阿富汗 Afghanistan

阿尔巴尼亚 Albania

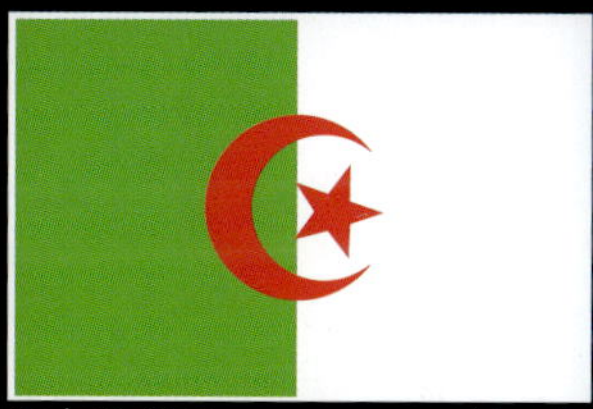
阿尔及利亚 Algeria

安道尔* Andorra

安哥拉 Angola

安提瓜和巴布达 Antigua and Barbuda

阿根廷 Argentina

亚美尼亚 Armenia

澳大利亚 Australia

奥地利* Austria

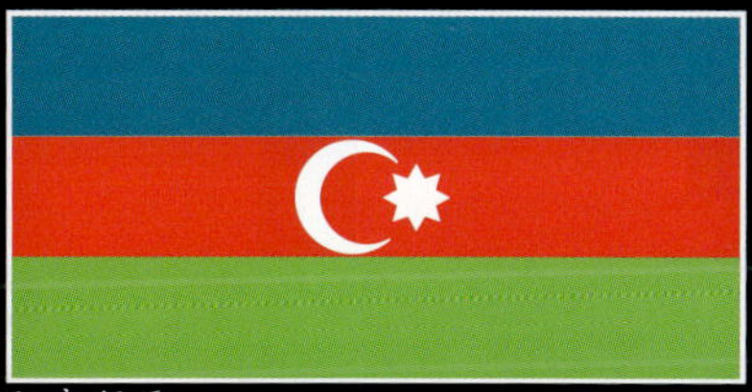
阿塞拜疆 Azerbaijan

巴哈马 The Bahamas

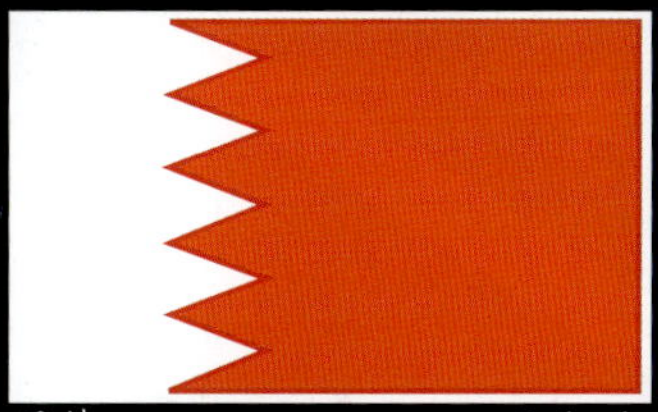
巴林 Bahrain

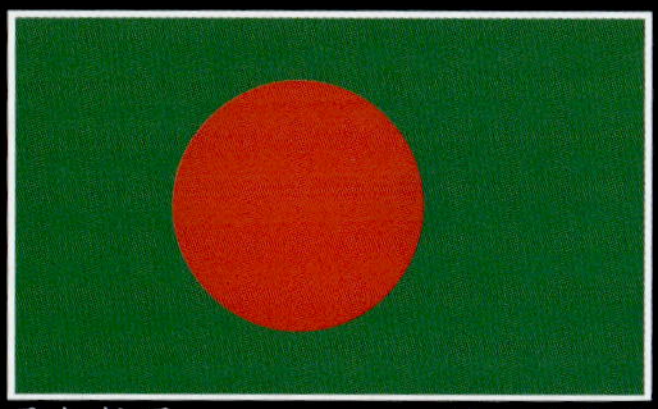
孟加拉国 Bangladesh

巴巴多斯 Barbados

白俄罗斯 Belarus

比利时 Belgium

伯利兹 Belize

贝宁 Benin

不丹 Bhutan

玻利维亚* Bolivia

波斯尼亚和黑塞哥维那 Bosnia and Herzegovina

博茨瓦纳 Botswana

巴西 Brazil

标记*的是政府旗帜，未标记*的是民用旗帜。两者均为正式国旗。

世界各国国旗 2

文莱 Brunei

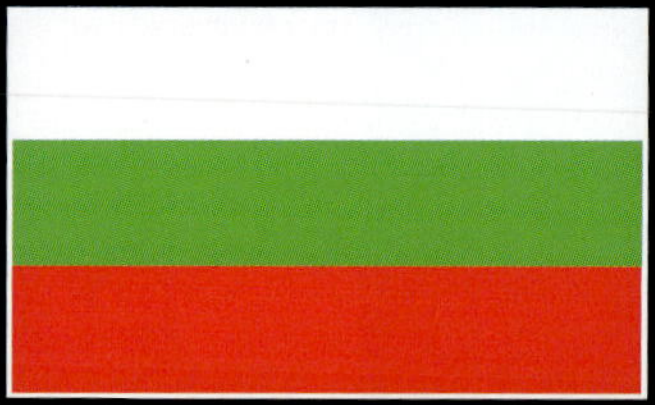
保加利亚 Bulgaria

布基纳法索 Burkina Faso

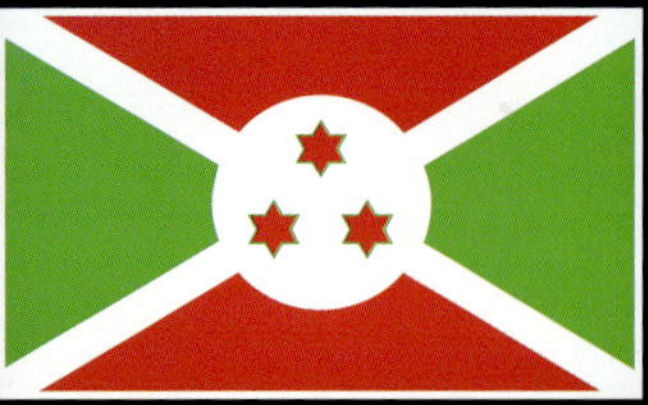
布隆迪 Burundi

柬埔寨 Cambodia

喀麦隆 Cameroon

加拿大 Canada

佛得角 Cape Verde

中非 Central African Republic

乍得 Chad

智利 Chile

中国 China

哥伦比亚 Colombia

科摩罗 Comoros

刚果(金)
Democratic Republic of the Congo

刚果(布) Republic of the Congo

哥斯达黎加* Costa Rica

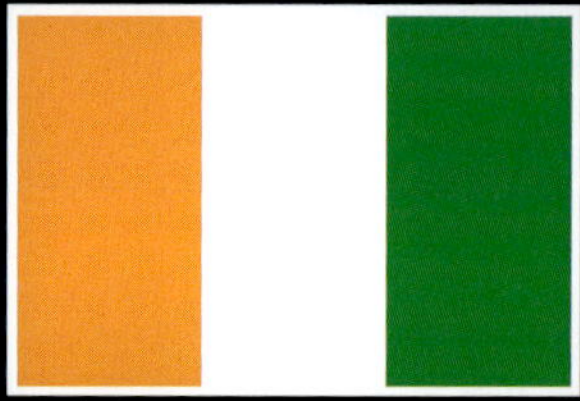
科特迪瓦 Côte d’Ivoire

克罗地亚 Croatia

古巴 Cuba

塞浦路斯 Cyprus

捷克 Czech Republic

丹麦 Denmark

吉布提 Djibouti

多米尼克 Dominica

多米尼加共和国* Dominican Republic

东帝汶 East Timor

厄瓜多尔* Ecuador

埃及 Egypt

萨尔瓦多 El Salvador

赤道几内亚 Equatorial Guinea

厄立特里亚 Eritrea

爱沙尼亚 Estonia

埃塞俄比亚 Ethiopia

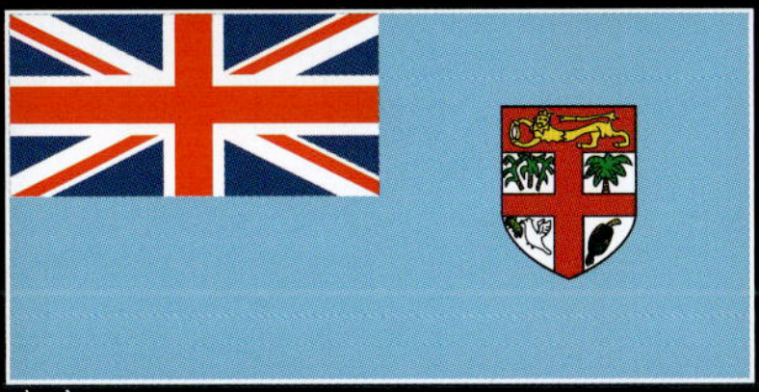
斐济 Fiji

芬兰* Finland

法国 France

加蓬 Gabon

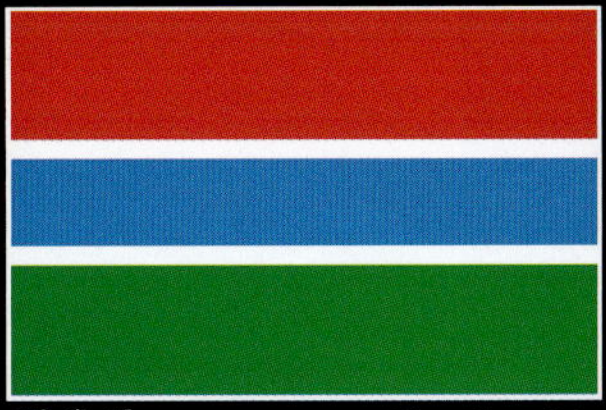
冈比亚 The Gambia

格鲁吉亚 Georgia

德国 Germany

加纳 Ghana

希腊 Greece

格林纳达 Grenada

危地马拉* Guatemala

几内亚 Guinea

几内亚比绍 Guinea-Bissau

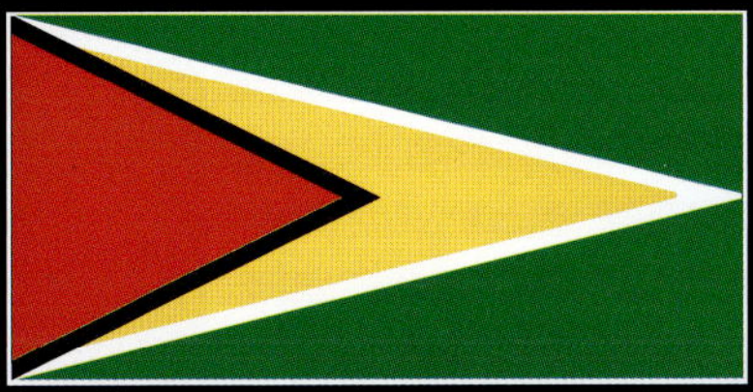
圭亚那 Guyana

海地* Haiti

洪都拉斯 Honduras

匈牙利 Hungary

冰岛 Iceland

印度 India

印度尼西亚 Indonesia

伊朗 Iran

الله اكبر
伊拉克 Iraq

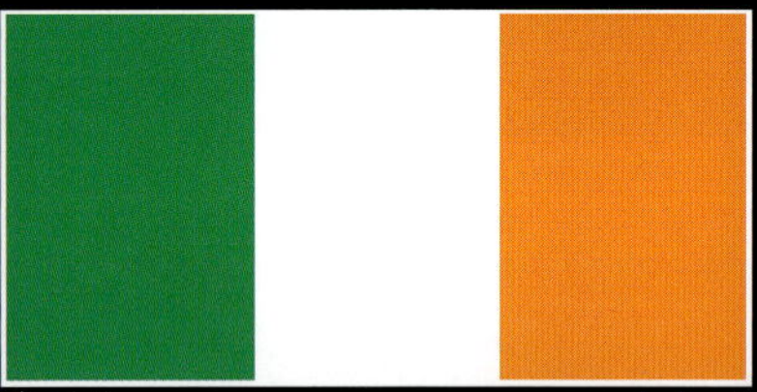
爱尔兰 Ireland

以色列 Israel

意大利 Italy

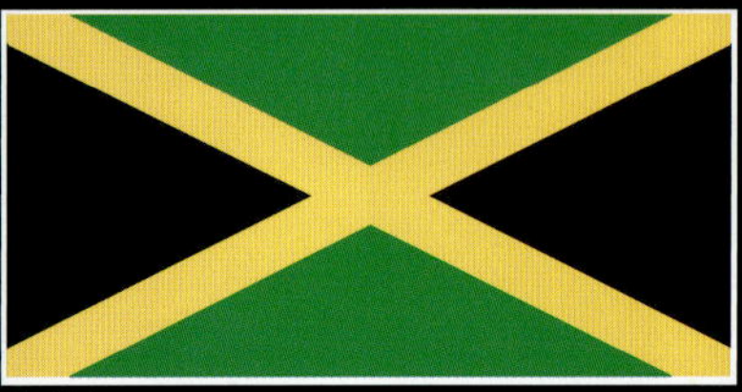
牙买加 Jamaica

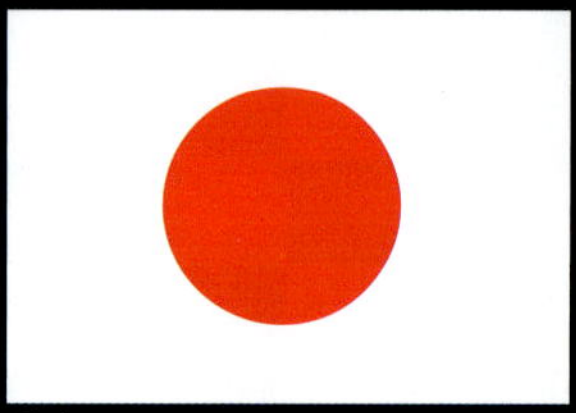
日本 Japan

约旦 Jordan

哈萨克斯坦 Kazakhstan

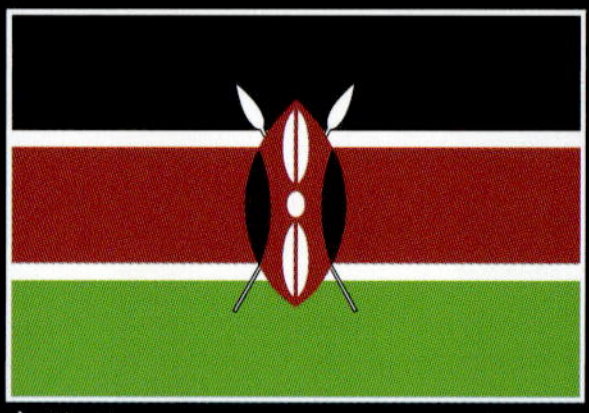
肯尼亚 Kenya

基里巴斯 Kiribati

朝鲜 North Korea

韩国 South Korea

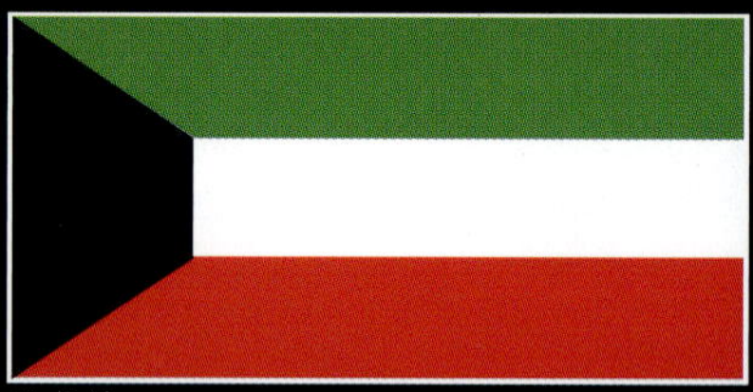
科威特 Kuwait

吉尔吉斯斯坦 Kyrgyzstan

老挝 Laos

拉脱维亚 Latvia

黎巴嫩 Lebanon

莱索托 Lesotho

利比里亚 Liberia

利比亚 Libya

列支敦士登 Liechtenstein

立陶宛 Lithuania

卢森堡 Luxembourg

马其顿 Macedonia

马达加斯加 Madagascar

马拉维 Malaŵi

马来西亚 Malaysia

马尔代夫 Maldives

马里 Mali

马耳他 Malta

马绍尔群岛 Marshall Islands

毛里塔尼亚 Mauritania

毛里求斯 Mauritius

墨西哥 Mexico

密克罗尼西亚 Micronesia, Federated States of

摩尔多瓦 Moldova

摩纳哥 Monaco

蒙古 Mongolia

黑山 Montenegro

摩洛哥 Morocco

莫桑比克 Mozambique

缅甸 Myanmar

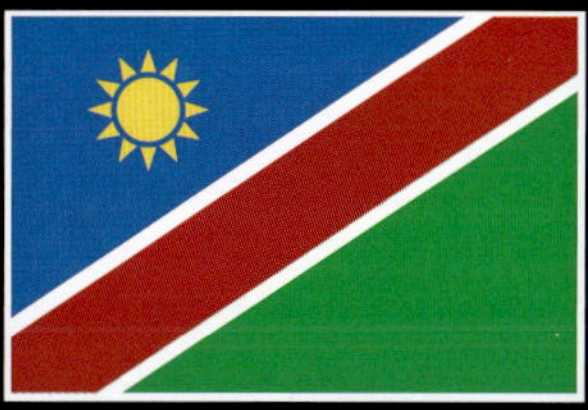
纳米比亚 Namibia

瑙鲁 Nauru

尼泊尔 Nepal

荷兰 The Netherlands

新西兰 New Zealand

尼加拉瓜* Nicaragua

尼日尔 Niger

尼日利亚 Nigeria

挪威 Norway

阿曼 Oman

巴基斯坦 Pakistan

帕劳 Palau

巴拿马 Panama

布亚新几内亚 Papua New Guinea

巴拉圭 Paraguay

秘鲁* Peru

菲律宾 Philippines

波兰 Poland

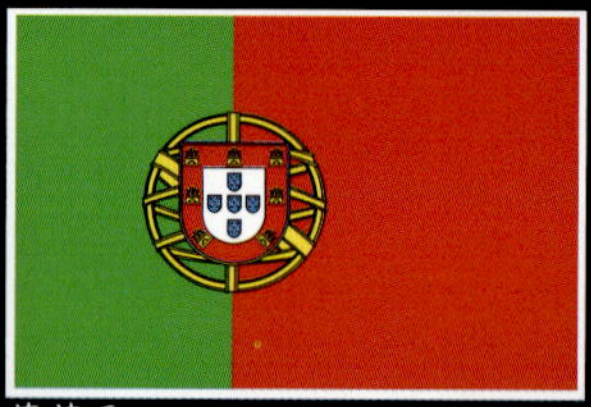
葡萄牙 Portugal

卡塔尔 Qatar

罗马尼亚 Romania

俄罗斯 Russia

卢旺达 Rwanda

圣基茨和尼维斯 Saint Kitts & Nevis

圣卢西亚 Saint Lucia

圣文森特和格林纳丁斯 Saint Vincent & the Grenadines

萨摩亚 Samoa

圣马力诺* San Marino

圣多美和普林西比 São Tomé and Principe

沙特阿拉伯 Saudi Arabia

塞内加尔 Senegal

塞尔维亚 Serbia

塞舌尔 Seychelles

塞拉利昂 Sierra Leone

新加坡 Singapore

斯洛伐克 Slovakia

斯洛文尼亚 Slovenia

所罗门群岛 Solomon Islands

索马里 Somalia

南非 South Africa

西班牙 Spain

斯里兰卡 Sri Lanka

苏丹 Sudan

苏里南 Suriname

斯威士兰 Swaziland

瑞典 Sweden

瑞士 Switzerland

叙利亚 Syria

塔吉克斯坦 Tajikistan

标记*的是政府旗帜，未标记*的是民用旗帜。两者均为正式国旗。

坦桑尼亚 Tanzania

泰国 Thailand

多哥 Togo

汤加 Tonga

特立尼达和多巴哥 Trinidad and Tobago

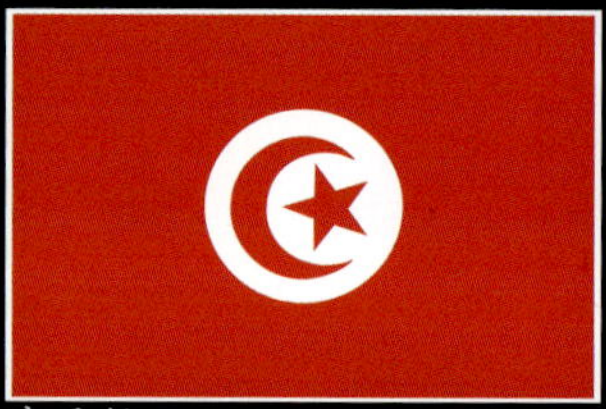
突尼斯 Tunisia

土耳其 Turkey

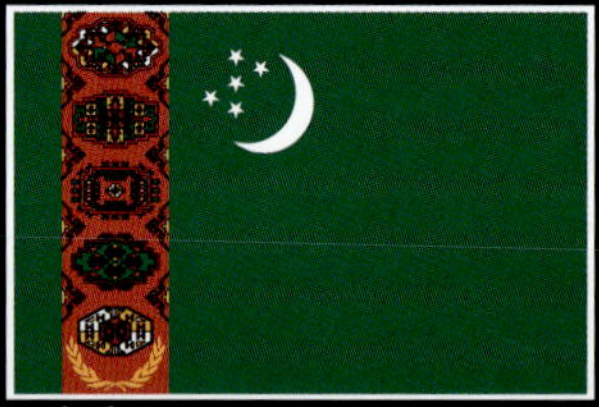
土库曼斯坦 Turkmenistan

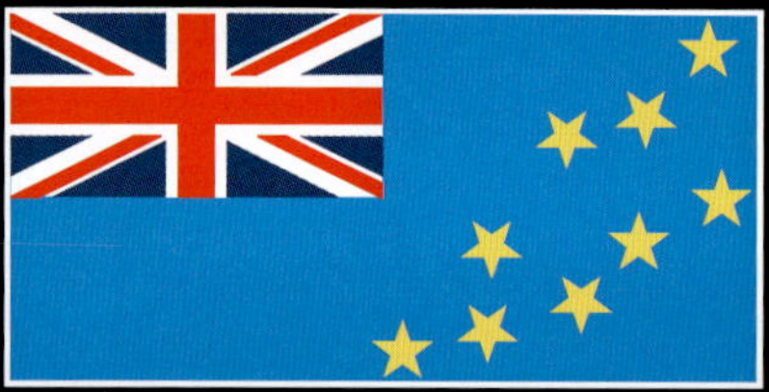
图瓦卢 Tuvalu

乌干达 Uganda

乌克兰 Ukraine

阿拉伯联合酋长国 United Arab Emirates

英国 United Kingdom

美国 United States

乌拉圭 Uruguay

乌兹别克斯坦 Uzbekistan

瓦努阿图 Vanuatu

梵蒂冈 Vatican City

委内瑞拉* Venezuela

越南 Vietnam

也门 Yemen

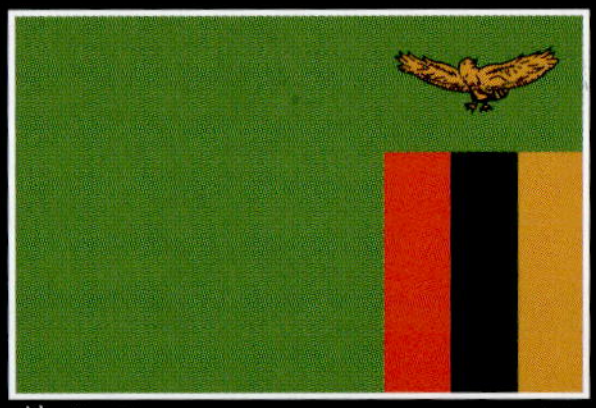
赞比亚 Zambia

津巴布韦 Zimbabwe

标记*的是政府旗帜，未标记*的是民用旗帜。两者均为正式国旗。

The New Encyclopædia Britannica

in 32 Volumes

FOUNDED 1768
15TH EDITION

ENCYCLOPÆDIA
Britannica

Encyclopædia Britannica, Inc.
Jacob E. Safra, Chairman of the Board
Jorge Aguilar-Cauz, President

Chicago

London/New Delhi/Paris/Seoul

Sydney/Taipei/Tokyo

The information on this page refers to
The New Encyclopædia Britannica.

First Edition	1768 – 1771
Second Edition	1777 – 1784
Third Edition	1788 – 1797
Supplement	1801
Fourth Edition	1801 – 1809
Fifth Edition	1815
Sixth Edition	1820 – 1823
Supplement	1815 – 1824
Seventh Edition	1830 – 1842
Eighth Edition	1852 – 1860
Ninth Edition	1875 – 1889
Tenth Edition	1902 – 1903

Printed in U. S. A.

Library of Congress Control Number: 2006921233
International Standard Book Number-10: 1-59339-292-3
International Standard Book Number-13: 978-1-59339-292-5

Britannica may be accessed at http://www.britannica.com on the Internet.

不列颠百科全书

国际中文版

修订版

Encyclopædia Britannica

International Chinese Edition

19

中国大百科全书出版社

《不列颠百科全书》国际中文版

索　引

一、条目中文标题索引（按汉语拼音音序排列）

A ～ R ································ 19—1 ～ 475

S ～ Z ································ 20—1 ～ 198

二、条目中文标题笔画索引 ································ 20—199 ～ 476

索　引
（一）

一、条目中文标题索引（按汉语拼音音序排列）

A ………………………………………… 1 ～ 46
B ………………………………………… 46 ～ 103
C ………………………………………… 103 ～ 116
D ………………………………………… 116 ～ 153
E ………………………………………… 154 ～ 157
F ………………………………………… 157 ～ 183
G ………………………………………… 183 ～ 210
H ………………………………………… 210 ～ 246
J ………………………………………… 246 ～ 274
K ………………………………………… 274 ～ 316
L ………………………………………… 316 ～ 368
M ………………………………………… 368 ～ 416
N ………………………………………… 416 ～ 434
O ………………………………………… 434 ～ 435
P ………………………………………… 435 ～ 456
Q ………………………………………… 456 ～ 469
R ………………………………………… 469 ～ 475

一、条目中文标题索引

（按汉语拼音音序排列）

说 明

1. 本索引是全书条目中文标题（即条目外文名称的中文译名）索引。条目中文标题按汉语拼音字母的顺序并辅以汉字笔画、起笔笔形顺序排列。同音时，按汉字笔画由少到多的顺序排列，笔画数相同的按起笔笔形一（横）、丨（竖）、丿（撇）、丶（点）、乛（折，包括亅㇆乚𡿨㇗等）的顺序排列。第一字相同时，按第二字，余类推。以拉丁字母、希腊字母和阿拉伯数字开头的条目中文标题，依次排在本索引的最后部分。

2. 条目中文标题用黑体字。

3. 条目中文标题后列有对照的外文（包括拼音）标题。标题后一般附有简短的定性（分类）。

4. 条目中文标题后的数码和拉丁字母分别指该条目所在的卷次、页码和版面区位，如 7—720a 指第 7 卷 720 页 a 区位。正文的版面区位划分如右图。

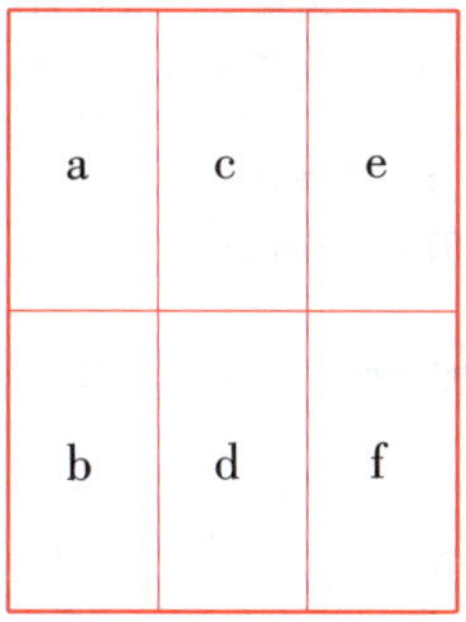
a
c
e
b
d
f

A

吖啶黄 acriflavine 染料 1—58a
阿埃多山脉 Haedo Range 乌拉圭山脉 7—404a
阿巴 Aba 尼日利亚城镇 1—3e
阿巴查 Abacha, Sani 尼日利亚军事领袖、国家元首 1—4b
阿巴丹 Ābādān 伊朗城市 1—4d
阿巴德王朝 ʻAbbādid DYNASTY 阿拉伯穆斯林王朝 1—5d
阿巴多 Abbado, Claudio 意大利指挥家 1—5f
阿巴厄 Abae 希腊古城镇 1—1c
阿巴哈人 Abaha (people) 非洲民族 1—4f
阿巴赫 Asbaje, Juana Inés de 墨西哥诗人 1—538f
阿巴卡利基 Abakaliki 尼日利亚城镇 1—4f
阿巴坎 Abakan 俄罗斯城市 1—5a
阿巴克尔（胖子） Arbuckle, Fatty 美国电影明星 1—444b
阿巴拉契科拉 Apalachicola 美国城市 1—405e
阿巴拉契人 Apalachee 北美民族 1—405d
阿巴拉契湾 Apalachee Bay 美国海湾 1—405e
阿巴拉契亚大山谷 Great Appalachian Valley 北美洲低地 7—268f
阿巴拉契亚高原区 Appalachian Highlands 美国高原区域 1—416c
阿巴拉契亚区域委员会 Appalachian Regional Commission 美国政府管理的机构 1—417a
阿巴拉契亚山脉 Appalachian Mountains 美国山脉 1—416c
阿巴拉契亚小道 Appalachian National Scenic Trail 美国山间小路 1—416e
阿巴拉契亚造山带 Appalachian orogenic belt 地质学 1—416f
阿巴里灵阿岛 Abariringa Atoll (Kiribati) 基里巴斯岛屿 1—5c
阿巴齐亚 Abbazia (Croatia) 克罗地亚城镇 1—7f
阿巴瑟亚纳克 Abasëyanık, Sait Faik 土耳其小说家 1—5c
阿巴思诺特 Arbuthnot, John 苏格兰数学家 1—444d
阿巴斯 Abbas, Ferhat 阿尔及利亚政治家 1—6d
阿巴斯 Abbas, Mahmoud 巴勒斯坦政治家 1—6f
阿巴斯港 Bandar-e ʻAbbās 伊朗港口 2—192d
阿巴斯·米尔扎 ʻAbbās Mīrzā 伊朗王储 1—7b
阿巴特 Abbate, Niccolò dell' 意大利画家 1—7e
阿拔斯 ʻAbbas 古代中东统治者之名 1—6a
阿拔斯二世 ʻAbbās II 埃及总督 1—6b
阿拔斯王朝 ʻAbbāsid DYNASTY 阿拉伯穆斯林王朝 1—7c
阿拔斯·希勒米帕夏 ʻAbbās Ḥilmī Pasha 埃及总督 1—6f
阿拔斯一世 ʻAbbās I 埃及总督 1—6a
阿拔斯一世 ʻAbbās I 波斯沙赫 1—6c
阿拜昂环礁 Abaiang Atoll 基里巴斯岛屿 1—4f
阿拜多斯 Abydos 土耳其古代城镇 1—38e
阿班凯 Abancay 秘鲁城市 1—5b
阿保机 A-pao-chi 中国辽代皇帝 1—1a
阿保机 Abaoji 中国辽代皇帝 1—5c
阿鲍齐特 Abauzit, Firmin 法国神学家 1—5d
阿贝 Abbe, Cleveland 美国气象学家 1—7f
阿贝 Abbe, Ernst 德国物理学家 1—7f
阿贝奥库塔 Abeokuta 尼日利亚城镇 1—20b
阿贝迪·阿尤·贝利 Abedi Ayew Pelé 加纳足球运动员 1—18b
阿贝尔 Abel, Carl Friedrich 德国作曲家 1—18c
阿贝尔 Abel, Niels Henrik 挪威数学家 1—18e
阿贝尔蒂内利 Albertinelli, Mariotto 佛罗伦萨画家 1—182c
阿贝尔·塔斯曼国家公园 Abel Tasman National Park 新西兰野生动物保护区 1—19b
阿贝耳 Abel, Sir Frederick Augustus 英国化学家、炸药专家 1—18d
阿贝格 Abegg, Richard Wilhelm Heinrich 德国物理化学家 1—18b

阿贝拉战役 Arbela, Battle of 古代马其顿与波斯之战 1—442c
阿贝马马环礁 Abemama Atoll 基里巴斯岛屿 1—19f
《阿贝赛报》 ABC 西班牙报纸 1—10e
阿贝歇 Abéché 乍得城镇 1—18a
阿本古鲁 Abengourou 科特迪瓦城镇 1—20a
阿本斯(古斯曼) Arbenz (Guzmán), Jacobo 危地马拉军人 1—442c
阿本斯贝格-特劳恩 Abensperg und Traun, Otto Ferdinand, Graf von (count of) 奥地利陆军元帅 1—20a
阿比德·布哈里 ʿAbīd al-Bukhārī 摩洛哥军事组织 1—23f
阿比多斯 Abydos 古埃及圣城 1—38c
阿比尔高 Abildgaard, Nicolai Abraham 丹麦画家 1—24c
阿比剧院 Abbey Theatre 爱尔兰都柏林剧院 1—8f
阿比林 Abilene 美国堪萨斯州城市 1—24c
阿比林 Abilene 美国得克萨斯州城市 1—24e
阿比庞人 Abipón 南美印第安人 1—25a
阿比让 Abidjan 科特迪瓦城市 1—24a
阿比维尔 Abbeville 美国路易斯安那州城镇 1—8b
阿比维尔 Abbeville 美国南卡罗来纳州城市 1—8c
阿比西尼亚 Abyssinia 埃塞俄比亚旧称 1—39c
阿比西尼亚猫 Abyssinian 猫品种 1—39c
阿比亚 Abia 尼日利亚州名 1—23e
阿庇安(亚历山大的) Appian of Alexandria 希腊历史学家 1—418f
阿庇亚大道 Appian Way 古罗马道路 1—419a
阿宾登 Abingdon 美国弗吉尼亚州城镇 1—24f
阿宾顿 Abingdon 英国城镇 1—24e
阿宾顿 Abington 美国马萨诸塞州城镇 1—24f
阿宾顿 Abington 美国宾夕法尼亚州城镇 1—25a
阿宾顿 Abington, Fanny 英国演员 1—25a
阿波火山 Apo, Mount 棉兰老岛活火山 1—410d
阿波加斯特 Arbogast 罗马帝国蛮族将领 1—443d
阿波里耐 Apollinaire, Guillaume 法国诗人 1—412a
阿波利那里斯 Apollinaris the Younger 基督教主教 1—412b
阿波利诺波利斯 Apollinopolis (Egypt) 埃及城镇 1—412c
阿波罗 Apollo 希腊宗教神祇 1—412c
阿波罗多罗斯 Apollodorus 雅典画家 1—413b
阿波罗多罗斯(雅典的) Apollodorus of Athens 希腊学者 1—413b
“阿波罗”计划 Apollo program 美国航天计划 1—412e
阿波罗精神 Apollonian 文学 1—413c
阿波罗剧院 Apollo Theatre 美国剧院 1—413a
阿波罗尼奥斯(罗得岛的) Apollonius of Rhodes 古希腊诗人、语法学家 1—413e
阿波罗尼奥斯(佩尔吉的) Apollonius of Perga 古希腊数学家 1—413c
阿波罗尼奥斯(特拉莱斯的) Apollonius of Tralles 古希腊雕刻家 1—413f
阿波罗尼奥斯(提亚纳的) Apollonius of Tyana 新毕达哥拉斯学派人物 1—413f
阿波罗尼奥斯(雅典人) Apollonius the Athenian 古希腊雕刻家 1—414a
阿波罗尼乌斯(提尔的) Apollonius of Tyre 拉丁传奇人物 1—414a
阿波洛多鲁斯(大马士革的) Apollodorus of Damascus 希腊工程师 1—413b
阿波马托克斯县府 Appomattox Court House 美国历史地名 1—421a
阿波美 Abomey 贝宁城镇 1—26f
阿波尼 Apponyi, Albert, Gróf 匈牙利政治家 1—421b
阿波皮 Apopis 埃及宗教恶魔 1—414e
阿波皮一世 Apopis I 古埃及国王 1—414e
阿波斯特尔群岛国家湖滨区 Apostle Islands National Lakeshore 美国威斯康星州西北部地区 1—415c
阿伯茨福德 Abbotsford 英国罗克斯堡区宅第 1—9b
阿伯德尔 Aberdare 英国城镇 1—20d
阿伯德尔山 Aberdare Range 肯尼亚山脉 1—20e
阿伯蒂比河 Abitibi River 加拿大河流 1—25b
阿伯蒂莱里 Abertillery 英国城镇 1—22f
阿伯丁 Aberdeen 英国城市 1—20f
阿伯丁伯爵(第四) Aberdeen, George Hamilton-Gordon, 4th Earl of 英国外交大臣、首相 1—21a
阿伯丁郡 Aberdeenshire 英国政务会辖区、历史郡 1—21c
阿伯尔 Abell, Kjeld 丹麦剧作家、社会评论家 1—19e
阿伯加文尼 Abergavenny 英国城镇 1—21e
阿伯康威 Aberconwy 英国威尔士区名 1—20c
阿伯拉尔 Abelard, Peter 法国神学家、哲学家 1—19b
阿伯拉哈 Abraha 埃塞俄比亚总督 1—27d
阿伯拉罕姆斯 Abrahams, Peter (Henry) 南非作家 1—28c
阿伯里斯特威斯 Aberystwyth 英国城镇 1—22f
阿伯塔巴德 Abbottābād 巴基斯坦城市 1—10c
阿博特和科斯蒂洛 Abbott, Bud; and Costello, Lou 美国演员搭档 1—9d
阿博维尔 Agboville 科特迪瓦城镇 1—118d
阿卜杜尔哈克·哈米德 Abdülhak Hâmid (Tarhan) 土耳其诗人、剧作家 1—16a
阿卜杜尔·卡拉姆 Abdul Kalam, A. P. J. 印度科学家、政治家 1—15c
阿卜杜尔·拉赫曼汗 ʿAbdor Raḥmān Khān 阿富汗国王 1—14f
阿卜杜·加尼 ʿAbd al-Ghanī 叙利亚作家 1—11a
阿卜杜卡迪尔 Abdelkader 阿尔及利亚领袖 1—13f
阿卜杜卡迪尔·伊本·穆希·迪恩·伊本·穆斯塔法·哈萨尼·杰扎伊里 ʿAbd al-Qādir ibn Muḥīy ad-Din ibn Musṭafā al-Ḥasanī al-Jazāʾirī (Algerian leader) 阿尔及利亚领袖 1—12a
阿卜杜拉 ʿAbd Allāh 苏丹政治和宗教领袖 1—12c
阿卜杜拉 ʿAbd Allāh 沙特阿拉伯国王 1—12d
阿卜杜拉 Abdullah 约旦国王 1—16d
阿卜杜拉 Abdulla, Muhammed Said 非洲小说家 1—16d
阿卜杜拉 Abdullah, Sheikh Muhammad 印度政治家 1—16f
阿卜杜拉·宾·阿卜杜尔·卡迪尔 Abdullah bin Abdul Kadir 马来亚作家 1—17a
阿卜杜拉二世 Abdullah II 约旦国王 1—16e
阿卜杜拉水道 ʿAbd Allāh, Khawr 伊拉克河口湾 1—12e
阿卜杜拉·伊本·侯赛因 ʿAbd Allāh ibn al-Ḥusayn 约旦国王 1—12e
阿卜杜拉·伊本·卢特夫·安拉·伊本·阿卜杜勒·拉希德·比赫达迪尼·哈菲兹·阿卜鲁 ʿAbd Allāh ibn Lutf Allāh ibn ʿAbd ar-Rashīd al-Bihdādīnī Ḥāfiẓ-i Abrū 波斯历史学家 1—12f
阿卜杜拉·伊本·祖拜尔 ʿAbd Allāh ibn az-Zubayr 阿拉伯穆斯林贵族 1—12f
阿卜杜勒·阿齐兹 Abd al-Aziz 摩洛哥苏丹 1—10f
阿卜杜勒·阿齐兹 Abdülaziz 奥斯曼苏丹 1—15f
阿卜杜勒·阿齐兹·伊本·阿卜杜勒·拉赫曼·伊本·费萨尔·伊本·图尔基·阿卜杜拉·伊本·穆罕默德·沙特 ʿAbd al-ʿAzīz ibn ʿAbd ar-Raḥmān ibn Fayṣal ibn Turkī ʿAbd Allāh ibn Muḥammad Al Saʿūd 沙特阿拉伯国王 1—10f
阿卜杜勒·哈菲德 Abd al-Hafid 摩洛哥苏丹 1—11a
阿卜杜勒-哈米德二世 Abdülhamid II 奥斯曼苏丹 1—16b
阿卜杜勒-哈米德一世 Abdülhamid I 奥斯曼苏丹 1—16b
阿卜杜勒·卡里姆·卡赛姆 ʿAbd al-Karīm Qāsim (Iraqi soldier) 伊拉克陆军军官 1—11c
阿卜杜勒·克里姆 Abd el-Krim 北非柏柏尔部落领袖 1—13d
阿卜杜勒·克里姆·古塔卜丁·伊本·易卜拉欣·吉里 ʿAbd al-Karīm Quṭb ad-Dīn ibn Ibrāhīm al-Jīlī 伊斯兰神秘主义者 1—11c
阿卜杜勒·拉赫曼 Abd ar-Rahman 摩洛哥苏丹 1—12f
阿卜杜勒·拉赫曼二世 ʿAbd ar-Raḥmān II 西班牙伍麦叶王朝统治者 1—13b

阿卜杜勒·拉赫曼三世 ʿAbd ar-Raḥmān III 西班牙伍麦叶王朝统治者 1—13b

阿卜杜勒·拉赫曼一世 ʿAbd ar-Raḥmān I 西班牙伍麦叶王朝统治者 1—13a

阿卜杜勒·马利克 ʿAbd al-Malik 伍麦叶王朝哈里发 1—11c

阿卜杜勒·迈吉德 Abdülmecid 奥斯曼苏丹之名 1—17b

阿卜杜勒·迈吉德二世 Abdülmecid II 奥斯曼哈里发、王储 1—17d

阿卜杜勒·迈吉德一世 Abdülmecid I 奥斯曼苏丹 1—17b

阿卜杜勒·慕敏 ʿAbd al-Muʾmin 阿尔摩哈德王朝哈里发 1—11d

阿卜杜勒-萨马德 ʿAbd-uṣ-Ṣamad, Khwāja 波斯画家 1—13e

阿卜杜勒瓦迪德王朝 ʿAbd al-Wādid DYNASTY 柏柏尔王朝 1—12a

阿卜杜勒·瓦哈卜 ʿAbd al-Wahhāb, Muḥammad 埃及作曲家、音乐家 1—12b

阿卜杜勒·伊拉 ʿAbd al-Ilāh 伊拉克摄政、王储 1—11a

阿卜·哈桑·阿里·伊本·侯赛因·麦斯欧迪 Abū al-Ḥasan ʿAlī ibn al-Ḥusayn al-Masʿūdī (Arab historian) 阿拉伯历史学家 1—34b

阿卜拉克萨斯 abraxas 一组受二元宗教崇拜的希腊字母 1—28e

阿布 Ābu 印度城市 1—33c

阿布·阿尔·哈桑 Abū al-Ḥasan 莫卧儿帝国画家 1—34a

阿布·阿里·哈桑·伊本·阿里 Abū ʿAlī Ḥasan ibn ʿAlī (Persian vizier) 波斯大臣 1—34d

阿布·阿里·穆斯塔法 Abū ʿAlī Muṣṭafā 巴勒斯坦民族主义者 1—34d

阿布·巴卡尔 Abu Bakar 马来柔佛国苏丹 1—34e

阿布巴卡尔 Abubakar, Abdusalam 尼日利亚军事领袖、国家元首 1—37f

阿布达尔-杰巴尔 Abdul-Jabbar, Kareem 美国篮球运动员 1—15b

阿布达利人 Abdālī 阿富汗部落联盟 1—13f

阿布达利苏丹国 ʿAbdali sultanate 也门古国 1—13f

阿布杜·卡迪尔·吉兰尼 ʿAbd al-Qādir al-Jīlānī 伊斯兰教神秘主义者 1—12a

阿布杜拉·伊本·阿巴斯 ʿAbd Allāh ibn al-ʿAbbās 伊斯兰教学者 1—12e

阿布·哈尼法 Abū Ḥanīfah 伊斯兰教法学家 1—35f

阿布哈兹 Abkhaziya 格鲁吉亚自治共和国 1—25c

阿布哈兹-阿迪格诸语言 Abkhazo-Adyghian languages 西北高加索语言 1—25d

阿布哈兹人 Abkhaz 西高加索民族 1—25c

阿布吉尔湾 Abū Qīr Bay 埃及海湾 1—37b

阿布吉尔湾战役 Aboukir Bay, Battle of 英法之间战役 1—27d

阿布吉拉伯 Abū Jirāb 埃及古地名 1—36b

阿布加尔传说 Abgar legend 基督教传说 1—23a

阿布·加法尔·阿卜杜拉·曼苏尔·伊本·穆罕默德 Abū Jaʿfar Abd Allāh al-Manṣūr ibn Muḥammad (caliph) 阿拔斯王朝哈里发 1—36a

阿布贾 Abuja (town and emirate, Nigeria) 尼日利亚城镇、酋长国名 1—37f

阿布贾 Abuja 尼日利亚区名 1—37f

阿布贾 Abuja 尼日利亚城市 1—38a

阿布·卡西姆 Abū al-Qāsim 伊斯兰外科医生 1—34c

阿布拉莫维奇 Abramowitsch, Shalom Jacob 俄罗斯作家 1—28c

阿布朗泰斯公爵 Abrantès, Andoche Junot, Duke (duc) d' 法国将军 1—28c

阿布朗泰斯公爵夫人 Abrantès, Laure Junot, Duchess (duchesse) d' 法国作家 1—28d

阿布雷乌 Abreu, Capistrano de 巴西历史学家 1—28f

阿布里科索夫 Abrikosov, Alexey A. 俄罗斯物理学家 1—28f

阿布鲁齐 Abruzzi 意大利地区 1—29a

阿布鲁齐 Abruzzi, Luigi Amedeo Giuseppe Maria Ferdinando Francesco, Duke (duca) d' 西班牙登山运动员、探险家 1—29c

阿布鲁韦斯 Abū Ruwaysh 埃及古地名 1—37b

阿布鲁佐 Abruzzo, Ben L. 美国气球飞行员 1—29c

阿布罗斯 Arbroath 苏格兰自治市 1—444b

阿布·蒙齐尔 Abū al-Mundhir (Islāmic scholar) 阿拉伯学者 1—34b

阿布·穆罕默德·阿里·伊本·艾哈迈德·伊本·赛义德·伊本·哈兹姆 Abū Muḥammad ʿAlī ibn Aḥmad ibn Saʿīdibn Ḥazm (Muslim historian) 穆斯林历史学家 1—36e

阿布·穆斯里姆 Abū Muslim 呼罗珊革命领袖 1—36e

阿布纳基人 Abnaki 北美印第安人 1—25f

阿布·纳斯尔 Abū Naṣr, Aḥmad Shāh Bahādur Mujāhidud-Dīn 莫卧儿皇帝 1—36f

阿布南河 Abuná River 南美河流 1—38b

阿布尼 Abney, Sir William de Wiveleslie 英国摄影化学家 1—26a

阿布·尼达尔 Abu Nidal 巴勒斯坦恐怖主义者 1—36f

阿布萨隆 Absalon 丹麦大主教 1—29e

阿布萨罗卡岭 Absaroka Range 美国山脉 1—29f

阿布沙赫赖因 Abū Shahrayn 伊拉克苏美尔古城遗址 1—37c

阿布山镇 Mount Ābu (India) 印度城市 11—440b

阿布斯 Abs, Hermann J(osef) 德国银行家 1—29d

阿布斯特贝辛根彩陶 Abstbessingen faience 德国陶器 1—31b

阿布-瓦法 Abū al-Wafāʾ 波斯天文学家、穆斯林数学家 1—34c

阿布维尔 Abbeville 法国城镇 1—8a

阿布维利文化期工艺 Abbevillian industry 欧洲史前石器工艺 1—8d

阿布-乌尔-法特-查拉-乌德-丁·穆罕默德·阿克巴 Abū-ul-Fatḥ Jalāl-ud-Dīn Muḥammad Akbar (Mughal emperor) 莫卧儿皇帝 1—37e

阿布西尔 Abū Ṣīr 埃及古代遗址 1—37d

阿布辛拜勒 Abu Simbel 埃及古代遗址 1—37c

阿布·优素福·耶古卜·伊本·阿卜杜勒·慕敏·曼苏尔 Abū Yūsuf Yaʿqūb ibn ʿAbd al-Muʾmin al-Manṣūr (Muslim ruler of Spain and North Africa) 北非、西班牙穆斯林统治者 1—37f

阿布月初九 Tisha be-Av 犹太人纪念日 17—112c

阿布扎比 Abu Dhabi 阿拉伯联合酋长国阿布扎比酋长国首都 1—35c

阿布扎比 Abu Dhabi 阿拉伯联合酋长国成员国 1—35a

阿部正弘 Abe Masahiro 日本政治家 1—18a

阿采尔努斯 Acernus (poet) 波兰诗人 1—48f

阿查法拉亚河 Atchafalaya River 美国河流 2—16c

阿查法拉亚湾 Atchafalaya Bay 墨西哥湾内海湾 2—16c

阿查瓜人 Achagua 南美洲民族 1—50f

阿昌庞 Acheampong, Ignatius Kutu 加纳陆军军官 1—51b

阿昌语 Achang language 中国语言 1—51a

阿昌族 Achang 中国民族 1—50f

阿城 Acheng 中国城市 1—51d

阿閦婆 Akṣobhya 佛教禅佛 1—158c

阿茨卡波察尔科 Atzcapotzalco 墨西哥城市 2—42b

阿茨卡波察尔科 Atzcapotzalco 墨西哥行政区 2—42b

阿达 ʿādah 伊斯兰教法律 1—63d

阿达卜 Adab 苏美尔古城 1—63a

阿达德 Adad 美索不达米亚神祇 1—63c

阿达尔 Adal 东非古国名 1—63e

阿达尔贝罗(阿登的) Adalbero OF ARDENNES 兰斯大主教 1—63f

阿达尔贝特 Adalbert 德意志大主教 1—64a

阿达尔贝特 Adalbert 意大利伦巴第国王 1—63f

阿达尔伯特,圣 Adalbert, SAINT 基督教布拉格主教 1—64b

阿达尔人 Adal (people) 非洲民族 1—63e

阿达河 Adda River 意大利河流 1—72a

阿达马瓦 Adamawa 尼日利亚酋长国 1—66a

阿达马瓦 Adamawa 尼日利亚州名 1—66c

阿达马瓦-东部诸语言 Adamawa-Eastern languages 中西非语言 1—66c

阿达马瓦高原 Adamawa Plateau 非洲火山高地 1—66d

阿达玛 Hadamard, Jacques-Salomon 法国数学家 7—400b

阿达米克 Adamic, Louis 美国作家 1—66d
阿达莫夫 Adamov, Arthur 法国作家 1—66f
阿达姆库斯 Adamkus, Valdas 立陶宛总统 1—66e
阿达姆南，圣 Adamnan, SAINT 基督教隐修院院长、学者 1—66e
阿达纳 Adana 土耳其城市 1—71b
阿达帕 Adapa 美索不达米亚神话人物 1—71d
阿达帕扎勒 Adapazarı 土耳其城市 1—71e
阿达圣餐杯 Ardagh Chalice 爱尔兰基督教会金属工艺品 1—457c
阿代尔 Ader, Clément 法国发明家 1—77c
阿代马尔 Adhémar DE CHABANNES 法兰克编年史家 1—77d
阿代马尔 Adhémar OF MONTEIL 法国主教 1—77d
阿代诺 Adernò (Sicily) 意大利城镇 1—77c
阿戴尔 Adair, John 苏格兰地图测绘家 1—63d
阿戴尔诉美国案（1908） Adair v. the United States 美国法院案例 1—63e
阿黛利海岸 Adélie Coast 南极洲海岸 1—75d
阿当梅人 Adangme 加纳民族 1—71c
阿当松 Adanson, Michel 法国植物学家 1—71d
阿道夫 Adolf 统治者之名 1—83d
阿道夫 Adolf 德意志国王 1—83e
阿道夫 Adolf 拿骚公爵、卢森堡大公 1—83e
阿道夫·腓特烈 Adolf Frederick 瑞典国王 1—83f
阿道诺家族 Adorno FAMILY 热那亚望族 1—84e
阿德奥达图斯 Adeodatus 教皇称号 1—77b
阿德奥达图斯二世 Adeodatus II 教皇 1—77c
阿德奥达图斯一世 Adeodatus I 教皇 1—77c
阿德拉 Adela 英国国王威廉一世的女儿 1—74e
阿德拉 Adelaer 挪威海军官员 1—74f
阿德拉德 Adelard OF BATH 英国经院哲学家 1—75d
阿德拉尔 Adrar 撒哈拉绿洲 1—85b
阿德拉尔 Adrar 西非地区名 1—85b
阿德拉诺 Adrano 意大利城镇 1—85a
阿德拉伊德，圣 Adelaide, SAINT 意大利皇后 1—75b
阿德莱德 Adelaide 澳大利亚城市 1—74f
阿德莱德港 Port Adelaide 澳大利亚港口 13—443e
阿德莱德河 Adelaide River 澳大利亚河流 1—75c
阿德勒 Adler, Alfred 奥地利精神病学家 1—79f
阿德勒 Adler, Cyrus 美国学者 1—80b
阿德勒 Adler, Dankmar 美国建筑师、工程师 1—80c
阿德勒 Adler, Felix 美国教育家 1—80d
阿德勒 Adler, Guido 奥地利音乐学家、教师 1—80e
阿德勒 Adler, Larry 美国口琴演奏家 1—80f
阿德勒 Adler, Mortimer J. 美国哲学家、教育家 1—81a
阿德勒 Adler, Nathan Marcus 不列颠帝国犹太教大拉比 1—81c
阿德勒 Adler, Sara 美国演员 1—81c
阿德勒 Adler, Victor 奥地利政治家 1—81d
阿德勒斯帕勒 Adlersparre, Georg, Greve (Count) 瑞典政治家 1—81e
阿德雷男爵 Adrets, François de Beaumont, baron des 法国军事首领 1—86b
阿德雷特 Adret, Solomon ben Abraham 西班牙犹太教精神领袖 1—86a
阿德里安 Adrian 教皇称号 1—86c
阿德里安 Adrian 美国城市 1—87a
阿德里安堡 Adrianople (Turkey) 土耳其城市 1—87b
《阿德里安堡条约》 Adrianople, Treaty of (1829) 欧洲历史 1—87b
阿德里安堡战役 Adrianople, Battle of 古罗马历史 1—87b
阿德里安二世 Adrian II 教皇 1—86c
阿德里安六世 Adrian VI 教皇 1—86f
阿德里安三世，圣 Adrian III, SAINT 教皇 1—86d
阿德里安四世 Adrian IV 教皇 1—86e
阿德里安五世 Adrian V 教皇 1—86f
阿德里安一世 Adrian I 教皇 1—86c
阿德里亚 Adria 意大利城市 1—86b
阿德利 Adderley, Herb 美国橄榄球运动员 1—72f
阿德利 Adderley, Nat 美国流行歌曲作家 1—72f
阿德隆 Adelung, Johann Christoph 德国学者 1—75e
阿德莫尔 Ardmore 美国城市 1—458e
阿德墨托斯 Admetus 希腊传说人物 1—81e
阿德默勒尔蒂群岛 Admiralty Islands 巴布亚新几内亚群岛 1—82f
阿德默勒尔蒂湾 Admiralty Inlet 加拿大西北地区峡湾 1—82e
阿德内·勒·鲁瓦 Adenet LE ROI 法国诗人、音乐家 1—76f
阿德亚曼 Adıyaman 土耳其城市 1—79d
阿登 Ardennes 欧洲地区 1—458b
阿登 Ardennes 法国省份 1—458c
阿登 Arden, John 英国剧作家 1—458a
阿登纳 Adenauer, Konrad 西德总理 1—76c
阿登纳文化 Adena culture 人类学 1—76a
阿登战役 Ardennes, Battle of the (1944～1945) 第二次世界大战史 1—458d
阿迪格 Adygeya 俄罗斯行政区域 1—91c
阿迪杰河 Adige River 意大利河流 1—78e
阿迪克勒斯特里特 Adwick le Street 英格兰城镇 1—91b
阿迪拉巴德 Ādilābād 印度城市 1—78f
阿迪朗达克山脉 Adirondack Mountains 美国山脉 1—79a
阿迪亚贝纳 Adiabene 伊拉克古代王国 1—78c
《阿底·格兰特》 Ādi Granth 印度锡克教经典 1—78a
阿底那陀 Ādinātha 耆那教圣者 1—78f
阿底提（无限无缚） Aditi 印度教女神 1—79c
阿底峡（殊胜） Atīśa 印度佛教改革家 2—26c
阿蒂博尼特河 Artibonite River 多米尼加共和国河流 1—529d
阿蒂基耶罗 Altichiero 意大利画家 1—256a
阿蒂加斯 Artigas 乌拉圭城市 1—531b
阿蒂加斯 Artigas, José Gervasio 乌拉圭革命领袖 1—531b
阿蒂斯蒙斯 Athis-Mons 法国城镇 2—24e
阿蒂特兰湖 Atitlán, Lake 危地马拉湖泊 2—26c
阿蒂西亚 Artesia 美国城市 1—526e
阿迭尔·沙赫王朝 ʿĀdil Shāhī DYNASTY 印度王朝 1—78f
阿丁 Artin, Emil 奥地利数学家 1—531e
阿丁顿 Addington, Henry 英国政治家 1—73a
阿杜安 Hardouin, Jean 法国耶稣会学者 7—473c
阿杜安-芒萨尔 Hardouin-Mansart, Jules (architect) 法国建筑家 7—473d
阿杜德·道拉 ʿAḍud ad-Dawlah 伊朗白益王朝统治者 1—87d
阿杜德·道拉 ʿAḍud al-Dawla (Turkish sultan) 土耳其苏丹 1—87e
阿杜尔河 Adour River 法国河流 1—85a
阿杜拉姆 ʿAdullam 以色列古地名 1—87e
阿杜瓦 Adwa 埃塞俄比亚城镇 1—90f
阿多埃基蒂 Ado-Ekiti 尼日利亚城镇 1—83a
阿多尼 Ādoni 印度城镇 1—84a
阿多尼斯 Adonis 希腊神话人物 1—84b
阿多尼亚斯 Adonias (Aguiar) Filho 巴西小说家 1—84b
阿多诺 Adorno, Theodor Wiesengrund 德国哲学家 1—84f
阿多瓦战役 Adwa, Battle of 历史事件 1—91a
阿多象国家公园 Addo Elephant National Park 南非公园 1—74c
阿恩 Hahn, Reynaldo 法国作曲家 7—408e
阿恩 Arne, Thomas (Augustine) 英国作曲家 1—506b
阿恩格里米尔 Arngrímur THE LEARNED (Icelandic folk poet) 冰岛民间诗人 1—506d
阿恩格里米尔·荣松 Arngrímur Jónsson (Icelandic historian) 冰岛历史学家 1—506e
阿恩施塔特 Arnstadt 德国城市 1—510c
阿恩斯贝格 Arnsberg 德国地区名 1—510a
阿恩斯贝格 Arnsberg 德国城市 1—510c

阿恩特 Arndt, Ernst Moritz 德国散文作家、诗人 1—506a
阿恩特 Arndt, Johann 德国基督教神学家 1—506b
阿尔 Halle, Adam de la (French playwright) 法国剧作家 7—428e
阿尔阿尔 ʻArʻar 沙特阿拉伯城镇 1—440b
阿尔巴 Alba 苏格兰古王国 1—172a
阿尔巴 Alba 意大利城镇 1—172b
阿尔巴 Alba 罗马尼亚县名 1—172b
阿尔巴堡 Cetatea Albă (Ukraine) 乌克兰城市 4—18c
阿尔巴富钦斯 Alba Fucens 意大利城镇 1—172e
阿尔巴拉格 Albalag, Isaac 犹太教哲学家 1—173b
阿尔巴雷罗陶罐 albarello 陶器 1—175f
阿尔巴隆加 Alba Longa 意大利古城 1—172f
阿尔巴尼 Albani, Francesco 意大利画家 1—173c
阿尔巴尼公爵 Albany, Henry Stewart, duke of 英国贵族 1—175f
阿尔巴尼亚 Albania 巴尔干半岛国家 1—173c
阿尔巴尼亚同盟 Albanian League 巴尔干历史 1—174d
阿尔巴尼亚文学 Albanian literature 文学 1—174e
阿尔巴尼亚语 Albanian language 欧洲语言 1—174c
阿尔巴诺 Albano, Francesco (Italian painter) 意大利画家 1—175a
阿尔巴诺湖 Albano, Lake 意大利火山口湖 1—175a
阿尔巴斯 Arbus, Diane 美国摄影家 1—444c
阿尔巴尤利亚 Alba Iulia 罗马尼亚县城 1—172f
阿尔班,圣 Alban, Saint 基督教徒 1—173b
阿尔班丘陵 Alban Hills 意大利山区 1—173b
阿尔班山 Monte Albán 墨西哥文化遗址 11—360d
阿尔卑斯 Alps 罗马帝国行省 1—252a
阿尔卑斯号角 alphorn 乐器 1—251b
阿尔卑斯莱茵河 Alpenrhein River 欧洲河流 1—249d
阿尔卑斯山湖群 Alpine lakes 欧洲湖群 1—251c
阿尔卑斯山脉 Alps 欧洲山脉 1—252a
阿尔卑斯山南共和国 Cisalpine Republic 意大利历史 4—246c
阿尔卑斯山区地域人种 Alpine local race 欧洲民族 1—251d
阿尔卑斯造山幕 Alpine orogeny 地质学 1—251e
阿尔贝 Albert, Eugen (Francis Charles) d' 德籍作曲家 1—180b
阿尔贝(艾克斯的) Albert of Aix 基督教教士、史学家 1—180a
阿尔贝(工人) Albert l'Ouvrier 法国工人代表 1—179f
阿尔贝德钢铁公司 ARBED SA 卢森堡公司 1—442b
阿尔贝蒂 Alberti, Domenico 威尼斯作曲家 1—181d
阿尔贝蒂 Alberti, Leon Battista 意大利人文主义者 1—181d
阿尔贝蒂家族 Alberti family 意大利银行家族 1—181c
阿尔贝蒂尼 Albertini, Luigi 意大利新闻工作者 1—182c
阿尔贝格 Arlberg 奥地利山口、隧道 1—493c
阿尔贝尼斯 Albéniz, Isaac (Manuel Francisco) 西班牙作曲家 1—177a
阿尔贝特 Albert 欧洲统治者之名 1—177d
阿尔贝特 Albert 勃兰登堡侯爵 1—178e
阿尔贝特 Albert 奥地利统治者 1—179a
阿尔贝特 Albert 普鲁士公爵 1—179a
阿尔贝特 Albert 萨克森国王 1—179c
阿尔贝特 Albert, Archduke 奥地利陆军元帅 1—179d
阿尔贝特 Albert, Heinrich 德国作曲家 1—180b
阿尔贝特(勃兰登堡的) Albert of Brandenburg 勃兰登堡侯爵 1—180a
阿尔贝特(大熊) Albert the Bear 勃兰登堡侯爵 1—180b
阿尔贝特(萨克森的) Albert of Saxony 日耳曼哲学家 1—180a
阿尔贝特(勇敢者) Albert the Courageous 萨克森公爵 1—180b
阿尔贝特·阿尼莫苏斯 Albert Animosus 萨克森公爵 1—179f
阿尔贝特版画收藏馆 Albertina Graphics Collection 奥地利艺术收藏馆 1—182b
阿尔贝特二世 Albert II 比利时国王 1—177f
阿尔贝特二世 Albert II 德意志、匈牙利、波希米亚国王 1—178d
阿尔贝特二世·阿尔齐比亚德斯 Albert II Alcibiades 勃兰登堡-库尔姆巴赫侯爵 1—178b
阿尔贝特七世 Albert VII 奥地利统治者 1—177e
阿尔贝特三世 Albert III Achilles 勃兰登堡选侯 1—178a
阿尔贝特三世 Albert III 萨克森公爵 1—179b
阿尔贝特五世 Albert V 德意志/神圣罗马帝国国王 1—177d
《阿尔贝特宪法》 Statuto Albertino 意大利历史 16—203b
阿尔贝特一世 Albert I 奥地利公爵、德意志国王 1—178c
阿尔贝特一世 Albert I 比利时国王 1—177e
阿尔贝特一世 Albert I 勃兰登堡侯爵 1—178a
阿尔贝特运河 Albert Canal 比利时水道 1—180d
阿尔贝维尔 Albertville 刚果(金)城镇 1—183b
阿尔比 Albi 法国城市 1—183b
阿尔比 Albee, Edward (Franklin) 美国剧作家 1—176e
阿尔比 Albee, Edward Franklin 美国剧场经理 1—176e
阿尔比恩 Albion 不列颠岛的古称 1—184a
阿尔比马尔公爵 Albemarle, George Monck, 1st Duke of 英国将军 1—176f
阿尔比努斯 Albinus, Decimus Clodius Septimius 罗马将军 1—183f
阿尔比诺尼 Albinoni, Tomaso Giovanni 意大利作曲家 1—183e
阿尔比诺瓦努斯·佩多 Albinovanus Pedo 罗马诗人 1—183f
阿尔比派 Albigenses 法国宗教派别 1—183c
阿尔宾大峡谷 Great Glen of Albin (Scotland) 苏格兰峡谷 7—272b
阿尔波尼 Alboni, Marietta 意大利歌唱家 1—184d
阿尔伯 Arber, Agnes 英国植物学家 1—442d
阿尔伯 Arber, Edward 英国学者 1—442e
阿尔伯 Arber, Werner 瑞士微生物学家 1—442e
阿尔伯克基 Albuquerque 美国城市 1—186b
阿尔伯马尔湾 Albemarle Sound 美国海湾 1—176f
阿尔伯特 Albert 摩纳哥公国亲王 1—178f
阿尔伯特(科隆的) Albert of Cologne 天主教主教、哲学家 1—180a
阿尔伯特二世 Albert II, prince de Monaco 摩纳哥元首 1—178f
阿尔博 Albo, Joseph 西班牙犹太哲学家、神学家 1—184c
阿尔博 Arbeau, Thoinot 法国舞蹈理论家 1—442b
阿尔博因 Alboin 日耳曼伦巴第人国王 1—184d
阿尔布克尔克 Albuquerque, Afonso de, the Great 葡萄牙军人、殖民者 1—186c
阿尔布拉山 Albula Alps 瑞士山脉 1—185f
阿尔布雷家族 Albret family 法国著名家族 1—185a
阿尔布雷希茨贝格 Albrechtsberger, Johann Georg 奥地利作曲家 1—185a
阿尔布马扎 Albumazar 阿拉伯穆斯林星占学家 1—100a
阿尔茨海默氏病 Alzheimer's disease 脑病 1—261b
阿尔达班 Artabanus 波斯王朝大臣 1—524a
阿尔达班 Artabanus 安息国王之名 1—524b
阿尔达班三世 Artabanus III 安息国王 1—524c
阿尔达班五世 Artabanus V 安息国王 1—524c
阿尔达班一世 Artabanus I 安息国王 1—524b
阿尔达比勒 Ardabīl 伊朗城镇 1—457b
阿尔达比勒地毯 Ardabīl Carpet 波斯地毯 1—457c
阿尔达布拉群岛 Aldabra Islands 印度洋环礁 1—192b
阿尔达河 Arda River 保加利亚河流 1—457b
阿尔达希尔 Ardashīr 古波斯国王之名 1—457d
阿尔达希尔二世 Ardashīr II 古波斯国王 1—457e
阿尔达希尔一世 Ardashīr I 古波斯国王 1—457d
阿尔代尔山 Adlergebirge (eastern Europe) 欧洲山脉 1—81e
阿尔代什 Ardèche 法国省份 1—457f
阿尔代亚 Ardea 意大利古城镇 1—457e
阿尔丹河 Aldan River 俄罗斯河流 1—192b
阿尔德 Alder, Kurt 德国化学家 1—193b
阿尔德科亚 Aldecoa, Ignacio 西班牙小说家 1—192c
阿尔德罗万迪 Aldrovandi, Ulisse 意大利博物学家 1—194f
阿尔迪 Hardy, Alexandre 法国剧作家 7—473f

阿尔蒂尔二世 Arthur II 布列塔尼公爵 1—528b
阿尔蒂尔三世 Arthur III 法国军官 1—528c
阿尔蒂尔一世 Arthur I 布列塔尼公爵 1—528b
阿尔蒂里 Altieri, Emilio (pope) 教皇 1—256b
阿尔蒂普拉诺 Altiplano 南美地区 1—256c
阿尔杜塞 Althusser, Louis 法国哲学家 1—255f
阿尔杜伊诺 Arduino, Giovanni 意大利地质学家 1—458e
阿尔多布朗迪尼 Aldobrandini, Ippolito (pope) 教皇 1—194a
阿尔法-罗密欧汽车公司 Alfa Romeo SpA 意大利汽车公司 1—214f
阿尔法罗·西凯罗斯 Alfaro Siqueiros, David 墨西哥画家 1—215c
阿尔法西 Alfasi, Isaac ben Jacob 犹太教学者 1—215c
阿尔菲奥斯河 Alpheus River 希腊河流 1—251a
阿尔菲耶里 Alfieri, Vittorio, Conte (Count) 意大利诗人 1—215d
阿尔费罗夫 Alferov, Zhores 苏联物理学家 1—215c
阿尔弗烈德 Alfred 韦塞克斯国王 1—218f
阿尔弗烈德之宝 Alfred Jewel 黄金饰物 1—219b
阿尔弗斯通 Ulverstone 澳大利亚城镇 17—334d
阿尔盖尔 Argall, Sir Samuel 英国冒险家 1—462a
阿尔盖罗 Alghero 意大利城镇 1—223c
阿尔甘灯 Argand burner 油灯 1—462a
阿尔甘图 Argand diagram 数学 1—462b
阿尔冈昆人 Algonquin 加拿大民族 1—224d
阿尔冈昆诸语言 Algonquian languages 北美语言 1—224c
阿尔高 Aargau 瑞士州名 1—3a
阿尔戈利斯 Argolís 希腊州名 1—465f
阿尔戈利斯湾 Argolis, Gulf of 希腊海湾 1—465f
阿尔戈斯 Argos 希腊城市 1—467a
阿尔戈维 Argovie (Switzerland) 瑞士州名 1—467c
阿尔戈英雄 Argonaut 希腊传说人物 1—466b
阿尔格伦 Ahlgren, Ernst 瑞典作家 1—134c
阿尔格伦 Algren, Nelson 美国作家 1—225d
阿尔格山 A'erge Mountains 中国山脉 1—95e
阿尔贡古 Argungu 尼日利亚城镇 1—467f
阿尔贡国家实验室 Argonne National Laboratory 美国能源部实验室 1—466f
阿尔贡金湖 Algonquin, Lake 北美古冰湖 1—224d
阿尔贡金省立公园 Algonquin Provincial Park 加拿大公园 1—224e
阿尔贡金圆桌 Algonquin Round Table 美国文艺团体 1—224e
阿尔古伯爵 Harcourt, Henri de Lorraine, comte de 法国军人 7—470e
阿尔果德 Arcot 印度城市 1—455c
阿尔汉格尔斯克 Arkhangelsk 俄罗斯城市 1—493a
阿尔汉格尔斯克 Arkhangelsk 俄罗斯州名 1—492f
阿尔赫西拉斯 Algeciras 西班牙海港 1—221c
阿尔赫西拉斯会议 Algeciras Conference 国际会议 1—221c
阿尔基洛科斯 Archilochus 希腊诗人 1—450a
阿尔及尔 Algiers 阿尔及利亚首都 1—223e
阿尔及利亚 Algeria 非洲国家 1—222c
阿尔及利亚革新派乌里玛协会 Algerian Reformist Ulama, Association of 穆斯林宗教团体 1—223b
阿尔吉达斯 Algirdas 立陶宛大公 1—224b
阿尔吉罗卡斯特罗 Argirocastro (Albania) 阿尔巴尼亚城市 1—465e
阿尔加迪 Algardi, Alessandro 罗马雕刻家 1—219e
阿尔加罗蒂 Algarotti, Francesco 意大利艺术鉴赏家 1—220a
阿尔加维 Algarve 葡萄牙省份 1—220a
阿尔加文化 El Argar 伊比利亚半岛史前文化 6—9f
阿尔杰 Alger, Horatio 美国作家 1—221d
阿尔杰(列日的) Alger of Liège 佛兰芒司铎 1—221d
阿尔杰罗斯·麦吉斯特(学者) Algerus Magister 佛兰芒司铎 1—223c
阿尔杰什 Argeş 罗马尼亚县名 1—465c
阿尔杰什河 Argeş River 罗马尼亚河流 1—465d
阿尔金岛 Arguin Island 毛里塔尼亚岛屿 1—467e
阿尔金山 Altun Shan 中国山脉 1—258b
阿尔喀诺俄斯 Alcinous 希腊神话人物 1—189d
阿尔卡拉大街 Alcalá, Calle de 西班牙马德里街道 1—186f
阿尔卡拉斯地毯 Alcaraz carpet 西班牙手工艺品 1—187e
阿尔卡雷克 Arqalyq 哈萨克斯坦城市 1—513b
阿尔卡莫 Alcamo 意大利城市 1—187d
阿尔卡姆内斯 Alcamenes 古希腊雕刻家 1—187d
阿尔卡萨尔-德圣胡安 Alcázar de San Juan 西班牙城镇 1—188b
阿尔卡萨基维尔 Alcazarquivir (Morocco) 摩洛哥城市 1—188c
阿尔卡特拉斯岛 Alcatraz Island 美国岩石岛 1—187f
阿尔卡特拉斯的禽学家 Birdman of Alcatraz 美国罪犯 2—490b
阿尔凯奥斯 Alcaeus 希腊诗人 1—186e
阿尔凯奥斯诗体 alcaic 古典希腊诗节 1—186f
阿尔坎塔拉 Alcântara, Osvaldo 非洲作家 1—187e
阿尔坎塔拉 Alcántara 西班牙城镇 1—187e
阿尔坎塔拉骑士团 Alcántara, Order of 西班牙基督教军人教派 1—187e
阿尔康 Alkan, (Charles-Henri-) Valentin 法国钢琴家、作曲家 1—232f
阿尔康 Archon 诺斯替教教义 1—454e
阿尔康公路 Alcan Highway 北美公路 1—187e
阿尔康铝业股份有限公司 Alcan Aluminium Limited 加拿大公司 1—187d
阿尔科阿 Alcoa 美国城市 1—190b
阿尔科巴萨 Alcobaça 葡萄牙城镇 1—190b
阿尔科克 Alcock, Sir John William 英国飞行家 1—190c
阿尔科纳神殿 Arkona 西斯拉夫人神殿 1—493b
阿尔科斯-德拉弗龙特拉 Arcos de la Frontera 西班牙城市 1—455c
阿尔科伊 Alcoy 西班牙城镇 1—191f
阿尔克马尔 Alkmaar 荷兰城市 1—233c
阿尔克迈翁 Alcmaeon 希腊传说人物 1—189e
阿尔克迈翁 Alcmaeon 希腊哲学家、生理学家 1—189f
阿尔克迈翁家族 Alcmaeonid family 古希腊家族 1—189f
阿尔克曼 Alcman 希腊诗人 1—190a
阿尔库勒夫 Arculf 基督教主教 1—457a
阿尔昆 Alcuin 盎格鲁-撒克逊学者 1—191f
阿尔勒 Arles 法国城市 1—493f
阿尔隆 Arlon 比利时地名 1—494f
阿尔马 Alma 加拿大城市 1—244b
阿尔马 Alma 美国城市 1—244b
阿尔马登 Almadén 西班牙城镇 1—244d
阿尔马格罗 Almagro, Diego de 西班牙军人 1—244e
阿尔马河战役 Alma, Battle of the 克里米亚战争 1—244b
阿尔马赫 Armah, Ayi Kwei 加纳小说家 1—496e
阿尔马雷克 Almalyk 乌兹别克斯坦城市 1—244f
阿尔马特雷丁 Armatrading, Joan 英国歌唱家、歌曲作家 1—497a
阿尔马维尔 Armavir 俄罗斯城市 1—497b
阿尔玛-塔德玛 Alma-Tadema, Sir Lawrence 英国画家 1—244c
阿尔曼萨水坝 Almansa Dam 西班牙水坝 1—245b
阿尔芒蒂耶尔 Armentières 法国城镇 1—500b
阿尔梅达 Almeida, Francisco de 葡萄牙军人、探险家 1—245d
阿尔梅达 Almeida, José Américo de 巴西小说家 1—245d
阿尔梅达 Almeida, José Valentim Fialho de 葡萄牙小说家、政论家 1—245e
阿尔梅达 Almeida, Lourenço de 葡萄牙船长 1—245e
阿尔梅达 Almeida, Manuel Antônio de 巴西作家 1—245f
阿尔梅季耶夫斯克 Almetyevsk 俄罗斯城市 1—246d
阿尔梅里亚 Almería 西班牙省份 1—246b
阿尔梅里亚 Almería 西班牙海港 1—246c

阿尔门达雷斯河 Almendares River 古巴河流 1—246a
阿尔门都斯 Almendros, Nestor 西班牙电影摄影师 1—246b
阿尔蒙 Almon, John 英国记者、作家 1—246e
阿尔蒙德 Almond, Gabriel A(braham) 美国政治学家 1—247b
阿尔摩哈德人 Almohads 柏柏尔人联合体 1—246e
阿尔莫拉 Almora 印度县城 1—247c
阿尔默洛 Almelo 荷兰城市 1—245f
阿尔姆克维斯特 Almqvist, Carl Jonas Love 瑞典作家 1—247e
阿尔内斯 Alness 英国村庄 1—248a
阿尔尼格 Arnig 尼泊尔建筑家 1—506f
阿尔尼科合金 alnico 冶金学 1—248b
阿尔尼克 Alnwick 英格兰区名 1—248b
阿尔尼克 Alnwick 英格兰城镇 1—248b
阿尔尼姆 Arnim, Achim von 德国戏剧家、诗人 1—507a
阿尔尼姆 Arnim, Bettina von 德国作家 1—507b
阿尔尼切斯(-巴雷拉) Arniches (y Barrera), Carlos 西班牙剧作家 1—506f
阿尔努斯河 Arnus (Italy) 意大利河流 1—510f
阿尔诺 Arnauld, Antoine 法兰西神学家 1—505d
阿尔诺 Arnauld, Jacqueline-Marie-Angélique 法兰西隐修院改革家 1—505e
阿尔诺 Arnauld, Jeanne-Catherine-Agnès 法兰西隐修院院长 1—505e
阿尔诺·达尼埃尔 Arnaut Daniel 法国诗人 1—505f
阿尔诺·当迪利 Arnauld d'Andilly, Robert 阿尔诺家族成员 1—505f
阿尔诺·德·马勒尔 Arnaut de Mareuil 法国行吟诗人 1—505f
阿尔诺河 Arno River 意大利河流 1—507f
阿尔诺家族 Arnauld family 法兰西贵族家庭 1—505d
阿尔帕德 Arpad 叙利亚古城 1—511e
阿尔帕德王朝 Árpád dynasty 匈牙利王朝 1—511f
阿尔派恩 Alpine 美国县城 1—251c
阿尔皮尼 Alpini, Prospero 意大利医生、植物学家 1—251f
阿尔皮诺 Arpino 意大利城镇 1—513a
阿尔皮诺 Arpino, Gerald 美国芭蕾舞编导 1—513b
阿尔普 Arp, Jean 法国雕刻家 1—511e
阿尔普亚拉地毯 Alpujarra rug 西班牙工艺品 1—252c
阿尔奇安 Alchian, Armen A(lbert) 美国经济学家 1—188e
阿尔奇弗龙 Alciphron 希腊修辞学家 1—189d
阿尔奇索厄 Alcithoë 希腊传说人物 1—189e
阿尔乔莫夫斯克 Artyormovsk 乌克兰城市 1—534e
阿尔乔姆 Artyom 俄罗斯城市 1—534d
阿尔切夫斯克 Alchevsk (Ukraine) 乌克兰城市 1—188e
阿尔琼 Arjun 锡克教祖师 1—489e
阿尔让侯爵 Argens, Jean-Baptiste de Boyer, marquis d' 法国作家 1—462d
阿尔让松侯爵 Argenson, René-Louis de Voyer de Paulmy, marquis d' 法国外交大臣 1—462e
阿尔萨斯 Alsace 法国规划区 1—252d
阿尔萨斯大运河 Grand Canal d'Alsace 法国水道 7—248c
阿尔萨斯狗 Alsatian (dog) 狗品种 1—253b
阿尔萨斯-洛林 Alsace-Lorraine 法国地区 1—252f
阿尔萨瓦 Arzawa 古安纳托利亚王国 1—537d
阿尔塞尼大师 Arsenius the Great 基督教隐修士 1—519d
阿尔塞尼乌斯·奥托里安 Arsenius Autorianus 拜占廷东正教牧首 1—519d
阿尔塞斯 Arses 波斯国王 1—519e
阿尔森 Alsen (Denmark) 丹麦岛屿 1—253b
阿尔沙坎 Arshakan (king of Parthia) 安息国王 1—519f
阿尔沙库尼王朝 Arshakuni dynasty 古伊朗王朝 1—519f
阿尔斯 Als 丹麦岛屿 1—252d
阿尔斯顿 Alston, Walter (Emmons) 美国棒球队经理 1—253b
阿尔斯兰泰佩 Arslantepe (Turkey) 土耳其古城 1—520e
阿尔斯梅尔 Aalsmeer 荷兰城市 1—1f
阿尔斯司铎 Ars, Jean-Baptiste-Marie Vianney, cure d' 法兰西天主教圣徒 1—517e
阿尔斯特 Aalst 比利时城市 1—2a
阿尔斯特 Ulster 爱尔兰古省份 17—331d
阿尔斯特伯爵 Ulster, earls of 英格兰-爱尔兰封爵贵族 17—331f
阿尔斯特伯爵 Ulster, Hugh de Lacy, earl of 盎格鲁-诺曼贵族 17—332a
阿尔斯特伯爵 Ulster, Lionel of Antwerp, earl of 英格兰贵族 17—332a
阿尔斯特伯爵(第二) Ulster, Richard de Burgh, 2nd earl of 爱尔兰贵族 17—332a
阿尔斯特伯爵(第三) Ulster, Edmund Mortimer, 3rd earl of 英格兰贵族 17—332b
阿尔斯特故事 Ulster cycle 爱尔兰盖尔语文学 17—332b
阿尔斯特河 Alster River 德国河流 1—253b
阿尔斯沃特 Ullswater 英格兰湖泊 17—329e
阿尔松 Alzon, Emmanuel d' 法国天主教士 1—261e
阿尔塔 Alta 希腊城市 1—253c
阿尔塔 Árta 希腊城市 1—523f
阿尔塔雷玻璃制品 Altare glass 意大利器皿 1—254c
阿尔塔米拉洞窟 Altamira 西班牙古迹 1—254a
阿尔塔穆拉 Altamura 意大利城市 1—254b
阿尔塔湾 Árta, Gulf of 希腊海湾 1—524a
阿尔塔夏 Artaxias 古亚美尼亚王国创建者 1—525a
阿尔塔薛西斯 Artaxerxes 波斯国王之名 1—524e
阿尔塔薛西斯二世 Artaxerxes II 波斯国王 1—524f
阿尔塔薛西斯三世 Artaxerxes III 波斯国王 1—525a
阿尔塔薛西斯一世 Artaxerxes I 波斯国王 1—524e
阿尔泰 Altay 俄罗斯边疆区名 1—254d
阿尔泰山 Altay Shan 亚洲山系 1—254e
阿尔泰诸语言 Altaic languages 亚洲语言 1—253d
阿尔泰自然保护区 Altaisky Nature Reserve 俄罗斯自然区 1—254a
阿尔特 Arlt, Roberto 阿根廷小说家 1—495a
阿尔特多费尔 Altdorfer, Albrecht 德意志画家 1—255a
阿尔特多夫 Altdorf 瑞士城市 1—254f
阿尔特胡修斯 Althusius, Johannes (Latin) 荷兰政治理论家 1—255e
阿尔特吉尔德 Altgeld, John Peter 美国州长 1—255d
《阿尔特兰施泰特条约》 Altranstädt, treaties of 欧洲历史 1—257e
阿尔特米西娅二世 Artemisia II 卡里亚王后 1—525f
阿尔特米西娅一世 Artemisia I 哈利卡纳苏斯女王 1—525f
阿尔特斯 Altus 美国城市 1—258b
阿尔特瓦特山 Altvatergebirge (eastern Europe) 东欧山脉 1—258b
阿尔特温 Artvin 土耳其城市 1—534d
阿尔滕堡 Altenburg 德国城市 1—255b
阿尔提斯 Altis 希腊宗教 1—256e
阿尔图格王朝 Artuqid dynasty 土库曼人王朝 1—534c
阿尔图纳 Altoona 美国城市 1—257e
阿尔托 Artaud, Antonin 法国剧作家 1—524c
阿尔托 Aalto, (Hugo) Alvar (Henrik) 芬兰建筑师 1—2b
阿尔托纳 Altona 德国区名 1—257e
阿尔瓦尔 Alwar 印度城市 1—260e
阿尔瓦尔弟兄会 Arval Brothers 古罗马祭司团 1—536e
阿尔瓦公爵 Alba, Fernando Álvarez de Toledo y Pimentel, 3er duque de (3rd duke of) 西班牙军人 1—172c
阿尔瓦拉多 Alvarado, Pedro de 西班牙征服者 1—259e
阿尔瓦雷斯 Álvarez, Juan 墨西哥总统 1—259e
阿尔瓦雷斯·金特罗兄弟 Álvarez Quintero, Serafín and Joaquín 西班牙剧作家 1—260a
阿尔瓦雷斯·佩雷拉 Álvares Pereira, Nuno (Portuguese soldier) 葡萄

牙军事领袖 1—259e
阿尔瓦塞特 Albacete 西班牙省份 1—172f
阿尔瓦塞特 Albacete 西班牙城市 1—173a
阿尔韦罗尼 Alberoni, Giulio 意大利政治家 1—177b
阿尔韦斯·德利马-席尔瓦 Alves de Lima e Silva, Luiz 巴西政治家 1—260d
阿尔维迪 Alberdi, Juan Bautista 阿根廷政治家 1—177b
阿尔维蒂 Alberti, Rafael 西班牙诗人 1—182a
阿尔维斯 Alves, Francisco de Paula Rodrigues 巴西总统 1—260d
阿尔维亚尔 Alvear, Marcelo T(orcuato) de 阿根廷政治家 1—260b
阿尔文斯勒本-埃尔克斯勒本伯爵 Alvensleben-Erxleben, Gustav, Graf von 普鲁士将军 1—260c
阿尔沃河 Arve River 欧洲河流 1—536e
阿尔沃诺斯 Albornoz, Gil Álvarez Carrillo de 西班牙枢机主教 1—184f
阿尔西布罗斯 Althiburos 突尼斯古城市 1—255e
阿尔西拉 Alcira 西班牙城市 1—189d
阿尔西拉 Alzira 西班牙城市 1—261d
阿尔西涅加斯 Arciniegas, Germán 哥伦比亚历史学家 1—455b
阿尔西诺伊 Arsinoe 埃及王后名 1—519f
阿尔西诺伊二世 Arsinoe II 埃及王后 1—520a
阿尔西诺伊三世 Arsinoe III 埃及王后 1—520b
阿尔西诺伊四世 Arsinoe IV 埃及王后 1—520d
阿尔西诺伊一世 Arsinoe I 埃及王后 1—519f
阿尔西品科 Archipenko, Alexander 美籍乌克兰裔雕刻家、画家 1—451f
阿尔辛多 Alcindor, Lew (basketball player) 美国篮球运动员 1—189d
阿尔-尤库瑟 Uqṣur, al- (Egypt) 埃及城镇 17—406c
阿尔泽 Arzew 阿尔及利亚港口 1—537d
阿尔泽特河畔埃施 Esch-sur-Alzette 卢森堡城镇 6—128b
阿尔扎马斯 Arzamas 俄罗斯城市 1—537c
阿尔扎马斯社 Arzamas society 俄国文学团体 1—537c
阿尔扎斯河 Árdhas (Europe) 欧洲河流 1—458e
阿尔志跋绥夫 Artsybashev, Mikhail Petrovich 俄国散文作家 1—534c
阿耳戈斯 Argus Panoptes 希腊传说人物 1—467f
阿耳忒弥斯 Artemis 希腊女神 1—525b
阿耳忒弥斯神庙 Artemis, Temple of 世界七大奇观之一 1—525e
阿耳瓦雷茨 Alvarez, Luis W(alter) 美国物理学家 1—259f
阿耳文 Alfvén, Hannes 瑞典天文学家 1—219c
阿法尔人 Afar 非洲民族 1—103a
阿法纳西耶夫 Afanasev, Aleksandr Nikolayevich 俄国文学史家 1—102f
阿凡 Afan (Wales) 英国城市 1—102f
阿方斯 Arfons, Art 美国赛车运动员 1—461f
阿方索 Alfonso 阿拉贡、纳瓦拉国王 1—216a
阿方索 Alfonso 统治者之名 1—216a
阿方索(纯洁的) Alfonso the Chaste 阿斯图里亚斯国王 1—218e
阿方索(非洲人) Alfonso the African 葡萄牙国王 1—218d
阿方索(高尚的) Alfonso the Magnanimous 阿拉贡国王 1—218f
阿方索(高尚的) Alfonso the Noble 莱昂国王 1—218f
阿方索(皇帝) Alfonso the Emperor 莱昂和卡斯蒂利亚国王 1—218e
阿方索(开明的) Alfonso the Liberal 阿拉贡国王 1—218f
阿方索(胖子) Alfonso the Fat 葡萄牙国王 1—218e
阿方索(善良的) Alfonso the Kind 阿拉贡国王 1—218e
阿方索(坦率的) Alfonso the Candid 阿拉贡国王 1—218d
阿方索(天主教徒) Alfonso the Catholic 阿斯图里亚斯国王 1—218d
阿方索(伟大的) Alfonso the Great 阿斯图里亚斯国王 1—218e
阿方索(修道士) Alfonso the Monk 莱昂和阿斯图里亚斯国王 1—218f
阿方索(勇敢者) Alfonso the Brave 卡斯蒂利亚和莱昂国王 1—218d
阿方索(战斗者) Alfonso the Battler 阿拉贡国王、纳瓦拉国王 1—218d
阿方索(征服者) Alfonso the Conqueror 葡萄牙国王 1—218e
阿方索(正义的) Alfonso the Just 卡斯蒂利亚和莱昂国王 1—218e
阿方索(智者) Alfonso the Wise 卡斯蒂利亚和莱昂国王 1—218f
阿方索八世 Alfonso VIII 卡斯蒂利亚国王 1—217e
阿方索二世 Alfonso II 阿拉贡国王 1—216c
阿方索二世 Alfonso II 阿斯图里亚斯国王 1—216f
阿方索环形山 Alphonsus 月球环形山 1—251b
阿方索九世 Alfonso IX 莱昂国王 1—217f
阿方索六世 Alfonso VI 莱昂国王 1—217b
阿方索七世 Alfonso VII 莱昂和卡斯蒂利亚国王 1—217d
阿方索三世 Alfonso III 阿拉贡国王 1—216c
阿方索三世 Alfonso III 阿斯图里亚斯国王 1—217a
阿方索十二世 Alfonso XII 西班牙国王 1—218b
阿方索十三世 Alfonso XIII 西班牙国王 1—218c
阿方索十世 Alfonso X 卡斯蒂利亚和莱昂国王 1—217f
阿方索十一世 Alfonso XI 卡斯蒂利亚和莱昂国王 1—218b
阿方索四世 Alfonso IV 阿拉贡国王 1—216c
阿方索四世 Alfonso IV 莱昂和阿斯图里亚斯国王 1—217a
阿方索五世 Alfonso V 阿拉贡国王 1—216c
阿方索五世 Alfonso V 莱昂国王 1—217a
《阿方索星表》 Alfonsine Tables 天文学 1—215f
阿方索一世 Alfonso I 意大利费拉拉公爵 1—216a
阿方索一世 Alfonso I 阿拉贡国王 1—216a
阿方索一世 Alfonso I 阿拉贡、纳瓦拉国王 1—216b
阿方索一世 Alfonso I 阿斯图里亚斯国王 1—216f
阿非利加 Africa 罗马历史 1—107b
阿非利加努斯 Africanus, Sextus Julius 基督教历史学家 1—112b
阿非利堪人联盟 Afrikaner Bond 非洲政党 1—112c
阿非利堪人兄弟会 Afrikaner-Broederbond 南非秘密团体 1—112d
阿非利堪斯语 Afrikaans language 南非语言 1—112c
阿菲永 Afyon 土耳其城市 1—113d
阿费克 Aphek 迦南王城 1—408b
阿费泰西王朝 Afṭasid dynasty 柏柏尔人王朝 1—113a
阿芬那留斯 Avenarius, Richard (Heinrich Ludwig) 德国哲学家 2—84d
阿丰 Arfon 威尔士区名 1—461f
阿丰索 Afonso 统治者之名 1—106d
阿丰索二世 Afonso II 葡萄牙国王 1—106e
阿丰索六世 Afonso VI 阿丰索六世 1—106f
阿丰索三世 Afonso III 葡萄牙国王 1—106e
阿丰索四世 Afonso IV 葡萄牙国王 1—106e
阿丰索五世 Afonso V 葡萄牙国王 1—106f
阿丰索一世 Afonso I 刚果王国国王 1—106d
阿丰索一世 Afonso I 葡萄牙国王 1—106d
阿夫顿间冰期 Aftonian Interglacial Stage 地质学 1—113d
阿夫季拉 Abdera 古希腊城镇 1—14c
阿夫拉姆河 Afram River 加纳河流 1—107a
阿夫朗什 Avranches 法国港口 2—91d
阿夫里迪人 Afrīdī 亚洲民族 1—112b
阿夫扎勒·奥丁·巴代勒·伊卜拉欣·伊本·哈加尼·希尔凡尼 Afẓal od-Dīn Bādel Ebrāhīm ebn ʿAlī Khāqānī Shīrvānī 波斯诗人 1—113e
阿弗拉阿蒂斯 Aphraates 叙利亚禁欲主义者 1—408f
阿弗拉克 ʿAflaq, 阿拉伯政治领袖 1—106c
阿弗拉尼乌斯 Afranius, Lucius 罗马将军 1—107a
阿弗莱克 Affleck, Thomas 美国家具工匠 1—104a
阿弗乐 Affre, Denis-Auguste 法国巴黎大主教 1—104b
阿弗里 Avery, John 英国海盗 2—87a

阿弗罗狄西亚 Aphrodisias 小亚细亚地区古城 1—409a
阿佛洛狄忒 Aphrodite 古希腊女神 1—409b
阿佛洛狄忒台地 Aphrodite Terra 金星表面高原台地 1—409d
阿伏伽德罗定律 Avogadro's law 物理学 2—90e
阿福花 asphodel 草本植物 1—557e
阿富汗 Afghanistan 中亚国家 1—105b
阿富汗地毯 Afghan carpet 工艺品 1—104c
阿富汗猎狗 Afghan hound 狗品种 1—104d
阿富汗人 Afghan 亚洲民族 1—104c
阿富汗人入寇时期 Afghan interlude 伊朗历史 1—104e
阿富汗语 Afghan language 亚洲语言 1—104f
阿富汗战争 Afghan Wars 英阿战争 1—105a
阿富汗战争 Afghan War 阿富汗内战 1—104f
阿富拉 ʻAfula 以色列城市 1—113d
阿盖 Agaie 尼日利亚城镇、酋长国名 1—114d
阿盖尔 Argyll 苏格兰地区 1—468a
阿盖尔-比特区 Argyll and Bute 苏格兰区名 1—468f
阿盖尔伯爵(第九) Argyll, Archibald Campbell, 9th Earl of 苏格兰新教领袖 1—468d
阿盖尔伯爵(第十)和公爵(第一) Argyll, Archibald Campbell, 10th Earl and 1st Duke of 苏格兰革命领袖 1—468d
阿盖尔伯爵(第五) Argyll, Archibald Campbell, 5th Earl of 苏格兰大法官 1—468b
阿盖尔伯爵、侯爵和公爵 Argyll, EARLS, MARQUESSES, AND DUKES OF 苏格兰封爵贵族 1—468b
阿盖尔公爵(第二) Argyll, John Campbell, 2nd Duke of 英国陆军元帅 1—468e
阿盖尔公爵(第三) Argyll, Archibald Campbell, 3rd Duke of 英国政治家 1—468e
阿盖尔侯爵(第一)和伯爵(第八) Argyll, Archibald Campbell, 1st Marquess and 8th Earl of 苏格兰反保王派领袖 1—468c
阿盖姆 Agam, Yaacov 以色列雕塑家 1—114e
阿高人 Agau 埃塞俄比亚民族 1—118b
阿戈巴尔德 Agobard, SAINT 法国大主教 1—125d
阿戈讷 Argonne 法国山林区 1—466f
阿戈斯蒂诺 Agostino DI DUCCIO 意大利雕刻家 1—126a
阿戈斯蒂诺 Agostino DI GIOVANNI 意大利雕刻家 1—126c
阿戈斯托利翁 Argostólion 希腊海港 1—467c
阿革劳罗斯 Aglauros 希腊神话人物 1—123e
阿格达斯 Arguedas, Alcides 玻利维亚小说家 1—467d
阿格达斯 Arguedas, José María 秘鲁小说家 1—467d
阿格迪斯蒂斯 Agdistis (religion) 古代神话 1—118e
阿格拉 Āgra 印度城市 1—126f
阿格拉蒙特-西莫尼 Agramonte y Simoni, Aristides 美国医师、细菌学家 1—127a
阿格兰德 Argelander, Friedrich Wilhelm August 德国天文学家 1—462c
阿格雷 Agre, Peter 美国医生 1—127b
阿格雷达 Agreda, María de 西班牙神学家 1—127c
阿格里奥尼亚节 Agrionia 希腊宗教节日 1—130a
阿格里巴扬教会 Aglipayan Church 菲律宾教会 1—123e
阿格里·戴可美特 Agri Decumates 德国古代地区 1—127d
阿格里汉岛 Agrihan 美国火山岛 1—129f
阿格里科拉 Agricola, Alexander 荷兰作曲家 1—127e
阿格里科拉 Agricola, Georgius 德意志科学家 1—127f
阿格里科拉 Agricola, Gnaeus Julius 罗马将军 1—128b
阿格里科拉 Agricola, Johann 德意志神学家 1—128c
阿格里科拉 Agricola, Martin 德意志作曲家 1—128c
阿格里科拉 Agricola, Rodolphus 荷兰人文主义者 1—128d
阿格里尼翁 Agrínion 希腊城镇 1—130a
阿格里帕 Agrippa, Marcus Vipsanius 罗马帝国宰相 1—130b
阿格里帕 Agrippa 希腊哲学家 1—130b
阿格里帕·冯·内特斯海姆 Agrippa von Nettesheim, Heinrich Cornelius 德国神秘学家 1—130d
阿格里真托 Agrigento 意大利城市 1—129e
阿格丽品娜(大) Agrippina THE ELDER 罗马贵族 1—130e
阿格丽品娜(小) Agrippina THE YOUNGER 罗马贵族 1—130e
阿格尼霍特利 Agnihotri, Shiv Narayan 印度社会改革家 1—124f
阿格尼人 Agni (people) 非洲民族 1—124e
阿格尼斯,圣 Agnes, SAINT 罗马殉教者 1—124b
阿格纽 Agnew, Spiro T(heodore) 美国副总统 1—124d
阿格农 Agnon, Shmuel Yosef 以色列小说家 1—124f
阿格诺 Haguenau 法国城镇 7—408b
阿格索 Aguesseau, Henri-François d' 法国法学家 1—131d
阿格特 Agate, James (Evershed) 英国戏剧评论家 1—117c
阿格瓦尔 Agarwālā 印度种姓 1—116b
阿格西劳斯二世 Agesilaus II 斯巴达国王 1—120f
阿根廷 Argentina 南美国家 1—463c
阿根廷海盆 Argentine Basin 大西洋海底盆地 1—465b
阿根廷娜 Argentina, La 西班牙舞蹈家 1—465a
阿根廷自然科学博物馆 Argentine Museum of Natural Sciences 阿根廷博物馆 1—465c
阿根廷总工会 Confederación General del Trabajo (CGT) 阿根廷工人组织 4—419c
阿贡 Agung 马打蓝王国苏丹 1—132c
阿贡 Agung, Abulfatah 爪哇苏丹王国统治者 1—132d
阿贡火山 Agung, Mount 印度尼西亚火山 1—132d
阿缑 Akow (Taiwan) 中国台湾县名 1—157e
阿古 Agoult, Marie(-Catherine-Sophie) de Flavigny, comtesse d' (countess of) 德国作家 1—126d
阿古柏 Yakub Beg 中国新疆割据政权头目 18—406a
阿古桑河 Agusan River 菲律宾河流 1—132e
阿古山 Agou, Mont (Togo) 多哥山脉 1—126d
阿古斯蒂尼 Agustini, Delmira 乌拉圭诗人 1—132e
阿古斯蒂诺 El Agustino 秘鲁区首府 6—9e
阿古斯丁一世 Agustín I 墨西哥皇帝 1—132e
阿古斯·萨利姆 Agus Salim, Hadji 印度尼西亚民族领袖 1—132d
阿骨打 A-Ku-Ta 中国金代创立者 1—1a
阿瓜迪亚 Aguadilla 波多黎各城镇 1—131a
阿瓜里科河 Aguarico River 厄瓜多尔河流 1—131b
阿瓜斯卡连特斯 Aguascalientes 墨西哥州名 1—131c
阿瓜斯卡连特斯 Aguascalientes 墨西哥城市 1—131c
阿关河 Aguán River 洪都拉斯河流 1—131a
阿圭略 Arguello, Alexis 尼加拉瓜职业拳击运动员 1—467e
阿桂 Agui 中国清代大臣 1—131e
阿哈(沙拜的) Aḥa OF SHABḤA 犹太学者 1—132f
阿哈德·哈阿姆 Aḥad Haʻam 犹太复国主义领袖 1—133a
阿哈加尔 Ahaggar 非洲高原 1—133b
阿哈马德沙 Aḥmad Shāh Durrānī 阿富汗国王 1—135d
阿哈米语 Ajami language 西班牙语古代方言 1—150d
阿哈伊亚 Akhaïa (Greece) 希腊地区 1—154c
阿含 agama 印度教著作 1—115a
阿赫 Aḥer (Jewish heretic) 犹太学者 1—133d
阿赫蒂萨里 Ahtisaari, Martti 芬兰政治家 1—138b
阿赫费肖赫菲克湾 Arfersiorfik Fjord 格陵兰海湾 1—461e
阿赫来姆人 Akhlame 叙利亚民族 1—155a
阿赫林 Ahlin, Lars 瑞典小说家 1—134c
阿赫马杜林娜 Akhmadulina, Bella 俄罗斯诗人 1—155b
阿赫马托娃 Akhmatova, Anna 苏联诗人 1—155c
阿赫玛德 Ali Haji bin Raja Amhad, Raja 布吉-马来王子 1—227b
阿赫默德 Ahmad, Mirza Ghulam 印度穆斯林派别的创立者 1—134e
阿赫默德 Ahmed, Fakhruddin Ali 印度政治家 1—136e
阿赫默德·巴巴 Aḥmad Bābā 苏丹法学家、文化领袖 1—134e
阿赫默德·沙赫 Aḥmad Shāh 印度莫卧儿皇帝 1—135d
阿赫默德·伊本·罕百里 Aḥmad ibn Ḥanbal 伊斯兰教义学家 1—

134f
阿赫默德·尤拉比帕夏·米斯里 Aḥmad ʿUrābī Pasha al-Miṣrī 埃及民族主义者 1—136b
阿赫默底亚教派 Aḥmadīyah 伊斯兰教派 1—135f
阿赫诺巴布斯 Ahenobarbus, Gnaeus Domitius 罗马将军 1—133c
阿赫诺巴布斯 Ahenobarbus, Lucius Domitius (Roman emperor) 罗马皇帝 1—133d
阿赫诺巴布斯 Ahenobarbus, Lucius Domitius 罗马贵族党领袖 1—133c
阿赫萨尔 Aḥsāʾī, al- 伊朗伊斯兰教领袖 1—138a
阿赫韦南马群岛 Ahvenanmaa (Finland) 芬兰岛屿 1—138e
阿亨巴赫 Achenbach, Andreas 德国画家 1—51d
阿亨巴赫 Achenbach, Oswald 德国画家 1—51d
阿胡拉·玛兹达 Ahura Mazdā 琐罗亚斯德教神祇 1—138d
阿霍 Aho, Juhani 芬兰小说家 1—137e
阿霍 Ajo 美国城镇 1—151f
阿霍姆人 Ahom 亚洲民族 1—137f
阿基尔岛 Achill Island 爱尔兰岛屿 1—52d
阿基劳斯 Archelaus 卡帕多西亚国王 1—447f
阿基劳斯 Archelaus 马其顿国王 1—447f
阿基里斯画匠 Achilles Painter 雅典画匠 1—52f
阿基利尼 Achillini, Alessandro 意大利哲学家、内科医生 1—53c
阿基利斯悖论 Achilles paradox 物理学 1—53a
阿基琉斯·塔提奥斯 Achilles Tatius 希腊教师、作家 1—53b
阿基米德 Archimedes 古希腊数学家 1—450b
阿基米德螺旋泵 Archimedes screw 提升水的机器 1—451d
阿基米德原理 Archimedes' principle 物理学 1—451c
阿基莫夫 Akimov, Nikolay Pavlovich 苏联舞台设计师 1—156c
阿基诺 Aquino, Benigno Simeon, Jr. 菲律宾政治家 1—428e
阿基诺(夫人) Aquino, Corazon 菲律宾政治家 1—428e
阿基坦 Aquitaine 法国大区名 1—429a
阿吉巴·本·约瑟 Akiba ben Joseph 犹太法学者 1—156a
阿吉德王朝 Argead DYNASTY 古代马其顿统治家族 1—462b
阿吉科约人 Agekoyo (people) 非洲民族 1—119c
阿吉拉尔 Aguilar, Grace 英国作家 1—131f
阿吉勒 ʿāqil 伊斯兰教法 1—426a
阿吉雷 Aguirre, Lope de 西班牙冒险家 1—132a
阿吉西子爵 Aguisy, Jean Grolier, vicomte d' 法国藏书家 1—132b
阿加 aga 土耳其官级称号 1—113f
阿加比 agape 希腊语名词(意为爱) 1—115d
阿加德兹 Agadez 尼日尔城镇 1—114b
阿加迪尔 Agadir 摩洛哥城市 1—114c
阿加迪尔事件 Agadir Incident 欧洲历史 1—114d
阿加尔塔拉 Agartala 印度城市 1—116a
阿加莱加群岛 Agalega Islands 毛里求斯群岛 1—114e
阿加·礼萨 Āqā Rezā 波斯画家 1—425d
阿加尼亚 Agana 美国城市 1—115c
阿加佩图斯 Agapetus 教皇称号 1—115d
阿加佩图斯二世 Agapetus II 教皇 1—115e
阿加佩图斯一世,圣 Agapetus I, SAINT 教皇 1—115d
阿加索克利斯 Agathocles 西西里统治者 1—118a
阿加塔 Agatha, SAINT 西西里殉教者 1—117f
阿加提阿斯 Agathias 拜占廷诗人 1—117f
阿加托,圣 Agatho, SAINT 教皇 1—118a
阿加西 Agassiz, Alexander (Emmanuel Rodolphe) 瑞士海洋动物学家 1—116b
阿加西 Agassiz, Elizabeth Cabot 美国博物学家、教育家 1—116c
阿加西 Agassiz, (Jean) Louis (Rodolphe) 美国博物学家 1—116d
阿加西湖 Agassiz, Lake 加拿大冰缘湖 1—116c
阿加扎 Agaja 达荷美国王 1—114d
阿加扎里 Agazzari, Agostino 意大利作曲家 1—118d
阿伽门农 Agamemnon 希腊传说人物 1—115b
阿伽门农墓 Tomb of Agamemnon 希腊考古遗址 17—144a
阿迦汗 Aga Khan 尼查尔支派精神领袖称号 1—113f
阿迦汗二世 Aga Khan II 尼查尔支派精神领袖 1—114a
阿迦汗三世 Aga Khan III 尼查尔支派精神领袖 1—114a
阿迦汗四世 Aga Khan IV 尼查尔支派精神领袖 1—114b
阿迦汗一世 Aga Khan I 尼查尔支派精神领袖 1—113f
阿迦·米拉克 Āqā Mīrak 波斯画家 1—425d
阿迦·穆罕默德·汗 Āghā Moḥammad Khān 伊朗统治者 1—122b
阿迦特叙事诗 Aqhat Epic 古代闪米特人传说 1—425f
阿迦同 Agathon 雅典诗人 1—118b
阿杰梅尔 Ajmer 印度城市 1—151e
阿捷纶 azlon 人造纤维 2—102b
阿金 Ah Kin 马雅宗教 1—132f
阿金-布里亚特 Agin-Buryatiya 俄罗斯自治区名 1—122c
阿金迪诺斯 Akindynos, Gregorios 拜占廷神学家 1—156d
阿金斯科耶 Aginskoye 俄罗斯城市 1—123a
阿喀琉斯 Achilles 希腊神话人物 1—52d
阿喀琉斯腱 Achilles tendon 解剖学 1—53c
阿喀斯 Acis 希腊神话人物 1—55a
阿卡 ʿAkko 以色列城市 1—157a
阿卡得 Akkad 伊拉克古地区 1—156f
阿卡德 ʿAqqād, ʿAbbās Maḥmūd al- 埃及记者 1—426b
阿卡德尔菲亚 Arkadelphia 美国城市 1—490a
阿卡德尔特 Arcadelt, Jacob 比利时作曲家 1—445b
阿卡德语 Akkadian language 美索不达米亚语言 1—156f
阿卡德语楔形文字 Akkadian writing 近东古代文字 1—157a
阿卡狄乌斯 Arcadius 东罗马皇帝 1—445f
阿卡迪亚 Acadia 法国前北美领地 1—41d
阿卡迪亚 Arcadia 古希腊山区 1—445b
阿卡迪亚 Arcadia 美国城市 1—445c
阿卡迪亚国家公园 Acadia National Park 美国公园 1—41e
阿卡迪亚诗社 arcádia 葡萄牙文学社团 1—445d
阿卡迪亚学院 Arcadia, Academy of 意大利文学院 1—445e
阿卡迪亚造山幕 Acadian orogeny 地质学 1—41f
阿卡尔派 Akālī 锡克教派别 1—152c
阿卡尔寺 Akāl Takht 印度锡克教寺庙 1—152b
阿卡胡特拉 Acajutla 萨尔瓦多海港 1—42a
阿卡卡瀑布 Akaka Falls 美国瀑布 1—152b
阿卡拉伊山脉 Acaraí Mountains 南美洲山脉 1—42d
阿卡里夫人 Acarie, Barbe-Jeanne Avrillot, Mme (French mystic) 法国神权主义者 1—42e
阿卡里瓜 Acarigua 委内瑞拉城市 1—42e
阿卡罗 Arcaro, Eddie 美国骑手 1—445f
阿卡罗阿 Akaroa 新西兰社区 1—152e
阿卡纳尼亚 Acarnania 希腊古地区 1—43f
阿卡普尔科 Acapulco 墨西哥港口 1—42c
阿卡沙秘录 Akashic record 神秘学 1—152f
阿卡西乌斯分裂 Acacian Schism 天主教历史 1—39f
阿开基木 akee (*Blighia sapida*) 木本植物 1—153d
阿开民王朝 Achaemenid DYNASTY 埃及王朝 1—50e
阿凯斯特斯 Acestes 希腊神话人物 1—48f
阿凯西劳斯 Arcesilaus 希腊哲学家 1—446a
阿坎巴罗 Acámbaro 墨西哥城市 1—42a
阿坎人 Akan 非洲民族 1—152c
阿坎诸邦 Akan states 西非历史国家 1—152e
阿科拉 Akola 印度城市 1—157d
阿科利人 Acoli (people) 非洲民族 1—55e
阿科马 Acoma 美国村庄 1—55e
阿科米纳图斯 Acominatus, Nicetas 拜占廷历史学家 1—55f
阿科斯塔 Acosta, Joaquín 哥伦比亚科学家 1—56e
阿科斯塔 Acosta, José de 西班牙神学家 1—56f
阿科斯塔 Acosta, Uriel 犹太哲学家 1—57a
阿科松博坝 Akosombo Dam 加纳填石坝 1—157d
阿克巴 Akbar 印度莫卧儿王朝皇帝 1—153a

阿克巴时代建筑 Akbar period architecture 建筑 1—153c
阿克顿 Acton (of Aldenham), John Emerich Edward Dalberg Acton, 1st Baron, 8th Baronet 英国历史学家、伦理学家 1—61e
阿克顿 Acton, Sir John Francis Edward, 6th Baronet 法国海军司令 1—62a
阿克尔 Arkell, Anthony John 英国历史学家 1—492f
阿克尔 Arkell, William Joscelyn 英国古生物学家 1—492f
阿克尔洛夫 Akerlof, George A. 美国经济学家 1—154b
阿克尔曼 Akkerman (Ukraine) 乌克兰城市 1—157a
阿克发-吉伐集团 Agfa-Gevaert Group 德国、比利时公司集团 1—121a
阿克纠宾斯克 Aktyubinsk 哈萨克斯坦州名 1—159b
阿克拉 Accra 加纳首都 1—47d
阿克拉内斯 Akranes 冰岛城镇 1—157e
阿克拉维克 Aklavik 加拿大村庄 1—157c
阿克赖特 Arkwright, Sir Richard 英国纺织工业家 1—493b
阿克雷里 Akureyri 冰岛城镇 1—159c
阿克里 Acre 巴西州名 1—57e
阿克里河 Acre River 巴西河流 1—58a
阿克利 Akeley, Carl (Ethan) 美国博物学家 1—153e
阿克伦 Akron 美国城市 1—157e
阿克罗波利特斯 Acropolites, George 拜占廷学者 1—58d
阿克罗蒂里 Akrotiri 塞浦路斯英国军事占领地 1—157f
阿克洛 Arklow 爱尔兰港口 1—493b
阿克曼 Ackermann, Konrad Ernst 德国演员 1—55b
阿克曼 Ackermann, Louise-Victorine 法国诗人 1—55b
阿克梅派 Acmeist 俄罗斯诗人团体 1—55c
阿克莫拉 Aqmola 哈萨克斯坦城市 1—426a
阿克莫林斯克 Akmolinsk (city, Kazakhstan) 哈萨克斯坦城市 1—157c
阿克姆-乌斯-蒙德什 Aquem-os-Montes (Portugal) 葡萄牙前省份 1—428a
阿克齐乌斯 Accius, Lucius 罗马诗人 1—45f
阿克萨科夫 Aksakov, Sergey Timofeyevich 俄罗斯小说家 1—158a
阿克塞尔罗德 Axelrod, Julius 美国生化药理学家 2—93a
阿克塞斯·莎莉 Axis Sally (propagandist) 美国叛国者 2—94a
阿克沙克 Akshak 美索不达米亚城市 1—158c
阿克什胡斯 Akershus 挪威郡名 1—154c
阿克斯霍姆岛 Axholme, Isle of 英格兰地区 2—93b
阿克斯明斯特 Axminster 英格兰城镇 2—94a
阿克斯明斯特地毯 Axminster carpet 英国工艺品 2—94a
阿克苏 Aksu 中国城市 1—158c
阿克苏河 Aksu River 中国河流 1—158e
阿克苏姆 Aksum 非洲古代王国 1—158f
阿克苏姆 Aksum 埃塞俄比亚古城镇 1—158f
阿克特翁 Actaeon 希腊神话人物 1—59c
阿克托别 Aqtöbe 哈萨克斯坦城市 1—426b
阿克瓦穆 Akwamu 加纳南部阿坎人国家 1—159f
阿克希萨尔 Akhisar 土耳其城镇 1—155a
阿克肖诺夫 Aksyonov, Vasily Pavlovich 俄罗斯小说家 1—159a
阿克谢利罗德 Akselrod, Pavel Borisovich 俄罗斯政治学家 1—158b
阿肯 Aken (Germany) 德国城市 1—153f
阿肯 Aken, Jerome van 佛兰德斯画家 1—153f
阿肯 Aquen, Jerome van 佛兰德斯画家 1—428b
阿肯 Aeken, Jeroen van 佛兰德斯画家 1—93d
阿肯那顿 Akhenaton 埃及国王 1—154d
阿肯色 Arkansas 美国州名 1—490a
阿肯色城 Arkansas City 美国城市 1—492c
阿肯色河 Arkansas River 美国河流 1—492d
阿肯色河航行系统 Arkansas River Navigation System 美国航运 1—492e
阿肯色站 Arkansas Post 美国历史村庄 1—492c
阿空加瓜河 Aconcagua River 智利河流 1—56a
阿空加瓜山 Aconcagua, Mount 阿根廷山峰 1—55f
阿孔蒂乌斯 Acontius 希腊传说人物 1—56b
阿孔齐奥 Aconcio, Giacomo 意大利基督教改革者 1—56a
阿库雷 Akure 尼日利亚城市 1—159c
阿库尼亚 Acuña (Mexico) 墨西哥城市 1—62d
阿库尼亚城 Ciudad Acuña 墨西哥城市 4—251d
阿库尼亚镇 Villa Acuña (Mexico) 墨西哥城市 17—562b
阿库修斯 Accursius, Franciscus 意大利法学家 1—48a
阿夸平-多哥岭 Akwapim-Togo Ranges 加纳山地 1—159f
阿夸伊博姆 Akwa Ibom 尼日利亚州名 1—159e
阿奎德内克岛 Aquidneck Island (Rhode Island, U.S.) 美国岛屿 1—428b
阿奎拉 Aquila 古《圣经》学者 1—428c
阿奎莱亚 Aquileia 罗马帝国城市 1—428c
阿奎纳多 Aguinaldo, Emilio 菲律宾领袖 1—131f
阿奎诺 Aquino 意大利古城 1—428d
阿奎维瓦 Aquaviva, Claudio 天主教耶稣会会长 1—427d
阿拉 Ara 印度城市 1—429b
阿拉 Aragh (Vanuatu) 瓦努阿图火山岛 1—435e
阿拉巴尔 Arrabal, Fernando 法国荒诞派剧作家 1—513c
阿拉巴马勾儿茶 rattan vine 木本植物 14—163e
阿拉贝斯坦 ʻArabestān (Iran) 伊朗行省 1—431a
阿拉比亚 Arabia 罗马行省 1—433a
阿拉伯半岛 Arabia 亚洲半岛地区 1—431a
阿拉伯的劳伦斯 Lawrence of Arabia 英国学者 9—530b
阿拉伯狒狒 hamadryas (*Papio hamadryas*) 哺乳动物 7—435e
阿拉伯复兴社会党 Arab Socialist Renaissance Party 阿拉伯政治组织 1—430e
阿拉伯谷地 Al-ʻArabah, Wadi 巴勒斯坦洼地 1—160b
阿拉伯国家联盟 Arab League 阿拉伯组织 1—430b
阿拉伯海 Arabian Sea 印度洋边缘海 1—433e
阿拉伯海盆 Arabian Basin 印度洋海底盆地 1—433b
阿拉伯河 al-ʻArab, Shaṭṭ 伊拉克河流 1—160a
阿拉伯河 Baḥr al-ʻArab 苏丹河流 2—142f
阿拉伯货币基金组织 Arab Monetary Fund 阿拉伯国家联盟组织 1—430d
阿拉伯经济和社会发展基金会 Arab Fund for Economic and Social Development 阿拉伯组织 1—429e
阿拉伯经济统一理事会 Arab Economic Unity, Council of 阿拉伯国家联盟组织 1—429e
阿拉伯军团 Arab Legion 约旦军队 1—400c
阿拉伯联合共和国 United Arab Republic (U.A.R.) 埃及-叙利亚历史联合体 17—351a
阿拉伯联合酋长国 United Arab Emirates (U.A.E.) 亚洲国家 17—350b
阿拉伯马 Arabian horse 马品种 1—433d
阿拉伯人 Arab 亚、非民族 1—429c
阿拉伯三角帆船 dhow 船舶 5—281a
阿拉伯沙漠 Arabian Desert (Egypt) 埃及沙漠 1—433b
阿拉伯沙漠 Arabian Desert 亚洲沙漠 1—433b
阿拉伯石油输出国组织 Arab Petroleum Exporting Countries, Organization of (OAPEC) 阿拉伯组织 1—430d
阿拉伯式花饰 arabesque 文学 1—431a
阿拉伯湾 Arabian Gulf (Asia) 印度洋边缘海 1—433d
阿拉伯文学 Arabic literature 阿拉伯文文学作品 1—434c
阿拉伯文学复兴 Arabic literary renaissance 阿拉伯文学运动 1—434b
阿拉伯语 Arabic language 北非、中东语言 1—434a
阿拉伯语学校 maktab 穆斯林小学 10—417f
阿拉伯装饰风格 arabesque 阿拉伯艺术 1—430e
阿拉伯字母系统 Arabic alphabet 语言学 1—433e
阿拉德 ʻArad 以色列城镇 1—434f

阿拉德 Arad 罗马尼亚城市 1—435a
阿拉德 Arad 罗马尼亚县名 1—435a
阿拉丁 Aladdin 文学故事人物 1—164d
阿拉丁·阿里·阿舍克·帕夏 Alâeddin Ali Aşik Paşa 土耳其诗人 1—164f
阿拉·丁·阿塔·马莱克·约韦尼 'Alā' od-Dīn 'Atā Malek Joveynī (Persian historian) 波斯历史学家 1—160e
阿拉杜拉 Aladura 尼日利亚宗教运动 1—164e
阿拉尔孔 Alarcón (y Mendoza), Juan Ruiz de (dramatist) 西班牙戏剧家 1—166e
阿拉尔孔-阿里萨 Alarcón y Ariza, Pedro Antonio de 西班牙作家 1—166e
阿拉尔树 arartree (*Tetraclinis articulata*) 木本植物 1—440d
阿拉法特 'Arafāt, Yāsir 巴勒斯坦政治家 1—435b
阿拉法与俄梅戛 Alpha and Omega 基督教 1—249e
阿拉弗拉海 Arafura Sea 西太平洋浅海 1—435d
阿拉戈 Arago, (Dominique-) François (-Jean) 法国物理学家 1—435e
阿拉戈斯 Alagoas 巴西州名 1—164f
阿拉戈伊尼亚斯 Alagoinhas 巴西城市 1—165a
阿拉贡 Aragon, Louis 法国诗人 1—436a
阿拉贡地区 Aragon 西班牙地区 1—435f
阿拉瓜 Aragua 委内瑞拉州名 1—436c
阿拉瓜里 Araguari 巴西城市 1—436d
阿拉瓜亚河 Araguaia River 巴西河流 1—436d
阿拉胡埃拉 Alajuela 哥斯达黎加省份 1—165c
阿拉胡埃拉 Alajuela 哥斯达黎加城市 1—165d
阿拉湖 Alakol, Lake 哈萨克斯坦盐湖 1—165d
阿拉加茨山 Aragats, Mount 亚美尼亚山脉 1—435e
阿拉贾许于克 Alaca Hüyük 古安纳托利亚遗址 1—164c
阿拉喀涅 Arachne 希腊神话人物 1—434e
阿拉卡茹 Aracaju 巴西城市 1—434d
阿拉科斯战役 Alarcos, Battle of 历史事件 1—166e
阿拉克切耶夫 Arakcheyev, Aleksey Andreyevich, Graf (Count) 俄国军官 1—437a
阿拉拉赫 Alalakh 叙利亚古城 1—165d
阿拉拉夸拉 Araraquara 巴西城市 1—440b
阿拉拉特 Ararat 澳大利亚城市 1—440b
阿拉里克 Alaric 西哥特人首领 1—166f
阿拉里克二世 Alaric II 西哥特国王 1—167a
阿拉曼 Alamán, Lucas 墨西哥政治家 1—165d
阿拉曼战役 Alamein, battles of el- 第二次世界大战史 1—165e
阿拉梅达 Alameda 美国城市 1—165e
阿拉米人 Aramaean 中东民族 1—438d
阿拉米语 Aramaic language 中东语言 1—438f
阿拉米字母 Aramaic alphabet 中东文字体系 1—438e
阿拉莫 Alamo 美国纪念地 1—165f
阿拉莫戈多 Alamogordo 美国县城 1—166a
阿拉莫萨 Alamosa 美国城市 1—166b
阿拉木图 Almaty 哈萨克斯坦城市 1—245c
阿拉尼亚 Aranha, José Pereira da Graça 巴西小说家 1—439d
阿拉帕 ālāpa 印度、巴基斯坦音乐 1—166d
阿拉帕霍人 Arapaho 北美民族 1—440a
阿拉帕耶夫斯克 Alapayevsk 俄罗斯城市 1—166e
阿拉萨里雀 aracari 巨嘴鸟 1—434d
阿拉萨图巴 Araçatuba 巴西城市 1—434d
阿拉善高原 Alxa Plateau 中国高原 1—260f
阿拉斯 Arras 法国城市 1—514b
阿拉斯 Arras, Gautier d' 早期法兰西作家 1—514c
阿拉斯 Alas (y Ureña), Leopoldo 西班牙小说家、评论家 1—167b
阿拉斯河 Aras River 亚洲河流 1—440d
阿拉斯花边 Arras lace 法国工艺品 1—514c
阿拉斯加 Alaska 美国州名 1—167c
阿拉斯加半岛 Alaska Peninsula 美国半岛 1—170e
阿拉斯加公路 Alaska Highway 北美公路 1—170e
阿拉斯加购买 Alaska Purchase 美国历史 1—170f
阿拉斯加黑鱼 Alaska blackfish (species *Dallia pectoralis*) 北极淡水鱼 1—170d
阿拉斯加马拉缪特狗 Alaskan Malamute 狗品种 1—170f
阿拉斯加山脉 Alaska Range 北美山脉 1—170f
阿拉斯加湾 Alaska, Gulf of 北太平洋海湾 1—170d
阿拉斯加王蟹 Alaskan king crab 节肢动物 1—170f
阿拉斯加洋流 Alaska Current 阿拉斯加湾洋流 1—170e
阿拉斯加棕熊 Alaskan brown bear 哺乳动物 1—170f
阿拉斯特 Alastor 复仇之神、精灵 1—171a
阿拉松 Arason, Jón 冰岛诗人 1—440e
阿拉特里 Alatri 意大利城镇 1—171a
阿拉托斯 Aratus 希腊诗人 1—440e
阿拉瓦 Álava 西班牙省份 1—171d
阿拉瓦 Arawa 巴布亚新几内亚城镇 1—441f
阿拉瓦克人 Arawak 美洲印第安人 1—441f
阿拉瓦克诸语言 Arawakan languages 南美印第安语言 1—442a
阿拉瓦利岭 Arāvalli Range 印度山系 1—441e
阿拉维杜王朝 Āravīḍu DYNASTY 印度历史 1—441e
阿拉维派 'Alawite 伊斯兰教派别 1—171e
阿拉乌丁 Ala'ud'din 马来柔佛王国苏丹 1—171b
阿拉谢希尔 Alaşehir 土耳其城镇 1—167c
阿拉约卢什地毯 Arraiolos rug 葡萄牙工艺品 1—513d
阿莱 Hallé, Sir Charles 英国钢琴家 7—428f
阿莱 Allais, Maurice 法国经济学家 1—235f
阿莱阿尔迪 Aleardi, Aleardo, Conte (Count) 意大利诗人 1—195b
阿莱安德罗 Aleandro, Girolamo 意大利天主教主教 1—195a
阿莱恩斯 Alliance 美国城市 1—240c
阿莱格雷蒂 Alegrete 巴西城市 1—195d
阿莱格里 Alegre, Caetano da Costa 非洲诗人 1—195d
阿莱格里亚 Alegría, Ciro 秘鲁小说家 1—195d
阿莱哈丁诺 Aleijadinho 巴西雕刻家 1—195e
阿莱赫姆 Aleichem, Sholem 犹太作家 1—195e
阿莱克桑德雷 Aleixandre, Vicente 西班牙诗人 1—195f
阿莱曼 Alemán, Mateo 西班牙小说家 1—196c
阿莱曼 Alemán, Miguel 墨西哥总统 1—196c
阿莱斯 Alès 法国城镇 1—197f
阿莱斯会议 Arles, Council of 西罗马帝国基督教主教会议 1—494a
阿赖耶识 ālaya-vijñāna 佛教 1—171f
阿兰 Alain 法国哲学家 1—165a
阿兰(里尔的) Alain DE LILLE 法国神学家 1—165b
阿兰布鲁克子爵(第一) Alanbrooke (of Brookeborough), Alan Francis Brooke, 1st Viscount 英国陆军元帅 1—166b
阿兰达伯爵 Aranda, Pedro Pablo Abarca de Bolea, conde de (count of) 西班牙大臣 1—439c
阿兰达人 Aranda 澳大利亚土著民族 1—439c
阿兰-傅尼耶 Alain-Fournier 法国作家 1—165c
阿兰胡埃斯 Aranjuez 西班牙城镇 1—439d
阿兰尼 Arany, János 匈牙利诗人 1—439e
阿兰人 Alani 黑海古民族 1—166d
阿兰萨斯国家野生动物禁猎区 Aransas National Wildlife Refuge 美国地区 1—439d
阿朗戈 Arango, Doroteo 墨西哥革命家 1—439d
阿朗松 Alençon 法国城镇 1—197a
阿朗松公爵 Alençon, (Hercule-) François, duc d' (duke of) 法国政治家 1—197a
阿朗松花边 Alençon lace 法国工艺品 1—197a
阿朗语 Alang language 越南语言 1—166c
阿劳 Aarau 瑞士城市 1—2d
阿劳 Arrau, Claudio 美国钢琴家 1—514d

阿劳卡 Arauca 哥伦比亚州名 1—441a
阿劳卡河 Arauca River 南美河流 1—441a
阿劳坎尼亚 Araucanía 智利区名 1—441b
阿劳坎人 Araucanian 南美印第安人 1—441c
阿劳西奥战役 Arausio, Battle of 欧洲历史 1—441e
阿勒 Ağrı 土耳其城市 1—127d
阿勒达拉 Ulladulla 澳大利亚城镇 17—329d
阿勒代尔 Allerdale 英格兰区名 1—239c
阿勒格尼高原 Allegheny Plateau 美国高原 1—236e
阿勒格尼河 Allegheny River 美国河流 1—236e
阿勒格尼山脉 Allegheny Mountains 美国山脉 1—236d
阿勒格尼造山幕 Alleghenian orogeny 地质学 1—236c
阿勒河 Aare River 欧洲河流 1—2f
阿勒卡莱 Alkalai, Judah ben Solomon Hai 西班牙的犹太人精神领袖 1—231d
阿勒奎帕 Aliquippa 美国城市 1—230b
阿勒里克 Aleric (antipope) 敌对教皇 1—197f
阿勒曼德舞 allemande 欧洲舞蹈 1—236f
阿勒曼尼人 Alemanni 欧洲民族 1—196d
阿勒纳哈扬 Nahyān, Shaykh Zāyid ibn Sulṭān Al 阿联酋总统 11—542f
阿勒努 ʿalenu 犹太教 1—197c
阿勒皮 Alleppey 印度城镇 1—239c
阿勒颇 Aleppo 叙利亚城市 1—197c
阿勒颇疖 aleppo boil (infection) 传染病 1—197e
阿勒山 Ağrı Dağı (Turkey) 土耳其山脉 1—127d
阿勒坦 Altan 蒙古可汗 1—254c
阿雷奥帕古斯 Areopagus 古雅典贵族会议 1—459f
阿雷蒂诺 Aretino, Leonardo 意大利学者 1—460f
阿雷蒂诺 Aretino, Pietro 意大利作家 1—461a
阿雷格里港 Pôrto Alegre 巴西州首府 13—452f
阿雷基帕 Arequipa 秘鲁省份 1—460a
阿雷基帕 Arequipa 秘鲁城市 1—460a
阿雷那小教堂 Arena Chapel 意大利基督教教堂 1—459b
阿雷尼格统 Arenig Series 地质学 1—459d
阿雷欧拉 Arreola, Juan José 墨西哥小说家、作家 1—514e
阿雷提乌斯(卡帕多西亚的) Aretaeus of Cappadocia 希腊医师 1—460e
阿雷图斯 Alytus 立陶宛城市 1—261b
阿雷瓦洛(贝尔梅霍) Arévalo (Bermejo), Juan José 危地马拉总统 1—461b
阿雷瓦洛·马丁内斯 Arévalo Martínez, Rafael 危地马拉小说家 1—461c
阿雷瓦西人 Arevaci 凯尔特人部落 1—461b
阿雷西福斯 Arrecifos (Caroline Islands) 太平洋加罗林群岛岛屿 1—514d
阿雷西沃 Arecibo 波多黎各市镇 1—458f
阿雷西沃河 Arecibo River 波多黎各河流 1—459a
阿雷西沃天文台 Arecibo Observatory 波多黎各天文台 1—459a
阿雷佐 Arezzo 意大利城市 1—461d
阿累鲁期 Allerød 地质学 1—239e
阿愣语 Haleng language 语言 7—420d
阿里 ʿAlī 早期哈里发 1—226b
阿里 Ali, Muhammad 美国拳击运动员 1—226d
阿里(大帝) ʿAlī the Great (western African monarch) 西非君主 1—226d
阿里阿德涅 Ariadne 希腊神话人物 1—469f
阿里昂 Arion 希腊诗人、乐师 1—472d
阿里奥巴尔赞 Ariobarzanes 波斯省长 1—472d
阿里奥斯托 Ariosto, Ludovico 意大利诗人 1—472d
阿里包 Aribau, Buenaventura Carles 西班牙经济学家、文学家 1—470e
阿里·贝伊 ʿAlī Bey 埃及马木路克总督 1—226f
阿里不哥 Arigböge 蒙古大汗 1—472a
阿里布尔 Alīpore 印度城镇 1—230a
阿里布尔杜阿尔 Alīpur Duār 印度城市 1—230b
阿里夫 ʿĀrif, ʿAbd al-Salām 伊拉克军官、政治家 1—471f
阿里·高哈尔 ʿAlī Gauhar 莫卧儿皇帝 1—226f
阿里格尔 Alīgarh 印度城市 1—229d
阿里哈克派 Ahl-e Ḥaqq 伊斯兰教派别 1—134c
阿里汗 Ali Khan, Liaquat 巴基斯坦总理 1—227a
阿里汗 Khan, Nusrat Fateh Ali 巴基斯坦歌手 9—255e
阿里卡 Arica 智利城市 1—470f
阿里卡拉人 Arikara 美洲印第安人 1—472a
阿里·里达 ʿAlī ar-Riḍā 伊斯兰教什叶派支派首脑 1—226e
阿里曼 Ahriman 琐罗亚斯德教神 1—137f
阿里米尼会议 Ariminum, Council of 基督教教义会议 1—472c
阿里努斯河 Arinos River 巴西河流 1—472c
阿里帕夏 Ali Paşa Tepelenë 奥斯曼帝国省督 1—227a
阿里帕夏 Âli Paşa, Mehmed Emin 奥斯曼帝国首席大臣 1—227a
阿里山 Ali Shan 中国山脉 1—227b
阿里什 ʿArīsh, Al- 埃及城市 1—473a
阿里斯蒂德 Aristide, Jean-Bertrand 海地政治家 1—473f
阿里斯顿(希俄斯的) Ariston of Chios 希腊哲学家 1—474f
阿里斯塔俄斯 Aristaeus 希腊神祇 1—473c
阿里斯塔科斯(萨莫色雷斯的) Aristarchus of Samothrace 古希腊文献校勘家 1—473d
阿里斯提得斯 Aristides the Just 雅典政治家、将军 1—474b
阿里斯提得斯 Aristides 雅典政治家、将军 1—474a
阿里斯提得斯·昆提利安 Aristides Quintilianus 希腊作者 1—474a
《阿里斯提亚斯书信》 Aristeas, Letter of 伪经之一 1—473e
阿里斯托布鲁斯二世 Aristobulus II 犹太国王 1—474c
阿里斯托布鲁斯一世 Aristobulus I 犹太国王 1—474c
阿里斯托芬 Aristophanes 古希腊喜剧作家 1—474f
阿里斯托芬(拜占廷的) Aristophanes of Byzantium 希腊文献校勘家 1—475f
阿里斯托吉顿 Aristogiton 古希腊刺客 1—474e
阿里斯托梅尼 Aristomenes 古希腊传说英雄 1—474e
阿里·索吉尔松(博学者) Ari Thorgilsson the Learned 冰岛历史学家 1—469c
阿里乌 Arius 埃及亚历山大基督教司铎 1—486a
阿里乌主义 Arianism 基督教异端 1—470a
阿里亚加 Arriaga (y Balzola), Juan Crisóstomo (Jacobo Antonio) 西班牙作曲家 1—515e
阿里亚拉姆尼斯 Ariaramnes 波斯国王 1—470c
阿里亚诺-伊尔皮诺 Ariano Irpino 意大利城镇 1—470b
阿里亚斯 Arias (Madrid), Arnulfo 巴拿马总统 1—470c
阿里亚斯·达维拉 Arias Dávila, Pedro 西班牙军人 1—470c
阿里亚斯·德萨维德拉 Arias de Saavedra, Hernando 西班牙探险家 1—470d
阿里亚斯·桑切斯 Arias Sánchez, Oscar 哥斯达黎加政治家 1—470e
阿里扬 Oryān (Persian poet) 波斯诗人 12—477f
阿里·伊本·艾比·塔列卜 ʿAlī ibn Abī Ṭālib (son-in-law of Muḥammad) 哈里发 1—227a
阿里·伊本·白益 ʿAlī ibn Būyeh (Būyid founder) 白益王朝统治者 1—227a
阿里·伊本·穆罕默德·朱尔贾尼 ʿAlī ibn Muḥammad al-Jurjānī 伊朗伊斯兰教教义学家 1—227a
阿历克塞 Alexius 拜占廷皇帝之名 1—214a
阿历克塞二世康尼努斯 Alexius II Comnenus 拜占廷皇帝 1—214c
阿历克塞三世安基卢斯 Alexius III Angelus 拜占廷皇帝 1—214d
阿历克塞四世安基卢斯 Alexius IV Angelus 拜占廷皇帝 1—214e
阿历克塞五世杜卡斯·穆泽弗卢斯 Alexius V Ducas Murtzuphlus 拜占廷皇帝 1—214e
阿历克塞一世康尼努斯 Alexius I Comnenus 拜占廷皇帝 1—214a

阿利阿克蒙河 Aliákmon River 希腊河流 1—227d
阿利安 Arrian 希腊历史学家 1—515e
阿利盖特河 Alligator Rivers 澳大利亚河流 1—241d
阿利坎特 Alicante 西班牙省份 1—227f
阿利坎特 Alicante 西班牙港口 1—227f
阿利皮乌斯 Alypius 希腊音乐作家 1—261a
阿利萨土丘 Alişar Hüyük 古安纳托利亚遗址 1—230b
阿利湿塔内米 Ariṣṭanemi 印度耆那教祖师 1—473c
阿利斯 Arliss, George 英国演员 1—494e
阿利斯塔克(萨摩斯的) Aristarchus OF SAMOS 古希腊天文学家 1—473d
阿利托(小) Alito, Samuel A(nthony), Jr. 美国最高法院大法官 1—231b
阿利雅 Alia, Ramiz 阿尔巴尼亚主席 1—227c
阿利亚特 Alyattes 吕底亚国王 1—260f
阿利亚托里克舞 aleatory dance 即兴舞蹈 1—195c
阿连德 Allende (Gossens), Salvador 智利总统 1—239a
阿连特茹 Alentejo 葡萄牙省份 1—197b
阿廖欣 Alekhine, Alexander 法国国际象棋大师 1—195f
阿列 Allier 法国省份 1—241b
阿列安努斯 Alienus, Aulis Caecina (Roman general) 罗马将军 1—229d
阿列蒂 Arletty 法国演员 1—494a
阿列河 Allier River 法国河流 1—241b
阿列克山德里 Alecsandri, Vasile 罗马尼亚诗人 1—195c
阿列克谢 Alexis 俄国皇帝 1—213a
阿列克谢 Alexis 俄国皇储 1—213b
阿列克谢 Alexis 俄国皇位继承人 1—213c
阿列克谢,圣 Alexis, SAINT 俄罗斯正教主教 1—213e
阿列克谢二世 Alexis II 俄罗斯正教牧首 1—213d
阿列克谢耶夫 Alekseyev, Konstanin Sergeyevich (theatre director) 俄罗斯演员、导演 1—196a
阿列克谢耶夫 Alekseyev, Mikhail Vasilyevich 俄军总司令 1—196a
阿列克谢耶夫 Alekseyev, Vasily Ivanovich 苏联举重运动员 1—196b
阿列克谢耶夫斯克 Alekseyevsk (Russia) 俄罗斯城市 1—196b
阿列克谢一世 Alexis I 俄罗斯正教会牧首 1—213c
阿列克辛 Aleksin 俄罗斯城市 1—196b
阿列日 Ariège 法国省份 1—471b
阿列维 Halévy, Élie 法国历史学家 7—420e
阿列维 Halévy, (Jacques-François-) Fromental(-Élie) 法国作曲家 7—420e
阿列维 Halévy, Ludovic 法国作家 7—420f
阿林-迪赛德 Alyn and Deeside 威尔士区名 1—261a
阿林顿伯爵(第一) Arlington, Henry Bennet, 1st earl of 英国大臣 1—494c
阿林厄姆 Allingham, Margery (Louise) 英国小说家 1—241d
阿林尼蒂 Arinnitti 古代赫梯人女神 1—472c
阿林斯基 Alinsky, Saul (David) 美国社会组织者 1—229f
阿灵顿 Arlington 美国马萨诸塞州城镇 1—494b
阿灵顿 Arlington 美国得克萨斯州城市 1—494c
阿灵顿 Arlington 美国弗吉尼亚州县名 1—494c
阿灵顿高地 Arlington Heights 美国村落 1—494d
阿灵顿国家公墓 Arlington National Cemetery 美国国家公墓 1—494e
阿留申-爱斯基摩诸语言 Aleut-Eskimo languages 语言 1—198d
阿留申海盆 Aleutian Basin 太平洋海底凹地 1—198d
阿留申岭 Aleutian Range 北美山脉 1—198f
阿留申群岛 Aleutian Islands 美国岛群 1—198e
阿留申人 Aleut 美国民族 1—198c
阿留申语 Aleut language 美国语言 1—198d
阿龙 Arron, Henck (Alphonsus Eugène) 苏里南总理 1—515f
阿龙 Aron, Raymond(-Claude-Ferdinand) 法国社会学家 1—511b
阿龙·辛康 Arung Singkang 印度尼西亚贵族 1—536c
阿隆 Allon, Yigal 以色列军人、政治家 1—242b
阿隆索 Alonso, Dámaso 西班牙诗人 1—248e
阿卢埃 Allouez, Claude-Jean 天主教耶稣会会士 1—242e
阿卢埃湾 Allouez Bay (Lake Superior, U.S.) 美国港湾 1—242f
阿卢科 Aluko, T(imothy) M(ofolorunso) 尼日利亚作家 1—258c
阿卢塞马斯 Alhucemas 西班牙在摩洛哥的飞地 1—226b
阿卢什塔 Alushta 乌克兰旅游胜地 1—259d
阿卢辛戈里 Allucingoli, Ubaldo(pope) 教皇 1—243e
阿卢伊人 Aluyi (people) 非洲民族 1—259d
阿鲁埃 Arouet, François-Marie 法国哲学家 1—511d
阿鲁巴岛 Aruba 加勒比海岛屿 1—534e
阿鲁浑 Arghūn 伊朗蒙古族伊尔汗 1—465d
阿鲁纳恰尔邦 Arunāchal Pradesh 印度邦名 1—535b
阿鲁普 Arrupe, Pedro 耶稣会总会长 1—517d
阿鲁群岛 Aru Islands 印度尼西亚岛群 1—534e
阿鲁萨 Arruza, Carlos 墨西哥斗牛士 1—517d
阿鲁沙 Arusha 坦桑尼亚区名 1—536d
阿鲁斯图克战争 Aroostook War 历史事件 1—511c
阿鲁台 Aruqtai 蒙古首长 1—536d
阿仑德-罗兰彗星 Arend-Roland, Comet 天文学 1—459b
阿伦 Aalen 德国城市 1—1f
阿伦 Alun 威尔士作家 1—259c
阿伦 Arun 英格兰区名 1—535b
阿伦 Allan, Sir Hugh 加拿大金融家、造船家 1—236a
阿伦 Arlen, Harold 美国作曲家 1—493d
阿伦 Arlen, Michael 英国作家 1—493e
阿伦伯爵 Arran, EARLS OF 苏格兰贵族 1—513e
阿伦伯爵 Arran, John Hamilton, earl of 苏格兰贵族 1—513f
阿伦伯爵 Arran, James Stewart, earl of 苏格兰贵族 1—513f
阿伦伯爵(第二) Arran, James Hamilton, 2nd earl of 苏格兰摄政 1—513f
阿伦伯爵(第三) Arran, James Hamilton, 3rd earl of 苏格兰贵族 1—513f
阿伦伯爵(第一) Arran, James Hamilton, 1st earl of 苏格兰副摄政 1—513e
阿伦达尔 Arendal 挪威港口 1—459c
阿伦岛 Arran 苏格兰岛屿 1—513e
阿伦德尔 Arundel 英格兰城镇 1—535d
阿伦德尔 Arundel, EARLS OF 英国贵族头衔 1—535e
阿伦德尔 Arundel, Thomas 英格兰政治家 1—536b
阿伦德尔伯爵(第二或第十四) Arundel, Thomas Howard, 2nd (or 14th) earl of, EARL OF SURREY, EARL OF NORFOLK 英格兰贵族 1—536a
阿伦德尔伯爵(第十二) Arundel, Henry Fitzalan, 12th earl of 英格兰贵族 1—535f
阿伦德尔伯爵(第四) Arundel, Richard Fitzalan, 4th Earl of, 10TH EARL OF SURREY 英格兰王室会议成员 1—535e
阿伦德尔伯爵(第五) Arundel, Thomas Fitzalan, 5th earl of, 11TH EARL OF SURREY 英格兰大臣 1—535e
阿伦德尔伯爵(第一或第十三) Arundel, Philip Howard, 1st (or 13th) earl of, EARL OF SURREY 英格兰贵族 1—535f
阿伦敦 Allentown 美国城市 1—239b
阿伦卡尔 Alencar, José (Martiniano) de 巴西小说家 1—196f
阿伦尼乌斯 Arrhenius, Svante (August) 瑞典物理化学家 1—515a
阿伦尼乌斯方程 Arrhenius equation 化学 1—515c
阿伦尼乌斯理论 Arrhenius theory 化学 1—515d
阿伦群岛 Aran Islands 爱尔兰岛屿 1—439a
阿伦斯基 Arensky, Anton (Stepanovich) 俄国作曲家 1—459e
阿伦特 Arendt, Hannah 美国政治学家 1—459c
阿罗 Arrow, Kenneth J(oseph) 美国经济学家 1—515f
阿罗 Haro, Luis Méndez de 西班牙首相 7—483b
阿罗汉 arhat 佛教 1—469a

阿罗隆多 Anawrahta 缅甸国王 1—321a
阿罗丘库 Arochukwu 尼日利亚城镇 1—510f
阿罗萨 Arosa 瑞士疗养胜地 1—511c
阿罗史密斯 Arrowsmith, Aaron 英国地理学家 1—516e
阿洛布罗克斯人 Allobroges 法国民族 1—242a
阿洛德 Aload 希腊传说人物 1—248c
阿洛群岛 Alor Islands 印度尼西亚群岛 1—248f
阿洛斯特 Alost (Belgium) 比利时城市 1—249a
阿洛韦 Alloway 苏格兰艾尔镇郊区名 1—242f
阿洛伊齐 Alojzy, Fortunat 波兰演员、作家 1—248e
阿洛伊修斯·贡扎加，圣 Aloysius GONZAGA, SAINT 天主教主保圣人 1—249a
阿马 Armagh 北爱尔兰旧郡 1—496b
阿马 Armagh 北爱尔兰城市 1—496c
阿马戴乌斯 Amadeus 统治者之名 1—261e
阿马戴乌斯 Amadeus 西班牙国王 1—262a
阿马戴乌斯八世 Amadeus Ⅷ 意大利萨伏依伯爵 1—261f
阿马戴乌斯六世 Amadeus Ⅵ 意大利萨伏依伯爵 1—261e
阿马戴乌斯七世 Amadeus Ⅶ 意大利萨伏依伯爵 1—261f
阿马迪 Amadi, Elechi 尼日利亚小说家 1—262b
阿马迪厄斯湖 Amadeus, Lake 澳大利亚泥盆 1—262a
阿马迪厄斯四重奏团 Amadeus Quartet 英国弦乐四重奏团 1—262a
《阿马迪斯·德·高尔》 Amadís of Gaul 欧洲文学 1—262c
阿马蒂家族 Amati FAMILY 意大利小提琴制造业家族 1—267a
阿马蒂克湾 Amatique Bay 中美洲海湾 1—267b
阿马蒂特兰湖 Amatitlán, Lake 危地马拉湖泊 1—267b
阿马杜·塞库 Ahmadu Seku 图库洛尔帝国君主 1—136b
阿马尔·达斯 Amar Dās 印度锡克教祖师 1—264e
阿马尔菲 Amalfi 意大利城镇 1—263b
阿马尔菲公爵 Amalfi, Ottavio Piccolomini, duca d' (duke of) 奥地利将军 1—263c
阿马戈萨岭 Amargosa Range 美国山脉 1—265d
阿马库罗三角洲 Delta Amacuro 委内瑞拉州名 5—231c
阿马拉 ʿAmārah, al- 伊拉克城市 1—264e
阿马拉布拉 Amarapura 缅甸城镇 1—265a
阿马拉里克 Amalaric 西哥特国王 1—263a
阿马拉珊萨 Amalasuntha 东哥特女王 1—263a
阿马拉瓦利 Amaravalli (India) 印度市镇 1—265a
阿马里克二世 Amalric Ⅱ 塞浦路斯国王 1—263f
阿马里克一世 Amalric Ⅰ 耶路撒冷国王 1—263f
阿马里洛 Amarillo 美国城市 1—265d
阿马林堡 Amalienborg 丹麦建筑群 1—263e
阿马林亚语 Amarinya language 埃塞俄比亚语言 1—265d
阿马纳 Amarna, Tell el- 埃及古代城市 1—265e
阿马纳风格 Amarna style 埃及艺术 1—266a
阿马纳殖民地 Amana Colonies 美国艾奥瓦殖民地 1—264b
阿马尼亚克 Armagnac 法国历史地区 1—496d
阿马帕 Amapá 巴西州名 1—264d
阿马苏斯 Amathus 塞浦路斯古城 1—267a
阿马托 armatole 希腊旧警察 1—496f
阿马西斯画匠 Amasis Painter 古希腊陶瓶画匠 1—266c
阿马西亚 Amasya 土耳其城市 1—266d
阿玛尔忒亚 Amalthaea 希腊神话人物 1—263f
阿玛莱特步枪 Armalite rifle 武器 1—496e
阿曼 Oman 亚洲国家 12—412e
阿曼 Amman, Jost 德国画家 1—292b
阿曼巴伊山 Amambaí Mountains 巴西高地 1—264a
阿曼拜 Amambay 巴拉圭省份 1—264a
阿曼门诺派 Amish 北美基督教派别 1—291b
阿曼纳蒂 Ammannati, Bartolommeo 意大利雕刻家 1—292c
阿曼尼 Armani, Giorgio 意大利时装设计师 1—496f
阿曼诺拉汗 Amānollāh Khān 阿富汗统治者 1—264d
阿曼湾 Oman, Gulf of 阿拉伯海海湾 12—413d
阿眉斯语 Amis language 中国语言 1—291a
阿眉斯族 Amis 中国台湾土著民族 1—290e
阿梅尔 Āmer 印度城镇 1—274f
阿梅里克斯 Americus 美国城市 1—285f
阿梅龙玻璃 Amelung glass 美国玻璃制品 1—273b
阿梅沙·斯彭塔 amesha spenta 琐罗亚斯德教天使长 1—287a
阿门多拉 Amendola, Giovanni 意大利新闻工作者 1—273d
阿门内莫普 Amenemope 埃及著作家 1—273f
阿门内姆哈特 Amenemhet 埃及国王名 1—273d
阿门内姆哈特二世 Amenemhet Ⅱ 埃及国王 1—273e
阿门内姆哈特三世 Amenemhet Ⅲ 埃及国王 1—273e
阿门内姆哈特一世 Amenemhet Ⅰ 埃及国王 1—273d
阿们 amen 宗教用语 1—273c
阿蒙 Amon 埃及神 1—294f
阿蒙森 Amundsen, Roald 挪威探险家 1—305a
阿蒙森湾 Amundsen Gulf 北冰洋海湾 1—305a
阿蒙通 Amontons, Guillaume 法国物理学家 1—295c
阿孟霍特普 Amenhotep, SON OF HAPU 古埃及高级官员 1—274c
阿孟霍特普 Amenhotep 埃及国王名 1—273f
阿孟霍特普二世 Amenhotep Ⅱ 埃及国王 1—274a
阿孟霍特普三世 Amenhotep Ⅲ 埃及国王 1—274b
阿孟霍特普四世 Amenhotep Ⅳ 埃及国王 1—274c
阿孟霍特普一世 Amenhotep Ⅰ 埃及国王 1—273f
阿米阿努斯·马尔切利努斯 Ammianus Marcellinus 罗马史学家 1—292f
阿米巴 amoeba 原生动物 1—294d
阿米达 Amida (Turkey) 土耳其城市 1—288e
阿米代尔 Armidale 澳大利亚城市 1—500c
阿米尔 Amiel, Henri Frédéric 瑞士作家 1—289a
阿米尔 ʿĀmir, ʿAbd al-Ḥakīm 埃及军官 1—290c
阿米尔·阿里 Amir Ali, Sayyid 印度法学家 1—290d
阿米尔泰乌斯(赛斯的) Amyrtaeus OF SAIS 埃及国王 1—306c
阿米和阿米勒 Amis and Amiles 法国传说人物 1—291a
阿米克 ʿAmūq 土耳其平原 1—305b
阿米兰特群岛 Amirante Isles 西印度洋珊瑚岛群 1—290e
阿米里亚 ʿĀmirīyah, al- 埃及工业区 1—290e
阿米利 ʿĀmilī, Bahā' ad-Dīn Muḥammad ibn Ḥusayn, al- 伊朗学者 1—289d
阿米鲁斯 Armilus 犹太教传说人物 1—500f
阿米尼乌斯 Arminius 日耳曼部族首领 1—501a
阿米欧 Amyot, Jacques 法国主教 1—306a
阿米奇 Amici, Giovanni Battista 意大利天文学家 1—288d
阿米苏斯 Amisus (Turkey) 土耳其城市 1—291c
阿米特努姆 Amiternum 意大利古代城镇 1—291e
阿米希诺 Ameghino, Florentino 阿根廷古生物学家 1—272e
阿密尔·霍斯陆 Amīr Khosrow 印度诗人、历史学家 1—290d
阿敏塔斯三世(或二世) Amyntas Ⅲ (or Ⅱ) 马其顿国王 1—306a
阿明 Amin, Hafizullah 阿富汗政治家 1—289e
阿明 Amin, Idi 乌干达军官、总统 1—289f
阿明尼乌 Arminius, Jacobus 荷兰基督教神学家 1—501a
阿明尼乌主义 Arminianism 基督教神学流派 1—500f
阿摩拉 amora 古犹太教学者 1—295d
阿摩里卡 Armorica 法国地区 1—501e
阿摩里卡丘陵 Armorican, Massif 法国地区 1—501e
阿摩尼奥斯 Ammonius HERMIAE 希腊哲学家 1—293d
阿摩司 Amos 希伯来先知 1—296a
《阿摩司书》 Amos, Book of 《旧约》 1—296b
阿莫巴赫 Amorbach 德国城市 1—295d
阿莫尔戈斯岛 Amorgós Island 希腊岛屿 1—295d
阿莫科公司 Amoco Corporation 美国公司 1—294c
阿莫勒 Āmol 伊朗城镇 1—294e
阿莫里特人 Amorite 亚、非民族 1—295e

阿莫罗佐·利马 Amoroso Lima, Alceu 巴西作家、哲学家 1—295f
阿莫斯女男爵 Amos, Valerie Ann, BARONESS AMOS, OF BRONDESBURY 英国政治家 1—296b
阿默拉沃蒂 Amarāvati 印度市镇 1—265a
阿默拉沃蒂雕刻 Amarāvatī sculpture 印度雕刻 1—265b
阿默兰 Hamelin, Ferdinand Alphonse 法国军人 7—440b
阿默舍姆 Amersham 英格兰城镇 1—286a
阿默斯福特 Amersfoort 荷兰城市 1—286a
阿默斯特 Amherst 加拿大城镇 1—287f
阿默斯特 Amherst 美国城镇 1—287f
阿默斯特 Amhurst, Nicholas 英国作家 1—288c
阿默斯特伯爵(第一) Amherst (of Arracan), William Pitt Amherst, 1st Earl 英国外交官 1—288a
阿默斯特男爵(第一) Amherst, Jeffrey Amherst, 1st Baron 英国陆军指挥官 1—288a
阿默斯特学院 Amherst College 美国文科学院 1—288b
阿姆 ʿAmm (Arabian god) 阿拉伯神 1—291e
阿姆倍伽尔 Ambedkar, Bhimrao Ramji 印度政治领袖 1—269c
阿姆达·锡安 Amda Tseyon 埃塞俄比亚统治者 1—272e
阿姆尔·伊本·库勒苏姆 ʿAmr ibn Kulthūm 阿拉伯诗人 1—301a
阿姆菲尔特 Armfelt, Gustaf Mauritz 瑞典政治家 1—500b
阿姆菲萨 Amphissa 希腊城市 1—299a
阿姆夫拉基亚湾 Amvrakikós Kólpos (Greece) 希腊海湾 1—305d
阿姆哈拉高原 Amhara Plateau 埃塞俄比亚山区 1—287e
阿姆哈拉人 Amhara 埃塞俄比亚民族 1—287c
阿姆哈拉语 Amharic language 埃塞俄比亚语言 1—287e
阿姆河 Amu Darya 亚洲河流 1—304d
阿姆科公司 Armco Inc. 美国公司 1—497c
阿姆拉特文化 Amratian culture 埃及历史 1—301b
阿姆兰·巴尔·谢什纳 Amram bar Sheshna 巴比伦犹太学者 1—301b
阿姆劳蒂 Amrāvati 印度城镇 1—301c
阿姆雷利 Amreli 印度城镇 1—301c
阿姆利则 Amritsar 印度城市 1—301c
《阿姆利则条约》 Amritsar, Treaty of 英国印度条约 1—301e
阿姆利则血案 Amritsar, Massacre of 印度历史 1—301e
阿姆罗赫 Amroha 印度城镇 1—301f
阿姆施泰滕 Amstetten 奥地利城镇 1—304c
阿姆斯 Ames, William 英格兰基督教神学家 1—286e
阿姆斯多尔夫 Amsdorf, Nikolaus von 德意志神学家 1—302a
阿姆斯特丹 Amsterdam 荷兰城市 1—302b
阿姆斯特丹 Amsterdam 美国城市 1—304b
阿姆斯特丹-莱茵运河 Amsterdam-Rhine Canal 荷兰航道 1—304c
阿姆斯特丹印坊画师 Amsterdam Cabinet, Master of the (late Gothic painter and engraver) 德国画家、雕刻家 1—304c
阿姆斯特尔芬 Amstelveen 荷兰城市 1—302b
阿姆斯特朗 Armstrong, Edwin H. 美国无线电发明家 1—503e
阿姆斯特朗 Armstrong, Henry 美国拳击运动员 1—504b
阿姆斯特朗 Armstrong, Henry Edward 英国有机化学家 1—504c
阿姆斯特朗 Armstrong, John 美国军人 1—504c
阿姆斯特朗 Armstrong, Lance 美国自行车运动员 1—504d
阿姆斯特朗 Armstrong, Louis (Daniel) 美国爵士乐演奏家 1—504e
阿姆斯特朗 Armstrong, Neil (Alden) 美国航天员 1—504f
阿姆斯特朗 Armstrong, Samuel Chapman 美国司令官 1—505b
阿姆斯特朗(克拉格赛德的) Armstrong (of Cragside), William George Armstrong, Baron 英国工业家 1—505b
阿木德人化石遗存 Amud remains 以色列考古化石 1—304e
阿睦尔撒纳 Amursana 中国清代封建主 1—305c
阿慕尔·伊本·阿斯 ʿAmr ibn al-ʿĀṣ 阿拉伯将领 1—300f
阿慕尔·伊本·阿斯清真寺 ʿAmr ibn al-ʿĀṣ, Mosque of 埃及伊斯兰建筑 1—301a
阿穆尔 Amur 俄罗斯州名 1—305b
阿穆尔 Armour, Philip Danforth 美国企业家 1—502e
阿穆尔河 Amur River 东亚河流 1—305b
阿穆尔河畔共青城 Komsomolsk-na-Amure 俄罗斯城市 9—343f
阿穆尔斯基伯爵 Amursky, Nikolay Nikolayevich Muravyov, Graf (Count) 俄罗斯探险家、政治家 1—305d
阿穆尔斯克 Amursk 俄罗斯城市 1—305c
阿穆斯戈人 Amuzgo 中美印第安人 1—305d
阿那克里翁 Anacreon 古希腊诗人 1—308b
阿那克西曼德 Anaximander 希腊哲学家 1—321c
阿那克西米尼(米利都的) Anaximenes OF MILETUS 希腊自然哲学家 1—321d
阿纳波利斯 Anápolis 巴西城市 1—316c
阿纳达科 Anadarko 美国城市 1—308c
阿纳德尔 Anadyr 俄罗斯城镇 1—308d
阿纳德尔湾 Anadyr, Gulf of 俄罗斯海湾 1—308d
阿纳海姆 Anaheim 美国城市 1—309a
阿纳河 Ana, Wādī (Europe) 欧洲河流 1—306f
阿纳康达 Anaconda 美国城市 1—307f
阿纳康达公司 Anaconda Company 美国公司 1—308a
阿纳科特斯 Anacortes 美国城市 1—308b
阿纳克莱图斯(二世) Anacletus (II) 敌对教皇 1—307e
阿纳克莱图斯,圣 Anacletus, SAINT 教皇 1—307e
阿纳姆 Arnhem 荷兰城市 1—506e
阿纳姆地 Arnhem Land 澳大利亚历史地区 1—506e
阿纳尼 Anagni 意大利城镇 1—308d
阿纳萨齐文化 Anasazi culture 北美历史 1—316f
阿纳斯塔西亚 Anastasia, Albert 美国暴徒 1—317c
阿纳斯塔西娅 Anastasia 俄国女大公爵 1—317b
阿纳斯塔修斯 Anastasius 统治者之名 1—317c
阿纳斯塔修斯(教廷图书馆馆长) Anastasius THE LIBRARIAN 罗马语言学者、主教 1—317f
阿纳斯塔修斯(西奈的),圣 Anastasius SINAITA, SAINT 基督教神学家 1—317f
阿纳斯塔修斯二世 Anastasius II 拜占廷皇帝 1—317d
阿纳斯塔修斯二世 Anastasius II 教皇 1—317e
阿纳斯塔修斯三世 Anastasius III 教皇 1—317e
阿纳斯塔修斯四世 Anastasius IV 教皇 1—317e
阿纳斯塔修斯一世 Anastasius I 拜占廷皇帝 1—317c
阿纳斯塔修斯一世,圣 Anastasius I, SAINT 教皇 1—317e
阿纳托姆岛 Anatom 太平洋瓦努阿图岛屿 1—320a
阿纳瓦克 Anáhuac 墨西哥历史地理区域 1—309a
阿纳扎布斯 Anazarbus 古安纳托利亚城市 1—321f
阿娜希蒂 Anāhiti 古伊朗神 1—309a
阿奈 ʿĀnah 伊拉克城镇 1—308f
阿奈峰 Anai Peak 印度山峰 1—309a
阿奈马莱丘陵 Anaimalai Hills 印度山地 1—309b
阿南 Anan 日本城市 1—315d
阿南布拉 Anambra 尼日利亚州名 1—315b
阿南达蒂尔塔 Ānandatīrtha (Hindu philosopher) 印度哲学家 1—315f
阿南达·玛希敦 Ananda Mahidol 暹罗国王 1—315f
阿南克 Ananke 希腊女神 1—315f
阿南克莱图斯,圣 Anencletus, SAINT (pope) 教皇 1—338f
阿难陀 Ānanda 佛教 1—315e
阿讷西 Annecy 法国城市 1—365f
阿内霍 Aného 多哥城镇 1—337f
阿内加达岛 Anegada Island 维尔京群岛岛屿 1—337f
阿内加达海峡 Anegada Passage 西印度群岛水道 1—337f
阿内里奥 Anerio, Felice 罗马作曲家 1—338f
阿内特 Arneth, Alfred, Ritter von 奥地利历史学家 1—506d
阿嫩达布尔 Anantapur 印度市镇 1—316a
阿嫩德纳格 Anantnāg 查漠和克什米尔城镇 1—316a

阿妮特 Anyte 希腊诗人 1—402e
阿尼 Ani 土耳其古城遗址 1—356b
阿尼埃洛 Aniello, Tommaso 意大利起义领袖 1—356f
阿尼奥洛 Agnolo di Cosimo 意大利画家 1—124f
阿尼奥洛 Agnolo, Baccio d' 意大利建筑师 1—124f
阿尼米克统 Animikie Series 地质学 1—359d
阿尼姆 Arnim, Hans Georg von 德意志军人 1—507d
阿尼姆伯爵 Arnim, Harry (Karl Kurt Eduard), Grafvon (count of) 普鲁士外交家 1—507d
阿尼人 Anyi 非洲民族 1—402e
阿尼塞图斯,圣 Anicetus, Saint 教皇 1—356d
阿尼乌斯 Anius 希腊神话人物 1—360b
阿尼亚查克国家保护区 Aniakchak National Monument and Preserve 美国地区 1—356c
阿尼亚诺 Agnano 意大利火山口 1—123e
阿涅莱维奇 Anielewicz, Mordecai 波兰英雄 1—356e
阿涅利 Agnelli, Giovanni 意大利实业家 1—124a
阿涅内河 Aniene River 意大利河流 1—356f
阿涅西 Agnesi, Maria Gaetana 意大利数学家、哲学家 1—124b
阿侬语 Anong language 中国语言 1—368f
阿努尔夫 Arnulf 德国皇帝 1—510c
阿努夫一世 Arnulf I 佛兰德伯爵 1—510f
阿努拉德普勒 Anuradhapura 斯里兰卡城市 1—401e
阿努拉德普勒王国 Anurādhapura, kingdom of 斯里兰卡古代国家 1—401e
阿努亚克人 Anuak 非洲民族 1—401b
阿努伊 Anouilh, Jean(-Marie-Lucien-Pierre) 法国剧作家 1—369c
阿诺 Arnow, Harriette 美国小说家、散文家 1—509f
阿诺 Arno, Peter 美国画家 1—507e
阿诺比乌斯(大) Arnobius the Elder 基督教著述家 1—507f
阿诺德 Arnold, Benedict 美国军官 1—508a
阿诺德 Arnold, Sir Edwin 英国诗人、学者 1—508c
阿诺德 Arnold, Harold De Forest 美国物理学家 1—508d
阿诺德 Arnold, Henry Harley 美国空军战略家 1—508d
阿诺德 Arnold, Matthew 英国文学评论家 1—508e
阿诺德 Arnold, Mary Augusta 美国作家 1—508e
阿诺德 Arnold, Samuel 英国作曲家 1—509c
阿诺德 Arnold, Thomas 英国教育家 1—509c
阿诺德(布雷西亚的) Arnold of Brescia 天主教隐修院院长 1—507f
阿诺德森 Arnoldson, Klas Pontus 瑞典政治家 1—509e
阿诺尔福 Arnolfo di Cambio 意大利雕刻家 1—509e
阿诺托 Hanotaux, (Albert-Auguste-) Gabriel 法国政治家、历史学家 7—462d
阿帕波库瓦人 Apapocuva 南美印第安人 1—406a
阿帕布罗萨语 Apabhramśa language 中古亚洲语言 1—405a
阿帕勒人 Aparni (Parthian tribe) 安息部落 1—406b
阿帕里 Aparri 菲律宾城市 1—406b
阿帕里西奥 Aparicio, Luis 委内瑞拉职业棒球运动员 1—406b
阿帕卢萨马 Appaloosa 美国马品种 1—417a
阿帕梅亚(西博土斯的) Apamea Cibotus 土耳其古城市 1—405f
阿帕纳斯湖 Apanás, Lake 尼加拉瓜水库 1—405f
阿帕切人 Apache 北美印第安人 1—405a
阿帕钦甘 Apatzingán 墨西哥城市 1—407c
阿帕塔尼人 Apa Tani 印度民族 1—404f
阿帕图里亚节 Apaturia 古希腊宗教节日 1—407c
阿槃提 Avanti 古印度王国 2—83e
阿佩 Ape (pseudonym) 意大利漫画家 1—407d
阿佩尔 Appel, Karel 荷兰画家 1—417e
阿佩尔 Appert, Nicolas(-François) 法国厨师 1—418c
阿佩尔综合征 Apert's syndrome (congenital malformation) 先天性畸形 1—408a
阿佩莱斯 Apelles 爱奥尼亚画家 1—407e
阿佩利孔 Apellicon of Teos 希腊图书收藏家 1—407f
阿佩皮 Apepi (Egyptian god) 埃及宗教中的恶魔 1—408a
阿朋人 Abung (people) 印度尼西亚民族 1—38b
阿彭策尔 Appenzell 瑞士州名 1—418b
阿彭策尔 Appenzell 瑞士城市 1—418b
阿皮尼 Harpignies, Henri 法国画家 7—485b
阿皮萨科 Apizaco 墨西哥城市 1—410c
阿皮亚 Apia (Kiribati) 基里巴斯珊瑚礁 1—409e
阿皮亚 Apia 萨摩亚首都 1—409e
阿皮亚 Appia, Adolphe 瑞士舞台设计师 1—418e
阿皮亚 Appiah, Kwame Anthony 美国哲学家、小说家 1—418f
《阿毗达磨俱舍论》 Abhidharmakośa 佛教著作 1—23d
《阿毗达磨义摄》 Abhidhammattha-saṅgaha 佛教著作 1—23c
阿匹斯 Apis 古埃及宗教神祇 1—410b
阿平厄姆 Uppingham 英格兰教区 17—405c
《阿婆陀那》 Apadāna 佛教故事集 1—405d
阿珀尔多伦 Apeldoorn 荷兰城市 1—407e
阿普 Arp, Halton Christian 美国天文学家 1—511d
阿普顿 Appleton, Sir Edward Victor 英国物理学家 1—420c
阿普顿层 Appleton layer 大气层 1—420d
阿普尔比 Applebee, Constance M.K. 英国运动员 1—420b
阿普尔顿 Appleton 美国城市 1—420c
阿普拉港 Apra Harbor 马里亚纳群岛港口 1—422e
阿普雷 Apure 委内瑞拉州名 1—425b
阿普雷彩陶 Aprey faience 法国陶器 1—422f
阿普雷河 Apure River 委内瑞拉河流 1—425b
阿普雷河畔圣费尔南多 San Fernando de Apure 委内瑞拉城市 15—8c
阿普里马克 Apurímac 秘鲁省份 1—425b
阿普里马克河 Apurímac River 秘鲁河流 1—425c
阿普里斯 Apries 埃及国王 1—423b
阿普利亚 Apulia (Italy) 意大利大区 1—425a
阿普列乌斯 Apuleius, Lucius 阿尔及利亚哲学家 1—424f
阿普-旁绍 Apu-Punchau (Inca religion) 印加人太阳神 1—424f
阿普塞尼山脉 Apuseni Mountains 罗马尼亚山脉 1—425c
阿普特阶 Aptian Stage 地质学 1—424e
阿普歇伦半岛 Apsheron Peninsula 阿塞拜疆半岛 1—423f
阿齐克韦 Azikiwe, Nnamdi 尼日利亚总统 2—101f
阿齐利文化期工艺 Azilian industry 石器文化 2—102a
阿齐纳人 Atsina 北美印第安人 2—37d
阿齐兹 'Azīz, al- 法蒂玛王朝哈里发 2—102b
阿奇 Arch, Joseph 英国农业劳工领袖 1—446b
阿啇雷亚莱 Acireale 意大利城镇 1—55a
阿奇姆博多 Arcimboldo, Giuseppe 意大利画家 1—455a
阿奇亚奥里 Acciaiuoli, Niccolò 意大利政治家 1—45d
阿耆尼 Agni 印度教 1—124e
阿契贝 Achebe, Chinua 尼日利亚小说家 1—51c
阿契美尼德王朝 Achaemenian dynasty 伊朗王朝 1—50d
阿契美尼斯 Achaemenes 波斯统治者 1—50c
阿契美尼斯 Achaemenes 波斯王子 1—50c
阿契塔 Archytas of Tarentum 古希腊科学家 1—454f
阿恰布 Akyab (Myanmar [Burma]) 缅甸城镇 1—160a
阿乔利人 Acholi 乌干达民族 1—53e
阿切尔 Archer, Frederick Scott 英国摄影家 1—448a
阿切尔 Archer, Thomas 英国建筑师 1—448b
阿切尔 Archer, William 英国戏剧评论家 1—448c
阿切斯国家公园 Arches National Park 美国公园 1—449d
阿切西剧团 Accesi, Compagnia degli 意大利剧团 1—45c
阿钦斯克 Achinsk 俄罗斯城市 1—53e
阿让 Agen 法国城镇 1—119c
阿让蒂耶尔 Argentière, L' (France-Italy) 法兰西-意大利关隘 1—463c
阿让库尔战役 Agincourt, Battle of 欧洲历史 1—122c

阿让唐花边 Argentan lace 法国工艺品 1—463a
阿让特伊 Argenteuil 法国城镇 1—463b
阿让托 Argenteau, Florimund Mercy d' 奥地利外交家 1—463b
阿热奈 Agenais 法国旧省份 1—119d
阿瑞斯 Ares 希腊神祇 1—460c
阿瑞托萨 Arethusa 希腊神话人物 1—460e
阿撒泻勒 Azazel 犹太教邪灵 2—100a
阿萨巴 Asaba 尼日利亚城镇 1—537f
阿萨巴斯卡河 Athabasca River 加拿大河流 2—17e
阿萨巴斯卡湖 Athabasca, Lake 加拿大湖泊 2—17c
阿萨巴斯卡区 Athabaska, District of 加拿大地区 2—17f
阿萨布 Aseb 埃塞俄比亚港口 1—543e
阿萨德 Assad, Bashar al- 叙利亚总统 1—559b
阿萨德 Assad, Ḥafiz al- 叙利亚总统 1—559b
阿萨蒂格岛 Assateague Island 美国岛屿 1—560b
阿萨卢赫 Asalluhe 苏美尔人神祇 1—538c
阿萨姆 Assam 印度邦名 1—559d
阿萨姆牛 mithan 牛品种 11—290f
阿萨姆兄弟 Asam, Cosmas Damian and Egid Quirin 巴罗克艺术代表人物 1—538c
阿萨姆语 Assamese language 印度语言 1—559e
阿萨尼亚 Azaña y Díaz, Manuel 西班牙总统 2—99c
阿萨息斯 Arsaces 安息王室称号 1—518a
阿萨息斯二世 Arsaces II (king) 安息国王 1—518a
阿萨息斯六世 Arsaces VI 安息国王 1—518a
阿萨息斯王朝 Arsacid DYNASTY 安息帝国王朝 1—518c
阿萨辛派 Assassin 中东伊斯兰教派别 1—559e
阿塞拜疆 Azerbaijan 伊朗西北地区 2—100c
阿塞拜疆 Azerbaijan 高加索地区国家 2—100e
阿塞拜疆人 Azerbaijani 民族 2—101d
阿塞尔 Asser 威尔士教士 1—561d
阿塞尔 Asser, Tobias Michael Carel 荷兰法学家 1—561e
阿塞尔内 Athelney 英格兰小高地 2—18f
阿塞拉 Asela 埃塞俄比亚城镇 1—543e
阿塞利 Aselli, Gaspare 意大利医生 1—543e
阿塞特 Aset (Egyptian religion) 埃及女神 1—543f
阿塞维多 Azevedo, Aluízio 巴西小说家 2—101d
阿塞维多·迪亚斯 Acevedo Díaz, Eduardo 乌拉圭作家、政治家 1—49f
阿塞西斯河 Athesis (Italy) 意大利河流 2—24e
阿散蒂地区 Ashanti Region 加纳行政区 1—544f
阿散蒂帝国 Ashanti empire 非洲历史 1—544e
阿散蒂人 Ashanti 非洲民族 1—544c
阿散索尔 Asansol 印度城市 1—538e
阿桑布勒 assemblé 芭蕾动作 1—561a
阿瑟 Arthur 美国村落 1—528c
阿瑟 Arthur, Chester A(lan) 美国总统 1—528c
阿瑟 Arthur, Ellen 美国总统夫人 1—528e
阿瑟 Arthur, Sir George, 1ST BARONET 英国殖民官员 1—528f
阿瑟 Arthur, Jean 美国电影演员 1—529a
阿瑟 Arthur, J. C. 美国植物学家 1—529a
阿瑟顿 Atherton 英格兰城镇 2—24c
阿瑟顿高原 Atherton Plateau 澳大利亚高原 2—24d
阿瑟尔 Athol 美国镇区 2—25d
阿瑟尔 Atholl 苏格兰赛德多山地区 2—25d
阿瑟港 Port Arthur 澳大利亚小海湾 13—443f
阿瑟港 Port Arthur 美国城市 13—444a
阿瑟基尔桥 Arthur Kill Bridge 美国桥梁 1—529b
阿瑟拉 Asherah 亚洲闪米特人女神 1—546f
阿森 Assen 荷兰城市 1—561d
阿森赖 Athenry 爱尔兰集镇 2—19e
阿森斯 Athens 美国亚拉巴马州城市 2—23e
阿森斯 Athens 美国佐治亚州城市 2—23f
阿森斯 Athens 美国俄亥俄州城市 2—24a
阿森斯 Athens 美国田纳西州城市 2—24a
阿森松 Ascension (Caroline Islands) 加罗林群岛火山岛 1—540a
阿森松 Ascension 南大西洋英属岛屿 1—540a
阿森一世 Asen I (Bulgarian tsar) 保加利亚沙皇 1—543f
阿沙尔 ʿĀshar min Ramaḍān, Madīnat al- 埃及城市 1—545a
阿沙芬堡 Aschaffenburg 德国城市 1—541a
阿尚博堡 Fort Archabault (Chad) 乍得城市 6—413b
阿舍克·帕夏 Aşık Paşa 土耳其诗人 1—554b
阿舍利文化期工艺 Acheulian industry 法国史前工艺 1—52c
阿舍斯莱本 Aschersleben 德国城市 1—541e
阿施 Asch, Sholem 美国小说家 1—540e
阿什贝里 Ashbery, John (Lawrence) 美国诗人 1—545d
阿什本 Ashbourne 英格兰城镇 1—545e
阿什比 Ashbee, Charles Robert 英国建筑师 1—545c
阿什伯顿 Ashburton 英格兰城镇 1—545e
阿什伯顿男爵(第一) Ashburton, John Dunning, 1st Baron 英国法官 1—545f
阿什伯勒 Asheboro 美国城市 1—546e
阿什杜德 Ashdod 巴勒斯坦城市 1—546c
阿什顿 Ashton, Sir Frederick (William Mallandaine) 英国芭蕾舞编导 1—549e
阿什菲尔德 Ashfield 英格兰区名 1—547b
阿什福德 Ashford 英格兰区名 1—547b
阿什哈巴德 Ashkhabad 土库曼斯坦首都 1—548d
阿什河城 Ashihho (China) 中国城市 1—547d
阿什及尔统 Ashgill Series 地质学 1—547b
阿什凯隆 Ashqelon 巴勒斯坦城市 1—549b
阿什克罗夫特 Ashcroft, Dame Peggy 英国舞台剧演员 1—546a
阿什肯纳齐 Ashkenazy, Vladimir 俄罗斯音乐家 1—548c
阿什拉维 Ashrawi, Hanan 巴勒斯坦教育工作者 1—549c
阿什兰 Ashland 美国肯塔基州城市 1—548d
阿什兰 Ashland 美国俄勒冈州城市 1—548e
阿什兰 Ashland 美国威斯康星州城市 1—548e
阿什利 Ashley, Maurice 美国国际象棋大师 1—548f
阿什利 Ashley, William Henry 美国国会议员 1—548f
阿什利勋爵 Ashley, Anthony Ashley Cooper, Baron 英格兰政治家 1—548f
阿什莫尔-卡捷群岛 Ashmore and Cartier Islands 澳大利亚海外领地 1—549a
阿什莫尔艺术与考古博物馆 Ashmolean Museum of Art and Archaeology 牛津大学博物馆 1—549a
阿什塔比拉 Ashtabula 美国城市 1—549d
阿什韦尔 Ashwell, Lena 英国演员 1—550e
阿什维尔 Asheville 美国城市 1—547a
阿室罗摩 ashrama 印度教 1—549c
阿舒尔 Ashur 美索不达米亚神灵 1—550a
阿术拉节 ʿĀshūrāʾ 伊斯兰教节日 1—550b
阿司匹林 aspirin 药物 1—558a
阿斯贝斯托斯 Asbestos 加拿大城镇 1—538f
阿斯别斯特 Asbest 俄罗斯城市 1—538f
阿斯伯里 Asbury, Francis 美国美以美会主教 1—539c
阿斯伯里帕克 Asbury Park 美国城市 1—539d
阿斯布约恩森和穆 Asbjørnsen, Peter Christen; and Moe, Jørgen Engebretsen 挪威民间传说搜集者 1—539b
阿斯堤阿那克斯 Astyanax 希腊传说人物 2—10c
阿斯蒂 Asti 意大利城市 2—4e
阿斯蒂帕莱阿岛 Astipálaia 希腊爱琴海岛屿 2—5a
阿斯顿 Aston, Francis William 英国物理学家 2—5c
阿斯菲 Asfi (Morocco) 摩洛哥省份和城市 1—543f
阿斯基亚·穆罕默德 Askia Muhammad 桑海帝国统治者 1—555a
阿斯基亚王朝 Askia DYNASTY 西非穆斯林家族 1—555a
阿斯加尔德 Asgard 古斯堪的纳维亚神话 1—543f

阿斯卡巴德 Askhabad (Turkmenistan) 土库曼斯坦首都 1—555a
阿斯卡里 Ascari, Alberto 意大利赛车运动员 1—539f
阿斯卡里 ʿAskarī, Jaʿfar al- 伊拉克政治家 1—554f
阿斯卡尼俄斯 Ascanius 古罗马传说人物 1—539e
阿斯卡尼亚王朝 Ascanian DYNASTIES 德意志家族 1—539e
阿斯科里 Ascoli, Graziadio Isaia 米兰语言学家 1—542e
阿斯科利皮切诺 Ascoli Piceno 意大利城市 1—542e
阿斯科特 Ascot 英格兰地名 1—543b
阿斯克 Usk 英国城市 17—423b
阿斯克尔和埃姆布拉 Askr and Embla 古斯堪的纳维亚神话人物 1—555b
阿斯克勒庇俄斯 Asclepius 古希腊罗马医药神 1—542d
阿斯克列皮阿德斯(比希尼亚的) Asclepiades OF BITHYNIA 希腊医师 1—542c
阿斯克列皮阿德斯诗体 asclepiad 希腊抒情诗体 1—542a
阿斯克列皮吉尼亚 Asclepigenia 希腊哲学家 1—542c
阿斯奎斯 Asquith, H(erbert) H(enry) 英国首相 1—558d
阿斯隆 Athlone 爱尔兰城市郊区 2—25c
阿斯隆伯爵(第一) Athlone, Godard van Reede, 1st earl of, BARON OF AGHRIM, HEER (Lord) VAN GINKEL 荷兰军人 2—25c
阿斯罗克 Asroc 美国武器 1—558f
阿斯马拉 Asmera 埃塞俄比亚城市 1—555c
阿斯纳尔 Aznar, José María 西班牙律师、总理 2—102b
阿斯南 Asnam, El- (Algeria) 阿尔及利亚城市 1—555d
阿斯内克 Asnyk, Adam 波兰诗人 1—555e
阿斯帕尔 Aspar, Flavius Ardaburius 罗马将军 1—556a
阿斯帕西娅 Aspasia 雅典社会活跃人物 1—556e
阿斯派灵山 Aspiring, Mount 新西兰山脉 1—558a
阿斯派灵山国家公园 Mount Aspiring National Park 新西兰公园 11—440b
阿斯彭 Aspen 美国城市 1—556e
阿斯彭杜斯 Aspendus 土耳其古城 1—557a
阿斯彭斯特伦 Aspenström, (Karl) Werner 瑞典诗人 1—557a
阿斯普伦德 Asplund, (Erik) Gunnar 瑞典建筑师 1—558d
阿斯普蛇 asp 爬行动物 1—556a
阿斯恰火山口 Askja 冰岛火山口 1—555a
阿斯塔纳 Astana 哈萨克斯坦城市 2—2b
阿斯塔特 Astarte 古代近东地区女神 2—2b
阿斯泰尔 Astaire, Fred 美国舞蹈家 2—1e
阿斯泰拉巴德 Asterābad (Iran) 伊朗城镇 2—3b
阿斯特 Astor, Brooke Russell 美国社会活动家、作家 2—5d
阿斯特 Astor, Caroline Webster Schermerhorn 美国贵妇人 2—5e
阿斯特 Astor, John Jacob 美国皮毛业大亨 2—5f
阿斯特 Astor (of Hever, of Hever Castle), John Jacob Astor, 1st Baron 英国新闻记者 2—6a
阿斯特 Astor, Mary 美国演员 2—6a
阿斯特伯里 Astbury, John 英国制陶工艺先驱 2—2d
阿斯特伯里-惠尔登陶瓷 Astbury-Whieldon ware 英国陶瓷 2—3a
阿斯特伯里陶器 Astbury ware 英国陶器 2—2e
阿斯特家族 Astor FAMILY 美国豪富家族 2—5c
阿斯特拉罕 Astrakhan 俄罗斯州名 2—6f
阿斯特拉罕 Astrakhan 俄罗斯城市 2—7a
阿斯特利 Astley, Philip 英国马术师 2—5b
阿斯特鲁(吕内勒的) Astruc OF LUNEL 犹太教狂热人士 2—9d
阿斯特子爵(第二) Astor (of Hever Castle), Waldorf Astor, 2nd Viscount, BARON ASTOR OF HEVER CASTLE 英国政治家 2—6c
阿斯特子爵夫人 Astor (of Hever Castle), Nancy Witcher Astor, Viscountess 英国政治家 2—6b
阿斯提亚格斯 Astyages 米底帝国末代国王 2—10b
阿斯图里亚斯 Asturias 西班牙自治区 2—9e
阿斯图里亚斯 Asturias, Miguel Ángel 危地马拉诗人 2—10a
阿斯托加 Astorga 西班牙城市 2—6d
阿斯托里亚 Astoria 美国城市 2—6d
阿斯托里亚海底峡谷 Astoria Canyon 太平洋东北部海底峡谷 2—6f
阿斯旺 Aswān 埃及省份 2—11a
阿斯旺 Aswān 埃及城市 2—11b
阿斯旺岛 Aswān, Jazīrat (Egypt) 埃及岛屿 2—11c
阿斯旺高坝 Aswān High Dam 埃及水坝 2—11c
阿苏阿 Azua 多米尼加共和国城市 2—104b
阿苏埃拉 Azuela, Mariano 墨西哥作家 2—104c
阿苏埃罗半岛 Azuero Peninsula 巴拿马半岛 2—104d
阿苏山 Aso, Mount 日本活火山 1—555e
阿苏斯 Assus 古希腊城市 2—1d
阿索尔伯爵(第二)和侯爵(第一) Atholl, John Murray, 2nd Earl and 1st Marquess of, EARL OF TULLIBARDINE, VISCOUNT OF BALQUHIDDER, LORD MURRAY, BALVANY, AND GASK 苏格兰保皇党领袖 2—25f
阿索尔伯爵(第四) Atholl, John Stewart, 4th Earl of 苏格兰贵族 2—25e
阿索尔伯爵、侯爵和公爵 Atholl, EARLS, MARQUESSES, AND DUKES OF 苏格兰贵族 2—25e
阿索尔侯爵(第二)和公爵(第一) Atholl, John Murray, 2nd Marquess and 1st Duke of, MARQUESS OF TULLIBARDINE, EARL OF STRATHTAY AND STRATHARDLE, VISCOUNT OF BALWHIDDER, GLENALMOND, AND GLENLYON, LORD MURRAY, BALVENIE, AND GASK 苏格兰贵族 2—26a
阿索格斯 Azogues 厄瓜多尔城市 2—102e
阿索林 Azorín 西班牙作家 2—103a
阿塔尔 Atar 毛里塔尼亚城镇 2—13a
阿塔尔 ʿAṭṭār, Farīd od-Dīn (Moḥammad ebn Ebrāhīm) 波斯诗人 2—38d
阿塔迦蒂斯 Atargatis 古代叙利亚女神 2—13a
阿塔卡马 Atacama 智利区名 2—12a
阿塔卡马高原 Atacama Plateau 安第斯山脉台地 2—12b
阿塔卡马海沟 Atacama Trench (Pacific Ocean) 太平洋海沟 2—12b
阿塔卡马人 Atacama 南美印第安人 2—11f
阿塔卡马沙漠 Atacama Desert 智利北部地区 2—12a
阿塔克斯 Attucks, Crispus 美洲殖民地反英烈士 2—41e
阿塔兰忒 Atalanta 希腊神话人物 2—12d
阿塔罗斯 Attalus 帕加马王国统治者之名 2—38b
阿塔罗斯 Attalus, Priscus 西罗马皇帝 2—38d
阿塔罗斯二世 Attalus II PHILADELPHUS 帕加马国王 2—38c
阿塔罗斯三世 Attalus III PHILOMETOR EUERGETES 帕加马国王 2—38c
阿塔罗斯一世 Attalus I SOTER 帕加马国王 2—38b
阿塔玛斯 Athamas 希腊神话人物 2—17f
阿塔纳里克 Athanaric 西哥特人首领 2—17f
阿塔纳修斯一世 Athanasius I 君士坦丁堡牧首 2—18a
阿塔帕梅 Atakpamé 多哥城镇 2—12d
阿塔图尔克，凯末尔 Atatürk, Kemal 土耳其共和国缔造者 2—13b
阿塔图尔克水坝 Ataturk Dam 土耳其水坝 2—15e
阿塔瓦尔帕 Atahuallpa 秘鲁印加帝国末代皇帝 2—12c
阿塔瓦斯德斯二世 Artavasdes II 亚美尼亚国王 1—524e
阿塔西 ʿAtāsī, Hāshim al- 叙利亚总统 2—13a
《阿闼婆吠陀》 Atharvaveda 印度古代经籍 2—18d
阿泰尔文化期工艺 Aterian industry 旧石器时代石器工艺 2—17a
阿泰尼昂 Attaignant, Pierre 欧洲印刷商 2—38a
阿泰斯特 Ateste 意大利古城 2—17a
阿陶尔夫 Ataulphus 西哥特人首领 2—15e
阿忒 Ate 希腊神话人物 2—16e
阿特巴拉 ʿAṭbarah 苏丹城镇 2—16b
阿特巴拉河 Atbara River 尼罗河支流 2—16b
阿特巴萨尔 Atbasar 哈萨克斯坦城市 2—16c
阿特巴伊 Itbāy 埃及地区 8—488f
阿特伯里 Atterbury, Francis 英国圣公会主教 2—39d
阿特博姆 Atterbom, Per Daniel Amadeus 瑞典文学家 2—39c

阿特尔 Attell, Abe 美国职业拳击运动员 2—38e
阿特尔 Atl, Doctor 墨西哥画家 2—26e
阿特尔伯勒 Attleboro 美国城市 2—41a
阿特金森 Atkinson, Sir Harry (Albert) 新西兰政治家 2—26d
阿特金斯美术馆 Atkins Museum of Fine Arts 美国堪萨斯城美术馆 2—26d
阿特拉 Hatra 伊拉克古城 7—509b
阿特拉斯 Atlas 希腊神话人物 2—28f
阿特拉斯 Atlas, Charles 美国健美师、体育家 2—29c
阿特拉斯山脉 Atlas Mountains 非洲山脉 2—29d
阿特拉托河 Atrato River 哥伦比亚河流 2—35c
阿特拉笑剧 fabula Atellana 意大利喜剧 6—208f
阿特里 Atri 意大利城镇 2—35e
阿特里亚 Atria (Italy) 意大利城市 2—35f
阿特利斯科 Atlixco 墨西哥城市 2—29f
《阿特利之歌》 Atli, Lay of 古代北欧英雄史诗 2—29e
阿特米多鲁斯 Artemidorus 希腊地理学家 1—525b
阿特米多鲁斯 Artemidorus Daldianus 罗马帝国占卜家 1—525b
阿特米萨 Artemisa 古巴城市 1—525f
阿特那哥拉斯 Athenagoras 希腊基督教哲学家 2—19d
阿特那哥拉斯一世 Athenagoras I 希腊正教牧首 2—19e
阿特纳奥斯 Athenaeus 希腊语法家 2—19d
阿特热 Atget, (Jean-) Eugène (-Auguste) 法国摄影家 2—17b
阿特柔斯 Atreus 希腊传说人物 2—35d
阿特柔斯宝库 Atreus, Treasury of 迈锡尼文化遗迹 2—35e
阿特尚纳赫 ʻAtshanah (Turkey) 叙利亚古城 2—37d
阿特索人 Ateso (people) 乌干达民族 2—17a
阿特威尔德 Artevelde, Jacob van 佛兰德人领袖 1—526f
阿特沃特 Atwater, Wilbur Olin 美国农业化学家 2—42a
阿特伍德 Atwood, Margaret (Eleanor) 加拿大诗人、小说家 2—42a
阿特伍德 Attwood, Thomas 英国经济学家 2—41e
阿滕伯勒 Attenborough, Sir David (Frederick) 英国广播事业家 2—38f
阿提卡 Attica 古希腊地区 2—39f
阿提卡 Attikí 希腊州名 2—40a
阿提库斯 Atticus, Herodes 希腊演说家 2—39f
阿提库斯 Atticus, Titus Pomponius 罗马骑士 2—40a
阿提拉 Attila 匈奴王 2—40b
阿提密喜安战役 Artemisium, Battle of 希波战争 1—526a
阿提斯 Attis 古罗马神祇 2—40c
阿图姆 Atum 古埃及太阳神 2—41f
阿图瓦 Artois 法国历史文化区 1—533f
阿图瓦伯爵 Artois, Charles-Philippe, comte d' (count of) 法国国王 1—533f
阿吞 Aton 古埃及太阳神 2—34d
阿托克 Attock 巴基斯坦县名 2—41c
阿托尼人 Atoni 印度尼西亚民族 2—35b
阿托品 atropine 药物 2—37b
阿瓦 Ava 中缅甸古都 2—82c
阿瓦查潘 Ahuachapán 萨尔瓦多城市 1—138c
阿瓦德 Awadh (India) 印度市镇 2—91f
阿瓦尔-安迪-迪多诸语言 Avar-Ando-Dido languages 高加索地区语言 2—83f
阿瓦尔人 Avar 民族 2—83e
阿瓦库姆·彼得罗维奇 Avvakum Petrovich 俄罗斯正教会大司铎 2—91e
阿瓦利 ʻAwālī 巴林国城市 2—92a
阿瓦隆 Avalon 传说中岛屿 2—83c
阿瓦隆半岛 Avalon Peninsula 加拿大半岛 2—83c
阿瓦隆造山幕 Avalonian orogeny 地质学 2—83d
阿瓦洛斯 Avalos, Fernando Francesco de 神圣罗马帝国军事领袖 2—83e
阿瓦什河 Awash River 埃塞俄比亚河流 2—92b
阿瓦士 Ahvāz 伊朗城镇 1—138d
阿旺 Awan 埃兰古代城市 2—92b
阿望桥村画派 Pont-Aven school 法国青年画家团体 13—426f
阿威罗 Aveiro 葡萄牙港口城市 2—84b
阿威罗伊 Averroës 伊斯兰宗教哲学家 2—85c
阿韦尔诺湖 Averno, Lake of 意大利火山口湖 2—85b
阿韦尔萨 Aversa 意大利城镇 2—86e
阿韦雷斯库 Averescu, Alexandru 罗马尼亚首相 2—85b
阿韦利诺 Avellino 意大利城市 2—84c
阿韦利诺 Averlino, Antonio di Pietro 意大利建筑师 2—85b
阿韦利亚内达 Avellaneda 阿根廷大布宜诺斯艾利斯行政区 2—84b
阿韦龙 Aveyron 法国省份 2—87f
阿韦鲁利诺 Averulino, Antonio di Pietro 意大利建筑师 2—86f
阿韦斯岛 Aves Island (Caribbean Sea) 加勒比海岛屿 2—87e
阿韦扎诺 Avezzano 意大利城镇 2—88a
阿维 Haüy, René-Just 法国矿物学家 7—516c
阿维 Haüy, Valentin 法国书法教授 7—516c
阿维措特 Ahuitzotl 阿兹特克人国王 1—138c
阿维狄乌斯·卡修斯 Avidius Cassius, Gaius 僭称罗马皇帝 2—88e
阿维尔尼人 Arverni 法国古凯尔特部落 1—536e
阿维拉 Ávila 西班牙省份 2—89d
阿维拉 Ávila 西班牙城市 2—89d
阿维拉·卡马乔 Ávila Camacho, Manuel 墨西哥总统 2—89e
阿维莱斯 Avilés 西班牙城市 2—89f
阿维尼翁 Avignon 法国城市 2—88f
阿维尼翁画派 Avignon school 法国后期哥特式画派 2—89b
阿维尼翁教廷 Avignon papacy 天主教历史 2—89a
阿维森 Avison, Charles 英国作曲家 2—90a
阿维森纳 Avicenna 穆斯林哲学科学家 2—88c
阿维丝布龙 Avicebron (Hebrew poet) 希伯来诗人 2—88c
阿维丝布鲁勒 Avencebrol (Hebrew poet) 希伯来诗人 2—84d
阿维斯塔字母 Avestan alphabet 中古波斯语文字体系 2—87e
《阿维斯陀》 Zend-Avesta (Zoroastrian scripture) 琐罗亚斯德教经典 18—507d
阿维斯陀语 Avestan language 古代伊朗语言 2—87e
阿维图斯 Avitus 西罗马皇帝 2—90b
阿魏 asafetida 树胶脂 1—538a
阿温巴人 Awemba (people) 非洲民族 2—92d
阿文纳萨尔 Avennasar (Muslim philosopher) 穆斯林哲学家 2—84e
阿文帕塞 Avempace 西班牙哲学家 2—84c
阿文提努斯 Aventinus 巴伐利亚历史学家 2—84e
阿沃拉 Avola 意大利西西里岛城镇 2—91b
阿沃洛沃 Awolowo, Obafemi 尼日利亚政治家 2—92d
阿沃斯塔 Avesta 瑞典城镇 2—87e
阿伍诺 Awoonor, Kofi 加纳小说家 2—92f
阿武隈山脉 Abukuma-sammyaku 日本山脉 1—38b
阿西 Ashi 犹太教学者 1—547c
阿西尔 Asir 沙特阿拉伯西南地区 1—554e
阿西尔格尔 Asīrgarh 印度堡垒 1—554e
阿西河 Nahr al-ʻAsī (Asia) 亚洲河流 11—542b
阿西莫夫 Asimov, Isaac 美国作家 1—554c
阿西纳拉岛 Asinara Island 地中海岛屿 1—554d
阿西尼博亚 Assiniboia 加拿大地区 1—562d
阿西尼博因河 Assiniboine River 加拿大河流 1—562f
阿西尼博因人 Assiniboin 美洲印第安人 1—562e
阿西尼乌斯·波利奥 Asinius Pollio, Gaius 罗马历史学家 1—554e
阿西诺 Asino 俄罗斯城市 1—554e
阿西斯 Assis 巴西城市 1—563a
阿西西 Assisi 意大利城镇 1—563a
阿西娅·杰巴尔 Assia Djebar 阿尔及利亚作家 1—562a
阿希 Ashe, Arthur (Robert) 美国网球运动员 1—546c

阿希达穆斯 Archidamus 斯巴达国王之名 1—449e
阿希达穆斯二世 Archidamus II 斯巴达国王 1—449e
阿希达穆斯三世 Archidamus III 斯巴达国王 1—449f
阿希达穆斯四世 Archidamus IV 斯巴达国王 1—449f
阿希达穆斯五世 Archidamus V 斯巴达国王 1—450a
阿希达穆斯一世 Archidamus I 斯巴达国王 1—449e
阿希尔 Ahīr 印度种姓 1—134a
阿希克帕夏扎德 Aşıkpaşazâde 奥斯曼历史学家 1—554c
阿希乔 Ahidjo, Ahmadou 喀麦隆总统 1—133e
阿希亚瓦 Ahhiyawā 安纳托利亚古代王国 1—133d
阿锡尔 Athyr (Egyptian goddess) 埃及女神 2—26c
阿孝夫 Aschoff, Karl Albert Ludwig 德国病理学家 1—541e
阿歇特 Hachette, Louis-Christophe-François 法国出版商 7—398f
阿谢隆 Acheron 希腊河流 1—51f
阿谢洛奥斯河 Achelous River 希腊河流 1—51c
阿谢姆 Ascham, Roger 英国学者 1—541a
阿修罗 asura 印度教神话 2—10e
阿雅克肖 Ajaccio 法国城镇 1—150c
阿雅拉 Ayala, Francisco 西班牙小说家 2—95a
阿亚·德拉托雷 Haya de la Torre, Víctor Raél 秘鲁政治家 7—529d
阿亚库乔 Ayacucho 秘鲁省份 2—94e
阿亚库乔 Ayacucho 秘鲁城市 2—94f
阿亚库乔港 Puerto Ayacucho 委内瑞拉区首府 14—15c
阿亚库乔战役 Ayacucho, Battle of 南美历史 2—94f
阿耶波多(第一) Āryabhaṭa I 印度天文学家 1—537a
"阿耶波多"号卫星 Aryabhata 印度人造卫星 1—537a
阿伊 Ay 埃及国王 2—94e
阿伊尔山 Aïr massif 尼日尔山丛 1—145c
阿伊卡故事 Ahikar, The Story of 民间故事 1—133f
阿依努人 Ainu 亚洲北部民族 1—142a
阿以莎 'Ā'ishah 穆罕默德之妻 1—148f
阿以战争 Arab-Israeli wars 阿拉伯-以色列军事冲突 1—429e
阿因 'ayn 阿拉伯语"名人"之意 2—97a
阿尤布·汗 Ayub Khan, Mohammad 巴基斯坦总统 2—98c
阿尤布王朝 Ayyūbid DYNASTY 穆斯林王朝 2—98f
阿尤恩 El Aaiún 摩洛哥城市 6—9e
阿瑜陀耶 Ayutthaya 泰国故都 2—98e
阿育王 Aśoka 印度皇帝 1—555f
阿约提亚 Ayodhyā 印度市镇 2—97b
阿月浑子属 Pistacia 植物学 13—326a
阿宰勒里多 Azay-le-Rideau 法国城镇 2—100a
阿赞德人 Azande 中非民族 2—99e
阿泽利奥 Azeglio, Massimo Taparelli, marchese d' 意大利作家、政治家 2—100b
阿泽姆格尔 Azamgarh 印度城镇 2—99c
阿扎尔 Hazard, Paul 法国教育家、思想史家 7—535b
阿扎尔派 Azalī 伊朗宗教教派 2—99c
阿扎克 Azak (Russia) 俄罗斯城市 2—99a
阿扎雷 Azare 尼日利亚城镇 2—99e
阿扎利亚 Ajaria 格鲁吉亚行政区域 1—150d
阿扎尼亚泛非主义者大会 Pan-Africanist Congress of Azania (PAC) 南非政治组织 13—2b
阿扎伊斯 Azaïs, Pierre-Hyacinthe 法国哲学家 2—99a
阿旃陀洞穴 Ajanta Caves 印度佛教庙宇 1—150d
阿真舍 Argentia 加拿大村庄 1—463b
阿真塔 Argenta 意大利城镇 1—462f
阿真泰拉 Argentera (France-Italy) 法兰西-意大利关隘 1—463b
阿治曼 'Ajmān 阿拉伯联合酋长国成员国 1—151c
阿周那 Arjuna 印度史诗中人物 1—489e
阿朱勒 'Ajjul, Tall al- 巴勒斯坦古代遗址 1—151c
阿兹 Ards 北爱尔兰区名 1—458e
阿兹拉伊来 'Izrā'īl 伊斯兰教天使 8—499a
阿兹纳 Arzner, Dorothy 美国电影导演 1—537e
阿兹特克历 Aztec calendar 中美洲古历法 2—103f
阿兹特克人 Aztec 中美洲民族 2—103d
阿兹特克-塔诺诸语言 Azteco-Tanoan languages 美洲印第安语言 2—104a
阿兹特克遗址国家保护地 Aztec Ruins National Monument 美国考古场地 2—103f
阿兹特克语 Aztec language 美洲印第安语言 2—103f
阿佐内 Azzone DEI PORCI 博洛尼亚法学家 2—104f
阿佐佩 Adzopé 科特迪瓦城镇 1—91e
锕(Ac) actinium 化学元素 1—60a
锕系 actinium series 化学元素 1—60b
锕系元素 actinide 化学元素 1—59f
哀悼 mourning 社会风俗习惯 11—447b
哀鸽 mourning dove (*Zenaida macroura*) 鸟类 11—447b
哀歌 elegy 诗学 6—32b
哀歌 lament 文学 9—464a
哀牢夷 Ailaoyi 中国古民族 1—141a
《哀乌尔》 Lament for the Destruction of Ur 文学 9—464b
埃 angstrom 计量单位 1—352c
埃阿 Ea 美索不达米亚水神 5—492d
埃阿科斯 Aeacus 希腊神话人物 1—91e
埃阿斯 Ajax 希腊传说人物大埃阿斯 1—150f
埃阿斯 Ajax 希腊传说人物小埃阿斯 1—150f
埃奥卡 EOKA 塞浦路斯民族主义运动组织 6—92f
埃奥利安群岛 Aeolian Islands (Italy) 意大利群岛 1—95a
埃奥利群岛 Eolie Islands 地中海火山群岛 6—93a
埃奥利斯 Aeolis 土耳其古代城市 1—95b
埃班 Eban, Abba (Solomon) 以色列外交家 5—515c
埃贝尔 Hébert, Anne 加拿大作家 7—549d
埃贝尔 Hébert, Jacques-René 法国新闻工作者 7—549d
埃贝哈德 Eberhard 法兰克尼亚公爵 5—516c
埃贝哈德一世 Eberhard I 符腾堡公爵 5—516c
埃本塞 Ebensee 奥地利城镇 5—516b
埃比斯科比乌斯 Episcopius, Simon 荷兰神学家 6—102f
埃庇卡摩斯 Epicharmus 希腊诗人 6—97e
埃庇米尼得斯 Epimenides 克里特先知 6—101b
埃庇米尼得斯悖论 Epimenides' paradox 逻辑学 6—101b
埃波雷迪亚 Eporedia (ancient Roman district and town, Italy) 古罗马城市 6—105b
埃伯巴赫 Eberbach, Heinrich 德国将军 5—516b
埃伯哈特 Eberhard, Johann August 德国哲学家 5—516d
埃伯哈特 Eberhart, Richard 美国诗人 5—516e
埃伯斯瓦尔德-菲诺 Eberswalde-Finow 德国城市 5—516f
埃伯斯纸草文稿 Ebers papyrus 古埃及医学文集 5—516f
埃博 Ebbo OF REIMS 法兰克王国大主教 5—515e
埃博拉病毒 Ebola 致出血热病毒 5—518c
埃博利 Eboli 意大利城镇 5—518e
埃博洛瓦 Ebolowa 喀麦隆城镇 5—518e
埃卜拉 Ebla 叙利亚古城遗址 5—517e
埃卜拉语 Eblaite language 古闪米特语言 5—518b
埃布埃 Éboué, Félix 乍得总督 5—519a
埃布莱玛 emblema 艺术品 6—57a
埃布隆冰期 Eburon glacial stage 地质学 5—519c
埃布罗恩 Ebroïn 法兰克王国宫相 5—519b
埃布罗河 Ebro River 西班牙河流 5—519b
埃布纳-埃申巴赫 Ebner-Eschenbach, Marie, Baroness (Freifrau) von 奥地利小说家 5—518c
埃布瓦 Herbois, Jean-Marie Collot d' 法国激进民主派成员 8—35f
埃布韦尔 Ebbw Vale 英国城镇 5—515e
埃达 Ada 美国城市 1—62f
《埃达》 Edda 冰岛文学作品 5—534f
埃达沃 Etāwah 印度城镇 6—143f
埃代 Ede 尼日利亚城镇 5—536b

埃代阿 Edéa 喀麦隆城镇 5—536b
埃丹 Edam 荷兰村镇 5—534c
埃丹干酪 Edam 食品 5—534d
埃当普公爵夫人 Étampes, Anne de Pisseleu, duchesse d' 法国贵族、国王情妇 6—143e
埃当普女公爵 Étampes, Gabrielle d'Estrées, duchesse d' (duchess of) 法国贵族 6—143e
埃德 Adur 英格兰区名 1—88f
埃德 Ede 荷兰城市 5—536b
埃德 Etah 印度城镇 6—143d
埃德伯特 Edbert 诺森伯里亚国王 5—534e
埃德尔 Ederle, Gertrude (Caroline) 美国游泳运动员 5—538d
埃德尔曼 Edelman, Gerald Maurice 美国生物化学家 5—536d
埃德尔曼 Edelman, Marian Wright 美国律师、民权活动家 5—536d
埃德加 Edgar 苏格兰国王 5—538f
埃德加 Edgar 英格兰国王 5—538f
埃德加(埃特尔英的) Edgar THE AETHELING 盎格鲁-撒克逊王子 5—539a
埃德加敦 Edgartown 美国城镇 5—539b
埃德拉巴德 Edlābād (India) 印度城市 5—546d
埃德兰 Hédelin, François 法国戏剧家 7—554d
埃德林克 Edelinck, Gerard 佛兰德斯铜版画家 5—536c
埃德门兹顿 Edmundston 加拿大城市 5—547d
埃德蒙 Edmond 美国城市 5—546e
埃德蒙 Edmund 统治者之名 5—546f
埃德蒙 Edmund 东英吉利国王 5—547a
埃德蒙 Edmund 英国贵族 5—547b
埃德蒙(兰利的) Edmund OF LANGLEY 英格兰贵族 5—547c
埃德蒙(伍德斯托克的) Edmund OF WOODSTOCK 英格兰贵族 5—547c
埃德蒙·贝克特爵士 Beckett, Sir Edmund 英国钟表专家 2—320f
埃德蒙德(阿宾顿的),圣 Edmund OF ABINGTON, SAINT 英格兰学者、大主教 5—547b
埃德蒙顿 Edmonton 加拿大城市 5—546e
埃德蒙二世 Edmund II 英格兰国王 5—547b
埃德蒙一世 Edmund I 英格兰国王 5—547a
埃德蒙兹 Edmunds, George Franklin 美国参议员 5—547c
埃德默 Edmer 英国历史学家 5—546d
埃德萨 Edessa (Turkey) 土耳其城市 5—538f
埃德森 Edson, Katherine Philips 美国改革家、公职人员 5—547f
埃德威格 Eadwig 英格兰国王 5—493a
埃德温 Edwin 诺森伯里亚国王 5—553d
埃德温·史密斯纸草文稿 Edwin Smith papyrus 古埃及医稿 5—553e
埃德修斯 Aedesius 希腊哲学家 1—92a
埃登 Edén, Nils 瑞典政治家 5—537c
埃迪布·阿德瓦尔 Edib Adıvar, Halide 土耳其小说家 5—540a
埃迪尔内 Edirne 土耳其城市 5—544a
《埃迪尔内条约》 Edirne, Treaty of 俄土战争条约 5—544c
埃迪卡拉动物群 Ediacara fauna 古生物学 5—539f
埃迪森 Eddison, E.R. 英国小说家 5—535e
埃迪斯通灯塔 Eddystone Lighthouse 航海 5—536a
埃蒂 Etty, William 英国画家 6—154a
埃蒂安纳 Estienne, Henri II 法国学者 6—140a
埃蒂安纳 Estienne, Robert I 法国学者 6—140b
埃丁根 Edingen (Belgium) 比利时城市 5—544a
埃冬 Aedon 希腊神话人物 1—92b
埃杜维 Aedui 法国凯尔特人部落 1—92b
埃多姆 Edom 约旦古地区 5—547e
埃多人 Edo 尼日利亚诸民族 5—547d
埃俄罗斯 Aeolus 希腊故事人物 1—95b
埃俄罗斯 Aeolus 希腊神话人物 1—95b
埃尔 ayre 英国歌曲体裁 2—97d
埃尔埃斯科里亚尔 El Escorial 西班牙村庄 6—10b
埃尔奥连特 El Oriente 厄瓜多尔行政区 6—11a
埃尔班科 El Banco 哥伦比亚城市 6—9f
埃尔比勒 Irbīl 伊拉克城镇 8—443a
埃尔布隆格 Elbląg 波兰城市 6—15b
埃尔布隆格 Elbląg 原波兰省份 6—15b
埃尔茨贝格尔 Erzberger, Matthias 德国政治家 6—126b
埃尔达 Elda 西班牙城市 6—16a
埃尔达 Eldad (BEN MAHLI) HA-DANI 犹太旅行家 6—16a
埃尔德 Elder, John 英国轮机工程师 6—16e
埃尔德 Elder, Kate 美国平原居民、边区娼妓 6—16e
埃尔德 Elder, Lonne, III 美国剧作家 6—16f
埃尔德古兹王朝 Eldegüzid DYNASTY 伊朗王朝 6—16b
埃尔德里奇 Eldridge, (David) Roy 美国音乐家 6—17d
埃尔德什 Erdös, Paul 波兰籍匈牙利数学家 6—112f
埃尔德斯 Elders, Joycelyn 美国医生 6—16f
埃尔登伯爵(第一) Eldon, John Scott, 1st Earl of, VISCOUNT ENCOMBE OF ENCOMBE, BARON ELDON OF ELDON 英国大法官 6—17a
埃尔蒂格雷 El Tigre 委内瑞拉城市 6—12e
埃尔顿 Elton, Charles 英国生物学家 6—53a
埃尔顿湖 Elton, Lake 俄罗斯盐湖 6—53d
埃尔多安 Erdogan, Recep Tayyip 土耳其政治人物 6—112f
埃尔多拉多 El Dorado 美国城市 6—10b
埃尔多拉多 Eldorado 传说中波哥大统治者 6—17b
埃尔多雷特 Eldoret 肯尼亚城镇 6—17d
埃尔费罗尔 El Ferrol 西班牙城市 6—10c
埃尔芬斯通 Elphinstone, Mountstuart 英国驻印度官员 6—51f
埃尔芬斯通 Elphinstone, William 苏格兰主教 6—51f
埃尔夫·阿奎坦公司 Elf Aquitaine 法国公司 6—35e
埃尔弗里克 Aelfric 盎格鲁-撒克逊作家 1—93e
埃尔戈 Helgaud 法国修士 7—572d
埃尔贡山 Elgon, Mount 非洲死火山 6—37c
埃尔哈特 Earhart, Amelia 美国飞行家 5—495f
埃尔加 Elgar, Sir Edward (William) 英国作曲家 6—36a
埃尔金 Elgin 苏格兰城市 6—36c
埃尔金 Elgin 美国城市 6—36d
埃尔金 Elgin, EARLS OF 苏格兰封爵贵族家族名 6—36d
埃尔金伯爵(第八) Elgin, James Bruce, 8th earl of, 12TH EARLOF KINCARDINE 英国政治家 6—36e
埃尔金伯爵(第九) Elgin, Victor Alexander Bruce, 9th earl of 英国驻印度总督 6—37a
埃尔金伯爵(第七) Elgin, Thomas Bruce, 7th earl of 英国外交家、艺术品收藏家 6—36e
埃尔金大理石雕刻艺术品 Elgin Marbles 伦敦不列颠博物馆收藏的希腊艺术品 6—37a
埃尔金斯 Elkins 美国城市 6—46e
埃尔津詹 Erzincan 土耳其城市 6—126c
埃尔卡诺 Elcano, Juan Sebastián de 西班牙探险家 6—15f
埃尔卡亚俄 El Callao 委内瑞拉城镇 6—10a
埃尔卡约 El Cayo (Belize) 伯利兹城市 6—10a
埃尔科 Elko 美国城市 6—46e
埃尔科岛 Elcho Island (Australia) 澳大利亚岛屿 6—16a
埃尔科拉诺 Ercolano 意大利城镇 6—112e
埃尔克 Ercker, Lazarus 德国冶金学家 6—112d
埃尔克城 Elk City 美国城市 6—46c
埃尔克岛国家公园 Elk Island National Park 加拿大公园 6—46c
埃尔克顿 Elkton 美国县城 6—46f
埃尔克哈特 Elkhart 美国城市 6—46d
埃尔克河 Elk River 美国河流 6—46d
埃尔克霍恩塔文战役 Elkhorn Tavern, Battle of (American Civil War) 美国历史 6—46e
埃尔克山 Elk Mountains 美国山脉 6—46d
埃尔克山丑闻 Elk Hills Scandal (U.S. history) 美国历史 6—46c
埃尔库拉诺·德·卡尔瓦略·埃·阿劳若 Herculano de Carvalho e

Araújo, Alexandre 葡萄牙历史学家、作家 8—36c
埃尔朗加 Erlangga 印度尼西亚统治者 6—120b
埃尔朗热贷款 Erlanger Loan 美国历史 6—120b
埃尔里诺 El Reno 美国城市 6—11d
埃尔利希 Ehrlich, Paul 美国生物学家 5—563f
埃尔利希 Ehrlich, Paul R(alph) 德国医学家 5—564a
埃尔隆伯爵 Erlon, Jean-Baptiste Drouet, Count (comte) d' 法国元帅 6—120c
埃尔迈恩街 Ermine Street 英国古罗马大道 6—120e
埃尔迈拉 Elmira 美国城市 6—50f
埃尔迈拉制度 Elmira system 美国刑罚制度 6—51a
埃尔曼 Elman, Mischa 美国小提琴家 6—50e
埃尔曼 Ellmann, Richard (David) 美国文学评论家 6—49c
埃尔芒·德瓦朗谢纳 Herman DE VALENCIENNES 法国诗人 8—40b
埃尔蒙特 El Monte 美国城市 6—10e
埃尔米特 Hermite, Charles 法国数学家 8—42e
埃尔米特圣母村 Notre-Dame-des-Ermites (Switzerland) 瑞士城镇 12—275c
埃尔莫, 圣 Elmo, SAINT 早期基督教主教 6—51b
埃尔莫尔兄弟 Elmore, Francis Edward and Alexander Stanley 英国选矿工艺学家 6—51b
埃尔莫罗国家保护区 El Morro National Monument 美国古迹保护区 6—10f
埃尔默洛 Ermelo 荷兰城市 6—120d
埃尔姆布里奇 Elmbridge 英国自治市 6—50e
埃尔姆赫斯特 Elmhurst 美国城市 6—50f
埃尔姆斯利 Elmslie, George Grant 美国建筑师 6—51c
埃尔穆波利斯 Hermoúpolis 希腊城市 8—43c
埃尔南德斯 Hernández, Felisberto 拉丁美洲作家 8—43d
埃尔南德斯 Hernández, Gregorio 西班牙雕刻家 8—43e
埃尔南德斯 Hernández, José 阿根廷诗人 8—43e
埃尔南德斯 Hernández, Miguel 西班牙作家 8—43f
埃尔南德斯 Hernández, Orlando 古巴棒球投手 8—44a
埃尔南德斯·科隆 Hernández Colón, Rafael 波多黎各总督 8—44a
埃尔帕拉伊索 El Paraíso 秘鲁前陶器时代遗址 6—11b
埃尔帕索 El Paso 美国城市 6—11b
埃尔普罗格雷索 El Progreso 洪都拉斯城市 6—11c
埃尔切 Elche 西班牙城镇 6—16a
埃尔萨里地毯 Ersari carpet 土库曼人工艺品 6—123b
埃尔萨塞 Elsasser, Walter M. 美国物理学家 6—52a
埃尔塞里托 El Cerrito 美国城市 6—10a
埃尔塞纳 Elsene (Belgium) 比利时城市 6—52b
埃尔塞沃 El Seíbo 多米尼加共和国城市 6—12e
埃尔森特罗 El Centro 美国城市 6—10a
埃尔沙拉纳 El Sherana 澳大利亚乡村社区、铀矿基地 6—12e
埃尔丝勒 Elssler, Fanny 奥地利芭蕾舞大师 6—52d
埃尔斯海默 Elsheimer, Adam 德国油画家 6—52b
埃尔斯霍特 Elsschot, Willem 比利时作家 6—52d
埃尔斯金 Erskine, John 苏格兰宗教改革家 6—123b
埃尔斯康普 Elskamp, Max 比利时诗人 6—52c
埃尔斯米尔岛 Ellesmere Island 加拿大岛屿 6—47b
埃尔斯米尔港和内斯顿 Ellesmere Port and Neston 英国区名 6—47b
埃尔斯米尔湖 Ellesmere, Lake 新西兰潟湖 6—47b
埃尔斯米尔男爵 Ellesmere, Thomas Egerton, Baron 英国律师、外交家 6—47b
埃尔斯沃思 Ellsworth 美国城市 6—49d
埃尔斯沃思 Ellsworth, Lincoln 美国探险家 6—49e
埃尔斯沃思 Ellsworth, Oliver 美国律师、外交家 6—50a
埃尔斯沃思地 Ellsworth Land 南极洲山麓地区 6—50b
埃尔泰 Erté 俄罗斯插图画家 6—123f
埃尔特尼恩特 El Teniente 智利矿区村庄 6—12e
埃尔廷治 Eltinge, Julian 美国歌舞剧明星 6—52f
埃尔瓦什 Elvas 葡萄牙城镇 6—53e
埃尔瓦什公爵 Elvas, William Carr Beresford, duke (duque) de 英国将军、葡萄牙元帅 6—53e
埃尔旺根 Ellwangen 德国城市 6—50c
埃尔韦(小姐) Hervé, Mademoiselle 法国演员 8—55b
埃尔韦-巴赞 Hervé-Bazin, Jean Pierre 法国作家 8—55b
埃尔维厄 Hervieu, Paul-Ernest 法国作家 8—55c
埃尔维拉会议 Elvira, Council of 西班牙教会会议 6—53f
埃尔伍德 Elwood 美国城市 6—53f
埃尔西利亚-苏尼加 Ercilla y Zúñiga, Alonso de 西班牙诗人 6—112d
埃尔西诺 Elsinore (Denmark) 丹麦城市 6—52c
埃尔约帕尔 El Yopal 哥伦比亚城市 6—12f
埃尔泽菲尔家族 Elzevir FAMILY 荷兰出版、印刷业家族 6—54f
埃尔祖鲁姆 Erzurum 土耳其城市 6—126d
埃耳门 Elmen, Gustav Waldemar 美国电气工程师 6—50f
埃法特岛 Éfaté 瓦努阿图岛屿 5—554d
埃菲尔 Eiffel, (Alexandre-) Gustave 法国土木工程师 5—566a
埃菲尔铁塔 Eiffel Tower 建筑 5—566b
埃菲克人 Efik 尼日利亚民族 5—555b
埃芬 Effen, Justus van 荷兰作家 5—554e
埃芬汉 Effingham 美国城市 5—555a
埃芬汉的霍华德(男爵第二) Effingham, Charles Howard, 2nd Baron Howard of 英格兰海军大臣 5—555a
埃丰阿莱耶 Effon-Alaiye 尼日利亚城镇 5—555b
埃佛勒斯 Everest, Sir George 英国大地测量学家 6—182d
埃佛勒斯峰 Everest, Mount 珠穆朗玛峰 6—182e
埃夫伯里 Avebury 英格兰教区 2—84a
埃夫勒 Évreux 法国城镇 6—186c
埃夫里 Évry 法国城镇 6—186e
埃夫里普 Euripus 爱琴海的海峡 6—166d
埃夫罗斯 Évros 希腊州名 6—186d
埃夫罗斯河 Évros (Europe) 欧洲河流 6—186d
埃夫罗塔斯河 Evrótas River 希腊河流 6—186d
埃弗丁恩 Everdingen, Allart van 荷兰画家 6—182d
埃弗格莱兹 Everglades 美国沼泽地区 6—182f
埃弗拉塔公社 Ephrata Community 美国新教定居点 6—97a
埃弗莱斯 Eveleth 美国城市 6—181e
埃弗雷特 Everett, Edward 美国政治家 6—182f
埃弗里特 Everett 美国华盛顿州城市 6—182e
埃弗里特 Everett 美国马萨诸塞州城市 6—182e
埃弗利兄弟合唱组 Everly Brothers, the 美国摇滚乐二重唱组合 6—183f
埃弗利姊妹 Everleigh, Ada and Minna 美国鸨母 6—183e
埃弗龙 Efron, Marina Ivanovna 俄罗斯诗人 5—555c
埃弗斯 Evers, Medgar (Wiley) 美国民权活动家 6—184a
埃弗斯-威廉斯 Evers-Williams, Myrlie 非洲裔美国民权活动家 6—184b
埃弗特 Evert, Chris 美国网球运动员 6—184c
埃弗谢德 Evershed, John 英国天文学家 6—184b
埃福德 Efod (Jewish philosopher) 犹太哲学家 5—555c
埃福罗斯 Ephorus 古希腊历史学家 6—96e
埃该翁 Aegaeon (Greek mythology) 希腊神话人物 1—92c
埃格 Egg, Augustus (Leopold) 英国画家 5—556e
埃格伯特 Egbert 韦塞克斯国王 5—555f
埃格尔 Eger (Czech Republic) 捷克城市 5—555f
埃格尔 Eger 匈牙利城镇 5—555f
埃格尔河 Eger River (Europe) 欧洲河流 5—556b
埃格尔斯顿 Eggleston, Edward 美国作家 5—557a
埃格朗丁 Églantine, Philippe(-François-Nazaire) Fabre d' 法国剧作家 5—557d
埃格列夫斯基 Eglevsky, André 美国舞蹈家 5—557d
埃格蒙特伯爵 Egmond, Lamoraal, graaf van (count of) 荷兰贵族

5—557f
埃格蒙特伯爵(第二) Egmont, John Perceval, 2nd earl of 英国政治家 5—557f
埃格蒙特山 Egmont, Mount 新西兰山脉 5—558a
埃格特·奥拉夫松 Eggert Ólafsson (Icelandic poet and antiquarian) 冰岛诗人 5—556f
埃格尤姆石碑 Eggjum Stone 挪威如尼文碑铭 5—556f
埃古伦 Eguren, José María 秘鲁诗人 5—559a
埃关加 Egwanga (Nigeria) 尼日利亚港镇 5—559a
埃亨 Ahern, Bertie 爱尔兰总理 1—133d
埃亨 Ahern, James (writer) 美国剧作家 1—133d
埃基巴斯图兹 Ekibastuz 哈萨克斯坦城市 6—8a
埃基多 ejido 墨西哥土地制度 6—7e
埃及 Egypt 非洲国家 5—559a
埃及博物馆 Egyptian Museum 古物馆 5—562a
埃及法 Egyptian law 法律 5—561e
埃及历 Egyptian calendar 历法 5—561c
埃及王冠 Crowns of Egypt 埃及历史 5—37a
埃及学 Egyptology 研究法老时代埃及的学科 5—562d
埃及艺术 Egyptian art 尼罗河流域古代艺术 5—560f
埃及语 Egyptian language 尼罗河谷语言 5—561c
埃及重脚兽 Arsinoitherium 古生物学 1—520d
埃及宗教 Egyptian religion 宗教 5—562b
埃吉尔·斯卡拉格里姆松 Egill Skallagrímsson 冰岛吟唱诗人 5—557c
埃吉里娅 Egeria 罗马宗教精灵 5—556b
埃济-德塔亚克洞窟 Eyzies-de-Tayac caves 考古 6—202c
埃加迪安群岛 Aegadian Islands 意大利岛群 1—92c
埃加迪群岛 Egadi Islands 意大利岛群 5—555d
埃加斯·莫尼兹 Egas Moniz, António 葡萄牙神经病学家 5—555d
埃杰顿 Edgerton, Harold E(ugene) 美国电气工程师 5—539b
埃杰顿 Egerton, Thomas 英格兰律师 5—556b
埃杰维特 Ecevit, Bülent 土耳其总理 5—521d
埃卡德 Eccard, Johannes 德国作曲家 5—519f
埃卡泰 Écarté 纸牌游戏 5—519e
埃坎卡教 ECKANKAR (ECK) 西方化的音流瑜伽 5—523f
埃柯夫 Ekhof, (Hans) Konrad (Dieterich) 德国演员 6—8a
埃科 Eco, Umberto 意大利文学评论家 5—526b
埃科菲斯克 Ekofisk 挪威近海油气田 6—9a
埃科伊人 Ekoi 非洲民族 6—9a
埃克 Eck, Johann 德意志神学家 5—523e
埃克 Egk, Werner 德国作曲家 5—557c
埃克巴坦那 Ecbatana 伊朗古城 5—519e
埃克尔 Eckhel, Joseph Hilarius 奥地利钱币学家 5—524e
埃克尔斯 Eccles, Sir John Carew 澳大利亚生理学家 5—520b
埃克尔斯 Eccles, William Henry 英国物理学家 5—520c
埃克弗里思 Ecgfrith 盎格鲁-撒克逊国王 5—521e
埃克哈德第四 Ekkehard IV 欧洲历史学家 6—8d
埃克哈德第一(老) Ekkehard I the Elder 欧洲诗人 6—8c
埃克豪特 Eekhoud, Georges 荷兰画家 5—554a
埃克豪特 Eeckhout, Gerbrand van den 荷兰画家 5—553e
埃克兰国家公园 Écrins National Park 法国自然保护区 5—531e
埃克勒夫 Ekelöf, Gunnar 瑞典诗人 6—7f
埃克曼 Ekman, Gösta 瑞典演员、导演 6—8e
埃克曼 Eckermann, Johann Peter 德国作家 5—524b
埃克曼 Ekman, V(agn) Walfrid 瑞典海洋物理学家 6—8e
埃克米尔亲王 Eckmühl, Louis-Nicolas Davout, Prince d' 法国将军 5—524e
埃克纳 Eckener, Hugo 德国航空工程师 5—524a
埃克塞尔西奥斯普林斯 Excelsior Springs 美国城市 6—188e
埃克塞尔西奥钻石 Excelsior diamond 南非金刚石 6—188e
埃克塞基亚斯 Exekias 希腊画家 6—191d
埃克塞特 Exeter 英格兰城市 6—192a
埃克塞特 Exeter 美国城镇 6—192b
埃克塞特菲利普斯学校 Phillips Exeter Academy 美国大学预备学校 13—243c
《埃克塞特诗集》 Exeter Book 古英语诗集 6—192c
埃克森公司 Exxon Corporation 美国公司 6—199e
埃克森-美孚公司 Exxon Mobil Corporation 美国公司 6—200b
埃克斯河 Exe, River 英国河流 6—190d
埃克斯卡利伯 Excalibur 亚瑟王传奇中的神剑名 6—188d
埃克斯茅斯 Exmouth 英格兰地名 6—193d
埃克斯茅斯湾 Exmouth Gulf 澳大利亚海湾 6—193d
埃克斯穆尔高地 Exmoor 英格兰高地 6—193c
埃克斯坦 Eckstine, Billy 美国歌手 5—524e
埃克斯托姆 Eckstorm, Fannie Pearson Hardy 美国作家、鸟类学家 5—524f
埃克苏马群岛 Exuma Cays 大西洋巴哈马群岛 6—199e
埃克托尔 Hector, Charles 法国军人 7—554a
埃克脱(小) Eckert, J(ohn) Presper, Jr. 美国工程师 5—524c
埃奎亚诺 Equiano, Olaudah 贝宁废奴主义者 6—108a
埃魁人 Aequi 古意大利民族 1—95e
埃昆西 Ekwensi, Cyprian (Odiatu Duaka) 尼日利亚作家 6—9d
埃拉尔 Érard, Sébastien 法国乐器制造家 6—109e
埃拉加巴卢斯 Elagabalus 罗马帝国皇帝 6—13a
埃拉斯都 Erastus, Thomas 瑞士医生、宗教教义论辩家 6—111f
埃拉斯都主义 Erastianism 基督教神学学说 6—111f
埃拉特 Elat 以色列港口城市 6—14d
埃拉托 Erato 希腊女神 6—112a
埃拉西斯特拉图斯(克奥斯的) Erasistratus of Ceos 希腊解剖学家 6—109f
埃拉泽 Elazığ 土耳其城市 6—14f
埃拉扎尔 Elazar, David 以色列军官 6—14e
埃莱夫西斯 Eleusis 古希腊城市 6—34d
埃莱夫西斯节 Eleusinia 古希腊节日 6—34c
埃莱夫西斯秘仪 Eleusinian Mysteries 古希腊宗教仪式 6—34c
埃莱亚诺(阿基坦的) Eleanor of Aquitaine 法王和英王王后 6—17e
埃兰 Elam 伊朗古国 6—13b
埃兰德 Erlander, Tage (Fritiof) 瑞典首相 6—119f
埃兰语 Elamite language 埃兰古国语言(已消亡) 6—13c
埃兰语楔形文字 Elamite writing 古代中东文字 6—13d
埃朗根 Erlangen 德国城市 6—120a
埃劳 Erlau (Hungary) 匈牙利城镇 6—120b
埃劳战役 Eylau, Battle of 欧洲历史 6—201e
埃勒曼 Ellerman, Annie Winifred (British writer) 英国作家 6—47a
埃勒默拉岭 Erramala Range 印度丘陵 6—122f
埃雷迪亚 Heredia 哥斯达黎加城市 8—37c
埃雷迪亚 Heredia, José Maria de 法国诗人 8—37c
埃雷克 Erech 伊拉克古城 6—113b
埃雷拉 Herrera, Fernando de 西班牙诗人 8—49b
埃雷拉 Herrera, Juan de 西班牙建筑师 8—49d
埃雷拉(老) Herrera, Francisco, the Elder 西班牙画家 8—49c
埃雷拉(小) Herrera, Francisco, the Younger 西班牙画家 8—49c
埃雷拉-雷西格 Herrera y Reissig, Julio 乌拉圭诗人 8—49e
埃雷利 Ereğli 土耳其中南部城镇 6—113d
埃雷利 Ereğli 土耳其北部城镇 6—113e
埃雷米泰 Eremita, Johannes 基督教修士、神学家 6—113e
埃雷特里亚 Eretria 古希腊城镇 6—114a
埃雷特纳王朝 Eretna dynasty 安纳托利亚王朝 6—114a
埃雷图娅 Eileithyia 希腊女神 6—1a
埃里昂 Hélion, Jean 法国画家 7—574a
埃里金纳 Erigena, John Scotus 基督教神学家 6—117e
埃里克 Erik 统治者之名 6—117f
埃里克 Erik 挪威国王 6—118c
埃里克 Erik the Red 欧洲拓殖者 6—118d
埃里克六世 Erik VI 丹麦国王 6—118a

埃里克七世 Erik VII 丹麦、挪威、瑞典联合王国国王 6—118b
埃里克三世 Erik III 挪威国王 6—118c
埃里克森 Ericsson, John 美国造船工程师 6—116d
埃里克十三世 Erik XIII 瑞典国王 6—118c
埃里克十四世 Erik XIV 瑞典国王 6—118c
埃里克松 Erikson, Erik H(omburger) 美国精神分析学家 6—118e
埃里克松 Ericson, Leif 挪威探险家 6—116d
埃里克松 Erikson, Leif 挪威探险家 6—118f
埃里克五世 Erik V 丹麦国王 6—118a
埃里克一世 Erik I 挪威、诺森伯兰国王 6—118c
埃里切 Erice 意大利城镇 6—116b
埃里温 Yerevan 亚美尼亚首都 18—441e
埃里希·冯·莱温斯基 Lewinski, Erich von 德国军人 10—50c
埃利奥 Hélyot, Hippolyte 法国历史学家 8—7f
埃利奥特 Eliot, Sir Charles (Norton Edgecumbe) 英国外交家 6—38d
埃利奥特 Eliot, Charles William 美国教育家 6—38d
埃利奥特 Elliott, Herb 澳大利亚运动员 6—48b
埃利奥特 Elliott, Harriet Wiseman 美国教育家 6—48a
埃利奥特 Eliot, Jared 北美殖民时期牧师 6—39b
埃利奥特 Eliot, John 英国传教士 6—39b
埃利奥特 Eliot, Sir John 英国清教徒、议会党人 6—39c
埃利奥特 Elyot, Sir Thomas 英国作家 6—54c
埃利奥特(-默里-凯宁芒德) Elliot(-Murray-Kynynmound), Gilbert 英国官员 6—47f
埃利奥特莱克 Elliot Lake 加拿大城市 6—47f
埃利奥特森 Elliotson, John 英国医师 6—48a
埃利蒂斯 Elytis, Odysseus 希腊诗人 6—54e
埃利都 Eridu 伊拉克古城 6—116e
《埃利都创世记》 Eridu Genesis 美索不达米亚经籍 6—116e
埃利孔山 Helicon, Mount 希腊山峰 7—573a
埃利潘蒂尼 Elephantine 埃及岛屿 6—34a
埃利色雷 Erythrae 土耳其古城 6—125c
埃利森 Ellison, Ralph (Waldo) 美国作家 6—49c
埃利斯 Ellis, (Henry) Havelock 英国散文家 6—48f
埃利斯岛 Ellis Island 美国岛屿 6—49a
埃利斯群岛 Ellice Islands (Pacific Ocean) 太平洋群岛 6—47d
埃利斯塔 Elista 俄罗斯城市 6—41d
埃利特 Ellet, Charles 美国钢索桥工程师 6—47c
埃利特 Ellet, Elizabeth Fries Lummis 美国历史作家 6—47c
埃利翁 Elion, Gertrude Belle 美国药物学家 6—38c
埃利乌斯·多纳图斯 Aelius Donatus 罗马语法学家 1—93f
埃利乌斯·斯提洛 Aelius Stilo 古罗马学者 1—93f
埃利西奥 Elísio, Filinto 葡萄牙诗人 6—41c
埃利希 Ehrlich, Eugen 奥地利法学家 5—563e
埃利希曼 Ehrlichman, John D(aniel) 美国政治顾问 5—564b
埃利亚(科尔托纳的) Elias of Cortona 意大利历史人物 6—37e
埃利亚代 Eliade, Mircea 美国宗教史学家 6—37d
埃利亚卡皮托利纳 Aelia Capitolina 亚洲古城市 1—93e
埃利亚努斯 Aelianus 希腊军事著作家 1—93f
埃利亚斯皮尼亚 Elías Piña 多米尼加共和国城市 6—37f
埃利赞 Relizane 阿尔及利亚城镇 14—216b
埃莉诺(卡斯蒂利亚的) Eleanor of Castile 英格兰王后 6—17f
埃莉诺(普罗旺斯的) Eleanor of Provence 英格兰王后 6—18a
埃列克特罗斯塔利 Elektrostal 俄罗斯城市 6—32c
埃列亚 Elea (Greek city-state) 古希腊城邦 6—17e
埃林顿 Ellington, Duke 美国作曲家 6—47d
埃留提利乌斯,圣 Eleutherius, Saint 教皇 6—34d
埃卢鲁 Elūru 印度城镇 6—53e
埃卢亚尔(-德苏维萨) Elhuyar (y de Suvisa), Fausto (d') 西班牙化学家 6—37c
埃鲁 Héroult, Paul-Louis-Toussaint 法国化学家 8—48e
埃吕尔 Ellul, Jacques (César) 法国政治学和社会学家 6—50b
埃律西昂 Elysium 希腊神话中的乐园 6—54d
埃伦巴勒伯爵 Ellenborough, Edward Law, Earl of, Viscount Southam of Southam, Baron Ellenborough of Ellenborough 英国驻印度总督 6—46f
埃伦贝格 Ehrenberg, Christian Gottfried 德国生物学家 5—563b
埃伦费尔斯 Ehrenfels, Christian, Freiherr von 奥地利哲学家 5—563d
埃伦斯堡 Ellensburg 美国城市 6—47a
埃伦塔尔 Aehrenthal, Aloys, Count Graf Lexa von 奥地利匈牙利外交大臣 1—93d
埃罗 Hérault 法国省份 8—33f
埃罗埃 Héroët, Antoine 法国诗人 8—47a
埃罗德 Erode 印度城镇 6—122a
埃罗德塞舍尔 Hérault de Séchelles, Marie-Jean 法国贵族、法官 8—34a
埃罗尔伯爵(第九) Erroll, Francis Hay, 9th earl of 苏格兰贵族 6—122f
埃罗尔德 Hérold, (Louis -Joseph-) Ferdinand 法国作曲家 8—48a
埃罗芒阿岛 Erromango 太平洋瓦鲁阿图火山岛 6—123a
埃罗伊兹 Héloïse 法国修女 8—4f
埃洛拉洞 Ellora Caves 印度古王朝庙宇 6—49d
埃洛雷 Ellore (India) 印度城镇 6—49d
埃洛石 halloysite 矿物 7—431b
埃洛希姆 Elohim 希伯来人的上帝、神祇 6—51d
埃洛希姆卷 Elohist source 《圣经·旧约》原始资料 6—51d
埃曼塔尔干酪 Emmentaler 瑞士干酪 6—61f
埃梅 Aymé, Marcel 法国小说家 2—96e
埃梅切塔 Emecheta, Buchi 尼日利亚小说家 6—58d
埃门 Emmen 荷兰城市 6—61e
埃蒙 Hémon, Louis 法国作家 8—10e
埃米茨堡 Emmitsburg 美国城镇 6—62c
埃米尔 emir 中东地区统治者称号 6—61c
埃米奖 Emmy Award 美国电视奖 6—62c
埃米利安 Aemilian 罗马皇帝 1—94b
埃米莉名单 EMILY's List 美国政治 6—60e
埃米柳斯·李必达 Aemilius Lepidus, Marcus 古罗马政治家 1—94c
埃米柳斯·帕皮尼安乌斯 Aemilius Papinianus 罗马法学家 1—94c
埃米特 Emmett, Daniel Decatur 美国作曲家 6—62b
埃米特 Emmet, Robert 爱尔兰民族主义领袖 6—62a
埃米特 Emmet, Thomas Addis 爱尔兰律师 6—62b
埃莫西约 Hermosillo 墨西哥城市 8—43b
埃默拉尔德 Emerald 澳大利亚城镇 6—58f
埃默里冰架 Amery Ice Shelf 印度洋浮冰体 1—286b
埃默森 Emerson, Peter Henry 英国摄影家 6—59e
埃姆布拉 Embla (mythology) 古斯堪的纳维亚神话中人物 6—56f
埃姆登 Emden 德国城市 6—58c
埃姆登 Emden, Robert 瑞士天体物理学家 6—58d
埃姆敦 Emden, Jacob Israel 丹麦犹太教教士 6—58c
埃姆海 Eemian Sea 地质学 5—554d
埃姆间冰期 Eemian Interglacial Stage 地质年代学 5—554c
埃姆塞尔 Emser, Hieronymus 德国神学家 6—66c
埃姆斯 Ames 美国城市 1—286b
埃姆斯 Eames, Emma (Hayden) 美国歌剧演员 5—495a
埃姆斯伯里 Amesbury 英格兰教区名 1—287a
埃姆斯伯里 Amesbury 美国城镇 1—287a
埃姆斯电报 Ems telegram 欧洲历史 6—66b
埃姆斯夫妇 Eames, Charles; and Eames, Ray 美国设计家、建筑师 5—494f
埃姆斯河 Ems River 德国河流 6—66b
埃姆斯河-威悉河-易北河运河 Ems-Weser-Elbe Canal (Germany) 德国运河 6—66b

埃姆斯兰 Emsland 德国地区 6—66c
埃纳 Aisne 法国省份 1—149a
埃纳比克 Hennebique, François 法国工程师 8—16a
埃纳尔·贝内迪克松 Einar Benediktsson (Icelandic poet) 冰岛诗人 6—1b
埃纳雷斯堡 Alcalá de Henares 西班牙城市 1—187a
埃纳雷斯堡大学 Alcalá de Henares, University of 西班牙大学 1—187b
埃奈斯库 Enesco, Georges 罗马尼亚作曲家 6—75f
埃奈西德穆 Aenesidemus 希腊哲学家 1—94e
埃内尔 Henner, Jean-Jacques 法国画家 8—16b
埃内斯特诸公国 Ernestine duchies 德意志中东部邦国 6—121d
埃尼威托克 Enewetak 马绍尔群岛共和国环礁 6—76a
埃涅阿斯 Aeneas 罗马神话人物 1—94c
埃努古 Enugu 尼日利亚州名 6—90c
埃努古 Enugu 尼日利亚城镇 6—90c
埃诺 Hainaut 比利时省份 7—412c
埃佩 Epe 尼日利亚港口城镇 6—94c
埃佩尔奈 Épernay 法国城镇 6—94e
埃佩尔农公爵 Épernon, Jean-Louis de Nogaret de La Valette, Duke (duc) d' 法国公爵 6—94f
埃佩耶斯 Eperjes (Slovakia) 斯洛伐克城镇 6—94e
埃皮达鲁斯 Epidaurus 希腊古城 6—98f
埃皮岛 Epi 太平洋瓦努阿图岛屿 6—97a
埃皮纳勒 Épinal 法国城镇 6—101c
埃皮奈 Épinay, Louise-Florence-Pétronille Tardieu d'Esclavelles, dame de La Live d' 法国作家 6—101c
埃平森林 Epping Forest 英国地区 6—105b
埃普瑟姆-尤厄尔 Epsom and Ewell 英国自治市 6—105b
埃奇河 Etsch (river, Italy) 意大利河流 6—153f
埃奇米阿津 Echmiadzin 亚美尼亚城市 5—522f
埃奇沃思 Edgeworth, Francis Ysidro 爱尔兰经济学家 5—539c
埃奇沃思 Edgeworth, Maria 爱尔兰作家 5—539d
埃奇沃思 Edgeworth, Richard Lovell 爱尔兰发明家 5—539e
埃乔 Edjo (Egyptian goddess) 埃及女神 5—546d
埃切加赖-埃萨吉雷 Echegaray y Eizaguirre, José 西班牙剧作家 5—521e
埃切利诺三世(罗马诺的) Ezzelino III da Romano 意大利贵族 6—203e
埃切维里亚 Echeverría, Esteban 阿根廷诗人、小说家 5—521f
埃切维里亚·阿尔瓦雷斯 Echeverría Álvarez, Luis 墨西哥总统 5—522a
埃瑞 Héré de Corny, Emmanuel 法国建筑师 8—37b
埃萨·德·克罗兹 Eça de Queirós, José Maria de 葡萄牙小说家 5—519d
埃萨吉拉寺 Esagila 古巴比伦庙宇 6—126e
埃塞俄比亚 Ethiopia 非洲国家 6—147a
埃塞俄比亚区 Ethiopian region 非洲生态学动物区 6—149c
埃塞俄比亚圣咏 Ethiopian chant 东非基督教仪式乐曲 6—148c
埃塞俄比亚文学 Ethiopian literature 文学 6—148d
埃塞俄比亚疣猴 guereza 哺乳动物 7—349c
埃塞俄比亚语 Ethiopic language 语言 6—149e
埃塞俄比亚正教会 Ethiopian Orthodox Church 基督教派别 6—149a
埃塞俄比亚诸语言 Ethiopic languages 语言 6—149e
埃塞俄比亚主义 Ethiopianism 非洲宗教运动 6—149c
埃塞俄比亚字母 Ethiopic alphabet 文字体系 6—149d
埃塞格 Esseg (Croatia) 克罗地亚城镇 6—135a
埃塞克斯 Essex 英格兰王国 6—136b
埃塞克斯 Essex 英格兰郡名 6—136b
埃塞克斯 Essex 美国市镇 6—136c
埃塞克斯伯爵 Essex, earls of 英格兰贵族封号 6—136c
埃塞克斯伯爵 Essex, Thomas Cromwell, earl of 英格兰统治者 6—136d
埃塞克斯伯爵 Essex, William Parr, earl of 英王亨利八世内弟 6—136d
埃塞克斯伯爵(第二) Essex, Robert Devereux, 2nd earl of 英格兰军人 6—136f
埃塞克斯伯爵(第三) Essex, Robert Devereux, 3rd earl of 英国贵族 6—137a
埃塞克斯伯爵(第一) Essex, Geoffrey de Mandeville, 1st earl of 英格兰贵族 6—136d
埃塞克斯伯爵(第一) Essex, Arthur Capel, 1st earl of 英格兰贵族 6—137b
埃塞克斯伯爵(第一) Essex, Walter Devereux, 1st earl of 英格兰军人 6—136d
埃塞克斯裁决 Essex Decision 英国法院裁决 6—137c
埃塞克斯派 Essex Junto 美国历史 6—137c
埃塞奎博河 Essequibo River 圭亚那河流 6—136a
埃塞特 Eset (Egyptian goddess) 古埃及女神 6—130b
埃瑟林顿 Etherington, Marie Susan 英国演员 6—145c
埃森 Essen 德国城市 6—135a
埃森 Essen, Louis 英国发明家 6—135b
埃绍 Esau, Katherine 美国植物学家 6—127b
埃施巴赫 Aeschbacher, Hans 瑞士雕刻家 1—97e
埃施韦勒 Eschweiler 德国城市 6—128e
埃什雷夫王朝 Eşref dynasty 土库曼王朝 6—134e
埃什南纳 Eshnunna 伊拉克古城 6—130f
埃什特雷拉山 Estrela Mountains 葡萄牙最高山脉 6—142a
埃什特雷马杜拉 Estremadura 葡萄牙省份 6—142a
埃思里奇 Etherege, Sir George 英国剧作家 6—145c
埃斯比约 Esbjerg 丹麦城市 6—127c
埃斯波 Espoo 芬兰城镇 6—133f
埃斯波斯-米纳 Espoz y Mina, Francisco 西班牙军事领袖 6—134a
埃斯波西托 Esposito, Phil 美国冰球运动员 6—133f
埃斯楚甫 Estrup, Jacob Brønnum Scavenius 丹麦政治家 6—142e
埃斯德赖隆平原 Esdraelon, Plain of 以色列北部低地 6—129f
埃斯登索罗 Estenssoro, Víctor Paz 玻利维亚总统 6—138f
埃斯蒂加里维亚元帅镇 Mariscal Estigarribia 巴拉圭城镇 10—517c
埃斯蒂斯帕克 Estes Park 美国城镇 6—139e
埃斯基尔斯蒂纳 Eskilstuna 瑞典城镇 6—131c
埃斯基耳 Eskil 丹麦大主教 6—131b
埃斯基久玛亚 Eski Dzhumaya (Bulgaria) 保加利亚城市 6—131b
埃斯基罗尔 Esquirol, Jean-Étienne-Dominique 法国精神病学家 6—134d
埃斯基涅斯 Aeschines 古雅典演说家 1—97f
埃斯基普拉斯 Esquipulas 危地马拉城镇 6—134c
埃斯基谢希尔 Eski şehir 土耳其城市 6—132a
埃斯卡兰特 Escalante, (Francisco) Silvestre Vélez de 西班牙探险家 6—127d
埃斯卡诺巴 Escanaba 美国城市 6—128a
埃斯科菲耶 Escoffier, (Georges-) Auguste 法国烹饪师 6—129a
埃斯科河 Escaut River (Europe) 欧洲河流 6—128b
埃斯科瓦尔-门多萨 Escobar y Mendoza, Antonio 西班牙神学家 6—128f
埃斯科韦多 Escobedo, Juan de 西班牙政治家 6—129a
埃斯克代尔 Eskdale (Scotland) 英国苏格兰区名 6—131a
埃斯克拉沃斯河 Escravos River 非洲河流 6—129b
埃斯孔迪多 Escondido 美国城市 6—129b
埃斯库德罗 Escudero, Vicente 西班牙舞蹈家 6—129d
埃斯库罗斯 Aeschylus 古雅典剧作家 1—98a
埃斯奎莫尔特 Esquimalt 加拿大自治镇 6—134b
埃斯昆特拉 Escuintla 危地马拉城市 6—129e
埃斯林根 Esslingen 德国城市 6—137d
埃斯灵亲王 Essling, André Masséna, Prince d' 法国将领 6—137d

埃斯马尔希 Esmarch, Friedrich von 德国外科医生 6—132a
埃斯梅拉达斯 Esmeraldas 厄瓜多尔城市 6—132b
埃斯诺-佩尔蒂埃 Esnault-Pelterie, Robert 法国航空先驱者 6—132b
埃斯帕特罗 Espartero, Baldomero, PRINCE (príncipe) DE VERGARA 西班牙摄政 6—132f
埃斯皮 Espy, James Pollard 美国气象学家 6—134b
埃斯皮内尔 Espinel, Vicente 西班牙作家 6—133b
埃斯皮尼亚苏山 Espinhaço Mountains 巴西山脉 6—133c
埃斯皮诺 Espino, Héctor 墨西哥职业棒球运动员 6—133c
埃斯皮诺萨 Espinosa, Pedro de 西班牙诗人 6—133c
埃斯普龙塞达-德尔加多 Espronceda y Delgado, José de 西班牙浪漫诗人 6—134a
埃斯塔卡多平原 Llano Estacado 美国平原 10—168d
埃斯塔勒 Herstal 比利时城市 8—53b
埃斯泰别墅 Villa d'Este 建筑 17—562c
埃斯泰尔戈姆 Esztergom 匈牙利城镇 6—143a
埃斯泰尔哈吉家族 Esterházy FAMILY 匈牙利马扎尔贵族世家 6—139b
埃斯泰因·奥斯格里松 Eysteinn Ásgrímsson (Icelandic poetmonk) 冰岛修士 6—202c
埃斯泰因一世(马格努松) Eystein I MAGNUSSON 挪威国王 6—202c
埃斯唐皮 estampie 舞蹈和音乐形式 6—138b
埃斯特 Este 意大利城镇 6—138d
埃斯特 Este, Marie Beatrice d' 英国王后 6—138e
埃斯特城 Ciudad del Este 巴拉圭城市 4—251e
埃斯特哈齐 Esterhazy, Ferdinand Walsin 法国军官 6—139d
埃斯特黑齐 Esterhazy 加拿大城镇 6—139b
埃斯特家族 Este, HOUSE OF 意大利王公世家 6—138e
埃斯特角城 Punta del Este 乌拉圭城市 14—29b
埃斯特拉达公爵 Duque de Estrada, Diego 西班牙军人 5—468e
埃斯特拉达·卡夫雷拉 Estrada Cabrera, Manuel 危地马拉总统 6—141e
埃斯特拉达·帕尔马 Estrada Palma, Tomás 古巴总统 6—141f
埃斯特拉德伯爵 Estrades, Godefroi (-Louis), comte d' 法国元帅 6—141f
埃斯特朗 Ångström, Anders Jonas 瑞典物理学家 1—352d
埃斯特雷马杜拉 Extremadura 西班牙自治地区 6—199b
埃斯特雷莫什 Estremoz 葡萄牙城市 6—142b
埃斯特利 Estelí 尼加拉瓜城市 6—138f
埃斯特瓦内斯·卡尔德隆 Estébanez Calderón, Serafín 西班牙作家 6—138f
埃斯特万 Estevan 加拿大城市 6—139f
埃斯特万·埃切维里亚 Esteban Echeverría 阿根廷行政区 6—138e
埃斯特维尔 Estherville 美国城市 6—140a
埃斯图内勒·德康斯坦 Estournelles de Constant, Paul-H(enri)-B(enjamin) d' 法国外交家 6—141d
埃斯托涅 Estaunié, Edouard 法国作家 6—138d
埃松 Essonne 法国省份 6—137e
埃苏斯 Esus 凯尔特神祇 6—143a
埃索 Esso 美国埃克森公司分公司 6—137e
埃塔 ETA 西班牙巴斯克人组织 6—143c
埃塔普尔 Étaples, Jacques Lefèvre d' 法国人文主义者 6—143f
埃唐普 Étampes 法国城市 6—143e
埃唐日阶 Hettangian Stage 地质学 8—63d
埃特贝克 Etterbeek 比利时城市 6—153f
埃特博莱文化期工艺 Ertebølle industry 北欧石器工艺 6—124b
埃特拉 Aethra 希腊神话人物 1—102a
埃特雷 Estrées, Gabrielle d' 法国国王情妇 6—142a
埃特里克-劳德代尔 Ettrick and Lauderdale 英国区名 6—153f
《埃特利亚朝圣记》 Peregrinatio Etheriae 基督教作品 13—161e
埃特林根 Ettlingen 德国城市 6—153f
埃特鲁斯坎人 Etruscan 意大利古代民族 6—153a
埃特鲁斯坎语 Etruscan language 意大利古代语言 6—153d
埃特鲁斯坎字母 Etruscan alphabet 文字体系 6—153d
埃特纳火山 Etna (Mount) 意大利活火山 6—152b
埃特泽尔 Etzel (Zionist terrorist organization) 犹太复国主义恐怖组织 6—154b
埃滕哈赫 Uitenhage 南非城镇 17—324b
埃提乌斯 Aëtius 基督教叙利亚主教 1—102a
埃提乌斯 Aetius, Flavius 罗马将军 1—102b
埃托比科克 Etobicoke 加拿大城市 6—152d
埃托河盐池 Etosha Pan 纳米比亚浅盐池 6—152e
埃托利亚 Aetolia 古希腊地区 1—102c
埃托利亚-阿卡纳尼亚 Aetolia and Acarnania 希腊州名 1—102c
埃托利亚同盟 Aetolian League 古希腊联邦国家 1—102d
埃瓦布群岛 Ewab Islands (Indonesia) 印度尼西亚岛群 6—186e
埃瓦茨 Evarts, William Maxwell 美国律师 6—181d
埃瓦尔 Eibar 西班牙城市 5—564c
埃瓦尔 Ewald, Johannes 丹麦诗人 6—186e
埃瓦戈拉斯 Evagoras 塞浦路斯的萨拉米斯国王 6—177d
埃瓦格里乌斯(本都的) Evagrius PONTICUS 基督教神秘主义作家 6—177d
埃瓦里斯图斯,圣 Evaristus, SAINT 教皇 6—181d
埃万德尔 Evander 古罗马神话人物 6—177e
埃维昂莱班 Évian-les-Bains 法国矿泉地 6—184d
埃维人 Ewe 非洲民族 6—187b
埃维亚 Euboea 希腊第二大岛 6—154c
埃维亚湾 Euboea, Gulf of 爱琴海海湾 6—154d
埃温鲁德 Evinrude, Ole 挪威发明家 6—185c
埃文 Avon 英格兰郡名 2—91b
埃文伯爵 Avon, (Robert) Anthony Eden, 1st Earl of 英国首相 2—91b
埃文河 Avon, River 英格兰河流 2—91b
埃文河 Avon, River 英格兰河流 2—91c
埃文河 Avon, River 英格兰河流 2—91d
埃文河畔布雷德福 Bradford-on-Avon 英格兰城镇 3—106d
埃文河畔斯特拉特福 Stratford-on-Avon 英国村镇 16—266f
埃文河畔斯特拉特福 Stratford-upon-Avon 英国城镇 16—267a
埃文克 Evenk 俄罗斯自治区 6—182c
埃文克人 Evenk 民族 6—182b
埃文克语 Evenk language 语言 6—182c
埃文人 Even 西伯利亚北部居民 6—182a
埃文斯 Evans, Alice 美国科学家 6—178f
埃文斯 Evans, Sir Arthur (John) 英国考古学家 6—179a
埃文斯 Evans, Bill 美国爵士乐钢琴家 6—179b
埃文斯 Evans, Chick 美国业余高尔夫球员 6—179c
埃文斯 Evans, Dame Edith 英国演员 6—179c
埃文斯 Evans, Frederick Henry 英国摄影家 6—179d
埃文斯 Evans, Gil 加拿大出生的作曲家 6—180a
埃文斯 Evans, George Henry 美国社会改革家 6—179e
埃文斯 Evans, George William 英国探险家 6—179e
埃文斯 Evans, John 美国医生 6—180b
埃文斯 Evans, Sir John 英国古文物专家 6—180b
埃文斯 Evans, Maurice 英裔舞台剧演员 6—180c
埃文斯 Evans, Oliver 美国发明家 6—180c
埃文斯 Evans, Walker 美国摄影家 6—180f
埃文斯顿 Evanston 美国城市 6—181a
埃文斯-普里查德 Evans-Pritchard, Sir Edward (Evan) 英国社会人类学家 6—181a
埃文斯维尔 Evansville 美国城市 6—181b
埃翁·德·博蒙 Éon de Beaumont, Charles (-Geneviève-Louis-Auguste-André-Timothée), chevalier d' (knight of) 法国特务 6—93b
埃沃拉 Evora, Cesaria 佛得角歌唱家 6—186b
埃沃隆博物馆 Evoluon 荷兰科技博物馆 6—185d
埃沃斯塔特沃斯 Ewostatewos 埃塞俄比亚圣者 6—188a

埃武拉 Évora 葡萄牙区首府 6—186a
埃西尔 Aesir 斯堪的纳维亚神话人物 1—99d
埃西哈 Ecija 西班牙城市 5—523e
埃希特纳赫 Echternach 卢森堡城镇 5—523d
埃歇尔 Escher, Alfred 苏黎世政界要人 6—128d
埃歇尔 Escher(von der Linth), Hans Conrad 瑞士政治家 6—128d
埃歇尔 Escher, M(aurits) C(ornelius) 荷兰艺术家 6—128d
埃歇尔 Escher, Rudolf (George) 荷兰作曲家 6—128e
埃辛顿港 Port Essington 澳大利亚小海湾 13—444f
埃亚德马 Eyadema, (Etienne) Gnassingbe 多哥总统 6—200a
埃亚西湖 Eyasi, Lake 坦桑尼亚湖泊 6—200b
埃伊纳岛 Aegina 希腊岛屿 1—92f
埃伊纳湾 Aegina, Gulf of (Greece) 希腊海湾 1—93a
埃因托芬 Einthoven, Willem 荷兰生理学家 6—4c
埃泽萨 Edessa 希腊城市 5—538e
锿(Es) einsteinium 化学元素 6—4b
癌 carcinoma 疾病 3—450d
癌基因 oncogene 遗传学 12—417a
矮凳 taboret 家具 16—416a
矮肥鸽 squab 鸟类 16—166e
矮梾木 dwarf cornel 木本植物 5—485c
矮栎 scrub oak 木本植物 15—159f
矮绿 leatherleaf (*Chamaedaphne calyculata*) 木本植物 9—546e
矮牵牛 petunia 草本植物 13—214b
矮人 midget 人类学 11—201b
矮缩 stunt 植物病害 16—289b
矮屉柜 lowboy 家具 10—253a
矮星 dwarf star 天文学 5—485e
矮妖 leprechaun 爱尔兰民间传说 10—31e
矮紫杉 dwarf yew 木本植物 5—485e
蔼益吉公司 AEG AG 德国公司 1—92b
霭覃 Eeden, Frederik Willem van 荷兰作家 5—553f
艾 AE 爱尔兰诗人 1—91e
艾奥纳团 Iona Community 苏格兰宗教团体 8—431a
艾奥山谷 Iao Valley 美国山谷 8—300a
艾奥瓦 Iowa 美国州名 8—433e
艾奥瓦城 Iowa City 美国城市 8—435f
艾奥瓦大湖区 Iowa Great Lakes 美国旅游区 8—436a
艾奥瓦大学实验学校 Laboratory Schools of the University of Iowa 美国教育 9—431b
艾奥瓦河 Iowa River 美国河流 8—436b
艾奥瓦人 Iowa 民族 8—433d
艾拜古苏尔 Ebba Ksour (Tunisia) 突尼斯城市 5—515d
艾拜克 Aybak 埃及苏丹 2—95b
艾贝尔 Abell, A(runah) S(hepardson) 美国报纸主编、发行人 1—19d
艾贝尔 Abel, John Jacob 美国药理学家、生理化学家 1—18d
艾贝尔 Abel, Rudolf (Ivanovich) 苏联情报官员 1—18f
艾贝尔 Abel, Theodora Mead 美国心理学家、教育家 1—19a
艾贝尔森 Abelson, Philip Hauge 美国物理化学家 1—19e
艾比 Abbey, Edwin Austin 美国画家 1—8f
艾宾豪斯 Ebbinghaus, Hermann 德国心理学家 5—515d
艾伯克龙比 Abercrombie, James 英国陆军上将 1—20c
艾伯克龙比 Abercrombie, Lascelles 英国诗人、评论家 1—20d
艾伯纳西 Abernathy, Ralph David 美国牧师、民权领袖 1—21f
艾伯斯 Albers, Josef 德国画家 1—177c
艾伯塔 Alberta 加拿大省份 1—180f
艾伯塔盆地 Alberta Basin 加拿大盆地 1—181b
艾伯特 Albert 敌对教皇 1—179a
艾伯特 Albert, PRINCE CONSORT OF GREAT BRITAIN AND IRELAND 英国维多利亚女王之夫 1—179e
艾伯特 Ebert, Friedrich 魏玛共和国总统 5—517a
艾伯特国家公园 Albert National Park 刚果(金)公园 1—180e
艾伯特湖 Albert, Lake 中非湖泊 1—180c
艾伯特纪念碑 Albert Memorial 英国建筑 1—180d
艾伯特利 Albert Lea 美国城市 1—180d
艾伯特尼罗河 Albert Nile 乌干达河流 1—180e
艾伯特王子城 Prince Albert 加拿大城市 13—513e
艾伯特王子国家公园 Prince Albert National Park 加拿大公园 13—513f
艾伯特王子山 Prince Albert Mountains 南极洲山群 13—513e
艾博特 Abbott, Berenice 美国摄影家 1—9c
艾博特 Abbot, Charles Greeley 美国天体物理学家 1—9b
艾博特 Abbott, Edith 美国社会工作者、教育家、作家 1—9e
艾博特 Abbott, Grace 美国社会工作者 1—9f
艾博特 Abbott, George (Francis) 美国导演、演员 1—9f
艾博特 Abbott, Jacob 美国作家 1—10a
艾博特 Abbott, Sir John (Joseph Caldwell) 加拿大法学家、政治家 1—10a
艾博特 Abbott, Lyman 美国牧师 1—10b
艾卜·伯克尔 Abū Bakr 阿拉伯哈里发 1—34f
艾卜哈 Abhā 沙特阿拉伯城市 1—23b
艾布·阿拔斯 Abū al-ʿAbbās as-Saffāḥ 阿拔斯王朝哈里发 1—33e
艾布·阿拔斯·阿卜杜拉·马蒙·伊本·拉希德 Abū al-ʿAbbās ʿAbd Allāh al-Maʾmūn ibn ar-Rashīd (caliph) 阿拔斯王朝国王 1—33e
艾布·阿卜杜拉·加法尔·伊本·穆罕默德 Abū ʿAbdollāh Jaʿfar ibn Moḥammad 波斯文诗人 1—33d
艾布·阿卜杜拉·穆罕默德·伊本·伊斯梅尔·布哈里 Abū ʿAbd Allāh Muḥammad ibn Ismāīl ʿal-Bukhārī 穆斯林学者 1—33d
艾布·阿里·侯赛因·伊本·阿卜杜拉·伊本·西拿 Abū ʿAlī al Ḥusayn ibn ʿAbd Allāh ibn Sīnā (Persian scientist) 波斯哲学家、医生 1—34d
艾布·阿塔希叶 Abū al-ʿAtāhiyah 阿拉伯诗人 1—33e
艾布·阿尤布·苏莱曼·伊本·叶海亚·伊本·盖比鲁勒 Abū Ayyūb Sulaymān ibn Yaḥyā ibn Gabirūt (Hebrew poet) 西班牙犹太诗人、哲学家 1—34e
艾布·奥斯曼·阿姆尔·伊本·巴赫尔·伊本·马赫布卜·贾希兹 Abū ʿUthmān ʿAmr ibn Baḥr ibn Maḥbūb al-Jāḥiẓ 阿拉伯穆斯林神学家 1—37f
艾布·伯克尔·穆罕默德·伊本·叶海亚·伊本·萨伊格赫·图吉比·安达卢西·萨拉库斯蒂 Abū Bakr Muḥammad ibn Yaḥyā ibn as-Sāyigh at-Tujībī al-Andalusī as-Saraqustī (Arabic philosopher) 西班牙哲学家 1—35a
艾布尔·法拉吉·伊斯法哈尼 Abū al-Faraj al-Iṣbahānī 阿拉伯文学家 1—33f
艾布·菲达 Abū al-Fidāʾ 艾尤布王朝历史学家、地理学家 1—33f
艾布哈巴赫 Abū Ḥabbah (Iraq) 伊拉克城市 1—35f
艾布·哈桑·阿里 Abū al-Ḥasan ʿAlī 摩洛哥苏丹 1—34a
艾布·胡达海发 Abū Ḥudhayfah (Muslim theologian) 阿拉伯穆斯林神学家 1—36a
艾布·加齐·伯哈杜 Abū al-Ghāzī Bahādur 希瓦可汗、历史学家 1—34a
艾布·卡利贾尔 Abū Kālījār al-Marzubān ibn Sulṭān ad-Dawlah 白益王朝苏丹 1—36b
艾布·卡西姆·曼苏尔 Abū ol-Qasem Manṣūr (Persian poet) 波斯诗人 1—37b
艾布勒·法德尔·阿拉姆 Abu l-Faḍl ʿAllāmī 印度历史学家、神学家 1—36c
艾布·马迪 Abu Madi, Iliya 阿拉伯诗人 1—36d
艾布·马吉德·马吉杜德·伊本·阿达姆 Abū al-Majd Majdūd ibn Ādam 波斯诗人 1—34b
艾布曼诉布思案 Ableman v. Booth 法院案例 1—25e
艾布·努瓦斯 Abū Nuwās 波斯诗人 1—37a
艾布·欧贝德·瓦利德·伊本·欧贝德·安拉·布赫图里 Abū ʿUbādah al-Walīd ibn ʿUbayd Allāh al-Buḥturī 阿拉伯作家 1—37e

艾布·赛义德·阿卜杜勒·马立克·伊本·古莱卜·艾斯马伊 Abū Saʿīd ʿAbd al-Malik ibn Qurayb al-Aṣmaʿī 阿拉伯学者 1—37c
艾布·赛义德·伊本·艾比·哈桑·叶萨尔·巴士里 Abū Saʿīd ibn Abī al-Ḥasan Yasār al-Baṣrī 阿拉伯伊斯兰教传教师 1—37c
艾布·泰马姆 Abū Tammām 阿拉伯诗人 1—37e
艾布·伊斯哈格·伊斯梅尔·伊本·盖西姆·伊本·苏韦德·伊本·凯桑 Abū Isḥāq Ismāʿīl ibn al-Qāsim ibn Suwayd ibn Kaysān (Arab poet) 阿拉伯诗人 1—36a
艾城 Ai 迦南古城 1—138e
艾达 Ida 盎格鲁人国王 8—318a
艾达藏品 Ada group 加洛林王朝艺术品 1—62f
艾丹 Aidan 达尔里阿达国王 1—139c
艾丹,圣 Aidan, Saint 古代英格兰基督教教士 1—139d
艾德 Ade, George 美国作家 1—74d
《艾德纲领》 Eider Program 丹麦政治政策 5—565c
艾德河 Eider River 德国河流 5—565d
艾德金斯诉儿童医院案 Adkins v. Children's Hospital 美国法院案例 1—79e
艾德礼 Attlee, Clement (Richard), 1st Earl Attlee of Walthamstow, Viscount Prestwood 英国首相 2—41a
艾德里安 Adrian (of Cambridge), Edgar Douglas Adrian, 1st Baron 英国电生理学家 1—87a
艾德斯 EDES 希腊民主国民军 5—538d
艾登 Aydın 土耳其城市 2—95b
艾登 Eden, Anthony 英国首相 5—537a
艾登王朝 Aydın dynasty 土库曼人王朝 2—95c
艾迪生 Addison (of Stallingborough), Christopher Addison, 1st Viscount, Baron Addison of Stallingborough 英国外科医师、政治家 1—73c
艾迪生 Addison, Joseph 英国散文家、诗人 1—73d
艾迪生 Addison, Thomas 英国医师 1—73e
艾迪生氏病 Addison's disease 隐袭性疾病 1—73f
艾迪生氏贫血 Addison's anemia 血液病 1—73f
艾迪塔罗德小道狗拉雪橇赛跑 Iditarod Trail Dog Sled Race 美国赛事 8—323b
艾娣 Eddy, Mary Baker 美国宗教领袖 5—535f
艾蒂安港 Port-Étienne (Mauritania) 毛里塔尼亚城镇 13—445a
艾丁湖 Aydingkol Lake 中国湖泊 2—95d
艾顿 Ayton, Sir Robert 苏格兰诗人 2—98b
艾厄沙 Aʿshā, al- 阿拉伯诗人 1—544c
艾厄特沃什 Eötvös, József, Báró 匈牙利作家 6—93d
艾恩德霍芬 Eindhoven 荷兰城市 6—1c
艾恩诺布 Iron Knob 澳大利亚城镇 8—451b
艾恩山 Iron Mountain 美国城市 8—451d
艾恩伍德 Ironwood 美国城市 8—452a
艾尔 Ayr 澳大利亚城镇 2—97c
艾尔 Ayr 苏格兰城市 2—97d
艾尔 Aelle 盎格鲁-撒克逊统治者 1—94a
艾尔 Aelle 英格兰国王 1—94a
艾尔 Ayer, Sir A(lfred) J(ules) 英国教育家、哲学家 2—95e
艾尔 Eyre, Edward John 英国探险家 6—201f
艾尔半岛 Eyre Peninsula 澳大利亚半岛 6—202b
艾尔德尔 Iredell, James 美国最高法院大法官 8—443b
艾尔顿 Ireton, Henry 英格兰军人 8—445e
艾尔夫赫亚克,圣 Aelfheah, Saint 坎特伯雷主教 1—93d
艾尔夫斯堡 Älvsborg 瑞典省份 1—260d
艾尔谷狸狗 Airedale terrier 最大的狸狗 1—146f
艾尔哈特(奥伯格的) Eilhart von Oberg 德国诗人 6—1a
艾尔湖 Eyre, Lake 澳大利亚大盐湖 6—202a
艾尔郡 Ayrshire 苏格兰历史郡 2—97f
艾尔郡白色绣制品 Ayrshire whitework 工艺品 2—98a
艾尔郡牛 Ayrshire 奶牛品种 2—97f
艾尔兰 Ireland, John 苏格兰作家 8—444f
艾尔兰 Ireland, John 美国大主教 8—445a
艾尔兰 Ireland, John (Nicholson) 英国作曲家 8—444f
艾尔雷德(里沃的),圣 Aelred of Rievaulx, Saint 英格兰著作家 1—94a
艾尔曼 Eiermann, Egon 德国建筑学家 5—565e
艾尔曼特 Armant (town, Egypt) 埃及古城 1—496f
艾尔默 Aylmer, John 英格兰教士 2—96b
艾尔斯 Ayres, Anne 美国修女 2—97e
艾尔斯伯里 Aylesbury 英格兰城镇 2—96a
艾尔斯伯里谷 Aylesbury Vale 英格兰区名 2—96a
艾尔斯岩 Ayers Rock 澳大利亚独体岩 2—95f
艾尔苏夫战役 Arsūf, Battle of 第三次十字军战役 1—521a
艾尔瓦德岛 Arwād, Jazīrat 叙利亚岛屿 1—536f
艾费尔阶 Eifelian Stage 地质学 5—565f
艾费尔丘陵 Eifel 德国高原区 5—565f
艾夫登 Avedon, Richard 美国摄影家 2—84a
艾夫斯 Ives, Frederic Eugene 美国发明家 8—493f
艾夫斯 Ives, James Merritt 美国平版印刷工人 8—493f
艾弗里 Avery, Byllye 美国保健事业活动家 2—86f
艾弗里 Avery, Milton (Clark) 美国画家 2—87a
艾弗里 Avery, Oswald (Theodore) 美国细菌学家 2—87b
艾弗里 Avery, Samuel Putnam 美国艺术家 2—87b
艾弗里 Avery, Tex 美国动画片导演 2—87c
艾弗里雅·切莱比 Evliya Çelebi 奥斯曼帝国旅行家 6—185c
艾弗森 Iverson, Allen (Ezail) 美国运动员 8—493c
艾甫斯 Ives, Charles (Edward) 美国作曲家 8—493d
艾格莱卜王朝 Aghlabid dynasty 阿拉伯王朝 1—122c
艾格莫尔特 Aigues-Mortes 法国城镇 1—140b
艾格瓦特 Laghouat 阿尔及利亚城镇 9—447b
艾根 Eigen, Manfred 德国物理学家 5—566c
艾哈德 Erhard, Ludwig 德国政治家、经济学家 6—115c
艾哈迈达巴德 Ahmadābād 印度县城 1—135e
艾哈迈德 Aḥmad 突尼斯统治者 1—134d
艾哈迈德 Ahmed 奥斯曼君王之名 1—136b
艾哈迈德二世 Ahmed II 奥斯曼苏丹 1—136c
艾哈迈德·格兰 Aḥmad Grāñ 索马里穆斯林领袖 1—134f
艾哈迈德·哈希姆 Ahmed Haşim 土耳其作家 1—136e
艾哈迈德汗 Ahmad Khan, Sir Sayyid 印度穆斯林学者 1—135b
艾哈迈德·杰夫代特·帕夏 Ahmed Cevdet Paşa 土耳其政治家 1—136e
艾哈迈德·曼苏尔 Aḥmad al-Manṣūr 摩洛哥统治者 1—134e
艾哈迈德·穆萨 Aḥmad Mūsa 伊儿汗宫廷画家 1—135c
艾哈迈德讷格尔 Ahmadnagar 印度城镇 1—136a
艾哈迈德三世 Ahmed III 奥斯曼苏丹 1—136d
艾哈迈德·韦菲克帕夏 Ahmed Vefik Paşa 奥斯曼政治家 1—136f
艾哈迈德·耶赛维 Ahmed Yesevi 突厥诗人 1—136f
艾哈迈德一世 Ahmed I 奥斯曼苏丹 1—136b
艾哈迈德·伊本·穆罕默德·伊本·艾卜伯克尔·伊本·赛义德 Aḥmad ibn Muḥammad ibn Abū Bakribn Saʿīd 西非富拉尼族穆斯林领袖 1—135a
艾哈迈德·伊本·图伦 Aḥmad ibn Ṭūlūn 埃及图伦王朝奠基人 1—135b
艾哈迈德·伊本·图伦清真寺 Aḥmad ibn Ṭūlūn, Mosque of 埃及清真寺 1—135b
艾哈迈德·伊本·易卜拉欣·加济 Aḥmad ibn Ibrāhīm al-Ghāzī 索马里穆斯林领袖 1—135a
艾哈迈迪 Aḥmadī, al- 科威特城镇 1—135f
艾哈迈迪 Ahmedi, Taceddin 安纳托利亚诗人 1—137a
艾哈迈都·哈马迪·布布 Ahmadu Hammadi Bubu 西非富拉尼族穆斯林领袖 1—136a
艾哈迈特·帕夏·布尔萨勒 Ahmet Paşa Bursali 土耳其诗人 1—137b
艾赫米姆 Akhmīm 埃及城镇 1—155f

艾赫泰勒 Akhṭal, al- 阿拉伯伍麦叶王朝诗人 1—156a
艾虎 fitch 哺乳动物 6—337b
艾吉 Agee, James 美国诗人 1—119b
艾吉永公爵 Aiguillon, Emmanuel-Armand (de Vignerot du Plessis) de Richelieu, duc d' 法国政治家 1—140c
艾菊 costmary (*Chrysanthemum balsamita*) 草本植物 4—534f
艾克尔伯格 Eichelberger, Robert L(awrence) 美国将军 5—564c
艾克夫 Acuff, Roy 美国声乐家 1—62c
艾克雷姆 Ekrem, Recaizade Mahmud 土耳其作家 6—9b
艾克曼 Eijkman, Christiaan 荷兰医生 5—568f
艾克曼-夏特良 Erckmann-Chatrian 法国两位地区派小说家 6—112e
艾克斯拉沙佩勒 Aix-la-Chapelle (Germany) 德国城市 1—149e
艾克斯拉沙佩勒会议 Aix-la-Chapelle, Congress of 欧洲历史 1—149e
《艾克斯拉沙佩勒条约》 Aix-la-Chapelle, Treaty of 欧洲历史 1—149f
艾克斯-马赛第一、第二和第三大学 Aix-Marseille I, II and III, Universities of 法国高等学府 1—149f
艾肯 Aiken 美国城市 1—140c
艾肯 Aiken, Conrad (Potter) 美国诗人 1—140d
艾肯 Aiken, Howard Hathaway 美国数学家 1—140e
艾肯赛德 Akenside, Mark 英国诗人、医师 1—154a
艾拉姆 Aram, Eugene 英国学者 1—438c
艾莱 Islay 大西洋岛屿 8—469c
艾莱伯爵 Islay, Archibald Campbell, earl of 苏格兰新教领袖 8—469c
艾莱恩 Alleyn, Edward 英国演员 1—239f
艾勒卜-艾尔斯兰 Alp-Arslan 塞尔柱苏丹 1—249a
艾勒汉卜拉宫 Alhambra 西班牙城堡 1—225e
艾雷尔 Ayrer, Jakob 德国剧作家 2—97e
艾丽斯 Alice 南非城镇 1—228a
艾丽斯斯普林斯 Alice Springs 澳大利亚城镇 1—228b
艾利 Ailey, Alvin, Jr. 美国舞蹈演员 1—141b
艾利安 Aelian 罗马作家 1—93e
艾利森 Allison, William B. 美国政治家 1—241e
艾利翁 Ayllón, Lucas Vázquez de 西班牙探险家 2—96a
艾吕雅 Éluard, Paul 法国诗人 6—53d
艾略特 Eliot, George 英国小说家 6—38f
艾略特 Eliot, T.S. 英国诗人 6—39d
艾伦 Allen, Ethan 美国军人 1—237c
艾伦 Allen, Elizabeth Anne Chase Akers 美国记者、诗人 1—237b
艾伦 Allen, Fred 美国幽默家 1—237d
艾伦 Allen, Florence Ellinwood 美国法官 1—237c
艾伦 Allen, Gracie 美国演员 1—237e
艾伦 Aaron, Hank 美国棒球运动员 1—3b
艾伦 Allen, Hervey 美国作家 1—237e
艾伦 Allen, Sir Hugh (Percy) 英国管风琴师、音乐教育家 1—237f
艾伦 Allen, Sir James 新西兰政治家 1—237f
艾伦 Allen, Paula Gunn 美国诗人、小说家 1—238a
艾伦 Allen, Richard 美国基督教主教 1—238b
艾伦 Allen, Steve 美国娱乐节目表演者 1—238b
艾伦 Allen, Viola (Emily) 美国演员 1—238c
艾伦 Allen, William 英格兰主教、学者 1—238d
艾伦 Allen, Woody 美国作家、演员 1—238d
艾伦比 Allenby (of Megiddo and of Felixstowe), Edmund Henry Hynman Allenby, 1st Viscount 英国陆军元帅 1—238f
艾伦沼泽 Allen, Bog of 爱尔兰沼泽 1—237b
艾马拉人 Aymara 南美印第安居民集团 2—96c
艾马拉诸语言 Aymaran languages 南美印第安语言 2—96d
艾米丽克 Emmerick, Blessed Anna Katharina 德国修女 6—61f
艾米利亚-罗马涅 Emilia-Romagna 意大利区名 6—60d
艾米斯 Amis, Sir Kingsley 英国作家 1—290f
艾米斯 Amis, Martin 英国作家 1—291a
艾敏 Amīn, (Muḥammad) al- 阿拔斯王朝哈里发 1—289e
艾敏帕夏 Emin Paşa, Mehmed 德国探险家 6—60f
艾莫雷斯山 Aimorés Mountains 巴西山区 1—141e
艾默尔氏虫属 Eimeria 原生动物 6—1a
艾默里 Amery, L(eopold Charles Maurice) S(tennett) 英国政治家 1—286b
艾默里 Amory, Thomas 英国政治家 1—296a
艾默伊登 IJmuiden 荷兰地名 8—330a
艾姆斯 Ames, Fisher 美国作家 1—286b
艾姆斯 Ames, Jessie Daniel 美国人权活动家 1—286b
艾姆斯 Ames, Leslie 英格兰板球运动员 1—286d
艾姆斯 Ames, Oakes 美国商人 1—286e
艾姆斯 Ames, Winthrop 美国戏剧演出人 1—286f
艾穆安 Aimoin 法国本笃会修士 1—141d
艾内姆 Einem, Gottfried von 德国作曲家 6—1c
艾欧纳 Iona 苏格兰岛屿 8—430f
艾皮努斯 Aepinus, Franz Maria Ulrich Theodor Hoch 德国物理学家 1—95c
艾奇孙 Acheson, Edward Goodrich 美国发明家 1—52b
艾奇逊 Atchison 美国县城 2—16d
艾奇逊 Acheson, Archibald 英国北美总督 1—51f
艾奇逊 Acheson, Dean (Gooderham) 美国政治家 1—51f
艾奇逊-托皮卡-圣菲铁路公司 Atchison, Topeka and Santa Fe Railway Company 美国公司 2—16d
艾青 Ai Qing 中国诗人 1—138e
艾萨克斯 Isaacs, Barnett 英国金融家 8—456e
艾塞克 Eszék (Croatia) 克罗地亚城镇、农业中心 6—143a
艾赛尼派 Essene 巴勒斯坦古教派 6—135c
艾瑟顿 Atherton, Gertrude Franklin 美国小说家 2—24c
艾瑟尔河 IJssel River 荷兰河流 8—330c
艾瑟尔湖 IJsselmeer 荷兰湖泊 8—330c
艾瑟尔圩地 IJsselmeer Polders 荷兰圩地 8—330d
艾森 Aisén 智利区名 1—148e
艾森埃尔茨 Eisenerz 奥地利城市 6—4f
艾森伯格 Eisenberg, Cora (puppeteer) 美国木偶戏剧大师 6—4f
艾森港 Puerto Aisén 智利城市 14—15c
艾森豪威尔 Eisenhower, Dwight D(avid) 美国总统 6—5a
艾森豪威尔杯 Eisenhower Trophy 高尔夫球赛奖杯 6—5e
艾森豪威尔主义 Eisenhower Doctrine 美国对外政策 6—5d
艾森曼 Eisenman, Peter (David) 美国建筑师 6—5e
艾森施塔特 Eisenstadt 奥地利城市 6—5f
艾森施塔特 Eisenstaedt, Alfred 美国摄影家 6—6a
艾森斯坦 Eisenstein, Ferdinand Gotthold Max 德国数学家 6—6b
艾森许滕施塔特 Eisenhüttenstadt 德国城市 6—5e
艾沙姆 Isham, John 英国作曲家 8—461c
艾沙姆 Isham, Ralph Heyward 美国珍稀手稿收藏家 8—461d
艾沙特帕夏 Essad Paşa (Toptani) 阿尔巴尼亚政治领袖 6—134e
艾什布尔 Aichbühl 德国考古遗址 1—139a
艾什顿-沃纳 Ashton-Warner, Sylvia (Constance) 新西兰教育家 1—549f
艾什尔里 Ashʿarī, Abū al-Ḥasan al- 阿拉伯伊斯兰教教义学家 1—545a
艾什·谢赫·阿克巴 Shaykh al-Akbar, Ash- (Muslim mystic) 穆斯林神秘主义者 15—288e
艾氏剂 aldrin 化合物 1—194d
艾斯莱本 Eisleben 德国城市 6—6e
艾斯利 Eiseley, Loren (Corey) 美国人类学家 6—4d
艾斯马伊 Aṣmaʿī, al- 阿拉伯学者 1—555b
艾斯纳 Eissner, Clara 德国社会学家 6—6f
艾斯纳 Eisner, Kurt 德国新闻工作者 6—6f
艾斯泰尔哈佐 Eszterháza (Hungary) 匈牙利农业公社 6—143b
艾斯特福德 eisteddfod 威尔士诗人聚会 6—7a

艾斯尤特 Asyūṭ 埃及省份 2—11e
艾斯尤特 Asyūṭ 埃及城市 2—11e
艾塔斯卡湖 Itasca, Lake 美国湖泊 8—488e
艾特尔鲍尔德 Aethelbald 盎格鲁-撒克逊统治者之名 1—101a
艾特尔鲍尔德 Aethelbald 麦西亚国王 1—101a
艾特尔鲍尔德 Aethelbald 韦塞克斯国王 1—101b
艾特尔伯赫特 Aethelberht 盎格鲁-撒克逊统治者之名 1—101b
艾特尔伯赫特 Aethelberht 西撒克逊国王 1—101c
艾特尔伯赫特一世 Aethelberht I 肯特国王 1—101b
艾特尔弗拉德 Aethelflaed 盎格鲁-撒克逊统治者 1—101c
艾特尔弗里思 Aethelfrith 伯尼西亚与德伊勒国王 1—101c
艾特尔雷德 Aethelred 盎格鲁-撒克逊统治者之名 1—101d
艾特尔雷德 Aethelred 麦西亚国王 1—101d
艾特尔雷德二世 Ethelred II 英格兰人的国王 6—144f
艾特尔雷德一世 Aethelred I 韦塞克斯、肯特国王 1—101e
艾特尔斯坦 Athelstan (Danish king of East Anglia) 东安吉利亚的丹麦国王 2—19a
艾特尔斯坦 Athelstan 英格兰的西撒克逊国王 2—19a
艾特尔韦德 Aethelweard 英格兰编年史家 1—101e
艾特尔伍尔夫 Aethelwulf 盎格鲁-撒克逊国王 1—101f
艾特尔英 Aetheling 英格兰贵族成员 1—101d
艾特肯 Aitken, John 英国物理学家、气象学家 1—149b
艾特肯 Aitken, Robert Grant 美国天文学家 1—149c
艾特肯 Aitken, William Maxwell 英国政治家、报纸业主 1—149c
艾特马托夫 Aytmatov, Chingiz 吉尔吉斯斯坦作家 2—98b
艾特纳 Eitner, Robert 德国音乐学家 6—7b
艾通 Aytoun, William Edmondstoune 苏格兰诗人 2—98c
艾文勋爵 Aven, John Hamilton, Lord 苏格兰贵族 2—84d
艾西拉 Asilah 摩洛哥城市 1—554c
艾希霍恩 Eichhorn, Johann Gottfried 德国《圣经》学者 5—564e
艾希科尔 Eshkol, Levi 以色列总理 6—130f
艾希勒 Eichler, August Wilhelm 德国植物学家 5—564f
艾希罗特 Eichrodt, Walther 德国《圣经》学者 5—565b
艾希曼 Eichmann, (Karl) Adolf 德国战犯 5—564f
艾希施泰特 Eichstätt 德国城市 5—565b
艾欣格 Aichinger, Gregor 德国作曲家 1—139b
艾兴多夫 Eichendorff, Joseph, Freiherr von 德国作家 5—564d
艾伊杜凯维支 Ajdukiewicz, Kazimierz 波兰逻辑学家 1—151a
艾伊尼阿·西尔维乌·皮科罗米尼 Piccolomini, Enea Silvio (pope) 教皇 13—288a
艾因 ʻAyn, al- 阿联酋城镇 2—97a
艾因贝达 Aïn Beïda 阿尔及利亚城镇 1—141e
艾因哈德 Einhard 法兰克历史学家 6—1d
艾因塞夫拉 Aïn Sefra 阿尔及利亚城镇 1—141f
艾因泰穆善特 Aïn Temouchent 阿尔及利亚城镇 1—141f
艾因西德伦 Einsiedeln 瑞士城镇 6—1e
艾因扎鲁特战役 ʻAyn Jālūt, Battle of 叙利亚历史 2—97b
艾鼬 polecat 哺乳动物 13—399a
艾于克鲁斯特 Aukrust, Olav 挪威地方诗人 2—56b
艾藻尔 Aizawl 印度城市 1—150a
艾泽尔斯贝格 Eiselsberg, Anton, Freiherr von (baron of) 奥地利外科医生 6—4e
艾扎里艾赫 ʻAyzarīyah, Al- (Jerusalem) 以色列村庄 2—98f
艾滋病 AIDS 病毒病 1—139d
砹(At) astatine 化学元素 2—2c
爱 charity 基督教神学 4—65b
爱 taṇhā 佛教 16—466a
爱奥尼亚 Ionia 古土耳其地区 8—431c
爱奥尼亚海 Ionian Sea 地中海一部分 8—432c
爱奥尼亚群岛 Ionian Islands 希腊群岛 8—432a
爱奥尼亚人 Ionian 古希腊民族 8—431e
爱奥尼亚音步 ionic foot 诗歌 8—432e
爱奥尼亚哲学学派 Ionian school 哲学学派 8—432c
爱奥尼亚柱式 Ionic order 古典建筑 8—432e
爱奥尼亚字母 Ionic alphabet 古希腊字母变体 8—432d
爱比克泰德 Epictetus 希腊艺术家 6—97f
爱比克泰德 Epictetus 希腊哲学家 6—98a
爱达荷 Idaho 美国州名 8—318b
爱达荷城 Idaho City 美国城市 8—320d
爱达荷福尔斯 Idaho Falls 美国城市 8—320e
爱德华 Edward 统治者之名 5—548f
爱德华 Edward 盎格鲁-撒克逊国王 5—548f
爱德华 Edward 英格兰国王 5—549a
爱德华 Edward 英格兰国王 5—549a
爱德华 Edward 葡萄牙国王 5—551f
爱德华 Edward 苏格兰国王 5—552a
爱德华(长腿) Edward Longshanks 英格兰国王 5—552b
爱德华(黑太子) Edward the Black Prince 英格兰王位继承人 5—552c
爱德华(卡那封的) Edward of Caernarvon 英格兰国王 5—552b
爱德华(老) Edward the Elder 盎格鲁-撒克逊国王 5—552d
爱德华(诺里奇的) Edward of Norwich 英格兰贵族 5—552b
爱德华(温莎的) Edward of Windsor 英格兰国王 5—552b
爱德华八世 Edward VIII 英国国王 5—551d
爱德华二世 Edward II 英格兰国王 5—549f
爱德华湖 Edward, Lake 东非湖泊 5—552e
爱德华六世 Edward VI 英格兰和爱尔兰国王 5—551a
爱德华·佩留爵士群岛 Sir Edward Pellew Group 澳大利亚群岛 15—401d
爱德华七世 Edward VII 英国国王 5—551c
《爱德华三世》 Edward III 戏剧 5—552a
爱德华三世 Edward III 英格兰国王 5—550a
爱德华四世 Edward IV 英格兰国王 5—550d
爱德华王子岛 Prince Edward Island 加拿大省份 13—513f
爱德华王子岛 Prince Edward Island 印度洋岛屿 13—514c
爱德华王子岛国家公园 Prince Edward Island National Park 加拿大公园 13—514c
爱德华五世 Edward V 英格兰国王 5—550f
爱德华一世 Edward I 英格兰国王 5—549b
爱德华兹 Edwards, Alfred George 威尔士大主教 5—552e
爱德华兹 Edwards, John 美国参议员 5—552e
爱德华兹 Edwards, Jonathan 美国神学家 5—552f
爱德华兹 Edwards, Lewis 威尔士牧师、教育家 5—553b
爱德华兹 Edwards, Sir Owen Morgan 威尔士作家 5—553c
爱德华兹 Edwards, Teresa 美国篮球运动员 5—553c
爱的家庭 Family of Love (16th-century sect) 欧洲宗教派别 6—228d
爱迪生 Edison 美国市镇 5—544d
爱迪生 Edison, Thomas Alva 美国发明家 5—544d
爱迪生效应 Edison effect (physics) 物理学 5—546d
爱丁堡 Edinburgh 苏格兰首府 5—540c
爱丁堡 Edinburg 美国城市 5—540b
爱丁堡城 Edinburgh, City of 苏格兰区名 5—543f
爱丁堡大学 Edinburgh, University of 苏格兰高等学府 5—543f
爱丁堡公爵 Edinburgh, Prince Philip, duke of 英国亲王 5—543f
《爱丁堡评论》 Edinburgh Review, The 苏格兰杂志 5—544a
爱丁堡绅士高尔夫球社 Honourable Company of Edinburgh Golfers 英国社团 8—160e
爱丁顿 Eddington, Sir Arthur Stanley 英国天文学家 5—535a
爱儿啤酒 ale 麦芽饮料 1—195a
爱尔巴桑 Elbasan 阿尔巴尼亚城镇 6—15a
爱尔福特 Erfurt 德国城市 6—114b
爱尔福特 Erfurth, Hugo 德国摄影师 6—114d
爱尔福特联盟议会 Erfurt Union Parliament 普鲁士会议 6—114d
爱尔兰 Ireland 欧洲国家 8—443b
爱尔兰抽彩 Irish Sweepstakes 抽彩给奖活动 8—448f

爱尔兰盖尔语 Erse language 爱尔兰语言 6—123b
爱尔兰㹴狗 Irish terrier 狗品种 8—449a
爱尔兰共和军 Irish Republican Army (IRA) 爱尔兰半军事组织 8—448d
爱尔兰国立大学 National University of Ireland 爱尔兰大学 12—37d
爱尔兰国营航空公司 Aer Lingus 爱尔兰航空公司 1—95e
爱尔兰海 Irish Sea 北大西洋属海 8—448f
爱尔兰猎狼狗 Irish wolfhound 狗品种 8—449b
爱尔兰铃铛花 bells of Ireland 草本植物 2—368e
爱尔兰马铃薯饥荒 Irish Potato Famine 爱尔兰历史 8—448a
爱尔兰麋 Irish elk 哺乳动物 8—447c
爱尔兰起义 Irish Rebellion 爱尔兰历史 8—448c
爱尔兰曲棍球 hurling 体育项目 8—265b
爱尔兰人联合会 United Irishmen, Society of 爱尔兰政治组织 17—352d
爱尔兰-撒克逊风格 Hiberno-Saxon style 英国艺术风格 8—69b
爱尔兰圣公会 Ireland, Church of 爱尔兰教会 8—444e
爱尔兰竖琴 Irish harp 乐器 8—447c
爱尔兰统一党 Fine Gael 爱尔兰政党 6—318b
爱尔兰统一党 United Ireland Party 爱尔兰政党 17—352d
爱尔兰王室警吏团 Black and Tan 英国历史 2—510a
爱尔兰文学 Irish literature 文学 8—447f
爱尔兰文艺复兴 Irish literary renaissance 爱尔兰文学史 8—447e
爱尔兰语 Irish language 语言 8—447d
《爱尔兰语词典》 Dictionary of the Irish Language 爱尔兰词典 5—302b
爱尔兰长老会 Presbyterian Church in Ireland 爱尔兰基督教会 13—495c
爱尔兰针织花边 Irish needle lace 工艺品 8—448a
爱尔兰制度 Irish system 刑罚方法 8—449a
爱尔兰紫杉 Irish yew 木本植物 8—449c
爱尔兰自治运动 Home Rule 爱尔兰历史 8—144a
爱尔米塔什博物馆 Hermitage 俄罗斯博物馆 8—42e
爱尔维修 Helvétius, Claude-Adrien 法国哲学家 8—7c
爱国彩陶 faience patriotique 法国陶器 6—214a
爱克 Eyck, Jan van 佛兰德斯画家 6—200c
爱克哈特(硕士) Eckhart, Meister 多明我会神学家 5—524d
爱里 Airy, Sir George Biddell 英国科学家 1—148e
爱利亚 Elea 意大利古城 6—17e
爱利亚学派 Eleaticism 古希腊哲学学派 6—18a
爱伦堡 Ehrenburg, Ilya Grigoryevich 苏联作家 5—563c
爱明内斯库 Eminescu, Mihail 罗马尼亚诗人 6—61b
爱默生 Emerson, Ellen Russell 美国人类文化学者 6—59d
爱默生 Emerson, Ralph Waldo 美国诗人 6—59f
爱泼斯坦 Epstein, Sir Jacob 英国雕刻家 6—105c
爱泼斯坦-巴尔二氏病毒 Epstein-Barr virus 疱疹病毒 6—105e
爱琴海 Aegean Sea 地中海海湾 1—92d
爱琴海诸文明 Aegean civilizations 历史 1—92c
爱情诗句 romance stanza 诗歌 14—368c
爱森纳赫 Eisenach 德国城市 6—4e
爱森斯坦 Eisenstein, Sergey (Mikhaylovich) 俄国电影导演 6—6c
爱沙尼亚 Estonia 欧洲国家 6—140c
爱沙尼亚文学 Estonian literature 文学 6—141a
爱沙尼亚语 Estonian language 语言 6—141a
爱神带水母 Venus's girdle 动物 17—510c
爱神星 Eros 火星轨道内小行星 6—122b
爱斯蒂斯 Aistis, Jonas 立陶宛诗人 1—149b
爱斯基摩-阿留申诸语言 Eskimo-Aleut languages 语言 6—131e
爱斯基摩狗 Eskimo dog 狗品种 6—131f
爱斯基摩蒙皮船 umiak 船 17—337b
爱斯基摩人 Eskimo 北极、亚北极地区民族 6—131c
爱娃·布劳恩 Braun, Eva 希特勒情妇 3—128d
爱西尼人 Iceni 古不列颠部落 8—315c
爱因斯坦 Einstein, Albert 美国物理学家 6—1f
爱因斯坦 Einstein, Alfred 美国音乐家 6—3f
爱因斯坦 Einstein, Hannah Bachman 美国社会工作者 6—4a
爱因斯坦质能关系 Einstein's mass-energy relation 物理学 6—4b
爱育黎拔力八达 Ayurparibhadra 中国元朝皇帝 2—98e
爱媛 Ehime 日本县名 5—563a
爱之匙乐队 Lovin' Spoonful, the 美国摇滚乐队 10—251f
爱知 Aichi 日本县名 1—139a
爱资哈尔大学 Azhar University, Al- 世界阿拉伯学研究中心 2—101d
爱资哈里 Azharī, Ismāʿīl al- 苏丹总理 2—101e
锾-钍年代测法 ionium-thorium dating 年代学 8—432e
安 An (Mesopotamian god) 苏美尔人祀奉之神 1—306c
安 On (ancient city) 埃及古城 12—416a
安阿伯 Ann Arbor 美国城市 1—362c
安巴楚米扬 Ambartsumian, Viktor 苏联天文学家 1—268d
安巴尔 Anbar 美索不达米亚古城 1—321f
安巴尔 Anbār, al- 伊拉克省份 1—321f
安巴拉 Ambāla 印度城市 1—268d
安巴托 Ambato 厄瓜多尔城市 1—269b
安贝尔 Amber (India) 印度城镇 1—269d
安贝格 Amberg 德国城市 1—269f
安贝里斯 Amberes, Gil de 西班牙雕刻家 1—269f
安比加布尔 Ambikāpur 印度城镇 1—270b
安波那 Amboina (Indonesia) 印度尼西亚岛屿、城市 1—270e
安伯谷 Amber Valley 英格兰区名 1—269e
安博人 Ambo 西南非民族 1—270d
安博塞利国家公园 Amboseli National Park 肯尼亚公园 1—271c
安布勒 Ambler, Eric 英国小说家 1—270b
安布里姆岛 Ambrym 太平洋岛屿 1—272c
安布里奇 Ambridge 美国自治镇 1—271d
安布里亚齐家族 Embriaci FAMILY 意大利热那亚家族 6—57c
安布罗吉尼 Ambrogini, Angelo (Renaissance scholar) 意大利诗人、人文主义者 1—271d
安布罗斯 Ambros, August Wilhelm 捷克音乐学家 1—271d
安布罗斯(卡马尔多利的) Ambrose OF CAMALDOLI 意大利人文学家、翻译家 1—272a
安布罗斯，圣 Ambrose, SAINT 米兰基督教主教 1—271e
安布罗斯圣咏 Ambrosian chant 宗教声乐 1—272b
安部公房 Abe Kōbō 日本小说家、戏剧家 1—17f
安部矶雄 Abe Isoo 日本社会主义运动领导人 1—17e
安岑格鲁贝 Anzengruber, Ludwig 奥地利剧作家 1—403b
安城 Anjō 日本城市 1—360c
安粗岩 latite 岩石 9—514f
安达卢西亚 Andalusia 西班牙地区 1—324a
安达卢西亚 Andalusia 美国城市 1—324b
安达曼海 Andaman Sea 印度洋一部分 1—324e
安达曼-尼科巴群岛 Andaman and Nicobar Islands 印度直辖区 1—324c
安达曼群岛 Andaman Islands 印度岛群 1—324d
安达曼人 Andamanese 亚洲民族 1—324f
安达曼语 Andamanese language 亚洲语言 1—325a
安达尼亚秘仪 Andania mysteries 宗教 1—325a
安大略 Ontario 加拿大省份 12—423a
安大略 Ontario 美国加利福尼亚州城市 12—423d
安大略 Ontario 美国俄勒冈州城市 12—423d
安大略湖 Ontario, Lake 北美五大洲湖之一 12—423d
安道尔 Andorra 欧洲公国 1—330b
安道尔 Andorra-la-Vella 安道尔公国首都 1—330d
安得拉邦 Andhra Pradesh 印度邦名 1—329b
安得罗尼库斯 Andronicus, Lucius Livius 罗马史诗创始人 1—336f

安德尔 Indre 法国省份 8—373f
安德尔河 Indre River 法国河流 8—374a
安德尔-卢瓦尔 Indre-et-Loire 法国省份 8—374a
安德尔斯 Anders, Władysław 波兰军官 1—325f
安德拉达-席尔瓦 Andrada e Silva, José Bonifácio de 巴西政治家 1—330e
安德拉德 Andrade, Mário (Raul) de (Morais) 巴西作家 1—330f
安德拉德 Andrade, (José) Oswald de (Sousa) 巴西作家 1—331a
安德拉希伯爵 Andrássy, Gyula, Gróf (Count) 匈牙利首相 1—331b
安德莱赫特 Anderlecht 比利时区名 1—325e
安德雷奥蒂 Andreotti, Giulio 意大利总理 1—333c
安德里奇 Andrić, Ivo 塞尔维亚-克罗地亚小说家 1—335d
安德里亚 Andria 意大利城市 1—335c
安德列亚 Andrea del Verrocchio (sculptor) 意大利画家、雕刻家 1—332e
安德列亚 Andrea di Cione 意大利画家 1—332e
安德列亚 Andrea Pisano (Italian sculptor) 意大利雕刻家 1—332e
安德列亚诺夫群岛 Andreanof Islands 美国岛群 1—332f
安德列耶夫 Andreyev, Leonid Nikolayevich 俄国小说家 1—335b
安德列一世 Andrew I 俄罗斯大公 1—333e
安德烈 Andreis, Felix de 意大利天主教传教士 1—333b
安德烈 André, John 英国陆军军官 1—331d
安德烈(神甫) André le Chapelain 法国作家 1—331c
安德烈(克里特的),圣 Andrew of Crete, Saint 克里特岛基督教大主教 1—334a
安德烈蒂 Andretti, Mario 美国赛车手 1—333d
安德烈尼 Andreini, Francesco 意大利喜剧演员 1—333a
安德烈尼 Andreini, Giovambattista 意大利喜剧演员 1—333a
安德烈尼 Andreini, Isabella 意大利演员 1—333b
安德烈亚 Andrea da Barberino 意大利民歌手 1—331e
安德烈亚 Andrea del Gobbo 意大利画家 1—332a
安德烈亚(裁缝之子) Andrea del Sarto 意大利画家 1—332a
安德烈亚(佛罗伦萨的) Andrea da Firenze 意大利壁画家 1—331f
安德烈亚尼 Andreani, Andrea 意大利版画家 1—332f
安德烈亚斯-萨乐美 Andreas-Salomé, Lou 德国作家 1—332f
安德鲁 Andrew, John Albion 美国反对奴隶制领袖 1—334b
安德鲁(该撒利亚的) Andrew of Caesarea 该撒利亚基督教主教 1—333f
安德鲁(卡尼奥拉的) Andrew of Carniola 天主教大主教 1—333f
安德鲁(隆瑞莫的) Andrew of Lonjumel 法国天主教修士 1—334a
安德鲁二世 Andrew II 匈牙利国王 1—333e
安德鲁斯 Andrews, Augustus George (English actor) 英国演员 1—334d
安德鲁斯 Andrews, Charles McLean 美国历史学家 1—334d
安德鲁斯 Andrews, Fannie Fern Phillips 美国作家 1—334d
安德鲁斯 Andrews, Frank M(axwell) 美国军人 1—334e
安德鲁斯 Andrews, Julie 美国电影演员 1—334f
安德鲁斯 Andrewes, Lancelot 英国神学家 1—334c
安德鲁斯 Andrews, Roy Chapman 美国博物学家 1—335a
安德鲁斯 Andrews, Thomas 爱尔兰化学家、物理学家 1—335b
《安德鲁索沃停战协定》 Andrusovo, Truce of 欧洲历史 1—337c
安德罗波夫 Andropov (Russia) 俄罗斯城市 1—336f
安德罗波夫 Andropov, Yury Vladimirovich 苏联政治家 1—336f
安德罗克勒斯 Androcles 罗马奴隶 1—335e
安德罗尼卡 Andronicus 拜占廷皇帝名 1—336c
安德罗尼卡(罗得的) Andronicus of Rhodes 希腊哲学家 1—336f
安德罗尼卡二世 Andronicus II Palaeologus 拜占廷皇帝 1—336d
安德罗尼卡三世 Andronicus III Palaeologus 拜占廷皇帝 1—336e
安德罗尼卡四世 Andronicus IV Palaeologus 拜占廷皇帝 1—336e
安德罗尼卡一世 Andronicus I Comnenus 拜占廷皇帝 1—336c
安德罗斯 Ándros 希腊岛屿 1—337a
安德罗斯 Andros, Sir Edmund 英国殖民官员 1—337b
安德罗斯岛 Andros Island 巴哈马岛屿 1—337b
安德罗斯科金河 Androscoggin River 美国河流 1—337c
安德洛玛刻 Andromache 希腊传说人物 1—335f
安德洛墨达 Andromeda 希腊神话人物 1—336a
安德热耶夫斯基 Andrzejewski, Jerzy 波兰小说家 1—337c
安德森 Anderson 美国印第安纳州城市 1—326d
安德森 Anderson 美国南卡罗来纳州城市 1—326d
安德森 Anderssen, Adolf 普鲁士国际象棋大师 1—328e
安德森 Anderson, Carl David 美国物理学家 1—326e
安德森 Anderson, Dame Judith 澳大利亚演员 1—327b
安德森 Anderson, Elda Emma 美国物理学家 1—326e
安德森 Anderson, Elizabeth Garrett 英国医师 1—326f
安德森 Andersen, Hjallis 挪威速度滑冰运动员 1—326b
安德森 Anderson, Helen Eugenie Moore 美国外交家 1—327a
安德森 Anderson, John Henry 苏格兰魔术师 1—327a
安德森 Anderson, Laurie 美国表演艺术家、作家 1—327c
安德森 Anderson, Lindsay 英国评论家 1—327c
安德森 Anderson, Marian 美国歌唱家 1—327d
安德森 Anderson, Mary 美国演员 1—327f
安德森 Anderson, Maxie 美国气球飞行员 1—327f
安德森 Anderson, Maxwell 美国剧作家 1—328a
安德森 Anderson, Philip W(arren) 美国物理学家 1—328b
安德森 Anderson, Richard Heron 美国南北战争南军将领 1—328c
安德森 Anderson, Sherwood 美国作家 1—328c
安德森 Anderson, Viv 英格兰职业足球运动员 1—328d
安德森氏病 Andersen's disease 遗传性疾病 1—326c
安德森维尔 Andersonville 美国村镇 1—328d
安德生 Andersen, Tryggve 挪威小说家 1—326c
安德斯 Anders, William A(lison) 美国航天员 1—325e
安德松 Andersson, Dan(iel) 瑞典诗人 1—328e
安德天皇 Antoku 日本天皇 1—396a
安德伍德 Underwood, Francis Henry 美国作家、律师 17—340e
安德伍德 Underwood, Oscar W(ilder) 美国国会议员 17—340f
安德希尔 Underhill, Evelyn 英国奥秘修行家、作家 17—340a
安迪 Antae 俄国民族 1—374b
安的列斯群岛 Antilles 西印度群岛 1—388a
安的列斯洋流 Antilles Current 大西洋洋流 1—388a
安第斯地槽 Andean Geosyncline 南美地质构造 1—325d
安第斯集团 Andean Group 南美组织 1—325d
安第斯山脉 Andes Mountains 南美山脉 1—328f
安第斯文明 Andean civilization 南美历史 1—325a
安第斯熊 Andean bear 哺乳动物 1—325a
安蒂奥基亚 Antioquia 哥伦比亚省份 1—392f
安蒂奥克大学 Antioch University 美国大学 1—391c
安蒂波迪斯群岛 Antipodes Islands 新西兰群岛 1—393e
安蒂波洛 Antipolo 菲律宾城市 1—393f
安蒂戈尼什 Antigonish 加拿大城镇 1—385e
安蒂科纳 Anticona (Peru) 秘鲁地名 1—384d
安蒂科斯蒂岛 Anticosti Island 加拿大岛屿 1—384d
安蒂姆(伊比利亚的) Anthimus of Iberia 瓦拉几亚主教、语言学家 1—378a
安蒂诺波利斯 Antinoöpolis 古埃及的罗马城市 1—390d
安蒂诺乌斯 Antinoüs 罗马皇帝的娈童 1—390d
安蒂特姆战役 Antietam, Battle of 美国历史 1—384f
安定 Valium 药物 17—453a
安定药 tranquilizer 药物 17—193c
安东 An-tung (China) 中国城市 1—306f
安东 Andong 韩国城市 1—330a
安东 Andong (China) 中国城市 1—330b
安东内利 Antonelli, Giacomo 枢机主教 1—396a
安东内斯库 Antonescu, Ion 罗马尼亚首相 1—396d
安东尼 Anthony, Katharine (Susan) 美国传记作家 1—378e
安东尼 Antony, Mark 罗马三执政之一 1—397d
安东尼 Anthony, Michael 西印度群岛作家 1—378f

安东尼 Anthony,Susan B(rownell) 美国女权运动先驱 1—378f
安东尼 Anthony,William Arnold 美国物理学家 1—379b
安东尼(波旁的) Anthony of Bourbon 纳瓦拉国王 1—378c
安东尼(基辅的) Anthony of Kiev 俄罗斯隐修活动创始人 1—378d
安东尼(蜜蜂) Anthony Melissa 拜占廷修士 1—378b
安东尼(诺夫哥罗德的) Anthony of Novgorod 俄罗斯修士 1—378d
安东尼(塔格里特的) Anthony of Tagrit 叙利亚神学家 1—378e
安东尼(埃及的),圣 Anthony of Egypt, Saint 基督教隐士 1—378c
安东尼(帕多瓦的),圣 Anthony of Padua, Saint 葡萄牙修士 1—378d
安东尼奥 António,Mário 安哥拉小说家 1—397a
安东尼奥 António, prior of Crato 葡萄牙教士 1—396f
安东尼奥港 Port Antonio 牙买加城市 13—443e
安东尼奥尼 Antonioni,Michelangelo 意大利电影导演 1—397b
安东尼·庇护 Antoninus Pius 罗马皇帝 1—396e
安东尼·赫拉波维茨基 Antony Khrapovitsky 俄罗斯正教主教 1—397f
安东尼拉贡 Anthony Lagoon 澳大利亚居民点 1—379c
安东尼娜 Antonina 巴西港口 1—396d
安东尼努斯,圣 Antoninus,Saint 基督教佛罗伦萨大主教 1—396e
安东尼墙 Antonine Wall 罗马人在不列颠修建的边墙 1—396d
安东尼王朝 Antonine 罗马王朝 1—396d
安杜哈尔 Andújar 西班牙城市 1—337d
安多弗 Andover 英格兰市镇 1—330d
安多弗 Andover 美国县城 1—330e
安多喀德斯 Andocides 雅典演说家 1—330a
安菲波利斯 Amphipolis 古希腊城市 1—299a
安菲特里特 Amphitrite 希腊神话人物 1—299d
安菲特律翁 Amphitryon 希腊神话人物 1—299e
安菲翁和西苏斯 Amphion and Zethus 希腊神话人物 1—298b
安芬森 Anfinsen,Christian B. 美国生物化学家 1—339e
安戈尔 Angol 智利城市 1—350a
安戈斯图拉战役 Angostura, Battle of 美国-墨西哥战争 1—351c
安哥拉 Angola 非洲国家 1—350a
安哥拉 Angora (city,Turkey) 土耳其城市 1—351b
安哥拉人民解放运动 Popular Movement for the Liberation of Angola 安哥拉政党 13—437c
安哥拉山羊 Angora goat 哺乳动物 1—351b
安格德 Angad 锡克教祖师 1—340a
安格尔 Ingres,Jean-Auguste-Dominique 法国画家 8—386d
安格尔西岛 Anglesey,Isle of 英国岛屿 1—346c
安格拉-杜斯雷斯 Angra dos Reis 巴西城市 1—352b
安格拉佩克纳 Angra Pequena (Namibia) 纳米比亚城镇 1—352b
安格雷扎巴德 Angrezābād (India) 印度城镇 1—352c
安格连 Angren 乌兹别克斯坦城市 1—352b
安格琳 Anglin,Margaret (Mary) 加拿大演员 1—347d
安格斯 Angus 苏格兰历史郡名 1—354b
安格斯伯爵 Angus, earls of 苏格兰贵族 1—354d
安格斯伯爵(第八) Angus,Archibald Douglas,8th Earl of, Earl of Morton 苏格兰贵族 1—354e
安格斯伯爵(第六) Angus,Archibald Douglas,6th Earl of 苏格兰贵族 1—354d
安格斯伯爵(第十) Angus,William Douglas,10th Earl of 苏格兰贵族 1—354f
安格斯牛 Angus 肉用牛 1—354d
安圭埃尔兄弟 Anguier,François; and Anguier,Michel-André 法国雕刻家 1—352e
安圭拉 Anguilla 英国属地 1—352e
安哈尔特 Anhalt 德国历史区域 1—354f
安哈瓦 Anhava,Tuomas 芬兰诗人 1—355a
安海塞纳曼 Ankhesenamen 埃及女王 1—361f
安河 Ain River 法国河流 1—141f
安赫尔瀑布 Angel Falls 委内瑞拉瀑布 1—340f
安赫莱斯 Angeles 菲律宾城市 1—341a
安赫莱斯 Angeles,Victoria de los 西班牙高音歌唱家 1—341b
安徽 Anhui 中国省份 1—355c
安徽四家 Four Masters of Anhui 中国清初画家 6—426d
安魂弥撒曲 requiem mass 音乐 14—238d
安霍伊塞-布希公司 Anheuser-Busch Companies,Inc. 美国啤酒公司 1—355b
安基卢斯 Angelus,Isaac (Byzantine emperor) 拜占廷皇帝 1—343e
安基卢斯家族 Angelus family 拜占廷家族 1—343d
安基提尔-杜佩隆 Anquetil-Duperron,A(braham)-H(yacinthe) 法兰西语言学家 1—370a
安吉奥利尼 Angiolini,Gasparo 意大利舞蹈编导、作曲家 1—345a
安吉尔 Angell,Sir Norman 英国经济学家 1—343b
安吉尔 Angell,Robert Cooley 美国社会学家 1—343c
安吉利科 Angelico,Fra 意大利画家 1—341f
安吉利斯港 Port Angeles 美国城市 13—443e
安吉洛 Angelou,Maya 美国诗人 1—343c
安吉亚拉 Anghiera,Peter Martyr d' 西班牙殉教士 1—344b
安集延 Andizhan 乌兹别克斯坦州名 1—329e
安集延 Andizhan 乌兹别克斯坦城市 1—329e
安加尔斯克 Angarsk 俄罗斯城市 1—340b
安加拉河 Angara River 俄罗斯河流 1—340a
安江 An Giang 越南省份 1—306d
安焦列里 Angiolieri,Cecco 意大利诗人 1—345a
安角 Ann,Cape 美国海岬 1—362b
安杰勒斯(西里西亚的) Angelus Silesius 宗教诗人 1—343e
安井曾太郎 Yasui Sōtarō 日本画家 18—429a
安居 vassa 佛教 17—478c
安喀塞斯 Anchises 希腊传说人物 1—322d
安卡拉 Ankara 土耳其首都 1—361c
安卡拉铭文 Monumentum Ancyranum 罗马铭文 11—375a
安卡拉特拉 Ankaratra 马达加斯加火山区 1—361e
《安卡拉条约》 Ankara, Treaty of 法兰西-土耳其条约 1—361e
安卡拉战役 Ankara,Battle of 土耳其历史 1—361d
安卡什 Ancash 秘鲁省份 1—322a
安卡斯瓦德 Anckarsvärd,Carl Henrik,Greve (Count) 瑞典政治家 1—323d
安凯厄斯 Ancaeus 希腊神话人物 1—322a
安康 Ankang 中国城市 1—361b
安科布拉河 Ankobra 非洲河流 1—362a
安科纳 Ancona 意大利城市 1—323d
安可 ankh 古埃及象形文字 1—361e
安克雷奇 Anchorage 美国城市 1—322e
安孔 Ancón 巴拿马城市 1—323d
安库德 Ancud 智利城镇 1—323e
安库斯·马基乌斯 Ancus Marcius 罗马国王 1—323f
安拉 Allāh 伊斯兰教神 1—235c
安拉阿巴德 Allahābād 印度城市 1—235e
安乐死 euthanasia 无痛苦致死 6—175f
安乐蜥 anole 爬行动物 1—368b
安立甘福音派 Anglican Evangelical 基督教派别 1—347b
安立甘公教派 Anglo-Catholicism 基督教派别 1—347f
安立甘宗 Anglican Communion 基督教派别 1—346f
安立甘宗修会 Anglican religious community 基督教组织 1—347c
安禄山 An Lushan 中国唐代节度使 1—306e
安曼 Amman 约旦首都 1—291e
安曼 Ammann,Othmar Herman 美国土木工程师 1—292b
安那克萨哥拉 Anaxagoras 希腊自然哲学家 1—321a
安纳巴 Annaba 阿尔及利亚城市 1—363a
安纳波利斯 Annapolis 美国县城 1—363e

安纳波利斯会议 Annapolis Convention 美国历史 1—363f
安纳波利斯军校 Annapolis Academy 美国军校 1—363f
安纳波利斯罗亚尔 Annapolis Royal 加拿大城镇 1—363f
安纳布尔纳峰 Annapūrna 尼泊尔山峰 1—364a
安纳德 Anand, Mulk Raj 印度英语作家 1—315d
安纳托利亚 Anatolia 亚洲半岛 1—318e
安纳托利亚诸语言 Anatolian languages 亚洲语言 1—319d
安娜 Anna 俄国女皇 1—362d
安娜 Anna 俄国摄政 1—362e
安娜(奥地利的) Anne of Austria 法国王后 1—365a
安娜(博热的) Anne of Beaujeu 法国摄政 1—365c
安娜(布列塔尼的) Anne of Brittany 法国王后 1—365c
安娜(法兰西的) Anne of France 法国摄政 1—365e
安娜(皮塞勒的) Anne de Pisseleu 法王情妇 1—365a
安娜贝格-布赫霍尔茨 Annaberg-Buchholz 德国城镇 1—363a
安娜和约雅敬,圣 Anne and Joachim, Saints 宗教人物 1—365f
安娜·康内娜 Anna Comnena 拜占廷撰史人 1—362f
安娜特 Anath 西闪米特人女神 1—318c
安奈林 Aneirin 威尔士诗人 1—337f
安南 Annam 亚洲国家越南旧名 1—363c
安南 Annan, Kofi 联合国秘书长 1—363d
安南·本·大卫 Anan ben David 犹太教异教徒 1—315d
安南伯格 Annenberg, Walter H. 美国出版家 1—366d
安南山脉 Annamese Cordillera 印度支那山脉 1—363c
安嫩代尔-埃斯克代尔 Annandale and Eskdale 苏格兰区名 1—363e
安妮 Anne 英国女王 1—364c
安妮 Anne Boleyn 英格兰王后 1—364f
安妮(丹麦的) Anne of Denmark 英格兰王后 1—365d
安妮(克利夫斯的) Anne of Cleves 英格兰王后 1—365c
安妮女王风格 Queen Anne style 英国装饰艺术 14—83c
安妮女王之战 Queen Anne's War 西班牙历史 14—83e
安尼阶 Anisian stage 地质学 1—360b
安尼克里斯 Anniceris 希腊哲学家 1—366e
安尼斯顿 Anniston 美国城市 1—367a
安尼娅·加莱里亚·福斯蒂纳 Annia Galeria Faustina 罗马皇后 1—366e
安宁 Anning 中国城市 1—366f
安努 Anu 美索不达米亚神祇 1—401a
安努毕斯 Anubis 古埃及神祇 1—401c
安诺,圣 Anno, Saint 天主教科隆大主教 1—367a
安培 Ampère, Jean-Jacques(-Antoine) 法国历史学家、语文学家 1—296d
安培 Ampère, André-Marie 法国物理学家 1—296c
安培 ampere 计量单位 1—296c
安培定律 Ampère's law 物理学 1—296e
安培计 ammeter 测量仪表 1—292e
安平 Anping 中国台湾区名 1—369e
安普 Anpu (Egyptian god) 埃及神祇 1—369f
安普西尔男爵(第一) Ampthill (of Ampthill), Odo William Leopold Russell, 1st Baron 英国外交家 1—300d
安齐奥 Anzio 意大利城镇 1—403d
安齐库王国 Anziku, Kingdom of 刚果前王国 1—403c
安齐拉贝 Antsirabe 马达加斯加城镇 1—398d
安齐拉纳纳 Antsiranana 马达加斯加城镇 1—398d
安齐隆 Ancillon, Charles 法国律师、教育家 1—323b
安齐隆 Ancillon, Johann Peter Friedrich 普鲁士政治家 1—323c
安齐洛蒂 Anzilotti, Dionisio 意大利法学家 1—403d
安琪利加白葡萄酒 Angelica 甜酒 1—341e
安庆 Anqing 中国城市 1—369f
安丘螺 Anchura 古生物学 1—323a
安全 safety 社会学 14—495a
安全保卫制度 security and protection system 安全保卫 15—179c
安全玻璃 safety glass 玻璃 14—495f
安全灯 safety lamp 灯具 14—496a
安全工程 safety engineering 社会学 14—495c
安全理事会 Security Council 联合国机构 15—180c
安全通行证 safe-conduct 国际法 14—495a
安热罗-苏真斯克 Anzhero-Sudzhensk 俄罗斯城市 1—403c
安茹 Anjou 法国文化区域 1—360d
安茹帝国 Angevin empire 英国历史 1—344a
安茹公爵 Anjou, dukes of 法国贵族头衔 1—360f
安茹公爵 Anjou, (Hercule-) François, Duke (duc) d' 法国公爵 1—360f
安茹公爵 Anjou, Gaston-Jean-Baptiste, Duke (duc) d' 法国亲王 1—361a
安茹公爵 Anjou, Philippe I de France, Duke (duc) d' 法国亲王 1—361a
安茹公爵 Anjou, Philippe, Duke (duc) d' 西班牙国王 1—361a
安茹王朝 Angevin dynasty 英格兰王室 1—344a
安茹王室 Anjou, house of 英格兰王室 1—361a
安萨-博雷戈沙漠州立公园 Anza-Borrego Desert State Park 美国旅游地区 1—402f
安萨尔 Ansar (Sudanese faction) 苏丹伊斯兰教派别 1—370b
安塞尔莫(巴吉奥的) Anselm of Baggio 教皇 1—370c
安塞尔莫(卢卡的) Anselm of Lucca 教皇 1—370e
安塞尔姆 Anselme, Nicolas (French actor) 法国演员 1—371a
安塞姆(拉昂的) Anselm of Laon 法国神学家 1—370e
安塞姆(圣玛丽的) Anselm of Saint Mary 法国系谱学家 1—370e
安塞姆(坎特伯雷的),圣 Anselm of Canterbury, Saint 英格兰中世纪经院哲学家 1—370c
安塞斯特里昂节 Anthesteria 古希腊节日 1—377f
安塞特运输工业股份有限公司 Ansett Transport Industries Limited 澳大利亚跨行业公司 1—371f
安色尔字体 uncial 古代书法 17—339a
安森 Anson, Cap 美国棒球运动员 1—372f
安森 Anson, George Anson, Baron 英国海军上将 1—372f
安沙尔和吉沙尔 Anshar and Kishar 美索不达米亚神话人物 1—372c
安山岩 andesite 岩石 1—329a
安申 Anshan 古代埃兰国城市 1—372a
安省 Ain 法国省份 1—141e
安顺 Anshun 中国城市 1—372d
安斯巴赫 Ansbach 德国城市 1—370b
安斯蒂 Anstey, Christopher 英国诗人 1—373b
安斯基 Ansky, S. 俄国犹太作家 1—372e
安斯加尔,圣 Ansgar, Saint 英格兰基督教传教士 1—371f
安斯帕赫 Anspach (Germany) 德国城市 1—373b
安斯沃思 Ainsworth, William Harrison 英国小说家 1—141f
安斯峡湾 And Fjord 挪威海峡湾 1—323f
安索阿德吉 Anzoátegui 委内瑞拉州名 1—403e
安索尼亚 Ansonia 美国城市 1—373a
安塔基亚 Antakya (Turkey) 土耳其城市 1—374d
《安塔拉传奇》 'Antar, Romance of 骑士故事 1—374f
安塔利亚 Antalya 土耳其港口 1—374d
安塔那那利佛 Antananarivo 马达加斯加首都 1—374e
安塔纳拉人 Antanala (people) 马达加斯加岛民族 1—374e
安太尔 Antheil, George 美国作曲家 1—377b
安泰俄斯 Antaeus 希腊神话人物 1—374b
安泰拉米 Antelami, Benedetto 意大利建筑师 1—376e
安泰莫罗人 Antaimoro 马尔加什民族 1—374c
安坦德罗人 Antandroy 马尔加什民族 1—374f
安特克拉 Antequera 西班牙城市 1—377b
安特克拉的费迪南德 Antequera, El de (Spanish: He of Antequera) 阿拉贡国王 1—377b
安特拉齐特 Antratsyt 乌克兰城市 1—398a

安特勒造山幕 Antler orogeny 地质学 1—395c
安特里姆 Antrim 北爱尔兰前郡名 1—398a
安特里姆 Antrim 北爱尔兰城市 1—398b
安特里姆侯爵和伯爵(第二) Antrim, Randal MacDonnell, Marquess and 2nd Earl of 英国天主教保王派重要人物 1—398c
安特鲁斯,圣 Anterus, Saint 教皇 1—377b
安特迈耶 Untermeyer, Louis 美国诗人、散文作家 17—403a
安特诺尔 Antenor 雅典雕刻家 1—377a
安特生 Andersson, Johan Gunnar 瑞典地质学家 1—328f
安特卫普 Antwerp 比利时省份 1—398e
安特卫普 Antwerp 比利时城市 1—398f
安特卫普动物园 Antwerp Zoo 比利时动物园 1—400f
安特卫普风格画家 Antwerp Mannerists 安特卫普佚名画家 1—400e
安特希尔 Ampthill 英格兰城镇 1—300d
安藤昌益 Andō Shōeki 日本哲学家 1—329f
安藤广重 Andō Hiroshige (Japanese artist) 日本艺术家 1—329f
安藤吉次郎 Andō Kichijirō (Japanese painter) 日本画家 1—329f
安藤忠雄 Ando Tadao 日本建筑师 1—329f
安梯丰 Antiphon 雅典演说家 1—393d
安提阿会议 Antioch, Council of 基督教会会议 1—391b
安提阿式礼仪 Antiochene rite 基督教 1—391c
安提阿学院 Antioch, School of 叙利亚基督教神学院 1—391b
安提阿正教会 Antioch, Orthodox Church of 东正教牧首区 1—391b
安提俄珀 Antiope 希腊传说人物 1—392f
安提法奈斯 Antiphanes 雅典喜剧作家 1—393d
安提戈涅 Antigone 希腊传说人物 1—385c
安提瓜和巴布达 Antigua and Barbuda 加勒比海岛国 1—387a
安提柯二世 Antigonus II Gonatas 马其顿国王 1—386c
安提柯三世 Antigonus III Doson 马其顿国王 1—386f
安提柯王朝 Antigonid dynasty 古马其顿统治家族 1—385d
安提柯一世(独眼的) Antigonus I Monophthalmus (One Eyed) 马其顿国王 1—385e
安提罗科斯 Antilochus 希腊传说人物 1—388a
安提马科斯(科洛丰的) Antimachus of Colophon 希腊诗人 1—388c
安提梅里纳人 Antimerina (people) 非洲民族 1—388f
安提米乌斯 Anthemius 西罗马皇帝 1—377e
安提姆斯六世 Anthimus VI 东正教牧首 1—377f
安提姆斯七世(察佐斯) Anthimus VII Tsatsos 东正教牧首 1—378a
安提姆斯一世 Anthimus I 希腊正教牧首 1—377f
安提帕特 Antipater 马其顿将军、摄政者 1—393b
安提帕特 Antipater 希律大帝之子 1—393c
安提帕特 Antipater 希罗德王朝创始人 1—393c
安提西尼 Antisthenes 希腊哲学家 1—394e
安替比林 antipyrine 药物 1—394b
安田靫彦 Yasuda Yukihiko 日本画家 18—428f
安田善次郎 Yasuda Zenjirō 日本实业家 18—429a
安条克 Antioch 弗里吉亚古城 1—390e
安条克 Antioch 古叙利亚城市 1—390f
安条克 Antioch 亚洲穆斯林公国 1—391a
安条克 Antiochus 塞琉西王国诸国王之名 1—391d
安条克 Antiochus Hierax 塞琉西国王之弟 1—392e
安条克(阿什凯隆的) Antiochus of Ascalon 希腊哲学家 1—392e
安条克二世 Antiochus II Theos 塞琉西国王 1—391e
安条克七世 Antiochus VII Sidetes 塞琉西国王 1—392d
安条克三世 Antiochus III 塞琉西国王 1—391e
安条克四世 Antiochus IV Epiphanes (God Manifest) 塞琉西国王 1—392b
安条克一世 Antiochus I Soter 塞琉西国王 1—391d
安廷 Antin, Mary 美国作家 1—390b
安徒生 Andersen, Hans Christian 丹麦作家 1—326a
安土桃山时代 Azuchi-Momoyama period 日本历史 2—104b
安托法加斯塔 Antofagasta 智利区名 1—395e
安托法加斯塔 Antofagasta 智利城市 1—395e
安托内洛 Antonello da Messina 意大利画家 1—396b
安托尼奥 Antonio, Nicolás 西班牙文学史家 1—397a
安托尼松 Anthoniszoon, Jeroen 北欧画家 1—378b
安托万 Antoine, André 法国演员 1—395f
安万特 Aventis 法国制药公司 2—84f
安汶 Ambon 印度尼西亚城市、岛屿 1—271b
安汶岛大屠杀 Amboina Massacre 亚洲历史 1—270e
安息 Parthia 伊朗古地区 13—66a
安息日 Sabbath 犹太教 14—482b
安息日河 Sabbath River 犹太教传说中河流 14—482c
安息日河 Sambation 犹太教传说中河流 14—562e
安息日联欢 Oneg Shabbat 犹太习俗 12—418b
安息日论 Sabbatarianism 基督教教义 14—482a
安息语 Parthian language 中古伊朗语言 13—66c
安谢塔 Anchieta, José de 葡萄牙耶稣会士 1—322c
安亚拉同盟 Anjala League 北欧历史 1—360c
安阳 Anyang 中国城市 1—402d
安养 Anyang 韩国城市 1—402c
安耶拉·梅里奇,圣 Angela Merici, Saint 乌尔苏拉会创立者 1—341a
安邺 Garnier, Francis 法国殖民者、探险家 7—18a
安赞 Chan 柬埔寨国王之名 4—42c
安赞二世 Chan II 柬埔寨国王 4—42d
安赞一世 Chan I 柬埔寨国王 4—42c
安葬 burial 处理人尸体的方式 3—264d
安泽尔梅特 Ansermet, Ernest 瑞士指挥家 1—371e
安中植 An Chung-sik 朝鲜画家 1—306d
桉属 Eucalyptus 植物学 6—154e
桉树矮林 mallee 植物学 10—433c
氨(NH_3) ammonia 化合物 1—293a
氨苄青霉素 ampicillin 药物 1—300b
氨酚喹 amodiaquine 药物 1—294d
氨基酸 amino acid 化合物 1—290b
氨碱法 ammonia-soda process 化学工业 1—293b
氨水 aqua ammonia 化学 1—426b
鹌鹑 quail 鸟类 14—72e
鮟鱇 goosefish 鱼类 7—210e
鞍 saddle 马具 14—491b
鞍背鸦 saddleback (*Creadion*, sometimes *Philesturnus*, *caruncutatus*) 鸟类 14—491d
鞍马 side horse 体操器械 15—352c
鞍牡蛎 saddle oyster 软体动物 14—491d
鞍山 Anshan 中国城市 1—372b
唵 Om 印度教咒语 12—411f
鞍作止利 Kuratsukuri Tori 日本雕刻家 9—400d
岸边区 Bankside 英国伦敦一地区 2—206c
岸和田 Kishiwada 日本城市 9—306f
岸礁 fringing reef 地质学 6—495f
岸驹 Ganku 日本画家 7—1f
岸信介 Kishi Nobusuke 日本政治家 9—306d
按立圣职 ordination 基督教仪式 12—450d
按摩 massage 医学 11—11a
按手礼 hands, imposition of 宗教礼仪 7—458e
按音速记机 stenotypy 速记机器 16—219e
按指数增减 indexation 经济 8—357d
胺 amine 化合物 1—290a
案情摘要 brief 法律文件 3—154e
暗利 Omri 以色列国王 12—415d
暗楼 triforium 建筑 17—218e

暗色调主义 tenebrism 绘画 16—538e
暗色土 Umbrisol 土壤 17—337a
暗示 suggestion 心理学 16—310d
暗示标志 rebus 写作原理 14—182e
暗滩 bank 海底被淹没高地 2—204b
暗箱 camera obscura 摄影装置 3—371f
暗星云 dark nebula 天文学 5—150c
暗铱铁矿 siserskite 矿物 15—403f
昂比石碑 Ängby Stone 瑞典古石碑 1—340c
昂布瓦斯 Amboise 法国城镇 1—270e
昂布瓦斯 Amboise, Georges d' 法国枢机主教 1—271a
昂布瓦斯阴谋 Amboise, Conspiracy of 法国历史 1—270f
昂德尔 Oundle 英国城镇 12—507c
昂德希尔 Underhill, John 美洲殖民地军官 17—340a
昂蒂布 Antibes 法国城镇 1—382e
昂蒂乌姆 Antium (Italy) 意大利城镇 1—395c
昂方坦 Enfantin, Barthélemy-Prosper 法国政治家 6—76a
昂戈 Ango, Jean 法国船主 1—349f
昂格维尔 Aungerville, Richard 英国藏书家 2—57c
昂古莱姆 Angoulême 法国城市 1—351c
昂古莱姆公爵 Angoulême, Charles, duc d' (duke of) 法国公爵 1—351d
昂古莱姆公爵 Angoulême, Charles de Valois, duc d' (duke of) 法国军事领袖 1—351e
昂古莱姆公爵 Angoulême, Louis-Antoine de Bourbon, duc d' (duke of) 法国公爵 1—351e
昂古莱姆女公爵 Angoulême, Diane de France, duchessede Montmorency et 法国公爵 1—351e
昂古莱姆王朝 Angoulême DYNASTY 法国王朝 1—351d
昂古穆瓦 Angoumois 法国前省份 1—352a
昂吉安 Enghien 比利时城市 6—78a
昂吉尔贝尔 Angilbert 法兰克诗人 1—344c
昂加瓦 Ungava 加拿大地区 17—341f
昂加瓦-魁北克陨石坑 Ungava-Quebec Crater 加拿大陨石坑 17—342a
昂加瓦湾 Ungava Bay 加拿大海湾 17—341f
昂克尔侯爵 Ancre, Concino Concini, marquis d' 意大利冒险家 1—323e
昂里奥 Hanriot, François 法国军人 7—463b
昂鲁什 Amrouche, Jean 阿尔及利亚诗人 1—301f
昂鲁什 Amrouche, Marguerite Taos 阿尔及利亚歌唱家、作家 1—301f
昂马克沙利克 Ammassalik 格陵兰城镇 1—292e
昂纳克 Honecker, Erich 德国共产党领袖 8—152e
昂热 Angers 法国城市 1—343f
昂萨格 Onsager, Lars 美国化学家 12—422f
昂塞尔兄弟 Unser, Bobby and Al 美国赛车手 17—402e
昂山 Aung San 缅甸民族领袖 2—57a
昂山素季 Aung San Suu Kyi 缅甸反对派领袖 2—57b
昂松戈 Ansongo 马里城镇 1—373a
昂特雷沙 entrechat 芭蕾舞动作 6—89f
昂瓦里 Anvarī 波斯诗人 1—401f
昂维尔瓦赫特统 Onverwacht series 地质学 12—423f
盎格鲁美洲 Anglo-America 北美洲文化实体 1—347e
盎格鲁-诺曼底群岛 Anglo-Normandes, Îles (Great Britain) 英国群岛 1—348f
盎格鲁-诺曼文学 Anglo-Norman literature 英格兰古法语文学 1—348c
盎格鲁人 Angle 日耳曼民族 1—346b
《盎格鲁-撒克逊编年史》 Anglo-Saxon Chronicle 英格兰编年史 1—349b
盎格鲁-撒克逊法律 Anglo-Saxon law 英格兰法律 1—349d
盎格鲁-撒克逊盟主 bretwalda 英国历史 3—145b
盎格鲁-撒克逊人 Anglo-Saxon 日耳曼民族 1—348f
盎格鲁-撒克逊艺术 Anglo-Saxon art 英国艺术 1—349a
盎格鲁-撒克逊语 Anglo-Saxon language 古英语 1—349d
盎司 ounce 重量单位 12—507c
凹版印刷 gravure printing 印刷方法 7—265f
凹槽和凸嵌线脚 fluting and reeding 建筑学 6—380a
凹脸蝠 slit-faced bat 哺乳动物 15—433f
凹舌兰 frog orchid (*Coeloglossum viride*) 草本植物 6—499d
凹室 alcove 建筑学 1—191e
凹形金属制品 hollowware 金属加工成品 8—133d
凹印 intaglio 印刷技法 8—403b
凹圆线脚 coving 建筑学 4—556c
敖德萨 Odessa 乌克兰州名 12—337a
敖德萨 Odessa 乌克兰港市 12—337b
敖德萨 Odessa 美国城市 12—337c
敖德萨陨石坑 Odessa Crater 美国陨坑 12—337d
螯合物 chelate 化合物 4—103e
螯虾 crayfish 甲壳动物 4—573f
翱翔运动 soaring 体育 15—467f
奥埃拉斯伯爵 Oeiras, Sebastião de Carvalho, conde de (count of) 葡萄牙改革家 12—342d
奥安尼斯 Oannes 美索不达米亚神名 12—315f
奥昂人 Oraon 印度民族 12—444a
奥巴岛 Aoba 瓦努阿图火山岛 1—403f
奥巴林 Oparin, Aleksandr 俄罗斯生物化学家 12—426c
奥巴马 Obama, Barack, Jr. 美国政治人物 12—317d
奥巴尼恩 O'Bannion, (Charles) Dion 美国匪徒 12—317e
奥巴桑乔 Obasanjo, Olusegun 尼日利亚将军 12—317e
奥贝尔 Aubert, Éticnne (pope) 教皇 2—42e
奥贝尔 Abeel, John (Seneca Indian leader) 印第安人领袖 1—18b
奥贝尔 O'Bail, John (Seneca Indian leader) 印第安人领袖 12—317c
奥贝尔 O'Beel, John (Seneca Indian leader) 印第安人领袖 12—317f
奥贝托一世 Oberto I 意大利封建主 12—320b
奥本 Auburn 美国亚拉巴马州城市 2—43c
奥本 Auburn 美国缅因州城市 2—43c
奥本 Auburn 美国纽约州城市 2—43c
奥本 Auburn 美国华盛顿州城市 2—43d
奥本海 Oppenheim, Lassa Francis Lawrence 德国法学家 12—434a
奥本海默 Oppenheimer, Sir Ernest 南非工业家 12—434a
奥本海默 Oppenheimer, J(ulius) Robert 美国物理学家 12—434b
奥本海姆 Oppenheim, E. Phillips 英国小说家 12—433f
奥本罗 Åbenrå 丹麦城市 1—20a
奥本制度 Auburn system 刑罚学 2—43d
奥比杜斯 Óbidos 巴西城镇 12—320e
奥比尼亚克 Aubignac, François Hédelin, abbé d' 法国剧作家 2—42e
奥比涅 Aubigné, Françoise d' 法国皇后 2—42f
奥比涅 Aubigné, Théodore-Agrippa d' 法国诗人 2—42f
奥比群岛 Obi Islands 印度尼西亚群岛 12—320e
奥比亚 obia 非洲民间传说 12—320e
奥波博 Opobo (Nigeria) 尼日利亚城镇 12—433a
奥波莱 Opole 波兰城市 12—433a
奥波莱 Opole 原波兰省份 12—433a
奥波莱 Opolskie 波兰省份 12—433b
奥伯豪森 Oberhausen 德国城市 12—318e
奥伯林 Oberlin 美国城市 12—318f
奥伯林 Oberlin, Johann Friedrich 德国教育家 12—318f
奥伯林学院 Oberlin College 美国高等学府 12—319a
奥伯龙 Oberon 法国诗歌中人物 12—319b
奥伯斯 Olbers, Wilhelm 德国天文学家 12—365d
奥伯斯佯谬 Olbers' paradox 天文学 12—365e

奥伯特 Oberth, Hermann (Julius) 德国科学家 12—319f
奥柏 Auber, Daniel-François-Esprit 法国作曲家 2—42d
奥勃拉兹佐夫 Obraztsov, Sergey (Vladimirovich) 苏联木偶戏大师 12—321e
奥勃朗 Oberon, Merle 英国和美国演员 12—319c
奥博德里人 Obodrite 欧洲中世纪民族 12—321a
奥博莫绍 Ogbomosho 尼日利亚城镇 12—345c
奥博特 Obote, Milton 乌干达总统 12—321d
奥布 Aube 法国省份 2—42c
奥布 Åbo (Finland) 芬兰城市 1—26b
奥布阿西 Obuasi 加纳城镇 12—324d
奥布河 Aube River 法国河流 2—42c
奥布赖恩 O'Brien, Edna 爱尔兰作家 12—322c
奥布赖恩 O'Brien, Flann 爱尔兰作家 12—322d
奥布赖恩 O'Brien, Fitz-James 美国作家 12—322d
奥布赖恩 O'Brien, James Bronterre 英国激进分子 12—322e
奥布赖恩 O'Brien, William 爱尔兰新闻记者 12—322f
奥布赖恩 O'Brien, (William) Parry 美国运动员 12—322e
奥布赖恩 O'Brien, William Smith 爱尔兰爱国者 12—322f
奥布雷 Aubray, Marie-Madeleine-Marguérite d' 法国投毒者 2—43b
奥布雷希特 Obrecht, Jakob 荷兰作曲家 12—321f
奥布里 Aubrey, John 英国文物研究者 2—43b
奥布廉诺维奇王朝 Obrenović DYNASTY 塞尔维亚历史 12—322b
奥布斯特费尔德 Obstfelder, Sigbjørn 挪威诗人 12—324c
《奥布条约》(1743) Åbo, Treaty of 欧洲历史 1—26b
奥藏方 Ozenfant, Amédée 法国画家 12—528d
奥查德 Orchard, William Edwin 英国天主教司铎 12—446d
奥查德森 Orchardson, Sir William Quiller 英国画家 12—446f
奥长石 oligoclase 矿物 12—374a
奥茨 Oz, Amos 以色列作家 12—527d
奥茨胡恩 Oudtshoorn 南非城镇 12—506a
奥村政信 Okumura Masanobu 日本画家 12—363f
奥达果斯特 Audaghost 前柏柏尔人城镇 2—45a
奥代什岛 Ghaudex (Malta) 马耳他岛屿 7—109d
奥戴拉菲家族 Ordelaffi FAMILY 意大利贵族 12—448c
奥戴莱 O Dalaigh, Cearbhall 爱尔兰总统 12—314b
奥得-哈弗尔运河 Oder-Havel Canal 德国运河 12—336e
奥得河 Oder River 欧洲河流 12—337a
奥得河畔法兰克福 Frankfurt an der Oder 德国城市 6—449d
奥得-尼斯线 Oder-Neisse Line 欧洲历史 12—336e
奥得湾 Oderhaff (Baltic Sea) 波罗的海海湾 12—337a
奥德 Aude 法国省份 2—45a
奥德 Oudh (India) 印度市镇 12—505e
奥德 Oud, Jacobus Johannes Pieter 荷兰建筑师 12—505a
奥德比-威格顿 Oadby and wigston 英格兰区名 12—314c
奥德尔 awdl 威尔士文学 2—92c
奥德费尔德 Oldfield, Barney 美国运动员 12—370f
奥德河 Ord River 澳大利亚河流 12—448b
奥德里亚 Odría, Manuel A. 秘鲁总统 12—340a
奥德利(沃尔登的) Audley (of Walden), Thomas Audley, Baron 英格兰大法官 2—46b
奥德姆 Odum, Howard W. 美国社会学家 12—340d
奥德纳尔德 Oudenaarde 比利时城市 12—505c
奥德纳尔德战役 Oudenaarde, Battle of 欧洲历史 12—505d
奥德尼·马格努松 Árni Magnusson (Icelandic antiquarian) 冰岛文物工作者 1—506f
奥德修斯 Odysseus 荷马史诗《奥德赛》中主人公 12—340d
奥德兹 Odets, Clifford 美国剧作家 12—337d
奥登 Auden, W(ystan) H(ugh) 英裔美国诗人 2—45b
奥登达尔斯勒斯 Odendaalsrus 南非城镇 12—336c
奥登林山 Odenwald 德国高地 12—336e
奥登纳图斯 Odaenathus, Septimius 罗马殖民地邦君 12—335f
奥迪贝蒂 Audiberti, Jacques 法国诗人 2—45d
奥地利 Austria 欧洲国家 2—69e
奥地利经济学派 Austrian school of economics 经济学 2—71d
奥地利美术馆 Österreichische Gallery 奥地利艺术博物馆 12—492d
奥地利狩猎地毯 Austrian Hunting Carpet 伊朗工艺品 2—71c
奥地利王朝 Austria, HOUSE OF 欧洲王朝 2—71b
奥地利王位继承战争 Austrian Succession, War of the 欧洲历史 2—71e
奥第 Ady, Endre 匈牙利诗人 1—91b
奥蒂河 Oti River 非洲河流 12—497b
奥蒂林河 Ottilien (Papua New Guinea) 巴布亚新几内亚河流 12—500c
奥蒂斯 Otis, Elisha Graves 美国发明家 12—497b
奥蒂斯 Otis, Harrison Gray 美国政治家 12—497c
奥蒂斯 Otis, Harrison Gray 美国报纸发行人 12—497c
奥蒂斯 Otis, James 美国政治活动家 12—497d
奥蒂西 oṛissī 印度舞蹈 12—462d
奥蒂泽尔 Altizer, Thomas J(onathan) J(ackson) 美国基督教神学家 1—256f
奥迭内 Odienné 科特迪瓦城镇 12—337f
奥丁 Odin 古斯堪的纳维亚主神 12—337f
奥杜邦 Audubon, John James 美国鸟类学家 2—46c
奥杜威文化期工艺 Oldowan industry 考古学 12—371b
奥杜威峡谷 Olduvai Gorge 坦桑尼亚考古遗址 12—371c
奥杜维尔·基罗斯 Oduber Quirós, Daniel 哥斯达黎加总统 12—340b
奥顿 Orton, Joe 英国剧作家 12—476d
奥顿伯格 Oldenburg, Claes 美国雕刻家 12—370d
奥多 Eudes DE CHÂTILLON-SUR-MARNE (pope) 教皇 6—157a
奥多(巴约的) Odo OF BAYEUX 诺曼贵族 12—338c
奥多(马恩河畔沙蒂永的) Odo OF CHÂTILLON-SUR-MARNE (pope) 教皇 12—338c
奥多(克吕尼的),圣 Odo OF CLUNY, SAINT 法国隐修院院长 12—338c
奥多德 O'Dowd, Bernard Patrick 澳大利亚诗人 12—340a
奥多里克 Odoric OF PORDENONE 方济各会修士 12—339f
奥多涅斯 Ordóñez, Antonio 西班牙斗牛士 12—450e
奥多涅斯 Ordóñez, Bartolomé 雕刻家 12—450e
奥多诺万 O'Donovan, Michael 爱尔兰作家 12—339d
奥多瓦卡尔 Odovacar (German king of Italy) 意大利国王 12—340a
奥多亚塞 Odoacer 意大利蛮族国王 12—338c
奥恩 Orne 法国省份 12—468b
奥恩布鲁格 Auenbrugger von Auenbrugg, Leopold 奥地利医师 2—46e
奥恩河 Orne River 法国河流 12—468c
奥尔 Orr, Bobby 美国运动员 12—471b
奥尔 Auer, Carl 奥地利化学家 2—46e
奥尔 Auer, Leopold 匈牙利小提琴家 2—46e
奥尔巴赫 Auerbach, Berthold 德国小说家 2—46f
奥尔巴赫 Auerbach, Erich 罗曼语学者 2—47a
奥尔巴尼 Albany 澳大利亚城镇 1—175a
奥尔巴尼 Albany 美国佐治亚州城市 1—175b
奥尔巴尼 Albany 美国县城、纽约州首府 1—175b
奥尔巴尼 Albany 美国俄勒冈州城市 1—175d
奥尔巴克 Auerbach, Red 美国职业篮球教练 2—47a
奥尔巴尼公爵 Albany, DUKES OF 苏格兰贵族封爵名 1—175d
奥尔巴尼公爵 Albany, Alexander Stewart, duke of 苏格兰公爵 1—175e
奥尔巴尼公爵(第二) Albany, John Stewart, 2nd duke of 苏格兰摄政者 1—175e
奥尔巴尼公爵(第一) Albany, Robert Stewart, 1st duke of 苏格兰摄政者 1—175d
奥尔巴尼河 Albany River 加拿大河流 1—175f

奥尔巴尼会议 Albany Congress 美国历史 1—175f
奥尔巴特 Allbutt, Sir Thomas Clifford 英国医师 1—236a
奥尔堡 Ålborg 丹麦城市 1—184e
奥尔比亚 Olbia 意大利城镇 12—365f
奥尔波特 Allport, Gordon W(illard) 美国心理学家、教育家 1—243a
奥尔伯里-沃东加 Albury-Wodonga 澳大利亚城市 1—186e
奥尔布赖特 Albright, Ivan (Le Lorraine) 美国画家 1—185b
奥尔布赖特 Albright, Madeleine 美国官员 1—185c
奥尔布赖特 Albright, Tenley (Emma) 美国滑冰运动员 1—185d
奥尔布赖特 Albright, W(illiam) F(oxwell) 美国《圣经》考古学家 1—185d
奥尔布赖特-诺克斯艺术馆 Albright-Knox Art Gallery 美国艺术博物馆 1—185e
奥尔布赖特氏综合征 Albright's syndrome 遗传性疾病 1—185f
奥尔布里希 Olbrich, Joseph (Maria) 德国建筑师 12—365f
奥尔德弗里思 Aldfrith 诺森伯里亚国王 1—193e
奥尔德海姆 Aldhelm 西撒克逊隐修院院长 1—193e
奥尔德卡斯尔 Oldcastle, Sir John 英格兰军人 12—369b
奥尔德里克·维塔尔 Orderic Vitalis 诺曼底历史学家 12—449d
奥尔德里奇 Aldrich, Bess Genevra Streeter 美国作家 1—194a
奥尔德里奇 Aldridge, Ira Frederick 美国悲剧演员 1—194c
奥尔德里奇 Aldrich, Nelson W(ilmarth) 美国参议员 1—194b
奥尔德里奇 Aldrich, Thomas Bailey 美国诗人 1—194c
奥尔德林(小) Aldrin, Edwin Eugene, Jr. 美国航天员 1—194e
奥尔德姆 Oldham 英格兰城市 12—370f
奥尔德姆 Oldham, John 英格兰诗人 12—370f
奥尔德姆 Oldham, Richard Dixon 英国地质学家 12—371a
奥尔德尼 Alderney 英国岛屿 1—193d
奥尔登 Alden, Cynthia May Westover 美国社会工作者、新闻记者 1—192d
奥尔登 Alden, Isabella Macdonald 美国儿童读物作家 1—192e
奥尔登 Alden, John 英格兰殖民地开拓者 1—192f
奥尔登巴内费尔特 Oldenbarnevelt, Johan van 尼德兰政治家 12—369c
奥尔登堡 Oldenburg 德国地名 12—370c
奥尔登堡 Oldenburg 德国城市 12—370d
奥尔登堡信义会 Lutheran Church of Oldenburg 德国基督教教会 10—300f
奥尔迪斯 Aldiss, Brian W(ilson) 英国小说家 1—193f
奥尔蒂冈 Ortigão, José Duarte Ramalho 葡萄牙作家 12—476b
奥尔蒂斯 Ortiz, Fernando 古巴人类学家 12—476c
奥尔丁顿 Aldington, Richard 英国小说家 1—193f
奥尔丁-纳施金 Ordyn-Nashchokin, Afanasy Lavrentyevich 俄国政治家 12—451b
奥尔杜 Ordu 土耳其城市 12—451b
奥尔顿 Alton 美国城市 1—257d
奥尔顿 Alton 英格兰城镇 1—257d
奥尔顿侯爵 Alton, Charles Talbot, Marquess of 英格兰政治家 1—257e
奥尔菲拉 Orfila, (Washington) Alejandro 阿根廷外交官 12—457a
奥尔夫 Orff, Carl 德国作曲家 12—456f
奥尔盖尔米尔 Aurgelmir 古斯堪的纳维亚神话人物 2—58e
奥尔盖尔陨石 Orgueil meteorite 一场生物学骗局中提到的陨石 12—459c
奥尔古德 Allgood, Sara 爱尔兰演员 1—240a
奥尔汗 Orhan 奥斯曼苏丹 12—459c
奥尔洪岛 Olkhon Island 俄罗斯岛屿 12—376f
奥尔霍迈诺斯 Orchomenus 希腊古城 12—448a
奥尔加山 Olgas 澳大利亚突岩 12—373b
奥尔加,圣 Olga, SAINT 俄罗斯统治者 12—373a
奥尔金 Holguín 古巴省份 8—125a
奥尔金 Holguín 古巴城市 8—125c
奥尔卡尼亚 Orcagna, Andrea 佛罗伦萨画家 12—446c
奥尔坎 Orkan, Władysław 波兰作家 12—462f
奥尔科特 Alcott, (Amos) Bronson 美国哲学家 1—191b
奥尔科特 Olcott, Henry Steel 美国哲学家 12—366a
奥尔科特 Alcott, Louisa May 美国作家 1—191d
奥尔莱 Orley, Bernard van 佛兰德斯画家 12—465c
奥尔利采山脉 Orlice Mountains 捷克山脉 12—465d
奥尔良 Orléanais 法国历史地区 12—463c
奥尔良 Orléans 法国城市 12—463d
奥尔良 Orléans, Anne-Marie-Louise d' 法国王族 12—465c
奥尔良(私生子) Orléans, BASTARD OF 法国军人 12—463e
奥尔良公爵 Orléans, DUKES OF 法国贵族 12—463e
奥尔良公爵 Orléans, Charles, duc d' 法国诗人 12—463f
奥尔良公爵 Orléans, Charles, duc d' 法国诗人 12—464a
奥尔良公爵 Orléans, Charles, duc d' 法国军人 12—464b
奥尔良公爵 Orléans, Ferdinand-Louis-Philippe-Charles-Henri, duc d' 法国贵族 12—465a
奥尔良公爵 Orléans, Gaston(-Jean-Baptiste), duc d' 法国亲王 12—464b
奥尔良公爵 Orléans, Henri, duc d' 法国国王 12—464a
奥尔良公爵 Orléans, Louis, duc d' 法国贵族 12—464e
奥尔良公爵 Orléans, Louis I, duc d' 法国贵族 12—463f
奥尔良公爵 Orléans, Louis II, duc d' 法国国王 12—464a
奥尔良公爵 Orléans, Louis-Philippe, duc d' 法国国王 12—465a
奥尔良公爵 Orléans, Louis-Philippe, duc d' 法国军人 12—464f
奥尔良公爵 Orléans, Louis-Philippe-Joseph, duc d' 法国亲王 12—464f
奥尔良公爵 Orléans, Louis-Philippe-Robert, duc d' 法国贵族 12—465a
奥尔良公爵 Orléans, Philippe I, duc d' 法国贵族 12—463e
奥尔良公爵(菲利普二世) Orléans, Philippe II, duc d' 法国摄政 12—464d
奥尔良公爵(菲利普一世) Orléans, Philippe I de France, duc d' 法国贵族 12—464c
奥尔良派 Orleanist 法国立宪君主主义者 12—463d
奥尔良维尔 Orléansville (Algeria) 阿尔及利亚城镇 12—465c
奥尔良之围 Orléans, Siege of 英法百年战争 12—465c
奥尔洛夫 Orlov, Aleksey Fyodorovich, Prince (Knyaz) 俄国政治家 12—465e
奥尔洛夫 Orlov, Aleksey Grigoryevich, Count (Graf) 俄国军人 12—466a
奥尔洛夫 Orlov, Grigory Grigoryevich, Graf (Count) 俄国军人 12—466b
奥尔洛夫伯爵 Orlov, Fyodor Grigoryevich, Graf (Count) 俄国军人 12—466b
奥尔洛夫公爵 Orlov, Nikolay Alekseyevich, Knyaz (Prince) 俄国外交官 12—466c
奥尔洛夫钻石 Orlov diamond 印度宝石 12—466d
奥尔曼兄弟乐队 Allman Brothers Band, the 美国摇滚乐队 1—241f
奥尔梅多 Olmedo, José Joaquín 厄瓜多尔诗人 12—378b
奥尔梅克文化 Olmec 墨西哥文化 12—377e
奥尔米 Olmi, Ermanno 意大利电影导演 12—378c
奥尔米茨 Olmütz (Czech Republic) 捷克城市 12—378e
《奥尔米茨条约》 Olmütz, Punctation of 欧洲普奥两国协议 12—378e
奥尔莫克 Ormoc 菲律宾城市 12—466a
奥尔默特 Olmert, Ehud 以色列政治人物 12—378b
奥尔尼 Olney, Richard 美国国务卿 12—378f
奥尔努瓦 Aulnoy, Marie-Catherine Le Jumel de Barneville, comtesse d' 法国作家 2—56d
奥尔诺斯包围战 Aornos, Siege of 巴基斯坦历史 1—404a
奥尔恰 Orchha 印度旧邦名 12—447b

奥尔恰 Orchha 印度古城 12—447b
奥尔赛博物馆 Orsay Museum 法国博物馆 12—472a
奥尔森 Olson, Charles (John) 美国诗人 12—379b
奥尔森 Olson, Elder (James) 美国诗人 12—379c
奥尔沙 Orsha 白俄罗斯城市 12—472a
奥尔施泰特公爵 Auerstedt, Louis-Nicolas Davout, Duke (duc) d' 法国将军 2—47b
奥尔施泰特战役 Auerstädt, Battle of 法国历史 2—47b
奥尔什丁 Olsztyn 原波兰省份 12—379d
奥尔什丁 Olsztyn 波兰城市 12—379d
奥尔斯顿 Allston, Robert (Francis Withers) 美国水稻种植家 1—243c
奥尔斯顿 Allston, Washington 美国画家、作家 1—243d
奥尔斯克 Orsk 俄罗斯城市 12—472c
奥尔斯佩格伯爵 Auersperg, Anton Alexander, Count (Graf) von 奥地利诗人 2—47b
奥尔斯佩格侯爵 Auersperg, Adolf (Karl Daniel), Prince (Fürst) von, DUKE (Herzog) VON GOTTSCHEE 奥地利首相 2—47b
奥尔索普子爵 Althorp, John Charles Spencer, Viscount 英国政治家 1—255e
奥尔塔 Horta 葡萄牙城市 8—185e
奥尔塔湖 Orta, Lake 意大利湖泊 12—472e
奥尔唐斯 Hortense 荷兰王后 8—186a
奥尔特 Olt 罗马尼亚县名 12—379e
奥尔特 Oerter, Al 美国铁饼运动员 12—342e
奥尔特 Oort, Jan Hendrik 荷兰天文学家 12—424d
奥尔特河 Olt River 罗马尼亚河流 12—379f
奥尔特加 Ortega, Domingo 西班牙斗牛士 12—472f
奥尔特加-加塞特 Ortega y Gasset, José 西班牙哲学家 12—473a
奥尔特加·萨维德拉 Ortega Saavedra, Daniel 尼加拉瓜总统 12—472f
奥尔特曼 Altman, Benjamin 美国商人、艺术收藏家 1—257a
奥尔特曼 Altman, Robert (B.) 美国电影导演 1—257a
奥尔特曼 Altman, Sidney 美国分子生物学家 1—257b
奥尔特峡谷 Olt Defile 罗马尼亚峡谷 12—379e
奥尔特云 Oort cloud 天文学 12—424e
奥尔托纳 Ortona 意大利城镇 12—476e
奥尔维耶托 Orvieto 意大利城镇 12—477a
奥尔维耶托陶器 Orvieto ware 工艺品 12—477a
奥尔西 Orsi, Paolo 奥地利考古学家 12—472a
奥尔西尼 Orsini, Felice 意大利民族主义者 12—472c
奥尔西尼 Orsini, Giovanni Gaetano 教皇 12—472c
奥尔西尼 Orsini, Pietro Francesco Vincenzo Maria (pope) 教皇 12—472c
奥尔西尼家族 Orsini FAMILY 意大利家族 12—472b
奥尔忠尼启则 Ordzhonikidze, Grigory Konstantinovich 苏联共产党领导人 12—451c
奥尔忠尼启则 Ordzhonikidze (Russia) 俄罗斯城市 12—451c
奥尔兹 Olds, Ransom Eli 美国发明家 12—371c
奥发 Offa 英格兰国王 12—343c
奥发(安格尔的) Offa OF ANGEL 盎格鲁族统治者 12—343e
奥发大堤 Offa's Dyke 英格兰工程 12—344a
奥法 Offa 尼日利亚城镇 12—343e
奥法莱恩 O'Faolain, Sean 爱尔兰作家 12—343a
奥法利 Offaly 爱尔兰郡名 12—343f
奥法利勋爵 Offaly, Thomas Fitzgerald, Lord 爱尔兰领袖 12—344a
奥菲尔斯 Ophüls, Max 德国电影导演 12—431c
奥芬巴赫 Offenbach, Jacques 法国作曲家 12—344b
奥芬巴赫 Offenbach 德国城市 12—344a
奥芬堡 Offenburg 德国城市 12—344b
奥佛尼乌斯·提格林努斯 Ofonius Tigellinus 罗马官员 12—344e
奥夫雷贡 Obregón, Álvaro 墨西哥总统 12—322a
奥夫雷贡城 Ciudad Obregón 墨西哥城市 4—252b
奥夫雷贡镇 Villa Obregón 墨西哥区名 17—562f
奥弗伯里 Overbury, Sir Thomas 英国作家 12—511d
奥弗顿 Overton, Richard 英国政论作家 12—512a
奥弗莱厄蒂 O'Flaherty, Liam 爱尔兰小说家 12—344d
奥弗涅 Auvergne 法国区名 2—81c
奥福德伯爵(第四) Orford, Horace Walpole, 4th Earl of 英国作家 12—457b
奥福德伯爵(第一) Orford, Robert Walpole, 1st Earl of 英国首相 12—457b
奥戈尔曼 O'Gorman, Juan 墨西哥建筑师 12—347c
奥戈高原 Ogo Highlands (Somalia) 索马里高原 12—347a
奥戈贾 Ogoja 尼日利亚城镇 12—347b
奥戈特 Ogot, Grace 肯尼亚小说家 12—347d
奥格 Haug, (Gustave-) Émile 法国地质学家 7—511a
奥格本 Ogburn, William Fielding 美国社会学家 12—345d
奥格登 Ogden 美国城市 12—345e
奥格登 Ogden, C(harles) K(ay) 英国语言学家 12—345f
奥格登 Ogden, Peter Skene 加拿大探险家 12—346a
奥格登斯堡 Ogdensburg 美国港口城市 12—346b
奥格尔比 Ogilby, John 英国印刷师 12—346d
奥格尔斯比 Oglesby, Richard (James) 美国参议员 12—346e
奥格尔索普 Oglethorpe, James Edward 英国军人 12—346e
奥格尔维 Ogilvy, David M(ackenzie) 英国广告经理人 12—346e
奥格雷迪 O'Grady, Standish James 爱尔兰作家 12—347e
奥格米奥斯 Ogmios 凯尔特神名 12—346f
奥格斯堡 Augsburg 德国城市 2—48c
《奥格斯堡和约》 Augsburg, Peace of 基督教文献 2—48e
奥格斯堡联盟战争 Augsburg, War of the League of 欧洲历史 2—48f
奥格斯堡联盟战争 League of Augsburg, War of the 欧洲历史 9—543d
《奥格斯堡临时敕令》 Augsburg Interim 德国历史 2—48f
《奥格斯堡信纲》 Augsburg Confession 基督教文献 2—48f
《奥格斯堡信纲辩》 Apology of the Augsburg Confession 基督教作品 1—414c
奥格乌尔 Ogwr 威尔士区名 12—348c
奥贡 Ogun 尼日利亚州名 12—347f
奥贡德 Ogunde, Hubert 尼日利亚剧作家 12—348a
奥贡莫拉 Ogunmola, Kola 尼日利亚演员 12—348b
奥古斯丁,圣 Augustine, SAINT 罗马帝国主教 2—49e
奥古斯丁(坎特伯雷的),圣 Augustine OF CANTERBURY, SAINT 坎特伯雷大主教 2—52c
奥古斯丁会 Augustinian 天主教修会 2—52c
奥古斯都 Augustus, Caesar 古罗马皇帝 2—53a
奥古斯都和平祭坛 Altar of Augustan Peace 意大利罗马的祭坛 1—254c
奥古斯都和平祭坛 Augustus' altar of peace 意大利罗马的祭坛 2—55f
奥古斯都时代 Augustan Age 拉丁文学的一个时代 2—49d
奥古斯都之宝 Gemma Augustea 浮雕宝石 7—50c
奥古斯塔 Augusta 意大利城镇 2—49b
奥古斯塔 Augusta 美国佐治亚州城市 2—49b
奥古斯塔 Augusta 美国缅因州城市 2—49c
奥古斯塔 Augusta 德意志皇后 2—49a
奥古斯塔 Augusta, Julia 凯撒大帝之妻 2—49d
奥古斯塔港 Port Augusta 澳大利亚城市 13—444b
奥古斯塔那福音信义会 Augustana Evangelical Lutheran Church 美国基督教教会 2—49e
奥古斯特 Augustus 统治者之名 2—52d
奥古斯特 Augustus 德意志新教领袖 2—55e
奥古斯特二世 Augustus II 波兰国王 2—52e
奥古斯特三世 Augustus III 波兰国王 2—52f
奥古斯特一世 Augustus I 波兰国王 2—52e

奥果韦河 Ogooué River 非洲河流 12—347b
奥哈拉 O'Hara, Frank 美国诗人 12—348f
奥哈拉 O'Hara, John (Henry) 美国小说家 12—349a
奥哈伊 Ojai 美国城市 12—356d
奥海恩 Ohain, Hans Pabst von 德国设计师 12—348d
奥豪森联盟 Auhausen, Union of (Germany) 德意志军事联盟 2—55f
奥赫达城 Ciudad Ojeda 委内瑞拉城市 4—252b
奥赫拉比斯瀑布 Augrabies Falls 南非瀑布 2—48c
奥赫里德 Ohrid 马其顿城镇 12—353f
奥赫里德湖 Ohrid, Lake 欧洲湖泊 12—354a
奥赫洛普科夫 Okhlopkov, Nikolay Pavlovich 苏联戏剧家 12—359d
奥赫热河 Ohře River 欧洲河流 12—353f
奥胡斯 Århus 丹麦城市 1—469b
奥胡斯州 Århus 丹麦州名 1—469a
奥湖 Awe, Loch 苏格兰湖泊 2—92c
奥怀希河 Owyhee River 美国河流 12—518c
奥基博 Okigbo, Christopher 尼日利亚诗人 12—359f
奥基夫 O'Keeffe, Georgia 美国画家 12—358f
奥基诺 Ochino, Bernardino 意大利宗教改革家 12—331c
奥基乔比湖 Okeechobee, Lake 美国湖泊 12—358f
奥吉布瓦人 Ojibwa 北美印第安人 12—356e
奥吉亚斯 Augeas 希腊传说中的国王 2—47c
奥加农 organum 乐器 12—459a
奥卡 Awka 尼日利亚城镇 2—92d
奥卡 Okha 印度城市 12—359c
奥卡-阿科科 Oka-Akoko 尼日利亚城镇 12—357b
奥卡河 Oka River 俄罗斯河流 12—357b
奥卡拉 Ocala 美国城市 12—324e
奥卡拉 Okāra 巴基斯坦城市 12—357f
奥卡拉 Okara, Gabriel (Imomotimi Gbaingbain) 尼日利亚作家 12—357f
奥卡罗兰 O'Carolan, Turlough 爱尔兰音乐家 12—325a
奥卡尼亚 Ocaña 哥伦比亚城市 12—324f
《奥卡森和尼克莱特》 Aucassin et Nicolette 法国叙事诗 2—44a
奥卡万戈 Okavango (Namibia) 纳米比亚地区 12—358a
奥卡万戈河 Okavango River 非洲河流 12—358a
奥凯 Aux Cayes (Haiti) 海地城镇 2—81f
奥凯利 O'Kelly, Sean T(homas) 爱尔兰总统 12—359b
奥凯内 Okene 尼日利亚城镇 12—359b
奥凯西 O'Casey, Sean 爱尔兰剧作家 12—325a
奥康姆 Ockham, William of 英国哲学家 12—332e
奥康姆的剃刀 Ockham's razor 经济法则 12—332e
奥康纳 O'Connor, Frank 爱尔兰作家 12—333d
奥康纳 O'Connor, Feargus Edward 英国政治领袖 12—333c
奥康纳 O'Connor, John Joseph Cardinal 英国政治领袖 12—333e
奥康纳 O'Connor, (Mary) Flannery 美国作家 12—333c
奥康纳 O'Connor, Rory (high king of Ireland) 爱尔兰国王 12—333f
奥康纳 O'Conor, Rory (high king of Ireland) 爱尔兰国王 12—334a
奥康纳 O'Connor, Sandra Day 美国最高法院大法官 12—333f
奥康内尔 O'Connell, Daniel 爱尔兰领袖 12—333a
奥康托 Oconto 美国城市 12—334a
奥柯里 O'Curry, Eugene 爱尔兰学者 12—335c
奥科兰帕迪乌斯 Oecolampadius, John 德国人文学家 12—341c
奥科诺麦斯 Oeconomus 瑞士宗教改革家 12—341d
奥科塔尔 Ocotal 尼加拉瓜城市 12—334a
奥科特兰 Ocotlán 墨西哥城市 12—334c
奥科特佩克 Ocotepeque (city, Honduras) 洪都拉斯城市 12—334a
奥科伊河 Ocoee River 美国河流 12—332f
奥克贝 Oak Bay 加拿大自治镇 12—314f
奥克弗诺基沼泽 Okefenokee Swamp 美国自然保护区 12—359a
奥克汉普顿 Okehampton 英格兰城镇 12—359b
奥克兰 Auckland 新西兰行政区 2—44b
奥克兰 Auckland 新西兰城市 2—44c
奥克兰 Oakland 美国城市 12—315b
奥克兰伯爵 Auckland, George Eden, Earl of, 2nd Baron Auckland, 2nd Baron Auckland of Auckland, Baron Eden of Norwood 英国驻印度总督 2—44d
奥克兰群岛 Auckland Islands 新西兰群岛 2—44e
奥克勒里 O'Clery, Michael 爱尔兰编年史家 12—332f
奥克里卡 Okrika 尼日利亚城镇 12—363c
奥克利 Oakley, Kenneth (Page) 英国人类学家 12—315d
奥克莉 Oakley, Annie 美国神枪手 12—315c
奥克马尔吉 Okmulgee 美国城市 12—363a
奥克尼和设得兰公爵 Orkney and Shetland, James Hepburn, Duke of 苏格兰贵族 12—463a
奥克尼群岛 Orkney Islands 苏格兰群岛 12—463a
奥克帕克 Oak Park 美国村庄 12—315a
奥克斯 Ochs, Adolph Simon 美国报业主 12—332a
奥克斯 Ochs, Peter 瑞士革命者 12—332b
奥克斯利 Oxley, John (Joseph William Molesworth) 英国探险家 12—522c
奥克斯纳德 Oxnard 美国城市 12—522d
奥克苏斯河 Oxus River (Asia) 亚洲河流 12—522e
奥克维尔 Oakville 加拿大自治镇 12—315e
奥克西坦语 Occitan language 法国南部语言 12—326a
奥克辛本 Ochsenbein, (Johann) Ulrich 瑞士政治家 12—332c
奥克亚 Aakjẽr, Jeppe 丹麦诗人、小说家 1—1f
奥库利 Oculi, Okello 乌干达作家 12—335c
奥库斯 Ochus 波斯国王 12—332c
奥奎尔山脉 Oquirrh Mountains 美国山脉 12—440a
奥拉迪亚 Oradea 罗马尼亚城市 12—440c
奥拉夫 Olaf 统治者之名 12—364b
奥拉夫 Olaf 瑞典国王 12—365a
奥拉夫(舍特科农) Olof Skötkonung 瑞典国王 12—379a
奥拉夫二世 Olaf II Haraldsson 挪威国王 12—364d
奥拉夫·格思弗里思松 Olaf Guthfrithson 都柏林国王 12—364b
奥拉夫三世 Olaf III Haakonsson 丹麦-挪威国王 12—364b
奥拉夫三世 Olaf III Haraldsson 丹麦-挪威国王 12—364e
奥拉夫四世 Olaf IV Haakonsson 丹麦-挪威国王 12—364e
奥拉夫四世 Olaf (IV) Magnusson 挪威国王 12—364e
奥拉夫松 Ólafsson, Eggert 冰岛诗人 12—365b
奥拉夫五世 Olaf V 挪威国王 12—364f
奥拉夫·西特里克松 Olaf Sihtricson 都柏林国王 12—364c
奥拉夫一世 Olaf I Tryggvason 挪威国王 12—364c
奥拉涅斯塔德 Oranjestad 荷属阿鲁巴岛港市 12—443f
奥拉宁鲍姆 Oranienbaum (Russia) 俄罗斯城镇 12—443e
奥拉帕 Orapa 博茨瓦纳城镇 12—444a
奥拉萨 Oglasa (Italy) 意大利岛屿 12—346e
奥拉托利会会士 Oratorian 天主教 12—444b
奥拉西 Olathe 美国城市 12—365d
奥莱龙岛 Oléron Island 法国岛屿 12—372e
奥莱希尼茨基 Oleśnicki, Zbigniew 波兰政治家 12—372f
奥赖 Ory, Kid 美国音乐家 12—477e
奥赖比 Oraibi 美国村庄 12—440e
奥兰 Oran 阿尔及利亚城市 12—441b
奥兰多 Orlando 美国城市 12—463b
奥兰多 Orlando, Vittorio Emanuele 意大利政治人物 12—463c
奥兰加巴德 Aurangābād 印度城镇 2—57c
奥兰妮 Arányi, Jelly d' 匈牙利小提琴家 1—439f
奥兰群岛 Åland Islands 芬兰群岛 1—166c
奥兰文化期工艺 Oranian industry 考古学 12—443e
奥兰治 Orange 美国加利福尼亚州城市 12—441e
奥兰治 Orange 美国康涅狄格州城镇 12—441e
奥兰治 Orange 美国新泽西州城市 12—441e
奥兰治 Orange 美国得克萨斯州城市 12—441e
奥兰治堡 Orangeburg 美国城市 12—443a

奥兰治党 Orange Order 爱尔兰政党 12—443e
奥兰治河 Orange River 非洲河流 12—443f
奥兰治蒙特 Oranjemund 纳米比亚城镇 12—443e
奥兰治人 Orangemen 爱尔兰政党 12—443b
奥兰治山脉 Orange Range (New Guinea) 新几内亚山脉 12—443f
奥兰治王室 Orange, HOUSE OF 欧洲贵族世家 12—443b
奥兰治沃克 Orange Walk 伯利兹城镇 12—443a
奥兰治自由邦 Orange Free State 南非省份 12—443d
奥朗日 Orange 法国城镇 12—441c
奥朗日会议 Orange, councils of 基督教 12—443c
奥朗则布 Aurangzeb 印度皇帝 2—57d
奥勒福斯玻璃 Orrefors glass 工艺品 12—471c
奥勒格宰 Orakzai 巴基斯坦少数民族特区 12—440f
奥勒利安 Aurelian 罗马皇帝 2—58b
奥勒利安壁垒 Aurelian Wall 罗马帝国壁垒 2—58c
奥勒利乌斯 Aurelius, Lucius Aelius 罗马皇帝 2—58d
奥勒姆 Orem 美国城市 12—456a
奥勒松 Ålesund 挪威渔港 1—198b
奥雷里伯爵(第一) Orrery, Roger Boyle, 1st Earl of, LORD BOYLE, BARON OF BROGHILL 爱尔兰贵族、作家 12—471e
奥雷利亚纳 Orellana, Francisco de 西班牙探险家 12—455f
奥雷姆 Oresme, Nicholas 法国学者、主教 12—456c
奥雷奇 Orage, Alfred Richard 英国社会思想家 12—440e
奥雷山脉 Ore Mountains 欧洲山脉 12—452a
奥雷斯 Aurès 阿尔及利亚山脉 2—58d
奥雷耶 Oreiller, Henri 法国运动员 12—455f
奥里 Orry, Jean 法国经济学家 12—471e
奥里奥尔 Auriol, Vincent 法兰西总统 2—59e
奥里克 Auric, Georges 法国作曲家 2—58f
奥里利亚 Orillia 加拿大城市 12—461b
奥里诺科河 Orinoco River 南美洲河流 12—461c
奥里萨 Orissa 印度邦名 12—462b
奥里萨巴 Orizaba 墨西哥城市 12—462e
奥里萨巴火山 Orizaba, Pico de (Mexico) 墨西哥火山 12—462f
奥里斯 aureus 古罗马货币单位 2—58e
奥里斯卡尼战役 Oriskany, Battle of 美国独立战争 12—462a
奥里斯塔诺 Oristano 意大利城镇 12—462e
奥里韦拉 Orihuela 西班牙城镇 12—461b
奥里维 Oribe, Manuel Ceferino 乌拉圭总统 12—459d
奥里雅语 Oṛiyā language 印度语言 12—462e
奥利埃 Olier, Jean-Jacques 天主教司铎 12—373c
奥利安 Olean 美国城市 12—372a
奥利安 Orion 希腊神话人物 12—461f
奥利布里乌斯 Olybrius 西罗马皇帝 12—379f
奥利茨基 Olitski, Jules 美国画家 12—375a
奥利芬特 Oliphant, Laurence 英国作家 12—374e
奥利芬特 Oliphant, Margaret Oliphant 苏格兰作家 12—374f
奥利弗 Oliver, Isaac 法国画家 12—375e
奥利弗 Oliver, King 美国音乐家 12—375f
奥利弗 Olivier, Laurence (Kerr), BARON OLIVIER OF BRIGHTON 法国画家 12—376b
奥利弗 Oliver, Sy 美国音乐家 12—375f
奥利金 Origen 希腊神学家 12—460e
奥利斯 Aulis 古希腊城镇 2—56c
奥利塔 Olita (Lithuania) 立陶宛城市 12—375a
奥利瓦雷斯 Olivares, Gaspar de Guzmán y Pimental, conde-duque de (count-duke of), DUQUE DE SANLÚCAR DE BARRAMEDA 西班牙首相 12—375a
奥利韦蒂公司 Olivetti & C.SpA 意大利公司 12—376a
奥利维耶 Ollivier, Émile 法国政治家 12—377b
奥利沃斯 Olivos 阿根廷城市 12—376f
奥良 Olhão 葡萄牙城镇 12—373b
奥辽沙 Olesha, Yury Karlovich 俄罗斯作家 12—372f
奥廖尔 Oryol 俄罗斯州名 12—477f
奥廖尔 Oryol 俄罗斯城市 12—477f
奥列格 Oleg 诺夫哥罗德统治者 12—372c
奥列霍沃-祖耶沃 Orekhovo-Zuyevo 俄罗斯城市 12—455f
奥列内奥克河 Olenyok River 俄罗斯河流 12—372e
奥列宁 Olenin, Boris 苏联政治家 12—372e
奥列斯库 aurresku 法国民间舞蹈 2—60b
奥林 Ohlin, Bertil (Gotthard) 瑞典经济学家 12—353b
奥林波堡 Fuerte Olimpo 巴拉圭城市 6—510e
奥林波斯山 Olympus, Mount 希腊山脉 12—411d
奥林达 Olinda 巴西城市 12—374c
奥林匹克国家公园 Olympic National Park 美国公园 12—411b
奥林匹克航空公司 Olympic Airways 希腊公司 12—380f
奥林匹克山 Olympic Mountains 美国山脉 12—411a
奥林匹克运动会 Olympic Games 体育 12—380f
奥林匹欧 Olympio, Sylvanus 多哥总统 12—411c
奥林匹斯火山 Olympus Mons 火星火山 12—411e
奥林匹亚 Olympia 古代宗教圣地 12—380a
奥林匹亚 Olympia 美国城市 12—380d
奥林匹娅斯 Olympias 马其顿王后 12—380e
奥林索斯 Olynthus 希腊古城 12—411e
奥龙 Oron 尼日利亚城镇 12—469d
奥龙特斯河 Orontes River 亚洲河流 12—469e
奥隆阿波 Olongapo 菲律宾城市 12—379b
奥隆奇人 Aurunci 古意大利部落 2—60c
奥卢 Oulu 芬兰省份 12—506f
奥卢 Oulu 芬兰城市 12—506f
奥鲁罗 Oruro 玻利维亚城市 12—476f
奥鲁斯 Aulus 古罗马人名 2—56f
奥伦堡 Orenburg 俄罗斯州名 12—456a
奥伦堡 Orenburg 俄罗斯城市 12—456b
奥伦吉 Aorangi 新西兰行政区 1—404a
奥伦尼克阶 Olenekian Stage 地质学 12—372c
奥伦塞 Orense 西班牙省份 12—456b
奥伦塞 Orense 西班牙城市 12—456b
奥罗宾多 Aurobindo, Śrī 印度教先知 2—59f
奥罗德斯二世 Orodes II 安息国王 12—469c
奥罗基达 Oroquieta 菲律宾城市 12—470b
奥罗拉 Aurora 美国科罗拉多州城市 2—60a
奥罗拉 Aurora 美国伊利诺伊州城市 2—60a
奥罗拉 Aurora (Roman mythology) 古罗马神话人物 2—60a
奥罗拉岛 Aurora (Vanuatu) 瓦努阿图岛屿 2—60a
奥罗莫人 Oromo 埃塞俄比亚民族 12—469d
奥罗诺 Orono 美国城镇 12—469e
奥罗维尔水坝 Oroville Dam 美国水坝 12—470b
奥罗修斯 Orosius, Paulus 西班牙神学家 12—470b
奥罗亚 Oroya (Peru) 秘鲁城市 12—470c
奥罗兹科 Orozco, José Clemente 墨西哥画家 12—470c
奥洛莫乌茨 Olomouc 捷克城市 12—379a
奥洛斯管 aulos 古希腊乐器 2—56e
奥马 Omagh 北爱尔兰区名 12—412a
奥马 Omagh 北爱尔兰城镇 12—412a
奥马奥尼 O'Mahony, John 爱尔兰民族主义者 12—412c
奥马哈 Omaha 美国城市 12—412c
奥马哈人 Omaha 北美印第安民族 12—412b
奥马利 O'Malley, Walter (Francis) 美国律师 12—412d
奥马鲁 Oamaru 新西兰城市 12—315e
奥曼 Oman, John Wood 英格兰神学家 12—413e
奥曼 Aumann, Robert J. 以色列数学家 2—57a
奥曼迪 Ormandy, Eugene 美国指挥家 12—466e
奥梅蒂库特利神 Ometecuhtli 阿兹特克神名 12—414f
奥梅格纳 Omegna, Roberto 意大利摄影师 12—414e
奥梅特佩岛 Ometepe Island 尼加拉瓜岛屿 12—415a

奥蒙德比奇 Ormond Beach 美国城市 12—466f
奥蒙德伯爵(第八) Ormonde, Piers Butler, 8th earl of 爱尔兰贵族 12—466f
奥蒙德伯爵(第十) Ormonde, Thomas Butler, 10th earl of 爱尔兰贵族 12—467a
奥蒙德伯爵(第十二)和公爵(第一) Ormonde, James Butler, 12th earl and 1st duke of 爱尔兰贵族 12—467a
奥蒙德伯爵和公爵 Ormonde, EARLS AND DUKES OF 爱尔兰贵族 12—466f
奥蒙德公爵(第二) Ormonde, James Butler, 2nd duke of 爱尔兰军人 12—467b
奥秘修行 mysticism 宗教 11—530a
奥莫化石遗存 Omo remains 考古学 12—415b
奥莫托索 Omotoso, Kole 尼日利亚作家 12—415c
奥姆 Orm 英国作家 12—466d
奥姆伯 Ombre 牌戏 12—414a
奥姆格尔吉 Omkarji (India) 印度朝圣中心 12—415a
奥姆斯比-戈尔 Ormsby-Gore, William George Arthur, 4TH BARON HARLECH 英国政治家 12—467c
奥姆斯特德 Olmsted, Frederick Law 美国建筑师 12—378d
奥姆真理教 AUM Shinrikyo 日本佛教教派 2—56f
奥纳人 Ona 南美印第安民族 12—416a
奥纳西斯 Onassis, Aristotle (Socrates) 希腊商人 12—416c
奥纳西斯 Onassis, Jacqueline Kennedy 美国第一夫人 12—416d
奥奈达 Oneida 美国城市 12—418d
奥奈达社团 Oneida Community 美国宗教团体 12—418d
奥内达人 Oneida 北美印第安民族 12—418c
奥内蒂 Onetti, Juan Carlos 乌拉圭小说家 12—421b
奥内库尔 Honnecourt, Villard de 法国建筑师 8—159e
奥内什蒂 Oneşti 罗马尼亚城市 12—421b
奥尼昂塔 Oneonta 美国城市 12—421a
奥尼查 Onitsha 尼日利亚城镇 12—421f
奥尼查市场文学 Onitsha market literature 尼日利亚文学 12—422b
奥尼尔 O'Neill, Conn 爱尔兰领袖 12—418e
奥尼尔 O'Neill, Daniel 爱尔兰军人 12—418e
奥尼尔 O'Neill, Eugene (Gladstone) 美国戏剧家 12—418f
奥尼尔 O'Neill, Gerard K(itchen) 美国物理学家 12—420b
奥尼尔 O'Neill, Hugh 爱尔兰反叛者 12—420c
奥尼尔 O'Neill, Hugh 爱尔兰军人 12—420c
奥尼尔 O'Neill, James 美国演员 12—420c
奥尼尔 O'Neill, John 美国军人 12—420d
奥尼尔 O'Neill, Owen Roe 爱尔兰反英领袖 12—420d
奥尼尔 O'Neill, Sir Phelim 爱尔兰反英领袖 12—420e
奥尼尔 O'Neill, Rose Cecil 美国插图画家 12—420e
奥尼尔 O'Neill, Shane 爱尔兰爱国者 12—420f
奥尼尔 O'Neal, Shaquille 爱尔兰领袖 12—418a
奥尼尔 O'Neill, Turlough Luineach 爱尔兰贵族 12—421a
奥尼亚 Oña, Pedro de 智利诗人 12—416a
奥尼亚特 Oñate, Juan de 西班牙殖民者 12—416d
奥涅格 Honegger, Arthur 法国作曲家 8—152f
奥涅加湖 Onega, Lake 俄罗斯湖泊 12—418b
奥农达加人 Onondaga 北美印第安民族 12—422f
奥努 Onu (ancient city) 埃及古城 12—423e
奥努亚兰 Ó Nuallain, Brian 爱尔兰作家 12—314c
奥帕蒂亚 Opatija 克罗地亚城镇 12—426e
奥帕林斯基 Opaliński, Krzysztof 波兰作家 12—426b
奥帕瓦 Opava 捷克城市 12—426f
奥佩 Opie, Eugene Lindsay 美国病理学家 12—431d
奥佩 Opie, John 英国画家 12—431e
奥佩尔 Opel, Fritz von 德国工业家 12—426f
奥佩特节 Opet 古埃及节日 12—430c
奥彭 Orpen, Sir William 英国画家 12—470d
奥皮茨 Opitz (von Boberfeld), Martin 德国诗人 12—431f
奥皮克 Öpik, Ernest Julius 爱沙尼亚天文学家 12—431e
奥皮塔尔 Hôpital, Michel de L' 法国政治家 8—169d
奥珀卢瑟斯 Opelousas 美国城市 12—427b
奥珀伦 Oppeln (Poland) 波兰城市 12—433f
奥珀斯 Opus 古希腊城市 12—438e
奥普蒂克 Optic, Oliver 美国作家 12—435a
奥普兰 Oppland 挪威郡名 12—434d
奥普艺术 Op art 几何化抽象艺术 12—425b
奥普战争 Austro-Prussian War (1866) 欧洲历史 2—72d
奥齐尔花样 ozier pattern 瓷器工艺 12—528e
奥奇瓦龙戈 Otjiwarongo 纳米比亚城镇 12—498a
奥乔 Outjo 纳米比亚城镇 12—509a
奥乔亚 Ochoa, Ellen 美国工程师 12—331d
奥乔亚 Ochoa, Severo 美国生物学家 12—331e
奥切 Orczy, Baroness Emmuska 英国小说家 12—448a
奥热罗 Augereau, Pierre-François-Charles, DUKE (duc) DE CASTIGLIONE 法国陆军军官 2—47e
奥热什科娃 Orzeszkowa, Eliza 波兰小说家 12—478b
奥日埃 Augier, (Guillaume-Victor) Émile 法国戏剧家 2—47f
奥瑞纳文化 Aurignacian culture 欧洲史前工艺 2—59b
奥瑞尼 Aurigny (Channel Islands) 英国岛屿 2—59d
《奥瑞斯忒亚》 Oresteia 古希腊悲剧 12—456d
奥萨 Osa 俄罗斯城市 12—478d
奥萨 Ossa 希腊山峰 12—487e
奥萨半岛 Osa Peninsula 哥斯达黎加半岛 12—478d
奥萨格人 Osage 北美印第安民族 12—478d
奥萨山 Ossa, Mount 澳大利亚山峰 12—487e
奥萨斯库 Osasco 巴西城市 12—481f
奥萨湾 Osa Gulf (Pacific Ocean) 哥斯达黎加海湾 12—478d
奥萨沃托米 Osawatomie 美国城市 12—481f
奥塞克利斯 Auseklis 波罗的海地区宗教神祇 2—60e
奥塞奇橙 Osage orange (*Maclura pomifera*) 木本植物 12—478f
奥塞奇河 Osage River 美国河流 12—479a
奥塞奇统 Osagian Series 地质学 12—479a
奥塞梯语 Ossetic language 东部伊朗语言 12—487f
奥塞·图图 Osei Tutu 阿散蒂国王 12—483f
奥赛 Houssay, Bernardo Alberto 阿根廷生理学家 8—196c
奥三棉示 Ozamis 菲律宾城市 12—528a
奥森 Osun 尼日利亚州名 12—495b
奥森 Aasen, Ivar (Andreas) 挪威语言学家 1—3d
奥沙利文 O'Sullivan, Mary Kenney 美国劳工领袖 12—494f
奥沙利文 O'Sullivan, Timothy H. 美国摄影家 12—495a
奥沙瓦 Oshawa 加拿大城市 12—484a
奥绍博 Oshogbo 尼日利亚城镇 12—484d
奥什 Osh 吉尔吉斯斯坦城市 12—484a
奥什 Hoche, (Louis-)Lazare 法国军人 8—112b
奥什科什 Oshkosh 美国城市 12—484d
奥氏体 austenite 冶金学 2—62c
奥属尼德兰 Austrian Netherlands 低地国家省份 2—71c
奥斯 Oss 荷兰城市 12—487d
奥斯本 Osborne, Dorothy, LADY TEMPLE 英国贵妇人 12—482b
奥斯本 Osborn, Henry Fairfield 英国贵妇人 12—482a
奥斯本 Osborne, John 英国剧作家 12—482c
奥斯本 Osborne, Thomas Mott 美国刑罚学家 12—482d
奥斯本男爵 Osborne, Sir Thomas, 2ND BARONET 英国政治家 12—482d
奥斯蒂亚 Ostia 意大利古城 12—492f
奥斯丁(坎特伯雷的),圣 Austin OF CANTERBURY, SAINT 坎特伯雷大主教 2—62f
奥斯丁会 Austin 天主教修会 2—62d
奥斯格里姆松 Ásgrímsson, Eysteinn 冰岛修士 1—544a
奥斯加克人 Ostyak (people) 西伯利亚西部民族 12—494f
奥斯佳克-沃古尔斯克 Ostyako-Vogulsk (Russia) 俄罗斯城市 12—494f

奥斯捷尔曼 Osterman, Andrey Ivanovich, Graf 俄国政治家 12—492c
奥斯卡 Oscar 瑞典国王 12—482f
奥斯卡二世 Oscar II 瑞典-挪威国王 12—483a
奥斯卡卢萨 Oskaloosa 美国城市 12—485a
奥斯卡一世 Oscar I 瑞典-挪威国王 12—482f
奥斯坎-翁布里亚诸语言 Osco-Umbrian languages 印欧语系意大利语族语言 12—483e
奥斯坎语 Oscan language 意大利语言 12—482f
奥斯兰德 Auslander, Joseph 美国小说家、抒情诗人 2—60f
奥斯勒 Osler, Sir William 加拿大医学教育家 12—485b
奥斯勒-朗迪-韦伯三氏病 Osler-Rendu-Weber disease 疾病 12—485c
奥斯林纳 Aušrinė (Baltic deity) 波罗的海地区宗教神祇 2—61a
奥斯陆 Oslo 挪威首都 12—485c
奥斯陆峡湾 Oslo Fjord 挪威海湾 12—485e
奥斯罗伊那 Osroëne 美索不达米亚古国 12—487d
奥斯马纳巴德 Osmānābād 印度城镇 12—486c
奥斯曼 Osman 奥斯曼苏丹之名 12—485e
奥斯曼 Haussmann, Georges-Eugène, Baron 法国官员 7—514b
奥斯曼·阿里 Osman Ali 印度土王 12—486a
奥斯曼·阿里汗 Usmān ʿAlī Khān, Mīr 印度统治者 17—423c
奥斯曼·丹·弗迪奥 Usman dan Fodio 富拉尼神秘主义者、哲学家 17—423c
奥斯曼帝国与土耳其史 Ottoman Empire and Turkey, history of the 土耳其历史 12—502d
奥斯曼·丁加 Osman Dinga 苏丹马赫迪派领袖 12—486b
奥斯曼二世 Osman II 奥斯曼苏丹 12—485f
奥斯曼宫廷地毯 Ottoman court carpet 工艺品 12—502d
奥斯曼·努里帕夏 Osman Nuri Paşa 奥斯曼军人 12—486b
奥斯曼一世 Osman I 土库曼公国统治者 12—485e
奥斯曼·伊本·阿凡 ʿUthmān ibn ʿAffān 穆斯林哈里发 17—430e
奥斯梅纳 Osmeña, Sergio 菲律宾总统 12—486c
奥斯蒙德 Osmund of Salisbury, Saint 索尔兹伯里主教 12—486f
奥斯纳布吕克 Osnabrück 德国城市 12—487b
奥斯皮塔莱特-德略夫雷加特 Hospitalet de Llobregat 西班牙城市 8—189d
奥斯塔 Aosta 意大利城市 1—404d
奥斯塔德 Ostade, Adriaen van 荷兰画家 12—488c
奥斯塔德 Ostade, Isack van 荷兰画家 12—488d
奥斯泰耶 Ostaijen, Paul van 比利时作家 12—488e
奥斯坦德 Ostend 比利时城市 12—490a
奥斯坦德公司 Ostend Company 奥地利公司 12—490b
《奥斯坦德宣言》 Ostend Manifesto 美国历史 12—490b
奥斯特 oersted 计量单位 12—342e
奥斯特 Ørsted, Hans Christian 丹麦物理学家 12—472d
奥斯特拉西亚 Austrasia 欧洲法兰克王国 2—69e
奥斯特勒 Oastler, Richard 英国工业改革家 12—316a
奥斯特里霍姆 Ostrihom (Hungary) 匈牙利城镇 12—494a
奥斯特利茨战役 Austerlitz, Battle of 欧洲历史 2—62d
奥斯特罗德 Osterode 德国城市 12—492d
奥斯特罗果尔斯基 Ostrogorsky, Moisey (Yakovlevich) 俄国政治学家 12—494a
奥斯特罗维茨-圣十字山 Ostrowiec świętokrzyski 波兰城镇 12—494d
奥斯特罗文卡 Ostrołęka 原波兰省份 12—494b
奥斯特罗文卡 Ostrołęka 波兰城市 12—494b
奥斯特洛夫斯基 Ostrovsky, Aleksandr Nikolayevich 俄国戏剧家 12—494c
奥斯特瓦尔德 Ostwald, Wilhelm 德国化学家 12—494d
奥斯特瓦尔德 Ostwald, Wolfgang 德国化学家 12—494f
奥斯汀 Austin 美国明尼苏达州城市 2—62d
奥斯汀 Austin 美国得克萨斯州城市 2—62e
奥斯汀 Austin, Alfred 英国桂冠诗人 2—63a
奥斯汀 Austin, Herbert Austin, Baron 英国奥斯汀公司董事长 2—63a
奥斯汀 Austen, Jane 英国作家 2—61b
奥斯汀 Austin, John 英国法学家 2—63a
奥斯汀 Austin, John Langshaw 英国哲学家 2—63c
奥斯汀 Austin, Louis Winslow 美国物理学家 2—63c
奥斯汀 Austin, Mary 美国小说家 2—63d
奥斯汀 Austin, Stephen 美国拓殖者 2—63e
奥斯托斯 Hostos, Eugenio María de 波多黎各教育家、作家 8—189e
奥斯瓦德 Oswald, Lee Harvey 美国匪徒 12—495d
奥斯瓦尔德(约克的),圣 Oswald of York, Saint 英格兰大主教 12—495d
奥斯威 Oswiu 诺森伯里亚国王 12—496b
奥斯威戈 Oswego 美国港市 12—495e
奥斯威辛 Auschwitz 波兰地名(集中营) 2—60d
奥斯威辛 Oświęcim 波兰城市 12—496a
奥斯沃尔德,圣 Oswald, Saint 盎格鲁-撒克逊国王 12—495c
奥斯沃斯特里 Oswestry 英格兰城镇 12—495f
奥苏纳 Osuna 西班牙城镇 12—495c
奥索尔诺 Osorno 智利城市 12—487b
奥索里 Ossory 爱尔兰古王国 12—488c
奥索尼乌斯 Ausonius, Decimus Magnus 拉丁诗人 2—60f
奥塔戈 Otago 新西兰行政区 12—496c
奥塔戈北部沿海 Coastal-North Otago 新西兰地方行政区 4—312f
奥塔姆瓦 Ottumwa 美国城市 12—503d
奥塔瓦洛 Otavalo 厄瓜多尔城镇 12—496e
奥塔维亚诺 Ottaviano 教皇 12—499a
奥塔维亚诺 Ottaviano de Monticello (antipope) 敌对教皇 12—499a
奥太 Horta, Victor, Baron 比利时建筑师 8—185f
奥唐奈 O'Donnell, Calvagh 爱尔兰领主 12—339a
奥唐奈 O'Donnell, Hugh 爱尔兰领主 12—339b
奥唐奈 O'Donnell, Hugh Roe 爱尔兰国王 12—339b
奥唐奈 O'Donnell, Leopoldo duque (duke) de Tetuán 西班牙首相 12—339b
奥唐奈 O'Donnell, Manus 爱尔兰领主 12—339c
奥唐奈 O'Donnell, Sir Niall Garve 爱尔兰部族首领 12—339d
奥唐奈 O'Donnell, Rory 爱尔兰领主 12—339d
奥陶纪 Ordovician Period 地质学 12—450f
奥特弗里德 Otfrid 日耳曼诗人 12—496e
奥特弗耶 Hautefeuille, Jean de 法国物理学家 7—515d
奥特金尼 Otetiani (Seneca Indian) 印第安人领袖 12—496e
奥特考尔特 Outcault, Richard Felton 美国漫画家 12—508d
奥特兰 Autlán 墨西哥城市 2—73c
奥特兰特 Otlet, Paul (-Marie-Ghislain) 比利时律师、目录学家 12—498a
奥特朗托 Otranto 意大利城镇 12—498e
奥特雷德 Oughtred, William 英国数学家 12—506c
奥特利乌斯 Ortelius, Abraham 比利时地图绘制家 12—473b
奥特芒 Hotman, François 法国法理学家 8—191a
奥特泰尔 Hotteterre, Jacques 法国音乐家 8—191c
奥特韦 Otway, Thomas 英国作家 12—503e
奥特韦勒瓷器 Ottweiler porcelain 工艺品 12—503d
奥滕多弗 Ottendorfer, Anna Sartorius Uhl 美国出版商 12—499e
奥廷加 Odinga, Oginga 肯尼亚副总统 12—338a
奥图尔 O'Toole, Peter 英国演员 12—498d
奥托 Otho 罗马皇帝 12—497a
奥托 Otto 统治者之名 12—500c
奥托 Otto 巴伐利亚国王 12—500d
奥托 Otto 希腊国王 12—501d
奥托 Otto of Freising 德意志主教 12—501e

奥托 Otto, Nikolaus August 德国工程师 12—501f
奥托 Otto, Rudolf 德国哲学家 12—502a
奥托(不伦瑞克的) Otto of Brunswick 神圣罗马帝国皇帝 12—501e
奥托(大帝) Otto the Great 神圣罗马帝国皇帝 12—501f
奥托波尼 Ottoboni, Pietro Vito 教皇 12—502c
奥托二世 Otto II 巴伐利亚公爵 12—500c
奥托二世 Otto II 神圣罗马帝国皇帝 12—501e
奥托二世 Otto II 巴伐利亚公爵 12—500f
奥托吕科斯 Autolycus 希腊神话人物 2—74e
奥托-曼格诸语言 Oto-Manguean languages 美洲印第安语言 12—498b
奥托米人 Otomí 中美印第安人 12—498d
奥托人 Oto 北美印第安人 12—498b
奥托三世 Otto III 神圣罗马帝国皇帝 12—501a
奥托四世 Otto IV 神圣罗马帝国皇帝 12—501b
奥托一世 Otto I 神圣罗马帝国皇帝 12—500d
奥托艺术 Ottonian art 艺术 12—503c
奥瓦通纳 Owatonna 美国城市 12—514f
奥万博 Owambo 纳米比亚地区 12—514e
奥万博兰 Ovamboland(Namibia) 纳米比亚地区 12—510c
奥万博人 Ovambo(people) 非洲民族 12—510c
奥万多 Obando, José María 哥伦比亚总统 12—317d
奥万多 Ovando, Nicolás de 哥伦比亚总统 12—510d
奥威尔 Orwell, George 英国作家 12—477c
奥威尔斯 Auwers, (Georg Friedrich Julius) Arthur von 德国天文学家 2—81e
奥威罗坑口 Aouelloul Crater 毛里塔尼亚坑口 1—404f
奥韦尔贝克 Overbeck, Johann Friedrich 德国画家 12—511b
奥韦尔韦格 Overweg, Adolf 德国天文学家 12—512d
奥韦拉米 Overami(king of Benin) 贝宁国王 12—511b
奥韦里 Owerri 尼日利亚城市 12—517a
奥韦里人 Owerri(people) 尼日利亚民族 12—517a
奥韦图姆 Ovetum(Spain) 西班牙城市 12—512d
奥维德 Ovid 罗马诗人 12—512e
奥维多上校镇 Coronel Oviedo 巴拉圭城市 4—518b
奥维耶多 Oviedo 西班牙城市 12—513b
奥文本杜人 Ovimbundu 安哥拉民族 12—513c
奥文顿 Ovington, Mary White 美国民权活动家 12—513d
奥文多 Owendo 加蓬港口 12—516e
奥翁拉姆文 Ovonramwen 贝宁国王 12—513f
奥沃 Owo 尼日利亚城镇 12—518c
奥西埃茨基 Ossietzky, Carl von 德国记者 12—488b
奥西安德尔 Osiander, Andreas 德意志神学家 12—484e
奥西奥拉 Osceola 美国城市 12—483b
奥西奥拉 Osceola 印第安人领袖 12—483c
奥西宁 Ossining 美国村庄 12—488b
奥西片科 Osipenko(Ukraine) 乌克兰城市 12—484f
奥西耶克 Osijek 克罗地亚城镇 12—484e
奥希金斯 O'Higgins, Kevin Christopher 爱尔兰政治家 12—349d
奥肖内西 O'Shaughnessy, Arthur 英国诗人 12—484a
奥谢夫妇 O'Shea, William Henry; and O'Shea, Katharine 爱尔兰民族主义者 12—484b
奥谢罗夫 Osheroff, Douglas D. 美国物理学家 12—484c
奥辛尼基 Osinniki 俄罗斯城市 12—484e
奥匈帝国 Austria-Hungary 欧洲历史 2—71b
《奥匈协约》 Ausgleich 奥匈帝国历史 2—60e
奥亚波基河 Oiapoque, Rio(South America) 美洲河流 12—354a
奥亚波克河 Oyapock River 美洲河流 12—525f
奥耶姆 Oyem 加蓬城镇 12—525f
奥耶斯基氏病 Aujeszky's disease 牛和猪的疾病 2—55f
奥伊金斯 O'Higgins 智利区名 12—349a
奥伊金斯 O'Higgins, Bernardo 智利国家元首 12—349b
奥伊金斯将军区 Libertador General Bernardo O'Higgins(Chile) 智利地区 10—76c
奥伊金斯领地 O'Higgins, Tierra de(Antarctica) 南极半岛的别名 12—349e
奥伊金斯领地 Tierra de O'Higgins (British Antarctic Territory) 英国南极领地 17—88f
奥伊考 Ajka 匈牙利城镇 1—151c
奥伊勒-凯尔平 Euler-Chelpin, Hans (Karl August Simon) von 瑞典生物化学家 6—160e
奥伊勒-凯尔平 Euler(-Chelpin), Ulf (Svante) von 瑞典生物化学家 6—160c
奥伊伦堡 Eulenburg, Botho (Wend August), Graf zu 普鲁士政治家 6—159d
奥伊伦堡 Eulenburg, Philipp, Fürst zu(prince of) 德国外交家 6—159e
奥伊罗特 Oyrot(Russia) 俄罗斯行政区域 12—526e
奥伊彭和马尔梅迪 Eupen-et-Malmédy 比利时地区 6—162a
奥伊斯特贝 Oyster Bay 美国城镇 12—527a
奥伊斯特拉赫 Oistrakh, David 苏联小提琴家 12—356c
奥伊斯特拉赫 Oistrakh, Igor 俄罗斯小提琴家 12—356c
奥伊廷 Eutin 德国城镇 6—176f
奥义书 Upanishad 印度宗教著作 17—403e
奥羽山脉 Ōu Mountains 日本山脉 12—504a
奥约 Oyo 尼日利亚州名 12—525f
奥约 Oyo 尼日利亚城镇 12—526b
奥约帝国 Oyo empire 非洲历史 12—526b
奥约诺 Oyono, Ferdinand Léopold 喀麦隆政治家 12—526c
奥约诺-姆比亚 Oyono-Mbia, Guillaume 喀麦隆作家 12—526d
奥扎克牙形石型 ozarkodiniform 古生物学 12—528b
奥扎纳姆 Ozanam, Antoine Frédéric 法国历史学家 12—528a
奥朱古 Ojukwu, (Chukwuemeka) Odumegwu 尼日利亚政治家 12—357a
奥兹玛计划 Ozma, Project 空间探测 12—528f
奥祖 Aozou 乍得城镇 1—404f
奥佐卢阿 Ozolua 贝宁国王 12—529a
澳北区 Northern Territory 澳大利亚自治领地 12—263d
澳大利亚 Australia 大洋洲国家 2—63f
澳大利亚阿尔卑斯山 Australian Alps 澳大利亚山脉 2—67a
澳大利亚爱国协会 Australian Patriotic Association(APA) 澳大利亚政治组织 2—68f
《澳大利亚百科全书》 Australian Encyclopaedia, The 澳大利亚全国性百科全书 2—67e
澳大利亚大盆地 Great Australian Basin(Australia) 澳大利亚自然区 7—269d
澳大利亚㹴狗 Australian terrier 狗品种 2—69a
澳大利亚工党 Australian Labor Party(ALP) 澳大利亚政党 2—68a
澳大利亚工会理事会 Australian Council of Trade Unions (ACTU) 澳大利亚劳工组织 2—67d
澳大利亚规则足球 Australian rules football 澳式足球运动 2—68f
澳大利亚国立大学 Australian National University 澳大利亚高等学府 2—68e
澳大利亚国庆日 Australia Day 澳大利亚节日 2—66b
澳大利亚海外领地 Australian External Territories 澳大利亚领地 2—67e
澳大利亚喇叭螺 baler 软体动物 2—168b
澳大利亚民主党 Australian Democrats 澳大利亚政党 2—67d
澳大利亚南极洲领地 Australian Antarctic Territory 澳大利亚领地 2—67a
澳大利亚瓶子草 Australian pitcher plant 草本植物 2—68f
澳大利亚区 Australian region 动物区 2—68f
澳大利亚圣诞树 Australian Christmas tree(species *Nuytsia floribunda*) 木本植物 2—67b
澳大利亚圣公会 Anglican Church of Australia 澳大利亚基督教会 1—346f

澳大利亚首都直辖区 Australian Capital Territory 澳大利亚政区 2—67b
澳大利亚统一党 United Australia Party (UAP) 澳大利亚政党 17—351b
澳大利亚土著民族 Australian Aborigine 大洋洲民族 2—66c
澳大利亚土著语言 Australian Aboriginal languages 大洋洲语言 2—66b
澳大利亚网球公开赛 Australian Open 世界网球赛事 2—68e
澳大利亚文学 Australian literature 文学 2—68b
澳大利亚野狗 dingo(*Canis dingo*) 哺乳动物 5—322e
《澳大利亚殖民政府法案》 Australian Colonies Government Act 英国法令 2—67c
澳大利亚自由党 Liberal Party of Australia 澳大利亚政党 10—73a
澳门 Macau 中国特别行政区 10—328e
澳蠕蛇 bandy-bandy (species *Vermicella annulata*) 爬行动物 2—196d
澳斯特罗尼西亚诸语言 Austronesian languages 南岛语系 2—72d
澳斯特罗亚细亚诸语言 Austroasiatic languages 东南亚语言 2—72a
澳新军团 ANZAC 第一次世界大战军事集团 1—403a
澳新军团日 ANZAC Day 澳大利亚、新西兰节日 1—403a
《澳新美安全条约》 ANZUS Pact 太平洋安全条约 1—403e
澳洲坚果 macadamia (*Macadamia*) 木本植物 10—326b

B

八齿鼠 degu(species *Octodon degus*) 动物 5—212c
八重法 Eightfold Way 物理学 5—568b
八达岭 Badaling 中国北京山峰 2—127c
八打雁 Batangas 菲律宾城市 2—274a
八大山人 Badashanren 中国清代画家 2—127e
八代 Yatsushiro 日本城市 18—429d
八度 octave 音乐 12—334d
八幡滨 Yawatahama 日本城市 18—430b
八幡神 Hachiman 日本神名 7—399a
八股文 baguwen 中国明、清科举文体 2—139c
八卦 bagua 中国筮占用图像 2—139a
八卦教 Baguajiao 中国清代教会 2—139a
八关会 P'alkwanhoe 朝鲜民族节日 12—567a
八国联军 Eight-Power Allied Forces 中国历史 5—567b
八行两韵诗 triolet 文学 17—223f
八行诗 ottava rima 诗歌 12—498f
八行诗体 huitain 法国诗体 8—228f
八号球 eight ball 台球游戏 5—566f
八户 Hachinohe 日本城市 7—399a
八吉祥 aṣṭamaṅgala 印度耆那教仪式用物品 2—2a
八角金盘 fatsia (*Fatsia japonica*) 日本灌木 6—250f
八角目 Illiciales 植物学 8—334d
八巨头联合会 Big Eight Conference 美国大学体育组织 2—467c
八里桥伯爵 Palikao, Charles-Guillaume-Marie-Apollinaire-Antoine Cousin-Montauban, comte de(count of) 法国将军 12—566a
八路军 Eighth Route Army 中国历史 5—568c
八氯 octachlor(insecticide) 化学 12—334c
八面沸石 faujasite 矿物 6—251b
八面体陨铁 octahedrite 陨石 12—334c
八旗制度 Banner system 中国清代满族社会组织形式 2—206e
八人画派 Eight, The 美国画家团体 5—566d
八色鸫 pitta 鸟类 13—330e
八圣王战争 Eight Saints, War of the 基督教史 5—567b
八十郎 Hikotarō (Japanese soldier) 日本军人 8—78e
八十年战争 Eighty Years' War 荷兰历史 5—568e
八十英里滩 Eighty Mile Beach 澳大利亚海滩 5—568e
八思巴 'Phags-pa 中国元代帝师、学者 13—217d
八头会议 Ashta Pradhan 印度首长咨询会议 1—549d
八王子 Hachiōji 日本城市 7—399b
八尾 Yao 日本城市 18—424c
八仙 Ba Xian 中国道教传说人物 2—106c
八旋律型 oktōēchos 音乐 12—363d
八音盒 music box 乐器 11—506b
八音律 octaves, law of 化学 12—334d
八印章 Aṣṭ chāp 一批印地语诗人称号 2—3a
八隅律 octet 化学 12—334e
八月 August 历法 2—49a
八正道 Eightfold Path 佛教教义 5—568b
巴 Ba 中国古代民族 2—105e
巴埃蒂卡山 Baetic Cordillera (Spain) 西班牙山脉 2—133b
巴埃斯 Báez, Buenaventura 多米尼加共和国总统 2—133d
巴埃斯特 Barghest 英国民间传说动物 2—228b
巴奥勒 Baol 西非历史地名 2—211e
巴巴奥约 Babahoyo 厄瓜多尔城市 2—107e
巴巴岛 Babar Island 印度尼西亚岛屿 2—107f
巴巴多斯 Barbados 西印度群岛岛国 2—217e
巴巴多斯海岭 Barbados Ridge 加勒比海海岭 2—218d
巴巴多斯樱桃 Barbados cherry 木本植物 2—218c
巴巴洛拉 Babalola, S(olomon) Adeboye 尼日利亚诗人 2—107e
巴巴塞纳 Barbacena 巴西城市 2—217d
巴巴·塔赫尔 Bābā Ṭāher 波斯早期诗人 2—107d
巴巴-亚加 Baba-Yaga 俄罗斯传说女妖 2—107d
巴班吉达 Babangida, Ibrahim 尼日利亚军事领袖 2—107e
巴贝夫 Babeuf, François-Noël 法国政治宣传家 2—110a
巴贝里 Barberi, Domenico, Blessed 奥秘神学家 2—220b
巴贝奇 Babbage, Charles 英国数学家、发明家 2—108b
巴贝斯虫病 babesiosis 家畜疾病 2—110a
巴贝托斯 Barbeitos, Arlindo (do Carmo Pires) 安哥拉诗人 2—219e
巴奔堡王室 Babenberg, House of 奥地利统治家族 2—109e
巴本 Papen, Franz von 德国政治家、外交家 13—23a
巴本 Barbon, Nicholas 英国经济学家 2—222a
巴本 Barbon, Praise-God 英格兰传教士 2—222b
巴本巴人 Babemba (people) 非洲民族 2—109e
巴本海姆 Pappenheim, Gottfried Heinrich, Count(Graf) zu 德意志军官 13—26b
巴本科 Babenco, Hector 巴西电影导演 2—109e
巴比 Barbie, Klaus 纳粹领导人 2—221c
巴比埃 Barbier, Antoine-Alexandre 法国图书馆学家 2—221d
巴比沟 Baby Yar 乌克兰万人坑 2—111d
巴比利恩 Barbellion, W. N. P. 英国作家 2—219e
巴比伦 Babylon 美索不达米亚古城 2—111e
巴比伦 Babylon 美国城镇 2—112e
巴比伦 Baburen, Dirck van 荷兰画家 2—111c
巴比伦历 Babylonian calendar 美索不达米亚古历 2—113a
巴比伦尼亚 Babylonia 古代文化地区 2—112e
巴比伦囚虏 Babylonian Exile 古犹太历史 2—113b
《巴比伦塔木德》 Babylonian Talmud 犹太教教义汇编 2—113b
巴比塞 Barbusse, Henri 法国小说家 2—222f
巴比氏树属 Barbeya 植物学 2—221a
巴比松画派 Barbizon school 法国画派 2—221f
巴比特 Babbitt, Isaac 美国发明家 2—108d
巴比特 Babbitt, Milton 美国作曲家 2—108e
巴比特合金 babbitt metal 冶金 2—108f
巴比土酸 barbituric acid 有机化合物 2—221f
巴比土酸盐 barbiturate 有机化合物 2—221e
巴比亚山 Babia, Mount 波兰最高山峰之一 2—110b
巴别尔 Babel, Isaak Emmanuilovich 苏联小说家 2—109b
巴别塔 Babel, Tower of 《圣经》传说 2—109c
巴宾顿 Babington, Anthony 英格兰阴谋家 2—110b
巴波 Barbo, Pietro 教皇 2—222a
巴伯 Babergh 英格兰区名 2—109f

巴伯 Barbour, John 苏格兰史诗作者 2—222d
巴伯 Barbour, Philip P(endleton) 美国最高法院大法官 2—222e
巴伯 Barber, Samuel 美国作曲家 2—219f
巴伯顿 Barberton 美国城市 2—220e
巴伯尔 Bābur 印度皇帝 2—111a
巴伯尔图阿普岛 Babelthuap 西太平洋岛屿 2—109d
巴伯拉 Barbera, Joseph (Roland) 美国动画片绘制者 2—220a
巴伯维尔 Barbourville 美国城市 2—222f
巴勃罗·拉赫伦萨市长镇 Mayor Pablo Lagerenza 巴拉圭城镇 11—54c
巴博勒 Bābol 伊朗城市 2—110e
巴布 Bāb, the 伊朗巴布教派创立者 2—107b
巴布迪尔 Boabdil (sultan of Granada) 格拉纳达苏丹 2—554d
巴布教 Bābism 伊朗宗教 2—110d
巴布科克 Babcock, Harold Delos 美国天文学家 2—109a
巴布科克 Babcock, Horace Welcome 美国天文学家 2—109a
巴布科克 Babcock, Stephen Moulton 美国农业化学家 2—109a
巴布里乌斯 Babrius 希腊寓言作者 2—110f
巴布纳 Pābna 孟加拉国城市 12—531a
巴布思 Barbooth 游戏 2—222b
巴布亚 Papua 印度尼西亚省份 13—26e
巴布亚湾 Papua, Gulf of 太平洋海湾 13—27a
巴布亚新几内亚 Papua New Guinea 太平洋岛国 13—27a
巴布亚诸语言 Papuan languages 语言 13—28a
巴布延群岛 Babuyan Islands 菲律宾岛屿 2—111d
巴差提朴 Prajadhipok 暹罗君主 13—483c
巴禅 Bachchan, Amitabh 印度电影演员 2—118a
巴茨 Batz, Jean, baron de 法国王党密谋分子 2—284c
巴茨瓦纳人 Batswana (people) 南部非洲民族 2—280d
巴达格里 Badagry 尼日利亚城镇 2—126e
巴达赫尚 Badakhshān 阿富汗历史地区 2—127c
巴达霍斯 Badajoz 西班牙省份 2—127a
巴达霍斯 Badajoz 西班牙城市 2—127b
巴达加人 Baḍaga 印度民族 2—126e
巴达洛纳 Badalona 西班牙城镇 2—127d
巴达曼 Bardhamān (India) 印度城市 2—226d
巴达米 Bādāmi 印度市镇 2—127d
巴达维亚 Batavia (Indonesia) 雅加达旧称 2—274a
巴达维亚 Batavia 美国城市 2—274a
巴达维亚共和国 Batavian Republic 欧洲历史 2—274b
巴丹半岛 Bataan Peninsula 菲律宾半岛 2—273a
巴丹吉林沙漠 Badain Jaran Desert 中国沙漠 2—126f
巴丹死亡行军 Bataan Death March 第二次世界大战事件 2—273a
巴德尔 Baader, Franz Xaver von 德国神学家 2—106c
巴德尔-迈因霍夫帮 Baader-Meinhof Gang 德国恐怖组织 2—106d
巴德加斯泰因 Badgastein 奥地利城镇 2—129e
巴德克 Baddeck 加拿大行政中心 2—127e
巴德兰兹国家公园 Badlands National Park 美国国家公园 2—130c
巴德明顿 Badminton 英格兰村庄 2—130c
巴德尼伯爵 Badeni, Kasimir Felix, Graf von 奥地利政治家 2—129d
巴德诺赫-斯特拉斯佩 Badenoch and Strathspey 苏格兰区名 2—129d
巴德西岛 Bardsey Island 威尔士小岛 2—226e
巴登 Baden 德国地区 2—127f
巴登 Baden 奥地利疗养地 2—128a
巴登 Baden 瑞士城市 2—128a
巴登-巴登 Baden-Baden 德国城市 2—128b
巴登-鲍威尔男爵(第一) Baden-Powell (of Gilwell), Robert Stephen-son Smyth Baden-Powell, 1st Baron 英国童子军创建人 2—128c
巴登-符腾堡 Baden-Württemberg 德国州名 2—128d
《巴登条约》 Baden, Treaty of (Sept. 7, 1714) 欧洲历史 2—128b
巴蒂 Baty, Gaston 法国剧作家 2—284a
巴蒂卡 Bartica 圭亚那城镇 2—250f
巴蒂克印花法 batik 蜡防印花法 2—279b
巴蒂斯塔 Batista (y Zaldívar), Fulgencio 古巴独裁者 2—279d
巴蒂斯特 Baptiste 法国演员 2—213b
巴蒂希尔 Battishill, Jonathan 英国作曲家 2—282c
巴蒂亚 Bathiat, Arlette-Leonie 法国演员 2—277d
巴丁 Bardeen, John 美国物理学家 2—226b
巴丁斯 Badings, Henk 荷兰作曲家 2—130a
巴东 Padang 印度尼西亚城市 12—538e
巴东高原 Padang Highlands 印度尼西亚高原 12—538e
巴豆油 croton oil 植物油 5—34d
巴都群岛 Batu Islands 印度尼西亚岛屿 2—283f
巴杜勒 Badulla 斯里兰卡城镇 2—131c
巴顿 Barton, Clara 美国红十字会创始人 2—252e
巴顿 Button, Dick 美国滑冰运动员 3—294a
巴顿 Barton, Derek H(arold) R(ichard) 英国化学家 2—252e
巴顿 Barton, Sir Edmund 澳大利亚首任总理 2—253a
巴顿 Barton, Elizabeth 英格兰狂言者 2—253a
巴顿 Barton, Frances 英国女演员 2—253b
巴顿 Patton, George S(mith) 美国陆军将领 13—93b
巴顿 Button, Stephen Decatur 美国建筑师 3—294b
巴顿 Button, Sir Thomas 英国航海家 3—294b
巴顿阶 Bartonian Stage 地质学 2—253b
巴多格里奥 Badoglio, Pietro 意大利军人、政治家 2—130e
巴多维内蒂 Baldovinetti, Alesso 意大利画家 2—165a
巴恩河 Bann, River 北爱尔兰河流 2—206d
巴恩河畔德罗赫德 Droichead na Banna (Northern Ireland) 北爱尔兰城镇 5—426b
巴恩斯 Barnes, Albert C(oombs) 美国发明家 2—235d
巴恩斯 Barnes, Barnabe 英国诗人 2—235e
巴恩斯 Barnes, George Nicoll 英国工党创始人 2—235e
巴恩斯 Barnes, Pancho 美国飞行家 2—235f
巴恩斯 Barnes, Robert 英格兰教士 2—236b
巴恩斯 Barnes, Thomas 英国新闻记者 2—236b
巴恩斯 Barnes, William 英国方言诗人 2—236b
巴恩斯利 Barnsley 英格兰城镇 2—237a
巴恩斯特布尔 Barnstable 美国城镇 2—237a
巴恩斯特珀尔 Barnstaple 英格兰城镇 2—237a
巴尔 Bar 黑山港口 2—213e
巴尔 Bar, François de 法国史料编纂者 2—213f
巴尔 Bahr, Hermann 奥地利小说家、戏剧家 2—142e
巴尔 Ball, Hugo 德国作家 2—172f
巴尔 Bart, Jean 法国私掠船船长 2—248a
巴尔巴拉,圣 Barbara, SAINT 基督教女殉教士 2—218d
巴尔巴雷利 Barbarelli, Giorgio (painter) 意大利画家 2—218e
巴尔巴里 Barbari, Jacopo de' 威尼斯画家 2—218e
巴尔巴罗萨(红胡子) Barbarossa (Redbeard) 柏柏里海盗、舰队司令 2—218e
巴尔贝·多尔维利 Barbey d'Aurevilly, Jules-Amédée 法国小说家 2—220f
巴尔贝里尼 Barberini, Maffeo (pope) 教皇 2—220c
巴尔贝里尼家族 Barberini FAMILY 罗马贵族世家 2—220b
巴尔贝-马尔布瓦侯爵 Barbé-Marbois, François, marquis de 法国政治家 2—219c
巴尔比罗利 Barbirolli, Sir John 英国指挥家 2—221d
巴尔比努斯 Balbinus, Decimus Caelius Calvinus 罗马皇帝 2—162e
巴尔博 Balbo, Cesare, Count (Conte) 皮埃蒙特政论作家 2—162f
巴尔博 Balbo, Italo 意大利法西斯头目 2—163a
巴尔博汀陶器 Barbotine ware 工艺品 2—222d
巴尔博亚 Balboa 巴拿马港口 2—163b
巴尔博扎 Barbosa, Jorge (Vera-Cruz) 非洲诗人 2—222c
巴尔布斯 Balbus, Lucius Cornelius 罗马富豪 2—163d

巴尔德尔 Balder 斯堪的纳维亚神话人物 2—164f
巴尔德佩尼亚斯 Valdepeñas 西班牙城市 17—448c
巴尔德撒纳斯 Bardesanes 叙利亚基督教人物 2—226c
巴尔德斯 Valdés, Alfonso de 西班牙思想家 17—448c
巴尔德斯 Valdés, Juan de 西班牙人文主义者 17—448d
巴尔德斯 Valdés, Juan Meléndez (Spanish poet) 西班牙诗人 17—448d
巴尔德斯·莱亚尔 Valdés Leal, Juan de Nisa 西班牙画家 17—448d
巴尔迪 Bardi, Giovanni, CONTE (count) DI VERNIO 佛罗伦萨音乐家 2—226d
巴尔迪家族 Bardi FAMILY 意大利贵族 2—226d
巴尔迪亚 Bardiya (king of Persia) 波斯国王 2—226e
巴尔的摩 Baltimore 美国城市 2—183c
巴尔的摩 Baltimore, David 美国病毒学家 2—184a
巴尔的摩—俄亥俄铁路 Baltimore and Ohio Railroad (B&O) 美国铁路 2—184b
巴尔的摩国立水族馆 National Aquarium in Baltimore, The 美国水族馆 12—11b
"巴尔的摩"号事件 Baltimore Incident 美国与智利之间纠纷 2—184c
巴尔的摩快帆船 Baltimore clipper 美国快速小帆船 2—184c
巴尔的摩男爵 Baltimore, BARONS 英国贵族 2—183d
巴尔的摩男爵(第二) Baltimore (of Baltimore), Cecilius Calvert, 2nd Baron 英国政治家 2—183f
巴尔的摩男爵(第三) Baltimore (of Baltimore), Charles Calvert, 3rd Baron 英国政治家 2—184a
巴尔的摩男爵(第一) Baltimore (of Baltimore), George Calvert, 1st Baron 英国政治家 2—183d
《巴尔的摩太阳报》 Baltimore Sun, The 美国报纸 2—184d
巴尔蒂斯 Balthus 法国画家 2—182a
巴尔东-格林 Baldung-Grien, Hans 德国画家 2—165c
巴尔都 Barthou, (Jean-) Louis 法国总理 2—250e
《巴尔杜条约》 Bardo, Treaty of 法国与突尼斯之间条约 2—226e
巴尔夫 Balfe, Michael William 爱尔兰音乐家 2—168d
巴尔富鲁什 Bārfurush (Iran) 伊朗城市 2—227f
巴尔干 Balkans 欧洲半岛 2—170e
巴尔干半岛 Balkan Peninsula 欧洲半岛 2—170b
巴尔干化 Balkanization 政治 2—170d
巴尔干流感 Balkan grippe 疾病 2—170a
巴尔干山脉 Balkan Mountains 欧洲山脉 2—170b
巴尔干同盟 Balkan League 欧洲近代史 2—170a
巴尔干同盟 Balkan League 欧洲近代史 2—170a
《巴尔干协约》 Balkan Entente 国际协定 2—170a
巴尔干战争 Balkan Wars 欧洲历史 2—170b
巴尔贡达丘陵 Pālkonda Hills 印度山地 12—567a
巴尔古津自然保护区 Barguzinsky Nature Reserve 俄罗斯自然保护区 2—228c
巴尔哈瓦塔 Barghawāṭah 柏柏尔部落联盟 2—228b
巴尔赫 Balkh 阿富汗村镇 2—172a
巴尔惠德 Balquhidder 苏格兰村庄 2—181b
巴尔加里斯 Bulgaris, Eugenius 希腊正教神学家 3—244f
巴尔加斯·略萨 Vargas Llosa, (Jorge) Mario (Pedro) 秘鲁小说家 17—472d
巴尔喀什 Balkhash 哈萨克斯坦城市 2—172b
巴尔喀什湖 Balkhash, Lake 哈萨克斯坦湖泊 2—172b
巴尔卡 Barca, Hamilcar 迦太基将军 2—223a
巴尔卡德 Pālghāt 印度城镇 12—565d
巴尔卡德山口 Pālghāt Gap 印度山口 12—565e
巴尔·科赫巴 Bar Kokhba 犹太人领袖 2—214d
巴尔克利 Bulkeley, Richard 英国军人、政治家 3—245e
巴尔拉赫 Barlach, Ernst 德国雕刻家 2—231e
巴尔拉纳德 Balranald 澳大利亚城镇 2—181c
巴尔马克家族 Barmakids 伊朗家族 2—232d
巴尔马塞达 Balmaceda, José Manuel 智利总统 2—179e
巴尔曼 Balmain, Pierre(-Alexandre-Claudius) 法国时装设计师 2—179e
巴尔梅尔 Bārmer 印度城市 2—232e
巴尔梅斯 Balmes, Jaime Luciano 西班牙哲学家 2—180a
巴尔米拉 Palmyra 叙利亚古城 12—574a
巴尔米拉环礁 Palmyra Atoll 美国无建制领土 12—574c
巴尔莫勒尔堡 Balmoral Castle 英国王室府第 2—180a
巴尔瑙尔 Barnaul 俄罗斯城市 2—235b
巴尔内弗斯 Balnaves, Henry 苏格兰政治家 2—180b
巴尔齐扎 Barzizza, Gasparino da 意大利教师 2—254e
巴尔奇 Balch, Emily Greene 美国社会学家 2—163e
巴尔切 Barca (Libya) 利比亚城镇 2—223a
巴尔切 Barce (Libya) 利比亚城镇 2—223b
巴尔钦 Balchin, Nigel (Marlin) 英国小说家 2—163f
巴尔曲式 Bar form 德国音乐 2—214c
巴尔萨 Bulsār (India) 印度城市 3—250a
巴尔-萨利比 Bar-Salibi, Jacob 叙利亚主教 2—214f
巴尔萨蒙 Balsamon, Theodore 拜占廷法律学家 2—181d
巴尔萨莫 Balsamo, Giuseppe 巴黎骗子魔术师 2—181d
巴尔萨斯河 Balsas River 墨西哥河流 2—181d
巴尔森托侯爵 Barsento, Emilio Pucci, marchese di (marquess of) 意大利时装设计师 2—247e
巴尔塔斯 Bartas, Guillaume de Salluste, seigneur du (lord of) 法国作家 2—248b
巴尔特 Bahrdt, Carl Friedrich 德国作家 2—144e
巴尔特 Barth, Heinrich 德国地理学家 2—248d
巴尔特 Barth, Paul 德国哲学家、社会学家 2—249b
巴尔特 Barthes, Roland (Gérard) 法国文学批评家 2—249c
巴尔特拉岛 Baltra Island 厄瓜多尔岛屿 2—184f
巴尔通氏体病 bartonellosis 疾病 2—253b
巴尔同盟 Bar, Confederation of 波兰历史 2—213f
巴尔托克 Bartók, Béla 匈牙利作曲家 2—251d
巴尔托利 Bartoli, Matteo Giulio 意大利语言学家 2—252b
巴尔托鲁(萨索费拉托的) Bartolus OF SAXOFERRATO 意大利法学家 2—252d
巴尔托洛 Bartolo, Andrea di 意大利画家 2—252c
巴尔托洛毛湖 Bartholomäusee 德国湖泊 2—250a
巴尔托洛齐 Bartolozzi, Francesco 意大利铜版画家 2—252d
巴尔韦德 Valverde 多米尼加共和国省份 17—457e
巴尔沃亚 Balboa, Vasco Núñez de 西班牙征服者 2—163c
巴尔武埃纳 Balbuena, Bernardo de 波多黎各诗人 2—163d
巴尔·希伯来 Bar Hebraeus 叙利亚学者 2—214d
巴尔希沙 Barṣīṣā 伊斯兰教传说人物 2—247f
巴尔扎克 Balzac, Honoré de 法国作家 2—185c
巴尔扎克 Balzac, Jean-Louis Guez de 法国文学家 2—185f
巴尔扎尼 Barzānī, Muṣṭafa al- 库尔德族军事领袖 2—254d
巴尔扎斯-布雷兹 Barzaz Breiz 民间歌谣集 2—254e
巴耳末 Balmer, Johann Jakob 瑞士数学家 2—179f
巴伐利亚 Bavaria 德国州名 2—288d
巴伐利亚阿尔卑斯山脉 Bavarian Alps 阿尔卑斯山一段 2—290c
巴伐利亚林山 Bavarian Forest 德国东南部山区 2—290c
巴伐利亚奶油 Bavarian cream 食品 2—290c
巴伐利亚王位继承战争 Bavarian Succession, War of the 普鲁士与奥地利之间冲突 2—290d
巴法塔 Bafatá 几内亚城镇 2—133f
巴菲特 Buffett, Warren Edward 美国企业家 3—234d
巴芬 Baffin 加拿大行政区 2—133f
巴芬 Baffin, William 英国航海家 2—134a
巴芬岛 Baffin Island 加拿大岛屿 2—134c
巴芬岛洋流 Baffin Island Current 海洋学 2—134c

巴芬河 Bafing River 非洲西部河流 2—134c
巴芬湾 Baffin Bay 北大西洋海湾 2—134a
巴夫利 Bavli, David ha- 叙利亚犹太哲学家 2—290e
《巴夫利塔木德》 Talmud Bavli (Jewish writ) 犹太教文献 16—448e
巴甫洛达尔 Pavlodar 哈萨克斯坦州名 13—103b
巴甫洛达尔 Pavlodar 哈萨克斯坦城市 13—103b
巴甫洛夫 Pavlov, Ivan Petrovich 苏联生理学家 13—103c
巴甫洛夫氏条件化作用 Pavlovian conditioning 生理学 13—103f
巴甫洛夫斯克 Pavlovsk 俄罗斯城市 13—104a
巴甫洛夫镇 Pavlovsky Posad 俄罗斯城市 13—104a
巴甫洛格勒 Pavlograd 乌克兰城市 13—103b
巴甫洛娃 Pavlova, Anna 俄国芭蕾舞蹈家 13—103d
巴甫洛沃 Pavlovo 俄罗斯城市 13—103f
巴富萨姆 Bafoussam 喀麦隆城镇 2—134d
巴盖里亚 Bagheria 意大利城镇 2—137b
巴干达人 Baganda (people) 非洲民族 2—134d
巴刚果人 Bakongo (people) 非洲民族 2—157f
巴港 Bar Harbor 美国城镇 2—214c
巴戈 Bago 菲律宾城市 2—138a
巴戈阿斯 Bagoas 波斯国王宠臣 2—138b
巴格 Bugge, (Elseus) Sophus 挪威语文学家 3—236b
巴格达 Baghdad 伊拉克首都 2—135e
巴格达画派 Baghdad school 伊斯兰教画派 2—136f
巴格达什 Baqdash, Khalid 叙利亚共产党领袖 2—213d
巴格达条约组织 Baghdad Pact Organization 国际组织 2—136e
巴格达铁路 Baghdad Railway 土耳其—波斯湾铁路 2—136f
巴格拉季昂 Bagration, Pyotr Ivanovich, Knyaz 俄国将军 2—138f
巴格拉提德王朝 Bagratid DYNASTY 亚美尼亚-格鲁吉亚王朝 2—138e
巴格兰 Baghlān 阿富汗城市 2—137c
巴格里茨基 Bagritsky, Eduard Georgiyevich 苏联诗人 2—138f
巴格利 Bagley, Sarah G. 美国劳工组织者 2—137d
巴格利 Bagley, William Chandler 美国教育家、作家 2—137e
巴格马蒂河 Bāghmati River 亚洲河流 2—137c
巴格诺尔德 Bagnold, Enid 英国小说家 2—137f
巴格诺尔德 Bagnold, Ralph A(lger) 英国地质学家 2—138a
巴格森 Baggesen, Jens (Immanuel) 丹麦文学家 2—135c
巴古拜 Baʿqūbah 伊拉克城市 2—213e
巴哈 Bāḥah, al- 沙特阿拉伯城镇 2—139f
巴哈都尔沙二世 Bahādur Shāh II 印度皇帝 2—139e
巴哈都尔沙一世 Bahādur Shāh I 印度皇帝 2—139e
巴哈杜尔布尔战役 Bāhādurpur, Battle of 印度帝位继承战争 2—139f
巴哈教 Bahāʾī faith 伊朗宗教 2—139f
巴哈兰布尔 Baharampur 印度城镇 2—141d
巴哈马 Bahamas, The 美洲国家 2—140c
巴哈寺 Bahāʾī temple 巴哈教礼拜寺 2—140c
巴哈瓦尔布尔 Bahāwalpur 巴基斯坦城市 2—141e
巴哈瓦尔讷格尔 Bahāwalnagar 巴基斯坦城镇 2—141d
巴哈·乌拉 Bahāʾ Ullāh 伊朗宗教领袖 2—139e
巴赫 Bach, Carl Philipp Emanuel 德国作曲家 2—114c
巴赫 Bach, Johann Christian 德国作曲家 2—114d
巴赫 Bach, Johann Christoph Friedrich 德国作曲家 2—114e
巴赫 Bach, Johann Sebastian 德国作曲家 2—114f
巴赫 Bach, Wilhelm Friedemann 德国作曲家 2—117e
巴赫蒂亚里地毯 Bakhtiari rug 伊朗地毯 2—156e
巴赫蒂亚里人 Bakhtyārī 伊朗民族 2—156f
巴赫拉恩 Bahrān (Zoroastrian deity) 琐罗亚斯德教神祇 2—144e
巴赫拉姆 Bahrām 波斯国王 2—144b
巴赫拉姆二世 Bahrām II 波斯国王 2—144b
巴赫拉姆六世·楚宾 Bahrām VI Chūbīn 波斯国王 2—144d
巴赫拉姆四世 Bahrām IV 波斯国王 2—144c
巴赫拉姆五世 Bahrām V 波斯国王 2—144c
巴赫拉姆一世 Bahrām I 波斯国王 2—144b
巴赫赖奇 Bahraich 印度城镇 2—143a
巴赫马尼苏丹国 Bahmanī SULTANATE 印度古国 2—142b
巴赫穆特 Bakhmut (Ukraine) 乌克兰城市 2—156d
巴赫奇萨赖 Bakhchysaray 乌克兰城市 2—156d
巴赫塔兰 Bākhtarān 伊朗城市 2—156d
巴胡巴利 Bāhubali 印度耆那教人物 2—144f
巴胡提 Bahūtī, al- 埃及伊斯兰教法教师 2—145a
巴胡图人 Bahutu (people) 非洲民族 2—145a
巴霍芬 Bachofen, Johann Jakob 瑞士法理学家 2—118d
巴霍纳尔 Bahonar, Mohammad Javad 伊朗政治家 2—142b
巴基 Bâkî 土耳其诗人 2—157a
巴基判决 Bakke decision 美国最高法院民事判决 2—157e
巴基斯坦 Pakistan 亚洲国家 12—552f
巴基斯坦教会 Pakistan, Church of 基督教会 12—554b
巴基西梅托 Barquisimeto 委内瑞拉城市 2—239e
巴吉尔米人 Bagirmi 非洲混血民族 2—137c
巴吉尔米王国 Bagirmi, Kingdom of 非洲历史 2—137c
巴季里克 Pazyryk 哈萨克斯坦墓葬遗址 13—107b
巴加拉人 Baqqārah 阿拉伯游牧民族 2—213d
巴加莫约 Bagamoyo 坦桑尼亚城镇 2—134d
巴加人 Baga 非洲民族 2—134d
巴加什(伊本·赛义德) Barghash (ibn Saʿīd) 桑给巴尔苏丹 2—228a
巴杰 Bājah 突尼斯城镇 2—153a
巴杰尔 Budgell, Eustace 英国作家 3—230a
巴杰罗博物馆 Bargello Museum 意大利博物馆 2—228a
巴杰罗绣制品 bargello work 意大利粗布刺绣品 2—228a
巴金 Ba Jin 中国作家 2—105f
巴金-达格纳姆 Barking and Dagenham 英格兰自治市 2—231c
巴卡 Vaca, Álvar Núñez Cabeza de 西班牙探险家 17—439f
巴卡布神 Bacab 马雅神话中四神 2—113c
巴卡洪德人 Bakahonde (people) 非洲民族 2—153d
巴卡拉玻璃制品 Baccarat glass 法国玻璃器皿 2—113f
巴卡拉牌 Baccarat 纸牌游戏 2—113e
巴凯尔哈德 Bāgherhāt 孟加拉国城镇 2—137b
巴凯利 Bacchelli, Riccardo 意大利作家 2—113f
巴科洛德 Bacolod 菲律宾城市 2—119d
巴科伊河 Bakoye River 非洲河流 2—157f
巴克 Barker, George 英国诗人 2—230f
巴克 Barker, Ma 美国匪帮头目 2—230f
巴克 Buck, Sir Peter 新西兰人类学家、政治家 3—222a
巴克本山 Backbone Mountain 美国山脉 2—119b
巴克德汗 Bakht Khan 印度军事统帅 2—156d
巴克尔根德 Baghelkhand 印度历史地区 2—137a
巴克帆船 bark 纵帆帆船 2—230b
巴克夫人 Barker, Lady Mary Anne 英国作家 2—230f
巴克豪斯 Backhaus, Wilhelm 德国钢琴家 2—119c
巴克好森 Barkhausen, Heinrich Georg 德国物理学家 2—231b
巴克好森效应 Barkhausen effect 物理学 2—231b
巴克赫伊斯山 Bakhuis Gebergte 苏里南山脉 2—157a
巴克黑文 Buckhaven 苏格兰港市 3—222f
巴克基利得斯 Bacchylides 希腊诗人 2—114a
巴克拉 Barkla, Charles Glover 英国物理学家 2—231c
巴克莱·德托利公爵 Barclay de Tolly, Mikhail Bogdanovich, Knyaz (Prince) 俄国元帅 2—225f
巴克莱银行 Barclays Bank PLC 英国金融企业 2—226a
巴克兰 Buckland, William 英国地质学家 3—223f
巴克勒奇公爵 Buccleuch, James Scott, duke of 英格兰反叛者 3—218d
巴克利 Barclay, Alexander 苏格兰诗人 2—225d
巴克利 Barkley, Alben W(illiam) 美国副总统 2—231d

巴克利 Barkly, Sir Henry 英国殖民官员 2—231d
巴克利 Barclay, John 苏格兰讽刺作家 2—225d
巴克利 Barclay, Robert 苏格兰贵格会领袖 2—225e
巴克利 Buckley, William F., Jr. 美国编辑、作家 3—224a
巴克利台地 Barkly Tableland 澳大利亚地区 2—231e
巴克马 Bakema, Jacob B(erend) 荷兰建筑师 2—153d
巴克曼 Bachman, John 美国博物学家 2—118c
巴克纳 Buckner, Simon Bolivar 美国将军 3—224b
巴克纳(小) Buckner, Simon Bolivar, Jr. 美国陆军将领 3—224b
巴克斯 Bacchus 希腊神话人物 2—114a
巴克斯 Bax, Sir Arnold (Edward Trevor) 英国作曲家 2—290e
巴克斯顿 Buxton 英格兰城镇 3—295c
巴克斯顿 Buxton, Sir Thomas Fowell, 1st BARONET 英国慈善家、政治家 3—295c
巴克斯马什 Bacchus Marsh 澳大利亚城镇 2—114a
巴克斯特 Baxter, Andrew 苏格兰哲学家 2—291a
巴克斯特 Baxter, George 英国印刷专家 2—291a
巴克斯特 Baxter, James K(eir) 新西兰诗人 2—291b
巴克斯特 Bakst, Léon 俄国艺术家 2—158a
巴克斯特 Baxter, Richard 英格兰牧师 2—291b
巴克塔普尔 Bhaktapur 尼泊尔市镇 2—449d
巴克维尔 Barkerville 加拿大城镇 2—231a
巴克乌 Bacău 罗马尼亚地区 2—113d
巴克乌 Bacău 罗马尼亚城市 2—113e
巴克乌斯,圣 Bacchus, SAINT 基督教圣人 2—114a
巴肯 Buchan (Scotland) 苏格兰区名 3—219c
巴肯 Buchan, Alexander 英国气象学家 3—219c
巴肯 Buchan, John, 1st BARON TWEEDSMUIR 苏格兰政治家、作家 3—219c
巴孔堆 Tall-e Bakun 伊朗史前遗址 16—445c
巴枯宁 Bakunin, Mikhail Aleksandrovich 俄国革命家 2—158f
巴库 Baku 阿塞拜疆首都 2—158c
巴库巴人 Bakuba (people) 林居半游牧民族 2—158f
巴库地毯 Baku rug 东高加索地毯 2—158e
巴库河 Barcoo River (Australia) 澳大利亚河流 2—226a
巴宽加 Bakwanga 刚果(金)城市 2—159b
巴拉 Bala 威尔士集镇 2—159b
巴拉 Balla, Giacomo 意大利画家 2—173e
巴拉 Bara, Theda 美国电影明星 2—215a
巴拉,圣玛德琳-索菲亚 Barat, Saint Madeleine-Sophie 法国天主教修女 2—217a
巴拉奥纳 Barahona 多米尼加共和国城市 2—215d
巴拉奥纳·德索托 Barahona de Soto, Luis 西班牙诗人 2—215d
巴拉巴克 Balabac 菲律宾岛屿 2—159c
巴拉本吉 Bāra Banki 印度城镇 2—215b
巴拉布 Baraboo 美国城市 2—215c
巴拉岛 Barra 苏格兰岛屿 2—239f
巴拉德 Ballard, Robert D(uane) 美国海洋学家 2—175c
巴拉德湾 Burrard Inlet 乔治亚海峡湾汊 3—275a
巴拉迪布 Parādip 印度城镇、海港 13—31a
巴拉迪尔 Balladur, Édouard 法国总理 2—174d
巴拉蒂耶里 Baratieri, Oreste 意大利将军 2—217a
巴拉丁 palatine 欧洲历史官职名 12—557c
巴拉丁礼拜堂 Palatine Chapel 德国皇家教堂 12—557c
巴拉丁领地 Palatinate 德国历史地区 12—557b
巴拉丁斯基 Baratynsky, Yevgeny Abramovich 俄国诗人 2—217b
巴拉-杜皮拉伊 Barra do Piraí 巴西城市 2—239f
巴拉顿菲赖德 Balatonfüred 匈牙利城镇 2—162e
巴拉顿湖 Balaton, Lake 欧洲湖泊 2—162d
巴拉尔 Balard, Antoine-Jérôme 法国化学家 2—162a
巴拉尔河 Pālār River 印度河流 12—556e
巴拉尔家族 Ballard FAMILY 法国印刷商家族 2—175b
巴拉甘 Barragán, Luis 墨西哥工程师、建筑师 2—240c
巴拉格尔 Balaguer (y Ricardo), Joaquín (Vidella) 多米尼加总统 2—159d
巴拉格尔 Balaguer (i Cirera), Victor 西班牙诗人、政治家 2—159f
巴拉格瓦纳思氏石松属 Baragwanathia 古生物学 2—215d
巴拉瓜里 Paraguarí 巴拉圭城市 13—32b
巴拉圭 Paraguay 南美洲国家 13—32c
巴拉圭茶 Paraguay tea 饮料 13—33f
巴拉圭河 Paraguay River 南美洲河流 13—33d
巴拉圭战争 Paraguayan War 南美洲历史 13—33f
巴拉绘画 Pāla painting 美术 12—554d
巴拉基列夫 Balakirev, Mily (Alekseyevich) 俄国作曲家 2—160a
巴拉卡 Baraka, Imamu Amiri 美国剧作家、诗人 2—215f
巴拉卡德 Bālāghāt 印度城镇 2—159d
巴拉卡德岭 Bālāghāt Range 印度山系 2—159d
巴拉卡尔多 Baracaldo 西班牙城市 2—215c
巴拉科阿 Baracoa 古巴城市 2—215c
巴拉科古代雕刻品博物馆 Barracco Museum of Antique Sculpture 罗马博物馆 2—240a
巴拉科沃 Balakovo 俄罗斯城市 2—160c
巴拉克 Barak, Ehud 以色列军人、政治家 2—215e
巴拉克河 Barāk River (India) 亚洲河流 2—215f
巴拉克拉瓦战役 Balaklava, Battle of 欧洲历史事件 2—160b
巴拉克宰王朝 Bārakzay DYNASTY 阿富汗统治家族 2—216a
巴拉腊特 Ballarat 澳大利亚城市 2—175a
巴拉莱卡琴 balalaika 俄罗斯弦乐器 2—160c
巴拉曼萨 Barra Mansa 巴西城市 2—240a
巴拉那 Paraná 阿根廷城市 13—37b
巴拉那 Paraná 巴西州名 13—37c
巴拉那高原 Paraná Plateau 南美洲高原 13—37e
巴拉那瓜 Paranaguá 巴西港口 13—38a
巴拉那河 Paraná River 南美洲河流 13—37e
巴拉那帕内马河 Paranapanema River 巴西河流 13—38b
巴拉那松 Paraná pine 木本植物 13—37d
巴拉那伊巴河 Paranaíba River 巴西河流 13—38a
巴拉瑙斯卡斯 Baranauskas, Antanas 立陶宛诗人 2—216b
巴拉尼 Bárány, Robert 奥地利耳科学家 2—216d
巴拉诺维奇 Baranovichi 白俄罗斯城镇 2—216c
巴拉人 Bara 马达加斯加民族 2—215a
巴拉瑟德 Bārāsat 印度城镇 2—216f
巴拉什 Balāsh 波斯国王 2—162a
巴拉什 Balassi, Bálint 匈牙利诗人 2—162c
巴拉斯 Barras, Paul-François-Jean-Nicolas, vicomte de 法国历史人物 2—240f
巴拉索尔 Balasore 印度城镇 2—162b
巴拉塔里亚湾 Barataria Bay 墨西哥湾小海湾 2—217a
巴拉塔树胶 balata 胶状物质 2—162c
巴拉特 Baalat 闪米特女神 2—106e
巴拉特 Balat (ancient city, Turkey) 土耳其古城 2—162c
巴拉王朝 Pāla DYNASTY 印度王朝名 12—554c
巴拉望 Palawan 菲律宾岛屿 12—558d
巴拉希 Palāshi (India) 印度古村名 12—556f
巴拉希哈 Balashikha 俄罗斯城市 2—162b
巴莱拉 Valera 委内瑞拉城市 17—451f
巴莱拉·伊·阿尔卡拉·加利亚诺 Valera y Alcalá Galiano, Juan 西班牙小说家 17—451f
巴莱沓 Baraita 古代犹太教律法 2—215e
巴莱托 balletto 声乐曲体裁 2—177a
巴莱语 Palaic language 古代印欧语言 12—555f
巴兰 Balaam 《圣经》中的先知 2—159c
巴兰格鲁德 Ballangrud, Ivar 挪威速滑运动员 2—174f
巴兰河 Baram River 婆罗洲河流 2—216a
巴兰基亚 Barranquilla 哥伦比亚城市 2—240e
巴兰卡贝梅哈 Barrancabermeja 哥伦比亚城市 2—240d

巴兰科 Barranco 秘鲁城市 2—240e
巴兰尼亚 Baranya 匈牙利州名 2—216e
巴兰钦 Balanchine,George 俄裔美国芭蕾舞编导 2—161a
巴兰斯 Ballance,John 新西兰总理 2—174e
巴兰坦 Ballantyne,Robert Michael 苏格兰作家 2—175a
巴兰西阿加 Balenciaga,Cristóbal 西班牙女装设计师 2—168b
巴朗德 Barrande,Joachim 法国地质学家 2—240e
巴朗加 barangay 菲律宾居民点形式 2—216b
巴朗什 Ballanche,Pierre-Simon 法国宗教与哲学家 2—174f
巴朗特男爵 Barante,Amable-Guillaume-Prosper Brugière,baron de 法国政治家 2—216c
巴劳 Balao 厄瓜多尔油港 2—161e
巴劳尔 Barrault,Jean-Louis 法国演员 2—241a
巴勒 Bâle (Switzerland) 瑞士城市 2—167e
巴勒贝克 Baalbek 黎巴嫩城镇 2—106f
巴勒城市半州 Bâle-Ville (Switzerland) 瑞士半州 2—167e
巴勒迪克 Baerle-Duc (Belgium) 比利时城市 2—133a
巴勒迪克 Bar-le-Duc 法国城市 2—214e
巴勒海托赫 Baarle-Hertog 比利时城市 2—107b
巴勒克埃西尔 Balıkesir 土耳其城市 2—169e
巴勒克布尔 Barrackpore 印度城镇 2—240b
巴勒克布尔兵变 Barrackpore Mutiny 英缅战争中事件 2—240b
巴勒莫 Palermo 意大利城市 12—562e
巴勒莫石刻 Palermo Stone 埃及考古 12—563a
巴勒什瓦尔 Bāleshwar (India) 印度城镇 2—168c
巴勒斯 Burroughs,Edgar Rice 美国小说家 3—275d
巴勒斯 Burroughs,John 美国散文家 3—275e
巴勒斯 Burroughs,William Seward 美国发明家 3—275e
巴勒斯 Burroughs,William S(eward) 美国小说家 3—275f
巴勒斯坦 Palestine 地中海东部地区 12—563c
巴勒斯坦解放组织 Palestine Liberation Organization (PLO) 巴勒斯坦政治组织 12—564a
巴勒斯坦权力机构 Palestinian Authority (PA) 巴勒斯坦自治区管理机构 12—564c
《巴勒斯坦塔木德》 Palestinian Talmud 犹太教文集 12—564d
巴勒提特 Baltit (Jammu and Kashmir) 查谟和克什米尔城镇 2—184e
巴勒瓦 Balewa,Sir Abubakar Tafawa 尼日利亚总理 2—168c
巴勒乡村半州 Bâle-Campagne (Switzerland) 瑞士半州 2—167e
巴勒延戈代 Pālayankottai 印度城镇 12—558d
巴雷尔 Barère (de Vieuzac),Bertrand 法国革命者 2—227d
巴雷尔 Barrell,Joseph 美国地质学家 2—242c
巴雷拉 Barrera,Carlos Arniches y 西班牙剧作家 2—242e
巴雷利 Bareilly 印度城市 2—227a
巴雷斯 Barrès,Maurice 法国作家、政治家 2—242e
巴雷特 Barrett,Elizabeth 英国诗人 2—243a
巴雷特 Barrett,Janie Porter 美国福利工作者、教育家 2—243b
巴雷特 Barrett,Kate Harwood Waller 美国医生 2—243b
巴雷特 Barrett,Lawrence 美国演员 2—243c
巴雷图斯 Barretos 巴西城市 2—243a
巴雷托 Barreto,Afonso Henriques de Lima 巴西作家 2—242f
巴雷托 Barreto,Francisco 葡萄牙军人、探险家 2—243a
巴厘 Bali 印度尼西亚省份 2—169b
巴厘巴板 Balikpapan 印度尼西亚港口 2—169e
巴厘牛 Bali cattle 哺乳动物 2—169e
巴厘人 Balinese 印度尼西亚民族 2—169f
巴黎 Paris 法国首都 13—42e
巴黎(省) Ville-de-Paris 法国省份 17—564e
巴黎伯爵 Paris,(Louis-)Philippe(-Albert) d'Orléans,comte de 法国王位觊觎者 13—51b
巴黎第一～第十三大学 Paris Ⅰ-ⅩⅢ,Universities of 法国大学 13—51f
巴黎歌剧院 Paris Opéra 法国歌剧院 13—52c
巴黎歌剧院芭蕾舞团 Paris Opéra Ballet 法国芭蕾舞团 13—52c
巴黎公社 Paris,Commune of 法国历史 13—50e
《巴黎公约》 Paris,Pact of 多边条约 13—51a
巴黎和会 Paris Peace Conference 国际会议 13—52d
《巴黎和平条约》 Paris,Peace of 国际条约 13—51a
巴黎花边 point de Paris 工艺品 13—389a
《巴黎竞赛》 Paris-Match 法国杂志 13—52b
巴黎刻本 Paris Codex 马雅文学 13—52a
巴黎炮 Paris Gun 军事 13—52b
巴黎盆地 Paris Basin 法国盆地 13—52a
《巴黎人报》 Parisien,Le 法国报刊 13—52f
巴黎圣母院 Notre-Dame de Paris 法国大教堂 12—275a
巴黎天文台 Paris Observatory 法国天文台 13—52b
巴黎条约 Paris,Treaties of 结束第一次世界大战的若干条约 13—51b
《巴黎条约》 Paris,Treaties of 结束拿破仑战争的条约 13—51c
《巴黎条约》 Paris,Treaty of 结束法英七年战争的条约 13—51c
《巴黎条约》 Paris,Treaty of 结束美国独立战争的条约 13—51d
《巴黎条约》 Paris,Treaty of 结束克里米亚战争的条约 13—51d
《巴黎条约》 Paris,Treaty of 结束美西战争的条约 13—51e
巴黎西昂叙 Parisiensus,Johannes 法国画家 13—52f
巴黎植物园 Jardin des Plantes 植物园 8—545c
巴里 Bari 意大利城市 2—228d
巴里 Barre 美国城市 2—241b
巴里 Barrie 加拿大城市 2—243d
巴里 Barry 威尔士城镇 2—246b
巴里 Barye,Antoine-Louis 法国雕刻家 2—253f
巴里 Barry,Sir Charles 英国建筑师 2—246b
巴里 Barri,Gerald de 威尔士历史学家 2—243d
巴里 Barry,James 英国美术家 2—246c
巴里 Barrie,Sir James (Matthew),BARONET 英国剧作家、小说家 2—243d
巴里 Barry,John 美国海军军官 2—246e
巴里 Barry,Marion 美国政治家 2—246f
巴里 Barry,Philip 美国剧作家 2—246f
巴里奥斯 Barrios,Eduardo 智利小说家 2—244c
巴里奥斯 Barrios,Justo Rufino 危地马拉总统 2—244d
巴里奥斯港 Puerto Barrios 危地马拉城镇 14—15d
巴里伯爵夫人 Barry,(Marie-)Jeanne Bécu,comtesse du 法国路易十五的情妇 2—246d
巴里德·沙赫王朝 Barīd Shāhī DYNASTY 比德尔国统治家族 2—228f
巴里洛切 Bariloche (Argentina) 阿根廷城镇 2—228f
巴里穆尔 Barrymore,Ethel 美国演员 2—247a
巴里穆尔 Barrymore,Georgiana 美国演员 2—247b
巴里穆尔 Barrymore,John 美国演员 2—247c
巴里穆尔 Barrymore,Lionel 美国演员 2—247d
巴里穆尔 Barrymore,Maurice 美国演员 2—247e
巴里纳斯 Barinas 委内瑞拉州名 2—228f
巴里纳斯 Barinas 委内瑞拉城市 2—229a
巴里尼 Parini,Giuseppe 意大利散文家、诗人 13—42c
巴里人 Bari 苏丹民族 2—228d
巴里什尼科夫 Baryshnikov,Mikhail (Nikolayevich) 美国芭蕾舞蹈家 2—254b
巴里通琴 baryton 弓弦乐器 2—254c
巴里之围 Bari,Siege of 欧洲历史 2—228e
巴力 Baal 古代近东神灵 2—106d
巴利 Bally 印度城镇 2—179c
巴利 Pāli 印度城镇 12—565f
巴利阿多利德 Valladolid 西班牙省份 17—453d
巴利阿多利德 Valladolid 西班牙城市 17—453e
巴利阿多利德大学 Valladolid,University of 西班牙高等学府 17—453e
巴利阿里群岛 Balearic Islands 西班牙省份 2—167f

巴利奥尔 Baliol, Edward de 苏格兰国王 2—169f
巴利奥尔 Baliol, John de 苏格兰国王 2—170a
巴利奥尔家族 Balliol FAMILY 欧洲中世纪家族 2—177d
巴利奥尼家族 Baglioni FAMILY 意大利贵族世家 2—137f
巴利卡斯尔 Ballycastle 北爱尔兰城镇 2—179c
巴利马尼 Ballymoney 北爱尔兰城镇 2—179d
巴利米纳 Ballymena 北爱尔兰城镇 2—179c
巴利纳 Ballina 澳大利亚港镇 2—177b
巴利纳 Ballina 爱尔兰城镇 2—177c
巴利纳斯洛 Ballinasloe 爱尔兰城镇 2—177c
巴利文文献 Pāli literature 佛教文献 12—566a
巴利语 Pāli language 宗教语言 12—565f
巴列霍 Vallejo, César (Abraham) 秘鲁诗人 17—454e
巴列姆阶 Barremian Stage 地质学 2—242d
巴列斯 Valles 墨西哥城市 17—454f
巴列塔 Barletta 意大利城市 2—231f
巴列维 Pahlavī (Iran) 伊朗港口 12—547b
巴列维 Mohammad Reza Shah Pahlavi 伊朗国王 11—310f
巴列维 Pahlavi, Reza Shah (shah of Iran) 伊朗国王 12—547b
巴列维港 Pahlavī, Bandar-e (Iran) 伊朗港口 12—547b
巴列维水坝 Pahlavi Dam 伊朗水坝 12—547c
巴列-因克兰 Valle-Inclán, Ramón María del 西班牙作家 17—454d
巴林 Bahrain 亚洲国家 2—143b
巴林 Barrin, Roland-Michel 新法兰西总督 2—244a
巴林德 Bārind 亚洲地区 2—229a
巴林顿 Barrington, George 爱尔兰冒险家 2—244b
巴林戈湖 Baringo, Lake 肯尼亚湖泊 2—229b
巴林家族 Baring FAMILY 英国家族 2—229a
巴林杰 Ballinger, Richard A(chilles) 美国内政部长 2—177c
巴灵顿 Barrington 美国城镇 2—244b
巴灵顿岛 Barrington Island (Galápagos Islands) 东太平洋岛屿 2—244c
巴隆 Balon, Jean 法国芭蕾舞蹈家 2—181b
巴隆 Baron, Michel 法国演员 2—238c
巴隆玛特莱洛卡纳 Borommatrailokanat (king of Siam) 暹罗国王 3—54f
巴卢 Ballou, Hosea 美国神学家 2—179a
巴卢巴人 Baluba (people) 刚果(金)民族 2—184f
巴卢尔卡德 Bālurghāt 印度城镇 2—185b
巴鲁克 Baruch, Bernard 美国金融家 2—253d
巴鲁尼 Bāruni 印度城镇 2—253e
巴鲁塔 Baruta 委内瑞拉城市 2—253e
巴鲁瓦 Barrois 欧洲古国 2—244f
《巴录启示录》 Baruch, Apocalypse of 基督教伪经 2—253d
《巴录书》 Baruch, Book of 古代宗教经籍 2—253e
巴吕 Balue, Jean 法国枢机主教 2—185a
巴吕兹 Baluze, Étienne 法国学者 2—185c
巴伦 Barron, Clarence W(alker) 美国报刊编辑、发行人 2—244f
巴伦博伊姆 Barenboim, Daniel 以色列钢琴家 2—227a
巴伦布尔 Pālanpur 印度城市 12—556d
巴伦河 Barron River 澳大利亚河流 2—245a
巴伦苏埃拉 Valenzuela, Fernando 墨西哥棒球运动员 17—451e
巴伦苏埃拉 Valenzuela, Fernando de, MARQUÉS (marquess) DE VILLA SIERRA 西班牙大臣 17—451f
巴伦西亚 Valencia 西班牙古国 17—449d
巴伦西亚 Valencia 西班牙自治区 17—449d
巴伦西亚 Valencia 西班牙省份 17—449d
巴伦西亚 Valencia 西班牙城市 17—449e
巴伦西亚 Valencia 委内瑞拉城市 17—449f
巴伦西亚 Valencia, Guillermo 哥伦比亚诗人、政治家 17—449f
巴伦西亚的阿尔武费拉公爵 Albufera da Valencia, Louis-Gabriel Suchet, duc d' (duke of) 法国元帅 1,—185f
巴伦西亚公爵 Valencia, Ramón María Narváez, duque de (duke of) 西班牙首相 17—450a
巴伦西亚湖 Valencia, Lake 委内瑞拉湖泊 17—450a
巴伦支 Barents, Willem 荷兰航海家 2—227b
巴伦支海 Barents Sea 北冰洋海域 2—227c
巴罗 Baro 尼日利亚城镇 2—237d
巴罗 Barrow (Alaska, U.S.) 美国城市 2—245e
巴罗 Barrot, (Camille-Hyacinthe-) Odilon 法国君主主义者 2—245d
巴罗 Barrow, Henry 英格兰律师、教士 2—245f
巴罗 Barrow, Isaac 英国文学家、神学家 2—245f
巴罗策人 Barotse (people) 赞比亚民族 2—239e
巴罗达 Baroda (India) 印度城市 2—237f
巴罗岛 Barrow Island 澳大利亚岛屿 2—246b
巴罗哈-内西 Baroja (y Nessi), Pío 西班牙作家 2—237f
巴罗和帕克 Barrow, Clyde; and Parker, Bonnie 美国强盗小集团 2—245e
巴罗河 Barrow, River 爱尔兰河流 2—246a
巴罗角 Point Barrow 美国城市 13—388e
巴罗克时期 Baroque period 西方艺术史 2—238f
巴罗内 Barone, Enrico 意大利数理经济学家 2—238d
巴罗尼乌斯 Baronius, Caesar 天主教教会史学家 2—238e
巴罗齐奥 Barozio, Giacomo 意大利建筑师 2—239e
巴罗奇 Barocci, Federico 意大利画家 2—237e
巴罗萨河谷 Barossa Valley 澳大利亚河谷 2—239d
巴罗斯 Barros, João de 葡萄牙历史学家 2—245b
巴罗斯·阿拉纳 Barros Arana, Diego 智利历史学家 2—245c
巴罗因弗内斯 Barrow-in-Furness 英格兰区名 2—246b
巴洛 Barlow, Joel 美国政府官员、诗人 2—232b
巴洛 Barlow, Peter 英国光学仪器制造者 2—232c
巴洛迪斯 Balodis, Jānis 拉脱维亚军官、政治家 2—181a
巴洛维杜人 Balovedu (people) 南非民族 2—181b
巴马科 Bamako 马里首都 2—186a
巴门达 Bamenda 喀麦隆城镇 2—187d
巴门会议 Barmen, Synod of 德国基督教会议 2—232e
巴门尼德 Parmenides 希腊哲学家 13—58d
巴米累克人 Bamileke 喀麦隆民族 2—187f
巴米扬 Bāmīān 阿富汗城镇 2—187e
巴莫 Ba Maw 缅甸政治家 2—106b
巴姆贝格尔 Bamberger, Ludwig 德国经济学家 2—186d
巴穆姆人 Bamum 西非民族 2—188a
巴拿巴,圣 Barnabas, SAINT 基督教早期教士 2—233a
《巴拿巴书信》 Barnabas, Letter of 基督教早期著作 2—233a
巴拿赫 Banach, Stefan 波兰数学家 2—189a
巴拿马 Panama 中美洲国家 13—4c
巴拿马病 Panama disease 香蕉病害 13—6d
巴拿马草目 Cyclanthales 植物学 5—85a
巴拿马城 Panama City 巴拿马首都 13—6b
巴拿马城 Panama City 美国城市 13—6d
巴拿马地峡 Panama, Isthmus of 中美洲地峡 13—5f
巴拿马金蛙 Panamanian golden toad (*Atelopus zetekialso*) 两栖动物 13—6e
巴拿马湾 Panama, Gulf of 太平洋小湾 13—5e
巴拿马运河 Panama Canal 中美洲运河 13—5f
巴拿马运河区 Panama Canal Zone 巴拿马地区 13—6b
巴那克 Barnack, Oskar 德国照相机设计者 2—233b
巴纳巴岛 Banaba 基里巴斯岛屿 2—188f
巴纳德 Barnard, Chester Irving 美国实业家 2—233e
巴纳德 Barnard, Christiaan (Neethling) 南非外科医师 2—233e
巴纳德 Barnard, Edward Emerson 美国天文学家 2—233f
巴纳德 Barnard, Frederick (Augustus Porter) 美国教育家 2—234b
巴纳德 Barnard, George Grey 美国雕刻家 2—234c
巴纳德 Barnard, Henry 美国教育家 2—234c
巴纳德 Barnard, Kate 美国福利工作领袖 2—234e
巴纳德堡 Barnard Castle 苏格兰城镇 2—234f

巴纳德夫人 Barnard, Lady Anne 苏格兰民歌作者 2—234e
巴纳德星 Barnard's star 天文学 2—235a
巴纳多 Barnardo, Thomas John 英国社会工作先驱 2—234f
巴纳夫 Barnave, Antoine (-Pierre-Joseph-Marie) 法国政治家 2—235b
巴纳姆 Barnum, P(hineas) T(aylor) 美国马戏团经理 2—237b
巴纳纳 Banana 刚果(金)海港 2—189a
巴纳纳尔岛 Bananal Island 巴西岛屿 2—189d
巴纳特 Banat 东欧古民族杂居区 2—189e
巴纳托 Barnato, Barney 南非金融家 2—235a
巴纳伊巴 Parnaíba 巴西城市 13—59a
巴纳伊巴河 Parnaíba River 巴西河流 13—59a
巴纳诸语言 Bahnaric languages 孟-高棉语系语支 2—142b
巴内尔 Banér, Johan 瑞典陆军元帅 2—197a
巴内杰亚 Banerjea, Sir Surendranath 现代印度奠基人 2—197a
巴尼 Baní 多米尼加共和国城市 2—202c
巴尼 Barney, Nora Stanton Blatch 美国土木工程师、女权主义者 2—236f
巴尼伯德 Pānīpat 印度城市 13—12e
巴尼伯德战役 Pānīpat, Battles of 印度历史 13—12f
巴尼哈蒂 Pānihāti 印度城市 13—12c
巴尼河 Bani River 马里河流 2—202e
巴尼姆兄弟 Banim, John and Michael 爱尔兰小说家 2—202f
巴尼-萨德尔 Bani-Sadr, Abolhasan 伊朗经济学家、政治人物 2—202c
巴尼特 Barnet 英格兰自治市 2—236c
巴尼特 Barnet, Miguel 古巴黑人文化专家、小说家 2—236e
巴尼特 Barnett, Samuel A(ugustus) 英国基督教牧师 2—236e
巴尼特战役 Barnet, Battle of 英国历史 2—236d
巴尼亚卢卡 Banja Luka 波斯尼亚-黑塞哥维那城市 2—203a
巴尼亚群岛 Banyak Islands 印度尼西亚岛群 2—209e
巴尼扬韦齐人 Banyamwesi (people) 坦桑尼亚民族 2—209e
巴涅尔 Parnell, Charles Stewart 爱尔兰民族主义者 13—59d
巴纽旺宜 Banjuwangi (Indonesia) 印度尼西亚港口 2—203e
巴努艾格莱卜王朝 Banū al-Aghlab DYNASTY 阿拉伯穆斯林王朝 2—209d
巴努哈夫西斯 Banū ḥafṣ (dynasty) 非洲王朝 2—209d
巴努马林 Banū Marīn (dynasty) 非洲王朝 2—209d
巴努齐里 Banū Zīrī (dynasty) 非洲王朝 2—209d
巴努扎亚 Banū Zayyān (dynasty) 非洲王朝 2—209d
巴佩迪人 Bapedi (people) 南非民族 2—212c
巴婆 pawpaw (*Asimina triloba*) 木本植物 13—101e
巴浦白蛉热 phlebotomus fever 疾病 13—253b
巴齐 Bazzi, Giovanni Antonio 意大利画家 2—300c
巴齐奥特 Baziotes, William 美国画家 2—300a
巴齐耶 Bazille, Jean-Frédéric 法国画家 2—299c
巴奇 Budge, Don 美国草地网球运动员 3—229f
巴奇 Budge, Sir (Ernest Alfred Thompson) Wallis 英国东方学家 3—229f
巴奇奥 Baccio DELLA PORTA 意大利画家 2—114c
巴奇巴奇 Budge Budge 印度市镇 3—230a
巴奇-基什孔 Bács-Kiskun 匈牙利州名 2—125a
巴奇勒 Batchelor, Joy 英国动画片作者 2—274b
巴奇恰 Baciccia 罗马画家 2—118e
巴乔达尼奥洛 Baccio D'AGNOLO 意大利木雕师、建筑师 2—114b
巴乔克人 Badjok (people) 非洲民族 2—130b
巴乔克韦人 Bajokwe (people) 非洲民族 2—153c
巴切莱特 Bachelet, Michelle 智利总统 2—118a
巴切勒 Bacheller, Irving (Addison) 美国记者、作家 2—118b
巴丘什科夫 Batyushkov, Konstantin Nikolayevich 俄国诗人 2—284b
巴热 Bagé 巴西城市 2—134e
巴萨 Bassar 多哥城镇 2—268a
巴萨 Baza 西班牙城市 2—298d
巴萨拉布 Basarab, Matthew 瓦拉几亚国君 2—255e
巴萨纳维奇乌斯 Basanavičius, Jonas 立陶宛医生 2—255d
巴萨尼 Bassani, Giorgio 意大利作家 2—267d
巴萨诺 Bassano, Jacopo 威尼斯画派画家 2—267e
巴萨诺-德尔格拉帕 Bassano del Grappa 意大利城镇 2—268a
巴萨诺公爵 Bassano, Hugues-Bernard Maret, duke (duc) de 法国外交家 2—267e
巴萨诺亲王 Basano, Manuel de Godoy, Prince (príncipe) de 西班牙首相 2—255e
巴萨万 Basāvan 莫卧儿帝国画家 2—255f
巴塞 Bassac (Laos) 老挝城市 2—267d
巴塞 Pakxé 老挝城镇 12—554c
巴塞尔 Basel 瑞士城市 2—256f
巴塞尔城市半州 Basel-Stadt 瑞士半州 2—257c
巴塞尔动物园 Basel Zoological Garden 瑞士私立动物园 2—257c
巴塞尔会议 Basel, Council of 天主教会会议 2—257b
巴塞尔曼 Bassermann, Albert 德国戏剧、电影演员 2—268e
巴塞尔曼 Bassermann, Ernst 德国政治家 2—268f
巴塞尔乡村半州 Basel-Landschaft 瑞士半州 2—257b
《巴塞尔信纲》 Basel, Confession of 基督教新教信仰声明 2—257a
巴塞尔艺术博物馆-公共艺术收藏馆 Kunstmuseum-Öffentliche Kunstsammlung Basel 瑞士文物、艺术收藏馆 9—399b
巴塞河 Pa Sak River 泰国河流 12—530d
巴塞罗 Barcelo, Gertrudis 墨西哥女商人 2—223b
巴塞罗那 Barcelona 西班牙省份 2—223c
巴塞罗那 Barcelona 西班牙城市 2—223d
巴塞罗那 Barcelona 委内瑞拉城市 2—225b
巴塞罗那椅 Barcelona chair 家具 2—225b
巴塞洛米厄斯 Bartholomaeus ANGLICUS 英国百科全书编纂人 2—250a
巴塞洛缪 Bartholomew, John George 英国地图制图家 2—250d
巴塞洛缪一世 Bartholomew I 东正教牧首 2—250b
巴塞圣苏 Basse Santa Su 冈比亚城镇 2—268b
巴塞特管 basset horn 乐器 2—268f
巴塞特洛 Bassetlaw 英格兰区名 2—269b
巴瑟尔顿 Busselton 澳大利亚城镇 3—286f
巴瑟斯特 Bathurst 澳大利亚城市 2—278a
巴瑟斯特 Bathurst 加拿大城市 2—278a
巴瑟斯特 Bathurst (The Gambia) 冈比亚首都 2—278b
巴瑟斯特伯爵(第三) Bathurst, Henry Bathurst, 3rd Earl 英国政治家 2—278b
巴瑟斯特岛 Bathurst Island 澳大利亚岛屿 2—278b
巴瑟斯特岛 Bathurst Island 加拿大岛屿 2—278b
巴森吉猎狗 basenji 狗品种 2—257d
巴珊 Bashan 巴勒斯坦古国 2—257e
巴生 Kelang 马来西亚城镇 9—215a
巴生港 Port Kelang 马来西亚港口 13—445f
巴师夏 Bastiat, (Claude-) Frédéric 法国经济学家 2—271c
巴湿伐那陀 Pārśvanātha 印度耆那教救世主 13—64e
巴什波祖克 bashi-bazouk 奥斯曼帝国雇佣兵 2—257f
巴什基尔采夫 Bashkirtseff, Marie 俄裔法国作家、艺术家 2—258a
巴什基尔人 Bashkir 突厥民族 2—258a
巴什科尔托斯坦 Bashkortostan 俄罗斯行政区域 2—258b
巴士底日 Bastille Day 法国节日 2—271f
巴士底狱 Bastille, the 法国国家监狱 2—271e
巴士拉 Basra 伊拉克城市 2—266b
巴氏染色 Pap smear 疾病检查方法 13—18b
巴氏杀菌法 pasteurization 食物防腐 13—82e
巴氏涂片 Papanicolaou's stain (medicine) 疾病检查方法 13—21e
巴思 Barth, Jean (French privateer) 法国私掠船船长 2—248e
巴思 Barth, John (Simmons, Jr.) 美国作家 2—248e

巴思伯爵(第一) Bath, William Pulteney, 1st Earl of, Viscount Pulteney of Wrington, Baron of Hedon 英国辉格党政客 2—277a
巴思伯爵和侯爵 Bath, earls and marquesses of 英国封爵贵族 2—276f
巴思大十字勋章获得者 G.C.B. 巴思勋位中最高等级者 7—40e
巴思二等爵士 K.C.B. 英国勋位 9—208b
巴思二等女爵士 D.C.B. 英国勋位 5—186a
巴思侯爵(第一) Bath, Thomas Thynne, 1st Marquess of, Viscount Weymouth, Baron Thynne of Warmister 英国政治家 2—277a
巴思下级爵士勋位 C.B. 英国勋位 3—545f
巴思最高荣誉勋位 Bath, The Most Honourable Order of the 英国勋位 2—276f
巴斯 Bath 英格兰城市 2—276a
巴斯 Bath 美国缅因州城市 2—276c
巴斯 Bath 美国北卡罗来纳州城镇 2—276c
巴斯 Bass, Charlotta Spears 美国编辑、民权活动家 2—266f
巴斯 Buss, Frances (Mary) 英国教育家 3—286f
巴斯 Bass, George 英国外科医生、海员 2—267a
巴斯 Bass, Sam 美国不法之徒 2—267b
巴斯比 Busby, Sir Matt 英国足球运动员 3—280f
巴斯德 Pasteur, Louis 法国化学家、微生物学家 13—81d
巴斯德氏杆菌病 pasteurellosis 细菌性疾病 13—82e
巴斯德氏杆菌属 Pasteurella 细菌学 13—82d
巴斯蒂安 Bastian, Adolf 德国人种学家 2—271b
巴斯蒂昂-勒帕热 Bastien-Lepage, Jules 法国画家 2—271d
巴斯蒂克 Bastwick, John 英格兰宗教狂热分子 2—272a
巴斯蒂亚 Bastia 法国城市 2—271a
巴斯-东北萨默塞特 Bath and North East Somerset 英格兰单一政区 2—277b
巴斯夫公司 BASF Aktiengesellschaft 德国公司 2—257e
巴斯海峡 Bass Strait 澳大利亚海峡 2—267c
巴斯金 Baskin, Leonard 美国雕刻家 2—264c
巴斯科姆 Bascom, Florence 美国地质学家 2—256a
巴斯科姆 Bascom, William R. 美国人类学家 2—256a
巴斯克地区 Basque Country 法国文化区 2—265c
巴斯克地区 Basque Country 西班牙自治区 2—265d
巴斯克港 Port aux Basques (Canada) 加拿大城镇 13—444c
巴斯克民族主义党 Basque Nationalist Party 西班牙政党 2—266a
巴斯克人 Basque 欧洲民族 2—265a
巴斯克斯·德·艾利翁 Vazquez de Ayllón, Lucas 西班牙探险家 17—483f
巴斯克维尔 Baskerville, John 英国印刷商和发明家 2—263a
巴斯克语 Basque language 欧洲语言 2—265e
巴斯克祖国与自由 Euzkadi Ta Azkatasuma (Basque organization) 西班牙政治组织 6—177d
巴斯孔塞洛斯 Vasconcelos, José 墨西哥教育家 17—476f
巴斯孔塞洛斯-索萨 Vasconcelos e Sousa, Luiz de 葡萄牙政治家 17—476f
巴斯马赤暴乱 Basmachi Revolt 中亚细亚暴乱 2—264e
巴斯塔姆 Basṭām 伊朗古城 2—270e
巴斯塔奈人 Bastarnae 欧洲民族 2—270e
巴斯泰得 bastide 欧洲村庄或集镇的形式 2—271d
巴斯特尔 Basse-Terre 法国瓜德罗普岛屿 2—268d
巴斯特尔 Basse-Terre 法国瓜德罗普城市 2—268d
巴斯特尔 Basseterre 圣基茨和尼维斯首都 2—269b
巴斯特罗普 Bastrop 美国城市 2—272a
巴斯特人 Baster 非洲民族集团 2—270f
巴斯托 Barstow 美国城市 2—247f
巴斯托 Barstow, Stan 英国小说家 2—248a
巴斯托阶 Barstovian stage 地质学 2—247f
巴斯维尔 Bassville, Nicolas-Jean Hugou de 法国新闻工作者 2—270b
巴斯鱼 bass 鱼类 2—266e
巴松皮埃尔 Bassompierre, François de 法国军人、外交家 2—269e
巴苏库人 Basuku (people) 刚果(金)民族 2—272b
巴苏鲁安 Pasuruan 印度尼西亚城市 13—84b
巴梭马 bar Sauma, Rabban 景教教士 2—214f
巴索夫 Basov, Nikolay Gennadiyevich 苏联物理学家 2—265a
巴索利绘画 Basohli painting 印度画派 2—264e
巴塔哥尼亚沙漠 Patagonia 美洲荒漠 13—84b
巴塔克人 Batak 印度尼西亚民族 2—273d
巴塔克人基督教会 Batak Protestant Christian Church 印度尼西亚基督教会 2—273e
巴塔里亚会员 Patarine 中世纪意大利改革家 13—84d
巴塔利亚 Batalha 葡萄牙城镇 2—273e
巴塔尼 Battānī, al- 阿拉伯天文学家 2—280e
巴塔瓦诺湾 Batabanó, Gulf of 加勒比海的海湾 2—273b
巴塔维人 Batavi 古代日耳曼人部落 2—274a
巴塔耶 Bataille, (Félix-) Henry 法国剧作家 2—273c
巴塔耶 Bataille, Georges 法国作家 2—273b
巴泰勒米-圣-伊莱尔 Barthélemy-Saint-Hilaire, Jules 法国哲学家、政治家 2—249b
巴泰斯克 Bataysk 俄罗斯城市 2—274b
巴坦群岛 Batan Islands 菲律宾群岛 2—273f
巴特 Butt, Dame Clara (Ellen) 英国歌唱家 3—291e
巴特 Butt, Isaac 爱尔兰民族主义领袖 3—291f
巴特 Barth, Karl 基督教神学家 2—248f
巴特 Bate, W(alter) Jackson 美国作家 2—274c
巴特迪克海姆 Bad Dürkheim 德国城市 2—126a
巴特尔 Battle 英格兰城镇 2—282c
巴特尔 Battle, Kathleen 美国歌剧歌员 2—282c
巴特尔弗里尔山 Bartle Frere, Mount 澳大利亚山名 2—250f
巴特尔福德 Battleford 加拿大城镇 2—283b
巴特尔克里克 Battle Creek 美国城市 2—282d
巴特尔斯维尔 Bartlesville 美国城市 2—250f
巴特菲尔德 Butterfield, William 英国建筑师 3—292e
巴特甘德斯海姆 Bad Gandersheim 德国城市 2—126b
巴特戈德斯贝格 Bad Godesberg 德国波恩市区名 2—126b
巴特哈尔茨堡 Bad Harzburg 德国城市 2—126c
巴特洪堡 Bad Homburg 德国城市 2—126c
巴特克罗伊茨纳赫 Bad Kreuznach 德国城市 2—126d
巴特库斯 Butkus, Dick 美国橄榄球运动员 3—289d
巴特拉姆 Bartram, John 美国博物学家 2—253c
巴特莱特海渊 Bartlett Deep (Caribbean Sea) 加勒比海海沟 2—251c
巴特赖兴哈尔 Bad Reichenhall 德国城市 2—126d
巴特勒 Butler, Alban 英国天主教司铎、教育家 3—289e
巴特勒 Butler, Benjamin F(ranklin) 美国政治家、军官 3—289e
巴特勒 Butler, (Frederick) Guy 南非诗人 3—289f
巴特勒 Butler, Henry Montagu 英国哈罗公学校长 3—290a
巴特勒 Butler, James 爱尔兰将军 3—290b
巴特勒 Butler, Joseph 英国圣公会主教 3—290b
巴特勒 Butler, Nicholas Murray 美国教育家、政治家 3—290b
巴特勒 Butler, Pierce 美国最高法院大法官 3—290c
巴特勒 Butler, Piers 英国贵族 3—290d
巴特勒 Butler, Reg 英国雕刻家 3—290e
巴特勒 Butler, R(ichard) A(usten), Baron Butler of Saffron Walden 英国政治家 3—290d
巴特勒 Butler, Thomas 英国贵族 3—291b
巴特勒特 Bartlett, John 美国书商、编辑 2—251a
巴特勒特 Bartlett, John Russell 美国目录学家 2—251b
巴特里克 Butterick, Ebenezer 美国制造商 3—293c
巴特里克,圣 Patrick, Saint 爱尔兰的主保圣人 13—90e
巴特里克王子岛 Prince Patrick Island 加拿大岛屿 13—515a
巴特利特 Bartlett, Sir Frederic C(harles) 英国心理学家 2—250f
巴特寮 Pathet Lao 老挝政党 13—87e

巴特列-奥多涅斯 Batlle y Ordóñez, José 乌拉圭总统 2—279e
巴特列·贝雷斯 Batlle Berres, Luis 乌拉圭总统 2—279e
巴特曼 Batman 土耳其城镇 2—280a
巴特曼斯湾 Batemans Bay 澳大利亚小海湾 2—274f
巴特芒 battement 芭蕾舞动作 2—280f
巴特梅根特海姆 Bad Mergentheim 德国城市 2—126d
巴特那 Patna 印度城市 13—89b
巴特那绘画 Patna painting 印度画派 13—89c
巴特纳 Batna 阿尔及利亚城市 2—280a
巴特瓦人 Batwa (people) 非洲俾格米人 2—284a
巴特沃思 Butterworth 南非城镇 3—293e
巴特西 Battersea 英格兰地区 2—281c
巴特西珐琅器皿 Battersea enamelware 英国珐琅制品 2—281d
巴特亚姆 Bat Yam 以色列城市 2—273a
巴特伊施尔 Bad Ischl 奥地利城镇 2—126c
巴滕 Batten, Jean 新西兰航空员 2—281a
巴滕贝格 Battenberg, Louis Alexander, prince of 英国海军元帅 2—281b
巴滕贝格家族 Battenberg FAMILY 欧洲著名家族 2—281a
巴滕贝格亲王 Battenberg, Louis Francis Albert Victor Nicholas, prince of 英国政治家 2—281c
巴滕施泰因男爵 Bartenstein, Johann Christoph, Freiherr von (baron of) 奥地利政治家 2—248c
巴滕斯 Boutens, Pieter Cornelis 荷兰诗人、学者 3—89d
巴提奈 Bāṭinah, Al- 阿曼沿海平原 2—279c
巴通阶 Bathonian Stage 地质学 2—277d
巴统 Batumi 格鲁吉亚城市 2—283f
巴图西人 Batusi (people) 俄罗斯、蒙古民族 2—284a
巴颓尼叶派 Bāṭinīyah 伊斯兰教派别 2—279c
巴吞鲁日 Baton Rouge 美国城市 2—280b
巴吞他尼 Pathum Thani 泰国城镇 13—88a
巴托 Bartow 美国城市 2—253c
巴托尔德 Bartold, Vasily V(ladimirovich) 俄国人类学家 2—252b
巴托尔德 Barthold, Wilhelm 俄国人类学家 2—249d
巴托尔迪 Bartholdi Frédéric-Auguste 法国雕刻家 2—249e
巴托里 Batory, Stefan (Polish king) 波兰国王 2—280c
巴托里 Báthory, Sigismund 特兰西瓦尼亚公爵 2—277e
巴托林 Bartholin, Caspar Berthelsen 丹麦医学家、神学家 2—249e
巴托林 Bartholin, Erasmus 丹麦物理学家 2—249f
巴托林 Bartholin, Thomas 丹麦解剖学家 2—249f
巴托罗人 Batoro (people) 乌干达民族 2—280c
巴托洛梅 Bartholomé, (Paul-) Albert 法国雕刻家 2—250a
巴托洛米奥 Bartolomeo, Fra 意大利画家 2—252c
巴托尼 Batoni, Pompeo Girolamo 意大利画家 2—280c
巴托什 Batoche 加拿大未建制地 2—280b
巴韦 Bhave, Vinoba 印度社会改革家 2—452a
巴文德王朝 Bāvand DYNASTY 伊朗古代王朝 2—288c
巴乌 bawu 中国气鸣乐器 2—290e
巴乌希斯 Baucis (Greek mythology) 希腊神话人物 2—284e
巴西 Brazil 南美洲国家 3—130f
巴西 Bassi, Agostino 意大利细菌学家 2—269d
巴西茶 Brazilian tea 类似茶的饮料 3—132f
巴西尔 Basil 统治者之名 2—259e
巴西尔 Basil 摩尔多瓦大公 2—260d
巴西尔 Basil THE CHAMBERLAIN 拜占廷太监大臣 2—260f
巴西尔 Basil, Colonel W. de 俄国演出经理人 2—261b
巴西尔(豺狼) Basil THE WOLF 摩尔多瓦大公 2—261b
巴西尔(马其顿人) Basil THE MACEDONIAN 拜占廷皇帝 2—261b
巴西尔登 Basildon 英格兰区名 2—261d
巴西尔登 Basildon 英格兰城镇 2—261d
巴西尔二世 Basil II 拜占廷皇帝 2—260b
《巴西尔法典》 Basilica 拜占廷法典 2—262a
巴西尔一世 Basil I 拜占廷皇帝 2—259e
巴西果 Brazil nut 植物 3—132d
巴西莱 Basile, Giambattista 那不勒斯军人、诗人 2—261d
巴西兰 Basilan 菲律宾岛屿、省份 2—261c
巴西勒(安西耳的) Basil OF ANCYRA 希腊基督教神学家 2—260f
巴西勒礼仪,圣 Basil, Liturgy of Saint 宗教礼仪 2—261b
巴西勒派 Basilian 基督教隐修派别 2—261e
巴西里德斯 Basilides 诺斯替教一派的创始人 2—262c
巴西利奥 Basilio, Carmen 美国职业拳击运动员 2—262c
巴西利奥·达·加马 Basílio da Gama 巴西诗人 2—262d
巴西利奥斯 Basilios 埃塞俄比亚正教会领袖 2—262d
巴西利卡 basilica 古罗马公共建筑物 2—261f
巴西利卡塔 Basilicata 意大利区名 2—262b
巴西利斯库斯 Basiliscus 东罗马僭帝 2—262d
巴西利亚 Brasília 巴西首都 3—125a
巴西利亚高原 Brazilian Highlands 巴西高原 3—132e
巴西民主运动党 Brazilian Democratic Movement, Party of the (PMDB) 巴西政党 3—132e
《巴西日报》 Jornal do Brasil, O 巴西报纸 9—88a
巴西肉烧豆 feijoada completa 巴西民族菜肴 6—266c
巴西社会民主党 Brazilian Social Democratic Party (PSDP) 巴西政党 3—132f
巴西石油总公司 Petrobrás 巴西公司 13—210a
巴西松 Brazilian pine (tree) 木本植物 3—132f
巴西苏木 brazilwood 木本植物 3—132f
巴西特 Bassett, John Spencer 美国历史学家 2—269c
巴西亚努斯 Bassianus, Varius Avitus 罗马皇帝 2—269e
巴西亚努斯·亚历克西亚努斯 Bassianus Alexianus, Gessius (Roman emperor) 罗马皇帝 2—269e
巴西洋流 Brazil Current 大西洋洋流分支 3—132d
巴西银行 Brasil, Banco do 巴西金融机构 3—124f
巴西棕榈 babassu palm (*Orbignya martiana*, *O. oleifera* or *O. speciosa*) 木本植物 2—107f
巴西棕榈蜡 carnauba wax 棕榈叶蜡 3—466c
巴希奥 Bajío 墨西哥地区 2—153c
巴希亚(本·约瑟·伊本·帕库达) Bahya ben Joseph ibn Pakuda 犹太教哲学家 2—145a
巴锡 Bassey, Dame Shirley 威尔士歌唱家 2—269c
巴锡 Bassi, Ugo 意大利爱国志士 2—269e
巴锡"伯爵" Basie, Count 美国爵士乐史上杰出人物 2—259d
巴锡基维 Paasikivi, Juho Kusti 芬兰总统 12—530e
巴辛 Bassin (U.S. Virgin Islands) 美属维尔京群岛港口 2—269e
巴亚 Baiae 意大利古城 2—146e
巴亚尔 Bayard, Pierre Terrail, seigneur de 法国军人 2—293d
巴亚尔塔港 Puerto Vallarta 墨西哥城市 14—17c
巴亚马雷 Baia Mare 罗马尼亚城市 2—146c
巴亚蒙 Bayamón 波多黎各城镇 2—293b
巴亚莫 Bayamo 古巴城市 2—293a
巴亚人 Baya 非洲民族 2—292f
巴颜喀拉山 Bayar Har Shan 中国青海省山脉 2—293c
巴彦图门 Bayan Tumen (Mongolia) 蒙古城镇 2—293c
巴耶 Bajer, Fredrik 丹麦政治家 2—153b
巴耶 Bayer, Johann 德国天文学家 2—294d
巴耶杜帕尔 Valledupar 哥伦比亚城市 17—454d
巴耶塞特 Bayezid 奥斯曼苏丹之名 2—296a
巴耶塞特二世 Bayezid II 奥斯曼苏丹 2—296b
巴耶塞特一世 Bayezid I 奥斯曼苏丹 2—296b
巴耶乌 Bayeu, Francisco 西班牙画家 2—295c
巴伊 Bailly, Jean-Sylvain 法国天文学家 2—149e
巴伊夫 Baïf, Jean-Antoine de 法国诗人 2—146e
巴伊·杰塔 Bhāī Jeṭhā (Sikh Gurū) 锡克教宗教领袖 2—449c
巴伊亚 Bahia 巴西州名 2—141f
巴伊亚 Bahia (city, Brazil) 巴西城市 2—142a
巴伊亚群岛 Bay Islands 洪都拉斯岛群 2—292a

巴以维安湖 Ballivián, Lake 南美洲更新世时期湖泊 2—178b
巴音塔拉 Pai-yin T'ai-lai (China) 中国城市 12—547d
巴永 Baillon, Andre 比利时小说家 2—149c
巴尤 Baillou, Guillaume de 法国医师 2—149d
巴约 Bayeux 法国城镇 2—295d
巴约挂毯 Bayeux Tapestry 中世纪刺绣工艺品 2—295f
巴约讷 Bayonne 法国城镇 2—297e
巴赞 Bazaine, Achille(-François) 法国元帅 2—298f
巴赞 Bazin, Hervé 法国作家 2—299d
巴赞 Bazin, Henri-Émile 法国工程师 2—299c
巴赞 Bazin, René(-François-Nicolas-Marie) 法国小说家 2—299f
巴赞 Basin, Thomas 法国主教 2—262f
巴泽多 Basedow, Johann Bernhard 德国教育改革家 2—256e
巴泽尔杰特 Bazalgette, Sir Joseph William 英国工程师 2—299a
巴泽兹湾 Buzzards Bay 大西洋小海湾 3—297a
巴曾 Barzun, Jacques 美国教师 2—254f
巴扎尔甘 Bazargan, Mehdi 伊朗教育家、政治人物 2—299a
巴扎鲁托岛 Bazaruto Island 莫桑比克岛屿 2—299b
巴扎兹 Bazzāz, 'Abd al-Raḥmān 伊拉克政治家 2—300b
巴占 Bacan 印度尼西亚岛屿 2—113c
巴真武里 Prachin Buri 泰国城镇 13—477f
巴兹敦 Bardstown 美国城市 2—226e
巴兹里斯克蛇 basilisk (legendary serpent) 欧洲古代传说 2—262e
巴兹纳 Bazna, Elyesa 德国间谍 2—300a
巴祖卡火箭筒 bazooka 武器 2—300a
巴佐尔 Bajor, Gizi 匈牙利女演员 2—153c
芭比娃娃 Barbie 塑料娃娃 2—221b
芭蕉 Bashō 日本俳句诗人 2—258d
芭蕉科 Musaceae 植物学 11—500a
芭蕾 ballet 舞蹈 2—175d
芭蕾舞动作 ballet movement 舞蹈 2—176b
芭蕾舞裙 tutu 舞蹈 17—296e
芭蕾舞位置 ballet position 舞蹈 2—176c
鲃 barb 鱼类 2—217c
拔都 Batu 钦察汗国创建者 2—283e
拔河 tug-of-war 体育 17—259f
拔克拉弗饼 baklava 食品 2—157e
拔染印花 discharge printing 纺织工业 5—338e
拔示巴 Bathsheba 《圣经》人物 2—277f
拔牙者密谋 Tiradentes Conspiracy 巴西历史 17—109a
菝葜属 Smilax 植物学 15—442e
跋蒂吠檀多 Bhaktivedanta, A(bhay) C(haranaravinda) 印度宗教领袖 2—450a
跋娑 Bhāsa 印度梵文剧作家 2—451c
跋娑伐 Basava 印度教改革家 2—255f
把杆 barre 芭蕾舞 2—241d
钯(Pd) palladium 化学元素 12—568a
靶恩 barn 计量单位 2—232f
靶理论 target theory 生物学 16—481e
耙 harrow 农具 7—491d
罢黜百家 bachubaijia 中国历史 2—118d
罢工 strike 16—277c
霸王计划 Overlord, Operation 第二次世界大战史 12—512a
霸王龙 tyrannosaur 古生物学 17—310a
霸鹟 tyrant flycatcher 鸟类 17—310f
霸鹟科 Tyrannidae (bird family) 动物学 17—310a
白矮星 white dwarf star 天文学 18—231e
白澳政策 White Australia Policy 澳大利亚反亚洲移民政策 18—231a
白柏 white cedar 木本植物 18—231d
白斑 leukoplakia 疾病 10—44b
白斑病 leukoderma (medicine) 疾病 10—44a
白斑羚 nyala (species *Tragelaphus angasi*) 哺乳动物 12—308b
白板 album 罗马布告栏 1—186a
白板 tabula rasa 哲学 16—416f
白贝罗 Buys Ballot, Christophorus H(enricus) D(idericus) 荷兰气象学家 3—296a
白贝罗定律 Buys Ballot's law 气象学 3—296b
白璧德 Babbitt, Irving 美国评论家、教师 2—108c
白变豆菜 white sanicle (plant) 草本植物 18—233f
白采尔科维 Belaya Tserkov 乌克兰城市 2—350f
白菜 Chinese cabbage 植物 4—168e
白城 Baicheng 中国城市 2—146d
白炽灯 incandescent lamp 照明灯 8—350d
白崇禧 Bai Chongxi 中国将领 2—145c
白川英树 Shirakawa Hideki 日本化学家 15—322c
白带 leukorrhea 疾病 10—44b
白蛋白 albumin 蛋白质 1—186a
白蛋白尿 albuminuria (medicine) 医学 1—186b
白癜风 vitiligo 疾病 18—24e
白俄罗斯 Belarus 东欧国家 2—349c
白俄罗斯 White Russia 欧洲东部旧地区名 18—233f
白俄罗斯岭 Belorussian Ridge 白俄罗斯高地 2—371a
白俄罗斯语 Belorussian language 东斯拉夫语言 2—370f
白额雁 white-fronted goose (species *Anser albifrons*) 鸟类 18—232c
白额鼬 grison 哺乳动物 7—316c
白垩 chalk 地质学 4—32b
白垩纪 Cretaceous Period 地质学 5—9a
白粉病 powdery mildew 植物病害 13—471e
白粉蝶 white butterfly 昆虫 18—231c
白粉藤属 Cissus 植物学 4—246e
白腹长尾猴 mona monkey (species *Cercopithecus mona*) 哺乳动物 11—328a
白腹鼬 ichneumon 哺乳动物 8—315e
白宫 White House 美国总统正式官邸 18—232d
白鲑 whitefish 鱼类 18—235c
白海 White Sea 北冰洋海域 18—233f
白海—波罗的海运河 White Sea—Baltic Canal 俄罗斯水道 18—234a
白河天皇 Shirakawa 日本天皇 15—322b
白喉 diphtheria 传染病 5—331d
白喉林莺 whitethroat (*Sylvia communis*) 鸟类 18—236e
白狐 white fox 哺乳动物 18—232c
白花菜目 Capparales 植物学 3—429d
白花丹目 Plumbaginales 植物学 13—375e
白花葫芦 white-flowered gourd 草本植物 18—232b
白花紫露草 wandering Jew 草本植物 18—90e
白化病 albinism 遗传缺陷疾病 1—183c
白化马 Albino 马品种 1—183e
白话文学 Baihua literature 中国文学 2—146f
白桦 white birch 木本植物 18—231b
白桦尺蛾 peppered moth (*Biston betularia*) 昆虫 13—153e
白鹏 wheatear 鸟类 18—220b
白金汉伯爵、侯爵和公爵 Buckingham, EARLS, MARQUESSES, AND DUKES OF 英格兰爵位 3—222f
白金汉公爵(第二) Buckingham, George Villiers, 2nd Duke of 英格兰政治家 3—223c
白金汉公爵(第二) Buckingham, Henry Stafford, 2nd Duke of 英格兰贵族 3—223a
白金汉公爵(第三) Buckingham, Edward Stafford, 3rd Duke of 英格兰贵族 3—223a
白金汉公爵(第一) Buckingham, George Villiers, 1st Duke of 英格兰政治家 3—223b
白金汉公爵(第一) Buckingham, Humphrey Stafford, 1st Duke of 英格兰贵族 3—222f
白金汉宫 Buckingham Palace 英国王宫 3—223e

白金汉和诺曼比公爵(第一) Buckingham and Normanby, John Sheffield, 1st duke of 英格兰政治家 3—223d
白金汉侯爵(第一) Buckingham, George Nugent Temple Grenville, 1st Marquess of 英格兰政界人士 3—223c
白金汉郡 Buckinghamshire 英格兰郡名 3—223f
白金汉郡花边 Buckinghamshire lace 工艺品 3—223f
白金汉运河 Buckingham Canal (India) 印度水道 3—223e
白鲸 beluga (*Delphinapterus leucas*) 哺乳动物 2—372c
白鲸 white whale 哺乳动物 18—235b
白居易 Bai Juyi 中国唐代诗人 2—145d
白拉奕 Kuala Belait 文莱城镇 9—386c
白镴 pewter 合金 13—215b
白兰地 brandy 酒精饮料 3—122d
白兰度 Brando, Marlon, (Jr.) 美国戏剧、电影演员 3—121d
白兰士 Blache, Paul Vidal de La 法国地理学家 2—509a
白浪划艇竞赛 white-water racing (canoeing) 体育项目 18—235b
白劳德 Browder, Earl (Russell) 美国共产党领袖 3—188e
白里安 Briand, Aristide 法国政治家 3—148b
白里欧 Brieux, Eugène 法国戏剧家 3—154f
白栎 white oak 木本植物 18—233b
白莲教起义 White Lotus Rebellion 中国清代农民起义 18—232f
白蛉 sand fly 昆虫 15—25c
白蛉热 pappataci fever 疾病 13—26a
白领犯罪 white-collar crime 法律 18—231e
白令 Bering, Vitus (Jonassen) 丹麦航海家 2—407d
白令海 Bering Sea 太平洋最北端水域 2—407f
白令海底峡谷 Bering Canyon 北太平洋海底峡谷 2—407e
白令海峡 Bering Strait 北冰洋和白令海间海峡 2—408a
白令海争端 Bering Sea Dispute 美、英、加间争端 2—407f
白榴石 leucite 矿物 10—42f
白榴岩 leucitite 岩石 10—42f
白龙江 Bailong Jiang 中国河流 2—149f
白龙尾 Bach Long Vi 越南岛屿 2—117f
白鹭 egret 鸟类 5—558e
白鹭羽 aigrette 饰物 1—140b
白洛嘉 Broca, Paul 法国外科医生 3—172d
白马寺 Baima Temple 中国佛教寺院 2—150c
白马语 Baima language 中国藏族语言 2—150a
白麦迥乃 Padma 'byung-gnas (Buddhist mystic) 印度教密宗僧人 12—540c
白毛茛 goldenseal (species *Hydrastis canadensis*) 草本植物 7—191b
白茅 cogon grass (*Imperata cylindrica*) 植物 4—332a
白眉猴 mangabey 哺乳动物 10—457a
白描 baimiao 中国绘画表现形式 2—150c
白内障 cataract 疾病 3—521f
白尼罗河 White Nile River 苏丹河流 18—233a
白袍 alb 天主教服饰 1—171f
白硼钙石 priceite 矿物 13—505c
白硼锰石 sussexite 矿物 16—361c
白朴 Bai Pu 中国元代杂剧作家 2—145f
白槭 white maple 木本植物 18—232f
白起 Bai Qi 中国战国时期秦国名将 2—146a
白铅矿 cerussite 矿物 4—12f
白人灵歌 blue-eyed soul 音乐 2—547e
白人至上 white supremacy 种族观点 18—234d
白萨西里 Basāsīrī, Arslān al-Muẓaffar al- 伊斯兰教军事领袖 2—255e
白色刺绣 whitework 工艺品 18—236e
白色堆饰 bianco sopra bianco 意大利陶器装饰 2—456d
白色云母 white mica 矿物 18—232f
白色主日 Whitsunday (Christian festival) 宗教节日 18—240b
白沙国家保护区 White Sands National Monument 美国新墨西哥州保护区 18—233f
白沙瓦 Peshāwar 巴基斯坦城市 13—193a
白鲨 white shark (species *Carcharodon carcharias*) 鱼类 18—234b
白山 Baishan 中国城市 2—152a
白蛇根 white snakeroot (*Eupatorium rugosum*) 草本植物 18—234c
白霜 hoarfrost 气象学 8—109d
白隼 gyrfalcon (*Falco rusticolus*) 鸟类 7—392e
白陶 white pottery 中国古代陶器 18—233e
白铁矿 marcasite 矿物 10—493d
白铜 cupronickel 合金 5—66d
白头澳鹏 tang 鸟类 16—461a
白头雕 bald eagle (*Haliaetus leucocephalus*) 鸟类 2—164c
白头鼬 tayra (*Eira barbara*) 哺乳动物 16—506e
白臀蜜鸟 apapane (*Himatione sanguinea*) 鸟类 1—405f
白臀叶猴 douc 哺乳动物 5—399c
白尾长尾猴 vervet 哺乳动物 17—526f
白尾鹿 white-tailed deer (*Odocoileus virginianus*) 哺乳动物 18—234f
白沃尔特河 White Volta River 西非河流 18—235b
白钨矿 scheelite 矿物 15—111a
白细胞 leukocyte 细胞学 10—43f
白细胞间素 interleukin (IL) 蛋白质 8—409e
白细胞减少症 leukopenia 疾病 10—44b
白细胞增多症 leukocytosis 疾病 10—44a
白鲜类 dittany 植物 5—345b
白藓 white moss 苔藓植物 18—233a
白辛树属 Pterostyrax 植物学 13—567e
白须长尾猴 DeBrazza's monkey (*Cercopithecus neglectus*) 哺乳动物 5—198b
白血病 leukemia 疾病 10—43e
白羊毛披肩带 pallium 教皇礼服 12—569a
白羊王朝 Ak Koyunlu 土库曼部落联盟 1—152a
白羊座 Aries 天文学 1—471e
白杨 Bai Yang 中国电影演员 2—146a
白洋淀 Baiyangdian 中国湖泊 2—152b
白衣派 Śvetāmbara 印度耆那教派别 16—368d
白衣神父 White Father 天主教非洲传信会会士 18—232b
白衣修士 White Canon (religious order) 宗教 18—231d
白衣修士 White Monk 宗教 18—233a
白衣修士剧院 Whitefriars Theatre 伦敦私人剧院 18—235e
白蚁 termite 昆虫 16—552b
白益王朝 Būyid DYNASTY 阿拉伯古王朝 3—206f
白银 Baiyin 中国城市 2—152b
白银时代 Silver Age 拉丁文学 15—376e
白隐 Hakuin 日本高僧 7—416f
白釉彩陶 faience blanche 法国陶器 6—213e
白语 Bai language 中国语言 2—145f
白云观 Baiyun Monastery 中国道教宫观 2—152c
白云矿区 Bayun Kuangqu 中国区名 2—298c
白云母 muscovite 矿物 11—501e
白云母薄片 isinglass 矿物 8—464b
白云岩 dolomite 岩石 5—367d
白云鱼 white cloud (species *Tanichthys albonubes*) 鱼类 18—231d
白噪音 white noise 音乐 18—233b
白罩衣 surplice 宗教礼服 16—355e
白哲特 Bagehot, Walter 英国经济学家 2—134e
白枝海绵属 Leucosolenia 动物学 10—43a
白芷 cow parsnip 草本植物 4—556d
白珠树属 Gaultheria 植物学 7—33f
白足鼠 white-footed mouse 哺乳动物 18—232b
白族 Bai 中国民族 2—145b
百多禄 Pigneau de Béhaine, Pierre-Joseph-Georges 天主教教士 13—299f

百分温标 centigrade temperature scale (physical science) 物理学 3—565b
百夫长 centurion 古罗马军队 4—6a
百官法庭 centumviri 古罗马法庭 4—6a
百官志 Notitia Dignitatum 古罗马文件 12—274b
百合 lily 草本植物 10—99f
百合花饰 fleur-de-lis 法国王室图案 6—358e
百合科 Liliaceae 植物学 10—97a
百合目 Liliales 植物学 10—97b
百户 hundred 英国历史 8—252d
百花挂毯 millefleur tapestry 工艺品 11—224c
百花齐放,百家争鸣 Hundred Flowers Bloom and Hundred Schools of Thought Contend 中国科学文化发展方针 8—252f
百花香瓶 potpourri 陶瓷容器 13—464e
百货公司 department store 商品零售企业 5—249f
百济 Paekche 朝鲜古王国 12—541b
百科全书 encyclopaedia 综合性工具书 6—70d
《百科全书》 Cyclopaedia 英国两卷本百科全书 5—86f
《百科全书》 Encyclopédie, L' 法文百科全书 6—72b
百浪多息 Prontosil 药物 13—534a
百老汇 Broadway 英格兰村庄 3—172b
百老汇 Broadway 美国纽约街名 3—172c
百里香 thyme (*Thymus vulgaris*) 植物 17—75c
百灵 lark 鸟类 9—500c
百灵庙 Bailingmiao 中国城镇 2—148f
百慕大 Bermuda 英属自治殖民地 2—418a
百慕大高压 Bermuda high 气象学 2—418e
百慕大赛 Bermuda Race 海洋帆船比赛 2—418f
百慕大三角区 Bermuda Triangle 北大西洋海区 2—418f
百衲被 crazy quilt 纺织品 4—574b
百年节 Secular Games 古罗马节日 15—178d
百年战争 Hundred Years' War 欧洲历史 8—252f
百日 Hundred Days 法国历史 8—252d
百日 Hundred Days 美国历史 8—252e
百日菊 zinnia 草本植物 18—556a
百日咳 whooping cough 急性呼吸道传染病 18—242b
百日维新 Hundred Days of Reform 中国历史 8—252e
百色 Baise 中国城市 2—151e
百事可公司 PepsiCo, Inc. 美国大联合企业 13—154d
百叶 louver 建筑 10—247f
百褶裙式椅 farthingale chair 家具 6—244e
柏科 Cupressaceae 植物学 5—66b
柏木陆均松 rimu (*Dacrydium cupressinum*) 木本植物 14—303b
柏树 cypress 木本植物 5—90d
柏松 cypress pine 木本植物 5—90f
柏油娃娃 Tar-Baby 美洲黑人民间故事 16—477b
摆 pendulum 悬挂摆动的物体 13—137d
摆榻节 lectisternium 古希腊、罗马风俗 9—552c
败酱草科 Valerianaceae 植物学 17—452a
败血症 septicemia 病理现象 15—219e
拜 By, John 英国军事工程师 3—297b
拜奥尔 Byoir, Carl 美国公共关系创始人 3—298e
拜巴尔斯一世 Baybars I 马木路克王朝的苏丹 2—293f
拜达里文化 Badarian culture 埃及古文化阶段 2—127d
拜达欧尼 Badā'ūnī, 'Abd al-Qādir 印度历史学家 2—127e
拜德尔·哈尼·贾莱代特 Badr Khānī Jāladat 库尔德人领袖 2—131b
拜德尔之战 Badr, Battle of 伊斯兰教军事胜利 2—131a
拜蒂克洛 Batticaloa 斯里兰卡城镇 2—282c
拜恩 Bayern (Germany) 德国州名 2—295a
拜恩阿尔卑斯山 Bayerische Alpen (Germany-Austria) 德-奥山脉 2—294e
拜恩湖 Bayrisches Meer (Germany) 德国湖泊 2—298b
拜恩林山 Bayerischer Wald 德国山区 2—294f
拜恩斯代尔 Bairnsdale 澳大利亚城镇 2—151d
拜尔 Bayer, Herbert 美国版画家 2—294c
拜尔 Beyer, Jinny 美国拼布设计师 2—447e
拜尔盖 Barqah (North Africa) 北非历史地区 2—239e
拜尔斯 Beyers, C. F. 南非政治家、将领 2—447f
拜尔扎伊尼 Berzsenyi, Dániel 匈牙利诗人 2—435b
拜耳 Baeyer, (Johann Friedrich Wilhelm) Adolphvon 德国化学家 2—133c
拜耳 Bayer, Friedrich 德国实业家 2—294c
拜耳公司 Bayer AG 德国化工医药公司 2—294e
拜哈丁·祖海尔 Bahā'ad-Dīn Zuhayr 阿拉伯诗人 2—139d
拜哈尔 Bahār, Mu ḥammad Taqī 伊朗诗人 2—141c
拜科莫 Baie-Comeau 加拿大城镇 2—146e
拜科努尔 Baikonur 俄罗斯太空中心 2—147c
拜拉达河 Baradā 叙利亚河流 2—215d
拜拉尼 Baranī, Ziyā'-ud-Dīn 印度史学家 2—216c
拜拉祖里 Balādhurī, al- 阿拉伯历史学家 2—159c
拜朗姆 bayram (Islām) 伊斯兰节日 2—297f
拜伦 Byron, George Gordon Byron, 6th Baron 英国诗人 3—300a
拜伦 Byron, John 英国海军上将 3—300d
拜伦贝 Byron Bay 澳大利亚城镇 3—300e
拜伦男爵(第一) Byron, John Byron, 1st Baron 英格兰骑士 3—300d
拜罗伊特 Bayreuth 德国城市 2—297f
拜尼阿斯甘 Beni Isguene 阿尔及利亚城镇 2—384f
拜塞尔 Beissel, Conrad 美国基督教人士 2—347a
拜斯 Bais 菲律宾城市 2—151e
拜斯泰采巴尼亚 Besztercebánya (Now Slovakia) 斯洛伐克城镇 2—439d
拜特布里奇 Beit Bridge 津巴布韦城镇 2—347a
拜特拉 Baṭrā (ancient Arabia) 阿拉伯古城 2—280c
拜特伦 Bethlen, Gábor 匈牙利国王 2—442f
拜特伦 Bethlen, István, Count 匈牙利总理 2—443b
拜图洛斯 baetylus 希腊宗教中圣石 2—133b
拜亚尔 Bayar, (Mahmud) Celâl 土耳其总统 2—293c
拜耶 Beyer, Absalon Pederssøn 挪威思想家 2—447e
拜占廷 Byzantium 古希腊城市 3—302f
拜占廷帝国 Byzantine Empire 世界历史 3—301c
拜占廷圣咏 Byzantine Chant 希腊东正教音乐 3—301b
拜占廷式礼仪 Byzantine rite 东正教礼仪 3—302f
拜占廷希腊语 Byzantine Greek language 古希腊语言 3—302d
拜占廷旋律型 ēchos 音乐 5—523d
拜占廷艺术 Byzantine art 中世纪艺术 3—300f
稗 barnyard grass (*Echinochloa crus-galli*) 草本植物 2—237c
稗麦 tare 草本植物 16—481d
扳机鱼 triggerfish 鱼类 17—219b
扳手 wrench 工具 18—344b
班巴拉人 Bambara 马里部落 2—186b
班巴拉诸邦 Bambara states 西非两个独立国家 2—186b
班堡 Bamburgh 英格兰堂区 2—187c
班鲍 Benbow, John 英国海军上将 2—376c
班贝格 Bamberg 德国城市 2—186c
班彪 Ban Biao 中国东汉史学家 2—188b
班伯里 Banbury 英格兰城镇 2—189f
班伯里 Bunbury 澳大利亚港镇 3—251b
班布蒂人 Bambuti (people) 刚果(金)民族 2—187d
班布里奇 Bainbridge 美国城市 2—150d
班布里奇 Banbridge 北爱尔兰城镇 2—189f
班布里奇 Bainbridge, William 美国海军军官 2—150e
班禅喇嘛 Panchen Lama 藏传佛教活佛 13—7d
班超 Ban Chao 中国东汉名将 2—188b
班达 Bānda 印度城镇 2—191f

班达 Bandar (India) 印度城市 2—192d
班达 Banda, H(astings) Kamuzu 马拉维总统 2—191f
班达伯格 Bundaberg 澳大利亚城市 3—251e
班达海 Banda Sea 南太平洋西部海域 2—192c
班达拉奈克 Bandaranaike, S(olomon) W(est) R(idgeway) D(ias) 斯里兰卡总理 2—192f
班达拉奈克(夫人) Bandaranaike, Sirimavo Ratwatte Dias 斯里兰卡总理 2—193b
班达尼工艺 bāndhanī work 印度扎染法 2—194b
班达群岛 Banda Islands 印度尼西亚岛群 2—192b
班达人 Banda 中非民族 2—191f
班达·辛格·巴哈都尔 Bandā Singh Bahādur 印度锡克族领袖 2—192d
班达亚齐 Banda Aceh 印度尼西亚城市 2—192b
班戴洛 Bandello, Matteo 意大利作家 2—194a
班德尔马 Bandırma 土耳其港口城镇 2—195b
班德拉 Bandeira (Filho), Manuel (Carneiro de Sousa) 巴西诗人 2—193d
班德拉斯 Banderas, Antonio 西班牙电影演员 2—194b
班德利尔 Bandelier, Adolph 美国人类学家 2—193e
班德利尔国家保护地 Bandelier National Monument 美国考古区 2—193f
班登 Bandon 爱尔兰城镇 2—195d
班登河 Bandon, River 爱尔兰河流 2—195d
班登河畔德罗赫德 Droichead na Bandan (Ireland) 爱尔兰城镇 5—426b
班迪内利 Bandinelli, Baccio 意大利雕刻家 2—195a
班迪内利 Bandinelli, Rolando 教皇 2—195b
班迪耶拉兄弟 Bandiera, Attilio; and Bandiera, Emilio 意大利革命者 2—194f
班都拉 Bandula, Maha 缅甸将军 2—195d
班都拉 bandura 乌克兰民族乐器 2—196a
班敦杜 Bandundu 刚果(金)城市 2—195e
班多拉琴 bandurria 弦乐器 2—196b
班夫 Banff 加拿大城镇 2—197b
班夫 Banff 苏格兰港口 2—197c
班夫-巴肯 Banff and Buchan 苏格兰区名 2—197d
班夫国家公园 Banff National Park 加拿大国家公园 2—197d
班夫郡 Banffshire 苏格兰历史郡名 2—197d
班福德 Bamford, Samuel 英国改革家 2—187e
班戈 Bangor 北爱尔兰城镇 2—201f
班戈 Bangor 美国城市 2—201f
班戈 Bangor 威尔士城市 2—202a
班公错 Bangong Co 中国湖泊 2—201e
班古拉 Bānkura 印度城镇 2—206d
班固 Ban Gu 中国东汉史学家 2—188d
班吉 Bangui 中非共和国首都 2—202a
班加罗尔 Bangalore 印度城市 2—197f
班加西 Banghāzī 利比亚城市 2—198b
班克黑得 Bankhead, Tallulah (Brockman) 美国演员 2—205b
班克罗夫特 Bancroft 加拿大村庄 2—190a
班克罗夫特 Bancroft (Zambia) 赞比亚矿区城镇 2—190a
班克罗夫特 Bancroft, Ann 美国探险家 2—190a
班克罗夫特 Bancroft, Edward 英国间谍 2—190b
班克罗夫特 Bancroft, George 美国历史学家 2—190c
班克罗夫特 Bancroft, Hubert Howe 美国历史学家 2—190d
班克罗夫特 Bancroft, Sir Squire 英国演员、剧团经理 2—190d
班克斯 Banks, Sir Joseph 英国探险家 2—205f
班克斯 Banks, Nathaniel P. 美国政治家、将领 2—206a
班克斯半岛 Banks Peninsula 新西兰半岛 2—206c
班克斯岛 Banks Island 加拿大岛屿 2—206b
班克斯群岛 Banks Islands 太平洋西南部岛群 2—206c
班纳克 Banneker, Benjamin 美国数学家、天文学家 2—206e
班纳曼 Bannerman, Henry 英国首相 2—207a
班纳坦 Bannatyne, George 苏格兰诗歌著者 2—206d
班乃 Panay 菲律宾岛屿 13—7a
班尼奥罗人 Banyoro (people) 乌干达民族 2—209f
班尼斯特 Bannister, Sir Roger (Gilbert) 英国神经病学家 2—207c
班尼亚 Bania 印度种姓 2—202f
班宁维尔 Banningville 刚果(金)城市 2—207b
班诺克本 Bannockburn 苏格兰城镇 2—207e
班诺克本战役 Bannockburn, Battle of 苏格兰历史 2—207e
班诺克人 Bannock 北美印第安部落 2—207d
班普顿 Bampton, John 英国牧师 2—188a
班契埃利 Banchieri, Adriano 意大利作曲家 2—189f
班热维尔 Bingerville 科特迪瓦城镇 2—477b
班塞尔·苏亚雷斯 Bánzer Suárez, Hugo 玻利维亚总统 2—210b
班桑 Bansang 冈比亚城镇 2—208b
班什 Binche 比利时城镇 2—476c
班舒瓦 Binchois, Gilles 比利时作曲家 2—476d
班斯法瑟 Bairnsfather, (Charles) Bruce 英国连环漫画家 2—151e
班斯卡-比斯特里察 Banská Bystrica 斯洛伐克城镇 2—208e
班斯特德 Banstead (England) 英格兰地区 2—208f
班斯瓦拉 Bānswāra 印度城市 2—208f
班特里湾 Bantry Bay 爱尔兰大西洋岸水湾 2—209a
班廷 Banting, Sir Frederick Grant 加拿大医师 2—209a
班图家园 Bantu Homeland (South Africa) 南非地区 2—209b
班图人 Bantu peoples 非洲民族 2—209b
班图斯坦 Bantustan (South Africa) 南非地区 2—209c
班图诺语言 Bantu languages 非洲语言 2—209b
班韦乌卢湖 Bangweulu 赞比亚湖泊 2—202b
班维尔 Bainville, Jacques 法国政论家 2—150f
班扬 Bunyan, John 英国清教徒牧师 3—255a
班扬 Bunyan, Paul 美国传说中的伐木巨人 3—255d
班昭 Ban Zhao 中国东汉史学家 2—188e
班珠尔 Banjul 冈比亚首都 2—203d
班卓琴 banjo 弦乐器 2—203b
班卓琴鲨 banjo shark 鱼类 2—203d
班卓琴座钟 banjo clock 时钟 2—203c
般度族五兄弟 Pāṇḍavas 印度传说人物 13—9b
斑赤蛱蝶 painted lady 昆虫 12—550b
斑点巴斯鱼 calico bass 鱼类 3—345c
斑点病 pinta 皮肤病 13—315e
斑点龟 spotted turtle (*Clemmys guttata*) 小型淡水龟 16—160c
斑点尾巴 Spotted Tail 美国印第安人首领 16—160b
斑点鳟 speckled trout 鱼类 16—13d
斑蝶 milkweed butterfly 昆虫 11—220b
斑腹雁 specklebelly 鸟类 16—13d
斑海豹 harbour seal (*Phoca vitulina*) 哺乳动物 7—470d
斑鸠 turtledove (*Streptopelia turtur*) 鸟类 17—294b
斑鸠菊 ironweed 植物 8—451f
斑鹿 chital (species *Cervus axis*, sometimes *Axis axis*) 哺乳动物 4—181b
斑马 zebra 哺乳动物 18—504d
斑马凤蝶 zebra swallowtail butterfly (*Iphiclides marcellus*, *Graphium marcellus*, or *Papilio marcellus*) 昆虫 18—504f
斑马鱼 zebra fish 鱼类 18—504f
斑猫 tabby 猫品种 16—413d
斑片试验 patch test 过敏性皮肤对照试验 13—84f
斑铜矿 bornite 矿物 3—53e
斑纹釉陶器 spatterware 陶器 16—9f
斑岩铜矿床 porphyry copper deposit 矿物 13—442d
斑蝇 otitid fly 昆虫 12—497f
斑噪钟鹊 chillawong 鸟类 4—157b
斑疹伤寒 typhus 疾病 17—309b
瘢痕 cicatrization 躯体装饰 4—234a

瘢痕 scar 生理学 15—103e
瘢痕疙瘩 keloid 皮肤病 9—218d
坂本龙马 Sakamoto Ryōma 日本皇权主义者 14—534b
坂仓准三 Sakakura Junzō 日本建筑师 14—534a
坂出 Sakaide 日本城市 14—533f
板齿犀 Elasmotherium 古生物学 6—13e
板谷波山 Itaya Hazan 日本陶瓷家 8—488f
板胡 banhu 中国弦乐器 2—202c
板块构造学 plate tectonics 板块学说 13—351c
板龙属 Plateosaurus 古生物学 13—353a
板门店 P'anmunjŏm 朝鲜村庄 13—14a
板硼钙石 inyoite 矿物 8—428f
板桥 Banqiao 中国台湾城市 2—208b
板球 CRICKET 体育项目 16—80a
板球 cricket 体育项目 5—11f
板上画 panel painting 美术 13—10c
板式变化体 banshi bianhuati 中国戏曲音乐结构 2—208d
板钛矿 brookite 矿物 3—183e
板条 lath 建筑材料 9—511a
板网球 paddle tennis 体育项目 12—538f
板岩 slate 地质 15—426d
板椅 wainscot chair 家具 18—66c
板垣退助 Itagaki Taisuke, HAKUSHAKU (Count) 日本自由党创立者 8—483b
板状甲状腺炎 ligneous thyroiditis 疾病 10—94c
板足鲎 eurypterid 古生物学 6—173e
版画制作 printmaking 艺术 13—517f
半阿里乌主义 Semi-Arianism 基督教异端 15—204b
半爆破音 semiplosive (semantics) 语言学 15—205f
半贝拉基主义 Semi-Pelagianism 基督教神学 15—204b
半边莲科 Lobeliaceae 植物学 10—173b
半导体 semiconductor 物理学 15—204c
半导体存储器 semiconductor memory 计算机存储设备 15—204f
半导体辐射探测器 semiconductor radiation detector 仪器 15—204f
半导体器件 semiconductor device 电子电路器件 15—204d
半导体闸流管 thyristor 电学 17—76b
半岛电视台 Jazeera, Al- 阿拉伯语有线电视新闻网 8—555b
半岛战役 Peninsular Campaign 美国历史 13—139e
半岛战争 Peninsular War 欧洲历史 13—139f
半刚石 ballas 工业用金刚石 2—175c
半棘肌 semispinalis muscle 解剖学 15—205f
半抗原 hapten 生物化学 7—468a
半女自在天 Ardhanārīśvara 印度教神祇 1—458d
半坡村 Pan-p'o-ts'un 中国仰韶文化遗址所在地 13—3d
半坡遗址 Banpo site 中国仰韶文化遗址 2—208a
半蹼白翅鹬 willet (*Catoptrophorus semipalmatus*) 鸟类 18—259f
半蹼雁 semipalmated goose 鸟类 15—205f
半蹼鹬 dowitcher 鸟类 5—406a
半人半马怪 centaur 希腊神话 3—564f
半人马星 Centaur object 天文学 3—565b
半人马座 α Alpha Centauri 恒星 1—249f
半人马座 β Beta Centauri 恒星 2—440b
半人马座 ω 星团 Omega Centauri 天文学 12—414e
半日花 sun rose 木本植物 16—337a
半乳糖 galactose 化合物 6—549d
半乳糖耐量试验 galactose tolerance test 医学检查 6—549d
半乳糖血症 galactosemia 遗传病 6—549d
半山 Banshan 中国政治家 2—208c
半山遗址 Banshan site 中国文化遗址 2—208c
半深海带 bathyal zone 海洋生态领域 2—278c
半诗 katauta 日本诗体 9—194e
半衰期 half-life 放射物理学 7—421d
半索动物 hemichordate 无脊椎动物 8—9a
半田 Handa 日本城市 7—456c
半纤维素 hemicellulose 化合物 8—9a
半箱龟 semibox turtle 爬行动物 15—204c
半押韵 half rhyme 诗歌韵律 7—421e
半音应用 chromaticism 音乐 4—211d
半影 penumbra 天文学 13—150a
半圆形后堂 chevet 建筑 4—135d
半圆形馅饼 turnover 食品 17—292b
半约 Half-Way Covenant 北美基督教 7—421f
半月鱼 halfmoon (*Medialuna californiensis*) 鱼类 7—422b
半知菌纲 Deuteromycetes 植物学 5—268e
半足鹑 hemipode 鸟类 8—10a
伴奏 accompaniment 音乐 1—46c
绊根草 Bermuda grass (*Cynodon dactylon*) 草本植物 2—418e
瓣 valve 解剖学 17—457a
瓣蹼鹬 phalarope 鸟类 13—218b
邦 Bang, Bernhard Lauritz Frederik 丹麦兽医 2—197e
邦 Bang, Herman 丹麦小说家 2—197e
邦阿西楠人 Pangasinan 菲律宾民族 13—11d
邦巴迪埃公司 Bombardier Inc. 加拿大制造商 3—19d
邦巴管 bombard 乐器 3—19c
邦巴辛绸 bombazine 纺织品 3—22b
邦板牙河 Pampanga River 菲律宾河流 12—576e
邦板牙人 Pampangan 菲律宾民族 12—576e
邦达 Benda, Julien 法国小说家 2—377a
邦达马河 Bandama River 科特迪瓦河流 2—192d
邦当 Bontemps, Arna (Wendell) 美国作家 3—36a
邦德 Bond, Carrie Jacobs 美国作曲家 3—26a
邦德 Bonde, Gustaf, Friherre (Baron) 瑞典政治家 3—26d
邦德 Bond, Julian 美国议员、民权运动领袖 3—26b
邦德 Bond, Sir Robert 纽芬兰自由党领袖 3—26b
邦德 Bond, William Cranch 美国天文学家 3—26c
邦德布鲁克 Bound Brook 美国城镇 3—83a
邦德反照率 Bond albedo 天文学 3—26d
邦德菲尔德 Bondfield, Margaret (Grace) 英国工会领袖 3—26e
邦德里峰 Boundary Peak 美国山峰 3—83a
邦迪 Bondi, Sir Hermann 英国数学家、宇宙学家 3—26e
邦迪 Bundy, McGeorge 美国政府官员 3—252b
邦迪 Bundy, Ted 美国罪犯 3—252c
邦蒂富尔 Bountiful 美国城市 3—83c
"邦蒂"号 Bounty 英国武装运输船 3—83c
邦蒂群岛 Bounty Islands 新西兰外围群岛 3—83c
邦杜库 Bondoukou 科特迪瓦城镇 3—26f
邦菲尔斯 Bonfils, Frederick Gilmer 美国报纸出版商 3—29a
邦盖群岛 Banggai Islands 印度尼西亚群岛 2—198a
邦戈尔 Bongor 乍得城镇 3—29e
邦戈鼓 bongo drum 拉丁美洲小鼓 3—29e
邦戈人 Bongo 苏丹民族 3—29c
邦加 Bangka 印度尼西亚岛屿 2—198b
邦加 Gbarnga 利比里亚城市 7—40e
邦加尔 Bongars, Jacques, SEIGNEUR (lord) DE BAULDRY ET DE LA CHESNAYE 法国外交家、古典学者 3—29b
邦角 Bon, Cape 突尼斯半岛 3—23a
邦卡莱溢洪道 Bonnet Carre Spillway 美国水利设施 3—33e
《邦咯条约》 Pangkor Engagement 英国政府与马来人条约 13—11d
邦科国家公园 Banco, Parc National du 科特迪瓦国家公园 2—190a
邦科姆帕格尼 Boncompagni, Ugo (pope) 教皇 3—25e
邦克岛 Bunker Island (Pacific Ocean) 太平洋岛屿 3—253a
邦克朗陶 Bang Klang Thao (Thai ruler) 泰国统治者 2—197f
邦克山战役 Bunker Hill, Battle of 美国历史 3—252f
邦库尔 Boncourt, Louis-Charles-Adélaïde Chamisso de 德国作家 3—

25e
《邦联条例》 Confederation, Articles of 美国宪法 4—419f
邦美蜀 Buon Me Thuot 越南城市 3—255f
邦纳 Bonner, Edmund 伦敦主教 3—33b
邦纳 Bunner, Henry Cuyler 美国作家 3—253a
邦纳尼河 Ponnāni River 印度河流 13—426d
邦纳斯费里 Bonners Ferry 美国城市 3—33c
邦纳维尔湖 Bonneville, Lake 美国史前湖泊 3—34a
邦纳维尔盐沼 Bonneville Salt Flats 美国赛车场 3—34a
邦奈亚尔河 Ponnaiyār River 印度河流 13—426d
邦尼 Bonny 尼日利亚油港 3—34d
邦尼 Bonney, Mary Lucinda 美国教育家、改革者 3—34b
邦尼 Bonney, Thérèse 美国摄影家、作家 3—34b
邦尼人 Bangni (people) 亚洲民族 2—201e
邦尼湾 Bonny, Bight of (Atlantic Ocean) 大西洋海湾 3—34d
邦尼与克莱德 Bonnie and Clyde 美国匪帮 3—34c
邦宁 Bonnin, Gertrude 美国作家、改革家 3—34c
邦塞拉德 Benserade, Isaac de 法国宫廷文人 2—390b
邦沙夫特 Bunshaft, Gordon 美国建筑师 3—254a
邦山 Bong Range 利比里亚山脉 3—29b
邦施泰滕 Bonstetten, Karl Viktor von 瑞士作家 3—35d
邦斯勒王朝 Bhonsle DYNASTY 印度王朝 2—452f
邦特 Bonthe 塞拉利昂海港 3—36b
邦特博克国家公园 Bontebok National Park 南非公园 3—35e
邦特库 Bontecou, Lee 美国艺术家 3—35f
邦特莱因 Buntline, Ned 美国冒险家、作家 3—254c
邦滕佩利 Bontempelli, Massimo 意大利作家 3—35f
邦韦辛(里瓦的) Bonvesin DA LA RIVA 意大利教师、诗人 3—36d
邦维尔 Banville, (Étienne-Claude-Jean-Baptiste-) Théodore (-Faullain) de 法国诗人 2—209d
邦兹 Bonds, Barry L(amar) 美国职业棒球选手 3—26a
帮派说唱乐 gangsta rap 黑人说唱乐的主要风格 7—1d
帮助犯 abettor 法律 1—23a
梆子 slit drum 乐器 15—433e
梆子腔 bangziqiang 中国戏剧声腔 2—202b
绑架 kidnapping 法律 9—269f
绑架奴隶 blackbirding 澳大利亚历史 2—518a
绑腿 puttee 护腿 14—39a
蚌 mussel 软体动物 11—512d
蚌虾 clam shrimp 甲壳动物 4—258e
棒球 baseball 体育 2—256b
棒球 BASEBALL 体育项目 16—57a
棒球名人堂 Baseball Hall of Fame 美国纪念性大厅 2—256d
棒球式台球 baseball 体育 2—256d
棒术 cane fencing 自卫技巧 3—399e
棒状病毒 rhabdovirus 病毒 14—257c
傍人属 Paranthropus 人类学 13—38d
磅 libra 计量单位 10—77d
磅 pound 英美计量单位 13—468e
磅清扬 Kâmpóng Chhnăng 柬埔寨城镇 9—151a
磅士卑 Kâmpóng Spœ 柬埔寨城镇 9—151b
磅税 poundage (English subsidy) 英国津贴 13—469d
磅同 Kâmpóng Thum 柬埔寨城镇 9—151b
磅逊 Kâmpóng Saôm 柬埔寨城镇 9—151a
磅湛 Kâmpóng Cham 柬埔寨城镇 9—151a
镑 pound (monetary unit) 货币单位 13—468e
包岑 Bautzen 德国城市 2—288a
包出制 putting-out system (manufacturing) 经济学 14—39b
包茨 Bouts, Dirck 尼德兰画家 3—90b
包尔绍德-奥包乌伊-曾普伦 Borsod-Abaúj-Zemplén 匈牙利州名 3—57a
包豪斯 Bauhaus 德国建筑设计学校 2—286b
包贾尼 Batthyány, Lajos, Count (Gróf) 匈牙利政治家 2—282b
包科尼山脉 Bakony Mountains 匈牙利山脉 2—157f
包鲁 Bauru 巴西城市 2—288a
包铝硬铝合金 alclad 冶金学 1—189e
包奇 Bauchi 尼日利亚州名 2—284d
包奇 Bauchi 尼日利亚城镇 2—284d
包奇高原 Bauchi Plateau (Nigeria) 尼日利亚高原 2—284e
包氏兽 Bauria 古生物学 2—287f
包塔 Bauta 古巴城市 2—288a
包塔利斯 Portalis, Jean-Étienne-Marie 法国律师、政治家 13—448c
包头 Baotou 中国城市 2—211f
包头地毯 Baotou carpet 中国工艺品 2—212b
包头龙 Euoplocephalus 恐龙 6—161f
包旋螺 Euphemites 古生物学 6—162b
包姚 Baja 匈牙利城镇 2—152d
包拯 Bao Zheng 中国北宋政治家 2—210d
包装 packaging 商品处理技术 12—537e
孢粉学 palynology 植物学 12—575e
孢子 spore 生物学 16—42b
孢子虫 sporozoan 原生动物 16—42d
孢子囊群 sorus 植物学 15—523c
孢子丝菌病 sporotrichosis 传染病 16—42d
孢子体 sporophyte 生物学 16—42c
胞间连丝 plasmodesma 植物学 13—349d
胞嘧啶 cytosine 化合物 5—96a
胞饮作用 pinocytosis 生理学 13—315b
胞族 phratry 社会群体 13—268c
褒奖 Citation 赛马 4—247e
褒曼 Bergman, Ingrid 电影演员 2—405f
雹 hail 气象学 7—410f
饱和 saturation 化学、物理学 15—78f
饱满感 satiety 生理学 15—77b
宝贝 cowrie 海产螺类 4—559d
宝坻 Baodi 中国天津市辖区 2—210f
宝鸡 Baoji 中国城市 2—211c
宝剑骑士团 Brothers of the Sword, Order of the 十字军组织 3—187a
宝洁公司 Procter & Gamble Company 美国公司 13—526d
宝莱坞 Bollywood 印度电影制片工业 3—15b
宝马汽车公司 Bayerische Motoren Werke AG (BMW) 德国汽车公司 2—294e
宝瓶座 Aquarius 天文学 1—426f
宝庆 Pao-ch'ing (China) 中国城市 13—17f
宝山 Baoshan 中国上海市区名 2—211e
宝生 Ratnasambhava 大乘佛教 14—163d
宝石 gemstone 矿物 7—50d
宝石玻璃制品 cameo glass 工艺品 3—371c
宝石红玻璃 ruby glass 深红色玻璃 14—438f
宝石兰 jewel orchid 草本植物 9—8a
宝塚 Takarazuka 日本城市 16—440e
宝座 curule chair 古罗马椅子 5—73d
宝座 throne 御座 17—66d
保安团 Heimwehr 奥地利地方组织 7—567d
保安语 Bonan language 中国语言 3—23f
保安族 Bonan 中国民族 3—23e
保大 Bao Dai 越南皇帝 2—210c
保德河 Powder River 美国河流 13—471d
保定 Baoding 中国城市 2—211a
保尔 Paul, Alice 美国女权运动领袖 13—99a
保尔 Paul, Jean 德国作家 13—99b
保尔 Paul, Wolfgang 德国物理学家 13—99b
保尔丁 Paulding, James Kirke 美国剧作家 13—99d
保和 Bohol 菲律宾岛屿 3—4a
保和海 Bohol Sea 北太平洋西部海 3—4b

保护关系 clientship 古罗马 4—289d
保护关系 protectorate 国际关系 13—542e
《保护文学和艺术作品的国际公约》 International Convention for the Protection of Literary and Artistic Works 版权法 8—414c
保护主义 protectionism 经济学 13—542c
保加利亚 Bulgaria 欧洲国家 3—242a
保加利亚惨案 Bulgarian Horrors 保加利亚历史 3—243e
保加利亚公教会 Bulgarian Catholic Church 天主教会 3—243e
保加利亚节奏 Bulgarian rhythm (music) 音乐 3—244f
保加利亚农民国家联盟 Bulgarian Agrarian National Union 保加利亚政党 3—243d
保加利亚人 Bulgar 东欧民族 3—241d
保加利亚文学 Bulgarian literature 欧洲文学 3—244a
保加利亚语 Bulgarian language 欧洲语言 3—243f
保加利亚正教会 Bulgarian Orthodox Church 东正教教会 3—244e
保甲制度 baojia system 中国历史 2—211d
保健组织 health maintenance organization (HMO) 社会福利 7—540d
保克海峡 Palk Strait 孟加拉湾海峡 12—566f
保拉 Paola 马耳他城镇 13—18a
保利 Paoli, Pasquale 意大利政治家 13—18a
保利努斯,圣 Paulinus, Saint 基督教传教士 13—100e
保龄球 bowling 球戏 3—95e
保龄球 BOWLING 体育项目 16—64a
保卢斯 Paulus, Friedrich von 德国元帅 13—101a
保罗 Paul 统治者之名 13—93e
保罗 Paul 希腊国王 13—93e
保罗 Paul 俄国沙皇 13—95b
保罗 Paul the Deacon 伦巴第历史学家、诗人 13—98f
保罗 Paolo uccello (painter) 佛罗伦萨画家 13—18b
保罗 Paul, Les 美国演奏家 13—99b
保罗 Paul, Lewis 英国发明家 13—99b
保罗 Paolo, Veneziano 威尼斯画家 13—18b
保罗(埃吉纳的) Paul of Aegina 亚历山大医师、作家 13—95d
保罗(萨莫萨塔的) Paul of Samosata 异端主教 13—95e
保罗(威尼斯的) Paul of venice 意大利神学家、哲学家 13—95f
保罗(底比斯的),圣 Paul of Thebes, saint 基督教苦修家 13—95e
保罗(诺拉的),圣 Paulinus of Nola, Saint 基督教诗人 13—100e
保罗(十字架的),圣 Paul of the Cross, Saint 天主教士 13—95e
保罗(使徒),圣 Paul the Apostle, Saint 基督教使徒 13—95f
保罗(隐士),圣 Paul the Hermit, Saint 基督教苦修家 13—98f
《保罗达腓立比人书》 Philippians, The Letter of Paul to the 《新约》 13—239d
《保罗达腓利门书》 Philemon, The Letter of Paul to 圣经《新约》 13—232c
《保罗达哥林多人书》 Corinthians, Letters of Paul to the 《新约》 4—508a
《保罗达歌罗西人书》 Colossians, The Letter of Paul to the 《新约》 4—365c
《保罗达加拉太人书》 Galatians, The Letter of Paul to the 《新约》 6—550f
《保罗达罗马人书》 Romans, The Letter of Paul to the 《新约》的一卷 14—373a
《保罗达提多书》 Titus, The Letter of Paul to 《新约》 17—121d
《保罗达提摩太书》 Timothy, Letters of Paul to 《新约》 17—102c
《保罗达帖撒罗尼迦人书》 Thessalonians, letters of Paul to the 《新约》 17—36f
《保罗达以弗所人书》 Ephesians, The Letter of Paul to the 《新约》 6—95e
保罗-阿方索 Paulo Afonso 巴西城市 13—100f
保罗-阿方索瀑布 Paulo Afonso Falls 巴西瀑布 13—100f
保罗-邦库尔 Paul-Boncour Joseph 法国政治家、外交部长 13—99c
保罗二世 Paul II 教皇 13—93f
保罗六世 Paul VI 教皇 13—94f
保罗派 Paulician 基督教派别 13—100a
保罗亲王 Paul Karageorgević, Prince 南斯拉夫摄政王 13—95d
保罗三世 Paul III 教皇 13—94b
保罗斯(马其顿的) Paullus Macedonicus, Lucius Aemilius 罗马将军 13—100e
保罗四世 Paul IV 教皇 13—94d
保罗五世 Paul V 教皇 13—94e
《保罗行传》 Paul, Acts of 基督教外典伪经 13—98f
保罗一世,圣 Paul I, Saint 教皇 13—93f
保民官 tribune 罗马史 17—215a
保讷格尔 Bhavnagar 印度城镇 2—452a
保萨尼阿斯 Pausanias 斯巴达将领 13—101c
保萨尼阿斯 Pausanias 希腊旅行家、地理学家 13—101c
保食神 Ukemochi no Kami 神道教女神 17—325a
保释 bail 法律 2—147d
保守党 Conservative Party (Canada) 加拿大政党 4—445f
保守党 Conservative Party 英国政党 4—446a
保守力 conservative force 物理学 4—445e
保守派犹太教 Conservative Judaism 宗教 4—445f
保守主义 conservatism 政治学、哲学 4—445b
保卫北爱尔兰协会 Ulster Defence Association (UDA) 北爱尔兰准军事组织 17—332c
保卫共和联盟 Rally for the Republic 法国政党 14—133e
保卫同盟 Schutzbund 奥地利政治组织 15—136e
保温瓶 Thermos flask 器皿 17—35d
保险 insurance 金融 8—402e
保险丝 fuse 电路安全装置 6—532c
保幼激素 juvenile hormone 昆虫激素 9—122c
保元之乱 Hōgen Disturbance 日本历史 8—119c
《保障法》 Guarantees, Law of 意大利法律 7—342f
保证 guaranty and suretyship 法律 7—342f
保证工资计划 guaranteed wage plan 经济学 7—342e
保证金 margin 金融 10—505d
保证金 recognizance 英美法律 14—184b
鸨 bustard 鸟类 3—287c
葆朴 Bopp, Franz 德国语言学家 3—42e
堡礁 barrier reef 珊瑚礁 2—244a
报酬递减律 diminishing returns, law of 经济学 5—318e
报春花 primrose 草本植物 13—511e
报春花科 Primulaceae 植物学 13—511f
报春花目 Primulales 植物学 13—512a
报德运动 Hōtoku 日本宗教运动 8—191b
报恩的死人 grateful dead 民间故事 7—262e
报业辛迪加 newspaper syndicate 新闻机构 12—153b
报纸 newspaper 出版物 12—152d
抱朴子 Pao-p'u-tzu (alchemist) 中国道教哲学家、炼金术士 13—17f
豹 leopard (*Leo pardus*) 哺乳动物 10—27e
豹斑鸟 pardalote(bird) 鸟类 13—40a
豹蛾 leopard moth (*Zeuzera pyrina*) 昆虫 10—28b
豹类 panther 哺乳动物 13—16e
豹猫 leopard cat (*Felis bengalensis*) 哺乳动物 10—27f
豹猫 ocelot (*Felis pardalis*) 哺乳动物 12—331a
豹鲨 leopard shark (*Triakis semifasciata*) 鱼类 10—28c
豹蛙 leopard frog (*Rana pipiens*) 两栖动物 10—27f
豹蜥 leopard lizard 爬行动物 10—28a
豹形海豹 leopard seal (*Hydrurga leptonyx*) 哺乳动物 10—28b
鲍 Bow, Clara 美国电影演员 3—91d
鲍 Baugh, Sammy 美国橄榄球运动员 2—286a
鲍比契 Babits, Mihály 匈牙利诗人、作家 2—110d
鲍彻 Bourchier, John 英国作家 3—84f

鲍彻 Bourchier, Thomas 英格兰枢机主教 3—84f
鲍瓷 Bow porcelain 英国软质瓷 3—92b
鲍德勒 Bowdler, Thomas 英国慈善家、文人 3—92f
鲍德利 Powderly, Terence V. 美国劳工领袖 13—471e
鲍德温 Baldwin 国家统治者名 2—165c
鲍德温 Baldwin, Faith 美国作家 2—166b
鲍德温 Baldwin, Frank Stephen 美国发明家 2—166c
鲍德温 Baldwin, Henry 美国最高法院大法官 2—166c
鲍德温 Baldwin, James (Arthur) 美国小说家 2—166c
鲍德温 Baldwin, James Mark 美国哲学家、心理学家 2—166e
鲍德温 Baldwin, Matthias William 美国制造商 2—166f
鲍德温 Baldwin, Robert 加拿大政治家 2—166f
鲍德温 Baldwin, Roger Nash 美国民权活动家 2—167a
鲍德温 Baldwin, Stanley, 1st Earl Baldwin of Bewdley, Viscount Corvedale of Corvedale 英国首相 2—167b
鲍德温二世 Baldwin II Porphyrogenitus 君士坦丁堡皇帝 2—165d
鲍德温二世 Baldwin II 耶路撒冷国王 2—165f
鲍德温九世 Baldwin IX 君士坦丁堡皇帝 2—165f
鲍德温六世 Baldwin VI 君士坦丁堡皇帝 2—165f
鲍德温三世 Baldwin III 耶路撒冷国王 2—166a
鲍德温四世 Baldwin IV 耶路撒冷国王 2—166a
鲍德温五世 Baldwin V 耶路撒冷国王 2—166b
鲍德温一世 Baldwin I 比利时国王 2—165c
鲍德温一世 Baldwin I 佛兰德伯爵 2—165c
鲍德温一世 Baldwin I 耶路撒冷国王 2—165f
鲍登 Bowdoin, James 美国政治领袖、物理学家 3—93a
鲍迪奇 Bowditch, Nathaniel 美国数学家、天文学家 3—92e
鲍迪奇 Bowdich, Thomas Edward 英国旅行家、作家 3—92d
鲍迪奇曲线 Bowditch curve (geometry) 数学 3—92f
鲍迪辛 Baudissin, Wolf Heinrich, Count (Graf) von 德国外交家、文学家 2—285b
鲍顿 Boughton, Rutland 英国歌剧作曲家 3—78f
鲍厄里 Bowery, the 美国纽约街区 3—94e
鲍恩 Bowen 澳大利亚港镇 3—93b
鲍恩 Bowen, Catherine (Shober) 美国作家 3—93b
鲍恩 Bowen, Elizabeth (Dorothea Cole) 英国小说家 3—93c
鲍恩 Bowen, I(ra) S(prague) 美国天体物理学家 3—93d
鲍恩费尔德 Bauernfeld, Eduard von 奥地利剧作家 2—286a
鲍恩氏苏铁属 Bowenia 植物学 3—93f
鲍尔 Ball, Albert 英国战斗机驾驶员 2—172d
鲍尔 Ball, Sir Alexander John, 1st Baronet 英国海军少将 2—172e
鲍尔 Baur, Ferdinand Christian 德国神学家 2—287e
鲍尔 Bower, Frederick, Orpen 英国植物学家 3—94a
鲍尔 Bauer, Georg 德国科学家 2—285d
鲍尔 Bauer, Gustav (Adolf) 德国政治家 2—285d
鲍尔 Bauer, Harold 美国钢琴家 2—285e
鲍尔 Ball, John 英格兰农民起义领袖 2—172f
鲍尔 Ball, Lucille 美国演员 2—173a
鲍尔 Bauer, Otto 奥地利政治家 2—285e
鲍尔 Bauer, Sebastian Wilhelm Valentin 德国潜艇发明家 2—285f
鲍尔 Ball, Thomas 美国雕刻家 2—173b
鲍尔 Bower, Walter 苏格兰编年史著作者 3—94b
鲍尔班克 Bowerbank, James Scott 英国博物学家 3—94c
鲍尔弗 Balfour, Francis Maitland 英国动物学家 2—169a
鲍尔康 Balcon, Sir Michael 英国电影制片人 2—164a
鲍尔氏试验 Bauer's test (medicine) 医学试验 2—286a
鲍尔斯 Bowles, Chester (Bliss) 美国广告商、政治家 3—95d
鲍尔斯 Powers, Francis Gary 美国 U-2 侦察机驾驶员 13—475b
鲍尔斯 Powers, Hiram 美国雕刻家 13—475c
鲍尔斯 Bowles, William Lisle 英国诗人、教士 3—95d
鲍格米勒派 Bogomil 基督教派别 2—568d
鲍河 Bow River 加拿大河流 3—92c
鲍华 Power, Tyrone (Edmund) 美国演员 13—474b
鲍克 Bowker, Richard Rogers 美国编辑、出版者 3—95c
鲍勒尔 Bowral 澳大利亚城镇 3—96f
鲍勒人 Baule 非洲民族 2—286f
鲍里斯 Boris Godunov 俄国沙皇 3—52b
鲍里斯三世 Boris III 保加利亚国王 3—52a
鲍里斯一世 Boris I 保加利亚国王 3—51e
鲍里索夫 Borisov 白俄罗斯城市 3—52b
鲍里索格列布斯克 Borisoglebsk 俄罗斯城市 3—52b
鲍灵格林 Bowling Green 美国肯塔基州城市 3—96a
鲍灵格林 Bowling Green 美国俄亥俄州城市 3—96a
鲍令 Bowring, Sir John 英国作家、外交官 3—96f
《鲍令条约》 Bowring Treaty 泰国与英国条约 3—97a
鲍罗丁 Borodin, Aleksandr (Porfiryevich) 俄罗斯作曲家、科学家 3—54c
鲍罗廷 Borodin, Mikhail Markovich 共产国际驻中国代表 3—54e
鲍曼 Bowman, Isaiah 美国地理学家、教育家 3—96c
鲍曼 Bowman, Sir William 英国外科医师、组织学家 3—96d
鲍曼峰 Baumann Peak 多哥山峰 2—287c
鲍蒙特 Beaumont, Francis 英国诗人、剧作家 2—314c
鲍蒙特 Beaumont, Sir John 英国诗人 2—314d
鲍姆 Baum, L(yman) Frank 美国作家 2—287a
鲍姆 Baum, Vicki 美国小说家 2—287b
鲍姆巴赫 Baumbach, Rudolf 德国诗歌作者 2—287c
鲍姆加登 Baumgarten, Alexander Gottlieb 德国哲学家、教育家 2—287d
《鲍姆斯法》 Baumes Laws 美国刑法 2—287c
鲍宁造山幕 Bowning orogeny 地质学 3—96e
鲍恰尼 Batsányi, János 匈牙利政治诗人 2—280d
鲍氏东非人 Zinjanthropus boisei 古人类学 18—555d
鲍斯 Bowes, Edward 美国广播界先驱 3—94e
鲍斯 Bose, Subhas Chandra 印度革命者 3—59e
鲍斯高 Bosco, Saint John 意大利天主教士 3—59b
鲍斯戈尔 Baunsgaard, Hilmar (Tormod Ingolf) 丹麦政治家 2—287e
鲍斯-莱昂 Bowes-Lyon, Elizabeth Angela Marguerite (queen consort of George VI of Great Britain) 英国王后、乔治六世之妻 3—94f
鲍斯韦尔 Boswell, James 英国作家 3—67e
鲍特韦尔 Boutwell, George Sewall 美国政治家 3—90c
鲍威尔 Powell 美国城市 13—472a
鲍威尔 Powell, Anthony 英国小说家 13—472b
鲍威尔 Powell, Bud 美国爵士乐钢琴家 13—472c
鲍威尔 Powell, Cecil Frank 英国物理学家 13—472e
鲍威尔 Powell, Colin 美国将军和政治人物 13—472e
鲍威尔 Powell, Eleanor 美国电影演员 13—472f
鲍威尔 Powell, Enoch 英国政治家、议员 13—473a
鲍威尔 Powell, John Wesley 美国地质学家、人种学家 13—473b
鲍威尔 Bowell, Sir Mackenzie 加拿大出版商、政界领袖 3—93b
鲍威尔 Powell, Maud 美国小提琴演奏家 13—473d
鲍威尔 Powell, William 美国电影演员 13—473e
鲍威尔(小) Powell, Adam Clayton, Jr. 美国黑人牧师、人权运动领袖 13—472a
鲍威尔(小) Powell, Lewis F(ranklin), Jr. 美国最高法院大法官 13—473c
鲍威尔河 Powell River 美国河流 13—473e
鲍威尔里弗 Powell River 加拿大自治镇 13—473e
鲍文 Bowen, Norman L(evi) 加拿大岩石学家 3—93e
鲍西考尔特 Boucicault, Dion 美国剧作家、演员 3—76f
鲍欣 Bauhin, Gaspard 瑞士医生、植物学家 2—286d
鲍耶 Bolyai, Farkas 匈牙利数学家、诗人 3—17f
鲍耶 Bolyai, János 匈牙利数学家 3—18a
鲍伊 Bowie, David 英国歌手、演员 3—95a
鲍伊 Bowie, James 美国英雄 3—95a
鲍伊 Bowie, William 美国测量学家 3—95b
鲍鱼 abalone 腹足动物 1—5a

鲍照 Bao Zhao 中国南朝文学家 2—210c

刨 plane 木工工具 13—341e

刨床 planer 切削机床 13—342a

暴风鹱 fulmar 海鸟 6—520e

暴力团 bōryokudan 日本匪帮 3—57c

暴徒造反 Rabulist riots 瑞典斯德哥尔摩的示威运动 14—103e

曝光表 exposure meter 摄影装置 6—196a

爆米花 popcorn 食品 13—432b

爆破 blasting 土木工程 2—530e

爆炸地震学 explosion seismology 地球物理学 6—195c

爆震 knocking 内燃机 9—323a

杯 cup 体积单位 5—64d

杯葛 Boycott, Charles Cunningham 英国地产经理人 3—100b

杯海百合 Cyathocrinites 古生物学 5—83c

杯菌 cup fungus 真菌类 5—64d

杯球戏法 cups and balls trick 魔术 5—66d

杯状地衣 cup lichen 生物学 5—65a

卑帝利 Pitṛ 印度教神秘主义 13—329d

卑尔根 Bergen 挪威城市 2—403f

卑弥呼 Himiko 日本统治者 8—86d

卑谬 Pyè 缅甸城镇 14—41f

卑南 P'i-nan (Taiwan) 中国台湾河流 13—278e

卑南语 Puyuma language 中国民族语言 14—40e

卑南族 Puyuma 中国民族 14—40d

背包徒步越野 backpacking 体育 2—119d

悲剧 tragedy 戏剧 17—190a

悲剧性错误 tragic flaw (drama) 戏剧 17—190e

悲世 Weltschmerz 文学 18—185a

悲无量心 karuna 佛教教义 9—189b

悲喜剧 tragicomedy 戏剧 17—190e

碑帖 bei and tie 中国书法艺术 2—341a

鹎 bulbul 鸟类 3—240d

北埃文 Northavon 英格兰区名 12—259a

北艾尔郡 North Ayrshire 苏格兰政务会辖区 12—248d

北爱尔兰 Northern Ireland 英国组成部分 12—261d

北爱尔兰皇家警察 Royal Ulster Constabulary (RUC) 北爱尔兰国家警察 14—432f

北爱尔兰联合党 Alliance Party of Northern Ireland 北爱尔兰政党 1—240e

北爱尔兰统一党 Ulster Unionist Party (UUP) 北爱尔兰政党 17—332c

北爱尔兰志愿军 Ulster Volunteer Force (UVF) 北爱尔兰军事组织 17—332e

北安普敦 Northampton 美国城市 12—258d

北安普敦 Northampton 英格兰城镇 12—258d

北安普敦伯爵 Northampton, Henry Howard, Earl of, BARON OF MARNHULL 英格兰阴谋家 12—258e

北安普敦伯爵(第二) Northampton, Spencer Compton, 2nd earl of, LORD COMPTON 英国保王军司令 12—258f

北安普敦伯爵和侯爵 Northampton, EARLS AND MARQUESSES OF 英格兰封爵贵族 12—258d

《北安普敦法令》 Northampton, Assize of 英国历史 12—258f

北安普敦侯爵 Northampton, William Parr, Marquess of, EARL OF ESSEX, BARON PARR 帕尔男爵 12—258e

北安普敦郡 Northamptonshire 英国郡名 12—259a

北岸 North Shore 新西兰城市 12—256f

北奥克兰半岛 North Auckland Peninsula 新西兰半岛 12—248d

北奥塞梯-阿拉尼亚 North Ossetia 俄罗斯西北部共和国 12—255f

北碚 Beibei 中国重庆市辖区 2—341c

北本内尔河 Northern Penner River (India) 印度河流 12—263c

北碧 Kanchanaburi 泰国城镇 9—153a

北滨海省 Côtes-d' Armor 法国省份 4—536b

北冰洋 Arctic Ocean 地球上最小的洋 1—456e

北博滕 Norrbotten 瑞典省份 12—241d

北布拉班特 Noord-Brabant 荷兰省份 12—230e

北部 North, the 美国地理区域 12—243f

北部非洲 North Africa 非洲地理区域 12—244c

北部高原 Mesa del Norte 墨西哥高原 11—138a

北部关东 Northern Kantō 日本工业区 12—262d

北部区 Northland 新西兰行政区 12—265a

北部省 Nord 法国省份 12—231f

北部省 Northern 南非省份 12—260e

北部台地 Northern Tableland (Australia) 澳大利亚高地 12—263c

北部湾 Beibu Gulf 中国南海海湾 2—341e

北查科 Chaco Boreal 南美特殊植被区 4—22e

北朝 Northern Dynasties 中国历史 12—261b

北茨城 Kita-Ibaraki 日本城市 9—308c

北达科他 North Dakota 美国州名 12—252a

北大年 Pattani 泰国城镇 13—92b

北大西洋公约组织 North Atlantic Treaty Organization (NATO) 国际组织 12—247d

北大西洋洋流 North Atlantic Current 大西洋洋流 12—247d

北戴河 Beidaihe 中国旅游景区 2—341f

北岛 North Island 新西兰岛屿 12—255d

北德平原 North German Plain 德国平原 12—254e

北德维纳河 Northern Dvina River 俄罗斯河流 12—261a

北德文 North Devon 英格兰区名 12—254b

北德文斯克 Severodvinsk 俄罗斯港市 15—240a

北德意志联邦 North German Confederation 德意志历史联盟 12—254d

北地群岛 Severnaya Zemlya 俄罗斯群岛 15—239e

北斗星 Big Dipper, The 天文学 2—467c

北顿涅茨克 Severodonetsk 乌克兰城市 15—240a

北多西特 North Dorset 英格兰区名 12—254c

北伐战争 Northern Expedition 中国历史 12—261b

北方邦 Uttar Pradesh 印度邦名 17—433d

北方林藓 boreal forest moss 植物 3—48c

北方蒙古地域人种 northern Mongoloid local race 亚洲地理人种 12—263b

北方气候期 Boreal Climatic Interval 气候学 3—48c

北方人 Northman 北欧民族 12—265b

北方森林 boreal forest 欧亚大陆北部森林 3—48c

北方使徒 Apostle of the North 英格兰教士 1—415c

北弗里西亚群岛 Nordfriesische Inseln (German) 德国群岛 12—233d

北弗里西亚群岛 North Frisian Islands 德国群岛 12—254d

北弗瓦列山 Severnye Uvaly 俄罗斯山岭 15—239e

北干巴鲁 Pekanbaru 印度尼西亚城市 13—126a

北鲑 sheefish 鱼类 15—292c

北哈福德夏尔 North Hertfordshire 英格兰区名 12—255a

北海 Beihai 中国城市 2—342b

北海 Butterworth 马来西亚城镇 3—293e

北海 North Sea 大西洋边缘海 12—256e

北海-波罗的海运河 Nord-Ostsee-Kanal (Germany) 俄罗斯西北部水道系统 12—232b

北海道 Hokkaido 日本岛屿 8—122e

北海公园 Beihai Park 中国园林 2—342c

北海峡 North Channel 欧洲海峡 12—251d

北海运河 North Sea Canal 荷兰水道 12—256f

北豪森 Nordhausen 德国城市 12—233d

北河二 Castor 天文学 3—514b

北河三 Pollux 天文学 13—408b

北荷兰省 Noord-Holland 荷兰省份 12—230e

北亨普斯特德 North Hempstead 美国城镇 12—254e

北回归线 Tropic of Cancer 地理学 17—234c

北回归线和南回归线 Cancer and Capricorn, Tropics of 地理学 3—396e
北饥饿草原 Severnaya Golodnaya Steppe (Kazakhstan) 哈萨克斯坦沙漠 15—239e
北极 North Pole 地轴北端 12—256c
北极低地 Vastitas Borealis 环绕着火星北极的平坦低地平原 17—478f
北极光 northern lights 大气现象 12—262e
北极海盆 North Polar Basin 北冰洋海底凹地 12—256b
北极狐 Arctic fox (species *Alopex lagopus*) 哺乳动物 1—456d
北极门国家公园和禁猎区 Gates of the Arctic National Park and Preserve 美国自然保护区 7—29d
北极区 Arctic 地理学 1—455c
北极圈 Arctic Circle 地理学 1—456d
北极星 Polaris 天文学 13—397d
北极星导弹 Polaris missile 武器 13—397d
北极星序 north polar sequence 天文学 12—256b
北极熊 polar bear 啮齿动物 13—396c
北加来海峡 Nord-Pas-de-Calais 法国大区 12—232b
北加浪岸 Pekalongan 印度尼西亚城镇 13—125f
北见 Kitami 日本城市 9—308f
北见山地 Kitami-sammyaku 日本山脉 9—308f
北江 Bei Jiang 中国河流 2—341a
北角流 North Cape Current 洋流 12—248e
北捷克州 Severočeský 捷克共和国州名 15—239f
北金斯敦 North Kingstown 美国城镇 12—255d
北京 Beijing 中国首都 2—342d
北京 Pekin 美国城市 13—126a
北京大学 Peking University 中国大学 13—127b
北京动物园 Beijing Zoological Garden 中国动物园 2—344d
北京狗 Pekingese 狗品种 13—127e
北京烤鸭 Beijing duck 食品 2—343f
北京农业大学 Beijing Agricultural University 中国大学 2—343f
北京人 Peking man 人类学 13—126c
北京师范大学 Beijing Normal University 中国大学 2—344a
北京天文馆 Beijing Planetarium 中国科普机构 2—344c
北九州 Kita-Kyūshū 日本城市 9—308c
北九州 Northern Kyūshū 日本城市 12—262d
北喀斯喀特国家公园 North Cascades National Park 美国公园 12—251c
北喀土穆 Khartoum North 苏丹城市 9—258a
北卡尔亚拉 Pohjois-Karjala 芬兰省份 13—387c
北卡累利阿 North Karelia (Finland) 芬兰省份 12—255d
北卡罗来纳 North Carolina 美国州名 12—248f
北卡罗来纳改革者协会 Regulators of North Carolina 美洲殖民史 14—206a
北卡内丁河 North Canadian River 美国河流 12—248e
北开普省 Northern Cape 南非省份 12—260f
北凯斯蒂文 North Kesteven 英格兰区名 12—255d
北坎顿 North Canton 美国城市 12—248e
北康沃尔 North Cornwall 英格兰区名 12—252a
北科利奇希尔 North College Hill 美国城市 12—251f
北莱茵-威斯特伐利亚 North Rhine-Westphalia 德国州名 12—256c
北雷德河 Red River of the North 北美河流 14—190a
北里奥格兰德 Rio Grande do Norte 巴西州名 14—309e
北里柴三郎 Kitasato Shibasaburo 日本医师 9—308f
北陆地区 Hokuriku Region 日本工业区 8—123a
北罗得西亚 Northern Rhodesia (Africa) 赞比亚旧称 12—263c
北罗得西亚 Rhodesia, Northern 赞比亚旧称 14—268c
北落师门 Fomalhaut 天文学 6—391b
北马里亚纳群岛 Northern Mariana Islands 太平洋群岛 12—262e
北美臭鼬 skunk 哺乳动物 15—422e
北美翠柏 incense cedar (*Calocedrus decurrens*) 木本植物 8—351c
北美杜鹃 rhodora (*Rhododendron canadense*) 木本植物 14—270a
北美椴木 basswood 木本植物 2—270c
北美狗鱼 muskellunge (species *Esox masquinongy*) 鱼类 11—511b
北美罗克韦尔公司 North American Rockwell Corporation 美国公司 12—247d
《北美评论》 North American Review 美国杂志 12—247c
北美沙漠 North American Desert 北美大陆西部地区 12—247a
北美山雀 chickadee 鸟类 4—146b
北美凸鲈 sauger 鱼类 15—83e
北美星云 North American Nebula 天文学 12—247c
北美驯鹿 caribou 哺乳动物 3—458c
北美野马 mustang (horse) 动物 11—515c
北美印第安妇女协会 North American Indian Women's Association (NAIWA) 美国非营利性组织 12—247b
北美洲 North America 世界第三大洲 12—244e
北美洲基督教归正会 Christian Reformed Church in North America 美国教会 4—206b
北美洲五旬节派联谊会 Pentecostal Fellowship of North America (PFNA) 美国基督教组织 13—149a
北美洲自由循道会 Free Methodist Church of North America 美国基督教派别 6—469b
《北美自由贸易协议》 North American Free Trade Agreement (NAFTA) 贸易条约 12—247b
北蒙特利尔 Montréal-Nord 加拿大城市 11—373d
北明奇 North Minch (Scotland) 苏格兰海峡 12—255e
北摩拉维亚州 Severomoravský 捷克共和国州名 15—240a
北挪威 Nord-Norge 挪威地理区域 12—232a
北诺福克 North Norfolk 英格兰区名 12—255e
北欧部长会议 Nordic Council of Ministers 斯堪的纳维亚政治组织 12—233e
北欧海盗 Viking 北欧航海武士 17—559d
北欧海盗船 longship 帆桨船 10—212a
北欧滑雪 Nordic skiing 体育 12—233f
北帕默斯顿 Palmerston North 新西兰城市 12—573d
北票 Beipiao 中国城市 2—345a
北普拉特河 North Platte River 美国河流 12—256b
北曲 beiqu 中国戏曲 2—345a
北日德兰 Nordjylland 丹麦州名 12—234a
北茹阿泽鲁 Juàzeiro do Norte 巴西城市 9—97f
北萨默塞特 North Somerset 英格兰区名 12—257a
北桑坦德 Norte de Santander 哥伦比亚省份 12—243a
北沙卡尔 Northern Sarkārs 印度历史地区 12—263c
北山羊 ibex 哺乳动物 8—302b
北闪米特字母 North Semitic alphabet 字母文字体系 12—256f
北上山地 Kitakami-sammyaku 日本山脉 9—308e
北水道 North Channel 加拿大水湾 12—251e
北苏拉威西 Sulawesi Utara 印度尼西亚省份 16—316e
北苏门答腊 Sumatera Utara 印度尼西亚省份 16—331a
北梭鱼 bonefish (*Albula vulpes*) 鱼类 3—28e
北索托人 Northern Sotho (people) 南非民族 12—263c
北太 Bac Thai 越南省份 2—113c
北太平洋铁路公司 Northern Pacific Railway Company 美国公司 12—263b
北泰恩赛德 North Tyneside 英格兰区名 12—257b
北唐 North Down 北爱尔兰区名 12—254c
北特伦德拉格 Nord-Trøndelag 挪威郡名 12—232b
北畠亲房 Kitabatake Chikafusa 日本武士 9—308d
北条家族 Hōjō FAMILY 日本家族 8—121f
北条时政 Hōjō Tokimasa 日本军人 8—122b
北条时宗 Hōjō Tokimune 日本摄政 8—122b
北条泰时 Hōjō Yasutoki 日本摄政 8—122c
北条义时 Hōjō Yoshitoki 日本军人 8—122c

北条政子 Hōjō Masako 日本政治人物 8—122a
北托纳旺达 North Tonawanda (New York, U.S.) 美国城市 12—257b
北威尔特 North Wiltshire 英格兰区名 12—258a
北魏 Northern Wei DYNASTY 中国历史 12—264c
北魏造像 Northern Wei sculpture 中国艺术 12—264f
北温哥华 North Vancouver 加拿大城市 12—257b
北沃尔兹 North Wolds (England) 英格兰自治市 12—258b
北沃里克 North Warwickshire 英格兰区名 12—257c
北西伯利亚低地 North Siberian Lowland 俄罗斯低地 12—257a
北西奈省 Shamāl Sīnā' 埃及省份 15—269a
北希罗普 North Shropshire 英格兰区名 12—257a
北小石城 North Little Rock 美国城市 12—255e
北学派 Vaḍakalai 印度教派别 17—442b
北亚当斯 North Adams 美国城市 12—244c
北亚克河 Yaque del Norte River 多米尼加共和国河流 18—426a
北洋军阀 Northern warlords 中国历史 12—264b
北伊罗戈 Ilocos Norte 菲律宾省份 8—339c
北印度教会 North India, Church of 基督教派别 12—255a
北印度寺庙建筑 North Indian temple architecture 建筑形式 12—255a
北原白秋 Kitahara Hakushū 日本诗人 9—308d
北约克 North York 加拿大城市 12—258b
北约克郡 North Yorkshire 英格兰郡名 12—258b
北斋 Hokusai 日本画家 8—123a
北芝加哥 North Chicago 美国城市 12—251e
贝 Bay, Josephine Holt Perfect 美国金融家 2—291e
贝 Bay, Michel de 比利时神学家 2—291f
贝阿德 Bayard, Thomas Francis 美国政治家 2—293e
贝阿恩 Béarn 法国历史文化区 2—307c
贝阿恩亲王 Béarn, Henri de Bourbon, prince de 法国国王 2—307c
贝阿斯河 Beās River 印度河流 2—307d
贝阿塔海岭 Beata Ridge 南加勒比海海底山岭 2—308b
贝阿沃尔 Beāwar 印度城镇 2—317a
贝奥赫特里克 Beorhtric 西撒克逊国王 2—396e
贝奥图克人 Beothuk 美洲印第安部落 2—396e
《贝奥武甫》 Beowulf 古英语英雄史诗 2—396f
贝班特 bhāībаnd (Hindi) 印度种姓自治机构 2—449d
贝比 Bebey, Francis 喀麦隆作家、音乐家 2—317d
贝比鲁树 bebeeru (tree) 木本植物 2—317a
贝采利乌斯 Berzelius, Jöns Jacob 瑞典化学家 2—435a
贝城 Bay City 美国城市 2—292a
贝楚斯 Becchus (Greek Orthodox leader) 希腊正教领袖 2—318c
贝茨 Bates, Daisy Gatson 美国新闻记者、民权活动家 2—275a
贝茨 Bates, Edward 美国律师 2—275b
贝茨 Bates, H(erbert) E(rnest) 英国小说家 2—275b
贝茨 Bates, H(enry) W(alter) 英国博物学家 2—275c
贝茨 Bates, Katharine Lee 美国作家 2—275d
贝茨 Beets, Nicolaas 荷兰牧师、作家 2—336c
贝茨氏拟态 Batesian mimicry 生物拟态现象 2—275e
贝茨维尔 Batesville 美国城市 2—275f
贝达 Baida (Libya) 利比亚城镇 2—146d
贝达 Bayḍā', Al- 也门城市 2—294b
贝达德 Bédard, Myriam 加拿大运动员 2—324b
贝代 Bedde 尼日利亚酋长国 2—324c
贝当 Pétain, (Henri-) Philippe 法国将军 13—196a
贝当古 Béthencourt, Jean de 诺曼-法国探险家 2—441f
贝岛 Nosy-Be 马达加斯加火山岛 12—273c
贝德贝克 Beiderbecke, Bix 美国爵士乐演奏家 2—341f
贝德尔丁 Bedreddin 奥斯曼神学家 2—327b
贝德福德 Bedford (district, England) 英格兰地区 2—324e
贝德福德 Bedford 英格兰自治市 2—324f
贝德福德 Bedford 英格兰地区 2—324e
贝德福德 Bedford 美国印第安纳州城市 2—324f
贝德福德 Bedford 美国马萨诸塞州城镇 2—324f
贝德福德 Bedford 美国宾夕法尼亚州自治镇 2—325a
贝德福德 Bedford 美国纽约州城镇 2—325a
贝德福德(第一公爵和第五伯爵) Bedford, William Russell, 1st duke and 5th earl of 英格兰贵族 2—325f
贝德福德伯爵(第二) Bedford, Francis Russell, 2nd earl of 英格兰政治家 2—325e
贝德福德伯爵(第一) Bedford, John Russell, 1st earl of 英格兰国王宠臣 2—325d
贝德福德伯爵和公爵 Bedford, EARLS AND DUKES OF 英国贵族头衔 2—325b
贝德福德公爵 Bedford, Jasper Tudor, duke of, EARL OF PEMBROKE 威尔士贵族 2—325c
贝德福德公爵 Bedford, John Plantagenet, duke of 英格兰军人、政治家 2—325b
贝德福德公爵(第十三) Bedford, John Robert Russell, 13th duke of 英格兰贵族 2—326a
贝德福德伯爵(第四) Bedford, Francis Russell, 4th earl of 英格兰政治家 2—325f
贝德福德公爵(第四) Bedford, John Russell, 4th duke of 英格兰政治家 2—325f
贝德福德公爵(第五) Bedford, Francis Russell, 5th duke of 英格兰贵族 2—326a
贝德福德郡 Bedfordshire 英格兰郡名 2—326a
贝德克尔 Baedeker, Karl 德国出版商 2—132b
贝德兰姆 Bedlam 英国医院 2—326c
贝德灵顿㹴狗 Bedlington terrier 狗品种 2—326d
贝德灵顿夏 Bedlingtonshire 英格兰地名 2—326e
贝德卢岛 Bedloe's Island (New York, U.S.) 美国纽约岛屿 2—326e
贝德瓦河 Betwa River 印度河流 2—445e
贝德沃思 Bedworth 英格兰城镇 2—327d
贝迪耶 Bédier, (Charles-Marie-) Joseph 法国学者 2—326b
贝蒂 Beatty, Sir (Alfred) Chester 英国工程师 2—310a
贝蒂 Beatty, Clyde (Raymond) 美国驯兽师 2—310a
贝蒂 Betti, Enrico 意大利数学家 2—445b
贝蒂 Beatty, (Henry) Warren 美国电影演员 2—310c
贝蒂 Beattie, James 苏格兰诗人 2—309e
贝蒂 Beatty, Louise Dilworth 美国歌唱家 2—310c
贝蒂 Beti, Mongo 非洲小说家 2—443f
贝蒂 Betti, Ugo 意大利剧作家 2—445c
贝蒂 Betty, William Henry West 英国演员 2—445c
贝蒂讷 Béthune 法国城镇 2—443d
贝蒂讷 Béthune, Maximilien de 法国政治家 2—443f
贝蒂荣 Bertillon, Alphonse 法国罪犯识别专家 2—432c
贝蒂荣 Bertillon, Jacques 法国统计学家 2—432d
贝蒂亚 Bettiah 印度城镇 2—445c
贝雕 scrimshaw 装饰品 15—157a
贝都因人 Bedouin 中东民族 2—326f
贝杜尔 Betūl 印度城镇 2—445d
贝敦 Baytown 美国城市 2—298c
贝多芬 Beethoven, Ludwig van 德国作曲家 2—332a
贝多斯 Beddoes, Thomas Lovell 英格兰诗人 2—324d
贝恩 Bain, Alexander 英国哲学家 2—150c
贝恩 Behn, Aphra 英国戏剧家 2—339f
贝恩 Benn, Gottfried 德国诗人 2—387d
贝恩 Behn, Sosthenes 美国企业家 2—340a
贝恩堡 Bernburg 德国城市 2—422e
贝恩卡斯特尔-屈斯 Bernkastel-Kues 德国城市 2—426e
贝恩斯 Baines, Thomas 英国艺术家 2—150e
贝恩斯 Baynes, Thomas Spencer 英国学者、编辑 2—297d
贝恩斯托夫伯爵 Bernstorff, Albrecht, Count (Graf) von 普鲁士政治

家 2—428e
贝恩斯托夫伯爵 Bernstorff, Johann-Heinrich, Count (Graf) von 德意志外交家 2—429b
贝尔 Bell, Andrew 苏格兰雕刻家 2—359d
贝尔 Bell, Andrew 苏格兰教士 2—359d
贝尔 Bell, Alexander Graham 美国电话发明人 2—358e
贝尔 Bell, Sir Charles 英国解剖学家 2—359e
贝尔 Bell, Clive 英国艺术评论家 2—359f
贝尔 Bell, Charles Frederic Moberly 英国记者 2—359e
贝尔 Bell, Cool Papa 美国棒球运动员 2—360a
贝尔 Bell, Daniel 美国社会学家 2—360b
贝尔 Bell, Eric Temple 美国数学家 2—360b
贝尔 Bell, Sir Francis Henry Dillon 新西兰政治家 2—360c
贝尔 Bähr, George 德国建筑师 2—142c
贝尔 Bell, George Kennedy Allen 英国基督教主教 2—360d
贝尔 Bell, Gertrude (Margaret Lowthian) 英国旅行家 2—360e
贝尔 Berr, Henri 法国历史学家 2—429c
贝尔 Bell, Henry 苏格兰工程师 2—360e
贝尔 Beer, Israel 以色列军事分析家 2—330e
贝尔 Bale, John 英格兰主教、戏剧家 2—167e
贝尔 Bell, John 美国政治家 2—361a
贝尔 Bell, John 苏格兰物理学家 2—360f
贝尔 Bell, John 英国出版商 2—360f
贝尔 Baer, Karl Ernst, Ritter von (knight of), EDLER (lord) VON HUTHORN 爱沙尼亚胚胎学家 2—132d
贝尔 Bell, Lawrence Dale 美国飞机设计家 2—361a
贝尔 Baer, Max 美国拳击运动员 2—133a
贝尔 Bert, Paul 法国生理学家 2—431b
贝尔 Baire, René-Louis 法国科学家 2—151d
贝尔贝 Bell Bay 澳大利亚港口 2—361b
贝尔布里奇 Baylebridge, William 澳大利亚作家 2—297a
贝尔彻 Belcher, Jonathan 美洲殖民地总督 2—350f
贝尔彻群岛 Belcher Islands 加拿大群岛 2—351a
贝尔岛 Bell Island 加拿大岛屿 2—361d
贝尔岛公爵 Belle-Isle, Charles(-Louis-Auguste) Fouquet, duc de (duke of), DUC DE GISORS 法国元帅、政治家 2—364a
贝尔岛海峡 Belle Isle, Strait of 加拿大东部海峡 2—364a
贝尔德 Baird, John Logie 苏格兰工程师 2—151b
贝尔德 Baird, Spencer Fullerton 美国博物学家 2—151c
贝尔德夫妇 Baird, Bil and Cora 美国木偶戏演员 2—151a
贝尔蒂埃 Berthier, Louis-Alexandre, PRINCE DE WAGRAM 法国军人 2—431f
贝尔蒂诺罗 Bertinoro, Obadiah (ben Abraham Yare) of 意大利犹太教教义家 2—432e
贝尔法斯特 Belfast 北爱尔兰城市 2—351f
贝尔法斯特 Belfast 美国城市 2—352b
贝尔法斯特湾 Belfast Lough 北爱尔兰东北水湾 2—352b
贝尔方丹 Bellefontaine 美国城市 2—364d
贝尔福 Balfour (of Whittingehame), Arthur James Balfour, 1st earl of 英国政治家 2—168e
贝尔福 Belfort 法国城镇 2—352b
贝尔福地区 Belfort, Territoire de 法国省份 2—352c
《贝尔福宣言》 Balfour Declaration 英国政治宣言 2—169b
贝尔富什 Belle Fourche 美国城市 2—363e
贝尔甘萨 Berganza, Teresa 西班牙歌唱家 2—403d
贝尔高姆 Belgaum 印度城市 2—352d
贝尔格 Berg, Alban 奥地利作曲家 2—401f
贝尔格 Berg, Lev Simonovich 俄罗斯动物学家 2—402e
贝尔格拉诺 Belgrano, Manuel 阿根廷军人 2—355e
贝尔格拉维亚 Belgravia 英国伦敦住宅区 2—355e
贝尔格莱德 Belgrade 塞尔维亚首都 2—355b
贝尔格莱德 Belle Glade 美国城市 2—363f
《贝尔格莱德条约》 Belgrade, Treaty of 国际和平条约 2—355d
贝尔根-贝尔森 Bergen-Belsen 德国纳粹集中营 2—404b
贝尔赫姆 Berchem, Nicolaes Pietersz(oon) 荷兰画家 2—398c
贝尔湖 Buir Nur 亚洲淡水湖 3—238b
贝尔基斯 Belkis (Turkey) 土耳其古城 2—358b
贝尔吉卡 Belgica 罗马省份 2—353e
贝尔加拉亲王 Vergara, Baldomero Espartero, príncipe de 西班牙摄政 17—514c
贝尔加马 Bergama 土耳其城市 2—403a
贝尔加马地毯 Bergama carpet 土耳其工艺品 2—403a
贝尔焦约索 Belgioioso 意大利城镇 2—353e
贝尔克雷迪伯爵 Belcredi, Richard, Count (Graf) 奥地利政治家 2—351a
贝尔罗克 Bell Rock 苏格兰北海暗礁 2—361f
贝尔曼 Bellman, Carl Michael 瑞典诗人、音乐家 2—367c
贝尔曼 Behrman, S(amuel) N(athaniel) 美国剧作家 2—340d
《贝尔贸易法案》 Bell Trade Act 美国法案 2—362a
贝尔梅霍 Bermejo, Bartolomé 西班牙画家 2—417e
贝尔梅霍河 Bermejo River 南美洲河流 2—417f
贝尔蒙多 Belmondo, Jean-Paul 法国电影演员 2—369c
贝尔蒙特 Belmont 美国加利福尼亚州城市 2—369c
贝尔蒙特 Belmont 美国威斯康星州村庄 2—369c
贝尔蒙特 Belmont, Alva 美国女权活动家 2—369f
贝尔蒙特 Belmonte, Juan 西班牙斗牛士 2—370b
贝尔蒙特大奖赛 Belmont Stakes 美国马赛 2—370a
贝尔蒙特家族 Belmont FAMILY 美国家族 2—369d
贝尔莫潘 Belmopan 伯利兹首都 2—370b
贝尔纳 Bénard, Abraham-Joseph 法国演员 2—376b
贝尔纳 Bernard, Claude 法国生理学家 2—420f
贝尔纳 Bernard, Émile 法国画家 2—421e
贝尔纳 Bernard, Henriette Rosine (actress) 法国演员 2—421e
贝尔纳 Bernard, Jean-Jacques 法国剧作家 2—421e
贝尔纳 Bernal, John Desmond 英国物理学家 2—419f
贝尔纳 Bernard, Samuel, COMTE (count) DE COUBERT 法国金融家 2—422a
贝尔纳 Bernard, Tristan 法国剧作家 2—422a
贝尔纳(克吕尼的) Bernard DE CLUNY 中世纪修士、诗人 2—420d
贝尔纳(沙特尔的) Bernard DE CHARTRES 法国哲学家 2—420b
贝尔纳丹·德·圣皮埃尔 Bernardin de Saint-Pierre, Jacques-Henri 法国作家 2—422b
贝尔纳德(芒通的),圣 Bernard DE MENTHON, SAINT 意大利代理主教 2—420e
贝尔纳德(锡耶纳的),圣 Bernard OF SIENA, SAINT 意大利神学家 2—420f
贝尔纳·德·旺塔杜尔 Bernard DE VENTADOUR 普罗旺斯行吟诗人 2—420e
贝尔纳诺斯 Bernanos, Georges 法国小说家 2—419f
贝尔纳斯 Byrnes, James F. 美国政治家 3—299f
贝尔纳特 Beernaert, Auguste-Marie-François 比利时政治家 2—331a
贝尔娜黛特(卢尔德的),圣 Bernadette OF LOURDES, SAINT 天主教女信徒 2—419d
贝尔尼 Berni, Francesco 意大利诗人 2—424e
贝尔尼尼 Bernini, Gian Lorenzo 意大利雕刻家 2—425a
贝尔尼尼 Bernini, Pietro 意大利雕刻家 2—426d
贝尔珀 Belper 英格兰城镇 2—371c
贝尔热拉克 Bergerac 法国城镇 2—404d
贝尔热拉克 Bergerac, Savinien Cyrano de 法国讽刺作家 2—404e
贝尔塞奥 Berceo, Gonzalo de 西班牙诗人 2—398b
贝尔森 Belsen (German Nazi concentration camp) 德国纳粹集中营 2—371c
贝尔森 Bellson, Louie 美国爵士乐鼓手 2—368e
"贝尔森野兽" Belsen, Beast of 德国纳粹集中营头目 2—371c
贝尔实验室 Bell Laboratories 美国科研机构 2—361e

贝尔斯 Bales,Peter 英国书法家 2—168c
贝尔斯坦 Beilstein,Friedrich Konrad 俄罗斯化学家 2—344f
贝尔塔巨炮 Big Bertha 德国武器 2—467a
贝尔塔尼 Bertani,Agostino 意大利医师 2—431c
贝尔特 Belter,John Henry 美国家具设计师 2—371f
贝尔特拉米 Beltrami,Eugenio 意大利数学家 2—372b
贝尔特兰 Beltrán,Pedro Gerado 秘鲁经济学家 2—372b
贝尔特利埃 Berthelier,Philibert 日内瓦政治领袖 2—431c
贝尔特统 Belt Series 地质学 2—371e
贝尔图 Berthoud,Ferdinand 瑞士钟表制造家 2—432c
贝尔图斯岭 Beartooth Range 美国落基山山岭 2—307c
贝尔托卢奇 Bertolucci,Bernardo 意大利电影导演 2—433a
贝尔托亚 Bertoia,Harry 意大利雕刻家、设计师 2—432e
贝尔维迪尔 Belvidere 美国城市 2—372e
贝尔维尔 Belleville 美国城市 2—365b
贝尔维尔 Bellville 南非城市 2—369b
贝尔维尤 Bellevue 美国城市 2—365c
贝尔温斯基 Berwiński,Ryszard Wincenty 波兰诗人 2—434c
贝尔系统 Bell System 美国电话系统 2—361f
贝尔谢巴 Beersheba 以色列城市 2—331b
贝尔佐尼 Belzoni,Giovanni Battista 埃及古迹发掘者 2—373c
贝耳俾 Beilby,Sir George Thomas 英国化学家 2—344e
贝夫河 Boeuf River 美国河流 2—565f
贝弗里奇 Beveridge,Albert J. 美国演说家、历史学家 2—446d
贝弗里奇 Beveridge (of Tuggal),William Henry Beveridge,1st Baron 英国经济学家 2—446e
贝弗利 Beverley 英格兰区名 2—446f
贝弗利 Beverly 美国城市 2—446f
贝弗利东约克自治市 East Yorks Borough of Beverley 英格兰区名、自治市名 5—508c
贝弗利希尔斯 Beverly Hills 美国城市 2—446f
贝格 Berg 神圣罗马帝国公国 2—401e
贝格曼 Bergmann,Ernst (Gustav Benjamin) von 德国外科医生 2—406c
贝格曼氏规律 Bergmann's Rule 动物学原理 2—406c
贝古瑟赖 Begusarai 印度城市 2—337f
贝哈尔 Pe-har 中国神祇 13—107e
贝哈格尔 Behaghel,Otto 德国语言学者 2—337f
贝哈姆 Beham,Hans Sebald 德国版画家 2—338b
贝海姆 Behaim,Martin 葡萄牙航海家 2—338a
贝汉 Behan,Brendan (Francis) 爱尔兰抗英志士、作家 2—338b
贝赫贝汉 Behbehān 伊朗城镇 2—339d
贝赫代特 Behdet (Egypt) 埃及城镇 2—339d
贝赫什提 Beheshti,Mohammad Hosayn 伊朗神职人员 2—339e
贝赫扎德 Behzād 波斯画家 2—340e
贝亨 Bergen (Belgium) 比利时城市 2—403f
贝亨奥普佐姆 Bergen op Zoom 荷兰城市 2—404b
贝霍瓦 Pehowa 印度城市 13—123d
贝玑 Péguy,Charles 法国诗人、哲学家 13—123c
贝吉施 Bergisches Land 德国西部地区 2—404f
贝吉施-格拉德巴赫 Bergisch Gladbach 德国城市 2—404f
贝济耶 Béziers 法国城市 2—448c
贝加尔湖 Baikal,Lake 俄罗斯湖泊 2—146f
贝加尔自然保护区 Baikalsky Nature Reserve 俄罗斯自然保护区 2—147b
贝加马斯卡 bergamasca 16世纪舞蹈 2—403b
贝加莫 Bergamo 意大利城市 2—403b
贝加斯 Begas,Reinhold 德国雕刻家 2—336d
贝贾人 Beja 非洲民族 2—347a
贝贾亚 Bejaïa 阿尔及利亚城镇 2—347c
贝杰曼 Betjeman,Sir John 英国诗人 2—444b
贝杰莫雷纳 Pech Morena (India) 印度城市 13—117b
贝京 Begin,Menachem 以色列总理 2—336e
贝居安会女修士 Beguines 中世纪北欧女修士 2—337e
贝卡 Biqā', Al- 黎巴嫩山谷 2—487c
贝卡富米 Beccafumi,Domenico 意大利画家、雕刻家 2—317f
贝卡里亚 Beccaria,Cesare 意大利犯罪学家、经济学家 2—318a
贝凯 Baikie,William Balfour 英国探险家 2—147b
贝凯什 Békés 匈牙利州名 2—348b
贝凯什乔包 Békéscsaba 匈牙利城镇 2—348b
贝凯西 Békésy,Georg von 美国物理学家 2—348c
贝壳币 wampum 货币 18—89d
贝壳采集 shell collecting 搜寻、鉴别活动 15—296a
贝壳放逐制度 ostracism 古希腊政治 12—493b
贝壳花 shell flower 草本植物 15—296b
贝壳花 shell flower (*Molucella laevis*) 草本植物 15—296c
贝壳杉属 Agathis 植物学 1—117f
贝可勒尔 Becquerel,(Antoine-)Henri 法国物理学家 2—323c
贝克 Baker,Anita 美国歌手 2—153e
贝克 Baker,Augustine 英国天主教修士 2—153f
贝克 Baker,Augusta Braxton 美国图书馆馆长、儿童文学作者 2—153e
贝克 Baker,Sir Benjamin 英国土木工程师 2—154a
贝克 Baker,Carlos (Heard) 美国小说家 2—154b
贝克 Beke,Charles Tilstone 英国圣经学者 2—348a
贝克 Baker,Chet 美国歌手 2—154b
贝克 Baker,Dame Janet 英国女歌唱家 2—154f
贝克 Baker,Ella 美国社区组织者、政治活动家 2—154c
贝克 Becke,Friedrich Johann Karl 奥地利矿物学家 2—319d
贝克 Baker,George 美国宗教领袖 2—154c
贝克 Back,Sir George 英国海军军官 2—118f
贝克 Baker,George Fisher 美国金融家 2—154d
贝克 Baker,George Pierce 美国戏剧教授 2—154d
贝克 Becque,Henry-François 法国剧作家 2—323b
贝克 Baker,Josephine 法国艺术家 2—155a
贝克 Beck,Józef 波兰军官 2—319c
贝克 Baker,James Addison,Ⅲ 美国政府官员 2—154e
贝克 Baeck,Leo 犹太教拉比、神学家 2—131f
贝克 Beck,Ludwig 德国将军 2—319d
贝克 Baker,LaFayette Curry 美国刑警首脑 2—155b
贝克 Baker,Newton D(iehl) 美国政治家 2—155c
贝克 Baker,Norma Jean (screen actress) 美国女演员 2—155c
贝克 Baker,Ray Stannard 美国新闻记者 2—155d
贝克 Baker,Sara Josephine 美国医生 2—155e
贝克 Baker,Sir Samuel White 英国探险家 2—155d
贝克 Baker,Theodore 美国音乐学家 2—155f
贝克岛 Baker Island 美国海外领地 2—156a
贝克尔 Bakr,Aḥmad ḥassan al- 伊拉克总统 2—158a
贝克尔 Becker,Carl (Lotus) 美国历史学家 2—319e
贝克尔 Bécquer,Gustavo Adolfo 西班牙诗人 2—323c
贝克尔 Becker,George Ferdinand 美国地质学家 2—320a
贝克尔 Becker,Gary S. 美国经济学家 2—319f
贝克尔 Becker,Wilhelm Adolf 德国考古学家 2—320b
贝克尔斯 Beccles 英格兰城镇 2—318d
贝克福德 Beckford,William 英国富商、官员 2—322c
贝克福德 Beckford,William 英国小说家 2—322d
贝克来特 Bakelite 化合物商品名 2—153d
贝克兰 Baekeland,Leo Hendrik 美国化学家 2—132c
贝克利 Beckley 美国城市 2—322d
贝克曼 Beckmann,Max 德国画家 2—322e
贝克男爵 Beck,Max Wladimir,Baron (Freiherr) von 奥地利首相 2—319d
贝克内尔 Becknell,William 美国商人 2—323a
贝克斯菲尔德 Bakersfield 美国城市 2—156b
贝克斯利 Bexley 伦敦自治市 2—447d
贝克斯希尔 Bexhill 英格兰城镇 2—447d

贝克诉卡尔案 Baker v. Carr 美国最高法院案例 2—156a
贝克特 Becket, Frederick Mark 美国冶金学家 2—320b
贝克特 Beckett, Margaret 英国政治人物 2—320f
贝克特 Beckett, Samuel (Barclay) 爱尔兰作家 2—320f
贝克特 Becket, Saint Thomas 英格兰大主教 2—320c
贝克特 Beckett, Sister Wendy 英国修女 2—322b
贝克韦尔 Bakewell, Robert 英国农业家 2—156b
贝克韦尔玻璃制品 Bakewell glass 美国玻璃制品 2—156c
贝克沃思 Beckwourth, Jim 美国山地居民 2—323a
贝拉 Beira 莫桑比克城市 2—345a
贝拉 Beira 葡萄牙前公国 2—345b
贝拉 Beyla 几内亚城镇 2—448a
贝拉 Bella, Stefano della 意大利版画家 2—362a
贝拉 Berra, Yogi 美国棒球运动员 2—429d
贝拉尔 Berār 印度地区 2—397d
贝拉尔卡萨尔 Belalcázar, Sebastián de 西班牙军人 2—349c
贝拉瓜斯 Veraguas 巴拿马省份 17—510f
贝拉基 Pelagius 基督教隐修士、神学家 13—128b
贝拉基二世 Pelagius II 教皇 13—128d
贝拉基一世 Pelagius I 教皇 13—128c
贝拉基主义 Pelagianism 基督教神学 13—128a
贝拉库拉人 Bella Coola 北美印第安人 2—362b
贝拉里 Bellary 印度城镇 2—362f
贝拉米 Bellamy, Edward 美国作家 2—362c
贝拉明 Bellarmine, Saint Robert 意大利主教 2—362e
贝拉萨特吉 Berazategui 阿根廷行政区名 2—397e
贝拉斯科 Belasco, David 美国戏剧演出人 2—350b
贝拉斯科·阿尔瓦拉多 Velasco Alvarado, Juan 秘鲁总统 17—491d
贝拉斯科·伊瓦拉 Velasco Ibarra, José María 厄瓜多尔总统 17—491d
贝拉斯克斯(库埃利亚尔的) Velázquez de Cuéllar, Diego 西班牙殖民者 17—493e
贝莱 Bellay, Guillaume du, SEIGNEUR (lord) DE LANGER 法国军人、著作家 2—362f
贝莱 Bellay, Jean du 法国主教、外交家 2—363a
贝莱 Bellay, Joachim du 法国诗人 2—363c
贝莱普群岛 Bélep, Îles 法属领地 2—351e
贝莱斯·德·格瓦拉 Vélez de Guevara, Luis 西班牙作家 17—494c
贝兰 Bélain, Pierre, SIEUR (sire) D'ESNAMBUC 法国商人 2—349b
贝兰(大) Berain, Jean, THE ELDER 法国工艺家 2—397b
贝兰卡 Bellanca, Dorothy Jacobs 美国工人领袖 2—362d
贝兰卡 Bellanca, Giuseppe Mario 美国飞机设计师 2—362d
贝兰特 Berent, Wacław 波兰小说家 2—401a
贝朗德·特尔里 Belaúnde Terry, Fernando 秘鲁总统 2—350d
贝朗瑞 Béranger, Pierre-Jean de 法国诗人 2—397c
贝朗瑞(图尔的) Berengar OF TOURS 法国神学家 2—399f
贝劳 Belau (country, Pacific Ocean) 太平洋岛群 2—350d
贝勒 Baylor, Elgin 美国篮球运动员 2—297c
贝勒岛 Belle-Île-en-Mer 法国岛屿 2—363f
贝勒库尔 Bellecour 法国剧作家、演员 2—364c
贝勒库尔夫人 Bellecour, Madame 法国演员 2—364c
贝勒奈斯 Berenice 罗马皇帝提图斯的情妇 2—400e
贝勒奈西 Berenice 埃及公主 2—400d
贝勒奈西 Berenice 埃及公主、皇后 2—400b
贝勒奈西二世 Berenice II 昔兰尼国王之女 2—400b
贝勒奈西三世 Berenice III 埃及王后 2—400c
贝勒奈西四世 Berenice IV 埃及公主 2—400d
贝勒奈西一世 Berenice I 埃及王后 2—400b
贝勒努斯 Belenus 凯尔特人神祇 2—351e
贝勒维尔 Belleville 加拿大城市 2—365b
贝雷戈瓦 Bérégovoy, Pierre 法国政治家 2—399d
贝雷斯福德 Beresford, John 爱尔兰政治领袖 2—401a
贝雷斯福德子爵 Beresford, William Carr Beresford, Viscount 英国将军、葡萄牙元帅 2—401b
贝雷塔公司 Beretta SpA 意大利公司 2—401d
贝类中毒 shellfish poisoning 医学 15—298f
贝里 Berry 法国历史文化区 2—430a
贝里 Bury 英格兰城镇 3—279d
贝里 Berry, Chuck 美国歌唱家 2—430c
贝里 Berry, Marthe McChesney 美国教育家 2—430e
贝里奥 Bériot, Charles-Auguste de 比利时小提琴家 2—408c
贝里奥港 Puerto Berrío 哥伦比亚城市 14—15d
贝里公爵 Berry, DUKES OF 法国贵族头衔 2—430b
贝里公爵 Berry, Charles-Ferdinand de Bourbon, duc de (duke of) 法国亲王 2—430c
贝里公爵 Berry, Jean de France, duc de (duke of) 法国王子 2—430b
贝里公爵 Berry, Louis-Auguste, duc de (duke of) 法国国王 2—430b
贝里公爵夫人 Berry, Marie-Caroline de Bourbon-Sicile, duchesse de (duchess of) 法国公爵夫人 2—430d
贝里克公爵 Berwick-upon-Tweed, James Fitzjames, Duke of, EARL OF TINMOUTH, BARON OF BOSWORTH, DUC (duke) DE FITZJAMES 英国贵族、法国元帅 2—434b
贝里克郡 Berwickshire 苏格兰郡名 2—434c
贝里克希尔 Berwickshire 苏格兰区名 2—434c
贝里曼 Bergman, Bo Hjalmar 瑞典诗人 2—405a
贝里曼 Bergman, Hjalmar Fredrik Elgérus 瑞典戏剧家、小说家 2—405a
贝里曼 Berryman, John 美国诗人 2—430f
贝里曼 Bergman, Torbern Olof 瑞典化学家 2—406b
贝里圣埃德蒙兹 Bury Saint Edmunds 英格兰城镇 3—279f
贝里斯拉根 Bergslagen 瑞典矿区 2—406e
贝里斯特罗姆 Bergström, Sune K. 瑞典生物化学家 2—407a
贝里亚尔 Periyār 印度河流、湖泊 13—171e
贝里亚尔野生动物保护区 Periyār Wild Life Sanctuary 印度野生动物保护区 13—171f
贝利 Pelé 巴西足球运动员 13—128f
贝利 Bailey, Ann 美国传奇人物 2—147e
贝利 Bailey, Anna Warner 美国爱国者 2—147e
贝利 Belli, Carlos Germán 秘鲁诗人 2—365e
贝利 Bailey, Sir Donald Coleman 英国工程师 2—147f
贝利 Bailey, Florence Augusta Merriam 美国鸟类学家 2—147f
贝利 Bailey, Frederick Augustus Washington 美国废奴主义者 2—148a
贝利 Bailey, Gamaliel 美国新闻工作者 2—148a
贝利 Belli, Giuseppe Gioacchino 意大利诗人 2—365e
贝利 Bailey, Hannah Clark Johnston 美国女政革家 2—148a
贝利 Bailey, James A(nthony) 美国马戏团主持人 2—148b
贝利 Bailey, Liberty Hyde 美国植物学家 2—148c
贝利 Baillie, Matthew 苏格兰病理学家 2—149b
贝利 Belli, Pierino 皮埃蒙特军人、法学家 2—365e
贝利 Baillie, Robert 基督教长老会牧师 2—149b
贝利 Baillie, Robert 基督教长老会人士 2—149b
贝利(杰维斯伍德的) Baillie OF JERVISWOOD 基督教长老会人士 2—149a
贝利奥 Berio, Luciano 意大利音乐家 2—408b
贝利多尔 Belidor, Bernard Forest de 法国工程师 2—355e
贝利夫人 Baillie, Lady Grizel 苏格兰诗人 2—149a
贝利-凯南 Bhêly-Quénum, Olympe 非洲法语小说家 2—452c
贝利尼 Bellini, Gentile 意大利画家 2—366b
贝利尼 Bellini, Giovanni 意大利画家 2—366c
贝利尼 Bellini, Jacopo 意大利画家 2—366f
贝利尼 Bellini, Lorenzo 意大利医师 2—366f
贝利尼 Bellini, Vincenzo 意大利歌剧作曲家 2—367a
贝利尼氏管 Bellini, duct of 解剖学 2—366b

贝利萨留 Belisarius 拜占廷大将 2—356b
贝利斯 Baylis, Lilian Mary 英国戏剧经理 2—297a
贝利斯 Bayliss, Sir William Maddock 英国生理学家 2—297b
贝利沃 Beliveau, Jean (Marc A.) 加拿大冰球运动员 2—356d
贝利欣根 Berlichingen, Götz von 德意志帝国骑士 2—410c
贝利亚 Beria, Lavrenty Pavlovich 苏联秘密警察首脑 2—407b
贝莉 Baillie, Joanna 苏格兰女诗人 2—149a
贝林 Behring, Emil (Adolf) von 德国细菌学家 2—340c
贝林 Berlin, Isaiah ben Judah Loeb 犹太学者 2—414e
贝林格 Berlinguer, Enrico 意大利共产党总书记 2—416d
贝林吉耶里 Berlinghieri, Bonaventura 意大利画家 2—416c
贝林加 Belinga 加蓬矿区 2—356a
贝林杰陨石坑 Barringer Crater (Arizona) 美国亚利桑那陨石坑 2—244a
贝林佐纳 Bellinzona 瑞士城市 2—367b
贝灵汉 Bellingham 美国城市 2—365f
贝隆 Belon, Pierre 法国博物学家 2—370e
贝娄娜 Bellona 古罗马女战神 2—367f
贝卢诺 Belluno 意大利城市 2—368f
贝卢斯科尼 Berlusconi, Silvio 意大利总理 2—417d
贝卢斯奇 Belluschi, Pietro 美国建筑师 2—369a
贝鲁格特 Berruguete, Alonso 西班牙雕刻家 2—429e
贝鲁格特 Berruguete, Pedro 西班牙画家 2—429f
贝鲁姆 Bærum 挪威村镇 2—133a
贝鲁特 Bayrūt 黎巴嫩省份 2—298b
贝鲁特 Beirut 黎巴嫩首都 2—345b
贝鲁特 Bierut, Bolesław 波兰政治家 2—466c
贝鲁特美国大学 Beirut, American University of 黎巴嫩私立大学 2—346f
贝律尔 Bérulle, Pierre de 法国枢机主教 2—433e
贝略 Bello, Andrés 智利诗人、学者 2—367d
贝伦 Belém 巴西城市 2—351b
贝伦 Belém 葡萄牙里斯本市区 2—351c
贝伦登 Bellenden, John 苏格兰作家 2—364e
贝伦登克尔岭 Bellenden Ker Range 澳大利亚山岭 2—364e
贝伦格尔 Berenguer (y Fusté), Dámaso, Count (conde) DE XAUEN 西班牙将军 2—400a
贝伦加尔 Berengar 国家统治者之名 2—399e
贝伦加尔 Berengar 神圣罗马皇帝 2—399e
贝伦加尔二世 Berengar II 意大利国王 2—399f
贝伦加尔一世 Berengar I 神圣罗马皇帝 2—399f
贝伦加里奥·达·卡尔皮 Berengario da Carpi, Jacopo 意大利医师 2—400a
贝伦森 Berenson, Bernard 美国艺术评论家 2—400e
贝伦森 Berenson, Senda 美国教育家、运动员 2—400f
贝伦斯 Behrens, Peter 德国建筑师 2—340b
贝罗索斯 Berosus 巴比伦祭司 2—429c
贝罗亚 Beroea (Greece) 希腊城市 2—429b
贝洛 Belleau, Rémy 法国学者、诗人 2—364b
贝洛 Bellow, Saul 美国小说家 2—368a
贝洛奥里藏特 Belo Horizonte 巴西城市 2—370c
贝洛克 Belloc, (Joseph-Pierre) Hilaire 英国作家 2—367e
贝洛三世 Béla III 匈牙利国王 2—349a
贝洛斯 Bellows, George Wesley 美国画家 2—368c
贝洛斯福尔斯 Bellows Falls 美国村庄 2—368d
贝洛四世 Béla IV 匈牙利国王 2—349a
贝洛托 Bellotto, Bernardo 意大利画家 2—368a
贝梅伦 Bemmelen, Reinout Willem van 荷兰地球物理学家 2—374a
贝母 fritillary 草本植物 6—497d
贝母兰属 Coelogyne 植物学 4—328e
贝姆 Bem, Józef Zachariasz 波兰军官 2—373c
贝拿勒斯 Banāras (India) 印度城市 2—189d
贝拿勒斯 Benares (India) 印度城市 2—376b
《贝拿勒斯条约》 Banaras, Treaties of 国际条约 2—189e
贝纳迪尔 Benadir 索马里沿海地区 2—376a
贝纳多特 Bernadotte (af Wisborg), Folke, Greve (Count) 瑞典军人 2—419e
贝纳多特 Bernadotte, Jean-Baptiste 瑞典国王 2—419f
贝纳多特王朝 Bernadotte, HOUSE OF 瑞典王朝 2—419d
贝纳尔德(比萨的) Bernard OF PISA (pope) 教皇 2—420f
贝纳科湖 Benaco (lake, Italy) 意大利湖泊 2—376a
贝纳拉 Benalla 澳大利亚城市 2—376b
贝纳姆 Beinum, Eduard (Alexander) van 荷兰指挥家 2—344f
贝纳塞拉夫 Benacerraf, Baruj 美籍免疫学家 2—376a
贝纳文特-马丁内斯 Benavente y Martínez, Jacinto 西班牙剧作家 2—376b
贝纳乌德 Benaud, Richie 澳大利亚板球运动员 2—376b
贝奈迪克特松 Benedictsson, Victoria 瑞典女作家 2—381e
贝奈斯 Beneš, Edvard 捷克斯洛伐克总统 2—382c
贝内贝拉克 Bene Beraq 以色列城市 2—378a
贝内德蒂 Benedetti, Mario 拉美小说家 2—378d
贝内德蒂伯爵 Benedetti, Vincent, Comte (Count) 法国外交家 2—378e
贝内德克骑士 Benedek, Ludwig August, Ritter von (knight of) 奥地利陆军元帅 2—378b
贝内德托 Benedetto DA MAJANO 意大利雕刻家 2—378f
贝内登 Beneden, Edouard (Joseph Louis-Marie) van 比利时动物学家 2—378c
贝内登 Beneden, Pierre-Joseph van 比利时寄生虫学家 2—378d
贝内迪克松 Benediktsson, Einar 冰岛诗人 2—381f
贝内·戈伊塔 Benet Goita, Juan 西班牙作家 2—382f
贝内克 Beneke, Friedrich Eduard 普鲁士哲学家 2—382b
贝内梅里塔-德圣克里斯托瓦尔 Benemérita de San Cristóbal (Dominican Republic) 多米尼加共和国城市 2—382c
贝内特 Bennett, Belle Harris 美国教会工作者 2—388b
贝内特 Bennett, Floyd 美国飞行家 2—388c
贝内特 Bennet, Henry 英国政治家 2—387f
贝内特 Bennet, John 英国作曲家 2—387f
贝内特 Bennett, James Gordon 美国报刊编辑 2—388c
贝内特 Bennett, Michael 美国舞蹈编导 2—388d
贝内特 Bennett (of Mickleham and of Calgary and Hopewell), Richard Bedford Bennett, Viscount 加拿大总理 2—388d
贝内特 Bennett, Tony 美国歌手 2—388e
贝内特 Bennett, Sir William Sterndale 英国音乐家 2—388f
贝内文托 Benevento 意大利城市 2—383a
贝内文托字体 Beneventan script 意大利文书写体 2—383a
贝内泽 Benezet, Anthony 美国教师、改革家 2—383b
贝内泽,圣 Bénézet, SAINT 基督教圣徒 2—383b
贝尼阿巴斯 Beni Abbès 阿尔及利亚城镇 2—384e
贝尼哈桑 Beni Hasan 埃及文化遗址 2—384e
贝尼河 Beni River 玻利维亚河流 2—384f
贝尼迈拉勒 Beni Mellal 摩洛哥城镇 2—384f
贝尼萨夫 Beni Saf 阿尔及利亚城镇 2—385a
贝尼斯 Bernis, François-Joachim de Pierre de 法国政治家、枢机主教 2—426e
贝尼苏韦夫 Banī Suwayf 埃及省份 2—202e
贝尼苏韦夫 Banī Suwayf 埃及城市 2—202e
贝尼特 Benét, Stephen Vincent 美国诗人 2—382e
贝尼特氏苏铁目 Bennettitales (plant fossil) 古生物学 2—389a
贝尼特斯·罗霍 Benítez Rojo, Antonio 古巴小说家、散文家 2—386d
贝尼维耶尼 Benivieni, Girolamo 意大利诗人 2—386d
贝宁 Benin 西非历史王国 2—385a
贝宁 Benin 西非国家 2—385b
贝宁城 Benin City 尼日利亚城市 2—386c

贝宁湾 Benin, Bight of 西非大西洋海湾 2—386b
贝努埃 Benue 尼日利亚州名 2—395c
贝努埃-刚果诸语言 Benue-Congo languages 非洲语言 2—395d
贝努埃河 Benue River 非洲河流 2—395d
贝努瓦 Benois, Alexandre 俄国戏剧美术家 2—389e
贝齐寮人 Betsileo 马达加斯加民族 2—444c
贝齐米萨拉卡人 Betsimisaraka 马达加斯加民族 2—444d
贝丘 shell mound 人类学 15—296e
贝屈 Bécu, (Marie-) Jeanne 法王路易十五的情妇 2—323f
贝热 Béjart, Maurice 法国舞蹈家 2—347e
贝瑞 Berry, Halle 美国电影演员 2—430d
贝萨里翁 Bessarion, John 拜占廷人文主义者 2—436e
贝萨·路易斯 Bessa Luís, Maria Agustina 葡萄牙小说家 2—436b
贝萨·维克托 Bessa Victor, Geraldo 安哥拉诗人 2—436c
贝塞尔 Bessel, Friedrich Wilhelm 德国天文学家 2—436f
贝塞尔函数 Bessel function 数学 2—437a
贝塞麦 Bessemer, Sir Henry 英国发明家 2—437c
贝塞麦炼钢法 Bessemer process 早期炼钢方法 2—437e
贝塞斯达-切维蔡斯 Bethesda-Chevy Chase 美国首都华盛顿西北郊 2—441f
贝桑松 Besançon 法国城市 2—435d
贝瑟默 Bessemer 美国城市 2—437c
贝瑟尼 Bethany 美国城市 2—441c
贝瑟尼 Bethany 耶路撒冷小村庄 2—441c
贝沙尔 Béchar 阿尔及利亚城镇 2—318d
贝圣路易斯 Bay Saint Louis 美国城市 2—292e
贝施 Beche, Sir Henry Thomas De La 英国地质学家 2—318e
贝什特 Besht (Jewish mystic) 犹太教领袖 2—436a
贝时璋 Bei Shizhang 中国生物学家 2—341b
贝斯 Bes 古埃及神祇 2—435c
贝斯 Bayes, Nora 美国歌唱家 2—295a
贝斯基德山脉 Beskid Mountains 东欧山脉 2—436a
贝斯克拉 Beskra (Algeria) 阿尔及利亚城镇 2—436a
贝斯特 Bast 古埃及猫头女神 2—270c
贝斯特 Best, Charles H(erbert) 加拿大生理学家 2—438d
贝斯沃特 Bayswater 英国伦敦居民区 2—298b
贝松 Besson, Jacques 法国工程师 2—438c
贝苏斯 Bessus 波斯总督 2—438d
贝塔尼 Bethanie 纳米比亚村落 2—441b
贝坦科尔特 Betancourt, Rómulo 委内瑞拉总统 2—440d
贝特 Bethe, Hans Albrecht 美国理论物理学家 2—441d
贝特阿勒法 Bet Alfa 以色列古代遗址 2—439d
贝特顿 Betterton, Thomas 英格兰演员 2—445a
贝特顿-克罗尔法 Betterton-Kroll process 熔炼方法 2—445b
贝特尔海姆 Bettelheim, Bruno 美国心理学家 2—444e
贝特朗 Bertrand, Joseph(-Louis-François) 法国数学家 2—433d
贝特朗 Bertrand, Louis(-Jacques-Napoléon) 法国作家 2—433d
贝特朗 Bertrand, Marcel-Alexandre 法国地质学家 2—433e
贝特朗(博恩的) Bertran de Born 法国军人 2—433b
贝特朗(盖克兰的) Bertrand du Guesclin (French soldier) 法国军人 2—433b
贝特朗伯爵 Bertrand, Henri-Gratien, comte (Count) 法国将军 2—433c
贝特洛 Berthelot, (Pierre-Eugène-) Marcellin 法国化学家 2—431d
贝特洛 Berthelot, Philippe(-Joseph-Louis) 法国外交家 2—431e
贝特曼 Bateman, Hester 英国银匠 2—274e
贝特曼 Bateman, H(ezekiah) L(inthicum) 美国演员、剧院经理 2—274d
贝特曼 Bateman, H(enry) M(ayo) 澳大利亚连环漫画家 2—274e
贝特曼·霍尔韦格 Bethmann Hollweg, Theobald von 德意志帝国首相 2—443b
贝特森 Bateson, William 英国生物学家 2—275e
贝特舍阿里姆 Bet She'arim 以色列文化遗址 2—439f
贝特谢安 Bet She'an 以色列城镇 2—439e
贝特耶拉 Beth Yerah 巴勒斯坦古代居民点 2—441b
贝托尔德(亨讷贝格的) Berthold von Henneberg 神圣罗马帝国首相 2—432a
贝托尔多 Bertoldo di Giovanni 意大利雕刻家 2—432f
贝托莱 Bertholet, Alfred 基督教学者 2—432b
贝托莱 Berthollet, Claude-Louis, Comte (Count) 法国化学家 2—432b
贝托姆 Bytom 波兰城市 3—300f
贝瓦 Bewa (Liberia) 西非河流 2—447b
贝瓦尔德 Berwald, Franz (Adolf) 瑞典作曲家 2—433f
贝文 Bevin, Ernest 英国政治家 2—447a
贝乌哈图夫 Bełchatów 波兰城市 2—350f
贝乌热茨 Belzec 波兰德国纳粹集中营 2—373b
贝乌斯 Baius, Michael 比利时神学家 2—152a
贝西 Bessey, Charles E. 美国植物学家 2—438a
贝西埃尔 Bessières, Jean-Baptiste, duc d'Istrie 法国元帅 2—438b
贝西奈公司 Pechiney 法国公司 13—117b
贝希尔 Becher, Johannes Robert 德国诗人、编辑 2—319a
贝希尔·谢哈布二世 Bashīr Shihāb II 黎巴嫩君主 2—257f
贝希特尔 Bechtel, Friedrich 德国古典语文学者 2—319b
贝希特斯加登 Berchtesgaden 德国城镇 2—398d
贝希托尔德伯爵 Berchtold, Leopold (Anton Johann Sigismund Joseph Korsinus Ferdinand), Graf von (count of) 奥匈帝国外交大臣 2—398f
贝螅属 Hydractinia 动物学 8—279d
贝歇尔 Becher, Johann Joachim 德国科学家 2—318f
贝辛斯托克-迪恩 Basingstoke and Deane 英格兰区名、市名 2—263a
贝休恩 Bethune, David 苏格兰枢机主教、政治家 2—443e
贝休恩 Bethune, James 苏格兰主教 2—443e
贝休恩 Bethune, Louise Blanchard 美国建筑师 2—443e
贝休恩 Bethune, Mary McLeod 美国教育家 2—443e
贝雅 Beja 葡萄牙区名 2—347b
贝雅 Beja 葡萄牙城市 2—347c
贝雅尔家族 Béjart family 法国戏剧世家 2—347c
贝雅特里齐 Beatrice 但丁为之奉献其诗歌的女子 2—309c
贝娅特丽克丝 Beatrix 荷兰女王 2—309e
贝叶斯 Bayes, Thomas 英国数学家 2—295a
贝叶斯定理 Bayes's theorem 数学定理 2—295a
贝伊 bey 土耳其人尊称 2—447e
贝永 Bayonne 美国城市 2—297f
贝聿铭 Pei, I(eoh) M(ing) 美籍华裔建筑师 13—123d
贝原益轩 Kaibara Ekiken 日本旅行家 9—134b
贝约 Bello 哥伦比亚城市 2—367d
贝赞特 Besant, Sir Walter 英国小说家 2—435e
贝赞特夫人 Besant, Annie 英国社会改革家 2—435e
贝札 Beza, Theodore 法国神学家 2—448a
贝专纳人 Bechuana (people) 南非民族 2—319c
贝兹 Baez, Joan 美国歌唱家、政治活动家 2—133e
贝兹鲁奇 Bezruč, Petr 捷克诗人 2—448e
贝兹瓦达 Bezwāda (India) 印度城镇 2—448f
贝佐斯 Bezos, Jeff(rey P.) 美国企业家 2—448e
备前陶器 Bizen ware 日本陶器 2—506c
备忘录 commentarii 罗马历史 4—384c
备战运动 Preparedness Movement 美国历史 13—494c
背风波 lee wave 气象学 9—556e
背风群岛 Leeward Islands 佛得角岛屿 9—558e
背风群岛 Leeward Islands 西印度群岛岛屿 9—558e
背景 setting 文学 15—235c
背阔肌 latissimus dorsi 解剖学 9—514e
背诵文 bhāṇavāra 巴利文佛经 2—450a
钡(Ba) barium 化学元素 2—229e

钡冰长石 hyalophane 矿物 8—276e
钡长石 celsian 矿物 3—558d
倍倍尔 Bebel, August 德国社会主义者 2—317a
倍比定律 multiple proportions, law of 化学 11—479f
倍尔 Pire, Dominique (Georges) 比利时教士 13—321d
倍利 Baily, Francis 英国天文学家 2—149f
倍利珠 Baily's beads 天文学 2—150a
倍数 multiplier 经济学 11—480d
倍性 ploidy 遗传学 13—373c
被告人权利 accused, rights of 法律 1—48a
被解放黑奴事务管理局 Freedmen's Bureau 美国历史机构 6—470e
被囊类 tunicate 脊索动物 17—269d
被子植物 angiosperm 植物学 1—345b
焙烤 baking 烹饪 2—157b
奔巴岛 Pemba Island 印度洋岛屿 13—133c
奔流瀑布 cataract 水文地理学 3—521f
奔宁山脉 Pennines 英格兰山脉 13—142c
奔萨 Penza 俄罗斯城市 13—150c
奔萨 Penza 俄罗斯州名 13—150c
锛 adz 工具 1—91d
本 pradhāna (Indian philosophy) 印度哲学 13—477f
本 reel 电影学 14—197a
本 Benn, Sir Ernest John Pickstone, 2ND BARONET 英国出版商 2—387c
本 Benn, Tony 英国政治家 2—387e
本·阿里 Ben Ali, Zine al-Abidine 突尼斯总统 2—374a
本阿弥光悦 Hon'ami Kōetsu 日本艺术家 8—151b
本·巴尔卡 Ben Barka, Mehdi 摩洛哥政治家 2—374b
本巴人 Bemba 非洲民族 2—373e
本·贝拉 Ben Bella, Ahmed 阿尔及利亚总理 2—374b
本贝丘拉 Benbecula 苏格兰岛屿 2—376c
本伯 Pampa 印度诗人、著作家 12—576d
本博 Bembo, Pietro 意大利枢机主教 2—373f
《本草纲目》 Bencao Gangmu 医学著作 2—376d
本初佛 Ādi-Buddha 佛教 1—78a
本初浸礼派信徒 Primitive Baptist 美国基督教派别 13—510f
本茨 Benz, Karl (Friedrich) 德国机械工程师 2—396a
本达 Benda, František 德国小提琴家 2—376f
本达 Benda, Georg (Anton) 德国作曲家 2—377a
本达 Benda, Wladyslaw Theodor 美国画家 2—377b
本代尔 Bendel 尼日利亚州名 2—377d
本德 Bend 美国城市 2—376f
本德 Bender, Charles Albert 美国棒球运动员 2—377c
本德-埃雷利 Bender-Ereğli (Turkey) 土耳其城镇 2—377e
本德尔汗德 Bundelkhand 印度历史地区 3—251f
本德拉人 Bundelā 印度民族 3—251e
本狄斯 Bendis 色雷斯女神 2—377f
本迪 Būndi 印度城市 3—252a
本迪戈 Bendigo 澳大利亚城市 2—377e
本迪戈 Bendigo 英格兰拳击家、教士 2—377e
本迪绘画 Būndi painting 印度画派 3—252a
本迪克斯 Bendix, Vincent 美国发明家 2—377f
本迪克斯公司 Bendix Corporation 美国公司 2—377f
本地猫 native cat 哺乳动物 12—40b
本地治里 Pondicherry 印度中央直辖区 13—425f
本地治里 Pondicherry 印度城镇 13—425f
本蒂沃廖 Bentivoglio, Guido 意大利外交家 2—393a
本蒂沃廖家族 Bentivoglio FAMILY 意大利贵族 2—393a
本都 Pontus 古安纳托利亚地区 13—429e
本笃会会士 Benedictine 天主教修士 2—381d
本顿 Benton 美国城市 2—393f
本顿 Benton, Thomas Hart 美国作家、民主党领袖 2—394a
本顿 Benton, Thomas Hart 美国画家 2—394b
本顿 Benton, William (Burnett) 美国广告商、政府官员 2—394c
本顿堡 Fort Benton 美国城市 6—413b
本顿港 Benton Harbor 美国城市 2—394f
本多利明 Honda Toshiaki 日本学者 8—151d
本费 Benfey, Theodor 德国语言学家 2—383c
本格 Bunge, Nikolay Khristyanovich 俄国经济学家、政治家 3—252d
本格尔 Bengel, J(ohann) A(lbrecht) 德国神学家 2—384b
本格拉 Benguela 安哥拉城市 2—384d
本格拉洋流 Benguela Current 海洋学 2—384d
本-古里安 Ben-Gurion, David 以色列总理 2—374e
本哈 Banhā 埃及城市 2—202c
本·哈达德一世 Ben-hadad I 大马士革国王 2—375b
本贾利 Boundiali 科特迪瓦城镇 3—83b
本间雅晴 Homma Masaharu 日本军人 8—146f
本杰 Pūnch 印度城镇 14—26a
本杰古尔 Panjgūr 巴基斯坦城镇 13—13b
本·杰隆 Ben Jelloun, Tahar 摩洛哥诗人、作家 2—375b
本杰明 Benjamin, Asher 美国建筑师 2—386f
本杰明 Benjamin, Judah P(hilip) 美国政治家 2—386f
本杰讷德河 Panjnad River 巴基斯坦河流 13—13c
本津 Będzin 波兰城市 2—327d
本居宣长 Motoori Norinaga 日本国学家、神道教义学者 11—435b
本肯多夫 Benckendorff, Aleksandr Khristoforovich, Count (Graf) 俄国将军、政治家 2—376f
本·拉登 bin Laden, Osama 基地组织头目 2—475f
本林尼斯 Ben Rinnes 苏格兰山脉 2—375d
本洛蒙德山 Ben Lomond 澳大利亚山岳 2—375c
本洛斯 Benlowes, Edward 英国诗人 2—387c
本纳 Panna 印度城市 13—14a
本内尔河 Penner River 印度河流 13—141f
本能 instinct 行为模式 8—399f
本尼 Benny, Jack 美国演员 2—389e
本尼狄克 Benedict 教皇和敌对教皇称号 2—378f
本尼狄克(十三世) Benedict (XIII) 敌对教皇 2—379f
本尼狄克(十世) Benedict (X) 敌对教皇 2—379d
本尼狄克(十四世) Benedict (XIV) 敌对敌对教皇 2—380a
本尼狄克(努尔西亚的),圣 Benedict OF NURSIA, SAINT 西方隐修制度之父 2—380f
本尼狄克八世 Benedict VIII 教皇 2—379c
本尼狄克·比斯科普,圣 Benedict BISCOP, SAINT 英格兰隐修院院长 2—380f
本尼狄克二世,圣 Benedict II, SAINT 教皇 2—379a
本尼狄克九世 Benedict IX 教皇 2—379c
本尼狄克六世 Benedict VI 教皇 2—379b
本尼狄克七世 Benedict VII 教皇 2—379b
本尼狄克三世 Benedict III 教皇 2—379a
本尼狄克十二世 Benedict XII 教皇 2—379e
本尼狄克十六世 Benedict XVI 教皇 2—380d
本尼狄克十三世 Benedict XIII 教皇 2—380a
本尼狄克十四世 Benedict XIV 教皇 2—380b
本尼狄克十五世 Benedict XV 教皇 2—380c
本尼狄克十一世(蒙福者) Benedict XI, BLESSED 教皇 2—379d
本尼狄克四世 Benedict IV 教皇 2—379a
本尼狄克五世 Benedict V 教皇或敌对教皇 2—379b
本尼狄克一世 Benedict I 教皇 2—378f
本尼迪克特 Benedict, Ruth 美国人类学家 2—381b
本尼格森 Bennigsen, (Karl Wilhelm) Rudolf von 汉诺威政治家 2—389b
本尼格森 Bennigsen, Leonty Leontyevich, Graf von (Count of) 俄国将军 2—389a
本尼特·比斯科普 Benet Biscop 苏格兰隐修院院长 2—382f
本尼维斯山 Ben Nevis 英国山脉 2—375d

本尼以色列人 Bene-Israel 印度犹太人 2—378a
本涅特 Bennett,(Enoch) Arnold 英国小说家 2—387f
本涅脱 Bennett,Willard Harrison 美国物理学家 2—388f
本宁顿 Bennington 美国城镇 2—389c
本宁顿战役 Bennington,Battle of 美国历史 2—389d
本努 Bannu 巴基斯坦城镇 2—207f
本诺,圣 Benno,SAINT 基督教教士 2—389d
本奇 Bench,Johnny (Lee) 美国棒球运动员 2—376e
本奇 Bunche,Ralph (Johnson) 美国外交家 3—251c
本奇利 Benchley,Robert (Charles) 美国戏剧评论员、演员 2—376e
本色丝花边 blonde lace 工艺品 2—540a
本森 Benson,Edward White 英国圣公会教士 2—390c
本森 Benson,Sir Frank (Robert) 英国演员兼剧团经理 2—390d
本生 Bunsen,Christian Karl Josias,Freiherr von (baron of) 普鲁士外交官、学者 3—253c
本生 Bunsen,Robert Wilhelm 德国化学家 3—253d
本生灯 Bunsen burner 燃烧装置 3—253f
《本生经》 Jātaka 佛教文献 8—549c
本苏莱曼 Ben Slimane 摩洛哥城镇 2—375d
本特 Bent,Charles 美国商人、官员 2—390e
本特 Bent,James Theodore 英国探险家 2—390e
本特尔布尔 Pandharpur 印度城镇 13—9c
本特利 Bentley,Arthur F(isher) 美国政治学家、哲学家 2—393a
本特利 Bentley,E(dmund) C(lerihew) 英国新闻记者、作家 2—393c
本特利 Bentley,Eric (Russell) 英国戏剧评论家、导演 2—393c
本特利 Bentley,Richard 英国教士、编辑 2—393e
本特松 Bengtsson,Frans Gunnar 瑞典作家 2—384d
本提 Benti 几内亚城镇 2—392d
本体 noumenon 哲学 12—276e
本体感觉 proprioception 生物学 13—537f
本体和喻体 tenor and vehicle 诗歌 16—544f
本体论 ontology 哲学 12—423e
本体同一论者 homoousian 基督教派别 8—149a
本体相类派 Homoean 基督教派别 8—147f
本田技研工业公司 Honda Motor Company,Ltd. 日本公司 8—151c
本田宗一郎 Honda Soichiro 日本实业家、工程师 8—151c
本廷克 Bentinck,Lord George 英国政治家 2—392d
本廷克 Bentinck,Lord William 英国官员 2—392e
本廷克 Bentinck,William Henry Cavendish 英国首相 2—393a
本图贡萨尔维斯 Bento Gonçalves 巴西城市 2—393f
本托尔 Bentol 利比里亚城市 2—393f
本威维斯 Ben Wyvis 苏格兰山岭 2—375e
本韦努蒂 Benvenuti,Nino 意大利职业拳击运动员 2—395e
本我 id 精神分析学说 8—317e
本西翁纳利 pensionary 荷兰官职 13—147e
本溪 Benxi 中国城市 2—395e
本星系群 Local Group 天文学 10—174b
本亚明 Benjamin,Walter 德国文学家 2—387a
本亚松 bunya pine (species *Araucaria bidwillii*) 木本植物 3—255a
本耶普 bunyip 澳大利亚民间传说 3—255e
本影 umbra 天文学 17—336a
本泽 Benzer,Seymour 美国分子生物学家 2—396c
本征值 eigenvalue 数学 5—566d
本州岛 Honshu 日本岛屿 8—160e
本-兹维 Ben-Zvi,Itzhak 以色列总统 2—375e
本尊 yi-dam 藏传佛教神祇 18—445a
苯(C_6H_6) benzene 化合物 2—396b
苯胺 aniline 化合物 1—357a
苯胺绿 aniline green (dye) 化合物 1—357b
苯巴比妥 phenobarbital 药物 13—223f
苯苄胺 phenbenzamine 药物 13—223e
苯丙氨酸 phenylalanine 化合物 13—225a
苯丙胺 amphetamine 药物 1—296f
苯丙酮尿症 phenylketonuria (PKU) 疾病 13—225a
苯海拉明 diphenhydramine 药物 5—331d
苯环己哌啶 PCP 药物 13—107c
苯甲醇 benzyl alcohol 化合物 2—396e
苯甲二氮䓬 diazepam 药物 5—292c
苯甲醛(C_6H_5CHO) benzaldehyde 化合物 2—396a
苯甲酸 benzoic acid 化合物 2—396d
苯教 Bon 中国西藏原始宗教 3—23a
苯醌 benzoquinone 化合物 2—396e
苯硫脲味觉检验 phenylthiocarbamide tasting 生物学 13—225b
苯醛绿 benzaldehyde green 化合物 2—396b
苯乙肼 phenelzine 药物 13—223e
苯乙烯 styrene 化合物 16—294c
笨脚兽 Barylambda 古生物学 2—254a
《笨拙周刊》 Punch 英国漫画刊物 14—26b
崩得 Bund 欧洲犹太工人组织 3—251d
崩龙人 Palaung 亚洲民族 12—558c
崩龙诸语言 Palaungic languages 亚洲语言 12—558c
崩塌 avalanche 地质学 2—82e
绷绣制品 tambour 刺绣品 16—451a
泵 pump 机械 14—23e
蚌埠 Bengbu 中国城市 2—383f
蹦床 trampoline 体育项目 17—192f
逼真 verisimilitude 文学 17—515e
鼻 nose 解剖学 12—272d
鼻病毒 rhinovirus 医学 14—264a
鼻出血 nosebleed 病理现象 12—272e
鼻窦炎 sinusitis 疾病 15—399d
鼻环 nose ring 装饰品 12—272e
鼻甲 nasal concha 解剖学 12—3b
鼻疽 glanders 疾病 7—150f
鼻尾丘 crag and tail (geology) 地质学 4—564c
鼻息肉 nasal polyp 疾病 12—3c
鼻腺 nasal gland 解剖学 12—3b
鼻烟 snuff 粉末状烟草 15—465f
鼻烟盒 snuffbox 容器 15—466a
鼻炎 rhinitis 疾病 14—263d
鼻音 nasal 语音学 12—3b
鼻肿瘤 nasal tumour 疾病 12—3c
匕首 dagger 小型刀器 5—107a
比阿戈 Biago,Bernardino di Betto di 意大利画家 2—455f
比阿特里斯 Beatrijs 中世纪欧洲文学 2—309d
比阿特丽斯 Beatrice 美国城市 2—309d
比埃里 bieri 加蓬部落木雕像 2—466a
比安 Bienne (Switzerland) 瑞士城镇 2—465e
比安科 Bianco,José 阿根廷小说家 2—456c
比安科峰 Bianco, Monte (France-Italy) 欧洲山峰 2—456c
比安库尔 Biencourt,Charles de,BARON DE SAINT-JUS 法国殖民者、商人 2—465d
比昂库马 Biankouma 科特迪瓦城镇 2—456e
比昂松 Bjørnson,Bjørnstjerne Martinius 挪威作家 2—508b
比奥比奥 Bío-Bío 智利区名 2—479c
比奥比奥河 Bío-Bío River 智利河流 2—479d
比奥蒂亚 Boeotia 希腊历史地名 2—564d
比奥蒂亚同盟 Boeotian League 欧洲历史 2—564d
比奥科 Bioko 赤道几内亚岛屿 2—482a
比鲍德 Bibaud,Michel 加拿大诗人、史学家 2—457a
比比恩纳家族 Bibiena,Galli da,FAMILY 意大利艺术家家族 2—457c
比伯 Biber,Heinrich 奥地利作曲家 2—457b
比伯 Bieber,Owen (Frederick) 美国劳工领袖 2—464e
比博普 bebop 爵士乐 2—317e

比布鲁斯 Byblos 黎巴嫩古代海港 3—297c
比才 Bizet, Georges 法国作曲家 2—506e
比查达 Vichada 哥伦比亚东部特区 17—536a
比彻尔 Beecher, Catharine Esther 美国教育家、著作家 2—329b
比彻尔 Beecher, Henry Ward 美国牧师 2—329c
比彻尔 Beecher, Lyman 美国教士 2—329d
比彻姆 Beecham, Sir Thomas 英国指挥家 2—329a
比达 Bida 尼日利亚城镇 2—463b
比达阿 bid'ah 伊斯兰教标新 2—463c
比达里战争 Padri War 东南亚历史 12—540d
比代 Budé, Guillaume 法国学者 3—229d
比得哥什 Bydgoszcz 波兰省份 3—297e
比得哥什 Bydgoszcz 波兰城市 3—297f
比得哥什运河 Bydgoszcz Canal 波兰运河 3—297f
比德 Bede the Venerable, Saint 英格兰神学家 2—324d
比德尔 Bīdar 印度城市 2—463c
比德尔 Beadle, George Wells 美国遗传学家 2—302c
比德尔 Biddle, John 英国神学家 2—463e
比德尔 Biddle, Nicholas 美国金融家 2—463f
《比德拉克条约》 Bidlack Treaty 新格拉纳达与美国条约 2—464b
比德里器皿 Bīdrī ware 印度金属制品 2—464c
比德迈风格 Biedermeier style 艺术风格 2—464e
《比德佩寓言》 Bidpai, The Fables of 印度寓言集 2—464c
比德韦尔 Bidwell, John 美国加州政界领袖 2—464d
比迪福德 Biddeford 美国城市 2—463e
比迪福德 Bideford 英格兰港口 2—464a
比东 Per Tum (ancient Egyptian city) 古埃及城市 13—156a
比顿 Beaton, Sir Cecil (Walter Hardy) 英国摄影家 2—308f
比顿 Beaton, David 苏格兰主教、政治家 2—309a
比顿 Beaton, James 苏格兰大主教 2—309b
比顿 Beaton, James 苏格兰格拉斯哥大主教 2—309b
比恩 Bean, Alan L(a Vern) 美国航天员 2—304c
比恩 Bean, Roy 美国治安法官、酒店老板 2—304d
比尔 Bhir 印度城镇 2—452f
比尔 Biel 瑞士城镇 2—465a
比尔 Buell, Don Carlos 美国将领 3—230c
比尔 Biel, Gabriel 德意志哲学家 2—465a
比尔 Beer, Sir Gavin (Rylands) de 英国动物学家 2—330e
比尔 Bill, Max 瑞士艺术家 2—472f
比尔 Beer, Wilhelm 德国天文学家 2—330e
比尔本贾尔岭 Pīr Panjāl Range 亚洲山系 13—320a
比尔博 Bilbo, Theodore G(ilmore) 美国政客 2—471f
比尔博姆 Beerbohm, Sir Max 英国漫画家、作家 2—330f
比尔德 Beard, Charles A(ustin) 美国历史学家 2—305d
比尔德贝格会议 Bilderberg Conference 欧美银行家、政治家年会 2—471f
比尔德狄克 Bilderdijk, Willem 荷兰诗人 2—472a
比尔德莫尔冰川 Beardmore Glacier 南极冰川 2—306b
比尔敦 Bearden, Romare (Howard) 美国画家 2—306a
比尔芬格 Bilfinger, Georg Bernhard 德国哲学家、数学家 2—472d
比尔根杰 Bīrganj 尼泊尔市镇 2—490f
比尔吉 Bürgi, Joost 瑞士数学家 3—261d
比尔卡 Birka 瑞典古城 2—491b
比尔卡班巴山 Vilcabamba, Cordillera de 秘鲁安第斯山脉山岭 17—561b
比尔宁凯比 Birnin Kebbi 尼日利亚城镇 2—493a
比尔宁库杜 Birnin Kudu 尼日利亚城镇 2—493a
比尔普姆 Bīrbhūm 印度县名 2—487e
比尔人 Bhīl 印度种族集团 2—452d
比尔森 Plzeň 捷克城市 13—380a
比尔斯 Birs (Iraq) 伊拉克古城 2—493e
比尔斯 Bierce, Ambrose (Gwinnett) 美国新闻记者 2—465f
比尔斯 Beers, Ethel Lynn 美国诗人 2—331b
比尔斯 Beals, Jessie Tarbox 美国摄影师 2—303e
比尔斯韦尔斯 Builth Wells 威尔士集镇 3—238b
比尔泽布贾 Birzebbuga 马耳他村庄 2—494e
比尔詹德 Bīrjand 伊朗城镇 2—491b
比尔诸语言 Pearic languages 柬埔寨语言 13—112d
比尔兹利 Beardsley, Aubrey (Vincent) 英国插图画家 2—306c
比法娜 Befana 意大利传说女仙 2—336c
比菲埃 Buffier, Claude 法国哲学家、历史学家 3—234e
比夫拉 Biafra 非洲历史 2—455d
比夫拉湾 Biafra, Bight of 西非海岸大西洋海湾 2—455e
比弗布鲁克男爵(第一) Beaverbrook (of Beaverbrook and of Cherkley), Sir (William) Maxwell Aitken, 1st Baron 加拿大金融家、英国政治家 2—316e
比弗岛 Beaver Island 美国密歇根湖岛屿 2—316e
比弗尔人 Beaver 加拿大印第安部落 2—316c
比弗黑德河 Beaverhead River (Montana, U.S.) 美国河流 2—316f
比弗斯 Beavers, Louise 美国演员 2—317a
比戈 Bigot, François 法国文官、律师 2—469c
比格尔海峡 Beagle Channel 南美海峡 2—303a
"比格尔"号 Beagle 英国船舶 2—303a
比格霍恩河 Bighorn River 美国河流 2—469b
比格霍恩山脉 Bighorn Mountains 美国山脉 2—469a
比格斯 Biggs, E(dward George) Power 美国管风琴家 2—468e
比格斯贝 Bigsby, John Jeremiah 英国医生、地质学家 2—469d
比格斯通湖 Big Stone Lake 美国湖泊 2—468a
比哈尔 Bihār 印度邦名 2—469e
比哈尔 Bihār (city, India) 印度城市 2—470a
比哈尔南部平原 Southern Bihār Plains 印度平原 15—553a
比哈尔谢里夫 Bihār Sharīf 印度城市 2—470a
比哈尔诸语言 Bihārī languages 亚洲语言 2—470b
比哈奇 Bihać 波黑城镇 2—469e
比荷卢经济联盟 Benelux Economic Union 三国经济联盟 2—382c
比荷卢三国 Benelux Countries (Belgium, The Netherlands, and Luxembourg) 低地国家 2—382b
比霍尔 Bihor 罗马尼亚县名 2—470b
比霍尔山 Bihor Massif 罗马尼亚山脉 2—470c
比基尼 Bikini 中太平洋环礁 2—471b
比加 Bega 澳大利亚城镇 2—336d
比贾布尔 Bijāpur 印度城市 2—470c
比贾尔地毯 Bījār carpet 伊朗手织毯 2—470d
比较解剖学 comparative anatomy 解剖学 4—396e
比较利益 comparative advantage 经济学 4—396d
比较伦理学 comparative ethics 伦理学 4—396f
比较心理学 comparative psychology 心理学 4—397c
比较语言学 comparative linguistics 语言学 4—397b
比杰诺尔 Bijnor 印度县城 2—471a
比卡 Biko, Stephen 南非黑人运动创始人 2—471c
比卡内尔 Bīkaner 印度城市 2—471a
比卡雀 becard 鸟类 2—317e
比卡兹 Bicaz 罗马尼亚城镇 2—460f
比科尔半岛 Bicol Peninsula 菲律宾半岛 2—461e
比科尔人 Bicol 菲律宾民族 2—461e
比克 Vic 西班牙城市 17—535a
比克戴克(夫人) Bickerdyke, Mary Ann 美国战地护理组织者 2—461d
比克尔 Bickel, Frederick McIntyre 美国演员 2—461d
比克罗夫特 Beecroft, John 英国商人、探险家 2—329e
比克瑙 Birkenau (German Nazi extermination camp) 纳粹集中营 2—491d
比克山 Bükk Mountains 匈牙利高原地区 3—239e
比克斯塔夫 Bickerstaffe, Isaac 爱尔兰剧作家 2—461d
比克特西 Bektashi 伊斯兰教团 2—348d
比肯 Beacon 美国城市 2—301f

比肯斯菲尔德 Beaconsfield 澳大利亚城镇 2—302a
比肯斯菲尔德 Beaconsfield 英格兰城镇 2—302a
比肯斯菲尔德伯爵 Beaconsfield, Benjamin Disraeli, Earl of 英国首相 2—302a
比拉 Bīrah, Al- 巴勒斯坦城镇 2—487c
比拉德纳格尔 Birātnagar 尼泊尔市镇 2—487e
比拉彗星 Biela's Comet 比拉发现的彗星 2—465a
比拉克 Birāk 利比亚绿洲 2—487c
比拉斯布尔 Bilāspur 印度县城 2—471d
比拉斯布尔 Bilāspur 印度中央邦城市 2—471d
比莱吉克 Bilecik 土耳其城市 2—472d
比莱讷格尔 Bhilai Nagar 印度城镇 2—452d
比兰德拉 Birendra Bir Bikram Shah Dev 尼泊尔国王 2—490d
比朗 Bullant, Jean 法国建筑师 3—247a
比勒 Bühler, Karl 德国精神病学家 3—237c
比勒拜斯 Bilbays 埃及城镇 2—471e
比勒达 Bildad 《圣经》人物 2—471f
比勒尔 Birrell, Augustine 英国政治家 2—493d
比勒费尔德 Bielefeld 德国城市 2—465b
比勒陀利乌斯 Pretorius, Andries (Wilhelmus Jacobus) 南非政界、军界要人 13—500d
比勒陀利乌斯 Pretorius, Marthinus Wessel 南非总统 13—500e
比勒陀利亚 Pretoria 南非首都 13—500b
比勒陀利亚大学 Pretoria, University of 南非大学 13—500c
比勒陀利亚动物园 Pretoria Zoo 南非动物园 13—500c
《比勒与大龙》 Bel and the Dragon 希腊文外典 2—348e
比雷埃夫斯 Piraeus 希腊城市 13—320c
比里当 Buridan, Jean 法国哲学家、科学理论家 3—265d
比里·帕侬荣 Pridi Phanomyong 泰国政治领袖 13—506d
比利 Beery, Wallace (Fitzgerald) 美国电影演员 2—331c
比利·毕晓普 Bishop, Billy (Canadian fighter pilot) 加拿大飞行员 2—496a
比利顿 Billiton 印度尼西亚县名 2—475b
比利克陶瓷 Belleek ware 爱尔兰瓷器 2—364d
比利牛斯大狗 Great Pyrenees 狗品种 7—274b
《比利牛斯和约》 Pyrenees, Peace of the 法西和约 14—46b
比利牛斯山地狗 Pyrenean Mountain dog 狗品种 14—46a
比利牛斯山脉 Pyrenees 欧洲山脉 14—46a
比利皮德 Pīlībhīt 印度县城 13—303d
比利其人 Belgae 高卢居民 2—352d
比利时 Belgium 欧洲国家 2—353e
比利时国家植物园 National Botanical Garden of Belgium 比利时植物园 12—12e
比利时国营军火工厂马格机枪 FN MAG (Belgian machine gun) 武器 6—383b
比利时航空公司 SABENA 比利时公司 14—482e
比利时马 Belgian horse 马品种 2—352f
比利时牧羊狗 Belgian sheepdog 狗品种 2—353c
比利时石油公司 Petrofina SA 比利时公司 13—210d
比利时文学 Belgian literature 欧洲文学 2—353a
《比利时信纲》 Belgic Confession 基督教文献 2—353d
比利小子 Billy the Kid 美国枪手 2—475b
比利亚 Villa, Pancho 墨西哥革命领导人 17—562a
比利亚雷亚尔-德洛斯因凡特斯 Villarreal de los Infantes 西班牙城市 17—564c
比利亚努埃瓦 Villanueva, Carlos Raúl 委内瑞拉建筑师 17—563f
比利亚努埃瓦-赫尔特鲁 Villanueva y Geltrú 西班牙城市 17—564a
比利亚维西奥萨 Villaviciosa 西班牙城镇 17—564e
比利亚·谢拉侯爵 Villa Sierra, Fernando de Valenzuela, marqués de (marquess of) 西班牙大臣 17—562f
比例代表制 proportional representation 政治学 13—537c
比良西科 villancico 西班牙歌曲体裁 17—563c
比量 anumāna 逻辑学 1—401d
比列加斯 Villegas, Esteban Manuel de 西班牙诗人 17—565a
比列纳 Villena 西班牙城市 17—565d
比林古乔 Biringuccio, Vannoccio 意大利冶金家 2—491a
比林斯 Billings, Josh 美国幽默作家 2—474e
比林斯 Billings, William 美国作曲家 2—475a
比灵斯 Billings 美国城市 2—474e
比灵斯盖特 Billingsgate 伦敦最古老的集市 2—475b
比龙 Biron, Ernst Johann, Reichsgraf von 德国冒险家 2—493c
比隆公爵 Biron, Armand-Louis de Gontaut, duc de (duke of) 法军指挥官 2—493c
比隆男爵 Biron, Armand de Gontaut, Baron de 法国军人 2—493b
比隆男爵和公爵 Biron, barons and dukes of 法国贵族 2—493b
比隆男爵和公爵 Biron, Charles de Gontaut, Baron and Duke (duc) de 法国军人 2—493c
比鲁尼 Bīrūnī, al- 波斯学者 2—494d
比罗比詹 Birobidzhan (region, Russia) 俄罗斯州名 2—493b
比罗比詹 Birobidzhan 俄罗斯城市 2—493b
比洛 Bülow, Adam Heinrich Dietrich, Freiherr von (baron of) 普鲁士军事理论家 3—249e
比洛 Bülow, Hans (Guido), Freiherr von (baron of) 德国钢琴家、指挥家 3—249f
比洛克西 Biloxi 美国城市 2—475c
比洛亲王 Bülow, Bernhard (Heinrich Martin Karl), Fürst von (prince of) 德意志帝国首相 3—249e
比蒙 Beamon, Bob 美国跳远运动员 2—303f
比米尼群岛 Bimini Islands 巴哈马岛群 2—475e
比目鱼 flatfish 鱼类 6—349f
比目鱼肌 soleus muscle 解剖学 15—495d
比那尔德里奥 Pinar del Río 古巴省份 13—306d
比那尔德里奥 Pinar del Río 古巴城市 13—306d
比纳特男爵 Bienerth, Richard, Freiherr von 奥地利首相 2—465d
比奈 Binet, Alfred 法国心理学家 2—476f
比内 Pinay, Antoine 法国政党领袖、总理 13—306e
比尼恩 Binyon, (Robert) Laurence 英国诗人、艺术家 2—479c
比尼人 Bini (people) 非洲民族 2—478c
比尼亚德尔马 Viña del Mar 智利游览胜地 17—567c
比诺-瓦里亚 Bunau-Varilla, Philippe-Jean 法国工程师 3—251a
比齐克牌 Bezique 纸牌游戏 2—448d
比齐乌斯 Bitzius, Albert (Swiss writer) 瑞士作家 2—505d
比奇 Beach, Alfred Ely 美国出版商、发明家 2—301b
比奇 Beach, Amy Marcy 美国音乐家 2—301c
比奇 Beach, Sir Michael Edward Hicks 英国政治家 2—301c
比奇 Beach, Sylvia 美国书商 2—301c
比奇德尔 Bichitr 印度画家 2—461b
比奇角 Beachy Head 英吉利海峡岬角 2—301f
比奇洛 Bigelow, Erastus Brigham 美国工业家 2—468d
比奇洛 Bigelow, John 美国作家 2—468d
比奇斯 Buchis 古埃及宗教传说动物 3—221b
比奇特尔 Bechtel, Stephen D(avison) 美国建筑工程师 2—319c
比奇沃思 Beechworth 澳大利亚城镇 2—329e
比切特 Bechet, Sidney 美国音乐家 2—319b
比丘 bhikku 佛教称谓 2—452c
比热 specific heat 物理学 16—13b
比热戈斯群岛 Bijagós Islands 几内亚比绍群岛 2—470c
比若 Bugeaud, Thomas-Robert, marquis de la Piconnerie, duc (duke) d'Isly 法国元帅 3—236a
比萨 Pisa 意大利城市 13—322f
比萨饼 pizza 食品 13—336b
比萨会议 Pisa, Council of 天主教会议 13—323b
比萨拉比亚 Bessarabia 东欧地区 2—436c
比萨斜塔 Leaning Tower of Pisa 意大利建筑 9—545a
比萨扬人 Bisaya 马来西亚民族 2—494e

比塞大 Banzart 突尼斯城市 2—210a
比塞塔 peseta 西班牙原货币单位 13—192f
比赛桥牌 Tournament Bridge (card game) 纸牌游戏 17—178f
比色法 colorimetry 化学 4—364e
比瑟姆 Bussum 荷兰城市 3—287a
比沙 Bichat, Marie-François-Xavier 法国解剖学家 2—460f
比尚达斯 Bishandās 印度画家 2—495c
比绍 Bissau 几内亚比绍首都 2—502d
比湿 specific humidity 气象学 16—13c
比什凯克 Bishkek 吉尔吉斯斯坦城市 2—495d
比什努布尔 Bishnupur 印度历史名城 2—495e
比属刚果 Belgian Congo 比利时前殖民地 2—352f
比属刚果狗 Belgian Congo dog 狗品种 2—352f
比斯贝克 Busbecq, Augier Ghislain de 佛兰德外交家、文人 3—280e
比斯比 Bisbee 美国城市 2—494f
比斯顿 Beeston, Christopher 英国戏剧演员、经理 2—331d
比斯顿-斯泰普尔福德 Beeston and Stapleford 英格兰社区 2—331d
比斯尔 Bissell, Melville Reuben 美国发明家 2—502e
比斯尔 Bissell, Richard (Pike) 美国作家 2—502f
比斯霍普 Bischop, Simon (Dutch theologian) 荷兰神学家 2—495b
比斯霍普 Bisschop, Simon (Dutch theologian) 荷兰神学家 2—502e
比斯开 Vizcaya 西班牙省份 18—28c
比斯开湾 Biscay, Bay of 北大西洋海湾 2—494f
比斯坎国家公园 Biscayne National Park 美国公园 2—495a
比斯坎湾 Biscayne Bay 北大西洋海湾 2—495a
比斯科普·巴杜辛 Biscop Baducing (7th-century British abbot) 英国隐修院院长 2—495b
比斯克 Biysk 俄罗斯城市 2—506b
比斯克拉 Biskra 阿尔及利亚城镇 2—498b
比斯肯·许埃特 Busken Huet, Conrad 荷兰作家 3—286a
比斯马亚 Bismāyah (Iraq) 伊拉克古城 2—502a
比斯米拉 basmalah 伊斯兰教祷词 2—264e
比斯努瓦 Busnois, Antoine 法国作曲家 3—286c
比斯然布尔 Bisrāmpur (India) 印度城镇 2—502d
比斯特 Bicester 英格兰城镇 2—460f
比斯特褐色颜料 bistre 绘画颜料 2—502f
比斯特里察 Bistriţa 罗马尼亚城镇 2—503a
比斯特里察-讷瑟乌德 Bistriţa-Năsăud 罗马尼亚县名 2—503b
比斯柱 bisj pole 宗教礼仪所用木柱 2—498a
比松 Buisson, Ferdinand-Édouard 法国教育家 3—238c
比苏姆 Büsum 德国城镇 3—288a
比索 peso 南美、菲律宾货币单位 13—193e
比索朗 Bissorã 几内亚比绍城镇 2—502f
比索通 Bīsitūn 伊朗村庄 2—497f
比特-阿迪尼 Bit-Adini 美索不达米亚古王国 2—503c
比特伯爵(第三) Bute, John Stuart, 3rd Earl of, Viscount Kingarth, Lord Mount Stuart, Cumrae, and Inchmarnock 英国首相 3—289a
比特岛 Bute 苏格兰岛屿 3—288f
比特郡 Buteshire 苏格兰郡名 3—289c
比特利斯 Bitlis 土耳其城市 2—503e
比特鲁特岭 Bitterroot Range 美国山岭 2—504e
比提 Beatty, David, 1st Earl Beatty, Viscount Borodale of Wexford, Baron Beatty of the North Sea and of Brooksby 英国海军元帅 2—310b
比铁尔 Vitier, Cintio 古巴诗人 18—24d
比通托 Bitonto 意大利城镇 2—504a
比图尔 Bithūr 印度市镇 2—503c
比图里吉人 Bituriges 高卢凯尔特部落 2—505c
比托尔 Butor, Michel 法国小说家 3—291d
比托拉 Bitola 马其顿城市 2—503f
比托勒格尔 Pithoragarh 印度城市 13—328e
比托叶夫 Pitoëff, Georges 俄国出生的导演、演出人 13—329c
比万 Bevan, Aneurin 英国政治家 2—446c
比韦斯 Vives, Amadeo 西班牙作曲家 18—27e
比维斯 Vives, Juan Luis 西班牙人文主义者 18—27e
比翁多 Biondo, Flavio 意大利历史学家 2—484d
比沃格拉夫影片公司 Biograph Company 美国电影制片厂 2—481a
比乌 Biu 尼日利亚城镇 2—505d
比乌埃拉琴 vihuela 乐器 17—559b
比乌高原 Biu Plateau 尼日利亚高原 2—505e
比西-拉比旦 Bussy-Rabutin, Roger de 法国浪子作家 3—287a
比西尼 Busignies, Henri-Gaston 美国电子工程师 3—284d
比希莫特 Behemoth 《圣经》中的巨兽 2—339e
比希尼亚 Bithynia 安纳托利亚古行政区 2—503c
比谢列 Bisceglie 意大利城镇 2—495a
比欣 Pishīn 巴基斯坦城镇 13—325c
比兴 Büsching, Anton Friedrich 德国地理学家 3—281b
比亚埃尔莫萨 Villahermosa 墨西哥城市 17—563b
比亚河 Bia River 西非河流 2—455d
比亚克岛 Biak Island 印度尼西亚岛屿 2—455f
比亚克拉拉 Villa Clara 古巴省份 17—562b
比亚里茨 Biarritz 法国城镇 2—456e
比亚里卡 Villarrica 巴拉圭城市 17—564c
比亚利克 Bialik, Ḥayyim Naḥman 希伯来文诗人 2—455f
比亚纳王子 Viana, Carlos de Aragon, principe de 纳瓦拉王位继承人 17—533d
比亚图斯·雷纳努斯 Beatus Rhenanus 德国人文主义者、作家 2—310c
比亚瓦-波德拉斯卡 Biała Podlaska 波兰省份 2—455f
比亚瓦-波德拉斯卡 Biała Podlaska 波兰城市 2—455f
比亚韦斯托克 Białystok 波兰旧省份 2—456b
比亚韦斯托克 Białystok 波兰城市 2—456b
比亚维森西奥 Villavicencio 哥伦比亚城市 17—564e
比耶 Bié 安哥拉省份 2—464e
比耶杜 Billetdoux, François 法国剧作家 2—473e
比耶尔克托尔普石碑 Björketorp Stone 瑞典古纪念碑 2—507f
比耶克斯岛 Vieques Island 波多黎各岛屿 17—553e
比耶拉 Biella 意大利城市 2—465b
比伊迪 Biyidi, Alexandre 非洲作家 2—506b
比尤卡斯尔十字碑 Bewcastle Cross 英格兰古石碑 2—447c
比尤纳帕克 Buena Park 美国城市 3—230d
比尤特锡尔弗博市 Butte-Silver Bow 美国城市 3—292a
比尤伊克 Bewick, Thomas 英国版画家 2—447c
比喻 parable 文学 13—29c
比约尔内博 Bjørneboe, Jens (Ingvald) 挪威作家 2—508a
比约林 Björling, Jussi (Johan Jonaton) 瑞典歌唱家 2—508a
比约讷堡 Björneborg (Finland) 芬兰城市 2—508b
比重 specific gravity 物理学 16—13a
比重计 hydrometer 仪器 8—286a
比浊法 turbidimetry (chemistry) 化学 17—277a
比兹塔特 Bierstadt, Albert 美国风景画家 2—466b
比佐泽罗 Bizzozero, Giulio 意大利病理学家 2—507c
吡啶 pyridine 化合物 14—46e
吡拉明 pyrilamine 药物 14—46e
吡咯 pyrrole 化合物 14—49b
吡喃 pyran 化合物 14—45e
吡嗪 pyrazine 化合物 14—45f
吡唑 pyrazole 有机化合物 14—46a
彼得 Peter 君士坦丁堡拉丁皇帝 13—196f
彼得 Peter 俄罗斯正教都主教 13—200f
彼得 Petre, Sir Edward 英国耶稣会会士 13—208d
彼得 Peter, Hugh 英格兰牧师 13—202f
彼得(安吉亚拉殉教士) Peter Martyr D'Anghiera 意大利历史学家 13—201d

彼得(奥雷奥里的) Petrus Aureoli 法国教士、哲学家 13—213b
彼得(德勒的) Peter of Dreux 布列塔尼公爵或伯爵 13—202a
彼得(甘地亚的) Peter of Candia 敌对教皇 13—201f
彼得(卡斯特尔诺的) Peter of Castelnau 法国殉教士 13—201f
彼得(库特奈的) Peter of Courtenay 君士坦丁堡皇帝 13—201f
彼得(里沃的) Peter des Rivaux 英格兰贵族 13—201b
彼得(伦巴第的) Peter Lombard 法国巴黎主教 13—201c
彼得(罗什的) Peter des Roches 英格兰外交家 13—201b
彼得(莫克莱尔) Peter Mauclerc 布列塔尼公爵或伯爵 13—201e
彼得(维罗纳的) Peter of Verona, Saint 意大利布道家 13—202a
彼得(殉教士) Peter Martyr 意大利殉教士 13—201c
彼得(殉教士韦尔米里) Peter Martyr vermigli 意大利宗教改革家 13—201e
彼得(隐修士) Peter the Hermit 法国苦行者 13—202e
彼得(尊敬的) Peter the Venerable 法国隐修院院长 13—202e
彼得(蒙布瓦歇的),蒙福者 Peter of Montboissier, Blessed 法国隐修院院长 13—202a
彼得(阿尔坎塔拉的),圣 Peter of Alcántara, Saint 西班牙修行家 13—201e
彼得(金口),圣 Peter Chrysologus, Saint 拉韦纳大主教 13—201a
彼得(使徒),圣 Peter the Apostle, Saint 耶稣基督门徒 13—202a
彼得(殉教士),圣 Peter Martyr, Saint 意大利异端裁判所法官 13—201d
彼得、保罗与玛丽 Peter, Paul and Mary 美国民歌手 13—203b
彼得伯勒 Peterborough 加拿大城市 13—203c
彼得伯勒 Peterborough 英格兰城市、区 13—203d
彼得伯勒 Peterborough 美国城镇 13—203d
彼得伯勒司法管辖区 Peterborough, Soke of 原英格兰行政郡 13—203e
彼得城 Petrodvorets 俄罗斯城市 13—210c
彼得·达米安,圣 Peter, Damian, Saint 意大利枢机主教 13—203b
彼得大帝(或佩德罗大帝) Peter the Great 皇帝名 13—202e
彼得大帝湾 Peter the Great Bay 日本海海湾 13—203c
彼得大帝一世 Peter I the Great, of Russia 俄国沙皇、改革家 13—197c
彼得二世 Peter II 法国布列塔尼公爵之子 13—196f
彼得二世 Peter II 黑山主教大公 13—197a
彼得二世 Peter II 俄国沙皇 13—199f
彼得二世 Peter II 南斯拉夫国王 13—200f
《彼得福音》 Peter, Gospel of 基督教伪经 13—202f
彼得格勒 Petrograd (Russia) 俄罗斯城市 13—210d
彼得黑德 Peterhead 苏格兰城镇 13—200e
彼得霍夫 Peterhof (Russia) 俄罗斯城市 13—203e
彼得·克莱佛尔,圣 Peter Claver, Saint 西班牙传教士 13—201a
彼得库夫 Piotrków 波兰旧省份 13—317c
彼得库夫-特雷布纳尔斯基 Piotrków Trybunalski 波兰城市 13—317c
彼得拉桑塔 Pietrasanta 意大利城镇 13—297d
彼得拉斯内格拉斯 Piedras Negras 墨西哥城市 13—294a
彼得卢大屠杀 Peterloo Massacre 英国历史 13—203e
彼得鲁奇 Petrucci, Ottaviano dei 意大利音乐出版商 13—213a
彼得罗(贡多拉的) Pietro della Gondola, Andrea di (architect) 意大利建筑师 13—297f
彼得罗(维尼亚的) Pietro della Vigna 罗马帝国首席大臣、法学家 13—297f
彼得罗巴甫洛夫斯克 Petropavlovsk 哈萨克斯坦城市 13—212d
彼得罗·达·科尔托纳 Pietro da Cortona 意大利建筑师、画家 13—297e
彼得罗夫 Petrov, Yevgeny 苏联幽默作家 13—212f
彼得罗夫斯克港 Petrovsk Port (Russia) 俄罗斯港口 13—213a
彼得罗·拉伊纳卢奇 Rainallucci, Pietro 敌对教皇 14—127a
彼得罗利尼 Petrolini, Ettore 意大利戏剧演员、作家 13—212a
彼得罗沙尼 Petroşani 罗马尼亚城市 13—212f
彼得罗维奇 Petrović, George, Serbo-Croatian dor-de petrović 塞尔维亚政治领袖 13—213a
彼得罗相 Petrosyan, Tigran V(artanovich) 苏联国际象棋大师 13—212f
彼得罗扎沃茨克 Petrozavodsk 俄罗斯城市 13—213a
彼得马里茨堡 Pietermaritzburg 南非城市 13—297a
彼得那战役 Pydna, Battle of 古罗马历史事件 14—41f
彼得·诺拉斯科,圣 Peter Nolasco, Saint 慈爱圣母创建人 13—201e
彼得;佩德罗 Peter 统治者之名 13—196e
《彼得启示录》 Peter, Apocalypse of 基督教伪经 13—202f
《彼得前书》、《彼得后书》 Peter, letters of 《新约》两卷 13—203a
彼得三世 Peter III 俄国沙皇 13—200a
彼得森 Peterson, Esther 美国消费者利益维护者 13—204c
彼得森 Peterson, Oscar 加拿大钢琴家 13—204d
彼得森 Peterson, Roger Tory 美国鸟类学家、作家 13—204e
彼得首位论 Petrine theory 天主教教义 13—210a
彼得斯 Peters, Carl 德国探险家 13—203f
彼得斯 Peters, Curtis Arnoux 美国漫画家 13—204a
彼得斯 Peters, Lenrie 冈比亚医生、作家 13—204a
彼得斯堡 Petersburg 美国弗吉尼亚州城市 13—204b
彼得斯堡 Petersburg 美国伊利诺伊州城市 13—204b
彼得斯堡 Pietersburg 南非城镇 13—297a
彼得斯堡战役 Petersburg Campaign 美国历史 13—204c
彼得斯菲尔德女男爵 Petersfield, Louise-Renée de Kérouaille, Baroness 英王查理二世情妇 13—204c
彼得松 Pétursson, Hallgrímur 冰岛诗人 13—214c
彼得松 Pieterszoon, Pieter 荷兰海军上将 13—297b
彼得一世 Peter I 法兰西卡佩王朝亲王 13—196e
彼得一世 Peter I 黑山主教、大公 13—196f
彼得一世 Peter I 塞尔维亚国王 13—200e
彼尔姆 Perm 俄罗斯州名 13—173b
彼尔姆 Perm 俄罗斯城市 13—173c
彼尔姆诸语言 Permic languages 欧洲语言 13—174e
彼尔特 Perthes, Jacques Boucher (de Crèvecoeur) de (French archaeologist) 法国考古学家 13—188c
彼科夫斯基 Bykovsky, Valery 苏联航天员 3—297f
彼拉多 Pilate, Pontius 罗马犹太巡抚 13—301f
彼斯捷尔 Pestel, Pavel Ivanovich 俄罗斯军官 13—195b
彼特拉克 Petrarch 意大利学者、诗人 13—207f
彼特留拉 Petlyura, Symon Vasilyevich 乌克兰社会党领导人 13—206f
彼特罗斯·菲拉尔戈斯 Petros Philargos (antipope) 敌对教皇 13—212f
彼翁 Bion 古希腊诗人 2—484d
彼泽森 Pedersen, Christiern 丹麦人文主义者 13—119a
秕糠诗派 Della-cruscan 英国诗歌流派 5—227f
秕糠学会 Crusca Academy 意大利语言学会 5—40a
笔 crayon 绘画工具 4—574a
笔 pen 书画工具 13—134b
笔螺 mitre shell 腹足动物 11—292e
笔铅 plumbago (mineral) 矿物 13—376a
笔石 graptolite 古生物学 7—260d
笔体学 graphology 心理学 7—260c
俾格米人 Pygmy 人类学 14—42b
俾路支 Balochistān 巴基斯坦省份 2—181a
俾路支地毯 Balochi rug 织物 2—180e
俾路支人 Balochi 亚洲民族 2—180c
俾路支兽 baluchitherium 古生物学 2—184f
俾路支语 Balochi language 现代伊朗语言 2—180e
俾斯麦 Bismarck 美国城市 2—498c
俾斯麦 Bismarck, Otto von 普鲁士政治家 2—498e
俾斯麦海 Bismarck Sea 太平洋西南部海域 2—501f
“俾斯麦”号 Bismarck 德国战列舰 2—498d

俾斯麦岭 Bismarck Range 巴布亚新几内亚山脉 2—501f
俾斯麦群岛 Bismarck Archipelago 太平洋俾斯麦海群岛 2—501f
俾约-瓦伦 Billaud-Varenne, Jean-Nicolas 法国律师 2—473b
币原喜重郎 Shidehara Kijūrō, DANSHAKU 日本外交家 15—311e
必打灵查亚 Petaling Jaya 马来西亚城市 13—196b
必和必拓集团 BHP Billiton 跨国公司 2—453a
毕奥 Biot, Jean-Baptiste 法国物理学家 2—486a
毕奥-萨伐尔定律 Biot-Savart law 物理学 2—486b
毕比 Beebe, (Charles) William 美国生物学家 2—328d
毕达哥拉斯 Pythagoras 希腊哲学家、数学家 14—49c
毕达哥拉斯 Pythagoras 希腊雕刻家 14—49d
毕达哥拉斯定理 Pythagorean theorem 数学 14—49d
毕达哥拉斯主义 Pythagoreanism 哲学流派和宗教团体 14—49f
毕尔巴鄂 Bilbao 西班牙城市 2—471d
毕尔格 Bürger, Gottfried August 德国文学家 3—260b
毕加尔 Pigalle, Jean-Baptiste 法国雕刻家 13—298d
毕加索 Picasso, Pablo (Ruiz y) 西班牙艺术家 13—283f
毕节 Bijie 中国城市 2—470e
毕拉克 Birāk, Tall 叙利亚古代遗址 2—487d
毕沙罗 Pissarro, Camille 法国印象派画家 13—325d
毕生发展心理学 life-span psychology 心理学 10—90b
毕昇 Bi Sheng 中国活字版印刷术发明人 2—455c
毕苏斯基 Piłsudski, Józef (Klemens) 波兰革命者、政治家 13—305a
毕希纳 Buchner, Eduard 德国生物化学家 3—221c
毕希纳 Büchner, Georg 德国剧作家 3—221c
毕希纳 Buchner, Hans 德国细菌学家 3—221e
毕希纳 Büchner, Ludwig 德国医生、哲学家 3—221e
毕晓普 Bishop, Elizabeth 美国诗人 2—496a
毕晓普 Bishop, Hazel 美国化学家 2—496c
毕晓普 Bishop, Sir Henry Rowley 英国作曲家 2—496c
毕晓普 Bishop, Isabel 美国画家 2—496d
毕晓普 Bishop, J(ohn) Michael 美国病毒学家 2—496e
毕晓普 Bishop, John Peale 美国作家 2—496f
毕晓普 Bishop, William Avery 加拿大飞行员 2—496f
毕晓普博物馆 Bishop Museum 美国博物馆 2—497a
毕晓普斯托福德 Bishop's Stortford 英格兰城镇 2—497e
毕晓普希尔 Bishop Hill State Historic Site 美国历史村 2—497a
毕晓普岩灯塔 Bishop Rock Lighthouse 康沃尔锡利群岛的灯塔 2—497b
毕星团 Hyades 天文学 8—276e
毕宿五 Aldebaran 天文学 1—192b
毕亚契达 Piazzetta, Giovanni Battista 意大利画家 13—282d
闭厂 lockout 劳资关系 10—180e
闭经 amenorrhea 生理学 1—274e
闭锁及狭窄 atresia and stenosis 病理现象 2—35c
庇厄塔斯 Pietas 罗马女神 13—297a
庇护 asylum 国际法 2—11d
庇护 Pius 教皇称号 13—332b
庇护八世 Pius Ⅷ 教皇 13—333e
庇护二世 Pius Ⅱ 教皇 13—332c
庇护九世 Pius Ⅸ 教皇 13—333f
庇护六世 Pius Ⅵ 教皇 13—333b
庇护七世 Pius Ⅶ 教皇 13—333d
庇护三世 Pius Ⅲ 教皇 13—332d
庇护十二世 Pius Ⅻ 教皇 13—334e
庇护十世，圣 Piux X, SAINT 教皇 13—334b
庇护十一世 Pius Ⅺ 教皇 13—334c
庇护四世 Pius Ⅳ 教皇 13—332e
庇护五世，圣 Pius V, SAINT 教皇 13—333a
庇护一世，圣 Pius I, SAINT 教皇 13—332b
庇里托俄斯 Pirithous 希腊神话人物 13—322a
庇隆 Perón, Juan 阿根廷总统 13—176c
庇隆夫人(爱娃) Perón, Eva 阿根廷总统夫人 13—176b
庇隆夫人(伊莎贝尔) Perón, Isabel 阿根廷总统夫人 13—176b
庇隆主义者 Peronist 阿根廷政治派别 13—176e
庇同和克勒奥庇斯 Biton and Cleobis 希腊传说人物 2—503f
庇西特拉图 Peisistratus 古雅典僭主 13—125c
哔叽 serge 织物 15—223f
铋(Bi) bismuth 金属元素 2—502a
秘鲁 Peru 南美洲国家 13—189a
秘鲁-玻利维亚邦联 Peruvian-Bolivian Confederation 南美洲历史 13—191f
秘鲁洋流 Peru Current 东南太平洋寒流 13—191a
秘鲁-智利海沟 Peru-Chile Trench 东太平洋海沟 13—191a
秘鲁总督辖区 Peru, Viceroyalty of 南美洲历史地区 13—190e
婢鲈 snook 鱼类 15—461f
蓖麻 castor-oil plant (*Ricinus communis*) 草本植物 3—514c
蓖麻油 castor oil 植物油 3—514b
辟尔唐人 Piltdown man 史前期人种 13—305c
辟支佛 pratyeka-buddha 佛教 13—486b
碧南 Hekinan 日本城市 7—571b
碧武里 Phetchaburi 泰国城镇 13—225e
碧玄岩 basanite 岩石 2—255e
碧瑶 Baguio 菲律宾城市 2—139b
碧玉 jasper 矿物 8—548b
碧玉炻器 jasperware 英国炻器 8—548e
碧云寺 Biyun Si 北京古寺 2—506b
篦齿纹器皿 combware 朝鲜古陶器 4—378d
篦齿纹陶器 comb pottery 朝鲜古陶器 4—376d
壁磅 Pyapon 缅甸城镇 14—41b
壁虎 gecko 爬行动物 7—42c
壁画 mural 绘画 11—490b
壁角柱 anta 建筑学 1—373f
壁龛 niche 建筑 12—169d
壁炉 fireplace 取暖设备 6—327e
壁炉柴架 andiron 炉具 1—329d
壁炉架 chimneypiece 建筑 4—159c
壁炉台 mantel 建筑 10—474d
壁式灯台 sconce 灯台 15—146b
壁台 console 家具 4—447c
壁毯 tapestry 工艺品 16—475a
壁细胞 parietal cell 细胞学 13—42b
壁纸 wallpaper 房屋装修用纸 18—83a
壁钟 bracket clock 英国摆钟 3—104f
壁柱 pilaster 建筑 13—301e
避雷针 lightning rod 避雷装置 10—94b
避世运动 Beat movement 美国文学和社会运动 2—308a
避暑山庄 Bishu Shanzhuang 中国景区 2—497f
避邪眼图案 apotropaic eye 绘画 1—416c
避役 chameleon 爬行动物 4—38a
避孕 contraception 生理学 4—470e
避孕套 condom 避孕用具 4—416e
臂 arm 解剖学 1—495a
臂钏 armlet 装饰 1—501c
臂神经丛 brachial plexus 解剖学 3—104b
臂行 brachiation 动物学 3—104b
璧 bi 中国古代玉器 2—455b
璧珥 Biddle, James 美国海军军官 2—463e
璧克馥 Pickford, Mary 美国电影演员 13—291a
躄鱼 frogfish 鱼类 6—499e
边材 sapwood 木质层 15—58f
边和 Bien Hoa 越南城市 2—465c
边际成本定价法 marginal-cost pricing 经济学 10—505e
边际生产力论 marginal productivity theory 经济学 10—505f
边际效用 marginal utility 经济学 10—505f

边疆幽默 frontier humour 美国文学 6—502b
边界层 boundary layer 流体力学 3—83a
边境歌谣 border ballad 英国文学 3—47c
边境㹴狗 border terrier 狗品种 3—47c
边沁 Bentham, George 英国植物学家 2—391b
边沁 Bentham, Jeremy 英国哲学家 2—391c
边沁 Bentham, Sir Samuel 英国工程师 2—392c
边水 Ben Thuy 越南城镇 2—375e
边维尔 Bienville, Jean-Baptiste Le Moyne de 法国探险家 2—465e
边音 lateral 语音学 9—510a
边值 boundary values 数学 3—83a
编缏带 braiding 织物 3—115a
编程性细胞死亡 apoptosis 细胞学 1—414f
编击乐器 chime 乐器 4—158e
编结花边 punto a groppo 工艺品 14—29c
编剧艺术 dramaturgy 戏剧 5—414c
编年史 chronicle 历史 4—213d
编年史家 annalist 罗马历史学家 1—363b
编枝小径 pleached alley 花园小道 13—367a
编织工艺 basketry 手工艺 2—264b
编钟 serial bells 中国古代乐器 15—225e
蝙蝠 bat 哺乳动物 2—272b
蝙蝠蝽 bat bug 昆虫 2—272f
蝙蝠蛾 swift 昆虫 16—382d
蝙蝠科 Vespertilionidae 动物学 17—528e
蝙蝠蝇 bat fly 昆虫 2—273a
蝙蝠鱼 batfish 鱼类 2—276a
鞭笞 flagellation 宗教 6—344a
鞭笞 flogging 维持纪律的常用方法 6—362b
鞭虫 whipworm 蠕虫 18—224f
鞭打损伤 whiplash 损伤类型 18—224c
鞭鸫 whipbird 鸟类 18—224b
鞭毛 flagellum 生物学 6—344b
鞭毛超纲 Mastigophora 生物学 11—15d
鞭毛虫 flagellate 原生动物 6—343f
鞭尾魟 whip-tailed ray 鱼类 18—224b
鞭尾蜥 whiptail (lizard) 爬行动物 18—224f
扁虫 flatworm 蠕虫 6—351a
扁蝽 flat bug 昆虫 6—349c
扁担山脉 Dângrêk Mountains 泰-柬边境山脉 5—134d
扁谷盗 flat grain beetle 昆虫 6—349d
扁甲 cucujid beetle 昆虫 5—50b
扁平餐具 flatware 餐具 6—350d
扁平足 flatfoot 疾病 6—350a
扁鹊 Bianque 中国古代医学家 2—456e
扁鲨 monkfish 鱼类 11—342c
扁桃 almond (*Prunus dulcis*) 木本植物 1—246f
扁桃体 tonsil 解剖学 17—153d
扁桃体炎 tonsillitis 疾病 17—153d
扁桃体周围脓肿 quinsy 疾病 14—94b
扁头袋鼩 planigale 哺乳动物 13—342f
扁头猫 flat-headed cat (*Felis planiceps*) 猫品种 6—349d
扁小蠹 flat bark beetle 昆虫 6—349b
扁形动物 platyhelminth 蠕虫 13—364d
扁形人物与圆形人物 flat and round characters 文学作品中所描绘的各种人物 6—349b
扁嘴霸鹟 spadebill 鸟类 15—564f
扁嘴雀 flatbill 鸟类 6—349e
弁才天 Benzaiten (Japanese goddess) 日本神话中福神 2—396a
弁庆 Benkei 日本武僧 2—387b
弁天 Benten 日本神话中福神 2—391a
变分法 calculus of variations 数学 3—337a
变构调控 allosteric control 生物化学 1—242d
变节 riddah 伊斯兰教历史 14—290f
变口目 Trepostomata 古生物学 17—211c
变狼狂 lycanthropy 精神病 10—307d
变鸣钟术 change ringing 英国鸣钟术 4—49b
变态 metamorphosis 生物学 11—151c
变态反应 allergy 医学 1—239d
变态心理学 abnormal psychology 心理学 1—26b
变体 transubstantiation 基督教神学 17—200a
变温性 poikilothermy 动物学 13—387e
变星 variable star 天文学 17—472f
变形性骨炎 osteitis deformans 疾病 12—490a
变性 denaturation 生物化学 5—241c
变性聚丙烯腈纤维 modacrylic 合成纤维 11—303c
变性土 vertisol 土壤 17—526d
变压器 transformer 电器 17—196e
变叶木 croton (*Codiaeum variegatum*) 木本植物 5—34d
变异 variation 生物学 17—473b
变音管 crook 乐器 5—29d
变应原 allergen 医学 1—239c
变质岩 metamorphic rock 岩石 11—150f
变质作用 metamorphism 地质学 11—151b
变奏 musical variation 音乐 11—509c
便秘 constipation 病理现象 4—456a
便士邮政 Penny Post 邮政业务 13—146b
《便西拉智训》 Ecclesiasticus 天主教次经 5—521b
便雅悯 Benjamin 《圣经》时代以色列人支派 2—386e
便雅悯(图德拉的) Benjamin OF TUDELA 犹太人拉比 2—386e
辨别 discrimination 心理学 5—339e
辨惑学 apologetics 基督教神学 1—414b
辨喜 Vivekananda 印度教领袖 18—27d
辩护律师 advocate 法律 1—90e
辩论 débat 文学 5—197d
辩论 debate 说理交锋 5—197d
《辩论报》 Journal des Débats, Le 法国报纸 9—93c
辩论诗 partimen 诗歌 13—68a
辩证法 dialectic 哲学 5—285b
辩证唯物主义 dialectical materialism 哲学 5—285b
标点符号 punctuation 文句符号 14—26c
标牌 sign 标记 15—362c
标题音乐 program music 音乐 13—528e
标志层 marker bed 地质学 10—520e
标致雪铁龙集团 PSA Peugeot Citroën SA 法国公司 13—561f
标准层 key bed (geology) 地质学 9—248c
标准差 standard deviation 统计学 16—187c
标准纯银 sterling 冶金学 16—225f
标准大气 standard atmosphere 大气模式 16—187b
标准化 standardization 工业 16—188a
标准化石 index fossil 地质学 8—357c
标准酒精度 proof 绝对酒精含量标准 13—534b
标准烈度酒 proof spirit 含标准酒精比例的酒 13—534c
标准模型 standard model 粒子物理学 16—187c
标准普尔 500 指数 S&P 500 股票市场指数 14—478a
标准石油公司和托拉斯 Standard Oil Company and Trust 美国公司 16—187e
标准时 standard time 法定时间 16—187f
标准种马 Standardbred 马品种 16—187f
飑 squall 气象学 16—166e
镖鲈 darter 鱼类 5—153f
瘰疽草 whitlow grass 草本植物 18—237d
表 watch 计时工具 18—133d
表壳虫目 Arcellinida 动物学 1—446a
表面活性剂 surface-active agent 化学 16—351d
表面硬化 surface hardening 钢材热、机械处理 16—351d

表面张力 surface tension 物理学 16—351f
表面张力波 capillary wave 物理学 3—425f
表皮 epidermis 皮肤外层 6—99d
表皮 epidermis 植物细胞层 6—99d
表皮角化症 hyperkeratosis 兽医学 8—292b
表皮牙 epidermal tooth 解剖学 6—99d
表饰 watch fob 怀表附件 18—134e
表述词 epithet 文字 6—104f
表现型 phenotype 遗传学 13—225a
表现主义 Expressionism 艺术流派 6—196b
表象论 representationism 哲学 14—234c
表演场 arena 建筑 1—459b
表业 vijñapti-karman 佛教 17—559d
鳔 swim bladder 鱼类浮力器官 16—384d
憋七 Sevens (card game) 纸牌游戏 15—238c
别德马 Viedma 阿根廷城市 17—547e
别德内 Bedny, Demyan 苏联诗人 2—326f
别动队员 ranger 美国军事人员 14—150b
别尔茨克 Berdsk 俄罗斯城市 2—399c
别尔哥罗德 Belgorod 俄罗斯州名 2—355a
别尔哥罗德 Belgorod 俄罗斯城市 2—355b
别尔哥罗德-德涅斯特罗夫斯基 Belgorod-Dnestrovsky 乌克兰城市 2—355b
别尔季切夫 Berdichev 乌克兰城市 2—399a
别尔季切夫斯基 Berdichevsky, Micah Joseph 俄国犹太作家 2—399a
别尔佳耶夫 Berdyayev, Nikolay Aleksandrovich 俄国宗教思想家、哲学家 2—399c
别尔江斯克 Berdyansk 乌克兰城市 2—399c
别尔斯克-比亚瓦 Bielsko-Biała 波兰旧省份 2—465c
别尔斯克-比亚瓦 Bielsko-Biała 波兰城市 2—465c
别府 Beppu 日本城市 2—397a
别赫捷列夫 Bekhterev, Vladimir 苏联神经生理学家 2—348c
别卡巴德 Bekabad 乌兹别克斯坦城市 2—348a
别克 Buick, David Dunbar 美国汽车制造商 3—237e
别拉亚河 Belaya River 俄罗斯河流 2—350f
别雷 Bely, Andrey 俄国理论家、诗人 2—372f
别雷哥罗德 Bely Gorod 俄国居民点 2—373a
别利齐 Belts 摩尔多瓦城市 2—372c
别利亚耶夫 Belyayev, Pavel 苏联航天员 2—373a
别廖索娃 Beriosova, Svetlana 立陶宛芭蕾演员 2—408c
别列津纳河 Berezina River 白俄罗斯河流 2—401e
别列斯捷奇科战役 Beresteczko, Battle of 波兰历史 2—401c
别列兹尼基 Berezniki 俄罗斯城市 2—401e
别林斯高晋 Bellingshausen, Fabian Gottlieb von 俄国探险家 2—366a
别林斯基 Belinsky, Vissarion Grigoryevich 俄国文学批评家 2—356a
别卢哈山 Belukha, Mount 俄罗斯山峰 2—372d
别洛戈尔斯克 Belogorsk 俄罗斯城市 2—370e
别洛列茨克 Beloretsk 俄罗斯城市 2—370f
别洛韦日森林 Belovezhskaya Forest 欧洲最大原始林区 2—371b
别洛沃 Belovo 俄罗斯城市 2—371b
别洛乌索夫 Belousov, Vladimir Vladimirovich 苏联地质学家 2—371a
别嘌呤醇 allopurinol 药物 1—242c
别曲 pyŏlgok 朝鲜高丽王朝诗歌形式 14—44a
别墅 villa 建筑 17—561e
别斯图热夫-留明 Bestuzhev-Ryumin, Aleksey Petrovich, Count (Graf) 俄国外交家 2—439d
别特帕克达拉草原 Betpak-Dala 哈萨克斯坦沙漠 2—444c
别西卜 Beelzebub 《圣经》中的鬼王 2—330c
别则 Beg-tse 藏传佛教护法神 2—336d
别兹博罗德科 Bezborodko, Aleksandr Andreyevich, Knyaz (Prince) 俄国外交大臣 2—448b
宾 Byng, John 英国海军将官 3—298b
宾 Byng of Vimy (of Thorpe-le-Soken), Julian Hedworth George Byng, Viscount 英国陆军元帅 3—298c
宾 Bing, Sir Rudolph 英国歌剧演出经理 2—477a
宾厄姆 Bingham, Amelia 美国演员 2—477b
宾厄姆 Bingham, George Caleb 美国画家 2—477c
宾厄姆 Bingham, George Charles 英国军人 2—477d
宾厄姆 Bingham, Hiram 美国考古学家 2—477d
宾厄姆顿 Binghamton 美国城市 2—477f
宾戈 bingo 游戏 2—477f
宾格尔 Bingöl 土耳其城市 2—478a
宾根 Bingen 德国城市 2—477a
宾基斯 Binkis, Kazys 立陶宛诗人 2—478c
宾杰里 Bendery 摩尔多瓦城市 2—377e
宾凯尔斯胡克 Bynkershoek, Cornelis van 荷兰法学家 3—298d
宾尼 Binney, Horace 美国律师、政治家 2—478d
宾尼 Binney, Thomas 英格兰牧师 2—478e
宾尼希 Binnig, Gerd 德国物理学家 2—478e
宾斯万格 Binswanger, Ludwig 瑞士精神病学家 2—479b
宾夕法尼亚 Pennsylvania 美国州名 13—142d
宾夕法尼亚大学 Pennsylvania, University of 美国大学 13—145d
宾夕法尼亚纪 Pennsylvanian period 地质学 13—146a
宾夕法尼亚街 Pennsylvania Avenue 美国华盛顿市街道 13—145e
宾夕法尼亚美术学院 Pennsylvania Academy of the Fine Arts 美国美术学院、博物馆 13—145e
宾夕法尼亚铁路公司 Pennsylvania Railroad Company 美国铁路公司 13—145f
宾夕法尼亚制度 Pennsylvania system 刑罚方法 13—146a
宾县 Bin Xian 中国县名 2—476a
宾州石油公司 Pennzoil Company 美国公司 13—146c
滨岸带 littoral zone 海洋生态领域 10—152d
滨瓣庆属 Mertensia 植物学 11—136c
滨北 Hamakita 日本城市 7—436b
滨海阿尔卑斯 Alpes-Maritimes 法国省份 1—249e
滨海阿尔卑斯山脉 Maritime Alps 欧洲山脉 10—517f
滨海阿特拉斯 Maritime Atlas (North Africa) 北非山脉 10—517f
滨海地区 Primorsky Kray 俄罗斯行政区 13—511d
滨海拉塞讷 Seyne-sur-Mer, La 法国城镇 15—248f
滨海区 Maritime 西非多哥经济区 10—517e
滨海塞纳省 Seine-Maritime 法国省份 15—191f
滨海绍森德 Southend-on-Sea 英格兰自治市 15—552b
滨海圣玛丽 Saintes-Maries-de-la-Mer 法国南部村庄 14—531c
滨海韦斯顿 Weston-super-Mare 英格兰埃文郡城镇 18—213f
滨海夏朗德省 Charente-Maritime 法国省份 4—63d
滨海肖勒姆 Shoreham-by-Sea 英格兰港口 15—332f
滨海诸省 Maritime Provinces 加拿大地理 10—518c
滨海自由城 Villefranche-sur-Mer 法国城镇 17—564f
滨湖尼亚加拉 Niagara-on-the-Lake 加拿大城镇 12—163f
滨口雄幸 Hamaguchi Osachi 日本政治家 7—435f
滨浪鹬 surfbird (*Aphriza virgata*) 鸟类 16—352d
滨藜属 Atriplex 植物学 2—36a
滨螺 periwinkle 腹足动物 13—171d
滨鸟 shorebird 鸟类 15—332e
滨松 Hamamatsu 日本城市 7—436c
滨田庄司 Hamada Shōji 日本艺术家 7—435b
滨外坝 offshore bar 地质学 12—344d
滨鹬 dunlin (*Calidris*, or *Erolia*, *alpina*) 鸟类 5—464a
滨鹬属 Calidris 动物学 3—345c
槟城 George Town 马来西亚城市 7—78c
槟港 Pangkalpinang 印度尼西亚城市 13—11d
槟知 Ben Tre 越南城市 2—375e

濒危物种 endangered species 生物学 6—72d
冰 ice 水的固态 8—310e
冰长石 adularia 矿物 1—87e
冰川 glacier 冰川学 7—147f
冰川锅穴 moulin 地质学 11—438e
冰川国家公园 Glacier National Park 加拿大公园 7—148c
冰川国家公园 Glacier National Park 美国公园 7—148c
冰川国家公园 Los Glaciares National Park 阿根廷公园 10—228a
冰川湖 tarn 冰川学 16—483d
冰川湾 Glacier Bay 美国海湾 7—148c
冰川湾国家公园和禁猎区 Glacier Bay National Park and Preserve 美国自然保护区 7—148c
冰川学 glaciology 地理学 7—148d
冰岛 Iceland 北大西洋岛国 8—313e
冰岛低压 Icelandic low 气象学 8—315a
冰岛国定教会 National Church of Iceland 基督教教会 12—13b
《冰岛家族萨迦》 Icelanders' sagas 冰岛散文故事 8—314f
冰岛文学 Icelandic literature 北欧文学 8—315a
冰岛藓 Iceland moss (*Cetraria islandica*) 苔藓植物 8—314e
冰岛语 Icelandic language 欧洲语言 8—314f
冰斗 cirque 冰川学 4—245e
冰海冰川 Mer de Glace 法国冰川 11—122e
冰后隙 bergschrund 冰川学 2—406e
冰架 ice shelf 冰川学 8—312b
冰间湖 polynya 冰川学 13—415e
冰晶石 cryolite 矿物 5—42c
冰块的形成 ice formation 冰川学 8—311f
冰砾阜 kame 冰川学 9—146d
冰期 glacial stage 地质学 7—147b
冰期 ice age 地质学 8—311b
冰淇淋 ice cream 食品 8—311c
冰碛 moraine 地质学 11—382e
冰碛物 till 地质学 17—95f
冰碛岩 tillite 岩石 17—97a
冰丘 pingo 山丘 13—312e
冰球 ICE HOCKEY 体育项目 16—119a
冰球 ice hockey 体育项目 8—312a
冰人 Iceman 人体干尸 8—315b
冰山 iceberg 冰川学 8—312f
冰上表演 ice show 娱乐 8—312c
冰上溜石 CURLING 体育项目 16—101a
冰上溜石 curling 体育项目 5—70a
冰上曲棍球 bandy 体育项目 2—196c
冰上驶帆运动 iceboating 运动项目 8—313c
冰上舞蹈 ice dancing 冰上运动 8—311d
冰蚀谷 glacial valley 冰川学 7—147d
冰水沉积 outwash 地质学 12—509d
冰丸 sleet 气象学 15—430d
冰隙 crevasse 冰川学 5—10b
冰心 Bingxin 中国作家 2—478b
冰穴 ice cave 冰川学 8—311c
冰雪植物区系 cryoflora 冰雪植物区系 5—41f
冰叶日中花 ice plant (*Mesembryanthemum crystallinum*) 草本植物 8—312b
冰鱼 icefish 鱼类 8—313e
冰原岛峰 nunatak 地质学 12—299e
冰缘学 periglaciology 地质学 13—168c
冰洲石 Iceland spar 矿物 8—314f
兵库 Hyōgo 日本县名 8—290d
兵鲇 Corydoras 鱼类 4—528c
兵器博物馆 Armoury Museum 俄罗斯博物馆 1—503a
兵营 camp 军队驻扎区 3—376a
兵鱼 soldierfish 鱼类 15—494e
槟榔 betel 木本植物 2—440f
槟榔亚纲 Arecidae 植物学 1—459a
槟榔屿 Penang 马来西亚岛屿 13—135a
丙氨酸 alanine 化合物 1—166d
丙醇 propyl alcohol 化合物 13—538a
丙二酸 malonic acid 化合物 10—435b
丙磺舒 probenecid 药物 13—523e
丙咪嗪 imipramine 药物 8—342c
丙三醇 glycerol 化合物 7—165e
丙酮 acetone 化合物 1—49c
丙烷 propane 化合物 13—535b
丙烯 propylene 化合物 13—538b
丙烯画 acrylic painting 绘画 1—59a
丙烯酸系化合物 acrylic compound 化合物 1—59a
饼海胆 cake urchin 棘皮动物 3—331e
饼酒同领派 Utraquist 基督教派别 17—432c
炳灵寺石窟 Grottoes at Bingling Monastery 中国石窟寺 7—322f
并居区 reducción 南美印第安人居住区 14—194f
并协原理 complementarity principle 物理学 4—399a
病毒 virus 微生物 18—15c
病毒粒子 virion 病毒学 18—14d
病毒性出血热 viral hemorrhagic fever 疾病 18—5d
病毒学 virology 医学 18—14e
病理学 pathology 医学 13—87f
病院 hotel dieu 法国中世纪医院 8—190f
病灶性发作 focal seizure 病理学 6—383e
拨弦键琴 harpsichord 乐器 7—485c
波埃都斯派 Boethusian 犹太教派 2—565f
波埃里奥 Poerio, Carlo 意大利革命者 13—385f
波别特诺斯采夫 Pobedonostsev, Konstantin Petrovich 沙皇俄国官员 13—382d
波波夫 Popov, Aleksandr 俄国物理学家、电气工程师 13—434b
波波夫 Popov, Alexey 苏联舞台剧导演 13—434d
波波夫 Popov, Oleg Konstantinovich 莫斯科马戏团演员 13—434e
波波湖 Poopó, Lake 玻利维亚湖泊 13—430f
波波卡特佩特 Popocatépetl 墨西哥死火山 13—433e
波波洛 popolo 意大利政治集团 13—434a
波波洛卡人 Popoloca 中美印第安人 13—434a
波波纳 Bobone, Giacinto 教皇 2—556e
波波维奇 Popovich, Pavel Romanovich 苏联航天员 13—434f
波长 wavelength 物理学 18—149f
波长计 wavemeter 物理学仪器 18—150a
波彻 Bocher, Joan 英格兰基督教信徒 2—559d
波城 Pau 法国城镇 13—93d
波茨措-迪-博尔哥伯爵 Pozzo di Borgo, Charles-André, Count 科西嘉岛贵族 13—477b
波茨敦 Pottstown 美国自治镇 13—467a
波茨坦 Potsdam 德国城市 13—464f
波茨坦 Potsdam 美国村庄、镇 13—465a
波茨坦会议 Potsdam Conference 第二次世界大战盟国会议 13—465a
波茨维尔 Pottsville 美国城市 13—467b
波茨维尔统 Pottsville Series 地质学 13—467c
波怛阇利 Patañjali 印度教作家、哲学家 13—84d
波代诺内 Pordenone 意大利画家 13—441a
波代诺内 Pordenone 意大利城市 13—441a
波导 waveguide 物理学 18—149e
波得定则 Bode's law 天文学 2—561c
波德勃拉 port de bras 芭蕾舞 13—444e
波德戈尔内 Podgorny, Nikolay 苏联政治家 13—383f
波德戈里察 Podgorica 黑山首都 13—383f
波德拉斯 Podlaskie 波兰省份 13—384d
波德莱尔 Baudelaire, Charles(-Pierre) 法国诗人 2—284e

波德申 Port Dickson 马来西亚城镇 13—444e
波德斯塔 podesta 意大利官职 13—383e
波的尼亚低地 Pohjanmaa 芬兰低地平原 13—387c
波的尼亚湾 Bothnia, Gulf of 波罗的海海湾 3—72c
波蒂埃 Pothier, Dom Joseph 法国修士、学者 13—463e
波蒂厄斯暴动 Porteous Riots 英国历史 13—448f
波蒂奇 Portage 美国城市 13—447f
波蒂奇 Portici 意大利城镇 13—451d
波蒂奇拉普雷里 Portage la Prairie 加拿大城市 13—447f
波动 wave motion 物理学 18—149a
波动力学 wave mechanics 物理学 18—149a
波动性气旋 wave cyclone 气象学 18—148f
波多黎各 Puerto Rico 西印度群岛美属自由联邦 14—16c
波多黎各海沟 Puerto Rico Trench 北大西洋海底凹地 14—17c
波多黎各民族解放武装力量 FALN 波多黎各民族主义组织 6—224e
波多利斯克 Podolsk 俄罗斯城市 13—385a
波多利亚 Podolia 乌克兰地区 13—384f
波多诺伏 Porto-Novo 贝宁首都 13—453a
波多韦柳 Pôrto Velho 巴西州首府 13—453c
波多野精一 Hatano Seiichi 日本学者 7—507a
波恩 Bonn 德国城市 3—32c
《波恩星表》 BD 天文学 2—300d
《波恩星表》 Bonner Durchmusterung (BD) 天文学 3—33b
波尔 Pole, Reginald 英格兰枢机主教 13—398c
波尔 Pole, Richard de la 英格兰贵族 13—398e
波尔 Poel, William 英国演员、剧院经理 13—385e
波尔 Pole, William de La 英格兰陆军司令、政治家 13—398e
波尔波拉 Porpora, Nicola (Antonio Giacinto) 意大利声乐教师、作曲家 13—442f
波尔布特 Pol Pot 高棉政治领袖 13—393e
波尔查诺 Bolzano, Bernhard 波希米亚数学家 3—18c
波尔迪-佩佐利博物馆 Poldi Pezzoli, Museo 意大利博物馆 13—398c
波尔蒂芒 Portimão 葡萄牙港口城镇 13—451e
波尔蒂芒新镇 Vila Nova de Portimão (Portugal) 葡萄牙城镇 17—560e
波尔丁 Polding, John Bede 澳大利亚天主教主教 13—398c
波尔都斯 Portus 古罗马港市 13—457a
波尔多 Bordeaux 法国城市 3—45c
《波尔多的于翁》 Huon de Bordeaux 古法语诗歌 8—263e
波尔多第一大学、第二大学、第三大学 Bordeaux I, II, and III, Universities of 法国大学 3—46a
波尔多公爵 Bordeaux, Henri Dieudonné, Duke (duc) de 法国贵族 3—46b
波尔多葡萄酒 Bordeaux wine 法国酒 3—46b
波尔加 Polgar, Judit 匈牙利国际象棋大师 13—399e
波尔加 Polgar, Zsuzsa 匈牙利国际象棋大师 13—399e
波尔卡 polka 舞蹈 13—405a
波尔克 Polk, James K(nox) 美国总统 13—404e
波尔克 Polk, Leonidas 美国圣公会主教 13—405a
波尔罗亚尔女隐修院 Port-Royal 法国西多会隐修院 13—447b
波尔森 Porson, Richard 英国学者 13—443b
波尔舍 Porsche, Ferdinand 奥地利汽车工程师 13—443a
波尔斯 Powles, Matilda Alice, Lady de Frece 英国喜剧演员 13—476a
波尔斯卡 polska 舞蹈 13—410c
波尔塔 Porta, Giambattista della 意大利自然哲学家 13—447e
波尔塔拉 Portolá, Gaspar de 西班牙军官 13—453e
波尔塔瓦 Poltava 乌克兰州名 13—410c
波尔塔瓦 Poltava 乌克兰城市 13—410c
波尔塔瓦战役 Poltava, Battle of 俄国-瑞典战争(1709-07-08) 13—410d
波尔图 Porto 葡萄牙港口城市 13—452e
波尔图葡萄酒 port 葡萄牙酒 13—443c
波尔沃 Porvoo 芬兰城市 13—457b
波尔沃思勋爵 Polwarth, Patrick Hume, Lord 苏格兰政治家 13—410e
波尔辛 Poulsen, Johannes 丹麦戏剧演员、导演 13—468c
波尔辛兄弟 Poulsen, Emil and Olaf 丹麦戏剧演员 13—468b
波菲利 Porphyry 希腊哲学家 13—442c
波弗蒂湾 Poverty Bay 南太平洋小海湾 13—471c
波弗特海 Beaufort Sea 北冰洋边缘海 2—312b
波伏瓦 Beauvoir, Simone (Lucie-Ernestine-Marie-Bertrand) de 法国女作家 2—315e
波冈达 Boganda, Barthélemy 中非民族主义领袖 2—567c
波哥大 Bogotá 哥伦比亚首都 3—1a
波格丹诺维奇 Bogdanovich, Peter 美国电影导演 2—568c
波哈斯卡 Pawhuska 美国城市 13—104b
波函数 wave function 物理学 18—149a
波河 Po River 意大利河流 13—381f
波河南共和国 Cispadane Republic 欧洲历史国家 4—246e
波痕 ripple mark 水文学 14—311f
波鸿 Bochum 德国城市 2—559f
波基普西 Poughkeepsie 美国城市 13—467e
波季 Poti 格鲁吉亚城市 13—463f
波江座α Alpha Eridani 天文学 1—250b
波将金 Potemkin, Grigory Aleksandrovich, Knyaz (Prince) 俄国军官、政治家 13—463a
波焦·布拉乔利尼 Poggio Bracciolini, Gian Francesco 意大利人文主义者、书法家 13—386f
波杰布尔 Bhojpur 印度古村庄 2—452f
波卡洪塔斯 Pocahontas 印第安波瓦坦族妇女 13—382e
波卡罗 Bokāro 印度城市 3—9b
波卡塔克河 Pawcatuck River 美国河流 13—104b
波卡特洛 Pocatello 美国城市 13—382f
波凯利尼 Boccherini, Luigi 意大利作曲家、大提琴家 2—558c
波科尔尼 Pokorny, Julius 欧洲语言学家 13—393d
波科克 Pocock, Lena Margaret (English actress) 英国演员 13—383d
波科曼人 Pocomam 马雅印第安人 13—383d
波科诺山 Pocono Mountains 美国高原地区 13—383d
波科乐队 Poco 美国乐队 13—383c
波克兰 Poquelin, Jean-Baptiste 法国剧作家莫里哀的原名 13—439c
波克罗夫斯基 Pokrovsky, Mikhail Nikolayevich 苏联历史学家、官员 13—393d
波克罗夫斯基大教堂 Pokrovsky Cathedral 俄罗斯莫斯科教堂 13—393e
波拉 Pola(Croatia) 克罗地亚港口、工业中心 13—394a
波拉布人 Polab 欧洲斯拉夫人 13—394a
波拉德 Pollard, A(lbert) F(rederick) 英国历史学家 13—405d
波拉德 Pollard, Fritz 美国橄榄球运动员 13—405e
波拉德 Pollard, Marjorie 英格兰女曲棍球运动员 13—405f
波拉尼 Polanyi, John C(harles) 加拿大化学家、教育家 13—396a
波拉尼 Polanyi, Karl (Paul) 经济人类学家、政治家 13—396b
波拉诺 Polano, Pietro Soave(Italian theologian) 意大利神学家 13—395f
波拉约洛 Pollaiuolo, Simone del 意大利建筑师 13—405d
波拉约洛兄弟 Pollaiuolo, Antonio del and Piero del 意大利雕刻家、画家 13—405c
波来古 Pleiku 越南城镇 13—368a
波莱尔 Borel, (Félix-Édouard-Justin-) Émile 法国数学家 3—48d
波莱斯瓦夫斯基 Bolesławski, Richard 电影、戏剧导演 3—11a
波兰 Poland 欧洲国家 13—394a
波兰会议王国 Congress Kingdom of Poland 波兰历史 4—428f
波兰式连衫裙 polonaise 服装 13—409e

波兰斯基 Polanski, Roman 波兰电影导演 13—396a
波兰提亚 Pollentia 意大利古城 13—406b
波兰王位继承战争 Polish Succession, War of the 欧洲历史 13—402b
波兰文学 Polish literature 东欧文学 13—401d
波兰语 Polish language 东欧语言 13—401c
波兰正教会 Orthodox Church of Poland 东正教自治教会 12—474a
波兰自治正教会 Autocephalous Orthodox Church of Poland 东正教会 2—73e
波兰走廊 Polish Corridor 欧洲地区 13—401c
波浪热 undulant fever 疾病 17—341b
波雷斯 Porres, Saint Martín de 秘鲁主保圣人 13—442f
波里 Pori 芬兰城市 13—441b
波里鲁阿 Porirua 新西兰城市 13—441c
波立特 Pollitt, Harry 英共总书记 13—406f
波利艾努斯 Polyaenus 马其顿修辞学家、律师 13—410f
波利奥 Pollio, Gaius Asinius 罗马演说家、史学家 13—406e
波利奥 Pollio, Marcus Vitruvius 罗马建筑师 13—406f
波利比奥斯 Polybius 希腊政治家、历史学家 13—411a
波利蒂斯 Politis, Nikolaos Sokrates 希腊法学家、外交官 13—404c
波利杜里 Polidoúri, Maria 希腊诗人 13—400e
波利格诺托斯 Polygnotus 希腊画家 13—413b
波利卡普,圣 Polycarp, SAINT 希腊基督教主教 13—411c
《波利卡普殉教记》 Martyrdom of Polycarp 基督教文献 10—552a
波利克拉特斯 Polycrates 萨摩斯岛僭主 13—412b
波利克里托斯 Polyclitus 希腊雕刻家 13—411f
波利尼西亚 Polynesia 太平洋地区 13—415b
波利尼西亚地理人种 Polynesian geographic race 人类学 13—415c
波利尼西亚诸语言 Polynesian languages 语言 13—415d
波利尼亚克家族 Polignac FAMILY 法国贵族世家 13—400e
波利齐亚诺 Politian 意大利诗人、古典学者 13—402e
波利萨里奥阵线 Polisario 西撒哈拉政治-军事组织 13—401b
波利瓦诺夫 Polivanov, Aleksey Andreyevich 沙俄将军、陆军大臣 13—404d
波粒二象性 wave-particle duality 物理学 18—149d
波列夫斯科伊 Polevskoy 俄罗斯城市 13—399e
波列斯拉夫 Boleslav 波希米亚统治者之名 3—10d
波列斯拉夫二世 Boleslav II 波希米亚公爵 3—10e
波列斯拉夫三世 Boleslav III 波希米亚公爵 3—10e
波列斯拉夫一世 Boleslav I 波希米亚公爵 3—10e
波列西耶沼泽 Polesye (eastern Europe) 东欧沼泽地 13—399d
波林 Boring, Edwin G(arrigues) 美国心理学家 3—51d
波林尼亚 Polymnia 希腊女神 13—414d
波龙戈斯 Porongos (Uruguay) 乌拉圭城市 13—441f
波隆纳鲁沃 Polonnaruwa 斯里兰卡城镇 13—410a
波鲁克斯 Pollux (Roman deity) 古希腊罗马神话 13—408b
波吕斐摩斯 Polyphemus 希腊神话人物 13—416b
波吕克塞娜 Polyxena 希腊神话人物 13—418f
波伦 Pollen, Daniel 新西兰总理 13—406b
波伦塔家族 Polenta FAMILY 意大利贵族世家 13—399c
波伦·翁德·哈尔巴黑 Bohlen und Halbach, Alfried von 德国工业家 3—3c
波伦·翁德·哈尔巴黑 Bohlen und Halbach, Gustav von 德国外交家 3—3c
波罗的海 Baltic Sea 北大西洋海湾 2—182e
《波罗的海公约》 Baltic Entente 波罗的海三国共同防御协定 2—182b
波罗的海国家 Baltic states 波罗的海东岸三国 2—183a
波罗的人 Balt 波罗的海沿海民族 2—181e
波罗的斯克 Baltiysk 俄罗斯城市 2—184e
波罗的诸语言 Baltic languages 印欧语系语族 2—182c
波罗的宗教 Baltic religion 波罗的海地区古代宗教 2—182e
波罗芬高原 Bolovens Plateau 老挝高原 3—16b
波罗伏洛干酪 provolone 意大利干酪 13—551c
波罗迦罗摩巴忽一世 Parākramabāhu I 斯里兰卡国王 13—34e
波罗蜜多 pāramitā 佛教 13—36f
波罗斯 Porus 印度王公 13—457a
波罗斯 Póros 希腊岛屿 13—441f
《波罗提木叉》 pātimokkha 佛教 13—88b
波萝勉 Prêy Veng 柬埔寨城镇 13—502b
波洛茨克 Polotsk 白俄罗斯城市 13—410b
波洛夫切人 Polovtsy (Euro-Asian tribal confederation) 民族 13—410b
波洛克 Pollock, Sir Frederick, 3RD BARONET 英国法学家 13—407a
波洛克 Pollock, Jackson 美国画家 13—407b
波洛克诉农家贷款和信托公司案 Pollock v. Farmers' Loan and Trust Company 美国法院案例 13—407d
波洛内兹 polonaise 舞蹈 13—409f
波洛奇克河 Polochic River 危地马拉河流 13—409e
波马雷 Pomare, Sir Maui 新西兰政治家、医师 13—419a
波梅尔 Böhmer, Johann Friedrich 德国历史学家 3—4a
波美拉尼亚 Pomerania 欧洲历史地区 13—419e
波美拉尼亚狗 Pomeranian 狗品种 13—420a
波美拉尼亚湖区 Pomeranian Lakeland 波兰地区 13—420a
波米利亚诺达尔科 Pomigliano d'Arco 意大利城镇 13—420b
波密 Bowo 中国西藏县名 3—96e
波莫纳 Pomona (island, Scotland) 苏格兰岛屿 13—420d
波莫纳 Pomona 美国城市 13—420d
波莫人 Pomo 美国印第安人 13—420c
波莫土 Paumotu (French Polynesia) 法属波利尼西亚岛群 13—101b
波拿巴 Bonaparte, Charles Joseph 美国律师 3—24b
波拿巴 Bonaparte, Charles-Louis-Napoléon 法国皇帝 3—24b
波拿巴 Bonaparte, Charles-Lucien, PRINCIPE (prince) DI CANINO E DI MUSIGNANO 法国科学家 3—24b
波拿巴 Buonaparte, Carlo Maria 法国拿破仑一世之父 3—256a
波拿巴 Bonaparte, Jérôme 法国拿破仑一世之小弟 3—24c
波拿巴 Bonaparte, Joseph 法国拿破仑一世之长兄 3—24c
波拿巴 Bonaparte, Joséphine 法国皇后 3—24d
波拿巴 Bonaparte, Lucien 法国议长,拿破仑一世的二哥 3—24f
波拿巴 Bonaparte, Louis 法国拿破仑一世之弟 3—24d
波拿巴 Bonaparte, Louis-Lucien 法国拿破仑三世之堂弟 3—24e
波拿巴 Buonaparte, (Maria) Letizia 法国拿破仑一世之母 3—256a
波拿巴 Bonaparte, (Marie-) Pauline 法国拿破仑的二妹 3—25a
波拿巴 Bonaparte, (Marie-Annonciade-) Caroline 法国拿破仑之小妹 3—24a
波拿巴 Bonaparte, (Marie-Anne-) Élisa 法国拿破仑一世之大妹 3—24b
波拿巴 Bonaparte, Napoléon 法国皇帝 3—24f
波拿巴 Bonaparte, (Napoléon-Eugène-) Louis 法国拿破仑三世之子 3—24e
波拿巴 Bonaparte, Napoléon-François-Charles-Joseph 法国皇帝 3—24f
波拿巴 Bonaparte, Napoléon-Joseph-Charles-Paul 法国拿破仑三世之堂弟 3—25a
波拿巴 Bonaparte, Pierre-Napoléon 法国拿破仑三世之堂弟 3—25a
波拿巴家族 Bonaparte FAMILY 法国家族 3—23f
波拿巴主义者 Bonapartist 法国历史 3—25b
波拿文都拉,圣 Bonaventure, SAINT 法国枢机主教 3—25c
波那 Bāṇa 印度梵文散文大师 2—188f
波纳佩 Pohnpei 加罗林群岛火山岛 13—387d
波尼 Bône (Algeria) 阿尔及利亚城镇 3—27a
波尼人 Pawnee 北美印第安人 13—104d
波尼亚托夫斯基 Poniatowski, Józef Antoni 波兰英雄、法国元帅 13—426b
波尼亚托夫斯基 Poniatowski, Stanisław 波兰军人、政府官员 13—

426c
波尼亚托夫斯基 Poniatowski, Stanisław (king of Poland) 波兰国王 13—426c
波宁顿 Bonington, Richard Parkes 英国画家 3—32a
波帕尔 Bhopāl 印度城市 2—453a
波帕扬 Popayán 哥伦比亚城市 13—432a
波旁 Bourbonnais 法国历史文化区 3—84e
波旁 Bourbon, Louis Auguste de 法国贵族 3—84d
波旁公爵 Bourbon, DUKES OF 法国封爵贵族称号 3—83f
波旁公爵 Bourbon, Louis Ⅲ, duc de (duke of) 法国亲王 3—84c
波旁公爵 Bourbon, Louis-Henri, duc de (duke of) 法国首相 3—84c
波旁公爵 Bourbon, Louis-Henri-Joseph, duc de (duke of) 法国亲王 3—84d
波旁公爵 Bourbon, Louis-Joseph, duc de (duke of) 法国亲王 3—84c
波旁公爵(第八) Bourbon, Charles Ⅲ, 8e duc de (8th duke of) 法国陆军元帅 3—84b
波旁公爵(第二) Bourbon, Pierre Ⅰ, 2e duc de (2nd duke of) 法国外交官 3—83f
波旁公爵(第六) Bourbon, Jean Ⅱ, 6e duc de (6th duke of) 法国贵族 3—84a
波旁公爵(第七) Bourbon, Pierre Ⅱ, 7e duc de (7th duke of) 法国摄政 3—84b
波旁公爵(第三) Bourbon, Louis Ⅱ, 3e duc de (3rd duke of) 法国贵族 3—84a
波旁公爵(第四) Bourbon, Jean Ⅰ, 4e duc de (4th duke of) 法国贵族 3—84a
波旁公爵(第五) Bourbon, Charles Ⅰ, 5e duc de (5th duke of) 法国贵族 3—84a
波旁公爵(第一) Bourbon, Louis Ⅰ, 1er duc de (1st duke of) 法国贵族 3—83f
波旁家族 Bourbon, HOUSE OF 欧洲统治家族 3—84d
波旁-孔代 Bourbon-Condé, Anne-Geneviève de 法国贵族 3—84e
波旁威士忌酒 bourbon whiskey 美国酒 3—84e
波佩 Popé 美国特瓦普埃布洛族领袖 13—432b
波蓬德塔 Popondetta 巴布亚新几内亚城镇 13—434a
波普 Poppo (pope) 教皇 13—435b
波普 Pope, John 美国将军 13—433a
波普 Pople, Sir John A. 英国数学家、化学家 13—433d
波普尔 Popper, Sir Karl 英国哲学家 13—435a
波普拉德 Poprad 斯洛伐克城市 13—435d
波普洛尼亚 Populonia 古罗马城市 13—439c
波普·沃纳橄榄球赛 Pop Warner Football 体育比赛 13—431f
波普艺术 Pop art 英美艺术 13—431c
波切夫斯特鲁姆 Potchefstroom 南非城镇 13—462f
波丘尼 Boccioni, Umberto 意大利雕刻家 2—559b
波丘派恩河 Porcupine River 北美河流 13—440f
波瑞阿斯 Boreas 希腊神话 3—48d
波若尼 Pozsony (Slovakia) 斯洛伐克首都 13—477b
波萨达 Posada, José Guadalupe 墨西哥版画家 13—457c
波萨达斯 Posadas 阿根廷城市 13—457c
波萨里卡 Poza Rica 墨西哥城市 13—476f
波塞冬 Poseidon 希腊宗教水神 13—457e
波塞多尼奥斯 Poseidonius 希腊哲学家 13—458a
波塞多尼亚 Poseidonia (Italy) 意大利古城 13—458a
波森 Posen (Poland) 波兰波兹南旧名 13—458b
波尚恩峡湾 Porsangen 挪威海湾 13—443a
波什格伦 Porsgrunn 挪威城镇 13—443b
波士顿 Boston 英格兰城镇 3—63a
波士顿 Boston 美国城市 3—63c
波士顿惨案 Boston Massacre 美国历史事件 3—67b
波士顿茶党案 Boston Tea Party 美国历史事件 3—67c
波士顿㹴狗 Boston terrier 狗品种 3—67d
《波士顿环球报》 Boston Globe, The 美国报纸 3—66e
波士顿警察罢工 Boston Police Strike 美国历史事件 3—67b
波士顿拉丁学校 Boston Latin School 美国学校 3—67a
波士顿马拉松赛 Boston Marathon 体育运动 3—67a
波士顿-缅因公司 Boston and Maine Corporation 3—66e
波士顿山 Boston Mountains 美国山脉 3—67b
波士顿图书馆 Boston Athenaeum 美国图书馆 3—66e
波士顿银行公司 Bank of Boston Corporation 美国金融机构 2—204d
波士顿乐队 Boston 美国摇滚乐队 3—66c
波舒哀 Bossuet, Jacques-Bénigne 法国天主教主教 3—62f
波数 wave number 物理学 18—149c
波斯 Persia 伊朗王国旧称 13—182c
波斯波利斯 Persepolis 古代伊朗都城 13—181d
《波斯古经》 Avesta 波斯古经籍 2—87e
波斯考尔 Porthcawl 威尔士海滨胜地 13—451d
波斯拉 Bostra 叙利亚古城遗址 3—67d
波斯猫 Persian (cat) 猫品种 13—182d
波斯尼亚和黑塞哥维那 Bosnia and Herzegovina 欧洲国家 3—60e
波斯尼亚河 Bosna River 欧洲河流 3—60e
波斯猞猁 Persian lynx 哺乳动物 13—183e
波斯特 Post, C(harles) W(illiam) 美国制造商 13—459b
波斯特 Post, Emily 美国论述社交礼仪权威 13—459b
波斯图穆斯 Postumus, Marcus Cassianius Latinius 罗马将军 13—461c
波斯托伊纳 Postojna 斯洛文尼亚城镇 13—461a
波斯湾 Persian Gulf 印度洋边缘海 13—182d
波斯王钻石 Shah diamond 宝石 15—255c
波斯文学 Persian literature 现代波斯语著述 13—183d
波斯语 Persian language 亚洲语言 13—183c
波斯御道 Persian Royal Road 亚洲古道 13—183e
波斯战争 Persian Wars 希腊-波斯历史 13—183e
波苏斯迪卡尔达斯 Poços de Caldas 巴西城市 13—383e
波速 wave velocity 物理学 18—149d
波索科罗拉多 Pozo Colorado 巴拉圭城镇 13—477b
波塔戈斯 Potagos, Panayotis 埃及医生、旅行家 13—461d
波塔基特 Pawtucket 美国城市 13—104f
波塔莱格里 Portalegre 葡萄牙城市 13—448b
波塔莱斯 Portales, Diego (José Víctor) 智利政治家 13—448b
波塔利斯 Portales 美国城市 13—448b
波塔瓦托米人 Potawatomi 北美印第安部落 13—462e
波塔沃托米枪杀事件 Pottawatomie Massacre 美国历史 13—465d
波坦察 Potenza 意大利城市 13—463c
波唐尼 Bordoni, Faustina 意大利歌唱家 3—48a
波特 Pott, August (Friedrich) 德国语言学家 13—465c
波特 Porter, Cole (Albert) 美国作曲家、歌词作家 13—449a
波特 Porter, David 美国海军军官 13—449b
波特 Porter, David Dixon 美国海军军官 13—449c
波特 Porter, Eliza Emily Chappell 美国教育家 13—450a
波特 Porter, Eliot (Furness) 美国摄影家 13—449f
波特 Porter, Eleanor Hodgman 美国小说家 13—449e
波特 Porter, Edwin S(tratton) 美国电影导演先驱 13—449d
波特 Porter, Fitz-John 美国将领 13—450b
波特 Porter, Gene Stratton 美国小说家 13—450b
波特 Porter, Sir George 英国化学家 13—450c
波特 Porter, Hal 澳大利亚作家、诗人 13—450d
波特 Potter, (Helen) Beatrix 英国儿童文学作家 13—465e
波特 Porter, Katherine Anne 美国小说家、文体大师 13—450d
波特 Porter, Keith Roberts 美国生物学家 13—450f
波特 Potter, (Martha) Beatrice (English socialist) 英国历史学家、改革先驱 13—465d
波特 Potter, Paulus 荷兰画家 13—466a
波特 Porter, Peter (Nevill Frederick) 英国诗人 13—450f

波特 Porter, Rodney Robert 英国生物化学家 13—451a
波特 Porter, Sarah 美国教育家 13—451a
波特 Porter, Sylvia Field 美国经济学家 13—451b
波特 Porter, William Sydney 美国作家 13—451c
波特尔 Pottle, Frederick A(lbert) 美国学者 13—466f
波特尔(亨格福德的) Portal (of Hungerford), Charles Frederick Algernon Portal, 1st Viscount 英国空军元帅 13—448a
波特尔堡 Fort Portal 乌干达城镇 6—415a
波特夫 Botev, Khristo 保加利亚爱国诗人 3—71d
波特吉特 Potgieter, (Andries) Hendrik 德兰士瓦的布尔人领袖 13—463e
波特拉什 Portrush 北爱尔兰城镇 13—454a
波特兰 Portland 澳大利亚城镇 13—451e
波特兰 Portland 美国缅因州城市 13—451e
波特兰 Portland 美国俄勒冈州港市 13—451f
波特兰岛 Portland, Isle of 英格兰半岛 13—452a
波特兰公爵(第三) Portland, William Henry Cavendish Bentinck, 3rd Duke of 英国首相 13—452b
波特兰花瓶 Portland Vase 玻璃器皿 13—452c
波特兰湾 Portland Inlet 加拿大海湾 13—452c
波特雷里约斯 Potrerillos 智利矿区 13—464e
波特里斯 Potteries, The 英格兰行政区 13—466a
波特列索夫 Potresov, Aleksandr Nikolayevich 俄国社会民主党人 13—464e
波特罗亚尔 Port Royal 美国岛屿、城镇 13—447b
波特斯·希尔 Portes Gil, Emilio 墨西哥政治家、外交家 13—451c
波特希特 Potgieter, Everhardus Johannes 荷兰散文作家、诗人 13—463d
波提切利 Botticelli, Sandro 意大利画家 3—74e
波提萨腊 Phothisan 老挝澜沧国王 13—260f
波图格萨 Portuguesa 委内瑞拉州名 13—456b
波图加莱特 Portugalete 西班牙城镇 13—456b
波托茨基 Potocki, Ignacy, Hrabia (count) 立陶宛政治家、大元帅 13—464a
波托茨基 Potocki, Stanisław Szczęsny 波兰政治家、将军 13—464b
波托茨基 Potocki, Wacław 波兰作家 13—464b
波托-里什 Porto-Riche, Georges de 法国剧作家 13—453b
波托马克河 Potomac River 美国河流 13—464b
波托韦洛 Portobelo 巴拿马村庄 13—453c
波托维耶霍 Portoviejo 厄瓜多尔城镇 13—453f
波托西 Potosí 玻利维亚城市 13—464c
波瓦-迪瓦尔津 Póvoa de Varzim 葡萄牙城镇、自治区 13—471e
波瓦坦 Powhatan 北美印第安人酋长 13—475f
波瓦坦人 Powhatan 北美印第安部落联盟 13—475e
波瓦坦之战 Powhatan War 北美历史 13—476a
波维兹基 Poweski, Piotr Skarga 波兰传教士、作家 13—475e
波翁塔伦蒂 Buontalenti, Bernardo 意大利舞台设计师 3—256b
波西斯 Persis 亚洲古国名 13—184c
波希米亚 Bohemia 捷克历史地区 3—1d
波希米亚玻璃制品 Bohemian glass 捷克刻花玻璃制品 3—2a
波希米亚地块 Bohemian Massif 捷克高地 3—2b
波希米亚-摩拉维亚高地 Bohemian-Moravian Highlands 捷克高原 3—2c
波希米亚森林 Bohemian Forest 欧洲山林 3—1f
波希米亚石榴子石 Bohemian garnet 矿物 3—2a
《波希米亚信纲》 Bohemian Confession 捷克基督教文献 3—1f
波希米亚学派 Bohemian school 捷克视觉艺术流派 3—2c
波希米亚语 Bohemian language 捷克语言 3—2b
波希战争 Greco-Persian Wars 希腊历史 7—278b
波形涡卷纹 running-dog pattern 古典建筑 14—450a
波雅尔 boyar 中世纪俄国社会上层分子 3—99e
波伊尔 Boyle, Kay 美国小说家 3—101d
波伊宁斯 Poynings, Sir Edward 英格兰驻爱尔兰总督 13—476e
波伊斯 Powys 威尔士郡名 13—476a
波伊斯 Powys, John Cowper 威尔士小说家、诗人 13—476b
波伊提乌 Boethius, Anicius Manlius Severinus 古罗马学者 2—565d
波因塞特 Poinsett, Joel R(oberts) 美国政治家 13—388b
波因特普莱森特 Point Pleasant 美国城市 13—389c
波音公司 Boeing Company 美国飞机制造商 2—564b
波鱼 rasbora 鱼类 14—156f
波阵面 wave front 物理学 18—148f
波兹南 Poznań 波兰旧省份 13—476f
波兹南 Poznań 波兰城市 13—477a
波兹南骚乱 Poznań Riots 波兰产业工人骚乱(1956) 13—477a
波佐利 Pozzuoli 意大利城镇、主教区 13—477d
玻恩 Born, Max 德国物理学家 3—52f
玻尔 Bohr, Aage N(iels) 丹麦物理学家 3—4c
玻尔 Bohr, Harald August 丹麦数学家 3—4c
玻尔 Bohr, Niels (Henrik David) 丹麦物理学家 3—4d
玻尔达 Borda, Jean-Charles de 法国数学家 3—45b
玻尔原子模型 Bohr atomic model 物理学 3—5d
玻耳兹曼 Boltzmann, Ludwig Eduard 奥地利物理学家 3—17d
玻耳兹曼常量 Boltzmann constant 物理学 3—17e
玻耳兹曼分布律 Boltzmann distribution law 物理学 3—17f
玻基辉橄岩 limburgite 岩石 10—103b
玻璃 glass 无机透明固体 7—152f
玻璃草 glasswort 草本植物 7—154e
玻璃吹制 glassblowing 工艺 7—154d
玻璃海绵 glass sponge 无脊椎动物 7—154c
玻璃花园 glass garden 温室 7—154a
玻璃晒图 cliché-verre 印刷术 4—288f
玻璃丝 spun glass 玻璃纤维 16—165f
玻璃碗琴 glass harmonica 乐器 7—154a
玻璃屋山 Glass House Mountains 澳大利亚山脉 7—154b
玻璃纤维 fibreglass 绝缘、增强材料 6—302a
玻璃鱼 glassfish 鱼类 7—154e
玻璃陨石 tektite 地球化学 16—518b
玻利瓦尔 bolivar 委内瑞拉货币单位 3—11f
玻利瓦尔 Bolívar 哥伦比亚省份 3—11f
玻利瓦尔 Bolívar 厄瓜多尔省份 3—12a
玻利瓦尔 Bolívar 委内瑞拉州名 3—12a
玻利瓦尔 Bolívar, Simón 南美政治家 3—12b
玻利瓦尔城 Ciudad Bolívar 委内瑞拉城市 4—251d
玻利瓦尔山 Bolívar, Cerro 委内瑞拉铁矿山 3—12a
玻利维亚 Bolivia 南美洲国家 3—12e
玻利希彩票 policy 抽彩给奖法 13—400e
玻色 Bose, Satyendra Nath 印度数学家、物理学家 3—59d
玻色-爱因斯坦统计法 Bose-Einstein statistics 物理学 3—60a
玻色子 boson 物理学 3—61f
玻意耳 Boyle, Richard 英格兰殖民者 3—101e
玻意耳 Boyle, Robert 爱尔兰化学家、自然哲学家 3—101e
玻意耳定律 Boyle's law 物理学 3—102a
钵伐底 Pārvatī 印度教神祇 13—70a
钵喇特崎拏 pradakṣiṇa 印度教、佛教礼仪 13—477f
钵啰惹 Prajāpati 古印度创世之神 13—483c
钵罗钵语 Pahlavi language 古代波斯语言 12—547c
钵罗钵字母 Pahlavi alphabet 古代波斯文字 12—547c
《般若波罗蜜多心经》 Prajñāpāramitāhṛdaya-sūtra 佛经名 13—483d
剥夺权利 attainder 英国法律 2—38a
剥离 exfoliation 地质学 6—192c
剥离法开采 strip-mining 采矿 16—279a
剥裂反应 stripping reaction 核物理学 16—279a
剥头皮 scalping 战争仪式 15—101b
剥脱性皮炎 exfoliative dermatitis 皮肤病 6—192e

菠菜 spinach (species *Spinacia oleracea*) 草本植物 16—31d
菠萝 pineapple (*Ananas comosus*) 草本植物 13—310e
铍 nielsbohrium 化学元素 12—181b
播云 cloud seeding 大气科学 4—303b
伯氨喹啉 primaquine 药物 13—509a
伯班克 Burbank 美国城市 3—257b
伯班克 Burbank, Luther 美国植物育种家 3—257b
伯比 Burpee, W(ashington) Atlee 美国种子商 3—274e
伯比奇 Burbidge, (Eleanor) Margaret 美国天文学家 3—257d
伯比奇 Burbage, Richard 英国戏剧演员 3—257a
伯比斯河 Berbice River 圭亚那河流 2—398b
伯朝拉海 Pechora Sea 俄罗斯海域 13—117d
伯朝拉河 Pechora River 俄罗斯河流 13—117c
伯达拉 Batāla 印度城市 2—273e
伯德 Bird, (Cyril) Kenneth 英国漫画家 2—488e
伯德 Byrd, Richard E(velyn) 美国海军少将 3—298e
伯德 Bird, Robert Montgomery 美国小说家 2—488e
伯德 Byrd, William 英国管风琴家、作曲家 3—299a
伯德 Byrd, William, OF WESTOVER 弗吉尼亚种植园主、作家 3—299d
伯德岛 Bird Island 加勒比海岛屿 2—489a
伯德格拉 Badagara 印度港市 2—126e
伯德金河 Burdekin River 澳大利亚河流 3—258b
伯德里纳特 Badrīnāth 印度圣地 2—131b
伯德曼 Boardman, Mabel Thorp 美国红十字会领导人 2—554f
伯德特 Burdett, Sir Francis, 5TH BARONET 英国政治家 3—258b
伯德特-库茨女男爵 Burdett-Coutts, Angela Georgina Burdett-Coutts, Baroness 英国慈善家 3—258c
伯蒂亚拉 Patiāla 印度县城 13—88b
伯丁 Badīn 巴基斯坦城镇 2—130a
伯顿 Burton, Harold H(itz) 美国最高法院大法官 3—277b
伯顿 Burton, Richard 英国演员 3—277c
伯顿 Burton, Sir Richard (Francis) 英国探险家、东方学家 3—277c
伯顿 Burton, Robert 英国作家 3—277e
伯顿 Burton, Virginia Lee 美国作家、插图画家 3—277f
伯顿 Burton, William Merriam 美国化学家 3—278a
伯恩 Bourne 美国城镇 3—88a
伯恩 Bourne, Francis 英国枢机主教 3—88b
伯恩 Byrne, (Francis) Barry 美国建筑师 3—299f
伯恩 Bourne, Geoffrey (Howard) 美国解剖学家 3—88c
伯恩 Bourne, Randolph Silliman 美国文学批评家 3—88c
伯恩巴克 Bernbach, William 美国广告经理人员 2—422e
伯恩哈德 Bernhard 基督教新教将领 2—423d
伯恩哈德 Bernhard, PRINCE OF THE NETHERLANDS, PRINCE OF LIPPE-BIESTERFELD 荷兰亲王 2—423e
伯恩哈德 Bernhard, Thomas 奥地利作家 2—423f
伯恩哈特 Bernhardt, Sarah 法国演员 2—424a
伯恩利 Burnley 英格兰城市 3—273e
伯恩茅斯 Bournemouth 英格兰海滨胜地 3—88d
伯恩-琼斯 Burne-Jones, Sir Edward Coley, 1ST BARONET 英国画家 3—271b
伯恩赛德 Burnside, Ambrose Everett 美国将领 3—274d
伯恩施坦 Bernstein, Eduard 德国政治理论家 2—427d
伯恩斯 Burnes, Sir Alexander 英国探险家、外交家 3—271d
伯恩斯 Burns, Eveline M. 美国经济学家、教育家 3—273e
伯恩斯 Burns, John Elliot 英国劳工领袖 3—274a
伯恩斯 Burns, Lucy 美国女权主义者 3—274a
伯恩斯 Burns, Tommy 加拿大拳击运动员 3—274d
伯恩斯和艾伦 Burns, George; and Allen, Gracie 美国喜剧演员 3—273f
伯恩斯坦 Bernstein, Aline Frankau 美国舞台设计师和作家 2—427d
伯恩斯坦 Bernstein, Henry (-Léon-Gustave-Charles) 法国剧作家 2—428a
伯恩斯坦 Bernstein, Jeremy 美国物理学家 2—428b
伯恩斯坦 Bernstein, Leonard 美国指挥家、作曲家 2—428c
伯恩斯托夫 Bernstorff, J. H. E., Count (Graf) von 丹麦政治家 2—429a
伯恩斯托夫伯爵 Bernstorff, Andreas Peter, Count (Graf) von 丹麦政治家 2—428e
伯恩斯托夫伯爵 Bernstorff, Christian Günther, Count (Graf) von 丹麦外交家 2—428f
伯尔 Burr, Aaron 美国副总统 3—274f
伯尔 Böll, Heinrich 德国作家 3—14d
伯尔达布格尔 Partāpgarh 印度城镇 13—64f
伯尔达布格尔 Partāpgarh 印度县名 13—64f
伯尔蒂斯坦 Baltistān 印度次大陆地区 2—184d
伯尔格山国家公园 Børge Mountains National Park 挪威公园 3—49c
伯尔卡拉人 Birkarlar 中世纪瑞典、芬兰商人 2—491c
伯尔拉赫 Berlage, Hendrik Petrus 荷兰建筑师 2—410b
伯尔纳(明谷的),圣 Bernard DE CLAIRVAUX, SAINT 天主教西多会修士 2—420c
伯尔纳会 Bernardine 天主教 2—422c
伯尔尼 Bern 瑞士州名 2—419a
伯尔尼 Bern 瑞士首都 2—419b
《伯尔尼公约》 Berne Convention 国际著作权协议 2—422f
伯尔尼纳山 Bernina Alps 瑞士山脉 2—424f
伯尔尼丘陵 Palni Hills 印度丘陵 12—574d
伯尔尼兹山 Bernese Alps 瑞士山脉 2—423b
伯尔尼兹山地狗 Bernese mountain dog 狗品种 2—423c
伯尔珀尼 Parbhani 印度城镇 13—39e
伯尔瓦尼 Barwāni 印度城市 2—253e
伯夫-梅里 Beuve-Méry, Hubert 法国出版商 2—446b
伯福德 Burford 英格兰城镇 3—259e
伯戈因 Burgoyne, John 英国将军 3—262c
伯格 Berg, Gertrude 美国演员、制片人和编剧 2—402d
伯格 Burgh, Hubert de 英国政法官 3—261c
伯格 Buerger, Martin Julian 美国晶体学家 3—233a
伯格 Berg, Patty 美国高尔夫球运动员 2—402e
伯格 Berg, Paul 美国生物化学家 2—402f
伯格 Burgh, Richard de 爱尔兰贵族 3—261d
伯格 Burgh, Ulick de 英国贵族 3—261d
伯格 Burke, Ulick de 英国贵族 3—266e
伯格 Burger, Warren E(arl) 美国最高法院大法官 3—260c
伯格波姆 Bergbom, Kaarlo 芬兰国立剧院创建者 2—403d
伯格达马人 Bergdama 非洲民族 2—403e
伯格尔 Berger, Victor (Louis) 美国社会党创建人 2—404c
伯格家族 Burgh FAMILY 英国家族 3—261c
伯格雷德 Burgred 麦西亚国王 3—262d
伯格曼 Bergman, (Ernst) Ingmar 瑞典剧作家、导演 2—405c
伯格纳 Bergner, Elisabeth 奥地利演员 2—406d
伯格氏病 Buerger's disease 疾病 3—233a
伯格斯 Burgers, Thomas François 德兰士瓦总统 3—260d
伯根 Bergen, Edgar 美国演员 2—404a
伯基特氏淋巴瘤 Burkitt's lymphoma 疾病 3—267e
伯吉尔(芒努松) Birger MAGNUSSON 瑞典国王 2—491a
伯吉尔王公 Birger JARL 瑞典统治者 2—490f
伯吉斯 Burgess, Anthony 英国作家 3—260e
伯吉斯 Burgess, Ernest Watson 美国社会学家 3—260f
伯吉斯 Burgess, Hugh 美国发明家 3—261b
伯吉斯 Burges, William 英国建筑师 3—260e
伯吉斯和麦克莱恩 Burgess, Guy; and Maclean, Donald (Duart) 英国外交官 3—261a
伯吉尤斯 Bergius, Friedrich 德国化学家 2—405a
伯杰 Bergey, David Hendricks 美国细菌学家 2—404e
伯杰龙 Bergeron, Tor Harold Percival 瑞典气象学家 2—404e

伯爵 count 欧洲贵族称号 4—542e
伯爵之战 Count's War 丹麦历史 4—545b
伯克 Bourke 澳大利亚城镇 3—87c
伯克 Burke, Edmund 英国政治家 3—265f
伯克 Burke, James 美国拳击运动员 3—266b
伯克 Burke, Kenneth (Duva) 美国文学批评家 3—266c
伯克 Bourke, Richard Southwell 爱尔兰政治人物 3—87d
伯克 Burke, Robert O'Hara 澳大利亚探险家 3—266d
伯克 Burke, Solomon 美国歌手 3—266e
伯克 Bourke, Ulick de 爱尔兰贵族 3—87d
伯克贝克 Birkbeck, George 英国医生 2—491c
伯克和黑尔 Burke, William; and Hare, William 英国杀人凶手 3—266f
伯克-怀特 Bourke-White, Margaret 美国摄影家 3—87d
伯克霍夫 Birkhoff, George David 美国数学家 2—492a
伯克郡 Berkshire 英格兰郡名 2—409e
伯克郡猪 Berkshire 家猪品种 2—410a
伯克利 Berkeley 美国城市 2—408d
伯克利 Berkeley, Busby 美国电影导演 2—408e
伯克利 Berkeley, George 爱尔兰哲学家 2—408e
伯克利 Berkeley, Sir Lennox 英国作曲家 2—409a
伯克利 Berkeley, Sir William 英国总督 2—409b
伯克姆斯特德 Berkhamsted 英格兰城镇 2—409e
伯克纳 Berkner, Lloyd Viel 美国物理学家 2—409e
《伯克氏系谱》 Burke's Peerage 英国贵族系谱 3—266f
伯克希尔山 Berkshire Hills 美国山脉 2—410a
伯肯黑德 Birkenhead 英格兰城市 2—491d
伯肯黑德伯爵(第一) Birkenhead, Frederick Edwin Smith, 1st Earl of 英国政治家 2—491e
伯拉戈兰湖 Burragorang, Lake 澳大利亚人工湖 3—275a
伯拉里加特战役 Barāri Ghāt, Battle of 印度历史 2—216e
伯兰 Belin, Édouard 法国工程师 2—355f
伯劳 shrike 鸟类 15—339e
伯劳科 Laniidae (bird family) 动物学 9—486f
伯勒穆拉 Bāramūla 印度次大陆城镇 2—216a
伯勒讷格尔 Baranagar 印度城镇 2—216b
伯勒伊 Beloeil 比利时村庄 2—370d
伯勒伊 Beloeil 加拿大城镇 2—370d
伯里 Bury, J(ohn) B(agnell) 英国古典学者 3—279d
伯里 Bury, Richard de 英格兰藏书家 3—279f
伯里伯达 Baripāda 印度城市 2—229b
伯里克利 Pericles 古代雅典政治家 13—167c
伯里特 Burritt, Elihu 美国和平运动人士 3—275c
伯利 Burleigh, Harry Thacker 美国歌唱家 3—268a
伯利 Berle, Milton 美国喜剧演员 2—410c
伯利恒 Bethlehem 巴勒斯坦中部城镇 2—442a
伯利恒 Bethlehem 南非城镇 2—442c
伯利恒 Bethlehem 美国城市 2—442d
伯利恒钢铁公司 Bethlehem Steel Corporation 美国公司 2—442f
伯利恒皇家医院 Bethlehem Royal Hospital (United Kingdom) 英国医院 2—442f
伯利男爵(第一) Burghley, William Cecil, 1st Baron 英国政治家 3—261d
伯利男爵(第一) Burleigh, William Cecil, 1st Baron 英国政治家 3—268b
伯利亚 Ballia 印度城镇 2—177b
伯利兹 Belize 中美洲国家 2—356d
伯利兹堡礁 Belize Barrier Reef 世界第二大珊瑚礁 2—357e
伯利兹城 Belize City 伯利兹海港 2—357f
伯利兹河 Belize River 中美洲河流 2—358a
伯林 Berlin, Irving 美国作曲家 2—414c
伯林 Berlin, Sir Isaiah 英国历史学家 2—414d
伯林 Burlin, Natalie Curtis 美国音乐学家 3—268d
伯林顿伯爵(第三) Burlington, Richard Boyle, 3rd Earl of 英国建筑师 3—269b
伯林纳 Berliner, Emil 美国发明家 2—416b
伯灵顿 Burlington 加拿大城市 3—268f
伯灵顿 Burlington 美国艾奥瓦州城市 3—268f
伯灵顿 Burlington 美国新泽西州城市 3—268f
伯灵顿 Burlington 美国北卡罗来纳州城市 3—269a
伯灵顿 Burlington 美国佛蒙特州城市 3—269a
伯灵顿北方圣菲公司 Burlington Northern Santa Fe Corporation 美国铁路公司 3—269b
伯罗奔尼撒 Peloponnese 希腊半岛 13—131e
伯罗奔尼撒同盟 Peloponnesian League 古希腊城邦军事联盟 13—131f
伯罗奔尼撒战争 Peloponnesian War 古希腊历史 13—131f
伯罗斯 Burrows, Ronald Montagu 英国考古学家 3—276c
伯洛伊特 Beloit 美国城市 2—370e
伯麦 Böhme, Jakob 德国哲学神秘主义者 3—3e
伯蒙德西 Bermondsey 英国伦敦地区 2—417f
伯米吉 Bemidji 美国城市 2—373f
伯明翰 Birmingham 英国城市 2—492c
伯明翰 Birmingham 美国城市 2—492e
伯纳比 Burnaby 加拿大自治区 3—271b
伯纳德 Bernard, Jessie (Shirley) 美国社会学家 2—421f
伯纳姆 Burnham, Daniel H(udson) 美国建筑师 3—272f
伯纳姆 Burnham, (Linden) Forbes (Sampson) 圭亚那总理 3—273c
伯纳姆男爵(第一) Burnham, (of Hall Barn, Beaconsfield), Edward Levy-Lawson, 1st Baron 英国报业主 3—273a
伯纳斯河 Banās River 印度河流 2—189e
伯纳斯-李 Berners-Lee, Sir Tim 英国计算机科学家 2—423a
伯纳斯男爵(第二) Berners, John Bourchier, 2nd Baron 英国作家 2—423a
伯奈斯 Bernays, Edward L. 美国公共关系业先驱 2—422c
伯奈斯 Bernays, Paul (Isaak) 瑞士数学家 2—422d
伯南布哥 Pernambuco 巴西州名 13—175c
伯内特 Burnett, Charles 美国电影制片人 3—271f
伯内特 Burnett, Chester Arthur 美国歌手、作曲家 3—272a
伯内特 Burnett, Frances Eliza 美国作家 3—272a
伯内特 Burnet, Sir (Frank) Macfarlane 澳大利亚医师 3—271e
伯内特 Burnett, James, Lord Monboddo 苏格兰法学家 3—272b
伯内特 Burnett, Leo 美国广告经理 3—272b
伯内特河 Burnett River 澳大利亚河流 3—272c
伯尼 Burnie 澳大利亚城镇 3—273d
伯尼 Burney, Fanny 英国作家 3—272d
伯尼 Birney, James Gillespie 美国废奴主义者 2—492f
伯尼哈尔山口 Banihāl Pass 印度次大陆北部山口 2—202f
伯尼斯·帕瓦希-毕晓普博物馆 Bernice P. Bishop Museum (Honolulu) 美国博物馆 2—424f
伯尼西亚 Bernicia 英国古代小王国 2—424f
伯努利 Bernoulli, Daniel 瑞士数学家 2—426f
伯努利 Bernoulli, Jakob 瑞士数学家 2—427a
伯努利 Bernoulli, Johann 瑞士数学家 2—427b
伯努利定理 Bernoulli's theorem 物理学 2—427c
伯努瓦 Benoit, Peter (Léonard Léopold) 比利时作曲家 2—390a
伯努瓦·德·圣莫尔 Benoît de Sainte-Maure 古法文诗人 2—389f
伯诺尼 Benoni 南非城镇 2—390a
伯奇菲尔德 Burchfield, Charles (Ephraim) 美国画家 3—257e
伯切尔氏斑马 quagga 非洲斑马 14—72e
伯塞恩 Bassein 印度市镇 2—268d
《伯塞恩条约》 Bassein, Treaty of 英-印条约 2—268d
伯森多费尔 Bösendorfer, Ignaz 奥地利钢琴制造家 3—60b
伯沙撒 Belshazzar 巴比伦王国摄政 2—371c
伯舒伯蒂 Pashupati 尼泊尔城镇 13—74b
伯斯蒂 Bastī 印度城镇 2—271a

伯斯力 Paisley, Ian (Richard Kyle) 英国教士 12—551d
伯特 Burt, Sir Cyril (Lodowic) 英国心理学家 3—277a
伯特利 Bethel 巴勒斯坦古城 2—441e
伯特林克 Böhtlingk, Otto von 德国语言学家 3—5e
伯西尔哈德 Basīrhāt 印度城市 2—263a
《伯西托本圣经》 Peshitta 古叙利亚文《圣经》 13—193d
伯颜 Bayan 中国元代大将军 2—293b
伯颜 Bayan 中国元末大臣 2—293b
伯伊斯 Buysse, Cyriel 比利时作家 3—296b
伯伊滕佐尔格 Buitenzorg (Indonesia) 印度尼西亚城市 3—238c
伯于斯 Buys, Paulus 荷兰政治家 3—296a
伯宰 Birdseye, Clarence 美国实业家 2—490c
伯祖尔格·阿拉维 Buzurg Ȧlavī 伊朗作家 3—296e
驳船 lighter 船舶 10—93d
驳船运河 Barge Canal (New York, U.S.) 美国运河 2—227f
帛画 silk painting 中国古代图画 15—371f
帛琉 Pelew (Caroline Islands) 太平洋岛群 13—130a
泊松 Poisson, Siméon-Denis 法国数学家 13—391d
泊松分布 Poisson distribution 统计学 13—391e
泊肃叶 Poiseuille, Jean-Louis-Marie 法国医师、生理学家 13—390c
柏 Kashiwa 日本城市 9—191b
柏柏尔人 Berber 北非土著民族 2—397e
柏柏尔诸语言 Berber languages 北非语言 2—398a
柏柏里 Barbary 北非沿海地区 2—218f
柏柏里海盗 Barbary pirate 北非海盗 2—219b
柏柏里马 Barbary (horse) 北非马品种 2—219a
柏柏里绵羊 Barbary sheep 哺乳动物 2—219b
柏布马 Barb 北非马品种 2—217c
柏格森 Bergson, Henri(-Louis) 法国哲学家 2—405e
柏格兹特胡德 Buxtehude, Dietrich 丹麦作曲家 3—295a
柏拉图 Plato 古希腊哲学家 13—354c
柏拉图学园 Platonic Academy 古意大利学者团体 13—358e
柏拉图主义 Platonism 哲学 13—358f
柏勒库纳斯 Pērkons 波罗的海地区神祇 13—172e
柏勒洛丰 Bellerophon 希腊传说英雄 2—364f
柏辽兹 Berlioz, (Louis-) Hector 法国作曲家 2—416e
柏林 Berlin 德国首都 2—410d
柏林 Berlin 美国康涅狄格州城镇 2—413f
柏林 Berlin 美国新罕布什尔州城市 2—414a
柏林-达勒姆植物园和植物博物馆 Berlin-Dahlem Botanical Garden and Botanical Museum 德国植物园 2—414f
柏林动物园 Berlin Zoo 德国动物园 2—416a
柏林动物园及水族馆 Berlin Zoological Garden and Aquarium 德国动物园 2—416a
柏林封锁和空运 Berlin blockade and airlift 国际危机 2—414e
柏林洪堡大学 Berlin, Humboldt University of 德国大学 2—414b
柏林画家 Berlin Painter 陶瓶画家 2—415a
柏林会议 Berlin, Congress of 欧洲国家外交会议 2—414a
柏林剧团 Berliner Ensemble 德国戏剧团体 2—416c
柏林墙 Berlin Wall 东、西柏林间围墙 2—415b
柏林绒绣 Berlin woolwork 德国工艺品 2—415f
柏林陶瓷 Berlin ware 柏林陶瓷 2—415c
柏林西非会议 Berlin West Africa Conference 欧洲国际会议 2—415e
柏林自由大学 Berlin, Free University of 德国大学 2—414b
柏罗丁 Plotinus 罗马哲学家 13—374a
柏姆-巴维克 Böhm-Bawerk, Eugen von 奥地利经济学家 3—3e
柏诺兹 Bednorz, J(ohannes) Georg 德国物理学家 2—326e
柏培尔曼 Pöppelmann, Matthäus Daniel 德国建筑师 13—434f
柏培拉 Berbera 索马里港口 2—398a
柏崎 Kashiwazaki 日本城市 9—191b
柏西埃和方丹 Percier, Charles; and Fontaine, Pierre(-François-Léonard) 法国建筑师 13—158b
勃尔尼 Burney, Charles 英国音乐史家 3—272c
勃艮第 Burgundy 法国规划区 3—263a
勃艮第罗马式风格 Burgundian Romanesque style 建筑艺术 3—262d
勃艮第葡萄酒 Burgundy wine 法国酒 3—264a
勃艮第乐派 Burgundian school 音乐 3—262f
勃固 Pegu 缅甸港市 13—122f
勃固山脉 Pegu Mountains 缅甸山脉 13—123b
勃克林 Böcklin, Arnold 瑞士画家 2—560b
勃拉姆斯 Brahms, Johannes 德国作曲家、钢琴家 3—113e
勃拉瓦茨基 Blavatsky, Helena Petrovna 俄国招魂术者 2—531e
勃拉希克 Blaschke, Wilhelm Johann Eugen 德国数学家 2—529c
勃兰登堡 Brandenburg 德国地区 3—120a
勃兰登堡 Brandenburg 德国州名 3—120d
勃兰登堡 Brandenburg 德国城市 3—120e
勃兰登堡门 Brandenburg Gate 德国柏林城门 3—120f
勃兰特 Brandt, Willy 德国政治家 3—122b
勃朗 Blanc, Louis 法国空想社会主义者 2—526c
勃朗峰 Blanc, Mont 阿尔卑斯山山峰 2—526f
勃朗峰隧道 Mont Blanc Tunnel 法国-意大利隧道 11—351f
勃朗宁 Browning, John Moses 美国武器设计师 3—197a
勃朗宁自动步枪 Browning automatic rifle (BAR) 武器 3—197d
勃朗特 Brontë, Anne 英国诗人、小说家 3—179a
勃朗特 Brontë, Charlotte 英国小说家 3—179b
勃朗特 Brontë, Emily (Jane) 英国小说家、诗人 3—180b
勃勒东 Breton, André 法国作家 3—144c
勃良安制度 Preanger system 荷兰税收制度 13—488a
勃列日涅夫 Brezhnev, Leonid Ilich 苏联政府首脑 3—147b
勃留洛夫 Bryullov, Karl Pavlovich 俄国画家 3—216d
勃留索夫 Bryusov, Valery Yakovlevich 俄国诗人、小说家 3—216d
勃鲁盖尔(大) Bruegel, Jan, THE ELDER 佛兰德斯画家 3—201a
勃鲁盖尔(大) Bruegel, Pieter, THE ELDER 佛兰德斯画家 3—201b
勃鲁盖尔(小) Bruegel, Pieter II, THE YOUNGER 佛兰德斯画家 3—201f
勃鲁格曼 Brugmann, (Friedrich) Karl 德国语言学家 3—202c
勃鲁西洛夫 Brusilov, Aleksey Alekseyevich 俄国将军 3—209c
勃吕克纳 Brückner, Eduard 德国地理学家 3—201a
勃洛克 Blok, Aleksandr Aleksandrovich 俄罗斯诗人、戏剧家 2—539d
勃纳尔 Bonnard, Pierre 法国画家 3—32e
勃生 Pathein 下缅甸城市 13—87e
勃特勒 Butler, Samuel 英国作家 3—290e
勃特勒 Butler, Samuel 英国作家 3—290f
钹 cymbal 乐器 5—88e
铂(Pt) platinum 化学元素 13—354b
亳州 Bozhou 中国城市 3—102f
博 Beaux, Cecilia 美国画家 2—316a
博阿尔内 Beauharnais, Eugène de 法国军人 2—313a
博阿尔内 Beauharnais, Eugénie-Hortense de 荷兰王后 2—313b
博阿尔内子爵 Beauharnais, Alexandre, Viscount (vicomte) de 法国贵族 2—312f
博阿尔内子爵夫人 Beauharnais, Marie-Josèphe-Rose, Vicomtesse de (viscountess of) 法国皇后 2—313b
博阿科 Boaco 尼加拉瓜城市 2—554d
博阿努瓦 Beauharnois 加拿大城市 2—313b
博阿滕 Boateng, Paul 英国政治家 2—555d
博阿维斯塔 Boa Vista 巴西城市 2—554d
博阿维斯塔岛 Boa Vista Island 佛得角岛屿 2—554d
博阿兹柯伊 Boğazköy 土耳其古城 2—567f
博埃 Boé 几内亚比绍城镇 2—563f
博埃 Boë, Franz de le 德国医生 2—564a
博埃 Boé, Jacques 法国诗人 2—564a
博埃城 Madina do Boé (Guinea-Bissau) 几内亚比绍城镇 10—369a
博巴桑-罗斯希尔 Beau Bassin-Rose Hill 毛里求斯城市 2—310d

博巴山 Popa, Mount 缅甸死火山 13—432a
博堡中心 Beaubourg, Centre (museum) 法国文化中心 2—310d
博比奥 Bobbio 意大利城镇 2—556a
博波尔 Beauport 加拿大城市 2—315a
博波卢 Bopolu 利比里亚城镇 3—42d
博博迪乌拉索 Bobo Dioulasso 布基纳法索城市 2—556c
博博利花园 Boboli Gardens 佛罗伦萨园林 2—556d
博博人 Bobo 布基纳法索民族 2—556c
博布里基 Bobriki (Russia) 俄罗斯城市 2—556e
博布里科夫 Bobrikov, Nikolay (Ivanovich) 俄国极端民族主义者 2—556e
博布鲁伊斯克 Bobruysk 白俄罗斯城市 2—556e
博布任斯基 Bobrzyński, Michał 波兰历史学家 2—556f
博察里斯 Botsaris, Markos 希腊独立战争领导人 3—73a
博彻尔 Bôcher, Maxime 美国数学家、教育家 2—559d
博彻兹 Borcherds, Richard Ewen 英国数学家 3—45b
博城 Bo 塞拉利昂城镇 2—554a
博茨瓦纳 Botswana 非洲国家 3—73a
博茨瓦纳人 Botswana (people) 非洲民族 3—73a
博达维里·阿罗塞纳 Bordaberry Arocena, Juan María 乌拉圭总统 3—45b
博代尔 Bodel, Jehan 法国诗人 2—560f
博丹 Bodin, Jean 法国政治哲学家 2—561f
博德 Bodø 挪威港口城镇 2—562d
博德 Border, Allan Robert 澳大利亚板球运动员 3—47c
博德 Bode, Wilhelm von 德国艺术评论家 2—560e
博德港事件 Bodø Affair 欧洲历史 2—562e
博德利图书馆 Bodleian Library 牛津大学图书馆 2—562a
博德鲁姆 Bodrum 土耳其城镇 2—562f
博·德·罗夏 Reau de Rochas, Alphonse(-Eugène) 法国工程师 2—310d
博德明 Bodmin 英格兰城镇 2—562c
博德默尔 Bodmer, Johann Georg 瑞士机械师 2—562b
博德默尔 Bodmer, Johann Jakob 瑞士历史学家 2—562b
博德瑟特 Beaudesert 澳大利亚城镇 2—311a
博德斯 Borders 苏格兰区名 3—47d
博德瓦尔高原 Potwar Plateau 巴基斯坦台地 13—467c
博登 Borden 加拿大城镇 3—46d
博登 Borden, Sir Frederick William 加拿大政治家 3—46d
博登 Borden, Gail 美国慈善家、发明家 3—46e
博登 Borden, Lizzie 美国电影制作人 3—46e
博登 Borden, Lizzie (Andrew) 美国杀人嫌疑犯 3—46f
博登 Borden, Sir Robert (Laird) 加拿大总理 3—46f
博登敦 Bordentown 美国城市 3—47b
博登港 Port Borden (Canada) 加拿大城镇 13—444d
博登海姆 Bodenheim, Maxwell 美国诗人 2—561a
博登湖 Bodensee (Europe) 欧洲湖泊 2—561a
博登施泰特 Bodenstedt, Friedrich Martin von 德国作家 2—561a
博登施泰因·冯·卡尔施塔特 Bodenstein von Karlstadt, Andreas Rudolf 德国神学家 2—561b
博杜阿卡利 Patuākhāli 孟加拉国城镇 13—93d
博杜安·德库尔特奈 Baudouin de Courtenay, Jan Niecisław 波兰语言学家 2—285d
博杜安二世 Baldwin II 佛兰德统治者 2—165e
博杜安四世 Baldwin IV 佛兰德伯爵 2—165e
博杜安五世 Baldwin V 佛兰德伯爵 2—165e
博杜安一世 Baldwin I 佛兰德统治者 2—165d
博杜安一世 Baudouin I (French) 比利时国王 2—285c
博顿 Bottome, Margaret McDonald 美国作家、宗教组织者 3—75e
博多 Baudot, Jean-Maurice-Émile 法国工程师 2—285b
博多河 Padma River 孟加拉国河流 12—540c
博多尼 Bodoni, Giambattista 意大利印刷家 2—562e
博多人 Bodo 印度民族 2—562d
博厄斯 Boas, Franz 美国人类学家 2—555b
博恩 Born, Bertran de 法国军人 3—52f
博恩 Bone, Henry 英国画家 3—27e
博恩 Bone, Sir Muirhead 英国画家 3—27e
博恩霍尔姆 Bornholm 丹麦岛屿、州名 3—53d
博恩霍尔姆氏病 Bornholm disease 疾病 3—53e
博尔 Bor 苏丹城市 3—43a
博尔 Bor 俄罗斯城市 3—43a
博尔 Bor 塞尔维亚城市 3—43b
博尔本德尔 Porbandar 印度城镇 13—439d
博尔布鲁克男爵 Bolebrooke (of Sussex), George Sackville-Germain, Baron 英国军人、政治家 3—10c
博尔查 Bolza, Oskar 德国数学家 3—18b
博尔德 Boulder 美国城市 3—80b
博尔德 Bordes, Charles 法国作曲家 3—47d
博尔德 Bordet, Jules(-Jean-Baptiste-Vincent) 比利时细菌学家 3—47e
博尔德城 Boulder City 美国城市 3—80b
博尔德雷伍德 Boldrewood, Rolf 澳大利亚小说家 3—10c
博尔德水坝 Boulder Dam 美国水坝 3—80c
博尔登 Bolden, Buddy 美国短号演奏家 3—10c
博尔迪盖雷 Bordighera 意大利城镇 3—47f
博尔迪尼奥 Bordinho, Maurício 敌对教皇 3—47f
博尔丁 Bourdin, Maurice (antipope) 敌对教皇 3—85c
博尔顿 Bolton 英格兰城镇 3—17b
博尔顿 Bolton, Edmund 英国历史学家 3—17b
博尔顿 Bolton, Guy (Reginald) 美国剧作家 3—17c
博尔顿 Boulton, Matthew 英国工程师 3—82e
博尔多内 Bordone, Paris 威尼斯画家 3—48a
博尔戈 Borgå (Finland) 芬兰城市 3—49c
博尔格 Bolger, James Brendan 新西兰政治家 3—11c
博尔格 Borge, Victor 美国演员 3—49c
博尔根 Borgen, Johan (Collet Müller) 挪威作家 3—49c
博尔贡吉尼-杜卡 Borgongini-Duca, Francesco 意大利枢机主教 3—51b
博尔古 Borgu 非洲西部内陆区 3—51c
博尔古 Borgu 尼日利亚酋长国 3—51c
博尔赫霍特 Borgerhout 比利时城镇 3—49d
博尔赫斯 Borges, Jorge Luis 阿根廷作家 3—49e
博尔基亚 Bolkiah Mu'izzaddin Waddaulah, Haji Hassanal 文莱苏丹 3—14c
博尔吉亚 Borgia, Cesare, DUC (duke) DE VALENTINOIS 意大利贵族 3—50b
博尔吉亚 Borgia, Saint Francis 西班牙贵族 3—50d
博尔吉亚 Borgia, Lucrezia 意大利贵族 3—50e
博尔吉亚 Borja, Rodrigo 教皇 3—52c
博尔吉亚-阿拉贡 Borja y Aragon, Francisco de 西班牙贵族 3—52c
博尔吉亚家族 Borgia FAMILY 西班牙贵族后裔家族 3—50a
博尔加尔 Bolgary 俄国古城 3—11c
博尔加坦加 Bolgatanga 加纳城镇 3—11c
博尔贾 Borja, Alfonso de (pope) 教皇 3—52c
博尔科姆 Bolcom, William (Elden) 美国作曲家 3—10a
博尔库 Borkou 乍得地区 3—52c
博尔库-恩内迪-提贝斯提 Borkou-Ennedi-Tibesti 乍得省份 3—52c
博尔曼 Borman, Frank 美国航天员 3—52e
博尔曼 Bormann, Martin 纳粹德国党魁 3—52e
博尔诺州 Borno 尼日利亚州名 3—53f
博尔萨 Borsa, Roger 阿普利亚公爵 3—57a
博尔塞纳 Bolsena 意大利城镇 3—16b
博尔索弗 Bolsover 英格兰城镇 3—16f
博尔特 Boult, Sir Adrian Cedric 英国指挥家 3—82c

博尔特 Boulter, Hugh 英格兰基督教大主教 3—82d
博尔特 Bolt, Robert 英国剧作家 3—17a
博尔特伍德 Boltwood, Bertram Borden 美国化学家、物理学家 3—17c
博尔西珀 Borsippa 伊拉克古城 3—57a
博尔扎诺 Bolzano 意大利城市 3—18c
博法 Boffa 几内亚渔港 2—566a
博弗尔 Beaufre, André 法国战略家 2—312e
博福尔公爵 Beaufort, François de Vendôme, duc de 法国亲王 2—311d
博福尔女公爵 Beaufort, Gabrielle d'Estrées, duchesse de (duchess of) 法国贵族 2—311e
博福特 Beaufort 美国城镇 2—311b
博福特 Beaufort 美国城市 2—311b
博福特 Beaufort, Edmund 英格兰贵族 2—311d
博福特 Beaufort, Henry 英格兰枢机主教 2—311e
博福特 Beaufort, Henry 英格兰贵族 2—312a
博福特家族 Beaufort FAMILY 英格兰贵族 2—311c
博福特统 Beaufort Series 地质学 2—312c
博盖塞陈列馆 Borghese Gallery 罗马国家博物馆 3—50a
博盖塞家族 Borghese FAMILY 意大利贵族世家 3—49f
博戈拉兹 Bogoraz, Vladimir Germanovich 俄罗斯人类学家 2—568f
博戈柳布斯基 Bogolyubsky, Andrey Yuryevich 俄罗斯历史人物 2—568d
博格 Borger 美国城市 3—49d
博格 Borg, Björn (Rune) 瑞典网球运动员 3—49b
博格达山 Bogda Shan 中国山脉 2—568b
博格拉 Bogra 孟加拉国城市 3—1b
博格勒姆 Borglum, (John) Gutzon (de la Mothe) 美国雕刻家 3—50f
博格诺里吉斯 Bognor Regis 英格兰堂区 2—568d
博根 Bogan, Louise 美国诗人 2—567c
博贡山 Bogong, Mount 澳大利亚山峰 2—568e
博古斯瓦夫斯基 Bogusławski, Wojciech 波兰演员、剧作家 3—1c
博哈多尔角 Bojador, Cape 非洲西海岸岬角 3—8d
博赫拉人 Bohrā 印度伊斯兰教徒 3—5e
博赫纳 Bochner, Salomon 美国数学家、教育家 2—559e
博霍尔特 Bocholt 德国城市 2—559f
博霍莫莱茨 Bohomolec, Franciszek 波兰剧作家 3—4b
博加德斯 Bogardus, James 美国发明家 2—567d
博加卢萨 Bogalusa 美国城市 2—567c
博加特 Bogart, Humphrey 美国电影演员 2—567e
博居斯 Bocuse, Paul 法国名厨 2—560e
博卡拉顿 Boca Raton 美国城市 2—557b
博卡利尼 Boccalini, Traiano 意大利作家 2—558b
博卡纳拉家族 Boccanegra FAMILY 2—558b
博卡热 Bocage, Manuel Maria Barbosa du 葡萄牙诗人 2—557c
博卡萨 Bokassa, Eddine Ahmed 中非共和国总统 3—9b
博凯 Boké 几内亚城镇 3—9c
博凯尔 Beaucaire 法国城镇 2—310d
博克 Bok, Bart J(an) 美国天文学家 3—8f
博克 Bok, Edward 美国编辑 3—9a
博克 Bock, Fedor von 德国陆军元帅 2—560a
博克 Bock, Hieronymus (Tragus) 德国植物学家 2—560a
博克龙 Boquerón 巴拉圭省份 3—43a
博克马尔语 bokmål 挪威书面语 3—9e
博克斯堡 Boksburg 南非工业中心 3—9e
博克斯霍尔陨石坑 Boxhole Meteorite Crater 澳大利亚陨石坑 3—98b
博客 blog 网络术语 2—539a
博肯南 Bokenam, Osbern 英国诗人 3—9c
博肯峡湾 Bokn Fjord 北海峡湾 3—9e
博库斯二世 Bocchus II 毛里塔尼亚国王 2—559a
博库斯一世 Bocchus I 毛里塔尼亚国王 2—559a
博拉 bola 南美印第安人武器 3—9f
博拉 Borah, William E(dgar) 美国参议员 3—43e
博拉博拉岛 Bora-Bora 南太平洋火山岛 3—43b
博拉峰 Borah Peak 美国山峰 3—43f
博拉马 Bolama 几内亚比绍港镇 3—10a
博拉奇 Borach, Fannie (comedienne) 美国喜剧演员 3—43b
博莱罗舞 bolero 西班牙舞 3—10d
博莱斯瓦夫 Bolesław 波兰统治者之名 3—10e
博莱斯瓦夫二世 Bolesław II 波兰国王 3—10f
博莱斯瓦夫三世 Bolesław III 波兰公爵 3—10f
博莱斯瓦夫一世 Bolesław I 波兰国王 3—10e
博兰德 Bolland, Jean 教会史学家 3—14f
博兰德会 Bollandist 比利时天主教团体 3—15a
博兰山口 Bolān Pass 巴基斯坦山口 3—10a
博朗吉尔 Bolāngir 印度城市 3—10a
博劳格 Borlaug, Norman Ernest 美国农业科学家 3—52d
博雷 Boré, (Jean) Étienne 美国制糖工业奠基人 3—48c
博雷尔 Borel, Jacques 法国作家 3—48e
博雷尔 Borel, Petrus 法国诗人、作家 3—48f
博雷加德 Beauregard, P(ierre) G(ustave) T(outant) 美国南北战争将领 2—315a
博雷利 Borelli, Giovanni Alfonso 意大利生理学家 3—49a
博里纳日 Borinage 比利时工业区 3—51d
博里萨尔 Barisāl 孟加拉国城镇 2—229c
博林 Boleyn, Anne (queen of England) 英格兰王后 3—11c
博林 Bullen, Anne (queen of England) 英格兰王后 3—247e
博林布鲁克 Bolingbroke, Henry 英格兰国王 3—11d
博林布鲁克子爵(第一) Bolingbroke, Henry Saint John, 1st Viscount, BARON SAINT JOHN OF LYDIARD TREGOZE 英国政治家 3—11d
博林根诗歌奖 Bollingen Prize 美国文学奖金 3—15a
博卢 Bolu 土耳其城市 3—17f
博卢-希奥马尔 Bólu-Hjálmar (Icelandic folk poet) 冰岛诗人 3—17f
博鲁杰尔德 Borūjerd 伊朗城镇 3—57c
博伦厄 Borlänge 瑞典城镇 3—52d
博罗 Borrow, George (Henry) 英国旅行家、语言学家 3—56f
博罗夫斯基 Borovský, Havel (Czech author) 捷克作家 3—56b
博罗夫斯基 Borowski, Tadeusz 波兰作家 3—56b
博罗季诺战役 Borodino, Battle of 法国历史 3—54f
博罗罗人 Bororo 南美印第安人 3—55e
博罗梅安群岛 Borromean Islands 意大利岛屿 3—56c
博罗梅奥 Borromeo, Saint Charles 枢机主教 3—56c
博罗米尼 Borromini, Francesco 意大利建筑师 3—56d
博罗特拉 Borotra, Jean 法国网球名将 3—55f
博罗维奇 Borovichi 俄罗斯城镇 3—56b
博洛尼亚 Bologna 意大利城市 3—15c
博洛尼亚 Bologna, Giovanni da 意大利雕刻家 3—15e
博洛尼亚 Bologna (Italian painter) 意大利画家 3—15c
博洛尼亚大学 Bologna, University of 意大利大学 3—15e
博洛尼亚画派 Bolognese school 意大利画派 3—15f
博洛尼亚石 Bologna stone 矿物 3—15f
博马 Boma 刚果(金)城市 3—18d
博马里斯 Beaumaris 威尔士城镇 2—313f
博马努瓦尔 Beaumanoir, Philippe de Remi, sire de 法国官员、法学家 2—313e
博马舍 Beaumarchais, Pierre-Augustin Caron de 法国戏剧家 2—313e
博梅纳尔(小姐) Beauménard, Mademoiselle (French actress) 法国戏剧演员 2—314a
博蒙 Beaumont, (Jean-Baptiste-Armand-Louis-Léonce) Élie de 法国地质学家 2—314b
博蒙特 Beaumont 美国城市 2—314a

博蒙特 Beaumont, William 美国外科军医 2—314e
博米希尔斯 Bomi Hills (Liberia) 利比里亚城市 3—22e
博姆 Böhm, Georg 德国作曲家 3—3c
博姆 Böhm, Karl 奥地利指挥家 3—3c
博姆 Böhm, Theobald 德国长笛演奏家 3—3d
博穆河 Bomu River 中非共和国河流 3—22e
博纳 Bona (Algeria) 阿尔及利亚城市 3—23b
博纳 Bonne, François de 法国公爵 3—33a
博纳 Bonnat, Léon 法国画家、教师 3—33a
博纳尔 Bonald, Louis-Gabriel-Ambroise, vicomte de (viscount of) 法国哲学家、政治家 3—23c
博纳尔 Bonheur, Rosa 法国画家、雕塑家 3—29e
博纳富瓦 Bonnefoy, Yves 法国诗人 3—33b
博纳科尔西家族 Bonacolsi family 意大利家族 3—23b
博纳姆案 Bonham's Case 司法 3—29e
博纳旺蒂尔岛 Bonaventure Island 加拿大岛屿 3—25d
博纳维尔 Bonneville, Benjamin-Louis-Eulalie de 美国陆军工程师 3—34a
博纳维斯塔 Bonavista 加拿大城镇 3—25d
博纳乌蒂 Bonaiuti, Andrea di (Florentine painter) 佛罗伦萨画家 3—23c
博奈尔岛 Bonaire 加勒比海岛屿 3—23b
博南扎河 Bonanza Creek 加拿大河流 3—23f
博讷 Beaune 法国城镇 2—314f
博内 Bonnet, Charles 瑞士博物学家 3—33c
博内 Bonnet, Georges-Étienne 法国政治家 3—33d
博内尔 Boner, Ulrich 瑞士作家、修士 3—28f
博内特 Bonet, Juan Pablo 西班牙牧师、教育家 3—29a
博尼法乔 Bonifacio 法国城镇 3—31e
博尼法西奥 Bonifacio, Andres 菲律宾爱国者 3—31f
博尼瓦尔 Bonivard, François 日内瓦爱国者 3—32c
博农奇尼 Bononcini, Giovanni 意大利作曲家 3—35a
博诺 Bono 西非古国 3—34d
博诺米 Bonomi, Ivanoe 意大利政治家 3—34f
"博诺姆·理查德"号和"塞拉皮斯"号海战 Bonhomme Richard and Serapis, engagement between 美-英海战 3—30c
博帕德 Boppard 德国城市 3—42f
博普 bop (music) 音乐 3—42c
博普塔茨瓦纳 Bophuthatswana 南非历史 3—42c
博奇考伊 Bocskay, István 特兰西瓦尼亚公爵 2—560d
博让西 Beaugency 法国城镇 2—312e
博热领主 Beaujeu, Pierre, seigneur de (lord of) 法国公爵 2—310c
博若莱 Beaujolais 法国古省份 2—313c
博若莱 Beaujolais 法国东南部大区 2—313c
博若莱葡萄酒 Beaujolais 法国名酒 2—313c
博若耶 Beaujoyeulx, Balthazar de 意大利作曲家、舞蹈编导 2—313d
博塞利 Boselli, Paolo 意大利政治家 3—60b
博塞特 Bossert, Helmuth Theodor 德国语文学家 3—62e
博沙尔 Bochart de Saron, Jean-Baptiste-Gaspard 法国律师、科学家 2—559c
博尚 Beauchamp, Alphonse de 法国历史学家 2—310e
博尚 Beauchamp, Kathleen Mansfield 英国女作家 2—310f
博尚 Beauchamp, Pierre 法国芭蕾舞蹈家 2—310f
博尚 Beauchamp, Richard 英格兰军人、外交家 2—311a
博尚 Beauchamp, Thomas Ⅱ de 英格兰贵族 2—311a
博尚男爵 Beauchamp, Edward Seymour, Baron 英格兰贵族 2—310f
博尚(阿什的)子爵 Beauchamp (of Hache), Edward Seymour, Viscount 英格兰摄政王 2—310f
博绍 Bauchau, Henry 比利时小说家、诗人 2—284c
博舍曼 Beauchemin, Nérée 加拿大法语诗人、医生 2—311a
博施 Bosch, Carl 德国化学家 3—58a
博施 Bosch, Robert 德国工业家 3—58f
博施公司 Bosch GmbH 德国公司 3—59a
博什(加维尼奥) Bosch (Gaviño), Juan 多米尼加作家、政治家 3—58e
博士 Dottore 意大利戏剧角色 5—396f
博士 Magi 《圣经》人物 10—381c
博思韦尔伯爵(第四) Bothwell, James Hepburn, 4th earl of, duke of Orkney Shetland 苏格兰贵族 3—72d
博思韦尔伯爵(第五) Bothwell, Francis Stewart Hepburn, 5th earl of 苏格兰贵族 3—72c
博斯 Beauce 法国地区 2—310e
博斯 Bosse, Abraham 法国画家、建筑师 3—62d
博斯 Bosch, Hiëronymus 北欧画家 3—58b
博斯 Bose, Sir Jagadis Chandra 印度植物生理学家 3—59c
博斯 Boss, Lewis 美国天文学家 3—62c
博斯伯爵 Bosch, Johannes, graaf van den (count of) 荷兰政治家 3—58d
博斯顿 Boston, Ralph 美国跳远运动员 3—66c
博斯科恩 Boscawen, Edward 英国海军上将 3—57f
博斯科维奇 Boscovich, Ruggero Giuseppe 意大利天文学家 3—59b
博斯曼 Bosman, Herman Charles 南非作家 3—60c
博斯普鲁斯海峡 Bosporus 亚欧两洲之间海峡 3—61f
博斯普鲁斯王国 Bosporus, Kingdom of the 古希腊国家 3—62b
博斯腾湖 Bositeng Lake 中国湖泊 3—60c
博斯托尔制度 Borstal system 英国感化制度 3—57b
博斯韦尔姐妹合唱团 Boswell Sisters, the 美国爵士乐团 3—68f
博斯沃思 Bosworth (England) 英格兰地区 3—69a
博斯沃思原野战役 Bosworth Field, Battle of 英国历史 3—69b
博苏姆推湖 Bosumtwi, Lake 加纳湖泊 3—67e
博索 Boso 普罗旺斯国王 3—61e
博索尼奥 Bousoño, Carlos 西班牙诗人、文学理论家 3—89c
博他仑 Phatthalung 泰国城镇 13—221f
博塔 Botta, Carlo Giuseppe Guglielmo 法国历史学家、政治家 3—74b
博塔 Botha, Louis 南非军人、政治家 3—71f
博塔 Botha, P(ieter) W(illem) 南非政治家 3—72a
博塔 Botta, Paul-Émile 法国外交官、考古学家 3—74c
博泰蒂河 Boteti River 博茨瓦纳河流 3—71d
博泰西尼 Bottesini, Giovanni 意大利提琴家、作曲家 3—74d
博特 Both, Jan 荷兰画家 3—71e
博特 Both, Pieter 荷兰殖民者 3—71f
博特 Bothe, Walther (Wilhelm Georg) 德国物理学家 3—72b
博特莱特莱河 Botletle River (Botswana) 博茨瓦纳河流 3—72e
博特罗 Botero, Fernando 哥伦比亚画家、雕塑家 3—71c
博特罗普 Bottrop 德国城市 3—75f
博特图尔特 Botetourt, Norborne Berkeley, Lord 英国殖民地总督 3—71d
博特温尼克 Botvinnik, Mikhail Moiseyevich 苏联国际象棋大师 3—76a
博图卡图 Botucatu 巴西城市 3—75f
博托 Boto, Eza 非洲作家 3—72e
博托库多人 Botocudo 南美印第安人 3—72e
博托沙尼 Botoşani 罗马尼亚县名 3—72e
博托沙尼 Botoşani 罗马尼亚城市 3—72f
博瓦迪利亚 Bobadilla, Francisco de 西班牙军人 2—555e
博韦 Beauvais 法国城市 2—315c
博韦 Bovet, Daniel 意大利药理学家 3—91a
博韦挂毯 Beauvais tapestry 法国挂毯 2—315d
博韦里 Boveri, Theodor Heinrich 德国细胞学家 3—90f
博物馆 museum 文化传播机构 11—502d
博物馆 Museum 埃及古代经典学术中心 11—503c
博物馆与美术馆 Museum and Picture Gallery 印度博物馆 11—503c
博希蒙德 Bohemond 安条克公爵、的黎波里伯爵名 3—2e

博希蒙德二世 Bohemond II 安条克公爵 3—3a
博希蒙德六世 Bohemond VI 安条克公爵 3—3b
博希蒙德七世 Bohemond VII 的黎波里伯爵 3—3b
博希蒙德三世 Bohemond III 安条克公爵 3—3a
博希蒙德四世 Bohemond IV 的黎波里伯爵 3—3a
博希蒙德五世 Bohemond V 安条克公爵 3—3b
博希蒙德一世 Bohemond I 安条克公爵 3—2e
博学喜剧 commedia erudita 戏剧形式 4—383e
博亚尔多 Boiardo, Matteo Maria 意大利诗人 3—6a
博亚卡 Boyacá 哥伦比亚省份 3—99d
博亚卡战役 Boyacá, Battle of 南美洲历史 3—99e
博耶 Boye, Karin (Maria) 瑞典作家 3—101a
博耶 Boyer, Paul D. 美国生物化学家 3—101b
博耶尔 Bojer, Johan 挪威小说家 3—8e
博伊安文化 Boian 罗马尼亚新石器文化 3—5f
博伊德 Boyd, Belle 美国戏剧演员、间谍 3—100c
博伊德 Boyd, Martin (à Beckett) 澳大利亚小说家 3—100d
博伊德 Boyd, William 美国电影演员 3—100e
博伊德(基马尔诺克的) Boyd (of Kilmarnock), Robert Boyd, 1st Lord 苏格兰政治家 3—100d
博伊德-奥尔 Boyd-Orr of Brechin Mearns, John Boyd Orr, Baron 苏格兰科学家 3—100e
博伊厄 Boie, Heinrich Christian 德国诗人、编辑 3—6a
博伊内堡 Boyneburg, Johann Christian, Baron (Freiherr) von 德国政治家 3—102c
博伊人 Boii 凯尔特部落 3—6c
博伊森莓 boysenberry 植物 3—102e
博伊斯 Boys, Sir Charles Vernon 英国物理学家 3—102d
博伊斯 Boece, Hector 苏格兰历史学家 2—564a
博伊斯 Beuys, Joseph 德国雕刻家 2—446b
博伊斯 Boyce, William 英国教堂音乐作曲家 3—99f
博伊斯特 Beust, Friedrich Ferdinand, Graf von 萨克森王国首相 2—445e
博伊斯镇 Boys Town 美国村镇 3—102d
博伊塔诺 Boitano, Brian 美国花样滑冰运动员 3—8b
博伊托 Boito, Arrigo 意大利诗人、作曲家 3—8c
博伊西 Boise 美国城市 3—7d
博伊西国家森林 Boise National Forest 美国森林 3—7e
博伊西河 Boise River 美国河流 3—7f
博伊西州立大学 Boise State University 美国大学 3—7f
博依那 Boina 马达加斯加古王国 3—7c
博因河 Boyne, River 爱尔兰河流 3—102c
博因河战役 Boyne, Battle of the 英国历史 3—102b
博英顿 Boyington, Pappy 美国飞行员 3—101c
博约马瀑布 Boyoma Falls 刚果(金)瀑布 3—102d
博赞基特 Bosanquet, Bernard 英国哲学家 3—57e
博扎奇 Borzage, Frank 美国电影导演、制片人 3—57d
博兹曼 Bozeman 美国城市 3—102e
博兹曼 Bozeman, John M. 美国“博兹曼小道”开辟者 3—102e
渤海 Bo Hai 中国内海 2—554a
渤海 Parhae 亚洲古国名 13—41c
搏牛 steer wrestling 牧人竞技项目 16—209a
箔 foil 金属片 6—386c
薄壁组织 parenchyma 植物组织 13—40d
薄层色谱法 thin-layer chromatography 分析化学 17—39d
薄层土 Leptosol 土壤学 10—33b
薄脆饼树 wafer ash 木本植物 18—61b
薄伽梵 Bhāgavata 印度教宗派 2—449b
《薄伽梵歌》 Bhagavadgītā 印度教经籍 2—449b
《薄伽梵往世书》 Bhāgavata-Purāna 印度教梵文经籍 2—449b
薄伽丘 Boccaccio, Giovanni 意大利诗人、学者 2—557c
薄寮 Bac Lieu 越南城镇 2—113c
薄膜乐器 mirliton 乐器 11—273a
薄片琴 lamellaphone 乐器 9—463e
薄片镶饰 veneer 工艺 17—497f
薄婆菩提 Bhavabhūti 印度剧作家、诗人 2—451f
薄软绸 foulard 纺织品 6—423c
薄纱花边 point de gaze 工艺品 13—389a
薄胎瓷 eggshell porcelain 中国瓷器 5—557b
薄皱贝属 Leptaena 古生物学 10—32b
薄荷 mint 草本植物 11—267a
薄荷醇 menthol 化合物 11—121b
薄荷属 Mentha 植物学 11—121a
卜雷加港 Marsā al-Burayqah 利比亚港口 10—533d
卜利达 Blida 阿尔及利亚城镇 2—534d
卜尼法斯 Boniface 教皇和敌对教皇称号 3—30c
卜尼法斯(萨伏依的) Boniface of Savoy 英格兰基督教大主教 3—31e
卜尼法斯,圣 Boniface, Saint 英格兰天主教传教士、改革家 3—31b
卜尼法斯(奎尔富特的),圣 Boniface of Querfurt, Saint 基督教传教士 3—31d
卜尼法斯八世 Boniface VIII 教皇 3—30f
卜尼法斯二世 Boniface II 教皇 3—30d
卜尼法斯九世 Boniface IX 教皇 3—31a
卜尼法斯六世 Boniface VI 教皇 3—30e
卜尼法斯七世 Boniface VII 教皇或敌对教皇 3—30e
卜尼法斯三世 Boniface III 教皇 3—30d
卜尼法斯四世,圣 Boniface IV, Saint 教皇 3—30d
卜尼法斯五世 Boniface V 教皇 3—30e
卜尼法斯一世,圣 Boniface I, Saint 教皇 3—30c
卜塔 Ptah 埃及神祇 13—566b
卟啉 porphyrin 生物色素 13—442b
卟啉症 porphyria 疾病 13—442a
补偿政策 Ethical Policy 荷兰殖民政策 6—145d
补锅鸟 tinkerbird 鸟类 17—106a
补体 complement 血液生化 4—398e
补贴 subsidy 经济政策 16—300d
补助金大军 Bonus Army 美国历史 3—36b
补助税 aid 欧洲中世纪捐税 1—139c
捕获法庭 prize court 国际法 13—522d
捕鲸 whaling 渔业 18—218b
捕鲸者鲨 whaler 鱼类 18—218a
捕虏体 xenolith 地质学 18—375b
捕食 predation 动物行为 13—489f
捕蝇草 catchfly (plant) 草本植物 3—522e
捕蝇草 Venus's-flytrap (species *Dionaea muscipula*) 植物 17—510b
捕蛛鸟 spider hunter 鸟类 16—29a
哺乳动物学 mammalogy 动物学 10—441e
哺乳类 mammal 动物学 10—441b
不参政 non expedit 天主教的规定 12—228a
不从国教派 Nonconformist 英国非国教派别 12—228b
不丹 Bhutan 亚洲国家 2—453e
不等蛤 jingle shell 双壳动物 9—29b
不定判 indeterminate sentence 法律 8—357c
不动产 immovable (legal concept) 法律 8—343e
不动明王 Fudō Myō-ō 日本佛教神 6—509f
不对称合成 asymmetric synthesis 化学 2—11d
不二论 Advaita 印度宗教哲学 1—88f
不法对外征伐 filibustering 美国历史 6—314f
不法行为 delict 罗马法 5—226a
不飞鸟属 Diatryma 古生物学 5—291c
不公正地划分选区 gerrymandering 美国政治 7—100b
不害 ahimsa 印度耆那教 1—134a
不合作运动 Noncooperation Movement 印度历史 12—228b
不合作主义 satyāgraha 哲学 15—80c
不可接触者 untouchable 印度社会等级 17—403b

《不可容忍法》 Intolerable Acts 北美殖民地法律 8—424f
不可知论 agnosticism 哲学 1—125b
不空成就 Amoghasiddhi 佛教禅定佛 1—294e
不来梅 Bremen 德国城市 3—139d
不来梅港 Bremerhaven 德国城市 3—140a
不来梅撰稿人 Bremer Beiträger 德国作家团体 3—140a
不列颠 Britain 欧洲国家 3—162e
《不列颠百科全书》 Encyclopaedia Britannica 大型百科全书 6—71d
不列颠博物馆 British Museum 英国博物馆 3—167d
不列颠(自然历史)博物馆 British Museum (Natural History) 英国博物馆 3—167e
不列颠哥伦比亚 British Columbia 加拿大省份 3—164b
《不列颠国际大百科事典》 Buritanika Kokusai Daihyakka-jiten 日文百科全书 3—265e
不列颠合金 britannia metal 白色合金 3—162f
不列颠桥 Britannia Bridge 威尔士铁路桥 3—162f
不列颠群岛 British Isles 欧洲西部沿海群岛 3—167b
不列颠人 Briton 民族 3—169f
不列颠入侵 British Invasion 音乐运动 3—167a
不列颠图书馆 British Library 英国图书馆 3—167c
不列颠战役 Britain, Battle of 欧洲历史 3—162e
不流血革命 Bloodless Revolution (England) 英国历史 2—542d
不伦瑞克 Braunschweig 德国行政区 3—129c
不伦瑞克 Braunschweig 德国城市 3—129f
不伦瑞克 Brunswick 美国佐治亚州城市 3—208a
不伦瑞克 Brunswick 美国缅因州城镇 3—208a
不眠修士 Acoemeti 拜占廷修士 1—55d
不明飞行物 unidentified flying object (UFO) 不能识别的空中物体 17—342f
不平等条约 unequal treaty 国际关系 17—341c
不确定性 indeterminacy 文学 8—357b
不确定性原理 uncertainty principle 物理学 17—338f
不矢忠派 Nonjuror 英国历史 12—229a
不受法律保护 outlawry 法律 12—509b
不协和音 dissonance (music) 音乐 5—343c
不朽 immortality 哲学、宗教 8—343c
不锈钢 stainless steel 合金钢 16—182a
不育 infertility (reproduction) 疾病 8—381a
不在地主所有权 absentee ownership 土地法 1—30a
不整囊菌类 Plectomycetes 微生物 13—367d
不置可否论 adiaphorism 基督教神学 1—78c
布阿吉尔贝尔 Boisguillebert, Pierre Le Pesant, sieur de (sire of) 法国经济学家 3—8a
布阿什 Buache, Philippe 法国地理学家 3—217a
布埃港 Port-Bouët 科特迪瓦自治镇 13—444d
布埃罗·巴列霍 Buero Vallejo, Antonio 西班牙剧作家 3—233b
布埃纳维斯塔战役 Buena Vista, Battle of 美洲历史 3—230e
布埃纳文图拉 Buenaventura 哥伦比亚港口 3—230e
布埃诺 Bueno, Maria Ester Audion 巴西网球运动员 3—230e
布埃亚 Buea 喀麦隆城市 3—230b
布奥尔-绍恩施泰因伯爵 Buol-Schauenstein, Karl Ferdinand, Graf von (count of) 奥地利帝国外交大臣 3—255f
布巴内斯瓦尔 Bhubaneshwar 印度城市 2—453c
布巴斯提斯 Bubastis 埃及古城 3—217b
布巴斯提斯王朝 Bubastite DYNASTY 埃及历史 3—217b
布贝尔 Buber, Martin 德国犹太宗教哲学家 3—217c
布本贝格 Bubenberg, Adrian von 瑞士军人、政治家 3—217c
布比延 Būbiyān 科威特岛屿 3—217f
布勃诺夫 Bubnov, Andrey Sergeyevich 苏联官员 3—217f
布查尔特 Buchalter, Louis 美国犯罪辛迪加首脑 3—219b
布彻 Butcher, Susan 美国雪橇狗驯狗师 3—288d
布达 Buda (Hungary) 匈牙利城镇 3—224f
布达拉宫 Potala Palace 中国藏传佛教建筑 13—461d
布达拉山 Potala Shan 中国西藏山脉 13—461e
布达佩斯 Budapest 匈牙利首都 3—224f
布代尔 Bourdelle, (Émile-) Antoine 法国雕刻家 3—85a
布袋 Hotei 日本神话人物 8—190c
布丹 Boudin, Eugène 法国画家 3—77c
布道恩 Budaun 印度城市 3—227d
布道坛 pulpit 教堂建筑 14—21f
布德里姆 Buderim 澳大利亚城镇 3—229f
布德万 Burdwān 印度城市 3—258d
布德韦斯 Budweis (Czech Republic) 捷克城市 3—230b
布狄卡 Boudicca 不列颠王后 3—77b
布迪诺特 Boudinot, Elias 美国律师、政府官员 3—77e
布蒂利耶 Bouthillier, Léon 法国投石党人 3—89f
布丁 pudding 食品 14—12f
布丁构造 boudinage 地质学 3—77d
布杜戈代 Pudukkottai 印度县城 14—13d
布恩 Boone 美国城市 3—39f
布恩 Boone 美国城镇 3—39f
布恩 Boone, Daniel 美国传奇式英雄 3—40a
布恩雷蒂罗瓷器 Buen Retiro ware 西班牙瓷器 3—230d
布恩斯博罗 Boonesborough 美国游览村 3—40b
布恩维尔 Boonville 美国城市 3—40b
布尔 Boole, George 英国数学家、逻辑学家 3—38f
布尔 Bull, John (English symbol) 英国漫画人物 3—245f
布尔 Bull, John 英国作曲家 3—245f
布尔 Bull, Olaf (Jacob Martin Luther) 挪威诗人 3—246a
布尔 Bull, Ole Bornemann 挪威小提琴家 3—246a
布尔 Boule, (Pierre-) Marcellin 法国地质学家 3—80d
布尔 Buhl, Vilhelm 丹麦首相 3—237c
布尔巴基 Bourbaki, Nicolas 法国数学家合用笔名 3—83e
布尔布纳 Bourboune, Mourad 阿尔及利亚小说家 3—84f
布尔达纳 Buldāna 印度城市 3—240e
布尔代 Bourdet, Édouard 法国戏剧家 3—85b
布尔代数 Boolean algebra 数学 3—39a
布尔代耶 Bourdeille, Pierre de 法国军人、编年史家 3—85a
布尔迪加尔阶 Burdigalian Stage 地质学 3—258c
布尔东 Bourdon, Sébastien 法国画家 3—85c
布尔东低音 bourdon (music) 音乐 3—85c
布尔杜尔 Burdur 土耳其城市 3—258d
布尔芬奇 Bulfinch, Charles 美国建筑师 3—240f
布尔戈涅宫剧院 Hôtel de Bourgogne, Théâtre de l' 巴黎剧院 0—190f
布尔戈斯 Burgos 西班牙省份 3—261f
布尔戈斯 Burgos 西班牙城市 3—262a
布尔戈斯 Burgos, José 菲律宾天主教司铎 3—262b
布尔格 Bourg-en-Bresse 法国城镇 3—85d
布尔格 Burg, Yosef 以色列政治家 3—259e
布尔根兰 Burgenland 奥地利州名 3—260a
布尔哈夫 Boerhaave, Hermann 荷兰医师 2—565b
布尔哈夫博物馆 Boerhaave Museum 荷兰博物馆 2—565b
布尔汉布 Burhānpur 印度城镇 3—264c
布尔汗布达山 Burhan Budai Shan 中国山脉 3—264b
布尔吉巴 Bourguiba, Habib (ibn Ali) 突尼斯总统 3—87a
布尔吉巴营 Manzil Bū Ruqaybah 突尼斯城镇 10—479e
布尔吉亚 Bulgya, Aleksandr Aleksandrovich 苏联作家 3—245c
布尔加科夫 Bulgakov, Macarius 俄罗斯正教主教 3—240f
布尔加科夫 Bulgakov, Mikhail Afanasyevich 苏联作家 3—241a
布尔加科夫 Bulgakov, Sergey Nikolayevich 俄罗斯经济学家、神学家 3—241c
布尔加鲁斯 Bulgarus 意大利法学家 3—245a
布尔加宁 Bulganin, Nikolay Aleksandrovich 苏联部长会议主席 3—241d

布尔加斯 Burgas 保加利亚城镇 3—259f
布尔克哈特 Burckhardt, Jacob (Christopher) 瑞士文化、艺术史家 3—257f
布尔克哈特 Burckhardt, Johann Ludwig 瑞士旅行家 3—258a
布尔莱马克斯 Burle Marx, Roberto 巴西园林建筑师 3—267f
布尔伦诗集抄本 Carmina Burana 德国民歌集 3—464e
布尔蒙 Bourmont, Louis-Auguste-Victor, Count (comte) de Ghaisnes de 法国军人、政治家 3—87f
布尔内斯 Bulnes, Manuel 智利总统 3—249d
布尔尼亚 Purnea 印度城市 14—34a
布尔诺 Brno 捷克城市 3—170f
布尔热 Bourget, Paul(-Charles-Joseph) 法国作家 3—86e
布尔人 Boer 南非民族 2—564f
布尔日 Bourges 法国城市 3—86d
《布尔日国事诏书》 Pragmatic Sanction of Bourges 法国历史文件 13—478e
布尔茹瓦 Bourgeois, Jeanne-Marie (comedienne) 法国喜剧演员 3—85f
布尔茹瓦 Bourgeois, Léon(-Victor-Auguste) 法国政治家 3—85f
布尔茹瓦 Bourgeois, Louise 美国雕刻家 3—86a
布尔茹瓦 Bourgeois, Loys 法国作曲家 3—86b
布尔萨 Bursa 土耳其城市 3—276c
布尔什维克 Bolshevik 俄国党派 3—16c
布尔什维克革命 Bolshevik Revolution 俄国历史 3—16d
布尔斯廷 Boorstin, Daniel J(oseph) 美国社会历史学家 3—40b
布尔索 Boursault, Edme 法国文人 3—89b
布尔索弗 Boulsover, Thomas 英国发明家 3—82c
布尔特曼 Bultmann, Rudolf (Karl) 德国《新约》学者 3—250a
布尔沃 Bulwer, (William) Henry Lytton (Earle), Baron Dalling and Bulwer of Dalling 英国外交家 3—250c
布尔沃-李顿 Bulwer-Lytton, Edward George Earle 英国政治家、作家 3—250d
布尔沃-李顿 Bulwer-Lytton, (Edward) Robert 英国外交家 3—250d
布尔沃-李顿 Bulwer-Lytton, Victor Alexander George Robert 英国驻孟加拉总督 3—250d
布尔溪战役 Bull Run, battles of 美国历史 3—246d
布尔战争 Boer War 南非战争 2—565a
布法里克 Boufarik 阿尔及利亚城镇 3—78b
布法罗 Buffalo 美国纽约州城市 3—233c
布法罗 Buffalo 美国怀俄明州城市 3—233d
布法罗山 Buffalo Range (Malaysia) 马来西亚山脉 3—234b
布法罗印第安人 Buffalo Indian 民族 3—234b
布丰伯爵 Buffon, Georges-Louis Leclerc, Count (Comte) de 法国博物学家 3—234e
布夫莱 Boufflers, Stanislas-Jean, chevalier de (knight of) 法国作家、军人 3—78c
布夫莱公爵 Boufflers, Louis-François, duc de (duke of) 法国元帅 3—78b
布弗朗 Boffrand, (Gabriel-) Germain 法国建筑师 2—566a
布盖格 Abqaiq 沙特阿拉伯城镇 1—27d
布干达 Buganda 东非王国 3—235e
布干维尔 Bougainville, Louis-Antoine de 法国航海家 3—78d
布干维尔岛 Bougainville Island 巴布亚新几内亚岛屿 3—78e
布格蒂丘陵 Bugti Hills 巴基斯坦丘陵区 3—237a
布格河 Bug River 欧洲河流 3—235b
布格罗 Bouguereau, William-Adolphe 法国画家 3—79b
布给 Bouguer, Pierre 法国科学家 3—79a
布根贝 Bugembe 乌干达城镇 3—236a
布古利马 Bugulma 俄罗斯城市 3—237a
布古鲁斯兰 Buguruslan 俄罗斯城市 3—237a
布哈河 Buha River 中国河流 3—237b
布哈拉 Bukhara 乌兹别克斯坦州名 3—238f
布哈拉 Bukhara 乌兹别克斯坦城市 3—238f
布哈拉地毯 Bokhara rug 工艺品 3—9d
布哈拉地毯 Bukhara rug 工艺品 3—239b
布哈兰塞 Bujalance 西班牙城市 3—238d
布哈里 Buākhar (Sudanese army) 苏丹黑人军队 3—217b
布哈里 Bukhārī, al- 穆斯林圣训学者 3—239b
布哈里 Buhari, Muhammad 尼日利亚军事领袖、国家元首 3—237b
布哈里堡 Ksar el-Boukhari 阿尔及利亚城镇 9—385c
布哈林 Bukharin, Nikolay Ivanovich 苏联理论家、经济学家 3—239c
布海拉 Buḥayrah, al- 埃及省份 3—237b
布赫 Buch, (Christian) Leopold, Freiherr von (baron of) 德国地质学家 3—219a
布赫尔 Bucher, (Adolf) Lothar 德国国际法专家 3—221a
布赫霍尔茨 Buchholz (Germany) 德国城市 3—221b
布赫图里 Buḥturī, al- 阿拔斯王朝诗人 3—237d
布痕瓦尔德 Buchenwald 纳粹德国集中营 3—221a
布胡山水库水坝 Boegoebergdam 南非水坝 2—564a
布胡斯 Bohuslän 瑞典历史省份 3—5f
布基纳法索 Burkina Faso 西非国家 3—267a
布吉人 Buginese 印度尼西亚民族 3—236c
布吉-伍吉 boogie-woogie 音乐风格 3—37a
布加 Buga 哥伦比亚城市 3—235c
布加 Būga, Kazimieras 立陶宛语言学家 3—235c
布加蒂 Bugatti, Ettore Arco Isidoro 意大利汽车制造商 3—235e
布加风 burga 气象学 3—259f
布加风 purga 气象学 14—32b
布加勒斯特 Bucharest 罗马尼亚首都 3—220d
《布加勒斯特条约》 Bucharest, Treaty of 欧洲历史 3—220f
布加耶夫 Bugaev, Boris Nikolayevich 俄国理论家、诗人 3—235c
布加耶夫 Bugayev, Boris Nikolayevich 俄国理论家、诗人 3—235e
布杰德拉 Boudjedra, Rachid 阿尔及利亚作家 3—77f
《布就筵席》 Shulḥan ʿarukh 犹太教著作 15—343c
布卡岛 Buka Island 巴布亚新几内亚岛屿 3—238e
布卡拉曼加 Bucaramanga 哥伦比亚城市 3—218a
布卡雷利-乌苏亚 Bucareli y Ursúa, Antonio María 西班牙军人、政治家 3—218a
布卡武 Bukavu 刚果(金)城市 3—238e
布坎南 Buchanan 利比里亚城镇 3—219d
布坎南 Buchanan, Franklin 美国海军军官 3—219d
布坎南 Buchanan, George 苏格兰人文主义者、作家 3—219e
布坎南 Buchanan, James 美国总统 3—219f
布坎南 Buchanan, James M. 美国经济学家 3—220b
布坎南 Buchanan, Patrick J. 美国新闻记者 3—220c
布科维纳 Bukovina 东欧地区 3—239f
布克陡崖 Book Cliffs 美国地理 3—37c
布克哈特 Burkhardt, Georg 德国作家 3—267a
布克凯洛陶器 bucchero ware 意大利古陶器 3—218c
布克迈尔(大) Burgkmair, Hans, The Elder 德国美术家 3—261e
布克曼运动 Buchmanism (religious movement) 宗教运动 3—221c
布克萨尔 Buxar 印度古城 3—295a
布克萨尔战役 Baksar, Battle of 英印战争 2—158a
布库鲁 Bukuru 尼日利亚城镇 3—239f
布拉班特 Brabant 欧洲封建公国 3—103b
布拉班特 Brabant 比利时省份 3—103d
布拉班特港 Port Brabant (Canada) 加拿大村庄 13—444d
布拉柴 Brazza, Pierre-Paul-François-Camille Savorgnan de 法国探险家、殖民官员 3—133c
布拉柴维尔 Brazzaville 刚果首都 3—133d
布拉茨克 Bratsk 俄罗斯城市 3—127b
布拉茨克水坝 Bratsk Dam 俄罗斯土坝 3—127c
布拉得雷 Bradley, James 英国天文学家 3—107d

布拉德 Bullard, Sir Edward (Crisp) 英国地球物理学家 3—247a
布拉德利 Bradley, Edward R. 美国广播新闻记者 3—107a
布拉德利 Bradley, F(rancis) H(erbert) 英国哲学家 3—107b
布拉德利 Bradley, Lydia Moss 美国慈善家 3—107f
布拉德利 Bradley, Marion Zimmer 美国作家 3—108a
布拉德利 Bradley, Tom 美国政治家 3—108b
布拉迪斯拉发 Bratislava 斯洛伐克首都 3—127b
布拉顿 Brattain, Walter H(ouser) 美国科学家 3—127c
布拉多尔湖 Bras d'Or Lake 加拿大湖泊 3—124e
布拉厄 Brahe, Tycho 丹麦天文学家 3—111e
布拉厄(小) Brahe, Per, Greve (Count), THE YOUNGER 瑞典政治家 3—111d
布拉菲 Bravais, Auguste 法国物理学家 3—130b
布拉菲点阵 Bravais lattice 物理学 3—130c
布拉风 bora 气象学 3—43b
布拉干萨 Bragança 巴西城市 3—110c
布拉干萨 Bragança 葡萄牙城市 3—110c
布拉干萨王室 Bragança, HOUSE OF 欧洲历史 3—110c
布拉戈维申斯克 Blagoveshchensk 俄罗斯城市 2—523b
布拉戈耶夫格勒 Blagoevgrad 保加利亚城镇 2—523a
布拉格 Prague 捷克首都 13—479d
布拉格 Bragg, Billy 英国歌手 3—110d
布拉格 Bragg, Sir William (Henry) 英国物理学家 3—111a
布拉格 Bragg, Sir (William) Lawrence 英国物理学家 3—110f
布拉格大学 Prague, University of 捷克大学 13—482a
布拉格定律 Bragg law 物理学 3—111c
布拉格动物园 Prague Zoological Garden 捷克动物园 13—482a
布拉格叛乱 Praguerie 法国叛乱 13—482b
布拉格扔出窗外 Prague, Defenestration of 欧洲历史 13—481f
布拉格学派 Prague school 语言学派 13—482a
布拉赫马地区 Brahmarṣi-deśa 印度历史地名 3—113c
布拉灰人 Brahui 巴基斯坦部落联盟 3—114e
布拉灰语 Brahui language 巴基斯坦语言 3—114e
布拉吉语 Braj Bhasa language 印度语言 3—116f
布拉加 Braga 葡萄牙城市 3—109f
布拉加 Braga (Joaquim), Teófilo (Fernandes) 葡萄牙诗人、政治家 3—110b
布拉加 Braga, Rubem 巴西作家 3—110a
布拉克 Braque, Georges 法国画家 3—124d
布拉克 Braak, Menno ter 荷兰评论家 3—103a
布拉克曼 Brackman, Barbara 美国被褥史专家 3—105b
布拉克内尔福里斯特 Bracknell Forest 英国城镇 3—105b
布拉克潘 Brakpan 南非城镇 3—117b
布拉马 Bramah, Joseph 英国工程师、发明家 3—117b
布拉马普尔 Brahmapur 印度城镇 3—113a
布拉马普特拉河 Brahmaputra River 亚洲河流 3—113b
布拉曼蒂诺 Bramantino 意大利画家、建筑师 3—117e
布拉曼特 Bramante, Donato 意大利建筑师、画家 3—117b
布拉姆 Bahram 英国赛马 2—144e
布拉姆 Brahm, Otto 德国文学评论家 3—112a
布拉内洛 Buranello, Il (composer) 意大利作曲家 3—256e
布拉尼 Blarney 爱尔兰村庄 2—529b
布拉尼氏鼠 Branick's rat 啮齿动物 3—123a
布拉诺 Burano 意大利威尼斯市郊区 3—256e
布拉诺花边 Burano lace 意大利工艺品 3—256e
布拉奇 Brač 克罗地亚岛屿 3—103e
布拉奇 Blatch, Harriot Eaton Stanton 美国妇女领袖 2—531b
布拉奇福德 Blatchford, Samuel 美国最高法院大法官 2—531c
布拉恰诺湖 Bracciano, Lake 意大利湖泊 3—103e
布拉乔利尼 Bracciolini, Gian Francesco Poggio 意大利人文主义者、书法家 3—103e
布拉萨 Bourassa, (Joseph-Napoléon) Henri 加拿大政治家 3—83d
布拉赛 Brassaï 法国诗人、画家 3—126a
布拉瑟·德·布尔布尔 Brasseur de Bourbourg, Charles-Étienne 法国天主教传教士、民族志学者 3—126b
布拉施卡玻璃模型 Blaschka glass 科学模型 2—529c
布拉什 Brush, Charles Francis 美国发明家 3—208f
布拉思韦特 Brathwait, Richard 英国诗人 3—126f
布拉斯 Brass 尼日利亚城镇 3—125d
布拉斯敦峰 Brasstown Bald 美国山峰 3—126e
布拉斯科维茨 Blaskowitz, Johannes 德国陆军元帅 2—529f
布拉斯科·伊巴内斯 Blasco Ibáñez, Vicente 西班牙作家、政治家 2—529c
布拉斯塔雷斯 Blastares, Matthew 希腊正教修士 2—530e
布拉索夫 Braşov 罗马尼亚县名 3—125b
布拉索夫 Braşov 罗马尼亚城市 3—125c
布拉索斯波特 Brazosport 美国工业综合体 3—133b
布拉索斯河 Brazos River 美国河流 3—133a
布拉特尔伯勒 Brattleboro 美国城镇 3—127e
布拉特利 Bratteli, Trygve (Martin) 挪威政治家 3—127d
布拉瓦岛 Brava Island 佛得角共和国岛屿 3—130b
布拉瓦海岸 Costa Brava 西班牙地理 4—532f
布拉瓦约 Bulawayo 津巴布韦城市 3—240a
布拉维 Bouraoui, Hédi (André) 突尼斯诗人、学者 3—83d
布拉沃 Bravo, Nicolás 墨西哥总统 3—130c
布拉西 Brassey, Thomas 英国铁路承包商 3—126c
布拉西达斯 Brasidas 斯巴达将领 3—124f
布拉西斯 Blasis, Carlo 意大利芭蕾舞教师 2—529d
布拉耶 Braille, Louis 法国教育家 3—115d
布拉耶盲字 Braille 国际盲文符号 3—115b
布拉扎 Brazza (Croatia) 克罗地亚岛屿 3—133b
布拉兹齐奥尼斯 Brazdžionis, Bernardas 立陶宛诗人、编辑 3—130e
布莱 Blais, Marie-Claire 加拿大法语作家 2—524d
布莱 Bly, Nellie 美国记者 2—553c
布莱 Boulez, Pierre 法国作曲家、钢琴家 3—81a
布莱 Bligh, William 英国海军将领 2—534d
布莱比 Blaby 英格兰区名 2—508f
布莱德湖 Bled, Lake 斯洛文尼亚冰川湖 2—532a
布莱恩 Blaine, James G(illespie) 美国政治家 2—523b
布莱尔 Blair, Bonnie 美国速滑运动员 2—523d
布莱尔 Blair, Francis P(reston) 美国记者、政治家 2—523d
布莱尔 Blair, James 美国教育家 2—524a
布莱尔 Blair, John 美国最高法院大法官 2—524a
布莱尔 Blair, Robert 苏格兰诗人 2—524b
布莱尔 Blair, Tony 英国首相 2—524b
布莱尔(小) Blair, Francis Preston, Jr. 美国政治家 2—523e
布莱尔港 Port Blair 印度城镇 13—444c
布莱基 Blakey, Art 美国鼓演奏家 2—526a
布莱基斯通岛 Blakistone Island 美国内河岛屿 2—526b
布莱金厄 Blekinge 瑞典省份 2—532d
布莱克 Blake, Eubie 美国钢琴家 2—524e
布莱克 Blake, Eugene Carson 美国牧师 2—524f
布莱克 Black, Hugo (La Fayette) 美国律师 2—509a
布莱克 Black, Jeremiah Sullivan 美国司法部长 2—509c
布莱克 Black, Joseph 英国化学家、物理学家 2—509c
布莱克 Black, Sir James (Whyte) 英国药理学家 2—509b
布莱克 Blake, Lillie Devereux 美国作家 2—524f
布莱克 Black, Max 美国分析哲学家 2—509e
布莱克 Blake, Robert 英国海军上将 2—525b
布莱克 Blake, William 英国诗人、画家 2—525c
布莱克 Black, Winifred Sweet 美国记者 2—509e
布莱克本 Blackburn, Gideon 美国牧师 2—518c
布莱克本 Blackburn, Helen 英国妇女领袖 2—518d
布莱克本 Blackburn, Joseph 英国画家 2—518d
布莱克本 Blackburn, Thomas 英国作家 2—518e

布莱克本-达温 Blackburn and Darwen 英格兰单一政区 2—518e
布莱克顿 Blackton,J(ames) Stuart 美国导演兼制片人 2—521a
布莱克弗赖尔 Blackfriars 英国伦敦区名 2—519d
布莱克富特 Blackfoot 美国城市 2—519c
布莱克河 Black River 美国河流 2—515b
布莱克河阶 Black Riveran Stage 地质学 2—515c
布莱克罗克 Blackrock 都柏林郊区 2—520b
布莱克罗克沙漠 Black Rock Desert 美国干旱地区 2—515c
布莱克洛克 Blakelock,Ralph Albert 美国画家 2—525e
布莱克门 Blackmun,Harry Andrew 美国最高法院大法官 2—519f
布莱克默 Blackmore,Sir Richard 英国作家、医生 2—519f
布莱克默 Blackmore,Richard Doddridge 英国小说家 2—519f
布莱克浦 Blackpool 英格兰城市 2—520a
布莱克山 Black Hills 美国山脉 2—512e
布莱克山脉 Black Mountains 美国山脉 2—514a
布莱克斯利 Blakeslee,Albert Francis 美国植物学家 2—525f
布莱克斯通 Blackstone,Sir William 英国法学家 2—520c
布莱克斯通河 Blackstone River 美国河流 2—520f
布莱克特 Blackett,Patrick M(aynard) S(tuart), Baron Blackett of Chelsea 英国物理学家 2—519a
布莱克梯特垂饰 bracteate 斯堪的纳维亚工艺品 3—105d
布莱克韦尔 Blackwell,Alice Stone 美国女权倡导者 2—521d
布莱克韦尔 Blackwell,Antoinette Brown 美国牧师 2—521d
布莱克韦尔 Blackwell,Elizabeth 美国医生 2—521e
布莱克韦尔 Blackwell,Emily 美国医生、教育家 2—521f
布莱克韦尔 Blackwell,John 威尔士作家 2—522a
布莱克沃特 Blackwater 澳大利亚城镇 2—521b
布莱克沃特河 Blackwater,River 爱尔兰河流 2—521b
布莱克沃特河 Blackwater,River 北爱尔兰河流 2—521c
布莱克伍德 Blackwood,Algernon Henry 英国作家 2—522a
布莱克伍德 Blackwood,Frederick Temple Hamilton-Temple- 英国外交家 2—522b
布莱克伍德 Blackwood,William 英国出版商 2—522b
布莱克希思 Blackheath 伦敦住宅区 2—519e
布莱里奥 Blériot,Louis 法国飞行家 2—533c
布莱洛克 Blalock,Alfred 美国外科医生 2—526b
布莱奈格温特 Blaenau Gwent 威尔士区名 2—523a
布莱奈伊 Blainey,Geoffrey (Norman) 澳大利亚历史学家 2—523c
布莱尼姆 Blenheim 新西兰城市 2—532e
布莱斯,圣 Blaise,Saint 小亚细亚基督教主教 2—524e
布莱斯谷 Blyth Valley 英格兰城市 2—553d
布莱斯特·加纳 Blest Gana, Alberto 智利作家 2—534a
布莱斯维尔 Blytheville 美国城市 2—553d
布莱希特 Brecht,Bertolt 德国诗人、剧作家 3—135f
布莱辛顿伯爵夫人 Blessington,Marguerite Gardiner,Countess of 爱尔兰女作家 2—533f
布赖比岛 Bribie Island 澳大利亚岛屿 3—148e
布赖代 Buraydah 沙特阿拉伯城镇 3—257a
布赖德(爱尔兰的),圣 Bride of Ireland,Saint 爱尔兰女隐修院院长 3—149d
布赖丁格 Breitinger,Johann Jakob 瑞士德语作家 3—139c
布赖顿 Brighton 英格兰城镇 3—156d
布赖顿-霍夫 Brighton and Hove 英格兰单一政区 3—156e
布赖恩 Brian 爱尔兰国王 3—147f
布赖恩 Bryan 美国城市 3—213d
布赖恩 Brian,Havergal 英国音乐家 3—147f
布赖恩 Bryan,Kirk 美国地质学家 3—213e
布赖恩 Bryan,William Jennings 美国政治家 3—213e
《布赖恩-查莫罗条约》 Bryan-Chamorro Treaty 美国-尼加拉瓜条约 3—214b
布赖恩特 Bryant,Sir Arthur (Wynne Morgan) 英国历史学家 3—214c
布赖恩特 Bryant,Bear 美国橄榄球教练 3—214c
布赖恩特 Bryant,William Cullen 美国诗人 3—214d
布赖尔 Bryher 英国作家 3—215f
布赖格斯 Brygos 欧洲艺术家 3—215e
布赖萨赫 Breisach 德国城市 3—139a
布赖斯 Brice,Fanny 美国演员 3—148e
布赖斯 Bryce (of Dechmont),James Bryce,Viscount 英国政治家 3—214e
布赖斯高 Breisgau 德国历史地区 3—139a
布赖斯高地区弗赖堡 Freiburg im Breisgau 德国城市 6—473e
布赖斯峡谷国家公园 Bryce Canyon National Park 美国公园 3—214f
布赖特 Bright,Sir Charles Tilston 英国工程师 3—155e
布赖特 Bright,John 英国政治家 3—156a
布赖特 Bright,Richard 英国医师 3—156b
布赖特·艾斯 Bright Eyes 美国作家 3—156d
布赖特氏病 Bright's disease 疾病 3—156f
布赖滕费尔德战役 Breitenfeld,Battle of 欧洲历史 3—139b
布兰 Brân 凯尔特人神话人物 3—117f
布兰 Blane,Sir Gilbert,1st Baronet 英国医师 2—528a
布兰查德 Blanchard,Thomas 美国发明家 2—527c
布兰达 Blanda,George (Frederick) 美国橄榄球运动员 2—527f
布兰代斯 Brandes,Edvard 丹麦作家、政治家 3—121a
布兰代斯 Brandes,Georg 丹麦文学批评家 3—121b
布兰代斯 Brandeis,Louis (Dembitz) 美国最高法院大法官 3—119d
布兰代斯大学 Brandeis University 美国大学 3—120a
布兰德 Brand,Hennig 德国化学家 3—119b
布兰德 Brand,Sir Johannes Henricus 南非政治家 3—119c
布兰德福德侯爵 Blandford,John Churchill,Marquess of 英国军人 2—528a
布兰登 Brandon 加拿大城市 3—121d
布兰登 Brandon,Charles 英国贵族 3—121e
布兰登山 Brandon Mountain 爱尔兰山脉 3—121f
布兰迪斯 Brandys,Kazimierz 波兰作家 3—122e
布兰迪万河 Brandywine Creek 美国河流 3—123a
布兰迪万河战役 Brandywine,Battle of the 美国历史 3—122f
布兰丁氏龟 Blanding's turtle (*Emys blandingi*) 爬行动物 2—528a
布兰福德 Branford 美国城镇 3—123a
布兰卡港 Bahía Blanca 阿根廷港口 2—142a
布兰科万公主 Brancovan,Anna de Noailles,princess 法国诗人 3—118f
布兰克 Blanc,Mel 美国演员 2—526e
布兰纳 Branner,Hans Christian 丹麦小说家 3—123b
布兰普顿 Brampton 加拿大城市 3—117f
布兰普顿岛 Brampton Island 澳大利亚岛屿 3—117f
布兰奇达伊 Branchidae (Greek religion) 古希腊遗址 3—118c
布兰奇菲尔德 Blanchfield,Florence A. 美国护士、军官 2—527e
布兰森 Branson 美国城市 3—123c
布兰森 Branson,Sir Richard 英国企业家 3—123d
布兰斯维克 Brunschvicg,Léon 法国哲学家 3—207f
布兰太尔 Blantyre 马拉维城市 2—529a
布兰特 Brandt,Alfred 德国土木工程师 3—121f
布兰特 Brandt,Bill 英国摄影家 3—121f
布兰特 Brandt,Georg 瑞典化学家 3—122b
布兰特 Brant,Joseph 北美印第安人领袖 3—123e
布兰特 Brant,Mary 印第安人首领 3—123f
布兰特 Brant,Sebastian 德国诗人 3—123f
布兰特福德 Brantford 加拿大城市 3—124a
布兰廷 Branting,Karl Hjalmar 瑞典政治家 3—124b
布兰维里耶 Boulainvilliers, Henri de,comte de (count of) Saint-Saire 法国历史学家、政论家 3—79e
布兰维利耶侯爵夫人 Brinvilliers,Marie-Madeleine-Marguérite d'Aubray,marquise de 法国杀人犯 3—158f

布朗 Brown, Alice 美国小说家、传记作家 3—188f
布朗 Brown, Alice Van Vechten 美国艺术教育家 3—189a
布朗 Brown, Sir Arthur Whitten 英国飞行员 3—189a
布朗 Brown, Charles 美国歌手 3—189b
布朗 Brown, Claude 美国作家 3—189d
布朗 Brown, Charles Brockden 美国作家 3—189c
布朗 Brown, Charlotte Emerson 美国俱乐部活动家 3—189c
布朗 Browne, Charles Farrar (U. S. humorist) 美国幽默作家 3—195c
布朗 Brun, Charles Le (French painter) 法国画家 3—203e
布朗 Brown, Earle 美国作曲家 3—189d
布朗 Browne, E(lliott) Martin 英国戏剧导演兼演出人 3—195c
布朗 Brown, Ernest William 美国数学家、天文学家 3—189e
布朗 Brown, Ford Madox 英国画家 3—189e
布朗 Brown, George 加拿大记者、政治家 3—189f
布朗 Brown, George Douglas 苏格兰小说家 3—190a
布朗 Brown, Henry Billings 美国最高法院大法官 3—190d
布朗 Brown, Herbert Charles 美国化学家 3—190d
布朗 Brown, Helen Gurley 美国作家和编辑 3—190c
布朗 Brown, Helen Hayes (American actress) 美国演员 3—190d
布朗 Browne, Hablot Knight 英国画家 3—195d
布朗 Brown, Hallie Quinn 美国教育家 3—190a
布朗 Brown, Harrison (Scott) 美国地球化学家 3—190b
布朗 Browne, Jackson 美国歌手 3—195d
布朗 Brown, James 美国声乐家、作曲家 3—190e
布朗 Brown, Jim 美国橄榄球运动员 3—190f
布朗 Brown, John 美国废奴主义斗士 3—191a
布朗 Brown, John 英国医师 3—191a
布朗 Brown, Joseph Emerson 美国州长 3—191c
布朗 Brown, Lancelot 英国园林设计大师 3—191d
布朗 Brown, Martha McClellan 美国禁酒倡导者 3—191f
布朗 Brown, Margaret Wise 美国儿童文学作家 3—191e
布朗 Brown, Michael S(tuart) 美国分子遗传学家 3—192a
布朗 Brown, Olympia 美国牧师、社会改革家 3—192c
布朗 Brown, Paul 美国橄榄球教练 3—192d
布朗 Browne, Robert 英国清教派公理会领导人 3—195f
布朗 Brown, Robert 苏格兰植物学家 3—192e
布朗 Brown, Ron 美国政治家 3—193b
布朗 Brown, Ruth 美国歌手、演员 3—193c
布朗 Brown, Robert Hanbury 英国天文学家、作家 3—193a
布朗 Brown, Thomas 英国诗人 3—193c
布朗 Brown, Thomas 英国玄学家 3—193d
布朗 Browne, Sir Thomas 英国医生、作家 3—195f
布朗 Browne, Thomas (Alexander) (Australian novelist) 澳大利亚小说家 3—196a
布朗 Brown, Trisha 美国舞蹈家 3—193e
布朗 Browne, William 英国诗人 3—196a
布朗 Brown, Willie 美国政治家 3—193f
布朗 Browne, William George 英国旅行家 3—196a
布朗 Brown, William Hill 美国小说家、戏剧家 3—193f
布朗(帝国伯爵) Browne, Maximilian Ulysses, Reichsgraf 奥地利陆军元帅 3—195e
布朗(夫人) Brown, Molly "泰坦尼克"号海难幸存者 3—192b
布朗大学 Brown University 美国大学 3—195b
布朗海军上将 Almirante Brown 阿根廷城镇 1—246d
布朗基 Blanqui, (Louis-)Auguste 法国社会主义者 2—528e
布朗科马 bronco (horse) 马品种 3—177f
布朗克斯 Bronx 美国纽约市行政区 3—180f
布朗克斯动物园 Bronx Zoo 纽约动物园 3—181a
布朗库堡 Castelo Branco 葡萄牙区名 3—509c
布朗库堡 Castelo Branco 葡萄牙城市 3—509d
布朗库河 Branco River 巴西河流 3—118f
布朗库角 Branco, Cape 巴西海角 3—118f
布朗库西 Brancusi, Constantin 罗马尼亚雕刻家 3—118f
布朗莱舞 branle 法国舞蹈 3—123a
布朗利 Brownlee, J. E. 加拿大政治家 3—197e
布朗洛 Brownlow, William G. 美国报纸主编、州长 3—197e
布朗宁 Browning, Elizabeth Barrett 英国诗人 3—196f
布朗宁 Browning, Robert 英国诗人 3—197a
布朗宁 Browning, Tod 美国电影导演 3—197c
布朗普顿教堂 Brompton Oratory 英国天主教教堂 3—177b
布朗热 Boulanger, Georges(-Ernest-Jean-Marie) 法国将军 3—79e
布朗热 Boulanger, Nadia 法国指挥家 3—79f
布朗森 Brownson, Orestes Augustus 美国作家 3—197f
布朗斯费尔德 Bransfield, Edward 英国海军军官 3—123c
布朗斯坦 Bronstein, Lev Davidovich (Russian leader) 俄国十月革命领导人 3—179a
布朗斯维尔 Brownsville 美国城市 3—198a
布朗斯维尔事件(1906) Brownsville Affair 美国种族事件 3—198a
布朗诉托皮卡教育局案 Brown v. Board of Education of Topeka 美国法院案例 3—195c
布朗特 Blount, Charles 英国贵族 2—545a
布朗特 Blount, Edward 英国出版商、翻译家 2—545a
布朗特 Blount, William 美国州长、参议员 2—545b
布朗特造山幕 Blountian orogeny 地质学 2—545c
布朗托姆 Brantôme, Pierre de 法国军人、编年史家 3—124c
布朗夏尔 Blanchard, Jean-Pierre-François 法国气球飞行家 2—527a
布朗歇 Blanche of Castile 法国王后 2—527d
布朗歇家族 Blanchet family 法国乐器制造者家族 2—527d
布朗语 Blang language 中国布朗族语言 2—528c
布朗运动 Brownian motion 物理学 3—196b
布朗族 Blang 中国民族 2—528b
布劳德尔 Braudel, (Paul Achille) Fernand 法国历史学家、教育家 3—127f
布劳迪 Broudy, Harry S(amuel) 美国教育哲学家 3—187c
布劳顿 Broughton, Jack 英格兰拳击冠军 3—187f
布劳顿男爵 Broughton (de Gyfford), John Cam Hobhouse, Baron 英国政治家、文人 3—188a
布劳恩 Braun, Alexander Carl Heinrich 德国植物学家 3—128b
布劳恩 Braun, (Karl) Ferdinand 德国物理学家 3—128d
布劳恩 Braun, Lily 德国女权运动者、作家 3—128f
布劳恩 Braun, Otto 德国政治家 3—128f
布劳恩 Braun, Wernher von 德国工程师 3—129a
布劳尔 Brouwer, Adriaen 佛兰德画家 3—188c
布劳尔 Brauer, Richard Dagobert 美国数学家 3—128b
布劳瑙 Braunau 奥地利城镇 3—129c
布劳内尔 Brownell, W(illiam) C(rary) 美国评论家 3—196b
布劳威尔 Brouwer, Dirk 美国天文学家 3—188d
布劳威尔 Brouwer, L(uitzen) E(gbertus) J(an) 荷兰数学家 3—188d
布劳希奇 Brauchitsch, (Heinrich Alfred) Walther von 德国陆军元帅 3—127f
布勒 Boulle, André-Charles 法国家具工匠 3—81c
布勒 Boulle, Pierre(-François-Marie-Louis) 法国小说家 3—81e
布勒蒂亚努 Brătianu, Constantin 罗马尼亚政治家 3—126f
布勒蒂亚努 Brătianu, Ionel 罗马尼亚政治家 3—127a
布勒蒂亚努 Brătianu, Ion (Constantin) 罗马尼亚政治家 3—126f
布勒豪特 Boulhaut (Morocco) 摩洛哥城镇 3—81c
布勒河 Buller River 新西兰河流 3—247e
布勒基尼 Bréquigny, Louis-Georges-Oudard-Feudrix de 法国学者 3—142c
布勒曼 Boulemane 摩洛哥城镇 3—80e
布勒特伊 Breteuil, Gabrielle-Émilie Le Tonnelier de (French scientific writer) 法国科学家 3—143f
布勒伊拉 Brăila 罗马尼亚县名 3—115a

布勒伊拉 Brăila 罗马尼亚城市 3—115b
布雷 Bray 英格兰城镇 3—130d
布雷 Bray 爱尔兰城镇 3—130d
布雷 Bray, Thomas 英格兰基督教教士 3—130e
布雷伯夫 Brébeuf, Saint Jean de 法国天主教传教士 3—135c
布雷达 Breda 荷兰城市 3—137d
《布雷达条约》 Breda, Treaty of 欧洲历史 3—137d
布雷德 Braid, James 英国高尔夫球运动员 3—114f
布雷德 Braid, James 英国外科医生 3—114f
布雷德伯里 Bradbury, Ray 美国作家 3—105e
布雷德福 Bradford 英格兰城市 3—106a
布雷德福 Bradford 美国城市 3—106a
布雷德福 Bradford, Roark (Whitney Wickliffe) 美国小说家 3—106b
布雷德福 Bradford, William 美国画家 3—106d
布雷德福 Bradford, William 美洲印刷商 3—106c
布雷德福 Bradford, William 英国殖民地总督 3—106c
布雷德利 Bradley, A(ndrew) C(ecil) 英国文学评论家 3—106f
布雷德利 Bradley, Bill 美国篮球运动员 3—107a
布雷德利 Bradley, Edward Riley 美国运动员 3—107b
布雷德利 Bradley, Joseph P. 美国最高法院大法官 3—107e
布雷德利 Bradley, Omar N(elson) 美国将领 3—108a
布雷德罗 Bredero, Gerbrand Adriaenszoon 荷兰诗人、剧作家 3—137e
布雷德洛 Bradlaugh, Charles 英国激进派人物 3—106e
布雷德曼 Bradman, Don 澳大利亚板球运动员 3—108c
布雷德韦尔 Bradwell, Myra Colby 美国律师、编辑 3—108f
布雷德韦尔诉伊利诺伊州 Bradwell v. State of Illinois 美国法院案例 3—108f
布雷德沃丁 Bradwardine, Thomas 英国基督教大主教、数学家 3—108f
布雷德肖 Bradshaw, John 英格兰法庭庭长 3—108c
布雷德肖 Bradshaw, Terry (Paxton) 美国橄榄球运动员 3—108d
布雷德运动 Braid movement 尼日利亚宗教运动 3—115a
布雷登顿 Bradenton 美国城市 3—105f
布雷迪 Brady, Alice 美国演员 3—109a
布雷迪 Brady, James Buchanan 美国金融家、慈善家 3—109b
布雷迪 Brady, Mathew B. 美国摄影师 3—109b
布雷迪 Brady, Nicholas 英国牧师、诗人 3—109d
布雷迪 Brady, William A(loysius) 美国演员、制片人 3—109d
布雷东·德·洛斯·埃雷罗斯 Bretón de los Herreros, Manuel 西班牙诗人、作家 3—144d
布雷顿 Breton, Nicholas 英国作家 3—144d
布雷顿角岛 Cape Breton Island 加拿大岛屿 3—419e
布雷顿角高地 Cape Breton Highlands 加拿大山地 3—419d
布雷顿森林会议 Bretton Woods Conference 国际金融会议 3—145a
布雷多尔本 Breadalbane 苏格兰历史地区 3—134a
布雷多尔本和霍兰伯爵(第一) Breadalbane and Holland, John Campbell, 1st earl of 苏格兰政治学家 3—134a
布雷多克 Braddock, Edward 英国指挥官 3—105e
布雷多克 Braddock, James J(oseph) 美国拳击运动员 3—105f
布雷恩 Braine, John 英国小说家 3—116c
布雷恩达尔 Bregendahl, Marie 丹麦作家 3—138b
布雷盖 Bréguet, Abraham-Louis 法国钟表制造家 3—138d
布雷盖 Bréguet, Louis-Charles 法国飞机制造家 3—138d
布雷格 Bragg, Braxton 美国军官 3—110e
布雷格 Bragg, Don 美国田径运动员 3—110f
布雷根茨 Bregenz 奥地利城镇 3—138b
布雷根茨林山 Bregenzerwald 奥地利山地 3—138c
布雷赫特 Brecht, Arnold 德国政治学家 3—135e
布雷克顿 Bracton, Henry de 英国法学家 3—105d
布雷克兰 Breckland 英格兰区名 3—137a
布雷克利子爵 Brackley, Thomas Egerton, Viscount, BARON ELLESMERE 英国法学家、外交家 3—105a
布雷克诺克 Brecknock (town, Wales) 威尔士城镇 3—137b
布雷克诺克伯爵(第一) Brecknock, John Jeffreys Pratt, 1st earl of 英国驻爱尔兰总督 3—137b
布雷克诺克郡 Brecknockshire 威尔士历史郡名 3—137b
布雷克斯皮尔 Breakspear, Nicholas (pope) 教皇 3—134e
布雷肯 Brecon 威尔士城镇 3—137c
布雷肯比肯斯国家公园 Brecon Beacons National Park 威尔士公园 3—137c
布雷肯阶 Breconian Stage 地质学 3—137c
布雷肯里奇 Breckenridge 美国城市 3—136d
布雷肯里奇 Brackenridge, Hugh Henry 美国小说家 3—104e
布雷肯里奇 Breckinridge, John C(abell) 美国副总统 3—136e
布雷肯里奇 Breckinridge, John 美国政治家 3—136d
布雷肯里奇 Breckinridge, Madeline McDowell 美国社会改革家 3—136e
布雷肯里奇 Breckinridge, Mary 美国护理助产士 3—136f
布雷肯里奇 Breckinridge, Sophonisba Preston 美国福利工作者 3—137a
布雷拉绘画陈列馆 Brera, Pinacoteca di 意大利博物馆 3—142d
布雷马 Braemar 苏格兰山村 3—109f
布雷默顿 Bremerton 美国城市 3—140b
布雷默尔 Bremer, Fredrika 瑞典作家 3—139f
布雷默斯多普 Bremersdorp (Swaziland) 斯威士兰城镇 3—140b
布雷纳德 Brainerd 美国城市 3—116c
布雷纳德 Brainerd, David 美国传教士 3—116d
布雷切尔 Bretscher, Willy 瑞士新闻工作者 3—145a
布雷萨诺内 Bressanone 意大利城镇 3—142f
布雷思韦特 Braithwaite, R(ichard) B(evan) 英国哲学家 3—116f
布雷斯 Bresse 法国自然区 3—142f
布雷斯 Blass, Bill 美国时尚设计师 2—530a
布雷斯 Brace, Charles Loring 美国社会改革者 3—103f
布雷斯丹 Bresdin, Rodolphe 法国雕刻师 3—142e
布雷斯格德尔 Bracegirdle, Anne 英国戏剧演员 3—104a
布雷斯劳 Breslau (Poland) 波兰城市 3—142f
布雷斯特 Brest 法国城市 3—143b
布雷斯特德 Breasted, James Henry 美国考古学家 3—135b
布雷松 Bresson, Robert 法国电影导演 3—143a
布雷特·汉诺弗 Bret Hanover 美国赛马 3—143e
布雷滕巴赫 Breytenbach, Breyten 南非作家 3—146f
布雷托诺 Bretonneau, Pierre-Fidèle 法国流行病学家 3—144f
布雷舞 bourrée 法国民间舞蹈 3—88f
布雷西亚 Brescia 意大利城市 3—142e
布雷西亚 Brescia, Girolamo 意大利画家 3—142e
布雷西亚 Brescia, Girolamo da 威尼斯画家 3—142e
布雷亚 Brea 美国城市 3—133d
布雷耶 Breyer, Stephen 美国最高法院大法官 3—146f
布雷泽 Brézé, Pierre II de 法国军人、政治家 3—147a
布雷兹特里特 Bradstreet, Anne 美国诗人 3—108e
布冷风 buran 气象学 3—256e
布里 Brie 法国自然区 3—154d
布里 Puri 印度县城 14—32d
布里 Burri, Alberto 意大利美术家 3—275b
布里 Bry, Theodor de (German) 德国雕版家、编辑 3—213d
布里埃内 Bourrienne, Louis-Antoine Fauvelet de 法国外交官 3—89b
布里安 Brienne, Étienne-Charles de Loménie de 法国主教、政治家 3—154f
布里昂 Burian, Emil František 捷克作家 3—265c
布里奥斯科 Briosco, Andrea 意大利雕刻家 3—159a
布里达尔维尔瀑布 Bridalveil Fall 美国大瀑布 3—149d
布里德尔 Bridel, Philippe-Sirice 瑞士文学家 3—149d

布里的西蒙 Brie, Simon de (pope) 教皇 3—154e
布里迪 Bridie, James 苏格兰剧作家 3—154c
布里顿 Britten, Benjamin 英国作曲家 3—170b
布里顿 Britton, Elizabeth Gertrude Knight 美国植物学家 3—170e
布里恩法律 Brehon laws 古爱尔兰法律 3—138e
布里恩尼奥斯 Bryennios, Philotheos 东正教神学家 3—215a
布里恩尼乌斯 Bryennius, Nicephorus 拜占廷军人 3—215b
布里恩扎公爵 Brienza, Francesco Caracciolo, duca di (duke of) 意大利那不勒斯海军舰队司令 3—154f
布里尔 Brill, Paul 佛兰德斯画家 3—157b
布里夫-拉盖亚尔德 Brive-la-Gaillarde 法国城镇 3—170f
布里盖拉 Brighella 意大利喜剧演员 3—155d
布里干酪 Brie 法国食品 3—154d
布里甘蒂亚 Brigantia (Celtic goddess) 凯尔特女神 3—155b
布里甘特人 Brigantes 古代英国部落 3—155a
布里格姆城 Brigham City 美国城市 3—155d
布里格斯 Briggs, Emily Pomona Edson 美国记者 3—155c
布里格斯 Briggs, Henry 英国数学家 3—155c
布里根蒂努斯湖 Brigantinus, Lacus (Europe) 欧洲湖泊 3—155c
布里吉特 Brigit 凯尔特女神 3—157a
布里吉特(爱尔兰的),圣 Brigit OF IRELAND, SAINT 爱尔兰女隐修院院长 3—157a
布里吉特(瑞典的),圣 Bridget OF SWEDEN, SAINT 瑞典主保圣人 3—153c
布里吉特修会 Bridgettine 天主教修会 3—153e
布里杰 Bridger, Jim 美国皮毛商 3—152f
布里金 Brechin 苏格兰自治市 3—135e
布里卡马 Brikama 冈比亚市镇 3—157b
布里科 Brico, Antonia 美国钢琴家、交响乐团指挥 3—149b
布里克里乌的宴会 Bricriu's Feast 爱尔兰文学 3—149c
布里克瑟姆 Brixham 英格兰城镇 3—170f
布里克森 Brixen (Italy) 意大利城镇 3—170f
布里莱索斯 Brilessos (Greece) 希腊山脉 3—157b
布里姆 Bream, Julian Alexander 英国吉他演奏家 3—134f
布里牧羊狗 briard 法国牧羊狗 3—148c
布里纳 Brynner, Yul 美国演员 3—215f
布里尼翁 Bourignon, Antoinette 奥秘神学家 3—87c
布里涅耳 Brinell, Johan August 瑞典冶金学家 3—158b
布里农 Brinon, Fernand de 法国新闻记者 3—158e
布里奇 Bridge, Frank 英国作曲家 3—152d
布里奇波特 Bridgeport 美国城市 3—152e
布里奇敦 Bridgetown 巴巴多斯首都 3—153d
布里奇顿 Bridgeton 美国城市 3—153c
布里奇曼 Bridgman, Laura Dewey 美国残疾人 3—153f
布里奇曼 Bridgman, P(ercy) W(illiams) 美国物理学家 3—154a
布里奇诺斯 Bridgnorth 英格兰区名 3—154c
布里奇斯 Bridges, Calvin Blackman 美国遗传学家 3—152f
布里奇斯 Bridges, Harry 美国劳工领袖 3—153a
布里奇斯 Brydges, James 英国贵族 3—215a
布里奇斯 Bridges, Robert (Seymour) 英国诗人 3—153b
布里奇斯 Brydges, Sir Samuel Egerton, 1ST BARONET 英国作家 3—215a
布里奇沃特 Bridgwater 英格兰港口 3—154c
布里奇沃特 Bridgewater, Francis Egerton, 3rd Duke of, MARQUESS OF BRACKLEY, EARL OF BRIDGEWATER, VISCOUNT BRACKLEY, BARON OF ELLESMERE 英国内河航运创始人 3—153e
布里奇沃特运河 Bridgewater Canal 英国水道 3—153e
布里塞 brisé 芭蕾舞步 3—159f
布里斯班 Brisbane 澳大利亚城市 3—159a
布里斯班 Brisbane, Albert 美国社会改革家 3—159b
布里斯班 Brisbane, Arthur 美国编辑、作家 3—159c
布里斯班 Brisbane, Sir Thomas Makdougall 英国军人、天文观测者 3—159c
布里斯班河 Brisbane River 澳大利亚河流 3—159e
布里斯班红胶木 Brisbane box (*Tristania conferta*) 木本植物 3—159e
布里斯班湾 Brisbane Water 澳大利亚湾汊 3—159e
布里斯托 Bristow, Benjamin Helm 美国律师、政治家 3—162d
布里斯托尔 Bristol 英格兰城市 3—161a
布里斯托尔 Bristol 美国康涅狄格州城市 3—161b
布里斯托尔 Bristol 美国宾夕法尼亚州自治镇 3—161c
布里斯托尔 Bristol 美国罗得岛州城镇 3—161c
布里斯托尔 Bristol 美国城镇 3—161d
布里斯托尔埃文河 Bristol Avon (river, England) 英国河流 3—162a
布里斯托尔伯爵 Bristol, EARLS OF 英格兰贵族 3—161d
布里斯托尔伯爵(第二) Bristol, George Digby, 2nd earl of 英格兰保王派 3—161e
布里斯托尔伯爵(第一) Bristol, John Digby, 1st earl of 英格兰外交官 3—161d
布里斯托尔伯爵(第一) Bristol, John Hervey, 1st earl of 英格兰议员 3—162a
布里斯托尔瓷器 Bristol ware 英国瓷器 3—162c
布里斯托尔动物园 Bristol Zoo 英国动物园 3—162d
布里斯托尔海峡 Bristol Channel 大西洋海湾 3—162a
布里斯托尔、克利夫顿及英国西部动物学会动物园 Bristol, Clifton and West of England Zoological Society's Gardens 英国动物园 3—162a
布里斯托尔-迈尔斯-斯奎布公司 Bristol-Myers Squibb Company 美国公司 3—162b
布里斯托尔湾 Bristol Bay 白令海海湾 3—162a
布里松 Brisson, Henri 法国总理 3—160a
布里松内 Briçonnet, Guillaume 法兰西天主教改革家 3—149c
布里索 Brissot (de Warville), Jacques-Pierre 法国政治领袖 3—160b
布里索尼诸语言 Brythonic languages 凯尔特语言语支 3—216c
布里索派 Brissotin (French Revolutionary) 法国大革命 3—160d
布里托玛尔提斯 Britomartis 希腊神话 3—169e
布里翁的西蒙 Brion, Simon de (pope) 教皇 3—159a
布里亚蒂亚 Buryatiya 俄罗斯行政区域 3—280b
布里亚尔蒙特 Brialmont, Henri-Alexis 比利时军人 3—147e
布里亚柔斯 Briareus 希腊神话 3—148d
布里亚-萨瓦兰 Brillat-Savarin, (Jean-) Anthelme 法国法学家 3—157c
布里亚特共和国 Buriat Republic (Russia) 俄罗斯行政区域 3—265d
布里亚特人 Buryat 蒙古民族 3—280a
布里扬松 Briançon 法国城市 3—148a
布里永领主 Brion, Philippe de Chabot, seigneur de (lord of) 法国海军元帅 3—159a
布里真德 Bridgend 威尔士城镇 3—152e
布立斯分类法 Bliss Classification 图书馆学 2—536a
布利安生 Brianchon, Charles-Julien 法国数学家 3—148a
布利长面式样 long-faced style of Buli (African art) 非洲艺术 10—206f
布利茨坦 Blitzstein, Marc 美国钢琴家、剧作家 2—536e
布利高 Blicher, Steen Steensen 丹麦作家 2—534c
布利格德湖 Pulicat Lake 印度咸水潟湖 14—20d
布利根 Blegen, Carl (William) 美国考古学家 2—532c
布利克森 Blixen, Karen, BARONESSE (Baroness) BLIXEN-FINECKE (Danish writer) 丹麦作家 2—536e
布利式样 Buli style 非洲木雕 3—245c
布利斯 Bliss, Sir Arthur (Edward Drummond) 英国作曲家 2—535d
布利斯 Bliss, Gilbert Ames 美国数学家 2—535e
布利斯 Bliss, Tasker Howard 美国军人、政治家 2—535f
布利斯 Bliss, William D(wight) P(orter) 美国社会改革家 2—535f
布利特 Bullitt, William C(hristian) 美国外交家 3—249b

布利特-谢尔南德尔层序 Blytt-Sernander system 地质学 2—553e
布利伊多普动物园 Blijdorp Zoo 荷兰动物园 2—534f
布良卡 Bryanka 乌克兰城市 3—214b
布良斯克 Bryansk 俄罗斯州名 3—214b
布良斯克 Bryansk 俄罗斯城市 3—214c
布列克 Bleek, Wilhelm (Heinrich Immanuel) 德国语言学家 2—532c
布列斯特 Brest 白俄罗斯州名 3—143c
布列斯特 Brest 白俄罗斯城市 3—143c
布列斯特-立陶夫斯克和约 Brest-Litovsk, treaties of 欧洲历史 3—143d
布列斯特-立陶夫斯克联合协议 Brest-Litovsk, Union of 欧洲宗教协议 3—143d
布列塔尼 Brittany 法国大区 3—169f
布列塔尼籁歌 Breton lay 诗歌 3—144e
布列塔尼文学 Breton literature 法国文学 3—144f
布列塔尼语 Breton language 语言 3—144e
布林德利 Brindley, James 英国工程师 3—157f
布林迪西 Brindisi 意大利城市 3—157f
布林格 Bullinger, Heinrich 瑞士基督教人士 3—249a
布林克 Brink, André Philippus 南非作家 3—158c
布林克 Brink, Bernhard ten 荷兰学者 3—158c
布林克曼 Brinkman, Johannes Andreas 荷兰建筑师 3—158d
布龙 Broun, Heywood (Campbell) 美国新闻工作者 3—188b
布龙 Brun, Rudolf 瑞士政治家 3—203f
布龙贝格 Bromberg (Poland) 波兰省份 3—176a
布龙齐诺 Bronzino, Il 佛罗伦萨画家 3—182a
布龙萨特·封·舍伦多夫 Bronsart von Schellendorf, Paul 普鲁士军人、作家 3—178d
布龙氏树科 Bruniaceae 植物学 3—207a
布龙泰 Bronte 意大利城镇 3—179a
布隆代尔 Blondel, André-Eugenè 法国物理学家 2—540b
布隆代尔 Blondel, Georges 法国历史学家 2—540c
布隆代尔 Blondel, Jacques-François 法国建筑师 2—540c
布隆代尔 Blondel, Maurice (Édouard) 法国哲学家 2—540d
布隆代尔·德·内斯莱 Blondel de Nesle 法国诗人 2—540b
布隆丹 Blondin 法国杂技演员 2—540d
布隆迪 Burundi 非洲国家 3—278b
布隆方丹 Bloemfontein 南非城市 2—538e
《布隆方丹公约》 Bloemfontein Convention 南非历史 2—539a
布隆费尔斯 Brunfels, Otto 德国植物学家 3—206d
布隆内尔 Brunner, Emil 瑞士神学家 3—207b
布隆尼亚尔 Brongniart, Adolphe-Théodore 法国植物学家 3—177f
布隆尼亚尔 Brongniart, Alexandre 法国矿物学家 3—178a
布隆希尔德 Brunhild 法国王后 3—206e
布卢盎 Bruant, Libéral 法国建筑师 3—198d
布卢彼得 Blue Peter 英国纯种赛马 2—548d
布卢登茨 Bludenz 奥地利城镇 2—546f
布卢尔 Bloor, Ella Reeve 美国政治组织者、作家 2—544e
布卢菲尔兹 Bluefields 尼加拉瓜城市 2—550c
布卢马尔特 Bloemaert, Abraham 荷兰画家 2—538d
布卢梅瑙 Blumenau 巴西城市 2—552c
布卢门塔尔伯爵 Blumenthal, Leonhard, Graf von 普鲁士陆军元帅 2—552e
布卢明顿 Bloomington 美国伊利诺伊州城市 2—544b
布卢明顿 Bloomington 美国印第安纳州城市 2—544b
布卢明顿 Bloomington 美国明尼苏达州城市 2—544c
布卢默 Bloomer, Amelia Jenks 美国改革家 2—543c
布卢默女裤 bloomers 服装 2—543d
布卢姆 Bloom, Claire 英国戏剧演员 2—543c
布卢姆伯格 Blumberg, Baruch S(amuel) 美国研究医师 2—552b
布卢姆菲尔德 Bloomfield 美国康涅狄格州城镇 2—543e
布卢姆菲尔德 Bloomfield 美国新泽西州城镇 2—543e
布卢姆菲尔德 Bloomfield, Leonard 美国语言学家 2—543f
布卢姆菲尔德 Bloomfield, Robert 英国诗人 2—543f
布卢姆菲尔德希尔斯 Bloomfield Hills 美国城市 2—544a
布卢姆加登 Bloomgarden, Kermit 美国戏剧演出人 2—544a
布卢姆斯堡 Bloomsburg 美国城镇 2—544c
布卢姆斯伯里 Bloomsbury 英国伦敦住宅区 2—544d
布卢姆斯伯里团体 Bloomsbury group 英国作家、哲学家和艺术家团体 2—544d
布卢人 Bulu 非洲民族 3—250b
布卢瓦 Blois 法国旧伯爵领地 2—539b
布卢瓦 Blois 法国城市 2—539c
布鲁 Brú, Hedin 丹麦法罗斯语作家 3—198c
布鲁 Buru 印度尼西亚岛屿 3—278b
布鲁昂熊 bruang 哺乳动物 3—198d
布鲁贝克 Brubeck, Dave 美国钢琴家、作曲家 3—198d
布鲁德内尔 Brudenell, James Thomas 英国将军 3—201a
布鲁顿 Bruton, John 爱尔兰总理 3—212f
布鲁厄姆 Brougham and Vaux, Henry Peter Brougham, 1st Baron 英国律师、政治家 3—187e
布鲁厄姆 Brougham, John 美国剧作家 3—187d
布鲁厄姆马车 brougham 英国马车 3—187c
布鲁恩 Bruhn, Erik 丹麦舞蹈家 3—202f
布鲁尔 Brewer, David J(osiah) 美国最高法院大法官 3—145f
布鲁尔 Brewer, Lucy 美国女兵 3—146a
布鲁菲尔德 Bluefield 美国城市 2—550b
布鲁赫 Bruch, Max 德国作曲家 3—199e
布鲁赫萨尔 Bruchsal 德国城市 3—200a
布鲁金斯 Brookings 美国城市 3—183c
布鲁金斯 Brookings 美国城市 3—183d
布鲁金斯 Brookings, Robert S(omers) 美国商人、慈善家 3—183d
布鲁金斯学会 Brookings Institution 美国研究机构 3—183e
布鲁克 Bruck 奥地利城镇 3—200b
布鲁克 Brooke, Alan Francis 英国元帅 3—182f
布鲁克 Brooke, Edward 美国律师 3—182f
布鲁克 Brooke, Henry 爱尔兰作家 3—183a
布鲁克 Brook, Peter (Stephen Paul) 英国戏剧导演 3—182c
布鲁克 Brooke, Rupert 英国诗人 3—183b
布鲁克岛 Brook Island (Pacific Ocean) 太平洋岛屿 3—182d
布鲁克菲尔德 Brookfield 美国芝加哥住宅区 3—183c
布鲁克菲尔德动物园 Brookfield Zoo 美国动物园 3—183c
布鲁克莱恩 Brookline 美国城镇 3—183f
布鲁克林 Brooklyn 美国纽约市行政区 3—183f
布鲁克林桥 Brooklyn Bridge 美国纽约市悬索桥 3—184b
布鲁克林艺术博物馆 Brooklyn Museum of Art 美国博物馆 3—184c
布鲁克林植物园 Brooklyn Botanic Garden and Arboretum 美国纽约市植物园 3—184a
布鲁克纳 Bruckner, (Josef) Anton 奥地利作曲家 3—200d
布鲁克男爵(第一) Brooke, Fulke Greville, 1st Baron (Eliza bethan writer) 英国作家 3—183a
布鲁克农场 Brook Farm 美国农场 3—182c
布鲁克斯 Brooks, Cleanth 美国教师 3—184c
布鲁克斯 Brooks, Gwendolyn (Elizabeth) 美国诗人 3—184d
布鲁克斯 Brooks, Louise 美国影星 3—184e
布鲁克斯 Brooks, Maria Gowen 美国诗人 3—184f
布鲁克斯 Brooks, Phillips 美国牧师 3—185a
布鲁克斯 Brooks, Rodney Allen 美国计算机、人工智能科学家 3—185e
布鲁克斯 Brooks, Romaine (Goddard) 美国画家 3—185f
布鲁克斯 Brooks, Van Wyck 美国作家 3—185b
布鲁克斯 Brooks, William Keith 美国动物学家 3—185c
布鲁克斯山脉 Brooks Range 美国山脉 3—185d
布鲁克王朝 Brooke raj 沙捞越历史 3—182e

布鲁利亚 Purūlia 印度城镇 14—34e
布鲁梅尔 Brummell, Beau 英国名流 3—203d
布鲁梅尔 Brumel, Valery (Nikolayevich) 苏联跳高运动员 3—203d
布鲁门巴赫 Blumenbach, Johann Friedrich 德国生理学家 2—552d
布鲁姆 Blum, Léon 法国社会党总理 2—551f
布鲁姆 Broome 澳大利亚港镇 3—186a
布鲁姆 Broome, William 英国学者、诗人 3—186b
布鲁姆 Brum, Baltasar 乌拉圭政治家 3—203b
布鲁纳 Bruner, Jerome S(eymour) 美国心理学家 3—206b
布鲁奈尔 Brunel, Olivier 佛兰芒商人 3—205e
《布鲁南堡战役》 Battle of Brunanburh, The 古英语诗 2—282e
布鲁内莱斯基 Brunelleschi, Filippo 意大利建筑师 3—205f
布鲁尼 Bruni, Leonardo 意大利人文主义者 3—206f
布鲁尼岛 Bruny Island 塔斯曼海岛屿 3—208c
布鲁农 Brugnon, Jacques 法国网球冠军 3—202d
布鲁诺 Bruno, Giordano 意大利哲学家 3—207d
布鲁诺(封·埃吉施海姆伯爵) Egisheim und Dagsburg, Bruno, Graf von 教皇 5—557c
布鲁诺，圣 Bruno THE CARTHUSIAN, SAINT 天主教加尔都西会创立人 3—207c
布鲁诺(奎尔富特的)，圣 Bruno OF QUERFURT, SAINT 基督教传教士 3—207c
布鲁诺(伟大的)，圣 Bruno THE GREAT, SAINT 科隆基督教大主教 3—207d
布鲁乔利 Brucioli, Antonio 意大利人文学家 3—200a
布鲁日 Bruges (Belgium) 比利时城市 3—202a
布鲁萨 Brusa (Turkey) 土耳其城市 3—208d
布鲁塞 Broussais, François-Joseph-Victor 法国医师 3—188b
布鲁塞尔 Brussels 比利时首都 3—209d
布鲁塞尔分类法 Brussels Classification (library science) 图书馆学 3—212b
布鲁塞尔狗 Brussels griffon 狗品种 3—212b
布鲁塞尔花边 Brussels lace 工艺品 3—212c
布鲁塞尔首都区 Brussels-Capital Region 比利时区名 3—212b
布鲁斯 blues 美国黑人音乐 2—551a
布鲁斯 Bruce, Blanche K(elso) 美国黑人参议员 3—199a
布鲁斯 Bruce, James 苏格兰探险家 3—199a
布鲁斯 Bruce, James 英国政治家 3—199b
布鲁斯 Bruce, Robert VIII de 苏格兰国王 3—199b
布鲁斯 Burrus, Sextus Afranius 罗马官员 3—276c
布鲁斯 Bruce, Thomas 英国外交家、收藏家 3—199b
布鲁斯(墨尔本的) Bruce (of Melbourne), Stanley Melbourne Bruce, Viscount 澳大利亚总理 3—199b
布鲁斯半岛 Bruce Peninsula 加拿大半岛 3—199d
布鲁斯基 Brusque 巴西城市 3—209d
布鲁斯家族 Bruce FAMILY 苏格兰古老家族 3—198f
布鲁斯氏杆菌病 brucellosis 疾病 3—199d
布鲁斯特 Brewster, William 新英格兰殖民地首脑 3—146c
布鲁斯特(小) Brewster, Kingman, Jr. 美国教育家、外交家 3—146b
布鲁斯特椅 Brewster chair 家具 3—146d
布鲁斯统 Bruce Series 地质学 3—199d
布鲁斯托隆 Brustolon, Andrea 意大利木器雕刻师 3—212e
布鲁特 Brut 英国历史 3—212e
布鲁特斯 Brutus, Dennis (Vincent) 南非诗人 3—213a
布鲁图 Brutus, Lucius Junius 古罗马传说人物 3—213a
布鲁图 Brutus, Marcus Junius 古罗马行政长官 3—213b
布鲁图 Burutu 尼日利亚城镇 3—279d
布鲁图·阿尔比努斯 Brutus Albinus, Decimus Junius 罗马将军 3—213c
布鲁肖语 Burushaski language 亚洲语言 3—279c
布吕恩 Brünn (Czech Republic) 捷克城市 3—207a
布吕尔 Brühl 德国城市 3—202e
布吕尔伯爵 Brühl, Heinrich, Graf von 萨克森选侯国首相 3—202e
布吕福特 Bluford, Guion S(tewart), Jr. 美国航天员 2—551f
布吕格曼 Bryggman, Erik 芬兰建筑师 3—215b
布吕赫 Brugge 比利时城市 3—202a
布吕赫-泽布吕赫运河 Brugge-Zeebrugge Canal 比利时水道 3—202b
布吕吉耶尔 Brugière, Amable-Guillaume-Prosper 法国政治家 3—202b
布吕克 Brücke, Ernst Wilhelm von 德国生理学家 3—200c
布吕克斯 Brüx (Czech Republic) 捷克城市 3—213c
布吕奈夫妇 Brunet, Andrée and Pierre 法国花样滑冰运动员 3—206c
布吕宁 Brüning, Heinrich 德国政治家 3—207a
布吕塞维茨 Brusewitz, Axel (Karl Adolf) 瑞典政治学家 3—208d
布吕歇尔 Blücher, Gebhard Leberecht von 普鲁士陆军元帅 2—546d
布吕耶尔 Bruyère, Jean de la 法国作家 3—213d
布律莱 Brûlé, Étienne 加拿大探险家 3—203b
布律纳 Brune, Guillaume(-Marie-Anne) 法国元帅 3—204a
布律内 Brunet, Jacques-Charles 法国目录学家 3—206d
布律内尔 Brunel, Isambard Kingdom 英国工程师 3—205b
布律内尔 Brunel, Sir Marc Isambard 英国工程师 3—205d
布律诺 Bruneau, Alfred 法国作曲家 3—204b
布仑司维克黑 Brunswick black 快干黑漆 3—208b
布仑斯惕 Brønsted, Johannes Nicolaus 丹麦物理化学家 3—178e
布仑斯惕-劳里理论 Brønsted-Lowry theory 化学 3—178f
布伦 Brun, Johan Nordahl 挪威诗人、政治家 3—203f
布伦戴奇 Brundage, Avery 国际奥委会主席 3—203f
布伦丹，圣 Brendan, SAINT 凯尔特基督教圣徒 3—140d
布伦德尔 Brendel, Alfred 奥地利钢琴家 3—140e
布伦德舍赫尔 Bulandshahr 印度城镇 3—240a
布伦德维尔 Blundeville, Ranulf de 英国伯爵 2—552f
布伦登 Blunden, Edmund Charles 英国诗人 2—552e
布伦顿 Brunton, Sir Thomas Lauder, 1ST BARONET 英国医师 3—208c
布伦海姆宫 Blenheim Palace 英格兰宅邸 2—532f
布伦海姆战役 Blenheim, Battle of 西班牙历史 2—532e
布伦纳 Brenner, Sydney 美国生物学家 3—141b
布伦纳罗山口 Brenner Pass 阿尔卑斯山隘口 3—141b
布伦南 Brennan, Christopher (John) 澳大利亚诗人、学者 3—140e
布伦南 Brennan, Tim (American author) 美国作家 3—140e
布伦南 Brennan, Walter 美国演员 3—140f
布伦南 Brennan, William J(oseph), Jr. 美国大法官 3—141a
布伦努斯 Brennus 高卢酋长 3—141c
布伦努斯 Brennus 高卢人领袖 3—141c
布伦齐 Broonzy, Big Bill 美国歌唱家 3—186c
布伦奇利 Bluntschli, Johann Kaspar 德国国际法著作家 2—553b
布伦瑞克 Brunswick, Ruth Jane Mack 美国心理学家 3—208b
布伦式轻机枪 Bren machine gun 武器 3—140c
布伦坦诺 Brentano, Bettina 德国作家 3—141d
布伦坦诺 Brentano, Clemens 德国诗人、小说家 3—141d
布伦坦诺 Brentano, Franz (Clemens) 德国哲学家 3—141f
布伦坦诺 Brentano, Heinrich von 德国政治家 3—142a
布伦坦诺 Brentano, Lujo 德国经济学家 3—142a
布伦特 Blunt, Anthony (Frederick) 英国美术史学家 2—552f
布伦特 Blunt, Wilfrid Scawen 英国诗人 2—553a
布伦特 Brent 英格兰自治市 3—141c
布伦特 Brent, Margaret 北美女权运动家 3—141d
《布伦特尔条约》 Purandhar, Treaty of 英国-马拉塔人条约 14—30d
布伦特兰 Brundtland, Gro Harlem 挪威总理 3—204a
布伦特里 Braintree 英格兰城镇 3—116d
布伦特里 Braintree 美国城镇 3—116d
布伦特伍德 Brentwood 英格兰区名 3—142b
布伦希尔特 Brunhild 古代日耳曼文学 3—206e

布伦兹 Brenz, Johannes 德意志宗教改革领导人 3—142b
布罗茨基 Brodsky, Joseph 美国诗人 3—174d
布罗德 Brod, Max 捷克作家 3—174a
布罗德河 Broad River 美国河流 3—171c
布罗德兰 Broadland 英格兰区名 3—172a
布罗德斯泰斯-圣彼得斯 Broadstairs and Saint Peter's 英格兰城镇 3—172a
布罗德伍德 Broadwood, John 英国钢琴制造家 3—172c
布罗多维奇 Brodovitch, Alexey 美国美术编辑、摄影师 3—174c
布罗菲 Brophy, Brigid (Antonia) 英国作家 3—186d
布罗费尔特 Brofeldt, Johannes (Finnish fiction writer) 芬兰小说家 3—174e
布罗格 Brøgger, Waldemar Christofer 挪威地质学家 3—174f
布罗赫 Broch, Hermann 德语作家 3—173a
布罗科蓬多 Brokopondo 苏里南城镇 3—176a
布罗克 Brock, Sir Isaac 英国军人、官员 3—173b
布罗克 Brock, Sir Thomas 英国雕刻家 3—173b
布罗克顿 Brockton 美国城市 3—173f
布罗克多夫-伦佐 Brockdorff-Rantzau, Ulrich, Graf von 德国外交部长 3—173c
布罗克豪斯 Brockhouse, Bertram N. 加拿大物理学家 3—173e
《布罗克豪斯百科全书》 Brockhaus Enzyklopädie 德国百科全书 3—173e
布罗克斯 Brockes, Barthold Heinrich 德国诗人 3—173d
布罗克斯伯恩 Broxbourne 英格兰自治市 3—198b
布罗克斯托 Broxtowe 英格兰区名 3—198b
布罗克维尔 Brockville 加拿大城市 3—173f
布罗克维尔伯爵 Broqueville, Charles, comte de 比利时政治家 3—186d
布罗肯宝光环 Brocken bow 气象学 3—173d
布罗肯山 Brocken 德国山脉 3—173c
布罗肯山人 Broken Hill man 民族 3—175f
布罗肯湾 Broken Bay 澳大利亚小海湾 3—175e
布罗肯希尔 Broken Hill (Zambia) 赞比亚城镇 3—175f
布罗肯希尔 Broken Hill 澳大利亚城市 3—175f
布罗肯希尔持股公司 Broken Hill Proprietary Company Limited (BHP) 澳大利亚公司 3—175f
布罗姆 Blom, Frans Ferdinand 丹麦考古学家 2—539f
布罗姆 Brome, Richard 英国作家 3—176a
布罗姆菲尔德 Bromfield, Louis 美国作家 3—176e
布罗姆利 Bromley 英格兰城镇 3—177a
布罗姆斯格罗夫 Bromsgrove 英格兰城镇 3—177b
布罗涅夫斯基 Broniewski, Władysław 波兰诗人 3—178b
布罗奇 Bharūch 印度县城 2—451b
布罗斯 Borås 瑞典城镇 3—43f
布罗斯 Brosse, Salomon de 法国建筑师 3—186f
布罗斯基 Broschi, Carlo 意大利歌唱家 3—186f
布罗松 Brorson, Hans Adolf 丹麦牧师 3—186e
布罗滕 Braaten, Oskar 挪威小说家、戏剧家 3—103b
布罗伊尔 Breuer, Josef 奥地利医师、生理学家 3—145b
布罗伊尔 Breuer, Marcel (Lajos) 匈牙利建筑师 3—145c
布罗伊公爵 Broglie, DUKES OF 法国贵族头衔 3—174f
布罗伊公爵(第二) Broglie, Victor-François, 2nd Duke (2e Duc) de 法国元帅 3—175a
布罗伊公爵(第三) Broglie, (Achille-Charles-Léonce-) Victor, 3e duc de 法国总理 3—175a
布罗伊公爵(第四) Broglie, (Jacques-Victor-) Albert, 4e duc de 法国法兰西学院院士 3—175b
布罗伊公爵(第一) Broglie, François-Marie, 1st Duke (1er Duc) de 法国元帅 3—174f
布罗兹 Broz, Josip (Yugoslav president) 南斯拉夫总统 3—198c
布罗兹区 Broads, The 英格兰内陆水道系统 3—172a
布洛 Blow, John 英国管风琴家 2—545c
布洛 Blow, Susan Elizabeth 美国教育家 2—545d
布洛贝尔 Blobel, Günter 美国细胞与分子生物学家 2—536f
布洛芬 ibuprofen 药物 8—310a
布洛赫 Bloch, Ernst 德国马克思主义哲学家 2—537c
布洛赫 Bloch, Felix 美国物理学家 2—537c
布洛赫 Bloch, Joseph Samuel 奥地利拉比、政治家 2—537d
布洛赫 Bloch, Konrad (Emil) 美国生物化学家 2—537d
布洛克 Bloch, Ernest 美国作曲家 2—537a
布洛克 Block, Herbert Lawrence 美国卡通画家 2—537f
布洛克 Bloch, Marc (Léopold Benjamin) 法国历史学家 2—537e
布洛克 Bullock, Wynn 美国摄影家 3—249b
布洛克岛 Block Island 美国岛屿 2—538b
布洛克西奇 Blocksidge, Charles William 澳大利亚作家 2—538d
布洛姆贝格 Blomberg, Werner (Eduard Fritz) von 德国将军 2—539f
布洛姆伯根 Bloembergen, Nicolaas 美国物理学家 2—538e
布洛涅 Boulogne 法国城市 3—82a
布洛涅 Boulogne, Jean 意大利雕刻家 3—82c
布洛诺夫斯基 Bronowski, Jacob 英国数学家 3—178c
布洛什科 Blasko, Béla (actor) 美国电影演员 2—529f
布洛瓦 Bloy, Léon 法国小说家 2—546d
布洛修斯 Blosius, Franciscus Ludovicus 尼德兰天主教改革家 2—544f
布洛伊勒 Bleuler, Eugen 瑞士精神病学者 2—534b
布迈丁 Boumedienne, Houari 阿尔及利亚总统 3—82f
布嫩语 Bunun language 中国台湾语言 3—254f
布嫩族 Bunun 中国台湾土著民族 3—254e
布尼奥罗 Bunyoro 东非王国 3—255e
布匿字母 Punic alphabet 腓尼基字母形式 14—26f
布宁 Bunin, Ivan Alekseyevich 俄国诗人、小说家 3—252e
布农维尔 Bournonville, August 丹麦舞蹈演员、编导 3—88e
布努埃尔 Buñuel, Luis 西班牙电影导演 3—254c
布切吉山 Bucegi Massif 罗马尼亚山脉 3—218d
布琼布拉 Bujumbura 布隆迪首都 3—238d
布琼尼 Budenny, Semyon Mikhaylovich 苏联元帅 3—229e
布热德 Poujade, Pierre(-Marie) 法国书商、政治人物 13—467e
布热季斯拉夫一世 Břetislav I 波希米亚公爵 3—144b
布热齐纳 Březina, Otakar 捷克诗人 3—147e
布戎 Bruun, Malte Conrad (geographer) 丹麦地理学家 3—213c
布儒斯特 Brewster, Sir David 苏格兰物理学家 3—146b
布儒斯特定律 Brewster's law 物理学 3—146e
布若佐夫斯基 Brzozowski, Stanisław (Leopold) 波兰作家 3—216f
布若佐夫斯基 Brzozowski, Tadeusz 波兰耶稣会总会长 3—216f
布萨 Pūsa 印度城镇 14—35c
布萨达 Bou Saâda 阿尔及利亚城镇 3—76b
布萨急流 Bussa Rapids 尼日尔河急流 3—286f
布萨克 Boesak, Allan (Aubrey) 南非基督教神职人员 2—565c
布萨克 Boussac, Marcel 法国实业家 3—89c
布萨日 uposatha 佛教 17—405a
布塞尔 Bucer, Martin 欧洲宗教改革家 3—218e
布·赛义德王朝 Āl Bū Saʿīd DYNASTY 阿曼王朝 1—160c
布瑟 Pousseur, Henri 比利时作曲家 13—469f
布森鲍姆 Busenbaum, Hermann 德国神学家 3—281c
布森戈 Boussingault, Jean-Baptiste 法国农业化学家 3—89d
布沙东 Bouchardon, Edmé 法国雕刻家 3—76c
布施 Busch, Wilhelm 德国画家、诗人 3—281b
布什 Bush, George W. 美国总统 3—281e
布什 Bush, George 美国总统 3—281c
布什 Bush, Laura Welch 美国第一夫人 3—282c
布什 Bush, Vannevar 美国工程师、政府官员 3—282d
布什尔 Būshehr 伊朗区域 3—283b
布什尔港 Bandar-e Būshehr 伊朗港口城市 2—192e
布什格尔 Pushkar 印度城市 14—36a

布什曼 Bushman, Francis X. 美国演员 3—283d
布什内尔 Bushnell, David 美国发明家 3—284a
布什内尔 Bushnell, Horace 美国神学家 3—284a
布思 Booth, Catherine 英国传道者 3—40c
布思 Booth, Charles 英国轮船主、社会学家 3—40c
布思 Booth, Edwin (Thomas) 美国悲剧演员 3—40d
布思 Booth, Evangeline Cory 美国救世军将军 3—41b
布思 Booth, George 英国政治家 3—41c
布思 Booth, John Wilkes 刺杀林肯总统的凶手 3—41c
布思 Booth, Mary Louise 美国新闻记者 3—41d
布思 Booth, Maud Ballington 美国救世军领袖 3—41f
布思 Booth, William 英国救世军创始人 3—41f
布思 Booth, William Bramwell 英国救世军将军 3—42a
布斯贝港 Boothbay Harbor 美国城镇 3—42b
布斯费里 Boothferry 英格兰城市 3—42b
布斯克吕 Buskerud 挪威郡名 3—286b
布斯拉沙姆 Buṣrā ash-Shām (ancient Syria) 叙利亚古城 3—286e
布斯塔曼特-西尔文 Bustamante y Sirvén, Antonio Sánchez de 古巴国际法学家 3—287b
布斯塔尼 Bustānī, Butrus al- 黎巴嫩学者 3—287b
布斯泰利 Bustelli, Franz Anton 德国瓷雕塑家 3—287d
布斯托阿西齐奥 Busto Arsizio 意大利城市 3—288a
布苏尔河 Pusur River 孟加拉国河流 14—37a
布索尼 Busoni, Ferruccio (Benvenuto) 意大利音乐家 3—286d
布塔 būṭā 装饰花纹 3—288a
布塔雷 Butare 卢旺达城市 3—288d
布塔里塔里环礁 Butaritari Atoll 太平洋环礁 3—288d
布泰德斯(西希昂的) Butades of Sicyon 古希腊陶工 3—288b
布特莱齐 Buthelezi, Mangosuthu G. 南非内政部长 3—289c
布特列洛夫 Butlerov, Aleksandr 俄国化学家 3—291b
布特罗斯-加利 Boutros-Ghali, Boutros 埃及学者、联合国秘书长 3—90a
布特南特 Butenandt, Adolf 德国生物化学家 3—289a
布特韦克 Bouterwek, Friedrich 德国哲学家 3—89e
布特维尔 Bouteville, François-Henri de Montmorency- 法国军人 3—89f
布通 Butung 印度尼西亚岛屿 3—294e
布图阿 Butua 非洲古王国 3—294e
布托 Buto 埃及宗教蛇神 3—291c
布托 Bhutto, Benazir 巴基斯坦总理 2—454f
布托 Bhutto, Zulfikar Ali 巴基斯坦总统 2—455a
布瓦埃尔迪厄 Boieldieu, François-Adrien 法国作曲家 3—6b
布瓦博德朗 Boisbaudran, Paul-Émile Lecoq de 法国化学家 3—7d
布瓦尔 Bouvard, Alexis 法国天文学家 3—90d
布瓦尔木属 bouvardia (genus *Bouvardia*) 植物学 3—90d
布瓦夫莱 Bouaflé 科特迪瓦城镇 3—76b
布瓦凯 Bouaké 科特迪瓦城市 3—76b
布瓦莱夫 Boylesve, René 法国小说家 3—102a
布瓦勒杜 Bois-le-Duc (The Netherlands) 荷兰城市 3—7d
布瓦雷 Poiré, Emmanuel 法国漫画家 13—390c
布瓦利 Boilly, Louis-Léopold 法国画家 3—7b
布瓦罗贝尔 Boisrobert, François Le Métel, seigneur de (lord of) 法国剧作家 3—8b
布瓦洛 Boileau(-Despréaux), Nicolas 法国诗人 3—6d
布瓦莫蒂埃 Boismortier, Joseph Bodin de 法国作曲家 3—8a
布瓦内斯瓦拉 Bhuvaneśvara (India) 印度城市 2—455b
布瓦热约夫斯基 Blazejowski, Carol 美国篮球运动员 2—531e
布瓦耶 Boyer, Charles 法国演员 3—101a
布瓦耶 Boyer, Jean-Baptiste de 法国作家 3—101b
布瓦耶 Boyer, Jean-Pierre 海地总统 3—101b
布韦 Boué, Ami 奥地利地质学家 3—78a
布维拉 Bouira 阿尔及利亚城镇 3—79d
布维特岛 Bouvet Island 南大西洋小岛 3—90d
布汶战役 Bouvines, Battle of 欧洲历史 3—90e
布西科特 Boursiquot, Dionysius Lardner (dramatist) 美国剧作家、演员 3—89c
布西里斯 Busiris 希腊神话人物 3—286a
布西亚半岛 Boothia Peninsula 加拿大半岛 3—42b
布希 Busch, Adolphus 美国啤酒商 3—281a
布锡考特 Boucicaut, Jean II le Meingre 法国元帅 3—77a
布歇 Boucher, François 法国画家、设计师 3—76c
布歇·德·彼尔特 Boucher (de Crèvecoeur) de Perthes, Jacques 法国考古学家 3—76d
布歇-德努瓦耶 Boucher-Desnoyers, Auguste-Gaspard-Louis 法国雕刻家 3—76e
布谢维尔 Boucherville 加拿大城镇 3—76e
布须曼兰 Boesmanland 纳米比亚历史地区 2—565d
布须曼人 Bushmen 民族 3—283f
布须曼诸语言 Bushman languages 语言 3—283e
布延斯 Boeyens, Adrian Florensz (pope) 教皇 2—565f
布扬松 Björnsson, Sveinn 冰岛总统 2—508d
布依语 Buyei language 中国语言 3—295e
布依族 Buyei 中国民族 3—295d
布宜诺斯艾利斯 Buenos Aires 阿根廷省份 3—230f
布宜诺斯艾利斯 Buenos Aires 阿根廷首都 3—231a
布永 Bouillon 比利时古城镇 3—79d
布约 Bouillaud, Jean-Baptiste 法国医学家 3—79c
布泽乌 Buzău 罗马尼亚县名 3—296c
布泽乌 Buzău 罗马尼亚城市 3—296c
布泽乌山口 Buzău Pass 罗马尼亚山口 3—296d
布扎蒂 Buzzati, Dino 意大利记者、小说家 3—297b
布祖基琴 bouzouki 希腊乐器 3—90f
布祖卢克 Buzuluk 俄罗斯城市 3—296e
步兵 infantry 军种 8—380d
步达生 Black, Davidson 加拿大医生 2—509a
步甲 ground beetle 昆虫 7—323c
步枪 rifle 武器 14—296c
步日耶 Breuil, Henri-Édouard-Prosper 法国考古学家 3—145e
步态舞 cakewalk 舞蹈 3—331f
步行鱼 walking fish 鱼类 18—76a
钚(Pu) plutonium 化学元素 13—378d
部 be 日本社会 2—300d
部多 bhut 印度教神话精灵 2—453e
部分性癫痫 partial epilepsy 疾病 13—67c
部分准备金制度 fractional reserve system 金融制度 6—434c
部雷 Boullée, Étienne-Louis 法国建筑师、教师 3—81e
部落 tribe 人类学 17—214d
部落 tribe 古罗马史 17—214d
部落民 burakumin 日本少数群体 3—256d
簿记 bookkeeping 会计学 3—38b

C

擦擦 tsha-tsha 藏传佛教 17—249a
擦洗灯心草 scouring rush (plant) 草本植物 15—154f
擦音 fricative 语音学 6—491a
擦音 spirant 语音学 16—34d
擦云鸟 cloud-scraper 鸟类 4—303b
擦子 eraser 文具 6—109e
材料加工 materials processing 工业 11—19e
材料科学 materials science 工学学科 11—21a
财产 property 法律 13—535f
财产估价 assessment 财务 1—561f
财产税 property tax 税 13—536c
财阀 zaibatsu 日本商业组织 18—492c
财富和收入的分配 wealth and income, distribution of 经济学 18—153d

财神 Caishen 中国道教 3—329f
财务代理 factoring 金融机构 6—210b
财务署 Exchequer 英国政府机构 6—189b
财务长官 procurator 古罗马政府官员 13—527a
财政部大档 Great Rolls of the Exchequer (English records) 英格兰历史 7—274e
财政部绘画雕刻局 Treasury Section of Painting and Sculpture 美国机构 17—204f
财政部艺术救济计划 Treasury Relief Art Project (TRAP) 美国艺术计划 17—204e
财政区 généralité 法国历史 7—57f
财政政策 fiscal policy 经济措施 6—329e
裁缝鸟 tailorbird 鸟类 16—431e
裁军 disarmament 政治 5—338b
采蒂涅 Cetinje 黑山城市 4—18c
采尔蒂斯 Celtis, Conradus 德国学者 3—560f
采尔马特 Zermatt 瑞士城镇 18—512c
采法特 Ẕefat 以色列圣城 18—506b
采格莱德 Cegled 匈牙利城镇 3—550a
采矿 mining 矿业 11—251c
采勒 Celle 德国城市 3—557b
采列 Celje 斯洛文尼亚城市 3—556a
采伦多夫 Zehlendorf 德国柏林市区名 18—506c
采石 quarry 矿业 14—78f
采西斯 Cēsis 拉脱维亚城市 4—16f
彩车 pageant wagon 戏剧 12—544f
彩翅蝇 picture-winged fly 昆虫 13—292d
彩光环 glory (diffraction phenomenon) 自然现象 7—161a
彩绘陶 pottery decorated with colour drawings 中国古代彩陶 13—466e
彩礼 bride-price 婚姻风俗 3—149d
彩色粉笔 pastel 绘画工具 13—80f
彩色龟 painted turtle (*Chrysemys picta*) 爬行动物 12—550d
彩色石印画 chromo (printmaking) 印刷 4—212c
彩色石印画 chromolithograph (printmaking) 印刷 4—212c
彩色印片法 Technicolor 电影制片方法 16—513a
彩色印刷 colour printing 印刷术 4—366b
彩诗 muwashshaḥ 诗歌体裁 11—519a
彩陶 faience 欧洲陶器 6—213d
彩线十字网 thread cross 中国西藏巫术用品 17—62d
彩釉镶嵌细工 alicatado 装饰 1—228b
彩鹬 painted snipe 鸟类 12—550c
菜豆 green bean (*Phaseolus vulgaris*) 蔬菜 7—289a
菜炖牛肉 goulash 食品 7—229a
菜蛾 diamondback moth (*Plutella maculipennis*) 昆虫 5—287a
菜花耳 cauliflower ear 病理现象 3—535f
菜园派 Kailyard school 苏格兰文学 9—135d
蔡锷 Cai E 中国近代军事家 3—324b
蔡尔德 Child, Charles Manning 美国作家 4—150d
蔡尔德 Child, Francis J(ames) 美国学者 4—150e
蔡尔德 Child, Sir John, Baronet 英国爵士 4—150e
蔡尔德 Child, Lydia Maria (Francis) 美国作家 4—151b
蔡尔德(夫人) Child, Julia 美国烹饪专家 4—150f
蔡尔德斯 Childers, Erskine H(amilton) 爱尔兰政治家 4—152f
蔡尔德斯 Childers, Hugh Culling Eardley 澳大利亚政治家 4—153a
蔡尔德斯 Childers, Robert Erskine 爱尔兰作家 4—153b
蔡伦 Cai Lun 中国造纸术革新家 3—324c
蔡平 Chapin, Harry 美国歌手、吉他手 4—57d
蔡司 Zeiss, Carl 德国企业家 18—506d
蔡斯 Chase, Mary Ellen 美国学者 4—87b
蔡斯 Chase, Philander 美国教育家 4—87c
蔡斯 Chase, Salmon P(ortland) 美国政治家 4—87c
蔡斯 Chase, Samuel 美国最高法院大法官 4—87d
蔡斯 Chase, William Merritt 美国画家 4—87e
蔡特金 Zetkin, Clara 德国女权主义者 18—513a
蔡襄 Cai Xiang 中国北宋书法家 3—324d
蔡元培 Cai Yuanpei 中国近代教育家 3—324e
参觐交代 sankin kōtai 日本历史 15—35d
参卡尔 Cankar, Ivan 斯洛文尼亚作家 3—402a
参考系 reference frame 物理学 14—197d
参谋部 general staff 军事机构 7—57b
参数变异法 parameters, variation of 数学 13—36e
参孙 Samson 古以色列英雄 15—1f
参议院 Senate 美国立法机构 15—208d
餐馆 restaurant 饭馆 14—243b
餐具 tableware 器皿、用具 16—415d
餐具柜 sideboard 家具 15—352f
餐桌饰架 epergne 装饰物 6—94d
残酷戏剧 Cruelty, Theatre of 法国戏剧 5—38c
残余地形 residual landform 地貌学 14—239f
残余权 remainder 英美法律 14—216c
残余议会 Rump Parliament 英国历史 14—448c
蚕豆病 favism 遗传疾病 6—254e
蚕蛾 silkworm moth 昆虫 15—372e
灿可夫 Tsankov, Aleksandŭr 保加利亚总理 17—247c
仓巴噶波 Tshangs-pa Dkar-po 藏传佛教 17—249a
仓敷 Kurashiki 日本城市 9—400c
仓吉 Kurayoshi 日本城市 9—400e
仓颉 Cangjie 中国汉字创造者 3—400f
仓洛语 Tsanglo language 语言 17—247b
仓舍 barn 农场建筑物 2—232f
仓鼠 hamster 哺乳动物 7—449d
仓鼠科 Cricetidae 动物学 5—11a
仓鸮 barn owl 猛禽 2—232f
苍耳 cocklebur 植物 4—323b
苍头燕雀 chaffinch (*Fringilla coelebs*) 鸣禽 4—25e
苍梧 Ts'ang-wu (China) 中国城市 17—247b
苍鹰 goshawk 鸟类 7—220e
沧江 Ch'anggang 朝鲜画家 4—49d
沧州 Cangzhou 中国城市 3—401a
藏经柜 ark 犹太教堂设备 1—489f
藏书 book collecting 收藏学 3—37d
藏书者标签 bookplate 收藏学 3—38d
操纵子 operon 生物学 12—430c
操作系统 operating system 计算机科学 12—429c
操作性条件反射 operant conditioning 心理学 12—429b
糙皮病 pellagra 疾病 13—130f
曹操 Cao Cao 中国古代军事家、政治家 3—416f
曹洞宗 Sōtō 日本佛教派别 15—524e
曹国舅 Cao Guojiu 中国道教八仙之一 3—417a
曹锟 Cao Kun 中国军阀 3—417b
曹丕 Cao Pi 中国皇帝 3—417c
曹雪芹 Cao Xueqin 中国小说家 3—417c
曹禺 Cao Yu 中国剧作家 3—417d
曹霑 Cao Zhan 中国小说家 3—417f
曹植 Cao Zhi 中国文学家 3—417f
曹仲达 Cao Zhongda 中国画家 3—418a
嘈鹬 tattler 鸟类 16—495c
槽齿类 thecodontian 原始首龙类 17—20f
槽轮机构 Geneva mechanism 机械装置 7—63a
草本沼泽 marsh 水文地理学 10—537b
草地槌球 lawn croquet (game) 体育 9—529f
草地滚球戏 lawn bowls (game) 体育 9—529f
草地褐蝶 meadow brown 昆虫 11—61f
草地鹨 meadowlark 鸟类 11—62b
草地网球 lawn tennis 体育 9—529f

草甸排草 creeping Jenny (*Lysimachia nummularia*) 草本植物 5—4b
草甸鼠 meadow mouse 哺乳动物 11—62a
草甸芸香 meadow rue 草本植物 11—62a
草海桐科 Goodeniaceae 植物学 7—208c
草加 Sōka 日本城市 15—490a
草蛉 lacewing 昆虫 9—436c
草履虫属 Paramecium 生物学 13—36c
草绿藻 grass-green algae 生物学 7—261b
草莓 strawberry 草本植物 16—272c
草皮 turf 园艺学 17—278e
草坪 lawn 园林 9—529f
草雀 grass finch 鸟类 7—261a
草裙舞 hula 舞蹈 8—229f
草书 caoshu 中国汉字书体 3—418a
草酸 oxalic acid 化合物 12—518d
草薙剑 Kusanagi 日本神话 9—405a
草鸮 grass owl 鸟类 7—261b
草写式速记术 tachygraphy 速记 16—418a
草雁 sheldgoose 鸟类 15—294f
草药志 herbal 医学文献 8—34a
草原 grassland 地理学 7—261f
草原风格 Prairie style 美国建筑风格 13—483a
草原古马 Merychippus 古生物学 11—137d
草原鸡 prairie chicken 鸟类 13—482e
草原狼 prairie wolf 哺乳动物 13—483a
草原犬鼠 prairie dog 啮齿动物 13—482ef
草原石鵖 whinchat (*Saxicola rubetra*) 鸟类 18—223e
草原兽瘟 steppe murrain (cattle disease) 动物疾病 16—225a
草原诸省 Prairie Provinces 加拿大三省的总称 13—483a
草月流 Sōgetsu 日本花道流派 15—487b
草螽 meadow grasshopper 昆虫 11—61f
草蛛 grass spider 昆虫 7—261b
《册府元龟》 Cefuyuangui 中国史学类书 3—550a
侧步 pacing 赛马用语 12—537b
侧分泌 lateral secretion 地质学 9—510a
侧进蛇 sidewinder (*Crotalus cerastes*) 爬行类 15—353c
侧颈龟 side-necked turtle 爬行类 15—352e
侧堂 aisle 教堂建筑 1—148f
侧线系统 lateral line system 动物学 9—510a
侧叶兰属 Pleurothallis 植物学 13—370e
测度 measure 数学 11—61b
测辐射热计 bolometer 仪器 3—16a
测光表 light meter 摄影 10—93b
测谎器 lie detector 测谎装置 10—84c
测交 testcross 遗传学 16—560e
测井 well logging 矿物勘测技术 18—178a
测距设备 distance-measuring equipment (DME) 航空 5—343c
测距仪 range finder 仪器 14—149f
测力器 dynamometer 工具 5—488e
测链 chain 计量单位 4—27f
测链 surveyor's chain 计量单位 16—358f
测量 measurement 物理学 11—64c
测量水准仪 surveyor's level 仪器 16—358f
测量学 surveying 土木工程 16—358c
测深仪 depth finder 仪器 5—251c
测速仪 log 仪器 10—187e
测温学 thermometry 物理学 17—34d
测向运动 orienteering 体育 12—460d
策策斯 Tzetzes, John 拜占廷学者 17—313f
策尔塔尔人 Tzeltal 民族 17—313e
策加耶 Tsegaye, Gabre-Medhin 埃塞俄比亚作家 17—248c
策杰尔包姆 Tsederbaum, Yuly Osipovich 俄国革命家 17—248c
策兰 Celan, Paul 欧洲诗人 3—551b
策姆林斯基 Zemlinsky, Alexander (von) 奥地利作曲家、指挥家 18—507a
策维埃 Tsévié 多哥城镇 17—248f
岑参 Cen Shen 中国诗人 3—562a
岑讷 Tønder 丹麦城市 17—147b
层 horizon 土壤学 8—174a
层理 stratification 地质学 16—267d
层流 laminar flow 物理学 9—465f
层压技术 lamination 工艺学 9—466a
层状硅酸盐 phyllosilicate 化合物 13—271a
叉 fork 餐具 6—408b
叉车 forklift truck 搬运车 6—408c
叉角羚 pronghorn (*Antilocapra americana*) 哺乳动物 13—533f
叉铃 sistrum 乐器 15—405b
叉藓 fork moss 藓类植物 6—408c
差别心理学 differential psychology 心理学 5—311c
差春骚 Chachoengsao 泰国城镇 4—22d
差动齿轮 differential gear 机械 5—309f
差分方程 difference equation 数学 5—309c
差热分析 differential thermal analysis (DTA) 化学 5—311d
插花 ikebana 日本古典艺术 8—330f
插晶菱沸石 levyne 矿物 10—49e
插剧 interlude 戏剧 8—410a
插曲 parabasis 古希腊戏剧 13—29c
插叙 in medias res 文学 8—349d
茶 tea 饮料 16—509c
茶藨子 currant 灌木 5—70d
茶藨子属 Ribes 植物学 14—276f
茶道 tea ceremony 日本风习 16—509f
茶碱 theophylline 药物 17—29b
茶具和咖啡具 tea and coffee service 器皿 16—509e
茶青霸鹟 elaenia (genus *Elaenia*) 鸟类 6—13a
茶室 cha-shitsu 日本园亭 4—21a
茶叶罐 caddy 器具 3—312d
《茶叶条例》 Tea Act 美国历史 16—509e
茶茱萸科 Icacinaceae 植物学 8—310d
查比尔 Jābir ibn Ḥayyān, Abū Mūsā 炼金术士 8—501d
查布 Chubb, Charles 英国发明家 4—218d
查布 Chubb, Thomas 自然神论者 4—218d
查布鱼 chub 鱼类 4—218b
查布陨石坑 Chubb Crater (Canada) 加拿大陨石坑 4—218e
查查波亚斯 Chachapoyas 秘鲁城市 4—22d
查茨沃思 Chatsworth 英格兰庄园 4—91e
查德,圣 Chad, SAINT 隐修院院长 4—24b
查德威克 Chadwick, Sir Edwin 英国医师 4—24d
查德威克 Chadwick, George Whitefield 作曲家 4—24e
查德威克 Chadwick, H(ector) Munro 英国语文学家 4—24f
查德威克 Chadwick, Sir James 英国物理学家 4—25a
查蒂诺人 Chatino 中美印第安人 4—91c
查恩伍德 Charnwood 英格兰自治市 4—84a
查恩语 Chan language 语言 4—42e
查尔德兰战役 Chāldirān, Battle of 奥斯曼人与伊朗人战争 4—31b
查尔迪 Ciardi, John 美国诗人 4—232f
查尔芬特-圣贾尔斯 Chalfont St. Giles 英格兰教区 4—31d
查尔卡斯 Charcas (Bolivia) 玻利维亚地理 4—61f
查尔默斯 Chalmers, Thomas 神学家 4—33a
查尔平原 Jarres, Plain of 老挝地区 8—546d
查尔丘特利奎 Chalchiuhtlicue 中美洲女神 4—30a
查尔斯 Charles, Eugenia 多米尼加总理 4—78f
查尔斯 Charles, Ezzard (Mack) 美国拳击运动员 4—79a
查尔斯 Charles, Ray 美国钢琴家 4—79b

查尔斯 Charles,Thomas 宗教领袖 4—79c
查尔斯(威尔士亲王) Charles,Prince of Wales 英国王位继承人 4—78a
查尔斯堡 Charlesbourg 加拿大城市 4—81a
查尔斯城 Charles City 美国艾奥瓦州城市 4—79f
查尔斯城 Charles City 美国弗吉尼亚州城市 4—79f
查尔斯城 Charles Town 美国西弗吉尼亚州城市 4—80e
查尔斯岛 Charles Island (Galápagos Island) 厄瓜多尔岛屿 4—80d
查尔斯敦 Charlestown 加勒比海海港 4—81e
查尔斯敦 Charlestown 美国市区名 4—81f
查尔斯顿 Charleston 美国南卡罗来纳州城市 4—81b
查尔斯顿 Charleston 美国伊利诺伊州城市 4—81b
查尔斯顿 Charleston 美国西弗吉尼亚州城市 4—81d
查尔斯顿 Charleston 社交爵士舞 4—81e
查尔斯河 Charles River 美国河流 4—80d
查尔维尔 Charleville 澳大利亚城镇 4—81f
查尔朱 Chardzhou 土库曼斯坦州名 4—63b
查尔朱 Chardzhou 土库曼斯坦城市 4—63c
查伐德斯基 Zavadsky,Yury Alexandrovich 苏联演员 18—503c
查法里纳斯群岛 Chafarinas Islands 摩洛哥群岛 4—25b
查菲 Chaffee,Adna R(omanza) 美国陆军军官 4—25c
查菲 Chaffee,Emory Leon 美国物理学家 4—25d
查菲 Chaffee,Roger B(ruce) 美国航天员 4—25d
查菲 Chafee,Zechariah,Jr. 美国法学家 4—25b
查戈斯群岛 Chagos Archipelago 英属印度洋领地 4—27b
查格雷斯河 Chagres River 巴拿马河流 4—27c
查加人 Chaga 班图语民族 4—25e
查加斯氏病 Chagas' disease 传染病 4—27a
查卡布科战役 Chacabuco,Battle of 拉丁美洲历史 4—22c
查考 Chacao 委内瑞拉城市 4—22d
查科 Chaco (plain,South America) 南美平原 4—22e
查科 Chaco 阿根廷省份 4—22e
查科文化国家历史公园 Chaco Culture National Historical Park 美国公园 4—22e
查科战争 Chaco War 南美洲历史 4—22f
查克马人 Chakma 孟加拉国部落居民 4—29d
查拉 Tzara,Tristan 法国作家 17—313c
查拉塞纳 Characene (ancient state,Babylonia) 古巴比伦城邦 4—59f
查拉特南戈 Chalatenango 萨尔瓦多城市 4—29e
查兰斯 Challans,Mary 英国小说家 4—32e
查理 Charles,Jacques-Alexandre-César 法国数学家 4—79a
查理 Charles 统治者之名 4—67f
查理 Charles 德意志/神圣罗马帝国皇帝 4—68c
查理 Charles 公爵爵位竞争者 4—68d
查理 Charles 勃艮第公爵 4—68e
查理 Charles 弗兰德伯爵 4—69b
查理 Charles 葡萄牙国王 4—75a
查理 Charles 普罗旺斯国王 4—75a
查理(阿拉贡的) Charles of Aragon 西班牙王子 4—78c
查理(安茹的) Charles of Anjou 那不勒斯国王 4—78c
查理(布卢瓦的) Charles of Blois 布列塔尼公爵 4—78c
查理(大胆的) Charles the Bold 勃艮第公爵 4—78d
查理(法兰西的) Charles of France 贝里公爵 4—78c
查理(疯人) Charles the Mad 法国国王 4—78e
查理(好人) Charles the Good 佛兰德伯爵 4—78e
查理(坏人) Charles the Bad 纳瓦拉国王 4—78d
查理(可爱的) Charles the Well-Beloved 法国国王 4—78e
查理(六世) Charles (Ⅵ) 西班牙贵族 4—75f
查理(卢森堡的) Charles of Luxembourg 神圣罗马帝国皇帝 4—78d
查理(美男子) Charles the Fair 法国国王 4—78d
查理(胖子) Charles the Fat 神圣罗马帝国皇帝 4—78e
查理(普罗旺斯的) Charles of Provence 普罗旺斯国王 4—78d
查理(七世) Charles (Ⅶ) 西班牙贵族 4—75f
查理(瘸子) Charles the Lame 那不勒斯国王 4—78e
查理(三世) Charles (Ⅲ) 小王位觊觎者 4—73d
查理(三世) Charles (Ⅲ) 德意志/神圣罗马帝国皇帝 4—75c
查理(傻瓜) Charles the Simple 法国国王 4—78e
查理(胜利者) Charles the Victorious 法国国王 4—78e
查理(秃头) Charles the Bald 德意志/神圣罗马帝国国王 4—78d
查理(瓦卢瓦的) Charles of Valois 瓦卢瓦公爵 4—78d
查理(五世) Charles (Ⅴ) 西班牙王子 4—75f
查理(小王位觊觎者) Charles,the Young Pretender 英国王子 4—78f
查理(一世) Charles (Ⅰ) 奥地利皇帝 4—68b
查理(英明的) Charles the Wise 法国国王 4—78f
查理(忠于职守者) Charles the Well-Served 法国国王 4—78f
查理·阿尔贝特 Charles Albert (elector of Bavaria) 巴伐利亚选侯 4—79c
查理·阿尔贝特 Charles Albert 意大利撒丁-皮埃蒙特国王 4—79d
查理·爱德华(小王位觊觎者) Charles Edward,the Young Pretender 英国斯图亚特王室成员 4—79f
查理·奥古斯特 Charles Augustus 歌德的庇护人 4—79e
查理八世 Charles Ⅷ 法国国王 4—70c
查理八世克努特松 Charles Ⅷ Knutsson 瑞典国王 4—75f
查理大帝 Charles the Great 法国洛林公爵皇帝 4—78e
查理大公 Charles, Archduke 奥地利大公 4—77e
查理大学 Charles University 捷克大学 4—80f
查理定律 Charles's law 物理学 4—81a
查理二世 Charles Ⅱ 大不列颠和爱尔兰国王 4—73a
查理二世 Charles Ⅱ 法兰西国王 4—70f
查理二世 Charles Ⅱ 那不勒斯国王 4—74e
查理二世 Charles Ⅱ 纳瓦拉国王 4—74f
查理二世 Charles Ⅱ 西班牙国王 4—75b
查理二世 Charles Ⅱ 匈牙利国王 4—73e
查理二世(或三世) Charles Ⅱ (or Ⅲ) 法国洛林公爵 4—74a
查理·腓特烈 Charles Frederick 巴登大公 4—80d
查理·费利切 Charles Felix 意大利萨伏依公爵 4—80d
查理九世 Charles Ⅸ 法国国王 4—70d
查理九世 Charles Ⅸ 瑞典国王 4—76b
查理六世 Charles Ⅵ 法国国王 4—69e
查理六世 Charles Ⅵ 神圣罗马帝国皇帝 4—72a
《查理六世国本诏书》 Pragmatic Sanction of Emperor Charles Ⅵ 神圣罗马帝国皇帝所颁命令 13—478f
查理·罗伯特(安茹的) Charles Robert of Anjou (king of Hungary) 匈牙利国王 4—80e
查理·马特 Charles Martel 法兰克王国宫相 4—78b
查理曼 Charlemagne 法兰克国王 4—65d
查理曼冠 Crown of Charlemagne 历史 5—36d
查理七世 Charles Ⅶ 法国国王 4—69f
查理七世 Charles Ⅶ 神圣罗马帝国皇帝 4—72b
查理七世 Charles Ⅶ 西班牙国王 4—74e
查理三世 Charles Ⅲ 德意志/神圣罗马帝国皇帝 4—68b
查理三世 Charles Ⅲ 法国伯爵 4—68a
查理三世 Charles Ⅲ 法兰克国王 4—71a
查理三世 Charles Ⅲ 法兰西国王 4—69c
查理三世 Charles Ⅲ 那不勒斯国王 4—74f
查理三世 Charles Ⅲ 西班牙国王 4—75c
查理三世 Charles Ⅲ 匈牙利国王 4—74e
查理三世 Charles Ⅲ 匈牙利国王和皇帝 4—73f
查理三世(或四世) Charles Ⅲ (or Ⅳ) 法国洛林公爵 4—74b
查理十二世 Charles Ⅻ 瑞典国王 4—76e
查理十六世古斯塔夫 Charles XVI Gustav 瑞典国王 4—77e
查理十三世 Charles XIII 瑞典国王 4—77a
查理十世 Charles Ⅹ 法国国王 4—70e
查理十世古斯塔夫 Charles X Gustav 瑞典国王 4—76c

查理十四世约翰 Charles XIV John 拿破仑帝国元帅 4—77b
查理十五世 Charles XV 瑞典和挪威联合王国国王 4—77d
查理十一世 Charles XI 瑞典国王 4—76d
查理士 Challis, James 英国教士 4—32e
查理四世 Charles IV 奥地利皇帝 4—73f
查理四世 Charles IV 德意志国王 4—71b
查理四世 Charles IV 法国和纳瓦拉国王 4—69c
查理四世 Charles IV 西班牙国王 4—75e
查理四世(或五世)·利奥波德 Charles IV (or V) Leopold 洛林和巴尔公爵 4—74c
《查理四世皇帝金玺诏书》 Golden Bull of Emperor Charles IV 欧洲历史 7—188d
查理·特奥多尔 Charles Theodore 德意志巴拉丁支选侯 4—80e
查理·威廉·斐迪南 Charles William Ferdinand 普鲁士陆军元帅 4—80f
查理五世 Charles V 法兰西国王 4—69d
查理五世 Charles V 神圣罗马帝国皇帝 4—71d
查理一世 Charles I 法兰克国王 4—69b
查理一世 Charles I 法兰克国王 4—70f
查理一世 Charles I 大不列颠和爱尔兰国王 4—72c
查理一世 Charles I 匈牙利国王 4—73e
查理一世 Charles I 法国公爵 4—73f
查理一世 Charles I 那不勒斯和西西里国王 4—74d
查理一世 Charles I 法兰西国王 4—74f
查理一世 Charles I 德意志/神圣罗马帝国皇帝 4—75b
查理一世(或二世) Charles I (or II) 法国公爵 4—73f
查理一世至二世 Charles I-II 那不勒斯一世至二世 4—68a
查理·伊曼纽尔 Charles Emmanuel 萨伏依公爵和撒丁国王名 4—80a
查理·伊曼纽尔二世 Charles Emmanuel II 意大利萨伏依公爵 4—80b
查理·伊曼纽尔三世 Charles Emmanuel III 意大利撒丁-皮埃蒙特国王 4—80c
查理·伊曼纽尔四世 Charles Emmanuel IV 意大利撒丁-皮埃蒙特国王 4—80c
查理·伊曼纽尔一世 Charles Emmanuel I 意大利萨伏依公爵 4—80b
查利尔 Charlier, Jean (French theologian and churchman) 法国神学家 4—82b
查灵克罗斯 Charing Cross 伦敦地名 4—64e
查洛纳 Challoner, Richard 英格兰天主教领袖 4—32f
查谟 Jammu 印度城市 8—532c
查谟和克什米尔 Jammu and Kashmir 印度邦名 8—532c
查谟和克什米尔 Jammu and Kashmir 印度次大陆西北地区 8—533a
查莫罗 Chamorro, Violeta Barrios de 尼加拉瓜总统 4—39c
查莫罗·巴尔加斯 Chamorro Vargas, Emiliano 尼加拉瓜总统 4—39d
查莫罗人 Chamorro 关岛土著居民 4—39c
查默斯 Chalmers, Alexander 英格兰传记作者 4—33a
查默斯 Chalmers, James 苏格兰传教士 4—33a
查纳克 Chanak (India) 印度城镇 4—43a
查尼 Charney, Jule Gregory 美国气象学家 4—83d
查诺克 Charnock, Job 英国东印度公司官员 4—83e
查帕拉湖 Chapala, Lake 墨西哥湖泊 4—56e
查珀尔希尔 Chapel Hill 美国城镇 4—57b
查普林 Chaplin, Sid 英国小说家 4—58a
查普曼 Chapman, Frank M(ichler) 美国鸟类学家 4—58a
查普曼 Chapman, George 英国诗人 4—58b
查普曼 Chapman, John Jay 美国诗人 4—58c
查普曼 Chapman, John 美国传教士 4—58c
查普曼 Chapman, Maria Weston 美国废奴运动活动家 4—58d
查普曼 Chapman, Sydney 英国数学家 4—58e
查普特佩克 Chapultepec 墨西哥城小山 4—59b
查普特佩克动物园 Chapultepec Zoological Park 墨西哥城动物园 4—59c
查士丁 Justin 罗马史学家 9—119a
查士丁二世 Justin II 拜占廷皇帝 9—119b
查士丁尼二世 Justinian II 拜占廷皇帝 9—120b
《查士丁尼法典》 Justinian, Code of 拜占廷法律 9—120c
《查士丁尼民法大全》 Corpus Juris Civilis (Roman law) 罗马法律 4—520f
查士丁尼一世 Justinian I 拜占廷皇帝 9—119d
查士丁一世 Justin I 拜占廷皇帝 9—119a
查斯丁(殉教士),圣 Justin MARTYR, SAINT 基督教教父 9—119c
查苏利奇 Zasulich, Vera Ivanovna 俄国革命家 18—503a
查塔姆 Chatham 加拿大安大略省城镇 4—91a
查塔姆 Chatham 加拿大新不伦瑞克省城镇 4—91a
查塔姆 Chatham 美国城镇 4—91b
查塔姆 Chatham 英格兰港口 4—91b
查塔姆伯爵(第一) Chatham, William Pitt, 1st Earl of 英国政治家 4—91b
查塔姆岛 Chatham Island (Galápagos Islands) 太平洋岛屿 4—91b
查塔姆海峡 Chatham Strait 北太平洋水道 4—91c
查塔姆群岛 Chatham Islands 南太平洋群岛 4—91b
查塔努加 Chattanooga 美国城市 4—91f
查塔努加战役 Chattanooga, Battle of 美国南北战争 4—92a
查特 jāti 印度教种姓 8—549d
查特顿 Chatterton, Thomas 英国诗人 4—92c
查特豪斯 Charterhouse 英格兰学校 4—86a
查特胡奇河 Chattahoochee River 美国河流 4—91e
查特吉 Chatterjee, Bankim Chandra 印度作家 4—92b
查特里斯 Charteris, Leslie 英国小说家 4—86a
查特斯堡 Charters Towers 澳大利亚城市 4—86b
查韦尔 Cherwell 英格兰牛津郡区名 4—129e
查韦斯 Chávez, Hugo 委内瑞拉政治家 4—96f
查韦斯 Chávez, Julio César 墨西哥职业拳击手 4—97a
查维斯 Chávez, Carlos 墨西哥指挥家 4—96d
查维斯 Chavez, Cesar (Estrada) 美国农场工人领袖 4—96e
查维斯 Chávez, Federico 巴拉圭总统 4—96f
查文文化 Chavín 秘鲁早期文化 4—97c
查希尔沙赫 Zahir Shah, Mohammad 阿富汗国王 18—492a
查希尔-乌德-丁·穆罕默德 Ẓahīr-ud-Dīn Muḥammad (emperor of India) 印度皇帝 18—492a
查亚峰 Jaya, Mount 印度尼西亚山峰 8—554d
查亚普拉 Jayapura 印度尼西亚城市 8—554d
查亚维查亚山 Jayawijaya Mountains 印度尼西亚山脉 8—554f
查耶夫斯基 Chayefsky, Paddy 美国剧作家 4—97c
查伊塔尼亚 Caitanya 印度教神秘主义者 3—330a
查伊塔尼亚运动 Caitanya sect 印度教 3—330b
察恩 Zahn, Ernst 瑞士作家 18—492b
察哈尔人 Chahar 蒙古人东支 4—27c
察汗乌苏 Qagan Us 中国集镇 14—52b
察合台 Chagatai 成吉思汗次子 4—27b
察里津 Tsaritsyn (city, Russia) 俄罗斯城市伏尔加格勒的前称 17—247e
察木多 Chab-do (China) 中国昌都旧称 4—21c
察木多 Qamdo (China) 中国地名 14—53d
察沃国家公园 Tsavo National Park 肯尼亚国家公园 17—247e
察佐斯 Tsatsos, Anthimus VII 君士坦丁堡牧首 17—247e
檫树 sassafras (*Sassafras albidum*) 木本植物 15—74c
刹帝利 Kshatriya 印度种姓 9—385e
拆分 resolution 化学 14—241b
柴达木盆地 Qaidam Pendi 中国青海省内陆盆地 14—52b
柴尔德 Child, Sir Josiah, 1ST BARONET 英国商人 4—150f
柴尔德 Childe, V(ere) Gordon 英国历史学家 4—152c

柴郡 Cheshire 英格兰郡名 4—130c
柴可夫斯基 Chaykovsky, Nikolay Vasilyevich 俄国民粹派领袖 4—97d
柴可夫斯基 Tchaikovsky, Peter Ilich 俄国作曲家 16—507d
柴门霍甫 Zamenhof, L. L. 俄国医生 18—495f
柴明达尔 zamindar 印度地主或官员 18—496a
柴纳克 Zanuck, Darryl F(rancis) 好莱坞巨头 18—498e
柴荣 Chai Rong 中国皇帝 4—27c
柴油机 diesel engine 机器 5—306e
柴油机通气管 snorkel 通气装置 15—462c
柴桢 Svay Riĕng 柬埔寨城镇 16—367d
豺 dhole (species *Cuon alpinus*) 犬科动物 5—280e
掺沙子 salting 美国工会组织策略 14—556a
掺质 dopant 半导体 5—387b
禅德语 Zend language 伊朗语言 18—507d
禅定 Buddhist meditation 佛教修习方式 3—229c
禅佛 Dhyāni-Buddha 佛教自生佛佛名 5—281d
禅画 Chan painting 中国画派 4—42f
禅那 dhyāna 印度哲学 5—281d
禅宗 Ch'an 大乘佛教 4—42d
禅宗 Chanzong 中国佛教宗派 4—55b
禅宗 Zen 日本佛教宗派 18—507c
缠丝玛瑙 sardonyx 矿物 15—65a
缠腰布 loincloth 服饰 10—192f
蝉 cicada 昆虫 4—233e
蝉虾 slipper lobster 动物学 15—433c
蟾蜍 toad 两栖动物 17—124b
蟾蜍凳 toadstool 真菌 17—125a
蟾蜍色胺 bufotenine 药物 3—235a
蟾蝽 toad bug 昆虫 17—124d
蟾毒素 bufotoxin 毒性物质 3—235a
蟾鱼 toadfish 鱼类 17—124e
产妇白腿肿 phlegmasia alba dolens (medicine) 疾病 13—253b
产后垂体坏死 postpartum pituitary necrosis 疾病 13—461b
产联 CIO 美国劳工组织 4—243a
产灵神 musubi 日本神灵 11—516a
产婆蟾 midwife toad (*Alytes obstetricans*) 两栖动物 11—203c
产褥期 puerperium 分娩后的调整阶段 14—15b
产褥热 puerperal fever 妇科病 14—15b
产痛 labour 医学 9—431e
产业 industry 生产性组织的群体 8—378f
产业革命 Industrial Revolution 现代历史 8—377e
产业工会 industrial union 工人组织 8—378c
产业工会联合会 Congress of Industrial Organizations 美国工人组织 4—429a
产业工会联合会 Industrial Organizations, Congress of 美国工会组织 8—377c
产业工人城 Barrio Obrero Industrial 秘鲁社区 2—244c
产业关系 organizational relations 经济学 12—458d
产业情报 industrial espionage 行业情报 8—376f
铲头虫 Dikelocephalus 古生物学 5—315c
铲鱼 spadefish 鱼类 16—1a
铲运机 scraper 机器 15—155b
忏悔祷词 Selihoth 犹太教用语 15—199d
忏悔节 Shrove Tuesday 基督教 15—341c
忏悔节诙谐戏剧 Fastnachtsspiel 德国戏剧 6—246e
忏悔录 confession 文学体裁 4—420e
颤痕 chatter mark 地质学 4—92a
颤杨 aspen 木本植物 1—556f
颤音琴 vibraphone 乐器 17—534b
颤藻属 Oscillatoria 植物学 12—483c
颤振及失真 flutter and wow 声音失真 6—380b
昌巴 Chamba 印度城市 4—33e
昌巴尔河 Chambal River 印度河流 4—33f
昌昌 Chan Chan 前印加时期大城市 4—42d
昌德拉吉里 Chandragiri 印度城镇 4—45c
昌德拉人 Chandelā 民族 4—43f
昌迪加尔 Chandīgarh 印度城市 4—44b
昌都 Changdu 中国城市 4—49a
昌加米腊王朝 Changamire DYNASTY 中非王朝 4—47e
昌克勒 Çankırı 土耳其城市 3—402c
昌平 Changping 中国区名 4—50a
昌西 Chauncy, Charles 美洲教士 4—95d
昌西 Chauncy, Charles 基督教公理会教士 4—95d
娼妓扒手 Moll Cutpurse 英国罪犯 11—322e
鲳 butterfish 鱼类 3—292e
鲳鲹 pompano 动物 13—421a
长安 Chang'an 中国县名 4—47f
长白山 Changbai Shan 中国山脉 4—47f
长白山自然保护区 Changbaishan Nature Reserve 中国自然保护区 4—48a
长呗 nagauta 日本音乐 11—539d
长鼻猴 proboscis monkey (*Nasalis larvatus*) 猴科动物 13—524c
长鼻类 proboscidean 哺乳动物 13—524a
长臂猿 gibbon 灵长目动物 7—117f
长臂猿科 Hylobatidae 动物学 8—288c
长柄大镰刀 scythe 农具 15—162c
长城 Great Wall of China 中国建筑 7—275f
长春 Ch'ang-ch'un (Taoist monk and traveler) 道家旅行者 4—46d
长春 Changchun 中国城市 4—48c
长春 Chōshun 日本画家 4—200e
长蝽 lygaeid bug 昆虫 10—311b
长刺歌雀 bobolink (*Dolichonyx oryzivorus*) 鸟类 2—556d
长刀鱼 knifefish 鱼类 9—321a
长岛 Long Island 美国纽约州岛屿 10—207c
长岛海峡 Long Island Sound 美国海峡 10—207e
长岛铁路公司 Long Island Rail Road Company 美国公司 10—207d
长岛战役 Long Island, Battle of 美国历史 10—207d
长凳 bench 家具 2—376d
长笛 flute 乐器 6—379e
长笛鱼 flutemouth 鱼类 6—380a
长短短格 dactyl 西方诗歌格律 5—103f
长短格音步 trochee 诗歌 17—229d
长短句相间诗体 epode 诗歌 6—105a
长耳蝠 long-eared bat 哺乳动物 10—206e
长耳豚鼠 mara 啮齿动物 10—486f
长耳鸮 long-eared owl (*Asio otus*) 鸟类 10—206e
长发教授 Professor Longhair 美国歌手、钢琴家 13—528a
长冈 Nagaoka 日本城市 11—538f
长歌 choka 诗歌 4—189f
长弓 longbow 英国古代兵器 10—209a
长谷川辰之助 Hasegawa Tatsunosuke 日本作家 7—502a
长谷川等伯 Hasegawa Tōhaku 日本画家 7—502a
长鼓 changko 朝鲜乐器 4—50a
长管炮 culverin 武器 5—57c
长号 trombone 乐器 17—232c
长号角 cornu 乐器 4—515d
长号筒 dung-chen 藏传佛教乐器 5—461d
长颌鱼 mormyrid 鱼类 11—398e
长湖 Long Lake (Saskatchewan, Canada) 加拿大湖泊 10—207f
长棘海星 crown-of-thorns starfish (*Acanthaster planci*) 棘皮动物 5—36e
长江 Chang Jiang 中国河流 4—46e
长江平原 Ch'ang Chiang P'ing-yüan (China) 中国平原 4—46d
长江三角洲 Changjiang Sanjiaozhou 中国三角洲 4—49d
长江三峡 Changjiang Sanxia 中国地理 4—49e

长江中下游平原 Changjiang Zhongxiayou Pingyuan 中国平原 4—49f
长角 Long Point 加拿大半岛 10—208d
长角蛉 owl-fly 昆虫 12—517f
长脚爷叔 daddy long legs (insect) 昆虫 5—104e
长脚爷叔 daddy longlegs 节肢动物 5—104e
长颈羚 gerenuk (*Litocranius walleri*) 哺乳动物 7—86e
长颈鹿 giraffe (species *Giraffa camelopardalis*) 哺乳动物 7—140e
长颈驼 Camelops 古生物学 3—370f
长距离赛跑 long-distance running 体育项目 10—206d
长靠椅 settee 家具 15—234e
长鳞鱼属 Birkenia 古生物学 2—491f
长岭山脉 Long Range Mountains 加拿大山脉 10—208e
长毛高卢 Gallia Comata 古罗马行省 6—559a
长毛猫 longhair 猫品种 10—209f
长矛 pike 古代和中世纪兵器 13—300f
长矛导弹 Lance missile 武器 9—472f
长明灯 ner tamid 犹太教 12—84c
长袍 cassock 宗教服装 3—506b
长篇小说 novel 文学 12—279e
长期议会 Long Parliament 英国历史 10—208c
长崎 Nagasaki 日本县名 11—539b
长崎 Nagasaki 日本城市 11—539b
长鳍金枪鱼 albacore (species *Thunnus alalunga*) 鱼类 1—173a
长枪党 Falange 西班牙政治组织 6—219a
长蠕孢属 Helminthosporium 真菌类 8—4c
长沙 Changsha 中国城市 4—50b
长沙发 sofa 家具 15—485a
长沙走马楼简牍 wooden and bamboo slips from Zoumalou, Changsha 中国文物 18—323b
长山群岛 Changshan Archipelago 中国群岛 4—50d
长山山脉 Langfjellet 挪威山脉 9—483b
长舌花蜂 euglossine bee 昆虫 6—159c
长蛇计划 Anaconda plan 美国南北战争 1—308b
长生草 live-forever (plant) 植物 10—159d
《长生殿》 Changsheng Dian 中国戏剧 4—50e
长石 feldspar 矿物 6—267d
长石砂岩 arkose 岩石 1—493b
长手 Macrocheir 波斯国王 10—363d
"长手" Longimanus 波斯国王 10—210e
长寿灌顶 tshe-dbang 藏传佛教仪式 17—249a
长牲 changsǔng 人面像柱 4—51a
长榻 couch 家具 4—540f
长滩 Long Beach 美国加利福尼亚州城市 10—206b
长滩 Long Beach 美国新泽西州市镇 10—206c
"长滩"号 Long Beach 美国军舰 10—206d
长筒号 buisine 乐器 3—238b
长筒厚底靴 buskin 悲剧别称 3—286c
长头蝽 unique-headed bug 昆虫 17—348f
长头丸 Chozumaru 日本诗人 4—201d
长腿鹬 stilt 鸟类 16—238d
长尾猴 guenon 灵长目动物 7—348e
长尾虎千代 Nagao Torachiyo (Japanese military leader) 日本军事领袖 11—538f
长尾鲨 thresher shark 鱼类 17—65b
"长尾鲨"号 Thresher 美国核潜艇 17—65b
长尾山雀科 Aegithalidae 生物学 1—93b
长尾豚鼠 pacarana (*Dinomys branickii*) 啮齿动物 12—531c
长尾吸蜜鹦鹉 lorikeet 鸟类 10—222e
长尾鳕 grenadier 鱼类 7—303a
长尾叶猴 langur 动物 9—486b
长尾鹦鹉 parakeet 鸟类 13—34c
长屋 longhouse 印第安人住房 10—210d
长屋教 Longhouse Religion 印第安人宗教 10—210e
长藓 long moss (plant) 植物 10—208c
长须鲸 razorback whale 哺乳动物 14—174f
长阳人 Changyang man 古人类学 4—51b
长野 Nagano 日本县名 11—538d
长野 Nagano 日本城市 11—538d
长音节缩短与短音节延长 systole and diastole 诗歌 16—408e
长英角岩 hälleflinta 矿物 7—429c
长英质岩石 felsic rock 火成岩 6—271a
长韵 long metre 诗体 10—208b
长征 Long March 中国历史 10—208a
长征 Truong Chinh 越南政治家 17—244f
"长征"号运载火箭 Changzheng launch vehicle 中国火箭系列 4—51c
长治 Changzhi 中国城市 4—51d
长周期变星 long-period variable star 天文学 10—208d
长足虻 long-legged fly 昆虫 10—207f
长左卫门 Chōzaemon 日本画家 4—201d
肠 intestine (anatomy) 解剖学 8—424e
肠促胰液肽 secretin 激素 15—178c
肠袋虫属 Balantidium 动物学 2—161e
肠梗阻 intestinal obstruction 病理现象 8—424d
肠激酶 enterokinase 生物化学 6—88e
肠挤压症 intestinal squeeze 病理现象 8—424d
肠扭转 volvulus 病理现象 18—46f
肠憩室 intestinal diverticulum 病理现象 8—424b
肠鳃虫 enteropneust 无脊椎动物 6—88e
肠套叠 intussusception 疾病 8—426b
肠体腔动物 enterocoelomate 胚胎学 6—88d
肠线 catgut 动物肠 3—524d
肠炎 enteritis 肠道病变 6—88d
肠液 intestinal juice 生物学 8—424d
肠抑胃素 enterogastrone 激素 6—88d
常陈一 Cor Caroli 天文学 4—496e
常春藤 ivy 植物学 8—495e
常春藤联合会 Ivy League 美国高等学府组织 8—496a
常德 Changde 中国城市 4—48e
常滑 Tokoname 日本城市 17—134b
常绿材柏 evergreen timber conifer (tree) 木本植物 6—183c
常绿植物 evergreen 植物 6—183c
常盘光长 Tokiwa Mitsunaga 日本画家 17—133f
常识哲学 common sense, philosophy of 哲学 4—300f
常熟 Changshu 中国城市 4—50e
常数 constant of 数学 4—449e
常微分方程 ordinary differential equation 数学 12—449d
常香玉 Chang Xiangyu 中国豫剧演员 4—47d
常项 constant 数学 4—449c
常昭 Tsuneaki (Japanese painter) 日本画家 17—251e
常州 Changzhou 中国城市 4—51f
偿债基金 sinking fund 金融 15—396a
嫦娥 Chang'e 中国神话 4—49b
厂官釉 Changguan glaze 中国瓷釉 4—49d
厂卫 changwei 中国明朝政府机构 4—51a
场外交易市场 over-the-counter market 经济 12—511b
场致发射 field emission 物理学 6—305f
敞廊 loggia 建筑 10—189e
敞篷四轮大马车 break 运输工具 3—134d
畅销书 best-seller 销售量居领先地位的书 2—438f
唱更人 wait 英国更夫 18—66f
唱经 cantillation 宗教 3—413a
唱盘 turntable 留声机部件 17—292c
唱诗班(合唱团) choir 音乐 4—189a
唱诗班席 choir 教堂建筑 4—189c

超鞭毛虫 hypermastigote 原生动物 8—292b
超导电性 superconductivity 物理学 16—345a
超对称性 supersymmetry 粒子物理学 16—348a
超额利润税 excess-profits tax 税种 6—188f
超感官知觉 extrasensory perception (ESP) 心理学 6—198d
超高频 UHF 通讯 17—323c
超高速缓冲存储器 cache memory 计算机部件 3—310a
超核 hypernucleus 物理学 8—292c
超级杯赛 Super Bowl 美国橄榄球比赛 16—344d
超级城市运动 stracittà 意大利文学运动 16—260b
超级机密 Ultra 盟军情报系统 17—333a
超级空中堡垒 Superfortress (aircraft) 美国重型轰炸机 16—345d
超级市场 supermarket 大型零售商店 16—346c
超级油轮 supertanker 船舶 16—348b
超精细结构 hyperfine structure 物理学 8—291e
超巨星 supergiant star 天文学 16—345d
超理论 metatheory 理论学 11—153f
超流性 superfluidity 物理学 16—345c
超敏反应 hypersensitivity 病理学 8—293c
超人 superman 德国哲学 16—346b
超人 Superman 美国连环画人物 16—346c
超日王 Vikramāditya (Indian emperor) 印度皇帝 17—560c
超声波 ultrasonics 物理学 17—333d
超声检查 ultrasound 医学诊断技术 17—333e
超数 hypernumbers 数学 8—292d
超碎片 hyperfragment 物理学 8—291f
超脱 ecstasy 宗教用语 5—531f
超外差接收 superheterodyne reception 信息技术 16—345f
超文本 hypertext 计算机科学 8—293f
超我 superego 精神分析学说 16—345b
超弦理论 superstring theory 粒子物理学 16—347f
超显微镜 ultramicroscope 显微镜装置 17—333c
超现实主义 Surrealism 视觉艺术、文学 16—356b
超限数 transfinite number 数学 17—196c
超新星 supernova 天文学 16—346e
超音段成分 suprasegmental 语音学 16—349a
超音速飞行 supersonic flight 飞行 16—347d
超引力 supergravity 物理学 16—345e
超越障碍赛 show jumping 马术 15—337c
超在禅定派 Transcendental Meditation (TM) 教派 17—195a
超子 hyperon 物理学 8—293b
超自然论 supernaturalism 宗教 16—346d
超嘴贝 Rhynchotreta 古生物学 14—272c
巢 nest 动物为安置自身筑成的结构 12—89b
巢菜 vetch 植物 17—531f
朝觐 hajj 伊斯兰教 7—415d
朝圣 pilgrimage 基督教 13—302f
朝圣节期 Pilgrim Festivals 犹太教名词 13—302f
朝圣瓶 pilgrim bottle 容器 13—302e
朝圣之路 Pilgrims' Way 英格兰古道 13—303c
朝鲜 Korea 亚洲历史 9—353c
朝鲜 Korea, North 亚洲国家 9—353d
朝鲜海峡 Korea Strait 亚洲海峡 9—356c
朝鲜泡菜 kimchi 食品 9—282e
朝鲜湾 Korea Bay 亚洲海湾 9—356c
朝鲜王朝 Chosŏn DYNASTY (Korea) 朝鲜历史 4—200e
朝鲜文学 Korean literature 文学 9—357b
朝鲜艺术 Korean art 视觉艺术 9—356d
朝鲜音乐 Korean music 东亚音乐类型 9—357d
朝鲜语 Korean language 语言 9—357a
朝鲜战争 Korean War 亚洲现代历史 9—358a
朝鲜族 Korean nationality 民族 9—357e
朝鲜族语 Korean nationality, language of 语言 9—357f
朝向 orientation 建筑 12—460d
朝向 qibla 伊斯兰教 14—60c
朝向风 ghibli 气象学 7—112e
朝阳 Chaoyang 中国城市 4—56b
嘲鸫 mockingbird 鸟类 11—303a
嘲鸫科 Mimidae 动物学 11—240a
嘲剧 hat cheo 戏剧 7—506f
潮安 Ch'ao-an (China) 中国城市 4—55c
潮白河 Chaobai He 中国河流 4—55d
潮波 tidal wave 海洋学 17—86f
潮虫 sow bug 动物学 15—558b
潮解 deliquescence 化学 5—227a
潮剧 Chaoju 中国戏曲剧种 4—55e
潮坪 tidal flat 海洋学 17—86d
潮汐 tide 天文学 17—86f
潮汐摩擦 tidal friction 天文学 17—86e
潮汐能发电 tidal power 电学 17—86f
潮州 Chaozhou 中国城市 4—56d
吵嚷伯劳 songshrike 鸟类 15—514f
炒锅 wok 烹饪用薄壁锅 18—306b
车车尔勒格 Tsetserleg 蒙古城镇 17—248f
车臣 Chechnya 俄罗斯共和国 4—98e
车床 lathe 机械 9—511a
车尔尼 Czerny, Carl 奥地利钢琴家、教师 5—100a
车尔尼雪夫斯基 Chernyshevsky, N(ikolay) G(avrilovich) 俄国政治家 4—127a
车里雅宾斯克 Chelyabinsk 俄罗斯城市 4—105c
车里雅宾斯克 Chelyabinsk 俄罗斯州名 4—105c
车辆安全装置 vehicular safety devices 交通 17—490e
车辆门道 Porte cochere 公共建筑入口 13—448e
车轮窗 wheel window (Gothic architecture) 哥特建筑 18—221d
车轮矿 bournonite 矿物 3—88e
车前属 Plantago 植物学 13—345e
车桑子 hopbush 植物 8—167c
车叶草 woodruff 草本植物 18—324c
车载图书馆 book van 图书馆 3—37f
车轴草 clover 植物 4—304b
车轴草叶象 clover leaf weevil 昆虫 4—304c
扯根菜科 Penthoraceae 草本植物 13—149d
扯根菜属 Penthorum 草本植物 13—149d
彻底的经验主义 radical empiricism 哲学 14—112e
彻尔宁 Tscherning, Anton Frederik 丹麦军事改革家 17—248a
彻莱梅里克 Çölemerik (Turkey) 土耳其省份 4—341b
撤诉 nolle prosequi 英美法律 12—226c
郴县 Cheng-hsien (China) 中国县名 4—121a
郴州 Chenzhou 中国城市 4—124b
臣服 liege 欧洲历史 10—87a
尘卷风 dust devil 气象学 5—479e
辰砂 cinnabar 矿物 4—242a
沉淀池 sedimentation tank 污水处理 15—184b
沉管法 immersed tube 水下施工技术 8—343b
沉积相 sedimentary facies 地质学 15—182f
沉积学 sedimentology 地质学 15—184b
沉积岩 sedimentary rock 岩石 15—183c
沉积作用 sedimentation 地质学 15—183f
沉降 settling 土壤力学 15—235f
沉降 subsidence 地质学 16—300c
沉箱 caisson 水下施工用具 3—329f
沉箱病 caisson disease 疾病 3—330a
陈瑄 Chen Xuan 中国明代大臣 4—117f
陈爱莲 Chen Ailian 中国舞蹈家 4—114b
陈伯达 Chen Boda 中国政治人物 4—114c
陈朝 Tran DYNASTY 越南王朝 17—193b

陈诚 Chen Cheng 中国国民党高级将领 4—114d
陈淳 Chen Chun 中国画家 4—114e
陈大齐 Chen Daqi 中国近代思想家 4—114f
陈独秀 Chen Duxiu 中国共产党创始人之一 4—115a
陈果夫 Chen Guofu 中国国民党政治家 4—115d
陈洪绶 Chen Hongshou 中国画家 4—115e
陈景润 Chen Jingrun 中国数学家 4—116b
陈镜开 Chen Jingkai 中国举重运动员 4—116a
陈炯明 Chen Jiongming 中国军阀 4—116c
陈立夫 Chen Lifu 中国国民党政治家 4—116e
陈亮 Chen Liang 中国思想家 4—116d
陈马六甲 Tan Malaka, Ibrahim Datuk 印度尼西亚共产党领袖 16—455b
陈纳德 Chennault, Claire L(ee) 美国将军 4—123f
陈纳特 Chenault, Kenneth 美国商人 4—120a
《陈旉农书》 Chen Fu Nongshu 中国农书 4—115c
陈其美 Chen Qimei 中国近代民主革命家 4—116f
陈容 Chen Rong 中国画家 4—117a
陈设饼 shewbread 犹太教 15—310e
陈胜吴广起义 Chen Sheng and Wu Guang uprising 中国历史 4—117b
陈省身 Chen Xingshen 美籍华裔数学家 4—117e
陈述样式 predicable 逻辑学 13—490a
陈水扁 Chen Shuibian 中国台湾民进党主席 4—117c
陈思王 Ch'en Ssu Wang 中国古代文学家 4—117c
陈思王 Ssu of Ch'en, Prince 中国古代文学家 16—174e
陈天华 Chen Tianhua 中国近代民主革命家 4—117c
陈抟 Chen Tuan 中国北宋道士 4—117d
陈兴道 Tran Hung Dao 越南军事战略家 17—193b
陈毅 Chen Yi 中国革命家 4—118a
陈寅恪 Chen Yinke 中国历史学家 4—118b
陈友谅 Chen Youliang 中国元末农民起义领袖 4—118e
陈玉成 Chen Yucheng 中国太平天国将领 4—118f
陈垣 Chen Yuan 中国历史学家 4—118e
陈云 Chen Yun 中国领导人 4—119a
陈祯禄 Tan Cheng Lock 马来亚华人领袖 16—455a
陈子昂 Chen Zi'ang 中国文学家 4—119e
梣 ash 木本植物 1—544a
梣叶草 fraxinella 草本植物 6—457a
梣叶槭 box elder (*Acer negundo*) 木本植物 3—97b
晨祷 shaharith 犹太教 15—256a
晨星 Morning Star (Cheyenne leader) 美国酋长 11—399a
衬架裙 crinoline 服装 5—17e
衬裙 petticoat 服装 13—213d
衬衫 shirt 衣服 15—324a
衬胸 stomacher 外衣 16—248d
称德天皇 Shōtoku Tennō (empress of Japan) 日本女天皇 15—336f
称义 justification 基督教神学 9—118f
谶纬 chenwei 中国汉代宗教迷信 4—124a
柽柳 tamarisk 木本植物 16—450b
柽柳目 Tamaricales 植物学 16—449e
蛏子 razor clam 海产贝类 14—174f
撑竿跳高 pole vault 田径运动 13—398f
成本 cost 经济学 4—532b
成本-效益分析 cost-benefit analysis 经济学 4—532c
成都 Chengdu 中国城市 4—122a
成都平原 Chengdu Plain 中国平原 4—122d
成骨不全 osteogenesis imperfecta 疾病 12—490f
成骨肉瘤 osteogenic sarcoma 疾病 12—491a
成骨细胞 osteoblast 细胞 12—490c
成核 nucleation 晶体学 12—290e
成化 Chenghua 中国明朝皇帝年号 4—122f
成吉思汗 Genghis Khan 蒙古皇帝 7—63c
成就法 sadhana 印度教和佛教密宗修炼法 14—492c
成均馆 Sŏnggyun'guan 朝鲜大学 15—513d
成矿区 metallogenic province 矿床学 11—148f
成人教育 adult education 教育 1—87f
成人期 adulthood 生理学 1—88e
《成实论》 Satyasiddhi-śāstra 佛书 15—80d
成实宗 Jōjitsu 佛教 9—75f
成髓细胞 myeloblast 生理学 11—523f
成汤 Chengtang 中国帝王 4—123b
成田 Narita 日本城市 11—576b
《成唯识论》 Chengweishilun 中国佛教典籍 4—123b
成纤维细胞 fibroblast 解剖学 6—302c
成岩作用 diagenesis 地质学 5—283e
成猪 hog 哺乳动物 8—118d
诚实花 honesty 草本植物 8—153b
承办 publican 古罗马公共事务承包人 14—10f
承德 Chengde 中国城市 4—121f
承兑汇票 acceptance 金融 1—45c
承阳大师 Jōyō Daishi (Buddhist monk) 日本高僧 9—95f
承租人 lessee 法律 10—39c
城邦 city-state 政治制度 4—250f
城邦 polis 古希腊城市国家 13—401a
城堡 castle 中世纪要塞 3—512d
城堡护卫 castle guard 欧洲历史 3—513b
城堡式府邸 château 封建领主庄园 4—89c
城隍 Chenghuang 中国古代神祇 4—122f
城津 Sŏngjin (North Korea) 朝鲜城市 15—514d
城陵矶 Chenglingji 中国港口 4—123a
城区更新 urban renewal 城市建设 17—412c
城市 city 人口集中地 4—250b
城市高速铁路 rapid transit 城市建设 14—155a
城市革命 urban revolution 社会学 17—412c
城市规划 urban planning 城市建设 17—412a
城市化 urbanization 社会学 17—412e
城市酒神节 City Dionysia (festival) 节日 4—250d
城市气候 urban climate 气象学 17—411e
城市同盟 hermandad 西班牙城市团体 8—40d
城市与区域规划学 ekistics 社会学 6—8b
城市政府 city government 行政机构 4—250d
城镇会议 town meeting 美国政治 17—180e
乘车节 Rathayātrā 印度节日 14—161e
乘船出逃者 boat people 难民 2—555d
乘马比武 joust 体育 9—93f
程长庚 Cheng Changgeng 中国京剧演员 4—120c
程颢与程颐 Cheng Hao and Cheng Yi 中国两学者 4—120e
程绍迥 Cheng Shaojiong 中国兽医学家 4—121a
程邃 Cheng Sui 中国画家 4—121b
程天放 Cheng Tianfang 中国国民党政治家 4—121c
程序法 adjective law 法律 1—79e
程砚秋 Cheng Yanqiu 中国京剧演员 4—121d
程颐 Ch'eng I 中国学者 4—121a
程逸 Uttaradit 泰国城镇 17—434b
程朱学派 Cheng-Zhu Xuepai 中国哲学 4—121e
惩戒法 Penal Laws 法律 13—134f
塍鹬 godwit 鸟类 7—176d
澄观 Chengguan 中国唐代佛教僧人 4—122d
澄江动物群 Chengjiang fauna 中国化石 4—123a
澄江堂主人 Chōkōdō Shujin 日本作家 4—190b
橙花马利筋 orange milkweed (plant) 草本植物 12—443e
橙尖粉蝶 orange-tip butterfly 昆虫 12—443a
吃人妖魔 ogre 民间故事 12—347e
蚩尤 Chi You 中国神话人物 4—138c
痴呆 dementia 病理现象 5—233a

池大雅 Ike Taiga 日本画家 8—330e
池坊 Ikenobō 日本花道流派 8—331a
池谷-关彗星 Ikeya-Seki,Comet 天文学 8—331b
池龟 pond turtle 甲壳动物 13—425e
池田 Ikeda 日本城市 8—330f
池田勇人 Ikeda Hayato 日本首相 8—330f
弛豫现象 relaxation phenomenon 物理学 14—214b
驰龙 dromaeosaur 古生物学 5—426c
持斧罗摩 Paraśurāma 印度教神话 13—39b
持续低音 drone 音乐 5—426e
持续音 pedal point 音乐 13—118f
匙 spoon 餐具 16—41a
匙唇兰 fairy slipper（*Calypso bulbosa*） 植物 6—217e
匙吻鲟 spoonbill 鱼类 16—41c
匙指虾 prawn 甲壳动物 13—486c
尺八 shakuhachi 日本乐器 15—268b
尺蛾 geometrid moth 昆虫 7—73b
尺骨 ulna 解剖学 17—330d
尺蠖 measuring worm 昆虫 11—65b
齿鲸 toothed whale 哺乳动物 17—155d
齿口虫 odontostome 原生生物 12—339e
齿绿松石 odontolite 化石 12—339e
齿轮 gear 机械 7—41f
齿扭贝 Stropheodonta 古生物学 16—282b
齿舌 radula 软体动物 14—119f
齿舌兰属 Odontoglossum 植物学 12—339d
齿条和小齿轮 rack and pinion 机械 14—107d
豉甲 whirligig beetle 昆虫 18—224f
赤膀鸭 gadwall（*Anas strepera*） 鸟类 6—543f
赤壁 Chibi 中国古战场遗址 4—139f
赤潮 red tide 海洋污染现象 14—191a
赤道 equator 地理学、天文学 6—106e
赤道地区 Istiwā'īyah,al- 苏丹南部地区 8—482e
赤道辐合带 equatorial convergence zone（meteorology） 气象学 6—106e
赤道几内亚 Equatorial Guinea 西非国家 6—107b
赤道逆流 equatorial countercurrent 海洋学 6—106e
赤道无风带 doldrums 气象学 5—363e
赤道洋流 equatorial current 海洋学 6—106f
赤峰 Chifeng 中国城市 4—148e
赤猴 patas monkey（*Erythrocebus*, or *Cercopithecus*, *patas*） 动物学 13—84d
赤经 right ascension 天文学 14—298d
赤颈鸭 wigeon 动物 18—248a
赤军 Red Army 日本恐怖主义组织 14—186f
赤栎 red oak 木本植物 14—189c
赤莲属 Erythronium 植物学 6—126a
赤鹿 red deer 偶蹄目动物 14—188a
赤霉素 gibberellin 生物化学 7—117e
赤水 Chishui 中国城市 4—180d
赤穗 Akō 日本城市 1—157c
赤塔 Chita 俄罗斯州名 4—181a
赤塔 Chita 俄罗斯城市 4—181b
赤陶 terra-cotta 工艺品 16—553f
赤铁矿 hematite 矿物 8—8b
赤铜矿 cuprite 矿物 5—66c
赤铜铁矿 delafossite 矿物 5—216d
赤纬 declination 天文学 5—203e
赤卫军城 Krasnogvardeysk（Russia） 俄罗斯城市 9—372c
赤胸朱顶雀 Linnet（*Carduelis*, or *Acanthis*, *cannabina*） 鸟类 10—124f
赤眼蜂 trichogrammatid 昆虫 17—216d
赤字财政 deficit financing 经济学 5—209b
炽热火山云 nuée ardente 地质学 12—292e
翅膀 wing 动物用以飞行的成对结构 18—287d
翅子藤科 Hippocrateaceae 植物学 8—91d
敕令 constitutiones principum 罗马立法 4—460f
充分理由论 good-reasons theory 伦理学 7—207e
充足理由原则 sufficient reason, principle of 哲学 16—307f
冲 opposition 天文学 12—434e
冲伯 Tshombe, Moise(-Kapenda) 刚果政治家 17—249a
冲刺 dash（race） 体育 5—159d
冲锋队 SA 德国纳粹党准军事组织 14—478b
冲锋枪 submachine gun 武器 16—298c
冲沟 gully 地质学 7—369f
冲击摆 ballistic pendulum 测量射体速度的装置 2—177e
冲击波 shock wave 物理学 15—328b
冲积层 alluvium 地质学 1—244a
冲积平原 alluvial plain 地理学 1—244a
冲积扇 alluvial fan 地质学 1—243e
冲浪运动 surfing 体育项目 16—352e
冲绳 Okinawa 日本县名 12—360a
冲绳 Okinawa 日本城市 12—360a
冲鹅 darter（water bird） 鸟类 5—153f
冲天炉 cupola furnace 冶金 5—66a
冲突 conflict 心理学 4—422a
《冲虚至德真经》 Ch'ung hsü chih te chen Ching 中国古典文献 4—221f
虫迹状处理 vermiculated work 建筑 17—517a
虫胶 shellac 昆虫分泌物产品 15—297a
虫蜡 insect wax 昆虫及其分泌物产品 8—397d
虫囊菌目 Laboulbeniomycetes 生物学 9—431c
虫漆 lac 染料 9—435a
虫胭脂 kermes 染料 9—241c
重氮化合物 diazo compound 化学 5—292c
重氮盐 diazonium salt 化学 5—292c
重光葵 Shigemitsu Mamoru 日本外交家 15—313a
重建时期 Reconstruction 美国历史 14—184d
重建主义 Reconstructionism 美洲犹太教派别 14—184f
重黎 Chong Li 中国神话 4—193c
重庆 Chongqing 中国城市 4—194a
重庆大学 Chongqing University 中国大学 4—194f
重言式 tautology 逻辑学 16—498c
重演律 recapitulation theory 生物学 14—183a
重整 reforming 化学 14—200a
重整化 renormalization 物理学 14—231e
重组 recombination 遗传学 14—184c
崇拜礼仪改革运动 Liturgical Movement 基督教 10—152f
崇德 Chongde 中国清朝皇帝年号 4—193d
崇德天皇 Sutoku 日本天皇 16—363a
崇高 sublime 文学评论 16—298b
崇明 Chongming 中国县名 4—193e
崇明岛 Chongming Dao 中国第三大岛 4—193f
崇祯 Chongzhen 中国明朝皇帝年号 4—195a
宠物 pet 动物 13—195c
冲床 punch press 机械 14—26b
冲压式喷气发动机 ramjet 航空 14—140c
抽彩给奖 lottery 博彩 10—231b
抽搐 tic 生理学 17—85b
抽签选举 sortition 古希腊选举方法 15—523c
抽纱制品 drawn thread work 工艺品 5—416f
抽象表现主义 Abstract Expressionism 美国绘画 1—32d
抽象-创作社 Abstraction-Création 法国画家团体 1—33a
抽象代数 abstract algebra 数学 1—31b
抽象诗 abstract poem 诗歌体裁 1—33a
抽象艺术 abstract art 艺术 1—32d

抽样 sampling 统计学 15—1b
仇恨罪 hate crime 法律 7—508a
筹资 finance 金融 6—317b
丑角 clown 喜剧角色 4—304f
丑妖怪 goblin 民间传说 7—171a
丑婴儿 changeling 欧洲民间传说 4—49d
臭虫 bedbug 昆虫 2—324b
臭椿 tree of heaven (*Ailanthus altissima*) 植物 17—207e
臭葱石 scorodite 矿物 15—148a
臭瓜 calabazilla (*Cucurbita foetidissima*) 藤本植物 3—332d
臭荠 wart cress 草本植物 18—114b
臭气 stinkdamp 化合物 16—240b
臭肉豆蔻 stinking nutmeg(tree) 木本植物 16—240c
臭氧(O_3) ozone 气体 12—529a
臭氧层 ozonosphere 大气科学 12—529c
臭氧化物 ozonide 化合物 12—529c
臭鼬草 skunk cabbage 草本植物 15—423a
《出埃及记》 Exodus 《圣经·旧约》 6—193e
出版业 publishing 书报杂志出版行业 14—10f
出光矿山公司 Idemitsu Kōsan Co., Ltd. 日本公司 8—322b
出汗 perspiration 生理学 13—187b
出家 pabbajjā 佛教 12—530f
出家制 rahbānīyah 伊斯兰教教义学 14—123d
出溶 exsolution 矿物学 6—197b
出生率 birth rate 统计学 2—494a
出曜经 Avadāna 佛教文献 2—82d
出云 Izumo 日本城市 8—499f
出云阿国 Izumo Okuni 日本舞蹈家 8—499f
出租马车 hackney 交通工具 7—399f
出租汽车 taxicab 交通 16—501c
出租人和承租人 lessor and lessee 法律 10—41b
初步教学字母表 Initial Teaching Alphabet 教育 8—388a
初传福音和口授教理 kerygma and catechesis 基督教 9—244b
初等教育 elementary education 教育 6—32d
初级律师 solicitor 律师 15—495f
初级学院 junior college 教育 9—112b
初级中学 junior high school 教育 9—112d
初龙 archosaur 爬行动物 1—454f
初唐四杰 Four Great Poets of Early Tang Dynasty 中国唐代文学家 6—425d
初选 primary election 政治 13—509b
初巡礼 Joyeuse Entrée 欧洲政治 9—95e
初夜权 seigneur, droit du 封建制度 15—191d
除草剂 herbicide 化学药剂 8—35d
除虫菊 pyrethrum 植物学 14—46d
锄 hoe 农具 8—113f
《锄恶利器》 Malleus maleficarum 神学文献 10—433e
锄足蟾 spadefoot toad 两栖动物 16—1a
蒭藁增二 Mira Ceti 天文学 11—270b
雏晶 crystallite 地质学 5—45a
雏菊 daisy 植物 5—113b
橱柜 cabinet 家具 3—305f
橱式写字台 secretary 写字台 15—178a
杵臼关节 spheroidal joint (anatomy) 解剖学 16—24f
储存 storage 保存方法 16—254b
储蓄 saving 经济学 15—89e
储蓄倾向 propensity to save 经济学 13—535e
储蓄银行 savings bank 金融机构 15—89f
储蓄与放款协会 savings and loan association 金融机构 15—89f
楚 Chu 中国先秦时期诸侯国 4—217b
楚辞 Chu ci 诗歌 4—217b
《楚辞》 Chuci 中国文学 4—219a
楚德湖 Chudskoye Ozero (Russia) 俄罗斯湖泊 4—219d
楚格 Zug 瑞士州名 18—571d
楚格 Zug 瑞士地名 18—571d
楚格峰 Zugspitze 德国山名 18—571e
楚河 Chu River 中亚河流 4—217d
楚加奇山 Chugach Mountains 北美洲山脉 4—219d
楚科夫斯基 Chukovsky, Korney Ivanovich 俄国文学评论家 4—220c
楚克迈尔 Zuckmayer, Carl 德国剧作家 18—571b
楚克奇 Chukchi 俄罗斯自治区 4—220b
楚克奇海 Chukchi Sea 北冰洋边缘海 4—220c
楚克奇人 Chukchi 俄罗斯民族 4—220a
楚鲁巴斯科 Churubusco 墨西哥联邦区属区 4—231b
楚梅布 Tsumeb 纳米比亚城镇 17—251b
楚姆佩 Zumpe, Johann Christoph 德国钢琴制造家 18—573a
楚姆托尔 Zumthor, Peter 瑞士建筑师 18—573b
楚图希尔人 Tzutujil 危地马拉马雅印第安人 17—314e
楚瓦什 Chuvashiya 俄罗斯西部共和国 4—231f
楚瓦什人 Chuvash 俄罗斯民族 4—231e
楚瓦什语 Chuvash language 阿尔泰语 4—231f
楚伊伦 Zuylen, Belle van (Swiss novelist) 瑞士小说家 18—576b
楚州 Chuzhou 中国江苏省淮安市辖区 4—232b
畜力车 cart 运输工具 3—486b
触觉 touch reception 生物学 17—174c
触觉小体 tactile corpuscle (biology) 生理学 16—420b
触毛虫 thigmotrich 原生动物 17—39b
触身式橄榄球 touch football 体育 17—174c
触手冠动物 lophophorate 无脊椎动物 10—217e
触手环假说 lophophore hypothesis 动物学 10—217e
触珠蛋白 haptoglobin 生理学 7—468a
川端康成 Kawabata Yasunari 日本小说家 9—202b
川合玉堂 Kawai Gyokudō 日本画家 9—202d
川剧 Chuanju 中国剧种 4—217f
川口 Kawaguchi 日本城市 9—202c
川圹 Xiangkhoang 老挝城镇 18—382b
川圹高原 Xiangkhoang, Plateau de 老挝高地 18—382c
川柳诗 senryū 日本诗体 15—214d
川内 Sendai 日本城市 15—208f
川崎 Kawasaki 日本城市 9—203a
川崎氏综合征 Kawasaki syndrome 疾病 9—203b
川崎制铁公司 Kawasaki Steel Corporation 日本公司 9—203b
川崎重工业公司 Kawasaki Heavy Industries, Ltd. 日本公司 9—203b
川西 Kawanishi 日本城市 9—203a
川续断 teasel 草本植物 16—512c
川续断目 Dipsacales 植物学 5—334a
川越 Kawagoe 日本城市 9—202c
氚(T或^{3}H) tritium 化学元素 17—227c
氚核 triton 化学 17—227f
穿贝海绵 clionid 动物学 4—294e
穿孔工艺 pierced work 工艺 13—295c
穿孔挂饰 bead 装饰品 2—302a
穿袍贵族 noblesse de robe 法国贵族等级 12—223a
穿山甲 pangolin 哺乳动物 13—11e
穿索针鱼 marlin 鱼类 10—524b
穿衣镜 cheval glass 镜 4—134f
传播 communication 交换信息 4—390e
传布 dispersion 生物学 5—341d
传承 Smṛti 印度教经籍 15—456b
传承派 Smārta sect 印度教正统派 15—440e
《传道书》 Ecclesiastes 基督教文学著作 5—520d
传递律 transitive law 数学、逻辑学 17—197d
传动器 transmission 机械 17—197f
传粉 pollination 孢粉学 13—406b

传教大师 Dengyō Daishi 日本高僧 5—243e
传票 summons 法律 16—333f
传奇故事 romance 文学 14—367c
传染性肠炎 infectious enteritis (disease of cats) 疾病 8—380f
传染性单核细胞增多症 infectious mononucleosis (disease) 疾病 8—380f
传染性黄疸 infectious jaundice 疾病 8—380f
传染性黄疸 jaundice, infectious 疾病 8—550a
传染性角膜炎 keratitis, infectious 牲畜疾病 9—239e
传染性黏液瘤病 infectious myxomatosis (disease of rabbits) 疾病 8—380f
传染性牛斑疹伤寒 bovine typhus, contagious 动物疾病 3—91d
传染性牛斑疹伤寒 contagious bovine typhus 动物疾病 4—464d
传染性丘疹 CE (contagious ecthyma; animal disease) 动物疾病 3—546c
传染性丘疹 ecthyma, contagious (animal disease) 动物疾病 5—532a
传热 heat transfer 物理学 7—544e
传声器 microphone 电声器件 11—194d
传说 legend 文学 9—561a
传闻证据 hearsay 法律 7—542a
传心术 telepathy 心理学 16—526b
传信会 Propagation of the Faith, Society for the 罗马教廷机构 13—535b
传真 facsimile 通信 6—209d
传真电报机 telautograph 通信 16—522c
传证令 subpoena 法律 16—300c
"魟鱼"号 Argonaut 美国潜艇 1—466e
船舶 ship 船 15—319f
船底座η Eta Carinae 天文学 6—143d
船歌 barcarole 音乐 2—223a
船菊石 Scaphites 古生物学 15—103b
船楼 castle 船体结构 3—513a
船桥 Funabashi 日本城市 6—522e
船蛆 shipworm 软体动物 15—321e
船坞 dock 船只检修设施 5—356a
船形容器 nef 工艺品 12—65c
船形调味汁碗 sauceboat 家用容器 15—81d
船闸 lock 航运 10—176d
船只捕获案 prize cases 美国法律史 13—522d
船只抵押借款契约 bottomry 海事契约 3—75f
船钟 ship's bell 古代船只报时钟 15—321e
喘气 panting 生理学 13—16e
喘息症 heaves 动物病 7—547e
串珠藻属 Batrachospermum 生物学 2—280c
钏路 Kushiro 日本城市 9—405d
创伤 wound 医学 18—340c
创伤后压力症候群 post-traumatic stress disorder 疾病 13—460a
疮痂病 scab 植物疾病 15—98f
窗 window 建筑 18—283d
窗翅蛾 window-winged moth 昆虫 18—283f
窗格苔藓虫 Fenestella 古生物学 6—273d
窗花格 tracery 建筑 17—185b
床 bed 家具 2—323f
床板珊瑚 Tabulata 古生物学 16—417a
床罩 bedspread 生活用品 2—327c
床之间 tokonoma 日本建筑 17—134a
创价学会 Sōka-gakkai 日本佛教团体 15—490b
创始者原理 founder principle 遗传学 6—424b
《创世记》 Genesis 基督教经典 7—58b
创世纪元 anno mundi 犹太人历法 1—367b
创世神话 creation myth 文化 5—1a
《创世外记》 Genesis Apocryphon 犹太教伪经 7—58c
《创世之书》 Sefer Yetzira 犹太教著作 15—187a
创业七圣 Seven Holy Founders 意大利基督教圣仆会创始人 15—237a
创意曲 invention 音乐 8—426f
创造力 creativity 心理学 5—1c
创造论 creationism 反进化论理论 5—1b
创造性进化论 creative evolution 哲学 5—1b
创造主义 Creacionismo 西班牙文学 4—574c
创制权 initiative (electoral process) 政治学 8—388b
吹管 blowpipe 助燃装置 2—546d
吹箭筒 blowgun 原始武器 2—546b
吹绵蚧 cottony-cushion scale (*Icerya purchasi*) 昆虫 4—539f
吹沫虫 spittlebug 昆虫 16—37d
吹模法 blow molding 玻璃生产方法 2—546a
吹牛军人 Miles Gloriosus 喜剧人物 11—214b
吹蚀 deflation 地质学 5—209c
吹田 Suita 日本城市 16—313e
垂钓鱼 anglerfish 鱼类 1—346b
垂耳鸟 wattlebird 鸟类 18—147b
垂耳鸦 kokako (*Callaeas cinerea*) 鸟类 9—336c
垂耳鸦科 Callaeidae 动物学 3—352f
垂花饰 swag 雕刻纹样 16—370a
垂体 pituitary gland 解剖学 13—331f
垂体功能减退 hypopituitarism 病理现象 8—295e
垂直起降飞机 VTOL airplane 飞行器 18—53f
槌球 croquet 体育 5—30d
锤 hammer 工具 7—445e
锤头鹳 hammerhead (*Scopus umbretta*) 鸟类 7—446c
锤头鲨 hammerhead shark 鱼类 7—446d
春孢器 aecium 真菌 1—92a
春川 Ch'unch'ŏn 韩国城市 4—221e
春鲑 spring salmon 鱼类 16—162f
春化 vernalization 植物学 17—520c
春季 spring 季节 16—161e
春节 Spring Festival 中国节日 16—162e
《春秋》 Chunqiu 中国编年史 4—222b
春秋时期 Spring and Autumn Period 中国历史 16—162c
春秋五霸 Chunqiu Wuba 中国历史 4—222d
春日井 Kasugai 日本城市 9—194b
春武里 Chon Buri 泰国城镇 4—192b
春雨奋兴运动 Latter Rain revival 基督教 9—515f
蝽 stinkbug 昆虫 16—239f
纯粹主义 Purism 法国绘画的流派 14—33a
纯橄榄岩 dunite 岩石 5—463b
纯合子 homozygote 生物学 8—151b
纯红母牛 red heifer 古犹太教祭牲 14—189a
纯碱 soda ash 化合物 15—482e
纯律 just intonation 音乐 9—118c
纯培养 pure culture 微生物学 14—31f
纯全派 Perfectionist (religious group) 宗教团体 13—165a
纯诗歌 pure poetry 文学 14—32a
纯文学 belles lettres 文学名词 2—365b
纯血马 Thoroughbred 马品种 17—58a
纯正浸礼会总联会 General Association of Regular Baptist Churches 美国宗教组织 7—55d
纯正希腊语 Katharevusa Greek language 语言学 9—195c
莼菜 water shield (*Brasenia schreberi*) 水生植物 18—138c
唇环、唇栓、唇板 lip ring, lip plug, and lip plate 民族学 10—129d
唇口目 Cheilostomata 动物学 4—102d
唇裂 cleft lip (congenital malformation) 先天畸形 4—278c
唇形科 Lamiaceae 植物学 9—464e
唇形目 Lamiales 植物学 9—465a
醇 alcohol 化合物 1—190d

醇溶谷蛋白 prolamin 蛋白质 13—532c

绰空 Shakkū (Buddhist reformer) 佛教改革家 15—268b

词 ci 中国文学 4—232d

词典 dictionary 工具书 5—301d

词符 logogram 文字 10—192a

词素 morpheme 语言学 11—402d

词形变化 accidence 语言学 1—45e

词源学 etymology 语言学 6—154a

词缀 affix 语言学 1—104a

茨 Munsch, Robert (Norman) 加拿大作家 11—486b

茨城 Ibaraki 日本县名 8—301a

茨雷斯 Cres 克罗地亚岛屿 5—7b

茨纳伊姆 Znaim (Czech Republic) 捷克城市 18—560d

茨瓦纳人 Tswana 民族 17—252f

茨韦布吕肯 Zweibrücken 德国城市 18—576e

茨韦格 Zweig, Arnold 德国犹太人作家 18—576e

茨韦格 Zweig, Stefan 奥地利作家 18—576f

茨维贝尔 Zwiebel 德国医生 18—577b

茨维考 Zwickau 德国城市 18—577a

茨维塔耶娃 Tsvetayeva, Marina Ivanovna 俄国诗人 17—252e

茨维特 Tsvet, Mikhail Semyonovich 俄国植物学家 17—252d

茨温利 Zwingli, Huldrych 瑞士宗教改革家 18—577b

茨欣瓦利 Tskhinvali 格鲁吉亚城市 17—250a

茨藻目 Najadales 植物学 11—545a

瓷器 china 陶瓷 4—164d

瓷器 porcelain 陶瓷 13—439d

瓷土 china clay 矿物 4—165c

瓷状岩 porcellanite 岩石 13—440b

辞格 speech, figure of 语言学 16—16d

慈爱圣母会 Lady of Mercy, Order of Our 天主教会 9—443b

慈爱圣母会会士 Mercedarian 天主教会成员 11—124b

慈姑 arrowhead 草本植物 1—516b

慈善基金会 philanthropic foundation 慈善组织 13—230d

慈善学校 charity school 教育 4—65c

慈善姊妹会 Mercy, Sisters of (R.S.M.) 天主教女修会 11—127f

慈无量心 maitrī 佛教教义 10—413a

慈禧 Cixi 中国皇后 4—256d

慈圆 Jien 日本僧人、历史学家 9—20e

慈藏律师 Chajang Yulsa 朝鲜佛教僧人 4—29c

磁暴 magnetic storm 大气科学 10—390e

磁测 magnetic survey 地球物理学 10—390f

磁层 magnetosphere 大气科学 10—392a

磁场 magnetic field 物理学 10—388e

磁赤铁矿 maghemite 矿物 10—380f

磁带录像机 video tape recorder 电子学 17—546d

磁带录音 tape recording 电子学 16—475a

磁单极子 magnetic monopole 物理学 10—389a

磁导率 magnetic permeability 物理学 10—389b

磁共振 magnetic resonance 物理学 10—390a

磁共振成像 magnetic resonance imaging 医学 10—390d

磁化率 magnetic susceptibility 物理学 10—390f

磁黄铁矿 pyrrhotite 矿物 14—49a

磁极 magnetic pole 物理学 10—389c

磁记录 magnetic recording 电子学 10—389c

磁镜 magnetic mirror 物理学 10—389a

磁控管 magnetron 电子学 10—392b

磁雷诺数 magnetic Reynolds number 物理学 10—390d

磁力 magnetic force 物理学 10—388e

磁流体动力发电机 magnetohydrodynamic power generator 发电机 10—391d

磁流体力学 magnetohydrodynamics (MHD) 物理学 10—391f

磁路 magnetic circuit 电学 10—388a

磁镍铁矿 trevorite 矿物 17—213b

磁偶极子 magnetic dipole 物理学 10—388c

磁泡存储器 magnetic bubble memory 计算机存储设备 10—388a

磁强计 magnetometer 测磁仪器 10—391f

磁山文化 Cishan culture 中国历史 4—246d

磁石 lodestone (mineral) 矿物 10—183d

磁体 magnet 物理学 10—386e

磁铁矿 magnetite 矿物 10—391c

磁铁矿石 magnetic iron ore (mineral) 矿物 10—388f

磁县 Ci Xian 中国县名 4—232d

磁心存储器 magnetic-core storage 计算机存储设备 10—388c

磁学 magnetism 物理学 10—391a

磁振子 magnon 物理学 10—393d

磁致伸缩 magnetostriction 物理学 10—392b

磁滞现象 hysteresis 物理学 8—297d

磁州窑 Cizhou kiln 中国瓷窑 4—256f

磁子 magneton 物理学 10—392a

雌黄 orpiment 矿物 12—471b

雌激素 estrogen 生理学 6—142c

雌蕊 pistil 植物学 13—326b

雌雄同体 hermaphroditism 生物学 8—41a

次兵卫 Jirobei (artist) 日本浮世绘画家 9—34d

次经 deuterocanonical books 犹太教、基督教经籍 5—268e

次女高音 mezzo-soprano 声乐 11—172f

次声 infrasonics 物理学 8—385a

次透辉石 salite 矿物 14—546c

次中音鼓 tenor drum 乐器 16—544f

次中音号 tenor horn 乐器 16—545a

伺服机构 servomechanism 自动装置 15—230a

刺鲅 wahoo (species *Acanthocybium solanderi*) 鱼类 18—64e

刺柏 juniper 植物 9—112d

刺胞动物 cnidarian 无脊椎动物 4—309c

刺滨螺 pricklywinkle 腹足动物 13—506c

刺菜蓟 cardoon (*Cynara cardunculus*) 草本植物 3—454f

刺刀 bayonet 武器 2—297d

刺蛾 slug caterpillar moth 昆虫 15—437f

刺萼茄 buffalo bur (*Solanum rostratum*) 植物 3—234a

刺钢丝 barbed wire 围栏钢丝 2—219d

刺果番荔枝 soursop (*Annona muricata*) 植物学 15—530c

刺果栎 bur oak (*Quercus macrocarpa*) 木本植物 3—256c

刺果松 bristlecone pine (species *Pinus aristata*) 松科小乔木 3—160d

刺果泽泻 burhead 草本植物 3—264e

刺魟 stingray 鱼类 16—239e

刺黄瓜 bur cucumber 植物学 3—256c

刺莲花科 Loasaceae 植物学 10—172b

刺鹩科 Acanthisittidae (bird family) 生物学 1—42c

刺龙属 Ceratosaurus 古生物学 4—9b

刺马甲子 Christ's thorn 灌木 4—211b

刺鳗 spiny eel 鱼类 16—33d

刺牛 rejoneo 斗牛 14—213b

刺丝胞 trichocyst 生物学 17—216c

刺丝囊 nematocyst 解剖学 12—73c

刺豚鼠 agouti 啮齿动物 1—126e

刺鲀 porcupine fish 鱼类 13—440e

刺尾飞蜥 spiny-tailed lizard 爬行动物 16—34b

刺尾鱼 tang (fish) 鱼类 16—461a

刺猬掌 hedgehog cactus 植物 7—554e

刺绣 embroidery 工艺 6—57d

刺绣样本 sampler 刺绣 15—1a

刺罂粟 prickly poppy 草本植物 13—506b

刺鱼 stickleback 鱼类 16—234e

刺鱼类 gasterosteiform 动物学 7—26b

赐地业主 cleruchy 古希腊历史 4—286f

赐地制 pronoia system 拜占廷封建制度 13—534a
赐职制 patronage system(U.S.) 政治 13—91f
葱科 Alliaceae 植物学 1—240b
葱绿玉髓 prase 矿物 13—485a
聪茨 Zunz, Leopold 德国犹太文学史家 18—574b
聪加人 Tsonga 民族 17—250b
从价税 ad valorem tax 经济学 1—62f
丛林 jungle 热带森林 9—111e
丛林狼 coyote (*Canis latrans*) 哺乳动物 4—560d
丛林狼狗 coydog 哺乳动物 4—560c
丛山雀 bushtit 鸟类 3—284c
从戏 cai luong 越南戏剧 3—324d
琮 cong 中国古代玉器 4—423a
粗布 crash 织物 4—570e
粗帆布 canvas 织物 3—415f
粗放农业 extensive agriculture 农作制度 6—197d
粗榧 plum-yew 木本植物 13—375d
粗花呢 tweed 纺织 17—300d
粗茎凤梨属 Puya 植物学 14—40a
粗蓝斜纹布工装裤 dungarees (apparel) 服装 5—461e
粗粒面粉 semolina 食品 15—206e
粗面安山岩 trachyandesite (rock) 岩石 17—186a
粗面石工 rustication 石工技术 14—466d
粗面岩 trachyte 岩石 17—186a
粗磨机 arrastra 机械 1—514c
粗硼砂 tincal (mineral) 矿物 17—104e
粗鳍鱼 dealfish 鱼类 5—194f
粗砂岩 grit 矿物 7—317a
粗斜棉布 denim 纺织品 5—244a
粗锌 spelter 锌块 16—18f
粗纸板 chipboard 纸产品 4—178a
粗质花边 Torchon lace 工艺品 17—159e
粗壮体型 mesomorph 体型分类 11—140b
粗籽黄花菜 clammyweed (*Polanisia trachysperma*) 草本植物 4—258f
促黄体激素 luteotropic hormone 生理学 10—294c
促进剂 accelerator 橡胶制造 1—44d
促进派革命 Promoters Revolution 泰国政变 13—533e
促卵泡激素 follicle-stimulating hormone (FSH) 生物化学 6—390e
促前胸腺素 prothoracotropin 生物化学 13—545b
促肾上腺皮质激素 adrenocorticotropic hormone (ACTH) 生物化学 1—85f
促胃液素 gastrin 生理学 7—27b
促狭鬼 poltergeist 神秘学名词 13—410d
促胸腺激素 thoracotropic hormone 生物学 17—54d
促胰酶素 pancreozymin (hormone) 生物化学 13—8c
猝倒病 damping-off 植物病 5—129d
酢浆草 wood sorrel 草本植物 18—321a
酢浆草属 Oxalis 植物学 12—518d
醋 vinegar 调味品 18—1a
醋栗 gooseberry 木本植物 7—210c
醋酸 acetic acid 化合物 1—49b
醋酸人造丝 acetate (textile) 纺织 1—49b
醋酸纤维 cellulose acetate 人造纤维 3—558b
醋酸乙烯酯 vinyl acetate 化学 18—2d
簇虫 gregarine 原生动物 7—297b
窜鸟 tapaculo 鸟类 16—474d
窜鸟科 Rhinocryptidae 动物学 14—264a
爨 Cuan 中国古代民族 5—46e
崔白 Cui Bai 中国画家 5—52e
崔济愚 Ch'oe Che-u 朝鲜东学教创始人 4—188c
崔泾 Ch'oe Kyŏng 朝鲜李朝画家 4—188d
崔可夫 Chuikov, Vasily Ivanovich 苏联元帅 4—219e
崔琦 Tsui, Daniel C. 华裔美国物理学家 17—251a
崔时亨 Ch'oe Si-hyŏng 朝鲜东学教领袖 4—188d
催产素 oxytocin 激素 12—525d
催化 catalysis 化学 3—520b
催化剂 catalyst 化学 3—520d
催化剂毒物 catalyst poison 化学 3—520e
催泪毒气 tear gas 化学 16—512b
催眠 hypnosis 心理学 8—294c
催乳激素 prolactin 生理学 13—532c
催生根 birthroot (plant) 草本植物 2—494a
催嚏草 sneezeweed 草本植物 15—460c
催欲 aphrodisiac 医学 1—408f
脆蛇蜥 glass snake 爬行动物 7—154c
脆银矿 stephanite 矿物 16—220b
脆云母 brittle mica 矿物 3—170d
淬火 quenching 金属加工工艺 14—86b
翠亨村 Cuihengcun 中国城镇 5—53b
翠菊 China aster 草本植物 4—165a
翠鴗 motmot 鸟类 11—434f
翠绿锂辉石 hiddenite 矿物 8—71e
翠鸟 kingfisher 鸟类 9—290b
翠鸟科 Alcedinidae (bird family) 生物学 1—188c
村山富市 Murayama Tomiichi 日本政治家 11—491f
村神 grāmadevatā 印度神 7—244c
村政府 municipio 地方民政机构 11—485a
皴 cun 中国绘画技法 5—60f
存货 inventory 贸易 8—426f
存款单 deposit, certificate of (CD) 金融 5—250d
存款账户 deposit account 金融 5—250d
存在的巨大链条 Great Chain of Being 哲学 7—270d
存在主义 Existentialism 哲学 6—193a
痤疮 acne 皮肤病 1—55c
措辞 diction 语言文字 5—301c
措林格尔 Zollinger, Albin 瑞士诗人、小说家 18—562f
锉刀 file 工具 6—314b
锉蛇 file snake 爬行动物 6—314b
错构瘤 hamartoma 病理学 7—437c
错觉 illusion 心理学 8—338b
错觉表现法 anamorphosis 视觉艺术 1—315c
错误陈述 misrepresentation 法律 11—276f

D

达巴迪兄弟 Abbadie, Antoine-Thomson d'; and Abbadie, Arnaud-Michel d' 法国地理学家、旅行家 1—5f
达比 Darby, Abraham 英国制造商 5—146f
达博 Dubbo 澳大利亚城市 5—439b
达博拉 Dabola 几内亚城镇 5—102b
达布 Darboux, (Jean-) Gaston 法国数学家 5—146e
达布蒂河 Tāpti River 印度河流 16—476d
达达 Datta, Michael Madhusudan 印度诗人 5—162f
达达 Datta, Narendranath (Indian mystic) 印度教精神领袖 5—162f
达达赫 Daddah, Moktar Ould 毛里塔尼亚总统 5—104c
达达尼尔海峡 Dardanelles 土耳其海峡 5—147b
《达达尼尔海峡条约》 Dardanelles, Treaty of the 欧洲历史 5—147c
达达尼尔海峡战役 Dardanelles Campaign 历史事件 5—147c
达达主义 Dada 西方艺术运动 5—104b
达德拉-纳加尔哈维利 Dādra and Nagar Haveli 印度区名 5—105a
达德利 Dudley 英格兰区名 5—446a
达德利 Dudley, Charles Benjamin 美国化学工程师 5—446b
达德利 Dudley, Dud 英国制造商 5—446c
达德利 Dudley, Edmund 英国政治家 5—446c
达德利 Dudley, Lady Jane 英格兰女王 5—446c
达德利 Dudley, John 英国贵族 5—446d

达德利 Dudley, Sir Robert 英国贵族 5—446d
达德利 Dudley, Thomas 英属殖民地总督 5—446d
达德利爵士 Dudley, Sir Robert 英国工程师 5—446d
达德利钻石 Dudley diamond (gem) 宝石 5—446e
达迪 Daddi, Bernardo 意大利画家 5—104d
达迪耶 Dadié, Bernard Binlin 科特迪瓦诗人 5—104f
达蒂尼 Datini, Francesco 意大利银行家 5—162a
达杜 Dādu 巴基斯坦城镇 5—105b
达杜 Dādū 印度教圣者 5—105a
达顿 Dutton, Clarence Edward 美国地质学家 5—482b
达恩 Dahn, (Julius Sophus) Felix 德国法理学家 5—109b
达恩利勋爵 Darnley, Henry Stewart, Lord 英国王室祖先 5—152e
达尔 Dahl, Roald 英国作家 5—108d
达尔巴赫里 Dayr al-Baḥrī 埃及考古遗址 5—183f
达尔贝达 Dār al-Bayḍā', ad- (Morocco) 摩洛哥城市 5—146a
达尔贝格 Dalberg, Karl Theodor von 德意志首主教 5—115c
达尔贝格公爵 Dalberg, Emmerich Joseph von Dalberg, duc de (duke of) 法国大臣 5—115c
达尔贝里 Dahlbergh, Eric, Count (Greve) 瑞典军人 5—108d
达尔德诸语言 Dardic languages 印度-伊朗语群 5—147e
达尔迪斯坦 Dardistān 巴基斯坦、克什米尔地区 5—147f
达尔富尔 Darfur 苏丹历史地区 5—148b
达尔戈梅日斯基 Dargomyzhsky, Aleksandr (Sergeyevich) 俄国作曲家 5—148c
达尔格伦 Dahlgren, John Adolphus Bernard 美国发明家 5—108e
达尔汗 Darhan 蒙古城镇 5—148d
达尔豪西 Dalhousie 加拿大城镇 5—116b
达尔豪西 Dalhousie 印度城市 5—116b
达尔豪西伯爵(第十一) Dalhousie, Fox Maule Ramsay, 11th earl of 英国大臣 5—116b
达尔豪西大学 Dalhousie University 加拿大高等学府 5—117a
达尔豪西侯爵和伯爵(第十) Dalhousie, James Andrew Broun Ramsay, marquess and 10th earl of 英国驻印总督 5—116c
达尔河 Dal River 瑞典河流 5—114e
达尔基斯 Dalkeith 苏格兰城市 5—118c
达尔加兰加陨石坑 Dalgaranga Crater 澳大利亚陨石坑 5—116b
达尔朗 Darlan, François 法国将领 5—150d
达尔里阿达 Dalriada 英国盖尔人古国 5—120e
达尔林普尔 Dalrymple, Alexander 英国地理学家 5—120f
达尔马迪纳 Dayr al-Madīnah 埃及古遗址 5—184a
达尔马提亚 Dalmatia 克罗地亚地区 5—119c
达尔马提亚公爵 Dalmatie, Nicolas Jean de Dieu Soult, duc de (duke of) 法国军人 5—120b
达尔马提亚狗 Dalmatian 狗品种 5—119f
达尔玛旺夏 Dharmavamsa 东爪哇国王 5—279f
达尔曼 Dahlmann, Friedrich (Christoph) 德意志历史学家 5—108f
达尔彭加 Darbhanga 印度城镇 5—146e
达尔斯 Dalles, The 美国城市 5—119b
达尔斯兰 Dalsland 瑞典旧省份 5—120f
达尔文 Darwin 澳大利亚港市 5—155c
达尔文 Darwin, Charles (Robert) 英国博物学家 5—155d
达尔文 Darwin, Erasmus 英国名医 5—158d
达尔文 Darwin, Sir George (Howard) 英国天文学家 5—158e
达尔文海梁 Darwin Rise 海底地形 5—158f
达尔文雀 Darwin's finch 鸟类 5—159b
达尔文氏蛙 Darwin's frog (*Rhinoderma darwinii*) 两栖动物 5—159b
达尔文主义 Darwinism 生物学学说 5—159a
达耳达诺斯 Dardanus 希腊神话人物 5—147e
达菲 Duffy, Sir Charles Gavan 爱尔兰民族主义者 5—448b
达费德 Dyfed 威尔士郡名 5—487f
达费林和阿瓦侯爵(第一) Dufferin and Ava, Frederick Temple Hamilton-Temple-Blackwood, 1st marquess of 英国外交家 5—448b
达佛尼斯 Daphnis 希腊神话人物 5—145c
达佛涅 Daphne 希腊神话人物 5—145a
达佛涅弗里亚节 Daphnephoria 希腊宗教节日 5—145b
达夫 Duff, Alexander 苏格兰教士 5—447f
达夫 Davel, Jean-Abraham-Daniel 瑞士民众领袖 5—166e
达夫 Duff, Mary Ann Dyke 美国悲剧演员 5—447f
达夫拉人 Dafla 亚洲民族 5—106a
达夫尼 Daphnae 埃及古城堡镇 5—145a
达盖尔 Daguerre, Louis-Jacques-Mandé 法国画家、物理学家 5—108b
达盖尔式照相法 daguerreotype 摄影 5—108c
达戈贝尔特 Dagobert 法兰克国王名 5—107d
达戈贝尔特二世 Dagobert Ⅱ 法兰克国王 5—107e
达戈贝尔特三世 Dagobert Ⅲ 法兰克国王 5—107e
达戈贝尔特一世 Dagobert Ⅰ 法兰克国王 5—107d
达戈伯特 Dagobert (leader of First Crusade) 十字军领袖 5—107e
达格班巴人 Dagbamba (people) 加纳民族 5—106d
达格达 Dagda 凯尔特宗教传说人物 5—106d
达格代尔 Dugdale, Sir William 英国文物学家 5—448f
达格岛 Dagö (Estonia) 爱沙尼亚岛屿 5—107d
达格利 Dagly, Gerhard 德国艺术家 5—107c
达贡巴人 Dagomba 加纳民族 5—107f
达古潘 Dagupan 菲律宾港市 5—108c
达哈翁 Dajabón 多米尼加共和国城镇 5—113d
达豪 Dachau 德国城市 5—103a
达豪 Dachau 纳粹集中营 5—103a
达荷美 Dahomey 西非王国 5—109c
达荷美 Dahomey (western Africa) 西非国家 5—109d
达荷美人 Dahomey (people) 非洲民族 5—109c
达赫 Dach, Simon 普鲁士诗人 5—102f
达赫兰 Dachlan, Kijai Hadji Ahmad 印度尼西亚伊斯兰教领袖 5—103b
达赫施泰因山 Dachstein 奥地利山脉 5—103c
达基耶·德佩尔贝 Darquier de Pellepoix, Louis 法国政客 5—153a
达吉基 Daqīqī 波斯诗人 5—145f
达吉斯坦 Dagestan 俄罗斯行政区域 5—106e
达吉斯坦地毯 Dagestan rug 俄罗斯工艺品 5—106f
达吉斯坦诸语言 Dagestanian languages 高加索语族 5—107a
达加尔 Dajjāl, ad- 伊斯兰教 5—113e
达加朱特 Tah-Gah-Jute (Iroquois Indian leader) 北美印第安人领袖 16—425c
达金氏液 Dakin's solution 防腐药 5—114c
达喀尔 Dakar 塞内加尔首都 5—113f
达卡 Dhākā 孟加拉国首都 5—278c
达坎 Daquin, Louis-Claude 法国作曲家 5—146a
达科 Dacko, David 中非总统 5—103e
达科鲁姆 Dacorum 英格兰地区 5—103f
达·科斯塔 da Costa, Uriel 犹太教理性派人物 5—101b
达科他河 Dakota River (U.S.) 美国河流 5—114e
达科他人 Dakota (American Indian) 北美大平原印第安民族 5—114e
达克莱克 Duck Lake 加拿大城镇 5—445c
达克山 Duck Mountain 加拿大高原 5—445d
达克斯 Dax 法国城镇 5—180e
达克斯伯里 Duxbury 美国城镇 5—483d
达克西尔·拉赫曼 Dākhīl Raḥmān, ad- (Umayyad ruler) 西班牙伍麦叶王朝君主 5—114b
达克战争 Dacke War 瑞典历史事件 5—103e
达肯菲尔德 Dukenfield, William Claude (American actor) 美国演员 5—452e
达拉卜 Dārāb 伊朗城镇 5—146d
达拉布卡鼓 darabukka 伊斯兰乐器 5—146d
达拉第 Daladier, Édouard 法国总理 5—114e

达拉赫 Darragh, Lydia Barrington 美国英雄 5—153b
达拉克 Darracq, (Pierre-) Alexandre 法国汽车制造商 5—153a
达拉姆 Dallam, Thomas 英格兰管风琴制造家 5—118d
达拉纳 Dalarna 瑞典省份 5—115b
达拉皮科拉 Dallapiccola, Luigi 意大利作曲家 5—118e
达拉齐 Darazī, Muḥammad ibn Ismāʿīl ad- 伊斯兰教宣教师 5—146e
达拉斯 Dallas 美国城市 5—118f
达拉斯 Dallas, George Mifflin 美国副总统 5—119a
达拉斯动物园 Dallas Zoo 美国动物园 5—119b
达莱卡尔利阿 Dalecarlia (Sweden) 瑞典省份 5—115e
达赖 Tarai 南亚地区 16—478d
达赖喇嘛 Dalai Lama 中国藏传佛教活佛称号 5—115a
达兰扎达嘎德 Dalandzadgad 蒙古城镇 5—115b
达朗伯 Alembert, Jean Le Rond d' 法国数学家 1—196d
达朗伯原理 d'Alembert's principle 物理学 5—115e
达朗·福盖尔 Dallán Forgaill 爱尔兰诗人 5—118d
达勒姆 Durham 英格兰郡名 5—473a
达勒姆 Durham 英格兰城市、区 5—473b
达勒姆 Durham 美国新罕布什尔州城镇 5—473c
达勒姆 Durham 美国北卡罗来纳州城市 5—473c
达勒姆牛 Durham (livestock) 牛品种 5—473d
达勒斯(弗里吉亚的) Dares Phrygius 特洛伊祭司、作家 5—148a
达雷 Daret, Jacques 法国画家 5—148b
达雷德统 Dalradian Series 地质学 5—120e
达雷尔 Durrell, Lawrence (George) 英国小说家、诗人 5—476f
达雷斯特 Arrest, Heinrich Louis d' 德国天文学家 1—515a
达雷斯特 Dareste de la Chavanne, Antoine(-Élisabeth-Cléophas) 法国历史学家 5—148a
达累斯萨拉姆 Dar es Salaam 坦桑尼亚城市 5—146b
达里奥 Darío, Rubén 尼加拉瓜诗人 5—149a
达里恩 Darien 美国城市 5—148f
达里恩 Darien 美国城镇 5—148f
达里维尔阶 Darriwilian Stage 地质学 5—153b
达里语 Dari language 伊朗语支语言 5—148d
达立普·辛格 Dalip Singh 印度锡克王国大君 5—118b
达利 Darley, George 英国诗人 5—150e
达利 Dalí, Salvador 西班牙画家 5—117c
达利戈达战役 Tālikota, Battle of 印度历史 16—444e
达利奇 Dulwich 英国伦敦住宅区 5—455a
达连 Darién 巴拿马历史地区 5—148e
达连湾 Darién, Gulf of 加勒比海海湾 5—148f
达林 Darin, Bobby 美国歌唱家、歌曲作家 5—149a
达林 Darling, Flora Adams 美国作家、历史学家 5—150f
达林 Darling, Grace 英国英雄 5—151a
达林 Darling, Jay Norwood 美国漫画家 5—151a
达林 Dalin, Olof von 瑞典作家 5—118b
达林顿 Darlington, Cyril Dean 英国生物学家 5—151d
达林和布尔沃男爵 Dalling and Bulwer (of Dalling), William Henry Lytton Earle Bulwer, Baron 英国外交官 5—119c
达灵顿 Darlington 英格兰城市、区 5—151d
达灵顿 Darlington 美国城市 5—151d
达令草地 Darling Downs 澳大利亚农牧区 5—151b
达令河 Darling River 澳大利亚河流 5—151b
达令山脉 Darling Range 澳大利亚山脉 5—151b
达卢 Dalou, (Aimé-) Jules 法国雕刻家 5—120b
达吕伯爵 Daru, Pierre-Antoine(-Noel-Mattieu-Bruno), Comte 法国官员 5—155b
达伦 Dalén, Nils (Gustaf) 瑞典发明家 5—115f
达罗 Darrow, Clarence (Seward) 美国律师 5—153c
达罗毗荼地域人种 Dravidian local race 印度地理人种亚群 5—416a
达罗毗荼风格 Drāviḍa style (Indian architecture) 印度建筑风格 5—415c
达罗毗荼诸语言 Dravidian languages 南亚地区语系 5—415c
达洛尼加 Dahlonega 美国城市 5—109a
达洛亚 Daloa 科特迪瓦城镇 5—120b
达马尔坦 Dammartin 法国伯爵领地 5—128d
达马津 Damazin, Ad- 苏丹城镇 5—127b
达马拉兰 Damaraland 纳米比亚历史地区 5—123e
达马树脂 dammar 清漆树脂 5—128c
达马斯基奥斯 Damascius 希腊哲学家 5—123f
达马斯金诺斯 Damaskinos 东正教雅典大主教 5—126f
达马松 dammar pine 植物 5—128d
达马苏斯二世 Damasus II 罗马教皇 5—127a
达马苏斯一世,圣 Damasus I, Saint 罗马教皇 5—126f
达马图鲁 Damaturu 尼日利亚城镇 5—127a
达马万德山 Demavend, Mount 伊朗山峰 5—232f
达玛鲁 damaru 宗教仪式用鼓 5—123e
达曼 Damān 印度城市 5—123d
达曼 Dammām, ad- 沙特阿拉伯城市 5—128c
达曼-第乌 Damān and Diu 印度区名 5—123d
达曼胡尔 Damanhūr 埃及城市 5—123e
达米埃塔 Damietta 埃及城市 5—127f
达米安 Damien, Father 比利时天主教司铎 5—127e
达米安 Damiens, Robert-François 法国狂热分子 5—127e
达米安,圣 Damian, Saint 基督教圣徒 5—127e
达米尔 Dāmir, ad- 苏丹城镇 5—128b
达米里 Damīrī, ad- 埃及穆斯林教义学家 5—128b
达摩-达古尔 Dharma-Ṭhākur 印度神名 5—279a
达摩克勒斯 Damocles 叙拉古廷臣 5—128e
达莫 Damoh 印度城镇 5—128f
达莫德尔河 Dāmodar River 印度河流 5—128f
达莫封 Damophon 古希腊雕刻家 5—128f
达默 Damme 比利时城市 5—128d
达默 Dahmer, Jeffrey 美国系列杀人犯 5—109a
达默 Dummer, Jeremiah 美洲殖民地驻英代表 5—456f
达姆 Dam, Henrik 丹麦生物化学家 5—123a
达姆达姆 Dum Dum 印度区名 5—455b
达姆-达姆热 Dum-Dumfever (disease) 疾病 5—455b
达姆甘 Dāmghān 伊朗城镇 5—127e
达姆拉利布塔 Tāmraliptā (India) 印度城市 16—454e
达姆罗施 Damrosch, Walter Johannes 美国音乐家 5—129e
达姆施塔特 Darmstadt 德国行政专区 5—151f
达姆施塔特 Darmstadt 德国城市 5—152b
达姆斯特泰尔 Darmesteter, Arsène 法国语言学者 5—151e
达姆斯特泰尔 Darmesteter, James 法国东方学家 5—151e
达穆 Damu 美索不达米亚神名 5—130c
达那俄斯 Danaus 希腊传说人物 5—131f
达纳 Dana, Charles A(nderson) 美国新闻记者 5—130f
达纳 Dana, James D(wight) 美国地质学家 5—130f
达纳 Dana, Richard Henry 美国律师 5—131d
达纳布尔 Dānāpur 印度城镇 5—131f
达纳基尔平原 Denakil Plain 埃塞俄比亚低地 5—241c
达纳基尔人 Danakil (people) 非洲民族 5—131e
达纳内 Danané 科特迪瓦城镇 5—131e
达纳炸药 dynamite 化学 5—488d
达瑙 Danao 菲律宾城市 5—131e
达内尔案 Darnel's case 英国历史案件 5—152d
达尼埃尔 Daniel, Arnaut 法国诗人 5—135a
达尼埃尔 Daniel, Gabriel 法国历史学家 5—135b
达尼埃尔(基辅的) Daniel of Kiev 俄国旅行家 5—134f
达尼埃尔(罗曼诺维奇) Daniel Romanovich 加利西亚、沃利尼亚君主 5—135a
达尼丁 Dunedin 新西兰港市 5—460e
达尼洛二世 Danilo II 门的内哥罗国君 5—135f

达尼洛一世 Danilo I 门的内哥罗国君 5—135f
达尼什曼德王朝 Dānishmend DYNASTY 土库曼王朝 5—136d
达尼韦 Duniway, Abigail Jane Scott 美国作家 5—463b
达农 Dunoon 苏格兰城镇 5—464f
达努女神之民 Tuatha Dé Danann 凯尔特神话 17—254c
达·蓬特 Da Ponte, Lorenzo 意大利诗人 5—101c
达皮丹 Dapitan 菲律宾港市 5—145c
达普桑峰 Dapsang (Jammu and Kashmir) 喜马拉雅山山峰 5—145d
达契亚 Dacia 罗马尼亚古地区 5—103c
《达萨姆·格兰特》 Dasam Granth 锡克教作品 5—159c
达塞人 Dāsa 印度民族 5—159c
达申斯基 Daszyński, Ignacy 波兰政治家 5—160c
达什柯娃 Dashkova, Yekaterina Romanovna Vorontsova, Knyaginya (Princess) 俄国贵族 5—159e
达舒尔 Dahshūr 埃及金字塔遗址 5—109e
达斯 Das, Chitta Ranjan 印度政治家 5—159b
达斯 Dass, Petter 挪威诗人 5—159e
达斯顿 Duston, Hannah Emerson 美国殖民地时期英雄 5—479e
达斯古普塔 Dasgupta, S(urendra) N(ath) 印度教哲学家 5—159c
达斯特格 dastgah 波斯音乐 5—160b
达斯万德 Dasvant 印度画家 5—160b
达松伐耳 Arsonval, Arsène d' 法国医生 1—520f
达索 Dassault, Marcel 法国飞机设计师 5—159f
达索企业 Dassault Industries 法国公司 5—159f
达特 Dart, Raymond A(rthur) 南非人类学家 5—153e
达特 Dart, Thurston 英国音乐学家 5—153e
达特福德 Dartford 英格兰自治市 5—154a
达特茅斯 Dartmouth 加拿大城市 5—154c
达特茅斯 Dartmouth 英格兰城镇 5—154c
达特茅斯 Dartmouth 美国城镇 5—154c
达特茅斯男爵(第二) Dartmouth, William Legge, 2nd Earl of, VISCOUNT LEWISHAM, BARON DARTMOUTH OF DARTMOUTH 英国政治家 5—154e
达特茅斯男爵(第一) Dartmouth (of Dartmouth), George Legge, 1st Baron 英国海军将领 5—154d
达特茅斯学院 Dartmouth College 美国高等学府 5—154e
达特茅斯学院案 Dartmouth College case 美国法院案例 5—154f
达特穆尔高地 Dartmoor 英格兰山地 5—154a
达特穆尔马 Dartmoor 马品种 5—154b
达托·伊拉迪耶 Dato Iradier, Eduardo 西班牙政治家 5—162b
达瓦尼 Dawānī 波斯哲学家 5—179a
达维德 David, Eduard Heinrich (Rudolph) 德国社会民主党领袖 5—170b
达维德斯库 Davidescu, Nicolae 罗马尼亚诗人 5—171e
达维德·斯特凡松 Davíd Stefánsson (Icelandic writer) 冰岛诗人 5—171e
达维多维奇 Davidović, Ljubomir 南斯拉夫首相 5—171f
达维拉 Davila, Arrigo Caterino 威尼斯历史学家 5—173d
达维拉 Dávila, Pedrarias (Spanish colonialist) 西班牙殖民地官员 5—173e
达维特 Davitt, Michael 爱尔兰政治家 5—178c
达文波特 Davenport 美国城市 5—166f
达文波特 Davenport, Charles Benedict 美国动物学家 5—167a
达文波特 Davenport, Edward Loomis 美国演员 5—167b
达文波特 Davenport, Fanny Lily Gypsy 美国演员 5—167c
达文波特 Davenport, John 英国牧师 5—167d
达文波特 Davenport, Thomas 美国发明家 5—167e
达文波特陶器 Davenport ware 英格兰陶器 5—167e
达文盖雷 Dāvangere 印度城镇 5—166d
达文特里 Daventry 英格兰城镇 5—167f
达沃城 Davao City 菲律宾城市 5—166d
达沃斯 Davos 瑞士城镇 5—178d
达斡尔语 Daghur language 中国达斡尔族语言 5—107b
达斡尔族 Daghur 中国民族 5—107a
达乌德 Daoud (Algeria) 阿尔及利亚城镇 5—144d
达乌德 Daud Khan, Mohammad 阿富汗政治家 5—163e
达武 Davout, Louis-Nicolas, DUC (duke) D'AUERSTEDT, PRINCE D'ECKMÜHL 法国将军 5—178e
达西 Darcy, Henri-Philibert-Gaspard 法国水利工程师 5—147a
达西 Darcy, Thomas Darcy, Lord 英格兰贵族 5—147a
达西埃 Dacier, Anne 法国文学评论家、翻译家 5—103d
达西定律 Darcy's law 水力学 5—147b
达仙德里亚 Taxandria (region, Belgium) 比利时高原地区 16—500f
达信 Taksin 暹罗将军 16—442c
达雅克人 Dayak 婆罗洲土著民族 5—182e
达亚 Daia (Roman emperor) 罗马皇帝 5—111c
达扬 Dayan, Moshe 以色列军人、政治家 5—183a
达耶难陀·娑罗室伐底 Dayananda Sarasvati 印度社会改革家 5—183c
达伊达拉节 Daedala 古希腊节日 5—105c
达因 dyne 计量单位 5—488f
达英·帕拉尼 Daing Parani 布吉人领袖 5—112e
达州 Dazhou 中国城市 5—185b
《答问》 responsa 犹太教书籍 14—242f
鞑靼 Tatarstan 俄罗斯一共和国 16—493c
鞑靼海峡 Tatar Strait 俄罗斯海峡 16—493b
鞑靼人 Tatar 民族 16—492d
鞑靼语 Tatar language 语言 16—493b
打鼾 snoring 睡眠症状 15—462b
打呵欠的人 Goyathlay (Apache Indian leader) 印第安人领袖 7—234a
打横 Tasikmalaya 印度尼西亚城市 16—489a
打箭炉 Ta-chien-lu (China) 中国古地名 16—412c
打拉根岛 Tarakan Island 印度尼西亚岛屿 16—478d
打兰 dram 计量单位 5—413f
打木栓 tip-cat 游戏 17—107f
打闹剧 slapstick 戏剧 15—426a
打油诗 doggerel 文学 5—361a
打字机 typewriter 机械 17—307e
大阿巴科 Great Abaco 巴哈马岛屿 7—268e
大阿德默勒尔蒂岛 Great Admiralty Island (Papua New Guinea) 巴布亚新几内亚岛屿 7—268e
大阿尔伯特,圣 Albert THE GREAT, SAINT 天主教哲学家 1—180b
大阿尔伯图斯,圣 Albertus MAGNUS, SAINT 天主教哲学家 1—182c
大阿尔冈昆诸语言 Macro-Algonquian languages 北美印第安语言 10—363a
大阿特拉斯山 Haut Atlas 摩洛哥山脉 7—514d
大安的列斯群岛 Greater Antilles 西印度群岛岛群 7—276c
大奥普里 Grand Ole Opry 美国音乐表演 7—251b
大澳大利亚湾 Great Australian Bight 澳大利亚海湾 7—269d
大巴德明顿 Great Badminton (England) 英格兰堂区 7—269e
大巴哈马 Grand Bahama 巴哈马岛屿 7—247e
大巴哈马浅滩 Great Bahama Bank 巴哈马大浅滩 7—269e
大巴哈马峡谷 Great Bahama Canyon 大西洋海底峡谷 7—269e
大巴里尔岛 Great Barrier Island 新西兰岛屿 7—269e
大巴灵顿 Great Barrington 美国城镇 7—269f
大巴萨 Grand Bassa (town, Liberia) 利比里亚城镇 7—247e
大巴萨姆 Grand-Bassam 科特迪瓦城市 7—247f
大巴山 Daba Shan 中国山脉 5—101f
大巴西勒,圣 Basil THE GREAT, SAINT 古代基督教教父 2—261a
大白菜 celery cabbage (*Brassica pekinensis*) 植物 3—553c
大白猪 Large White (breed of pig) 猪品种 9—499d
《大百科全书》 Grande Encyclopédie, La 法国百科全书 7—253a
《大百科事典》 Dai hyakkajiten 日本百科全书 5—110c
大阪 Ōsaka 日本府名 12—479a

大阪 Ōsaka 日本城市 12—479b
大阪-神户都会区 Ōsaka-Kōbe Metropolitan Area 日本都会区 12—479c
大棒政策 Big Stick Policy 美国历史 2—468a
《大宝律令》 Taihō code 日本历史 16—430d
大堡礁 Great Barrier Reef 澳大利亚珊瑚礁区 7—269e
大爆炸宇宙模型 big-bang model 宇宙演化理论 2—466d
大北方探险 Great Northern Expedition 俄国历史 7—273d
大北方战争 Great Northern War 欧洲历史 7—273e
大北铁路公司 Great Northern Railway Company 美国铁路企业 7—273d
大贝尔特海峡 Great Belt 丹麦海峡 7—270b
大贝尔特山 Big Belt Mountains 美国山脉 2—466e
大本德 Great Bend 美国城市 7—270b
大本德国家公园 Big Bend National Park 美国国家公园 2—466f
大本教 Ōmoto 日本宗教 12—415c
大本钟 Big Ben 伦敦大钟 2—466e
大鼻龙属 Captorhinus 古生物学 3—432f
大别山 Dabie Shan 中国山脉 5—102a
大波蒂奇国家保护地 Grand Portage National Monument 美国历史遗址 7—251b
大波兰 Wielkopolskie 波兰中西部省份 18—245e
大波兰地区奥斯特鲁夫 Ostrów Wielkopolski 波兰城市 12—494d
大波兰地区戈茹夫 Gorzów Wielkopolski 原波兰省份 7—220b
大波兰地区戈茹夫 Gorzów Wielkopolski 波兰城市 7—220b
大波兰湖区 Great Poland Lakeland 波兰湖泊地区 7—274a
大玻璃杯 Humpen glass 德国酒器 8—249e
《大般若波罗蜜多经》 Prajñāpāramitā 佛经名 13—483c
大不里士 Tabrīz 伊朗城市 16—416b
大不里士地毯 Tabrīz carpet 工艺品 16—416b
大不里士画派 Tabrīz school 绘画流派 16—416d
大不列颠 Great Britain 欧洲岛屿 7—270c
"大不列颠"号 Great Britain 航船 7—270c
大不列颠和爱尔兰浸礼联会 Baptist Union of Great Britain and Ireland 不列颠列岛基督教组织 2—213a
大布莱克河战役 Big Black River, Battle of 美国历史 2—467b
大仓喜八郎 Ōkura Kihachirō 日本财阀 12—364a
大草原城 Grande Prairie 加拿大城市 7—253a
大查科 Gran Chaco 南美洲平原 7—245e
大柴旦 Da Qaidam 中国城镇 5—101d
大肠 large intestine 解剖学 9—499c
大肠激躁病 Irritable bowel syndrome (IBS) 疾病 8—453f
大肠细菌 coliform bacteria 细菌 4—344f
大潮 spring tide 天文学 16—162f
大城 Phra Nakhon 泰国曼谷都市区之一部分 13—267e
大乘 Mahāyāna 佛教派别 10—399d
《大乘起信论》 Mahāyāna-śraddhotpāda-śāstra 佛教经典 10—399e
大川 Ōkawa 日本城市 12—358c
大川周明 Ōkawa Shūmei 日本政论家 12—358c
大村 Ōmura 日本城市 12—415f
大村益次郎 Ōmura Masujirō 日本学者、军人 12—415f
大迪克桑斯水坝 Grande Dixence Dam 瑞士重力坝 7—252e
大迪斯默尔沼泽 Great Dismal Swamp (U.S.) 美国沼泽地区 7—271c
大地测量学 geodesy 测绘学 7—70b
大地电流 telluric current 地球物理学 16—530b
大地懒 Megatherium 古生物学 11—81d
大地母亲 Earth Mother 宗教 5—498d
大地水准面 geoid 测绘学 7—71e
大蒂顿国家公园 Grand Teton National Park 美国公园 7—252a
大雕像 colossus 雕刻 4—365c
大调音阶 major scale 音乐 10—414b
大东 Daitō 日本城市 5—113d
"大东方"号 Great Eastern 航船 7—271e
大东诸岛 Daitō Islands 琉球群岛岛群 5—113d
大陡崖 Great Escarpment 非洲地貌 7—271f
大斗兽场 Colosseum 意大利罗马竞技场 4—365a
大豆 soybean (*Glycine max*, or *G. soja*) 植物学 15—558e
大都 Dadu 中国元朝首都 5—105b
大都 Taidu (China) 中国古都 16—429f
大都会歌剧院协会 Metropolitan Opera Association 美国歌剧公司 11—162a
大都会区 metropolitan area 都市区域 11—161e
大都会艺术博物馆 Metropolitan Museum of Art 美国博物馆 11—161f
大渡河 Dadu He 中国河流 5—105b
大多伦多市动物园 Metro Toronto Zoo 加拿大动物园 11—161c
大耳蝠 big-eared bat 哺乳动物 2—467c
大耳狐 bat-eared fox (species *Otocyon megalotis*) 哺乳动物 2—272f
大发作 grand mal 病理学 7—250e
大法官 lord chancellor 英国官职 10—219a
大法官法院 Chancery, Court of 英国衡平法法院 4—43c
大帆船瓷器 carrack porcelain 中国青花瓷器 3—479f
《大方广佛华严经》 Avata ṃsaka-sūtra 佛教经典 2—83f
大狒狒 chacma 动物 4—22e
大分 Ōita 日本县名 12—356d
大分水岭 Great Dividing Range 澳大利亚山脉 7—271d
大分子 macromolecule 化学 10—363e
大风 gale 气象学 6—551e
大风雪 blizzard 气象学 2—536e
大风子科 Flacourtiaceae 植物学 6—342d
大福克斯 Grand Forks 美国城市 7—249f
大复活节周期 Great Paschal period (calendars) 历法 7—273e
大干旱期 Great Droug 气候学 7—271d
大干线铁路 Grand Trunk Railway 加拿大铁路 7—252b
大冈忠相 Ōoka Tadasuke 日本法官 12—424c
大港 Dagang 中国天津市区名 5—106c
大高加索 Great Caucasus 欧洲山脉 7—270c
大哥伦比亚 Gran Colombia 南美历史国家 7—245f
大格里姆斯比 Great Grimsby (England) 英格兰城镇 7—272b
大格列高利 Gregory THE GREAT (pope) 罗马教皇 7—301a
大格洛克纳山 Grossglockner 奥地利山峰 7—321a
大公 grand duke 欧洲贵族称号 7—249d
大公 grandee 西班牙贵族称号 7—253b
《大公报》 Dagong Bao 中国报纸 5—107f
大公会 Great Sanhedrin 犹太人立法、司法机关 7—275b
大公爵 archduke 哈布斯堡王室称号 1—447d
大宫 Ōmiya 日本城市 12—415a
"大共和"号 Great Republic 美国快速帆船 7—274d
大古力水坝 Grand Coulee Dam 美国水坝 7—249d
大鼓 bass drum 乐器 2—267b
大馆 Ōdate 日本城市 12—336a
大管 bassoon 木管乐器 2—269f
大规模杀伤性武器 weapon of mass destruction (WMD) 武器 18—153f
大衮 Dagan 闪米特农神 5—106c
大国家党 Grand National Party (GNP) 韩国政党 7—251a
大国主神 Ōkuninushi 日本宗教 12—364a
大海鲢 tarpon 鱼类 16—484f
大海雀 great auk (*Pinguinus impennis*) 鸟类 7—269c
大韩 Taehan 东北亚古国 16—421b
大汉山 Tahan, Mount 马来半岛山峰 16—425d
大号 tuba 乐器 17—254d
大和 Yamato 日本城市 18—411d
大和古琴 yamato koto (musical instrument) 乐器 18—411e
大和绘 Yamato-e 绘画 18—411d

大和郡山 Yamato-Kōriyama 日本城市 18—411e
大河 Ca, River 3—303a
大河狸属 Castoroides 古生物学 3—514d
大赫尔莫波利斯 Hermopolis Magna 埃及古城 8—43b
大黑 Daikoku 日本神名 5—111f
大黑麦岛 Great Rye Island 斯洛伐克岛屿 7—274e
大红斑 Great Red Spot 天文学 7—274c
大狐猴 indri (*Indri indri*) 灵长动物 8—374b
大狐猴科 Indriidae 动物学 8—374c
大湖瀑布国家公园 Stora Sjöfallets National Park 瑞典公园 16—254a
大花草目 Rafflesiales 植物学 14—121d
大化革新 Taika era reforms 日本历史 16—430f
大黄 rhubarb 草本植物 14—271a
大会堂 Kneset ha-Gedola 犹太教组织 9—320f
大吉岭 Darjeeling 印度城镇 5—150a
大吉尼奥尔 Grand Guignol 戏剧 7—250a
大急流城 Grand Rapids 美国城市 7—251f
大戟 spurge 植物 16—165f
大戟科 Euphorbiaceae 植物学 6—162e
大戟目 Euphorbiales 植物学 6—162f
大戟属 Euphorbia 植物学 6—162e
大祭司 pontifex 罗马宗教 13—428e
大加那利岛 Gran Canaria 北大西洋岛屿 7—245e
大家庭 extended family 社会学 6—197b
大甲溪 Dajia Xi 中国台湾河流 5—113d
大剪刀 shears 工具 15—291c
大间歇泉 Great Geysir (Iceland) 冰岛间歇泉 7—272b
大江健三郎 Ōe Kenzaburō 日本小说家 12—340f
大奖赛 Grand Prix racing 汽车赛 7—251e
大蕉 plantain (*Musa paradisiaca*) 植物 13—345e
大蕉鹃 plantain-eater (bird) 鸟类 13—348a
大角 Arcturus 天文学 1—457a
大角斑羚 eland 哺乳动物 6—13d
大角羊 bighorn 哺乳动物 2—468f
大脚野人 Sasquatch 野人 15—74b
大教堂学校 cathedral school 教育 3—525a
大津 Ōtsu 日本城市 12—498f
大净 ghusl 伊斯兰教 7—114d
大竞技场 Circus Maximus 罗马竞技场 4—245c
大久保利通 Ōkubo Toshimichi 日本政治家 12—363d
大酒杯 tankard 酒器 16—467d
大酒神节 Great Dionysia 希腊节日 7—271c
大剧院 Bolshoi Theatre 俄罗斯戏剧团体 3—16e
大剧院 Grosses Schauspielhaus 德国剧院 7—320e
大剧院芭蕾舞团 Bolshoi Ballet 俄罗斯芭蕾舞团 3—16d
大觉国师 Daigak Guksa 高丽僧人 5—111d
大觉醒 Great Awakening 美洲宗教运动 7—269d
大卡鲁 Great Karroo 南非盆地 7—272c
大卡萨斯 Casas Grandes 墨西哥城镇 3—497c
大凯河 Great Kei River 南非河流 7—272d
大坎皮纳 Campina Grande 巴西城市 3—382c
大科学 Big Science 科学研究风格 2—467d
大孔代 Great Condé, the 法国将军 7—270e
大孔蒂 Grand Conti, le 法国贵族 7—249c
大孔蒂 Great Conti, the 法国贵族 7—270e
大口径前膛枪 blunderbuss 武器 2—552f
大拉比院 chief rabbinate 犹太教 4—148b
大来佐武郎 Okita Saburo 日本经济学家 12—360b
大老 tairō 日本行政职务 16—434d
大烙饼 bannock 苏格兰食品 2—207e
大叻 Da Lat 越南城市 5—101b
大理 Dali 中国城市 5—117a
大理查 Richard LE GRANT 英格兰坎特伯雷大主教 14—282c
大理石纹陶器 marbled pottery 陶器 10—491f
大理石状骨病 marble bone disease 疾病 10—491e
大理岩 marble 岩石 10—490d
大理院 Parlement 法国历史上的最高法院 13—57b
大力罗摩 Balarāma 印度教神话 2—161f
大力神火箭 Titan rocket 航天器运载火箭 17—114e
大丽花属 Dahlia 植物学 5—108e
大利奥 Leo THE GREAT 教皇 10—18c
大利拉 Delilah 圣经人物 5—226b
大连 Dalian 中国港市 5—117e
大联邦旗 Grand Union Flag 美国历史 7—252c
大凉山 Daliang Shan 中国山脉 5—118a
大梁 girder 建筑 7—142b
大量生产 mass production 生产方式 11—5e
大裂谷 Great Rift Valley (Africa) 非洲大裂谷 7—274d
大鳞大麻哈鱼 quinnat 鱼类 14—93f
大陵五 Algol 天文学 1—224b
大菱鲆 turbot (*Scophthalmus maximus*) 鱼类 17—277e
大羚羊 oryx 哺乳动物 12—478a
大流沙 Syrtis Major (Mediterranean Sea) 地中海海湾 16—407e
大流沙地带 Syrtis Major 天文学 16—407e
大流士 Darius 波斯国王名 5—149d
大流士二世 Darius II Ochus 波斯国王 5—149f
大流士三世 Darius III 波斯国王 5—150a
大流士一世 Darius I 波斯国王 5—149d
大柳草 great willow herb 植物 7—276c
大娄山 Dalou Shan 中国山脉 5—120c
大卢基 Velikiye Luki 俄罗斯城市 17—494d
大陆 continent 地理学 4—466a
大陆地盾 continental shield 地质学 4—468e
大陆分水岭 Continental Divide 北美分水岭 4—466f
大陆封锁政策 Continental System 欧洲历史 4—468f
大陆罐头公司 Continental Can Company 美国制造商 4—466d
大陆航空公司 Continental Airlines, Inc. 美国航空公司 4—466b
大陆会议 Continental Congress 美国历史 4—466d
大陆集团公司 Continental Group, Inc. 美国制造商 4—468b
大陆架 continental shelf 地质学 4—468d
大陆漂移 continental drift 地质学 4—466f
大陆坡 continental slope 地质学 4—468f
大陆气团 continental air mass 气象学 4—466d
大陆石油公司 Continental Oil Company (Conoco) 美国公司 4—468c
大伦敦 Greater London 英国都会郡 7—276e
大罗克坎迪山 Big Rock Candy Mountain 美国碳酸盐丘陵综合体 2—467d
大麻 hemp (species *Cannabis sativa*) 植物 8—11b
大麻 marijuana 植物或药物 10—511f
大麻哈鱼 chum salmon (*Oncorhynchus keta*) 鱼类 4—221b
大麻科 Cannabaceae 植物学 3—402c
大麻麻醉剂 hashish 药物 7—503a
大麻属 Cannabis 植物学 3—402d
大马南岛 Grand Manan Island 加拿大岛屿 7—250f
大马士革 Damascus 叙利亚首都 5—124a
大马士革波纹金属镶嵌 damascening 工艺 5—123f
大马士革大清真寺 Damascus, Great Mosque of 伊斯兰教寺院 5—126c
大马士革地毯 Damascus rug 工艺品 5—126d
大马士革钢 Damascus steel 古代钢材 5—126e
大马士革黑种草 love-in-a-mist (*Nigella damascena*) 植物 10—249d
《大马士革文献》 Damascus Document 犹太教典籍 5—126c
大迈阿密河 Great Miami River (Ohio, U.S.) 美国河流 7—273a

大迈哈莱 Maḥallah al-Kubrā, Al- 埃及城市 10—397d
大麦 barley 谷类植物 2—232a
大曼彻斯特 Greater Manchester 英格兰都会郡 7—276f
大冒险 Grand Hazard 骰子游戏 7—250a
大门德雷斯河 Büyük Menderes Nehri (Turkey) 土耳其河流 3—296c
大门剧团 Gate Theatre 爱尔兰戏剧 7—28f
大门乐队 Doors, the 美国乐队 5—387a
大名 daimyo 日本大领主 5—112e
《大明律》 Daminglü 中国法典 5—128a
大摩拉瓦河 Velika Morava (Serbia) 塞尔维亚河流 17—494d
大莫卧儿钻石 Great Mogul diamond 印度金刚石 7—273a
大牟田 Ōmuta 日本城市 12—415f
大拇指将军汤姆 Tom Thumb, General 美国侏儒 17—143a
大拇指汤姆 Thumb, Tom 美国侏儒演员 17—69e
大牧场 ranch 农业 14—146a
大南北 Dai Namboku 日本剧作家 5—111b
大南滩 Great South Beach (New York, U.S) 美国纽约州一狭长沙嘴 7—275d
大脑 cerebrum 解剖学 4—10e
大脑裂 cerebral fissure 解剖学 4—10b
大脑皮质 cerebral cortex 解剖学 4—10a
大脑性麻痹 cerebral palsy 病理学 4—10b
大奴湖 Great Slave Lake 加拿大湖泊 7—275b
大帕拉迪索国家公园 Gran Paradiso National Park 意大利国家公园 7—246b
大帕拉迪索山 Gran Paradiso 意大利山峰 7—246a
大叛乱 Great Rebellion 英国历史 7—274c
大疱性类天疱疮 bullous pemphigoid 皮肤病 3—249d
大陪审团 grand jury 法律 7—250c
大盆地 Great Basin 北美洲地理区 7—270a
大盆地国家公园 Great Basin National Park 美国国家公园 7—270a
大鹏 roc 传奇中的巨鸟 14—337a
《大毗卢遮那成佛神变加持经》 Mahāvairocana-sūtra 佛教作品 10—399b
大平原 Great plains 北美洲地理区 7—273f
大平原印第安人 Plains Indian 民族 13—339b
大平正芳 Ōhira Masayoshi 日本首相 12—353a
大苹果舞 big apple 美国舞蹈 2—466c
大瀑布 Grand Falls (Labrador, Canada) 加拿大瀑布 7—249f
大瀑布城 Grand Falls 加拿大新不伦瑞克省城镇 7—249f
大瀑布城 Grand Falls 加拿大纽芬兰岛城镇 7—249f
大瀑布城 Great Falls 美国城市 7—271f
大气 atmosphere 大气科学 2—30a
大气华 atmospheric corona 气象学 2—30f
大气环流 atmospheric circulation 气象学 2—30f
大气科学 atmospheric science 地球科学 2—31b
大气透视法 atmospheric perspective (visual arts) 气象学 2—31a
大气湍流 atmospheric turbulence 气象学 2—31b
大气压 atmosphere 压强单位 2—30e
大气折射 atmospheric refraction 大气科学 2—31b
大迁徙 Great Trek 南非历史 7—275e
大迁移 Great Migration 美国历史 7—273a
大浅滩 Grand Banks 加拿大大陆架 7—247e
大巧如拙 Taikō Josetsu 日本画家 16—431a
大秦景教流行中国碑 Xi'an monument 中国基督教 18—380c
大青鲨 great blue shark 鱼类 7—270c
大清河 Daqing He 中国河流 5—145e
大清洗 Great Purge 苏联历史 7—274b
《大清一统志》 Daqing Yitong Zhi 中国古代专志 5—145f
大庆 Daqing 中国城市 5—145d
大庆油田 Ta-ch'ing oil field (China) 中国石油产地 16—412c
大邱 Taegu 韩国城市 16—421a
大犬座α Alpha Canis Majoris 天文学 1—249f
大人 monsignor 天主教教士称号 11—351a
《大日经》 Dainichi-kyō 佛教经典 5—112f
大萨瓜 Sagua la Grande 古巴城市 14—499d
大萨索山 Gran Sasso d'Italia 意大利山群 7—246b
大塞本 Nagyszeben (Romania) 罗马尼亚城市 11—541d
大赛普里斯沼泽 Big Cypress Swamp 美国大森林沼泽 2—467c
大桑迪河 Big Sandy River 美国河流 2—467d
大瑟尔 Big Sur 美国风景区 2—468a
大沙岛 Great Sandy Island (Queensland, Australia) 澳大利亚岛屿 7—275a
大沙丘国家公园和保护区 Great Sand Dunes National Park and Preserve 美国地理区 7—275a
大沙沙漠 Great Sandy Desert 澳大利亚荒漠 7—275a
大舢板 launch 船载小艇 9—520a
大赦 amnesty 法律 1—294a
大赦国际 Amnesty International (AI) 国际组织 1—294a
大赦年 Jubilee, Year of 天主教节期 9—98d
大神农架 Dashennongjia 中国山地 5—159d
大圣伯纳德山口 Great Saint Bernard Pass 欧洲山口 7—274e
大师巡回赛 Masters Tournament 高尔夫邀请赛 11—14f
大诗 mahakavya 梵文诗体 10—397c
大诗琴 archlute 乐器 1—454d
大石斑鱼 jewfish 鱼类 9—8e
《大史》 Mahāvaṃsa 斯里兰卡编年史 10—399b
大矢车菊 basket-flower (*Centaurea americana*) 植物 2—263b
大使 ambassador 外交官员 1—269a
大士 mahāpuruṣa 印度教、耆那教、佛教名词 10—398b
《大事》 Mahāvastu 佛教经典 10—399b
《大事典》 Dai jiten 日本词典 5—110e
大手印 mahāmudrā 佛教 10—397e
大鼠 rat 啮齿动物 14—160b
大鼠耳蝠 large mouse-eared bat 哺乳动物 9—499d
大数定理 law of large numbers 统计学 9—529a
大斯卡西斯河 Great Scarcies River 西非河流 7—275b
大斯普林 Big Spring 美国城市 2—467f
大寺 Mahāvihāra 斯里兰卡佛寺 10—399c
大苏丹诸语言 Macro-Sudanic languages (Africa) 非洲语言 10—363c
大苏河 Big Sioux River 美国河流 2—467f
大苏铁属 Encephalartos 植物学 6—69a
大苏语诸语言 Macro-Siouan languages 北美印第安语言 10—363c
大蒜芥 rocket 草本植物 14—342d
《大唐西域记》 Datangxiyuji 佛教史籍 5—161b
大特尔诺沃 Veliko Tŭrnovo 保加利亚古城镇 17—494e
大特克 Grand Turk 西印度群岛岛屿 7—252b
大特拉弗斯湾 Grand Traverse Bay 美国湖湾 7—252a
大提琴 cello 乐器 3—557d
大田 Taejŏn 韩国城市 16—421b
大厅 great hall 建筑 7—272b
大通曼哈顿公司 Chase Manhattan Corporation, The 美国持股公司 4—87f
大同 Datong 中国城市 5—162c
大同 Datong 儒家学说 5—162e
大同江 Taedong River 朝鲜河流 16—420f
大同盟战争 Grand Alliance, War of the 欧洲历史 7—247c
大统一理论 grand unified theory 物理学 7—252c
大统一理论 GUT 物理学 7—382a
大头虫 Bumastus 古生物学 3—250d
大头杜父鱼 cabezone 鱼类 3—305c
大头蝇 thick-headed fly 昆虫 17—38a
大屠杀 Holocaust 欧洲历史 8—135d
大屠杀纪念日 Holocaust remembrance days 国际纪念日 8—136b

大瓦代恩 Grosswardein (Romania) 罗马尼亚城市 7—321c
大王 maharaja 印度行政管理等级 10—398c
大隈重信 Ōkuma Shigenobu 日本首相 12—363e
大卫 David 统治者之名 5—167f
大卫 David 古以色列国王 5—167f
大卫 David 米开朗琪罗雕刻 5—169e
大卫 David, Félicien-César 法国作曲家 5—170b
大卫 David, Jacques-Louis 法国画家 5—170d
大卫,圣 David, Saint 威尔士主保圣人 5—169f
大卫·当热 David d'Angers, Pierre-Jean 法国雕刻家 5—171d
大卫·德·梅瑞纳 David de Mayrena, Marie-Charles 法国冒险家 5—171e
大卫之盾 David, Star of 犹太人标志 5—171a
《大温克勒·普林斯》 Grote Winkler Prins 荷兰百科全书 7—321f
大汶口文化 Dawenkou culture 中国新石器时代文化 5—179b
大蚊 crane fly 昆虫 4—569b
大乌斯河 Great Ouse (England) 英国河流 7—273e
大乌斯秋格 Veliky Ustyug 俄罗斯城市 17—494f
大雾山 Great Smoky Mountains 美国山脉 7—275c
大雾山国家公园 Great Smoky Mountains National Park 美国国家公园 7—275c
大西部山脉 Great Western Mountains 澳大利亚山脉 7—276b
大西岛 Atlantis 传说中的岛 2—28f
"大西方"号 Great Western 航船 7—276b
大西洋 Atlantic Ocean 世界第二大洋 2—28c
大西洋岸比利牛斯 Pyrénées-Atlantiques 法国省份 14—46b
大西洋岸卢瓦尔 Loire-Alantique 法国省份 10—193d
大西洋城 Atlantic City 美国城市 2—28a
大西洋大海鲢 silver king 鱼类 15—377a
大西洋鲑 Atlantic salmon (species *Salmo salar*) 鱼类 2—28e
大西洋海岸联合会 Atlantic Coast Conference (ACC) 美国体育组织 2—28b
大西洋里奇菲尔德公司 Atlantic Richfield Company (ARCO) 美国公司 2—28d
大西洋鲭鲨 porbeagle 鱼类 13—439d
大西洋省 Atlántico 哥伦比亚省份 2—28e
《大西洋宪章》 Atlantic Charter 第二次世界大战史 2—27f
大西洋沿岸水道 Atlantic Intracoastal Waterway 美国沿海水道 2—28b
大西洋与太平洋茶叶公司 Great Atlantic & Pacific Tea Company, Inc. (A&P) 美国公司 7—269a
《大西洋月刊》 Atlantic, The 美国刊物 2—27e
大西洋战役 Atlantic, Battle of the 第二次世界大战史 2—27d
大西洋诸语言 Atlantic languages 尼日尔-刚果语系的语支 2—28b
大希腊 Magna Graecia 古意大利城市 10—385c
大悉达 mahāsiddha 佛教 10—398f
大细胞核 macronucleus 生物学 10—363f
大峡谷 Grand Canyon 美国峡谷 7—248c
大峡谷统 Grand Canyon Series 地质学 7—249b
大夏 Bactria 亚洲古代国名 2—125f
《大宪章》 Magna Carta 英国历史 10—383a
大乡绅 thane 英国历史 17—13c
大萧条 Great Depression 经济 7—270f
大协奏曲 concerto grosso 音乐 4—411a
大写字母 majuscule 书法 10—414f
大兴 Daxing 中国北京市辖区 5—180f
大兴安岭 Greater Khingan Range 中国山脉 7—276d
大猩猩 gorilla 灵长目动物 7—216e
大型海洋水族馆 oceanarium 咸水水族馆 12—327f
大型褐藻 kelp 海生植物 9—218d
大型猎物狩猎文化 Big-Game Hunting culture 古代北美文化 2—467c
大型土壤动物 macrofauna 生物学 10—363e
大型游览马车 charabanc 车 4—59e
大雄 Mahāvīra 耆那教创始人 10—399c
大雄寺 Somapura Mahāvīra 孟加拉国佛教寺院 15—504d
大熊湖 Great Bear Lake 加拿大湖泊 7—270b
大熊猫 panda, giant 哺乳动物 13—8c
大熊座 Ursa Major 天文学 17—418c
大熊座ζ Zeta Ursae Majoris (star) 天文学 18—513a
大选侯 Great Elector, the 勃兰登堡选侯 7—271f
《大学》 Daxue 儒家经典 5—180f
大学 university 高等学府 17—377b
大学才子 University wit 英国戏剧创作先驱 17—400f
大学城 Ciudad Universitaria 西班牙马德里区名 4—252c
大学附校 university extension 教育机构 17—400b
大学联合公司 Associated Universities, Inc. (AUI) 美国组织 1—563e
大学文科 liberal arts 教育 10—72c
大学学院 university college 高等教育机构 17—377f
大学预科 Gymnasium 德国中等学校 7—389b
大雪山 Daxue Shan 中国山名 5—181b
大勋位菊花章 Chrysanthemum, Order of the 日本最高勋章 4—215a
大巡回马赛 Grand Circuit 美国马赛 7—249c
大驯犬 mastiff 狗品种 11—15b
大驯犬蝙蝠 mastiff bat 哺乳动物 11—15c
大蕈甲 pleasing fungus beetle 昆虫 13—367c
大雅茅斯 Great Yarmouth 英国城镇 7—276c
大岩脉 Great Dyke 津巴布韦低山区 7—271e
大岩桐 gloxinia 植物学 7—163b
大盐湖 Great Salt Lake 美国湖泊 7—274f
大眼鲷 bigeye 鱼类 2—468e
大眼鰤鲈 walleyed pike 鱼类 18—81c
大眼鳕 bib (*Trisopterus*, or *Gadus*, *luscus*) 鱼类 2—457a
大扬琴 dulcimer 弦乐器 5—453d
大洋城 Ocean City 美国马里兰州旅游地 12—326f
大洋城 Ocean City 美国新泽西州旅游地 12—326f
大洋岛 Ocean Island (Kiribati) 基里巴斯岛屿 12—327d
大洋沟 oceanic trench 地质学 12—329b
大洋沟 trench, oceanic 地质学 17—209b
大洋环流 ocean current 海洋学 12—327a
大洋鲈 ocean perch 鱼类 12—327e
大洋洲 Oceania 世界大洲 12—320a
大洋洲艺术 Oceanic arts 艺术 12—328a
大洋洲诸语言 Oceanic languages 语言 12—328e
大窑文化 Dayao culture 中国旧石器时代文化 5—183c
大冶 Daye 中国城市 5—183d
大叶蜜花 honey bush (*Melianthus major*) 植物 8—153e
大衣橱 armoire 家具 1—501c
大隐修院 abbey 宗教建筑 1—8d
大英帝国 British Empire 英国历史 3—164f
大英帝国二等男爵士 K.B.E. 英国勋位 9—208b
大英帝国二等女爵士 D.B.E. 英国勋位 5—185e
大英帝国奖章 B.E.M. 英国奖章 2—373c
大英帝国三等爵士勋位 C.B.E. 英国勋位 3—545f
大英帝国四等爵士 O.B.E. 英国勋位 12—317f
大映影片公司 Daiei Motion Picture Company 日本制片厂 5—111c
大鱼河 Great Fish River 南非河流 7—272a
"大隅"号卫星 Ōsumi 日本人造卫星 12—495b
大隅诸岛 Ōsumi Archipelago 日本岛屿 12—495b
大屿山 Dayushan 中国岛屿 5—184e
大禹 Da Yu 中国传说人物 5—101e
大庾岭 Dayu Ling 中国山脉 5—184d
大御所时代 Ōgosho period (Japanese history) 日本历史 12—347d

大垣 Ōgaki 日本城市 12—345a
大圆弧航线 great circle route 航海 7—270e
大院君 Taewŏn-gun 朝鲜摄政王 16—421f
大跃进 Great Leap Forward 中国历史 7—272f
大运河 Grand Canal 中国运河 7—247f
大运河 Grand Canal 意大利运河 7—248b
《大藏经》 Dazangjing 佛教经典 5—185a
《大藏经》 Ta-ts'ang Ching 佛教经典 16—412c
大泽米属 Macrozamia 植物学 10—363f
大斋节 Lent 基督教节日 10—14c
大斋首日 Ash Wednesday 基督教节日 1—544b
大章克申 Grand Junction 美国城市 7—250b
大昭寺 Dazhao Monastery 中国佛教寺院 5—185a
大正天皇 Taishō 日本天皇 16—435a
大智赤神 In Ruad Ro-fhessa (Celtic religion) 凯尔特宗教 8—349e
大钟琴 carillon 乐器 3—459a
大仲马 Dumas, Alexandre, PÈRE 法国作家 5—455c
大众部 Mahāsaṅghika 佛教派别 10—398f
大众汽车公司 Volkswagen AG 德国公司 18—39e
大众艺术 popular art 艺术 13—435e
大烛教 Kuga Sorta 宗教 9—389f
大主教 archbishop 基督教会职称 1—447c
大助祭 archdeacon 基督教会职称 1—447d
大篆 dazhuan 中国书法 5—185d
大庄园 latifundium 罗马史 9—511c
大自流盆地 Great Artesian Basin 澳大利亚盆地 7—268f
大棕蝠 serotine 哺乳动物 15—226e
大足 Dazu 中国县名 5—185d
大足石刻 Dazu stone sculptures 中国文物 5—185e
大嘴雀 grosbeak 鸟类 7—320a
大罪 deadly sin 基督教 5—194a
呆鸟 gooney 鸟类 7—210b
呆小病 cretinism 疾病 5—9e
傣语 Dai language 中国民族语言 5—111a
傣语诸语言 Tai languages 东南亚语言 16—427e
傣族 Dai 中国民族 5—109f
傣族 Tai 东南亚民族 16—427a
代 dey 奥斯曼海盗头目头衔 5—277b
代 era 奥斯曼海盗头目头衔 6—109e
代阿布洛岭 Diablo Range 美国山脉 5—283c
代阿布洛峡谷 Canyon Diablo (meteor crater, Arizona) 美国亚利桑那陨石坑 3—416c
代奥吉里 Deogir (India) 印度古城市 5—249a
代奥克尔 Deoghar 印度城镇 5—249a
代奥里亚 Deoria 印度城镇 5—249c
代奥米德群岛 Diomede Islands 白令海峡岛群 5—327a
代奥赛山 Deosai Mountains 印度山脉 5—249d
代巴哈贝 Deba Habe 尼日利亚城镇 5—197c
代办 chargé d'affaires 国际法 4—64b
代比尔 Debir (ancient Palestine) 巴勒斯坦古城镇 5—197e
代表制 representation 政治学 14—234b
代博湖 Débo, Lac 马里湖泊 5—198a
代布勒 déblé 非洲工艺 5—197f
代称 kenning 语法 9—227f
代达罗斯 Daedalus 希腊神话建筑师 5—105e
代达罗斯雕刻 Daedalic sculpture 古希腊艺术 5—105d
代蒂瀑布 Dettifoss 冰岛瀑布 5—267f
代顿 Dayton 美国俄亥俄州城市 5—184b
代顿 Dayton 美国田纳西州城市 5—184c
代尔夫特 Delft 荷兰城市 5—222d
代尔夫特陶器 delftware 锡釉陶器 5—222d
代尔门霍斯特 Delmenhorst 德国城市 5—228e
代尔斯贝格 Delsberg (Switzerland) 瑞士城市 5—230b
代尔祖尔 Dayr az-Zawr 叙利亚城镇 5—184a
代芬特尔 Deventer 荷兰城市 5—271d
代盖赫利耶 Daqahlīyah, ad- 埃及省份 5—145d
代盖马 Degema 尼日利亚港镇 5—211c
代根多夫 Deggendorf 德国城市 5—211e
代赫里 Dehri 印度城市 5—212f
代赫里格尔瓦尔 Tehri-Garhwāl 印度城镇 16—516b
代赫纳沙漠 Dahnā', ad- 沙特阿拉伯沙漠 5—109c
代胡克 Dahūk 伊拉克城镇 5—109e
代肯 Deken, Aagje 荷兰女作家 5—215c
代理 agency 法律 1—119f
代理 agent 计算机用语 1—120c
代理权 attorney, power of 法律 2—41c
代利 Daehlie, Bjørn 挪威越野滑雪运动员 5—105f
代利杰里 Tellicherry 印度城市 16—530b
代鲁塔陶器 Deruta ware 意大利锡釉陶器 5—255e
代码 code 通信 4—326b
代莫内西群岛 Demonesi Insulae (Turkey) 土耳其群岛 5—238c
代姆雷 Demre (Turkey) 土耳其古城镇 5—241a
代目狗 Seeing Eye dog 动物 15—186d
代牧 vicar 教会职称 17—535b
代尼兹利 Denizli 土耳其城市 5—244e
代数方程 algebraic equation 数学 1—220c
代数几何 algebraic geometry 数学 1—220d
代数曲面 algebraic surface 数学 1—221b
代数数 algebraic number 数学 1—221a
代数拓扑 topology, algebraic 数学 17—157c
代数学 algebra 数学 1—220b
代斯诺斯 Desnos, Robert 法国诗人 5—262f
代斯鱼 dace 鱼类 5—102e
代诉人 proctor 法律 13—526e
代特莫尔德 Detmold 德国行政区 5—266f
代特莫尔德 Detmold 德国城市 5—267b
代替 substitution 诗歌 16—300f
代托纳比奇 Daytona Beach 美国城市 5—184d
代瓦吉里 Devagiri (village, India) 印度村庄 5—270c
代瓦斯 Dewās 印度城市 5—275d
代西奥 Desio 意大利城镇 5—261b
代希瓦勒-芒特拉维尼亚 Dehiwala-Mount Lavinia 斯里兰卡城市区 5—212c
代孕法 surrogate motherhood 代孕生育 16—358a
代扎 Dedza 马拉维城镇 5—205a
玳瑁斑纹陶器 tortoiseshell ware 工艺品 17—168d
玳瑁壳 tortoiseshell 装饰材料 17—168d
带齿兽 taeniodont 古生物学 16—421c
带虫 bootlace worm 动物学 3—42c
带传动 belt drive 机器传动装置 2—371d
带广 Obihiro 日本城市 12—320f
带绦虫属 Taenia 动物学 16—421c
带通滤波器 band-pass filter 电子装置 2—191d
带尾蜥蜴 girdle-tailed lizard 蜥蜴 7—142b
带纹 slick 水面污染 15—431a
带纹海豹 ribbon seal (*Histriophoca fasciata*) 哺乳动物 14—275e
带鱼 cutlass fish 鱼类 5—79b
带状疱疹 herpes zoster 疾病 8—49a
带状饰 strapwork 装饰艺术 16—262f
带状铁矿建造 banded-iron formation (BIF) 地质学 2—193c
带座凹室 exedra 建筑学 6—190f
袋貂 possum 哺乳动物 13—459a
袋猴 cuscus 哺乳动物 5—75e
袋獾 Tasmanian devil (species *Sarcophilus harrisii*, sometimes *S. ursinus*) 哺乳动物 16—490c

袋剑虎 Thylacosmilus 古生物学 17—75b
袋狼 Tasmanian wolf (*Thylacinus cynocephalus*) 哺乳动物 16—490e
袋狸 bandicoot 哺乳动物 2—194c
袋狸鼠 bandicoot rat (species *Bandicota indica*) 哺乳动物 2—194e
袋鼠 kangaroo 哺乳动物 9—156b
袋鼩 marsupial mouse 哺乳动物 10—543a
袋形动物 aschelminth 无脊椎动物 1—541b
袋鼹鼠 marsupial mole 哺乳动物 10—542f
袋鼬类 dasyurid 哺乳动物 5—160c
袋貂 numbat (*Myrmecobius fasciatus*) 哺乳动物 12—295a
逮捕 arrest 法律 1—514e
戴 Day, Arthur L(ouis) 美国地球物理学家 5—181c
戴 Day, Benjamin Henry 美国新闻工作者 5—181c
戴 Day, Clarence (Shepard) 美国作家 5—181d
戴 Day, Doris 美国歌唱家 5—181e
戴 Day, Dorothy 美国记者、社会改革者 5—181f
戴 Day, John 英格兰剧作家 5—181f
戴 Day, Sir Robin 英国电视记者 5—182a
戴 Day, Stephen 英属北美殖民地印刷商 5—182a
戴 Day, William R(ufus) 美国政治家、大法官 5—182b
戴阿克 Deák, Ferenc 匈牙利政治家 5—194c
戴爱莲 Dai Ailian 中国舞蹈家 5—110a
戴安娜 Diana, PRINCESS OF WALES 英国王妃 5—287e
戴德金 Dedekind, (Julius Wilhelm) Richard 德国数学家 5—204f
戴德姆 Dedham 美国城镇 5—204f
戴德伍德 Deadwood 美国城市 5—194b
戴东原 Tai Tung-yüan 中国古代思想家 16—428d
戴顿 Dayton, Jonathan 美国政治家 5—184c
戴顿 Deighton, Len 美国政治家 5—214a
戴尔 Dyer, Sir Edward 英格兰诗人 5—487d
戴尔 Dale, Sir Henry (Hallett) 英国生理学家 5—115d
戴尔 Dyer, Sir James 英格兰法官 5—487d
戴尔 Dyer, John 英国诗人 5—487f
戴尔 Dyer, Mary Barrett 美国宗教人物 5—487e
戴尔 Dyer, Reginald Edward Harry 英国将领 5—487f
戴尔 Dale, Richard 美国军官 5—115e
戴尔 Dare, Virginia 美洲出生的第一个英格兰孩子 5—147f
戴尔马 Delmas, Jacques(-Pierre-Michel) 法国政治家 5—228e
戴夫南特 Davenant, Sir William 英国诗人 5—166e
戴高乐 Gaulle, Charles(André Marie Joseph) de 法国总统 7—33b
戴高乐派 Gaullists (French political party) 法国政治派别 7—33f
戴假发者 Pelucón (member of a Chilean political group) 智利政治派别 13—132f
戴进 Dai Jin 中国画家 5—110d
戴菊 kinglet 鸟类 9—290e
戴凯巴路斯 Decebalus 达契亚人领袖 5—202a
戴克 Dyck, Anthonie van 佛兰德斯画家 5—487a
戴克里先 Diocletian 罗马皇帝 5—325c
戴克里先宫 Diocletian, Palace of 建筑 5—325f
戴克里先式窗 Diocletian window 建筑 5—326a
戴孔蒂 Conti, Michelangiolo dei (pope) 教皇 4—465f
戴逵 Dai Kui 中国雕塑家 5—110e
戴利 Daly, (John) Augustin 美国剧作家 5—121d
戴利 Daly, Marcus 美国企业家 5—121d
戴利 Daly, Reginald Aldworth 美国地质学家 5—121e
戴利 Daley, Richard J(oseph) 美国芝加哥市长 5—116a
戴利河 Daly River 澳大利亚河流 5—121f
戴-刘易斯 Day-Lewis C(ecil) 英国诗人 5—182c
戴流士 Delius, Frederick (Theodore Albert) 英国作曲家 5—227c
戴罗·乔伊奥 Dello Joio, Norman 美国作曲家 5—228d
戴蒙德港 Diamond Harbour 印度城镇 5—286f
戴蒙德火山口 Diamond Head 美国夏威夷海角 5—286f
戴蒙德角 Diamond, Cape 加拿大海角 5—286d
戴明 Deming, W. Edwards 美国统计学家 5—235a
戴莫雷斯特 Demorest, Ellen Louise Curtis 美国商人 5—238d
戴默尔 Dehmel, Richard 德国诗人 5—212d
戴姆伯特 Daimbert 意大利大主教 5—112c
戴姆勒 Daimler, Gottlieb (Wilhelm) 德国工程师 5—112c
戴姆勒-奔驰汽车公司 Daimler-Benz AG 德国公司 5—112d
戴佩里埃 Des Périers, Bonaventure 法国作家 5—256e
戴塞尔 Deyssel, Lodewijk van 荷兰作家 5—277c
戴森 Dyson, Freeman (John) 英国物理学家 5—489e
戴森 Dyson, Sir Frank (Watson) 英国天文学家 5—489d
戴森霍费 Deisenhofer, Johann 德国生物化学家 5—214f
戴胜 hoopoe (*Upupa epops*) 鸟类 8—165e
戴斯 Dyce, Alexander 苏格兰编辑 5—486f
戴斯 Dies, Martin, Jr. 美国政治家 5—306c
戴斯 Dyce, William 苏格兰画家 5—486f
戴维 David 巴拿马城市 5—169e
戴维 David AP GRUFFUDD 威尔士土王 5—170a
戴维 David AP LLYWELYN 威尔士王 5—170a
戴维 Davie, Donald Alfred 英国诗人 5—172c
戴维 Davy, Edward 英国化学家、发明家 5—178e
戴维 Dávid, Ferenc 基督教神学家 5—170c
戴维 David, Gerard 尼德兰画家 5—170c
戴维 Davy, Sir Humphry 英国化学家 5—178f
戴维 Davey, Norris Frank 新西兰作家 5—167f
戴维 David, Sir T(annatt) W(illiam) Edgeworth 澳大利亚地质学家 5—171b
戴维德(南莫的) Dafydd NANMOR 威尔士诗人 5—106b
戴维德·艾布·爱德华 Dafydd AP EDMWND 威尔士诗人 5—106b
戴维德·艾布·格维利姆 Dafydd AP GWILYM 威尔士诗人 5—106b
戴维灯 Davy lamp 安全照明工具 5—179a
戴维二世 David II 苏格兰国王 5—169d
戴维港 Port Davey 澳大利亚小海湾 13—444e
戴维教派 Branch Davidians 宗教 3—118b
戴维森 Davidson, Bruce 美国摄影家 5—171f
戴维森 Davidson, John 苏格兰诗人 5—172a
戴维森 Davidson, Thomas 苏格兰博物学家 5—172b
戴维森 Davison, William 英格兰女王秘书 5—178b
戴维森(兰贝斯的) Davidson (of Lambeth), Randall Thomas Davidson, Baron 英国坎特伯雷大主教 5—172a
戴维丝 Davis, Bette 美国演员 5—174b
戴维斯 Davis 美国城市 5—173e
戴维斯 Davies, Arthur B(owen) 美国画家 5—172c
戴维斯 Davis, Arthur Hoey 澳大利亚作家 5—174a
戴维斯 Davis, Alexander Jackson 美国建筑师 5—173e
戴维斯 Davis, Angela (Yvonne) 美国活动家 5—173f
戴维斯 Davis, Charles Harold 美国画家 5—174d
戴维斯 Davis, Charles Henry 美国军官、科学家 5—174d
戴维斯 Davis, Sir Colin (Rex) 英国乐队指挥 5—174e
戴维斯 Davis, David 美国政治家 5—174e
戴维斯 Davies, David Ivor 威尔士作曲家 5—172d
戴维斯 Davis, Dwight F(illey) 美国运动员 5—174e
戴维斯 Davis, Elmer (Holmes) 美国新闻播音员 5—174f
戴维斯 Davis, H(arold) L(enoir) 美国小说家 5—175a
戴维斯 Davis, Henry Winter 美国政治家 5—175a
戴维斯 Davis, Jefferson 美国南部邦联总统 5—175b
戴维斯 Davis, Joe 英国运动员 5—175d
戴维斯 Davies, Sir John 英国诗人 5—172e
戴维斯 Davies, John (grammarian) 威尔士语法学家 5—172e
戴维斯 Davis, John 英国航海家 5—175e
戴维斯 Davies (of Hereford), John 英国诗人 5—172e
戴维斯 Davis, John W. 美国政治家 5—175f

戴维斯 Davis, Katharine Bemen 美国刑罚学家、作家 5—175f
戴维斯 Davis, Kingsley 美国社会学家 5—176b
戴维斯 Davies, Marion 美国演员 5—172f
戴维斯 Davis, Miles 美国音乐家 5—176c
戴维斯 Davis, Paulina Kellogg Wright 美国女权主义者、社会改革家 5—176e
戴维斯 Davies, Peter Maxwell 英国作曲家 5—173a
戴维斯 Davis, Rebecca Blaine Harding 美国作家 5—177b
戴维斯 Davis, Richard Harding 美国作家 5—177b
戴维斯 Davies, Robertson 加拿大剧作家 5—173b
戴维斯 Davies, Samuel 英属北美殖民地牧师 5—173c
戴维斯 Davies, (Sarah) Emily 英国教育家 5—172e
戴维斯 Davis, Stuart 美国画家 5—177c
戴维斯 Davis, Thomas Osborne 爱尔兰作家、政治家 5—177d
戴维斯 Davies, William Henry 英国诗人 5—173d
戴维斯 Davis, William Morris 美国地理学家 5—177e
戴维斯(兰蒂纳姆的) Davies (of Llandinam), David Davies, 1st Baron 英国政治学家 5—172d
戴维斯(老) Davis, Benjamin Oliver, Sr. 美国陆军将领 5—174a
戴维斯(小) Davis, Benjamin Oliver, Jr. 美国空军将领 5—174a
戴维斯(小) Davis, Raymond, Jr. 美国物理学家 5—177a
戴维斯杯 Davis Cup 体育奖杯 5—177f
戴维斯海峡 Davis Strait 大西洋海湾 5—178a
戴维斯和迪伊 Davis, Ossie; and Dee, Ruby 美国夫妻演出队 5—176e
戴维斯山 Davis, Mount 美国山名 5—176d
戴维斯山脉 Davis Mountains 美国山脉 5—178a
戴维孙 Davisson, Clinton Joseph 美国物理学家 5—178c
戴维一世 David I 苏格兰国王 5—169c
戴维营 Camp David 美国地名 3—376a
《戴维营协议》 Camp David Accords 埃及-以色列协议 3—376b
戴文进 Tai Wen-chin 中国古代画家 16—428d
戴西 Dicey, Albert Venn 英国法学家 5—294b
戴震 Dai Zhen 中国思想家 5—111b
黛德丽 Dietrich, Marlene 德国电影演员 5—308c
黛莱达 Deledda, Grazia 意大利作家 5—222b
黛伦 Deren, Maya 美国导演、表演艺术家 5—253c
黛特 Deirdre 爱尔兰文学 5—214e
黛瓦达西 Devadāsī 印度原妇女种姓 5—270c
丹巴 Damba 安哥拉城镇 5—127b
丹巴德 Dhānbād 印度城镇 5—278f
丹比伯爵 Danby, Thomas Osborne, Earl of 英格兰政治家 5—132a
丹波伊斯 d'Amboise, Jacques 美国芭蕾舞演员 5—127c
丹伯里 Danbury 美国城市 5—131f
丹伯里制帽工会案 Danbury Hatters' Case 美国案件 5—132a
丹达卡兰亚 Dandakāranya 印度自然区域 5—132f
丹达拉 Dandarah 埃及城镇 5—132f
丹德尔斯 Daendels, Herman Willem 荷兰军人 5—105f
丹德农岭 Dandenong Ranges 澳大利亚山脉 5—133b
丹迪·丁蒙㹴狗 Dandie Dinmont terrier 狗品种 5—133b
丹第 Indy, (Paul-Marie-Theodore-) Vincent d' 法国作曲家 8—379a
丹蒂卡特 Danticat, Edwidge 美国作家 5—141d
丹蒂斯库斯 Dantiscus, Johannes 波兰诗人 5—141e
丹东 Dandong 中国城市 5—133e
丹东 Danton, Georges(-Jacques) 法国革命领袖 5—141e
丹毒 erysipelas 皮肤感染 6—125a
丹毒丝菌属感染 erysipelothrix infection 传染病 6—125a
丹兑 Sandoway 缅甸城镇 15—29e
丹多洛 Dandolo, Enrico 威尼斯执政官 5—133d
丹多洛 Dandolo, Vincenzo 意大利化学家 5—133e
丹多洛家族 Dandolo FAMILY 威尼斯执政官家族 5—133d
丹佛 Denver 美国城市 5—248e
丹佛-里奥格兰德西方铁路公司 Denver and Rio Grande Western Railroad Company 美国铁路企业 5—248f
丹弗姆林 Dunfermline 苏格兰区名 5—461a
丹弗姆林 Dunfermline 苏格兰城市 5—461b
丹弗斯 Danvers 美国城镇 5—143c
丹格里加 Dangriga 伯利兹城镇 5—134e
丹绘 tan-e 日本绘画 16—455a
丹吉尔 Tangier 摩洛哥省份 16—464c
丹江口 Danjiangkou 中国城市 5—136e
丹江口水利枢纽工程 Danjiangkou Key Water Control Project 中国水利工程 5—136f
丹杰菲尔德 Dangerfield, Thomas 英国告密者 5—134b
丹夸 Danquah, J(oseph Kwame Kyeretwi) B(oakye) 加纳政治家 5—137e
丹老 Mergui 缅甸城镇 11—129e
丹老群岛 Mergui Archipelago 缅甸群岛 11—129e
丹龙·腊贾努巴 Damrong Rajanubhab 泰国亲王 5—129e
丹麦 Denmark 欧洲国家 5—244f
丹麦边墙 Danewirk 丹麦古边境壁垒 5—134b
丹麦大狗 Great Dane 狗品种 7—270f
丹麦海峡 Denmark Strait 格陵兰与冰岛间海峡 5—246a
丹麦皇家芭蕾舞团 Royal Danish Ballet 丹麦芭蕾舞团 14—431b
丹麦区 Danelaw 英国史 5—134a
丹麦人俄吉 Ogier THE DANE 法国文学 12—346c
丹麦人民福音信义会 Evangelical Lutheran People's Church of Denmark 丹麦国定教会 6—178d
丹麦水族馆 Denmark's Aquarium 丹麦科研、展出机构 5—246a
丹麦税 Danegeld 英国史 5—134a
丹麦文学 Danish literature 欧洲文学 5—136c
丹麦语 Danish language 欧洲语言 5—136b
丹奈 Dannay, Frederic 美国作家 5—137a
丹尼 Dennie, Joseph 美国作家 5—246c
丹尼尔 Daniel, Peter V(ivian) 美国最高法院大法官 5—135c
丹尼尔 Daniel, Samuel 英国诗人 5—135c
丹尼尔森 Danielsen, Karen 美国精神分析学家 5—135e
丹尼尔斯 Daniels, Josephus 美国外交家 5—135d
丹尼尔松 Danielsson, Anders 瑞典农民领袖 5—135e
丹尼列夫斯基 Danilevsky, Nikolay Yakovlevich 俄国博物学家 5—135e
丹尼洛娃 Danilova, Alexandra 俄罗斯芭蕾舞演员 5—135f
丹尼森 Denison 美国城市 5—244d
丹尼森 Dennison, Aaron Lufkin 美国制表家 5—246f
丹尼斯 Dennis 美国城镇 5—246d
丹尼斯 Dennis, Eugene 美国政治家 5—246e
丹尼斯 Dennis, John 英国评论家、作家 5—246e
丹尼斯 Dennis, Nigel 英国作家 5—246f
丹尼斯, 圣 Denis, SAINT 巴黎主教 5—244b
丹尼斯肖恩舞蹈学校 Denishawn School of Dancing and Related Arts 美国舞蹈教育和演出机构 5—244c
丹尼特 Dennett, Mary Coffin Ware 美国改革家 5—246b
丹聂耳 Daniell, John Frederic 英国化学家 5—135d
丹·帕奇 Dan Patch 美国赛马 5—130e
丹皮尔 Dampier 澳大利亚城镇 5—129a
丹皮尔 Dampier, William 英国海盗 5—129a
丹普尔 Temple, Le 法国王家监狱 16—534c
丹齐 Danzi, Franz (Ignaz) 德国作曲家 5—143e
丹人 Dan 非洲民族 5—130d
丹戎 Danjon, André-Louis 法国天文学家 5—137a
丹戎加兰 Tanjung Karang 印度尼西亚城市 16—466f
丹萨兰 Dansalan (Philippines) 菲律宾城市 5—137e
丹斯 Dines, William Henry 英国气象学家 5—320f
丹斯(小) Dance, George, THE YOUNGER 英国建筑师 5—132a
丹徒 Tan-t'u (China) 中国县名 16—455e
丹维尔 Danville 美国伊利诺伊州城市 5—143d

丹维尔 Danville 美国肯塔基州城市 5—143d
丹维尔 Danville 美国弗吉尼亚州城市 5—143e
丹下健三 Tange Kenzō 日本建筑师 16—463e
丹因 Dine, Jim 美国画家 5—320e
《丹珠尔》 Bstan-'gyur 佛教著作 3—216f
担轮幼虫 trochophore 动物 17—229e
担子果 basidiocarp 微生物 2—259b
担子菌纲 Basidiomycetes 微生物学 2—259b
单板类 monoplacophoran 软体动物 11—346a
单孢子虫 haplosporidian 原生动物 7—467f
单笔石 Monograptus 古生物学 11—345a
单纯疱疹 herpes simplex 疾病 8—48f
单打式墙网球 squash tennis 体育项目 16—169a
单斗挖掘机 power shovel 挖土和起重机械 13—474e
单杠 horizontal bar 体育器械 8—174b
单轨铁路 monorail 铁路 11—346f
单棍 singlestick 格斗比赛 15—395b
单核吞噬细胞系统 mononuclear phagocyte system 生理学 11—345d
单核细胞增多症 mononucleosis 疾病 11—345d
单簧管 clarinet 乐器 4—263a
单簧口琴 Jew's harp 乐器 9—9e
单角鲀 filefish 海产鱼 6—314c
单晶 single crystal 结晶物质 15—395a
单克隆抗体 monoclonal antibody 免疫学 11—344a
单孔类 monotreme 哺乳动物 11—347f
单肋蛤 Monopleura 古生物学 11—346b
单马两轮轻便车 one-horse shay 美国马车 12—417f
单马双轮篷车 cabriolet 法国马车 3—309c
单面大活页歌谣 broadside ballad 欧洲文学 3—172a
单面山 cuesta 地质学 5—52c
单宁 tannin 生物化学 16—468f
单片滤波器 monolithic filter 电子器件 11—345a
单鳍六线鱼 Atka mackerel 鱼类 2—26d
单鳍鳕 cusk (*Brosme brosme*) 鱼类 5—77b
单鳍鱼类 sweeper 鱼类 16—379b
单人剧 monodrama 戏剧 11—344c
单人纸牌戏 Solitaire 纸牌游戏 15—497c
单身女子 feme sole 法律 6—271c
单声部音乐 monophony 音乐 11—345e
单糖 monosaccharide 生物化学 11—347a
单体 monomer 化学 11—345b
单桅小帆船 sloop 帆船 15—434f
单位信托公司 unit trust 金融机构 17—349c
单斜晶系 monoclinic system 晶体学 11—343f
单斜岭 homoclinal ridge (landform) 地质学 8—147f
单性结实 parthenocarpy 植物学 13—65d
单性现象 unisexuality 生物学 17—349a
单旋律独唱曲 monody 音乐 11—344d
单一婚制 henogamy 社会学 8—16c
单一税 single tax 税务 15—395a
单一尾韵诗 monorhyme 诗歌 11—347a
单翼机 monoplane 飞机 11—346b
单音步诗行 monometer 诗歌 11—345c
单原子气体 monatomic gas 物理学 11—330e
单子 monad 哲学 11—328f
单子叶植物 monocotyledon 植物学 11—344a
单座两轮马车 sulky 敞篷轻便车 16—325f
鲋类 danio 鱼类 5—136b
胆矾 blue vitriol 矿物 2—549c
胆矾 chalcanthite 矿物 4—29f
胆固醇 cholesterol 化合物 4—190f
胆红素 bilirubin 脊椎动物胆汁中色素 2—472f
胆碱 choline 化合物 4—191b
胆碱能药 cholinergic drug 药物 4—191b
胆囊 gallbladder 解剖学 6—557b
胆囊炎 cholecystitis 疾病 4—190d
胆囊造影术 cholecystography 诊断方法 4—190d
胆色素 bilin 生物色素 2—472e
胆石 gallstone 生物化学 6—561e
胆汁 bile 生物化学 2—472c
但丁 Dante 意大利诗人 5—138a
《但以理书》 Daniel, The Book of 《圣经》 5—135a
但泽 Danzig (Poland) 波兰城市 5—143f
但泽公爵 Dantzig, François-Joseph Lefebvre, Duke (duc) de 法国元帅 5—142e
但泽湾 Danzig, Gulf of 波罗的海海湾 5—143f
但支派 Dan 希伯来部族 5—130e
诞生石 birthstone 表示出生月份的宝石 2—494a
淡红银矿 proustite 矿物 13—549a
淡路岛 Awaji Island 日本岛屿 2—91f
淡马鲁 Temerloh 马来西亚城镇 16—531e
淡啤酒艾菊 ale cost (herb) 草本植物 1—195a
淡水 Danshui 中国城镇 5—137f
淡水海绵 freshwater sponge 海绵动物 6—484d
淡水河 Danshui He 中国河流 5—137f
淡水螺 freshwater snail 软体动物 6—484d
淡水鸭 freshwater duck 水禽 6—484d
弹道学 ballistics 军事科学 2—177e
弹劾 impeachment 法律 8—345c
弹簧 spring 机械零件 16—162a
弹簧秤 spring balance 称重工具 16—162d
弹球 marble 游戏 10—491c
弹球机 pinball machine 游艺机 13—306f
弹射器 catapult 机械装置 3—521e
弹涂鱼 mudskipper 鱼类 11—463b
弹尾虫 springtail 昆虫 16—164e
弹药 ammunition 武器 1—293e
弹震症 shell shock 神经性疾病 15—297a
蛋 egg 食品 5—556c
蛋白结合碘试验 protein-bound iodine test 医学 13—543b
蛋白酶 proteinase 生物化学 13—543c
蛋白尿 proteinuria 病理现象 13—543c
蛋白石 opal 矿物 12—425d
蛋白水解酶 proteolytic enzyme 生物化学 10—540c
蛋白酥皮 meringue 食品 11—131c
蛋白相纸 albumen paper 摄影 1—186a
蛋白杏仁饼 macaroon 食品 10—327f
蛋白质 protein 生物化学 13—542f
蛋白质浓缩物 protein concentrate 饮食添加剂 13—543b
蛋白质营养不良 protein malnutrition 疾病 13—543c
蛋彩画 tempera painting 绘画 16—532c
蛋黄果 canistel (*Lucuma nervosa*) 植物 3—401f
蛋黄酱 mayonnaise 食品 11—54a
蛋箭饰 egg and dart 建筑 5—556e
蛋奶糕 custard 食品 5—77c
氮(N) nitrogen 化学元素 12—204d
氮化物 nitride 化合物 12—203f
氮麻醉 nitrogen narcosis 生理学 12—205f
氮欣快 nitrogen euphoria (medicine) 生理学 12—205c
氮循环 nitrogen cycle 生物化学 12—205b
氮族元素 nitrogen group element 化学元素 12—205e
当甘公爵 Enghien, Henri-Jules de Bourbon, Duke (duc) d' 法国孔代亲王 6—78a
当甘公爵 Enghien, Louis-Antoine-Henri de Bourbon-Condé, Duke (duc) d' 法国王子 6—78a

当古 Dancourt, Florent Carton 法国剧作家 5—132e
当归属 angelica 植物学 1—341d
当量 equivalent weight 化学 6—109c
当坦 Dantin, Louis 加拿大法语诗人 5—141e
当特尔卡斯托海峡 D'Entrecasteaux Channel 澳大利亚海峡 5—248c
当特尔卡斯托群岛 D'Entrecasteaux Islands 太平洋岛群 5—248d
挡土墙 retaining wall 土木工程 14—245d
党锢 dang gu 中国东汉政治事件 5—134c
党卫军 SS 德国纳粹部队 16—174c
党项 Dangxiang 中国古代民族 5—134e
氹仔岛 Dangzai Island 中国澳门地名 5—134e
荡双桨 sculling 体育 15—161b
档案馆 archives 档案保存机构 1—453f
刀 knife 工具 9—321a
刀耕火种农业 slash-and-burn agriculture 农业 15—426b
刀嘴海雀 razor-billed auk (*Alca torda*) 鸟类 14—174e
氘 deuterium 氢同位素 5—268c
氘核 deuteron 重氢核 5—268e
导弹 guided missile 武器 7—353f
导弹 missile 武器 11—277b
导弹预警卫星 Midas 美国军用卫星 11—197f
导管 vessel 植物学 17—529c
导航 navigation 航行技术 12—51b
导生制 monitorial system 教育 11—340e
导数 derivative 数学 5—253e
导演 directing 表演艺术 5—336b
导演 régisseur 戏剧导演 14—204f
岛风字体 Insular script 书法 8—402b
岛根 Shimane 日本县名 15—315b
岛弧 island arc 地质学 8—469a
岛津久光 Shimazu Hisamitsu KOSHAKU 日本藩主 15—315e
岛津齐彬 Shimazu Nariakira 日本藩主 15—315e
岛津氏 Shimazu FAMILY 日本武士家族 15—315d
岛津重豪 Shimazu Shigehide 日本藩主 15—315f
岛鹃 coua 鸟类 4—540d
岛崎藤村 Shimazaki Tōson 日本诗人 15—315c
岛山 inselberg 地质学 8—398f
《岛史》 Dīpavaṃsa 斯里兰卡文献 5—331c
岛田 Shimada 日本城市 15—315b
岛屿 island 地质学 8—467e
岛屿式舞台 island stage 戏剧舞台形式 8—469b
岛原 Shimabara 日本城市 15—315a
岛原暴动 Shimabara Rebellion 日本历史 15—315b
蹈火 fire walking 宗教仪式 6—327b
倒地铃 balloon vine (species *Cardiospermum halicacabum*) 木质藤本植物 2—178e
倒挂金钟属 Fuchsia 植物学 6—508f
倒立鱼 headstander 鱼类 7—538f
倒提壶 hound's-tongue 植物 8—193d
倒叙 flashback 电影、文学手法 6—349a
倒置法 hyperbaton 文学 8—291a
倒装 inversion 文学 8—427e
悼念诗节 In Memoriam stanza 诗歌 8—349d
悼婴节 Holy Innocents, Feast of the 基督教节日 8—141b
盗窃 theft 犯罪行为 17—20f
盗窃狂 kleptomania 精神错乱病症 9—316d
盗蟹 robber crab 蟹类 14—325c
盗用 embezzlement 犯罪行为 6—56f
道 dao 中国哲学 5—143f
道 mārga 印度教名词 10—503a
道 Dou, Gerrit 荷兰画家 5—397b
道 Dow, Charles Henry 美国记者 5—405b
道 Dow, Herbert H. 美国化学家 5—405c
道 Dow, Neal 美国政治家 5—405d
道安 Dao'an 中国僧人 5—143f
道布尔戴 Doubleday, Abner 美国军人 5—398f
道布尔戴 Doubleday, Frank Nelson 美国出版商 5—398f
道布莱特上衣 doublet 服装 5—399a
道成肉身 Incarnation 基督教 8—350e
道乘 tariqa 伊斯兰教 16—482e
道春 Dōshun (Japanese scholar) 日本学者 5—393c
道绰 Daochuo 中国僧人 5—144a
道达尔法国石油公司 TOTAL Compagnie Française des Pétroles (TOTAL CFP) 法国公司 17—171e
道德重建运动 Moral Re-Armament (MRA) 美国宗教团体 11—383a
《道德重整》杂志 Advocate of Moral Reform 美国杂志 1—90e
道德教育 Ethical Culture 教育运动 6—145d
《道德经》 Daodejing 中国道教经典 5—144a
道德剧 morality play 中世纪戏剧剧种 11—383e
道德神学 moral theology 基督教神学 11—383a
道蒂 Doughty, Charles Montagu 英国旅行家 5—399e
道丁男爵(第一) Dowding, Hugh Caswall Tremenheere Dowding, 1st Baron 英国元帅 5—405f
道恩伯爵 Daun, Leopold Joseph, Graf von 奥地利军官 5—165d
道尔比尼 Orbigny, Alcide Dessalines d' 法国古生物学家 12—445c
道尔顿 Dalton, John 英国化学家、气象学家 5—121b
道尔顿定律 Dalton's law 物理学 5—121c
道尔顿陶瓷 Doulton ware 英格兰陶瓷 5—403c
道费里 Dauferi (pope) 教皇 5—164e
道格拉斯 Douglas 英国城市 5—399f
道格拉斯 Douglas 美国郊区名 5—399f
道格拉斯 Douglas 美国亚利桑那州城市 5—399f
道格拉斯 Douglas 美国佐治亚州城市 5—400a
道格拉斯 Douglas 美国怀俄明州城市 5—400a
道格拉斯 Douglas, Aaron 美国艺术家 5—400e
道格拉斯 Douglas, Archibald 苏格兰贵族 5—400e
道格拉斯 Douglass, Andrew Ellicott 美国天文学家 5—402f
道格拉斯 Douglas, Clifford (Hugh) 英国经济学家 5—400e
道格拉斯 Douglas, David 苏格兰植物学家 5—400f
道格拉斯 Douglas, Donald (Wills) 美国飞机设计师 5—400f
道格拉斯 Douglass, Frederick 美国人权领袖 5—402f
道格拉斯 Douglas, Gawin 苏格兰诗人 5—401a
道格拉斯 Douglas, (George) Norman 苏格兰作家 5—401f
道格拉斯 Douglas, George 苏格兰小说家 5—401b
道格拉斯 Douglas, Helen Mary Gahagan 美国演员 5—401b
道格拉斯 Douglas, James 苏格兰贵族 5—401c
道格拉斯 Douglas, James 美国采矿工程师 5—401c
道格拉斯 Douglas, Sir James 加拿大政治家 5—401e
道格拉斯 Douglas, Keith Castellain 英国诗人 5—401e
道格拉斯 Douglas, Margaret 英格兰贵族 5—401f
道格拉斯 Douglas, Stephen A(rnold) 美国政治家 5—401f
道格拉斯 Douglas, Thomas 苏格兰慈善家 5—402b
道格拉斯 Douglas, William 苏格兰贵族 5—402b
道格拉斯 Douglas, William O(rville) 美国大法官 5—402b
道格拉斯 DC-3 Douglas DC-3 (U.S. aircraft) 飞机 5—402c
道格拉斯伯爵 Douglas, EARLS OF 苏格兰贵族 5—400b
道格拉斯伯爵(第八) Douglas, William Douglas, 8th earl of 苏格兰贵族 5—400c
道格拉斯伯爵(第二) Douglas, James Douglas, 2nd earl of 苏格兰贵族 5—400b
道格拉斯伯爵(第九) Douglas, James Douglas, 9th earl of 苏格兰贵族 5—400d
道格拉斯伯爵(第四) Douglas, Archibald Douglas, 4th earl of 苏格兰军人 5—400c

道格拉斯伯爵(第一) Douglas, William Douglas, 1st earl of 苏格兰贵族 5—400b
道格拉斯-霍姆 Douglas-Home, Sir Alec 英国首相 5—402d
道格拉斯爵士 Douglas, Sir James 苏格兰贵族 5—401d
道格拉斯氏海况和长浪分级表 Douglas scale 海洋学 5—402e
道格拉斯氏杉 Douglas fir 植物 5—402c
道光 Daoguang 中国清朝皇帝年号 5—144b
道加瓦河 Daugava River (Europe) 欧洲河流 5—164e
道家 Taoist school 中国古代哲学流派 16—473b
道教 Taoism 中国宗教 16—472e
道镜 Dōkyō 日本佛僧 5—363c
道坎塔斯 Daukantas, Simanas 立陶宛历史学家 5—165a
道拉 Daura 尼日利亚城镇 5—166b
道拉达巴德 Daulatābād 印度村庄、古城 5—165b
道拉德 Daulat 印度画家 5—165a
道拉吉里峰 Dhaulāgiri 尼泊尔峰群 5—279f
道拉尼 Darányi, Kálmán 匈牙利政治家 5—146d
道兰德 Dowland, John 英国作曲家 5—406b
道勒斯沃勒姆 Dowlaiswaram 印度城镇 5—406b
道利什 Dawlish 英格兰城镇 5—179f
道路 road 交通 14—323d
道路手册 itinerarium 古罗马帝国路线图 8—489d
道尼尔 Dornier, Claudius 德国工程师 5—390e
道奇 Dodge, Bernard Ogilvie 美国植物学家 5—357e
道奇 Dodge, Grace Hoadley 美国慈善家 5—357f
道奇 Dodge, Grenville Mellen 美国工程师 5—358a
道奇 Dodge, Josephine Marshall Jewell 美国教育家 5—358b
道奇 Dodge, John V. 美国编辑、出版商 5—358b
道奇 Dodge, Mary Abigail 美国散文作家 5—358c
道奇 Dodge, Mary Mapes 美国儿童读物作家 5—358c
道奇 Dodge, William E. 美国企业家 5—358d
道奇堡 Fort Dodge 美国城市 6—413d
道奇城 Dodge City 美国城市 5—358e
道奇森 Dodgson, Charles Lutwidge (novelist) 英国小说家 5—358e
道奇兄弟 Dodge, Horace E.; and Dodge, John F. 美国汽车制造商 5—358a
道-琼斯平均指数 Dow Jones average 金融 5—405e
道森 Dawson 加拿大城市 5—180b
道森 Dowson, Ernest (Christopher) 英国诗人 5—407f
道森 Dawson, George Geoffrey 英国记者 5—180c
道森 Dawson, Sir John William 加拿大地质学家 5—180d
道森河 Dawson River 澳大利亚河流 5—180e
道森克里克 Dawson Creek 加拿大城市 5—180d
道生 Daosheng 中国东晋僧人 5—144b
道士 daoshi 中国道教徒 5—144c
道氏化学公司 Dow Chemical Company 美国企业 5—405d
道斯 Dawes, Sophie 英格兰冒险家 5—179d
道斯 Dawes, William Rutter 英国天文学家 5—179d
《道斯土地分配法案》 Dawes General Allotment Act 美国法律 5—179e
道威斯 Dawes, Charles G(ates) 美国副总统 5—179c
《道威斯计划》 Dawes Plan 第一次世界大战史 5—179e
道维 Dowie, John Alexander 美国布道家 5—406a
道元 Dōgen 日本僧人 5—360e
《道藏》 Daozang 中国道教经典 5—144d
道长 Michinaga (Japanese regent) 日本统治者 11—190e
道昭 Dōshō 日本僧人 5—393c
稻草人 scarecrow 农业 15—104d
稻荷神 Inari 日本护稻神 8—349f
稻米母亲 Rice Mother 印度尼西亚神话人物 14—280a
稻雀 ricebird 鸟类 14—280c
稻鼠 rice rat 啮齿动物 14—280c
稻泽 Inazawa 日本城市 8—350b
得格·巴哈都尔 Tegh Bahādur 印度锡克教祖师 16—515b
得奖纪念碑亭 choragic monument 建筑物 4—197a
得救预定论 predestination 基督教教义 13—489f
得克萨斯 Texas 美国州名 17—2e
得克萨斯城 Texas City 美国城市 17—6b
得克萨斯石油公司 Texaco Inc. 美国公司 17—2d
得克萨斯-太平洋铁路公司 Texas and Pacific Railway Company 美国公司 17—6b
得克萨斯巡逻队 Texas Rangers 美国治安部队 17—6f
得克萨斯仪器公司 Texas Instruments Incorporated (TI) 美国制造商 17—6c
得克萨斯州诉怀特案 Texas v. White 美国法院案例 17—6f
得梅因 Des Moines 美国城市 5—256b
得梅因河 Des Moines River 美国河流 5—256d
《得梅因记事报》 Des Moines Register, The 美国报纸 5—256d
得莫丰 Demophoon 希腊神话人物 5—238c
得墨忒耳 Demeter 希腊女神 5—233c
得票最多者当选制 plurality system 选举法 13—377d
得土安 Tétouan 摩洛哥城市 16—562d
得土安公爵 Tetuán, Leopoldo O'Donnell, duque (duke) de 西班牙政治家 17—1a
锝(Tc) technetium 化学元素 16—512e
德 de 中国哲学术语 5—186b
德 virtue 基督教 18—15a
德阿 Déat, Marcel 法国政客 5—196a
德埃利 Ailly, Pierre d' 法兰西神学家 1—141c
德昂语 De'ang language 中国民族语言 5—195e
德昂族 De'ang 中国民族 5—195d
德奥班德学院 Deoband school 印度伊斯兰学院 5—249a
德奥合并 Anschluss 欧洲历史 1—370b
德奥塔鲁斯 Deiotarus 加拉西亚国王 5—214c
德巴基 De Bakey, Michael Ellis 美国外科医生 5—186c
德巴里 Bary, Heinrich Anton de 德国植物学家 2—253f
德拜 Debye, Peter (Joseph William) 美国物理化学家 5—199f
德拜-休克尔方程 Debye-Hückel equation 物理化学 5—200a
德班 Durban 南非港市 5—471e
德班 D'Urban, Sir Benjamin 英国将领 5—471f
德贝赖纳 Döbereiner, Johann Wolfgang 德国化学家 5—353f
德比 Derby 澳大利亚城镇 5—251f
德比 Derby 英格兰城市 5—251f
德比 Derby 美国城市 5—252a
德比伯爵 Derby, earls of 英格兰贵族 5—252b
德比伯爵 Derby, Henry, earl of 英格兰国王 5—252b
德比伯爵(第七) Derby, James Stanley, 7th earl of 英格兰贵族、将领 5—252c
德比伯爵(第三) Derby, Edward Stanley, 3rd earl of 英格兰贵族 5—252c
德比伯爵(第十四) Derby, Edward (George Geoffrey Smith) Stanley, 14th earl of 英国政治家 5—252d
德比伯爵(第一) Derby, Thomas Stanley, 1st earl of 英格兰贵族 5—252b
德比瓷器 Derby ware 英格兰瓷器 5—252e
德比尔 de Beer, Sir Gavin (Rylands) 英国动物学家 5—186c
德比尔斯联合矿业公司 De Beers Consolidated Mines, Ltd. 南非企业 5—186d
德比郡 Derbyshire 英格兰郡名 5—252f
德比郡戴尔斯 Derbyshire Dales 英格兰区名 5—253b
德比马赛 Derby 英国马赛 5—252a
德·比斯内 De Busne, Antoine (composer) 法国作曲家 5—186f
德彪西 Debussy, Claude 法国作曲家 5—199b
德波尔特 Desportes, Alexandre-François 法国画家 5—263d
德波尔特 Desportes, Philippe 法国诗人 5—263e
德波林 Deborin, Abram Moiseyevich 苏联哲学家 5—198a

德博尔德-瓦尔摩尔 Desbordes-Valmore, Marceline 法国诗人 5—257e
德·博诺 De Bono, Emilio 意大利将领 5—186e
德布劳 Deburau, Jean-Gaspard 法国演员 5—199b
德布勒森 Debrecen 匈牙利城市 5—198c
德布雷 Debré, Michel(-Jean-Pierre) 法国政治家 5—198c
《德布雷特氏贵族名鉴》 Debrett's Peerage 英国贵族名录 5—198e
德布林 Döblin, Alfred 德国作家 5—354a
德布鲁 Debreu, Gerard 美国经济学家 5—198e
德布罗意 Broglie, (Louis-César-Victor-) Maurice, 6ᵉ duc de 法国物理学家 3—175c
德布罗意 Broglie, Louis-Victor(-Pierre-Raymond), 7ᵉ duc de 法国物理学家 3—175c
德布罗意波 de Broglie wave 物理学 5—186f
德布兹 Debs, Eugene V. 美国劳工领袖 5—198f
德处 gunasthana 印度耆那教 7—371e
德川纲吉 Tokugawa Tsunayoshi 日本幕府将军 17—135c
德川光圀 Tokugawa Mitsukuni 日本藩主 17—134f
德川吉宗 Tokugawa Yoshimune 日本幕府将军 17—135d
德川家光 Tokugawa Iemitsu 日本幕府将军 17—134d
德川家康 Tokugawa Ieyasu 日本幕府建立者 17—134d
德川齐昭 Tokugawa Nariaki 日本藩主 17—135a
德川庆喜 Tokugawa Yoshinobu 日本幕府将军 17—135d
德川时代 Tokugawa period 日本历史 17—135b
德川秀忠 Tokugawa Hidetada 日本幕府将军 17—134c
德川昭致 Tokugawa Keiki 日本幕府将军 17—134f
德达 Thatta 巴基斯坦城镇 17—16e
德岛 Tokushima 日本城市 17—135f
德·蒂尔托夫 de Tirtoff, Romain (designer) 俄国舞台布景、服装设计师 5—191c
德蒂亚 Datia 印度城市 5—161e
德蒂耶蒙 Tillemont, (Louis-) Sébastien Le Nain de 法国历史学家 17—96b
德尔 Dell, Floyd 美国小说家 5—227e
德尔布吕克 Delbrück, Berthold 德国语言学家 5—221e
德尔布吕克 Delbrück, (Martin Friedrich) Rudolph von 德意志帝国政治家 5—221f
德尔布吕克 Delbrück, Max 美国生物学家 5—221f
德尔布兰克 Delblanc, Sven 瑞典小说家 5—221e
德尔斐 Delphi 古希腊神庙遗址 5—229e
德尔卡塞 Delcassé, Théophile 法国政治家 5—222a
德尔·卡斯蒂略 Del Castillo, Michel 西班牙政治家 5—215e
德尔雷比奇 Delray Beach 美国城市 5—230b
德尔里奥 Del Rio 美国城市 5—215f
德尔马瓦半岛 Delmarva Peninsula 美国半岛 5—228d
德尔蒙特 Ciocchi del Monte, Giovanni Maria (pope) 教皇 4—243a
德尔蒙特 Monte, Giovanni Maria Ciocchi del (pope) 教皇 11—360c
德尔·蒙特食品公司 Del Monte Food 美国食品公司 5—215e
德尔纳 Darnah 利比亚城镇 5—152c
德尔普特 Derpt (Estonia) 爱沙尼亚旧大学城 5—255a
德尔塔 Delta 加拿大城镇 5—230b
德尔塔 Delta 美国城市 5—231a
德尔塔 Delta 尼日利亚州名 5—230c
德尔塔航空公司 Delta Air Lines, Inc. 美国公司 5—231b
"德尔塔"号运载火箭 Delta 美国火箭 5—231a
德尔特约尔 Dörtyol 土耳其城镇 5—392d
德尔图良 Tertullian 迦太基基督教神学家 16—558a
德尔维涅 Delvigne, Henri-Gustave 法国军人、发明家 5—232a
德尔维斯·穆罕默德·齐利 Derviş Mehmed Zilli (Ottoman traveler) 土耳其旅行家 5—255f
德尔维希 dervish 伊斯兰苏非派教团成员 5—255f
德尔沃 Delvaux, Paul 比利时画家 5—231f
德芳侯爵夫人 Deffand, Marie de Vichy-Chamrond, marquise du 法国文人 5—208e
德费尔 Defferre, Gaston 法国政治家 5—209a
德芬特 Deventer, Conrad Theodor van 荷兰政治家 5—271d
德夫 Dove, Arthur G. 美国画家 5—404c
德·夫里厄斯 De Vries, Peter 美国小说家 5—192c
德弗 D'Urfey, Thomas 英国剧作家 5—472d
德弗尔斯莱克 Devils Lake 美国城市 5—272d
德弗里恩特 Devrient, Eduard 德国演员、导演 5—274d
德弗里恩特 Devrient, Emil 德国演员 5—274e
德弗里恩特 Devrient, Karl August 德国演员 5—274e
德弗里恩特 Devrient, Ludwig 德国演员 5—274e
德弗里恩特 Devrient, Max 德国演员 5—274f
德弗里恩特 Devrient, Otto 德国演员 5—275a
德弗里斯 Vries, Adriaen de 荷兰雕刻家 18—53d
德弗里斯 Vries, Hugo (Marie) de 荷兰植物学家 18—53d
德弗罗 Devereux, Robert 英格兰贵族 5—271e
德弗罗 Devereux, Walter 英格兰军人 5—271e
德弗斯 Devers, Jacob L. 美国将领 5—271e
德福雷斯特 DeForest, John William 美国作家 5—209f
德福雷斯特 De Forest, Lee 美国发明家 5—187b
德富芦花 Tokutomi Rōka 日本小说家 17—136a
德富苏峰 Tokutomi Sohō 日本历史学家 17—136a
德干高原 Deccan 印度南部地区 5—201e
德干绘画 Deccani painting 印度画派 5—201f
德格湖 Derg, Lough 爱尔兰湖泊 5—253d
德格雷尔 Degrelle, Léon 比利时政治领袖 5—212c
德格雷河 De Grey River 澳大利亚河流 5—187f
德格伊 DGI 古巴情报机构 5—278b
德古 Decoux, Jean 法国将领 5—204d
德国 Germany 欧洲国家 7—95a
《德国百科全书》 Konversationslexikon 百科全书 9—348b
德国电子同步加速器实验室 DESY 物理学研究机构 5—265b
德国福音会 Evangelical Church in Germany, The 德国宗教机构 6—177f
德国工会联合会 Deutscher Gewerkschaftsbund (DGB) 德国工会组织 5—269d
德国雇员工会 Deutsche Angestellten-Gewerkschaft (DAG) 德国工会组织 5—269a
德国国家人民党 German National People's Party 德国政党 7—90e
德国国家社会主义工人党 National Socialist German Workers' Party 德国政党 12—37a
德国国家社会主义工人党 Nationalsozialistische Deutsche Arbeiterpartei 德国政党 12—39e
德国联合福音信义会 United Evangelical Lutheran Church of Germany 德国基督教会 17—352a
德国麻疹 German measles 疾病 7—90d
《德国民法典》 German Civil Code 德国法典 7—89b
德国牧羊狗 German shepherd 使役狗 7—90e
德国社会民主党 Social Democratic Party of Germany 德国政党 15—471a
《德国天文学会星表》 AG catalog 天文学 1—113e
德国图书馆 Deutsche Bücherei 德国莱比锡图书馆 5—269c
德国硬毛指示猎狗 German wirehaired pointer 狗品种 7—91d
德国装甲师 panzer division 陆军部队 13—17d
德国 88 毫米炮 German 88 武器 7—89a
德哈尔托赫 de Hartog, Jan 美国作家 5—187f
德哈哈比 Dhahabī, al- 摩洛哥统治者 5—278c
德·哈维兰 De Havilland, Sir Geoffrey 英国飞机设计师 5—187f
德·哈维兰 de Havilland, Olivia (Mary) 美国电影演员 5—188a
德·哈维兰DH-98型蚊式飞机 De Havilland DH-98 Mosquito (British aircraft) 飞机 5—188a
德·赫拉夫 Graaff, Simon de 荷兰政治家 7—234f

德黑兰 Tehrān 伊朗首都 16—515e
德黑兰会议 Tehrān Conference 第二次世界大战历史 16—516b
德化瓷 Dehua porcelain 中国瓷器 5—212f
德怀特 Dwight, John 英国陶艺师 5—486a
德怀特 Dwight, Timothy 美国教育家、诗人 5—486b
德加 Degas, (Hilaire-Germain-) Edgar 法国画家 5—210d
德加桑 Desgarcins, Magdeleine-Marie 法国演员 5—260f
德·加斯贝利 De Gasperi, Alcide 意大利政治家 5—187c
德加塔加 De gata ga (Cherokee chief) 切罗基酋长 5—187e
德加维教团 Darqāwā 伊斯兰教派别 5—152f
德卡波利斯 Decapolis 古希腊城市联盟 5—200f
德卡兹公爵 Decazes, Élie, Duke (duc) 法国政治家 5—201e
德·凯尔万氏甲状腺炎 de Quervain's thyroiditis 疾病 5—190f
德凯特 Decatur, Stephen 美国军官 5—201c
德坎普 De Camp, Maria Theresa 英国演员 5—187a
德康 Decamps, Alexandre(-Gabriel) 法国画家 5—200c
德科文 De Koven, (Henry Louis) Reginald 美国作曲家 5—188f
德克 Dekker, Eduard Douwes 荷兰作家 5—215d
德克 Dekker, Thomas 英国剧作家 5—215d
德克哈托格岛 Dirk Hartog Island 澳大利亚岛屿 5—337f
德克勒克 de Klerk, F. W. 南非总统 5—188b
德克罗利 Decroly, Ovide 比利时教育家 5—204e
德克森 Dirksen, Everett Mckinley 美国政治家 5—338a
德克西普斯 Dexippus, Publius Herennius 罗马历史家 5—277a
德肯 Decken, Karl Klaus von der 德国探险家 5—203c
德·库宁 de Kooning, Elaine 美国画家 5—188c
德·库宁 de Kooning, Willem 美国画家 5—188d
德·昆西 De Quincey, Thomas 英国散文家 5—190f
德拉 Dar'ā 叙利亚城镇 5—146c
德拉波尔塔 della Porta, Giambattista (philosopher) 意大利自然哲学家 5—227f
德拉布尔 Drabble, Margaret 英国小说家 5—408d
德拉福斯 Delafosse, Charles (Baroque painter) 法国画家 5—216d
德拉哥 Drago, Luis María 阿根廷政治家 5—410e
德拉贡海峡 Dragon's Mouths 加勒比海海峡 5—412b
德拉古 Draco 雅典立法者 5—409a
德拉瓜湾 Delagoa Bay 莫桑比克海湾 5—216f
德拉河 Drâa, Oued 摩洛哥河流 5—408d
德拉赫滕 Drachten 荷兰城镇 5—409a
德拉加尔迪 De la Gardie, Jacob Pontusson, Greve (Count) 瑞典政治家 5—188f
德拉加尔迪 De la Gardie, Magnus Gabriel, Greve (Count) 瑞典政治家 5—189a
德拉加济汗 Dera Ghāzi Khān 巴基斯坦城镇 5—251d
德拉·卡萨 Della Casa, Giovanni 意大利诗人 5—227f
德拉康蒂乌斯 Dracontius, Blossius Aemilius 北非诗人 5—409b
德拉克洛瓦 Delacroix, Eugène 法国画家 5—216a
德拉克马 drachma 希腊货币单位 5—408e
德拉克曼 Drachmann, Holger Henrik Herholdt 丹麦作家 5—408f
德拉肯斯山脉 Drakensberg 非洲山脉 5—413e
德拉库尔 Delacour, Jean Theodore 美国鸟类学家 5—215f
德拉拉梅 De La Ramée, Maria Louise 英国作家 5—189b
德拉朗德 Delalande, Michel-Richard 法国作曲家 5—217a
德拉雷伊 De la Rey, Jocobus Hercules 布尔人领袖 5—189d
德拉鲁 De la Rue, Warren 英国天文摄影家、发明家 5—189e
德拉伦塔 de la Renta, Oscar 美国服装设计师 5—189b
德拉·罗比亚 Della Robbia, Andrea 佛罗伦萨雕刻家 5—228a
德拉·罗比亚 Della Robbia, Giovanni 佛罗伦萨雕刻家 5—228a
德拉·罗比亚 Della Robbia, Luca 佛罗伦萨雕刻家 5—228b
德·拉·罗奇 de la Roche, Mazo 加拿大作家 5—189d
德拉罗虚 Delaroche, (Hippolyte-) Paul 法国画家 5—217f
德拉马德里 Madrid (Hurtado), Miguel de la 墨西哥总统 10—374b
德拉·梅尔 de la Mare, Walter (John) 英国作家 5—189a
德拉梅里 Lamerie, Paul de 英国银匠 9—464b
德拉门 Drammen 挪威城市 5—414d
德拉蒙德 Drummond, Henry 英国银行家 5—430a
德拉蒙德 Drummond (of Hawthornden), William 苏格兰诗人 5—430b
德拉蒙德 Drummond, William Henry 加拿大诗人 5—430b
德拉蒙德维尔 Drummondville 加拿大城市 5—430d
德拉米尔男爵(第三) Delamere (of Vale Royal), Hugh Cholmondeley, 3rd Baron 英国东非殖民者领袖 5—217c
德拉米尔男爵(第一) Delamere (of Dunham Massie), George Booth, 1st Baron 英格兰政治家 5—217b
德拉姆伯爵(第一) Durham, John George Lambton, 1st earl of 英格兰贵族 5—473d
德拉姆河 Dramselva 挪威河流 5—414d
德拉姆黑勒 Drumheller 加拿大城市 5—429e
德拉尼 Delany, Martin R(obison) 美国废奴主义者 5—217f
德拉诺 Delano, Jane A(rminda) 美国护士、教育家 5—217e
德拉瀑布 Della Falls 加拿大瀑布群 5—227f
德拉奇 Drač (Albania) 阿尔巴尼亚港市 5—408d
德拉热 Delage, Yves 法国动物学家 5—216e
德拉瓦河 Drava River 欧洲河流 5—415c
德拉·瓦莱 Della Valle, Federico 意大利戏剧家 5—228c
德拉沃尔 De La Warr, Thomas West, 12th Baron 英格兰北美殖民者 5—189f
德拉伊斯梅尔汗 Dera Ismāīl Khān 巴基斯坦城镇 5—251d
德莱阿耶 Delehaye, Hippolyte 比利时学者 5—222b
德莱昂 De Leon, Daniel 美国社会主义者 5—190a
德莱顿 Dryden, John 英国作家 5—432f
德莱顿 Dryden, John Fairfield 美国参议员 5—433b
德莱厄尔 Dreyer, Carl Theodor 丹麦电影导演 5—422f
德莱恩 Delane, John Thadeus 英国《泰晤士》报主笔 5—217d
德莱蒙 Delémont 瑞士城市 5—222b
德莱尼 Delaney, Shelagh 英国剧作家 5—217e
德莱塞 Dreiser, Theodore 美国小说家 5—418e
德赖登 Dryden, Hugh L(atimer) 美国物理学家 5—432e
德赖弗斯 Dreyfuss, Henry 美国工业设计家 5—423c
德赖弗斯 Dreyfuss, Richard 美国电影演员 5—423d
德赖库尔斯 Dreikurs, Rudolf 美国精神病学家 5—418e
德赖托图格斯群岛 Dry Tortugas 美国岛群 5—432d
德兰 Derain, André 法国画家 5—251e
德兰薄花呢 delaine 毛纺织品 5—217a
德兰士瓦 Transvaal 南非省份 17—200b
德兰士瓦人 Homo transvaalensis 人类学 8—147e
德兰士瓦索托人 Transvaal Sotho (people) 南非民族 17—200d
德兰西 DeLancey, James 纽约殖民地法官 5—217c
德朗 De Long, George Washington 美国探险家 5—190a
德朗布尔 Delambre, Jean-Baptiste-Joseph 法国天文学家 5—217b
德朗达尔 Deslandres, Henri-Alexandre 法国物理学家 5—261e
德朗西 Drancy 法国工业区 5—414e
德勒 Dreux 法国城镇 5—422b
德勒格沙尼战役 Drăgăşani, Battle of 希腊独立战争史 5—410e
德勒克吕泽 Delescluze, (Louis-) Charles 法国革命者 5—222c
德勒兹 Deleuze, Gilles 法国哲学家 5—222c
德雷贝尔 Drebbel, Cornelis (Jacobszoon) 荷兰发明家 5—417f
德雷伯 Draper, Henry 美国医生、天文学家 5—414f
德雷达瓦 Dire Dawa 埃塞俄比亚城镇 5—335e
德雷德·斯科特裁决 Dred Scott decision 美国历史事件 5—418a
德雷顿 Drayton, Michael 英国诗人 5—416f
德雷尔 Hérelle, Félix d' 法国微生物学家 8—38e
德雷尔 Dreyer, Johan Ludvig Emil 丹麦天文学家 5—423a
德雷福斯 Dreyfus, Alfred 法国军官 5—423b
德雷克 Drake, Edwin Laurentine 美国石油工人 5—412d

德雷克 Drake, Sir Francis 英国海军将领 5—412e
德雷克 Drake, Frances Ann Denny 美国戏剧演员 5—412e
德雷克 Drake, Joseph Rodman 美国诗人 5—413c
德雷克海峡 Drake Passage 大西洋-太平洋航道 5—413d
德雷克塞尔 Drexel, Anthony Joseph 美国银行家 5—422e
德雷克塞尔 Drexel, Katharine, BLESSED 美国天主教修女 5—422e
德雷帕尼乌斯 Drepanius, Latinius Pacatus 罗马演说家 5—420a
德雷珀 Draper, Charles Stark 美国航空工程师 5—414e
德雷塞 Dresser, Christopher 英国设计家 5—421f
德雷斯 Drees, Willem 荷兰政治家 5—418c
德雷夏克 Dreyschock, Alexander 波希米亚音乐家 5—423e
德雷泽 Dreyse, Nikolaus von 德国发明家 5—423e
德雷泽步枪 Dreyse rifle 武器 5—423f
德蕾珀 Draper, Ruth 美国独剧演员 5—415a
德肋撒(修女) Teresa, MOTHER 印度修女 16—550b
德肋撒(阿维拉的),圣 Teresa OF ÁVILA, SAINT 西班牙修女 16—550c
德肋撒(利雪的),圣 Theresa OF LISIEUX, SAINT 天主教修女 17—31d
德累斯顿 Dresden 德国城市 5—420a
德累斯顿刻本 Dresden Codex 马雅文献 5—420e
德累斯顿银行 Dresdner Bank AG 德国银行 5—420e
德累斯顿战役 Dresden, Battle of 欧洲历史 5—420d
德里 Delhi 印度城市 5—222d
德里 Derry (Northern Ireland) 北爱尔兰城市 5—255c
德里达 Derrida, Jacques 法国哲学家 5—255b
德里大学 Delhi, University of 印度高等学府 5—225b
德里动物园 Delhi Zoological Park 印度动物园 5—225d
德里加尔斯基 Drygalski, Erich Dagobert von 德国地理学家 5—433c
德里疖 Delhi boil (infection) 传染病 5—225b
德里久尔 Trichūr 印度城镇 17—217a
德里纳河 Drina River 巴尔干河流 5—425c
德里欧·拉罗舍尔 Drieu La Rochelle, Pierre 法国作家 5—424b
德里施 Driesch, Hans Adolf Eduard 德国胚胎学家 5—423f
德里苏丹国 Delhi sultanate 印度穆斯林王国 5—225c
《德里协定》 Delhi Pact 印巴关系史 5—225b
德利布 Delibes, (Clément-Philibert-) Léo 法国作曲家 5—225f
德利尔 Delisle, Guillaume 法国地图制图家 5—227b
德利尔 Delille, Jacques 法国诗人、古典学者 5—226c
德利尔 Delisle, Joseph-Nicolas 法国天文学家 5—227b
德利西亚斯城 Ciudad Delicias 墨西哥城市 4—251f
德林 Delyn 威尔士区名 5—232b
德林达依 Tenasserim 缅甸地区 16—537d
德林克沃特 Drinkwater, John 英国诗人 5—425d
德令哈 Delingha 中国城市 5—226c
德龙 Drôme 法国省份 5—426d
德卢斯 Duluth 美国城市 5—455a
德鲁 Drew, Charles Richard 美国医生 5—422b
德鲁 Drew, Daniel 美国金融家 5—422c
德鲁 Drew, Georgiana Emma 美国演员 5—422c
德鲁 Drew, Jane 英国建筑师 5—422c
德鲁 Drew, Louisa Lane 美国演员 5—422d
德鲁(老) Drew, John, Sr. 美国演员 5—422d
德鲁(小) Drew, John, Jr. 美国演员 5—422c
德鲁埃 Drouet, Jean-Baptiste 法国革命家 5—427d
德鲁埃 Drouet, Jean-Baptiste, COMTE D'ERLON 法国元帅 5—427e
德鲁埃 Drouais, Jean-Germain 法国画家 5—427d
德鲁格 Drug (India) 印度城市 5—428c
德鲁克 Drucker, Peter F(erdinand) 美国企业管理学家 5—428b
德鲁蒙德·德·安德拉德 Drummond de Andrade, Carlos 巴西诗人 5—430c
德鲁帕德 dhrupad 印度斯坦古声乐曲式 5—281b
德鲁日科夫卡 Druzhkivka 乌克兰城市 5—432b
德·鲁斯 Roos, S(joerd) H(endrik) de 荷兰字体设计家 14—391a
德鲁苏斯 Drusus, Marcus Livius 罗马政治家 5—431a
德鲁苏斯(小) Drusus, Marcus Livius 罗马保民官 5—431b
德鲁苏斯·凯撒 Drusus Caesar 罗马执政官 5—431b
德鲁苏斯·日尔曼尼库斯 Drusus Germanicus, Nero Claudius 罗马执政官 5—431d
德鲁翁·安蒂冈努斯 Druon Antigonus 比利时传说人物 5—430e
德鲁西拉 Drusilla, Livia 罗马贵族 5—431a
德鲁伊特 Druid 凯尔特人知识阶层 5—429a
德鲁兹教派 Druze 中东宗教派别 5—431e
德鲁兹人暴乱 Druze revolt 叙利亚历史事件 5—432a
德鲁兹山 Durūz, Mount ad- 叙利亚山名 5—477d
德吕克 Deluc, Jean André 英国地质学家 5—231e
德律安·德·吕 Drouyn de Lhuys, Edmond 法国政治家 5—427f
德律风根公司 Telefunken AG 德国公司 16—522e
德伦特 Drenthe 荷兰省份 5—419f
德罗贝塔-塞维林堡 Drobeta-Turnu Severin 罗马尼亚城市 5—425f
德罗戈(欧特维尔的)的 Drogo DE HAUTEVILLE 阿普利亚伯爵 5—426a
德罗戈贝奇 Drohobych 乌克兰城市 5—426b
德罗赫达 Drogheda 爱尔兰港区 5—426a
德罗莫尔 Dromore 北爱尔兰城镇 5—426e
德罗斯特 Drost, Aernout 荷兰作家 5—427b
德罗斯特-许尔斯霍夫 Droste-Hülshoff, Annette, Freiin von 德国诗人 5—427c
德罗特宁霍尔摩剧院 Drottningholm Theatre 瑞典宫廷剧院 5—427c
德罗西耶 Desrosiers, Léo-Paul 加拿大作家 5—263f
德罗肖特 Droeshout, Martin 英国版画家 5—426a
德罗伊森 Droysen, Johann Gustav 普鲁士历史学家 5—428a
德罗伊特威奇 Droitwich 英格兰城镇 5—426c
德罗兹 Droz, Numa 瑞士总统 5—428b
德罗兹多夫 Drozdov, Vasily Mikhaylovich (Russian Orthodox patriarch) 东正教莫斯科牧首 5—428b
德洛尔 Delors, Jacques (Lucien Jean) 法国政治家 5—229b
德洛尔姆 Delorme, Marion 法国名妓 5—228f
德洛尔姆 Delorme, Philibert 法国建筑师 5—228f
德洛莫 Dhlomo, R(olfus) R(eginald) R(aymond) 非洲小说家 5—280d
德洛莫锡战役 Drummossie, Battle of 英国历史事件 5—430d
德洛内 Delaunay, Charles-Eugène 法国天文学家 5—218a
德洛内 Delaunay, Robert 法国画家 5—218b
德洛内 Delaunay, Sonia 法国画家 5—218c
德洛尼 Deloney, Thomas 英国民谣、散文作家 5—228e
德马拉托斯 Demaratus 斯巴达国王 5—232e
德马雷 Desmarest, Nicolas 法国地质学家 5—262a
德马雷 Desmarets, Nicolas, MARQUIS DE MAILLEBOIS 法国大臣 5—262a
德马雷(圣索兰的) Desmarets de Saint-Sorlin, Jean 法国作家 5—262b
德玛神 dema deity 新几内亚神话 5—232b
德茂特 Dermoût, Maria 荷兰小说家 5—255a
德梅 Demetz, Frédéric-Auguste 法国法理学家 5—234c
德梅尔特 Dehmelt, Hans Georg 美国物理学家 5—212e
德梅拉拉河 Demerara River 圭亚那河流 5—233b
德美联盟 German-American Bund 美国亲纳粹组织 7—89a
德米尔 deMille, Agnes 美国舞蹈家 5—234c
德米尔 deMille, Cecil B. 美国电影导演 5—234e
德米尔 De Mille, James 加拿大作家 5—190b
德米雷尔 Demirel, Süleyman 土耳其政治家 5—235b
德米特里 Demetrius 大夏国王 5—233e
德米特里 Demetrius 统治者之名 5—233e
德米特里(阿洛佩加的) Demetrios OF ALOPEKA 希腊雕塑家 5—233d
德米特里(法莱隆的) Demetrius OF PHALERON 希腊政治家、哲学家

5—234b
德米特里二世 Demetrius Ⅱ 马其顿国王 5—233f
德米特里二世(胜利者) Demetrius Ⅱ Nicator (Victor) 叙利亚国王 5—234a
德米特里·卡尔孔狄利斯 Demetrius Chalcondyles 意大利教师、哲学家 5—234a
德米特里克 Dmytryk, Edward 美国电影导演 5—352e
德米特里·特里克利尼乌斯 Demetrius Triclinius 拜占廷学者 5—234b
德米特里·西多内斯 Demetrius Cydones 拜占廷学者、政治家 5—234b
德米特里一世 Demetrius Ⅰ Poliorcetes 马其顿国王 5—233f
德米特里一世(保护者) Demetrius Ⅰ Soter (Preserver) 叙利亚国王 5—234a
德明 Deming 美国城市 5—235a
德谟 deme 古希腊农村地区 5—233a
德谟克利特 Democritus 希腊哲学家 5—237e
德·摩尔根 De Morgan, Augustus 英国数学家 5—190c
德莫尔德 Demolder, Eugène 比利时小说家 5—238a
德莫夫斯基 Dmowski, Roman 波兰政治家 5—352d
德莫特 Dermot MacMurrough 爱尔兰伦斯特王 5—254f
德姆卢格 Tamlūk 印度城市 16—453d
德姆西 Dempsey, Sister Mary Joseph 美国护士 5—240f
德穆楚克栋鲁普 Demchukdongrub 蒙古首领 5—232f
德穆兰 Desmoulins, (Lucie-Simplice-)Camille(-Benoist) 法国记者 5—262d
德穆思 Demuth, Charles 美国画家 5—241b
德纳芙 Deneuve, Catherine 法国演员 5—242a
德纳姆 Denham, Dixon 英国军人、探险家 5—243e
德纳姆 Denham, Sir James Steuart, 4th Baronet 苏格兰经济学家 5—243e
德纳姆 Denham, Sir John 英国诗人 5—243f
德尼 Denis, Maurice 法国画家 5—244b
德尼茨 Dönitz, Karl 德国军官 5—383d
德尼利昆 Deniliquin 澳大利亚城镇 5—244a
德·尼罗 De Niro, Robert 美国电影演员 5—190d
德聂斯特河 Dniester River 欧洲河流 5—353c
德农 Denon, Dominique Vivant, Baron 法国艺术家 5—247a
德努瓦耶男爵 Desnoyers, Auguste-Gaspard-Louis, Baron 法国版画家 5—263a
德帕迪厄 Depardieu, Gérard 法国电影演员 5—249d
德帕尔马 De Palma, Brian (Russell) 美国导演、电影剧本作者 5—190e
德帕尔马 De Palma, Ralph 美国运动员 5—190e
德普菲尔德 Dörpfeld, Friedrich Wilhelm 德国教育家 5—391a
德普费尔德 Dörpfeld, Wilhelm 德国考古学家 5—391a
德普雷 Desprez, Jean-Louis 法国画家 5—263f
德普雷蒂斯 Depretis, Agostino 意大利政治家 5—251b
德钦丹东 Than Tun, Thakin 缅甸共产党领袖 17—13a
德热林-鲁西二氏综合征 Déjerine-Roussy syndrome 神经失调 5—215c
德日进 Teilhard de Chardin, Pierre 法国哲学家 16—516f
《德萨凡拉梅》 Thesavalamai 泰米尔人法律 17—35f
德萨瓜德罗河 Desaguadero River (Nicaragua) 尼加拉瓜河流 5—256f
德萨利讷 Dessalines, Jean-Jacques 海地皇帝 5—263f
德塞 Dese 埃塞俄比亚城镇 5—258f
德塞 Desaix de Veygoux, Louis-Charles-Antoine 法国军人 5—257a
德塞阿多河 Deseado River 阿根廷河流 5—259a
德塞夫勒 Deux-Sèvres 法国省份 5—270a
德赛 Desai, Morarji 印度总理 5—256f
德·桑克蒂斯 De Sanctis, Francesco 意大利文学评论家 5—191a
德山 Tokuyama 日本城市 17—136b
德尚 Deschamps (de Saint-Amand), Émile 法国诗人 5—258d
德尚 Deschamps, Eustache 法国诗人 5—258e
德绍 Dessau 德国城市 5—264a
德绍 Dessau, Paul 德国作曲家 5—264b
德事隆公司 Textron Inc. 美国工业制造企业 17—7d
德属东非 German East Africa 原德国殖民地 7—89d
德属西南非洲 German South West Africa 原德国殖民地 7—90f
德斯巴勒 Desborough, John 英格兰军人 5—257f
德斯蒂·德·特拉西 Destutt de Tracy, Antoine-Louis-Claude, Count (comte) 法国哲学家 5—265a
德斯丁 Destinn, Emmy 捷克歌唱家 5—264c
德斯基 Deskey, Donald 美国工艺设计师 5—261d
德斯蒙德 Desmond 爱尔兰古地区 5—262c
德斯蒙德伯爵(第十四或第十五) Desmond, Gerald Fitzgerald, 14th (or 15th) earl of 爱尔兰贵族 5—262d
德斯帕德 Despard, Edward Marcus 英国军官 5—263a
德斯彭瑟父子 Despenser, Hugh Le and Hugh Le 英格兰国王爱德华二世宠臣 5—263b
德斯皮奥 Despiau, Charles 法国雕刻家 5—263c
德斯普兰斯 Des Plaines 美国城市 5—256f
德斯普兰斯河 Des Plaines River 美国河流 5—256f
德斯坦伯爵 Estaing, Charles-Hector, Count (comte) d' 法国舰队司令 6—138a
《德苏互不侵犯条约》 German-Soviet Nonaggression Pact 德国-苏联条约 7—91a
德索托 Soto, Hernando de 西班牙探险家 15—524e
德索瓦 Dessoir, Ludwig 德国演员 5—264c
德太耶 Detaille, (Jean-Baptiste-)Édouard 法国画家 5—265c
德特雷 Detrez, Conrad 比利时小说家 5—267b
德特鲁瓦 Detroy, Jean-François (French painter) 法国画家 5—267f
德田秋声 Tokuda Shūsei 日本小说家 17—134b
德图 Thou, Jacques-Auguste de 法国政治家 17—59d
德图什 Destouches, André Cardinal 法国作曲家 5—264d
德图什 Destouches, Philippe Néricault 法国戏剧家 5—264d
德托尼-范可尼二氏综合征 de Toni-Fanconi syndrome 疾病 5—191c
德瓦 Deva 罗马尼亚城市 5—270b
德·瓦勒拉 de Valera, Eamon 爱尔兰政治家 5—191d
德·瓦卢娃 de Valois, Dame Ninette 爱尔兰舞蹈家 5—191f
德瓦旺·瓦罗巴卡 Devawongse Varoprakar, Prince 暹罗外交大臣 5—270e
德万托罗 Dewantoro, Ki Hadjar 印度尼西亚教育家 5—275c
德威弗尔 Dwyfor 威尔士区名 5—486d
德威金斯 Dwiggins, William Addison 美国字体、装帧设计家 5—486a
德威特 DeWitt, Lydia Maria Adams 美国实验病理学家 5—276e
德维 Devey, George 英国建筑师 5—271e
德·维奥 De Vio, Tommaso 意大利神学家 5—192c
德维尔 Deville, Édouard Gaston (Daniel) 加拿大测量专家 5—272b
德维尔 Deville, Henri-Étienne Sainte-Claire 法国化学家 5—272c
德维因 De Vinne, Theodore L(ow) 美国印刷史作者 5—192b
德·温特 De Wint, Peter 英国画家 5—192d
德文 Devon 英格兰郡名 5—273c
德文波特 Devonport 澳大利亚城镇 5—273f
德文斯克 Dvinsk (Latvia) 拉脱维亚城市 5—484b
德文特河 Derwent, River 英格兰河流 5—255f
德文特河 Derwent River 澳大利亚河流 5—255f
德文特湖 Derwent Water 英格兰湖泊 5—256a
德文特赛德 Derwentside 英格兰区名 5—256a
德文希尔伯爵 Devonshire, Charles Blount, Earl of 英格兰驻爱尔兰国王代表 5—274a
德文希尔伯爵(第一) Devonshire, William Cavendish, 1st Earl of 英格

兰贵族 5—274a
德文希尔伯爵和公爵 Devonshire, EARLS AND DUKES OF 英格兰贵族 5—274a
德文希尔公爵(第八) Devonshire, Spencer Compton Cavendish, 8th Duke of 英国政治家 5—274c
德文希尔公爵(第四) Devonshire, William Cavendish, 4th Duke of 英国首相 5—274b
德文希尔公爵(第一) Devonshire, William Cavendish, 1st Dukeof 英国政治家 5—274a
德翁 Dehon, Léon-Gustave 法国天主教司铎 5—212e
德沃尔夫 de Wolfe, Elsie 美国装饰设计师 5—192d
德沃金 Dworkin, Andrea 美国女权主义者、作家 5—486c
德沃托 De Voto, Bernard (Augustine) 美国作家 5—192c
德沃夏克 Dvořák, Antonín (Leopold) 波希米亚作曲家 5—484c
德乌斯(诺盖罗·拉莫斯) Deus (Nogueira Ramos), João de 葡萄牙诗人 5—268a
德武戈什 Długosz, Jan 波兰历史学家 5—352b
德西德里乌斯 Desiderius (pope) 罗马教皇 5—261b
德·西卡 De Sica, Vittorio 意大利电影导演 5—191b
德西洛埃 Siloé, Diego de 西班牙雕刻家 15—374b
德西洛埃 Siloé, Gil de 西班牙雕刻家 15—374d
德西特 Sitter, Willem de 荷兰数学家 15—406f
德西乌斯 Decius, Gaius Messius Quintus Trajanus 罗马皇帝 5—203b
德·希里科 de Chirico, Giorgio 意大利画家 5—187a
德系犹太人 Ashkenazi 欧洲民族 1—548b
德夏内尔 Deschanel, Paul(-Eugène-Louis) 法国政治家 5—258e
德谢莱特 Déchelette, Joseph 法国考古学家 5—202e
德·亚米契斯 De Amicis, Edmondo 意大利作家 5—186b
德阳 Deyang 中国城市 5—277b
德耶尔 De Geer, Gerhard (Jakob), Friherre (Baron) 瑞典地质学家 5—187e
德伊勒 Deira 英格兰古王国 5—214d
德意志博物馆 Deutsches Museum 德国博物馆 5—269e
德意志工匠联盟 Deutscher Werkbund 德国工匠艺人协会 5—269d
德意志国民议会 German National Assembly 德国历史 7—90e
德意志花饰 deutsche Blumen 陶瓷装饰 5—269b
德意志基督教徒派 German Christian 德国宗教团体 7—89b
德意志剧团 Deutsches Theater 德国剧团 5—269f
德意志联邦铁路公司 Deutsche Bundesbahn 德国公司 5—269c
德意志民主共和国 German Democratic Republic 德国历史 7—89d
德意志银行 Deutsche Bank AG 德国金融机构 5—269a
《德意志之歌》 Deutschlandlied 德国国歌 5—270a
德裔宾州人 Pennsylvania Dutch 定居美国的德国移民 13—145e
德语 German language 语言 7—89d
《德语词典》 Deutsches Wörterbuch 德国词典 5—269f
德语文学 German literature 文学 7—89f
德扎尔格 Desargues, Girard 法国数学家 5—257c
德扎尔格定理 Desargues's theorem 数学 5—257d
德州 Dezhou 中国城市 5—277e
德祖利埃 Deshoulières, Antoinette du Ligier de la Garde 法国诗人 5—262f
灯 lamp 照明器具 9—466e
灯草雀 junco 鸟类 9—109e
灯船 lightship 导航信标 10—94b
灯笼 lantern 照明工具 9—489a
灯笼辣椒 bell pepper 植物 2—361f
灯笼眼鱼 lantern-eye fish 鱼类 9—489b
灯笼鱼 lantern fish 鱼类 9—489b
灯泡 light bulb 照明灯 10—93b
灯丝灯 filament lamp 照明灯 6—313c
灯塔 lighthouse 导航信标 10—93e
灯心 wick 吸引灯油燃烧的纤维束 18—243e
灯心草 rush 草本植物 14—454a
灯心草目 Juncales 植物学 9—109d
灯芯绒 corduroy 织物 4—504d
登巴德尼亚王朝 Dam̐badeṇiya DYNASTY 锡兰王朝 5—127b
登巴萨 Denpasar 印度尼西亚城市 5—247a
登比 Denbigh 威尔士集镇 5—241d
登比郡 Denbighshire 威尔士郡名 5—241d
登别 Noboribetsu 日本城市 12—223b
登博斯 Den Bosch (The Netherlands) 荷兰城市 5—241c
登博维察 Dîmboviţa 罗马尼亚县名 5—318a
登册的保有权 copyhold 法律 4—495a
登登压腰鼓 dùndún pressure drum 约鲁巴人乐器 5—460d
登顿 Denton 美国城市 5—248c
登革热 dengue 疾病 5—243d
登海尔德 Helder, Den 荷兰城市 7—571e
登京格·诺尔盖 Tenzing Norgay 尼泊尔登山运动员 16—547c
登陆艇 landing craft 军用船只 9—476d
登纳 Denner, Johann Christoph 德国乐器制造家 5—246b
登普斯特 Dempster, Arthur Jeffrey 美国物理学家 5—240f
登普西 Dempsey, Jack 美国拳击运动员 5—240b
登普西 Dempsey, Miles Christopher 英国陆军军官 5—240d
登普西 Dempsey, Nonpareil Jack 美国拳击运动员 5—240e
登奇 Dench, Dame Judi 英国演员 5—241e
《登山宝训》 Sermon on the Mount 《圣经》 15—226d
登山运动 mountaineering 体育 11—445c
登斯莫尔 Densmore, Frances 美国人类文化学家 5—247d
登苏夏努 Densuşianu, Ovid 罗马尼亚作家 5—247d
登塔图斯 Dentatus, Manius Curius 罗马将军 5—247f
登特 Dent, Edward John 英国钟表制造商 5—247e
登霄 miʿrāj 伊斯兰传说 11—271e
等孢球虫属 Isospora 生物学 8—473f
等称虫属 Isotelus 古生物学 8—474b
等持 samadhi 印度哲学 14—559e
等待线论 waiting-line theory (management science) 经济 18—67d
等高栽种 contour farming 农业 4—470c
等级 caste 昆虫类群 3—508c
等级规则(帆船赛) rating rule 帆船级别的规则 14—162c
等价 equivalence 数学、逻辑学 6—109c
等角投影 isometric drawing 制图学 8—472d
等角线 rhumb line (navigation) 制图学 14—271c
等离子层顶 plasmapause 大气科学 13—349c
等离子体 plasma 物理学 13—349b
等离子体振荡 plasma oscillation 物理学 13—349c
等色岩 shonkinite 矿物 15—331d
等熵面图 isentropic chart 气象学 8—460e
等同 equivalence 数学、逻辑学 6—109b
等位基因 allele 生物学 1—236f
等温线 isotherm 气象学 8—474c
等效原理 equivalence principle 物理学 6—109c
等斜线 loxodrome 制图学 10—256f
等压线 isobar 气象学 8—471b
等音音程 enharmonic 音乐 6—83f
等雨率线 isomer 气象学 8—472a
等值线制图法 contour mapping 制图学 4—470c
等周问题 isoperimetric problem 数学 8—473a
等足类 isopod 动物学 8—473b
邓巴 Dunbar 苏格兰城市 5—458b
邓巴 Dunbar, Paul Laurence 美国作家 5—458c
邓巴 Dunbar, William 苏格兰诗人 5—458c
邓巴伯爵(第九) Dunbar, Patrick Dunbar, 9th earl of 苏格兰贵族 5—458b
邓巴顿 Dunbarton 苏格兰区名 5—458e

邓巴顿 Dumbarton 苏格兰城市 5—456b
邓巴顿郡 Dumbartonshire 苏格兰旧郡名 5—456c
邓春区 Dang Xuan Khu（Vietnamese Communist leader） 越南共产党领袖 5—134b
邓达斯 Dundas 格陵兰美国空军基地 5—459e
邓达斯 Dundas, Henry 英国政治家 5—459f
邓迪 Dundee 苏格兰港市 5—459f
邓迪 Dundee, Angelo 美国职业拳击教练、经理 5—460a
邓迪城 Dundee City 苏格兰区名 5—460c
邓迪子爵（第一） Dundee, John Graham of Claverhouse, 1st Viscount of 苏格兰军人 5—460b
邓多克 Dundalk 爱尔兰海港 5—459e
邓恩 Dunne, Finley Peter 美国新闻记者 5—464c
邓恩 Dunne, Irene 美国演员 5—464c
邓弗里斯 Dumfries 苏格兰城市 5—456d
邓弗里斯-加洛韦 Dumfries and Galloway 苏格兰行政区 5—456e
邓弗里斯郡 Dumfriesshire 苏格兰旧郡名 5—456e
邓甘嫩 Dungannon 北爱尔兰城镇 5—461e
邓翰 Dunham, Katherine 美国舞蹈家、人类学者 5—461f
邓加文 Dungarvan 爱尔兰城镇 5—461e
邓稼先 Deng Jiaxian 中国核物理学家 5—242b
邓杰内斯 Dungeness 英格兰海岬 5—461f
邓杰内斯蟹 Dungeness crab（*Cancer magister*） 甲壳动物 5—461f
邓凯尔德 Dunkeld 苏格兰古城 5—463d
邓克岛 Dunk Island 澳大利亚岛屿 5—463d
邓肯 Duncan 美国城市 5—458e
邓肯 Duncan, David Douglas 美国新闻摄影记者 5—458f
邓肯 Duncan, Isadora 美国舞蹈家 5—459a
邓肯 Duncan, Otis Dudley 美国社会学家 5—459c
邓肯 Duncan, Robert（Edward） 美国诗人 5—459d
邓肯 Duncan, Ronald 英国剧作家、诗人 5—459d
邓肯岛 Duncan Island（Galapagos Islands） 加拉帕戈斯群岛岛屿 5—459e
邓肯二世 Duncan II 苏格兰国王 5—458f
邓肯一世 Duncan I 苏格兰国王 5—458e
邓莱里 Dún Laoghaire 爱尔兰城市 5—457e
邓洛普持股公司 Dunlop Holdings PLC 英国公司 5—464a
邓莫尔伯爵（第四） Dunmore, John Murray, 4th Earl of 英属北美殖民地总督 5—464b
邓莫尔伯爵之战 Lord Dunmore's War 美国历史 10—219c
邓南特 Dunant, Henri 瑞士人道主义者 5—457e
邓南遮 D'Annunzio, Gabriele 意大利作家 5—137b
邓尼金 Denikin, Anton Ivanovich 俄国将军 5—244a
邓尼拉男爵 Dunira, Henry Dundas, Baron 英国政治家 5—463a
邓尼奇 Dunwich 英格兰城镇 5—465f
邓尼特角 Dunnet Head 苏格兰岬角 5—464d
邓宁 Dunning, John 英国法官 5—464d
邓宁 Dunning, John R(ay) 美国核物理学家 5—464d
邓萨尼 Dunsany, Edward John Moreton Drax Plunkett, 18th baron of 爱尔兰作家 5—465b
邓斯 Duns 苏格兰区首府 5—464f
邓斯克瓦塔瓦 Tenskwatawa（Shawnee Indian leader） 美国印第安人领袖 16—546a
邓斯纳恩 Dunsinane 苏格兰山峰 5—465b
邓斯·司各脱 Duns Scotus, John 苏格兰哲学家、神学家 5—464f
邓斯塔布 Dunstable, John 英格兰作曲家 5—465c
邓斯坦（坎特伯雷的），圣 Dunstan of Canterbury, Saint 英格兰大主教 5—465c
邓斯特 Dunster 英格兰城镇 5—465e
邓斯特 Dunster, Henry 美国教育家 5—465e
邓斯特布尔 Dunstable 英格兰城镇 5—465b
邓唐纳德伯爵（第十） Dundonald, Thomas Cochrane, 10th earl of 英国海军上将 5—460d
邓希尔 Dunhill, Thomas Frederick 英国作曲家 5—462b
邓小平 Deng Xiaoping 中国领导人 5—242c
邓小平理论 Deng Xiaoping Theory 中国政治理论 5—243a
邓颖超 Deng Yingchao 中国政治家 5—243b
凳 stool 家具 16—253d
镫骨固定 stirrup fixation 病理学 16—242a
氐羌 Di-Qiang 中国古代民族 5—282b
低步舞 basse danse 宫廷男女对舞 2—268a
低岛鹿 Key deer 哺乳动物 9—248c
低地 Lowlands 苏格兰自然地理区 10—256c
低地国家 Low Countries 欧洲地区 10—252d
低共熔混合物 eutectic 物理学 6—175e
低级歌舞表演 burlesque show 美国文娱节目 3—268c
低磷酸盐血症 hypophosphatemia 病理现象 8—295d
低俗喜剧 low comedy 戏剧 10—252d
低碗柜 court cupboard 家具 4—549d
低位沼泽 fen 地理学 6—271f
低温技术 cryogenics 物理学 5—42a
低血糖 hypoglycemia 病理现象 8—295c
低血压 hypotension 病理现象 8—295e
低氧 hypoxia 病理现象 8—296d
低音 bass 音乐 2—266e
低音提琴 double bass 弦乐器 5—398a
低语音 vocal fry 语音学 18—31e
堤岸 Cho Lon 越南城市 4—186d
堤岸权 riparian right 法律 14—310f
堤丰 Typhon 希腊神话人物 17—308e
堤家族 Tsutsumi family 日本家族 17—252b
堤喀 Tyche 希腊女神 17—304e
滴滴涕 DDT 化学合成杀虫剂 5—186a
滴定 titration 化学 17—120e
滴定管 burette 仪器 3—259e
滴色主义 Tachism 绘画风格 16—417d
滴水石 dripstone（architecture） 建筑 5—425d
镝（Dy） dysprosium 化学元素 5—490a
狄 Di 中国民族 5—281f
狄阿多库斯（佛提塞的） Diadochus of Photice 基督教神学家 5—283d
狄安娜 Diana 古罗马女神 5—287d
狄安娜长尾猴 diana monkey（*Cercopithecus diana*） 哺乳动物 5—288a
狄奥达蒂 Diodati, Giovanni 基督教牧师 5—326a
狄奥多；狄奥多尔 Theodore 统治者之名 17—24b
狄奥多尔 Theodore 敌对教皇 17—24d
狄奥多尔（阿斯齐达斯） Theodore Ascidas 希腊神学家 17—24e
狄奥多尔（巴尔·科奈） Theodore bar Konai 叙利亚学者 17—24f
狄奥多尔（莱托的） Theodore of Rhaithu 神学家、修士 17—25a
狄奥多尔（莫普苏埃斯蒂亚的） Theodore of Mopsuestia 叙利亚神学家 17—25a
狄奥多尔（坎特伯雷的），圣 Theodore of Canterbury, Saint 坎特伯雷大主教 17—24f
狄奥多尔（斯图狄乌斯隐修院的），圣 Theodore Studites, Saint 隐修院院长 17—25b
狄奥多尔二世 Theodore II 埃塞俄比亚皇帝 17—24d
狄奥多尔二世 Theodore II 教皇 17—24d
狄奥多尔夫（奥尔良的） Theodulf of Orléans 法兰克神学家 17—27d
狄奥多尔一世 Theodore I 教皇 17—24d
狄奥多尔一世至三世 Theodore I—III 俄国沙皇 17—24e
狄奥多二世 Theodore II Lascaris 尼西亚的拜占廷皇帝 17—24c
狄奥多拉 Theodora 拜占廷皇后 17—23f
狄奥多拉 Theodora 拜占廷女皇 17—24a
狄奥多莱（昔尔的） Theodoret of Cyrrhus 叙利亚神学家、主教 17—

25c
狄奥多里克 Theodoric 东哥特人国王 17—25d
狄奥多里克 Theodoric 敌对教皇 17—26a
狄奥多里克陵墓 Theodoric, Mausoleum of 建筑 17—26a
狄奥多里克;提奥多里克 Theodoric 统治者之名 17—25d
狄奥多鲁斯·阿布·库拉 Theōdūrus Abū Qurrah 叙利亚神学家 17—27e
狄奥多罗斯 Diodorus Cronus 希腊哲学家 5—326c
狄奥多罗斯(西西里的) Diodorus Siculus 希腊历史学家 5—326c
狄奥多图斯 Theodotus 拜占廷学者 17—27d
狄奥多图斯(安卡拉的) Theodotus of Ancyra 安卡拉主教 17—27c
狄奥多图斯(诺斯替教徒) Theodotus the Gnostic 东派诺斯替教理论家 17—27c
狄奥多托斯二世 Diodotus II 大夏国王 5—326d
狄奥多托斯一世 Diodotus I 大夏国王 5—326d
狄奥多西 Theodosius 统治者之名 17—26c
狄奥多西(亚历山大的) Theodosius of Alexandria 亚历山大牧首 17—26f
狄奥多西(巴勒斯坦的),圣 Theodosius of Palestine, Saint 巴勒斯坦圣徒 17—27a
狄奥多西大帝 Theodosius the Great 罗马帝国皇帝 17—27b
狄奥多西二世 Theodosius II 东罗马皇帝 17—26f
狄奥多西三世 Theodosius III 拜占廷皇帝 17—26f
狄奥多西一世 Theodosius I Boradiotes 君士坦丁堡牧首 17—26c
狄奥多西一世 Theodosius I 罗马帝国皇帝 17—26d
狄奥多一世 Theodore I Lascaris 尼西亚皇帝 17—24b
狄奥法内斯(坚信者),圣 Theophanes the Confessor, Saint 拜占廷神学家 17—28c
狄奥凡(希腊人) Theophanes the Greek 拜占廷画家 17—28c
狄奥菲拉克图斯(奥克里达的) Theophylactus of Ochrida 希腊神学家 17—29a
狄奥菲拉托 Teofilatto (pope) 教皇 16—547d
狄奥菲鲁斯(亚历山大的),圣 Theophilus of Alexandria, Saint 亚历山大牧首 17—28e
狄奥斐卢斯 Theophilus 东罗马帝国皇帝 17—28d
狄奥格诺斯图斯(亚历山大的) Theognostus of Alexandria 希腊神学家 17—27f
狄奥格诺斯托斯 Theognostos 拜占廷神学家 17—27f
狄奥根尼斯之灯 Diogenes, Lamp of (monument) 雅典纪念建筑 5—327a
狄奥克莱斯 Diocles 希腊哲学家、医学家 5—325c
狄奥莱普特斯(菲拉德尔斐亚的) Theoleptus of Philadelphia 希腊神学家 17—28a
狄奥尼西(加尔都西会士) Dionysius the Carthusian 基督教神学家 5—328d
狄奥尼西(小) Dionysius Exiguus 古罗马教会法学家 5—328a
狄奥尼西,圣 Dionysius, Saint 罗马教皇 5—328c
狄奥尼西奥斯(大) Dionysius the Elder 叙拉古僭主 5—328d
狄奥尼西奥斯(哈利卡纳苏斯的) Dionysius of Halicarnassus 希腊历史学家 5—328b
狄奥尼西奥斯(小) Dionysius the Younger 叙拉古僭主 5—328e
狄奥尼西奥斯·朗吉努斯 Dionysius Longinus 希腊文学评论家 5—328f
狄奥尼修斯(特尔马尔的) Dionysius Telmaharensis 叙利亚教会牧首 5—328c
狄奥尼修斯(大),圣 Dionysius the Great, Saint 古罗马基督教神学家 5—328e
狄奥尼修斯(亚历山大的),圣 Dionysius of Alexandria, Saint 古罗马基督教神学家 5—328a
狄奥普 Diop, Birago 非洲诗人 5—329d
狄奥普 Diop, David 非洲诗人 5—329e
狄奥斯科鲁斯 Dioscorus 基督教亚历山大牧首 5—330e
狄奥斯科鲁斯 Dioscorus 罗马教皇 5—330e
狄奥托科普洛 Theotokópoulos, Doménikos (painter) 希腊画家 17—30b
狄布 Dib, Mohammed 阿尔及利亚作家 5—292d
狄布涅尔 Dibner, Bern 美国工程师 5—293d
狄布泰德斯 Dibutades (Greek sculptor) 希腊雕刻家 5—293f
狄德罗 Diderot, Denis 法国文学家、哲学家 5—303b
狄迪莫斯 Didymus Chalcenterus 希腊学者 5—304b
狄迪莫斯(盲人) Didymus the Blind 基督教神学家 5—304c
狄第乌斯·尤里安 Didius Julianus, Marcus 罗马皇帝 5—303d
狄杜玛 Didyma 古希腊遗址 5—304a
狄多 Dido 希腊传说人物 5—303e
狄俄墨得斯 Diomedes 希腊传说人物 5—327b
狄俄尼索斯 Dionysus 希腊罗马宗教中的酒神 5—328f
狄俄尼索斯节 Dionysia (Greco-Roman religion) 希腊罗马节日 5—327f
狄俄尼索斯精神 Dionysian 戏剧 5—327f
狄俄尼索斯剧场 Dionysus, Theatre of 雅典古希腊剧场 5—329c
狄俄涅 Dione 希腊神话人物 5—327d
狄俄斯库里 Dioscuri 希腊罗马神话人物 5—330f
狄尔斯 Diels, Otto Paul Hermann 德国化学家 5—305d
狄尔泰 Dilthey, Wilhelm 德国哲学家 5—317d
狄更生 Dickinson, Emily (Elizabeth) 美国诗人 5—299f
狄更斯 Dickens, Charles (John Huffam) 英国小说家 5—295a
狄骥 Duguit, Léon 法国法学家 5—449b
狄洁里都号角 didjeridu 乐器 5—303e
狄卡果仁 dika nut 植物 5—315c
狄凯阿科斯 Dicaearchus 希腊哲学家 5—293f
狄克 Dick, George Frederick 美国医生 5—294e
狄克氏花属 Dyckia 植物学 5—487a
狄克提斯(克里特岛的) Dictys Cretensis 克里特岛作家 5—302d
狄克逊 Dixon, George 美国拳击运动员 5—349c
狄克逊 Dixon, Henry Horatio 爱尔兰植物学家 5—349d
狄拉克 Dirac, P(aul) A(drien) M(aurice) 英国物理学家 5—335c
狄克逊 Dixon, Roland B(urrage) 美国文化人类学家 5—349d
狄克逊 Dixon, Thomas 美国作家 5—349e
狄利克雷 Dirichlet, Peter Gustav Lejeune 德国数学家 5—337c
狄利克雷定理 Dirichlet's theorem 数学 5—337e
狄利克雷问题 Dirichlet problem 数学 5—337d
狄龙 Dillon 美国城市 5—317b
狄龙 Dillon, John 爱尔兰政治家 5—317b
狄马德斯 Demades 雅典政治家 5—232d
狄摩西尼 Demosthenes 雅典将军 5—238e
狄摩西尼 Demosthenes 雅典政治家 5—238f
狄纳尔科斯 Dinarchus 雅典演说词作家 5—320b
狄诺克拉底 Dinocrates 古希腊建筑师 5—323f
狄萨兰属 Disa 植物学 5—338b
狄塞耳 Diesel, Rudolf (Christian Karl) 德国工程师 5—306d
狄赛德里奥 Desiderio da Settignano 佛罗伦萨雕刻家 5—260f
狄氏剂 dieldrin 杀虫剂 5—305c
狄斯科耳狄亚 Discordia (in Roman mythology) 罗马神话 5—339c
狄斯帕特 Dis Pater 罗马宗教神名 5—338a
狄特里希·封·贝尔恩 Dietrich von Bern 日耳曼传说人物 5—308e
狄翁 Dion 叙拉古统治者 5—327b
狄翁 Dion, Céline 加拿大歌唱家 5—327c
狄翁(雄辩家) Dion Chrysostom 古希腊修辞学家 5—327c
狄乌迪弟,圣 Deusdedit, SAINT 罗马教皇 5—268c
迪 Dee, John 英国数学家 5—205b
迪埃格诺人 Diegueño 北美印第安人 5—305a
迪安 Dean, Dizzy 美国运动员 5—195a
迪安 Dean, James (Byron) 美国电影演员 5—195a
迪安 Dean, John Wesley, III 美国律师 5—195b
迪安颇会议 Diamper, Synod of 天主教史 5—287b

迪昂 Duhem, Pierre(-Maurice-Marie) 法国物理学家 5—449d
《迪奥》 Deor 古英语诗 5—249c
迪奥 Dior, Christian 法国时装设计师 5—330b
迪奥多蒂翁 Theodotion 犹太学者 17—27c
迪奥尼西·巴尔-萨利比 Dionysius BAR-SALIBI 叙利亚主教 5—328a
迪奥尼修斯周期 Dionysian period 历法 5—327f
迪奥斯科里斯 Dioscorides, Pedanius 希腊医生 5—330d
迪奥特 Dyott, Thomas W. 美国商人 5—488f
迪巴 Dībā al-Hisn 阿拉伯半岛港镇 5—292e
迪拜 Dubayy 阿联酋成员国、城镇 5—438f
迪邦谷 Dibāng Valley 印度地区 5—292f
迪贝利乌斯 Dibelius, Martin 德国《圣经》学者 5—293c
迪比费 Dubuffet, Jean(-Philippe-Arthur) 法国画家 5—443b
迪比克 Dubuque 美国城市 5—443c
迪比奇 Diebitsch, Johann (Karl Friedrich Anton), Graf (Count) 俄国军官 5—304e
迪比奇-扎巴尔坎斯基 Dibich-Zabalkansky, Ivan Ivanovich 俄国军官 5—293d
迪比亚 Du Buat, Pierre-Louis-Georges 法国工程师 5—434f
迪波 Duport, Louis(-Antoine) 法国舞蹈家 5—467c
迪波尔 Duport, Adrien(-Jean-François) 法国政治家 5—467c
迪博 Dubos, René (Jules) 美国微生物学家 5—442e
迪布丁 Dibdin, Charles 英国作曲家 5—293a
迪布丁 Dibdin, Thomas Frognall 英国目录学者 5—293c
迪布鲁格尔 Dibrugarh 印度城镇 5—293e
迪布瓦 Dubois, Eugène 荷兰解剖学家、地质学家 5—442c
迪布瓦 Dubois, (François-Clément-) Théodore 荷兰解剖学家、地质学家 5—442e
迪布瓦 Dubois, Guillaume 法国枢机主教 5—442c
迪布瓦 Dubois, Jean-Antoine 法国天主教司铎 5—442d
迪布瓦 Dubois, Pierre 法国律师 5—442d
迪茨 Diez, Friedrich Christian 德国语言学家 5—309b
迪茨 Dietz, Howard 美国流行歌词作家 5—308e
迪茨 Dietz, Robert S. 美国地球物理学家 5—308f
迪德利 Diddley, Bo 美国歌手 5—302f
迪迪米岛 Didyme Insula (Italy) 意大利岛屿 5—304a
迪多 Dudo OF SAINT-QUENTIN 法国历史学家 5—446e
迪多家族 Didot FAMILY 法国印刷、出版业者 5—303f
迪多克 Dudok, Willem Marinus 荷兰建筑师 5—446e
迪厄多内 Dieudonné, Jean(-Alexandre-Eugène) 法国数学家 5—309a
迪厄拉富瓦 Dieulafoy, Marcel-Auguste 法国考古学家 5—000a
迪恩 Deane, Silas 美国外交官 5—195c
迪恩森林 Dean, Forest of 英格兰森林 5—195a
迪恩森林 Forest of Dean 英格兰森林 6—406d
迪尔 Deal 英格兰城镇 5—194f
迪尔 Dīr 巴基斯坦城镇 5—335c
迪尔 Deere, John 美国发明家 5—206e
迪尔 Dill, Sir John Greer 英国元帅 5—316d
迪尔伯恩 Dearborn 美国城市 5—195f
迪尔伯恩 Dearborn, Henry 美国陆军部长 5—196a
迪尔伯恩堡 Dearborn, Fort 美国碉堡 5—195f
迪尔福 Durfort, Louis de 英国军人 5—472e
迪尔福家族 Durfort FAMILY 法国贵族 5—472e
迪尔公司 Deere & Company 美国农机制造商 5—206e
《迪尔集》 Deer, The Book of 基督教文献 5—206d
迪尔克从男爵(第二) Dilke, Sir Charles Wentworth, 2ND BARONET 英国政治家 5—316b
迪尔穆恩 Dilmun 古王国名 5—317d
迪尔塞梅洛琴 dulce melos 乐器 5—453d
迪法恩斯 Defiance 美国城市 5—209b
迪费 Dufay, Guillaume 法国作曲家 5—447e
迪芬贝克 Diefenbaker, John G(eorge) 加拿大总理 5—304f
迪夫里伊 Divriği 土耳其城镇 5—348b
迪夫斯 Dievs 波罗的海地区天神 5—309a
迪弗吉埃 Duvergier de Hauranne, Jean, ABBÉ DE SAINTCYRAN 法国隐修院院长 5—483b
迪戈 Dihigo, Martin 古巴职业棒球运动员 5—314f
迪戈加西亚 Diego Garcia 印度洋岛屿 5—305a
迪格比 Digby 加拿大城镇 5—312c
迪格比 Digby, George 英国政治家 5—312c
迪格比 Digby, John 英格兰外交官 5—312c
迪格比 Digby, Sir Kenelm 英国哲学家、外交官 5—312c
迪格尼斯·阿克里塔斯 Digenis Akritas 拜占廷史诗英雄 5—312d
迪格斯 Diggs, Annie LePorte 美国改革家、政治家 5—313b
迪古尔河 Digul River 印度尼西亚河流 5—314f
迪河 Dee, River 苏格兰河流 5—205b
迪河 Dee, River 北威尔士、英格兰河流 5—205b
迪基 Dickey, Bill 美国运动员 5—299b
迪基 Dickey, James (Lafayette) 美国作家 5—299b
迪基 Dickey, Sarah Ann 美国教育家 5—299c
迪加辛斯基 Dygasiński, Adolf 波兰作家 5—488a
迪金 Deakin, Alfred 澳大利亚总理 5—194e
迪金 Deakin, Arthur 英国工会领袖 5—194e
迪金森 Dickinson 美国城市 5—299d
迪金森 Dickinson, Anna Elizabeth 美国演讲者 5—299d
迪金森 Dickinson, John 美国政治家 5—300b
迪金森 Dickinson, Jonathan 北美殖民地牧师 5—300c
迪卡尔布 De Kalb 美国城市 5—188b
迪卡斯男爵 Du Casse, Pierre-Emmanuel-Albert, Baron 法国军事史学家 5—435b
迪卡斯特里法院 dicastery 古雅典司法机构 5—293f
迪开石 dickite 矿物 5—300c
迪凯纳 Duquesne, Abraham, MARQUIS DU QUESNE 法国军人 5—468e
迪凯努瓦 Duquesnoy, François 罗马雕刻家 5—468f
迪凯特 Decatur 美国亚拉巴马州城市 5—201b
迪凯特 Decatur 美国佐治亚州城市 5—201b
迪凯特 Decatur 美国伊利诺伊州城市 5—201b
迪康热 Cange, Charles du Fresne, seigneur du (lord of) 法国学者 3—400e
迪科·迪欧龙 Ducos du Hauron, (Arthur-) Louis 法国物理学家 5—445e
迪克 Deak, Nicholas L(ouis) 美国银行家 5—194d
迪克 Dicke, Robert H(enry) 美国物理学家 5—294f
迪克海姆 Dürkheim (Germany) 德国城市 5—175d
迪克森 Dixon 美国城市 5—349b
迪克森 Dickson, Carr (American author) 美国作家 5—300d
迪克森 Dixon, George 英国航海家 5—349c
迪克森 Dixon, Jeremiah 英国土地测量员 5—349d
迪克森 Dickson, John Robinson 爱尔兰医生 5—300d
迪克森 Dickson, Leonard Eugene 美国数学家 5—300d
迪克森海峡 Dixon Entrance 太平洋海上通道 5—349f
迪克斯 Dix, Dorothea Lynde 美国社会改革家 5—348d
迪克斯 Dix, John Adams 美国政治家 5—348e
迪克斯 Dix, Otto 德国画家 5—348e
迪克斯 Dirks, Rudolph 美国画家 5—337f
迪克西 Dixie 美国南部区域俗称 5—348f
迪克西兰 Dixieland 美国音乐 5—349a
迪克西民主党人 Dixiecrat 美国政治党派 5—349a
迪库尔 Dicuil 爱尔兰僧侣、地理学家 5—302d
迪夸 Dikwa 尼日利亚城镇、酋长国名 5—315d
迪拉斯 Duras, Marguerite 法国作家 5—471c
迪朗 Durand, Guillaume 法国天主教教会法学者 5—470a
迪朗蒂 Duranti, William 法国天主教教会法学者 5—471b
迪朗杜 Durandus, William 法国天主教教会法学者 5—470c
迪朗杜(圣普尔桑的) Durandus OF SAINT-POURÇAIN 法国天主教主教

5—470c
迪朗-吕埃尔 Durand-Ruel, Paul 法国画商 5—470b
迪朗斯河 Durance 法国河流 5—469f
迪里安巴 Diriamba 尼加拉瓜城市 5—337c
迪里耶战役 Dirʿīyah, Battle of ad- 阿拉伯半岛历史 5—337f
迪林 Deering, William 美国企业家 5—206f
迪林格 Deringer, Henry 美国军械工匠 5—253e
迪林格手枪 derringer 武器 5—255c
迪林杰 Dillinger, John (Herbert) 美国匪徒 5—316f
迪隆河 Dillon (eastern South Island, New Zealand) 新西兰河流 5—317a
迪吕 DuLhut, Daniel Greysolon, Sieur 法国探险家 5—453e
迪律伊 Duruy, Victor 法国学者、官吏 5—477d
迪伦 Düren 德国城市 5—472a
迪伦 Dylan, Bob 美国歌星 5—488a
迪伦马特 Dürrenmatt, Friedrich 瑞士作家 5—477b
迪罗克 Duroc, Géraud - Christophe - Michel, DUC (duke) DE FRIOUL 法国将军 5—476d
迪马乔 DiMaggio, Joe 美国棒球运动员 5—317e
迪马什契 Dimashqī, ad- (Muslim scholar) 伊拉克穆斯林学者 5—317f
迪梅尼尔小姐 Dumesnil, Mademoiselle 法国演员 5—456d
迪美 Diémer, Louis -Joseph 法国钢琴家 5—305f
迪蒙 Dumont, François 法国画家 5—456f
迪蒙·迪尔维尔 Dumont d'Urville, Jules-Sébastien-César 法国航海家 5—456f
迪米特里奥斯 Dimitrios 东正教牧首 5—318f
迪米特里耶维奇 Dimitrijević, Dragutin 塞尔维亚军官 5—318f
迪莫波利斯 Demopolis 美国城市 5—238d
迪莫纳 Dimona 以色列城镇 5—319c
迪穆里埃 Dumouriez, Charles-François du Périer 法国将军 5—457b
迪纳堡 Dünaburg (Latvia) 拉脱维亚城市 5—457e
迪纳尔阶 Dienerian Stage 地质学 5—306a
迪纳杰布尔 Dinājpur 孟加拉国城镇 5—319d
迪纳拉山脉 Dinaric Alps 欧洲山脉 5—320b
迪纳利国家公园和禁猎区 Denali National Park and Preserve 美国保护区 5—241c
迪奈维里 Dīnawarī, ad- 波斯天文学家、植物学家 5—320c
迪南 Dinant 法国城镇 5—320a
迪南 Dinan 比利时城镇 5—319e
迪南黄铜器皿 dinanderie 中世纪比利时工艺品 5—319f
迪内弗尔 Dinefwr 威尔士区名 5—320e
迪内森 Dinesen, Isak 丹麦作家 5—320f
迪尼斯 Dinis 葡萄牙国王 5—323c
迪尼斯 Dinis, Júlio 葡萄牙作家 5—323d
迪涅莱班 Digne-les-Bains 法国城镇 5—314e
迪努瓦伯爵 Dunois, Jean d'Orléans, comte de 法国军官 5—464e
迪帕克 Duparc, (Marie-Eugène-) Henri 法国作曲家 5—466c
迪潘 Dupin, Louis Ellies 法兰西教会史学家 5—466e
迪佩龙 Duperron, Jacques Davy 法国枢机主教 5—466d
迪皮特伦 Dupuytren, Guillaume, Baron 法国外科医师 5—468d
迪皮特伦氏挛缩 Dupuytren's contracture 病理学 5—468d
迪皮伊 Dupuy, Charles-Alexandre 法国政治家 5—468c
迪皮伊 Dupuy, Pierre 法国历史学家 5—468c
迪普 Depew, Chauncey Mitchell 美国律师、政治家 5—250a
迪普拉 Duprat, Antoine 法国大法官 5—467e
迪普莱西-莫尔奈 Duplessis-Mornay, Philippe 法国外交家 5—466f
迪塞普申岛 Deception Island 南设得兰群岛岛屿 5—202e
迪塞普申湾 Deception Bay 澳大利亚海湾、城镇 5—202e
迪赛德 Deeside (Scotland) 苏格兰区名 5—207a
迪赛德 Deeside (Wales) 威尔士区名 5—207a
迪森塔 Di Centa, Manuela 意大利滑雪运动员 5—282a
迪石 Rach Gia 越南城市 14—105c
迪斯伯里 Dewsbury 英格兰区属地方名 5—276f
迪斯卡弗里湾 Discovery Bay 澳大利亚海湾 5—339e
迪斯坎特 descant 音乐 5—257f
迪斯科 disco 流行音乐 5—339a
迪斯科岛 Disco Island (Greenland) 格陵兰岛屿 5—340e
迪斯科岛 Disko Island (Greenland) 格陵兰岛屿 5—339b
迪斯累里 Disraeli, Benjamin, EARL OF BEACONSFIELD 英国首相 5—342e
迪斯默尔沼泽 Dismal Swamp 美国沼泽 5—340e
迪斯尼 Disney, Walt 美国动画电影先驱 5—340f
迪斯尼公司 Disney Company 美国公司 5—341b
迪斯泰法诺 Di Stefano, Alfredo 阿根廷足球运动员、经理 5—282c
迪特里希 Dietrich, Josef 德国党卫军军官 5—308b
迪特里希 Dietrich, Paul-Henri 法国哲学家 5—308d
迪特罗谢 Dutrochet, (René-Joachim-) Henri 法国生理学家 5—482a
迪特马申 Dithmarschen 德国地区 5—345a
迪特斯·冯·迪特斯多夫 Ditters von Dittersdorf, Carl 奥地利小提琴家 5—345c
迪瓦卡罗庞迪塔 Divākarapaṇḍita 柬埔寨国王宠臣 5—345f
迪瓦尼耶 Dīwānīyah, ad- 伊拉克城市 5—348d
迪瓦尼字体 dīwānī script 文字 5—348c
迪万 divan 伊斯兰政府单位 5—346a
迪韦 Duve, Christian René de 比利时生物化学家 5—483a
迪韦 Duvet, Jean 法国版画家 5—483b
迪韦齐斯 Devizes 英格兰城镇 5—273a
迪维尼 Divini, Eustachio 意大利光学家 5—347e
迪维尼奥 du Vigneaud, Vincent 美国生物化学家 5—437a
迪维诺 Divino, El (poet) 西班牙诗人 5—347e
迪维诺波利斯 Divinópolis 巴西城市 5—347e
迪维维耶 Duvivier, Julien (Henri Nicolas) 法国电影导演 5—483c
迪翁五胞胎 Dionne QUINTUPLETS 加拿大人物 5—327e
迪沃 Divo 科特迪瓦城镇 5—348a
迪乌夫 Diouf, Abdou 塞内加尔总统 5—331a
迪西 Ducis, Jean-François 法国戏剧家 5—445a
迪歇恩 Duchenne, Guillaume -Benjamin -Amand 法国医生 5—444e
迪歇纳 Duchesne, André 法国历史学家 5—444e
迪歇纳 Duchesne, Louis-Marie-Olivier 法国天主教教会史学家 5—444f
迪歇纳 Duchesne, Saint Rose Philippine 法国传教士 5—444f
迪歇纳老爷 Duchesne, Père (Father) 法国政治新闻工作者 5—444f
迪雅尔丹 Dujardin, Félix 法国生物学家 5—450c
迪亚巴克尔 Diyarbakır 土耳其城市 5—350a
迪亚贝利 Diabelli, Anton 奥地利作曲家 5—282e
迪亚丁 Dujardin, Karel 荷兰画家 5—450c
迪亚吉塔人 Diaguita 南美印第安人 5—284f
迪亚拉河 Diyālā River 亚洲河流 5—350a
迪亚曼蒂纳 Diamantina 巴西城市 5—286b
迪亚曼蒂纳河 Diamantina River 澳大利亚河流 5—286b
迪亚米尔 Diamir (Jammu and Kashmir) 查谟和克什米尔山峰 5—286b
迪亚娜(法兰西的) Diane DE FRANCE, DUCHESS (duchesse) DE MONTMORENCY ET ANGOULÊME 法国女公爵 5—288c
迪亚娜(普瓦蒂埃的) Diane DE POITIERS, DUCHESS (duchesse) DEVALENTINOIS 法国贵族 5—288c
迪亚斯 Diaz, Abby Morton 美国小说家 5—291d
迪亚斯 Dias, Antônio Gonçalves (Brazilian wrifer) 巴西作家 5—289c
迪亚斯 Dias, Bartolomeu 葡萄牙探险家 5—289c
迪亚斯 Díaz del Castillo, Bernal 西班牙军人、作家 5—292b
迪亚斯 Dias, Dinís 葡萄牙航海家 5—289f
迪亚斯 Díaz, Porfirio 墨西哥总统 5—291e
迪亚斯·奥尔达斯 Díaz Ordaz, Gustavo 墨西哥总统 5—292c
迪亚斯·德索利斯 Díaz de Solís, Juan 西班牙探险家 5—292b

迪亚兹 Diaz, Armando 意大利将军 5—291e
迪亚兹·德·拉·佩纳 Diaz de La Peña, Narcisse-Virgile 法国画家 5—292a
迪耶普 Dieppe 法国港镇 5—306b
迪尤布 Dube, John Langalibalele 南非作家、教育家 5—439d
迪尤拉人 Dyula 西非民族 5—490b
迪尤森 Dewson, Mary Williams 美国经济学家 5—276f
迪兹富勒 Dezfūl 伊朗城市 5—277d
迪兹水坝 Dez Dam 伊朗水坝 5—277c
的的喀喀湖 Titicaca, Lake 南美湖泊 17—119b
的黎波里 Ṭarābulus (Lebanon) 黎巴嫩城市 16—478b
的黎波里 Tripoli 利比亚首都 17—225b
的黎波里塔尼亚 Tripolitania 北非历史地区 17—225d
的黎波里战争 Tripolitan War 历史事件 17—225d
的里雅斯特 Trieste 意大利城市 17—218c
“的里雅斯特”号 Trieste 探海艇 17—218d
荻生徂徕 Ogyū Sorai 日本儒者 12—348c
荻原朔太郎 Hagiwara Sakutarō 日本诗人 7—407c
敌对教皇 antipope 伪教皇 1—393f
敌基督 Antichrist 基督教 1—383d
笛福 Defoe, Daniel 英国小说家 5—209c
笛卡儿 Descartes, René 法国数学家、哲学家 5—257f
笛卡儿主义 Cartesianism 哲学 3—488f
抵抗运动 resistance 反纳粹统治的地下组织 14—240c
抵押 mortgage 法律 11—408e
抵押财物 hypothec 法律 8—296a
抵制 boycott 政治行动 3—100a
抵制英货公约 Nonimportation Agreements 美国殖民历史 12—229a
底本 Dibon 古摩押首都 5—293d
底比斯 Thebes 埃及古都 17—19b
底辟 diapir 地质学 5—289a
底波拉 Deborah 《圣经》人物 5—198a
底层水 bottom water 海洋最低水层 3—75d
底格里斯河 Tigris River 亚洲河流 17—92e
底流 undertow 海流 17—340c
底拿 Dinah 《圣经》人物 5—319d
底特律 Detroit 美国城市 5—267c
底特律河 Detroit River 美国河流 5—267f
底特律艺术馆 Detroit Institute of Arts 美国博物馆 5—267e
骶骨 sacrum 解剖学 14—490b
骶髂关节 sacroiliac 解剖学 14—490b
地 bhūmi 大乘佛教 2—453d
地伯 landgrave 欧洲贵族称号 9—476d
地槽 geosyncline 地质学 7—84e
地层学 stratigraphy 地质学 16—267f
地磁场 geomagnetic field 地球物理学 7—72e
地磁极性倒转 geomagnetic reversal 地球物理学 7—72f
地磁学 geomagnetics 地球物理学 7—72f
地电 Earth current 地球物理学 5—498c
地鸫 ground thrush 鸟类 7—324d
地盾 shield (geology) 地质学 15—311f
地垛 butte 地形 3—292a
地方警察 Préfecture de Police 法国警察部队 13—492a
地方武装团队 posse comitatus 古代英国机构 13—458f
地方长官 corregidor 西班牙政府官员 4—521d
《地方志》 Dindsheanchas 古爱尔兰文献 5—320d
地方自治 home rule 政治学 8—143f
地方自治会 zemstvo 俄国政府 18—507b
地风火乐队 Earth, Wind and Fire 美国乐队 5—498c
地肤属 Kochia 植物学 9—331b
地核 core 地球物理学 4—504e
地花蜂 mining bee 昆虫 11—258a
地窖 cellar 建筑 3—556f
地鹃 ground cuckoo 鸟类 7—323e
地拉那 Tiranë 阿尔巴尼亚首都 17—109a
地蜡 ozokerite 矿物蜡 12—529a
地雷 land mine 武器 9—474d
地垒和地堑 horst and graben 地质学 8—185d
地理人种 geographic race 人类学 7—71c
地理信息系统 GIS 执行地理分析的计算机系统 7—143e
地理旋回 geographic cycle 地貌学 7—71c
地理学 geography 自然科学 7—71d
地利贝伊 derebey 安纳托利亚领主 5—253c
地栗 groundnut 植物学 7—324e
地鸡 ground roller 鸟类 7—324a
地灵 kobold 日耳曼民间传说 9—329b
地幔 mantle 地球物理学 10—475e
地幔岩 pyrolite 岩石 14—47c
地貌 landform 地貌学 9—476c
地貌成因区 morphogenetic region 地貌学 11—402f
地貌旋回 geomorphic cycle 地貌学 7—73e
地貌学 geomorphology 地理学 7—73f
地米斯托克利 Themistocles 雅典政治家 17—22c
地面靶射箭 clout shooting 体育 4—303f
地面镶砌 tessellated pavement 建筑 16—559c
地名学 toponymy 地名分类研究 17—158d
地母 Terra Mater (Roman goddess) 古罗马土地女神 16—554c
地平经度 azimuth 天文学 2—102a
地平纬度和地平经度 altitude and azimuth 天文学 1—256e
地平纬圈 almucantar 天文学 1—248a
地平线 horizon 天文学 8—174a
地壳 crust 地球物理学 5—40c
地壳均衡 isostasy 地球物理学 8—473f
地钱属 Marchantia 植物学 10—497b
地堑 graben (geology) 地质学 7—235b
地球 Earth 地球科学 5—497e
地球化学 geochemistry 地球科学 7—69e
地球化学旋回 geochemical cycle 地球化学 7—69d
地球科学 Earth sciences 科学 5—498e
地球物理学 geophysics 地球科学 7—74a
地球仪 globe 能转动的现形地图 7—160a
地球资源技术卫星 Earth Resources Technology Satellite 人造卫星 5—498d
地球资源技术卫星 ERTS 人造卫星 6—124c
地区开发规划 regional development program 政府规划 14—204e
地热能 geothermal energy 地球物理学 7—84f
地声探测器 Geophone 地球物理仪器 7—74a
地松鼠 ground squirrel 哺乳动物 7—324b
地毯 rug and carpet 装饰性织物 14—444a
地毯草 carpet grass (*Axonopus affinis*) 草本植物 3—477f
地毯尺蛾 carpet moth 昆虫 3—478a
地毯藓 carpet moss 苔藓植物 3—477f
地头 jitō 日本古代庄园总管 9—34e
地图 map 地图学 10—483e
地图集 atlas 地图学 2—29b
地图投影 cartographic projection 地图学 3—490f
地外生命 extraterrestrial life 空间科学 6—198d
地网 counterpoise 电子学 4—543f
地峡 isthmus 地理学 8—482d
地峡运动会 Isthmian Games 古希腊赛事 8—482c
地下党卫队 Odessa 德国纳粹组织 12—337c
地下电影 underground film 电影 17—339e
地下礼堂 kiva 印第安人建筑 9—310f
地下墓窟 catacomb 墓地 3—518b
地下暖坑 hypocaust 建筑 8—294f
地下水 groundwater 水文学 7—325a

地下水位 water table 水文学 18—139d
地下丝绒乐队 Velvet Underground, the 美国乐队 17—495f
地下铁道 subway 交通工具 16—301b
"地下铁道" Underground Railroad 美国历史 17—339f
地蟹 land crab 甲壳动物 9—474b
地心体系 geocentric system 天文学 7—69c
地形降水 orographic precipitation 气象学 12—469c
地形图 topographic map 地理学 17—156f
地衣 lichen 植物 10—81f
地衣红 cudbear 染料 5—51c
地役权 easement 法律 5—501d
地役权 servitude 财产法 15—229f
地榆 burnet 草本植物 3—271e
地狱 hell 宗教 7—575b
地狱 Jigoku 日本佛教传说 9—21b
地狱 naraka 宗教 11—574a
地狱犬 hellhound 神话 8—1e
地域人种 local race 人类学 10—174b
地缘政治学 geopolitics 政治学 7—74b
地藏 Kṣitigarbha 佛教菩萨名 9—385f
地照 earthshine 天文学 5—501a
地震 earthquake 地震学 5—499f
地震波 seismic wave 地震学 15—192f
地震带 seismic belt 地震学 15—192d
地震海波 seismic sea wave 地震学 15—192d
地震勘测 seismic survey 地震学 15—192d
地震学 seismology 地球物理学 15—194b
地震仪 seismograph 地震学 15—193a
地质海洋学 geologic oceanography 地质学 7—71f
地质年代学 geochronology 地质学 7—69e
地质时期 geologic time 地质学 7—71f
地质学 geology 地球科学 7—72b
地掷球 boccie 体育项目 2—559b
地中海 Mediterranean Sea 世界最大陆间海 11—78d
地中海地域人种 Mediterranean local race 人类学 11—78c
地中海粉蛾 Mediterranean flour moth 昆虫 11—78c
地中海季风 etesian wind 气象学 6—144d
《地中海领事全书》 Consulate of the Sea, Book of the 法令汇编 4—461c
地中海茅草 esparto 植物学 6—133a
地中海贫血 thalassemia 疾病 17—11b
地中海热 Mediterranean fever 疾病 11—78c
地中海实蝇 Mediterranean fruit fly 昆虫 11—78c
地中海夏旱灌木群落 maquis 植物学 10—486b
地中海植被 Mediterranean vegetation 植物学 11—78e
地珠 ground pearl 昆虫 7—323f
地蛛 ground spider 昆虫 7—324a
地转运动 geostrophic motion 流体力学 7—84d
弟兄联盟 Unitas Fratrum 基督教派别 17—349e
帝刹 dīkṣā 印度宗教礼仪 5—315d
帝冠 Imperial Crown 查理曼皇冠 8—346d
帝龟 Archelon 古生物学 1—448a
帝国 Reich 德国政治 14—207a
帝国大厦 Empire State Building 美国建筑 6—64a
帝国风格 Empire style 法国新古典主义艺术 6—64b
帝国化学工业公司 Imperial Chemical Industries PLC (ICI) 英国公司 8—345f
帝国集团公司 Imperial Group, PLC 英国烟草商 8—346e
帝国枢密法院 Reichskammergericht 神圣罗马帝国最高法院 14—207e
帝国特惠制 imperial preference 经济 8—346e
帝国行政区 Kreis 神圣罗马帝国历史 9—374e
帝国议会 Diet 神圣罗马帝国立法机构 5—307b
帝国战争博物馆 Imperial War Museum 英国博物馆 8—347a
帝国直辖市 imperial city 神圣罗马帝国城市 8—346a
帝国主义 imperialism 政治学 8—347a
帝俊 Di Jun 中国神话人物 5—282b
帝力 Dili 东帝汶首都 5—316a
帝权 imperium 古罗马政治 8—347d
帝汶 Timor 马来群岛岛屿 17—101e
帝汶海 Timor Sea 印度洋海域 17—101f
帝座 Ras Algethi 天文学 14—156c
递归函数 recursive function 逻辑学、数学函数 14—186b
第奥 Dio (India) 印度城镇 5—325b
第八颅神经 eighth cranial nerve 解剖学 5—568c
第比利斯 Tbilisi 格鲁吉亚首都 16—507b
第比斯 Thebes 希腊城市 17—20c
第波罗 Dipolog 菲律宾城市 5—333e
第博尼哥罗(亲王) Dipo Negoro, Pangeran (Prince) 印度尼西亚民族英雄 5—333c
第二巴库 Second Baku (Russia) 俄国地区 15—176d
第二次北方战争 Northern War, Second 欧洲历史 12—263f
第二次布匿战争 Punic War, Second 古罗马历史 14—27a
第二次梵蒂冈会议 Vatican Council, second 天主教会普世会议 17—480a
第二次海湾战争 Persian Gulf War, Second 国际冲突 13—182f
第二次马恩河会战 Marne, Second Battle of the 法国历史 10—527b
第二次世界大战 World War II 世界史 18—337c
第二次索姆河战役 Somme, Second Battle of the 第一次世界大战史 15—506e
第二次鸦片战争 Second Opium War 中国历史 15—176f
第二次犹太人起义 Jewish Revolt, Second 犹太王国历史 9—9d
第二帝国风格 Second Empire style 建筑风格 15—176d
第二国际 International, Second 国际组织 8—411c
第谷·布拉厄 Tycho Brahe (Danish astronomer) 丹麦天文学家 17—304f
第谷环形山 Tycho 月球环形山 17—304e
第谷体系 Tychonic system 天文学 17—304f
第谷新星 Tycho's Nova 天文学 17—304f
第勒尼安海 Tyrrhenian Sea 地中海海湾 17—312d
第聂伯河 Dnieper River 欧洲河流 5—353b
第聂伯罗彼得罗夫斯克 Dnipropetrovsk 乌克兰州名 5—353e
第聂伯罗彼得罗夫斯克 Dnipropetrovsk 乌克兰城市 5—353e
第聂伯罗捷尔任斯克 Dniprodzerzhinsk 乌克兰城市 5—353d
第欧根尼 Diogenes 希腊哲学家 5—326e
第欧根尼(阿波罗尼亚的) Diogenes of Apollonia 希腊哲学家 5—327a
第欧根尼·拉尔修 Diogenes Laërtius 希腊作家 5—326f
第戎 Dijon 法国城市 5—315a
第三次布匿战争 Punic War, Third 古罗马历史 14—27c
第三等级 Third Estate 法国历史 17—40b
第三帝国 Third Reich 纳粹德国 17—40b
第三国际 International, Third 国际组织 8—411e
第三纪 Tertiary Period 地质学 16—557d
第三厅 Third Department 俄国机构 17—40a
第三者保存的契据 escrow 法律 6—129d
第四点计划 Point Four Program 美国外援政策 13—389b
第四国际 International, Fourth 国际组织 8—412a
第四纪 Quaternary Period 地质学 14—80e
第乌 Diu 印度城镇 5—345e
第五共和国运动 Movement for the Fifth Republic 委内瑞拉政党 11—449a
第五君主国派 Fifth Monarchy Men 英国历史教派 6—309b
第五、六次会议 Quinisext Council 普世教会会议 14—93f
第五纵队 fifth column 军事小集团 6—309b

第一次北方战争 Northern War, First 欧洲历史 12—263f
第一次布匿战争 Punic War, First 古罗马历史 14—26f
第一次梵蒂冈会议 Vatican Council, First 天主教史 17—480a
第一次海湾战争 Persian Gulf War, First 国际冲突 13—182e
第一次马恩河会战 Marne, First Battle of the 法国历史 10—527b
第一次世界大战 World War I 世界史 18—337a
第一次索姆河战役 Somme, First Battle of the 第一次世界大战史 15—506d
第一次犹太人起义 Jewish Revolt, First 犹太王国历史 9—9d
第一动因 first cause 哲学 6—328f
第一夫人 first lady 美国总统妻子 6—329a
第一国际 International, First 国际组织 8—411b
第一基督教科学会 First Church of Christ, Scientist 美国督教教会 6—329a
第一劝业银行 Dai-Ichi Kangyo Bank 日本银行 5—110c
第一乌拉尔斯克 Pervouralsk 俄罗斯城市 13—192b
第一银行 Bank One 美国银行 2—204f
第一银行系统公司 First Bank System, Inc. 美国公司 6—328f
第一州际银行公司 First Interstate Bancorp 美国银行持股公司 6—329a
棣美弗 Moivre, Abraham de 法国数学家 11—313e
蒂阿罗哈 Te Aroha 新西兰城市 16—509a
蒂阿瑙湖 Te Anau, Lake 新西兰湖泊 16—509a
蒂奥农塔蒂人 Tionontati 美国印第安人 17—107e
蒂奥王国 Tyo, Kingdom of (African history) 非洲历史 17—307c
蒂巴尔迪 Tibaldi, Pellegrino 意大利画家 17—81d
蒂鲍 Thibaut, Anton Friedrich Justus 德国法学家 17—37f
蒂贝特 Tibbett, Lawrence 美国歌唱家 17—81d
蒂贝托特 Tibetot, John 英国军官 17—84f
蒂宾根 Tübingen 德国行政区 17—256a
蒂宾根 Tübingen 德国城市 17—256b
蒂宾根大学 Tübingen, University of 德国大学 17—256c
蒂波 Thibault, Jacques-Anatole-François 法国作家 17—37e
蒂波特山丑闻 Teapot Dome Scandal 美国历史 16—512a
蒂博 Thibaud, Jacques 法国小提琴家 17—37e
蒂博多 Thibodaux 美国城市 17—38a
蒂达格尔 Titāgarh 印度城镇 17—114c
蒂蒂拉雀 tityra 鸟类 17—121f
蒂顿岭 Teton Range 美国山岭 16—562d
蒂多雷岛 Tidore Island 印度尼西亚岛屿 17—87c
蒂尔 Tiel 荷兰城镇 17—88a
蒂尔堡 Tilburg 荷兰城市 17—94f
蒂尔伯里 Tilbury 英格兰港口 17—95a
蒂尔登 Tilden, Bill 美国运动员 17—95a
蒂尔登 Tilden, Samuel J(ones) 美国政治人物 17—95b
蒂尔登-海斯事件 Tilden-Hayes affair 美国历史 17—95c
蒂尔迪 Tildy, Zoltán 匈牙利政治家 17—95c
蒂尔加滕 Tiergarten 德国柏林区名 17—88e
蒂尔曼 Tillman, Benjamin R(yan) 美国政治家 17—97a
蒂尔瑙 Tyrnau (Slovakia) 斯洛伐克城镇 17—311f
蒂尔索·德·莫利纳 Tirso de Molina 西班牙戏剧家 17—111a
蒂尔托夫 Tirtoff, Romain de (designer) 俄国设计师 17—111d
蒂尔西特 Tilsit (Russia) 俄罗斯历史地名 17—97c
《蒂尔西特条约》 Tilsit, Treaties of 欧洲历史 17—97d
蒂法尼 Tiffany, Charles Lewis 美国珠宝商 17—89d
蒂法尼 Tiffany, Louis Comfort 美国画家 17—89d
蒂芬 Tiffin 美国城市 17—89f
蒂夫人 Tiv 尼日利亚民族 17—122a
蒂弗顿 Tiverton (England) 苏格兰区名 17—122b
蒂弗顿 Tiverton 美国城镇 17—122b
蒂格 Teague, Walter Dorwin 美国工业设计家 16—511a
蒂格尔 Tiger, Theobald 德国作家 17—90c
蒂格雷 Tigre 阿根廷城市 17—92c
蒂黑 Tychy 波兰城镇 17—305a
蒂华纳 Tijuana 墨西哥城市 17—93a
蒂吉纳 Tighina 摩尔多瓦城市 17—91c
蒂加登 Teagarden, Jack 美国音乐家 16—510f
蒂卡尔 Tikal 危地马拉马雅古遗址 17—93b
蒂科 Tiko 喀麦隆城镇 17—94c
蒂克 Tieck, (Johann) Ludwig 德国作家 17—87e
蒂克 Ticker, Reuben (singer) 美国歌剧演员 17—86b
蒂克尔 Tickell, Thomas 英国作家 17—86a
蒂克利奥 Ticlio 秘鲁安第斯山脉山隘 17—86c
蒂克纳 Ticknor, George 美国教育家 17—86b
蒂克斯伯里 Tewkesbury 英格兰城镇 17—2a
蒂克斯伯里 Tewkesbury 英格兰自治市 17—2a
蒂克斯伯里 Tewksbury 英格兰城镇 17—2c
蒂克斯伯里战役 Tewkesbury, Battle of 英国历史 17—2b
蒂拉赫 Tīrāh 巴基斯坦山地 17—109a
蒂拉斯波尔 Tiraspol 摩尔多瓦城市 17—109b
蒂兰兹氏凤梨属 Tillandsia 植物学 17—96b
蒂勒 Tulle 法国城镇 17—264e
蒂勒 Tiller, (Terence) Rogers 英国作家 17—96c
蒂勒尔 Tyrrell, Sir James 英格兰军人 17—312c
蒂勒尔湖 Tyrrell, Lake 澳大利亚浅洼地 17—312c
蒂雷纳 Turenne, Henri de La Tour d'Auvergne, vicomte de 法国元帅 17—278c
蒂里湖 Tyri, Lake 挪威湖泊 17—311e
蒂里杰米尔山 Tirich Mir 巴基斯坦山峰 17—110a
蒂里特 Tyrwhitt, Thomas 英国学者 17—312e
蒂利 Tilly, Johann Tserclaes, Graf von 巴伐利亚将领 17—97b
蒂利 Tilley, Sir Samuel Leonard 加拿大政治家 17—96d
蒂利 Tilley, Vesta 英国歌唱家 17—96e
蒂利特 Tillett, Benjamin 英国工会领袖 17—96c
蒂利希 Tillich, Paul (Johannes) 美国哲学家 17—96e
蒂龙 Tyrone 北爱尔兰旧郡名 17—311f
蒂龙伯爵(第二) Tyrone, Hugh O'Neill, 2nd Earl of 爱尔兰反英领袖 17—312a
蒂龙伯爵(第一) Tyrone, Conn O'Neill, 1st Earl of 爱尔兰领袖 17—312a
蒂鲁伯蒂 Tirupati 印度城市 17—111e
蒂鲁布尔 Tiruppūr 印度城市 17—111e
蒂鲁内尔韦利 Tirunelveli 印度城市 17—111d
蒂鲁奇奇拉帕利 Tiruchchirāppalli 印度城市 17—111d
蒂伦豪特 Turnhout 比利时城市 17—201f
蒂伦尼乌斯 Dillenius, Johann Jakob 德国植物学家 5—316f
蒂罗尔 Tirol 奥地利州名 17—110c
蒂马鲁 Timaru 新西兰城市 17—98a
蒂曼 Thimann, Kenneth V(ivian) 美国植物生理学家 17—39b
蒂米 Timmi (Algeria) 阿尔及利亚绿洲 17—101c
蒂米什 Timiş 罗马尼亚县名 17—100f
蒂米什河 Timiş River 欧洲河流 17—101a
蒂米什-切尔纳隘口 Timiş-Cerna Gap 南喀尔巴阡山脉隘口 17—101a
蒂米什瓦拉 Timişoara 罗马尼亚城市 17—101a
蒂明斯 Timmins 加拿大城市 17—101c
蒂默特 Tumut 澳大利亚城镇 17—267b
蒂默特河 Tumut River 澳大利亚河流 17—267b
蒂姆罗德 Timrod, Henry 美国诗人 17—102f
蒂南 Tinné, Alexandrine-Pieternella-Françoise 荷兰探险家 17—106b
蒂尼安岛 Tinian 美属北马里亚纳群岛火山岛 17—105f
蒂诺 Tino di Camaino 意大利雕刻家 17—106c
蒂诺斯岛 Tínos 希腊岛屿 17—106c
蒂欧尼欧格阶 Tioughnioga Stage 地质学 17—107f
蒂皮特披肩 tippet 服饰 17—108c
蒂珀卡努河 Tippecanoe River 美国河流 17—108b

蒂珀卡努之战 Tippecanoe, Battle of 美国历史 17—108b
蒂珀雷里 Tipperary 爱尔兰郡名 17—108b
蒂珀雷里 Tipperary 爱尔兰城镇 17—108c
蒂奇 Teach, Edward 美国海盗 16—510b
蒂奇菲尔德侯爵 Titchfield, William Henry Cavendish Bentinck, Marquess of 英国首相 17—115f
蒂奇马什 Titchmarsh, Edward Charles 英国数学家 17—115f
蒂萨 Tisza, István, Gróf (Count) 匈牙利首相 17—113f
蒂萨 Tisza, Kálmán 匈牙利首相 17—113f
蒂萨河 Tisza River 欧洲河流 17—114a
蒂塞利乌斯 Tiselius, Arne 瑞典生物化学家 17—112b
蒂森家族 Thyssen FAMILY 德国家族 17—76f
蒂森克虏伯集团 Thyssen Krupp AG 德国公司 17—77b
蒂森有限责任公司 Thyssen AG 德国公司 17—77b
蒂申多夫 Tischendorf, Konstantin von 德国《圣经》评论家 17—112a
蒂施拜恩 Tischbein, Johann Heinrich Wilhelm 德国画家 17—112a
蒂斯代尔 Teasdale, Sara 美国诗人 16—512b
蒂斯德鲁斯 Thysdrus 古罗马城市 17—76e
蒂斯河 Tees, River 英格兰河流 16—514e
蒂斯河谷 Teesdale 英格兰区名 16—514e
蒂斯河畔斯托克顿 Stockton-on-Tees 英格兰自治区 16—245a
蒂斯匡特姆 Tisquantum (American Indian) 美洲印第安人译员 17—112d
蒂斯朗 Tisserand, Félix 法国天文学家 17—112e
蒂斯塔河 Tīsta River 亚洲河流 17—113e
蒂索 Tissot, James 法国画家 17—112e
蒂特尔 Tittle, Y. A. 美国运动员 17—121a
蒂特卢兹 Titelouze, Jean 法国音乐家 17—115f
蒂特马尔 Thietmar 梅泽堡主教、编年史家 17—39a
蒂瓦万 Tivaouane 塞内加尔城镇 17—122b
蒂维 Tiwi 菲律宾城镇 17—122d
蒂维厄特河 Teviot, River 苏格兰河流 17—2a
蒂沃利 Tivoli 丹麦游乐园 17—122c
蒂沃利 Tivoli 意大利城镇 17—122c
蒂夏契克 Tichatschek, Joseph (Aloys) 波希米亚歌唱家 17—85b
蒂亚尔 Tyard, Pontus de 勃艮第诗人 17—304c
蒂亚格拉贾 Tyagaraja 印度作曲家 17—304c
蒂亚瓦纳科 Tiahuanaco 玻利维亚文化遗址 17—77c
蒂耶里 Thierry 佛兰德伯爵 17—38c
蒂耶里(沙特尔的) Thierry DE CHARTRES 法国神学家 17—38d
蒂耶里堡 Château-Thierry 法国城镇 4—89e
蒂永维尔 Thionville 法国城镇 17—39f
蒂永维尔 Thionville, Merlin de 法国革命者 17—40a
蒂尤厄姆 Tuam 爱尔兰城镇 17—253e
缔约神官 fetial 古罗马宗教官员 6—297d
碲(Te) tellurium 化学元素 16—530c
碲金矿 calaverite 矿物 3—334f
碲铜矿 rickardite 矿物 14—289d
滇池 Dian Chi 中国湖泊 5—287c
颠茄 belladonna (*Atropa belladonna*) 草本植物 2—362b
颠僧 Dao Khung (Vietnamese philosopher) 越南哲学家 5—143f
癫痫 epilepsy 疾病 6—100e
典当业 pawnbroking 抵押贷款 13—104c
典故 allusion 文学手段 1—243e
典雅爱情 courtly love 中世纪欧洲文学 4—550c
典雅风格 preciosity 法国文学 13—488f
点斑鸭 freckled duck (*Stictonetta naevosa*) 鸟类 6—457f
点彩画法 pointillism 绘画 13—390b
点苍山 Diancang Shan 中国山名 5—288b
点火系统 ignition system 内燃机 8—327b
点间赛 point-to-point 跑马赛 13—389e
点群 point group 晶体学 13—389b
点绣针法 petit point 刺绣 13—206b
碘(I) iodine 化学元素 8—429c
碘仿 iodoform 有机化合物 8—429f
碘缺乏 iodine deficiency 病理现象 8—429e
碘酸盐矿物 iodate mineral 矿物 8—429c
碘值 iodine value 化学 8—429e
电 electricity 电学 6—23c
电报机 telegraph 通信 16—522f
电场 electric field 电学 6—20e
电池 battery 电化学 2—281e
电池 cell 电学 3—556e
电传打字机 teleprinter 通信工具 16—526f
电磁场 electromagnetic field 电磁学 6—26c
电磁辐射 electromagnetic radiation 电磁学 6—26c
电磁感应 induction, electromagnetic 电磁学 8—374f
电磁铁 electromagnet 电磁器件 6—25e
电动机 electric motor 机器 6—21c
电动机发电机组 motor generator 电力机械 11—435d
电动势 electromotive force 电学 6—27a
电动势序 electromotive series 化学 6—27a
电镀 electroplating 电化学 6—30f
电镀锌 electrogalvanizing 电化学 6—25a
电风琴 electric organ (musical instrument) 乐器 6—21f
电风琴 telharmonium 乐器 16—529a
电负性 electronegativity 电化学 6—28d
电感 inductance 电学 8—374c
电荷 electric charge 电学 6—19e
电荷共轭 charge conjugation 粒子物理学 4—64a
电荷守恒 charge conservation 物理学 4—64a
电弧 electric arc 电学 6—19c
电弧焊 arc welding 金属加工 1—445a
电弧炉 arc furnace 冶金装置 1—444f
电化学 electrochemistry 化学 6—24d
电化学反应 electrochemical reaction 化学 6—23f
电话机 telephone 通信工具 16—526b
电击 electrical shock 生物物理学 6—23b
电机和电子工程师学会 Electrical and Electronics Engineers, Institute of (IEEE) 美国科学技术组织 6—23a
电机与电子工程 electrical and electronics engineering 工程学 6—22e
电极 electrode 电学 6—24e
电极化 electric polarization 电学 6—21f
电极化率 electric susceptibility 电学 6—22d
电价键 electrovalent bond 化学 6—31f
电解 electrolysis 电化学反应 6—25c
电解池 electrolytic cell 电化学装置 6—25d
电解抛光 electrolytic polishing 电化学加工 6—25e
电解质 electrolyte 化学、物理学 6—25d
电介质 dielectric 电磁学 5—305c
电介质加热 dielectric heating 物理学 5—305d
电惊厥疗法 ECT 治疗方法 5—532a
电开关 electric switch 电路元件 6—22e
电抗 reactance 电学 14—175c
电缆 cable 电子导线 3—306b
电离 ionization 化学、物理学 8—432f
电离层 ionosphere 大气科学 8—433b
电离电势 ionization potential 化学 8—433b
电离氢区 H II region 天文学 7—394a
电离室 ionization chamber 辐射探测器 8—433a
电力 electric power 电学 6—22b
电流 electric current 电学 6—20a
电流计 galvanometer 测量仪器 6—564d
电炉 electric furnace 冶金装置 6—21a

电路 electric circuit 电学 6—19f
电鳗 electric eel (*Electrophorus electricus*) 鱼类 6—20d
电脑科幻小说 cyberpunk 文学 5—84a
电鲶 electric catfish (*Malapterurus electricus*) 鱼类 6—19d
电偶极子 electric dipole 电磁学 6—20b
电抛光 electropolishing 电化学加工 6—31d
电喷流 electrojet 大气科学 6—25a
电瓶车 electric automobile 电池驱动车 6—19c
电气石 tourmaline 矿物 17—178a
电气体动力学 electrogasdynamics 物理学 6—25a
电桥 bridge 仪表 3—152d
电热法 electrothermic process 冶炼工艺 6—31f
电热器 electric heater 供暖装置 6—21c
电容 capacitance 电学 3—418f
电容率 permittivity 电学常量 13—174f
电容式加热 capacitance heating 物理学 3—419c
电弱理论 electroweak theory 物理学 6—31f
电声合成器 electronic sound synthesizer 音乐合成器 6—30c
电声合成器 synthesizer, electronic sound 音乐合成器 16—403c
电势 electric potential 电学 6—22a
电视 television 大众传媒 16—527f
电视电话 videophone 通信设备 17—547a
电视红外观测卫星 Television and Infra-Red Observation Satellite 人造卫星 16—528c
电视游戏 video game 游戏 17—546d
电位移 electric displacement 电学 6—20c
电信系统 telecommunications system 通信 16—522c
电刑 electrocution 行刑方法 6—24e
电休克疗法 electroshock therapy 医疗 6—31d
电压表 voltmeter 仪器 18—45e
电压调整器 voltage regulator 电子器件 18—42b
电眼 electric eye 电子管 6—20e
电鳐 electric ray 鱼类 6—22d
电影 motion picture 文化艺术 11—432c
电影城 Cinecittà 意大利电影摄制中心 4—241a
电影导演作者论 auteur theory 电影理论 2—72f
电影脚本 scenario 戏剧文学 15—107b
电影节 film festival 影片评价集会 6—315f
电影俱乐部 ciné-club 电影艺术团体 4—240f
电影剧本 script 戏剧文学 15—157e
电影摄影 cinematography 摄影艺术 4—241c
电影摄影机 motion-picture camera 摄影机 11—433c
电影视镜 Kinetoscope 放影工具 9—285a
电影艺术和科学学会 Motion Picture Arts and Sciences, Academy of 美国电影界组织 11—433b
电影专利公司 Motion Picture Patents Company 美国公司 11—433d
电泳 electrophoresis 化学 6—30e
电致发光 electroluminescence 物理学 6—25b
电致伸缩 electrostriction 物理学 6—31e
电铸 galvanoplasty (technology) 电加工技术 6—564d
电铸版技术 electrotyping 印刷术 6—31f
电铸成型 electroforming 电加工技术 6—25a
电子 electron 物理学 6—27d
电子表格 spreadsheet 计算机软件 16—161b
电子大钟琴 electronic carillon 乐器 6—28e
电子电荷 electron charge 物理学 6—27e
电子风琴 electronic organ 乐器 6—30a
电子伏 electron volt 计量单位 6—28d
电子俘获 electron capture 物理学 6—27e
电子感应加速器 betatron 粒子物理学 2—440e
电子功函数 electronic work function 物理学 6—30c
电子构型 electronic structure 物理学 6—30c
电子管 electron tube 电子器件 6—28c
电子光学 electron optics 物理学 6—28a
电子计算机排字 computerized typesetting 计算机科学 4—406e
电子计算机音乐 computer music 计算机科学 4—404d
电子炉 electronic oven 烹饪装置 6—30c
电子能谱学 electron spectroscopy 物理学 6—28b
电子偶产生 pair production 物理学 12—550f
电子偶素 positronium 物理学 13—458f
电子枪 electron gun 电子学 6—27f
电子窃听 electronic eavesdropping 侦破技术 6—29a
电子亲合势 electron affinity 化学 6—27e
电子散射 electron scattering 物理学 6—28b
电子商务 e-commerce 经济 5—492a
电子摄影术 electrophotography 摄影 6—30f
电子束 electron beam 电子学 6—27e
电子顺磁共振 electron paramagnetic resonance (EPR) 物理学 6—28a
电子同步加速器 electron synchrotron 粒子物理学 6—28b
电子位置指示器 EPI (navigation) 导航 6—97a
电子显微镜 electron microscope 高分辨率光学仪器 6—28a
电子学 electronics 物理学 6—30d
电子衍射 electron diffraction 物理学 6—27f
电子游戏 electronic game 游戏 6—29c
电子乐器 electronic instrument 乐器 6—29d
电子乐器 electrophone 乐器 6—30e
电子自旋共振 ESR 物理学 6—134e
电子组态 electronic configuration 原子物理学 6—28f
电阻 resistance 电学 14—240c
电阻表 ohmmeter 仪表 12—353d
电阻抗 electrical impedance 电磁学 6—23b
电阻率 resistivity 电学 14—240e
电阻器 resistor 电气元件 14—240f
佃户死时的贡献 heriot 欧洲历史 8—39e
佃租 tallage 中世纪欧洲税收 16—445f
垫圈 washer 机械零件 18—117d
垫藓 cushion moss 苔藓植物 5—76d
淀川 Yodo River 日本河流 18—452a
淀粉 starch 化合物 16—196f
淀粉酶 amylase 生物化学 1—305e
淀粉样变性 amyloidosis 疾病 1—305f
奠边府战役 Dien Bien Phu, Battle of 越南历史 5—305f
奠基石 cornerstone 建筑学 4—514b
殿堂 mansion 中世纪布景装置 10—473b
殿下 monseigneur 法国贵族称号 11—351a
靛蓝 indigo 染料 8—368d
靛青蛇 indigo snake (*Drymarchon corais*) 爬行动物 8—368e
刁文池 Deo Van Tri 越南泰族土司 5—249a
貂 marten 哺乳动物 10—543d
貂羚 sable antelope (*Hippotragus niger*) 哺乳动物 14—484a
雕 eagle 鸟类 5—493c
雕版 engraving 制版技术 6—83d
雕齿兽 Glyptodon 古生物学 7—166e
雕魟 eagle ray 鱼类 5—494a
雕刻 sculpture 艺术 15—161d
雕刻玻璃制品 engraved glass 工艺品 6—83d
雕空绣 cutwork 手工艺 5—80f
雕门岛 Tioman, Pulau 南海岛屿 17—107e
雕漆 lacquer engraving 中国工艺品 9—437f
雕线刀 burin 雕刻工具 3—265e
雕鸮 eagle owl (*Bubo bubo*) 鸟类 5—493f
鲷 porgy 鱼类 13—441a
吊环 rings 体操器械 14—305c
吊兰属 Chlorophytum 植物学 4—185d
吊桥 drawbridge 桥梁 5—416b

吊竹梅属 Zebrina 植物学 18—505a
钓鱼 fishing 体育 6—335c
钓鱼虫 angleworm 环节动物 1—346e
钓鱼岛 Diaoyu Dao 中国岛屿 5—288d
钓钟柳属 Penstemon 植物学 13—147e
调 key 音乐 9—247e
调查者号海峡 Investigator Strait 澳大利亚海峡 8—428a
调布 Chōfu 日本城市 4—188e
调律 temperament (music) 音乐 16—532e
调审令 certiorari 法律 4—12e
调式 mode 音乐 11—303e
调性 tonality 音乐 17—146e
调音与调律 tuning and temperament 音乐 17—270a
迭戈苏亚雷斯 Diégo-Suarez (Madagascar) 马达加斯加城镇 5—305a
迭句 refrain 诗形式 14—200d
叠杯 Häufebecher 银制酒器 7—510d
叠层石 stromatolite 地质学 16—280d
叠氮化物 azide 化合物 2—101f
叠接式结构 clinker construction 古代造船方法 4—293b
叠瓦蛤 Inoceramus 古生物学 8—394b
叠柱式 superposed order 建筑学 16—347b
蝶 Itchō (Japanese painter) 日本画家 8—489a
蝶耳狗 papillon 狗品种 13—25a
蝶酰谷氨酸 pteroylglutamic acid 维生素 13—567f
鲽 plaice (*Pleuronectes platessa*) 鱼类 13—338c
鲽形目 Pleuronectiformes (fish order) 鱼类 13—370d
丁博克罗 Dimbokro 科特迪瓦城市 5—318a
丁布尔比 Dimbleby, Richard (Frederick) 英国广播记者 5—317f
丁部领 Dinh Bo Linh 越南皇帝 5—323b
丁岑霍费父子 Dientzenhofer, Christoph and Kilian Ignaz 德国建筑师 5—306a
丁醇 butyl alcohol 化合物 3—294e
丁村人 Dingcun man 中国人类化石 5—322b
丁德尔国家公园 Dinder National Park 苏丹公园 5—320c
丁德尔河 Dinder River 非洲河流 5—320d
丁迪古尔 Dindigul 印度城市 5—320d
丁二烯 butadiene 化合物 3—288b
丁冈 Dingane 南非祖鲁人国王 5—322b
丁格尔 Dingle 爱尔兰半岛、海湾 5—322e
丁格尔施泰特伯爵 Dingelstedt, Franz Ferdinand, Freiherr von 德国诗人 5—322c
丁格利 Tinguely, Jean 瑞士艺术家 17—105e
丁光训 Ding Guangxun 中国神学家 5—321b
丁鲹 tench (species *Tinca tinca*) 鱼类 16—537e
丁吉拉伊 Dinguiraye 几内亚城镇 5—322f
丁吉斯瓦约 Dingiswayo 班图酋长 5—322e
丁加奴 Terengganu 马来西亚地区 16—550b
丁金斯 Dinkins, David 美国政治人物 5—323e
丁卡人 Dinka 苏丹民族 5—323d
丁克尔斯比尔 Dinkelsbühl 德国城市 5—323e
丁玲 Ding Ling 中国作家 5—321d
丁尼生 Tennyson (of Aldworth and Freshwater), Alfred Tennyson, 1st Baron 英国诗人 16—544c
丁若钟 Chŏng Yak-jong 朝鲜天主教人士 4—193d
丁斯拉肯 Dinslaken 德国城市 5—325a
丁苏吉亚 Tinsukia 印度城镇 17—106d
丁酸 butyric acid 化合物 3—294f
丁托列托 Tintoretto 威尼斯画家 17—106f
丁烷 butane 化合物 3—288c
丁威迪 Dinwiddie, Robert 英国殖民地官员 5—325a
丁文江 Ding Wenjiang 中国地质学家 5—321e
丁烯 butene 化合物 3—289b
丁香 clove 木本植物 4—304a
丁香花 lilac 木本植物 10—96d
丁香石竹 clove pink 草本植物 4—304b
丁香树 clove tree 热带乔木 4—304b
丁-伊拉赫教派 Dīn-i Ilāhī 印度宗教运动 5—319d
丁颖 Ding Ying 中国农学家 5—321f
丁肇中 Ting, Samuel C(hao) C(hung) 美国物理学家 17—105a
叮人小虫 gnat 昆虫 7—167a
町人 chōnin 日本市民阶级 4—195c
町田 Machida 日本城市 10—347b
钉 nail 建筑材料 11—543b
钉十字架 crucifixion 古代刑罚 5—37e
耵聍栓塞 earwax impaction 耳病 5—501c
顶垂体 roof pendant 地质学 14—390d
顶复虫 apicomplexan 原生动物 1—410a
顶骨 parietal bone 解剖学 13—42b
顶楼 attic 建筑 2—39e
顶饰 brattishing 建筑装饰 3—127d
顶饰珊瑚 Lophophyllum 古生物学 10—217e
顶死 dieback 植物病症 5—304d
顶相 chinsō 肖像画 4—177c
顶针 thimble 缝纫用具 17—39c
顶真诗 echo verse 文学 5—523b
鼎 ding 中国礼器 5—321a
鼎湖山自然保护区 Dinghushan Nature Reserve 中国自然保护区 5—322d
订婚 betrothal 婚姻习俗 2—444c
定比定律 definite proportions, law of 化学 5—209b
定朝 Jōchō 日本佛像雕刻家 9—42c
定家 Teika 日本诗人 16—516f
《定居记》 Landnámabók 冰岛历史 9—477e
定理 theorem 数学、逻辑学 17—29e
定量化学分析 quantitative chemical analysis 化学 14—74c
定期存款 time deposit 金融 17—99c
定期远洋船 ocean liner 海运 12—327d
定日镜 heliostat 天文仪器 7—574c
定天镜 coelostat 天文仪器 4—329a
定星镜 siderostat 天文仪器 15—353b
定性化学分析 qualitative chemical analysis 化学 14—73e
定窑 Ding kiln 中国瓷窑 5—321b
定音鼓 timpani 乐器 17—102d
定约桥牌 CONTRACT BRIDGE 纸牌游戏 16—79a
定约桥牌 contract bridge 纸牌游戏 4—471d
定植制度 Culture System 印度尼西亚税收 5—57b
定州 Dingzhou 中国城市 5—322f
丢番图(亚历山大的) Diophantus OF ALEXANDRIA 希腊数学家 5—329f
丢番图方程 Diophantine equation 数学 5—329e
丢卡利翁 Deucalion 希腊传说人物 5—267f
丢勒 Dürer, Albrecht 德国画家 5—472a
丢尼修(大法官) Dionysius THE AREOPAGITE 《圣经》人物 5—328c
铥(Tm) thulium 化学元素 17—69d
东 Duong 柬埔寨国王 5—466a
东阿格德尔 Aust-Agder 挪威郡名 2—61a
东埃文河 East Avon (river, England) 英格兰河流 5—503c
东艾尔 East Ayrshire 苏格兰区名 5—503c
东奥兰治 East Orange 美国城市 5—506f
东奥罗拉 East Aurora 美国村名 5—503b
东澳大利亚洋流 East Australian Current 太平洋洋流 5—503c
东澳斯特罗尼西亚语 Eastern Austronesian languages 大洋洲诸语言 5—510b
东巴教 Dongbajiao 中国宗教 5—381d
东巴文 Dongba character 中国文字 5—381c

东柏林 East Berlin 德国柏林历史区划 5—503d
东宝影片公司 Tōhō Motion Picture Company 日本公司 17—132a
东北 Tohoku 日本地区 17—132b
东北安普敦 East Northamptonshire 英国区名 5—506f
东北边区 North East Frontier Agency (India) 印度邦名 12—254d
东北德比 North East Derbyshire 英格兰区名 12—254c
东北地区派 Northeastern school 巴西文学 12—260d
东北法夫 North East Fife 苏格兰区名 12—254d
东北高加索诸语言 Northeast Caucasian languages 高加索语言 12—260a
东北航路 Northeast Passage 俄罗斯海上航路 12—260b
东北林肯郡 North East Lincolnshire 英格兰区名 12—254d
东北欧地域人种 northeast European local race 高加索地理人种 12—260a
东北平原 Northeast Plain 中国平原 12—260b
东北斯瓦尔巴自然保护区 Northeast Svalbard Nature Reservation 挪威自然保护区 12—260d
东比利牛斯 Pyrénées-Orientales 法国省份 14—46c
东布罗夫斯基 Dąbrowski, Jan Henryk 波兰将军 5—102d
东布罗夫斯卡 Dąbrowska, Maria 波兰作家 5—102b
东部地区 Sharqīyah, Ash- 沙特阿拉伯地理区 15—283e
东部独角仙 unicorn beetle (*Dynastes tityus*) 昆虫 17—342d
东部非洲 eastern Africa 非洲地区 5—509d
东部高地 Eastern Highlands (India) 印度东部群山 5—510e
东部裂谷(非洲) Eastern Rift Valley (Africa) 非洲地理 5—511e
东部林地印第安人 Eastern Woodlands Indian 北美洲土著 5—512c
东部沙漠 Eastern Desert 埃及大沙漠 5—510d
东部山脉 Purvachal 印度山脉 14—34f
东部省 Sharqīyah, Ash- 埃及省份 15—283e
东部裕固语 Eastern Yugur language 中国民族语言 5—512e
东朝鲜暖流 Korea Warm Current, East 日本海洋流 9—356c
东川 Dongchuan 中国城市 5—381e
东村山 Higashi-Murayama 日本城市 8—73c
东大阪 Higashi-Ōsaka 日本城市 8—73c
东大寺 Tōdai Temple 日本佛寺 17—128b
东德 East Germany 德国历史国名 5—504d
东德斯 Donders, Frans Cornelis 荷兰眼科医师 5—378b
东德文 East Devon 英格兰区名 5—504b
东邓巴顿 East Dunbartonshire 苏格兰区名 5—504b
东迪勒姆 East Dereham 英格兰城镇 5—504a
东底特律 East Detroit 美国城市 5—504a
东帝汶 East Timor 东南亚国家 5—508a
东方大漆 Oriental lacquer 清漆树脂 12—460c
东方海 Mare Orientale 月球地貌 10—501e
"东方"号飞船 Vostok 苏联航天器 18—51c
东方航空公司 Eastern Air Lines, Inc. 美国公司 5—510a
东方红柏 eastern red cedar (*Juniperus virginiana*) 木本植物 5—511d
东方教会法纲要 nomocanon 拜占廷法律汇编 12—227d
东方疖 Oriental sore 疾病 12—460d
东方快车 Orient-Express 豪华列车 12—460b
东方问题 Eastern Question 欧洲外交史 5—511c
东方犹太人 Oriental Jew 民族 12—460b
东非 East Africa 非洲地理 5—502b
东非大裂谷 East African Rift Valley 非洲地理 5—502e
东非大羚羊 beisa 哺乳动物 2—347a
东非地域人种 East African local race 人类学 5—502c
东非湖泊 East African lakes 东非湖群 5—502b
东非山地 East African mountains 东非山脉 5—502d
东佛兰德 East Flanders 比利时省份 5—504c
东弗里斯兰 East Friesland 德国文化区 5—504d
东福尔 Østfold 挪威郡名 12—492e
东福克兰岛 East Falkland 大西洋岛屿 5—504c
东高加索诸语言 East Caucasian languages 语言 5—503d
东哥特人 Ostrogoth 欧洲古代民族 12—494a
东格里夸兰 Griqualand East 南非古地名 7—315c
东格林尼治 East Greenwich 美国县城 5—504e
东格林斯特德 East Grinstead 英格兰城镇 5—504f
东格陵兰地槽 East Greenland orogen 地质学 5—504e
东格陵兰洋流 East Greenland Current 北冰洋洋流 5—504e
东莞 Dongguan 中国城市 5—382b
东哈萨克斯坦 Vostochno-Kazakhstan 哈萨克斯坦州名 18—51c
东哈特福德 East Hartford 美国城镇 5—505a
东哈特福德夏 East Hertfordshire 英格兰区名 5—505b
东海 Dong Hai 太平洋边缘海 5—380a
东海 Östersjön (Europe) 欧洲海洋 12—492d
东海 Ostsee (Europe) 波罗的海德语名称 12—494d
东海滨 Eastern Seaboard 美国地区 5—512b
东海道 Tōkaidō 日本古道路 17—133a
东海地区 Tōkai region 日本工业区 17—132f
东海银行 Tōkai Bank Ltd. 日本银行 17—132f
东汉普顿 East Hampton 美国城镇 5—505a
东汉普夏 East Hampshire 英格兰区名 5—504f
东黑文 East Haven 美国城镇 5—505a
东胡 Donghu 中国古民族 5—382c
东基尔布赖德 East Kilbride 苏格兰区名 5—506c
东加里曼丹 Kalimantan Timur 印度尼西亚省份 9—141c
东加洛韦 East Galloway (Scotland) 苏格兰旧郡名 5—504d
东坚巴兰 Purba Champāran 印度县名 14—30e
东剑桥 East Cambridgeshire 英格兰区名 5—503d
东江 Dong Jiang 中国河流 5—379f
东角 East Cape (eastern Russia) 俄罗斯海角 5—503d
东捷克州 Východočeský 捷克州名 18—56d
东进 Drang nach Osten 德意志政策 5—414e
东晋 Eastern Chin 中国古代王朝 5—510c
东京 Tokyo 日本首都 17—136c
东京 Tonkin 法国殖民时期越南北部 17—152e
东京大学 Tokyo University 日本高等学府 17—137b
东京都 Tokyo 日本都市区 17—136c
东京国立博物馆 Tokyo National Museum 日本博物馆 17—137a
东京-横滨都会区 Tokyo-Yokohama metropolitan area 日本城市集群 17—137c
东京玫瑰 Tokyo Rose (propagandist) 日本播音员 17—137a
东京湾 Tokyo Bay 日本海湾 17—100f
东京湾 Tonkin, Gulf of 南海海湾 17—152e
《东京湾决议案》 Gulf of Tonkin Resolution 美国历史 7—368a
东京银行 Tokyo, Bank of 日本银行 17—136f
东京证券交易所 Tokyo Stock Exchange 日本证券市场 17—137a
东久迩稔彦 Higashikuni Naruhiko 日本首相 8—73d
东开普 Easternc Cape 南非省份 5—510b
东克利夫兰 East Cleveland 美国城市 5—503f
东拉贾斯坦高地 East Rājasthān Uplands 印度高地 5—507b
东兰辛 East Lansing 美国城市 5—506c
东莨菪碱 scopolamine 生物碱 15—147c
东黎巴嫩山脉 Lubnān ash-Sharqī 黎巴嫩山脉 10—265b
东利物浦 East Liverpool 美国城市 5—506d
东辽 Tung-liao (China) 中国城市 17—268d
东林 Tung-lin 中国历史 17—268d
东林党 Donglin clique 中国历史 5—382d
东林齐 East Lindsey 英格兰区名 5—506d
东伦敦 East London 南非港市 5—506d
东伦弗鲁 East Renfrewshire 苏格兰区名 5—507c
东罗马帝国 Roman Empire, Eastern 欧洲历史 14—363f
东洛锡安 East Lothian 苏格兰区名 5—506e
东马来西亚 East Malaysia 马来西亚地区 5—506e

东马派 Dönme 犹太教派 5—384c
东盟区域论坛 ASEAN Regional Forum (ARF) 亚太地区多边论坛 1—543d
东莫克琼克 East Mauch Chunk 原美国城镇 5—506e
东莫林 East Moline 美国城市 5—506f
东南宾夕法尼亚计划生育组织诉凯西案 Planned Parenthood of Southeastern Pennsylvania v. Casey 美国法院案例 13—344a
东南大学 Southeast University 中国大学 15—551f
东南岛 Sudest Island 巴布亚新几内亚岛屿 16—306a
东南联合会 Southeastern Conference 美国大学体育组织 15—552a
东南斯瓦巴德自然保护区 Southeast Svalbard Nature Reservation 挪威保护区 15—551f
东南苏拉威西 Sulawesi Tenggara 印度尼西亚省份 16—316d
东南西里伯斯 Southeast Celebes (Indonesia) 印度尼西亚省份 15—551f
东南亚 Southeast Asia 亚洲地区 15—550c
东南亚地域人种 Southeast Asian local race 人类学 15—551e
东南亚国家联盟 ASEAN 亚洲国际组织 1—543c
东南亚条约组织 Southeast Asia Treaty Organization (SEATO) 地区性防御组织 15—551a
东南亚艺术 Southeast Asian arts 艺术 15—551b
东南亚疣猪 babirusa (*Babirousa babyrussa*) 哺乳动物 2—110c
东南沿海丘陵 Southeast China Coastal Hilly Regions 中国地貌 15—551f
东南州 South-Eastern (state, Nigeria) 尼日利亚州名 15—544f
东努沙登加拉 Nusa Tenggara Timur 印度尼西亚省份 12—304c
东欧平原 East European Plain 欧洲平原 5—504c
东欧平原 Vostochno-Yevropeyskaya Ravnina (Russia) 东欧区域 18—51c
东普鲁士 East Prussia 德国旧省份 5—507b
东普罗维登斯 East Providence 美国城市 5—507b
东萨塞克斯 East Sussex 英格兰郡名 5—507f
东山文化 Dong Son culture 印度支那史前文化 5—380e
东胜 Dongsheng 中国城市 5—382e
东圣路易 East Saint Louis 美国城市 5—507d
东斯海尔德 Eastern Schelde 荷兰运河 5—512a
东斯科舍海盆 East Scotia Basin 大西洋海底凹槽 5—507e
东斯洛伐克 Východní Slovensko 斯洛伐克州名 18—56c
东斯塔福德 East Staffordshire 英格兰区名 5—507f
东苏丹诸语言 Eastern Sudanic languages 非洲语言 5—512b
东太平洋海隆 East Pacific Rise 太平洋海底山脉 5—507a
东条英机 Tōjō Hideki 日本首相 17—132d
东西伯利亚海 East Siberian Sea 北冰洋海域 5—507e
东西两派教会分裂 East-West Schism (Christianity) 基督教历史 5—508c
东乡平八郎 Tōgō Heihachirō, KōSHAKU (Marquess) 日本军人 17—131f
东乡语 Dongxiang language 中国民族语言 5—383b
东乡族 Dongxiang 中国民族 5—383a
东叙利亚礼仪 East Syrian rite (liturgies) 宗教仪式 5—508a
东亚艺术 East Asian arts 艺术 5—502f
东洋工业公司 Tōyō Kōgyō Company 日本公司 17—183f
东洋区 Oriental region 动物地理区 12—460c
东仪天主教会 Eastern rite church 东方基督教会 5—511e
东印度公司 East India Company (Dutch) 荷兰公司 5—505b
东印度公司 East India Company 英国公司 5—505b
东印度公司 East India Company (French) 法国公司 5—505c
东印度绘画 Eastern Indian painting 印度艺术 5—510f
东印度贸易船 East Indiaman 帆船 5—505c
东印度群岛 East Indies 东南亚岛群 5—505d
东印度铜像 Eastern Indian bronze 印度艺术 5—510e
东英吉利亚 East Anglia 英格兰行政区 5—502e
东营 Dongying 中国城市 5—383c
东映影片公司 Tōei Company, Ltd. 日本公司 17—129c
东吁 Toungoo 缅甸城镇 17—176c
东吁王朝 Toungoo DYNASTY 缅甸历史 17—176d
东约克 East York 加拿大自治市 5—508c
东约克郡 East Riding of Yorkshire 英格兰单一政区 5—507c
东约特兰 Östergötland 瑞典省份 12—492c
东爪哇 Jawa Timur 印度尼西亚省份 8—552f
东镇区 Eastern Townships 加拿大行政区 5—512b
东正教 Eastern Orthodoxy 基督教 5—511a
东芝公司 Toshiba Corporation 日本公司 17—171b
东芝加哥 East Chicago 美国港市 5—503d
东枝 Taunggyi 缅甸城镇 16—496f
东洲斋写乐 Tōshūsai Sharaku 日本画家 17—171c
冬孢子 teliospore 植物 16—529b
冬瓜 wax gourd (*Benincasa hispida*) 植物 18—150f
冬季 winter 季节 18—290c
冬季战争 Winter War 欧洲历史 18—290f
冬绿 wintergreen 植物 18—291b
冬青 holly 植物 8—133e
冬青科 Aquifoliaceae 植物学 1—428b
冬青属 Ilex 植物学 8—333d
冬乌头 winter aconite 草本植物 18—290d
氡(Rn) radon 化学元素 14—119d
鸫 thrush 鸟类 17—66f
鸫歌鸲 sprosser 鸟类 16—165d
鸫科 Turdidae 动物学 17—278a
董必武 Dong Biwu 中国革命家 5—379d
董鸡 water cock (*Gallicrex cinerea*) 鸟类 18—135e
董里 Trang 泰国城镇 17—193c
董其昌 Dong Qichang 中国画家 5—380c
董源 Dong Yuan 中国画家 5—380f
董仲舒 Dong Zhongshu 中国哲学家 5—381a
董卓 Dong Zhuo 中国汉朝权臣 5—381c
动鞭毛虫 zooflagellate 原生动物 18—566e
动鞭毛虫纲 Zoomastigophorea 动物学 18—567a
动产和不动产 movable and immovable 法律 11—448e
动冠伞鸟 cock-of-the-rock 鸟类 4—320f
动画 animation 艺术 1—359b
动机 motivation 心理学 11—434a
动机 motive 音乐 11—434d
动机争胜性行为 agonism 动物学 1—125e
动金甲藻 zooxanthella 原生动物 18—567b
动静脉瘘 arteriovenous fistula 疾病 1—526c
动力学 dynamics 物理学 5—488d
动力转向机构 power steering 汽车装置 13—475a
动量 momentum 物理学 11—326e
动量守恒 momentum, conservation of 物理学 11—326e
动脉 artery 解剖学 1—526d
动脉导管未闭 patent ductus arteriosus 病理现象 13—86b
动脉瘤 aneurysm 疾病 1—339d
动脉炎 arteritis 疾病 1—526c
动脉硬化 arteriosclerosis 疾病 1—526b
动脉粥样硬化 atherosclerosis 病理学 2—24b
动能 kinetic energy 物理学 9—284d
动情期 estrus 动物学 6—142e
动态雕刻 kinetic sculpture 艺术 9—284e
动吻类 kinorhynch 海生无脊椎动物 9—294e
动物 animal 生物学 1—357b
动物标本剥制术 taxidermy 标本制作 16—501d
动物崇拜 animal worship 宗教 1—358d
动物传染病 zoonosis 动物疾病 18—567a
动物磁性 animal magnetism 生理学 1—358d
动物地理区域 zoogeographic region 生物地理学 18—566f

动物地理学 zoogeography 生物地理学 18—566f
动物毒液 venom 动物学 17—507a
动物故事 beast tale 文学 2—307e
动物交织图饰 animal interlace 装饰艺术 1—358d
动物胶 glue 胶黏剂 7—165a
动物乐队 Animals, the 英格兰乐队 1—359b
动物区系区 faunal region 生物地理学 6—252d
动物群带 faunizone 地质学 6—252e
动物通讯 animal communication 动物学 1—358a
动物行为 animal behaviour 动物学 1—357c
动物叙事诗 beast epic 文学体裁 2—307d
动物学 zoology 生物学 18—566f
动物育种 animal breeding 动物学 1—357e
动物寓言 beast fable 文学 2—307e
动物寓言 bestiary 文学体裁 2—439a
动物园 zoo 公园 18—565b
动小球藻 zoochlorella 藻类 18—566e
动胸龟科 Kinosternidae 动物学 9—295a
动研究 motion study 工业 11—434a
动议 motion 议会程序 11—431f
动员 mobilization 军事行动 11—300d
动质虫目 Kinetoplastida 动物学 9—285a
动作电位 action potential 生理学 1—61a
冻疮 chilblain 疾病 4—150d
冻结核 freezing nucleus 气象学 6—472e
冻伤 frostbite 疾病 6—503c
冻土 Gelisol 土壤分类 7—48a
冻原 tundra 地理学 17—267e
侗语 Dong language 中国语言 5—380b
侗族 Dong 中国民族 5—379b
栋布 Dombes 法国历史地区 5—368d
栋布罗瓦-古尔尼恰 Dąbrowa Górnicza 波兰城市 5—102b
栋杜山 Tondou Massif 中非共和国山名 17—147c
栋多 Dundo 安哥拉城镇 5—460c
栋方志功 Munakata Shikō 日本画家 11—482a
栋盖尔 Tangail 孟加拉国城市 16—463d
栋格 Tonk 印度城镇 17—152d
栋格尔布尔 Dungarpur 印度城镇 5—461e
栋古拉 Dunqulah 苏丹城镇 5—464f
栋雷米拉皮塞勒 Domrémy-la-Pucelle 法国乡村 5—375e
洞里萨湖 Tonle Sap 柬埔寨湖泊 17—152f
洞室 grotto 园林艺术 7—322f
洞庭湖 Dongting Hu 中国湖泊 5—002f
洞熊 cave bear 古生物学 3—539d
洞穴 cave 地质学 3—539b
洞穴沉积 cave deposit 地质学 3—539e
洞穴学 speleology 地质水文学 16—18e
洞穴鱼 cave fish 鱼类 3—539e
洞穴珠 cave pearl 地质学 3—541a
洞螈 olm (*Proteus anguinus*) 两栖动物 12—377d
洞状陷穴 cenote 天然井 3—563a
胴甲鱼 antiarch 古生物学 1—382d
兜甲 lorica 动物学 10—222d
兜帽海豹 hooded seal (*Cystophora cristata*) 哺乳动物 8—162b
兜水母 lobed comb jelly 腔肠动物 10—172f
兜网球 lacrosse 球戏 9—439a
兜状荷包牡丹 Dutchman's-breeches (species *Dicentra cucullaria*) 植物 5—481d
斗湖 Tawau 马来西亚港口 16—499f
斗六 Douliu 中国城市 5—403c
斗篷草 lady's mantle 植物 9—443e
斗篷加短剑戏剧 cloak and dagger theatre 西班牙戏剧 4—296c
斗篷式长袍 cope 基督教法衣 4—487f
斗篷蜥属 Chlamydosaurus 动物学 4—183c
斗拳狗 boxer 狗品种 3—97e
斗勺 kovsh 俄国酒器 9—368b
抖草 quaking grass 草本植物 14—73e
斗鸡 cockfighting 游戏 4—322d
斗牛 bullfighting 体育 3—248c
斗牛㹴狗 bull terrier 英国狗品种 3—246f
斗牛狗 bulldog 英国狗品种 3—247c
斗牛狗蝠 bulldog bat 动物 3—247c
斗牛士 matador 斗牛表演者 11—17c
斗殴 affray 法律 1—104b
斗士 champion 英国历史 4—41b
斗兽场斗牛㹴狗 pit bull terrier 狗品种 13—327a
斗兽大会 venationes 罗马历史 17—496d
豆 bean 植物种子 2—303f
豆 dou 中国青铜器 5—397a
豆瓣绿属 Peperomia 植物学 13—151f
豆腐 tofu 食品 17—129e
豆科 Leguminosae (plant family) 植物学 9—563f
豆蔻丘陵 Cardamom Hills 印度山地 3—451b
豆蔻山脉 Krâvanh Mountains 柬埔寨山脉 9—373e
豆粒 pisolite 结晶质沉积物 13—325d
豆目 Fabales 植物学 6—204f
豆娘 damselfly 昆虫 5—130b
豆薯 jícama (species *Pachyrhizus erosus*, or *P. tuberosus*) 植物 9—20c
豆象 seed beetle 昆虫 15—185d
豆蟹 pea crab 甲壳动物 13—108a
逗牛 bullbaiting 游戏 3—247b
逗熊 bearbaiting 游戏 2—305b
痘病 pox disease 疾病 13—476b
痘病毒 poxvirus 微生物 13—476c
窦 sinus 解剖学 15—399c
《窦娥冤》 Dou E Yuan 中国文学作品 5—397c
窦建德 Dou Jiande 中国农民起义领袖 5—397d
窦状隙 sinusoid 解剖学 15—399e
都柏林 Dublin 爱尔兰郡名 5—439e
都柏林 Dublin 爱尔兰首都 5—439e
都柏林大学 Dublin, University of 爱尔兰高等学府 5—442a
都柏林湾匙指虾 Dublin Bay prawn 甲壳动物 5—442a
都布按三司 three local offices 中国历史 17—64a
都城 Miyakonojō 日本城市 11—296f
都德 Daudet, Alphonse 法国小说家 5—163f
都德 Daudet, (Alphonse-Marie-) Léon 法国记者、小说家 5—164d
都督 captain general 西属美洲殖民地长官 3—432e
都铎 Tudor, Henry 英格兰国王 17—259c
都铎 Tudor, Jasper 威尔士贵族 17—259c
都铎 Tudor, Margaret (queen of Scotland) 苏格兰女王 17—259c
都铎 Tudor, Mary 英格兰女王 17—259c
都铎风格 Tudor style 建筑 17—259c
都铎王室 Tudor, HOUSE OF 英格兰王室 17—258f
都江堰 Dujiang Weirs 中国水利工程 5—450d
都江堰 Dujiangyan 中国城市 5—451a
都拉斯 Durrës 阿尔巴尼亚港市 5—477b
都兰 Dulan 中国县名 5—453a
都灵 Turin 意大利城市 17—281a
都灵彩陶 Turin faience 工艺品 17—281d
都灵大学 Turin, University of 意大利高等学府 17—281d
都灵尸衣 Turin, Shroud of 基督教 17—281b
都灵纸莎草纸文献 Turin Papyrus 埃及象形文字手稿 17—281e
都玛 dolma 食品 5—367a
都匀 Duyun 中国城市 5—483e
都主教 metropolitan 宗教首脑 11—161e

督护 adelantado 西班牙官职 1—75c
督统 intendente 西班牙官职 8—407a
督政府 Directory 法国革命政体 5—337b
督政府时期风格 Directoire style 法国艺术风格 5—337a
毒常春藤 poison ivy 植物 13—391b
毒豆 laburnum 植物 9—434b
毒蛾 tussock moth 昆虫 17—296a
毒番石榴 poison guava(plant) 木本植物 13—391a
毒风 poison wind 气象学 13—391c
毒理学 toxicology 科学 17—182b
毒麦 darnel 草本植物 5—152d
毒牛芹 cowbane 植物 4—556f
毒苹果 manchineel (*Hippomane mancinella*) 木本植物 10—450f
毒芹 water hemlock 植物 18—136a
毒杀芬 toxaphene 杀虫剂 17—182a
毒砂 arsenopyrite 矿物 1—519e
毒参 poison hemlock 草本植物 13—391a
毒素 toxin 生物化学 17—182c
毒物 poison 生物化学 13—390d
毒性多结节性甲状腺肿 toxic multinodular goitre (endocrine disorder) 疾病 17—182b
独白 monologue 文学、戏剧 11—345a
独白 soliloquy 戏剧 15—497a
独版印刷 monoprint (printmaking) 版画技法 11—346f
独臂匪徒 one-armed bandit 赌博用具 12—417f
独裁 dictatorship 政体形式 5—300f
独裁官 dictator 罗马历史 5—300f
独幅版画 monotype 版画技法 11—348b
独角鲸 narwhal (*Monodon monoceros*) 哺乳动物 12—2e
独角兽 unicorn 神话动物 17—342b
独角仙 rhinoceros beetle 昆虫 14—263f
独角鱼 unicorn fish 鱼类 17—342f
独脚金 witchweed 植物 18—299c
独居石 monazite 矿物 11—330e
独立城 Independence 美国堪萨斯州城市 8—354c
独立城 Independence 美国密苏里州城市 8—354c
独立岛 Independence Island (Kiribati) 基里巴斯岛屿 8—356f
独立电视台 Independent Television (ITV) 英国电视网 8—357a
独立国家联合体 Commonwealth of Independent States 国家联合体 4—390c
独立基督会 Undenominational Fellowship of Christian Churches and Churches of Christ 宗教 17—339e
独立派 Independent 基督教 8—356f
独立沙龙 Salon des Indépendants 法国年度画展 14—551e
《独立宣言》 Independence, Declaration of 美国历史 8—354d
独龙语 Derung language 中国语言 5—255d
独龙族 Derung 中国民族 5—255c
独木舟 dugout 小船 5—449b
独木舟杉 canoe cedar 植物 3—406c
独栖蜂 solitary bee 昆虫 15—497d
独山 Dushan 中国县名 5—478c
独身 celibacy 宗教 3—555d
独桅纵帆船 cutter 快速小帆船 5—80c
独弦琴 monochord 乐器 11—343f
独弦琴歌手 guslar 巴尔干民间歌手 7—380b
独行菜 garden cress (*Lepidium sativum*) 草本植物 7—11c
独行骑警 Lone Ranger 美国传播媒介中虚构人物 10—205e
独占产业 Monopoly 游戏 11—346e
读本 yomihon 日本文学作品 18—454a
读经台 ambo 基督教讲台 1—270d
《读卖新闻》 Yomiuri shimbun 日本报纸 18—454a
《读者文摘》 Reader's Digest 美国杂志 14—176d
渎圣 sacrilege 亵渎圣物 14—489f
髑髅地 Calvary (site of Jesus' Crucifixion) 耶稣受难地 3—358e
髑髅派和黑脸派 Kāpālika and Kālāmukha 印度苦修集团 9—171e
笃信 Atsunobu (Japanese philosopher) 日本哲学家 2—37e
堵布益 Dupuis, Jean 法国商人 5—468b
赌博 gambling 博奕游戏 6—567e
赌注登记 bookmaking 赌博 3—38c
睹梨娑罗 Triśalā 耆那教救世主大雄之母 17—226d
杜阿尔斯 Duārs 印度地区 5—438e
杜阿尔特 Duarte, Fausto (Castilho) 几内亚比绍作家 5—438e
杜阿尔特 Duarte, Juan Pablo 多米尼加共和国政治家 5—438f
杜阿拉 Douala 喀麦隆港市 5—397f
杜埃 Douai 法国城镇 5—397e
杜埃 Douai, Merlin de 法国法学家 5—397e
《杜埃-兰斯圣经》 Douai-Reims Bible 天主教经典 5—397f
杜埃娄娜 Duellona (Roman goddess) 罗马女神 5—447d
杜埃兹 Duèse, Jacques 罗马教皇 5—447d
杜埃兹 Euze, Jacques d' 教皇 6—177c
杜安-亨脱定律 Duane-Hunt law 物理学 5—438e
杜邦 du Pont, Pierre Samuel 美国制造商 5—436c
杜邦 du Pont, Pierre-Samuel 法国经济学家 5—436c
杜邦公司 DuPont Company 美国公司 5—467a
杜邦家族 du Pont FAMILY 美籍法裔家族 5—436b
杜比 Duby, Georges 法国历史学家 5—443d
杜比尼 Daubigny, Charles-François 法国画家 5—163b
杜宾斯基 Dubinsky, David 美国工人领袖 5—439e
杜波伊斯 Du Bois, W(illiam) E(dward) B(urghardt) 美国社会学家 5—434a
杜伯曼 Tubman, William V(acanarat) S(hadrach) 利比里亚总统 17—256e
杜勃罗留波夫 Dobrolyubov, Nikolay Aleksandrovich 俄国文学批评家 5—354c
杜博 Du Bos, Charles 法国文学批评家 5—434f
杜布雷 Dupleix, Joseph-François 法属印度总督 5—466e
杜布罗夫尼克 Dubrovnik 克罗地亚港口 5—442f
杜布纳 Dubna 俄罗斯城市 5—442a
杜布诺夫 Dubnow, Simon M. 俄国历史学家 5—442b
杜布切克 Dubček, Alexander 捷克政治家 5—439b
杜布瓦 Du Bois, Franz 德国医师 5—434a
杜布瓦-雷蒙 Du Bois-Reymond, Emil Heinrich 德国生理学家 5—434e
杜德克 Dudek, Louis 加拿大诗人 5—446a
杜狄格尼 Dodeigne, Eugène 法国雕刻家 5—357d
杜蒂科林 Tuticorin 印度城镇 17—296d
杜多伽摩尼 Duṭṭhagāmaṇī 锡兰国王 5—482b
杜恩 Duun, Olav 挪威小说家 5—482c
杜恩·卡姆 Dun Karm (Maltese poet) 马耳他诗人 5—457e
杜尔 Touré, (Ahmed) Sékou 几内亚总统 17—177d
杜尔 Touré, Samory 宗教改革家 17—177d
杜尔巴 durbar 印度宫廷 5—471f
杜尔贝科 Dulbecco, Renato 意大利病毒学家 5—453c
杜尔哥 Turgot, Anne-Robert-Jacques, BARON DE L'AULNE 法国经济学家 17—280e
杜尔格 Durg 印度城市 5—472e
杜尔加布尔 Durgāpur 印度城市 5—473a
杜尔诺沃 Durnovo, Pyotr Nikolayevich 俄国政治家 5—476c
杜尔塞湾 Dulce, Gulf of 太平洋海湾 5—453d
杜尔舍鲁金 Dur Sharrukin 亚述古城 5—469b
杜尔温塔什 Dur Untashi (Iran) 伊朗古城 5—469c
杜尔西达斯 Tulsīdās 印度诗人 17—265a
杜飞 Dufy, Raoul 法国画家 5—448d
杜弗尔 Dufaure, (Jules-)Armand(-Stanislas) 法国政治家 5—447d
杜伏威 Du Fuwei 中国农民领袖 5—435d
杜甫 Du Fu 中国诗人 5—435b

杜父鱼 sculpin 鱼类 15—161b
杜富尔 Dufour, Guillaume-Henri 瑞士工程师 5—448d
杜富尔峰 Dufourspitze 瑞士山峰 5—448d
杜盖 Dughet, Gaspard 意大利画家 5—448f
杜格伊 thugyi 缅甸地方官员 17—69b
杜哈梅 Duhamel, Jean-Marie-Constant 法国数学家、物理学家 5—449c
杜河 Doubs River 法国河流 5—399c
杜赫宁 Dukhonin, Nikolay Nikolayevich 俄国将军 5—452f
杜赫斯特 Dewhurst, Colleen 美国演员 5—276d
杜黑 Douhet, Giulio 意大利将军 5—403b
杜霍波尔派 Dukhobor 俄国农村教派 5—452e
杜加 Dougga (Tunisia) 突尼斯城市 5—399e
杜金卡 Dudinka 俄罗斯城市 5—446a
杜鹃 cuckoo 鸟类 5—49c
杜鹃花 rhododendron 木本植物 14—269b
杜鹃花目 Ericales 植物学 6—115e
杜卡 Dukas, Paul(-Abraham) 法国作曲家 5—451c
杜卡基斯 Dukakis, Michael S(tanley) 美国政治家 5—451a
杜卡拉姆 Tukārām 印度诗人 17—261e
杜卡斯 Ducas, Irene (Byzantine empress) 拜占廷皇后 5—443e
杜卡斯家族 Ducas FAMILY 拜占廷皇族 5—443e
杜凯提奥斯 Ducetius 西西里领袖 5—444a
杜坎甫 Du Camp, Maxime 法国作家 5—435a
杜科蒙 Ducommun, Élie 瑞士作家 5—445d
杜克 Duke, James Buchanan 美国企业家 5—452b
杜克 Duke, Vernon 美国作曲家 5—452c
杜克大学 Duke University 美国大学 5—452d
杜克拉山口 Dukla Pass 欧洲山口 5—452f
杜克罗 Ducrow, Andrew 英国马术演员 5—445e
杜拉铝 duralumin 合金 5—469c
杜拉尼 Dulany, Daniel 美洲殖民地律师 5—453b
杜拉尼 Dulany, Daniel 美国律师 5—453b
杜拉-欧罗波斯 Dura-Europus 叙利亚古城遗址 5—469c
杜拉斯诺 Durazno 乌拉圭省份 5—471d
杜拉斯诺 Durazno 乌拉圭城市 5—471d
杜兰 Duran, Profiat 犹太哲学家 5—469d
杜兰 Durán, Roberto 巴拿马拳击运动员 5—469e
杜兰 Duran, Simeon ben Zemah 西班牙犹太教拉比 5—469e
杜兰德 Durand, Asher B(rown) 美国画家 5—469f
杜兰戈 Durango 墨西哥州名 5—470d
杜兰戈 Durango 墨西哥城市 5—470d
杜兰戈 Durango 美国城市 5—470e
杜兰尼 Durrānī, Aḥmad Shāh 阿富汗统治者 5—476f
杜兰尼人 Durrānī 阿富汗民族 5—476f
杜兰特 Durant 美国城市 5—470e
杜兰特 Durante, Francesco 意大利作曲家 5—471a
杜兰特 Durante, Jimmy 美国演员 5—471b
杜兰特 Durant, William Crapo 美国实业家 5—471a
杜兰特夫妇 Durant, Will and Ariel 美国作家 5—470f
杜兰线 Durand Line 阿富汗与巴基斯坦边界线 5—470b
杜朗 Durang, John 美国舞蹈家 5—470c
杜朗 Durão, José de Santa Rita 巴西诗人 5—471b
杜勒卡迪尔王朝 Dulkadir DYNASTY 土库曼王朝 5—453e
杜勒斯 Dulles, Allen W(elsh) 美国外交家 5—454a
杜勒斯 Dulles, John Foster 美国国务卿 5—454b
杜雷 Dooley, Thomas Anthony 美国医生 5—386a
杜里 Dury, John 苏格兰牧师 5—477d
杜里埃兄弟 Duryea, Charles E.; and Duryea, J. Frank 美国发明家 5—477e
杜里乌斯河 Durius (Europe) 欧洲河流 5—475d
杜立德 Doolittle, James H(arold) 美国将军 5—386c
杜利特尔 Doolittle, Hilda 美国诗人 5—386b
杜利亚 Dhūlia 印度城镇 5—281d
杜林 Doolin, Bill 美国匪徒 5—386a
杜林 Dühring, (Karl) Eugen 德国哲学家 5—449d
杜隆 Dulong, Pierre-Louis 法国化学家、物理学家 5—454e
杜隆-珀蒂定律 Dulong-Petit law 化学 5—454f
杜鲁门 Truman, Harry S. 美国总统 17—242a
杜鲁门主义 Truman Doctrine 美国政治 17—242d
杜罗河 Douro River 欧洲河流 5—404a
杜罗切 Durocher, Leo 美国棒球运动员 5—476e
杜洛克猪 Duroc 猪品种 5—476d
杜马 Duma 俄国立法机构 5—455b
杜马 Dumas, Jean-Baptiste-André 法国化学家 5—455f
杜马格特 Dumaguete 菲律宾城市 5—455c
杜梅 Doumer, Paul 法国总统 5—403e
杜梅格 Doumergue, Gaston 法国总统 5—403f
杜蒙 Du Mont, Allen B. 美国工程师 5—435f
杜米埃 Daumier, Honoré(-Victorin) 法国画家 5—165b
杜米托尔 Durmitor 黑山山脉 5—476c
杜莫里埃 du Maurier, Dame Daphne 英国作家 5—435e
杜莫里埃 du Maurier, George 英国画家、作家 5—435e
杜莫里埃 du Maurier, Sir Gerald 英国演员 5—435e
杜姆古尔 Tumkūr 印度城市 17—266b
杜姆加 Dumka 印度城镇 5—456f
杜姆亚特 Dimyat (Egypt) 埃及城市 5—319d
杜姆亚特 Dumyāṭ (Egypt) 埃及城市 5—457d
杜姆亚特 Dumyāṭ 埃及省份 5—457d
杜木兹 Dumuzi (Mesopotamian deity) 美索不达米亚神祇 5—457d
杜牧 Du Mu 中国诗人 5—436a
杜纳什·本·拉卜拉特 Dunash BEN LABRAT 希伯来诗人、语法学家、善辩论者 5—457f
杜纳什·本·塔明 Dunash BEN TAMIM 犹太医生 5—458a
杜纳耶茨河 Dunajec River 波兰河流 5—457e
杜奈尔 Dunér, Nils Christofer 瑞典天文学家 5—461a
杜庞卢 Dupanloup, Félix-Antoine-Philibert 法国天主教开明派代言人 5—466c
杜佩雷 Dupré, Jules 法国画家 5—467f
杜佩雷 Dupré, Marcel 法国管风琴演奏家 5—467f
杜佩雷 Dupré, Marie-Jules 法国军官 5—468a
杜普莱西斯 Duplessis, Maurice (Le Noblet) 加拿大政治家 5—466f
杜普雷 Dupré, Giovanni 意大利雕刻家 5—467e
杜普雷 Duprez, Gilbert(-Louis) 法国歌唱家 5—468a
杜普林沼地战役 Dupplin Moor, Battle of 英国历史 5—467d
杜普伊 Dupuit, Arsène-Jules-Étienne-Juvénal 法国工程师 5—468b
杜齐 Dutse 尼日利亚集镇 5—482a
杜乔 Duccio, Agostino di 意大利雕刻家 5—444a
杜乔·第·博尼塞纳 Duccio DI BUONINSEGNA 意大利画家 5—443f
杜萨 Dousa, Janus 荷兰政治家 5—404a
杜萨布尔 Du Sable, Jean-Baptist-Point 美国商人 5—436e
杜塞尔多夫 Düsseldorf 德国行政区 5—478f
杜塞尔多夫 Düsseldorf 德国城市 5—479b
杜塞尔多夫画派 Düsseldorf school 德国画派 5—479d
杜塞克 Dussek, Jan Ladislav 波希米亚作曲家 5—478e
杜尚 Duchamp, Gaston 法国画家 5—444d
杜尚 Duchamp, Marcel 法国画家 5—444b
杜尚别 Dushanbe 塔吉克斯坦首都 5—478d
杜尚-维庸 Duchamp-Villon, Raymond 法国雕刻家 5—444d
杜省 Doubs 法国省份 5—399b
杜什曼 Dushman, Saul 美国物理化学家 5—478e
杜丝 Duse, Eleonora 意大利演员 5—477e
杜斯 Does, Johan van der 荷兰政治家 5—359d
杜斯堡 Doesburg, Theo van 荷兰画家 5—359d
杜松人 Dusun 马来西亚民族 5—479f

杜松子酒 gin 香料型蒸馏酒 7—135b
杜特 Dutt, Utpal 印度演员、编导 5—482a
杜特拉 Dutra, Eurico Gaspar 巴西总统 5—481f
杜托伊特 Du Toit, Jakob Daniel 南非作家 5—436f
杜托伊特 Du Toit, Stephanus Jacobus 南非政治家 5—436f
杜瓦 Dewar, Sir James 英国化学家、物理学家 5—275c
杜瓦尔 Duvall, Gabriel 美国最高法院大法官 5—482e
杜瓦尔 Duvall, Robert 美国演员 5—482f
杜瓦尔卡 Dwārkā 印度城镇 5—485f
杜瓦利埃 Duvalier, François 海地总统 5—482d
杜瓦利埃 Duvalier, Jean-Claude 海地总统 5—482e
杜瓦讷内 Douarnenez 法国城镇 5—398a
杜万瓜河 Dwangwa River 马拉维河流 5—485a
杜威 Dewey, George 美国军官 5—275e
杜威 Dewey, John 美国哲学家、教育家 5—275f
杜威 Dewey, Melvil 美国图书馆学家 5—276b
杜威 Dewey, Thomas E. 美国州长 5—276b
杜威十进分类法 Dewey Decimal Classification 图书馆学 5—276c
杜韦里埃 Duveyrier, Henri 法国探险家 5—483c
杜韦姆 Duwaym, Ad- 苏丹城市 5—483d
杜维恩男爵 Duveen (of Millbank), Joseph Duveen, Baron 英国商人 5—483a
杜维利耶 Douvillier, Suzanne Théodore Vaillande 法裔美国舞蹈家 5—404a
杜维姆 Tuwim, Julian 波兰诗人 17—298e
杜维内克 Duveneck, Frank 美国画家 5—483a
杜文秀 Du Wenxiu 中国回民起义领袖 5—437b
杜香 Stefan Dušan 塞尔维亚国王 16—209a
杜亚拉人 Duala 喀麦隆民族 5—437e
杜亚美 Duhamel, Georges 法国小说家 5—449b
杜伊金克 Duyckinck, Evert Augustus 美国文学批评家 5—483e
杜伊利乌斯 Duilius, Gaius 罗马统帅 5—450a
杜伊斯堡 Duisburg 德国城市 5—450a
杜伊塔马 Duitama 哥伦比亚城市 5—450c
杜佑 Du You 中国宰相、历史学家 5—437c
杜仲目 Eucommiales 植物学 6—156c
度会神道 Watarai Shintō 日本宗教 18—133c
度量衡 weights and measures 计量标准 18—170c
度量空间 metric space 数学 11—160e
度母 Tārā 佛教 16—477d
度支官 quaestor 古罗马官员 14—72d
渡边长武 Watanabe Osamu 日本轻量级摔跤运动员 18—133c
渡边华山 Watanabe Kazan 日本学者和画家 18—133b
渡渡鸟 dodo (*Raphus cucullatus*) 古生物学 5—358f
渡津者 Tirthankara 耆那教 17—111c
渡鸦 raven 鸟类 14—166c
镀覆 plating 冶金学 13—354a
镀金时代 Gilded Age 美国历史 7—129e
镀金银器 vermeil 工艺品 17—516f
镀铅锡钢板 terneplate 冶金 16—553c
镀锡钢板 tinplate 冶金 17—106d
镀锌 galvanizing 冶金 6—564c
镀银 silvering 玻璃加工制镜法 15—377d
端午节 Dragon Boat Festival 中国传统节日 5—411b
端午节 Tano 朝鲜节日 16—469b
端正行为 Derekh Eretz 犹太教 5—253c
端足类 amphipod 甲壳动物 1—298e
短鼻水羚 lechwe 哺乳动物 9—550e
短波无线电通信 shortwave radio 通信 15—335b
“短衬衫”号 Cutty Sark 苏格兰快帆船 5—80f
短翅水鸡 takahe (species *Notornis mantelli*) 鸟类 16—440b
短翅小海雀 dovekie (*Alle alle*) 鸟类 5—404d
短道速滑 short-track speed skating 体育 15—334b
短笛 piccolo 乐器 13—287f
短叠句 bob and wheel 诗歌韵律 2—555e
短耳鸮 short-eared owl (*Asio flammeus*) 鸟类 15—333a
短歌 tanka 日本文学 16—467d
短号 cornet 乐器 4—514c
短角牛 Shorthorn 牛品种 15—335a
短脚猎狗 basset hound 狗品种 2—269a
短距离跑 sprint 体育项目 16—165a
短距离赛 sprint 体育项目 16—165c
短距起降飞机 STOL airplane 飞机 16—247a
《短裤圣经》 Breeches Bible 基督教著作 3—137f
短链 chatelaine 饰物 4—90d
短毛家猫 domestic shorthair 哺乳动物 5—370c
短膜虫属 Crithidia 动物学 5—19a
短篇小说 short story 文学 15—333d
短期国库券 treasury bill 金融 17—204e
短期培信班 cursillo 天主教 5—71e
短期议会 Short Parliament 英国历史 15—333d
短诗节 verset 文学 17—525f
短途游览两轮马车 jaunting car 敞篷马车 8—550b
短尾矮袋鼠 quokka 哺乳动物 14—97c
短尾雕 bateleur (species *Terathopius ecaudatus*) 鸟类 2—274c
短尾鴗 tody 鸟类 17—129b
短尾猫 bobcat (*Felis rufa*) 哺乳动物 2—556a
短尾鼩鼱 short-tailed shrew (*Blarina brevicauda*) 哺乳动物 15—334a
短尾吸蜜鹦鹉 lory 鸟类 10—224b
短尾鹦哥 caique 鸟类 3—326d
短雪橇运动 lugeing 体育项目 10—275c
短韵律 short metre 诗歌 15—333d
短褶裙 kilt 苏格兰服装 9—280f
段祺瑞 Duan Qirui 中国军阀首领 5—438c
断层 fault 地质学 6—252b
断骨热 breakbone fever (disease) 疾病 3—134d
断口 fracture 矿物学 6—434c
断头台 guillotine 斩首刑具 7—357d
缎木 satinwood (*Chloroxylon swietenia*) 木本植物 15—77d
缎纹织物 satin 纺织 15—77c
椴树 linden 木本植物 10—116f
椴树科 Tiliaceae 植物学 17—95f
锻工 smith 冶金工人 15—443a
锻铁炉 forge 冶金设备 6—407d
锻造 forging 冶金方法 6—408a
堆花装饰 pâte-sur-pâte 瓷器的装饰方法 13—85a
堆行机 windrower 农业机械 18—283f
对-氨基苯甲酸 para-aminobenzoic acid (PABA) 化合物 13—29b
对-氨基水杨酸 para-aminosalicylic acid (PAS) 药物 13—29c
对瓣兰属 Zygopetalum 植物学 18—578c
对笔石属 Didymograptus 古生物学 5—304b
对策论 game theory 数学 6—569a
对唱比赛 agon 古希腊戏剧 1—125e
对称 symmetry 生物学 16—398c
对称性 symmetry 结晶学 16—398e
对称性 symmetry 物理学 16—398f
对当方阵 opposition, square of 逻辑 12—434e
对非存在的否认 Not-Being, denial of 哲学 12—273d
《对古人的询问》 Interrogation of the Old Men, The 爱尔兰文学 8—423b
对华 anticorona 大气科学 1—384d
对话体作品 dialogue 文学 5—285d
对句 couplet 文学 4—546e
对句韵诗 masnawi 诗歌 11—2a
对抗式程序 adversary procedure 法律 1—89f

对立表 opposites, table of 哲学 12—434e
对流 convection 物理学 4—474a
对流层 troposphere 大气科学 17—235b
对硫磷 parathion 杀虫剂 13—39c
对马 Tsushima 朝鲜海峡内群岛 17—251f
对马海峡之战 Tsushima, Battle of 日-俄海战 17—252a
对骂竞赛 flyting 苏格兰诗人竞骂 6—382f
对美利坚合众国国旗宣誓效忠 Pledge of Allegiance to the Flag of the United States of America 美国历史 13—367e
对偶性 duality 数学 5—438c
对日照 gegenschein 天文学 7—44b
对数 logarithm 数学 10—189a
对位 counterpoint 音乐 4—543d
对舞 contredanse 欧洲舞蹈 4—472b
对象恒常性 object constancy (psychology) 心理学 12—320f
对象语言 object language 语言学 12—320f
对乙酰氨基酚 acetaminophen 药物 1—49a
对议会的忠告 Parliament, Admonition to 英格兰清教徒宣言 13—57e
对应 contrapposto 艺术 4—471f
对应原理 correspondence principle 物理学 4—522a
对映体 enantiomorph 化学 6—68d
对照 antithesis 修辞学 1—395a
对撞束储存环 colliding-beam storage ring 物理学 4—348b
兑巴 thod pa (in Buddhism) 佛教祭器 17—41f
吨 ton 计量单位 17—146d
吨税和磅税 tonnage and poundage 英国国王津贴 17—153a
吨位 tonnage 航运 17—153a
敦 dui 中国古食器 5—449e
敦巴顿橡树园会议 Dumbarton Oaks Conference 联合国史 5—456b
敦巴顿橡树园研究图书馆和收藏馆 Dumbarton Oaks Research Library and Collection 美国文化机构 5—456c
敦贺 Tsuruga 日本城市 17—251e
敦煌 Dunhuang 中国城市 5—462b
敦煌石窟 Dunhuang caves 中国佛教艺术 5—462e
敦刻尔克 Dunkirk 法国港镇 5—463e
敦刻尔克 Dunkirk 美国港市 5—463e
敦讷尔兰 Dunderlands 挪威河谷 5—460c
墩 pier 建筑 13—294b
墩身 dado 古典建筑结构 5—105a
蹲伏猎狗 setter 狗品种 15—234f
炖 braising 烹饪方法 [illegible] 110e
钝刀 Dull Knife 印第安酋长 5—453f
钝吻鳄 alligator (genus *Alligator*) 爬行动物 1—241b
钝吻海豚 porpoise 哺乳动物 13—442d
钝叶草属 Stenotaphrum 植物学 16—219e
盾背螽斯 shield-backed katydid 昆虫 15—311f
盾牌钱 shield money (feudal law) 封建法律 15—312b
盾皮鱼 placoderm 古生物学 13—337e
盾尾蛇 shieldtail snake 爬行动物 15—312c
盾形饰牌 escutcheon 家具装饰物 6—129e
盾形纹章 arms, coat of 纹章学 1—503b
顿 caesura 诗法 3—321a
顿巴斯 Donbass (Ukraine and Russia) 东欧煤田 5—378a
顿河 Don River 俄罗斯河流 5—376d
顿河畔罗斯托夫 Rostov-na-Donu 俄罗斯城市 14—412c
顿绝 aposiopesis 辩术 1—415a
顿涅茨河 Donets River 欧洲河流 5—378f
顿涅茨克 Donetsk 乌克兰州名 5—379a
顿涅茨克 Donetsk 乌克兰城市 5—379a
顿涅茨煤田 Donets Basin 东欧煤田 5—378e
顿悟 insight 佛教 8—399c
顿悟 insight 心理学 8—399b
遁世者 sannyasi 印度教 15—37e
楯螺湖期 Ancylus stage 地质学 1—323f
多巴胺 dopamine 化合物 5—387b
多巴湖 Toba, Lake 印度尼西亚湖泊 17—125d
多邦通 Daubenton, Louis-Jean-Marie 法国博物学家 5—163a
多贝尔 Dobell, Sydney Thompson 英国诗人 5—353f
多贝瓦尔 Dauberval, Jean 法国芭蕾舞蹈家 5—163a
多倍性 polyploidy 遗传学 13—416d
多比 Doby, Larry 美国棒球运动员 5—355a
多比传 Tobit 《圣经》外典 17—126b
多变小冠花 crown vetch (*Coronilla varia*) 地被植物 5—37a
多伯曼氏短尾狗 Doberman pinscher 狗品种 5—354a
多勃雷宁 Dobrynin, Anatoly Fyodorovich 苏联外交家 5—354d
多布雷 Daubrée, Gabriel-Auguste 法国地球化学家 5—163d
多布里奇 Dobrich 保加利亚城镇 5—354c
多布罗夫斯基 Dobrovský, Josef 捷克语言学者 5—354d
多布罗加 Dobruja 欧洲历史区域 5—354d
多布尼人 Dobuni 古不列颠部落 5—355a
多布森 Dobson, Austin 英国作家 5—354e
多布森 Dobson, Frank 英国雕刻家 5—354f
多布森 Dobson, William 英国画家 5—354f
多布希纳 Dobšiná 斯洛伐克乡镇 5—354e
多布赞斯基 Dobzhansky, Theodosius 美国遗传学家 5—355b
多重布景 multiple setting 舞台技术 11—480a
多重处理 multiprocessing 计算机科学 11—480e
多重人格 multiple personality 心理学 11—479e
多刺楤木 angelica tree (species *Aralia spinosa*) 木本植物 1—341e
多达贝达山 Doda Betta 印度山峰 5—357a
多弹头分导重返大气层运载工具 MIRV 武器 11—274c
多德勒尔 Doderer, Heimito von 奥地利小说家 5—357d
多德雷赫特 Dordrecht 荷兰城市 5—388d
多蒂腰布 dhoti 印度服饰 5—280f
多调性 polytonality 音乐 13—418c
多丁顿 Dodington, George Bubb, BARON MELCOMBE OF MELCOMBE-REGIS 英国政客 5—358e
多东斯 Dodoens, Rembert 佛兰芒医生、植物学家 5—359a
多动症 hyperactivity 疾病 8—290e
多斗拱式 tap'o style 朝鲜建筑 16—476b
多顿 Dowden, Edward 爱尔兰作家 5—405f
多多马 Dodoma 坦桑尼亚首都 5—359a
多多纳 Dodona 希腊伊庇鲁斯古神殿 5—359b
多恩 Don 凯尔特神话人物 5—376a
多恩 Donne, John 英国诗人 5—384f
多恩贝格尔 Dornberger, Walter Robert 德国工程师 5—390d
多恩比恩 Dornbirn 奥地利城市 5—390e
多尔 Dor 以色列定居点 5—387e
多尔 Dole, Bob 美国参议员 5—363f
多尔 Dorr, Julia Caroline Ripley 美国小说家、诗人 5—391b
多尔 Dole, Sanford Ballard 夏威夷总统、美国州长 5—364a
多尔 Dorr, Thomas Wilson 美国政治家 5—391b
多尔半岛 Door Peninsula 美国半岛 5—386f
多尔比 Dalby 澳大利亚城镇 5—115c
多尔德会议 Dort, Synod of 基督教会议 5—392b
多尔蒂 Daugherty, Harry Micajah 美国律师 5—164f
多尔蒂 Doherty, Peter C. 澳大利亚免疫学家 5—362e
多尔蒂 Dougherty, Walter Hampden (American actor) 美国演员 5—399e
多尔蒂兄弟 Doherty, Laurie; and Doherty, Reggie 英国网球运动员 5—362d
多尔顿 Dalton 美国城市 5—121a
多尔顿 Dalton, William (vaudeville star) 美国轻歌舞剧明星 5—121c
多尔顿兄弟 Dalton BROTHERS 美国西部匪徒 5—121a

多尔顿制 Dalton Plan 教育方法 5—121c
多尔多涅 Dordogne 法国省份 5—388b
多尔多涅河 Dordogne River 法国河流 5—388c
多尔菲斯 Dollfus, Audouin(-Charles) 法国天文学家 5—366b
多尔干-涅涅茨自治区 Dolgano-Nenets autonomous okrug (Russia) 俄罗斯行政区 5—364c
多尔甘人 Dolgan 俄罗斯民族 5—364c
多尔戈鲁基 Dolgoruky, Vasily Lukich, Knyaz (Prince) 俄国公爵、外交家 5—364d
多尔戈鲁基 Dolgoruky, Vasily Vladimirovich, Knyaz (Prince) 俄国公爵、军官 5—364e
多尔戈鲁基家族 Dolgoruky FAMILY 俄国公爵世族 5—364c
多尔戈普鲁德内 Dolgoprudny 俄罗斯城市 5—364c
多尔衮 Dorgon 中国清初摄政王 5—388f
多尔金 Dorking 英格兰商镇 5—390a
多尔迈耶 Dallmeyer, John Henry 英国发明家 5—119c
多尔曼 Dollmann, Friedrich 德国陆军指挥官 5—366d
多尔曼 Dollmann, Georg (Carl Heinrich) von 德国建筑师 5—366e
多尔曼 Doorman, Karel (Willem Frederik Marie) 荷兰将军 5—386f
多尔梅奇 Dolmetsch, (Eugène) Arnold 英国音乐家 5—367b
多尔内 Dorner, Isaak August 德国神学家 5—390e
多尔帕特 Dorpat (Estonia) 爱沙尼亚城市 5—391a
多尔奇 Dolci, Carlo 意大利画家 5—363d
多尔切斯特男爵(第一) Dorchester (of Dorchester), Guy Carleton, lst Baron 英属北美总督 5—388b
多尔日 Dolj 罗马尼亚县名 5—365b
多尔氏绵羊 Dall sheep (*Ovis dalli*) 北美大角羊 5—118d
多尔斯-罗维拉 Ors y Rovira, Eugenio d' 西班牙作家 12—471f
多尔斯滕 Dorsten 德国城市 5—392a
多尔西 Dorsey, George A. 美国人种学家 5—391e
多尔西 Dorsey, James Owen 美国人种学家 5—391e
多尔西 Dorsey, Thomas Andrew 美国音乐家 5—392a
多尔西兄弟 Dorsey, Jimmy; and Dorsey, Tommy 美国管弦乐队领队 5—391f
多发性骨髓瘤 multiple myeloma 疾病 11—479e
多发性硬化 multiple sclerosis (MS) 疾病 11—480a
多凡堡 Fort-Dauphin (Madagascar) 马达加斯加城镇 6—413c
多菲内 Dauphiné 法国历史文化区域 5—166a
多菲内山 Dauphiné Alps 法国山脉 5—166b
多芬 dauphin 法国王储称号 5—165f
多芬 Dauphin 加拿大城镇 5—165f
多芬岛 Dauphin Island 美国岛屿 5—166a
多佛 Dover 美国特拉华州城市 5—404e
多佛 Dover 美国新罕布什尔州城市 5—404e
多佛尔 Dover 英格兰区名 5—404d
多佛尔 Dover 英格兰城镇 5—404e
多佛尔海峡 Dover, Strait of 英法间海峡 5—404f
《多佛尔条约》 Dover, Treaty of 欧洲历史 5—404f
多夫勒山 Dovre Mountains 挪威山脉 5—405a
多夫仁科 Dovzhenko, Aleksandr (Petrovich) 苏联电影导演 5—405a
多甘 Dorgan, Thomas Aloysius 美国漫画家、记者 5—388e
多哥 Togo 非洲国家 17—130f
多哥兰 Togoland 非洲历史 17—131f
多哥山 Togo Mountains (Africa) 非洲山脉 17—131f
多格博人 Togbo (people) 非洲民族 17—129f
多格拉王朝 Dogra DYNASTY 印度王朝 5—361c
多格里布人 Dogrib 加拿大印第安部落集团 5—361d
多格滩 Dogger Bank 北海沙洲 5—361a
多格特 Doggett, Thomas 英格兰演员 5—361b
多格特上衣和徽章赛 Doggett's Coat and Badge 划船比赛 5—361b
多贡人 Dogon 马里种族集团 5—361b
多国公司 multinational corporation (MNC) 跨国公司 11—479a
多哈 Doha 卡塔尔首都 5—362c
多汗症 hyperhidrosis 病理现象 8—291f
多颌牙形石型 polygnathiform 古生物学 13—413a
多赫纳尼 Dohnányi, Ernst von 匈牙利作曲家 5—362f
多花蔷薇 sweetbrier (*Rosa eglanteria* or *R. rubiginosa*) 木本植物 16—380c
多环盆地 multiringed basin 天文学 11—480f
多肌炎 polymyositis 疾病 13—415a
多级火箭 staged rocket 航天运载器 16—180d
多济 Dozy, Reinhart Pieter (Anne) 荷兰阿拉伯学家 5—408c
多晶体 polycrystal 晶体学 13—412b
多镜面望远镜 Multiple Mirror Telescope (MMT) 天文光学仪器 11—479d
多锯鲈 wreckfish (*Polyprion americanus*) 鱼类 18—343a
多克 Dock, Christopher 北美殖民地教师 5—356b
多孔动物门 Porifera (animal phylum) 无脊椎动物 13—441c
多孔菌 pore fungus 真菌 13—441a
多孔菌目 Polyporales 真菌 13—416f
多孔螅 millepore 无脊椎动物 11—225b
多库恰耶夫 Dokuchayev, Vasily Vasilyevich 俄罗斯地貌学家 5—363b
多拉 Dorat, Jean 法国古希腊语学者 5—387f
多拉蒂 Dorati, Antal 美国指挥家 5—387f
多拉尔 Dollar, William (Henry) 美国芭蕾舞蹈家 5—365f
多榔菊 leopard's bane 植物 10—28d
多朗德 Dollond, George 英国光学家 5—366e
多朗德 Dollond, John 英国光学仪器制造者 5—366f
多朗德 Dollond, Peter 英国光学仪器制造者 5—366f
多勒 Dole 法国城镇 5—363f
多雷 Dolet, Étienne 法国人文学者、印刷商 5—364b
多雷 Doré, (Paul-) Gustave 法国版画家 5—388d
多里安人 Dorian 古希腊民族 5—389d
多里昂 Dorion, Sir Antoine Aimé 加拿大政治家 5—389f
多里斯 Doris 希腊古地区 5—390a
多里斯 Douris 古希腊陶瓶画家 5—403f
多里亚 Doria, Andrea 热那亚政治家 5—389a
多里亚调式 Dorian mode 音乐 5—389f
多里亚家族 Doria FAMILY 热那亚家族 5—389a
多立斯柱式 Doric order 建筑 5—389f
多利特尔医生 Dolittle, Doctor 美国小说人物 5—365b
多利·瓦登鳟 Dolly Varden trout (*Salvelinus malma*) 鱼类 5—367a
多利西 Dolisie (Congo) 刚果城市 5—365b
多连灯烛台 menorah 犹太教礼仪用具 11—117d
多列士 Torez 乌克兰城市 17—160b
多列士 Thorez, Maurice 法国政治家 17—55b
多林 Dolin, Sir Anton 英国芭蕾舞蹈家 5—364f
多林格尔 Döllinger, Johann Joseph Ignaz von 德国神学家 5—366c
多灵魂说 multiple souls 宗教观念 11—480c
多硫化物 polysulfide 化合物 13—417e
多瘤病毒 polyomavirus 病毒 13—416a
多瘤齿兽 multituberculate 古生物学 11—481a
多路传输 multiplexing 电子学 11—480c
多氯联苯 polychlorinated biphenyl (PCB) 化合物 13—411e
多伦 Duolun 中国城市 5—465f
多伦多 Toronto 加拿大城市 17—162d
多伦多大学 Toronto, University of 加拿大大学 17—164a
多伦多电视塔 CN Tower 加拿大电视塔 4—309b
《多伦多明星日报》 Toronto Star, The 加拿大报纸 17—164b
多伦多证券交易所 Toronto Stock Exchange (TSE) 加拿大证券交易所 17—164b
多罗磨王国 Tarumanegara 西爪哇王国 16—487e
多罗西斯 Dorotheus 罗马法学家 5—390f
多罗·辛格 Tara Singh 锡克教领袖 16—477f

多洛雷斯河 Dolores River 美国河流 5—367f
多洛雷斯口号 Grito de Dolores 墨西哥历史 7—317a
多洛米蒂山 Dolomites 意大利山群 5—367f
多洛米厄 Dolomieu, Dieudonné 法国地质学家 5—367d
多洛氏法则 Dollo's law 生物学原理 5—366f
多马,圣 Thomas, SAINT 《圣经》人物 17—42c
多马克 Domagk, Gerhard 德国细菌学家 5—368c
多毛纲假说 polychaete hypothesis 古生物学 13—411d
多毛类 polychaete 动物学 13—411d
多毛症 hypertrichosis 病理现象 8—294a
多梅尼基诺 Domenichino 意大利画家 5—369b
多梅尼基诺 Domenichino, Il (composer) 意大利作曲家 5—369c
多米尼加共和国 Dominican Republic 西印度群岛国家 5—373e
多米尼加海峡 Dominica Channel 西印度群岛海峡 5—373d
多米尼科 Domenico VENEZIANO 意大利画家 5—369d
多米尼克 Dominica 加勒比海岛国 5—372f
多米尼克(上帝之母的) Dominic OF THE MOTHER OF GOD 教皇国奥秘神学家 5—372e
多米宁 Dominion 加拿大城镇 5—374e
多米诺骨牌 dominoes 博戏 5—375a
多米特 Domett, Alfred 新西兰作家、总理 5—371f
多面形琢型 brilliant cut 钻石加工方法 3—157d
多明戈 Domingo, Plácido 西班牙演唱家 5—372c
多明戈·德·古斯曼,圣 Domingo DE GUZMÁN, SANTO 西班牙天主教神父 5—372c
多明格斯·巴斯蒂达 Domínguez Bastida, Gustavo Adolfo (Spanish writer) 西班牙作家 5—372d
多明金 Dominguín 西班牙斗牛士 5—372d
多明我会 Dominican 天主教组织 5—373d
多明我,圣 Dominic, SAINT 西班牙天主教神父 5—372e
多姆 Ḍom 印度种姓 5—368c
多姆纳 Domna, Julia (Roman empress) 古罗马皇后 5—375e
多姆山省 Puy-de-Dôme 法国省份 14—40a
多那太罗 Donatello 意大利雕刻家 5—377b
多纳 Donner, Georg Raphael 奥地利雕刻家 5—385c
多纳蒂 Donati Corso 佛罗伦萨贵族 5—377d
多纳蒂 Donati, Giovanni Battista 意大利天文学家 5—377e
多纳特氏草属 Donatia 植物学 5—377e
多纳图派 Donatist 北非基督教派别 5—377f
多纳图斯 Donatus, Aelius 古罗马语法学家 5—377f
多奈 Donnay, Maurice(-Charles) 法国剧作家 5—384e
多南 Donen, Stanley 美国电影导演 5—378d
多瑙河 Danube River 欧洲河流 5—142f
多瑙河画派 Danube school 风景画派 5—143a
多瑙河文化 Danubian culture 新石器文化 5—143c
多瑙沃特 Donauwörth 德国港市 5—378a
多瑙新城 Dunaújváros 匈牙利城镇 5—458a
多尼戈尔 Donegal 爱尔兰郡名 5—378b
多尼戈尔 Donegal 爱尔兰城镇 5—378c
多黏菌素 polymyxin 抗生素 13—415b
多涅拉伊蒂斯 Donelaitis, Kristijonas 立陶宛诗人 5—378c
多努 Daunou, Pierre-Claude-François 法国政治家 5—165d
多努斯 Donus 罗马教皇 5—385f
多诺 Dono, Paolo di (Florentine painter) 佛罗伦萨画家 5—385d
多诺莫尔考察团 Donoughmore Commission 英国考察团 5—385e
多诺索 Donoso, José 智利小说家 5—385d
多诺万 Donovan, William J(oseph) 美国外交官、军人 5—385f
多偶婚制 polygamy 婚姻 13—412f
多胚 polyembryony 生物学 13—412c
多普勒 Doppler, Christian 奥地利物理学家 5—387d
多普勒效应 Doppler effect 物理学 5—387d
多鳍鱼 bichir 鱼类 2—461b
多切斯特 Dorchester 英格兰城镇 5—388a
多情善感风格 empfindsamer Stil 音乐思潮 6—63e
多饶起义 Dózsa Rebellion 匈牙利农民起义 5—408c
多软骨炎 polychondritis 疾病 13—411f
多塞 Dausset, Jean-Baptiste-Gabriel-Joachim 法国免疫学家 5—166c
多塞特伯爵(第二) Dorset, Henry Beaufort, 2nd Earl of 英国贵族 5—391d
多塞特伯爵(第一) Dorset, Edmund Beaufort, 1st Earl of 英国贵族 5—391d
多塞特侯爵(第三) Dorset, Henry Grey, 3rd Marquess of 英国贵族 5—391d
多塞特文化 Dorset culture 考古学 5—391d
多瑟 Dauser, Sue Sophia 美国护士 5—166c
多森 Dothan 美国城市 5—396d
多神经炎 polyneuritis 疾病 13—415d
多神论 polytheism 宗教 13—418a
多斯·帕索斯 Dos Passos, John 美国作家 5—392f
多斯桑托斯 dos Santos, José 安哥拉民族主义者 5—393c
多斯特·穆罕默德汗 Dōst Moḥammad Khān 阿富汗国王 5—393f
多索 Dosso 尼日尔城镇 5—393d
多索·多西 Dosso Dossi 意大利画家 5—393e
多胎产 multiple birth 动物学 11—479a
多态现象 pleomorphism 微生物学 13—369f
多态现象 polymorphism 生物学 13—414d
多糖 polysaccharide 化合物 13—417c
多特蒙德 Dortmund 德国城市 5—392b
多特蒙德-埃姆斯运河 Dortmund-Ems Canal 德国运河 5—392c
多头市场 bull market 经济 3—246b
多托蒙 Dotremont, Christian 比利时诗人 5—396e
多瓦高地 Dowa Highlands 马拉维高地 5—405f
多瓦勒 Dorval 加拿大城市 5—392d
多维尔 Deauville 法国海滨胜地 5—197c
多闻天王 Vaiśravaṇa 宗教 17—445c
多乌巴亚泽特 Doğubayazıt 土耳其城镇 5—361f
多西狄奥斯 Dosítheos 耶路撒冷牧首 5—393d
多西河 Doce River 巴西河流 5—356a
多西特 Dorset 英格兰郡名 5—391c
多西亚瓷器 Doccia porcelain 欧洲瓷器 5—355f
多细胞生物体 multicellular organism 生物学 11—478f
多香果 allspice 木本植物 1—243b
多向飞碟射击 trapshooting 体育项目 17—202b
多向色性 pleochroism 光学 13—369d
多项描记器 polygraph 仪器装置 13—413d
多叶缬木 bog rosemary (*Andromeda polifolia*) 灌木植物 2—567b
多伊 Doe, Samuel K(anyon) 利比亚总统 5—359c
多伊布勒尔 Däubler, Theodor 德国诗人 5—163c
多伊尔 Doyle, Richard 英国画家 5—408b
多伊奇 Deutsch(painter) 瑞士画家、作家 5—269a
多伊西 Doisy, Edward Adelbert 美国生物化学家 5—363b
多音节诗体 arte mayor 西班牙诗歌形式 1—525a
多余的人 superfluous man 俄国文学 16—345c
多语种《圣经》合参 polyglot Bible 《圣经》多语种文本 13—413a
多元论和一元论 pluralism and monism 哲学理论 13—377c
多元主义 pluralism 政治科学 13—377b
多韵散文 polyphonic prose 文学 13—416c
多治见 Tajimi 日本城市 16—440a
多柱厅 hypostyle hall 建筑 8—295e
多兹 Dodds, Alfred-Amédée 法国军人 5—357b
多兹利 Dodsley, Robert 英国作家、出版商 5—359b
多足类 myriapod 动物学 11—526c
《夺牛长征记》 Cattle Raid of Cooley, The 古爱尔兰文学 3—532a
朵玛 gtor-ma 中国藏传佛教供品 7—331f
舵 rudder 船部件 14—439e

E

阿弥陀佛 Amitābha 佛教佛名 1—291c
阿弥陀宗 Amidism 佛教派别 1—289a
《俄巴底亚书》 Obadiah, Book of 《圣经》篇章 12—317c
俄波战争 Russo-Polish War 俄国与波兰历史事件 14—466a
《俄德再保险条约》 Reinsurance Treaty 俄德秘密条约 14—211f
俄狄浦斯 Oedipus 希腊神话人物 12—341d
俄狄浦斯情结 Oedipus complex 心理学 12—341e
《俄狄浦斯王》 Oedipus Rex 古希腊文学 12—342a
俄尔甫斯 Orpheus 希腊传说人物 12—470e
俄耳甫斯主义 Orphism 绘画 12—470f
俄斐 Ophir 《圣经》地名 12—430f
俄国科学院 Sciences, Academy of 俄国研究机构 15—143b
俄国灵猩 borzoi 俄国猎狗 3—57d
俄国内战 Russian Civil War 俄国历史 14—463a
俄国社会民主工党 Russian Social-Democratic Workers' Party 俄国政党 14—465b
俄国式茶炊 samovar 金属茶壶 14—564d
俄国形式主义 Russian Formalism (literary criticism) 文学评论 14—463c
俄国1905年革命 Russian Revolution of 1905 俄国历史 14—464e
俄国1917年革命 Russian Revolution of 1917 俄国历史 14—465a
俄亥俄 Ohio 美国州名 12—349e
俄亥俄帮 Ohio Gang 美国历史 12—352f
俄亥俄倡议 Ohio Idea 美国历史 12—352f
俄亥俄公司 Ohio Company 美国公司 12—352f
俄亥俄河 Ohio River 美国河流 12—353a
俄柯阶 Ochoan Stage 地质学 12—331f
俄克拉何马 Oklahoma 美国州名 12—360c
俄克拉何马城 Oklahoma City 美国城市 12—362e
俄克拉何马城爆炸 Oklahoma City bombing 恐怖袭击事件 12—362f
俄克拉何马城动物园 Oklahoma City Zoological Park 美国动物园 12—363a
俄克喜林库斯 Oxyrhynchus 古埃及城市 12—525c
俄刻阿诺斯 Oceanus 希腊神话 12—331a
俄勒冈 Oregon 美国城市 12—452d
俄勒冈 Oregon 美国州名 12—452e
俄勒冈葡萄 Oregon grape 木本植物 12—455c
《俄勒冈人报》 Oregonian, The 美国报纸 12—455e
俄勒冈山洞国家自然保护区 Oregon Caves National Monument 美国自然保护区 12—455c
俄勒冈市 Oregon City 美国城市 12—455c
俄勒冈问题 Oregon Question 国际争端 12—455d
俄勒冈小道 Oregon Trail 美国历史 12—455e
俄勒冈紫杉 Oregon yew 木本植物 12—455e
俄罗斯 Russia 欧洲国家 14—459e
俄罗斯芭蕾舞团 Ballets Russes 艺术团体 2—177a
《俄罗斯编年史》 Russian Primary Chronicle 中世纪文献 14—464e
俄罗斯公教会 Russian Catholic church 俄国教会 14—462f
俄罗斯公司 Russia Company (English merchants) 英国贸易机构 14—462e
俄罗斯国立博物馆 Russian State Museum 俄国博物馆 14—465c
俄罗斯蓝猫 Russian Blue 猫品种 14—462f
俄罗斯平原 Russian Plain 东欧平原 14—464e
俄罗斯苏维埃联邦社会主义共和国 Russian Soviet Federated Socialist Republic 俄罗斯历史名称 14—465c
俄罗斯文学 Russian literature 文学 14—463d
俄罗斯无产阶级作家联合会 Russian Association of Proletarian Writers 苏联作家组织 14—462f
俄罗斯油橄榄 Russian olive (small tree) 木本植物 14—464a
俄罗斯正教会 Russian Orthodox church 俄国教会 14—464b
俄罗斯族 Russ 中国少数民族 14—464a
俄美公司 Russian-American Company 俄国公司 14—462e
俄纽斯 Oeneus 希腊传说人物 12—342d
俄诺涅 Oenone 希腊神话人物 12—342d
俄瑞斯忒斯 Orestes 希腊神话人物 12—456e
俄赛里斯 Osiris 埃及神名 12—484f
俄斯特拉发 Ostrava 捷克城市 12—493d
俄土战争 Russo-Turkish wars 俄国与奥斯曼帝国的战争 14—466a
俄歇效应 Auger effect 原子物理学 2—47d
俄语 Russian language 欧洲语言 14—463c
莪默·伊本·阿比·拉比亚 ʿUmar ibn Abī Rabīʿah 阿拉伯诗人 17—334f
莪相 Ossian 爱尔兰诗人 12—487f
莪相民谣 Ossianic ballads 爱尔兰文学 12—488a
峨眉山 Emeishan 中国城市 6—58e
锇(Os) osmium 化学元素 12—486d
鹅耳枥 hornbeam 植物 8—176a
鹅膏属 Amanita 生物学 1—264b
鹅口疮 thrush 疾病 17—67a
鹅妈妈 Mother Goose 虚构的人物 11—431b
鹅棋 goose 棋戏 7—210c
鹅掌柴 schefflera 植物学 15—111c
蛾 moth 昆虫 11—430e
蛾兰 moth orchid 草本植物 11—431a
蛾螺 whelk 腹足纲动物 18—222e
蛾摩拉 Gomorrah 《旧约》 7—199f
蛾鸮 moth owl 鸟类 11—431a
额尔古纳河 Ergun He 中俄界河 6—115b
额尔齐斯河 Ertix He 中国河流 6—124b
额枋 architrave 建筑学 1—453e
额济纳河 Ejin He 中国河流 6—7e
额外雇工 featherbedding 劳动规则 6—259a
恶心 nausea 病理现象 12—48b
厄巴纳 Urbana 美国俄亥俄州城市 17—412e
厄巴纳 Urbana 美国伊利诺伊州城市 17—412e
厄伯伦德 Aparanta (India) 印度沿海平原 1—406b
厄德,圣 Eudes, Saint John 法国天主教教士 6—157a
厄登堡 Ödenburg (Hungary) 匈牙利城镇 12—336c
厄俄斯 Eos 罗马神话女神 6—93c
厄恩 Earn 苏格兰湖泊、河流 5—497b
厄恩哈特 Earnhardt, (Ralph) Dale 美国汽车赛赛手 5—497b
厄恩湖 Erne, Lough 英国湖泊 6—120e
厄恩肖 Earnshaw, Thomas 英国制表家 5—497c
厄尔 Eure 法国省份 6—164a
厄尔 Earle, Alice Morse 美国作家、古文物家 5—496a
厄尔 Earle, John 英国牧师 5—496b
厄尔巴岛 Elba 意大利岛屿 6—14f
厄尔布尔士山脉 Elburz Mountains 伊朗山脉 6—15e
厄尔布鲁士山 Elbrus, Mount 俄罗斯山峰 6—15d
厄尔河 Eure River 法国河流 6—164b
厄尔利 Early, Jubal A(nderson) 美国将领 5—496b
厄尔-卢瓦 Eure-et-Loir 法国省份 6—164a
厄尔马那里克 Ermanaric 东哥特人国王 6—120c
厄尔曼 Ulman, Douglas Elton (actor) 美国演员 17—330c
厄尔尼诺 El Niño 海温异常升高现象 6—10f
厄菲阿尔特 Ephialtes 希腊政治家 6—96d
厄缶 Eötvös, Roland, Baron von 匈牙利物理学家 6—93e
厄弗冷(叙利亚人),圣 Ephraem Syrus, Saint 叙利亚神学家 6—96f
厄福德 Ufford, Robert de 英格兰军人、政治家 17—321b
厄瓜多尔 Ecuador 南美洲国家 5—532e
厄加勒斯角 Agulhas, Cape 南非岬角 1—132b
厄加勒斯洋流 Agulhas Current 大洋环流 1—132b

厄喀德那 Echidna 希腊神话女怪 5—522b
厄科 Echo 希腊神话仙女 5—523a
厄克贝里 Ekeberg, Anders Gustav 瑞典化学家 6—7f
厄克特 Urquhart, Sir Thomas 英国翻译家 17—417f
厄拉多塞(昔兰尼的) Eratosthenes of Cyrene 希腊科学作家、天文学家 6—112b
厄拉多塞筛法 Eratosthenes, sieve of 数学 6—112b
厄赖法冰盖 Öræfajökull 冰岛火山 12—440e
厄兰 Öland 瑞典岛屿 12—365c
厄兰格 Erlanger, Joseph 美国生理学家 6—120a
厄勒 El 西闪米特人神祇 6—9e
厄勒布鲁 Örebro 瑞典省份 12—452a
厄勒布鲁 Örebro 瑞典城市 12—452b
厄勒海峡 Øresund (Baltic Sea) 波罗的海海峡 12—456f
厄勒克赛派 Elkesaite 犹太教派别 6—46d
厄勒克特拉 Electra 希腊神话人物 6—19b
厄里戈妮 Erigone 希腊神话人物 6—117f
厄里倪厄斯 Erinys (Greco-Roman mythology) 希腊罗马神话女神 6—118f
厄里什基迦勒 Ereshkigal 美索不达米亚女神 6—114a
厄里斯 Eris 希腊罗马神话人物 6—119a
厄立特里亚 Eritrea 东非国家 6—119b
厄立特里亚人民解放阵线 Eritrean People's Liberation Front (EPLF) 厄立特里亚政治组织 6—119e
厄利萨 Elissa (Greek mythology) 希腊神话人物 6—41d
厄鲁 Heureaux, Ulises 多米尼加共和国总统 8—64a
厄洛斯 Eros 希腊神祇 6—122a
厄梅尔 Ömer (Ottoman poet) 奥斯曼诗人 12—414f
厄南,圣 Eunan, Saint 爱尔兰学者 6—161b
厄普 Earp, Wyatt (Berry Stapp) 美国边疆开拓者 5—497c
厄普代克 Updike, Daniel Berkeley 美国印刷商、学者 17—403f
厄普代克 Updike, John (Hoyer) 美国作家 17—404a
厄普顿 Upton, Francis Robbins 美国数学家、物理学家 17—406b
厄普菲尔德 Upfield, Arthur William 澳大利亚小说家 17—404d
厄普约翰 Upjohn, Richard 美国建筑师 17—404e
厄瑞克忒翁庙 Erechtheum 希腊雅典庙宇 6—113b
厄瑞克透斯 Erechtheus 希腊传说人物 6—113c
厄塞尔 Ösel (Estonia) 爱沙尼亚岛屿 12—483f
厄斯金 Erskine, John 苏格兰贵族 6—123c
厄斯金 Erskine, John 美国教育家、音乐家和小说家 6—123c
厄斯金 Erskine (of Restormel), Thomas Erskine, 1st Baron 英国律师 6—123d
厄斯特谷 Østerdalen 挪威谷地 12—492b
厄斯特兰 Østlandet 挪威地理区域 12—492f
厄斯特松德 Östersund 瑞典城市 12—492e
厄廷根-施拉滕豪芬彩陶 Öttingen-Schrattenhofen faience 工艺品 12—500c
厄瓦耳 Ewald, Paul Peter 德国物理学家 6—187a
厄乌德琴 ʿūd 乐器 17—318d
厄谢尔 Ussher, James 爱尔兰基督教神职人员 17—424b
厄亚塞特 Ørjasaeter, Tore 挪威诗人 12—462f
厄运诗人 poète maudit 失意诗人 13—386b
厄泽尔 Oeser, Adam Friedrich 匈牙利画家 12—342f
厄扎尔 ghazal 伊斯兰文学 7—109e
厄扎尔 Özal, Turgut 土耳其总统 12—527f
厄兹塔尔阿尔卑斯山 Ötztal Alps 欧洲山脉 12—504a
呃逆 hiccup 生理学 8—69c
轭木 yoke 器具 18—452f
恶魔 demon 宗教 5—238b
恶目 evil eye 迷信 6—185b
恶性脓疱 malignant pustule 疾病 10—431a
恶性贫血 pernicious anemia 疾病 13—175e
恶性炭疽 woolsorters' disease 疾病 18—328f
恶性肿瘤 cancer 疾病 3—396a
恶作剧故事 trickster tale 民间故事 17—217a
鄂毕河 Ob River 俄罗斯河流 12—317b
鄂毕湾 Ob, Gulf of 俄罗斯海湾 12—317a
鄂毕-乌戈尔诸语言 Ob-Ugric languages 欧洲语言 12—317c
鄂尔多斯高原 Ordos Plateau 中国高原 12—450f
鄂尔多斯沙地 Ordos Desert 中国沙漠 12—450f
鄂尔浑碑文 Orhon inscriptions 突厥文字 12—459d
鄂尔泰 Oèr-t'ai 中国清代大臣 12—342d
鄂霍茨克海 Okhotsk, Sea of 太平洋边缘海 12—359d
鄂君启节 Prince E's tallies 中国古青铜器 13—514c
鄂伦春语 Oroqen language 中国语言 12—470a
鄂伦春族 Oroqen 中国民族 12—469f
鄂木斯克 Omsk 俄罗斯州名 12—415d
鄂木斯克 Omsk 俄罗斯城市 12—415e
鄂图卡 Otakar 波希米亚国王之名 12—496c
鄂图卡二世 Otakar II 波希米亚国王 12—496d
鄂图卡一世 Otakar I 波希米亚国王 12—496c
鄂温克语 Ewenki language 中国语言 6—187d
鄂温克族 Ewenki 中国民族 6—187b
鄂州 Ezhou 中国城市 6—202f
萼距花属 Cuphea 植物学 5—65d
遏制 containment 美国外交 4—464d
腭 palate 解剖学 12—557a
腭化 palatalization 语音学 12—557a
腭裂 cleft palate 先天畸形 4—278d
腭音 palatal 语音学 12—556f
腭针鱼 needlefish 鱼类 12—64d
鹗 osprey (*Pandion haliaetus*) 鸟类 12—487c
鳄 crocodile 爬行动物 5—22d
鳄梨 avocado (*Persea americana*) 木本植物 2—90b
鳄鳞鱼 alligator fish 鱼类 1—241d
鳄鸟 crocodile bird (*Pluvianus aegyptius*) 鸟类 5—22d
《鳄鱼》 Krokodil 苏联杂志 9—380d
鳄鱼苹果 alligator apple 木本植物 1—241d
恩贝里斯 Emberres, Gil de 西班牙雕刻家 6—56f
恩波里亚 Emporia 美国城市 6—65e
恩波利 Empoli 意大利城镇 6—65d
恩伯里 Embury, Philip 美国教士 6—58c
恩博马 Embomma 刚果(金)城市 6—57c
恩博瓦斯战争 Emboabas, War of the 巴西历史 6—57b
恩布 Amb 巴基斯坦邦君 1—268d
恩布 Embu 肯尼亚城镇 6—58c
恩布登 Embden, Gustav Georg 德国生理化学家 6—56d
恩德贝勒人 Ndebele 南非民族 12—56c
恩德贝勒人 Ndebele 津巴布韦民族 12—56d
恩德比地 Enderby Land 南极洲地区 6—72f
恩德尔 Ender, Otto 奥地利总理 6—72f
恩德里彻 Endlicher, Stephan (Ladislaus) 奥地利植物学家 6—73b
恩德培 Entebbe 乌干达城市 6—87f
恩德斯 Enders, John Franklin 美国病毒学家 6—73a
恩迪科特 Endecott, John 英国殖民总督 6—72e
恩底弥昂 Endymion 希腊神话人物 6—75c
恩典 grace 基督教神学 7—237c
恩东加 Ndongo 非洲历史王国 12—57a
恩多拉 Ndola 赞比亚城镇 12—56f
恩厄尔布雷克特(恩厄尔布雷克特松) Engelbrekt Engelbrektsson 瑞典民族英雄 6—76e
恩菲尔德 Enfield 英国自治市 6—76c
恩菲尔德 Enfield 美国城镇 6—76c
恩盖迪 ʿEn Gedi 以色列考古遗址 6—67a
恩冈代雷 Ngaoundéré 喀麦隆城镇 12—159e
恩戈科河 Ngoko River (Cameroon) 喀麦隆河流 12—160c

恩戈罗恩戈罗保护区 Ngorongoro Conservation Area 坦桑尼亚国家保护区 12—160d
恩戈罗恩戈罗火山口 Ngorongoro Crater 坦桑尼亚火山口 12—160d
恩戈尼人 Ngoni 非洲民族 12—160c
恩戈齐 Ngozi 布隆迪城镇 12—160e
恩戈伊 Ngoy 中非历史国家 12—160e
恩格班迪人 Ngbandi 非洲民族 12—159f
恩格尔 Engle, Robert F. 美国经济学家 6—79d
恩格尔巴特 Engelbart, Douglas (Carl) 美国计算机科学家 6—76e
恩格尔菲尔德 Englefield, Sir Francis 英格兰女王顾问 6—79e
恩格尔曼 Engelmann, George 美国植物学家 6—76f
恩格尔伍德 Englewood 美国城市 6—79f
恩格霍尔姆 Engholm, Björn 德国政治家 6—78b
恩格朗瓦 Ngelengwa (African ruler) 非洲统治者 12—160a
恩格勒 Engler, Adolf 德国植物学家 6—79e
恩格斯 Engels 俄罗斯城市 6—76f
恩格斯 Engels, Friedrich 德国哲学家 6—76f
恩根吉 Ngengi, Kamau (president of Kenya) 肯尼亚总统 12—160a
恩贡德人 Ngonde (people) 非洲民族 12—160c
恩古巴内 Ngubane, Jordan Kush 祖鲁族小说家 12—160e
恩古吉 Ngugi, wa Thiong'o 东非小说家 12—160f
恩古鲁 Nguru 尼日利亚城镇 12—161b
恩古尼人 Nguni 非洲民族 12—161a
恩基 Enki (Mesopotamian deity) 美索不达米亚神祇 6—84c
恩加 Enga 巴布亚新几内亚省份 6—76c
恩加达人 Ngada 印度尼西亚民族 12—159d
恩加丁 Engadin 瑞士谷地 6—76d
恩加米湖 Ngami, Lake 博茨瓦纳湖泊 12—159e
恩加诺岛 Enggano Island 印度尼西亚岛屿 6—77e
恩加塔 Ngata, Sir Apirana Turupa 新西兰毛利族领袖 12—159f
恩贾梅纳 N'Djamena 乍得首都 12—56e
恩卡纳西翁 Encarnación 巴拉圭城市 6—68e
恩卡伊 Nkayi 刚果城镇 12—210b
恩坎普 Encamp 安道尔村庄 6—68e
恩康桑巴 Nkongsamba 喀麦隆城镇 12—210d
恩科勒人 Nkole 非洲民族 12—210b
恩科莫 Nkomo, Joshua 津巴布韦民族主义领袖 12—210c
恩科塔科塔 Nkhotakota 马拉维城镇 12—210b
恩科西 Nkosi, Lewis 南非作家 12—210d
恩克 Encke, Johann Franz 德国天文学家 6—69f
恩克 Enke, Karin 德国速滑运动员 6—84b
恩克尔 Enckell, Rabbe (Arnfinn) 芬兰诗人 6—69f
恩克赫伊曾 Enkhuizen 荷兰城市 6—84c
恩克彗星 Encke's Comet 天文学 6—70a
恩克鲁玛 Nkrumah, Kwame 加纳民族领袖 12—210e
恩孔德人 Nkonde(people) 非洲民族 12—210d
恩奎斯特 Enquist, Per-Olov 瑞典作家 6—86b
恩赖特 Enright, D(ennis) J(oseph) 英国诗人 6—86c
恩利勒 Enlil 美索不达米亚神祇 6—85a
恩麦卡尔 Enmerkar 古代苏美尔人英雄 6—85a
恩梅开江 Nmai Hka 缅甸河流 12—211b
恩米巴拉格西 Enmebaragesi 巴比伦国王 6—85a
恩纳 Enna 意大利城市 6—85b
恩纳吉亚公司 Energia 俄罗斯航空公司 6—75c
恩内迪 Ennedi 乍得高原地区 6—85b
恩尼斯 Ennis 爱尔兰郡首府 6—85c
恩尼斯基林 Enniskillen 英国城镇 6—85d
恩尼乌斯 Ennius, Quintus 罗马诗人 6—85d
恩诺迪乌斯 Ennodius, Magnus Felix 拉丁语诗人 6—85e
恩潘盖尼 Empangeni 南非城镇 6—62f
恩培多克勒 Empedocles 希腊哲学家 6—63a
恩普森 Empson, Sir Richard 英格兰律师 6—65e
恩塞纳达 Ensenada 墨西哥城市 6—86d
恩塞纳达侯爵 Ensenada, Zenón de Somodevilla y Bengoechea, marqués de la (marquess of) 西班牙政治家、首相 6—86d
恩桑杰 Nsanje 马拉维城镇 12—285c
恩森 Emson, Sir Richard 英格兰律师 6—66c
恩舍尔兹维克 Örnsköldsvik 瑞典城市 12—469b
恩施 Enshi 中国城市 6—86e
恩斯 Enns 奥地利城镇 6—85e
恩斯赫德 Enschede 荷兰城市 6—86c
恩斯特 Ernest 统治者之名 6—120f
恩斯特 Ernst, Max 德国画家、雕刻家 6—121d
恩斯特 Ernst, Paul 德国作家 6—121e
恩斯特 Ernst, Richard R. 瑞士化学家 6—121f
恩斯特·奥古斯特 Ernest Augustus 汉诺威公爵和选侯 6—121a
恩斯特·奥古斯特 Ernest Augustus 汉诺威国王 6—121b
恩斯特·奥古斯特 Ernest Augustus 汉诺威选侯及国王之名 6—121a
恩斯特·奥古斯特(二世) Ernest Augustus (Ⅱ) 觊觎汉诺威王位者 6—121c
恩斯特二世 Ernest Ⅱ 萨克森-科堡-哥达公爵 6—120f
恩斯特·路易 Ernest Louis 黑森-达姆施塔特大公 6—121c
恩斯特一世 Ernest Ⅰ 萨克森-科堡-哥达公爵 6—120f
恩斯特一世 Ernest Ⅰ 萨克森-哥达-阿尔滕堡公爵 6—121a
恩苏卡 Nsukka 尼日利亚城市 12—285d
恩苏克什丹纳 Ensuhkeshdanna 古代苏美尔统治者 6—87c
恩索尔 Ensor, James (Sydney), Baron 比利时画家 6—87a
恩特雷里奥斯 Entre Ríos 阿根廷省份 6—89f
恩特普赖斯 Enterprise 美国城市 6—88e
恩图曼 Omdurman 苏丹城镇 12—414c
恩图曼战役 Omdurman, Battle of 埃及历史 12—414d
恩维尔帕夏 Enver Paşa 奥斯曼帝国将领 6—90e
恩维加多 Envigado 哥伦比亚城市 6—90f
恩西地毯 ensi rug 地板铺盖用品 6—86f
恩西纳 Encina, Juan del 西班牙剧作家 6—69e
恩西纳斯 Enzinas, Francisco de 西班牙学者 6—91d
恩辛加·姆维姆巴 Nzinga Mbemba 刚果王国国王 12—313e
恩泽库 Nzekwu, Onuora 尼日利亚教师 12—313c
恩泽雷科雷 Nzérékoré 几内亚城镇 12—313e
恩泽利港 Anzalī, Bandar-e 伊朗港口 1—403a
蒽 anthracene 化合物 1—379c
蒽醌 anthraquinone 化合物 1—379e
蒽醌染料 anthraquinone dye 纺织 1—379f
儿茶 catechu 植物提取物 3—523a
儿茶酚胺 catecholamine 化合物 3—523a
儿歌 nursery rhyme 文学 12—303e
儿科 pediatrics 医学专科 13—119d
儿科疾病 childhood diseases and disorders 疾病 4—153c
儿童发展 child development 行为学过程 4—151c
儿童法院 children's court (law) 法律 4—153f
儿童福利 child welfare 社会学 4—152b
儿童精神病学 child psychiatry 医学 4—151e
儿童剧团 children's company 英国戏剧 4—153e
儿童十字军 Children's Crusade 欧洲历史 4—153f
儿童文学 children's literature 文学作品 4—154b
儿童心理学 child psychology 心理学 4—152a
儿童牙科 pedodontics 医学专科 13—120b
儿童游戏 children's game 游戏 4—153f
儿童之家 children's house 学前教育 4—154a
儿玉源太郎 Kodama Gentarō 日本政治家 9—331f
鸸鹋 emu 鸟类 6—66c
鸸鹋鹩莺 emu-wren 鸟类 6—66e
鲕粒 oölite 岩石 12—424c
鲕绿泥石 chamosite 矿物 4—39e

尔德 ʻĪd 伊斯兰教节日 8—317f
尔格 erg 计量单位 6—114e
尔龚语 Ergong language 中国语言 6—114f
尔苏语 Ersu language 中国语言 6—123e
《尔雅》 Erya 中国古典文学 6—124e
耳 ear 解剖学 5—495b
耳鲍 ear shell 贝类 5—495e
耳喉科学 otolaryngology 医学 12—498c
耳环 earring 垂饰物 5—497e
耳机 earphone 电声转换器 5—497d
耳挤压症 ear squeeze 疾病 5—495e
耳廓 auricle 解剖学 2—59a
耳鸣 tinnitus 病理现象 17—106b
耳栓 earplug 装饰品 5—497d
耳堂 transept 建筑 17—195e
耳形图案 auricular style 装饰艺术 2—59a
耳硬化 otosclerosis 疾病 12—498e
耳语音 whisper 语音 18—225f
洱海 Erhai 中国湖泊 6—115c
铒 erbium 化学元素 6—112c
二苯氮䓬类药物 dibenzazepine 抗抑郁药 5—293c
二长岩 monzonite 矿物 11—375b
二齿兽 cynodont 古生物学 5—89d
二齿兽属 Dicynodon 古生物学 5—302e
二醇 glycol 化合物 7—166b
二次方程 quadratic equation 数学 14—71e
二等兵 private 军衔 13—521e
二叠纪 Permian Period 地质学 13—174b
二叠纪盆地 Permian Basin 美国沉积盆地 13—174a
二段式 binary form 音乐 2—476b
二噁英 dioxin 化合物 5—331b
二分点 equinox 天文学 6—108e
二分点风暴 equinoctial storm 气象学 6—108d
二分法 dichotomy 逻辑 5—294d
二宫尊德 Ninomiya Sontoku 日本土地改革家 12—199a
二硅酸盐 disilicate(mineralogy) 矿物 5—340d
二合元音 diphthong 语音学 5—331e
二胡 erhu 中国乐器 6—115d
二极管 diode 电子管 5—326a
二甲苯 xylene 化合物 18—399e
二甲基氨基乙基苯基苯胺 dimethylaminoethylbenzanilide 药物 5—318d
二甲基色胺 DMT 药物 5—352e
二甲亚砜 dimethyl sulfoxide 化合物 5—318c
二尖瓣关闭不全 mitral insufficiency 疾病 11—292b
二尖瓣狭窄 mitral stenosis 疾病 11—292c
二进制数系 binary number system 数学 2—476b
二里头文化 Erlitou culture 中国早期青铜器文化 6—120c
二连浩特 Erenhot 中国城市 6—113f
二硫化碳 carbon disulfide 化合物 3—444b
二律背反 antinomy 哲学 1—390c
二氯苯 dichlorobenzene 化合物 5—294c
二氯二苯基三氯乙烷 dichlorodiphenyltrichloroethane 化合物 5—294c
二氯化汞 bichloride of mercury 化合物 2—461c
二氯甲烷 dichloromethane 化合物 5—294d
二论 Dvaita 印度哲学学派 5—483f
二茂铁 ferrocene 化合物 6—293b
二难推理 dilemma 逻辑学 5—315e
二胚虫 dicyemid 寄生虫 5—302e
二七惨案 February Seventh Massacre 中国历史 6—259c
二七年一代 1927,Generation of 西班牙诗人、作家 12—196f
二千畿尼赛 Two Thousand Guineas 英国马赛 17—303f
二巯基丙醇 dimercaprol 药物 5—318c
二区轮作制 two-field system 农业耕作体制 17—303d
二十六 Twenty-six 游戏 17—302d
二十人画派 Vingt,Les 艺术家团体 18—1d
二十人画社 Twenty,The Society of the (art) 艺术家团体 17—302a
二十世纪福斯影片公司 Twentieth Century-Fox Film Corporation 美国公司 17—301e
二十世纪运动 Novecento movement 意大利画家团体 12—279e
《二十四史》 Chinese history,24-set series of 中国史书 4—170d
《二十五条信纲》 Twenty-five Articles of Religion 基督教信仰纲要 17—302b
二十一点 Blackjack 纸牌游戏 2—519e
二十一条 Twenty-one Demands 中国历史 17—302c
二世 Nisei 美籍日裔 12—201f
二糖 disaccharide 生物化学 5—338b
二天 Niten (Japanese artist) 日本艺术家 12—203a
二条良基 Nijo Yoshimoto 日本诗人 12—191d
二头肌 biceps muscle 解剖学 2—460f
二王 Ni-ō 日本佛教神话护教神 12—162d
二项式定理 binomial theorem 数学 2—479a
二形翼龙属 Dimorphodon 古生物学 5—319c
二溴化乙烯 dibromoethane 化合物 5—293e
二氧化硅 silica 化合物 15—368e
二氧化碳 carbon dioxide 化合物 3—444a
二叶亭四迷 Futabatei Shimei 日本小说家 6—534a
二乙醚 diethyl ether 化合物 5—307d
二乙酰吗啡 diacetylmorphine (drug) 药物 5—283c
二音步 dipody 诗歌韵律 5—333c
二元论 dualism 哲学 5—438b
二元论 dualism 宗教 5—437e
二元制王朝 Dual Monarchy 奥匈帝国史 5—437d
二元组织 dual organization 社会学 5—437d
二月 February 历法 6—259c
二月革命 February Revolution 俄国历史 6—259c
二月三日站 Tres de Febrero 阿根廷行政区 17—211c
二爪猎蛛 two-clawed hunting spider 蛛形纲动物 17—303d
二征 Trung Sisters 越南英雄 17—244e
二趾树懒 unau 哺乳动物 17—338e

F

发电机 electric generator 机器 6—21b
发电机理论 dynamo theory 物理学 5—488e
发电站乐队 Kraftwerk 德国乐队 9—369f
发动机 engine 机器 6—78b
发光 luminescence 物理学 10—280f
发光虫 glowworm 昆虫 7—163a
发光器 photophore 发光动物器官 13—266a
发光强度 luminous intensity 物理学 10—281f
发光涂料 luminous paint 化工 10—282a
发光藓 luminous moss 植物 10—281f
发酵 fermentation 化学反应 6—285e
发酵粉 baking powder 焙烤食品用发酵剂 2—157e
发句 hokku (Japanese poetry) 日本文学 8—122f
发罗拉 Vlorë 阿尔巴尼亚海港 18—31a
《发罗拉宣言》 Vlorë proclamation 巴尔干历史 18—31b
发热 fever 病理现象 6—299f
发嗓音 vocalization 动物学 18—31f
发色团 chromophore 化学 4—212d
发射星云 emission nebula 天文学 6—61e
发身期 puberty 人类生理学术语 14—3c
发生炉煤气 producer gas 化合物 13—527c
发声 sound production 动物学 15—528c
发网菌属 Stemonitis 生物学 16—217a

"发现者"号卫星 Discoverer 美国实验卫星系列 5—339d
发癣菌属 Trichophyton 真菌 17—216f
发芽 budding 无性繁殖形式 3—229c
发音 articulation 语音学 1—529f
发育 development 生物学 5—270e
发育不全 agenesis 病理现象 1—120c
发育异常 dysplasia 病理现象 5—489f
发展心理学 developmental psychology 心理学 5—271c
发作性睡病 narcolepsy 疾病 11—575c
伐诃那 vāhana 印度教神话 17—443d
伐卡塔卡王朝 Vākāṭaka Dynasty 印度王朝 17—446c
伐腊毗 Valabhī 古印度城市 17—446f
伐腊毗 Vallabha 印度教哲学家 17—453d
伐腊毗派 Vallabhācārya 印度教教派 17—453d
伐兰狄甘 Vallandigham, Clement L(aird) 美国政治家 17—453f
伐丽流 Wareru 缅甸勃固国王 18—106c
伐楼拿 Varuṇa 印度教神灵 17—475e
伐佐夫 Vazov, Ivan (Minchov) 保加利亚文学家 17—483f
罚款 amercement 英国法律 1—275a
阀 valve 控制流体的装置 17—457a
阀键 valve 音乐 17—457d
筏 raft 水运工具 14—122b
筏驮摩那 Vardhamāna (Jainist teacher) 耆那教祖师 17—471d
筏罗诃 Varāha 印度教大神化身 17—470e
筏摩那 Vāmana 印度教大神化身 17—457e
法 dharma 印度教、佛教、耆那教名词 5—279a
法昂 Fa Ngum 老挝国王 6—204e
法贝尔·斯塔普伦西斯 Faber Stapulensis, Johannes 法国人文主义者 6—206a
法贝尔兄弟 Faber, Lothar von; and Faber, Eberhard 德国铅笔制造商 6—205f
法贝热 Fabergé, Peter Carl 俄国珠宝首饰匠人 6—206a
法本化学工业公司 IG Farben 德国公司 8—325c
法比安 Fabian, Warner 美国作家 6—206b
法比安,圣 Fabian, Saint 教皇 6—206b
法比奥拉,圣 Fabiola, Saint 意大利基督教信徒 6—206c
法布尔 Fabre, Émile 法国剧作家 6—207c
法布尔 Fabre, Jean Henri 法国昆虫学家 6—207c
法布尔·德格朗丁 Fabre d'Églantine, Philippe(-François-Nazaire) 法国剧作家 6—207d
法布里 Fabry, Charles 法国物理学家 6—208e
法布里蒂厄斯 Fabritius, Barent 荷兰画家 6—208b
法布里蒂厄斯 Fabritius, Carel 荷兰画家 6—208c
法布里齐 Fabrizi, Nicola 意大利复兴运动领袖 6—208d
法布里齐乌斯 Fabricius ab Aquapendente, Hieronymus 意大利外科医生 6—208a
法布里齐乌斯 Fabricius, Johann Christian 丹麦昆虫学家 6—207f
法布里齐乌斯·卢西努斯 Fabricius Luscinus, Gaius 罗马政治家 6—208b
法布里氏病 Fabry's disease 遗传性疾病 6—208e
法布里希乌斯 Fabricius, Johann Albert 德国学者 6—207e
法布里休斯 Fabricius, Johannes 荷兰天文学家 6—208a
法布里亚诺 Fabriano 意大利城镇 6—207e
法布里亚诺 Fabriano, Gentile da 意大利画家 6—207e
法常 Fa-ch'ang 中国画家 6—204e
法称 Dharmakīrti 印度佛教哲学家 5—279b
法代赫·辛格 Fateh Singh, Sant 印度锡克教领袖 6—248f
法道 sorcery 术士操纵自然力的举动 15—521a
法德 Fardd, Eben 威尔士诗人 6—238f
法登 Fadden, Sir Arthur William 澳大利亚总理 6—210c
法谛哈 fātiḥah 《古兰经》章节 6—250b
法蒂玛 Fāṭimah 伊斯兰教创始人之女 6—250c
法蒂玛 Fátima 葡萄牙村庄 6—250c
法蒂玛王朝 Fāṭimid dynasty 穆斯林王朝 6—250d
法蒂曼 Fadiman, Clifton 美国编辑、作家 6—210e
法典 law code 法律文件 9—528e
法定劳动 statute labour 徭役制度 16—203a
法定期限 prescription 法律 13—496d
法俄同盟 Dual Alliance 国际关系 5—437c
法厄同 Phaethon 希腊神话 13—217a
法恩海姆 Farnham, Eliza Wood Burhans 美国改革家、作家 6—242c
法恩群岛 Farne Islands 北海岛群 6—241f
法恩斯沃思 Farnsworth, Philo Taylor 美国电视先驱 6—242d
法恩扎 Faenza 意大利城镇 6—210f
法恩扎釉陶 Faenza majolica 意大利陶器 6—210f
法尔岛 Fire Island 美国长岛岸外大沙嘴 6—326d
法尔德 Fylde 英格兰区名 6—536f
法尔德 Fard, Wallace D. 美国宗教领袖 6—238e
法尔格 Fargue, Léon-Paul 法国诗人 6—239c
法尔卡 Falca, Pietro 威尼斯艺术家 6—219c
法尔康涅 Falconet, Étienne-Maurice 法国雕刻家 6—219f
法尔科内托 Falconetto, Giovanni Maria 意大利画家 6—220a
法尔克 Falke, Gustav 德国诗人、小说家 6—221c
法尔克 Falk, (Paul Ludwig) Adalbert 德国诗人、小说家 6—221b
法尔克贝格 Falkberget, Johan Petter 挪威小说家 6—221c
法尔孔 Falcón 委内瑞拉州名 6—219c
法尔芒 Farman, Henri 法国飞行员、飞机设计师 6—240f
法尔芒 Farman, Maurice 法国飞机制造家 6—240f
法尔茅斯 Falmouth 英格兰城镇 6—224d
法尔茅斯 Falmouth 美国城镇 6—224e
法尔纳巴佐斯 Pharnabazus 波斯军人、政治家 13—220d
法尔内塞 Farnese, Alessandro 教皇 6—242a
法尔内塞 Farnese, Alessandro, duca (duke) di Parma e Piacenza 尼德兰摄政 6—242a
法尔内塞府邸 Farnese, Palazzo 文艺复兴时建筑 6—242c
法尔内塞家族 Farnese family 意大利贵族家族 6—241f
法尔内塞剧院 Farnese, Teatro 意大利剧院 6—242c
法尔森 Falsen, Christian Magnus 挪威政治家 6—225f
法尔斯 Fārs 伊朗地理区域 6—244c
法尔斯塔夫 Falstaff, Sir John 喜剧人物 6—226a
法尔斯特岛 Falster 丹麦岛屿 6—226a
法尔斯湾 Valsbaai (South Africa) 南非海湾 17—456d
法尔斯语 Fārsī language 伊朗语言 6—244d
法夫 Fife 英国政务会辖区、历史郡 6—308f
法夫尔 Favre, Claude 法国语法学家 6—255a
法夫尔 Favre, (Gabriel-Claude-) Jules 法国外交部长 6—255a
法弗舍姆 Faversham 英国教区(城镇) 6—254e
法盖 Faguet, Émile 法国评论家 6—212d
法冈瓦 Fagunwa, D(aniel) O(lorunfemi) 尼日利亚作家 6—212e
法戈 Fargo 美国城市 6—239b
法戈 Fargo, William George 美国捷运业先驱 6—239b
法规 kanun 奥斯曼帝国法典 9—170c
法国 France 西欧国家 6—436b
法国巴黎银行 BNP Paribas 法国银行 2—553f
法国出租小马车 fiacre 交通工具 6—301b
法国大革命 French Revolution 法国历史 6—480e
法国东印度公司 French East India Company 法国贸易公司 6—477b
法国斗牛狗 French bulldog 狗品种 6—476d
法国-佛兰德斯学派 Franco-Flemish school (music) 音乐风格 6—446c
法国感伤喜剧 comédie-larmoyante 法国戏剧形式 4—379a
法国革命战争和拿破仑战争 French revolutionary and Napoleonic wars 欧洲历史 6—481e
法国工人民主联合会 French Democratic Confederation of Labour 法国

工会联盟 6—477a
法国公共马车 diligence 交通工具 5—316a
法国共产党 French Communist Party 法国政党 6—476e
法国共和历 French republican calendar 法国历法 6—480e
法国锅菜 cassoulet 食品 3—506d
法国国家图书馆 Bibliothèque Nationale 法国图书馆 2—460c
法国国营铁路公司 Société Nationale des Chemins de Fer Français (SNCF) 法国公司 15—477c
法国航空公司 Air France 法国航空机构 1—144b
法国花边 point de France 工艺品 13—388f
法国锦标赛 French Championships 国际网球赛 6—476d
法国科学院 Sciences, Academy of 法国机构 15—143a
法国煤矿公司 Charbonnages de France 法国公司 4—61e
法国-尼德兰学派 Franco-Netherlandish school 音乐风格 6—446e
法国摄政时期风格 Régence style 装饰艺术 14—202a
法国新闻社 Agence France-Presse (AFP) 法国新闻机构 1—119e
法国兴业银行 Société Générale 法国银行 15—477c
法国艺术歌曲 mélodie 音乐 11—98e
法国印度公司 French India Company 法国贸易公司 6—478d
法国印度公司 Indes, Compagnie Française des 法国贸易公司 8—357b
法国总工会 French Confederation of Christian Workers 法国工人组织 6—477a
法国最高法院 Cour de Cassation 法国法律 4—546f
法哈尔多 Fajardo 波多黎各城镇 6—218e
法荷战争 Franco-Dutch War 欧洲历史 6—446c
法赫德 Fahd 沙特阿拉伯国王 6—212e
法赫尔丁·拉齐 Fakhr ad-Dīn ar-Rāzī 伊斯兰教义学家 6—218f
法赫鲁丁二世 Fakhr ad-Dīn II 黎巴嫩统治者 6—218e
法赫萨湾 Faxa Bay 冰岛海湾 6—255e
法吉宾湖 Faguibine, Lake 马里湖泊 6—212e
法吉达尔 fawjdār 印度莫卧儿王朝官职 6—255d
法吉尔 fakir 宗教名词 6—219a
法家 Legalism 中国哲学 9—560d
法杰恩 Farjeon, Eleanor 英国作家 6—240b
法捷耶夫 Fadeyev, Aleksandr 苏联作家 6—210d
法金汉 Falkenhayn, Erich (Georg Anton Sebastian) von 德意志帝国参谋总长 6—221d
法经 dharmasutra 印度法学 5—279e
《法句经》 Dhammapada 佛教经典 5—278e
法坎 Fakkān (United Arab Emirates) 阿联酋港口城镇 6—219a
法克塔 Facta, Luigi 意大利首相 6—210a
法夸尔 Farquhar, George 英国剧作家 6—243a
法拉 farad 计量单位 6—235b
法拉 Farāh 阿富汗城镇 6—237e
法拉 Farʿah, Tall al- 巴勒斯坦古代遗址 6—237f
法拉比 Fārābī, al- 穆斯林哲学家 6—235b
法拉德·穆罕默德 Farrad Mohammed 美国宗教领袖 6—243c
法拉第 faraday 计量单位 6—235c
法拉第 Faraday, Michael 英国科学家 6—235c
法拉第电解定律 Faraday's laws of electrolysis 化学 6—237d
法拉第感应定律 Faraday's law of induction 物理学 6—237c
法拉第效应 Faraday effect 物理学 6—237c
法拉杜法伊 Faradofay (Madagascar) 马达加斯加城镇 6—237e
法拉尔 Farrar, Geraldine 美国歌唱家 6—243d
法拉尔 Farrar, Margaret Petherdridge 美国报纸编辑 6—243e
法拉格特 Farragut, David (Glasgow) 美国海军上将 6—243c
法拉汗地毯 Ferahan carpet 伊朗工艺品 6—278e
法拉河 Farāh River 阿富汗河流 6—238a
法拉赫 Farah, Nuruddin 索马里作家 6—237e
法拉赫丘 Fa' rah, Tall (Iraq) 伊拉克古城 6—237f
法拉里斯 Phalaris 西西里的僭主 13—218b
法拉纳 Faranah 几内亚城镇 6—238a
法拉沙人 Falasha 非洲民族 6—219b
法拉兹达格 Farazdaq, al- 阿拉伯诗人 6—238b
法莱梅河 Falémé River 西非河流 6—220f
法莱斯 Falaise 丹麦城镇 6—219a
法赖吉 Faraj 埃及和叙利亚统治者 6—238a
法兰多拉舞 farandole 舞蹈 6—238b
法兰克福 Frankfort, Henri 美国考古学家 6—449b
法兰克福 Frankfort 美国肯塔基州首府 6—449a
法兰克福国民议会 Frankfurt National Assembly 德意志机构 6—449e
《法兰克福汇报》 Frankfurter Allgemeine Zeitung 德国报纸 6—450d
法兰克福香肠 frankfurter 食品 6—450a
法兰克福学派 Frankfurt School 德国学术派别 6—449f
法兰克尼亚 Franconia 德国历史地区 6—447b
法兰克-普罗旺斯方言 Franco-Provençal dialect 法国方言 6—446f
法兰克人 Frank 欧洲民族 6—447d
法兰绒 flannel 纺织物 6—348c
法兰绒木 flannelbush (*Fremontodendron californicum*) 植物 6—348c
法兰士约瑟夫地群岛 Franz Josef Land 俄罗斯群岛 6—454d
法兰西堡 Fort-de-France 法国海外省马提尼克岛首府 6—413c
法兰西岛 Île-de-France 法国大区 8—332e
法兰西岛方言 Francien *dialect* 古法兰西方言 6—440b
法兰西共同体 French Community 法兰西国家联盟组织 6—476f
法兰西归正 Reformed Church of France 法国基督教会 14—199e
法兰西国家 French State 法国历史 6—482d
法兰西海岸 French Shore 加拿大沿海地区 6—482c
法兰西剧院 Théâtre-Français, Le 法国剧院 17—18d
法兰西-坎塔布连艺术流派 Franco-Cantabrian school 欧洲史前艺术 6—446c
法兰西联邦 French Union 法兰西政治实体 6—482d
《法兰西晚报》 France-Soir 法国报纸 6—439a
法兰西喜剧院 Comédie-Française 法国国家剧院 4—378e
法兰西行动 Action Française 法国历史 1—60e
法兰西学院 France, Collège de 法国研究机构、教育中心 6—439a
法兰西学院 French Academy 法国文学院 6—475f
法兰西银行 France, Banque de 法国国家银行 6—438f
法郎 franc 货币单位 6—436a
法朗士 France, Anatole 法国作家 6—438d
法老 pharaoh 古埃及国王的通称 13—219d
法勒 Farrar, Frederic William 英国宗教作家 6—243d
法勒斯莱本 Fallersleben, August Heinrich Hoffmann von 德国爱国诗人 6—223d
法雷尔 Farrell, Eileen 美国高音歌唱家 6—243f
法雷尔 Farel, Guillaume 法国宗教改革家 6—239a
法雷尔 Farrell, James T(homas) 美国小说家 6—243f
法雷尔 Farrell, Suzanne 美国舞蹈家 6—244a
法雷尔 Farrer, William James 澳大利亚农业家 6—244b
法雷纳 Farina, Giuseppe 意大利赛车手 6—239e
法雷斯 Farès, Nabile 阿尔及利亚卡比尔族诗人 6—239a
法里阿 Fāriʿah, Tall al- 巴勒斯坦古代遗址 6—239c
法里埃罗 Falier, Marin 威尼斯执政 6—221a
法里博 Faribault 美国城市 6—239d
法里达巴德 Farīdābād 印度城镇 6—239d
法里德·奥丁·艾布·哈米德·穆罕默德 Farīd od-Dīn Abū-Ḥamīd Moḥammad 波斯诗人 6—239d
法里德果德 Farīdkot 印度城镇 6—239e
法里古勒 Farigoule, Louis-Henri-Jean 法国作家 6—239e
法里纳蒂 Farinati, Paolo 意大利画家 6—240a
法里纳奇 Farinacci, Prospero 意大利法学家 6—239f
法里纳奇 Farinacci, Roberto 意大利政客 6—239f
法里内利 Farinelli 意大利歌唱家 6—240a
法里尼 Farini, Luigi Carlo 意大利历史学家 6—240b
法里特汗 Farīd Khān 印度皇帝 6—239d

法里雅 Falla, Manuel de 西班牙作曲家 6—223a
法利 Farley, Harriet 美国作家、编辑 6—240c
法利 Farley, James A(loysius) 美国政治家 6—240d
法利埃 Fallières, (Clément-) Armand 法国总统 6—223d
法利人 Fali 喀麦隆民族 6—220f
法利赛人 Pharisee 犹太教派别 13—219d
法利希人 Falisci 意大利古代民族 6—221b
法利希语 Faliscan language 意大利语言 6—221b
法林 Farim 几内亚比绍城镇 6—239e
法林公司 Filene's 美国百货商店 6—314d
法隆寺 Hōryū Temple 日本佛教寺院 8—187f
法卢 Falloux, Frédéric-Alfred-Pierre, comte de 法国政治家 6—224c
法鲁 Faro 葡萄牙城市 6—242e
法鲁卡巴德-法塔赫格尔 Farrukhābād-cum-Fatehgarh 印度自治市 6—244c
法鲁克·贝格 Farrukh Beg 印度莫卧儿帝国画家 6—244b
法鲁克一世 Farouk I 埃及国王 6—243a
法吕迪 Faludi, Susan 美国女权主义者 6—226b
法律 law 社会科学 9—528a
法律冲突 laws, conflict of 法律 9—532e
法律格言 legal maxim 英美法采用的概括性命题 9—560b
《法律汇编》 Ecloga 拜占廷法律 5—525f
《法律入门》 Epanagoge 拜占廷法典 6—94b
法律上的假设 legal fiction 法律 9—560a
法律援助 legal aid 法律 9—559f
法律注释家 legal glossator 罗马法学者 9—560a
法伦 Falun 瑞典城镇 6—226b
法论 dharmashastra 古印度法学 5—279d
法罗 Faro 纸牌游戏 6—242e
法罗群岛 Faeroe Islands 丹麦自治社区 6—211b
法罗斯岛灯塔 Pharos of Alexandria 埃及亚历山大城港口古灯塔 13—220d
法罗斯语 Faeroese language 法罗群岛语言 6—211e
法洛 Farlow, William Gilson 美国植物病理学家 6—240e
法洛阶 Farlovian Stage 地质学 6—240d
法洛皮奥 Fallopius, Gabriel 意大利解剖学家 6—223f
法洛氏四联症 Fallot, tetralogy of 先天性心脏畸形 6—224a
法马古斯塔 Famagusta 塞浦路斯港口 6—226c
法玛 Fama 希腊罗马神话 6—226c
《法美同盟条约》 Franco-American Alliance 法国与北美殖民地协定 6—446b
法门阶 Famennian Stage 地质学 6—226e
法门寺塔基地宫 Famensi Pagoda, The Underground Palace at 中国佛教建筑 6—226f
法明顿 Farmington 美国康涅狄格州城镇 6—241d
法明顿 Farmington 美国缅因州城镇 6—241d
法明顿 Farmington 美国新墨西哥州城市 6—241e
法明顿河 Farmington River 利比里亚河流 6—241e
法默 Farmer, Fannie (Merritt) 美国烹饪专家 6—241a
法默 Farmer, James 美国民权活动家 6—241b
法纳 Fana 挪威卑尔根市一部分 6—232a
法纳 fana 苏非派禁欲修炼方法 6—232b
法纳比 Farnaby, Giles 英国作曲家 6—241e
法纳尔人 Phanariote 奥斯曼帝国文官 13—219a
法尼亚斯 Phanias 希腊哲学家 13—219c
法宁格 Feininger, Andreas (Bernhard Lyonel) 美国摄影家 6—266d
法宁格 Feininger, Lyonel (Charles Adrian) 美国美术家 6—266e
法农 Fanon, Frantz (Omar) 西印度群岛哲学家 6—233e
法诺 Fano 意大利城镇 6—233d
法奇软糖 fudge 食品 6—509f
法契内蒂 Facchinetti, Giovanni Antonio (pope) 教皇 6—209a
法然 Hōnen 日本高僧 8—153a
法萨卢斯战役 Pharsalus, Battle of 古罗马历史 13—220e
法萨诺 Fasano 教皇 6—244f
法塞特 Fassett, Cornelia Adele Strong 美国画家 6—246a
法绍达事件 Fashoda Incident 英法非洲领土之争 6—245d
法式薄饼 crepe 食品 5—6d
法式台球 French billiards 体育项目 6—476c
法式馅饼 pâté 食品 13—85a
法属阿法尔和伊萨领地 Afars and Issas, French Territory of the (Africa) 法国东非殖民地 1—103b
法属波利尼西亚 French Polynesia 法国海外领地 6—479e
法属赤道非洲 French Equatorial Africa 法属中非领地 6—477c
法属刚果 French Congo 法属中非领地 6—476f
法属圭亚那 French Guiana 法国海外省 6—477c
法属南方和南极领地 Terres Australes et Antarctiques Françaises 法国海外领地 16—555d
法属索马里 French Somaliland (Africa) 法属东非领地 6—482d
法属西非 French West Africa 法属非洲殖民地 6—482d
法属印度支那 French Indochina (Southeast Asia) 法属东南亚殖民地 6—478d
法术 magic 准宗教现象 10—381d
法斯 Faes, Pieter van der (Baroque portraitist) 英国画家 6—211e
法斯宾德 Fassbinder, Rainer Werner 德国导演 6—245f
法斯里历 Faṣlī era 印度历法 6—245e
法斯耐特杯 Fastnet Cup 帆船比赛奖 6—246f
法斯托夫 Fastolf, Sir John 英格兰军人 6—246f
法索伯顿 falsobordone 音乐 6—226a
法他摩根娜 Fata Morgana 传奇中的幻景 6—248c
法塔赫 Fatah 巴勒斯坦政治和军事组织 6—248c
法塔赫·阿里·沙阿 Fath ʿAlī Shāh 波斯国王 6—249b
法塔赫·阿里·提普 Fateh Ali Tipu (sultan of Mysore) 印度迈索尔苏丹 6—248f
法塔赫布尔 Fatehpur 印度城镇 6—249a
法塔赫布尔西格里 Fatehpur Sīkri 印度城镇 6—249a
法特米 Fatemi, Hosayn 伊朗政治家 6—249b
法庭代索 prosbul 犹太教律法用语 13—538b
法庭之友 amicus curiae 法律 1—288e
法瓦 Favart, Charles-Simon 法国戏剧家 6—254d
法瓦拉 Favara 意大利城镇 6—254d
法韦尔 Faber, Cecilia Böhl de 西班牙作家 6—205f
法位学 tagmemics 语言学 16—424e
法沃里努斯 Favorinus 罗马帝国哲学家 6—254e
法乌娜 Fauna 古罗马女神 6—252c
法乌努斯 Faunus 古意大利神灵 6—252e
法乌司密斯文化期工艺 Fauresmith industry 史前非洲石器工艺 6—253c
法西 Fassi, Carlo 意大利花样滑冰教练 6—246a
法西 Fasi, Rabbi Isaac 犹太学者 6—245e
法西利德斯 Fasilides 埃塞俄比亚皇帝 6—245e
法西斯 fasces 古罗马权力标志 6—244f
法西斯主义 fascism 极权主义政治运动 6—245b
法希 Fāsī, al- (traveler and writer) 非洲旅行家 6—245e
法希 Fāsī, al- 西北非学者 6—245e
法希尔 Fāshir, Al- 苏丹城镇 6—245d
法显 Faxian 中国东晋僧人、旅行家、翻译家 6—255e
法相宗 Faxiangzong 中国佛教学派 6—255f
法辛盖尔衬裙 farthingale 欧洲服装 6—244d
《法学汇编》 Pandects 古罗马文献 13—9c
法亚 Faya 乍得城市 6—256a
法亚尔岛 Faial Island 北大西洋葡属岛屿 6—213b
法扬斯 Fajans, Kasimir 美国物理化学家 6—218d
法伊夫 Phyfe, Duncan 美国家具设计师 13—270a
法伊夫 Fyffe, Will 苏格兰喜剧演员 6—536e
法医学 forensic medicine 医学分支学科 6—405d
法医学 medical jurisprudence 研究医学资料与法律问题关系的科

学 11—72a
法因斯 Fiennes, William 英国政治家 6—308c
法因斯坦 Feinstein, Dianne Goldman 美国政治家 6—266f
法因斯坦 Feinstein, Isidor (journalist) 美国新闻记者 6—267a
法英北美殖民地争夺战 French and Indian War 法英战争 6—476a
法尤姆 Fayyūm, al- 埃及省份 6—257a
法尤姆 Fayyūm, al- 埃及城市 6—257c
法尤姆城 Madīnat al-Fayyūm (Egypt) 埃及城镇 10—369b
法尤姆肖像 Fayum portrait 埃及殡葬肖像 6—256f
法语 French language 欧洲语言 6—478d
《法语宝库》 Tresor de la langue française 辞书 17—211e
《法语词典》 Dictionnaire de la langue française 法国辞书 5—302c
法语文学 French literature 文学 6—478f
《法语字顺类比词典》 Dictionnaire alphabétique et analogique de la langue française 法国辞书 5—302c
法院 court 法律 4—548e
法藏 Fazang 中国佛教大师 6—257c
法扎巴德 Faizābād 印度城市 6—218d
法正 alcalde 西班牙官员称谓 1—187c
珐花 fahua glaze 中国琉璃器物 6—213a
珐琅制品 enamelwork 工艺品 6—67d
帆 sail 船的风动设备 14—503d
帆板运动 windsurfing 体育项目 18—286e
帆布 duck 织物 5—445c
帆布背潜鸭 canvasback (species *Aythya valisineria*) 鸟类 3—416a
帆船 YACHTING 体育项目 16—158a
帆船 yacht 船舶 18—401e
帆船运动 sailing 体育项目 14—504a
帆鳉 molly 鱼类 11—323e
帆具 rigging 帆船装备 14—298b
帆水母 purple sail 刺胞动物 14—34b
帆蜥鱼 lancet fish 鱼类 9—473b
番红花 saffron (*Crocus sativus*) 草本植物 14—496e
番红花属 Crocus 植物学 5—22e
番荔枝 sweetsop (species *Annona squamosa*) 木本植物 16—381a
番荔枝科 Annonaceae 植物学 1—367b
番荔枝类 custard apple 植物学 5—77d
番木瓜 papaya (*Carica papaya*) 木本植物 13—22e
番茄 tomato (*Lycopersicon esculentum*) 草本植物 17—143d
番茄红素 lycopene 化合物 10—308e
番茄螟蛉 tomato fruitworm 昆虫 17—143e
番石榴 guava 木本植物 7—346a
番薯 sweet potato (*Ipomoea batatas*) 草本植物 16—379e
番薯属 Ipomoea 植物学 8—437a
番摊 Fan-Tan 赌博游戏 6—231b
番摊 Fan-Tan 纸牌游戏 6—231c
番西邦山 Fan Si Pan 越南最高峰 6—231b
番樱桃木 myrtlewood (tree) 木本植物 11—528f
番樱桃属 Eugenia 植物学 6—158a
翻板写字台 davenport 家具 5—166f
翻板桌 drop-leaf table 家具 5—427b
翻车鲀 mola 鱼类 11—314e
翻光面 facet 宝石抛光面 6—209b
翻滚花甲 tumbling flower beetle 昆虫 17—265f
翻石鹬 turnstone 鸟类 17—292b
藩 han 日本历史 7—451f
藩切 Phan Thiet 越南海港 13—219a
凡勃伦 Veblen, Thorstein (Bunde) 美国经济学家、社会学家 17—484b
凡城 Van 土耳其城市 17—458b
凡·戴克 Van Dyck, Sir Anthony 佛兰德斯画家 17—460e
凡岛 Fanø 丹麦岛屿 6—233d
凡尔登 Verdun 加拿大城市 17—513b
凡尔登 Verdun 法国城镇 17—513b
《凡尔登条约》 Verdun, Treaty of 欧洲历史 17—513c
凡尔登战役 Verdun, Battle of 第一次世界大战史 17—513c
凡尔纳 Verne, Jules 法国作家 17—520c
凡尔赛 Versailles 法国城市 17—525a
凡尔赛宫 Versailles, Palace of 法国国家地标建筑 17—525d
《凡尔赛和约》 Versailles, Treaty of 协约国与德国的条约 17—525c
凡·高 Gogh, Vincent (Willem) van 荷兰画家 7—183a
凡湖 Van, Lake 土耳其湖泊 17—458c
凡男爵 Fain, Agathon-Jean-François, Baron 法国历史学家 6—214b
矾 vitriol 化学 18—25c
矾红 iron red glaze 中国瓷釉彩料 8—451d
矾土 alumina 化合物 1—258d
钒(V) vanadium 化学元素 17—463a
钒钙铀矿 tyuyamunite 矿物 17—313b
钒酐 vanadic anhydride 化学 17—462f
钒钾铀矿 carnotite 矿物 3—471a
钒铅矿 vanadinite 矿物 17—462f
钒酸盐矿物 vanadate mineral 矿物 17—462e
烦恼 kilesa (Buddhism) 佛教哲学名词 9—278a
烦恼 kleśa (Buddhism) 佛教哲学名词 9—316e
樊焦 Fangio, Juan Manuel 阿根廷赛车手 6—233b
樊尚(博韦的) Vincent of Beauvais 法国学者 17—568b
樊尚(莱兰的) Vincent of Lérins, Saint 基督教神学家 17—568c
繁殖 propagation 园艺学术语 13—535a
反暴力伤害妇女局 Violence Against Women Office 美国政府机构 18—4a
反苯环丙胺 tranylcypromine 药物 17—201c
反驳陪审团 traverse jury 法律 17—204b
反刍动物 ruminant 偶蹄目反刍动物 14—448a
反氘核 antideuteron 物理学 1—384f
《反共产国际协定》 Anti-Comintern Pact 世界近代史 1—381a
反共济运动 Anti-Masonic Movement 美国历史 1—381c
反间谍 counterespionage 间谍活动 4—543c
反教权主义 anticlericalism 天主教 1—383e
反馈 feedback 生物学概念 6—264d
反馈抑制 feedback inhibition 生物化学 6—264d
《反扩大参政权者》 Anti-Suffragist, The 美国期刊 1—382b
反粒子 antiparticle 物理学 1—393b
反联邦党 Anti-Federalists 美国历史 1—381b
反流分布法 countercurrent distribution 化学 4—543b
反律法论 antinomianism 基督教神学 1—390c
反论 paradox 逻辑学 13—31b
反歧视行动 affirmative action 美国政治 1—103f
反气旋 anticyclone 气象学 1—384e
反情报 counterintelligence 反侦察措施 4—543d
反沙龙联盟 Anti-Saloon League 美国游说禁酒组织 1—381c
反射 reflection 物理学 14—197f
反射 reflex 生物学 14—198a
反射炉 reverberatory furnace 冶金学 14—251b
反圣灵派 Pneumatomachian 基督教异端 13—381a
反坦克武器 antitank weapon 武器 1—394f
反题 converse 逻辑学 4—474c
反铁磁性 antiferromagnetism 物理学 1—385b
反托拉斯法 antitrust law 法律 1—395b
反物质 antimatter 物理学 1—388c
反小说 antinovel 文学 1—390e
反信风 antitrade wind 气象学 1—395b
反应热 reaction, heat of 化学 14—175e
反应素 reagin 生物化学 14—177f
反应速率 reaction rate 化学 14—175f
反应停 thalidomide 化学药品 17—11f

反英雄 antihero 戏剧、故事中的人物 1—387e
反语 irony 语言表达方式 8—452b
反照率 albedo 天文学 1—176d
反质子 antiproton 物理学 1—394b
反中微子 antineutrino 物理学 1—390c
反中子 antineutron 物理学 1—390c
反转 inversion 化学 8—427d
反转录病毒 retrovirus 病毒 14—247c
反宗教改革 Counter-Reformation 基督教历史 4—543a
反嘴鸻科 Recurvirostridae 动物学 14—186c
反嘴鹬 avocet 鸟类 2—90d
返回诗节 antistrophe 诗歌 1—394f
返回性 homing 动物学 8—146b
犯意 mens rea 法律 11—118a
犯罪集团 syndicate 犯罪组织 16—402b
犯罪学 criminology 对犯罪非法律方面的研究 5—17c
犯罪与青少年犯罪 crime and delinquency 法律 5—12c
饭尾宗祇 Iio Sōgi 日本僧人 8—329e
饭冢 Iizuka 日本城市 8—329f
泛白细胞减少症 panleucopenia (disease of cats) 猫疾病 13—13f
泛大陆 Pangaea 地质学 13—11b
《泛大陆条约》 Transcontinental Treaty 世界历史 17—195b
泛函分析 functional analysis 数学 6—523e
泛化 generalization 心理学 7—57f
泛醌 ubiquinone 化合物 17—317c
泛灵论 animism 宗教最初形态 1—359e
泛美公路 Pan-American Highway 连接南北美洲的公路网 13—2d
泛美会议 Pan-American conferences 美洲国际会议 13—2c
泛美世界航空公司 Pan American World Airways, Inc. 美国公司 13—2e
泛美运动会 Pan American Sports Games 体育比赛 13—2d
泛日耳曼主义 Pan-Germanism 政治运动 13—3a
泛神论 pantheism 哲学 13—16a
泛斯堪的纳维亚主义 Pan-Scandinavianism 政治运动 13—3d
泛斯拉夫主义 Pan-Slavism 政治运动 13—3d
泛酸 pantothenic acid 水溶性维生素 13—16f
泛突厥主义 Pan-Turkism 政治运动 13—4a
泛乌拉尔阿尔泰主义 Pan-Turanianism 政治运动 13—4a
泛心论 panpsychism 哲学 13—15b
泛雅典娜节 Panathenaea 希腊宗教节日 13—7a
泛亚美国妇女组织 Organization of Pan Asian American Women 美国组织 12—458c
泛音 overtone 声学 12—512b
范艾伦 Van Allen, James Alfred 美国物理学家 17—458d
范艾伦辐射带 Van Allen radiation belt 空间科学 17—458e
范比伦 Van Buren 美国城市 17—458f
范布勒 Vanbrugh, Sir John 英国建筑师 17—463d
范布伦 Van Buren, Hannah 美国总统夫人 17—458f
范布伦 Van Buren, Martin 美国总统 17—459a
范成大 Fan Chengda 中国南宋诗人 6—230e
范畴 category 逻辑学 3—523c
范戴克 Van Dyke, Henry 美国作家 17—461a
范德比特 Vanderbilt, Amy 美国作家 17—466a
范德比尔特 Vanderbilt, Cornelius 美国航运和铁路巨头 17—466a
范德比尔特 Vanderbilt, William Henry 美国铁路巨头 17—466c
范德比尔特家族 Vanderbilt FAMILY 美国家族 17—465f
范德尔拜尔帕克 Vanderbijlpark 南非城镇 17—465e
范德格拉夫 Van de Graaff, Robert Jemison 美国物理学家 17—459b
范德格里夫特 Vandegrift, Alexander A(rcher) 美国军官 17—465d
范德胡斯特 Hulst, Hendrik Christoffel van de 荷兰天文学家 8—232a
范德林 Vanderlyn, John 美国画家 17—466c
范德曼 Van Deman, Esther Boise 美国考古学家 17—459c
范德曼 Van Deman, Ralph H(enry) 美国情报官员 17—459d
范德米尔 Meer, Simon van der 荷兰物理工程师 11—79f
范德珀莱 Van Depoele, Charles Joseph 美国发明家 17—459e
范德瓦耳斯 Waals, Johannes Diederik van der 荷兰物理学家 18—58c
范德瓦耳斯力 van der Waals forces 化学、物理学 17—459f
范德万特 Van Devanter, Willis 美国最高法院大法官 17—460a
范登堡 Vandenberg, Arthur H(endrick) 美国政治家 17—465e
范登布鲁克 Broek, J. H. van den 荷兰建筑师 3—174e
范迪门 Diemen, Anthony van 荷兰殖民地官员 5—305e
范迪门地区 Van Diemen's Land 澳大利亚旧区名 17—460b
范迪门湾 Van Diemen Gulf 印度洋海湾 17—460a
范蒂 Fanti, Manfredo 意大利将领 6—234c
范多伦 Van Doren, Carl (Clinton) 美国作家 17—460b
范多伦 Van Doren, Mark 美国诗人 17—460c
范范尼 Fanfani, Amintore 意大利总理 6—232c
范扶累克 Van Vleck, John H. 美国物理学家、数学家 17—462c
范海斯 Van Hise, Charles Richard 美国地质学家 17—461b
范亨尼普 van Gennip, Yvonne 荷兰速度滑冰运动员 17—461b
范霍恩 Van Horne, Sir William Cornelius 加拿大铁路官员 17—461c
范科特兰 Van Cortlandt, Stephanus 荷属美洲殖民地商人、官员 17—459b
范可尼氏综合征 Fanconi syndrome 疾病 6—232b
范克利克 Van Kleeck, Mary Abby 美国社会研究者、改革家 17—461c
范宽 Fan Kuan 中国北宋画家 6—231a
范勒伯格 Van Lerberghe, Charles 比利时诗人、作家 17—461e
范卢 Van Lew, Elizabeth L. 美国南北战争时密探 17—461e
范伦斯勒 Van Rensselaer, Mariana Alley Griswold 美国作家、评论家 17—462b
范洛 Van Loo, Charles-André 法国画家 17—461f
范曼德 Mander, Carel van 荷兰画家、诗人 10—454a
范内(老) Vane, Sir Henry, THE ELDER 英格兰政治家 17—466f
范内(小) Vane, Sir Henry, THE YOUNGER 英格兰清教徒 17—467a
范宁环礁 Fanning Atoll (Kiribati) 基里巴斯环礁 6—233c
范朋克 Fairbanks, Douglas 美国电影演员 6—215d
范皮布尔斯 Van Peebles, Melvin 美国制片人 17—462a
范思哲 Versace, Gianni 意大利时装设计师 17—524f
范托夫 Hoff, Jacobus Henricus van't 荷兰物理化学家 8—114f
范韦克滕 Van Vechten, Carl 美国作家 17—462c
范文程 Fan Wencheng 中国清代大臣 6—231c
范文澜 Fan Wenlan 中国历史学家 6—231d
范西塔特男爵(德纳姆的) Vansittart (of Denham), Robert Gilbert Vansittart, Baron 英国外交家、作家 17—468d
范肖 Fanshawe, Sir Richard, 1ST BARONET 英国诗人 6—233e
范宴 Han'en (Buddhist reformer) 日本佛教改革家 7—459a
范赞特 Van Zandt, Marie 美国歌剧演员 17—462d
范缜 Fan Zhen 中国南朝哲学家 6—231e
范仲淹 Fan Zhongyan 中国北宋政治家、文学家 6—231f
贩奴合同 asiento de negros 供应奴隶的协议 1—554a
梵 brahma 印度教 3—112c
梵蒂冈博物馆和美术馆 Vatican Museums and Galleries 美术收藏馆 17—480b
梵蒂冈城 Vatican City 欧洲国家 17—479e
梵蒂冈教皇宫 Vatican palace 教皇府邸 17—480b
梵蒂冈教廷图书馆 Vatican Apostolic Library 梵蒂冈官方图书馆 17—479d
梵社 Brahmo Samaj 印度教派别 3—113e
梵世间 brahma-loka 印度教、佛教 3—112d
《梵书》 Brāhmaṇa 印度教著作 3—112f
梵天 Brahmā 印度教 3—112b

梵天花 urena（*Urena lobata*） 植物 17—414c
梵行 brahmacharya 佛教 3—112d
梵语 Sanskrit language 印度语族语言 15—38d
梵语文学 Sanskrit literature 文学 15—38e
梵住 brahmavihāra 佛教哲学 3—113c
方 phon 响度单位 13—256d
方差 variance 数学 17—473b
方达 Fonda, Henry (Jaynes) 美国电影演员 6—391e
方达 Fonda, Jane 美国电影演员 6—391f
方丹 Fontaine, Hippolyte 法国工程师 6—392c
方丹戈 fandango 西班牙民间歌舞 6—232c
方丹-拉图尔 Fantin-Latour, Henri 法国画家 6—234d
方旦软糖 fondant 食品 6—392a
方鲷 boarfish 鱼类 2—555b
方法的怀疑 methodic doubt 哲学 11—158d
方沸石 analcime 矿物 1—309c
方格法 squaring 绘画 16—167e
方钴矿 skutterudite 矿物 15—423b
方黄铜矿 cubanite 矿物 5—48d
方济各(梅罗讷的) Francis of Meyronnes 法国哲学家 6—441f
方济各(阿西西的),圣 Francis of Assisi, Saint 方济各会创始人 6—441d
方济各(保拉的),圣 Francis of Paola, Saint 天主教小兄弟会创始人 6—441f
方济各(塞尔斯的),圣 Francis of Sales, Saint 天主教日内瓦主教 6—442a
方济各会士 Franciscan 方济各会成员 6—443e
方济各会属灵派修士 Spiritual 基督教 16—35d
方尖碑 obelisk 纪念碑 12—318a
方解石 calcite 矿物 3—335c
方块杰克 Jack of Diamonds 俄国艺术家团体 8—503c
方块舞 square dance 美国舞蹈 16—167b
方镁石 periclase 矿物 13—167c
方钠石 sodalite 矿物 15—482e
方硼石 boracite 矿物 3—43c
方旗骑士 banneret 欧洲中世纪荣誉称号 2—207a
方铅矿 galena 矿物 6—552c
方石英 cristobalite 矿物 5—18e
《方士秘录》 Chilam Balam, Books of 马雅文学 4—150d
方塔娜 Fontana, Lavinia 意大利画家 6—393c
方头鱼 tilefish 鱼类 17—95e
方钍石 thorianite 矿物 17—56c
方尾鳟 squaretail (trout) 鱼类 16—167e
方向场 direction field 数学 5—336e
方形钢琴 square piano 乐器 16—167c
方言 dialect 语言 5—285a
方言学 dialectology 语言学 5—285d
方彝 fangyi 中国青铜器 6—233c
方以智 Fang Yizhi 中国明清思想家、科学家 6—233a
方照 quadrature 天文学 14—71f
方阵 phalanx 军事学 13—218a
方柱石 scapolite 矿物 15—103d
芳丹 Fontanne, Lynn 美国演员 6—393e
芳蒂联邦 Fanti confederacy 非洲历史 6—234d
芳蒂人 Fanti 非洲民族 6—234b
芳人 Fang 非洲民族 6—232f
芳汀那干酪 Fontina 意大利干酪 6—394d
芳廷 Fonteyn, Dame Margot 英国芭蕾舞家 6—394b
芳香树 perfume tree 木本植物 13—165e
芳香族化合物 aromatic compound 化合物 1—511a
钫(Fr) francium 化学元素 6—444a
防波堤 breakwater 防波工程结构 3—134e
防弹背心 bulletproof vest 防护衣 3—248a
防毒面具 gas mask 防化装备 7—22f
防府 Hōfu 日本城市 8—118c
防腐剂 antiseptic 生物化学 1—394e
防腐剂 preservative 生物化学 13—497a
防染印花 resist printing 纺织工业 14—240b
防线 limes 罗马史 10—104a
防御机制 defense mechanism 精神分析学 5—208c
《防止核扩散条约》 Non-proliferation of Nuclear Weapons, Treaty on the 国际协定 12—228a
妨害行为 nuisance 法律 12—293f
妨害治安 disorderly conduct 法律 5—341c
房间隔缺损 atrial septal defect 病理现象 2—35f
房山 Fangshan 中国北京市辖区 6—233b
房屋建造 building construction 建筑 3—237e
房总半岛 Bōsō Peninsula 日本半岛 3—61e
鲂鮄 sea robin 鱼类 15—167c
仿佛哲学 as if, philosophy of 哲学 1—537f
仿哥特式建筑 Gothic Revival 建筑学 7—224f
仿金铜 ormolu 铜锌合金 12—466f
仿马约利卡陶器 mezza majolica 陶器 11—172e
仿生学 bionics 边缘学科 2—484e
仿洋瓷器 Jesuit ware 中国瓷器 9—5e
仿英雄体诗 mock-epic 文学 11—302f
纺车 spinning wheel 纺织 16—32d
纺锤䗴 Fusulina 古生物学 6—533f
纺纱 spinning 纺织 16—32c
纺织品 textile 纺织 17—7b
纺足虫 embiid (insect) 昆虫 6—56f
放大机 enlarger 摄影设备 6—84c
放大率 magnification 光学 10—392c
放大器 amplifier 电子学 1—300b
放电灯 electric discharge lamp 照明器件 6—20c
放火 arson 刑法 1—520e
放弃 abandonment 财产法 1—5b
放射虫 radiolarian 原生动物 14—117c
放射黏孢子虫 actinomyxidian 微生物 1—60d
放射系 radioactive series 物理学 14—115c
放射性 radioactivity 物理学 14—115e
放射性沉降 fallout 核物质沉积作用 6—224b
放射性沉降 radioactive fallout 物理学 14—115b
放射性活度 activity 物理学 1—61d
放射性碳年代测定法 radiocarbon dating 年代学 14—117b
放射性同位素 radioactive isotope 化学 14—115b
放射学 radiology 医学 14—117c
放射治疗学 radiation therapy 医学 14—110f
放射状花边 nanduti 工艺品 11—554b
放线菌 actinomycete 微生物 1—60c
放线菌病 actinomycosis 疾病 1—60c
放映机 projector 放映影片的器械 13—531a
放逐 banishment 法律 2—203a
飞边 ruff 服饰 14—443a
飞标 boomerang 投掷器 3—39d
飞尘腐蚀法 aquatint 印刷术 1—427b
飞弹 flying bomb 武器 6—381c
飞碟 flying saucer 不明飞行物 6—382a
飞鲂鮄 flying gurnard 鱼类 6—381f
飞狐 flying fox 哺乳动物 6—381f
飞狐猴 flying lemur (mammal) 哺乳动物 6—382a
飞虎队 Flying Tigers 美国空军援华抗日机构 6—382d
飞蝗类 locust 昆虫 10—182d
飞机 airplane 航空器 1—147c
飞轮 flywheel 机器组件 6—383a
飞鸟乐队 Byrds, the 美国乐队 3—299d

飞鸟时代 Asuka period 日本历史 2—10c
飞蓬 fleabane 植物 6—354b
飞人舞 voladores, juego de los 舞蹈 18—34b
飞驒山脉 Hida Range 日本山脉 8—70f
飞蛇 flying snake 爬行动物 6—382a
飞升 levitation 巫术 10—48b
飞鼠 flying squirrel 啮齿动物 6—382b
飞艇 airship 航空器 1—148b
飞蜥属 Draco 动物学 5—409a
飞翔 flight 动物行动方式 6—360c
飞行堡垒 Flying Fortress (U.S. aircraft) 军用飞机 6—381f
飞行记录器 flight recorder 记录仪器 6—360d
飞行竞赛 air racing 航空 1—145c
飞行模拟机 flight simulator 飞行训练仪器 6—360e
飞行医生服务 flying doctor service 医疗服务 6—381d
飞行玉米卷兄弟乐队 Flying Burrito Brothers, the 美国乐队 6—381c
飞絮柳 pussy willow 木本植物 14—37a
飞燕草 larkspur 植物 9—500e
飞燕草属 Delphinium 植物学 5—230b
飞鱼 flying fish 鱼类 6—381e
非暴力反抗 civil disobedience 政治 4—253d
非标准分析 nonstandard analysis 微积分 12—230a
非常征用 angary 国际法 1—340b
非对映异构体 diastereoisomer 化学 5—290c
非法集会 unlawful assembly 法律 17—401c
非法侵入 trespass 法律 17—211e
非法占有 adverse possession 法律 1—90a
非婚生 illegitimacy 法律 8—334c
非金属 nonmetal 化学 12—229b
非均相反应 heterogeneous reaction 化学 8—61f
非理性主义 irrationalism 哲学 8—453a
非利士人 Philistine 古代民族 13—242b
非命 ajiva 耆那教 1—151a
非欧几里得几何 non-Euclidean geometry 几何学 12—227e
非热带性口炎性腹泻 nontropical sprue 疾病 12—230e
非斯 Fès 摩洛哥城市 6—295e
非同成分熔化 incongruent melting 物理学 8—353e
非谐音 cacophony 文学 3—310f
非性病性梅毒 bejel 疾病 2—347f
非虚构小说 nonfiction novel 文学 12—228c
非预谋杀人 manslaughter 法律 10—473b
非整倍性 aneuploidy (biology) 生物学 1—339d
非整比化合物 nonstoichiometric compound 化合物 12—230c
非正式婚姻 common-law marriage 法律 4—388b
非政府组织 nongovernmental organization (NGO) 民间志愿组织 12—228e
非指导式心理治疗 nondirective psychotherapy 心理治疗方法 12—228c
非洲 Africa 世界第二大洲 1—107c
非洲-阿拉伯大裂谷 Afro-Arabian Rift Valley (Africa) 东非峡谷 1—112d
非洲艾虎 zorille (*Ictonyx* [sometimes *Zorilla*] *striatus*) 哺乳动物 18—567e
非洲艾鼬 African polecat 哺乳动物 1—111b
非洲俾格米地域人种 African Pygmy local race 人类学 1—111b
非洲传教会 Missionaries of Africa, Society of 天主教组织 11—278e
非洲刺毛鼠 spiny mouse 啮齿动物 16—34a
非洲丛伯劳 bush-shrike' 鸟类 3—283a
非洲工会统一组织 African Trade Union Unity, Organization of (OATUU) 非洲工人组织 1—111f
非洲国家杯 African Cup of Nations 非洲足球比赛 1—109e
非洲荷兰归正会 Dutch Reformed Church in Africa 南非基督教组织 5—481b
非洲经济发展阿拉伯银行 Arab Bank for Economic Development in Africa 阿拉伯金融组织 1—429d
非洲开发银行 African Development Bank (ADB) 非洲金融组织 1—109e
非洲猎狗 African hunting dog (species *Lycaon pictus*) 狗品种 1—110a
非洲猎狮狗 African lion dog 狗品种 1—110f
非洲流行音乐 African popular music 非洲流行音乐 1—111b
非洲马病 African horse sickness (AHS) 马病 1—110a
非洲人国民大会 African National Congress (ANC) 南非政党 1—110f
非洲人美以美会 African Methodist Episcopal Church 美国基督教 1—110f
非洲人美以美锡安会 African Methodist Episcopal Zion Church 美国基督教 1—110f
非洲树蛇 boomslang (*Dispholidus typus*) 爬行动物 3—39e
非洲水羚 waterbuck 哺乳动物 18—139f
非洲统一组织 African Unity, Organization of (OAU) 非洲组织 1—112a
非洲希腊正教会 African Greek Orthodox Church 东非基督教 1—109f
非洲蚁熊 African ant bear 哺乳动物 1—109b
非洲艺术 African arts 非洲本土艺术 1—109b
非洲运动会 African Games 体育 1—109f
非洲之星 Star of Africa 钻石 16—196c
非洲中心论 Afrocentrism 文化、政治运动 1—112e
非洲诸语言 African languages 语言 1—110b
非洲猪热 African swine fever 猪病 1—111e
非洲锥虫病 nagana 牲畜疾病 11—538d
非洲紫罗兰 African violet 草本植物 1—112a
菲埃希 Fieschi, Giuseppe Maria 法国密谋者 6—308d
菲奥德兰 Fiordland (region, New Zealand) 新西兰地区 6—323f
菲奥雷 Fiore, Pasquale 意大利法学家 6—324a
菲奥雷利 Fiorelli, Giuseppe 意大利考古学家 6—324b
菲奥里洛 Fiorillo, Tiberio 意大利喜剧演员 6—324b
菲比霸鹟 phoebe 鸟类 13—255a
菲比岛 Phoebe Island (Pacific Ocean) 太平洋岛屿 13—255b
菲比格 Fibiger, Johannes (Andreas Grib) 丹麦病理学家 6—301e
菲布拉别针 fibula 服饰 6—302e
菲查伦 Fitzalan, Henry 英格兰贵族 6—338a
菲查伦 Fitzalan, Richard 英王查理二世反对者 6—338a
菲查伦 Fitzalan, Thomas 英格兰财政大臣 6—338a
菲茨奥斯本 FitzOsbern, William, 1st Earl of Hereford, Seigneur de Breteuil 法国贵族 6—339e
菲茨奥斯伯特 FitzOsbert, William 英格兰平民领袖 6—339f
菲茨赫伯特(夫人) Fitzherbert, Maria (Anne) 威尔士亲王秘密妻子 6—339d
菲茨吉本 Fitzgibbon, John 爱尔兰大法官 6—339d
菲茨吉本 Fitzgibbon, Sister Irene 美国天主教修女 6—339c
菲茨杰拉德 Fitzgerald 美国城市 6—338a
菲茨杰拉德 FitzGerald, Edward 英国作家 6—338a
菲茨杰拉德 Fitzgerald, Ella 美国歌唱家 6—338c
菲茨杰拉德 Fitzgerald, F(rancis) Scott (Key) 美国小说家 6—338d
菲茨杰拉德 FitzGerald, Garret (Michael) 爱尔兰总理 6—338f
菲茨杰拉德 FitzGerald, George Francis 爱尔兰物理学家 6—338f
菲茨杰拉德 Fitzgerald, Gerald 爱尔兰贵族 6—339a
菲茨杰拉德 Fitzgerald, James Fitzmaurice 爱尔兰贵族 6—339a
菲茨杰拉德 Fitzgerald, Lord Edward 爱尔兰起义者 6—338b
菲茨杰拉德 Fitzgerald, Robert 美国诗人、教育家 6—339b
菲茨杰拉德 FitzGerald, R.D. 澳大利亚诗人 6—339b
菲茨杰拉德 Fitzgerald, Thomas 爱尔兰起义领袖 6—339c
菲茨罗伊 Fitzroy, Augustus Henry 英国首相 6—339f

菲茨罗伊 Fitzroy, Henry 英格兰王子 6—339f
菲茨罗伊 Fitzroy, James 英格兰王位要求者 6—340a
菲茨罗伊 Fitzroy, Robert 英国海军军官、地理学家 6—340a
菲茨罗伊河 Fitzroy River 澳大利亚西北部河流 6—340a
菲茨罗伊河 Fitzroy River 澳大利亚东部河流 6—340b
菲茨莫里斯 Fitzmaurice, William Petty- 英国首相 6—339e
菲茨尼尔 Fitzneale, Richard 英格兰财政大臣 6—339e
菲茨威廉博物馆 Fitzwilliam Museum 英国艺术博物馆 6—340e
菲茨沃尔特 Fitzwalter, Robert 英格兰贵族领袖 6—340e
菲茨沃尔特子爵 Fitzwalter, Thomas Radcliffe, Viscount 英格兰外交使臣 6—340e
菲茨西蒙斯 Fitzsimmons, Fat Freddie 美国棒球运动员 6—340c
菲茨西蒙斯 Fitzsimmons, Robert 美国拳击运动员 6—340c
菲茨西蒙斯 Fitzsimmons, Sunny Jim 美国驯马师 6—340d
菲茨锡德马 Fitzthedmar, Arnold 英格兰高级市政官 6—340d
菲德勒 Fiedler, Arthur 美国音乐家 6—304c
菲德勒 Fiedler, Leslie 美国文学评论家 6—304d
菲登扎 Fidenza 意大利城镇 6—304b
菲狄斯 Fides 古罗马女神 6—304b
菲迪亚斯 Phidias 雅典雕刻家 13—226c
菲敦 Pheidon 阿尔戈斯国王 13—222e
菲顿 Fitton, Mary 文学人物 6—337f
菲尔比 Philby, H. Saint John 英国探险家 13—232a
菲尔比 Philby, Kim 英国情报官员 13—232b
菲尔波 Firpo, Louis 阿根廷职业拳击手 6—328e
菲尔波茨 Phillpotts, Eden 英国作家、戏剧家 13—243f
菲尔波茨 Phillpotts, Henry 英国圣公会主教 13—244a
菲尔布里克 Philbrick, Herbert Arthur 美国特工人员 13—232a
菲尔茨 Fields, Dame Gracie 英国喜剧演员 6—307e
菲尔德 Field, Cyrus W(est) 美国金融家 6—304e
菲尔德 Field, David Dudley 美国律师 6—304e
菲尔德 Field, Eugene 美国诗人 6—305a
菲尔德 Field, John 爱尔兰作曲家 6—305b
菲尔德 Field, Marshall 美国商人 6—305b
菲尔德 Field, Nathan 英国演员 6—305c
菲尔德 Field, Stephen J(ohnson) 美国最高法院大法官 6—305c
菲尔德自然历史博物馆 Field Museum of Natural History 美国博物馆 6—306d
菲尔登 Fielden, John 英国激进改革家 6—306e
菲尔丁 Fielding, Henry 英国小说家 6—306f
菲尔丁 Fielding, Sir John 英国法官 6—307c
菲尔丁 Fielding, William Stevens 加拿大新闻记者 6—307d
菲尔多西 Ferdowsī 波斯诗人 6—282e
菲尔莫尔 Fillmore 美国城市 6—315b
菲尔默 Filmer, Sir Robert 英国政治理论家 6—316d
菲尔讷 Furnes (Belgium) 比利时城市 6—530a
菲尔诺 Furneaux, Tobias 英国探险家 6—529f
菲尔绍 Virchow, Rudolf (Carl) 德国病理学家、人类学家 18—5f
菲尔斯滕瓦尔德 Fürstenwalde 德国城市 6—531d
菲尔特 Fürth 德国城市 6—531e
菲尔希纳 Filchner, Wilhelm 德国探险家 6—314a
菲尔希纳冰架 Filchner Ice Shelf 南极洲冰架 6—314a
菲尔谢(沙特尔的) Fulcher of Chartres 法国随军牧师 6—517d
菲尔兹 Fields, Dorothy 美国诗人、作家 6—307e
菲尔兹 Fields, James T(homas) 美国出版家 6—307e
菲尔兹 Fields, Lew 美国喜剧演员 6—307f
菲尔兹 Fields, W.C. 美国演员 6—307f
菲尔兹奖 Fields Medal 数学奖 6—308b
菲菲内拉 Fifinella 英国纯种赛马 6—309b
菲弗 Feiffer, Jules 美国漫画家 6—266a
菲盖拉-达福什 Figueira da Foz 葡萄牙港市 6—310f
菲格 Figg, James 英国拳击运动员 6—310b
菲格雷多 Figueiredo, João Baptista de oliveira 巴西总统 6—310f
菲格雷斯·费雷尔 Figueres Ferrer, José 哥斯达黎加总统 6—311a
菲格涅尔 Figner, Vera Nikolayevna 俄国民粹派领导人 6—310e
菲古卢斯 Figulus, Daniel Ernst 德国神学家 6—311c
菲古卢斯 Figulus, Publius Nigidius 罗马学者、作家 6—311c
菲吉格 Figuig 摩洛哥城镇 6—311b
菲克塞尔 Füchsel, Georg Christian 德国地质学家 6—508e
菲拉德尔斐亚 Philadelphia (Jordan) 约旦首都 13—226e
菲拉赫 Villach 奥地利城市 17—562f
菲拉加托 Filagato, Giovanni 敌对教皇 6—313b
菲拉雷特 Filarete 意大利建筑师、作家 6—313c
菲拉雷特 Philaret 俄罗斯正教牧首 13—230f
菲拉雷特 Philaret 俄罗斯正教神学家 13—231a
菲拉列托斯 Philaretus 佛兰芒哲学家 13—231b
菲莱 Philae 埃及小岛 13—230a
菲莱蒙 Philemon 雅典新喜剧诗人 13—232c
菲莱泰罗斯 Philetaerus 帕加马王国国王 13—232d
菲兰杰里 Filangieri, Carlo, prince (principe) di Satriano, duke (duca) di Taormina 意大利将军 6—313c
菲勒塞德斯(希罗斯的) Pherecydes of Syros 古希腊神话作家 13—225d
菲勒塔斯(科斯岛的) Philetas of Cos 希腊诗人、语法学家 13—232e
菲雷蒂埃 Furetière, Antoine 法国作家 6—529c
菲雷粉 filé 香料、增稠剂 6—314b
菲里什达 Firishtah 印度作家 6—328c
菲力普(平民) Philippe Égalité 法国亲王 13—239b
菲利 fili 爱尔兰古代诗人 6—314e
菲利波 Phélypeaux, Jean-Frédéric 法国大臣 13—223c
菲利多尔 Philidor, André 法国乐师、作曲家 13—232e
菲利多尔 Philidor, François-André 法国作曲家 13—232f
菲利克斯 Felix 教皇和敌对教皇之称号 6—268b
菲利克斯 Felix 西班牙乌赫尔基督教主教 6—268f
菲利克斯(二世) Felix (II) 敌对教皇 6—268c
菲利克斯(五世) Felix (V) (antipope) 敌对教皇 6—268f
菲利克斯(瓦洛瓦的),圣 Felix of Valois, Saint 天主教修士 6—269b
菲利克斯三世(或二世),圣 Felix III (orII), Saint 教皇 6—268c
菲利克斯四世(或三世),圣 Felix IV (or III), Saint 教皇 6—268c
菲利克斯一世,圣 Felix I, Saint 教皇 6—268b
菲利门和巴乌希斯 Philemon and Baucis 希腊神话 13—232c
菲利帕(埃诺的) Philippa of Hainaut 英格兰王后 13—239b
菲利蓬 Philipon, Charles 法国讽刺画家 13—238f
菲利皮 Philippi 希腊小山城 13—239d
菲利皮 Philippi 美国城市 13—239d
菲利浦 Philippe, Charles-Louis 法国小说家 13—239c
菲利浦电器公司 Philips Electronics, NV 荷兰公司 13—242a
菲利普 Philip 德意志国王 13—235a
菲利普 Philip 德意志新教领袖 13—235c
菲利普 Phillip, Arthur 英国海军上将 13—242d
菲利普 Philipe, Gérard 法国演员 13—238e
菲利普 Philip, John 苏格兰传教士 13—238d
菲利普 Philipp, Isidor 法国钢琴家 13—239a
菲利普(爱丁堡公爵) Philip, Duke of Edinburgh 女王伊利莎白二世的丈夫 13—237e
菲利普(波卡诺克特的) Philip of Pokanoket 万帕诺亚格族首长 13—238a
菲利普(高尚的) Philip the Magnanimous 德意志新教领袖 13—238c
菲利普(善良的) Philip the Good 勃艮第公爵 13—238c
菲利普(士瓦本的) Philip of Swabia 德意志国王 13—238a
菲利普阿 Fílippoi (Greece) 希腊小山城 6—315b
菲利普岛 Phillip Island 澳大利亚岛屿 13—242d
菲利普港地区 Port Phillip District 澳大利亚殖民地的旧称 13—446f
菲利普港湾 Port Phillip Bay 澳大利亚海湾 13—446f
菲利普港协会 Port Phillip Association 澳大利亚欧洲移民组织 13—446e

菲利普·莫里斯公司 Philip Morris Companies Inc. 美国公司 13—238d
菲利普三叶虫 Phillipsia 古生物学 13—243e
菲利普斯 Philips, Peter 英国作曲家 13—241f
菲利普斯 Phillips, Lena Madesin 美国律师、俱乐部活动家 13—243d
菲利普斯 Phillips, Stephen 英国演员、诗人 13—242e
菲利普斯 Phillips, Wendell 美国废奴主义斗士 13—242f
菲利普斯 Phillips, William D. 美国物理学家 13—243a
菲利普斯陈列馆 Phillips Collection 美国私人美术收藏馆 13—243b
菲利普斯曲线 Phillips curve 经济学 13—243b
菲利普斯石油公司 Phillips Petroleum Company 美国公司 13—243d
菲利普斯学校 Phillips Academy 美国大学预备学校 13—243b
菲利普王战争 King Philip's War 美洲历史 9—289c
菲利普维尔 Philippeville (Algeria) 阿尔及利亚省份 13—239d
菲利斯托斯 Philistus 希腊历史学家 13—242c
菲利翁 Filion, Hervé 加拿大运动员 6—315a
菲隆布 Philombe, René 非洲作家、剧作家 13—244f
菲鲁扎巴德 Fīrūzābād 伊朗城镇 6—329e
菲鲁扎巴迪 Fīrūzābādī, al- 伊朗词典编纂家 6—329e
菲律宾 Philippines 亚洲国家 13—240e
菲律宾独立教会 Philippine Independent Church 菲律宾教会 13—239f
菲律宾革命 Philippine Revolution 菲律宾历史 13—240b
菲律宾海 Philippine Sea 北太平洋西部海域 13—240c
菲律宾海沟 Philippine Trench 北太平洋西部海沟 13—240d
菲律宾海渊 Philippine Deep (Pacific Ocean) 北太平洋西部海沟 13—239f
菲律宾海之战 Philippine Sea, Battle of the 美日舰队海战 13—240c
菲律宾起义 Philippine Insurrection 菲律宾历史 13—239f
菲律宾语 Pilipino language 亚洲语言 13—303d
菲律宾诸语言 Philippine languages 亚洲语言 13—240a
《菲律宾自治领与独立法》 Philippine Commonwealth and Independence Act 菲律宾历史 13—239e
菲罗克忒忒斯 Philoctetes 希腊传说人物 13—244c
菲罗特 Vierordt, Karl von 德国医学家 17—553e
菲罗兹布尔 Ferozepur (India) 印度城市 6—289f
菲罗兹布尔 Fīrozpur 印度城市 6—328e
菲罗兹布尔-奇尔格 Fīrozpur Jhirka 印度城市 6—328e
菲罗兹沙战役 Fīroz Shāh, Battle of 锡克教徒与英军冲突 6—328d
菲洛波努斯 Philoponus, John 希腊神学家、哲学家 13—245a
菲洛德穆 Philodemus 希腊诗人、哲学家 13—244d
菲洛克塞努斯(马布格的) Philoxenus OF MABBUG 叙利亚主教、神学家、作家 13—252f
菲洛劳斯 Philolaus 希腊哲学家 13—244e
菲洛皮门 Philopoemen 亚该亚同盟的将军 13—245a
菲洛斯特拉托斯(莱姆尼亚人) Philostratus THE LEMNIAN 古希腊作家 13—252e
菲洛斯特拉托斯(雅典人) Philostratus, Flavius, THE ATHENIAN 古希腊作家 13—252e
菲洛斯托吉乌斯 Philostorgius 拜占廷史学家 13—252d
菲洛修斯·科基诺斯 Philotheus Kokkinos 东正教神学家、修士 13—252f
菲美 Pheme (Greek mythology) 希腊神话 13—223c
菲尼格拉 Finiguerra, Maso 意大利艺术家 6—319e
菲尼克斯 Phoenix 美国城市 13—256a
菲尼克斯城 Phenix City 美国城市 13—223f
菲尼克斯群岛 Phoenix Islands 太平洋珊瑚环礁群 13—256c
菲尼克斯维尔 Phoenixville 美国自治镇 13—256c
菲尼斯泰尔 Finistère 法国省份 6—319e
菲涅耳 Fresnel, Augustin-Jean 法国物理学家 6—484f
菲涅耳透镜 Fresnel lens 光学 6—485a
菲诺港 Portofino 意大利渔村 13—453d
菲奇 Fitch, Clyde 美国剧作家 6—337b
菲奇 Fitch, John 美国工业家 6—337b
菲奇 Fitch, Ralph 英国旅行家 6—337c
菲奇 Fitch, Val Logsdon 美国核物理学家 6—337d
菲奇堡 Fitchburg 美国城市 6—337e
菲奇诺 Ficino, Marsilio 意大利哲学家 6—303b
菲瑟特·霍夫特 Visser 't Hooft, Willem Adolph 荷兰神学家 18—20b
菲森 Füssen 德国城市 6—533c
菲沙尔特 Fischart, Johann 德国讽刺作家 6—330b
菲舍尔 Fischer, Ernst Otto 德国化学家 6—330e
菲舍尔 Fischer, Johann Michael 德国建筑师 6—330f
菲舍尔 Fischer, Ludwig 德国男低音歌剧演唱家 6—331a
菲舍尔 Vischer, Friedrich Theodor von 德国文学批评家 18—16e
菲舍尔-迪斯科 Fischer-Dieskau, Dietrich 德国歌剧歌唱家 6—331b
菲舍尔·冯·埃尔拉赫 Fischer von Erlach, Johann Bernhard 奥地利建筑师 6—331c
菲舍尔家族 Vischer FAMILY 德国家族 18—16d
菲施霍夫 Fischhof, Adolf 奥地利政治理论家 6—331e
菲什 Fish, Hamilton 美国国务卿 6—332f
菲什伯恩 Fishburne, Laurence 美国演员 6—333e
菲什河 Fish River 纳米比亚河流 6—333e
菲斯海尔 Visscher, Anna (Roemersdochter) 荷兰诗人 18—20a
菲斯海尔 Visscher, Roemer (Pieterszoon) 荷兰诗人 18—20a
菲斯克 Fiske, Bradley Allen 美国海军军官、发明家 6—336a
菲斯克 Fiske, Fidelia 美国传教士 6—336b
菲斯克 Fiske, Harrison Grey 美国剧作家 6—336c
菲斯克 Fiske, Helen Maria (writer) 美国作家 6—336c
菲斯克 Fiske, John 美国历史学家、哲学家 6—336c
菲斯克 Fiske, Minnie Maddern 美国演员 6—336d
菲斯克 Fisk, James 美国金融投机商 6—335f
菲斯克 Fisk, Wilbur 美国教育家 6—336a
菲斯托斯 Phaestus 希腊古城 13—217a
菲特 Fyt, Jan 佛兰德斯画家 6—537f
菲特·封·戈尔森瑙 Vieth von Golssenau, Arnold Friedrich 德国小说家 17—554d
菲特纳 fitnah 穆斯林内部斗争 6—337e
菲希特尔山 Fichtel Hills 德国山脉 6—303a
菲亚纳兰楚阿 Fianarantsoa 马达加斯加城镇 6—301b
菲亚特公司 Fiat SpA 意大利跨国公司 6—301c
菲耶斯基(小) Fieschi, Gian Luigi, IL GIOVANNE (the Younger) 意大利贵族 6—308d
菲耶斯基家族 Fieschi FAMILY 意大利热那亚贵族世家 6—308c
菲耶索莱 Fiesole 意大利城镇 6—308e
菲英 Fyn 丹麦州名 6—536f
菲英岛 Funen 丹麦第二大岛 6—526b
菲约德勒姆冰河 Jökulsá á Fjöllum 冰岛河流 9—76b
菲兹 Phiz 英国画家 13—253a
鲱形类 clupeiform 鱼类 4—306e
鲱鱼 herring 鱼类 8—50d
肥达 Widal, (Georges-) Fernand-Isidore 法国医师 18—244d
肥大细胞 mast cell 生物学 11—14a
肥鹅肝 foie gras 法国佳肴 6—386b
肥料 fertilizer 农业 6—295d
肥美的星期二 Mardi Gras 法国节日 10—501a
肥胖性生殖器退化 adiposogenital dystrophy 疾病 1—79a
肥胖症 obesity 病态 12—320b
肥沃的阿拉比亚 Arabia Felix 古代地理 1—433a
肥沃新月 Fertile Crescent 近东地区 6—294d

肥皂 soap 洗涤用品 15—467a
肥皂草 soapwort 植物 15—467e
肥皂剧 soap opera 连续剧 15—467b
肥皂鱼 soapfish 鱼类 15—467d
淝水之战 Battle of the Feishui 中国古代著名战役 2—282f
腓肠肌 gastrocnemius muscle 解剖学 7—27c
腓骨 fibula 解剖学 6—302e
腓力 Philip 希律大帝之子 13—235e
腓力 Philip 敌对教皇 13—236c
腓力 Philip 罗马皇帝 13—236d
腓力(阿拉伯人) Philip the Arabian 罗马皇帝 13—238b
腓力(奥古斯特) Philip Augustus 法国国王 13—237f
腓力(高个子) Philip the Tall 法国国王 13—238c
腓力(鲁夫尔的) Philip of Rouvres 勃艮第公爵 13—238a
腓力(马其顿的) Philip of Macedon 马其顿国王 13—238a
腓力(美男子) Philip the Fair 法国国王 13—238c
腓力(瓦卢瓦的) Philip of Valois 法国国王 13—238a
腓力(英俊的) Philip the Handsome 西班牙卡斯蒂利亚国王 13—238c
腓力(勇敢者) Philip the Bold 勃艮第公爵 13—238b
腓力(传福音者),圣 Philip the Evangelist, Saint 早期基督教会执事 13—238b
腓力(使徒),圣 Philip the Apostle, Saint 耶稣十二门徒之一 13—238a
腓力比库斯·巴达尼斯 Philippicus Bardanes 拜占廷皇帝 13—239e
腓力二世 Philip II 勃艮第公爵 13—233a
腓力二世 Philip II 法国国王 13—233e
腓力二世 Philip II 马其顿国王 13—235e
腓力二世 Philip II 西班牙国王 13—236f
腓力;菲利普 Philip 统治者之名 13—232f
腓力六世 Philip VI 法国国王 13—234f
腓力三世 Philip III 勃艮第公爵 13—233c
腓力三世 Philip III 法国国王 13—234b
腓力三世 Philip III 西班牙国王 13—237b
腓力四世 Philip IV 法国国王 13—234c
腓力四世 Philip IV 西班牙国王 13—237c
腓力五世 Philip V 法国国王 13—234e
腓力五世 Philip V 马其顿国王 13—236b
腓力五世 Philip V 西班牙国王 13—237d
腓力一世 Philip I 勃艮第公爵 13—233a
腓力一世 Philip I 法国国王 13—233d
腓力一世 Philip I 西班牙卡斯蒂利亚国王 13—236e
腓力一世至二世 Philip I-II 纳瓦拉国王 13—236c
腓尼基 Phoenicia 亚洲历史地区 13—255b
腓尼基语 Phoenician language 古代语言 13—255f
腓尼基字母 Phoenician alphabet 古代文字 13—255e
腓特烈 Frederick 统治者之名 6—458b
腓特烈(好战者) Frederick the Warlike 萨克森选侯 6—465b
腓特烈(红胡子) Frederick Barbarossa 士瓦本公爵 6—464f
腓特烈(皇后) Frederick, Empress 德皇腓特烈三世之妻 6—465b
腓特烈(洛林的) Frederick of Lorraine 教皇 6—465a
腓特烈(美男子) Frederick the Fair 德意志国王 6—465a
腓特烈(虔诚者) Frederick the Pious 莱茵巴拉丁选侯 6—465a
腓特烈(三世) Frederick (III) 德意志国王 6—460e
腓特烈(雅士) Frederick the Gentle 萨克森选侯 6—465a
腓特烈(雅士) Frederick the Mild 萨克森选侯 6—465a
腓特烈(正直者) Frederick the Righteous 莱茵巴拉丁选侯 6—465a
腓特烈(智者) Frederick the Wise 萨克森选侯 6—465b
腓特烈·奥古斯特 Frederick Augustus 萨克森选侯及国王之名 6—465b
腓特烈·奥古斯特二世 Frederick Augustus II (elector) 波兰国王 6—465b
腓特烈·奥古斯特二世 Frederick Augustus II 萨克森国王 6—465c
腓特烈·奥古斯特一世 Frederick Augustus I (elector) 波兰国王 6—465b
腓特烈·奥古斯特一世 Frederick Augustus I 萨克森国王 6—465b
腓特烈八世 Frederick VIII 丹麦国王 6—459d
腓特烈·查理 Frederick Charles, Prince of Prussia 普鲁士亲王 6—465d
腓特烈大帝 Frederick the Great 普鲁士国王 6—465a
腓特烈二世 Frederick II 丹麦、挪威国王 6—458d
腓特烈二世 Frederick II 西西里国王 6—460c
腓特烈二世 Frederick II 普鲁士国王 6—461d
腓特烈二世 Frederick II 萨克森选侯 6—464c
腓特烈二世(或一世) Frederick II (or I) 西西里国王 6—464d
腓特烈港 Frederikshavn 丹麦港市 6—467e
腓特烈港 Friedrichshafen 德国城市 6—493b
腓特烈·亨利 Frederick Henry, Prince of Orange 奥兰治公爵 6—465e
腓特烈九世 Frederick IX 丹麦国王 6—459e
腓特烈克斯塔 Fredrikstad 挪威城镇 6—468a
腓特烈六世 Frederick VI 丹麦、挪威国王 6—459b
腓特烈六世 Frederick VI 西西里国王、士瓦本公爵 6—464d
腓特烈七世 Frederick VII 丹麦国王 6—459c
腓特烈三世 Frederick III 普鲁士国王 6—458c
腓特烈三世 Frederick III 丹麦、挪威国王 6—458e
腓特烈三世 Frederick III 普鲁士国王 6—459e
腓特烈三世 Frederick III 神圣罗马帝国皇帝 6—460f
腓特烈三世 Frederick III 巴拉丁选侯 6—461a
腓特烈三世 Frederick III 萨克森选侯 6—464c
腓特烈三世 Frederick III 神圣罗马帝国皇帝 6—464d
腓特烈三世(或二世) Frederick III (or II) 西西里国王 6—464d
腓特烈斯堡 Frederiksborg 丹麦州名 6—467d
腓特烈斯贝 Frederiksberg 丹麦自治市 6—467d
腓特烈斯哈尔 Fredrikshald (Norway) 挪威城镇 6—467f
腓特烈斯霍布 Frederikshåb 格陵兰城镇 6—467e
腓特烈四世 Frederick IV 丹麦、挪威国王 6—459a
腓特烈四世 Frederick IV 巴拉丁选侯 6—461b
腓特烈·威廉 Frederick William, crown prince of Prussia 普鲁士国王 6—467b
腓特烈·威廉 Frederick William 统治者之名 6—466a
腓特烈·威廉 Frederick William 勃兰登堡选侯 6—466a
腓特烈·威廉 Frederick William 黑森-卡塞尔选侯 6—466b
腓特烈·威廉二世 Frederick William II 普鲁士国王 6—466d
腓特烈·威廉三世 Frederick William III 普鲁士国王 6—466e
腓特烈·威廉四世 Frederick William IV 普鲁士国王 6—466f
腓特烈·威廉一世 Frederick William I 普鲁士国王 6—466c
腓特烈五世 Frederick V 丹麦、挪威国王 6—459a
腓特烈五世 Frederick V 巴拉丁选侯 6—461b
腓特烈西亚 Fredericia 丹麦城市、港口 6—458a
腓特烈一世 Frederick I 巴拉丁选侯 6—458b
腓特烈一世 Frederick I 勃兰登堡系始祖 6—458b
腓特烈一世 Frederick I 丹麦、挪威国王 6—458c
腓特烈一世 Frederick I 德意志国王 6—459f
腓特烈一世 Frederick I 普鲁士国王 6—461c
腓特烈一世 Frederick (I) 瑞典国王 6—464e
腓特烈一世 Frederick I 萨克森选侯 6—464c
斐波那契数 Fibonacci numbers 数学 6—301f
斐迪南 Ferdinand 统治者之名 6—279c
斐迪南 Ferdinand 普鲁士陆军元帅 6—279d
斐迪南 Ferdinand 保加利亚国王 6—279e
斐迪南(善良的) Ferdinand the Benign 奥地利皇帝 6—282d
斐迪南(一世) Ferdinand (I) 奥地利皇帝 6—279c
斐迪南二世 Ferdinand II 神圣罗马帝国皇帝 6—280a
斐迪南二世 Ferdinand II 托斯卡纳大公 6—282b
斐迪南二世 Ferdinand II 意大利那不勒斯国王 6—280d
斐迪南二世 Ferdinand II 意大利西西里国王 6—282d

斐迪南·马克西米连·约瑟夫 Ferdinand Maximilian Joseph (emperor of Mexico) 墨西哥皇帝 6—282e
斐迪南·玛里亚 Ferdinand Maria 巴伐利亚选侯 6—282e
斐迪南三世 Ferdinand Ⅲ 神圣罗马帝国皇帝 6—280b
斐迪南三世 Ferdinand Ⅲ 阿拉贡国王 6—280d
斐迪南三世 Ferdinand Ⅲ 托斯卡纳大公 6—282c
斐迪南四世 Ferdinand Ⅳ 波希米亚、匈牙利国王 6—280c
斐迪南四世 Ferdinand Ⅳ 意大利两西西里国王 6—280d
斐迪南五世 Ferdinand Ⅴ 奥地利国王 6—279d
斐迪南一世 Ferdinand Ⅰ 神圣罗马帝国皇帝 6—279e
斐迪南一世 Ferdinand Ⅰ 意大利那不勒斯国王 6—280c
斐迪南一世 Ferdinand Ⅰ 罗马尼亚国王 6—280e
斐迪南一世 Ferdinand Ⅰ 托斯卡纳大公 6—282a
斐迪南一世 Ferdinand Ⅰ 意大利西西里国王 6—282c
斐多 Phaedo 哲学家 13—216e
斐济 Fiji 南太平洋国家 6—312b
斐济语 Fijian language 语言 6—313b
斐勒得 veld 南非开阔地 17—493e
斐洛 Philo Judaeus 犹太哲学家 13—244a
斐索 Fizeau, Armand-Hippolyte-Louis 法国物理学家 6—342a
斐扬俱乐部 Feuillants, Club of the 法国政治俱乐部 6—299e
榧螺 olive shell 海螺 12—375e
榧树属 Torreya 植物学 17—166e
蜚蠊 roach (insect) 昆虫 14—323a
吠鹿 barking deer 哺乳动物 2—231c
吠舍 Vaisya 印度种姓等级 17—445c
吠舍离 Vaiśālī 印度古城 17—444f
吠檀多派 Vedānta 印度哲学 17—486c
吠檀多提悉迦 Vedāntadeśika 印度教神学家 17—486c
吠陀 Veda 印度教文献 17—486b
吠陀教 Vedic religion 印度宗教 17—486e
吠陀圣咏 Vedic chant 印度宗教赞美诗 17—486e
废奴运动 abolitionism 欧洲、美洲社会改革运动 1—26d
废物处理 waste disposal 环境保护 18—133b
废物利用 materials salvage 资源再循环 11—20a
沸点 boiling point 物理学 3—7b
沸绿岩 teschenite 岩石 16—558e
沸石 zeolite 矿物 18—509e
沸石相 zeolitic facies 地质学 18—509f
狒狒 baboon 哺乳动物 2—110e
肺 lung 解剖学 10—284f
肺癌 lung cancer 疾病 10—285b
肺不张 atelectasis 疾病 2—16e
肺草 lungwort 草本植物 10—286d
肺草 lungwort (lichen) 地衣植物 10—286d
肺尘埃沉着病 pneumoconiosis 疾病 13—381b
肺充血 lung congestion 病理现象 10—285d
肺动脉瓣狭窄 pulmonary stenosis 病理现象 14—21f
肺梗塞形成 lung infarction 疾病 10—285e
肺螺 pulmonate 腹足类动物 14—21f
肺泡 pulmonary alveolus 解剖学 14—21d
肺泡蛋白质沉积症 alveolar proteinosis 疾病 1—260c
肺气肿 emphysema 疾病 6—63e
肺蠕虫 lungworm 蠕虫 10—286c
肺栓塞 pulmonary embolism 病理现象 14—21e
肺循环 pulmonary circulation 生理学 14—21d
肺压缩 lung squeeze (medicine) 病理现象 10—285f
肺炎 pneumonia 疾病 13—381c
肺炎克雷伯斯氏菌 Klebsiella pneumoniae 微生物 9—314b
肺炎球菌 pneumococcus (*Streptococcus pneumoniae*) 微生物 13—381a
肺衣 tree lungwort (*Lobaria pulmonaria*) 地衣植物 17—207c
肺疫 lung plague 动物病 10—285f
肺鱼 lungfish 鱼类 10—286a
肺鱼亚纲 Dipnoi 动物学 5—333a
肺原性心脏病 pulmonary heart disease 疾病 14—21e
费奥多西亚 Feodosiya 乌克兰城市 6—278b
费奥克季斯托夫 Feoktistov, Konstantin Petrovich 苏联航天员 6—278b
费奥里 Fiori da Urbino 意大利画家 6—324b
费边·安布斯图斯 Fabius Ambustus, Quintus 罗马政治家 6—206d
费边·马克西姆斯 Fabius Maximus Cunctator, Quintus 罗马政治家 6—206d
费边·皮克托 Fabius Pictor, Quintus 罗马历史学家 6—206f
费边社 Fabian Society 伦敦社会主义团体 6—206b
费伯 Ferber, Edna 美国小说家 6—279b
费伯 Faber, Frederick William 英国神学家 6—205f
费伯 Faber, Peter 法国神学家 6—206a
费勃罗内斯 Febronius, Justinus 德国神学家 6—259c
费城 Philadelphia 美国城市 13—226e
费城百年纪念博览会 Philadelphia Centennial Exposition 贸易博览会 13—229f
费城动物园 Philadelphia Zoological Gardens 美国动物园 13—230a
《费城问询报》 Philadelphia Inquirer, The 美国报纸 13—229f
费达拉 Fedala (Morocco) 摩洛哥港市 6—260b
费代里奇 Federici, Camillo 意大利剧作家、演员 6—263e
费德 Feyder, Jacques 法国电影导演 6—300c
费德尔布 Faidherbe, Louis(-Léon-César) 法属塞内加尔总督 6—213c
费德雷尔 Federer, Heinrich 瑞士小说家 6—263d
费德林 Fedorenko, Nikolai Trofimovich 苏联外交家 6—264a
费德鲁斯 Phaedrus 罗马寓言作家 13—216f
费迪南德(不坚定的) Ferdinand the Fickle 葡萄牙国王 6—282d
费迪南德(大众渴望的) Ferdinand the Desired 西班牙国王 6—282d
费迪南德(圣) Ferdinand, Saint 卡斯蒂利亚、莱昂国王 6—282d
费迪南德(天主教徒) Ferdinand the Catholic 阿拉贡国王 6—282d
费迪南德(伟大的) Ferdinand the Great 卡斯蒂利亚、莱昂国王 6—282e
费迪南德(英俊的) Ferdinand the Handsome 葡萄牙国王 6—282e
费迪南德二世 Ferdinand Ⅱ 葡萄牙女王之夫 6—280e
费迪南德二世 Ferdinand Ⅱ 阿拉贡国王 6—281c
费迪南德二世 Ferdinand Ⅱ 西班牙莱昂国王 6—281f
费迪南德六世 Ferdinand Ⅵ 西班牙国王 6—280f
费迪南德七世 Ferdinand Ⅶ 西班牙国王 6—281a
《费迪南德七世国事诏书》 Pragmatic Sanction of King Ferdinand Ⅶ 西班牙国王法令 13—479a
费迪南德三世 Ferdinand Ⅲ 卡斯蒂利亚、莱昂国王 6—282a
费迪南德四世 Ferdinand Ⅳ 卡斯蒂利亚、莱昂国王 6—282a
费迪南德五世 Ferdinand Ⅴ 阿拉贡国王 6—280f
费迪南德一世 Ferdinand Ⅰ 阿拉贡国王 6—281b
费迪南德一世 Ferdinand Ⅰ 葡萄牙国王 6—280d
费迪南德一世 Ferdinand Ⅰ 西班牙卡斯蒂利亚国王 6—281e
费蒂 Fetti, Domenico 意大利画家 6—298a
费蒂斯 Fétis, François-Joseph 奥地利音乐学者 6—297d
费蒂希 Fittig, Rudolf 德国化学家 6—337f
费定 Fedin, Konstantin Aleksandrovich 苏联作家 6—263f
费多 Feydeau, Georges(-Léon-Jules-Marie) 法国戏剧家 6—300b
费多尔 Fyodor 俄国沙皇名 6—536f
费多尔二世 Fyodor Ⅱ 俄国沙皇 6—537a
费多尔三世 Fyodor Ⅲ 俄国沙皇 6—537a
费多尔一世 Fyodor Ⅰ 俄国沙皇 6—537a
费恩 Fens 英国沼泽地区 6—277d
费恩 Fain, Sammy 美国作曲家 6—214c
费恩茨尔贝格 Faynzilberg, Ilya Arnoldovich 苏联作家 6—256c
费恩兰 Fenland 英国区名 6—276e
费恩兰 Fenland (region, England) 英国沼泽地区 6—276e

费恩斯 Fiennes, Celia 英国作家 6—308b
费尔 Fell, John 英国牧师、作家 6—269d
费尔奥克斯战役 Fair Oaks, Battle of (1862) 美国历史 6—215a
费尔巴哈 Feuerbach, Anselm 德国画家 6—299a
费尔巴哈 Feuerbach, Ludwig (Andreas) 德国哲学家 6—299b
费尔巴哈 Feuerbach, Paul (Johann Anselm), Ritter von (knight of) 德国法学家 6—299d
费尔班克斯 Fairbanks 美国城市 6—215c
费尔邦斯 Fairbanks, Charles Warren 美国副总统 6—215c
费尔贝恩 Fairbairn, Stephen 英国赛艇运动员 6—215b
费尔贝恩 Fairbairn, Sir William 英国土木工程师 6—215b
费尔柴尔德 Fairchild, David Grandison 美国植物学家 6—215e
费尔柴尔德 Fairchild, Mary Salome Cutler 美国图书馆馆长 6—215f
费尔柴尔德半导体公司 Fairchild Semiconductor Corporation 美国电子公司 6—216a
费尔德 Velde, Adriaen van de 荷兰画家 17—493f
费尔德 Feld, Eliot 美国舞蹈家 6—267b
费尔德 Velde, Esaias van de 荷兰画家 17—494a
费尔德 Velde, Henry (Clemens) van de 比利时教师、建筑师 17—494b
费尔德基希 Feldkirch 奥地利城市 6—267b
费尔德克 Veldeke, Heinrich von (German poet) 德国诗人 17—494c
费尔德曼 Feldman, Morton 美国作曲家 6—267c
费尔丁 Fälldin, Thorbjörn 瑞典首相 6—223c
费尔顿(夫人) Felton, Rebecca Ann 美国政治家、参议员 6—271b
费尔法克斯 Fairfax 美国城市 6—216b
费尔法克斯 Fairfax, Edward 英国诗人 6—216b
费尔法克斯 Fayrfax, Robert 英国作曲家 6—256c
费尔法克斯(卡梅伦的)男爵(第二) Fairfax (of Cameron), Ferdinando Fairfax, 2nd Baron 英国将领 6—216c
费尔法克斯(卡梅伦的)男爵(第三) Fairfax (of Cameron), Thomas Fairfax, 3rdBaron 英国议会军总司令 6—216c
费尔菲尔德 Fairfield 美国加利福尼亚州城市 6—216d
费尔菲尔德 Fairfield 美国康涅狄格州城镇 6—216e
费尔菲尔德 Fairfield 美国艾奥瓦州城市 6—216e
费尔干纳 Fergana 乌兹别克斯坦州名 6—283d
费尔干纳 Fergana 乌兹别克斯坦城市 6—283e
费尔干纳谷地 Fergana Valley 亚洲大凹地 6—283e
费尔黑文 Fairhaven 美国城镇 6—216e
费尔凯塞杜古 Ferkessedougou 科特迪瓦城镇 6—284f
费尔洛 Ferlo 塞内加尔行政区 6—285a
费尔蒙特 Fairmont 美国城市 6—216e
费尔莫 Fermo 意大利城镇 6—287c
费尔莫尔 Fillmore, Millard 美国总统 6—315c
费尔莫尔 Fillmore, Myrtle Page 美国宗教领袖 6—315e
费尔默伊登 Vermuyden, Sir Cornelius 英国工程师 17—519f
费尔南德尔 Fernandel 法国喜剧演员 6—288c
费尔南德斯 Fernandes, Álvaro 葡萄牙船长、探险家 6—288c
费尔南德斯 Fernandes, António 葡萄牙探险家、历史学家 6—288d
费尔南德斯 Fernández, Gregorio (Spanish sculptor) 西班牙雕塑家 6—288e
费尔南德斯 Fernandes, João 葡萄牙旅行家 6—288d
费尔南德斯 Fernández, Juan 西班牙航海家 6—288e
费尔南德斯 Fernández, Lucas 西班牙剧作家 6—288e
费尔南德斯 Fernández, Manuel Félix (president of Mexico) 墨西哥总统 6—288f
费尔南德斯·德·阿维利亚内达 Fernández de Avellaneda, Alonso 作者笔名 6—288f
费尔南德斯·德·科尔多瓦 Fernández de Córdoba, Gonzalo 西班牙军事领袖 6—288f
费尔南德斯·德·利萨尔迪 Fernández de Lizardi, José Joaquín 墨西哥编辑、作家 6—289a
费尔南德斯·德·莫拉廷 Fernández de Moratín, Leandro 西班牙剧作家 6—289a
费尔南德斯·德·纳瓦莱特 Fernández de Navarrete, Juan 西班牙画家 6—289b
费尔南德斯·雷纳 Fernández Reyna, Leonel 多米尼加共和国总统 6—289c
费尔南德斯·雷塔马尔 Fernández Retamar, Roberto 古巴诗人、作家 6—289b
费尔南迪纳岛 Fernandina Island 厄瓜多尔岛屿 6—289e
费尔南多波 Fernando Po (Equatorial Guinea) 几内亚湾岛屿 6—289f
费尔南多-迪诺罗尼亚岛 Fernando de Noronha Island 南大西洋岛屿 6—289f
费尔普斯 Phelps, Almira Hart Lincoln 美国教育家、作家 13—222f
费尔普斯 Phelps, Samuel 英国演员、演出经理 13—223a
费尔普斯 Phelps, William Lyon 美国学者、评论家 13—223b
费尔瑟姆 Felltham, Owen 英国作家、诗人 6—270e
费尔森 Velsen 荷兰城市 17—495c
费尔森 Fersen, Fredrik Axel von 瑞典政治家 6—294b
费尔森 Fersen, Hans Axel von 瑞典政治家、外交家 6—294c
费尔斯通 Firestone, Harvey S(amuel) 美国企业家 6—327f
费尔特德 Fertöd 匈牙利农业公社 6—295e
费尔特雷 Feltre 意大利山镇 6—271b
费尔特林 Veltlin (Italy) 意大利地区 17—495c
费尔韦 Fairway 英国纯种赛马 6—216f
费尔韦 Verwey, Albert 荷兰诗人、学者 17—527a
费尔韦瑟山 Fairweather, Mount 加拿大山峰 6—216f
费尔西纳 Felsina 意大利古城 6—271a
费夫尔 Febvre, Lucien Paul Victor 法国历史学家 6—259d
费弗沙姆伯爵(第二) Feversham, Louis de Durfort, 2nd earl of 英国军人 6—300a
费根鲍姆 Feigenbaum, Edward Albert 美国系统分析专家 6—266b
费霍-蒙特内格罗 Feijóo y Montenegro, Benito Jerónimo 西班牙教师、作家 6—266d
费基 Feke, Robert 北美画家 6—267a
费季索夫 Fetisov, Vyacheslav 苏联冰球运动员 6—297f
费加罗 Figaro 法国喜剧人物 6—310a
《费加罗报》 Figaro, Le 法国巴黎晨报 6—310b
费康 Fécamp 法国海滨胜地、渔港 6—259e
费克 Fick, August 德国语言学家 6—303c
费肯汉 Feckenham, John de 英格兰隐修院院长 6—260a
费拉博斯科(第二) Ferrabosco, Alfonso, II 英国作曲家 6—290a
费拉博斯科(第一) Ferrabosco, Alfonso, I 意大利作曲家 6—289f
费拉德尔菲亚 Philadelphia 美国城市 13—226e
费拉-迪圣安娜 Feira de Santana 巴西城市 6—267a
费拉尔 Ferrar, Nicholas 英格兰牧师、议员 6—290b
费拉拉 Ferrara 意大利城市 6—290b
费拉拉-佛罗伦萨会议 Ferrara-Florence, Council of 宗教会议 6—290c
费拉拉公爵夫人 Ferrara, Renée de France, Duchessa di (Duchess of) 意大利和法国宗教改革者 6—290c
费拉里 Ferrari, Enzo 意大利汽车制造商 6—290d
费拉里 Ferrari, Giuseppe 意大利历史学家 6—290e
费拉里 Ferrari, Lodovico 意大利数学家 6—290e
费拉里斯 Ferraris, Galileo 意大利物理学家 6—290f
费拉罗 Ferraro, Geraldine A(nne) 美国政治家 6—290f
费拉温 Feraoun, Mouloud 阿尔及利亚小说家 6—279a
费拉西人骨架 Ferassie Skeletons, La 人类学 6—279a
费莱凯岛 Faylakah 科威特岛屿 6—256c
费兰梯 Ferranti, Sebastian Ziani de 英国电机工程师 6—290a
费勒 Feller, Bob 美国棒球运动员 6—269f

费勒姆 Fareham 英格兰区名 6—238f
费勒姆女伯爵 Fareham, Louise-Renée de Kéroualle, countess of 英王情妇 6—238f
费雷 Ferré, Charles-Théophile 法国革命家 6—291b
费雷 Ferré, Luis A. 波多黎各总督 6—291b
费雷 Ferré, Rosario 拉丁美洲作家 6—291c
费雷尔 Ferrel, William 美国气象学家 6—291f
费雷尔环流圈 Ferrel cell 大气环流模式 6—291f
费雷拉 Ferreira, António 葡萄牙诗人 6—291d
费雷拉 Ferreira, Manuel 葡萄牙裔小说家、学者 6—291d
费雷拉 Ferreira, Virgílio 葡萄牙教师、小说家 6—291e
费雷拉·德·卡斯特罗 Ferreira de Castro, José Maria 葡萄牙作家 6—291e
费里 Ferri, Ciro 意大利画家 6—292b
费里 Ferry, Jules(-François-Camille) 法国总理 6—293f
费里埃 Ferrié, Gustave-Auguste 法国科学家 6—292c
费里尔 Ferrier, Kathleen 英国女低音歌唱家 6—292c
费里尔 Ferrier, Susan Edmonstone 苏格兰小说家 6—292d
费里港 Port Fairy 澳大利亚城镇 13—445a
费里兰 Ferryland 加拿大村庄 6—294b
费里维尔 Ferryville (Tunisia) 突尼斯城镇 6—294b
费利布里热协会 Félibrige 法国文学社团 6—267e
费利克斯 Félix, Élisa (French actress) 法国演员 6—269b
费利克斯托 Felixstowe 英国城镇 6—269b
费利尼 Fellini, Federico 意大利电影导演 6—270a
费林 Fearing, Kenneth (Flexner) 美国诗人、小说家 6—257f
费灵 Felling 英格兰地名 6—269f
费鲁 Ferro 西班牙岛屿 6—293a
费鲁兹萨普尔 Fairuz Sapur (ancient town, Iraq) 伊拉克古城 6—216f
费伦巴赫 Fehrenbach, Konstantin 德国总理 6—265e
费伦贝格 Fellenberg, Philipp Emanuel von 瑞士教育改革家 6—269d
费伦蒂诺 Ferentino 意大利城镇 6—283d
费伦奇 Ferenczi, Sándor 匈牙利精神分析学家 6—283c
费洛斯 Fellows, Sir Charles 英国考古学家 6—270d
费马 Fermat, Pierre de 法国数学家 6—285b
费马大定理 Fermat's last theorem 数学 6—285e
费马素数 Fermat prime 数学 6—285d
费马原理 Fermat's principle 光学 6—285e
费米 Fermi, Enrico 美国物理学家 6—286a
费米-狄拉克统计法 Fermi-Dirac statistics 物理学 6—286e
费米国家加速器实验室 Fermi National Accelerator Laboratory 美国粒子物理学研究中心 6—286f
费米克法院 fehmic court 中世纪法庭 6—265d
费米面 Fermi surface 物理学 6—287a
费米能级 Fermi level 物理学 6—286f
费米子 fermion 亚原子粒子 6—287b
费奈隆 Fénelon, François de Salignac de La Mothe- 法国大主教 6—273b
费南迪纳比奇 Fernandina Beach 美国城市 6—289d
费内奇 Fenech Adami, Eddie 马耳他政治家 6—273a
费内斯特拉 Fenestella 罗马诗人 6—273c
费琴科冰川 Fedchenko Glacier 塔吉克斯坦冰川 6—260b
费若果 feijoa (species *Feijoa sellowiana*) 植物 6—266c
费萨尔 Fayṣal, ibn ʿAbd al-ʿAzīz ibn ʿAbd ar-Raḥmān as-Saʿūd 沙特阿拉伯国王 6—256e
费萨尔二世 Fayṣal II 伊拉克国王 6—256e
费萨尔一世 Fayṣal I 伊拉克国王 6—256d
费萨拉巴德 Faisalābād 巴基斯坦县名 6—218a
费瑟 Feather, Victor (Grayson Hardie), Baron Feather of the City of Bradford 英国工会领导人 6—258d
费森登 Fessenden, Reginald Aubrey 美国无线电先驱 6—296c
费森登 Fessenden, William Pitt 美国政治家 6—296d
费申尼内诗 Fescennine verse 意大利诗集 6—296a
费申尼内诗集抄本 carmina Fescennina (poetry) 意大利诗集 3—464f
费什 Fesch, Joseph 法国红衣主教 6—296a
费斯特代克 Vestdijk, Simon 荷兰作家 17—530a
费斯图斯 Festus, Sextus Pompeius 拉丁文法学家 6—296e
费索恩 Faithorne, William 英格兰铜版画家 6—218c
费泰干酪 feta 希腊干酪 6—297a
费特 Fet, Afanasy Afanasyevich 俄国诗人、翻译家 6—296f
费特希耶 Fethiye 土耳其城镇 6—297c
费雯丽 Leigh, Vivien 英国演员 9—567f
费西 Faesi, Robert 瑞士诗人、戏剧家 6—211f
费希尔 Fisher, Andrew 澳大利亚总理 6—334a
费希尔 Fischer, Bobby 美国国际象棋大师 6—330c
费希尔 Fisher, Bud 美国漫画家 6—334a
费希尔 Fisher, Clara 美国演员 6—334b
费希尔 Fischer, Edmond H. 美国生物化学家 6—330d
费希尔 Fisher, Herbert Albert Laurens 英国历史学家 6—334b
费希尔 Fisher, Irving 美国经济学家 6—334c
费希尔 Fisher, Saint John 英国主教 6—334e
费希尔 Fisher, Sir R(onald) A(ylmer) 英国遗传学家 6—335a
费希尔(基尔弗斯通的) Fisher (of Kilverstone), John Arbuthnot Fisher, 1st Baron 英国海军上将 6—334f
费希纳 Fechner, Gustav Theodor 德国哲学家 6—259f
费希特 Fichte, Johann Gottlieb 德国哲学家 6—302e
费孝通 Fei Xiaotong 中国社会学家 6—265e
费歇尔 Fischer, Emil (Hermann) 德国化学家 6—330d
费歇尔 Fischer, Hans 德国生物化学家 6—330e
费(歇尔)-托(罗普希)反应 Fischer-Tropsch reaction 化学 6—331c
费耶 Phayre, Sir Arthur Purves 英国驻缅甸专员 13—222b
费耶尔 Fejér 匈牙利州名 6—267a
费耶特维尔 Fayetteville 美国阿肯色州城市 6—256b
费耶特维尔 Fayetteville 美国北卡罗来纳州城市 6—256b
费伊 Fay, Sidney Bradshaw 美国历史学家 6—255f
费因曼 Feynman, Richard P(hillips) 美国物理学家 6—300d
费因曼图 Feynman diagram 物理学 6—300e
费英格 Vaihinger, Hans 德国哲学家 17—443e
费赞 Fezzan 北非历史地区 6—301a
费扎巴德 Feyzābād 阿富汗城镇 6—301a
痱子 prickly heat 疾病 13—506a
镄 fermium 人工合成化学元素 6—287c
分 minute 计量单位 11—268d
分贝 decibel (dB) 计量单位 5—202f
分布函数 distribution function 数学 5—344b
分拆 partition 数学 13—68d
分成制 métayage 土地租佃形式 11—154b
分顶式四轮马车 landau 交通工具 9—475c
分肥制 spoils system 美国历史 16—39b
分割韵 broken rhyme 诗歌韵律 3—175f
分隔马 cutting horse 轻型骑乘马 5—80d
分光法 Divisionism 绘画技法 5—348a
分光光度学 spectrophotometry 光谱学 16—14c
分节 segmentation 动物躯体构造形式 15—188b
分解代谢 catabolism 生物化学 3—518a
分金 parting 冶金学 13—68b
分居 separation 法律 15—217f
分类 classification 生物学 4—269f
分类测度学 taximetrics 分类学 16—501e
分类法 classification (library science) 图书馆学 4—270a
分类阶元 taxon 生物学 16—502a
分类理论 classification theory 社会学 4—270a
分类学 taxonomy 生物学 16—502a

分离变量法 variables, separation of 数学 17—472f
分离主义者联盟 Sonderbund 瑞士宗教组织 15—508d
分裂 fission 生物学 6—336e
分裂 Raskol 俄国正教会史 14—158c
分泌 secretion 生物学 15—178d
分娩 parturition 生理学 13—69c
分年级学校 graded school 教育 7—238d
分派劳役制 repartimiento 西属美洲殖民地史 14—233b
分配理论 distribution theory 经济学 5—344c
分配律 distributive law 数学 5—344f
分谱 partbook 音乐 13—64f
分期偿付或摊销 amortization 财务会计名词 1—295f
分期付款信贷 installment credit 信贷措施 8—399e
分区制 zoning 城市规划 18—565b
分生孢子 conidium 真菌 4—430d
分生孢子盘 acervulus 微生物学 1—48f
分生组织 meristem 植物学 11—131d
分时 time-sharing 计算机科学 17—100a
分室鹦鹉螺 chambered nautilus 软体动物 4—34b
分体论 mereology 逻辑学 11—129a
分析 analysis 物理学、化学 1—311b
分析命题 analytic proposition 逻辑学 1—315a
分析心理学 analytic psychology 心理学 1—315b
分析学 analysis 数学 1—310c
分析语 analytic language 语言学 1—314d
分析哲学 Analytic philosophy 哲学 1—314e
分线规 divider 测量工具 5—346c
分形 fractal 数学 6—434a
分音符 diaeresis 音乐 5—283e
分支放射 branching 物理学 3—118c
分枝杆菌属 Mycobacterium 微生物学 11—523b
分子 molecule 化学 11—318e
分子筛 molecular sieve 化学 11—318d
分子生物学 molecular biology 生物学 11—318c
分子束 molecular beam 物理学 11—317f
分组套牛 team roping 美国牧放人竞技 16—511e
芬博阿多蒂尔 Finnbogadóttir, Vigdís 冰岛总统 6—321f
芬德 Fender, Leo 美国发明家、电子乐器制造商 6—273a
芬德利 Findlay 美国城市 6—317f
芬德利背斜 Findlay Arch 地质学 6—318a
芬迪国家公园 Fundy National Park 加拿大公园 6—526b
芬迪湾 Fundy, Bay of 加拿大海湾 6—526a
芬顿 Fenton, Elijah 英国诗人 6—277e
芬顿 Fenton, Lavinia 英国演员 6—277e
芬顿 Fenton, Roger 英国摄影家 6—277f
芬恩 Fenn, John B. 美国化学家 6—276e
芬恩·麦库尔 Finn MacCumhaill (Irish hero) 爱尔兰传说人物 6—321e
芬戈人 Fingo (people) 南非民族 6—319d
芬格湖群 Finger Lakes 美国冰川湖 6—318e
芬吉王朝 Funj DYNASTY 苏丹王朝 6—527c
芬克 Fink, Albert 美国工程师 6—319f
芬克 Funk, Isaac Kauffman 美国出版家 6—527c
芬克 Fink, Mike 美国船员、传奇英雄 6—320a
芬克 Fink, Theodore 澳大利亚政治家 6—320a
芬克河 Finke River 澳大利亚河流 6—320a
芬克与瓦格纳词典 Funk & Wagnalls dictionaries 英语词典 6—527d
芬莱 Finlay, Carlos J. 古巴流行病学家 6—321c
芬兰 Finland 北欧国家 6—320b
芬兰热气浴 sauna 沐浴 15—84f
芬兰湾 Finland, Gulf of 北欧海湾 6—321b
芬兰文学 Finnish literature 文学 6—322d
芬兰-乌戈尔诸语言 Finno-Ugric languages 欧洲语言 6—323b
芬兰-乌戈尔宗教 Finno-Ugric religion 宗教 6—323d
芬兰信义会 Finland, Church of 芬兰教会 6—321b
芬兰语 Finnish language 欧洲语言 6—322c
芬兰语诸民族 Finnic PEOPLES 欧洲民族 6—322a
芬兰正教会 Orthodox Church of Finland 芬兰教会 12—474a
芬里尔 Fenrir 北欧神话中的狼 6—277c
芬利 Finley, Charlie 美国保险业董事 6—321d
芬利 Finlay, George 英国历史学家 6—321d
芬利 Finley, Martha 美国儿童读物作家 6—321e
芬洛 Venlo 荷兰城市 17—507a
芬马克 Finnmark 挪威郡名 6—323b
芬尼 Finney, Charles Grandison 美国律师 6—321f
芬尼亚故事 Fenian cycle 爱尔兰文学 6—276d
芬尼运动成员 Fenian 爱尔兰秘密社团成员 6—276c
芬宁梅因纳斯 Vening Meinesz, Felix Andries 荷兰地球物理学家 17—506a
芬诺 Fenno, John 美国出版家 6—277b
芬诺洛萨 Fenollosa, Ernest F. 美国东方学家 6—277b
芬奇 Vinci, Leonardo da 意大利艺术家、科学家 17—568e
芬奇 Finch, Robert (Duer Clayton) 加拿大诗人 6—317f
芬森 Finsen, Niels Ryberg 丹麦医生 6—323f
芬什港 Finschhafen 巴布亚新几内亚港镇 6—323f
芬太尼 fentanyl 药物 6—277e
酚 phenol 化合物 13—223f
酚红试验 phenolsulfonphthalein test 临床检查方法 13—224b
酚醛树脂 phenol-formaldehyde resin (plastic) 化合物 13—224a
酚噻嗪 phenothiazine 兽医用药物 13—224f
酚酞 phenolphthalein 化合物 13—224a
酚系数 phenol coefficient 化学 13—224a
坟墓 tomb 墓葬 17—143f
汾河 Fen He 中国河流 6—272a
焚风 foehn 气象学 6—384c
焚化炉 incinerator 焚化设备 8—352c
焚书坑儒 fenshu-kengru 中国历史 6—277e
鼢鼠 zokor 啮齿类动物 18—562a
粉孢子 oidium 真菌 12—354a
粉笔画 chalk drawing 绘画 4—32b
粉彩地 fundamiji 日本工艺 6—525f
粉蠹 powder-post beetle 昆虫 13—471d
粉红色系列色料 famille rose 中国彩瓷色系 6—227c
粉红色仙犰狳 pichiciego 哺乳动物 13—288c
粉蚧 mealybug 昆虫 11—62d
粉螟 flour moth (*Ephestia*, or *Anagasta*, *kuehniella*) 昆虫 6—374d
粉末镀锌 sherardizing 冶金 15—305e
粉末冶金 powder metallurgy 冶金学 13—471c
粉青陶瓷 punch'ŏng pottery 朝鲜彩绘青瓷 14—26c
粉砂 silt 矿物 15—375a
粉砂岩 siltstone 岩石 15—375a
粉虱 whitefly 昆虫 18—235d
粉纹夜蛾 cabbage looper 昆虫 3—304f
奋斗 mujāhadah 伊斯兰教苏非派用语 11—472b
奋锐党 Zealot 古代犹太教派别 18—504c
奋森氏牙龈炎 Vincent's gingivitis 疾病 17—568d
奋兴运动 revivalism 基督教 14—252a
忿激派 Enragé 法国组织派别 6—86b
愤怒的青年 Angry Young Men 英国文学 1—352c
粪便 feces 排泄物 6—259f
粪肥 manure 农业 10—478a
粪化石 coprolite 古生物学 4—494c
粪类圆线虫 threadworm (*Strongyloides stercoralis*) 寄生虫 17—63a
粪蝇 dung fly 昆虫 5—461d
丰臣秀次 Toyotomi Hidetsugu 日本武士 17—184b

丰臣秀吉 Toyotomi Hideyoshi 日本封建领主 17—184c
丰臣秀赖 Toyotomi Hideyori 日本封建领主 17—184b
丰川 Toyokawa 日本城市 17—183f
丰迪 Fondi 意大利城镇 6—392a
丰迪拉克 Fond du Lac 美国城市 6—391e
丰镐遗址 Feng and Hao sites 中国考古遗址 6—273d
丰国 Toyokuni (artist) 日本艺术家 17—184a
丰克 Funk, Walther 德国经济学家 6—527d
丰满水库 Fengman Shuiku 中国水库 6—275e
丰桥 Toyohashi 日本城市 17—183f
丰饶角 horn of plenty 装饰 8—176a
丰人 Fon 非洲民族 6—391c
丰塞卡 Fonseca, Manuel Deodoro da 巴西总统 6—392b
丰塞卡湾 Fonseca, Gulf of 太平洋水湾 6—392b
丰沙尔 Funchal 葡萄牙城市 6—522f
丰盛港 Mersing 马来西亚港口 11—136b
丰塔纳 Fontana, Carlo 意大利建筑师、出版家 6—392f
丰塔纳 Fontana, Domenico 意大利建筑师 6—393b
丰塔纳侯爵 Fontanes, Louis, marquis de 法国文学家 6—393d
丰特夫罗拉拜 Fontevrault-l'Abbaye 法国村庄 6—394a
丰特奈尔 Fontenelle, Bernard Le Bovier, sieur de 法国科学家 6—393e
丰特努瓦战役 Fontenoy, Battle of 欧洲历史 6—393f
丰田 Toyota 日本城市 17—184a
丰田汽车公司 Toyota Motor Corporation 日本公司 17—184a
丰原 Fengyuan 中国城市 6—276b
丰中 Toyonaka 日本城市 17—184a
丰子恺 Feng Zikai 中国漫画家 6—275b
风 wind 气象学 18—280f
风暴 storm 气象学 16—255d
风暴性大火 fire storm 火灾 6—327b
风车 windmill 风能装置 18—283a
风成声 eolian sound 物理学 6—93a
风笛 bagpipe 管乐器 2—138b
风洞 wind tunnel 空气动力学 18—282a
风格 maniera 艺术风格 10—461b
风格化演出法 theatricalism 戏剧 17—19b
风格派 Stijl, De 荷兰艺术家团体 16—236e
风格学 stylistics 语言学 16—293f
风格主义 Mannerism 意大利艺术风格 10—467d
风寒 windchill 气象学 18—282c
风花 windflower 植物 18—282e
风化 efflorescence 化学 5—555a
风化 weathering 化学 18—155f
风化硅土 tripoli 矿物 17—225c
风机 fan 送风装置 6—230d
风景如画风格 Picturesque style 建筑学 13—292d
风景诗 topographical poetry 诗歌类型 17—156f
风棱石 ventifact 矿物 17—507d
风棱石(平原) gibber 澳大利亚地理 7—117e
风铃 wind-bell 风推动发声的共振部件 18—281b
风铃草 bellflower 草本植物 2—365c
风陵渡 Fenglingdu 中国渡口 6—275e
风吕 furo 日本式沐浴 6—531b
风玫瑰图 wind rose 气象学 18—282a
风鸣琴 Aeolian harp 弦乐器 1—94e
风鸟科 Paradisaeidae (bird family) 动物学 13—31a
风切变 wind shear 气象学 18—282a
风区 fetch 海洋学 6—297b
风骚女仆 soubrette 戏剧人物 15—525e
《风尚》 Esquire 美国杂志 6—134c
风尚喜剧 manners, comedy of 戏剧 10—467e
风湿病 rheumatism 疾病 14—261b
风湿热 rheumatic fever 疾病 14—261a
风水地理说 p'ungsuchirisol 朝鲜宗教 14—26f
风俗画 genre painting 艺术 7—66c
风俗主义 costumbrismo 西班牙文学 4—534f
风速计 anemometer 仪表 1—338b
风塔 Winds, Tower of the 雅典计时建筑物 18—284a
风味小菜 relish 食品 14—216a
风险 risk 经济学 14—312e
风箱 bellows 机械装置 2—368c
风箱树 buttonbush 植物 3—294d
风蝎 wind scorpion 昆虫 18—282a
风信子 hyacinth 植物 8—276c
风雅 adab 文学 1—63b
风雨板 weatherboard 建筑 18—155e
《风月法令》 Ventôse Decrees 法国历史 17—508a
风疹 rubella 疾病 14—436a
风筝 kite 游戏 9—309e
枫丹白露 Fontainebleau 法国城镇 6—392d
枫丹白露画派 Fontainebleau, school of 艺术 6—392e
枫-德-哥姆洞穴 Font-de-Gaume 法国洞穴 6—392c
枫香树 sweet gum 木本植物 16—379d
封闭盆地 bolson 地貌 3—16f
封臣 vassal 历史 17—478c
封丹 Fontaine, Jean de La (poet) 法国诗人 6—392d
封地 appanage 法国历史 1—417b
封建土地占用制 feudal land tenure 土地制度 6—298d
封建主义 feudalism 社会制度 6—298e
封蜡 sealing wax 密封材料 15—171a
封锁 blockade 战争行动 2—538c
封·维勒布兰德氏病 von Willebrand's disease 病理学 18—47e
封檐板 bargeboard 建筑 2—227f
封印木属 Sigillaria 古生物学 15—360f
封斋 ṣawm 伊斯兰教 15—94a
砜 sulfone 化合物 16—320f
疯草 locoweed 植物 10—182a
疯马 Crazy Horse 美国印第安人首领 4—574a
疯人哈里发 Mad Caliph 埃及统治者 10—364c
峰峦俱乐部 Sierra Club 美国组织 15—357e
锋 front 气象学 6—501e
蜂巢珊瑚 Favosites 古生物学 6—254f
蜂巢屋 beehive house 原始房屋 2—330a
蜂巢星团 Beehive (stars) 天文学 2—329f
蜂巢状装饰 honeycomb work (architecture) 建筑 8—154d
蜂虎 bee-eater 鸟类 2—328a
蜂虎科 Meropidae (bird family) 动物学 11—133f
蜂蜡 beeswax 工蜂分泌物 2—331e
蜂虻 bee fly 昆虫 2—328b
蜂蜜 honey 蜂产品 8—153c
蜂蜜酒 mead 饮料 11—60f
蜂鸟 hummingbird 鸟类 8—248d
蜂窝 Beehive, The 法国巴黎居住区 2—329f
蜂窝框架构筑法 cellular framing (architecture) 建筑学 3—557f
蜂箱墓 beehive tomb 希腊古迹 2—330a
冯道 Feng Dao 中国五代宰相 6—273e
冯德尔 Vondel, Joost van den 荷兰作家 18—48a
冯桂芬 Feng Guifen 中国政论家 6—273e
冯国璋 Feng Guozhang 中国直系军阀首领 6—273e
冯·吉尔克氏病 von Gierke's disease 病理学 18—47b
冯梦龙 Feng Menglong 中国文学家 6—273f
冯内古特 Vonnegut, Kurt, Jr. 美国小说家 18—48a
冯·诺伊曼 von Neumann, John 美国数学家 18—47c
冯塔纳 Fontane, Theodor 德国作家 6—393c
冯特 Wundt, Wilhelm 德国生理学家 18—359e

冯维辛 Fonvizin, Denis Ivanovich 俄国戏剧家 6—394d
冯·许格尔 von Hügel, Friedrich, FREIHERR (Baron) VON HÜGEL 天主教哲学家 18—47c
冯雪峰 Feng Xuefeng 中国作家 6—274b
冯友兰 Feng Youlan 中国哲学家 6—274c
冯玉祥 Feng Yuxiang 中国爱国将领 6—274e
冯云山 Feng Yunshan 中国太平天国领袖 6—274e
冯至 Feng Zhi 中国诗人、翻译学 6—275a
缝合线 stylolite 地质学 16—294a
缝匠肌 sartorius muscle 解剖学 15—71f
缝纫机 sewing machine 机器 15—244a
讽刺画 caricature 绘画 3—458c
讽刺诗 iambe 诗歌 8—299e
讽刺文 lampoon 文学 9—468c
讽刺文 pasquinade 文学体裁 13—75e
讽刺作品 satire 艺术形式 15—77e
讽喻 allegory 艺术、文学 1—236e
凤蝶 swallowtail butterfly 昆虫 16—371c
凤冠雉 curassow 鸟类 5—67a
凤凰 fenghuang 中国神话中的神鸟 6—275e
凤凰 phoenix 古埃及、古希腊神话中的鸟 13—256b
凤凰公园暗杀事件 Phoenix Park murders 英国历史事件 13—256c
凤凰木 royal poinciana (*Delonix regia*) 木本植物 14—432c
凤晶 Ho Sho 日本女诗人 8—108e
凤梨目 Bromeliales 植物学 3—176c
凤山 Fengshan 中国城市 6—276a
凤头鹦鹉 cockatoo 鸟类 4—321c
凤头雨燕 crested swift 鸟类 5—8d
凤仙花属 Impatiens 植物学 8—345b
奉化 Fenghua 中国城市 6—275d
奉贤 Fengxian 中国上海市辖区 6—276b
佛得角 Cape Verde 非洲岛国 3—423c
佛得角 Verde, Cape 非洲岛国 17—511f
佛得角半岛 Cape Verde Peninsula 塞内加尔半岛 3—424b
佛得角海盆 Cape Verde Basin 大西洋海底凹地 3—424b
佛顶尊胜 Usnīsavijayā 佛教菩萨 17—423e
佛法僧 roller 鸟类 14—360b
佛法僧科 Coraciidae (bird family) 动物学 4—496e
佛法僧类 coraciiform 鸟类 4—496e
佛光山 Foguang Shan 中国佛教圣地 6—386a
佛光寺 Foguang Monastery 中国古佛寺 6—385f
佛教 Buddhism 宗教 3—228a
佛教混合梵语 Buddhist Hybrid Sanskrit language 语言 3—229b
佛教结集大会 Buddhist council 佛教徒国际会议 3—229a
佛教密宗 Tantric Buddhism 佛教 16—470b
佛兰德(斯) Flanders 欧洲中世纪公国 6—347f
佛兰德(斯) Flanders 比利时行政大区 6—348a
佛兰德牧牛狗 Bouvier des Flanders 欧洲牧牛狗 3—90e
佛兰德斯大师 Flémalle, Master of 佛兰德斯画家 6—355a
佛兰德斯式砌合 Flemish bond 砖石建筑 6—356f
佛兰德斯学派 Flemish school (music) 音乐风格 6—357b
佛兰德斯艺术 Flemish art 艺术 6—356d
佛兰芒布拉班特 Flemish Brabant 比利时省份 6—356f
佛兰芒人和瓦隆人 Fleming and Walloon 比利时民族 6—356c
佛兰芒语 Flemish language 欧洲语言 6—357a
佛兰芒运动 Flemish movement 比利时民族主义运动 6—357b
佛朗哥 Franco, Francisco 西班牙统治者 6—445d
佛罗里达 Florida 古巴城市 6—368c
佛罗里达 Florida 美国州名 6—368c
佛罗里达 Florida 乌拉圭城市 6—372c
佛罗里达海峡 Florida, Straits of 北美海峡 6—372c
佛罗里达群岛 Florida Keys 美国岛群 6—372d
佛罗里达湾 Florida Bay 美国海湾 6—372d
佛罗里达洋流 Florida Current 大西洋洋流 6—372d
佛罗伦萨 Florence 意大利城市 6—363f
佛罗伦萨大学 Florence, University of 意大利大学 6—367a
佛罗伦萨会议 Florence, Council of 宗教会议 6—367a
佛罗伦萨马赛克 Florentine mosaic 艺术 6—367d
佛罗伦萨网形粗布刺绣品 Florentine canvas work 工艺品 6—367c
佛罗伦萨钻石 Florentine diamond 宝石 6—367c
佛罗伦修斯 Florentius, Georgius 法兰克学者 6—367d
佛洛顿战役 Flodden, Battle of 英国历史 6—362a
佛蒙特 Vermont 美国州名 17—517e
佛帕 Foppa, Vincenzo 意大利画家 6—397f
佛山 Foshan 中国城市 6—419f
佛狮 Lion of Fo 中国艺术 10—128e
佛手瓜 chayote (*Sechium edule*) 藤本植物 4—97e
佛斯 Foss, Lukas 美国作曲家 6—420a
《佛所行赞》 Buddhacarita 释迦牟尼传记 3—228a
佛塔 pagoda 佛教建筑 12—545e
佛坛 butsudan 日本家庭佛教祭坛 3—291e
佛提乌,圣 Photius, SAINT 君士坦丁堡牧首 13—261a
佛提乌分裂 Photian Schism 东西两派教会之间的争论 13—260f
佛统 Nakhon Pathom 泰国城镇 11—547b
佛陀 Buddha 佛教创始人 3—227e
佛音 Buddhaghosa 印度佛教学者 3—228a
佛子岭水库 Foziling Reservoir 中国水库 6—433e
否认原则 nullification 美国历史 12—294e
夫差 Fuchai 中国春秋时期吴王 6—508b
夫兰克 Frank, Ilya Mikhaylovich 苏联物理学家 6—448a
夫兰克 Franck, James 美国物理学家 6—444f
夫兰克-赫兹实验 Franck-Hertz experiment 物理学 6—445b
夫琅和费 Fraunhofer, Joseph von 德国物理学家 6—456d
夫琅和费线 Fraunhofer lines 物理学 6—456e
夫累铭 Fleming, Sir John Ambrose 英国电气工程师 6—355d
夫权 manus 罗马法律 10—478a
呋喃 furan 化合物 6—529b
麸皮 bran 食物 3—118a
跗骨 tarsal 解剖学 16—486a
孵育 incubation 动物学 8—353f
弗班克 Firbank, (Arthur Annesley) Ronald 英国小说家 6—324e
弗比什 Furbish, Catharine 美国植物学家 6—529b
弗德尔 Feder, Gottfried 德国政治活动家 6—260c
弗德里克 Fdérik 毛里塔尼亚村庄 6—257e
弗德台地国家公园 Mesa Verde National Park 美国公园 11—138b
弗登 Virden 加拿大城镇 18—6b
弗登 Virden 美国城市 18—6b
弗迪格里斯河 Verdigris River 美国河流 17—513a
弗尔贝格 Forberg, Friedrich Karl 德国哲学家 6—398b
弗尔菲 Furphy, Joseph 澳大利亚作家 6—531c
弗尔讷 Veurne 比利时城市 17—532e
弗尔萨姆文化遗存 Folsom complex 北美古文化 6—391a
弗尔斯特 Förster, Josef Bohuslav 捷克作曲家 6—412a
弗尔斯特-尼采 Förster-Nietzsche, Elisabeth 德国编辑 6—412c
弗格拉什 Făgăraş 罗马尼亚城镇 6—212c
弗格拉什山脉 Făgăraş Mountains 罗马尼亚山脉 6—212d
弗格森 Ferguson, Abbie Park 美国教育家 6—283f
弗格森 Ferguson, Adam 苏格兰哲学家 6—284a
弗格森 Ferguson, Elizabeth Graeme 美国作家 6—284b
弗格森 Ferguson, Harry George 爱尔兰工业家 6—284c
弗格森 Ferguson, Patrick 英国军人 6—284c
弗格森 Ferguson, Robert 苏格兰阴谋家 6—284d
弗格森 Fergusson, Robert 苏格兰诗人 6—284e
弗格森 Ferguson, Samuel David 非洲圣公会第一位美国人主教 6—284d
弗格森 Ferguson, Tom R. 美国骑马牧者冠军 6—284e

弗格森岛 Fergusson Island 巴布亚新几内亚岛屿 6—284f
弗格斯福尔斯 Fergus Falls 美国城市 6—283f
弗吉尔统 Virgilian series 地质学 18—8b
"弗吉尼厄斯"号事件 Virginius affair 美国历史 18—14c
弗吉尼亚 Virginia 南非城镇 18—9f
弗吉尼亚 Virginia 美国城市 18—9f
弗吉尼亚 Virginia 美国州名 18—9f
弗吉尼亚比奇 Virginia Beach 美国城市 18—13c
弗吉尼亚城 Virginia City 美国蒙大拿州城市 18—13e
弗吉尼亚城 Virginia City 美国内华达州城镇 18—13e
弗吉尼亚大学 Virginia, University of 美国大学 18—13b
弗吉尼亚海角战役 Virginia Capes, Battle of 美国历史 18—13d
《弗吉尼亚和肯塔基决议》 Virginia and Kentucky Resolutions 美国历史 18—13c
弗吉尼亚里尔舞 Virginia reel 舞蹈 18—14b
弗吉尼亚鹿 Virginia deer 哺乳动物 18—14b
弗吉尼亚爬山虎 Virginia creeper (*Parthenocissus quinquefolia*) 植物 18—13f
弗吉尼亚瀑布 Virginia Falls 加拿大瀑布 18—14b
《弗吉尼亚人权宣言》 Virginia Declaration of Rights 美国史 18—14a
弗克拉布鲁克 Vøcklabruck 奥地利城市 18—32a
弗拉奥伯爵 Flahaut de la Billarderie, Auguste (-Charles-Joseph), comte de 法国军官 6—345b
弗拉奥提斯 Phraortes 米底国王 13—268b
弗拉察 Vratsa 保加利亚城镇 18—53c
弗拉迪米雷斯库 Vladimirescu, Tudor 瓦拉几亚英雄 18—30a
弗拉迪斯拉斯 Vladislas 统治者之名 18—30a
弗拉迪斯拉斯二世 Vladislas II 波希米亚国王 18—30b
弗拉迪耶 vrātya 印度苦行者 18—53c
弗拉尔丁恩 Vlaardingen 荷兰城市 18—28f
弗拉法希灵 fravashi 宗教 6—456f
弗拉盖 Flaget, Benedict Joseph 美国主教 6—344d
弗拉戈纳尔 Fragonard, Jean-Honoré 法国画家 6—435a
弗拉格 Flagg, James Montgomery 美国画家 6—344e
弗拉格勒 Flagler, Henry M(orrison) 美国金融家 6—344e
弗拉格斯塔 Flagstad, Kirsten 挪威歌唱家 6—344f
弗拉格斯塔夫 Flagstaff 美国城市 6—345a
弗拉基米尔 Vladimir 俄罗斯州名 18—29b
弗拉基米尔 Vladimir 俄罗斯城市 18—29b
弗拉基米尔二世 Vladimir II Monomakh 基辅大公 18—29d
弗拉基米尔-苏兹达尔画派 Vladimir-Suzdal school 绘画 18—29e
弗拉基米尔-沃伦斯基 Vladimir-Volynsky 乌克兰城市 18—30a
弗拉基米尔一世 Vladimir I 基辅大公 18—29d
弗拉季卡夫卡兹 Vladikavkaz 俄罗斯城市 18—29b
弗拉卡斯托罗 Fracastoro, Girolamo 意大利医生、天文学家 6—433f
弗拉克斯宾德 Flachsbinder, Jan (Polish Renaissance poet) 波兰诗人 6—342c
弗拉克斯曼 Flaxman, John 英国雕刻家 6—353b
弗拉库斯 Flaccus, Aulus Persius (Roman satirist) 罗马讽刺作家 6—342b
弗拉库斯 Flaccus, Gaius Valerius (Roman epic poet) 罗马史诗诗人 6—342c
弗拉库斯 Flaccus, Marcus Verrius (Roman teacher) 罗马学者 6—342c
弗拉库斯 Flaccus, Quintus Horatius (Roman lyric poet) 罗马诗人 6—342c
弗拉曼克 Vlaminck, Maurice de 法国画家 18—30d
弗拉-毛罗环形山 Fra Mauro 月球环形山 6—433f
弗拉米尼努斯 Flamininus, Titus Quinctius 罗马将军 6—347c
弗拉米尼乌斯 Flaminius, Gaius 罗马政治家 6—347d
弗拉明科 flamenco 舞蹈和音乐 6—346e
弗拉姆 Frahm, Karl Herbert 德国政治家 6—435c
弗拉姆斯蒂德 Flamsteed, John 英国天文学家 6—347e
弗拉纳根 Flannagan, John Bernard 美国雕刻家 6—348b
弗拉其人 Vlach 欧洲民族 18—28f
弗拉塞德人 Flathead 美国民族 6—350b
弗拉施 Frasch, Herman 美国化学家 6—454f
弗拉施法 Frasch process 采矿方法 6—454f
弗拉斯阶 Frasnian Stage 地质学 6—455f
弗拉斯卡蒂 Frascati 意大利城镇 6—454e
弗拉索夫 Vlasov, Andrey Andreyevich 苏联军人 18—30f
弗拉泰利尼家族 Fratellini FAMILY 法国马戏演员世家 6—456a
弗拉特黑德河 Flathead River 北美河流 6—350d
弗拉特黑德湖 Flathead Lake 美国湖泊 6—350c
弗拉特斯 Phraates 安息国王之名 13—267f
弗拉特斯二世 Phraates II 安息国王 13—267f
弗拉特斯三世 Phraates III 安息国王 13—267f
弗拉特斯四世 Phraates IV 安息国王 13—268a
弗拉特斯五世 Phraates V 安息国王 13—268a
弗拉维安，圣 Flavian, SAINT 君士坦丁堡牧首 6—352a
弗拉维安二世(安提阿的) Flavian II OF ANTIOCH 安提阿牧首 6—352a
弗拉维安一世(安提阿的) Flavian I OF ANTIOCH 安提阿主教 6—351f
弗拉维大斗兽场 Flavian Amphitheatre 罗马大斗兽场 6—352b
弗拉维尼 Flavigny, Marie-Catherine-Sophie de 法国作家 6—352b
弗拉维王朝 Flavian DYNASTY 古罗马王朝 6—352a
弗拉维乌斯 Flavius 罗马人名 6—352b
弗拉维乌斯 Flavius, Gnaeus 罗马法律学者 6—352b
弗拉希乌斯·伊利里库斯 Flacius Illyricus, Matthias 欧洲宗教改革家 6—342c
弗拉兴 Flushing (The Netherlands) 荷兰城市 6—379d
弗拉兴 Flushing 美国市区 6—379e
弗莱彻 Fletcher, Alice Cunningham 美国人类学家 6—357e
弗莱彻 Fletcher, Harvey 美国物理学家 6—358a
弗莱彻 Fletcher, John 英国戏剧家 6—358b
弗莱彻 Fletcher, Phineas 英格兰诗人 6—358e
弗莱彻(老) Fletcher, Giles, THE ELDER 英国诗人、作家 6—357f
弗莱彻(小) Fletcher, Giles, THE YOUNGER 英国诗人 6—358a
弗莱德曼 Friedman, Ignacy 波兰钢琴家 6—492d
弗莱厄蒂 Flaherty, Robert (Joseph) 美国记录片之父 6—345c
弗莱福兰 Flevoland 荷兰省份 6—359c
弗莱格尔 Flegel, Eduard Robert 德国探险家 6—354e
弗莱河 Fly River 巴布亚新几内亚河流 6—380f
弗莱河龟 Fly River turtle 爬行动物 6—381a
弗莱克诺 Flecknoe, Richard 英格兰诗人 6—354c
弗莱克斯纳 Flexner, Abraham 美国教育家 6—359d
弗莱克斯纳 Flexner, Simon 美国病理学家 6—359e
弗莱梅尔 Flémalle, Bertholet 佛兰德斯画家 6—354f
弗莱明 Fleming, Sir Alexander 苏格兰细菌学家 6—355b
弗莱明 Fleming, Sir Arthur Percy Morris 英国雷达工程师 6—355c
弗莱明 Fleming, Ian (Lancaster) 英国作家 6—355c
弗莱明 Fleming, Peggy (Gale) 美国花样滑冰运动员 6—355e
弗莱明 Fleming, Renée 美国女高音歌唱家 6—355f
弗莱明 Fleming, Richard H(owell) 美国海洋学家 6—356a
弗莱明 Fleming, Sir Sandford 加拿大土木工程师 6—356a
弗莱明 Fleming, Victor 美国导演 6—356b
弗莱明 Flemming, Walther 德国遗传学家 6—357b
弗莱明 Fleming, Williamina Paton Stevens 美国天文学家 6—356b
弗莱氏试验 Frei test 诊断方法 6—473c
弗莱特纳 Flettner, Anton 德国发明家 6—358e
弗莱谢尔 Fleischer, Nat 美国体育记者 6—354f
弗莱谢尔兄弟 Fleischer, Dave and Max 美国动画家 6—354e
弗赖 Frey, Adolf 瑞士作家 6—489d
弗赖 Fry, Christopher 英国剧作家 6—505e

弗赖 Fry, Elizabeth 英国慈善家 6—506a
弗赖 Fry, Roger (Eliot) 英国美术理论家 6—506a
弗赖堡 Freiburg (Switzerland) 瑞士州首府 6—473e
弗赖堡 Freiburg 德国行政区 6—473c
弗赖堡阿尔贝特-路德维希大学 Freiburg, Albert Ludwig University of 德国大学 6—473e
弗赖贝格 Freiberg 德国城市 6—473c
弗赖本托斯 Fray Bentos 乌拉圭城市 6—457a
弗赖伯格 Freyberg (of Wellington and of Munstead), Bernard Cyril Freyberg, 1st Baron 新西兰总司令 6—489e
弗赖丹克 Freidank 德国诗人 6—473f
弗赖利格拉特 Freiligrath, (Hermann) Ferdinand 德国诗人 6—474c
弗赖施塔特 Freistadt 奥地利城镇 6—474d
弗赖斯暴动 Fries's Rebellion 美国历史 6—494c
弗赖斯-格林 Friese-Greene, William 英国摄影机发明家 6—494b
弗赖塔格 Freytag, Gustav 德国作家 6—490d
弗赖-维斯林 Frey-Wyssling, Albert F(riedrich) 瑞士植物学家 6—489e
弗赖辛 Freising 德国城市 6—474c
弗赖伊 Frye, Northrop 加拿大文学评论家 6—506b
弗赖与德鲁 Fry, E. Maxwell; and Drew, Jane 英国建筑师 6—505e
弗兰巴德 Flambard, Ranulf 英格兰大臣 6—345e
弗兰伯勒角 Flamborough Head 英国岬角 6—346b
弗兰茨 Francis 神圣罗马帝国皇帝 6—440c
弗兰茨 Franz, Robert 德国作曲家 6—454d
弗兰茨二世 Francis II 神圣罗马帝国皇帝 6—441a
弗兰茨·斐迪南 Franz Ferdinand 奥地利大公 6—454d
弗兰茨一世 Francis I 奥地利皇帝 6—440b
弗兰茨一世 Francis I 神圣罗马帝国皇帝 6—441a
弗兰格尔 Wrangel, Ferdinand Petrovich 俄国探险家 18—342a
弗兰格尔 Wrangel, Pyotr Nikolayevich, Baron 俄国军人 18—342b
弗兰格尔伯爵 Wrangel, Karl Gustav, Greve (Count) 瑞典军人 18—342a
弗兰格尔岛 Wrangel Island 俄罗斯远东岛屿 18—342c
弗兰科 Franco (antipope) 敌对教皇 6—445d
弗兰科尼亚山峡 Franconia Notch 美国山峡 6—447c
弗兰克 Frank, Anne 德国日记作者 6—447e
弗兰克 Francke, August Hermann 德国宗教领袖 6—445b
弗兰克 Franck, César (Auguste) 比利时裔法国作曲家 6—444b
弗兰克 Frank, Hans 德国政治家 6—447f
弗兰克 Frank, Jacob 波兰宗教领袖 6—448a
弗兰克 Frank, Karl Hermann 苏台德区德国纳粹分子 6—440b
弗兰克 Frank, Leonhard 德国作家 6—448b
弗兰克 Frank, Robert 美国摄影家 6—448c
弗兰克 Franck, Sebastian 巴伐利亚神学家 6—445a
弗兰克尔 Frankel, Zacharias 德国神学家 6—448d
弗兰克福特 Frankfurter, Felix 美国最高法院大法官 6—450b
弗兰克画师 Francke, Meister 德国画家 6—445c
弗兰克兰 Frankland, Sir Edward 英国化学家 6—450f
弗兰克兰(夫人) Frankland, Agnes Surriage, Lady 美国殖民地时期的名人 6—450e
弗兰克林山 Franconian Forest 德国高地 6—447c
弗兰克斯 Franks, Sir Augustus Wollaston 英格兰艺术品收藏家 6—454b
弗兰肯斯坦 Frankenstein 作品中的怪物 6—448e
弗兰肯塔尔 Frankenthal 德国城市 6—448e
弗兰肯特勒 Frankenthaler, Helen 美国画家 6—448f
弗兰肯图恩 Frankenthurn, Paul, Freiherr Gautsch von 奥地利首相 6—449a
弗兰纳 Flanner, Janet 美国作家 6—348d
弗兰普顿 Frampton, Sir George James 英国艺术家 6—435f
弗兰契斯卡·达·里米尼 Francesca da Rimini 意大利文学人物 6—439b
弗兰恰比焦 Franciabigio 意大利画家 6—440a
弗兰切斯基尼 Franceschini, Baldassare 意大利画家 6—439c
弗兰切斯基尼 Franceschini, Marcantonio 意大利画家 6—439c
弗兰切斯科 Francesco di Cristofano 意大利画家 6—439d
弗兰森 Franzén, Frans Mikael 芬兰裔瑞典诗人 6—454e
弗兰西斯 Francis 统治者之名 6—440b
弗兰西斯 Francis, Lydia Maria 美国作家 6—442c
弗兰西斯(昂古莱姆的) Francis of Angoulême 法国国王 6—441d
弗兰西斯二世 Francis II 布列塔尼公爵 6—440c
弗兰西斯二世 Francis II 法国国王 6—440f
弗兰西斯·斐迪南 Francis Ferdinand, archduke of Austria-Este 奥地利大公 6—442e
弗兰西斯一世 Francis I 布列塔尼公爵 6—440c
弗兰西斯·约瑟夫 Francis Joseph 奥匈帝国皇帝 6—442f
弗朗丹 Flandin, Pierre-Étienne 法国政治家 6—348a
弗朗蒂努斯 Frontinus, Sextus Julius 罗马军人、著者 6—502c
弗朗基港 Port-Francqui 刚果(金)城镇 13—445a
弗朗卡 Franca 巴西城市 6—436a
弗朗科尼 Franconi, Antonio 法国马戏创始人 6—447a
《弗朗克兰-布荣条约》 Franklin-Bouillon Agreement 法国-土耳其历史 6—453f
弗朗齐歇克矿泉村 Františkovy Lázně 捷克城镇 6—454c
弗朗奇亚 Francia 意大利艺术家 6—439f
弗朗恰 Vrancea 罗马尼亚县名 18—53b
弗朗切斯(罗马的),圣 Frances of Rome, Saint 意大利修女 6—439b
弗朗切斯科-迪乔治 Francesco di Giorgio 意大利艺术家 6—439d
弗朗瑞 Franju, Georges 法国导演 6—447c
弗朗塞斯卡蒂 Francescatti, Zino 法国小提琴演奏家 6—439c
弗朗什孔泰 Franche-Comté 法国历史地区 6—439e
弗朗斯维尔 Franceville 加蓬城镇 6—439d
弗朗特岭 Front Range 美国山脉 6—502a
弗朗西斯 Francis, James Bicheno 美国水利工程师 6—442b
弗朗西斯 Francis, Sir Philip 英国政治家 6—442c
弗朗西斯 Francis, Sam 美国画家 6—442d
弗朗西斯 Francis, Thomas, Jr. 美国微生物学家 6—442e
弗朗西斯(一世) Francis (I) 托斯卡纳大公 6—441c
弗朗西斯堡 Fort Frances 加拿大城镇 6—413e
弗朗西斯·博尔吉亚 Francis Borgia, Saint 西班牙耶稣会总会长 6—441d
弗朗西斯敦 Francistown 博茨瓦纳城镇 6—444a
弗朗西斯二世 Francis II 两西西里国王 6—441d
弗朗西斯卡 Francesca, Piero della (painter) 意大利画家 6—400b
弗朗西斯一世 Francis I 法国国王 6—440d
弗朗西斯一世 Francis I 两西西里国王 6—441c
弗朗西亚 Francia, José Gaspar Rodríguez de 巴拉圭独裁者 6—440a
弗朗谢·德斯佩雷 Franchet d'Esperey, Louis-Félix-François 法国元帅 6—439e
弗劳德 Froude, James Anthony 英国历史学家 6—503f
弗劳德 Froude, Richard Hurrell 英国神学家 6—504a
弗劳德 Froude, William 英国工程师 6—504b
弗劳德数 Froude number 物理学 6—504c
弗劳登塔尔 Freudenthal, Axel Olof 芬兰语言学家 6—489c
弗劳恩费尔德 Frauenfeld 瑞士州首府 6—456c
弗劳恩洛布 Frauenlob 德国吟游诗人 6—456d
弗劳尔 Flower, Lucy Louisa Coues 美国福利工作者 6—375d
弗劳尔 Flower, Sir William Henry 英国动物学家 6—375e
弗劳利(小) Frawley, Patrick Joseph, Jr. 美国企业家 6—456f
弗勒德 Flood, Curt 美国棒球运动员 6—362e
弗勒德 Flood, Henry 英格兰-爱尔兰政治家 6—362e
弗勒丁 Fröding, Gustaf 瑞典诗人 6—498e
弗勒里 Fleury 法国演员 6—359a
弗勒里 Fleury, André-Hercule de 法国红衣主教 6—359b

弗勒利希氏综合征 Fröhlich's syndrome 疾病 6—500b
弗勒侣斯 Fleurus 比利时城市 6—358f
弗勒侣斯战役 Fleurus, Battle of 欧洲历史 6—359a
弗勒明 Fleming, Paul 德国诗人 6—355e
弗勒什毛尔蒂 Vörösmarty, Mihály 匈牙利诗人、戏剧家 18—49d
弗雷 Freyr 古斯堪的纳维亚神话 6—490b
弗雷 Frey, Roger 法国政治家 6—489d
弗雷(蒙塔尔瓦) Frei (Montalva), Eduardo 智利总统 6—473b
弗雷德 Wrede, Karl Philipp, Fürst von 巴伐利亚陆军元帅 18—343a
弗雷德霍姆 Fredholm, (Erik) Ivar 瑞典数学家 6—467f
弗雷德加留斯 Fredegarius 法兰克历史学家 6—457f
弗雷德里克 Frederic, Harold 美国记者 6—458a
弗雷德里克 Frederick, PRINCE OF WALES 威尔士亲王 6—464f
弗雷德里克 Frederick 美国城市 6—464e
弗雷德里克顿 Fredericton 加拿大城市 6—467c
弗雷德里克·路易斯 Frederick Louis, PRINCE OF WALES 威尔士亲王 6—465f
弗雷德里克斯堡 Fredericksburg 美国城市 6—467b
弗雷德里克斯堡战役 Fredericksburg, Battle of 美国南北战争 6—467c
弗雷德里克斯塔德 Frederiksted 美属维尔京群岛城镇 6—467e
弗雷德罗 Fredro, Aleksander 波兰喜剧家 6—468a
弗雷尔-奥尔邦 Frère-Orban, Hubert Joseph Walther 比利时首相 6—483c
弗雷格 Frege, (Friedrich Ludwig) Gottlob 德国数学家 6—472f
弗雷克茨-莫杰夫斯基 Frycz-Modrzewski, Andrzej (writer) 波兰作家 6—506b
弗雷里 Freyre, Gilberto de Mello 巴西社会学家 6—490c
弗雷里克斯 Frerichs, Friedrich Theodor von 德国病理学家 6—483d
弗雷林 Freleng, Friz 美国动画片设计家 6—474d
弗雷隆 Fréron, Louis(-Marie-Stanislas) 法国新闻工作者 6—483e
弗雷米 Frémy, Edmond 法国化学家 6—475d
弗雷明汉 Framingham 美国城镇 6—435f
弗雷姆 Frame, Janet 新西兰作家 6—435c
弗雷纳 Fresnay, Pierre 法国演员 6—484e
弗雷瑞斯 Fréjus 法国城镇 6—474d
弗雷什菲尔德 Freshfield, Douglas William 英国探险家 6—484c
弗雷什沃特 Freshwater 英国堂区 6—484c
弗雷斯科巴尔第 Frescobaldi, Girolamo 意大利作曲家 6—484a
弗雷斯科巴尔第家族 Frescobaldi FAMILY 意大利银行世家 6—483f
弗雷斯尼约 Fresnillo 墨西哥城市 6—485b
弗雷斯诺 Fresno 美国城市 6—485b
弗雷西内 Freycinet, Charles-Louis de Saulces de 法国总理 6—489f
弗雷西内 Freycinet, Louis-Claude de Saulces de 法国制图学家 6—490a
弗雷西内 Freyssinet, (Marie-) Eugène(-Léon) 法国工程师 6—490c
弗雷西内半岛 Freycinet Peninsula 澳大利亚半岛 6—490b
弗雷歇 Fréchet, (René-) Maurice 法国数学家 6—457d
弗雷谢特 Fréchette, Louis-Honoré 加拿大诗人 6—457e
弗雷泽 Frietschie, Barbara Hauer 美国爱国者 6—494d
弗雷泽 Fraser, Dawn 澳大利亚游泳运动员 6—455a
弗雷泽 Frazier, E(dward) Franklin 美国社会学家 6—457b
弗雷泽 Frazier, Joe 美国拳击运动员 6—457d
弗雷泽 Frazer, Sir James George 英国人类学家 6—457a
弗雷泽 Fraser, (John) Malcolm 澳大利亚总理 6—455a
弗雷泽 Fraser, Peter 新西兰总理 6—455b
弗雷泽 Fraser, Simon 加拿大探险家 6—455d
弗雷泽 Fraser, Simon 英国詹姆斯二世追随者 6—455d
弗雷泽(北角的) Fraser (of North Cape), Bruce Austin Fraser, 1st Baron 英国海军上将 6—454f
弗雷泽岛 Fraser Island 澳大利亚岛屿 6—455e
弗雷泽河 Fraser River 加拿大河流 6—455e
弗雷泽纽斯 Fresenius, Carl Remigius 德国化学家 6—484c
弗雷泽峡谷 Fraser Canyon 加拿大峡谷 6—455d
弗蕾德贡德 Fredegund 法兰克人墨洛温王后 6—457f
弗蕾迪 Friday, Nancy 美国女权主义者 6—491f
弗蕾娅 Freyja 斯堪的纳维亚女神 6—490b
弗里堡 Fribourg 瑞士州名 6—490f
弗里堡 Fribourg 瑞士州首府 6—491a
弗里波特 Freeport 巴哈马城镇 6—471e
弗里波特 Freeport 美国伊利诺伊州城市 6—471f
弗里波特 Freeport 美国得克萨斯州城市 6—471f
弗里代克-米斯泰克 Frýdek-Místek 捷克城市 6—506b
弗里德 Freed, Arthur 美国电影制片人 6—470c
弗里德 Fried, Alfred Hermann 奥地利和平主义者 6—491f
弗里德尔 Friedel, Charles 法国化学家 6—492a
弗里德尔 Friedel, Georges 法国晶体学家 6—492b
弗里德兰德 Friedländer, Ludwig Heinrich 德国历史学家 6—492c
弗里德兰战役 Friedland, Battle of 欧洲历史 6—492c
弗里德里希 Friedrich, Caspar David 德国画家 6—493a
弗里德曼 Friedmann, Andrei 美国摄影家 6—493a
弗里德曼 Friedmann, Aleksandr Aleksandrovich 俄国数学家 6—493a
弗里德曼 Friedman, Jerome Isaac 美国物理学家 6—492d
弗里德曼 Freedman, Maurice 英国学者 6—470e
弗里德曼 Friedman, Milton 美国经济学家 6—492e
弗里德曼夫妇 Friedman, William F(rederick); and Friedman, Elizebeth S(mith) 美国密码学家 6—492f
弗里登 Friedan, Betty (Naomi) 美国女权主义者 6—492a
弗里登赖希 Friedenreich, Arthur 巴西足球运动员 6—492c
弗里敦 Freetown 塞拉利昂首都 6—472c
弗里多林(塞京根的),圣 Fridolin OF SÄCKINGEN, SAINT 爱尔兰传教士 6—491f
弗里多尼亚 Fredonia 美国村庄 6—467f
弗里尔 Friel, Brian 爱尔兰剧作家 6—493c
弗里尔 Frere, Sir (Henry) Bartle (Edward), 1ST BARONET 英属殖民地官员 6—483b
弗里尔 Frere, John 英国考古学家 6—483c
弗里尔 Frere, John Hookham 英国外交家 6—483c
弗里尔艺术陈列馆 Freer Gallery of Art 美国博物馆 6—472a
弗里吉亚 Phrygia 古安纳托利亚地区 13—268e
弗里吉亚帽 Phrygian cap 服装 13—268f
弗里吉亚语 Phrygian language 古代语言 13—269a
弗里季亚调式 Phrygian mode 音乐 13—269b
弗里克 Frick, Henry Clay 美国企业家 6—491b
弗里克 Frick, Wilhelm 德国内政部长 6—491b
弗里克美术收藏馆 Frick Collection 美国艺术陈列馆 6—491c
弗里兰 Vreeland, Diana Dalziel 美国编辑、时装专家 18—53c
弗里林海森 Frelinghuysen, Frederick Theodore 美国政治家 6—474f
弗里曼 Freeman, Douglas Southall 美国作家 6—471b
弗里曼 Freeman, Morgan 美国演员 6—471c
弗里曼 Freeman, Mary Eleanor Wilkins 美国作家 6—471b
弗里曼 Freeman, Sir Ralph 英国土木工程师 6—471d
弗里曼 Freeman, Richard Austin 英国通俗小说作家 6—471d
弗里曼特尔 Fremantle 澳大利亚港市 6—475a
弗里蒙特 Fremont 美国城市 6—475a
弗里蒙特 Frémont, Jessie Ann Benton 美国作家 6—475a
弗里蒙特 Frémont, John C(harles) 美国探险家 6—475c
弗里莫尔 Friml, (Charles) Rudolf 美国作曲家 6—495c
弗里尼库 Phrynichus 雅典悲剧诗人 13—269b
弗里尼库 Phrynichus 雅典旧喜剧诗人 13—269c
弗里尼库(阿拉伯的) Phrynichus ARABIUS 希腊语法、修辞学家 13—269c
弗里尼欣 Vereeniging 南非城镇 17—513f

《弗里尼欣和约》 Vereeniging, Peace of 南非历史 17—513f
弗里奇 Fritzsche, Hans 德国新闻记者 6—497e
弗里施 Frisch, Karl von 奥地利动物学家 6—496a
弗里施 Frisch, Max (Rudolf) 瑞士剧作家 6—496b
弗里施 Frisch, Otto Robert 奥地利物理学家 6—496c
弗里施林 Frischlin, Philipp Nikodemus 德国语言学家 6—496d
弗里思 Frith, William Powell 英国画家 6—497d
弗里斯 Fries, Elias (Magnus) 瑞典植物学家 6—494a
弗里斯 Friis, Johan 丹麦政治家 6—495c
弗里斯 Fries, Jakob Friedrich 德国哲学家 6—494a
弗里斯科 Frisco (U.S.) 美国城市 6—496e
弗里斯兰 Friesland 荷兰省份 6—494b
弗里乌尔公爵 Frioul, Géraud-Christophe-Michel Duroc, duc de (duke of) 法国将军 6—495f
弗里乌角 Frio, Cape 巴西岬角 6—495f
弗里西 Frisi, Paolo 意大利物理学家 6—496e
弗里西亚 Frisia 欧洲历史地区 6—496e
弗里西亚群岛 Frisian Islands 欧洲群岛 6—497a
弗里西亚文学 Frisian literature 文学 6—497b
弗里西亚语 Frisian language 荷兰-德国语言 6—497a
弗里希 Frisch, Frank 美国棒球运动员 6—496a
弗里希 Frisch, Ragnar (Anton Kittil) 挪威经济学家 6—496c
弗里亚 Fria 几内亚区首府 6—490e
弗丽嘉 Frigg 古斯堪的纳维亚神话人物 6—495b
弗利 Forlì 意大利城市 6—408d
弗利克集团 Flick Group 德国工业企业 6—360a
弗利蓬 Phlipon, Jeanne-Marie 法国政治家 13—253b
弗利特伍德 Fleetwood, Charles 英国议会军将军 6—354c
弗利特伍德·麦克乐队 Fleetwood Mac 英国布鲁斯乐队 6—354d
弗利辛恩 Vlissingen 荷兰城市 18—31a
弗烈德里克斯 Frédérix, Jacques 法国导演 6—467e
弗林 Flynn, Elizabeth Gurley 美国政治领袖 6—382d
弗林 Flynn, Errol (Leslie Thomson) 美国电影演员 6—382e
弗林 Flynn, John 澳大利亚教士 6—382e
弗林德斯 Flinders, Matthew 英国航海家 6—361a
弗林德斯岛 Flinders Island 澳大利亚岛屿 6—361b
弗林德斯河 Flinders River 澳大利亚河流 6—361c
弗林德斯岭 Flinders Ranges 澳大利亚山峰 6—361b
弗林弗伦 Flin Flon 加拿大城市 6—360f
弗林格蒂 Ferlinghetti, Lawrence 美国诗人 6—285a
弗林克 Flinck, Govert 荷兰画家 6—361a
弗林特 Flint 美国城市 6—361e
弗林特 Flint, Austin 美国内科医生 6—361d
弗林特 Flint, F.S. 英国诗人 6—361d
弗林特岛 Flint Island 基里巴斯环礁 6—361e
弗林特郡 Flintshire 威尔士郡名 6—361f
弗林特岭洞系 Flint Ridge Cave System 美国地质地区 6—361e
弗留利-威尼斯朱利亚 Friuli-Venezia Giulia 意大利区名 6—497f
弗龙托 Fronto, Marcus Cornelius 罗马雄辩家 6—502c
弗隆特纳克伯爵 Frontenac, Louis de Buade, comte de Palluau et de 法国北美殖民地总督 6—502a
弗卢埃林 Flewelling, Ralph Tyler 美国哲学家 6—359c
弗卢德 Fludd, Robert 英国哲学家 6—376e
弗卢朗 Flourens, Marie-Jean-Pierre 法国生理学家 6—374f
弗卢门多萨河 Flumendosa River 意大利河流 6—378d
弗鲁 Frueh, Al 美国漫画家 6—504d
弗鲁孟提乌斯·圣 Frumentius, Saint 埃塞俄比亚主教 6—505c
《弗鲁瓦和布朗歇弗洛》 Floire et Blancheflor 法国浪漫故事 6—362d
弗路朗斯 Flourens, Gustave 法国巴黎公社领袖 6—374e
弗吕厄 Flüe, Saint Nicholas of 瑞士民间英雄 6—376f
弗吕霍夫拖车公司 Fruehauf Trailer Corporation 美国公司 6—504e
弗伦茨贝格 Frundsberg, Georg von 日耳曼军人 6—505d
弗伦克尔-康拉特 Fraenkel-Conrat, Heinz L(udwig) 美国生物化学家 6—434f
弗伦奇 French, Daniel Chester 美国雕刻家 6—475d
弗伦奇 French, Sir George Arthur 英国军人 6—475e
弗伦奇 French, John (Denton Pinkstone), 1st Earl of Ypres, Viscount French of Ypres and of High Lake 英国陆军元帅 6—475e
弗伦奇布罗德河 French Broad River 美国河流 6—476c
弗伦奇岛 French Island 澳大利亚岛屿 6—478d
弗伦森 Frenssen, Gustav 德国小说家 6—482f
弗伦斯堡 Flensburg 德国城市 6—357c
弗罗贝尼乌斯 Frobenius, Georg 德国数学家 6—498a
弗罗贝尼乌斯 Frobenius, Leo (Viktor) 德国人种学家 6—498b
弗罗本 Froben, Johann 瑞士印刷家 6—498a
弗罗比舍 Frobisher, Sir Martin 英格兰探险家 6—498c
弗罗比舍湾 Frobisher Bay 北大西洋海湾 6—498d
弗罗茨瓦夫 Wrocław 波兰省份 18—349a
弗罗茨瓦夫 Wrocław 波兰城市 18—349b
弗罗曼 Frohman, Charles 美国剧院经理 6—500c
弗罗芒 Froment, Nicolas 法国画家 6—500e
弗罗芒坦 Fromentin, Eugène 法国画家 6—500f
弗罗姆 Fromm, Erich 美国心理学家 6—500f
弗罗姆湖 Frome, Lake 澳大利亚间歇湖 6—500e
弗罗沙默 Frohschammer, Jakob 德国哲学家 6—500c
弗罗斯特 Frost, A(rthur) B(urdett) 美国插图画家 6—502e
弗罗斯特 Frost, John 英国社会改革家 6—502f
弗罗斯特 Frost, Robert (Lee) 美国诗人 6—502f
弗罗斯特 Frost, Sarah Frances 英国演员 6—503c
弗罗托拉 frottola 意大利世俗歌曲 6—503f
弗罗西诺内 Frosinone 意大利城市 6—502d
弗罗伊登施塔特 Freudenstadt 德国城市 6—489b
弗洛贝格 Froberger, Johann Jakob 德国作曲家 6—498b
弗洛多德 Flodoard 法兰克编年史家 6—362a
弗洛尔 Flor, Roger de 西班牙雇佣兵首领 6—363c
弗洛格斯塔德 Fløgstad, Kjartan 挪威诗人 6—362c
弗洛凯 Floquet, Charles(-Thomas) 法国政治家 6—363c
弗洛勒斯 Flores 印度尼西亚岛屿 6—367d
弗洛勒斯海 Flores Sea 南太平洋海域 6—367f
弗洛勒斯人 Homo floresiensis 生物分类学名称 8—147b
弗洛雷斯 Flores 危地马拉省份 6—367e
弗洛雷斯 Flores 危地马拉城市 6—367d
弗洛雷斯 Flórez (de Setién y Huidobro), Enrique 西班牙历史学家 6—368a
弗洛里 Florey, Howard Walter Florey, Baron 澳大利亚病理学家 6—367f
弗洛里 Flory, Paul J. 美国物理化学家 6—373f
弗洛里安 Florian 罗马皇帝 6—368b
弗洛里奥 Florio, John 英格兰辞书编纂家 6—373a
弗洛里达布兰卡伯爵 Floridablanca, José Moñino y Redondo, conde de (count of) 西班牙政治家 6—372e
弗洛里多 Floridor 法国演员 6—372f
弗洛里纳 Flórina 希腊城市 6—373a
弗洛里森特 Florissant 美国城市 6—373c
弗洛里森特化石床国家保护区 Florissant Fossil Beds National Monument 美国科罗拉多州中部多化石的山谷 6—373d
弗洛里森特组 Florissant Formation 地质学 6—373d
弗洛里斯 Flores, Isabel de 秘鲁宗教人物 6—367e
弗洛里斯岛 Flores Island 北大西洋葡属岛屿 6—367e
弗洛里斯五世 Floris V 荷兰伯爵 6—373b
弗洛里兄弟 Floris, Cornelis II and Frans 比利时艺术家 6—373b
弗洛里亚努 Floriano 巴西城市 6—368b
弗洛里亚诺波利斯 Florianópolis 巴西港口、州首府 6—368b
弗洛鲁斯 Florus, Publius Annius 非洲罗马历史学家 6—373e
弗洛伦斯 Florence 美国亚拉巴马州城市 6—366e

弗洛伦斯 Florence 美国亚利桑那州城市 6—366e
弗洛伦斯 Florence 美国南卡罗来纳州城市 6—366f
弗洛伦斯 Florence, William Jermyn 美国演员 6—367a
弗洛伦斯(伍斯特的) Florence of Worcester 英格兰修士 6—366f
弗洛伦斯基 Florensky, Pavel Alexandrovich 俄罗斯神学家 6—367b
弗洛伦西奥-巴雷拉 Florencio Varela 阿根廷城市 6—367b
弗洛伦西亚 Florencia 哥伦比亚城市 6—367b
弗洛森比格 Flossenbürg 德国集中营 6—373f
弗洛托 Flotow, Friedrich, Baron (Freiherr) von 法国作曲家 6—374a
弗洛伊德 Freud, Anna 英国心理学家 6—485c
弗洛伊德 Floyd, John Buchanan 美国政治家 6—376d
弗洛伊德 Freud, Sigmund 奥地利精神分析奠基人 6—485d
弗洛伊德(美男子) Floyd, Pretty Boy 美国劫匪 6—376d
弗洛伊德派批评理论 Freudian criticism 文学批评 6—489c
弗马纳 Fermanagh 英国区名 6—285b
弗美尔 Vermeer, Johannes 荷兰画家 17—516d
弗米利恩 Vermillion 美国城市 17—517d
弗纳尔 Vernal 美国城市 17—520b
弗纳尔德 Fernald, Merritt Lyndon 美国植物学家 6—288b
弗内森 Venaissin (French county and fief) 法国伯爵领地 17—496d
弗内斯 Furness 英国行政区 6—530a
弗内斯 Furness, Frank Heyling 美国建筑师 6—530b
弗内斯 Furness, Horace Howard 美国编纂家 6—530c
弗尼斯 Furniss, Harry 英国漫画家 6—530c
弗尼瓦尔 Furnivall, Frederick James 英国学者 6—531a
弗农 Vernon 加拿大城市 17—522b
弗诺群岛 Furneaux Group 澳大利亚岛屿和礁石 6—530a
弗奇格特 Furchgott, Robert F. 美国药理学家 6—529c
弗瑞诺 Freneau, Philip (Morin) 美国诗人 6—482e
弗思 Firth, Sir Charles (Harding) 英国历史学家 6—329c
弗思 Firth, John R(upert) 英国语言学家 6—329c
弗思 Firth, Sir Raymond (William) 新西兰人类学家 6—329d
弗斯特 Veuster, Joseph de 比利时天主教司铎 17—532f
弗瓦迪斯瓦夫 Władysław 波兰统治者之名 18—303c
弗瓦迪斯瓦夫二世 Władysław II Jagiełło 波兰国王 18—303d
弗瓦迪斯瓦夫三世 Władysław III Warneńczyk 波兰国王 18—303f
弗瓦迪斯瓦夫四世 Władysław IV Vasa 波兰国王 18—304a
弗瓦迪斯瓦夫一世 Władysław I 波兰国王 18—303c
弗沃茨瓦韦克 Włocławek 波兰省份 18—304c
弗沃茨瓦韦克 Włocławek 波兰城市 18—304b
弗歇尔男爵夫人 Feuchères, Sophie Dawes, baronne de 英国冒险家 6—298b
弗亚德 Feuillade, Louis 法国电影导演 6—299e
弗依耶 Feuillet, Raoul-Auger 法国舞蹈家 6—299f
伏安法 voltammetry 化学 18—45c
伏打 Volta, Alessandro Giuseppe Antonio Anastasio 意大利物理学家 18—41e
伏都教 voodoo 海地宗教 18—48c
伏尔甘 Vulcan 罗马神名 18—54b
伏尔加-波罗的海航道 Volga-Baltic Waterway 俄罗斯水道 18—38a
伏尔加格勒 Volgograd 俄罗斯城市 18—38f
伏尔加格勒州 Volgograd 俄罗斯州名 18—38e
伏尔加河 Volga River 俄罗斯河流 18—38c
伏尔加河-顿河运河 Volga-Don Ship Canal 俄罗斯运河 18—38b
伏尔加阶 Volgian Stage 地质学 18—38e
伏尔加斯基 Volzhsky 俄罗斯城市 18—47a
伏尔加-乌拉尔石油与天然气区 Volga-Ural Petroleum and Gas Province 俄罗斯产油区 18—38d
伏尔塔瓦河 Vltava River 捷克河流 18—31b
伏尔泰 Voltaire 法国作家 18—42c
伏龙芝 Frunze (Kyrgyzstan) 吉尔吉斯斯坦城市 6—505d
伏龙芝 Frunze, Mikhail Vasilyevich 苏联高级军官 6—505d
伏罗希洛夫 Voroshilov, Kliment Yefremovich 苏联领导人 18—49c
伏罗希洛夫格勒 Voroshilovgrad (Ukraine) 乌克兰城市 18—49c
伏罗希洛夫斯克 Voroshilovsk (Ukraine) 乌克兰城市 18—49d
伏牛山 Funiu Shan 中国山脉 6—527b
伏特 volt 计量单位 18—41e
伏特加 vodka 蒸馏酒 18—32b
伏天 dog days 气象学 5—360a
伏窝 brooding 动物学 3—182b
伏羲 Fu-hsi 中国神话帝王 6—506f
伏伊伏丁那 Vojvodina 塞尔维亚自治省 18—34a
伏翼 pipistrelle 动物 13—319b
芙莱妮 Phryne 希腊名妓 13—269b
芙蓉 Seremban 马来西亚城镇 15—222f
芙耶拉 vyāla 印度艺术 18—56a
扶垛 buttress 建筑 3—294d
扶轮国际 Rotary International 群众性服务社团 14—413c
扶南 Funan 印度支那古王国 6—522f
孚日 Vosges 法国省份 18—50e
孚日山 Vosges 法国山脉 18—50e
孚兹 Wurtz, Charles-Adolphe 法国化学家 18—360e
苻坚 Fu Jian 中国皇帝 6—507a
服王役 rājākariya 锡兰土地制度 14—129e
服务大师公司 Service Master Company, The 美国公司 15—229d
服务行业 service industry 经济学 15—229c
服务性俱乐部 service club 团体 15—229b
服役土地占有权 sergeanty 封建法律 15—224a
服装 dress 生活 5—420f
服装工业 garment industry 工业 7—16d
服装及纺织工人混合工会 Amalgamated Clothing and Textile Workers Union 美国工人组织 1—263d
氟 fluorine 化学元素 6—378f
氟化物缺乏 fluoride deficiency 生物化学 6—379a
氟利昂 Freon 化合物 6—482f
氟磷灰石 fluorapatite 矿物 6—378d
氟磷锰石 triplite 矿物 17—224f
氟碳铈矿 bastnaesite 矿物 2—272a
氟烷 halothane 化合物 7—433b
氟乙烯 fluoroethylene 化合物 6—379c
氟中毒 fluorosis 病理学 6—379c
俘获 capture 核物理学 3—432f
祓 harai 日本神道教礼仪 7—468c
祓除邪恶 lustration 古希腊、古罗马祭祀仪式 10—293b
浮标 buoy 航海 3—256b
浮岛 chinampa 人工岛 4—166e
浮雕 relief 雕刻 14—215c
浮雕蚀刻法 relief etching 印刷 14—215e
浮雕绣制品 stump work (embroidery) 工艺品 16—288f
浮雕压印 embossing 工艺 6—57c
浮浪幼体 planula 动物学 13—348e
浮力定律 buoyancy, law of (physics) 物理学 3—256c
浮梁 Fou-liang (China) 中国旧县名 6—422c
浮桥 pontoon bridge 桥 13—429a
浮士德 Faust 西方文学传奇人物 6—253d
浮世绘 ukiyo-e 日本风俗画 17—325b
浮选 flotation 选矿 6—373f
浮岩 pumice 泡沫状火山玻璃 14—23c
浮游动物 zooplankton 生物学 18—567b
浮游生物 plankton 生物 13—343a
浮游植物 phytoplankton 生物学 13—278c
符号 symbol 传达信息的基元 16—397c
符号学 semiotics 应用学科 15—205c

符合计数 coincidence counting 物理学 4—335f
符拉迪沃斯托克 Vladivostok 俄罗斯港口 18—30b
符箓 fulu 中国道教术语 6—521f
符山石 vesuvianite 矿物 17—531a
符腾堡 Württemberg 古代德意志邦国 18—360c
符腾堡信义会 Lutheran Church in Württemberg 德国基督教教会 10—300e
涪陵 Fuling 中国城市 6—517f
辐合与辐散 convergence and divergence 气象学 4—474b
辐散 divergence (meteorology) 气象学 5—346a
辐射 radiation 物理学 14—110d
辐射计 radiometer 仪器 14—117f
辐射损伤 radiation injury 病理学 14—110e
辐射损伤年代测定法 radiation-damage dating 测定年代的方法 14—110d
辐射压强 radiation pressure 物理学 14—110f
蜉蝣 mayfly 昆虫 11—52b
蜉蝣类 ephemeropteran 动物学 6—95c
福 Fo, Dario 意大利剧作家 6—383b
福阿德帕夏 Fuad Paşa, Mehmed 土耳其政治家 6—507e
福阿德一世 Fu'ād I 埃及国王 6—507d
福安 Fuan 中国城市 6—507f
福玻斯 Phoebus (Greek god) 希腊神名 13—255b
福柏 Phoebe 希腊神话 13—255a
福布尔东 fauxbourdon 音乐 6—254c
福布斯 Forbes 澳大利亚城镇 6—398b
福布斯 Forbes (of Culloden), Duncan 苏格兰政治家 6—398b
福布斯 Forbes, Edward 英国博物学家 6—398c
福布斯 Forbes, George William 新西兰总理 6—398d
福布斯 Forbes, James David 苏格兰物理学家 6—398d
福布斯 Forbes, Steve 美国出版商 6—398e
福布斯-罗伯逊 Forbes-Robertson, Sir Johnston 英国演员 6—398e
福布斯氏病 Forbes' disease 遗传性疾病 6—398f
福布希效应 Forbush effect 天文学 6—399e
福岛 Fukushima 日本县名 6—516c
福德 Forde, Francis Michael 澳大利亚总理 6—403f
福德利尼尔造纸机 Fourdrinier machine 机器 6—426f
福地 Cockaigne 想象国度 4—321b
福蒂纳图斯 Fortunatus, Venantius 意大利诗人、主教 6—418c
福蒂斯 Fortes, Meyer 英国人类学家 6—416e
福蒂斯丘 Fortescue, Sir John 英格兰法学家 6—416f
福多尔 Fodor, Eugene 美国旅行作家 6—504b
福尔 Fall, Albert Bacon 美国内政部长 6—222f
福尔 Faure, (François-) Félix 法国总统 6—252f
福尔 Fort, Paul 法国诗人 6—413a
福尔巴克 Forbach 法国城镇 6—398a
福尔班 Forbin, Claude de 法国军官 6—399d
福尔茨 Foltz, Clara Shortridge 美国律师和改革家 6—391b
福尔达 Folda 挪威峡湾 6—387f
福尔德 Ford, Francis Xavier 美国传教士 6—401a
福尔蒂斯 Fortis, Alessandro 意大利政治家 6—418a
福尔盖(马赛的) Folquet de Marseille 法国诗人、教士 6—391a
福尔盖(图卢兹的) Foulques de Toulouse 法国诗人、教士 6—423d
福尔哈贝尔 Faulhaber, Michael von 德国红衣主教 6—251c
福尔杰 Folger, Henry Clay 美国律师 6—387f
福尔杰莎士比亚图书馆 Folger Shakespeare Library 美国社会与文化研究中心 6—388a
福尔金提乌斯(鲁斯佩的),圣 Fulgentius of Ruspe, Saint 非洲主教 6—517e
福尔柯克 Falkirk 英国区名 6—221e
福尔柯克 Falkirk 英国城镇 6—221e
福尔克曼氏挛缩 Volkmann's contracture 病理学 18—39c
福尔克纳 Falconer, Martha Platt 美国社会工作者 6—219e
福尔里弗 Fall River 美国城市 6—222f
福尔马林 formalin 甲醛的水溶液 6—409b
福尔曼 Forman, Andrew 苏格兰外交家 6—409c
福尔曼 Foreman, George 美国拳击运动员 6—405d
福尔米翁 Phormion 雅典海军统帅 13—257d
福尔米亚 Formia 意大利城镇 6—409e
福尔摩斯 Holmes, Sherlock 小说人物 8—135a
福尔摩苏斯 Formosus 教皇 6—410b
福尔姆斯泰彻尔 Formstecher, Solomon 犹太哲学家 6—410b
福尔内 Forner, Juan Pablo 西班牙文学评论家 6—410c
福尔斯 Fowles, John 英国小说家 6—429f
福尔斯 Foulis, Robert 苏格兰出版商 6—423d
福尔斯彻奇 Falls Church 美国城市 6—224d
福尔斯特 Forster, Georg 德国探险家 6—411f
福尔斯湾 False Bay 南非港湾 6—224f
福尔图娜 Fortuna 古罗马女神 6—418b
福尔图尼 Fortuny, Mariano 西班牙画家 6—418f
福尔图尼 Fortuny, Mariano 西班牙艺术家 6—418f
福尔维娅 Fulvia 马可·安东尼之妻 6—522b
福尔西,圣 Fursey, Saint 爱尔兰圣者 6—531d
福弗尔 Forfar 苏格兰城镇 6—407d
福弗尔 Forfarshire (Scotland) 英国郡名 6—407d
福冈 Fukuoka 日本县名 6—516b
福冈 Fukuoka 日本城市和港口 6—516c
福格尔 Fogel, Robert William 美国经济学家 6—385b
福格特 Vogt, Johan Herman Lie 挪威地质学家 18—32f
福格特兰 Vogtland 德国地区 18—33a
福格艺术博物馆 Fogg Art Museum 美国博物馆 6—385d
福古岛 Fogo Island 佛得角岛屿 6—385e
福基斯 Phocis 古希腊中部地区 13—254f
福基翁 Phocion 雅典政治家、将军 13—254d
福吉谷 Valley Forge 美国历史 17—455c
福加扎罗 Fogazzaro, Antonio 意大利小说家 6—385b
福贾 Foggia 意大利城市 6—385e
福建 Fujian 中国省份 6—512d
福杰蒂 Fogerty, Elsie 英国戏剧台词教员 6—385c
福金 Fokine, Michel 俄罗斯舞蹈家 6—386f
福井 Fukui 日本县名 6—515f
福井谦一 Fukui Kenichi 日本化学家 6—516a
福卡多斯河 Forcados River 尼日利亚河流 6—399f
福卡斯 Phocas 拜占廷皇帝 13—254d
福卡斯 Focas, Antonio de Curtis Gagliardi Griffo 意大利喜剧演员 6—383e
福凯斯 Fougasse (cartoonist) 英国漫画家 6—423c
福康安 Fukang'an 中国清代将领 6—515d
福科斯 Phocus 希腊神话 13—254f
福克尔 Fokker, Anthony Herman Gerard 荷兰飞机制造商 6—387b
福克尔 Forkel, Johann Nikolaus 德国作家 6—408c
福克兰 Falkland 英国前王室驻地 6—221e
福克兰海峡 Falkland Sound 大西洋海峡 6—222e
福克兰群岛 Falkland Islands 大西洋群岛 6—221f
福克兰群岛战争 Falkland Islands War 英国-阿根廷战争 6—222d
福克兰子爵(第二) Falkland, Lucius Cary, 2nd Viscount of 英格兰贵族 6—221f
福克纳 Faulkner, William (Cuthbert) 美国小说家 6—251d
福克沙尼 Focşani 罗马尼亚城市 6—384a
福克斯 Fox, Charles James 英国外交大臣 6—430d
福克斯 Fox, Della May 美国演员、歌手 6—431a
福克斯 Fox, George 英国宗教领袖 6—431b
福克斯 Fawkes, Guy 英国军人 6—255d
福克斯 Fox, Henry 英国政客 6—431c
福克斯 Fox, Henry Richard Vassall 英国政治家 6—431c
福克斯 Foxe, John 英国清教派传教人员 6—432c

福克斯 Foxx, Jimmie 美国棒球运动员 6—433a
福克斯 Folkers, Karl August 美国化学家 6—389f
福克斯 Foxx, Redd 美国喜剧演员 6—433a
福克斯 Foxe, Richard 英格兰基督教政治家 6—432d
福克斯 Fox, Vicente Quesada 墨西哥总统 6—431d
福克斯 Fox, Sir William 新西兰政治家 6—431e
福克斯广播公司 Fox Broadcasting Company 美国电视广播公司 6—431f
福克斯姐妹 Fox, Margaret and Catherine 美国巫师 6—431c
福克斯人 Fox 北美印第安部落 6—429f
福克斯通 Folkestone 英国城镇 6—389f
福克-乌夫公司 **Fw-190** Focke-Wulf Fw-190 (German aircraft) 德国战斗机 6—384a
福肯贝克 Forckenbeck, Max(imilian Franz August) von 德国政治家 6—400e
福拉尔(骑士) Folard, Jean-Charles, chevalier de 法国军人 6—387c
福拉尔贝格 Vorarlberg 奥地利州名 18—48e
福莱 Fauré, Gabriel(-Urbain) 法国作曲家 6—253a
福莱斯特 Forrestal, James V(incent) 美国国防部长 6—411b
福莱特 Follett, Mary Parker 美国社会学家 6—390e
福兰德特国家公园 Forlandet National Park 挪威公园 6—408d
福勒 Fowler, H(enry) W(atson) 英国辞书编纂家 6—428f
福勒 Fowler, John 英国农机工程师 6—429b
福勒 Fowler, Sir John, 1st Baronet 英国土木工程师 6—429b
福勒 Fowler, Lydia Folger 美国医生、作家 6—429b
福勒 Fowler, William A. 美国天体物理学家 6—429d
福雷 Forez 法国古地区 6—407c
福雷尔 Forel, Auguste-Henri 瑞士精神病学家 6—405c
福雷尔 Forel, François-Alphonse 瑞士医生、科学家 6—405c
福雷尔 Forrer, Ludwig 瑞士政治家 6—410d
福雷斯蒂尔半岛 Forestier Peninsula 澳大利亚半岛 6—406f
福雷斯特 Forester, C(ecil) S(cott) 英国历史小说家 6—406d
福雷斯特 Forrest, Edwin 美国演员 6—410d
福雷斯特 Forrest, Sir John 澳大利亚探险家 6—410e
福雷斯特 Forrester, Jay Wright 美国电机工程师、管理专家 6—411b
福雷斯特 Forrest, Leon 非洲裔美国作家 6—410f
福雷斯特 Forrest, Nathan Bedford 美国将领 6—411a
福雷斯特城 Forrest City 美国城市 6—411b
福雷斯特黑思 Forest Heath 英国区名 6—406c
福雷斯特希尔 Forest Hills 美国纽约市区住宅区 6—406c
福里埃尔 Fauriel, Claude(-Charles) 法国学者、作家 6—253c
福里奥 Forio 意大利城镇 6—408b
福里德布尔 Farīdpur 孟加拉国城市 6—239e
福里斯 Forres 英国小自治市 6—410d
福利奥特 Foliot, Gilbert 伦敦主教 6—388e
福利国家 welfare state 政治体制 18—177d
福利经济学 welfare economics 经济学 18—177c
福利尼奥 Foligno 意大利城镇 6—388d
福利事业 welfare service 社会学 18—177d
福莉西塔斯 Felicitas 古罗马神祇 6—267f
福林 forint 匈牙利货币单位 6—408b
福临 Fulin 中国皇帝 6—517f
福楼拜 Flaubert, Gustave 法国文学家 6—351c
福禄考 phlox 草本植物 13—253e
福禄培尔 Froebel, Friedrich (Wilhelm August) 德国教育家 6—498f
福禄寿 Fukurokuju 日本神话中的福神 6—516c
福禄寿 Fu-Lu-Shou 中国神话中的三位天神 6—507b
福伦 Follen, Adolf Ludwig 德国诗人 6—390d
福伦丹 Volendam 荷兰城镇 18—38a
福伦戈 Folengo, Teofilo 意大利作家 6—387f
福罗拉 Flora 古罗马女神 6—363d
福曼 Forman, Miloš 捷克斯洛伐克电影导演 6—409d
福门特 Forment, Damián 西班牙雕刻家 6—409e
福米加 Formica 贴面材料 6—409f
福莫萨 Formosa 阿根廷省份 6—410a
福莫萨 Formosa 阿根廷城市 6—410a
福尼克斯 Phoenix 希腊神话 13—255f
福恰 Foça (Turkey) 古代爱奥尼亚城市 6—383e
福琼 Fortune, T. Thomas 美国新闻工作者 6—418d
福萨诺 Fossano 意大利城镇 6—420c
福赛 Fossey, Dian 美国动物学家 6—420d
福赛思 Forsyth, Alexander John 英国发明家 6—412e
福赛思 Forsyth, Peter Taylor 英国基督教牧师 6—412f
福瑟吉尔 Fothergill, John 英国内科医生 6—422b
福瑟吉尔木属 Fothergilla 植物学 6—422b
福山 Fukuyama 日本城市 6—516d
福思伯爵 Forth, Patrick Ruthven, Earl of, Earl of Brentford, Lord Ruthven of Ettrick 英国军事指挥官 6—417a
福斯 Fosse, Bob 美国歌舞剧导演 6—420c
福斯 Fosse, Charles de La (French painter) 法国艺术家 6—420c
福斯 Voss, Johann Heinrich 德国诗人 18—51a
福斯 Force, Juliana Rieser 美国博物馆馆长 6—400a
福斯 Fox, William 好莱坞电影事业家 6—431e
福斯迪克 Fosdick, Harry Emerson 美国牧师 6—419e
福斯蒂纳 Faustina, Annia Galeria 罗马皇帝之妻 6—254a
福斯河 Forth, River 英国河流 6—417a
福斯河 Forth River 英国河流 6—417c
福斯卡里 Foscari, Francesco 意大利威尼斯执政官 6—419c
福斯科洛 Foscolo, Ugo 意大利作家、诗人 6—419e
福斯路 Fosse Way 英国古罗马道路 6—420c
福斯曼 Forsman, Georg Zacharias 芬兰政治家 6—411c
福斯曼 Forssmann, Werner 德国外科医生 6—411c
福斯桥 Forth Bridge 英国铁路桥 6—417b
福斯特 Forster 澳大利亚城镇 6—411d
福斯特 Forster, E(dward) M(organ) 英国作家 6—411d
福斯特 Foster, Sir George Eulas 加拿大政治家 6—421c
福斯特 Foster, Hannah Webster 美国小说家 6—421c
福斯特 Forster, John 英国作家 6—412a
福斯特 Foster, John W(atson) 美国外交家、国务卿 6—421d
福斯特 Foster, Sir Michael 英国生理学家 6—421d
福斯特 Foster, Sir Norman 英国建筑师 6—421e
福斯特 Foster, Stephen (Collins) 美国作曲家 6—421f
福斯特 Forster, Thomas 英格兰詹姆斯党人 6—412b
福斯特 Forster, William Edward 英国政治家 6—412b
福斯特 Foster, William Z(ebulon) 美国共产党领袖 6—422a
福斯特(夫人) Foster, Abigail Kelley 美国废奴主义者 6—421b
福斯图斯(里兹的),圣 Faustus of Riez, Saint 法国主教 6—254a
福塔莱萨 Fortaleza 巴西港市 6—416d
福塔斯 Fortas, Abe 美国最高法院大法官 6—416d
福特 Ford, Edmund Brisco 英国遗传学家 6—400f
福特 Ford, Ford Madox 英国作家 6—400f
福特 Ford, Gerald R. 美国总统 6—401b
福特 Ford, Henry 美国工业家 6—401c
福特 Ford, John 美国电影导演 6—403d
福特 Ford, John 英国戏剧家 6—403c
福特(第二) Ford, Henry, II 美国汽车工业家 6—403b
福特基金会 Ford Foundation 美国慈善机构 6—403d
福特纳 Fortner, Wolfgang 德国作曲家 6—418a
福特南-梅森公司 Fortnum & Mason 英国百货商店 6—418b
福特汽车公司 Ford Motor Company 美国公司 6—403e
福田赳夫 Fukuda Takeo 日本首相 6—515f
《福韦尔传奇》 Roman de Fauvel 法国文学 14—363c
福西厄斯 Vossius, Gerardus Johannes 荷兰学者 18—51b
福西特夫人 Fawcett, Dame Millicent Garrett 英国女权运动领导人 6—255b

福西亚 Phocaea 古代爱奥尼亚城市 13—254c
福希海默 Forchheimer, Philipp 奥地利水利工程师 6—400e
福辛纽-达罗萨 Focinho da Rosa (Portugal) 葡萄牙海角 6—384a
福星 Fuxing 中国神话天神 6—535d
福煦 Foch, Ferdinand 法国元帅 6—383e
福伊 Fowey 英国港口 6—428d
福伊 Foy, Eddie 美国喜剧演员 6—433b
福伊尔潟湖 Foyle, Lough 爱尔兰海湾 6—433d
福伊特 Foyt, A(nthony) J(oseph), (Jr.) 美国赛车手 6—433d
福伊特 Voit, Carl von 德国生理学家 18—33e
福伊希特万格 Feuchtwanger, Lion 德国作家 6—298b
福音归正会 Evangelical and Reformed Church 美国基督教会 6—177f
福音联合弟兄会 Evangelical United Brethren Church (EUB) 美国基督教会 6—178e
福音联盟 Evangelical Alliance 基督教组织 6—177e
福音联盟 Evangelical Union 基督教组织 6—178e
福音派教会 evangelical church 基督教会 6—177f
福音书 Gospel 基督教经典 7—221c
福音文字 Estrangela 叙利亚早期文字 6—142a
福音音乐 gospel music 音乐 7—221d
福泽谕吉 Fukuzawa Yukichi 日本教育家 6—516d
福州 Fuzhou 中国城市 6—535e
蝠鲼 devil ray 鱼类 5—272a
甫斯特尔·德·库朗日 Fustel de Coulanges, Numa Denis 法国历史学家 6—533e
抚顺 Fushun 中国城市 6—532e
斧 ax 工具 2—93a
斧锛类工具 celt 新石器时代工具 3—559d
斧石 axinite 矿物 2—93b
斧头鱼 hatchetfish 鱼类 7—507b
府兵制 fubing system 中国古代军事制度 6—508a
府中 Fuchū 日本城市 6—509a
俯冲轰炸机 Sturzkampfflugzeug (German aircraft) 德国飞机 16—292a
俯冲消减带 subduction zone 地质学 16—297c
釜山 Pusan 韩国港市 14—35d
釜石 Kamaishi 日本城市 9—145a
辅导 guidance 教育 7—353f
辅酶 Q coenzyme Q 生物化学 4—329c
辅音 consonant 语音学 4—447e
辅助因子 cofactor 生物化学 4—330a
脯氨酸 proline 化合物 13—532f
腐败选区 rotten borough 英国历史 14—417a
腐臭花 carrion flower 植物 3—484a
腐烂病 rot 植物病害 14—412f
腐泥 sapropel 地质学 15—58d
腐朽病 decay (plant disease) 植物病害 5—201d
腐殖酸 humic acid 化学 8—247f
腐殖质 humus 土壤学 8—251a
簠 fu 中国古代食器 6—506d
獛 genet 哺乳动物 7—58d
父名 patronymic 人名 13—91f
父母 parent 亲属关系 13—40e
父亲节 Father's Day 美国节日 6—249c
父权 patria potestas 罗马法律 13—90b
负电子 negatron 物理学 12—66b
负粪甲虫 casebearing beetle 昆虫 3—498c
负鞘幼虫 casebearer 昆虫 3—498b
负鼠 opossum 哺乳动物 12—433c
负鼠虾 opossum shrimp 甲壳动物 12—433e
负像 negative 摄影 12—66b
负重训练 weight training 体育 18—170a
负子蟾 Surinam toad (*Pipa pipa*) 两栖动物 16—354b
负子蝽 giant water bug 昆虫 7—117a
妇产科学 obstetrics and gynecology 医学 12—324a
妇科 gynecology 医学 7—390f
妇科检查 gynecological examination 医学 7—390f
《妇女参军平等法案》 Women's Armed Services Integration Act 美国法律 18—315c
《妇女参政史》 History of Woman Suffrage 美国女权运动历史 8—101b
妇女地位总统委员会 President's Commission on the Status of Women 美国组织 13—497c
妇女工会联盟 Women's Trade Union League (WTUL) 美国组织 18—316c
妇女和平党 Woman's Peace Party (WPP) 美国组织 18—314e
妇女和平与自由国际联盟 Women's International League for Peace and Freedom (WILPF) 美国和平组织 18—315d
《妇女家庭杂志》 Ladies' Home Journal 美国期刊 9—441d
妇女解放运动 women's liberation movement 社会运动 18—315f
妇女陆地服务队 Women's Land Army (WLA) 美国组织 18—315e
妇女全国效忠联盟 Women's National Loyal League 美国组织 18—316b
妇女选举权 woman suffrage 法律 18—312d
妇女选民联盟 League of Women Voters 美国政治组织 9—543d
《妇女》杂志 Ms. 美国杂志 11—458e
《妇女杂志》 Woman's Journal 美国周刊 18—314d
妇女争取和平罢工 Women Strike for Peace (WSP) 国际组织 18—315b
附睾 epididyme 解剖学 6—99d
附睾炎 epididymitis 疾病 6—99e
附鬼 dybbuk 犹太传说 5—486e
附加 upādhi 印度哲学 17—403d
附加句 trope 宗教音乐 17—234a
附加体 episome 微生物学 6—103a
附生凤梨属 Aechmea 植物学 1—91f
附生兰属 Epidendrum 植物学 6—99c
附生植物 epiphyte 植物学 6—101f
附誓书面陈述 affidavit 法律 1—103e
附属礼拜堂 chantry 教堂建筑 4—54e
附体 possession 宗教和民间传说 13—459a
阜姆 Fiume (Croatia) 克罗地亚城市 6—340f
阜姆问题 Fiume question 意-南纷争 6—340f
阜新 Fuxin 中国城市 6—535d
阜阳 Fuyang 中国城市 6—535d
复本位制 bimetallism 货币制度 2—475d
复仇悲剧 revenge tragedy 戏剧 14—250f
复仇女神 Fury 希腊罗马神话 6—532a
复旦大学 Fudan University 中国大学 6—509c
复地运动 Reconquista 伊比利亚历史 14—184c
复调音乐 polyphony 音乐 13—416c
复分析 analysis, complex 数学 1—311c
复古神道 Fukko Shintō 日本宗教 6—515e
复归权 reversion 英美法律 14—251e
复合材料 composite material 材料科学 4—399e
复合墩 compound pier 建筑学 4—400b
复合核模型 compound-nucleus model 原子核物理学 4—400a
复合三段论 sorites 逻辑学 15—522c
复合音 combination tone 音乐 4—377b
复活 resurrection 宗教 14—244f
复活节 Easter 基督教节日 5—508e
复活节岛 Easter Island 智利属太平洋岛屿 5—509a
复活节岛断裂带 Easter Fracture Zone 太平洋海底断裂带 5—508f
复活节起义 Easter Rising 爱尔兰反英事件 5—509b

复活节日期之争 Paschal controversies 基督教 13—73a
复活节仙人掌 Easter cactus (*Rhipsalidopsis gaertneri*) 植物 5—508e
复节奏 polyrhythm 音乐 13—417c
复理石 flysch 岩石 6—382e
复生礼 reanimation rite 埃及宗教礼仪 14—181d
复式桥牌 Duplicate Bridge 游戏 5—466f
复视 double vision 生理学 5—398e
复数 complex number 数学 4—399b
复协奏(唱)风格 concertato style 音乐风格 4—410c
复兴党 Ba'th Party 阿拉伯政党 2—277c
复兴金融公司 Reconstruction Finance Corporation (RFC) 美国政府机构 14—184e
复兴运动 Risorgimento 统一意大利的思想文化运动 14—312e
复压室 recompression chamber (medical technology) 医疗技术 14—184c
复椰子 double coconut (palm) 植物 5—398c
复印机 duplicating machine 机械 5—467a
副标题 subtitle 文学 16—301a
副棘鳍鱼 paracanthopterygian 鱼类 13—30a
副结核病 paratuberculosis 家畜疾病 13—39e
副矿物 accessory mineral 矿物学 1—45d
副醛 paraldehyde 化合物 13—34e
副热带高压 subtropical high 气象学 16—301a
副热带无风带 horse latitude 气象学 8—180f
副伤寒 paratyphoid fever 疾病 13—39e
副翼 aileron 飞行器部件 1—141a
赋 fu 中国古代文体 6—506d
赋格 fugue 音乐曲式 6—511e
赋格式曲调 fuging tune 赞美诗曲式 6—511c
赋色 coloration 生物学 4—364a
傅抱石 Fu Baoshi 中国画家 6—506e
傅华萨 Froissart, Jean 欧洲中世纪诗人 6—500d
傅科 Foucault, Jean-Bernard-Léon 法国物理学家 6—422c
傅科 Foucault, Michel (Paul) 法国哲学家 6—422d
傅科摆 Foucault pendulum 物理装置 6—422e
傅里叶 Fourier, (Jean-Baptiste-) Joseph, Baron 法国数学家 6—427b
傅里叶变换 Fourier transform 数学 6—427c
傅里叶分析 analysis, Fourier 数学、数学物理 1—312b
傅立叶 Fourier, (François-Marie-) Charles 法国社会理论家 6—427a
傅立叶主义 Fourierism 社会改革理论 6—427d
傅尼耶 Fournier, Henri-Alban 法国作家 6—427e
傅斯年 Fu Sinian 中国文史语言学家 6—507c
傅鹰 Fu Ying 中国化学家、教育家 6—507d
富埃尔特河 Fuerte River 墨西哥河流 6—510e
富埃泰·昂·图尔囊 fouetté en tournant 芭蕾舞动作 6—423b
富埃特文图拉岛 Fuerteventura Island 西班牙岛屿 6—510f
富布赖特 Fulbright, J. William 美国参议员 6—517b
富布赖特奖学金 Fulbright scholarship 美国奖学金 6—517c
富查伊拉 Al-Fujayrah 阿拉伯联合酋长国成员国 1—160d
富川 Puch'ŏn 韩国城市 14—12d
富春江 Fuchun Jiang 中国河流 6—509a
富蒂乌斯 Voetius, Gisbertus 荷兰神学家 18—32d
富恩特斯 Fuentes, Carlos 墨西哥作家 6—510c
富尔 Faure, Edgar(-Jean) 法国总理 6—252e
富尔贝尔(沙特尔的),圣 Fulbert OF CHARTRES, SAINT 法兰西主教 6—517a
富尔达 Fulda 德国城市 6—517d
富尔达河 Fulda River 德国河流 6—517e
富尔德 Fould, Achille 法国政治家 6—423c
富尔顿 Fulton 美国城市 6—520f
富尔顿 Fulton, Mary Hannah 美国医生 6—520f
富尔顿 Fulton, Robert 美国发明家 6—521a
富尔根蒂尤 Fulgentius, Fabius Planciades 非洲拉丁文著作家 6—517e
富尔克 Fulk 统治者之名 6—518b
富尔克 Fulk 耶路撒冷国王 6—518c
富尔克 Fulk, ARCHBISHOP OF REIMS 兰斯大主教 6—518c
富尔克 Foulques, Gui (pope) 教皇 6—423d
富尔克三世 Fulk III NERRA 安茹伯爵 6—518b
富尔克四世 Fulk IV 安茹伯爵 6—518b
富尔克五世 Fulk V 耶路撒冷国王 6—518c
富尔内隆 Fourneyron, Benoît 法国水轮机发明家 6—427e
富尔人 Fur 苏丹民族 6—527f
富尔特斯 Fuertes, Dolores Adios (U.S. actress) 美国演员 6—510e
富冈 Tomioka 日本城市 17—144f
富冈铁斋 Tomioka Tessai 日本画家 17—144f
富格尔家族 Fugger FAMILY 德国商人世家 6—511a
富硅高岭石 anauxite 矿物 1—321a
富国岛 Phu Quoc Island 越南岛屿 13—269d
富基埃-坦维尔 Fouquier-Tinville, Antoine-Quentin 法国律师 6—425b
富加德 Fugard, Athol 南非剧作家 6—510f
富凯 Fouquet, Charles(-Louis-Auguste) 法国元帅 6—424e
富凯 Fouqué, Friedrich Heinrich Karl de La Motte, Baron 德国作家 6—424e
富凯 Fouquet, Jean 法国画家 6—424f
富凯 Fouquet, Nicolas 法国财政大臣 6—425a
富克斯 Fuchs, (Emil) Klaus (Julius) 德国物理学家 6—508b
富克斯 Fux, Johann Joseph 奥地利作曲家 6—535c
富克斯 Fuchs, Leonhard 德国植物学家 6—508c
富克斯 Fuchs, Lukas 美国作曲家 6—508e
富克斯 Fuchs, Sir Vivian Ernest 英国探险家、地质学家 6—508e
富拉尔基 Fula'erji 中国工业区 6—516e
富拉尼帝国 Fulani empire 苏丹西部穆斯林神权国家 6—517a
富拉尼人 Fulani 非洲民族 6—516e
富兰克林 Franklin 美国历史州名 6—451a
富兰克林 Franklin 美国宾夕法尼亚州城市 6—451a
富兰克林 Franklin 美国田纳西州城市 6—451b
富兰克林 Franklin, Aretha 美国歌唱家 6—451b
富兰克林 Franklin, Benjamin 美国政治家 6—451b
富兰克林 Franklin, Sir John 英国探险家 6—453c
富兰克林 Franklin, John Hope 美国历史学家 6—453e
富兰克林 Franklin, Rosalind (Elsie) 英国科学家 6—453f
富兰克林-戈登河国家公园 Franklin-Lower Gordon Wild Rivers National Park 澳大利亚国家公园 6—454a
富兰克林炉 Franklin stove 火炉 6—454a
富兰克林树 franklinia (*Franklinia alatamaha* or *Gordonia alatamaha*) 植物 6—454b
富兰克林学会 Franklin Institute 美国科技中心 6—453f
富勒 Fuller, Andrew 英国神学家 6—518d
富勒 Fuller, George 美国画家 6—518d
富勒 Fuller, Henry Blake 美国小说家 6—518d
富勒 Fuller, J(ohn) F(rederick) C(harles) 英国陆军军官 6—518e
富勒 Fuller, Loie 美国舞蹈家 6—518f
富勒 Fuller, Melville Weston 美国最高法院大法官 6—519c
富勒 Fuller, R(ichard) Buckminster 美国建筑学家 6—519d
富勒 Fuller, Roy 英国诗人、小说家 6—519f
富勒 Fuller, (Sarah) Margaret 美国文学家 6—519b
富勒 Fuller, Sarah 美国教育家 6—520a
富勒 Fuller, Thomas 英格兰作家 6—520b
富勒顿 Fullerton 美国城市 6—520e
富勒尔 Furrer, Jonas 瑞士联邦主席 6—531c
富勒姆 Fulham (England) 英格兰城市 6—517f
富勒烯 fullerene 化合物 6—520c

富里酸 fulvic acid 腐殖酸 6—522b
富马酸 fumaric acid 化合物 6—522c
富纳富提环礁 Funafuti Atoll 图瓦卢珊瑚礁 6—522f
富内斯 Funes 西班牙城市 6—526c
富尼埃 Fournier, Jacques (pope) 教皇 6—427f
富尼埃 Fournier, Pierre-Simon 法国雕版工人 6—427f
富农 kulak 俄国历史 9—392c
富齐诺盆地 Fucino Basin 意大利湖盆 6—509b
富气 wet gas 天然烃类混合物 18—214f
富强 Phu Cuong (Vietnam) 越南城市 13—269d
富萨罗湖 Fusaro, Lake of 意大利潟湖 6—532b
富塞利 Fuseli, Henry 瑞士画家 6—532d
富山 Toyama 日本县名 17—183b
富士 Fuji 日本城市 6—512a
富士宫 Fujinomiya 日本城市 6—513a
富士山 Fuji, Mount 日本最高峰 6—512a
富士通有限公司 Fujitsu Limited 日本公司 6—513e
富士银行 Fuji Bank 日本银行 6—512c
富斯塔特 Fusṭāt, al- 埃及古城 6—533d
富斯塔特陶器 Fusṭāt ware 伊斯兰陶器 6—533d
富斯特 Fust, Johann 德国印刷企业家 6—533c
富塔贾隆 Fouta Djallon 几内亚山岳地区 6—428c
富塔-托罗 Fouta-Toro 塞内加尔半沙漠地区 6—428d
富特 Foote, Andrew (Hull) 美国海军官员 6—397c
富特 Foote, Mary Anna Hallock 美国小说家、插图画家 6—397d
富特 Foote, Robert Bruce 英国地质学家 6—397d
富特 Foote, Samuel 英国演员、剧作家 6—397e
富特 Foot, Michael 英国工党领袖 6—396d
富特旺根 Furtwangen 德国城市 6—531e
富特文格勒 Furtwängler, Adolf 德国考古学家 6—531e
富特文格勒 Furtwängler, (Gustav Heinrich Ernst Martin) Wilhelm 德国指挥家 6—531f
富铁镁铁橄榄石 ferrohortonolite 矿物 6—293c
富图纳群岛 Futuna Islands 太平洋两火山岛 6—534b
富屯溪 Futun Xi 中国河流 6—534b
富托克字母 futhark (writing system) 欧洲古文字 6—534b
富瓦 Foix 法国封建伯爵领地 6—386e
富瓦 Foix 法国城镇 6—386e
富瓦 Foy, Maximilien(-Sébastien) 法国军事领袖 6—433c
富歇 Foucher, Simon 法国哲学家 6—423b
富歇 Fouché, Joseph, DUC (duke) D'OTRANTE 法国政治家 6—422f
富营养化 eutrophication 生态学 6—176f
富韵 rime riche 韵律学 14—302b
富兹利 Füssli, Johann Heinrich 瑞士画家 6—533c
富祖里 Fuzuli, Mehmed bin Süleyman 突厥诗人 6—536b
腹地 hinterland 城市附属地区 8—90b
腹股沟淋巴肉芽肿 climatic bubo (disease) 疾病 4—292b
腹股沟肉芽肿 granuloma inguinale 疾病 7—257b
腹肌 abdominal muscle 解剖学 1—14e
腹菌类 Gasteromycetes 植物学 7—26b
腹菌目 Hymenogastrales 植物学 8—289a
腹毛类 gastrotrich 无脊椎动物 7—28c
腹膜 peritoneum 解剖学 13—171a
腹膜炎 peritonitis 疾病 13—171b
腹腔 abdominal cavity 解剖学 1—14c
腹腔镜检查 laparoscopy 医学 9—494e
腹水 ascites 病理现象 1—542a
腹纤毛虫 hypotrich 原生动物 8—296c
腹泻 diarrhea 病理现象 5—289a
腹足类 gastropod 软体动物 7—28c

G

咖喱 curry 食品 5—71c
嘎巴拉 kapāla 人头骨碗 9—171e
嘎尔 Kadra 中国藏族乐舞 9—128e
嘎那角 Ke Ga, Point 越南地理区 9—208c
嘎坦罐鼓 ghatam 乐器 7—109d
轧别丁 gabardine 织物 6—538b
钆(Gd) gadolinium 化学元素 6—543d
噶尔 Gar 中国县名 7—6e
噶尔丹 Dga'-ldan 中国蒙古族首领 5—278a
噶举派 Bka'-brgyud-pa 中国藏传佛教派别 2—508d
噶伦堡 Kālimpong 印度城市 9—141e
噶玛派 Karma-pa 中国藏传佛教派别 9—184c
噶乌 ga'u 中国护身佛盒 7—30c
该利亚克统 Gyliakian Series 地质学 7—388e
该林西亚斯 Galinthias 希腊神话人物 6—555e
该尼墨得斯 Ganymede 希腊神话人物 7—3c
该亚 Gaea 希腊女神 6—544a
该隐 Cain 《圣经·旧约》人物 3—325f
该隐派 Cainite 诺斯替教派别 3—326c
改编 arrangement 音乐 1—514a
改编 transcription 音乐 17—195c
改编诗 found poem 文学 6—423d
改革法案 Reform Bill 英国议会法案 14—198b
改进党 Kaishintō 日本政党 9—136c
改良党 Reform Party 加拿大历史政党 14—198e
改土归流 gaitu-guiliu 中国清代政治措施 6—548c
改形及毁损 body modifications and mutilations 文化 2—563b
改宗者 converso 西班牙历史 4—474f
钙(Ca) calcium 化学元素 3—335d
钙长辉长无球粒陨石 eucrite 岩石 6—156e
钙长石 anorthite 矿物 1—369b
钙沸石 scolecite 矿物 15—146b
钙铬榴石 uvarovite 矿物 17—434d
钙铝黄长石 gehlenite 矿物 7—44c
钙铝榴石 grossular 矿物 7—321c
钙镁橄榄石 monticellite 矿物 11—369b
钙锰橄榄石 glaucochroite 矿物 7—155c
钙钠柱石 wernerite 矿物 18—191d
钙缺乏 calcium deficiency 营养失调 3—336a
钙十字沸石 phillipsite 矿物 13—243f
钙铁辉石 hedenbergite 矿物 7—554d
钙铁榴石 andradite 宝石 1—331b
钙霞石 cancrinite 矿物 3—396f
钙铀云母 autunite 矿物 2—81b
钙质海绵 calcareous sponge 动物 3—335a
钙质壳 calcrete 地质学 3—336b
盖 Gay, Jean-Baptiste-Sylvère (French statesman) 法国政治家、历史学家 7—37f
盖奥特 Guyot, Arnold Henry 美国地质学家、教育家 7—386b
盖贝尔 Geibel, (Franz) Emanuel (August) von 德国诗人、戏剧家 7—44d
盖博 Gable, Clark 美国电影演员 6—539b
盖布 Geb 古埃及神 7—42b
盖茨 Gates, Frederick T(aylor) 美国慈善家 7—28f
盖茨 Gates, Horatio 美国将军 7—29a
盖茨 Gates, John Warne 美国金融家 7—29b
盖茨 Getz, Stan 美国音乐家 7—105a
盖茨 Gates, William H. 美国计算机软件设计师、商人 7—29b
盖茨黑德 Gateshead 英格兰城镇 7—29d
盖茨克尔 Gaitskell Hugh (Todd Naylor) 英国政治家 6—548b
盖达塞克 Gajdusek, D(aniel) Carleton 美国医生 6—549a
盖德 Guesde, Jules 法国新闻工作者 7—351b
盖恩莱希 Gernreich, Rudi 美国时装设计师 7—99a
盖恩斯巴勒 Gainsborough 英国纯种赛马 6—547d

盖恩斯伯勒 Gainsborough 英国城镇 6—547d
盖恩斯的米尔战役 Gaines's Mill, Battle of 美国南北战争 6—547c
盖恩斯维尔 Gainesville 美国佛罗里达州城市 6—547c
盖恩斯维尔 Gainesville 美国佐治亚州城市 6—547c
盖尔 Gale, Richard Nelson 英国陆军军官 6—551f
盖尔 Gale, Zona 美国小说家 6—551f
盖尔比山 Gharbī, Jabal al- (Lebanon) 黎巴嫩山脉 7—108f
盖尔比耶 Gharbīyah, al- 埃及省份 7—108f
盖尔伯 Gelber, Jack 美国剧作家 7—47c
盖尔达耶 Ghardaïa 阿尔及利亚城镇 7—108f
盖尔德罗德 Ghelderode, Michel de 比利时戏剧家 7—110e
盖尔德纳湖 Gairdner, Lake 澳大利亚盐沼 6—548a
盖尔范德 Gelfand, Aleksandr Izrail Lazarevich 俄罗斯社会学家 7—47f
盖尔丰德 Gelfond, Aleksandr Osipovich 俄罗斯数学家 7—47f
盖尔·冯·施韦彭堡 Geyr von Schweppenburg, Leo 德国指挥官 7—105e
盖尔纳(蓬圣马桑斯的) Guernes de Pont-Sainte-Maxence 法国作家 7—350b
盖尔人联盟 Gaelic League 爱尔兰文学史 6—544c
盖尔森基兴 Gelsenkirchen 德国城市 7—49a
盖尔斯堡 Galesburg 美国城市 6—552d
盖尔扬 Gharyān 利比亚城镇 7—109a
盖尔语 Gaelic language 爱尔兰语言 6—544c
盖尔语复兴 Gaelic revival 爱尔兰文学 6—544c
盖耳-曼 Gell-Mann, Murray 美国物理学家 7—48a
盖夫勒蒙 Guèvremont, Germaine 加拿大作家 7—351f
盖革 Geiger, Hans 德国物理学家 7—44f
盖革计数器 Geiger counter 仪器 7—45b
盖格 Geiger, Abraham 犹太学者 7—44e
盖格 Geiger, Rudolf Oskar Robert Williams 德国气象学家 7—44f
盖格 Gág, Wanda Hazel 美国艺术家、作家 6—544f
盖格尔 Geiger, Theodor Julius 德国社会学家 7—45a
盖基 Geikie, Sir Archibald 英国地质学家 7—45c
盖吉兹 Gyges 吕底亚国王 7—388e
盖叫天 Gai Jiaotian 中国京剧艺术家 6—546e
盖津 Gezing 印度城镇 7—107a
盖凯杜 Guéckédou 几内亚城镇 7—348b
盖克兰 Guesclin, Bertrand du 法国民族英雄 7—351a
盖克沃尔王朝 Gaekwar dynasty 印度统治家族 6—544b
盖拉 Kaira (India) 印度城市 9—135f
盖拉德 Gailhard, John 英国作家 6—546f
盖拉德卡特 Gaillard Cut 巴拿马人工水道 6—547b
盖拉德斯卡家族 Gherardesca family 意大利贵族世家 7—111f
盖拉尼 Gaylānī, Rashīd ʻA lī al- 伊拉克律师和政治人物 7—38f
盖莱克 Gierek, Edward 波兰共产党领导人 7—123c
盖兰 Guérin, (Georges-) Maurice de 法国诗人 7—349f
盖兰 Guérin, Mother Theodore 法裔美国宗教领袖 7—350a
盖兰 Guérin, Pierre-Narcisse, Baron 法国画家 7—349f
盖朗热 Guéranger, Prosper-Louis-Pascal 法国天主教修士 7—349a
盖勒马 Guelma 阿尔及利亚省份 7—348d
盖勒马 Guelma 阿尔及利亚城市 7—348d
盖勒特 Gellert 威尔士传说 7—48c
盖勒特 Gellert, Christian Fürchtegott 德国作家 7—48c
盖勒尤卜 Qalyūb 埃及城镇 14—53b
盖勒尤卜 Qalyūbīyah, Al- 埃及省份 14—53b
盖雷 Guéret 法国城市 7—349c
盖里济姆山 Gerizim, Mount 巴勒斯坦山峰 7—87d
盖利 Gayley, James 美国冶金学家 7—39a
盖利克足球 Gaelic football 爱尔兰式足球 6—544b
盖利默 Gelimer 汪达尔国王 7—48a
盖-吕萨克 Gay-Lussac, Joseph-Louis 法国化学家、物理学家 7—38b
盖洛普 Gallup 美国城市 6—561f
盖洛普 Gallup, George (Horace) 美国民意测验者 6—561f
盖洛韦 Galloway, Joseph 英国美洲殖民地律师 6—561d
盖马高原 Kaema Highlands 朝鲜高原 9—129c
盖纳 Gaines, Joseph 美国拳击运动员 6—547c
盖尼麦 ghanīmah 伊斯兰战利品 7—108e
盖尼特拉 Kenitra 摩洛哥城市 9—225a
盖齐 Ghezzi, Pier Leone 意大利漫画家 7—112c
盖奇 Gage, Frances Dana Barker 美国社会改革家、作家 6—545c
盖奇 Gage, Matilda Joslyn 美国女权倡导者 6—545d
盖奇 Gage, Thomas 英国将领 6—545e
盖塞里克 Gaiseric 汪达尔人国王 6—548a
盖沙布·钱德尔·森 Keshab Chunder Sen 印度教哲学家 9—244c
盖世太保 Gestapo 纳粹德国政治警察 7—103d
盖朔夫 Geshov, Ivan Evstatiev 保加利亚政治家 7—102b
盖斯 Hess, Germain Henri 俄国化学家 8—58d
盖斯岛 Qeys Island 波斯湾岛屿 14—56b
盖斯凯尔 Gaskell, Elizabeth Cleghorn 英国作家 7—24a
盖斯科因 Gascoigne, George 英国诗人 7—23c
盖斯科因 Gascoyne, David (Emery) 英国诗人 7—23e
盖斯勒 Geissler, (Johann) Heinrich (Wilhelm) 德国吹玻璃工人 7—46a
盖斯热加和定律 Hess's law of heat summation 化学 8—60c
盖斯特-金-奈帝福有限公司 Guest, Keen & Nettlefolds, PLC 英国工程公司集团 7—351c
盖索恩-哈迪 Gathorne-Hardy, Gathorne 英国政治家 7—29e
盖塔 Guettard, Jean-Étienne 法国地质学家、矿物学家 7—351d
盖塔 Geta, Publius Septimius 罗马皇帝 7—104a
盖塔拉洼地 Qattara Depression 埃及利比亚沙漠盆地 14—55f
盖塔人 Getae 欧洲古代民族 7—104b
盖坦 Gaitán, Jorge Eliécer 哥伦比亚政治家 6—548b
盖特尔 Kaithal 印度城市 9—136e
盖特曼 hetman 波兰军衔 8—63d
盖提夫 Qaṭīf Al- 沙特阿拉伯城镇 14—55e
盖图里亚 Gaetulia 北非古地区 6—544e
盖瓦 imbrex 希腊-罗马建筑 8—341f
盖瓦姆 Ghavam el-Saltaneh, Ahmad 伊朗首相 7—109d
盖翁切尔 Keonjhar 印度城镇 9—236e
盖沃尔斯贝格 Gevelsberg 德国城市 7—105d
盖西 Gessi, Romolo 意大利探险家、军人 7—102d
盖伊 Guy 统治者之名 7—384b
盖伊 Guy 耶路撒冷国王 7—384c
盖伊 Guy, Buddy 美国音乐家 7—384e
盖伊 Gaye, Marvin (Pentz) 美国歌手、歌曲作者 7—38f
盖伊 Guy, Thomas 英国慈善家 7—384f
盖伊(勃艮第的) Guy of Burgundy (pope) 教皇 7—384d
盖伊(沃里克的) Guy of Warwick 英国传奇英雄 7—384d
盖依 Gay, John 英国戏剧作家 7—37f
盖依 Gay, Sophie 法国作家 7—38a
盖尤斯 Gaius 古罗马人名 6—548c
盖尤斯 Gaius 罗马法学家 6—548c
盖泽尔 Geisel, Ernesto 巴西总统 7—45d
盖泽尔 Geisel, Theodor Seuss 美国作家、插图画家 7—45e
概率论 probability theory 数学 13—523a
概念 concept 哲学 4—409e
概念形成 concept formation 哲学 4—409f
概念主义 conceptismo 西班牙文学 4—410b
干板 dry plate 摄影 5—432d
干冰 Dry Ice 化学 5—432c
干草 hay 农业 7—528c
干草原 Steppe, the 欧亚地理区 16—224d
干草原猫 steppe cat 哺乳动物 16—224f
干城章嘉峰 Kānchenjunga 亚洲山峰 9—153b

干船坞 dry dock 船舶检修设施 5—432b
干达人 Ganda 乌干达民族 6—571d
干地亚 Candia (city, Crete) 克里特城市 3—397e
干地亚海 Candia, Sea of (Europe) 爱琴海南部海域 3—397e
干腐病 dry rot 植物病害 5—432d
干谷 arroyo 地理学 1—517c
干旱 drought 气候学 5—427e
干旱尘暴区 Dust Bowl 美国区域 5—479d
干旱林 dry forest 生态学 5—432c
干画 dry painting 绘画 5—432d
干胶印 dry offset 印刷 5—432d
干刻法 drypoint 铜版画技法 5—433d
干酪 cheese 食品 4—100d
干酪根 kerogen 化合物 9—242a
干尼亚 Khaniá 希腊城市 9—256a
干尼亚湾 Khaniá, Gulf of 希腊海湾 9—256a
干漆 kanshitsu 日本雕刻装饰技术 9—164c
干砌墙结构 drywall construction 建筑 5—433e
干扰 jamming 电子学 8—532b
干扰素 interferon 药物 8—409a
干热焚风 zonda 气象学 18—563c
干涉 interference 物理学 8—408e
干尸 mummy 经过防腐处理的尸体 11—481d
干湿表 psychrometer 湿度表 13—565f
干细胞 stem cell 细胞学 16—216e
干舷高 freeboard 船舶载重安全界限 6—470c
干性油 drying oil 天然、化合脂油 5—433c
干盐湖 playa 地质学 13—365d
干燥 seasoning 木材加工 15—173e
干燥综合征 sicca syndrome 疾病 15—349c
甘氨酸 glycine 生物化学 7—165f
甘巴加陡崖 Gambaga Scarp 加纳高地 6—566a
甘比尔群岛 Gambier Islands 法属玻利尼西亚群岛 6—567d
甘比诺 Gambino, Garlo 美国犯罪集团首脑 6—567d
甘必大 Gambetta, Léon 法国政治家 6—566b
甘布尔雨期 Gamblian Pluvial Stage 地质学 6—567e
甘布尔泽夫山 Gamburtsev Mountains 南极冰盖下山脉 6—568e
甘茨 Ganz, Rudolph 美国音乐家 7—3e
甘德 Gander 加拿大城镇 6—571e
甘德斯海姆 Gandersheim (Germany) 德国城市 6—571e
甘德与石申 Gan De and Shi Shen 中国古代天文学家 6—570f
甘迪亚 Candía 西班牙港市 6—576a
甘地 Gandhi, Mohandas Karamchand 印度民族主义领袖 6—572c
甘地 Gandhi, Rajiv 印度总理 6—575e
甘地(夫人) Gandhi, Indira (Priyadarshini) 印度总理 6—572b
甘地讷格尔 Gāndhīnagar 印度城市 6—576a
甘多 Gando (Nigeria) 尼日利亚城镇 6—576a
甘多尔福堡 Castel Gandolfo 意大利村庄、城堡 3—508c
甘恩 Gahn, Johan Gottlieb 瑞典矿物学家 6—546d
甘格拉 Gangra (Turkey) 土耳其省份 7—1c
甘汞(Hg_2Cl_2) calomel 矿物 3—357b
甘哈国家公园 Kānha National Park 印度国家公园 9—158a
甘吉布勒姆 Kānchipuram 印度城镇 9—153b
甘贾 Gyandzha 阿塞拜疆城市 7—388b
甘杰拉巴拉 Kānchrāpāra 印度城镇 9—153c
甘蓝 cabbage 植物 3—304d
甘露衣 manna 草本植物 10—467a
甘米银 Camiguin 菲律宾岛屿 3—374b
甘末林 Gamelin, Maurice(-Gustave) 法国陆军总司令 6—569e
甘尼阿达约 Ganioda'yo 印第安人部族首领 7—1e
甘尼森 Gunnison 美国城市 7—373a
甘尼森布莱克峡谷国家公园 Black Canyon of the Gunnison National Park 美国国家公园 2—510d
甘尼特 Gannett, Frank Ernest 美国报纸出版家 7—2a
甘尼特公司 Gannett Co., Inc. 美国报业集团 7—2b
甘宁汉 Cunningham, Sir Alexander 英国陆军军官、考古学家 5—62d
甘烹碧 Kamphaeng Phet 泰国城镇 9—150f
甘斯 Gans, Eduard 德国法学家 7—2b
甘斯 Gans, Joe 美国拳击运动员 7—2c
甘肃 Gansu 中国省份 7—2d
甘特 Gante, Pedro de 天主教方济各会修士 7—3c
甘特斯维尔 Guntersville 美国城市 7—374d
甘托克 Gangtok 印度城市 7—1e
甘油三酯 triglyceride 化学 17—219c
甘蔗 sugarcane(*Saccharum officinarum*) 草本植物 16—309f
《甘珠尔》 Bka'-'gyur 佛经 2—508e
杆 rod 英国旧长度单位 14—345e
杆锥晶束 bacillite 矿物学 2—118e
杆沸石 thomsonite 矿物 17—53e
杆石属 Bactrites 古生物学 2—125f
肝 liver 解剖学 10—159f
肝癌 liver cancer 疾病 10—160b
肝豆状核变性 hepatolenticular degeneration (metabolic disorder) 疾病 8—29e
肝功能试验 liver function test 医学 10—160e
肝静脉 hepatic vein 解剖学 8—29b
肝素 heparin 药物 8—29a
肝吸虫 liver fluke 动物 10—160d
肝炎 hepatitis 疾病 8—29c
肝叶草 liverleaf (plant) 植物 10—160e
肝硬变 cirrhosis 疾病 4—246a
坩埚 crucible 化学实验器皿 5—37d
坩埚法 crucible process 冶金工艺 5—37e
坩埚炉 crucible furnace 冶金设备 5—37e
柑橘 orange 木本植物 12—441f
柑橘赛 Orange Bowl 体育项目 12—443d
柑橘园 orangery 建筑 12—443b
酐 anhydride 化合物 1—355f
感恩节 Thanksgiving Day 美国节日 17—14b
感光度 speed 照相术 16—17b
感化院 reformatory 对青少年进行改造的机构 14—199c
感觉 sensation 神经学 15—214e
感觉 sense 生理学 15—214f
感觉论 sensationalism 心理学 15—214f
感觉运动技能 sensorimotor skill 习得能力 15—215d
感情的谬误 affective fallacy 文学 1—103c
感情误置 pathetic fallacy 文学 13—87f
感染 infection 病理现象 8—380d
感伤喜剧 sentimental comedy 戏剧 15—216a
感伤小说 sentimental novel 文学 15—216b
感受器 receptor 神经系统 14—183b
感受性训练 sensitivity training 心理治疗技术 15—215c
感应加热 induction heating 电磁学 8—374f
橄长岩 troctolite 岩石 17—229f
橄榄科 Burseraceae 植物学 3—276f
橄榄球 football 美式球戏 6—396f
橄榄球 football 加拿大式球戏 6—397a
橄榄山 Olives, Mount of 巴勒斯坦山脉 12—376a
橄榄石 olivine 矿物 12—376d
橄榄岩 peridotite 岩石 13—168a
橄榄陨铁 pallasite 陨石 12—568e
赣方言 Gan dialect 中国汉语方言 6—571a
赣江 Gan Jiang 中国河流 6—571a
赣县 Kan-hsien (China) 中国地名 9—151e
赣州 Ganzhou 中国城市 7—3f

冈本绮堂 Okamoto Kidō 日本剧作家 12—357d
冈比西斯 Cambyses 古波斯统治者之名 3—368d
冈比西斯二世 Cambyses Ⅱ 波斯国王 3—368e
冈比西斯一世 Cambyses Ⅰ 安申统治者 3—368e
冈比亚 Gambia,The 西非国家 6—566d
冈比亚河 Gambia River 西非河流 6—567b
冈伯格 Gomberg,Moses 美国化学家 7—198c
冈布里奇 Gombrich,Sir Ernst Hans Josef 奥地利出生的艺术史学家 7—198e
冈布龙陶瓷 Gombroon ware 陶瓷器 7—198e
冈仓觉三 Okakura Kakuzō 日本艺术评论家 12—357d
冈察罗娃 Goncharova,Natalya 俄国艺术家 7—201d
冈察洛夫 Goncharov,Ivan Aleksandrovich 俄国小说家 7—201b
冈达 ghaṇṭā 中国藏传佛教法铃 7—108e
冈德盖 Gundagai 澳大利亚城镇 7—371f
冈底斯山 Gangdisi Shan 中国山脉 6—576e
冈都巴德 Gundobad 勃艮第国王 7—372b
冈多弗纳斯 Gondophernes 印度-安息国王 7—203a
冈恩 Gunn,Thom 英国诗人 7—372d
冈弗林特微体化石 Gunflint microfossils 古生物学 7—372b
冈格拉 Kāngra 印度城市 9—157d
冈谷 Okaya 日本城市 12—358d
冈内 Gennes,Pierre-Gilles de 法国物理学家 7—64e
冈妮 Gonne,Maud 爱尔兰爱国者 7—205c
冈尼达 Gunnedah 澳大利亚城镇 7—372f
冈崎 Okazaki 日本城市 12—358e
冈崎源七 Okazaki Genshichi 日本画家 12—358f
冈人 Gang (people) 非洲文化语言集团 6—576d
冈萨雷斯 Gonzales,Alberto R. 美国律师、法官 7—206a
冈萨雷斯 González,Julio 西班牙雕刻家 7—206c
冈萨雷斯 González,Manuel 墨西哥军人、总统 7—206d
冈萨雷斯 Gonzales,Pancho 美国运动员 7—206b
冈萨雷斯·德·克拉维霍 González de Clavijo,Ruy 西班牙外交官 7—206d
冈萨雷斯·德·门多萨 González de Mendoza,Pedro,CARDINAL 西班牙教士、外交家 7—206e
冈萨雷斯·马丁内斯 González Martínez,Enrique 墨西哥诗人、医生 7—207a
冈萨雷斯·马克斯 González Márquez,Felipe 西班牙总理 7—206f
冈山 Okayama 日本城市 12—358d
冈斯 Gance,Abel 法国电影导演 6—571c
冈特 Gunter,Edmund 英国数学家 7—374c
冈特 Gaunt,John of 英格兰亲王 7—34c
冈田米山人 Okada Beisanjin 日本画家 12—357c
冈田启介 Okada Keisuke 日本首相 12—357c
冈田为恭 Okada Tamechika 日本画家 12—357c
冈瓦纳古大陆 Gondwanaland 地质学 7—203a
刚果 Congo 非洲国家 4—426c
刚果(金) Congo 非洲国家 4—425a
刚果海底峡谷 Congo Canyon 大西洋峡谷 4—427e
刚果河 Congo River 非洲河流 4—428a
刚果红 Congo red 染料 4—428a
刚果黄麻 Congo jute (plant) 植物 4—428a
刚果人 Kongo 非洲民族 9—345d
刚果薮狗 Congo bush dog 狗品种 4—427e
刚果王国 Kongo kingdom 中非西部王国 9—345d
刚果自由邦 Congo Free State 非洲历史 4—427f
刚毛藻属 Cladophora 植物学 4—257c
刚玉 corundum 矿物 4—527b
肛管 anal canal 解剖学 1—309b
肛门 anus 解剖学 1—401f
肛门期 anal stage 心理学 1—309c
钢 steel 冶金 16—206f
钢笔画 pen drawing 美术作品 13—134d
钢鼓 steel drum 乐器 16—207d
钢片琴 celesta 乐器 3—553d
钢琴 piano 乐器 13—279e
港湾 harbour 地理学 7—470a
港务官 shabunder 马来亚官员 15—251e
杠杆 lever 简单机械 10—45d
高 Gow,Niel 苏格兰小提琴家 7—233a
高阿岛 Gaua (Vanuatu) 瓦努阿图岛屿 7—30c
高傲自大 hubris 希腊哲学 8—220a
高浜虚子 Takahama Kyoshi 日本诗人 16—440a
高背长椅 settle 家具 15—235c
高鼻羚羊 saiga (*Saiga tatarica*) 哺乳动物 14—502e
高侧窗 clerestory 建筑 4—285d
高层建筑 high-rise building 建筑 8—75b
高潮 climax 文学 4—292d
高潮突降 anticlimax 修辞方法 1—384c
高村光云 Takamura Kōun 日本雕刻家 16—440d
高达 Gauḍa 印度古地名 7—31a
高岛屋有限公司 Takashimaya Co.,Ltd. 日本百货公司 16—441b
高德温 Goldwyn,Samuel 美国电影制片人 7—195b
高登 Gordon,Ruth 美国作家、演员 7—215a
高等法院 High Court of Justice 英国法院 8—74d
高等法院首席法官 lord chief justice 英国官职 10—219b
高等海事法庭 High Court of Admiralty 英国法院 8—74c
高等教育 higher education 教育 8—75f
高等小学 Hauptschule 德国教育 7—513a
高等宗教事务法院(委员会) High Commission,Court of 英国法院 8—74a
高低杠 uneven parallel bars 体育器械 17—341d
高迪 Gaudí Cornet,Antoni 西班牙建筑师 7—31a
高地 Highlands 苏格兰地区 8—77a
高地 high place 以色列人拜神处 8—75a
高地弗林格 highland fling 苏格兰舞蹈 8—76e
高地运动会 Highland Games 体育 8—76f
高杜瓦德亚姆琴 gottuvadyam 琵琶家族的长颈弦乐器 7—227b
高度表 altimeter 仪表 1—256b
高尔 Gower 英国半岛 7—233a
高尔 Gall 美国苏族军事领袖 6—555e
高尔 Gower,John 英格兰诗人 7—233b
高尔,圣 Gall,SAINT 爱尔兰修士 6—555f
高尔察克 Kolchak,Aleksandr Vasilyevich 俄国北极探险家 9—338c
高尔顿 Galton,Sir Francis 英国科学家 6—563c
高尔夫球 GOLF 体育项目 16—98b
高尔夫球 golf 体育项目 7—195c
高尔夫式台球 golf 体育项目 7—195f
高尔基 Gorky (Russia) 俄罗斯城市 7—217e
高尔基 Gorky,Arshile 美国画家 7—217e
高尔基 Gorky,Maksim 苏联作家 7—218a
高尔斯 Gowers,William Timothy 英国数学家 7—233c
高尔斯华绥 Galsworthy,John 英国作家 6—562e
高尔特 Galt,Sir Alexander Tilloch 加拿大政治家 6—563a
高尔特 Galt,John 英国作家 6—563b
高峰让吉 Takamine,Jokichi 日本生物化学家 16—440c
高夫 Gough,Sir Hubert de la Poer 英国将领 7—228c
高冈 Takaoka 日本城市 16—440e
高岗 Gao Gang 中国领导人 7—4b
高庚 Gauguin,(Eugène-Henri-)Paul 法国画家 7—32d
高句丽 Koguryŏ 古朝鲜王国 9—333c
高句丽风格 Koguryŏ style 朝鲜视觉艺术 9—333d
高句丽遗址 Gaogouli sites 中国辽宁、吉林高句丽城址遗迹 7—5e

高胱氨酸尿症 homocystinuria 病理现象 8—147f
高槻 Takatsuki 日本城市 16—441c
高哈蒂 Gauhāti (Assam, India) 印度城镇 7—32f
高后 Gaohou 中国皇后 7—5c
高级大菜 grande cuisine 法式名菜 7—252d
高级律师 barrister 法律 2—244e
高级神职人员 prelate 天主教会神职人员 13—492f
高级审判法院 Supreme Court of Judicature 英国法律 16—349d
高加梅拉战役 Gaugamela, Battle of 亚洲历史 7—31f
高加索 Caucasus 欧亚地理 3—534d
高加索地理人种 Caucasoid geographic race 欧洲地理人种 3—534c
高加索诸民族 Caucasian PEOPLES 民族 3—533d
高加索诸语言 Caucasian languages 语言 3—533f
高加索自然保护区 Kavkazsky Nature Reserve 俄罗斯地理区 9—201f
高架桥 viaduct 建筑 17—533c
高架渠 aqueduct 工程 1—427e
高架铁路 elevated transit line 交通运输 6—34e
高剑父 Gao Jianfu 中国画家 7—4c
高克恭 Gao Kegong 中国画家 7—4e
高拉土丘 Tepe Gawra 美索不达米亚古代居民点 16—547e
高勒 Gawler 澳大利亚城镇 7—37e
高勒岭 Gawler Ranges 澳大利亚山脉 7—37e
高里伯爵(第三) Gowrie, John Ruthven, 3rd earl of 苏格兰阴谋分子 7—233d
高里亚拉河 Kauriālā (central Asia) 中亚河流 9—200d
高丽古棋 nyout 朝鲜古老棋戏 12—312e
高丽王朝 Koryŏ DYNASTY 朝鲜历史 9—361b
高利 Gaulli, Giovanni Battista (Italian painter) 意大利画家 7—33f
高利贷 usury 法律 17—425c
高凉菜 kalanchoe 植物 9—138e
高粱 sorghum 谷物 15—522a
高岭 Cao Lanh 越南城市 3—417c
高岭化土 kaolisol 土壤 9—171c
高岭石 kaolinite 矿物 9—171c
高岭土 kaolin 矿物 9—171a
高隆班,圣 Columban, SAINT 爱尔兰传教士 4—367e
高卢 Gaul 欧洲古地名 7—32f
高卢卢格杜南西斯 Gallia Lugdunensis (Roman province) 古罗马省份 6—559a
高卢纳尔榜南西斯 Gallia Narbonensis (ancient Gaul) 古罗马省份 6—559b
高卢圣咏 Gallican chant 宗教音乐 6—559d
《高卢信纲》 Gallican Confession 基督教归正会信纲 6—559d
高卢语 Gaulish language 欧亚古代语言 7—33b
高卢战争 Gallic Wars 罗马历史 6—559d
高卢主义 Gallicanism 法兰西宗教和政治理论 6—559e
高炉 blast furnace 冶金 2—530b
高马达 Gaumata (pretender to Persian throne) 自封波斯国王 7—34b
高帽德发冠架 commode 妇女发饰 4—386a
高门 Sublime Porte 奥斯曼土耳其政府 16—298b
高棉人 Khmer 亚洲民族 9—260f
高棉文学 Khmer literature 东南亚文学 9—261a
高棉野牛 kouprey (species *Bos sauveli*) 动物 9—367b
高棉语 Khmer language 亚洲语言 9—261a
高敏 Gao Min 中国跳水运动员 7—4f
高明 Gao Ming 中国剧作家 7—5a
高鸣鹤 whooping crane (*Grus americana*) 鸟类 18—242c
高乃依 Corneille, Pierre 法国诗人、剧作家 4—511e
高乃依 Corneille, Thomas 法国剧作家 4—512e
高平 Cao Bang 越南城镇 3—416f
高平原 High Plains 美国草原 8—75a
高其佩 Gao Qipei 中国画家 7—5a
高奇·封·弗兰肯图恩 Gautsch von Frankenthurn, Paul, Freiherr (Baron) 奥地利首相 7—36d
高崎 Takasaki 日本城市 16—441a
高跷 stilt 娱乐工具 16—238e
高砂 Takasago 日本城市 16—440f
高山 Takayama 日本城市 16—441c
高山矮曲林地 elfin woodland 高海拔矮小森林 6—35f
高山病 mountain sickness 疾病 11—445b
高山滑雪 Alpine skiing 体育项目 1—251e
高山岭 Mount Lofty Ranges 澳大利亚丘陵 11—441c
高山牧场经济 alpwirtschaft 经济 1—252c
高山热 mountain fever 疾病 11—444d
高山族 Gaoshan 中国民族 7—5f
高杉晋作 Takasugi Shinsaku 日本军事领袖 16—441b
高尚的野蛮人 noble savage 文学 12—222f
高射炮 antiaircraft gun 武器 1—382c
高深曲线 hypsometric curve 地质学 8—296f
高適 Gao Shi 中国诗人 7—5c
高斯 gauss 物理学 7—34c
高斯 Gauss, Carl Friedrich 德国数学家 7—34d
高斯 Ghose, Śrī Aurobindo (Indian philosopher) 印度哲学家 7—113b
高斯定理 Gauss's theorem 物理学 7—35d
高斯分布 Gaussian distribution (mathematics) 数学 7—35d
高斯氏原理 Gause's principle (biology) 生物学 7—34c
高斯消去法 Gauss elimination 数学 7—35d
高松 Takamatsu 日本城市 16—440c
高速公路 expressway 公路主干线 6—196f
高台 dais 建筑 5—113a
高台教 Cao Dai 越南宗教派别 3—416f
高特利集团 Altria Group 美国公司 1—257f
高滕 Gauteng 南非省份 7—35e
高屉柜 highboy 家具 8—75e
高韦里河 Cauvery River 印度圣河 3—536e
高位神 High God 人类学 8—74e
高温计 pyrometer 测温仪器 14—47d
高温气候期 Hypsithermal Climatic Interval 地质学 8—296f
高文 Gawain 民间传奇人物 7—37d
《高文爵士和绿衣骑士》 Sir Gawayne and the Grene Knight 中古英语诗篇 15—401e
高羲东 Koh Hui-dong 朝鲜美术家 9—333d
高雄 Gaoxiong 中国县名 7—6a
高雄 Gaoxiong 中国城市 7—6b
高雄县 Kao-hsiung Hsien (Taiwan) 中国台湾县名 9—170e
高血糖 hyperglycemia 医学 8—291f
高血压病 hypertension 疾病 8—293d
高压舱 hyperbaric chamber 医学 8—290f
高压釜 autoclave 容器 2—73e
高雅喜剧 genteel comedy 戏剧 7—66f
高要 Gaoyao (China) 中国城市 7—6d
高要 Kao-yao (China) 中国城市 9—170e
高原 plateau 地形 13—352a
高原病 altitude sickness 疾病 1—256f
高原肖肖尼诸语言 Plateau Shoshonean languages 北美印第安语言 13—352e
高原肖肖尼诸语言 Shoshonean languages, Plateau 北美印第安语言 15—335c
高原印第安人 Plateau Indian 北美印第安民族 13—352c
高原州 Plateau 尼日利亚州名 13—351f
高知 Kōchi 日本县名 9—331a
高知阶 Kochian Stage 地质学 9—331c

高止山脉 Ghāts 印度山脉 7—109d
高志航 Gao Zhihang 中国国民党空军将领 7—5d
高兹耶达 Goizueta, Roberto Crispulo 美国商人 7—184d
高宗 Kojong 朝鲜国君 9—336b
高座石 perched rock 地质学 13—157e
羔羊肉 lamb 食品 9—460d
睾丸 testis 解剖学 16—561b
睾丸癌 testicular cancer 疾病 16—561a
睾丸炎 orchitis 疾病 12—447f
睾丸甾酮 testosterone 激素 16—561c
膏桐 jatropha 植物 8—549e
糕饼 cake 食品 3—331c
糕点面团 pastry 食品 13—83f
糕点战争 Pastry War 墨西哥与法国间冲突 13—84a
缟玛瑙 onyx 矿物 12—424b
告解室 confessional 天主教 4—421a
锆(Zr) zirconium 化学元素 18—558d
锆石 zircon 矿物 18—558c
戈巴比斯 Gobabis 纳米比亚城镇 7—170b
戈巴特 Gobat, Charles-Albert 瑞士政治家 7—170b
戈贝尔 Gobel, Jean-Baptiste-Joseph 法国大主教 7—170c
戈贝尔 Goebel, Karl (Immanuel Eberhard) von 法国大主教 7—177a
戈壁 Gobi 亚洲荒漠 7—170d
戈宾诺伯爵 Gobineau, Joseph-Arthur, comte de (count of) 法国外交官、作家 7—170e
戈布兰家族 Gobelin BZFAMILY 法国染织师家族 7—170c
戈茨 Gotch, Frank 美国摔跤运动员 7—222f
戈达德 Goddard, Mary Katherine 美国印刷商、出版商 7—172e
戈达德 Goddard, Robert Hutchings 美国火箭之父 7—172f
戈达德(奥尔本的) Goddard (of Aldbourne), Rayner Goddard, Baron 英国法官 7—172f
戈达德家族 Goddard FAMILY 美国工匠家族 7—172e
戈达尔 Godard, Benjamin(-Louis-Paul) 法国作曲家 7—172b
戈达尔 Godard, Jean-Luc 法国导演 7—172b
戈代加讷尔 Kodaikānal 印度城镇 9—331d
戈黛娃夫人 Godiva, Lady 盎格鲁-撒克逊贵妇 7—174d
戈丹 Gaudin, Martin-Michel-Charles, DUC (duke) DE GAËTE 法国财政大臣 7—31e
戈德堡 Goldberg, Arthur J. 美国劳工律师 7—187e
戈德堡 Goldberg, Rube 美国漫画家 7—187e
戈德堡 Goldberg, Whoopi 美国喜剧演员、制片人 7—188a
戈德尔布尔 Godarpura 印度朝圣地 7—172d
戈德法登 Goldfaden, Abraham 犹太作家 7—191d
戈德弗雷(方丹的) Godfrey OF FONTAINES 亚里士多德学派哲学家 7—173f
戈德弗鲁瓦(克莱尔的) Godefroid DE CLAIRE 比利时金匠 7—173c
戈德弗鲁瓦家族 Godefroy FAMILY 法国家族 7—173c
戈德哈伯 Goldhaber, Maurice 美国物理学家 7—192a
戈德华特 Goldwater, Barry M(orris) 美国政治家 7—194f
戈德金 Godkin, E(dwin) L(awrence) 美国编辑 7—174e
戈德里 Kotri 巴基斯坦城镇 9—365f
戈德里克(诺克顿的)子爵 Goderich of Nocton, Frederick John Robinson, Viscount 英国首相 7—173e
戈德马克 Goldmark, Josephine Clara 美国社会改革家 7—192f
戈德马克 Goldmark, Karl 匈牙利作曲家 7—192f
戈德马克 Goldmark, Peter Carl 匈牙利工程师 7—193a
戈德曼 Goldmann, Nahum 以色列犹太复国主义者领袖 7—192e
戈德曼彻斯特 Godmanchester (England) 英国城镇 7—174f
戈德斯米德 Goldsmid, Sir Frederick John 英国陆军将领 7—194a
戈德斯米德 Goldsmid, Sir Isaac Lyon, 1ST BARONET 犹太金融家 7—194b
戈德斯坦 Goldstein, Eugen 德国物理学家 7—194e
戈德温 Godwine 韦塞克斯伯爵 7—176d
戈德温 Godwin, Edward (William) 英国建筑师、作家 7—176a
戈德温 Godwin, Francis 英格兰主教、历史学家 7—176b
戈德温 Godwin, Mary Wollstonecraft (writer and feminist) 英国作家 7—176b
戈德温 Godwin, William 英国哲学家 7—176b
戈德温奥斯丁峰 Godwin Austen, Mount (Jammu and Kashmir) 查谟和克什米尔山峰 7—176c
戈德亚姆 Kottayam 印度城市 9—366b
戈登 Gordon 苏格兰区名 7—213c
戈登 Gordon, Anna Adams 美国社会改革家 7—213e
戈登 Gordon, Aaron David 犹太复国主义作家、哲学家 7—213d
戈登 Gordon, Adam Lindsay 澳大利亚作家 7—213d
戈登 Gordon, Charles George 英国将军 7—213f
戈登 Gordon, Charles William 加拿大长老会牧师 7—214b
戈登 Gordon, George 英国阴谋家 7—214b
戈登 Gordon, Jeff 美国赛车手 7—214c
戈登 Gordon, John Brown 美国将军 7—214c
戈登 Gordon, Judah Leib 犹太作家 7—214d
戈登 Gordon, Laura de Force 美国律师、编辑 7—214d
戈登 Gordon, Patrick 俄国将军 7—214e
戈登 Gordon, Richard F(rancis), Jr. 美国航天员 7—214f
戈登 Gordon, Walter Lockhart 加拿大商人、政府官员 7—215b
戈登 Gordon, William 苏格兰詹姆斯党人 7—215b
戈登河 Gordon River 澳大利亚河流 7—215b
戈登魏泽 Goldenweiser, Alexander (Alexandrovich) 美国人类学家 7—191c
戈登勋爵 Gordon, Lord George 英国贵族 7—214b
戈迪埃-布尔泽斯卡 Gaudier-Brzeska, Henri 法国雕塑家 7—31d
戈迪菲 Gadifer DE LA SALLE 法国军人 6—543c
戈迪默 Gordimer, Nadine 南非小说家 7—213a
戈蒂 Gotti, John 美国黑社会头目 7—226b
戈蒂埃 Gaultier, Denys 法国演奏家 7—34a
戈蒂埃 Gautier, Hubert 法国工程师 7—36a
戈蒂埃 Gautier, Léon 法国文学史家 7—36a
戈蒂埃 Gautier, Théophile 法国诗人 7—36b
戈蒂埃(阿拉斯的) Gautier D'ARRAS 法国小说家 7—35f
戈蒂埃(梅斯·昂洛埃兰的) Gauthier DE MÉS EN LOHERAINS (poet) 法国诗人、教士 7—35f
戈蒂埃(梅斯的) Gautier DE METZ 法国诗人、教士 7—36a
戈东诺夫 Godunov, Boris (Fyodorovich) 俄国沙皇 7—175f
戈顿 Gorton, Sir John Grey 澳大利亚总理 7—219e
戈多尔芬 Godolphin, Sidney 英国诗人 7—174f
戈多尔芬 Godolphin, Sidney Godolphin, 1st Earl of 英格兰政治家 7—175a
戈多夫斯基 Godowsky, Leopold 美国钢琴家、作曲家 7—175b
戈多斯基 Godowsky, Leopold Jr. 美国音乐家、摄影科技工作者 7—175c
戈多伊 Godoy, Manuel de 西班牙首相 7—175d
戈多伊克鲁斯 Godoy Cruz 阿根廷地区 7—175e
戈尔 Kol (India) 印度城市 9—337d
戈尔 Gore, Albert 美国副总统 7—215d
戈尔 Gore, Charles 英国神学家 7—215d
戈尔巴乔夫 Gorbachev, Mikhail 苏联共产党总书记、总统 7—211e
戈尔茨 Goltz, (Gustav Adolf Joachim) Rüdiger, Grafvon der (count of) 普鲁士军人、作家 7—197f
戈尔茨 Goltz, (Wilhelm Leopold) Colmar, Freiherrvon der (baron of) 德国军官 7—197e
戈尔茨坦 Goldstein, Joseph L(eonard) 美国分子遗传学家 7—194e
戈尔德 Gold, Thomas 英国天文学家 7—186a
戈尔德贝格 Goldberg, Dora 美国歌唱家 7—187e

戈尔德菲尔德　Goldfield　美国县城　7—191d
戈尔德科斯特　Gold Coast　澳大利亚城市　7—186c
戈尔德曼　Goldman, Emma　国际无政府主义者　7—192d
戈尔德曼　Goldmann, Max (theatre director)　奥地利导演　7—192e
戈尔德施米特　Goldschmidt, Meïr Aron　丹麦作家　7—193d
戈尔德施米特　Goldschmidt, Richard B(enedict)　美国动物学家、遗传学家　7—193e
戈尔德施米特　Goldschmidt, Victor Mordechai　德国矿物学家　7—193e
戈尔德施米特　Goldschmidt, Victor Moritz　挪威矿物学家、岩石学家　7—193f
戈尔登　Golden　美国城市　7—188a
戈尔狄安　Gordian　罗马皇帝之名　7—212f
戈尔狄安二世　Gordian II　罗马皇帝　7—212f
戈尔狄安三世　Gordian III　罗马皇帝　7—213a
戈尔狄安一世　Gordian I　罗马皇帝　7—212f
戈尔迪　Goldie, Sir George (Dashwood Taubman)　英国殖民地官员　7—192a
戈尔迪娃与格林科夫　Gordeeva, Yekaterina; and Grinkov, Sergey　俄罗斯出生的花样滑冰搭档　7—212e
戈尔迪乌姆　Gordium　古安纳托利亚城市　7—213b
戈尔迪乌姆结　Gordian knot　谚语词　7—213a
戈尔迪乌斯虫　gordian worm　无脊椎动物　7—213a
戈尔丁　Golding, Louis　英国作家　7—192b
戈尔丁　Golding, Sir William (Gerald)　英国小说家　7—192c
戈尔菲托　Golfito　哥斯达黎加城市　7—195f
戈尔甘　Gorgān　伊朗城镇　7—215f
戈尔贡佐拉　Gorgonzola　意大利城镇　7—216d
戈尔哈布尔　Kolhāpur　印度城市　9—339a
戈尔吉　Golgi, Camillo　意大利医师、细胞学家　7—195f
戈尔加斯　Gorgas, William Crawford　美国军医　7—216a
戈尔孔达　Golconda　印度城堡　7—185c
戈尔洛夫卡　Gorlovka　乌克兰城市　7—219b
戈尔诺-阿尔泰　Gorno-Altay　俄罗斯行政区　7—219b
戈尔诺-阿尔泰斯克　Gorno-Altaysk　俄罗斯城市　7—219c
戈尔诺-巴达赫尚　Gorno-Badakhshan　塔吉克斯坦州名　7—219c
戈尔诺普利河　Karnaphuli River　孟加拉国河流　9—185c
戈尔恰科夫公爵　Gorchakov, Aleksandr Mikhaylovich, Prince (Knyaz)　俄国政治家　7—212c
戈尔恰科夫公爵　Gorchakov, Mikhail Dmitriyevich, Prince (Knayz)　俄国军官、政治家　7—212e
戈尔日　Gorj　罗马尼亚县名　7—217c
戈尔韦　Galway　爱尔兰港市　6—565a
戈尔韦郡　Galway　爱尔兰郡名　6—564f
戈尔兹伯勒　Goldsboro　美国城市　7—193c
戈耳工　Gorgon　希腊神话　7—216c
戈耳什密特　Goldschmidt, Hans　德国化学家　7—193d
戈夫半岛　Gove Peninsula　澳大利亚半岛　7—231e
戈夫岛　Gough Island　大西洋岛屿　7—228d
戈弗雷　Godfrey, Arthur (Morton)　美国娱乐节目表演者　7—174b
戈弗雷　Godfrey, Sir Edmund (Berry)　英国地方官员　7—174c
戈弗雷　Godfrey, Thomas　美洲殖民地发明家　7—174c
戈弗雷(布永的)　Godfrey of Bouillon　下洛林公爵　7—173f
戈弗雷(圣维克托的)　Godfrey of Saint-Victor　法国修士、哲学家　7—174a
戈甘纳　Gokaṇṇa (Sri Lanka)　斯里兰卡城镇　7—184f
戈格斯　Gorgas, Josiah　美国军事官员　7—215f
戈贡达战役　Gogūnda, Battle of　印度历史　7—183f
戈赫卢　Kohlu　巴基斯坦区名　9—335b
戈吉斯　Gorges, Sir Ferdinando　英国殖民地开拓者　7—216a
戈加蒂　Gogarty, Oliver St. John　爱尔兰作家　7—182f
戈卡莱　Gokhale, Gopāl Krishna　印度社会改革家　7—185a
戈拉布德　Koraput　印度城镇　9—352a
戈拉尔　Kolār　印度城市　9—338a
戈拉尔戈德菲尔兹　Kolār Gold Fields　印度城市　9—338a
戈莱鲁湖　Kolleru Lake　印度湖泊　9—339e
戈莱伦河　Coleroon River　印度河流　4—343d
戈兰茨　Gollancz, Sir Victor　英国出版家、作家　7—197a
戈兰高地　Golan Heights　中东地区　7—185a
戈勒克布尔　Gorakhpur　印度城镇　7—211d
戈雷岛　Gorée Island　塞内加尔岛屿　7—215e
戈里　Gorrie, John　美国医师　7—219d
戈里　Gorrio, Tobia (Italian poet and composer)　意大利诗人、作曲家　7—219e
戈里齐亚　Gorizia　意大利城市　7—217d
戈利钦　Golitsyn, Boris Alekseyevich　俄国政治家　7—196d
戈利钦　Golitsyn, Dmitry Mikhaylovich, Knyaz (Prince)　俄国政治家　7—196e
戈利钦　Golitsyn, Vasily Vasilyevich, Knyaz (Prince)　俄国公爵、政治家　7—196f
戈利亚德　Goliad　美国城市　7—196b
戈列尼谢夫-库图佐夫　Golenishchev-Kutuzov, Mikhail Illarionovich, Prince　俄国陆军总司令　7—195c
戈林　Göring, Hermann　德国纳粹党魁　7—217b
戈伦　Goren, Charles H.　美国桥牌权威　7—215e
戈罗卡　Goroka　巴布亚新几内亚城镇　7—219c
戈罗特芬德　Grotefend, Georg Friedrich　德国教师、语言学家　7—321f
戈洛夫金　Golovkin, Gavriil Ivanovich, Graf (Count)　俄国伯爵、政治家　7—197d
戈洛夫宁　Golovnin, Vasily Mikhaylovich　俄国海军军官、航海家　7—197e
戈洛文　Golovin, Fyodor Alekseyevich, Graf (Count)　俄国伯爵、政治家　7—197c
戈马尔　Gomarus, Franciscus　加尔文宗神学家　7—198b
戈马尔派　Gomarist　基督教派别　7—198a
戈麦斯　Gomes, Diogo　葡萄牙探险家　7—199a
戈麦斯　Gómez, Juan Vicente　委内瑞拉独裁者　7—199b
戈麦斯(卡斯特罗)　Gómez (Castro), Laureano Eleuterio　哥伦比亚总统　7—199c
戈麦斯-巴埃斯　Gómez y Báez, Máximo　古巴革命军司令　7—199e
戈麦斯·法利亚斯　Gómez Farías, Valentín　墨西哥自由主义领导人　7—199e
戈麦斯帕拉西奥　Gómez Palacio　墨西哥城市　7—199e
戈梅拉　Gomera　西班牙岛屿　7—100a
戈梅利　Gomel　白俄罗斯州名　7—198f
戈梅利　Gomel　白俄罗斯城市　7—199a
戈梅斯·德·阿维利亚内达　Gómez de Avellaneda, Gertrudis　古巴剧作家、诗人　7—199d
戈梅斯·德·拉·塞尔纳　Gómez de la Serna, Ramón　西班牙作家　7—199d
戈默蒂河　Gomati River　印度河流　7—198c
戈姆玛特斯瓦拉　Gommateśvara　印度耆那教　7—199f
戈纳尔迪雅　Gonardīya (Hindu author)　印度作家、哲学家　7—200f
戈纳勒克　Konārak　印度历史名村　9—344c
戈纳伊夫　Gonaïves　海地城市　7—200e
戈尼卡普特拉　Gonikāputra (Hindu author)　印度作家　7—205b
戈尼罗　Gaunilo　法兰西本笃会隐修士　7—34b
戈帕克　hopak　乌克兰民间舞蹈　8—167c
戈培尔　Goebbels, (Paul) Joseph　纳粹德国宣传部长　7—176e
戈齐　Gozzi, Carlo, Conte　意大利作家　7—234b
戈齐　Gozzi, Gasparo, Conte (Count)　意大利作家　7—234c
戈瑞　gray　物理学　7—266a
戈赛克　Gossec, François-Joseph　法国作曲家　7—222b
戈瑟尔斯　Goethals, George Washington　美国陆军军官、工程师　7—177e

戈申 Goshen 美国城市 7—220f
戈申 Goschen (of Hawkhurst), George Joachim Goschen, 1st Viscount 英国经济学家 7—220c
戈斯 Gosse, Sir Edmund 英国翻译家、文学批评家 7—221f
戈斯 Gosse, Philip Henry 英国博物学家 7—222a
戈斯波特 Gosport 英格兰自治市 7—221e
戈斯茨基 Goślicki, Wawrzyniec 波兰主教、外交家 7—221b
戈斯福德 Gosford 澳大利亚城市 7—220d
戈斯福德 Gosford, Archibald Acheson, 2nd earl of, BARON WORLINGHAM 英属北美总督 7—220e
戈斯拉尔 Goslar 德国城市 7—221b
戈斯诺尔德 Gosnold (town, Massachusetts, U.S.) 美国城镇 7—221c
戈斯诺尔德 Gosnold, Bartholomew 英国探险家、殖民者 7—221c
戈塔尔泽斯 Godarz (kings of Parthia) 帕提亚国王 7—172d
戈塔尔泽斯 Gotarzes 安息国王之名 7—222e
戈塔尔泽斯二世 Gotarzes II 安息国王 7—222e
戈塔尔泽斯一世 Gotarzes I 安息国王 7—222e
戈泰 Gauthey, Emiland-Marie 法国工程师 7—35f
戈特布扎德 Ghotbzadeh, Sadegh 伊朗政治人物 7—114a
戈特夫里德(斯特拉斯堡的) Gottfried VON STRASSBURG 德国诗人 7—225e
戈特哈尔德,圣 Gotthard, SAINT 基督教隐修院院长 7—226a
戈特赫尔夫 Gotthelf, Jeremias 瑞士小说家 7—226a
戈特霍布 Godthåb (Greenland) 格陵兰城市 7—175f
戈特拉 Godhra 印度城镇 7—174d
戈特利布 Gottlieb, Adolph 美国画家 7—226d
戈特罗 gotra 印度种姓制度 7—225d
戈特曼 Gottman, Jean 法国地理学家 7—226e
戈特沙尔克 Gottschalk, Louis Moreau 美国钢琴家 7—226f
戈特沙尔克(奥尔拜斯的) Gottschalk OF ORBAIS 罗马教士、神学家 7—226f
戈特舍德 Gottsched, Johann Christoph 德国文学评论家 7—227a
戈提那 Gortyn 希腊古代城市 7—219f
戈瓦切尔姐妹 Goitschel, Christine; and Goitschel, Marielle 法国高山滑雪运动员 7—184d
戈韦纳多岛 Governador Island 巴西岛屿 7—231e
戈翁 Gowon, Yakubu 尼日利亚政治家、军人 7—233c
戈武霍夫斯基 Gołuchowski, Agenor (Maria Adam), Graf (Count) 波兰贵族、政治家 7—198a
戈武霍夫斯基 Gołuchowski, Agenor (Romuald), Graf (Count) 奥地利外交家 7—198a
戈西河 Kosi River 亚洲河流 9—362c
戈歇氏病 Gaucher's disease 疾病 7—30c
戈雅 Goya (y Lucientes), Francisco (José) de 西班牙画家 7—233e
戈亚尼亚 Goiânia 巴西城市 7—184a
戈亚斯 Goiás 巴西州名 7—184a
戈伊迪利诸语言 Goidelic languages 欧洲语言 7—184b
戈伊尔 Koil (India) 印度城市 9—335d
戈伊斯 Góis, Damião de 葡萄牙人文主义者 7—184b
戈佐岛 Gozo 马耳他岛屿 7—234b
戈佐利 Gozzoli, Benozzo 意大利画家 7—234d
仡佬语 Gelao language 中国语言 7—46f
仡佬族 Gelao 中国民族 7—46e
哥白尼 Copernicus, Nicolaus 波兰天文学家 4—489c
哥白尼环形山 Copernicus 月球环形山 4—489b
哥白尼体系 Copernican system 天文学 4—489b
哥本哈根 Copenhagen 丹麦首都 4—488e
哥本哈根大学植物园 Copenhagen University Botanical Garden 丹麦植物园 4—488f
哥本哈根皇家瓷器 Royal Copenhagen porcelain 丹麦瓷器 14—431a
哥宾德·辛格 Gobind Singh 锡克教祖师 7—170e
哥达 Gotha 德国城市 7—223c
哥达瓦里河 Godāvari River 印度河流 7—172d
哥打巴鲁 Kota Baharu 马来西亚城市 9—364e
哥打巴托河 Cotabato River (Philippines) 菲律宾河流 4—535a
哥打巴托市 Cotabato City 菲律宾城市 4—535a
哥打丁宜 Kota Tinggi 马来西亚城镇 9—364f
哥打基纳巴卢 Kota Kinabalu 马来西亚城市 9—364e
哥得兰 Gotland 瑞典岛屿 7—225b
哥德巴赫 Goldbach, Christian 德国数学家 7—187d
哥德堡-布胡斯 Göteborg och Bohus 瑞典省份 7—223a
哥德尔 Gödel, Kurt 美国数学家、逻辑学家 7—173d
哥尔德斯密斯 Goldsmith, Oliver 英国作家 7—194c
哥尔多尼 Goldoni, Carlo 意大利剧作家 7—193b
哥兰德 Garand, John C. 美国工程师 7—7c
哥兰德步枪 Garand rifle 武器 7—7d
哥里 Gori 格鲁吉亚城市 7—216d
哥利岑 Golitsyn, Boris Borisovich, Knyaz (Prince) 俄国物理学家 7—196d
哥伦比亚 Colombia 美洲国家 4—355b
哥伦比亚 Columbia 美国马里兰州新社区 4—367f
哥伦比亚 Columbia 美国密西西比州城市 4—367f
哥伦比亚 Columbia 美国密苏里州城市 4—367f
哥伦比亚 Columbia 美国宾夕法尼亚州城市 4—368a
哥伦比亚 Columbia 美国南卡罗来纳州城市 4—368a
哥伦比亚 Columbia 美国田纳西州城市 4—368b
《哥伦比亚百科全书》 Columbia Encyclopedia 美国百科全书 4—368c
哥伦比亚冰原 Columbia Icefield 加拿大冰原 4—368d
哥伦比亚大学 Columbia University 美国大学 4—369b
哥伦比亚德 columbiad 文学 4—369c
哥伦比亚高原 Columbia Plateau 美国高原 4—369a
哥伦比亚革命武装 FARC 哥伦比亚军事组织 6—238c
哥伦比亚共和国 Colombia, Republic of (1822～1830) 南美历史共和国 4—356e
哥伦比亚广播公司 Columbia Broadcasting System 美国广播公司 4—368c
哥伦比亚河 Columbia River 北美洲河流 4—369a
《哥伦比亚河条约》 Columbia River Treaty 加拿大与美国条约 4—369b
哥伦比亚山 Columbia Mountains 加拿大山脉 4—368e
哥伦比亚深海平原 Colombian Abyssal Plain 加勒比海海底平原 4—356e
哥伦比亚特区 District of Columbia 美国联邦特区 5—344f
哥伦比亚影片公司 Columbia Pictures, Inc. 美国电影公司 4—368e
哥伦布 Columbus 美国佐治亚州城市 4—370c
哥伦布 Columbus 美国印第安纳州城市 4—370c
哥伦布 Columbus 美国密西西比州城市 4—370d
哥伦布 Columbus 美国内布拉斯加州城市 4—370d
哥伦布 Columbus 美国俄亥俄州城市 4—370e
哥伦布 Columbus, Bartholomew 意大利探险家 4—370f
哥伦布 Columbus, Christopher 意大利探险家 4—371a
哥伦布 Columbus, Diego 意大利探险家 4—375a
哥伦布纪念日 Columbus Day 美国节日 4—374f
哥伦布骑士团 Knights of Columbus 天主教国际组织 9—321f
哥伦西尔,圣 Columcille, SAINT 基督教传教士 4—375a
哥穆尔卡 Gomułka, Władysław 波兰政治家 7—200b
哥萨克 Cossack 欧洲民族 4—532a
哥斯达黎加 Costa Rica 中美洲国家 4—533b
哥特堡 Göteborg 瑞典海港、城市 7—222f
哥特库斯 Gothicus 罗马皇帝 7—225b
哥特人 Goth 欧洲民族 7—223b
哥特式艺术 Gothic art 艺术 7—223e

哥特体字 Gothic script 文字 7—225b
哥特瓦尔德 Gottwald, Klement 捷克斯洛伐克政治家 7—227b
哥特瓦尔德夫 Gottwaldov (city, Czech Republic) 捷克城市 7—227c
哥特小说 Gothic novel 文学 7—224e
哥特语 Gothic language 语言 7—224d
哥特字母 Gothic alphabet 文字 7—223d
哥瓦尔坦 Govardhan 印度画家 7—231e
哥欣尼 Goscinny, René 法国作家 7—220d
哥休特人 Gosiute 北美印第安人 7—221a
哥窑 Ge kiln 中国瓷窑 7—41e
哥印拜陀 Coimbatore 印度县城 4—335a
鸽 dove 鸟类 5—404b
鸽 pigeon 鸟类 13—298f
鸽麦藓 pigeon wheat 植物 13—299d
鸽形类 columbiform 鸟类 4—369c
鸽鹰 pigeon hawk 鸟类 13—299c
割礼 circumcision 宗教礼仪 4—244e
割礼 khitān 宗教礼仪 9—260b
割穗机 header 农业机械 7—538d
歌 Cantar 西班牙文学 3—410d
歌唱 singing 音乐 15—394c
歌唱剧 Singspiel 德国喜歌剧 15—395b
歌川丰国 Utagawa Toyokuni 日本画家 17—425f
歌川国芳 Utagawa Kuniyoshi 日本画家 17—425f
歌川国贞 Utagawa Kunisada 日本画家 17—425e
歌德 Goethe, Johann Wolfgang von 德国作家 7—178a
《歌蒂女士之书》 Godey's Lady's Book 女性月刊 7—173e
歌革 Gog 宗教、神话 7—182f
歌集 cancioneiro 葡萄牙语抒情诗集 3—396f
歌剧 opera 配音乐的戏剧 12—428c
歌剧院 Opéra 法国剧院 12—429a
歌利亚 Goliath 《圣经》人物 7—196c
歌麿 Utamaro 日本画家 17—429b
歌鹏 song-babbler 鸟类 15—511d
歌曲 song 音乐 15—509a
歌人 rāwī 阿拉伯文学中职业朗诵者 14—168c
歌舞伎 kabuki 日本剧种 9—125b
歌舞片 musical film 歌舞故事影片 11—508c
歌舞杂耍表演 vaudeville 娱乐节目 17—481d
歌仔戏 gezaixi 中国戏剧 7—106b
革拉特科夫 Gladkov, Fyodor Vasilyevich 苏联作家 7—149c
革兰氏染色 gram stain 微生物学 7—244b
革隆 Gelon 西西里城邦僭主 7—48e
革马拉 Gemara 犹太教 7—49c
革命 revolution 政治学 14—252b
革命法庭 Revolutionary Tribunal 法国历史 14—253b
革命峰 Revolution Peak 塔吉克斯坦山峰 14—252f
革命工团主义 revolutionary syndicalism 政治哲学 14—253b
革命制度党 Institutional Revolutionary Party 墨西哥政党 8—400f
《革命周报》 Revolution, The 美国报纸 14—252e
革末 Germer, Lester Halbert 美国物理学家 7—98b
革新党 Reform Party (New Zealand) 新西兰政党 14—198e
革新教会 Renovated Church 苏联教会联合组织 14—232a
革新运动 Reforma, La 墨西哥历史 14—198e
阁楼 loft 建筑 10—187c
格 figure 逻辑学 6—311c
格奥尔格 George, Stefan 德国诗人 7—78a
格奥尔格第二 George II 萨克森-迈宁根公国君主 7—76e
格贝尔 Geber 中世纪炼金术著作的作者化名 7—42b
格本 Goeben, August Karl von 普鲁士将军 7—177b
格庇德人 Gepidae 日耳曼部落 7—85a
格布尔特拉 Kapūrthala 印度城市 9—173d
格布哈德(多林施坦-希尔施贝格的) Gebhard of Dollnstein-Hirschberg (pope) 教皇 7—42b
格茨 Götz, Hermann 瑞士作曲家 7—227c
格达半岛 Gyda Peninsula 俄罗斯半岛 7—388d
格但斯克 Gdańsk 波兰省份 7—40f
格但斯克 Gdańsk 波兰城市 7—41a
格但斯克湾 Gdańsk, Gulf of 波罗的海海湾 7—41b
格德 Ged, William 英国苏格兰金匠 7—42e
格德勒 Goerdeler, Karl Friedrich 德国市政官员 7—177c
格德林 Gedling 英格兰自治市 7—43b
格德罗西亚 Gedrosia 巴基斯坦古地名 7—43b
格迪米纳斯 Gediminas 立陶宛大公 7—43a
格迪斯 Geddes, James 美国土木工程师 7—42e
格迪斯 Geddes, Norman Bel 美国舞台设计师 7—42f
格迪斯 Geddes, Sir Patrick 苏格兰生物学家、社会学家 7—43a
格蒂 Getty, J(ean) Paul 美国石油企业家 7—104c
格蒂哈尔 Katihār 印度城镇 9—196a
格蒂信托基金会 Getty Trust 美国基金会 7—104d
格丁根 Göttingen 德国城市 7—226c
格丁根大学 Göttingen, University of 德国大学 7—226c
格丁根林苑派 Göttinger Hain 德国文艺团体 7—226d
格丁尼亚 Gdynia 波兰城镇 7—41b
格尔采尔 Geltzer, Yekaterina Vasilyevna 俄罗斯舞蹈家 7—49a
格尔茨 Görz (Italy) 意大利城市 7—220b
格尔茨 Geertz, Clifford (James) 美国文化人类学学者 7—43f
格尔茨 Görtz, Georg Heinrich, Baron (Freiherr) von 德国政治家 7—219f
格尔达纳卡拉 Kertanagara 爪哇国王 9—243d
格尔夫波特 Gulfport 美国城市 7—368f
格尔盖伊 Görgey, Artér 匈牙利军官 7—216b
格尔津文化 Gerzean culture 古埃及历史 7—101d
格尔利茨 Görlitz 德国城市 7—219a
格尔木 Golmud 中国城市 7—197b
格尔纳尔 Karnāl 印度城市 9—185c
格尔纳尔战役 Karnāl, Battle of 波斯与莫卧儿战役 9—185c
格尔尼卡 Guernica 西班牙城市 7—350b
格尔绍姆·本·犹大 Gershom ben Judah 犹太教学者 7—100c
格尔松尼迪斯 Gersonides 犹太教学者 7—101b
格尔索巴瀑布 Gersoppa Falls (India) 印度瀑布 7—101c
格尔雄·伦斯 Gershon Loans, Joseph ben 犹太人律师 7—100c
格尔泽人 Guerze (people) 西非民族 7—351a
格根堡 Gegenbaur, Karl 德国解剖学家 7—44a
格哈得 Gerhard, Johann 德国神学家 7—86f
格哈尔特 Gerhaert von Leyden, Nikolaus 荷兰雕塑家 7—86f
格哈特 Gerhardt, Elena 德国歌唱家 7—87b
格卡尔普 Gökalp, Ziya 土耳其作家 7—184e
格科巴 Gqoba, William Wellington 班图作家 7—234e
格克切岛 Gökçeada 土耳其岛屿 7—185a
格拉 Gera 德国城市 7—85a
格拉贝 Grabbe, Christian Dietrich 德国剧作家 7—235a
格拉贝尔 Glaber, Radulfus 法国历史学家 7—147a
格拉布 Glubb, Sir John Bagot 英国军事官员 7—163c
格拉布街 Grub Street 文学 7—327e
格拉布斯 Grubbs, Robert H. 美国化学家 7—327e
格拉布斯基 Grabski, Władysław 波兰总理 7—235b
格拉茨 Graz 奥地利城市 7—268a
格拉茨 Glatz (Poland) 波兰城市 7—155a
格拉德 Kalāt 巴基斯坦城镇 9—139a
格拉德贝克 Gladbeck 德国城市 7—148f
格拉德斯通 Gladstone 澳大利亚城市 7—149d
格拉登 Gladden, Washington 美国公理会牧师 7—148f
格拉迪斯·波特动物园 Gladys Porter Zoo 美国动物园 7—150c
格拉蒂安 Gratian 意大利教会法学者 7—263a

《格拉蒂安教令》 Gratian's Decretum 宗教法规 7—263a
格拉蒂尼 Glatigny,(Joseph-)Albert-Alexandre 法国诗人 7—155a
格拉顿 Grattan,Henry 爱尔兰政治家 7—263a
格拉厄姆 Graham,Isabella Marshall 苏格兰裔美国教育家 7—241a
格拉夫 Graf,Oskar Maria 德国作家 7—239c
格拉夫 Graaf,Reinier de 荷兰医师 7—234e
格拉夫 Graf,Steffi 德国运动员 7—239d
格拉夫 Graf,Urs 瑞士艺术家 7—239d
格拉夫顿 Grafton 澳大利亚城市 7—240c
格拉夫顿 Grafton 美国城市 7—240d
格拉夫顿公爵(第三) Grafton,Augustus Henry Fitzroy,3rd duke of 英国首相 7—240d
格拉夫顿公爵(第一) Grafton,Henry Fitzroy,1st Duke of,Earl of Euston,Viscount Ipswich,Baron Sudbury 英国贵族 7—240e
格拉夫斯特伦 Grafström,Gillis 瑞典花样滑冰运动员 7—240b
格拉弗夏姆 Gravesham 英国自治市 7—264f
格拉哥里字母 Glagolitic alphabet 文字 7—150d
格拉古 Gracchus,Gaius Sempronius 罗马护民官 7—235d
格拉古 Gracchus,Tiberius Sempronius 罗马护民官 7—236d
格拉赫 Gerlach,(Ernst) Ludwig von 普鲁士法官、政治家 7—88a
格拉赫 Gerlach,Helmut (Georg) von 德国记者、政治家 7—87e
格拉赫 Gerlach,(Karl Friedrich) Otto von 普鲁士神学家、教育家 7—88a
格拉赫 Gerlach,(Ludwig Friedrich) Leopold von 普鲁士政治家 7—87f
格拉赫 Gerlach,Walther 德国物理学家 7—88a
格拉克曼 Gluckman,(Herman) Max 南非社会人类学家 7—164d
格拉肯斯 Glackens,William (James) 美国画家 7—148e
格拉雷阿努斯 Glareanus,Henricus 瑞士音乐家、人道主义者 7—151c
格拉鲁斯 Glarus 瑞士城市 7—151c
格拉鲁斯 Glarus 瑞士州名 7—151d
格拉鲁斯山 Glarus Alps 瑞士山脉 7—151d
格拉马草 grama grass 植物学 7—244b
格拉玛 Granma 古巴省份 7—255c
《格拉玛报》 Granma 古巴报纸 7—255d
格拉蒙 Gramont,Antoine-Agénor-Alfred,duc de (duke of) 法国外交家、政治家 7—245c
格拉摩根 Glamorgan(Wales) 威尔士古地名 7—150e
格拉摩根伯爵 Glamorgan,Edward Somerset,earl 英格兰保皇主义者 7—150e
格拉摩根谷 Vale of Glamorgan 威尔士郡名 17—449a
格拉姆 Gramme,Zénobe-Théophile 法国电器工程师 7—245b
格拉姆斯 Glamis 苏格兰城堡、村庄 7—150e
格拉纳达 Granada 西班牙古国名 7—246c
格拉纳达 Granada 尼加拉瓜城市 7—246d
格拉纳达 Granada 西班牙省份 7—246d
格拉纳达 Granada 西班牙城市 7—246e
格拉纳多斯 Granados,Enrique 西班牙作曲家 7—246f
格拉讷河畔奥拉杜尔 Oradour-sur-Glane 法国村庄 12—440d
格拉尼卡斯河战役 Granicus,Battle of the 希腊历史 7—254e
格拉尼特 Granit,Ragnar Arthur 瑞典生理学家 7—254e
格拉尼特城 Granite City 美国城市 7—255a
格拉尼特峰 Granite Peak 美国山峰 7—255b
格拉诺列尔斯 Granollers 西班牙城市 7—255e
格拉齐尼 Grazzini,Anton Francesco 意大利诗人、剧作家 7—268c
格拉齐亚尼 Graziani,Rodolfo,marchese (marquess) di Neghelli 意大利陆军元帅 7—268c
格拉萨·阿拉尼亚 Graça Aranha,José Pereira da 巴西小说家、外交官 7—235d
格拉斯 Grasse 法国城镇 7—261c
格拉斯 Glass,Carter 美国政治家 7—153e
格拉斯 Grasse,François-Joseph-Paul,comte de (count of) 法国海军司令 7—261d
格拉斯 Grass,Günter (Wilhelm) 德国诗人、剧作家 7—260f
格拉斯 Glas,John 苏格兰长老会牧师 7—151e
格拉斯 Glass,Philip 美国作曲家 7—153f
格拉斯顿伯里 Glastonbury 英国城镇 7—154f
格拉斯哥 Glasgow 英国城市 7—152a
格拉斯哥 Glasgow,Ellen (Anderson Gholson) 美国作家 7—152b
格拉斯哥大学 Glasgow,University of 英国大学 7—152d
格拉斯曼 Grassmann,Hermann Günther 德国数学家 7—262c
格拉斯米尔 Grasmere 英国地区 7—260e
格拉斯派 Glasite (sect) 基督教派别 7—152e
格拉斯佩尔 Glaspell,Susan 美国作家 7—152e
格拉索 Grasso,Ella 美国政府官员 7—262d
格拉提安 Gratian 罗马皇帝 7—262f
格拉沃莱 Gravelet,Jean-François 法国杂技演员 7—264a
格拉沃利讷 Gravelines 法国城镇 7—264a
格拉西安(伊·莫拉莱斯) Gracián(y Morales),Baltasar 西班牙哲学家、作家 7—237f
格拉西奥萨岛 Graciosa Island 北大西洋火山岛 7—237f
格拉西亚斯 Gracias 洪都拉斯城市 7—237f
格拉肖 Glashow,Sheldon Lee 美国理论物理学家 7—152d
格拉泽 Glaser,Donald A(rthur) 美国物理学家 7—151e
格拉泽 Glaser,Milton 美国平面设计师 7—151f
格拉祖诺夫 Glazunov,Aleksandr (Konstaninovich) 俄罗斯作曲家 7—156a
格拉佐夫 Glazov 俄罗斯城市 7—156a
格莱恩 Grahn,Lucile 德国舞蹈编导 7—243a
格莱卡斯 Glycas,Michael 拜占廷史学家、神学家 7—165e
格莱肯 Gleichen,Melchior,Graf von Hatzfeldt und 神圣罗马帝国元帅 7—156e
格莱美奖 Grammy Awards 音乐奖项 7—245c
格莱姆 Gleim,Johann Wilhelm Ludwig 德国诗人 7—156f
格莱内尔格河 Glenelg River 澳大利亚河流 7—157e
格莱斯贝 Glace Bay 加拿大城镇 7—147a
格莱斯顿 Gladstone,William Ewart 英国政治家 7—149e
格莱斯顿子爵(第一) Gladstone,Herbert John Gladstone,1st Viscount 英国政治家 7—149d
格莱维茨 Gleiwitz (Poland) 波兰城镇 7—156f
格赖埃尔茨 Greyerz (Switzerland) 瑞士区名 7—307d
格赖夫 Greiff,León de 拉丁美洲诗人 7—301e
格赖夫斯瓦尔德 Greifswald 德国城市 7—301f
格兰 Gran (Hungary) 匈牙利城镇 7—245e
格兰比 Granby 加拿大城市 7—247a
格兰比侯爵 Granby,John Manners,marquess of 英国陆军军官 7—247b
格兰扁 Grampian 苏格兰行政区 7—245d
格兰扁山 Grampian Mountains 澳大利亚山岭 7—245d
格兰扁山脉 Grampians,The 苏格兰高地 7—245d
格兰茨 Grants 美国城市 7—256f
格兰茨帕斯 Grants Pass 美国城市 7—257a
格兰代尔 Grindel,Eugène 法国作家 7—314d
格兰德艾兰 Grand Island 美国城市 7—250a
格兰德港 Grand Harbour 马耳他港湾 7—250a
格兰德港 Porto Grande (Cape Verde) 佛得角城市 13—453a
格兰德河 Grand River 美国河流 7—252a
格兰德河 Grand River 美国河流 7—252a
格兰德河 Rio Grande 巴西河流 14—309c
格兰德河 Rio Grande 北美洲河流 14—309c
格兰德圣地亚哥河 Río Grande de Santiago 墨西哥河流 14—309e
格兰德营 Campo Grande 巴西城市 3—383d
格兰迪 Grandi,Alessandro 意大利作曲家 7—253d
格兰第 Grandi,Dino,conte (count) di Mordano 意大利官员 7—253d

格兰丁 Grandin, Temple 美国科学家、工业设计师 7—253e
格兰福德 Glanford 英格兰自治市 7—151a
格兰戈尔 Gringore, Pierre 法国演员、作家 7—314f
格兰杰 Grainger, Percy (Aldridge) 美国作曲家 7—243e
格兰杰 Granger, Clive W.J. 英国威尔士经济学家 7—254d
格兰靳特 Grandgent, Charles Hall 美国语言学家 7—253c
格兰其运动 Granger movement 美国农民组织 7—254d
格兰奇 Grange, Red 美国橄榄球运动员 7—254b
格兰奇茅斯 Grangemouth 英国城镇 7—254c
格兰瑟姆 Grantham 英国城镇 7—256f
格兰塔字母 Grantha alphabet 文字 7—256e
格兰特 Grant, Bernie 英国政治人物 7—255f
格兰特 Grant, Cary 美国电影演员 7—255f
格兰特 Grant, Duncan (James Corrowr) 英国画家 7—256a
格兰特 Grant, James Augustus 英国探险家 7—256b
格兰特 Grant, Ulysses S. 美国总统 7—256c
格兰特 Grant, Zilpah Polly 美国教育家 7—256d
格兰特将军国家纪念堂 General Grant National Memorial 美国格兰特总统陵墓 7—56c
格兰特陵园 Grant's Tomb (New York City) 美国格兰特总统陵墓 7—257a
格兰维尔 Grandville 法国漫画家 7—254a
格兰维尔 Glanvill, Joseph 英国哲学家 7—151a
格兰维尔 Glanville, Ranulf de 英国法官 7—151b
格兰维尔-巴克 Granville-Barker, Harley 英国戏剧家、评论家 7—257e
格兰维尔伯爵 Granville, Ebzarls of 英国贵族 7—257d
格兰维尔伯爵(第二) HGranville, Granville George Leveson-Gower, 2nd Earl 英国外交大臣 7—257e
格兰维尔伯爵(第一) Granville, John Carteret, 1st Earl 英国政治家 7—257d
格朗布瓦 Grandbois, Alain 加拿大诗人 7—252c
格朗德河 Grande River, La 加拿大河流 7—253b
格朗德瀑布 Grande Cascade 法国瀑布 7—252d
格朗德特尔 Grande-Terre 加勒比海岛屿 7—253b
格朗梅尔 Grand-Mère 加拿大城市 7—250f
格朗蒙 Granmont, Louis 法国海盗 7—255d
格朗普雷 Grand Pré 加拿大村庄 7—251d
格朗让 Grandjean, Philippe 法国活字镌刻家 7—253f
格朗尚会和泰泽会 Grandchamp and Taizé communities 欧洲基督教组织 7—252c
格朗特 Graunt, John 英国统计学家 7—260c
格朗维尔 Granville 法国城镇 7—257d
格朗维尔 Granvelle, Antoine Perrenot de 西班牙大臣 7—257c
格劳 Grau, Shirley Ann 美国作家 7—263c
格劳贝尔 Glauber, Johann Rudolf 荷兰化学家 7—155b
格劳贝尔 Glauber, Roy J. 美国物理学家 7—155b
格劳贝尔盐 Glauber's salt 化学 7—155b
格劳宾登 Graubünden 瑞士州名 7—263c
格劳登茨 Graudenz (Poland) 波兰城市 7—263d
格劳恩 Graun, Karl Heinrich 德国作曲家 7—263d
格劳科斯 Glaucus 希腊神话人物 7—155e
格劳普纳 Graupner, Christoph 德国作曲家 7—263e
格劳秀斯 Grotius, Hugo 荷兰法学家、学者 7—322b
格勒纳 Groener, (Karl Eduard) Wilhelm 德国将领、政治家 7—317e
格勒诺布尔 Grenoble 法国城镇 7—303d
格勒诺布尔第一大学、第二大学、第三大学 Grenoble I, II, and III, Universities of 法国大学 7—303e
格勒兹 Greuze, Jean-Baptiste 法国画家 7—305e
格雷 Grey Earles 英国封爵贵族 7—306c
格雷 Gray, Asa 美国植物学家 7—266a
格雷 Gray, Elisha 美国发明家 7—266c
格雷 Grey, Sir Edward, 3rd Baronet 英国政治家 7—306f
格雷 Grey, Sir George 英国殖民地官员 7—307a
格雷 Gray, Horace 美国最高法院大法官 7—266d
格雷 Grey, Henry 英国贵族 7—307b
格雷 Gray, Harold (Lincoln) 美国漫画家 7—266c
格雷 Gray, Sir James 英国动物学家 7—266e
格雷 Gray, Robert 美国船长、勘探者 7—266e
格雷 Gray, Thomas 英国诗人 7—266e
格雷 Gray, Walter de 英格兰教士 7—267a
格雷 Grey, Zane 美国作家 7—307c
格雷邦 Gréban, Arnoul 法国作家 7—277a
格雷杯 Grey Cup 加拿大橄榄球赛奖杯 7—307d
格雷贝 Graebe, Carl 德国化学家 7—239a
格雷贝尔 Grebel, Konrad 瑞士基督教领导人 7—277c
格雷伯爵(第二) Grey, Charles Grey, 2nd Earl 英国首相 7—306d
格雷伯爵(第三) Grey, Henry George Grey, 3rd Earl 英国政治家 7—306e
格雷伯爵(第一) Grey, Charles Grey, 1st Earl, Viscount Howick 英国将军 7—306c
格雷布纳 Graebner, (Robert) Fritz 德国人种学家 7—239b
格雷茨 Graetz, Heinrich 德国历史学家 7—239c
格雷茨基 Gretzky, Wayne 加拿大冰球运动员 7—305c
格雷大风 gregale 气象学 7—297a
格雷德 Grade, Lew, Baron Grade of Elstree 英国电影制片人 7—238b
格雷迪 Grady, Henry Woodfin 美国新闻记者 7—239a
格雷蒂尔萨迦 Grettis saga 冰岛家族萨迦之一 7—305c
格雷厄姆 Graham, Billy 美国布道家 7—240e
格雷厄姆 Graham, Catharine Macaulay 英国历史学家 7—240f
格雷厄姆 Grahame, Kenneth 英国作家 7—242e
格雷厄姆 Graham, George 英国制表师 7—240f
格雷厄姆 Graham, James 英格兰将领 7—241b
格雷厄姆 Graham, Sir James (Robert George), 2nd Baronet 英国政治家 7—241b
格雷厄姆 Graham, Martha 美国舞蹈家 7—241c
格雷厄姆 Graham, Otto (Everett, Jr.) 美国橄榄球运动员 7—242b
格雷厄姆 Graham, Sylvester 美国牧师 7—242c
格雷厄姆 Graham, Thomas 英国化学家 7—242d
格雷厄姆(夫人) Graham, Katharine 美国出版商 7—241c
格雷厄姆(克拉弗豪斯的) Graham of Claverhouse, John 苏格兰军人 7—242e
格雷厄姆地 Graham Land (Antarctica) 南极洲半岛 7—242e
格雷厄姆-怀特 Grahame-White, Claude 英国飞行家 7—242f
格雷厄姆斯敦 Grahamstown 南非城市 7—242f
格雷费 Gräfe, Albrecht (Friedrich Wilhelm Ernst) von 德国眼外科医师 7—239f
格雷费 Gräfe, Karl Ferdinand von 德国外科医师 7—239f
格雷夫森德 Gravesend 英国城镇 7—264e
格雷夫斯 Graves, Michael 美国建筑师 7—264a
格雷夫斯 Graves, Morris (Cole) 美国画家 7—264b
格雷夫斯 Graves, Robert (von Ranke) 英国诗人 7—264c
格雷夫斯 Graves, Robert James 爱尔兰医师 7—264d
格雷夫斯氏病 Graves' disease 疾病 7—264e
格雷戈拉斯 Gregoras, Nicephorus 拜占廷人文主义学者 7—297d
格雷戈里 Gregory, Cynthia 美国芭蕾舞蹈家 7—301b
格雷戈里 Gregory, Horace (Victor) 美国诗人、评论家 7—301b
格雷戈里 Gregory, Wilton D. 美国天主教高级教士 7—301d
格雷戈里夫人 Gregory, Isabella Augusta, Lady 爱尔兰剧作家 7—301c
格雷格 Gregg, John Robert 美国速记法发明者 7—297b
格雷格速记法 Gregg shorthand 快速书写符号系统 7—297c
格雷古瓦 Grégoire, Henri 法国教士 7—297c
格雷果里 Gregory, James 苏格兰数学家、天文学家 7—301c
格雷郡主 Grey, Lady Jane 英格兰女王 7—307b

格雷灵 Grayling 美国城市 7—267e
格雷罗 Guerrero 墨西哥州名 7—350d
格雷罗 Guerrero, Francisco 西班牙作曲家 7—350e
格雷罗 Guerrero, Vicente 墨西哥独立英雄 7—350e
格雷洛克山 Greylock, Mount 美国山峰 7—308b
格雷茅斯 Greymouth 新西兰城市 7—308b
格雷塞 Gresset, Jean-Baptiste-Louis 法国诗人、剧作家 7—304d
格雷森 Grayson, David 美国记者 7—267f
格雷沙姆 Gresham, Walter Quintin 美国政治家 7—304c
格雷山 Grey Hills 英国山脉 7—307d
格雷斯 Görres, (Johann) Joseph von 德国作家 7—219d
格雷斯 Grace, William Gilbert 英国板球运动员 7—237d
格雷斯 Grace, William R(ussell) 美国商人 7—237d
格雷斯港 Harbour Grace 加拿大城镇 7—470c
格雷斯公司 Grace & Company 美国公司 7—237e
格雷斯里 Gressly, Amanz 瑞士地质学家 7—304e
格雷斯曼 Gressmann, Hugo 德国宗教学者 7—304f
格雷斯(摩纳哥的)王妃 Grace of Monaco, Princess 美国演员、摩纳哥王妃 7—237c
格雷特黑德 Greathead, James Henry 英国土木工程师 7—276f
格雷特湖 Great Lake 澳大利亚湖泊 7—272d
格雷特里 Grétry, André-Ernest-Modeste 法国作曲家 7—305b
格雷特纳 Gretna 美国城市 7—305a
格雷特纳格林 Gretna Green 苏格兰村庄 7—305a
格雷特内克 Great Neck 美国村庄 7—273d
格雷万 Grévin, Jacques 法国诗人、剧作家 7—306a
格雷维 Grévy (François-Paul-) Jules 法国总统 7—306b
格雷维尔 Greville, Fulke, 1st Baron Brooke 英国作家 7—305f
格雷欣 Gresham, Sir Thomas 英国金融家 7—304b
格雷欣法则 Gresham's law 经济学 7—304c
格雷晏阿尔卑斯山脉 Graian Alps 欧洲山脉 7—243a
格里 Gerry, Elbridge 美国副总统 7—100a
格里爱尔 Glière, Reinhold (Moritsevich) 俄罗斯作曲家 7—158f
格里鲍耶陀夫 Griboyedov, Aleksandr Sergeyevich 俄国剧作家 7—308d
格里博弗尔 Gribeauval, Jean-Baptiste Vaquette de 法国军官、工程师 7—308c
格里布 Greb, Harry 美国拳击运动员 7—277a
格里尔 Greer, Germaine 英国作家 7—297a
格里尔 Grier, Robert C(ooper) 美国最高法院大法官 7—309a
格里尔帕策 Grillparzer, Franz 奥地利剧作家 7—312a
格里尔森 Grierson, Sir George Abraham 爱尔兰语言学家 7—309b
格里尔森 Grierson, John 英国电影制片人 7—309c
格里菲 Griffey, Ken 美国棒球手 7—309e
格里菲思 Griffith, Arthur 爱尔兰新闻工作者 7—310b
格里菲思 Griffith, D(avid) W(ark) 美国电影导演 7—310d
格里菲思 Griffith, Emile (Alphonse) 美国拳击运动员 7—310f
格里菲思 Griffiths, John Willis 美国造船技师 7—311a
格里菲思 Griffith, Sir Richard John, 1st Baronet 爱尔兰地质学家、土木工程师 7—310f
格里菲斯 Griffith 澳大利亚城镇 7—310b
格里芬 Griffin, Donald Redfield 美国生物物理学家 7—309f
格里芬 Griffing, Josephine Sophia White 美国改革家 7—310a
格里芬 Griffin, Walter Burley 美国建筑师、园林设计师 7—310a
格里芬菲尔德 Griffenfeld, Peder Schumacher, greve af (count of) 丹麦政治家 7—309d
格里夫 Grieve, Christopher Murray 苏格兰诗人 7—309d
格里福斯 Griffes, Charles (Tomlinson) 美国作曲家 7—309e
格里甘岛 Grigan (Mariana Islands) 马里亚纳群岛岛屿 7—311b
格里戈尔·纳列卡齐 Gregory Narekatzi, Saint 亚美尼亚诗人 7—299e
格里戈里耶夫 Grigoryev, Apollon Aleksandrovich 俄国文学批评家、诗人 7—311d
格里戈洛维奇 Grigorovich, Yuri (Nikolayevich) 俄罗斯舞蹈家 7—311d
格里格 Grieg, Edvard (Hagerup) 挪威作曲家 7—308e
格里格 Grieg, (Johan) Nordahl Brun 挪威诗人、戏剧家 7—309a
格里格森 Grigson, Geoffrey (Edward Harvey) 英国编辑、诗人 7—311e
格里哈尔瓦 Grijalba, Juan de 西班牙探险家 7—311f
格里哈尔瓦河 Grijalva River 墨西哥河流 7—311f
格里焦尼 Grigioni (Switzerland) 瑞士州名 7—311b
格里克 Gehrig, Lou 美国棒球运动员 7—44c
格里夸人 Griqua 南非民族 7—315c
格里利 Greeley 美国城市 7—286a
格里利 Greely, Adolphus Washington 美国军官 7—286d
格里利 Greeley, Horace 美国报纸编辑 7—286b
格里马尔迪 Grimaldi, Joseph 英国演员 7—312d
格里马尔迪家族 Grimaldi family 意大利热那亚世家 7—312d
格里马鲁斯 Grimalus, Laurentius (Polish prelate) 波兰主教、外交家 7—312d
格里美豪森 Grimmelshausen, Hans Jacob Christoph von 德国小说家 7—313d
格里蒙德 Grimond, Jo 英国政治家 7—313f
格里摩阿尔德 Grimoard, Guillaume de (pope) 教皇 7—313f
格里莫阿尔德 Grimoald 墨洛温王朝官员 7—313f
格里默德 Grimald, Nicholas 英国学者、诗人 7—312c
格里姆凯姐妹 Grimké, Sarah (Moore) and Angelina (Emily) 美国废奴主义者 7—312e
格里姆讷格尔 Karīmnagar 印度城市 9—182a
格里姆塞 Grímsey 格陵兰海岛屿 7—314a
格里姆斯比 Grimsby 英格兰城镇 7—314a
格里姆索普男爵(第一) Grimthorpe (of Grimthorpe), Edmund Beckett, 1st Baron 英国律师、钟表制造家 7—314b
格里姆肖 Grimshaw, Beatrice (Ethel) 澳大利亚作家、旅行家 7—314a
格里木定律 Grimm's law 语言学 7—313e
格里尼 Grigny, Nicolas de 法国作曲家 7—311c
格里尼乌斯 Grinius Kazys 立陶宛爱国者、政治家 7—314f
格里涅夫斯基 Grinevsky, Aleksandr Stepanovich 苏联作家 7—314f
格里诺 Guarino, Battista 意大利学者 7—344a
格里诺 Greenough, Horatio 美国雕刻家 7—295a
格里诺克 Greenock 苏格兰城市 7—294f
格里彭贝里 Gripenberg, Bertel Johan Sebastian, Friherre (baron) 芬兰诗人 7—315a
格里彭斯塔特 Gripenstedt, Johan August, Friherre 瑞典政治家 7—315b
格里塞尔达 Griselda 欧洲传奇人物 7—315f
格里塞利·科丘·穆斯塔法·贝伊 Göriceli Koçu Mustafa Bey (Turkish reformer) 奥斯曼帝国政治家 7—216d
格里申 Grishin, Yevgeny 苏联速度滑雪运动员 7—315f
格里什克 Gereshk 阿富汗城镇 7—86e
格里顺 Grishun (Switzerland) 瑞士州名 7—316a
格里斯 Gris, Juan 西班牙艺术家 7—315d
格里斯巴赫 Griesbach, Johann Jakob 德国基督教神学家 7—309c
格里斯巴赫阶 Griesbachian Stage 地质学 7—309d
格里斯沃尔德 Griswold, Alfred Whitney 美国教育家 7—316e
格里斯沃尔德 Griswold, Rufus Wilmot 美国记者、评论家 7—316f
格里斯沃尔德诉康涅狄格州 Griswold v. State of Connecticut 美国法院案例 7—316f
格里松 Grisons (Switzerland) 瑞士州名 7—316d
格里索姆 Grissom, Virgil I(van) 美国航天员 7—316d
格里瓦斯 Grivas, Georgios (Theodoros) 塞浦路斯爱国者 7—317b
格里西 Grisi, Carlotta 意大利演员 7—316a
格里西 Grisi, Giulia 意大利歌唱家 7—316b
格里希诺 Grishino (Ukraine) 乌克兰城市 7—316a

格利登 Glidden, Joseph Farwell 美国发明家 7—158b
格利盖尔 Gelligaer 威尔士社区 7—48d
格利合唱 glee 音乐 7—156e
格利塞里乌斯 Glycerius 西罗马皇帝 7—165e
格利桑 Glissant, Édouard 马提尼克作家 7—159c
格利森 Gleason, Jackie 美国喜剧演员 7—156c
格利森 Gleason, Kate 美国实业家 7—156d
格利沙德 glissade 芭蕾舞术语 7—159c
格利维采 Gliwice 波兰城镇 7—159d
格利乌斯 Gellius, Aulus 拉丁文作家 7—48d
格利雅 Grignard, (François-Auguste-) Victor 法国化学家 7—311b
格利雅试剂 Grignard reagent 化学 7—311c
格利扬 Kalyān 印度城市 9—144e
格列高利 Gregory 教会统治者名 7—298a
格列高利(八世) Gregory (VIII) 罗马敌对教皇 7—298e
格列高利(里米尼的) Gregory of Rimini 意大利哲学家、神学家 7—300b
格列高利(六世) Gregory (VI) 罗马敌对教皇 7—298c
格列高利(西奈的) Gregory of Sinai 希腊正教修士 7—300c
格列高利,圣 Gregory, Saint (pope) 罗马教皇 7—299e
格列高利(纳西昂的),圣 Gregory of Nazianzus, Saint 拜占廷神学家 7—299e
格列高利(尼斯的),圣 Gregory of Nyssa, Saint 拜占廷哲学家、神学家 7—300a
格列高利(启蒙者),圣 Gregory the Illuminator, Saint 亚美尼亚使徒 7—301a
格列高利(图尔的),圣 Gregory of Tours, Saint 法兰克主教、历史学家 7—300d
格列高利(托马都古斯),圣 Gregory Thaumaturgus, Saint 希腊基督教使徒 7—300f
格列高利八世 Gregory VIII 罗马教皇 7—298f
格列高利大学 Gregorian University 罗马天主教大学 7—298a
格列高利二世(塞浦路斯的) Gregory II Cyprius 希腊正教会牧首 7—299d
格列高利二世,圣 Gregory II, Saint 罗马教皇 7—298b
格列高利改革 Gregorian Reform 宗教改革 7—297f
格列高利九世 Gregory IX 罗马教皇 7—298f
格列高利历 Gregorian calendar 历法 7—297e
格列高利六世 Gregory VI 罗马教皇 7—298d
格列高利·帕拉马斯,圣 Gregory Palamas, Saint 希腊神学家 7—300f
格列高利七世,圣 Gregory VII, Saint 罗马教皇 7—298d
格列高利三世,圣 Gregory III, Saint 罗马教皇 7—298b
格列高利圣咏 Gregorian chant 宗教音乐 7—297f
格列高利十二世 Gregory XII 罗马教皇 7—299b
格列高利十六世 Gregory XVI 罗马教皇 7—299d
格列高利十三世 Gregory XIII 罗马教皇 7—299c
格列高利十世(蒙福者) Gregory X, Blessed 罗马教皇 7—299a
格列高利十四世 Gregory XIV 罗马教皇 7—299c
格列高利十五世 Gregory XV 罗马教皇 7—299d
格列高利十一世 Gregory XI 罗马教皇 7—299b
格列高利斯 Gregorius (medieval Svrian scholar) 叙利亚哲学家 7—298a
格列高利四世 Gregory IV 罗马教皇 7—298c
格列高利五世 Gregory V 罗马教皇 7—298c
格列高利一世,圣 Gregory I, Saint 罗马教皇 7—298a
格列柯 Greco, El 西班牙画家 7—277e
格列柯 Greco, Emilio 意大利雕刻家 7—278a
格列恰尼诺夫 Grechaninov, Aleksandr (Tikhonovich) 俄罗斯作曲家 7—277d
格林 Green, Adolf (songwriter) 美国歌曲作家 7—286e
格林 Green, Al 美国歌手 7—286e
格林 Green, Anne Catherine Hoof 美国印刷商 7—287a
格林 Green, Anna Katharine 美国小说家 7—287a
格林 Grin, Aleksandr Stepanovich 苏联作家 7—314c
格林 Green, Bartholomew 美国新闻工作者 7—287b
格林 Greene, Belle da Costa 美国图书馆馆长 7—290d
格林 Green, Charles 英国气球飞行家 7—287b
格林 Green, Duff 美国新闻工作者 7—287c
格林 Glyn, Elinor 英国作家 7—166c
格林 Green, George 英国数学家 7—287d
格林 Green, Henry 英国小说家、工业家 7—287e
格林 Green, Hetty 美国金融家 7—287e
格林 Grimm, Hans (Emil Wilhelm) 德国作家 7—312f
格林 Greene, (Henry) Graham 英国作家 7—291a
格林 Green, Julien (Hartridge) 美国作家 7—287e
格林 Grein, Jack Thomas 英国评论家、剧作家 7—301f
格林 Greene, Nancy 加拿大运动员 7—291d
格林 Greene, Nathanael 美国将领 7—291e
格林 Green, Paul (Eliot) 美国作家 7—287f
格林 Greene, Robert 英国作家 7—291f
格林 Green, T(homas) H(ill) 英国教育家、哲学家 7—288a
格林 Green, William 美国劳工领袖 7—288b
格林班克方程 Green Bank equation 天文学 7—288d
格林班克天文台 Green Bank Observatory 美国天文台 7—288e
格林贝 Green Bay 美国城市 7—288f
格林伯格 Greenberg, Joseph H(arold) 美国人类学家、语言学家 7—290d
格林达尔 Grindal, Edmund 英格兰坎特伯雷大主教 7—314c
格林德包恩庄园 Glyndebourne 英国庄园 7—166d
格林德尔瓦尔德 Grindelwald 瑞士谷地 7—314d
格林杜尔 Glyndŵr 英国区名 7—166d
格林菲尔德 Greenfield 美国印第安纳州城市 7—292b
格林菲尔德 Greenfield 美国马萨诸塞州城镇 7—292b
格林菲尔德村 Greenfield Village 美国村庄 7—292c
格林菲尔德 Greenfield, Elizabeth Taylor 美国歌唱家 7—292c
格林夫人 Green, Alice Stopford 爱尔兰历史学家 7—286f
格林公园 Green Park 英国皇家公园 7—289c
格林河 Green River 美国河流 7—289d
格林河 Green River 美国河流 7—289e
格林加德 Greengard, Paul 美国神经生物学家 7—292d
格林卡 Glinka, Mikhail (Ivanovich) 俄罗斯作曲家 7—159a
格林里弗 Green River 美国犹他州城市 7—289e
格林里弗 Green River 美国怀俄明州城市 7—289f
格林利夫 Greenleaf, Ralph 美国台球运动员 7—294e
格林纳 Greener, William 英国制造商、发明家 7—291f
格林纳达 Grenada 西印度群岛岛屿 7—302b
格林纳达 Grenada 美国城市 7—302e
格林纳丁斯群岛 Grenadines 西印度群岛岛链 7—303b
格林纳韦 Greenaway, Kate 英国美术家 7—290b
格林男爵 Grimm, Friedrich Melchior, Freiherr von (baron of) 德裔评论家 7—312e
格林内尔 Grinnell 美国城市 7—315a
格林内尔氏定理 Grinnell's axiom 生物学 7—315a
格林尼治 Greenwich 英格兰自治市 7—296a
格林尼治 Greenwich 美国城镇 7—296c
格林尼治村 Greenwich Village 美国居民区 7—296e
格林尼治公爵 Greenwich, John Campbell, Duke of 英国官员、军人 7—296c
格林尼治平时 Greenwich Mean Time (GMT) 天文学 7—296c
格林尼治天文台 Royal Greenwich Observatory 英国天文机构 14—431e
格林尼治子午线 Greenwich meridian 天文学 7—296d
格林山 Green Mountains 美国山脉 7—289b
格林山兄弟会 Green Mountain Boys 美国历史 7—289b
格林斯伯勒 Greensboro 美国城市 7—295d
格林斯潘 Greenspan, Alan 美国经济学家 7—295e

格林苏斯 Grynswth, Syr Meurig 威尔士诗人 7—331c

格林湾 Green Bay 美国湖湾 7—288e

格林维尔 Greeneville 美国田纳西州城镇 7—292b

格林维尔 Greenville 美国密西西比州城市 7—295e

格林维尔 Greenville 美国北卡罗来纳州城市 7—295f

格林维尔 Greenville 美国俄亥俄州城市 7—295f

格林维尔 Greenville 美国南卡罗来纳州城市 7—295f

格林维尔 Greenville 美国得克萨斯州城市 7—296a

格林伍德 Greenwood 美国密西西比州城市 7—296e

格林伍德 Greenwood 美国南卡罗来纳州城市 7—296f

格林伍德 Greenwood, Arthur 英国政治家 7—296f

格林兄弟 Greene, Charles Sumner; and Greene, Henry Mather 美国建筑师 7—290f

格林兄弟 Grimm, Jacob Ludwig Carl and Wilhelm Carl 德国民间文学研究者 7—312f

格陵兰 Greenland 丹麦岛屿 7—293d

格陵兰冰原 Greenland Ice Sheet 格陵兰地理 7—294c

格陵兰海 Greenland Sea 北冰洋边缘海 7—294c

格陵兰鲨 Greenland shark (*Somniosus microcephalus*) 鱼类 7—294d

格陵兰洋流 Greenland Current 海洋洋流 7—294b

格令 grain 计量单位 7—243c

格隆基 Gronchi, Giovanni 意大利总统 7—318b

格卢克 Gluck, Alma 美国歌手 7—163d

格卢克夫妇 Glueck, Sheldon; and Glueck, Eleanor 美国犯罪学家 7—165a

格鲁 Grew, Nehemiah 英国植物学家 7—306c

格鲁阿罗港 Portogruaro 意大利城镇 13—453e

格鲁本曼兄弟 Grubenmann, Hans Ulrich; and Grubenmann, Johannes 瑞士木工、桥梁设计师 7—327f

格鲁恩 Gruen, Victor 美国建筑师 7—328a

格鲁尔 Groulx, Lionel-Adolphe 加拿大教士、历史学家 7—323a

格鲁菲德 Gruffydd, William John 威尔士诗人 7—328b

格鲁吉亚 Georgia 亚洲国家 7—79b

格鲁吉亚文学 Georgian literature 文学 7—83e

格鲁吉亚语 Georgian language 语言 7—83d

格鲁吉亚正教会 Georgian Orthodox Church 东正教自主教会 7—84a

《格鲁吉耶夫斯克条约》 Georgievsk, Treaty of 俄国与格鲁吉亚缔结的历史协定 7—84d

格鲁克 Gluck, Christoph Willibald, RITTER (knig) VON GLUCK 德国作曲家 7—163e

格鲁曼 Grumman, Leroy Randle 美国工程师 7—329d

格鲁米约男爵 Grumiaux, Arthur, Baron 比利时小提琴家 7—329d

格鲁姆巴赫 Grumbach, Wilhelm von 德国骑士、冒险家 7—329c

格鲁姆布里奇 Groombridge, Stephen 英国天文学家 7—318d

格鲁派 Dge-lugs-pa 中国藏传佛教教派 5—278a

格鲁琼兹 Grudziądz 波兰城市 7—328a

格鲁特岛 Groote Eylandt 澳大利亚岛屿 7—318f

格鲁特河 Groot River 南非河流 7—318e

格鲁特舒尔 Groote Schuur 南非大庄园 7—319a

格鲁西人 Grusi 非洲文化语言集团 7—331b

格吕菲乌斯 Gryphius, Andreas 德国诗人 7—331d

格吕克施塔特 Glückstadt 德国城市 7—164d

格吕克斯堡公爵 Glücksberg, Élie, duc de (duke of) 法国政治家 7—164d

格吕内瓦尔德 Grünewald, Matthias 德国画家 7—330c

格吕耶尔 La Gruyère 瑞士区名 9—422c

格吕耶尔干酪 Gruyère 瑞士食品 7—331b

格律 metre 诗歌 11—160b

格律词典 gradus 文学词典 7—239a

格律恩 Grün, Anastasius 奥地利诗人、政治家 7—329e

格仑莫尔 Glenmore 英国森林公园 7—157a

格伦 Gruen, David (Israeli statesman) 以色列总理 7—328a

格伦 Glenn, John H(erschel), Jr. 美国航天员 7—157e

格伦埃林 Glen Ellyn 美国住宅区 7—156f

格伦达洛谷 Glendalough, Vale of 爱尔兰峡谷 7—157d

格伦代尔 Glendale 美国亚利桑那州城市 7—157c

格伦代尔 Glendale 美国加利福尼亚州城市 7—157c

格伦代夫 Glendive 美国蒙大拿州城市 7—157d

格伦道尔 Glendower, Owen 威尔士民族英雄 7—157d

格伦迪太太 Grundy, Mrs. 英国戏剧人物 7—330b

格伦费尔 Grenfell, Sir Wilfred (Thomason) 英国医务传教士 7—303c

格伦吉摇滚 grunge 音乐 7—330d

格伦凯恩伯爵(第四) Glencairn, William Cunningham, 4th earl of 苏格兰阴谋家 7—157b

格伦凯恩伯爵(第五) Glencairn, Alexander Cunningham, 5th earl of 苏格兰贵族 7—157a

格伦科 Glencoe 苏格兰峡谷 7—157b

格伦科惨案 Glencoe, Massacre of 苏格兰历史 7—157c

格伦罗西斯 Glenrothes 英国城镇 7—158a

格伦斯福尔斯 Glens Falls 美国城市 7—158a

格伦特维 Grundtvig, N(ikolai) F(rederik) S(everin) 丹麦主教、诗人 7—329f

格伦维尔 Grenville, George 英国政治家 7—303e

格伦维尔 Grenville, George Nugent Temple 英国政治家 7—303f

格伦维尔 Grenville, Richard 英国政治家 7—303f

格伦维尔 Grenville, Sir Richard 英国海军指挥官 7—304a

格伦维尔男爵 Grenville (of Wotton-under-Bernewood), William Wyndham Grenville, Baron 英国政治家 7—304a

格伦维尤 Glenview 美国村庄 7—158a

格伦伍德斯普林斯 Glenwood Springs 美国城市 7—158a

格伦因尼斯 Glen Innes 澳大利亚城镇 7—157a

格罗 Gros, Antoine-Jean, Baron 法国画家 7—319f

格罗茨 Grosz, George 德国画家 7—321d

格罗德诺 Hrodno 白俄罗斯城市 8—203c

格罗顿 Groton 美国康涅狄格州城市 7—322d

格罗顿 Groton 美国马萨诸塞州城镇 7—322d

格罗夫 Grove, Frederick Philip 加拿大小说家 7—326f

格罗夫 Grove, Sir George 英国音乐评论家 7—326f

格罗夫 Grove, Lefty 美国职业棒球运动员 7—327a

格罗夫 Grove, Sir William Robert 英国物理学家 7—327a

格罗夫纳 Grosvenor, Gilbert H(ovey) 美国地理学家、作家 7—321d

格罗里埃 Grolier de Servières, Jean, VICOMTE (viscount) D'AGIUSY 法国藏书家 7—317f

格罗宁根 Groningen 荷兰省份 7—318b

格罗宁根 Groningen 荷兰城市 7—318c

格罗皮厄斯 Gropius, Walter (Adolph) 美国建筑师、教育家 7—319a

格罗塞 Grosse, Hans Werner 德国飞行员 7—320d

格罗塞托 Grosseto 意大利城市 7—321a

格罗史密斯 Grossmith, George 英国演员、歌唱家 7—321b

格罗斯 Gross, Samuel David 美国外科医师 7—320b

格罗斯波因特 Grosse Pointe 美国底特律住宅区 7—320e

格罗斯-罗森 Gross-Rosen 德国历史 7—320d

格罗斯泰斯特 Grosseteste, Robert 英国主教、学者 7—320f

格罗斯文特人 Gros Ventres 北美印第安人 7—320a

格罗塔列 Grottaglie 意大利城镇 7—322e

格罗特 Grote, George 英国历史学家 7—321e

格罗特 Groth, Klaus 德国诗人 7—322a

格罗托夫斯基 Grotowski, Jerzy 波兰导演 7—322e

格罗辛 Grocyn, William 英国学者 7—317d

格罗兹尼 Grozny 俄罗斯车臣城市 7—327e

格洛布 Globe 美国城市 7—159f

格洛弗 Glover, Savion 美国舞蹈家、编舞 7—162f

格洛弗斯维尔 Gloversville 美国城市 7—163a
格洛克 Grock 瑞士演员 7—317d
格洛克纳山 Glockner (Austria) 奥地利山峰 7—160e
格洛马河 Glomma 挪威河流 7—160f
格洛斯特 Gloucester 英格兰城市 7—161d
格洛斯特 Gloucester 美国城市 7—161d
格洛斯特伯爵 Gloucester, Robert, Earl of 英格兰贵族 7—161e
格洛斯特伯爵(第八) Gloucester, Gilbert de Clare, 8th earl of, 9TH EARL OF CLARE 威尔士贵族 7—162a
格洛斯特伯爵(第七) Gloucester, Richard de Clare, 7th earl of, 8TH EARL OF CLARE, 6TH EARL OF HERTFORD 英国贵族 7—162a
格洛斯特伯爵和公爵 Gloucester, EARLS AND DUKES OF 英格兰封爵贵族 7—161e
格洛斯特公爵 Gloucester, Humphrey Plantagenet, duke of 英格兰贵族 7—162b
格洛斯特公爵 Gloucester, Henry Stuart, duke of 英格兰贵族 7—162c
格洛斯特公爵 Gloucester, Richard Plantagenet, duke of 英格兰国王 7—162c
格洛斯特公爵 Gloucester, Thomas of Woodstock, duke of 英格兰贵族 7—162b
格洛斯特郡 Gloucestershire 英国郡名 7—162d
格洛瓦茨基 Glowacki, Aleksander (writer) 波兰作家 7—163a
格马尼库斯·凯撒 Germanicus Caesar 罗马将军 7—94b
《格梅林故事》 Gamelyn, The Tale of 英国故事诗 6—569f
格蒙登 Gmunden 奥地利城镇 7—166f
格姆鲁布保护地 Kāmrūp Sanctuary (India) 印度保护地 9—151c
格纳登徐滕惨案 Gnadenhütten Massacre 美国历史 7—167a
格纳莱河 genale (Ethiopia and Somalia) 非洲河流 7—53b
格奈斯特 Gneist, Rudolf von 德国法学家 7—167e
格奈乌斯 Cneius 古罗马人名 4—309c
格奈乌斯 Gnaeus 古罗马人名 7—167a
格奈泽瑙 Gneisenau, August, Count (Graf) Neidhardt von 普鲁士陆军元帅 7—167c
格讷拉 Kanara 印度地区 9—152d
格尼 Gurney, Sir Goldsworthy 英国发明家 7—379a
格尼洛耶海 Gniloye More (Ukraine) 乌克兰亚速海海域 7—168a
格涅兹诺 Gniezno 波兰城镇 7—167f
格平根 Göppingen 德国城市 7—211c
格乔 Guecho 西班牙城镇 7—348a
格人 Ge 南美印第安人 7—41c
《格萨尔王传》 Gesaerwang Zhuan 中国藏族英雄史诗 7—101c
格塞尔 Gesell, Arnold (Lucius) 美国心理学家 7—101f
格赛特 Gossett, Louis, Jr. 美国演员 7—222c
格施塔德 Gstaad 瑞士山村 7—331e
格什姆岛 Qeshm 波斯湾岛屿 14—56b
格什温 Gershwin, George 美国作曲家 7—100d
格什温 Gershwin, Ira 美国诗人 7—100f
格式塔心理学 Gestalt psychology 心理学 7—103b
格思里 Guthrie, Edwin Ray 美国心理学家 7—382d
格思里 Guthrie, Janet 美国赛车手 7—382e
格思里 Guthrie, Jimmy 英国摩托车运动员 7—382f
格思里 Guthrie, Woody 美国歌手、作曲家 7—383a
格思里 Guthrie, Sir (William) Tyrone 英国戏剧导演 7—382f
格思鲁姆 Guthrum 丹麦国王 7—383b
格斯 Guess, George 美国切罗基族领导人 7—351c
格斯顿 Guston, Philip 美国画家 7—381f
格-斯二氏综合征 Grönblad-Strandberg syndrome 病理学 7—318b
格斯勒 Gessler, Otto (Karl) 德国政治家 7—102e
格斯纳 Gesner, Conrad 瑞士医生、博物学家 7—102b
格斯纳 Gessner, Salomon 瑞士作家、艺术家 7—102f
格斯特 Guest, Edgar A(lbert) 美国作家 7—351c
格斯滕贝格 Gerstenberg, Heinrich Wilhelm von 德国诗人 7—101c
格塔 giddha 印度舞蹈 7—122b
格特尔 Goetel, Ferdynand 波兰作家 7—177e
格廷 Girtin, Thomas 英国画家 7—143d
格瓦拉 Guevara, Antonio de 西班牙文人 7—351d
格瓦拉 Guevara, Che 南美洲革命家 7—351e
格瓦拉 Guevara, Luis Vélez de 西班牙作家 7—351f
格威纳特 Gwinnett, Button 美国商人、爱国者 7—387e
格维兹门迪尔·吉斯拉松·哈加林 Gudmundur Gíslason Hagalin (Icelandic writer) 冰岛作家 7—348a
格维兹门松 Gudmundsson, Kristmann 冰岛小说家 7—347f
格维兹门松 Gudmundsson, Tómas 冰岛诗人 7—348a
格温 Gwyn, Nell 英国演员 7—387f
格温 Gwynn, Tony 美国棒球运动员 7—388a
格温特 Gwent 威尔士旧郡名 7—387d
格沃古夫 Głogów 波兰城市 7—160e
格沃兹杰瓦群岛 Gvozdeva, Ostrova (Bering Strait) 白令海群岛 7—387b
格雅 Gayā 印度城镇 7—38e
格言 proverb 民间文学 13—550b
格言诗 gnomic poetry 诗歌 7—168a
格义 geyi 中国佛教 7—105d
格语诸语言 Ge languages 南美印第安语言 7—41f
格泽纽斯 Gesenius, (Heinrich Friedrich) Wilhelm 德国《圣经》学家、语言学家 7—102a
搁栅 joist 建筑 9—75f
蛤 clam 软体动物 4—258c
隔离 isolation 医学 8—471f
隔行正反针编结法 stockinette stitch (knitting) 纺织工艺 16—244d
膈 diaphragm 解剖学 5—288f
镉(Cd) cadmium 化学元素 3—313f
镉中毒 cadmium poisoning 病理现象 3—314b
葛底斯堡 Gettysburg 美国城镇 7—104e
《葛底斯堡演说》 Gettysburg Address 美国历史 7—104f
葛底斯堡战役 Gettysburg, Battle of 美国历史 7—104e
葛洪 Ge Hong 中国道家学者 7—41d
葛拉斯堡罗 Glassboro 美国城镇 7—154d
葛兰宝 Grable, Betty 美国演员 7—235b
葛兰西 Gramsci, Antonio 意大利政治家 7—245e
葛利普 Grabau, Amadeus William 美国地质学家、古生物学家 7—234f
葛琳皓 Greenhow, Rose O'Neal 美国间谍 7—293b
葛缕子 caraway 草本植物 3—439b
葛罗米柯 Gromyko, Andrey Andreyevich 苏联政治家 7—317f
葛逻禄联盟 Qarluq confederation 中亚突厥部落联盟 14—54a
葛瑞菲斯·乔伊纳 Griffith Joyner, (Delorez) Florence 美国短跑运动员 7—311a
葛饰北斋 Katsushika Hokusai (Japanese artist) 日本艺术家 9—197d
"葛斯比"号焚船事件 Gaspee, Burning of the 美国历史 7—25c
葛藤 kudzu vine 植物 9—389c
葛玄 Ge Xuan 中国道士 7—41f
葛伊 Guèye, Lamine 塞内加尔政治家 7—352a
葛洲坝水利枢纽工程 Gezhouba Key Water Control Project 中国水利工程 7—106e
葛兹(铁手) Götz WITH THE IRON HAND 德国骑士 7—227c
个旧 Gejiu 中国城市 7—46a
个人计算机 personal computer (PC) 微型计算机 13—184c
个人所得税 personal income tax 税收 13—185a
个人统治 personalismo 拉美政治 13—185c
个人主义 individualism 哲学 8—369b
个体生态学 autecology 生态学 2—72f
个体心理学 individual psychology 精神病学 8—369a

个性化评名 charactonym 文学 4—60c
各各他 Golgotha 基督受难地 7—196a
各务原 Kagamigahara 日本城市 9—131a
各向异性 anisotropy 物理学 1—360b
铬(Cr) chromium 化学元素 4—212a
铬铅矿 crocoite 矿物 5—22e
铬酸盐矿物 chromate mineral 化合物 4—211c
铬铁 ferrochromium 合金 6—293b
铬铁矿 chromite 矿物 4—212a
根 indriya 印度哲学 8—374c
根 root 植物病害 14—395d
根 root 数学 14—395f
根癌病 crown gall 植物病害 5—36b
《根本中观颂》 Mūlamadhyamakakārikā 佛教著作 11—473a
根伯什 Gömbös, Gyula 匈牙利首相 7—198d
根茨 Gentz, Friedrich 奥地利记者 7—69b
根措夫特 Gentofte 丹麦城市区 7—69a
根德格河 Gandak River 亚洲河流 6—571e
根德拉 Kandla 印度城镇 9—154e
根费尔湖 Genfersee (Europe) 欧洲湖泊 7—63c
根付 netsuke 装饰品 12—94c
根纳普 Gennep, Arnold van 法国人种志学者、民俗学家 7—64d
根瑙杰 Kannauj 印度城镇 9—159a
根尼亚古马里 Kanniyākumāri 印度城镇 9—159a
根舍 Genscher, Hans-Dietrich 德国政治家 7—66e
根室 Nemuro 日本城市 12—75d
根室 Gunther, John 美国记者、作家 7—375a
根斯巴克 Gernsback, Hugo 美国发明家、出版商 7—99a
根斯博罗椅 Gainsborough chair 英国扶手椅 6—547f
根特 Ghent 比利时城市 7—110f
根特-布鲁日画派 Ghent-Bruges school 手抄本装饰画家集团 7—111e
根特-泰尔讷曾运河 Ghent-Terneuzen Canal 比利时水道 7—111e
《根特条约》 Ghent, Treaty of 美国历史 7—111d
《根特协定》 Ghent, Pacification of 荷兰历史 7—111c
根西 Guernsey 英国岛屿 7—350b
根西牛 Guernsey 牛品种 7—350d
根肿病 clubroot 植物病害 4—305f
根肿菌纲 Plasmodiophoromycetes 生物学 13—349d
根状茎 rhizome 植物学 14—264d
根足鞭毛虫 rhizomastigote 原生动物 14—264c
根足虫 rhizopod 原生动物 14—264d
跟 heel 解剖学 7—555d
更格卢鼠 kangaroo rat 啮齿动物 9—156e
更新世 Pleistocene Epoch 地质学 13—368c
更新统 Pleistocene Series 地质学 13—369b
庚斯博罗 Gainsborough, Thomas 英国画家 6—547d
耕地 tillage 农业 17—96a
耿氏效应 Gunn effect 电学 7—372e
梗塞 infarction 病理现象 8—380d
工笔与写意 gongbi and xieyi 中国绘画技法 7—204b
工兵 sapper 军事工程兵 15—57d
工程 engineering 工程学 6—78b
工程地质学 engineering geology 地质学 6—78d
工程制图 drawing, engineering 工程设计 5—416e
工程制图 engineering drawing 制图 6—78d
工党 Labor Party (Australia) 澳大利亚政党 9—431b
工党 Labour Party 英国政党 9—433a
工党 Labour Party 爱尔兰政党 9—433c
工党和社会党国际 Labour and Socialist International (LSI) 国际组织 9—432c
工会 trade union 职工协会 17—187f
工会妇女联盟 Coalition of Labor Union Women 美国妇女工会组织 4—311d
工会化企业 union shop 企业管理 17—348e
工匠党 Workingmen's Party 美国劳工组织 18—333c
工具 tool 文化史 17—154c
工具主义 instrumentalism 哲学 8—401c
工模具制作 tool and die making 工业 17—154d
工人阿尔贝 Ouvrier, Albert l' 法国工人代表 12—509e
工人反对派 Workers' Opposition 苏联共产党派别 18—333a
工人国际法国支部 French Section of the Worker's International (French political party) 法国政党 6—482c
工人国际法国支部 SFIO (France) 法国政党 15—249a
工人力量总工会 Confédération Générale du Travail-Force Ouvrière (CGTFO) 法国工人组织 4—420a
《工人日报》 Daily Worker 美国报纸 5—112c
《工人日报》 Worker, The (newspaper) 美国报纸 18—332f
工人司铎 worker-priest 宗教 18—332f
工人协会诉亨特案 Commonwealth v. Hunt 美国最高法院案例 4—390d
工伤补偿金 workers' compensation 工人抚恤金 18—333a
工团主义 syndicalism 政治 16—402a
工业城 Cité Industrielle 城市规划 4—247e
工业管理学 industrial engineering 工业工程设计 8—376e
工业黑化 industrial melanism 生物学 8—377c
工业化 industrialization 经济 8—378e
工业设计 industrial design 工业 8—376a
工业心理学 industrial psychology 心理学 8—377c
工业医学 industrial medicine 医学 8—377a
工业用搬运车辆 industrial truck 车 8—378b
工业用金刚石 industrial diamond 金刚石 8—376d
工艺博物馆 Polytechnical Museum 俄罗斯莫斯科科技博物馆 13—417f
工艺美术运动 Arts and Crafts Movement 美学 1—534a
工资理论 wage theory 经济学 18—61c
工资-物价管制 wage-price control 经济学 18—61b
《工资与工时法》 Wages and Hours Act 美国法律 18—61d
工作 work 社会生存所必需的劳动 18—332b
工作权利法 right-to-work law 美国法律 14—298e
工作站 workstation 高性能计算机系统 18—333d
弓背鱼 featherback (fish) 鱼类 6—259a
弓道 kyūdō 日本箭术 9—417e
弓箭 bow and arrow 兵器 3—91f
弓鳍鱼 bowfin (*Amia calva*) 淡水鱼类 3—94f
弓琴 musical bow 弦乐器 11—507e
弓式诗琴 bow lute (musical instrument) 乐器 3—92b
弓形竖琴 arched harp 乐器 1—447e
弓形体病 toxoplasmosis 疾病 17—182e
公 catholic 基督教 3—527f
公安委员会 General Security, Committee of 法国历史 7—57a
公案 koan 日本佛教 9—327e
公报 gazette 新闻 7—40c
《公祷书》 Common Prayer, The Book of 基督教礼仪书 4—388e
公敌榜 proscription 古罗马布告 13—538d
公地 commons 公共地块 4—388f
公地优先购买权 preemption 美国历史 13—491a
《公告》 Declaratory Act 英国历史 5—203d
公共工程署 Public Works Administration (PWA) 美国政府机构 14—10f
公共关系 public relations 社会学 14—9e
公共广播社 Public Broadcasting Service (PBS) 美国公司 14—4a
公共交通 mass transit 运输系统 11—6c
《公共礼仪书》 Common Order, Book of 宗教著作 4—388d
公共汽车 bus 交通工具 3—280d
公共事业规划署 Work Projects Administration 美国机构 18—332e

公共事业振兴署 Works Progress Administration (WPA) 美国机构 18—333c
公共事业振兴署联邦戏剧计划 WPA Federal Theatre Project 美国政府管理的戏剧运动 18—341f
公共事业振兴署联邦艺术计划 WPA Federal Art Project 美国罗斯福政府制定的计划 18—341d
公共事业振兴署联邦作家计划 WPA Federal Writers' Project 美国政府为作家等提供就业的计划 18—341f
公共卫生 public health 维护健康生活的社会制度 14—5a
公共行政管理 public administration 管理学 14—3f
公共艺术收藏馆 Öffentliche Kunstmuseum 瑞士收藏馆 12—344c
公共浴场 thermae 洗浴场所 17—32a
公共运输 public transportation 交通运输 14—10e
公共资源保护队 Civilian Conservation Corps (CCC) 美国历史 4—256a
公海 high seas 法律 8—75d
公行 cohong 中国行会 4—334d
公行 cong-hong 中国行会 4—423b
公河 Kong River 亚洲河流 9—345a
公会议主义 conciliarism 天主教 4—411f
公教弟兄会 Christian Brother 天主教 4—205b
公教进行会 Catholic Action 天主教 3—527f
公教青年工人运动 Young Christian Workers 比利时天主教运动 18—464e
公爵 duke 欧洲贵族称号 5—451d
公爵夫人花边 duchesse lace 工艺品 5—445a
公开市场业务 open-market operation 经济 12—427f
公理 axiom 逻辑学 2—93e
公理方法 axiomatic method 逻辑学 2—93e
公理主义 Congregationalism 新教徒运动 4—428c
公立中学 lycée 法国教育 10—307f
公路 highway 交通 8—77c
公路自行车赛 road race 体育 14—324a
公麋党 Bull Moose Party 美国政治派别 3—246b
《公民报》 Burger, Die 南非报纸 3—260b
公民大会 Ecclesia 古希腊公民大会 5—520c
公民警卫队 Civil Guard 西班牙警察 4—254b
公民投票 plebiscite 政治 13—367c
公民议会 apella 斯巴达国民大会 1—407e
公民资格 citizenship 法律 4—248e
公亩 are 计量单位 1—458f
公墓 cemetery 墓地 3—561d
公牛 bull 家畜 3—245e
公牛崇拜 bull cult 史前宗教活动 3—246b
公平交易 Square Deal 美国历史 16—167c
公平贸易法 fair-trade law 美国经济法 6—215a
公平施政 Fair Deal 美国国内改革计划 6—214f
公顷 hectare 计量单位 7—553e
公设辩护人 public defender 法律 14—4d
公社 commune 中世纪西欧自治城镇 4—390e
公社战士 Federate 法国巴黎公社拥护者 6—263d
公司 corporation 工商业组织形式 4—519d
公司财务 corporate finance 金融 4—519b
公司画派 Company school 印度艺术 4—395f
公司所得税 corporate income tax 税务 4—519d
公司债券 debenture stock 金融 5—197e
公诉人 prosecutor 法律 13—538f
公孙弘 Gongsun Hong 中国学者 7—204e
公孙龙 Gongsun Long 中国战国时期哲学家 7—204f
公孙鞅 Gongsun Yang 中国战国时期改革家 7—205a
公学 public school 英国教育 14—10b
公议 ijmāʿ 伊斯兰教 8—330a
公益 istiṣlāḥ 伊斯兰教 8—482d
公谊会 Friends, Society of 基督教新教派别 6—493d
公谊会世界协商委员会 Friends World Committee for Consultation (FWCC) 基督教公谊会国际组织 6—493f
公营企业 public enterprise 公有的企业组织 14—4e
公用事业 public utility 服务行业 14—10e
公用征收 expropriation (property law) 财产法 6—197b
公寓式住宅 apartment house 建筑物 1—406e
公园 park 供消遣游憩的场所 13—53b
公债 public debt 政府的债务 14—4b
公证人 notary 法律 12—273e
公众赛会 ludi publici 古罗马赛会 10—272d
公主款式 princess style 服饰 13—515e
功 work 物理学 18—332d
功德 puñña 佛教 14—28e
功绩勋章 Merit, Medal for 美国勋章 11—131d
功绩勋章 Merit, Order of (O.M.) 英国荣誉褒奖制度 11—131e
功绩勋章 Pour le Mérite 普鲁士勋章 13—469d
功利主义 Utilitarianism 伦理学 17—430f
功率 power 物理学 13—473e
功能主义 Functionalism 建筑学 6—524e
功能主义 functionalism 社会学 6—524f
功能主义 functionalism 心理学 6—525a
功能主义 functionalism 语言学 6—524f
攻城锤 battering ram 中世纪武器 2—281c
攻击性拟态 aggressive mimicry 生物学 1—122a
供给曲线 supply curve 经济学 16—349a
供暖 heating 机械装置、系统 7—545c
供求 supply and demand 经济学 16—348e
供认 confession 法律 4—420d
供水系统 water-supply system 输送淡水的设施 18—139a
肱骨 humerus 解剖学 8—247e
宫 palace 建筑 12—554d
宫本武藏 Miyamoto Musashi 日本武士美术家 11—296f
宫城 Miyagi 日本县名 11—296d
宫川长春 Miyagawa Chōshun 日本画家 11—296c
宫岛 Miya-shima (Japan) 日本濑户内海岛屿 11—296c
宫岛(日本) Shrine Island (Japan) 日本濑户内海岛屿 15—340e
宫古 Miyako 日本城市 11—296e
宫内大臣供奉剧团 Chamberlain's Men 英格兰剧团 4—35e
宫内节育器 IUD 避孕 8—491a
宫女画 odalisque 绘画 12—335f
宫崎 Miyazaki 日本县名 11—297a
宫崎友禅 Miyazaki Yūzen 日本画家 11—297b
宫廷恋歌 air de cour 音乐 1—143c
宫廷诗 chant royal 法国诗体 4—53d
宫廷史诗体 Kavya 印度文学 9—202a
宫廷游艺总管 Revels, Master of the 英国宫廷官员 14—250d
宫外孕 extrauterine pregnancy 疾病 6—199b
宫位 house 占星术 8—194d
宫相 mayor of the palace 欧洲官员 11—54c
宫泽喜一 Miyazawa Kiichi 日本首相 11—297b
恭亲王 Gong Qinwang 中国亲王 7—203f
䳍 tinamou 鸟类 17—104b
龚古尔兄弟 Goncourt, Edmond and Jules 法国作家 7—201e
龚开 Gong Kai 中国画家 7—203e
龚帕斯 Gompers, Samuel 美国劳工领袖 7—199f
龚贤 Gong Xian 中国画家 7—203f
龚自珍 Gong Zizhen 中国文学家、思想家 7—204a
觥 gong 中国青铜酒器 7—203d
巩膜炎 scleritis 疾病 15—145d
巩特尔 Gunther 勃艮第国王 7—374d
巩义 Gongyi 中国城市 7—205a
汞(Hg) mercury 化学元素 11—127a

汞齐 amalgam 合金 1—263c
汞溴红 merbromin 抗菌剂 11—123a
汞中毒 mercury poisoning 毒害作用 11—127d
拱 arch 建筑 1—446a
拱点 apse 天文学 1—423f
拱顶 vault 建筑 17—482d
拱肩 spandrel 建筑 16—4e
拱门缘饰 archivolt 建筑 1—454c
拱檐线脚 hoodmold 建筑 8—162c
拱鹰架 centring (construction) 建筑结构 4—5f
珙桐 dove tree (*Davidia involucrata*) 小乔木 5—404c
共产党和工人党情报局 Cominform 国际共产主义机构 4—381f
共产国际 Comintern 共产党国际组织 4—382a
共产国际 Communist International 共产党国际组织 4—391f
共产主义 communism 政治经济组织制度 4—391b
共轭体系 conjugated system 化学 4—432b
共犯 accomplice 法律 1—46e
共沸物 azeotrope 化学 2—100c
共工 Gonggong 中国神话人物 7—204c
共和党 Republican Party 法国政党 14—237a
共和党 Republican Party 爱尔兰政党 14—237b
共和党 Republican Party 美国今日民主党的前身 14—237b
共和党 Republican Party 美国两大政党之一 14—237d
共和党 Republicans, The 德国政党 14—238a
共和党独立派 Mugwump 美国政治派别 11—466c
共和国大军 Grand Army of the Republic (GAR) 美国退伍军人组织 7—247e
共济会会员 Mason 秘密团体 11—2d
共济会制 Freemasonry 宗教信条 6—471d
共济失调 ataxia 医学 2—15e
共济制 Gesellschaft 社会学 7—102a
共价键 covalent bond 化学 4—553f
共进会 Gongjinhui 中国清代政治团体 7—204d
共聚物 copolymer 化学 4—491d
共谋罪 conspiracy 法律 4—447f
共奶血亲 raḍāʿ 伊斯兰教法律 14—108a
共栖 commensalism 生物学 4—384b
《共青团真理报》 Komsomolskaya Pravda 苏联报纸 9—343f
共生 symbiosis 生物学 16—397c
共生次序 paragenesis 地质学 13—31f
共时语言学 synchronic linguistics 语言学 16—401b
共同财产 community property 法律 4—393b
共同管领 condominium 法律 4—416e
共同基金 mutual fund 金融 11—518f
共同生活兄弟会 Common Life, Brethren of the 宗教组织 4—388c
共同市场 Common Market 国际经济组织 4—388d
共同通讯社 Kyōdō Tsūshinsha 日本通讯社 9—413e
共同意志 general will 法国哲学 7—57e
共同语 koine 语言学 9—335d
共相 universal 哲学 17—374f
共享制与共济制 Gemeinschaft and Gesellschaft 社会学 7—49e
共振 resonance 物理学 14—241c
共振论 resonance, theory of 化学 14—241d
共振器 resonator 声学 14—241e
共振态 resonance 粒子物理学 14—241c
贡巴来尔洞穴 Les Combarelles 法国古遗址 10—35e
贡版王朝 Konbaung DYNASTY (Myanmar [Burma]) 缅甸历史 9—344d
贡贝 Gombe 尼日利亚城镇、酋长国名 7—198c
贡贝尔 Gombert, Nicolas 佛兰德斯作曲家 7—198d
贡比涅 Compiègne 法国城镇 4—398c
贡比约恩山 Gunnbjørn Mountain 格陵兰山峰 7—372f
贡伯戈讷姆 Kumbakonam 印度城市 9—395b
贡布 Kâmpôt 柬埔寨城镇 9—151c
贡布罗维奇 Gombrowicz, Witold 波兰作家 7—198f
贡达 Gonda 印度城镇 7—202b
贡德尔 Gonder 埃塞俄比亚城市 7—202c
贡德勒格马河 Gundlakamma River 印度河流 7—372a
贡德人 Gond 印度土著民族 7—202a
贡德瓦纳 Gondwana 印度历史地区 7—203a
贡迪家族 Gondi FAMILY 法国世家 7—202d
贡迪萨尔沃 Gundisalvo, Domingo 西班牙哲学家、语言学家 7—372a
贡迪温迪 Goondiwindi 澳大利亚城镇 7—210b
贡都利奇 Gundulić, Ivan (Franov) 克罗地亚诗人、剧作家 7—372b
贡多马尔伯爵 Gondomar, Diego Sarmiento de Acuña, Count (conde) de 西班牙外交家 7—202f
贡嘎山 Gongga Shan 中国山峰 7—204b
贡戈拉-阿尔戈特 Góngora y Argote, Luis de 西班牙诗人 7—204d
贡戈拉河 Gongola River 尼日利亚河流 7—204d
贡格尔 Gungl, Joseph 奥匈帝国作曲家 7—372c
贡根 Konkan 印度平原 9—346e
贡古尼亚纳 Gungunhana 南非班图人国王 7—372c
贡贾人 Gonja (people) 非洲民族 7—205c
贡金 benevolence 英国税制 2—383a
贡克尔 Gunkel, (Johann Friedrich) Hermann 德国《圣经》学者 7—372d
贡普洛维奇 Gumplowicz, Ludwig 波兰社会学家、法理学家 7—371b
贡萨尔维斯 Gonçalves, António Aurélio 非洲小说家 7—200f
贡萨尔维斯 Gonçalves, Nuno 葡萄牙画家 7—200f
贡萨尔维斯·迪亚斯 Gonçalvez Dias, Antônio 巴西诗人 7—201a
贡萨加 Gonzaga, Tomás António 葡萄牙诗人 7—206a
贡萨加·米什科夫斯基 Gonzaga Myszkowski, Aleksander Wielopolski, Margrave (Margrabia) 波兰政治家 7—206a
贡萨洛·费尔南德斯·德·科尔多瓦 Gonzalo Fernández de Córdoba 西班牙军事家 7—207a
贡斯当 Constant, Benjamin 法国-瑞士小说家 4—449c
贡特拉姆 Guntram 勃艮第国王 7—375a
贡荼利尼 Kuṇḍalinī 佛教 9—396d
贡土尔 Guntūr 印度县城 7—375b
贡扎加王朝 Gonzaga DYNASTY 意大利王朝 7—205f
贡兹冰期 Günz Glacial Stage 地质学 7—375c
贡兹-明德间冰期 Günz-Mindel Interglacial Stage 地质学 7—375c
勾兑威士忌酒 blended whiskey 酒类 2—532e
勾缝 pointing 建筑学 13—390b
勾践 Goujian 中国春秋末期越国君 7—228e
勾玉 magatama 玉石饰物 10—378e
佝偻病 rickets 疾病 14—289f
沟齿鼩 solenodon 动物 15—495a
沟道效应 channeling 物理学 4—52d
沟繁缕科 Elatinaceae 水生草本植物 6—14e
沟腹虫 solenogaster 软体动物 15—495b
沟口健二 Mizoguchi Kenji 日本电影导演 11—297e
沟鳞鱼 Bothriolepis 古生物学 3—72c
沟酸浆 monkey flower 草本植物 11—341f
钩虫病 hookworm disease 疾病 8—164f
钩端螺旋体病 leptospirosis 疾病 10—33c
钩口线虫病 ancylostomiasis 疾病 1—323f
钩手水母属 Gonionemus 动物学 7—205b
钩虾 gammarid 甲壳动物 6—570c
钩针织品 crochet 工艺品 5—21d
钩嘴鵙 vanga-shrike 鸟类 17—467c
钩嘴鹛科 Pomatorhinidae 动物学 13—419b
狗 dog (*Canis familiaris*) 哺乳动物 5—359e
狗鰔 weakfish 鱼类 18—153c

狗橇比赛 dogsled racing 体育 5—361d
狗鲨 dogfish 鱼类 5—360f
狗鱼 pike 鱼类 13—300e
狗鱼鲈 pikeperch 鱼类 13—301c
狗鱼属 Esox 动物学 6—132e
构成主义 Constructivism 艺术 4—460f
构象 conformation 化学 4—422b
构形色 schemochrome 生物学 15—113a
构型 configuration 化学 4—421d
构造变动 diastrophism 地质学 5—290d
构造地质学 structural geology 地质学 16—282e
构造论 constitution theory 哲学 4—460c
构造原理 Aufbau principle 物理学 2—47c
构造运动学 tectonics 地质学 16—513f
构造主义 structuralism 心理学 16—283b
构造作用 tectonism 地质学 16—513f
购书会 book club 图书销售组织 3—37c
购物中心 shopping centre 商业 15—332a
购置佛罗里达 Florida, Purchase of 美国与西班牙协议 6—372c
孤雌生殖 parthenogenesis 生物学 13—65d
孤鸽 solitaire 古生物学 15—497c
孤立双四面体硅酸盐 sorosilicate 矿物学 15—523a
孤立语 isolating language 语言学 8—471e
孤立字母 ḥurūf al-muqaṭṭaʿah (Islām) 伊斯兰教 8—266d
孤山 monadnock 地貌学 11—328f
菰 wild rice (*Zizania aquatica*) 茎叶粗大的禾草 18—252b
辜振甫 Gu Zhenfu 中国台湾企业家 7—333d
觚 gu 中国酒器 7—331f
古埃及通俗体文字 demotic script 象形文字草写体 5—240a
古安 Gouin, Sir (Jean) Lomer 加拿大政治家 7—228e
古昂人 Guang 非洲民族 7—338d
古巴 Cuba 西印度群岛岛国 5—46f
古巴棒球联盟 Cuban League 拉丁美洲棒球联合会 5—48c
古巴导弹危机 Cuban missile crisis 美苏关系事件 5—48c
古巴独立运动 Cuban Independence Movement 古巴历史 5—48a
古巴共产党 Communist Party of Cuba 古巴政党 4—391f
古班 Guban 索马里平原 7—347b
古版书 incunabula 出版物 8—354b
古邦 Kupang 印度尼西亚城市 9—399d
古保加利亚语 Bulgarian language, Old 语言 3—244a
古杯类 archaeocyathid 古生物学 1—446d
古北口 Gubeikou 中国长城关口 7—347c
古贝尔伯爵 Coubert, Samuel Bernard, comte de (count of) 法国教育家 4—540d
古比奥 Gubbio 意大利城镇 7—347b
古比雪夫 Kuibyshev (Russia) 俄罗斯城市 9—390f
古比雪夫 Kujbyšev (Russia) 俄罗斯城市 9—391e
古比雪夫 Kuybyshev (city and region, Russia, U.S.S.R.) 俄罗斯城市 9—409e
古波斯语楔形文字 Old Persian writing 古代中东文字 12—368c
古伯察 Huc, Evariste Régis 法国天主教传教士 8—220a
古布金 Gubkin 俄罗斯城市 7—347c
古草食有袋科 Diprotodontidae 古生物学 5—333f
古昌 Qūchān 伊朗城镇 14—81c
古茨科 Gutzkow, Karl (Ferdinand) 德国作家 7—384a
古磁性 paleomagnetism 地球物理学 12—561e
古达米斯 Ghadāmis 利比亚绿洲 7—107a
古代雕刻展览馆 Glyptothek 德国博物馆 7—166f
古代基督教艺术 paleo-Christian art 宗教艺术 12—559c
古代萨迦 fornaldar saga 斯堪的纳维亚文学 6—410c
古德 Goode, G(eorge) Brown 美国动物学家 7—208b
古德伯 Cuddapah 印度城市 5—51c
古德弗雷德 Godfrey 丹麦国王 7—173e
古德里安 Guderian, Heinz (Wilhelm) 德国将领 7—347d
古德里基 Goodridge, Sarah 美国画家 7—209c
古德里克 Goodricke, John 英国天文学家 7—209b
古德里奇 Goodrich, Samuel Griswold 美国出版家、作家 7—208f
古德里奇公司 Goodrich Company 美国公司 7—209a
古德洛尔 Cuddalore 印度城镇 5—51c
古德曼 Goodman, Benny 美国音乐家 7—208d
古德耐特-拉文小道 Goodnig-Loving Trail 美国古牛车小道 7—208e
古德帕斯丘 Goodpasture, E(rnest) W(illiam) 美国病理学家 7—208f
古德瑟 Goodsir, John 苏格兰解剖学家 7—209c
古德温 Goodwin, Thomas 美国教士 7—209d
古德温暗沙 Goodwin Sands 英格兰暗礁 7—209e
古德伊尔 Goodyear, Charles 美国发明家 7—209e
古迪 Goudy, Frederic W(illiam) 美国印刷工作者 7—228b
古迪梅尔 Goudimel, Claude 法国作曲家 7—228a
古迪纳夫岛 Goodenough Island 巴布亚新几内亚岛屿 7—208d
古地理学 paleogeography 地理学 12—559f
古地质学 paleogeology 地质学 12—560d
古蒂埃尔 Gouthière, Pierre 法国金属制造工 7—231d
古蒂人 Guti 美索不达米亚民族 7—383c
古典芭蕾 classical ballet 芭蕾 4—268f
古典滑雪 Classic skiing 滑雪 4—268e
古典经济学 classical economics 英国经济学派 4—268f
古典式摔跤 Greco-Roman wrestling 体育 7—278e
古典文学 classical literature 古希腊古罗马文学 4—269b
古典主义和新古典主义 Classicism and Neoclassicism 美学观点 4—269c
古多尔 Goodall, Jane 英国动物行为学家 7—208a
古尔 Goole 英国港口 7—210a
古尔 Gull, Sir William Withey, 1st Baronet 英国生理学家 7—369c
古尔·艾米尔陵 Gūr-e amīr 蒙古帖木儿陵墓 7—378a
古尔班通古特沙漠 Gurbantunggut Desert 中国沙漠 7—378b
古尔邦节 Id al-Adha 伊斯兰教节日 8—318a
古尔本 Goulburn 澳大利亚城市 7—229b
古尔本河 Goulburn River 澳大利亚河流 7—229b
古尔本群岛 Goulburn Islands 澳大利亚群岛 7—229b
古尔伯加 Gulbarga 印度城市 7—367d
古尔达斯布尔 Gurdāspur 印度城市 7—378b
古尔代盖 Ghurdaqah, al- 埃及城市 7—114b
古尔德 Gould, Chester 美国连环漫画家 7—220d
古尔德 Gould, Glenn Herbert 加拿大钢琴家 7—229d
古尔德 Gould, Jay 美国金融家 7—229e
古尔德 Gould, John 英国鸟类学家 7—229f
古尔德 Gould, Morton 美国音乐家 7—230a
古尔德 Gould, Stephen Jay 美国古生物学家 7—230b
古尔德贝格 Guldberg, Cato Maximilian 挪威化学家 7—367d
古尔冈 Gurgaon 印度城市 7—378c
古尔戈 Gourgaud, Gaspard 法国军人、历史学家 7—231a
古尔格 Coorg 印度县名 4—486d
古尔捷耶夫 Gurdjieff, George Ivanovitch 亚美尼亚哲学家、神秘主义者 7—378b
古尔马人 Gurma 非洲民族 7—378e
古尔蒙 Gourmont, Remy de 法国作家 7—231b
古尔默尔格 Gulmarg 查谟和克什米尔城镇 7—370a
古尔萨 Goursat, Édouard(-Jean-Baptiste) 法国数学家 7—231b
古尔斯特兰德 Gullstrand, Allvar 瑞典眼科学家 7—369e
古尔苏丹国 Ghūrid sultanate 阿富汗古国名 7—114c
古尔瓦 Goolwa 澳大利亚城镇 7—210a
古尔诸语言 Gur languages 非洲语言 7—378a
古坟时代 Tumulus period 日本文化 17—267a
古风时期 Archaic period 历史学 1—447b

古风式微笑 Archaic smile 希腊雕刻 1—447b
古根海姆 Guggenheim, Peggy 美国艺术品收藏家 7—352b
古根海姆博物馆 Guggenheim Museum 美国艺术馆 7—352d
古根海姆父子 Guggenheim, Meyer and Daniel 美国企业家 7—352b
古根海姆收藏馆 Guggenheim Collection 美国艺术收藏馆 7—352c
古古什 Googoosh 伊朗歌手、演员 7—209f
古河 Koga 日本城市 9—333a
古吉拉特 Gujarāt 印度邦名 7—365f
古吉拉特木雕 Gujarāt woodwork 印度雕刻 7—366c
古吉拉特平原 Gujarāt Plains 印度平原 7—366c
古吉拉特语 Gujarati language 印度-雅利安语言 7—366e
古教会斯拉夫语 Old Church Slavonic language 语言 12—367b
古杰拉特 Gujrāt 巴基斯坦城市 7—367a
古杰拉特战役 Gujrāt, Battle of 印度历史 7—367a
古杰兰瓦拉 Gujrānwāla 巴基斯坦城市 7—366f
《古今图书集成》 Gujin Tushu Jicheng 中国类书 7—366e
古今之争 ancients and moderns 文学争论 1—323b
古晋 Kuching 马来西亚城镇 9—388b
古柯 coca (*Erythroxylum coca*) 植物学 4—318b
古科沃 Gukovo 俄罗斯城市 7—367a
古拉 Gula (Mesopotamian deity) 美索不达米亚神名 7—367a
古拉格 Gulag 苏联历史 7—367b
古拉格人 Gurage 非洲民族 7—378a
古拉姆·阿赫默德 Ghulam Ahmad, Mirza 印度穆斯林领袖 7—114b
古拉特 Goulart, João (Belchior Marques) 巴西总统 7—229a
古剌地毯 Kula carpet 土耳其工艺品 9—392b
古来氏 Quraysh 沙特阿拉伯古代部落名 14—98b
古莱阿 Kolea 阿尔及利亚城镇 9—338f
古赖亚特 Qurayyāt, al- 沙特阿拉伯省份 14—98c
《古兰经》 Qur'ān 伊斯兰教经典 14—97e
古老的荣耀 Old Glory (U.S. flag) 美国国旗的别称 12—367f
古勒语 Gullah 语言 7—369d
古里水坝 Guri Dam 委内瑞拉水库、水电站 7—378d
古里耶夫 Guryev 哈萨克斯坦城市 7—379e
古力丹 Coulee Dam 美国城镇 4—541d
古利 Gully, John 英国拳击运动员 7—369f
古利明 Guelmim 摩洛哥城镇 7—348d
古利斯坦 Guliston 乌兹别克斯坦城市 7—368f
古鬣狗科 Borhyaenidae 动物学 3—51d
古流 Ko 日本花道流派 9—327b
古隆人 Gurung 尼泊尔民族 7—379d
古卢 Gulu 乌干达城镇 7—370b
古卢 Kullu 印度城市 9—393b
古鲁 Gurū 锡克教领袖 7—379c
古鲁 guru 印度教 7—379d
古鲁格舍德拉 Kurukshetra 印度城市 9—404d
古罗堡 Fort-Gouraud (Mauritania) 毛里塔尼亚矿区村庄 6—413e
古罗马广场 forum 古罗马城市露天场地 6—419b
古罗人 Guro 非洲民族 7—379a
古马勒河 Gumal River 阿富汗河流 7—370e
古马勒山口 Gumal Pass 巴基斯坦山口 7—370e
古梅尔 Gumel 尼日利亚城镇、酋长国名 7—370f
古米廖夫 Gumilyov, Nikolay Stepanovich 俄国诗人、理论家 7—370f
古默尔赫德 Kumarhata (India) 印度城镇 9—394e
古姆 Gumm, Frances (American actress) 美国演员 7—371a
古姆蒂河 Gumti (India) 印度河流 7—371c
古姆星云 Gum Nebula 天文学 7—370d
古纳 Guna 印度城市 7—371e
古诺 Gounod, Charles(-François) 法国作曲家 7—230c
古诺尔斯语 Old Norse language 古冰岛语言 12—368b
古普鲁士语 Old Prussian language 语言 12—368c
古奇 Gooch, Sir Daniel, 1st Baronet 英国工程师 7—207a
古奇 Gooch, George Peabody 英国历史学家 7—207b
古气候学 paleoclimatology 地质学 12—559e
古契柯夫 Guchkov, Aleksandr Ivanovich 俄国政治家 7—347c
古钱形珍珠菜 moneywort (plant) 草本植物 11—335c
古热 Gouges, Olympia de 法国社会改革家、作家 7—228b
古人类学 paleoanthropology 人类古生物学 12—559c
古戎 Goujon, Jean 法国雕刻家 7—228f
古如仁波且 Guru Rimpoche (Buddhist mystic) 印度佛教密宗僧人 7—379d
古撒克逊语 Old Saxon language 语言 12—368e
古瑟布勒 Kusapura (India) 印度城镇 9—405a
古森斯 Goossens, Sir Eugene 英国音乐家 7—211a
古绍 Gusau 尼日利亚城镇 7—379e
古生代 Paleozoic Era 地质学 12—562b
古生物群演替规律 faunal succession, law of 地层学 6—252d
古生物学 paleontology 生物学、地质学 12—561e
古什布赫文布尔 Kushbhawanpur (India) 印度城镇 9—405d
《古事记》 Kojiki 日本史籍 9—336b
古书手抄本 codex 历史手稿 4—326d
古水文学 paleohydrology 水文学 12—561a
古斯贝 Goose Bay (Newfoundland) 加拿大城镇 7—210c
古斯堪的纳维亚人 Norseman 北欧民族 12—242f
古斯拉琴 gusla 乐器 7—380a
古斯曼 Guzmán, Jacobo Arbenz 危地马拉总统 7—386d
古斯曼 Guzmán, Martín Luis 墨西哥作家 7—386d
古斯曼·布兰科 Guzmán Blanco, Antonio 委内瑞拉总统 7—386e
古斯曼城 Ciudad Guzmán 墨西哥城市 4—252a
古斯曼·费尔南德斯 Guzmán Fernández, (Silvestre) Antonio 多米尼加共和国总统 7—386f
古斯曼-皮门塔尔 Guzmán y Pimental, Gaspar (Spanish prime minister) 西班牙总理 7—387a
古斯曼氏凤梨属 Guzmania 植物学 7—387a
古斯塔夫 Gustav 瑞典国王之名 7—380d
古斯塔夫二世·阿道夫 Gustav II Adolf 瑞典国王 7—380e
古斯塔夫二世福音联合会 Gustavus Adolphus Union 基督教组织 7—381f
古斯塔夫六世·阿道夫 Gustav VI Adolf 瑞典国王 7—381e
古斯塔夫三世 Gustav III 瑞典国王 7—381b
古斯塔夫森 Gustafson, Ralph Barker 加拿大诗人 7—380c
古斯塔夫四世·阿道夫 Gustav IV Adolf 瑞典国王 7—381c
古斯塔夫松 Gustafsson, Toini 瑞典滑雪运动员 7—380c
古斯塔夫五世 Gustav V 瑞典国王 7—381d
古斯塔夫一世·瓦萨 Gustav I Vasa 瑞典国王 7—380d
古塔 Cuthah 伊拉克古城 5—78f
古塔巴拉塔树胶 gutta balata (gum) 植物胶 7—383f
古塔波胶 gutta-percha 植物胶 7—383f
古泰拜·伊本·穆斯林 Qutaybah ibn Muslim 阿拉伯人将军 14—98d
古腾贝格 Gutenberg, Beno 美国地震学家 7—382a
古体诗 ancient-style poem 中国文学 1—323a
古田 Gutian 中国县名 7—383c
古田织部 Furuta Oribe 日本茶道大师 6—532a
古铁雷斯·纳赫拉 Gutiérrez Nájera, Manuel 墨西哥诗人、散文作家 7—383d
古铁雷斯·索拉纳 Gutiérrez Solana, José 西班牙画家、作家 7—383e
古铁雷兹 Gutiérrez, Gustavo 天主教神学家 7—383d
古廷 Quthing 莱索托村庄 14—98e
古托·葛林 Guto'r Glyn 威尔士诗人 7—383f
古瓦哈蒂 Guwāhāti 印度城镇 7—384a
古瓦耶 Goyer, Salomon de (painter) 荷兰画家 7—234b
古维翁-圣西尔 Gouvion-Saint-Cyr, Laurent, marquis de 法国军人、政

治家 7—231d
古文 guwen 中国古代文体 7—384b
古文书学 diplomatics 文献学 5—332c
古文字学 paleography 文字学 12—560d
古西伯利亚人 Paleosiberian 民族 12—561e
古西伯利亚诸语言 Paleosiberian languages 语言 12—561f
古西-赫鲁斯塔利内 Gus-Khrustalny 俄罗斯城市 7—379e
古西人 Gusii 非洲民族 7—379f
古希腊共同语 Koine 语言学 9—335e
古希腊椅 klismos 家具 9—318b
古蜥鲸 Basilosaurus 古生物学 2—262e
古细菌 archaebacterium 细菌 1—446c
古新世 Paleocene epoch 地质学 12—559d
古信托制 use 英国财产法 17—422c
古叙利亚语 Syriac language 语言 16—406b
古叙利亚语文献 Syriac literature 文献 16—406c
古叙利亚字母 Syriac alphabet 文字体系 16—406b
古学 Kogaku 日本新儒学派别 9—333a
古亚细亚诸语言 Paleo-Asiatic languages 语言 12—559c
古羊齿属 Archaeopteris 植物学 1—446f
古蝎甲龙属 Palaeoscincus 古生物学 12—555e
古英语 Old English language 语言 12—367d
古英语字体 Old English script 文字 12—367e
古元 Gu Yuan 中国画家 7—333b
古陨击坑 astrobleme 地质学 2—7b
古冢 burial mound 墓地 3—265b
古椎鱼属 Palaeospondylus 古生物学 12—555f
古兹密特 Goudsmit, Samuel Abraham 美国物理学家 7—228a
古兹匹德 Goodspeed, Edgar J(ohnson) 美国《圣经》学者 7—209d
谷 valley 地质学 17—455b
谷氨酸 glutamic acid 生物化学 7—165b
谷氨酸钠 sodium glutamate 化合物 15—484a
谷氨酸一钠(味精) monosodium glutamate (MSG) 化合物 11—347b
谷氨酰胺 glutamine 生物化学 7—165c
谷蛋白 gluten 生物化学 7—165c
谷盗 bark-gnawing beetle 昆虫 2—230d
谷德 Gould, Benjamin Apthorp 美国天文学家 7—229c
谷德伦 Gudrun 北欧传说人物 7—348a
谷登堡 Gutenberg, Johannes 德国工匠、发明家 7—382b
《谷登堡圣经》 Gutenberg Bible 印刷史 7—382c
谷地色拉 corn salad (species *Valerianella olitoria*) 植物 4—510f
谷蛾 tineid moth 昆虫 17—104f
谷胱甘肽 glutathione 生物化学 7—165c
谷精草目 Eriocaulales 植物学 6—118f
谷崎润一郎 Tanizaki Jun'ichirō 日本小说家 16—466e
谷神星 Ceres 天文学 4—11a
谷文晁 Tani Bunchō 日本画家 16—466b
谷物 cereal 植物 4—9e
谷物法 Corn Law 英国历史 4—510d
谷物分成制 sharecropping 农业 15—280b
谷物海岸 Grain Coast 西非海岸 7—243d
谷物升运器 grain elevator 农业机械 7—243d
谷物条播机 grain drill 农业机械 7—243d
谷象 grain weevil (*Sitophilus granarius*) 昆虫 7—243e
股白肿 milk leg 疾病 11—219e
股份 stock 金融 16—242d
股份不定信托公司 open-end trust 金融 12—427d
股份公司 joint-stock company 公司制度 9—75c
股份固定信托公司 closed-end trust 金融 4—299f
股骨 femur 解剖学 6—271f
股票行情自动收录器 ticker 机器 17—86a
股票买卖特权 stock option 金融学 16—243a
股四头肌 quadriceps femoris muscle 解剖学 14—72a
股息 dividend 金融 5—346b
骨 bone 解剖学 3—27a
骨癌 bone cancer 疾病 3—27f
骨鳔鱼 ostariophysan 鱼类 12—488f
骨齿工具工艺 Osteodontokeratic tool industry 考古学 12—490f
骨传导 bone conduction 生理学 3—28c
骨单位 osteon 解剖学 12—491d
骨的佩吉特氏病 Paget's disease of bone 疾病 12—545a
骨封·雷克林豪森氏病 von Recklinghausen's disease of bone 疾病 18—47e
骨骼 skeleton 解剖学 15—414d
骨骼肌 skeletal muscle 解剖学 15—414d
骨关节炎 osteoarthritis 疾病 12—490c
骨化性肌炎 myositis ossificans 疾病 11—525f
骨坏死 osteonecrosis 疾病 12—491d
骨灰 Ashes 板球赛获胜象征 1—547a
骨灰瓷 bone china 含骨灰的硬质瓷 3—28a
骨灰堂 columbarium 丧葬艺术 4—367e
骨痂 callus 骨科学 3—357a
骨巨细胞瘤 giant cell tumour of bone 疾病 7—116e
骨疗学 osteopathy 医学 12—491e
骨料 aggregate 建筑材料 1—121d
骨鳞鱼 Osteolepis 古生物学 12—491b
骨瘤 osteoma 疾病 12—491c
骨螺 murex 螺类 11—494c
骨膜 periosteum 解剖学 13—169e
骨囊肿 bone cyst 疾病 3—28c
骨牌理论 domino theory 美国外交政策 5—374f
骨盆 pelvic girdle 解剖学 13—132f
骨品 kolp'um 朝鲜历史 9—341b
骨肉瘤 osteosarcoma 病理学 12—492b
骨软骨病 osteochondrosis 疾病 12—490d
骨软骨瘤 osteochondroma 疾病 12—490d
骨软化 osteomalacia 病理现象 12—491c
骨舌鱼 bony tongue 鱼类 3—36e
骨舌鱼 osteoglossomorph 鱼类 12—491a
骨石化病 osteopetrosis 疾病 12—491f
骨髓 bone marrow 解剖学 3—28d
骨髓瘤病 myelomatosis 疾病 11—524a
骨髓瘤蛋白 myeloma protein 病理现象 11—524a
骨髓炎 osteomyelitis 疾病 12—491c
骨炭 bone black 化学 3—27f
骨网织细胞肉瘤 reticulum cell sarcoma of bone 恶性肿瘤 14—246b
骨细胞 osteocyte 细胞 12—490f
骨纤维性结构不良 fibrous dysplasia 先天性发育障碍 6—302e
骨折 fracture 外科病 6—434d
骨折脱位 fracture-dislocation 外科病 6—434f
骨质疏松症 osteoporosis 疾病 12—491f
骨转移癌 bone lesion 疾病 3—28c
钴(Co) cobalt 化学元素 4—313d
钴华 erythrite 矿物 6—125c
钴缺乏 cobalt deficiency 病态 4—314a
鼓 drum 乐器 5—429b
鼓槌树 drumstick tree (*Moringa pterygosperma*) 小乔木 5—430d
鼓动宣传 agitprop 政治 1—123c
鼓浪屿 Gulangyu 中国岛屿 7—367c
鼓膜 tympanic membrane 解剖学 17—306d
鼓丘 drumlin 地质学 5—429f
鼓形圆桌 drum table 家具 5—429e
鼓藻 desmid 藻类 5—262c
鼓胀 bulging 地质学 3—245c

鹘 accipiter 鸟类 1—45e
簋 gu 中国礼器 7—332a
固定氮 nitrogen fixation 化学反应 12—205c
固定低音 basso ostinato (music) 音乐 2—269e
固定剧团 stock company 戏剧 16—242e
固定旋律 cantus firmus 音乐 3—415a
固结成岩作用 induration 地质学 8—375c
固溶体 solid solution 化学 15—496c
固态器件 solid-state device 电子器件 15—496d
固特异轮胎及橡胶公司 Goodyear Tire & Rubber Company 美国公司 7—209f
固体 solid 物质状态 15—496a
固体潮 Earth tide 地球物理学 5—499b
固体探测器 solid-state detector 探测器 15—496d
故宫 Gugong 中国皇宫 7—352d
故宫博物院 Palace Museum 中国博物馆 12—555a
故事 skaz 文学 15—414b
顾拜旦 Coubertin, Pierre, baron de 法国教育家 4—540d
顾夫·德姆维尔 Couve de Murville, (Jacques) Maurice 法国外交家 4—553c
顾闳中 Gu Hongzhong 中国画家 7—332b
顾颉刚 Gu Jiegang 中国历史学家 7—332d
顾恺之 Gu Kaizhi 中国画家 7—332f
顾圣 Cushing, Caleb 美国律师 5—75f
顾实汗 Gushi Khan 中国黄教护法王 7—379e
顾特卜·沙希王朝 Quṭb Shāhī DYNASTY 印度王朝 14—98d
顾特卜-乌德-丁·艾伯克 Quṭb-ud-Dīn Aybak 印度穆斯林统治者 14—98e
顾绣 Gu-family embroidery 中国刺绣 7—332b
顾炎武 Gu Yanwu 中国思想家、经学家 7—333a
顾祝同 Gu Zhutong 中国将领 7—333e
雇佣兵队长 condottiere 意大利历史 4—417c
雇佣军 mercenary 职业士兵 11—124e
瓜波雷河 Guaporé River 南美洲河流 7—342b
瓜达 Guarda 葡萄牙城市 7—343a
瓜达尔基维尔河 Guadalquivir River 西班牙河流 7—334c
瓜达尔卡纳尔 Guadalcanal 太平洋岛屿 7—334b
瓜达尔卡纳尔战役 Guadalcanal, Battle of 第二次世界大战史 7—334b
瓜达拉哈拉 Guadalajara 墨西哥城市 7—333f
瓜达拉哈拉 Guadalajara 西班牙省份 7—334a
瓜达拉哈拉 Guadalajara 西班牙城市 7—334a
瓜达拉哈拉大学 Guadalajara, University of 墨西哥大学 7—334b
瓜达卢佩 Guadalupe 墨西哥城市 7—334e
瓜达卢佩 Guadalupe 西班牙城镇 7—334e
瓜达卢佩教堂 Guadalupe, Basilica of 墨西哥宗教中心 7—334e
瓜达卢佩圣母 Guadalupe, Our Lady of 宗教 7—334f
《瓜达卢佩伊达尔戈和约》 Guadalupe Hidalgo, Treaty of 美国-墨西哥历史 7—335a
瓜达卢普峰 Guadalupe Peak 美国山峰 7—335b
瓜达卢普阶 Guadalupian stage 地质学 7—335b
瓜代拉堡 Alcalá de Guadaira 西班牙城镇 1—187a
瓜德尔 Gwādar 巴基斯坦城镇 7—387b
瓜德罗普 Guadeloupe 法国海外省份 7—335b
瓜迪克斯 Guadix 西班牙城镇 7—336a
瓜迪亚纳河 Guadiana River 欧洲河流 7—336a
瓜尔迪 Guardi, Francesco 威尼斯画家 7—343b
瓜尔迪 Guardi, Giovanni Antonio 威尼斯画家 7—343c
瓜尔内里家族 Guarneri FAMILY 意大利小提琴制造家族 7—344b
瓜分波兰 Poland, Partitions of 波兰历史 13—395e
瓜卡纳亚沃湾 Guacanayabo, Gulf of 古巴海湾 7—333f
瓜拉丁加奴 Kuala Terengganu 马来西亚城镇 9—386e
瓜拉江沙 Kuala Kangsar 马来西亚城镇 9—386c
瓜拉立卑 Kuala Lipis 马来西亚城镇 9—386c
瓜拉拿藤 guarana (*Paullinia cupana*) 植物 7—342c
瓜拉尼人 Guaraní 南美印第安人 7—342c
瓜拉尼亚 Guaragna, Salvatore (composer) 美国艺术家 7—342c
瓜拉廷格塔 Guaratinguetá 巴西城市 7—343a
瓜兰达 Guaranda 厄瓜多尔城市 7—342c
瓜里科 Guárico 委内瑞拉州名 7—343e
瓜里内人 Guarine (people) 委内瑞拉印第安人 7—343e
瓜里尼 Guarini, (Giovanni) Battista 意大利诗人 7—343e
瓜里尼 Guarini, Guarino 意大利建筑师、数学家 7—343f
瓜里诺(维罗纳的) Guarino VERONESE 意大利人文主义者 7—344a
瓜廖尔 Gwalior 印度城市 7—387c
瓜鲁柳斯 Guarulhos 巴西城市 7—344b
瓜鲁雅 Guarujá 巴西城市 7—344b
瓜伦多卡德 Goalundo Ghāt 孟加拉国城镇 7—169e
瓜纳巴拉湾 Guanabara Bay 大西洋海湾 7—337e
瓜纳巴纳树 guanabana (tree) 木本植物 7—337e
瓜纳华托 Guanajuato 墨西哥州名 7—338a
瓜纳华托 Guanajuato 墨西哥城市 7—338b
瓜纳卡斯特 Guanacaste 哥斯达黎加省份 7—337f
瓜纳卡斯特山脉 Guanacaste, Cordillera de 哥斯达黎加山脉 7—337f
瓜纳雷 Guanare 委内瑞拉城市 7—338b
瓜纳瓦科阿 Guanabacoa 古巴城市 7—337e
瓜尼瓜尼科山脉 Guaniguanico, Cordillera de 古巴山脉 7—341a
瓜浦 Guap (Caroline Islands) 西太平洋群岛 7—342b
瓜却美·艾浦·梅里尔 Gwalchmai AP MEILYR 威尔士诗人 7—387b
瓜仁太阳鱼 pumpkinseed 鱼类 14—25d
瓜斯 Guas, Juan 西班牙建筑师 7—344c
瓜斯塔拉 Guastalla 意大利城镇 7—344d
瓜托人 Guató 南美印第安人 7—345f
瓜维亚雷 Guaviare 哥伦比亚省份 7—346b
瓜维亚雷河 Guaviare River 哥伦比亚河流 7—346c
瓜维亚雷河畔圣何塞 San José del Guaviare 哥伦比亚城市 15—13d
瓜希拉 Guajira, La 哥伦比亚省份 7—336d
瓜希拉半岛 Guajira Peninsula, La 南美洲半岛 7—336d
瓜希罗人 Goajiro 南美印第安人 7—169e
瓜希沃人和奇里夸人 Guahibo and Chiricoa 南美印第安人 7—336b
瓜雅拉米林 Guajará-Mirim 巴西城市 7—336d
瓜亚基尔 Guayaquil 厄瓜多尔城市 7—346c
瓜亚基尔会晤 Guayaquil Conference 南美洲历史 7—346e
瓜亚马 Guayama 波多黎各城镇 7—346c
瓜亚斯河 Guayas River 厄瓜多尔水系 7—346e
瓜叶菊 cineraria 观赏植物 4—241e
瓜伊拉瀑布 Guaíra Falls 南美洲瀑布 7—336c
瓜伊马斯 Guaymas 墨西哥城市 7—346f
瓜伊马延 Guaymallén (Argentina) 阿根廷城市 7—346f
瓜伊纳沃 Guaynabo 波多黎各城镇 7—347a
瓜伊尼亚 Guainía 哥伦比亚特别区 7—336b
瓜伊尼亚河 Guainía River 南美洲河流 7—336b
刮除法 sgraffito 视觉艺术 15—250c
刮鸣乐器 scraper 乐器 15—155b
寡妇鸟 widowbird 鸟类 18—245b
寡毛类 oligochaete 环节动物 12—374a
寡糖 oligosaccharide 生物化学 12—374b
寡头垄断 oligopoly 经济学 12—374b
寡头政治 oligarchy 政治学 12—373c
挂浆陶器 slipware 泥釉陶器 15—433c
怪面蛛 ogre-faced spider 昆虫 12—347f
怪兽形滴水嘴 gargoyle 建筑学 7—15a
关白 kampaku 日本官职 9—150d

关丹 Kuantan 马来西亚城市 9—386f
关岛 Guam 马里亚纳群岛岛屿 7—336e
关帝 Guandi 中国武神 7—338c
关东平原 Kantō Plain 日本平原 9—169f
关东山脉 Kantō Range 日本山脉 9—169f
关汉卿 Guan Hanqing 中国剧作家 7—337b
关节 joint 解剖学 9—74d
关节腱鞘囊肿 joint ganglion 疾病 9—75c
关节炎 arthritis 疾病 1—527c
关门海底隧道 Kanmon Tunnel 日本海底隧道 9—158f
关切人和卡纳里奥人 Guanche and Canario 加那利群岛民族 7—338b
关税 tariff 国际贸易 16—482a
《关税及贸易总协定》 General Agreement on Tariffs and Trade (GATT) 国际关系 7—55b
关税同盟 customs union 贸易协定 5—78b
关税同盟 Zollverein 德意志关税联盟 18—563a
关塔那摩 Guantánamo 古巴省份 7—341b
关塔那摩 Guantánamo 古巴城市 7—341c
关塔那摩湾 Guantánamo Bay 加勒比海海湾 7—341c
关仝 Guan Tong 中国画家 7—337d
关图 Gwandu 尼日利亚城镇、酋长国名 7—387d
关孝和 Seki Kōwa 日本数学奠基人 15—195a
《关于教皇体制的附件》 Appendix on the Papacy (1537) 基督教信仰声明 1—418b
《关于体育运动的布告》 Sports, Book of 英国历史 16—42d
关羽 Guan Yu 中国武神 7—337e
关原之战 Sekigahara, Battle of 日本历史 15—195a
关中平原 Guanzhong Pingyuan 中国平原 7—341f
观阿弥 Kan'ami 日本演员 9—152c
《观察家报》 Observer, The 英国报纸 12—323d
观景殿的躯干 Belvedere Torso 古希腊雕像 2—372e
观景楼 belvedere 建筑 2—372d
观念学派 Idéologie 法国哲学运动 8—322b
观鸟 bird-watching 娱乐活动 2—489f
观世流 Kanze school 日本能剧 9—170d
观世音 Avalokiteśvara 佛教菩萨 2—83a
《观无量寿经》 Amitāyur-dhyāna-sūtra 佛教经典 1—291d
观音 Guanyin 佛教菩萨 7—341f
观音 Kannon 日本佛教 9—159b
观兆卜 augury 占卜 2—49a
观众厅 auditorium 建筑 2—46a
官话 Mandarin language 中国语言 10—452d
官阶表 Ranks, Table of 俄国陆海军和文职员官阶 14—152a
官僚机构 bureaucracy 社会学 3—258f
官能团 functional group 化学 6—524d
官厅水库 Guanting Reservoir 中国水库 7—341d
官窑 Guan Kiln 中国瓷窑 7—337c
《官员任职法》 Tenure of Office Act 美国历史 16—547b
冠 crown 头饰 5—36a
冠齿兽属 Coryphodon 古生物学 4—528d
冠螺 helmet shell 贝壳动物 8—2e
冠裸鼻鸱 mopoke 鸟类 11—382c
冠冕 coronet 英国头饰 4—518d
冠鼠 crested rat 哺乳动物 5—8d
冠雉 guan 鸟类 7—337b
冠状动脉 coronary artery 解剖学 4—517f
冠状动脉搭桥术 coronary bypass 外科治疗法 4—517f
冠状动脉硬化性心脏病 coronary heart disease 疾病 4—518a
冠状循环 coronary circulation 生理学 4—517f
棺 coffin 装殓尸体的容器 4—330f
棺文 Coffin Texts 古埃及文献 4—331c
馆林 Tatebayashi 日本城市 16—494a
管 guan 中国乐器 7—337a
管 pipe 乐器 13—318a
管胞 tracheid 植物组织 17—185e
管鼻类 tubinares (bird order) 鸟类 17—255f
管巢蛛 sac spider 节肢动物 14—485c
管虫 tube worm 动物 17—255a
管道 conduit 输送管 4—418a
管道 pipeline 装有控制设备的管路 13—318c
管风琴 organ 乐器 12—457c
管海葵 tube anemone 无脊椎动物 17—254f
管口鱼 trumpet fish 鱼类 17—244a
管理机构 regulatory agency 美国政府委员会 14—206b
管理经济学 managerial economics 经济学 10—445d
管区 legation 教皇国行政区划 9—560f
管辖 jurisdiction (law) 法律 9—116d
管弦乐队 orchestra 音乐 12—446f
管弦乐法 orchestration 音乐 12—447b
管与鼓 pipe and tabor 乐器 13—318a
管乐队 band 音乐 2—190e
管乐器 wind instrument 乐器 18—281c
管钟 tubular bells 乐器 17—257a
管仲 Guan Zhong 中国政治家、思想家 7—337e
管子 Guanzi 中国政治家、思想家 7—342a
贯休 Guanxiu 中国画家、诗人 7—341e
冠军花 campion 草本植物 3—383a
惯犯 habitual offender 法律 7—398d
惯性 inertia 物理学 8—379c
惯性制导系统 inertial guidance system 电子系统 8—379d
灌丛火灾 brush fire 林学 3—209a
灌丛婴猴 bush baby 哺乳动物 3—282d
灌顶 abhiseka 佛教仪式 1—23e
灌溉 irrigation 农业 8—453e
灌木 shrub 木本植物 15—341c
灌木草原 Bushveld 非洲南部自然地理区 3—284d
灌木蒿 sagebrush 木本植物 14—498f
灌木忍冬 bush honeysuckle 木本植物 3—282e
灌木罂粟 bush poppy (*Dendromecon rigida*) 木本植物 3—283a
鹳 stork 鸟类 16—255a
鹳形类 ciconiiform 鸟类 4—235c
鹳嘴牻牛儿苗 storksbill 植物 16—255d
罐装 canning 食品贮藏 3—403c
光 light 物理学 10—91f
光斑 facula 天文学 6—210c
光变曲线 light curve 天文学 10—93b
光测弹性 photoelasticity 光学 13—262d
光抽运 optical pumping 物理学 12—436a
光存储器 optical storage 计算机科学 12—436a
光蛋白 photoprotein 生物化学 13—266a
光的感受 photoreception 生物学 13—266a
光电倍增管 photomultiplier tube 电子学 13—265d
光电导性 photoconductivity 物理学 13—262a
光电管 photoelectric cell 电子学 13—262e
光电效应 photoelectric effect 物理学 13—262e
光电阴极 photocathode 光电管部件 13—261d
光度计 photometer 测量装置 13—264f
光度学 photometry 天文学 13—265a
光复会 Guangfuhui 中国革命团体 7—339c
光复主义者 Irredentist 意大利爱国者 8—453e
光管 photocell 物理学 13—261d
光管 phototube 电子学 13—267d
光合作用 photosynthesis 生物学 13—266f
光滑猎狗鲨 smooth hound 鱼类 15—456a
光化 Guanghua (China) 中国城市 7—339c

光化 Kuang-hua (China) 中国城市 9—386f
光化当量定律 photochemical equivalence law 化学 13—261d
光化学反应 photochemical reaction 化学 13—261e
光辉道路派 Shining Path 秘鲁共产党组织 15—317d
《光辉之书》 Sefer ha-zohar 犹太教著作 15—186f
光检 candling 禽卵分级方法 3—398d
光解 photolysis 化学 13—264f
光亮主义 Luminism 美国绘画 10—281e
光量子 light quantum 物理学 10—93c
光卤石 carnallite 矿物 3—465c
光轮 halo 艺术 7—432d
光敏作用 photosensitization 化学 13—266e
《光明之书》 Sefer ha-bahir 犹太教著作 15—186e
《光明之子对黑暗之子之战》 War of the Sons of Light Against the Sons of Darkness, The 犹太教文献 18—102b
光能测定仪 actinometer 化学仪器 1—60b
光年 light-year 天文学 10—93d
光谱 spectrum 物理学 16—15f
光谱化学分析 spectrochemical analysis 化学分析方法 16—14b
光谱学 spectroscopy 物理学 16—14d
光气 phosgene 气体 13—257e
光球 photosphere 天文学 13—266e
光荣革命 Glorious Revolution (England) 英格兰历史 7—161a
光生伏打效应 photovoltaic effect 物理学 13—267e
光瞳 pupil 光学 14—29e
光头党 skinhead 青年亚文化群 15—419e
光效应艺术 Optical art 几何化抽象艺术 12—435c
光行差常数 aberration, constant of 天文学 1—22f
光绪 Guangxu (Chinese emperor) 中国皇帝 7—339f
光学 optics 物理学 12—436c
光学对映体 optical antipode (chemistry) 化学 12—435c
光学干涉仪 optical interferometer 仪器 12—435d
光学晶体学 optical crystallography 晶体学 12—435c
光学录声 optical sound recording 电影 12—436a
光学像 optical image 光学 12—435d
光学原理 optics, principles of 光学 12—436c
光叶南芥 tower mustard 植物 17—180d
光阴派 Dahrīyah 伊斯兰教派 5—109d
光影图像 photogram 照相印刷 13—264b
光玉髓 carnelian 宝石 3—467e
光悦 Kōetsu (Japanese painter) 日本画家 9—332d
光泽 lustre 矿物学 10—293c
光照派 Alumbrado 天主教派别 1—258d
光致电离 photo-ionization 物理学 13—261c
光致发光 photoluminescence 物理学 13—264f
光致复原作用 photorecovery 生物学 13—266d
光致嬗变 phototransmutation 物理学 13—267d
光致蜕变 photodisintegration 物理学 13—262c
光致转化作用 photodynamism 生物学 13—262d
光州 Kwangju 韩国城市 9—411b
光周期现象 photoperiodism 生物学 13—265e
光轴 optical axis 光学 12—435c
光子 photon 亚原子粒子 13—265e
胱氨酸 cystine 氨基酸 5—94f
胱氨酸病 cystinosis 疾病 5—94f
胱氨酸尿症 cystinuria 疾病 5—95a
胱氨酸贮积病 cystine storage disease 疾病 5—94f
广播 broadcasting 传媒 3—171d
广彩 Canton enamel 中国瓷器 3—414b
广场 agora 古希腊聚会场所 1—125f
广岛 Hiroshima 日本县名 8—94e
广岛 Hiroshima 日本城市 8—94e
广东 Guangdong 中国省份 7—338e
广东话 Cantonese language 中国方言 3—414c
广告 advertising 商业 1—90b
广告色画 gouache 绘画技法 7—227d
广西 Guangxi 中国自治区名 7—339c
广西壮族自治区 Chuang Autonomous Region of Kwangsi (China) 中国自治区名 4—218a
广学会 Guangxuehui 中国出版机构 7—340a
广腰亚目 Symphyta 动物学 16—400c
广义 Quang Ngai 越南城镇 14—74a
广翼蝎 giant water scorpion 节肢动物 7—117b
广元 Guangyuan 中国城市 7—340a
《广韵》 Guang yun 中国古代韵书 7—340b
广治 Quang Tri 越南城镇 14—74b
广重 Hiroshige 日本版画家 8—94c
广州 Guangzhou 中国城市 7—340c
广州 Canton 美国伊利诺伊州城市 3—413c
广州 Canton 美国马萨诸塞州城市 3—413d
广州 Canton 美国密西西比州城市 3—413d
广州 Canton 美国俄亥俄州城市 3—413d
广州 Canton 美国南达科他州城市 3—413f
广州平原 Canton Delta (China) 中国平原 3—414a
广州起义 Guangzhou Uprising 中国历史 7—340f
广州十三行 Canton system 中国历史 3—414b
归尔甫派与吉伯林派 Guelf and Ghibelline 意大利政治派别 7—348b
归谬法 reductio ad absurdum 逻辑学 14—195a
归纳 induction 逻辑学 8—374e
归仁 Qui Nhon 越南城市 14—89f
归有光 Gui Youguang 中国散文家 7—352f
归约 reduction 传统逻辑 14—195a
归正会联合会 Reformed League 德国基督教归正宗教会 14—199f
归正宗 Reformed church 基督教派别 14—199d
圭迪 Guidi, Tommaso di Giovanni di Simone (painter) 意大利画家 7—354a
圭迪家族 Guidi FAMILY 意大利家族 7—354a
圭多 Guido DELLE COLONNE 意大利法学家、作家 7—354a
圭多(阿雷佐的) Guido OF AREZZO 意大利音乐家 7—354b
圭多(克雷马的) Guido DA CREMA (antipope) 敌对教皇 7—354a
圭多(锡耶纳的) Guido DA SIENA 意大利画家 7—354a
圭尔夫 Guelph 加拿大城市 7—348e
圭尔奇诺 Guercino, Il 意大利画家 7—349b
圭库鲁诸语言 Guaycuruan languages 南美部落语言 7—346f
圭拉-德梅莱纳 Güira de Melena 古巴城市 7—363a
圭拉杜鹃 guira (*Guira guira*) 鸟类 7—362f
圭鲁 Gweru 津巴布韦城镇 7—387e
圭洛 Gwelo (town, Zimbabwe) 津巴布韦城镇 7—387d
圭米人 Guaymí 中美洲印第安人 7—347a
圭内斯 Güines 古巴城市 7—361e
圭内斯 Gwynedd 威尔士郡名 7—387f
圭尼维尔 Guinevere 英国传说人物 7—361e
圭恰尔迪尼 Guicciardini, Francesco 意大利政治家、历史学家 7—353d
圭斯卡德 Guiscard, Robert 诺曼底伯爵 7—363b
圭斯卡德 Guiscard, Roger 西西里伯爵 7—363b
圭托内(阿雷佐的) Guittone D'AREZZO 意大利诗人 7—364e
圭亚那 Guianas, The 南美洲地区 7—353b
圭亚那 Guyana 南美洲国家 7—385a
圭亚那城 Ciudad Guayana 委内瑞拉城市 4—251f
圭亚那高原 Guiana Highlands 南美洲高原 7—353a
圭亚那洋流 Guiana Current 海洋洋流 7—353a
龟 gui 中国神话 7—352d
龟 turtle 爬行动物 17—293f

龟背竹属 Monstera 植物学 11—351d
龟鳖目 Chelonia (reptilian order) 动物学 4—104e
龟蟾科 Myobatrachidae 动物学 11—525b
龟甲 tortoise beetle 昆虫 17—168c
龟科 Testudinidae 动物学 16—561c
龟尾 Kumi 韩国城市 9—395e
规范 norm 社会学 12—237f
规范理论 gauge theory 物理学 7—32b
规范伦理学 normative ethics 伦理学 12—241a
硅(Si) silicon 化学元素 15—369f
硅肺 silicosis 疾病 15—371a
硅谷 Silicon Valley 美国城市 15—370f
硅化木 petrified wood 木化石 13—209e
硅灰石 wollastonite 矿物 18—310f
硅胶 silica gel 化合物 15—368f
硅孔雀石 chrysocolla 矿物 4—216b
硅镁石 humite 矿物 8—248b
硅硼钙石 datolite 矿物 5—162c
硅铍石 phenakite 矿物 13—223d
硅氢化物 silicon hydride (chemistry) 化合物 15—370f
硅酸 silicic acid 化合物 15—369f
硅酸钠 sodium silicate 化合物 15—484b
硅酸盐矿物 silicate mineral 矿物学 15—369d
硅酮 silicone 化合物 15—370f
硅烷 silane 化合物 15—367c
硅锌矿 willemite 矿物 18—259c
硅氧矿物 silica mineral 矿物学 15—368f
硅藻 diatom 浮游生物 5—290f
硅藻门 Bacillariophyta 植物学 2—118e
硅藻土 diatomaceous earth 岩石 5—291a
硅质海绵 siliceous sponge 海绵 15—369e
硅质壳 silcrete 土壤 15—367e
硅质岩 siliceous rock 岩石 15—369e
鲑 salmon 鱼类 14—548c
鲑莓 salmonberry 草本植物 14—549a
鲑形类 salmoniform 动物学 14—549c
鲑属 Salmo 动物学 14—548c
鲑鳟 salmon trout 鱼类 14—548f
轨道 orbit 天文学 12—445e
轨道地球物理观测台 Orbiting Geophysical Observatory (OGO) 美国人造卫星 12—446c
轨道马车 horsecar 有轨电车的前身 8—182f
轨道速度 orbital velocity 天文学 12—446b
轨道天文台 Orbiting Astronomical Observatory(OAO) 美国科学卫星 12—446b
轨函数 orbital 化学、物理学 12—445f
轨距 gauge 铁路运输 7—32b
鬼 ghost 迷信观念 7—113b
鬼 gui 迷信观念 7—352d
鬼 oni 日本民间传说 12—421c
鬼笔菌 stinkhorn 植物 16—240b
鬼蛾 ghost moth 昆虫 7—113e
鬼蝠 ghost bat 动物 7—113c
鬼故事 ghost story 文学 7—113f
鬼火 jack-o'-lantern 火光 8—503d
鬼节 Day of the Dead 墨西哥节日 5—182d
鬼臼 mayapple (*Podophyllum peltatum*) 草本植物 11—51a
鬼伞属 Coprinus 食用伞菌 4—494c
鬼舞道门 Ghost Dance 美国印第安人崇拜形式 7—113e
鬼蟹 ghost crab 甲壳动物 7—113d
鬼星团 Praesepe 天文学 13—478c
鬼鱼 spookfish 鱼类 16—41a
鬼针草属 Bidens 植物学 2—464a
鬼子母神 Hārītī 佛教神名 7—477e
簋 gui 中国古代食器 7—352e
柜橱 cupboard 家具 5—65b
贵橄榄石 peridot 矿物 13—167f
贵港 Guigang 中国城市 7—354d
贵格会 Quaker 基督教公谊会 14—73b
贵格食品饮料公司 Quaker Foods and Beverages 美国公司 14—73c
贵公子 childe 古代出身贵族或理想成为骑士的青年 4—152c
贵贱婚 morganatic marriage 法律 11—394a
贵金属 noble metal 化学 12—222f
贵绅 priyayi 印度尼西亚社会阶级 13—522d
贵霜王朝 Kushān DYNASTY 亚洲古代王朝 9—405b
贵霜艺术 Kushān art 亚洲古代艺术 9—405c
贵阳 Guiyang 中国城市 7—364e
贵由 Güyük 蒙古皇帝 7—386d
贵州 Guizhou 中国省份 7—365a
贵族 patrician 古罗马特权阶级 13—90d
贵族板球场 Lord's Cricket Ground 体育 10—219f
贵族党和平民党 Optimates and Populares 古罗马政治集团 12—437c
《贵族名录大全》 Complete Peerage, The 英国系谱学 4—399a
贵族私人法院 court baron 中世纪法庭 4—549d
《贵族宪章》(1785) Gentry, Charter to the 俄国历史 7—69a
贵族掌管的裁判庭 court leet 英国法律 4—549e
贵族政治 aristocracy 政治学 1—474d
桂冠诗人 poet laureate 英国诗人称号 13—386a
桂河 Kwai River (Thailand) 泰国河流 9—410e
桂江 Gui Jiang 中国河流 7—352f
桂离宫 Katsura Imperial Villa 日本建筑 9—197b
桂林 Guilin 中国城市 7—356c
桂平 Guiping 中国城市 7—362d
桂太郎 Katsura Tarō, KŌSHAKU (Duke, or Prince) 日本首相 9—197c
桂樱 cherry laurel (*Prunus laurocerasus*, also *Laurocerasus officinalis*) 常绿灌木 4—128c
桂园 Keien (Japanese poet) 日本诗人 9—212f
跪拜礼 supplicatio 古罗马宗教礼节 16—348e
滚木比赛 birling 户外运动 2—492b
滚木球 bowls 球戏 3—96b
滚木球 BOWLS 体育项目 16—67a
滚球 boules 法国式球戏 3—80f
滚石乐队 Rolling Stones 英国音乐小组 14—360e
滚珠轴承 ball bearing 机械 2—173c
滚子轴承 roller bearing 机械 14—360c
棍球 stickball 游戏 16—234e
郭富 Gough, Sir Hugh 英国军人 7—228c
郭公虫 checkered beetle 昆虫 4—99b
郭沫若 Guo Moruo 中国作家、学者 7—375e
郭守敬 Guo Shoujing 中国天文学家、水利学家 7—376a
郭嵩焘 Guo Songtao 中国外交官 7—376b
郭泰祺 Guo Taiqi 中国政府官员 7—376c
郭熙 Guo Xi 中国画家 7—376e
郭象 Guo Xiang 中国哲学家 7—377a
郭忠恕 Guo Zhongshu 中国画家 7—377b
郭子仪 Guo Ziyi 中国将领 7—377c
锅鼓 kettledrum 乐器 9—246e
锅炉 boiler 蒸汽装置 3—6e
锅炉修理工 Boilermaker, The (boxer) 美国拳击运动员 3—7a
锅形锣 kettle gong 乐器 9—246e
锅穴 kettle 地质学 9—246d
聊狐 fennec (species *Fennecus zerda*) 哺乳动物 6—276f
国大党 Congress Party (India) 印度政党 4—429d
国防高级研究计划局 Defense Advanced Research Projects Agency 美国政府机构 5—207d

国防经济学 defense economics 经济学 5—208b
国分寺 Kokubunji 日本城市 9—337c
国歌 national anthem 代表国家的歌曲 12—11a
国会季刊 Congressional Quarterly（CQ） 美国出版集团 4—429e
国会图书馆 Congress, Library of 美国图书馆 4—428e
国会图书馆分类法 Library of Congress Classification 图书馆学 10—78f
国会纵火案 Reichstag fire 德国历史 14—208a
国吉康雄 Kuniyoshi, Yasuo 美国画家 9—397d
国籍 nationality 法律 12—39c
国际奥林匹克委员会 International Olympic Committee 国际体育组织 8—417e
国际芭蕾舞比赛 International Ballet Competitions 舞蹈赛事 8—413a
国际芭蕾舞团 International Ballet 英国舞蹈团体 8—412f
国际笔会 PEN, International 国际作家组织 13—134c
《国际边界水域条约》 International Boundary Waters Treaty 美-英条约 8—413b
国际标准化组织 International Organization for Standardization（ISO） 国际组织 8—418a
国际标准刊号 International Standard Serial Number（ISSN） 国际期刊简明代号 8—419c
国际标准书号 International Standard Book Number（ISBN） 国际书籍出版编号 8—419b
国际冰情巡逻队 International Ice Patrol 国际组织 8—416a
国际捕鲸委员会 International Whaling Commission（IWC） 国际组织 8—420e
国际大学协会 International Association of Universities（IAU） 国际组织 8—412e
国际单位 International Unit（IU） 药理学单位 8—420d
国际单位制 International System of Units 计量 8—419f
国际地球物理年 International Geophysical Year（IGY） 世界性研究活动 8—415e
国际电话电报公司 International Telephone and Telegraph Corporation 美国公司 8—420b
国际电信联盟 International Telecommunication Union（ITU） 联合国机构 8—420a
国际法 international law 国际公法 8—416e
国际法院 International Court of Justice 国际组织 8—414c
国际防核战医师组织 International Physicians for the Prevention of Nuclear War 国际组织 8—418f
国际非洲协会 Association Internationale Africaine 非洲组织 1—564e
国际风格 International Style 建筑风格 8—419c
国际妇女服装工人联合会 International Ladies' Garment Workers' Union（ILGWU） 美国和加拿大工会 8—416c
国际妇女节 International Women's Day（IWD） 国际节日 8—420f
国际妇女俱乐部总联合会 General Federation of Women's Clubs International 美国组织 7—56a
国际妇女理事会 International Council of Women 国际组织 8—414c
国际刚果协会 Association Internationale du Congo 殖民组织 1—564e
《国际歌》 Internationale, L' 歌曲 8—421a
国际工人协会 International Working Men's Association 国际组织 8—420f
国际海事组织 International Maritime Organization（IMO） 联合国机构 8—417c
国际和平公园 International Peace Garden 美国和加拿大公园 8—418e
国际黑天觉悟会 Hare Krishna 美国宗教派别 7—475d
国际汇兑 international exchange 经济学 8—415b
国际货币基金组织 International Monetary Fund（IMF） 联合国机构 8—417d
国际基督徒勉励会 International Society of Christian Endeavor 基督教团体 8—419a
国际计量局 International Bureau of Weights and Measures（BIPM） 国际组织 8—413d
国际金融公司 International Finance Corporation（IFC） 联合国机构 8—415d
国际禁雷运动 International Campaign to Ban Landmines（ICBL） 国际组织 8—413f
国际经济合作银行 International Bank for Economic Cooperation（IBEC） 国际组织 8—413a
国际开发协会 International Development Association（IDA） 联合国机构 8—415a
国际空间站 International Space Station（ISS） 航空航天 8—419a
国际劳工组织 International Labour Organization（ILO） 联合国机构 8—416b
国际乐施会 OXFAM International 英国民间机构 12—519c
国际联盟 Nations, League of 国际合作组织 12—39e
国际贸易 international trade 经济学 8—420c
国际民用航空组织 International Civil Aviation Organization（ICAO） 国际组织 8—414b
国际农业发展基金 International Fund for Agricultural Development（IFAD） 联合国机构 8—415e
国际日界线 international date line 地理学 8—415a
国际商用机器公司 International Business Machines Corporation（IBM） 美国公司 8—413d
国际射箭联合会赛 FITA round 射箭比赛项目 6—337a
国际狮子俱乐部协会 Lions Clubs, International Association of 美国协会 10—128f
国际收割机公司 International Harvester Company 美国公司 8—415f
国际收支 international payment 经济学 8—418b
国际收支 payments, balance of 经济学 13—105e
国际私法 private international law 国际法 13—521e
国际田径总会 International Association of Athletics Federations（IAAF） 国际组织 8—412e
国际跳棋 checkers 游戏 4—99c
国际通信卫星联盟 International Telecommunications Satellite Consortium 国际组织 8—420b
国际通信卫星组织 Intelsat 国际组织 8—406e
国际投资银行 International Investment Bank 国际金融机构 8—416b
国际文献联合会 International Federation for Information and Documentation（FID） 国际组织 8—415c
《国际先驱论坛报》 International Herald Tribune（IHT） 法国报纸 8—416a
国际现代艺术展览会 International Exhibition of Modern Art 艺术展览 8—415c
国际象棋 chess 体育项目 4—131b
国际象棋 CHESS 体育项目 16—78a
国际协定 international agreement 国际法 8—412b
国际刑警组织 Interpol 国际组织 8—422c
国际刑事法庭 International Criminal Court（ICC） 国际组织 8—414f
国际刑事警察组织 International Criminal Police Organization 国际组织 8—415a
国际音标 International Phonetic Alphabet（IPA） 语音学 8—418e
国际语 Interlingua 语言学 8—409e
国际原子能机构 International Atomic Energy Agency（IAEA） 国际组织 8—412f
国际载重线标志 International Load Line（marine engineering） 国际标志 8—417c
国际纸业公司 International Paper Company 美国公司 8—418a

国际紫外探测器 International Ultraviolet Explorer (IUE) 天文观测卫星 8—420d
国际自由工会联合会 International Confederation of Free Trade Unions (ICFTU) 国际组织 8—414b
国际纵队 International Brigades 西班牙历史 8—413b
国际组织 international organization 主权国家间组织 8—417e
国家安全部 Stasi 东德秘密警察 16—199f
国家安全局 National Security Agency (NSA) 美国政府情报机构 12—36d
国家安全委员会 National Security Council (NSC) 美国总统行政部门机构 12—36d
国家保护区 national monument 美国国家保护区 12—17b
《国家报》 País, El 西班牙报纸 12—551a
国家博物馆 Rijksmuseum 荷兰艺术收藏馆 14—299f
国家党 National Party 澳大利亚政党 12—18b
国家地理学会 Institut Géographique National (IGN) 法国机构 8—400d
国家地理学会 National Geographic Society 美国科学团体 12—15b
《国家地理杂志》 National Geographic Magazine 美国杂志 12—15b
国家法院 Conseil d'État 法国法院 4—444c
国家复兴署 National Recovery Administration (NRA) 美国历史机构 12—35f
国家公路 National Road 美国公路 12—36b
国家公园 national park 政府保护地区 12—18b
国家海滨 national seashore 美国政府设立的游览区 12—36c
国家海洋博物馆 National Maritime Museum 英国国家博物馆 12—17b
国家航空和航天局 National Aeronautics and Space Administration (NASA) 美国政府组织 12—10e
国家计划委员会 Gosplan 苏联中央机构 7—221e
国家剧院 National Theatre (United Kingdom) 英国剧院 12—37b
国家恐龙化石保护区 Dinosaur National Monument 美国自然保护区 5—324e
国家陆军博物馆 National Army Museum 英国博物馆 12—11c
《国家评论》 National Review 美国杂志 12—36a
国家森林 national forest 美国林区 12—14f
国家社会主义 National Socialism 德国集权主义运动 12—36e
国家神道 State Shintō 日本宗教 16—201a
国家首都区 National Capital Region 美国纪念地 12—12f
国家碳化氢公司 ENI 意大利公司 6—83f
国家图书馆 National Central Library 中国台湾图书馆 12—13a
国家行动党 National Action Party 墨西哥政党 12—10d
国家邮政博物馆 National Postal Museum 英国伦敦的博物馆 12—35d
国家政治保安局 GPU 苏联警察机构 7—234e
国家政治保安总局 OGPU 苏联机构 12—347e
国教 established church 国家或民族正统宗教或教派 6—137e
国库收入承包制 iltizām 奥斯曼帝国税收制度 8—340a
国立巴伐利亚绘画陈列馆 Bavarian State Picture Galleries 德国博物馆 2—290d
国立大众剧院 Théâtre National Populaire (TNP) 法国剧院 17—18f
国立德累斯顿艺术收藏馆 Staatliche Kunstsammlungen Dresden 德国艺术博物馆 16—174e
国立动物园 National Zoological Park 美国动物园 12—38c
国立根特大学 Ghent, State University of 比利时大学 7—111d
国立故宫博物院 National Palace Museum 中国台湾博物馆 12—18a
国立国会图书馆 National Diet Library 日本图书馆 12—14b
国立考古博物馆 National Archaeological Museum 古希腊博物馆 12—11c
国立莱顿大学 Leiden, State University of 荷兰大学 9—567c
国立历史博物馆 National Museum of History 中国台湾博物馆 12—17e
国立列日大学 Liège, State University of 比利时大学 10—87b
国立罗马博物馆 National Roman Museum 意大利博物馆 12—36c
国立美术馆 National Art Gallery 新西兰美术馆 12—11d
国立美术馆 National Gallery of Art 美国博物馆 12—15a
国立美术馆 National Gallery 英国博物馆 12—14f
国立莫斯科大学 Moscow State University 俄罗斯大学 11—420e
国立乔治·蓬皮杜艺术与文化中心 Centre National d'Art et de Culture Georges Pompidou (Paris) 法国巴黎文化机构 4—5a
国立人类学博物馆 National Museum of Anthropology 墨西哥博物馆 12—17c
国立射电天文台 National Radio Astronomy Observatory 美国天文台 12—35d
国立水族馆 National Aquarium 美国水族馆 12—11b
国立维多利亚美术馆 National Gallery of Victoria 澳大利亚博物馆 12—15b
国立卫生研究院 National Institutes of Health (NIH) 美国政府机构 12—15f
国立乌得勒支大学 Utrecht, State University of 荷兰大学 17—432e
国立现代艺术馆 National Gallery of Modern Art 意大利博物馆 12—15a
国立肖像画陈列馆 National Portrait Gallery 英国博物馆 12—35b
国立音乐学院 Académie Nationale de Musique 法国剧院 1—40d
国立朱里奥别墅博物馆 Villa Giulia, Museo Nazionale di 意大利博物馆 17—562c
国民保健服务计划 National Health Service (NHS) 英国健康保险条例 12—15c
国民党 Kuomintang 中国政党 9—399c
国民钢铁公司 National Steel Corporation 美国公司 12—37a
国民革命党 National Revolutionary Party 墨西哥政党 12—36b
国民公会 National Convention 法国历史 12—13e
国民共和党 National Republican Party 美国历史政党 12—36a
国民军组织 Irgun Zvai Leumi 巴勒斯坦犹太恐怖组织 8—445f
国民生产总值 gross national product (GNP) 经济学 7—320d
国民收款机公司 National Cash Register Company 美国公司 12—13a
国民收入核算 national income accounting 经济学 12—15e
国民威斯敏斯特银行 National Westminster Bank 英国银行控股公司 12—37e
国民议会 National Assembly 法国历史上议会名称 12—11d
国民银行 national bank 美国私人银行 12—12b
国木田独步 Kunikida Doppo 日本作家 9—397c
《国土报》 Ha'aretz 以色列报纸 7—395e
国外安全总署 DGSE 法国情报机构 5—278b
国外传教事业 mission 基督教传教活动 11—278b
国王 king 君主 9—285b
国王病 king's evil 疾病 9—291d
国王法院 aula regis 英国法律 2—56b
国王供奉剧团 King's Men 英国剧团 9—291f
国王谷 Kings, Valley of the 埃及山谷 9—291b
国王领地 King Country 新西兰北岛地区 9—288f
国王篇 Kingis Quair, The 苏格兰文学 9—290d
国学 Kokugaku 日本学术研究运动 9—337c
国营百货公司 GUM 俄罗斯公司 7—370d
国营农场 sovkhoz 苏联农业 15—558b
国有化 nationalization 经济政策 12—39d
国子监 Guozijian 中国古代教育机构 7—377d
虢国墓地 Guo tomb 中国历史古迹 7—376e
果 phala 印度哲学 13—217e
果阿 Goa 印度邦名 7—169a
果斑 fruit spot 植物病害症状 6—505b
果冻 jelly 食品 8—564b
果蝠 fruit bat 哺乳动物 6—505a
果戈理 Gogol, Nikolay (Vasilyevich) 俄国作家 7—183d

果浆软糖 marshmallow 食品 10—541e
果酱树 marmalade tree 木本植物 10—525d
果胶 pectin 碳水化合物 13—118d
果壳游戏 shell game 魔术 15—296c
果鲁穆奇字母 Gurmukhi alphabet 锡克教文字体系 7—378f
果仁糖 praline 食品 13—483f
果实 fruit 植物学 6—504f
果糖 fructose 化合物 6—504c
果糖磷酸激酶 phosphofructokinase 酶 13—259b
果糖尿症 fructosuria 疾病 6—504d
果谐 Sgor-gzhas 中国藏族歌舞 15—250b
果蝇 vinegar fly 昆虫 18—1b
果月十八日政变 Fructidor, Coup of 18 法国历史 6—504c
果汁冰糕 sherbet 食品 15—305f
过程哲学 process philosophy 哲学派别 13—525d
过渡礼仪 passage rite 礼仪活动 13—76a
过渡态理论 transition-state theory 化学 17—197c
过渡元素 transition element 化学 17—197c
过敏反应 anaphylaxis 生理学 1—316b
过山蕨 walking fern 植物 18—75f
过失 negligence 法律 12—66e
过酸 peracid (chemistry) 化学 13—156a
过氧化氢 hydrogen peroxide 化学 8—284a
过氧化氢酶 catalase 生物学 3—519b
过氧化氢酶缺乏症 acatalasia 疾病 1—44a
过氧化物 peroxide 化合物 13—177b
过氧酸 peroxy acid 化合物 13—177c

H

《哈巴谷书》 Habakkuk, The Book of 《圣经》文献 7—396f
哈巴罗夫斯克 Khabarovsk 俄罗斯地区 9—252a
哈巴罗夫斯克 Khabarovsk 俄罗斯城市 9—252b
哈巴内克 Habeneck, François-Antoine 法国音乐家 7—397c
哈巴尼耶湖 Ḥabbānīyah, Hawr al- 伊拉克湖泊 7—397a
哈巴什 Ḥabash, Georges 巴勒斯坦政治家 7—396f
哈包 Hába, Alois 捷克作曲家 7—396d
哈贝尔 Harbel 利比里亚城镇 7—469d
哈贝尔 Hubbell, Carl (Owen) 美国运动员 8—218a
哈比布拉汗 Ḥabībollāh Khān 阿富汗统治者 7—398a
哈伯 Haber, Fritz 德国物理化学家 7—397d
哈伯-博施法 Haber-Bosch process 化学 7—397e
哈伯德 Hubbard, Cal 美国运动员、裁判员 8—217e
哈伯德 Hubbard, Elbert (Green) 美国出版家 8—217f
哈伯兰特 Haberlandt, Gottlieb 奥地利植物学家 7—397f
哈伯勒 Harborough 英格兰区名 7—470a
哈伯特 Hubbert, Marion King 美国地球物理学家 8—218a
哈勃 Hubble, Edwin Powell 美国天文学家 8—218b
哈勃常数 Hubble's constant 天文学 8—218e
哈勃勒 Haberler, Gottfried von 美国经济学家 7—398a
哈勃太空望远镜 Hubble Space Telescope (HST) 天文学 8—218c
哈博罗内 Gaborone 博茨瓦纳首都 6—541b
哈布尘暴 haboob 气象学 7—398e
哈布尔河 Khābūr River 亚洲河流 9—252c
哈布纳菲尼泽 Hafnarfjördhur 冰岛城镇 7—404e
哈布斯堡王朝 Habsburg, House of 欧洲王朝 7—398e
哈布希 Ḥabshī 历史 7—398f
哈茨费尔特 Hatzfeldt, Melchior, Graf von Gleichen und (count of Gleichen and) 德国元帅 7—510d
哈茨霍恩 Hartshorne, Charles 美国哲学家、神学家 7—495f
哈茨山 Harz 德国山脉 7—500e
哈茨山脉 Hartz Mountains 澳大利亚山脉 7—496c
哈茨维尔 Hartsville 美国城市 7—496a
哈达 Hatta, Mohammad 印度尼西亚政治家 7—509e
哈达德 Hadad 闪米特神名 7—400a
哈达德 Haddad, Malek 阿尔及利亚诗人 7—400d
哈达尔化石遗迹 Hadar remains 考古学 7—400c
哈达萨 Hadassah 美国妇女犹太复国主义组织 7—400c
哈代 Hardy, Godfrey Harold 英国数学家 7—474a
哈代 Hardy, Oliver 美国演员 7—474b
哈代 Hardy, Thomas 英国作家 7—474b
哈代贾 Hadejia 尼日利亚城镇、酋长国名 7—401a
哈代拉 Hadera 以色列城市 7—401a
哈代-魏因贝格二氏定律 Hardy-Weinberg law 数学 7—474e
哈当厄高原 Hardanger Plateau 挪威高原 7—471b
哈当厄峡湾 Hardanger Fjord 挪威峡湾 7—471b
哈得来 Hadley, George 英国物理学家、气象学家 7—402b
哈得来环流圈 Hadley cell 气象学 7—402c
哈得斯 Hades 希腊神名 7—401b
哈得孙 Hudson, Henry 英国探险家 8—221a
哈得孙海底峡谷 Hudson Canyon 大西洋海底峡谷 8—221f
哈得孙海峡 Hudson Strait 大西洋海峡 8—222b
哈得孙河 Hudson River 美国河流 8—221f
哈得孙河画派 Hudson River school 美国画派 8—222a
哈得孙湾 Hudson Bay 加拿大内陆海 8—221e
哈得孙湾公司 Hudson's Bay Company 加拿大公司 8—222c
哈得孙造山幕 Hudsonian orogeny 地质学 8—222b
哈德尔 Ḥaḍr, al- (city, ancient Iraq) 伊拉克古城 7—402e
哈德菲尔德 Hadfield, Sir Robert Abbott 英国冶金学家 7—401c
哈德格里姆松 Hallgrímsson, Jónas 冰岛诗人 7—430c
哈德吉·阿古斯·萨利姆 Hadji Agus Salim 印度尼西亚民族主义领袖 7—402a
哈德拉毛 Hadhramaut 也门地名 7—401c
哈德拉毛 Ḥaḍramawt 阿拉伯古王国 7—402e
哈德里安堡 Hadrianople (Turkey) 土耳其城市 7—403b
哈德里亚 Hadria (Italy) 意大利城市 7—402e
哈德利 Hadley, Henry (Kimball) 美国作曲家 7—402b
哈德利 Hadley, John 英国数学家 7—402b
哈德利谷 Hadley Rille 月谷 7—402d
哈德良 Hadrian 罗马皇帝 7—402e
哈德良别墅 Hadrian's Villa 意大利古建筑 7—403b
哈德良长城 Hadrian's Wall 英格兰边墙 7—403b
哈德鲁梅 Hadrumetum 突尼斯古城 7—403d
哈德斯菲尔德 Huddersfield 英格兰城镇 8—220e
哈德威克伯爵(第一) Hardwicke, Philip Yorke, 1st earl of, Viscount Royston 英国大法官 7—473e
哈登 Haddon, Alfred Cort 英国人类学家 7—400e
哈登 Harden, Sir Arthur 英国生物化学家 7—471c
哈登 Hawarden 威尔士城镇 7—523f
哈登贝格 Hardenberg, Friedrich Leopold, Freiherr von (baron of) 德国诗人 7—471d
哈登贝格 Hardenberg, Karl August, Fürst von 普鲁士政治家 7—471d
哈登菲尔德 Haddonfield 美国城镇 7—400f
哈迪 Hadi, Sayyid Shaykh bin Ahmad, al- 马来作家 7—401e
哈迪 Hardee, William J(oseph) 美国军人 7—471c
哈迪 Hardey, Mother Mary Aloysia 美国宗教领袖 7—471f
哈迪 Hardie, J(ames) Keir 英国工人领袖 7—472a
哈迪 Hādī, al- 阿拔斯哈里发 7—401d
哈迪德 Hadid, Zaha 英国建筑师 7—401e
哈迪克努特 Hardecanute 丹麦国王、英格兰国王 7—471b
哈蒂 Harty, Sir (Herbert) Hamilton 英国音乐家 7—496c
哈蒂夫 khedive 埃及称号 9—259c
哈蒂斯堡 Hattiesburg 美国城市 7—510a
哈蒂亚岛 Hātia Island 孟加拉国岛屿 7—509a
哈丁 Harding, Chester 美国画家 7—472c
哈丁 Harding, Saint Stephen 基督教西多会创始人 7—472d

哈丁 Hardin, John Wesley 美国匪徒 7—472c
哈丁顿 Haddington 苏格兰城镇 7—400e
哈丁男爵(第一) Hardinge (of Penshurst), Charles Hardinge, 1st Baron 英国外交家 7—472f
哈丁子爵(第一) Hardinge (of Lahore and Kings Newton), Henry Hardinge, 1st Viscount 英国驻印度总督 7—473a
哈定 Harding, Warren G(amaliel) 美国总统 7—472e
哈顿 Hatton, Sir Christopher 英格兰贵族 7—510b
哈恩 Hahn, Otto 德国化学家 7—408b
哈恩 Jaén 西班牙城市 8—515c
哈恩 Jaén 西班牙省份 8—515c
哈恩-哈恩 Hahn-Hahn, Ida (Marie Luise Gustave), Gräfin von (countess of) 德国作家 7—408e
哈尔 Hall (Austria) 奥地利城市 7—425a
哈尔 Hall, Carl Christian 丹麦政治家 7—425b
哈尔堡 Harburg 德国工业区 7—470d
哈尔滨 Harbin 中国城市 7—469d
哈尔伯施塔特 Halberstadt 德国城市 7—417f
哈尔茨格罗德 Harzgerode 德国城市 7—500e
哈尔-戴雅尔 Har Dayal, Lala 印度革命家 7—468b
哈尔德韦克 Harderwijk 荷兰城市 7—471f
哈尔登 Halden 挪威城镇 7—418e
哈尔登 Harden, Maximilian Felix Ernst 德国记者 7—471d
哈尔迪 Haldi 乌拉尔图神名 7—418e
哈尔迪加特战役 Haldīghāt, Battle of 印度历史 7—418e
哈尔迪曼德 Haldimand, Sir Frederick 英国军人 7—418e
哈尔蒂山 Haltia, Mount 芬兰山峰 7—434c
哈尔蒂亚 haltia 北欧神祇 7—434c
哈尔多尔·拉克斯内斯 Halldór (Gudjonsson Kiljan) Laxness (Icelandic novelist) 冰岛小说家 7—428d
哈尔·哥宾德 Hargobind 锡克教祖师 7—476b
哈尔格萨 Hargeysa 索马里城镇 7—476a
哈尔胡夫 Harkhuf 上埃及南部总督 7—477f
哈尔基季基 Chalcidice 希腊州名 4—30c
哈尔基季基同盟 Chalcidian League 古希腊联盟 4—30c
哈尔基斯 Chalcis 希腊城市、州首府 4—30d
哈尔吉塔 Harghita 罗马尼亚县名 7—476b
哈尔科夫 Kharkiv 乌克兰州名 9—257c
哈尔科夫 Kharkov 乌克兰城市 9—257c
哈尔克岛 Kharg Island 伊朗岛屿 9—256e
哈尔·克里香 Hari Krishen 锡克教祖师 7—476d
哈尔·拉伊 Har Rāī 锡克教祖师 7—468b
哈尔里克山 Karlik Shan 中国山脉 9—182f
哈尔姆斯塔德 Halmstad 瑞典城镇 7—432c
哈尔纳克 Harnack, Adolf (Karl Gustav) von 德国神学家 7—482d
哈尔内斯 Jarnés, Benjamín 西班牙小说家 8—546a
哈尔帕戈斯 Harpagus 米底王国军人 7—484b
哈尔齐斯克 Khartsyzsk 乌克兰城市 9—258a
哈尔施塔特 Hallstatt 考古学 7—431b
哈尔斯 Hals, Frans 荷兰画家 7—433c
哈尔斯德费尔 Harsdörfer, Georg Philipp 德国诗人 7—492b
哈尔塔米 Ḥaltami (ancient country) 伊朗古代王国 7—434c
哈尔特山 Haardt Mountains 德国山脉 7—395d
哈尔托赫 Hartog, Dirck 荷兰探险家 7—495e
哈尔托赫 Hartog, Jan de 美国作家 7—495f
哈尔西恩岛 Halcyon Island (Pacific Ocean) 太平洋岛屿 7—417f
哈尔西(小) Halsey, William F(rederick), Jr. 美国军人 7—433e
哈耳摩尼亚 Harmonia 希腊神话人物 7—480f
哈菲兹 Ḥāfeẓ 波斯诗人 7—404c
哈菲兹 Ḥāfīz, 'Abdal-Ḥalīm 埃及歌手 7—404d
哈菲兹·阿卜鲁 Ḥāfiẓ-i Abrū 波斯历史学家 7—404e
哈菲兹·易卜拉欣 Ḥāfiẓ Ibrāhīm, Muḥammad 埃及诗人 7—404d
哈佛 Harvard, John 新英格兰殖民地开拓者 7—496f
哈佛 Havre 美国城市 7—519f
哈佛大学 Harvard University 美国大学 7—497c
哈佛大学阿诺德植物园 Arnold Arboretum of Harvard University 美国植物园 1—509e
哈佛大学图书馆 Harvard University Library 美国图书馆 7—497d
哈佛光谱分类 Harvard classification system 天文学 7—497a
哈佛-史密森天体物理中心 Harvard-Smithsonian Center for Astrophysics 美国天文研究中心 7—497b
哈夫丹 Halfdan 丹麦国王 7—422b
哈夫尔(小) Havell, Robert, Jr. 美国画家 7—519b
哈夫利切克 Havlicek, John 美国篮球运动员 7—519f
哈夫利切克·博罗夫斯基 Havlíček Borovský, Karel 捷克作家 7—519f
哈夫洛克 Havelock, Sir Henry 英国军人 7—519c
哈夫洛克 Havelock 斯威士兰城镇 7—519c
哈夫斯泰因 Hafstein, Hannes 冰岛政治家、诗人 7—405b
哈夫西德王朝 Ḥafṣid DYNASTY 柏柏尔王朝 7—405b
哈弗尔河 Havel River 德国河流 7—519b
哈弗福德学院 Haverford College 美国学校 7—519c
哈弗福韦斯特 Haverfordwest 威尔士城镇 7—519d
哈弗斯氏系统 haversian system (bone) 解剖学 7—519e
哈弗他拉 Haftarah 犹太教 7—405c
《哈该神谕》 Aggeus, The Prophecy of (Old Testament) 基督教经典 1—121b
《哈该书》 Haggai, The Book of 《圣经·旧约》篇章 7—406e
哈格德 Haggard, Sir H(enry) Rider 英国小说家 7—406f
哈格多恩 Hagedorn, Friedrich von 德国诗人 7—405e
哈格拉 Ha-gra (Jewish scholar) 犹太学者 7—394c
哈格雷夫 Hargrave, Lawrence 澳大利亚航空先驱 7—476c
哈格里夫斯 Hargreaves, James 英国发明家 7—476d
哈根 Hagen 德国城市 7—405f
哈根 Hagen 日耳曼神话人物 7—405f
哈根 Hagen, Johann Georg 奥地利天文学家 7—405f
哈根 Hagen, Walter (Charles) 美国运动员 7—406a
哈根贝克 Hagenbeck, Carl 德国动物商人 7—406a
哈根贝克动物园 Hagenbeck Zoo 德国动物园 7—406b
哈哈勋爵 Haw-Haw, Lord 德国宣传家 7—520a
哈基姆 Ḥākim, al- 法蒂玛王朝统治者 7—415f
哈基姆 Ḥakīm, Tawfīq (Ḥusayn) al- 埃及作家 7—416a
哈吉 ḥājib 马木路克王朝官职 7—415c
哈吉 Haji, Raja 布吉军人、政治家 7—415b
哈吉·艾敏 Hajj Amīn, al- 伊斯兰教法学家 7—415e
哈吉布尔 Hājīpur 印度城镇 7—415d
哈吉·哈里发 Haci Halife 土耳其历史学家、地理学家 7—399b
哈吉·哈里发 Ḥājjī Khalīfa 土耳其历史学家、地理学家 7—415f
哈吉·欧麦尔·伊本·赛义德·塔尔 Hadj Omar ibn Sa'īd Tal, el- (Tukulor leader) 图库洛尔人首领 7—402a
哈吉-塔尔汉 Khadzhi-Tarkhan 俄国城市 9—252e
哈加达 Haggada 犹太教文献 7—406e
哈加达 Haggada 犹太教文献 7—406e
哈加林 Hagalín, Gudmundur G. 冰岛作家 7—405c
哈加纳 Haganah 犹太军事组织 7—405d
哈加尼 Khāqānī 波斯诗人 9—256d
哈杰尔山脉 Ḥajar, al- 阿曼山脉 7—414f
哈金斯 Huggins, Charles B(renton) 美国医学家 8—223f
哈金斯 Huggins, Godfrey (Martin) 津巴布韦总理 8—223f
哈金斯 Huggins, Sir William 英国天文学家 8—223f
哈金斯 Harkins, William Draper 美国化学家 7—478a
哈卡 Jaca 西班牙城市 8—502c
哈卡里 Hakkâri 土耳其城市 7—416b
哈卡斯人 Khakass 民族 9—253d
哈卡西亚 Khakasiya 俄罗斯的共和国 9—253c
哈康 Haakon 挪威国王名 7—394e

哈康(西居尔松) Haakon Sigurdsson 挪威贵族 7—395c
哈康二世·西居尔松 Haakon II Sigurdsson 挪威国王 7—394f
哈康六世·马格努松 Haakon VI Magnusson 挪威国王 7—395b
哈康七世 Haakon VII 挪威国王 7—395b
哈康三世·斯维勒松 Haakon III Sverresson 挪威国王 7—394f
哈康四世·哈康松 Haakon IV Haakonsson 挪威国王 7—394f
哈康五世·马格努松 Haakon V Magnusson 挪威国王 7—395a
哈康一世·阿达尔施泰因福斯特雷 Haakon I Adalsteinsfostre 挪威国王 7—394e
哈考特 Harcourt, Sir William (George Granville Venables Vernon) 英国律师 7—470e
哈科特港 Port Harcourt 尼日利亚港口城镇 13—445c
哈克尔 Hackl, Georg 德国小雪橇运动员 7—399e
哈克卢特 Hakluyt, Richard 英国地理学家 7—416c
哈克曼 Hackman, Gene 美国电影演员 7—399e
哈克尼 Hackney 英国自治市 7—399e
哈克尼马 Hackney 马品种 7—399f
哈克尼斯 Harkness, Anna M. Richardson 美国慈善家 7—478a
哈克尼小型马 Hackney pony 马品种 7—399f
哈克特 Hackett, James Henry 美国演员 7—399d
哈肯萨克 Hackensack 美国城市 7—399c
哈肯施米特 Hackenschmidt, George 英国运动员 7—399d
哈库利宁 Hakulinen, Veikko 芬兰越野滑雪运动员 7—417a
哈拉贝 jarabe 舞蹈 8—545a
哈拉比 Ḥalabī, al- (Muslim scholar) 穆斯林学者 7—417a
哈拉尔 Harald 统治者之名 7—468d
哈拉尔二世 Harald II Eiriksson 挪威国王 7—468e
哈拉尔三世 Harald III Sigurdsson 挪威国王 7—468e
哈拉尔四世 Harald IV 挪威国王 7—468f
哈拉尔五世 Harald V 挪威国王 7—469a
哈拉尔一世 Harald I 丹麦国王 7—468d
哈拉尔一世 Harald I 挪威国王 7—468d
哈拉夫 Khalaf, Ṣalāḥ 巴勒斯坦政治激进主义者 9—253e
哈拉和林 Karakorum 蒙古帝国古都 9—178d
哈拉吉 kharāj 伊斯兰教税收 9—256e
哈拉卡 Halakhah 犹太教律法 7—417b
哈拉雷 Harare 津巴布韦首都 7—469b
哈拉伦 Hallaren, Mary Agnes 美国军官 7—428c
哈拉帕 Harappā 巴基斯坦村庄 7—469a
哈拉帕 Jalapa 墨西哥城市 8—522b
哈拉帕 Jalapa 危地马拉省份 8—522a
哈拉帕 Jalapa 危地马拉城市 8—522a
哈拉帕文明 Harappān civilization 印度历史 7—469b
哈拉斯 Halas, George Stanley 美国运动员 7—417c
哈拉斯和巴奇勒 Halas, John; and Batchelor, Joy 英国电影导演 7—417d
哈拉廷人 Ḥarāṭīn 民族 7—469c
哈拉智 Ḥallāj, al- 伊斯兰神秘主义者 7—427f
哈拉兹泰·德·摩克沙 Haraszthy de Mokcsa, Agoston 美国葡萄栽培先驱 7—469c
哈来姆 harem 伊斯兰习俗 7—475e
哈莱阿卡拉 Haleakala 美国火山 7—420b
哈莱因 Hallein 奥地利城市 7—429c
哈兰 Halland 瑞典省份 7—428c
哈兰 Harran 古罗马城市 7—486a
哈朗语 Halăng language 东南亚语言 7—417c
哈乐根 Harlequin 意大利戏剧角色 7—479b
哈乐根丑角戏 harlequinade 戏剧 7—479f
哈乐根卷心菜蝽 harlequin cabbage bug (*Murgantia histrionica*) 昆虫 7—479e
哈勒 Haller, Albrecht von 瑞士生物学家 7—429d
哈勒 Haller, Bertold 瑞士宗教改革家 7—429f
哈勒比德 Halebīd 印度村庄 7—420c
哈勒尔 Hārer 埃塞俄比亚城市 7—475f
哈勒格瓦迪 Ḥalq al-Wādī 突尼斯城镇 7—433b
哈勒赫 Harlech 威尔士村庄 7—478e
哈勒克 Halleck, Fitz-Greene 美国诗人 7—429a
哈勒克 Halleck, Henry W(ager) 美国军人 7—429b
哈勒默梅尔 Haarlemmermeer 荷兰城市 7—395f
哈勒姆 Haarlem 荷兰城市 7—395e
哈勒姆 Harlem 美国纽约市区名 7—478e
哈勒姆 Hallam, Arthur Henry 英国作家 7—428a
哈勒姆湖 Haarlem Lake 荷兰垦区 7—395f
哈勒姆环球旅行队 Harlem Globetrotters 美国篮球队 7—479a
哈勒姆家族 Hallam Family 美国戏剧世家 7—428b
哈勒姆文艺复兴 Harlem Renaissance 美国文学 7—479a
哈雷 Halle 德国城市 7—428d
哈雷 Halley, Edmond 英国天文学家 7—429f
哈雷夫 Ḥalaf, Tall 考古学 7—417a
哈雷彗星 Halley's Comet 天文学 7—430b
哈雷-维滕贝格马丁·路德大学 Halle-Wittenberg, Martin Luther University of 德国大学 7—428f
哈雷新城 Halle Neustadt 德国城市 7—428f
哈里奥特 Harriot, Thomas 英国数学家 7—487b
哈里发 caliph 穆斯林国家统治者称号 3—351b
哈里发帝国 Caliphate 亚洲古国 3—351b
哈里根 Harrigan, Edward 美国演员 7—486c
哈里河 Harīrūd 中亚河流 7—477d
哈里杰 Khārijah, Al- 埃及城市 9—257a
哈里杰绿洲 Wāḥāt al-Khārijah, Al- 埃及绿洲 18—64c
哈里里 Ḥarīrī, al- 阿拉伯学者 7—477c
哈里里丘 Ḥarīrī, Tall al- (Syria) 叙利亚古城 7—477c
哈里里丘 Tall al-Ḥarīrī (archaeological site, Syria) 叙利亚古城 16—445c
哈里曼 Harriman, Edward Henry 美国金融家 7—486c
哈里曼 Harriman, Florence Jaffray 美国外交官 7—486d
哈里曼 Harriman, W(illiam) Averell 美国政治家 7—486d
哈里齐 Harizi, Judah ben Solomon 希伯来诗人 7—477e
哈里奇 Harwich 英格兰城镇 7—500c
哈里森 Harrison 美国城市 7—489e
哈里森 Harrison, Anna 美国总统夫人 7—489e
哈里森 Harrison, Benjamin 美国总统 7—489e
哈里森 Harrison, Elizabeth 美国教育家 7—490a
哈里森 Harrison, Frederic 英国作家 7—490b
哈里森 Harrison, Francis Burton 美国驻菲律宾总督 7—490a
哈里森 arrison, G(eorge) Donald 美国管风琴设计家、制造家 7—490c
哈里森 Harrison, John 英国钟表制造家 7—490c
哈里森 Harrison, Peter 美国建筑师 7—490d
哈里森 Harrison, Sir Rex (Carey) 英国演员 7—490d
哈里森 Harrison, Ross Granville 美国动物学家 7—490e
哈里森 Harrison, Thomas 英国军人 7—490f
哈里森 Harrison, William Henry 美国总统 7—491a
哈里森 Harrison, Wallace K(irkman) 美国建筑师 7—490f
哈里斯 Harris (Scotland) 苏格兰岛屿 7—487b
哈里斯 Harris, Alexander 英国作家 7—487c
哈里斯 Harris, Sir Arthur Travers, 1st Baronet 英国军人 7—487c
哈里斯 Harris, Benjamin 英国书商、作家 7—487d
哈里斯 Harris, Barbara Clementine 美国神职人员 7—487d
哈里斯 Harris, Frank 美国新闻记者 7—487e
哈里斯 Harris, George Washington 美国作家 7—487e
哈里斯 Harris, Joel Chandler 美国作家 7—487f
哈里斯 Harris, John Wyndham Parkes Lucas Beynon 英国作家 7—488a
哈里斯 Harris, Louis 美国民意测验者、公众舆论分析家 7—488a
哈里斯 Harris, Marvin 美国人类学家 7—488b

哈里斯 Harris, Patricia Roberts 美国公职人员 7—488c
哈里斯 Harris, Renatus 英国乐器制造商 7—488c
哈里斯 Harris, Roy 美国作曲家 7—488d
哈里斯 Harris, Townsend 美国政治家 7—488e
哈里斯 Harris, William Torrey 美国教育家 7—488f
哈里斯 Harris, Zellig S(abbetai) 美国语言学家 7—489a
哈里斯堡 Harrisburg 美国宾夕法尼亚州城市 7—489c
哈里斯堡 Harrisburg 美国伊利诺伊州城市 7—489c
哈里斯昌德拉山 Harischandra Range 印度山脉 7—477d
哈里斯运动 Harris movement 非洲基督教运动 7—489b
哈里亚纳 Haryāna 印度邦名 7—500c
哈立德 Khālid 沙特阿拉伯国王 9—253f
哈立德 Khālid al-Qasrī 伊拉克总督 9—254a
哈立德国王军用城市 King Khālid Military City 沙特阿拉伯城市 9—289b
哈立德·伊本·瓦利德 Khālid ibn al-Walīd 阿拉伯穆斯林将军 9—254b
哈利 Haley, Alex 美国作家 7—421a
哈利 Haley, Bill 美国歌手、歌曲作者 7—421b
哈利 Haley, Margaret Angela 美国教育家 7—421c
哈利 Harley, Robert 英国政治家 7—479f
哈利 Haley, Sir William 英国贵族、编辑家 7—421c
哈利伯顿 Halliburton, Richard 美国作家 7—430c
哈利伯顿 Haliburton, Thomas Chandler 加拿大作家 7—422c
哈利德·齐亚·乌沙克勒吉尔 Halid Ziya Ushakligil (Turkish author) 土耳其作家 7—422f
哈利登山战役 Halidon Hill, Battle of 英国历史 7—423e
哈利法克斯 Halifax 加拿大城市 7—423e
哈利法克斯 Halifax 英格兰城镇 7—424a
哈利法克斯 Halifax 美国城镇 7—424b
哈利法克斯伯爵(第二) Halifax, George Montagu Dunk, 2nd earl of 英国政治家 7—424d
哈利法克斯伯爵(第一) Halifax, Charles Montagu, 1st earl of 英国政治家 7—424c
哈利法克斯伯爵(第一) Halifax, Edward Frederick Lindley Wood, 1st earl of 英国政治家 7—424d
哈利法克斯侯爵、伯爵和子爵 Halifax, MARQUESSES, EARLS, AND VISCOUNTS OF 英国贵族封号 7—424b
哈利法克斯侯爵(第一) Halifax, George Savile, 1st Marquess of 英国政治家 7—424b
哈利卡纳苏斯 Halicarnassus 古希腊城市 7—422e
哈利卡纳苏斯的摩索拉斯陵墓 Halicarnassus, Mausoleum of 考古学 7—422f
哈利昆小丑天牛 harlequin beetle 昆虫 7—479d
哈利勒 Khalīl, al-Ashraf Ṣalāḥ ad-Dīn 埃及苏丹 9—254c
哈利勒 Halil, Patrona 土耳其反叛者 7—424e
哈利勒·伊本·艾哈迈德 Khalīl ibn Aḥmad, al- 阿拉伯语文学家 9—254c
哈利路亚 hallelujah 犹太教礼拜仪式 7—429d
哈利姆帕夏 Halim Paşa, Said 奥斯曼政治家 7—424e
哈利瑟赫尔 Hālisahar 印度城市 7—424f
哈利斯河 Halys (Turkey) 土耳其河流 7—434d
哈利斯科 Jalisco 墨西哥州名 8—522e
哈列维 ha-Levi, Isaac ben Moses 法籍犹太哲学家 7—394c
哈列维 ha-Levi, Judah (Jewish poet) 犹太诗人 7—394d
哈林顿 Harington, Sir John 英国作家 7—477a
哈林顿 Harrington, James 英国哲学家 7—486e
哈林顿伯爵(第一) Harrington, William Stanhope, 1st earl of 英国外交家 7—487a
哈林盖 Haringey 英格兰自治市 7—477a
哈林格 halling 挪威舞蹈 7—430e
哈灵根 Harlingen 美国城市 7—479f
哈灵水道 Haringvliet 荷兰水道 7—477b
哈鲁特和马鲁特 Hārūt and Mārūt 伊斯兰神名 7—496e
哈伦 Harlan 美国城市 7—478b
哈伦 Harlan, John Marshall 美国最高法院大法官 7—478b
哈伦 Harlan, John Marshall 美国最高法院大法官 7—478d
哈伦代尔比奇 Hallandale Beach 美国城市 7—428c
哈伦·赖世德 Hārūn ar-Rashīd 阿拔斯王朝哈里发 7—496d
哈罗 Harrow 英国自治市 7—491d
哈罗德 Harold 统治者之名 7—483c
哈罗德 Harrod, Sir (Henry) Roy (Forbes) 英国经济学家 7—491b
哈罗德二世 Harold II 英格兰国王 7—483c
哈罗德公司 Harrods 英国百货商店 7—491b
哈罗德一世 Harold I 英格兰国王 7—483c
哈罗盖特 Harrogate 英国区名 7—491c
哈罗公学 Harrow School 英国学校 7—491e
哈罗海峡 Haro Strait 太平洋海峡 7—483b
哈罗兹堡 Harrodsburg 美国城市 7—491c
哈洛 Harlow 英格兰城镇 7—480a
哈洛 Harlow, Jean 美国演员 7—480a
哈洛韦尔 Hallowell, A(lfred) Irving 美国人类学家 7—431b
哈马 Ḥamāh 叙利亚城市 7—436a
哈马达尼 Hamadānī, al- 伊朗教义学家 7—435e
哈马丹 Hamadan 伊朗城市 7—435b
哈马丹地毯 Hamadan rug 工艺品 7—435d
哈马德·拉维耶 Ḥammād ar-Rāwiyah 阿拉伯古籍编纂家 7—445a
哈马尔 Hamar 挪威城市 7—437b
哈马尔湖 Ḥammār, Lake 伊拉克沼泽湖 7—445b
哈马尔托洛斯 Hamartolos, George 拜占廷历史学家 7—437c
哈马黑拉 Halmahera 印度尼西亚岛屿 7—432b
哈马马特 Hammāmāt, al- 突尼斯渔港 7—445a
哈马米 Hammāmī, Said 巴勒斯坦民族主义者 7—445b
哈马舍尔德 Hammarskjöld, Dag (Hjalmar Agne Carl) 瑞典政治家 7—445c
哈马舍尔德 Hammarskjöld, (Knut) Hjalmar (Leonard) 瑞典首相 7—445d
哈马斯塔沙尔 Khāmastāshar Māyo, Madīnat 埃及城镇 9—254f
哈麦丹风 harmattan 气象学 7—480c
哈曼 Hamann, Johann Georg 普鲁士宗教思想家 7—437b
哈曼 Harman, Martin Coles 英国理财家 7—480a
哈梅内伊 Khamenei, Ali 伊朗总统 9—255a
哈蒙 Harmon, Tom 美国橄榄球运动员 7—480e
哈蒙德 Hammond 美国城市 7—447b
哈蒙德 Hammond, John Hays 美国工程师 7—447b
哈蒙德 Hammond, Laurens 美国商人 7—447c
哈蒙德 Hammond, Walter Reginald 英国运动员 7—447d
哈蒙德(小) Hammond, John Hays, Jr. 美国发明家 7—447c
哈蒙德·英尼斯 Hammond Innes, Ralph 英国小说家 7—447d
哈蒙兹波特 Hammondsport 美国村庄 7—447e
哈米德-阿巴德 Hamid-Abad (Turkey) 土耳其城市 7—441b
哈米德王朝 Hamid DYNASTY 亚洲历史 7—441a
哈米尔 Hamill, Dorothy Stuart 美国运动员 7—441c
哈米尔卡尔·巴尔卡 Hamilcar Barca 迦太基将军 7—441b
哈米吉多顿 Armageddon 《圣经·新约》 1—496a
哈米特 Hammett, (Samuel) Dashiell 美国作家 7—447a
哈密 Hami 中国城市 7—440f
哈密顿 Hamilton, Sir William Rowan 爱尔兰数学家 7—443d
哈密顿函数 Hamiltonian function 数学 7—444a
哈密尔顿 Hamilton 澳大利亚城市 7—441c
哈密尔顿 Hamilton 百慕大首府 7—441c
哈密尔顿 Hamilton 加拿大城市 7—441c
哈密尔顿 Hamilton 新西兰城市 7—441d
哈密尔顿 Hamilton 苏格兰区名 7—441d
哈密尔顿 Hamilton 苏格兰自治市 7—441e
哈密尔顿 Hamilton 美国城市 7—441e

哈密尔顿河 Hamilton River (Labrador, Canada) 加拿大河流 7—444a
哈莫狄奥斯和阿里斯托吉顿 Harmodius and Aristogiton 希腊传说人物 7—480d
哈莫尼 Harmony 美国城镇 7—482a
哈默 Hammer, Armand 美国企业家 7—445f
哈默 Hamer, Fannie Lou 美国民权活动家 7—440c
哈默尔恩 Hameln 德国城市 7—440c
哈默费斯特 Hammerfest 挪威城镇 7—446b
哈默林 Hamerling, Robert 奥地利诗人 7—440d
哈默施米特 Hammerschmidt, Andreas 波希米亚作曲家 7—446e
哈默斯利岭 Hamersley Range 澳大利亚山岭 7—440d
哈默斯米思和富勒姆 Hammersmith and Fulham 英格兰自治市 7—446f
哈默斯坦 Hammerstein, Oscar, II 美国歌词作家、歌剧演出人 7—446f
哈默诉达根哈特案 Hammer v. Dagenhart 美国法院案例 7—446b
哈姆 Hamm 德国城市 7—444e
哈姆丹王朝 Ḥamdānid DYNASTY 穆斯林阿拉伯王朝 7—439f
哈姆登 Hamden 美国城镇 7—440a
哈姆迪贝伊 Hamdi Bey, Osman 土耳其政治家、艺术家 7—440a
哈姆拉沙漠 Ḥamrā', al-Ḥammādah al- 利比亚沙漠 7—449d
哈姆雷特 Hamlet 传说的丹麦王子 7—444d
哈姆林 Hamlin, Hannibal 美国副总统 7—444e
哈姆林氏猴 Hamlyn's monkey 哺乳动物 7—444e
哈姆斯沃思 Harmsworth, Alfred Charles William 英国报纸发行人 7—482c
哈姆斯沃思 Harmsworth, Harold Sidney 英国报业主 7—482c
哈姆斯沃思杯 Harmsworth Cup 体育竞赛奖 7—482d
哈姆扎 Ḥamzah ibn ʿAlī 德鲁兹教派领袖 7—450a
哈木德王朝 Ḥammūdid DYNASTY 西班牙历史 7—447e
哈拿 Hannah 犹太先知 7—461d
哈纳 Hana 美国村庄 7—454e
哈纳谷 Haná Valley 捷克农业区 7—454e
哈纳莱伊 Hanalei 美国村庄 7—455a
哈乃斐学派 Ḥanafīyah 伊斯兰教派 7—455a
哈奈根 Khānaqīn 伊拉克城镇 9—255f
哈瑙 Hanau 德国城市 7—455b
哈内曼 Hahnemann, (Christian Friedrich) Samuel 德国医生 7—408f
哈尼峰 Harney Peak 美国山峰 7—483a
哈尼夫 hanif 伊斯兰教 7—460c
哈尼什群岛 Ḥanīsh Islands 红海群岛 7—460c
哈尼特 Harnett, William (Michael) 美国画家 7—482f
哈尼语 Hani language 中国语言 7—460b
哈尼族 Hani 中国民族 7—460a
哈奴曼 Hanumān 印度神话 7—466d
哈派群岛 Ha'apai Group 南太平洋岛群 7—395d
哈皮瓦利-古斯贝 Happy Valley-Goose Bay 加拿大城镇 7—467f
哈浬 Hapi 古埃及神名 7—467e
哈珀 Harper 利比里亚城镇 7—484b
哈珀 Harpur, Charles 澳大利亚诗人 7—485e
哈珀 Harper, Ida A. Husted 美国新闻记者 7—484d
哈珀 Harper, Robert Almer 美国植物学家 7—484d
哈珀 Harper, Stephen 加拿大总理 7—484e
哈珀 Harper, William Rainey 美国语言学家、教育家 7—484f
哈珀斯费里 Harpers Ferry 美国城镇 7—485a
哈珀兄弟 Harper BROTHERS 美国出版家 7—484c
《哈珀杂志》 Harper's Magazine 美国期刊 7—485b
哈普 Hap (Egyptian deity) 埃及神名 7—467d
哈普古德 Hapgood, Isabel Florence 美国翻译家、作家 7—467d
哈齐札基斯 Hatzidakis, George N. 希腊语言学家 7—510e
哈其鹿地毯 Hatchlu rug 土库曼斯坦工艺品 7—507d
《哈奇法》 Hatch Act 美国法律 7—507b
哈奇森 Hutcheson, Francis 苏格兰哲学家 8—270a
哈恰图良 Khachaturian, Aram 苏联作曲家 9—252c
哈切特 Hatchett, Charles 英国化学家 7—507c
哈钦森 Hutchinson 美国城市 8—270d
哈钦森 Hutchinson, Alfred 南非作家 8—270e
哈钦森 Hutchinson, Anne 美国宗教家 8—270e
哈钦森 Hutchinson, G(eorge) Evelyn 美国动物学家 8—270f
哈钦森 Hutchinson, Sir Jonathan 英国病理学家 8—271a
哈钦森 Hutchinson, Thomas 英国殖民地总督 8—271a
哈钦斯 Hutchins, Robert M(aynard) 美国教育家 8—270b
哈人 Ha 非洲民族 7—394b
哈萨 Hasa, Al- 沙特阿拉伯地区 7—500f
哈萨艾勒 Hazael 大马士革国王 7—534f
哈萨克地毯 Kazakh rug 工艺品 9—205d
哈萨克高地 Kazakh Uplands 哈萨克斯坦高地 9—205e
哈萨克人 Kazakh 民族 9—205a
哈萨克斯坦 Kazakhstan 中亚国家 9—205e
哈萨克语 Kazakh language 语言 9—205c
哈萨克族 Hazak 中国民族 9—204f
哈萨维尤尔特 Khasavyurt 俄罗斯城市 9—258a
哈塞 Hasse, Ernst 德国民族主义者领袖 7—504d
哈塞 Hasse, Johann Adolph 德国作曲家 7—504d
哈塞尔 Hassel, Odd 挪威物理化学家 7—504e
哈塞尔特 Hasselt, André (Henri Constant) Van 比利时诗人 7—505a
哈塞赫穆伊 Khasekhemwy 埃及国王 9—258b
哈塞克 Ḥasakah, Al- 叙利亚城镇 7—500f
哈桑 Hassan 印度城镇 7—504c
哈桑 Ḥasan 伊斯兰教哲人 7—501a
哈桑 Ḥasan al-Bannā' 埃及政治、宗教领袖 7—501b
哈桑阿卜杜勒 Hasan Abdāl 巴基斯坦城镇 7—501a
哈桑·阿里·沙 Ḥasan ʿAlī Shāh 伊斯兰教派伊玛目 7—501c
哈桑·巴士里 Ḥasan al-Baṣrī, al- 穆斯林宗教领袖 7—501b
哈桑·本萨巴 Ḥasan-e Ṣabbāḥ 伊斯兰教派领袖 7—501c
哈桑二世 Hassan II 摩洛哥国王 7—504b
哈桑卢 Hasanlu 考古学 7—501d
哈桑姆 Hassam, (Frederick) Childe 美国画家 7—504a
哈桑塔尼港 Mina Hassan Tani (Morocco) 摩洛哥港口 11—241e
哈桑一世 Hassan I 摩洛哥苏丹 7—504b
哈桑·伊本·穆罕默德·瓦赞·扎耶提 Ḥasan ibn Muḥammad al-Wazzān al-Zayyātī, al- 阿拉伯旅行家 7—501d
哈桑·伊本·萨比特 Ḥassān ibn Thābit 阿拉伯诗人 7—504c
哈瑟尔特 Hasselt 比利时城市 7—504f
哈瑟维 Hathaway, Anne 莎士比亚之妻 7—508e
哈森克勒费尔 Hasenclever, Walter 德国作家 7—502c
哈森普夫卢格 Hassenpflug, Hans Daniel (Ludwig Friedrich) 德国政治家 7—505a
哈什迭乌 Hasdeu, Bogdan Petriceicu 罗马尼亚语言学家 7—501e
哈斯 Haas, Ernst 奥地利摄影家 7—396a
哈斯 Hass, Robert 美国诗人、翻译家 7—503f
哈斯 Haas, Walter A. 美国商人 7—396b
哈斯代·本·亚伯拉罕·克雷斯卡斯 Ḥasdai ben Abraham Crescas 犹太哲学家 7—501e
哈斯德鲁巴 Hasdrubal 迦太基将领 7—501f
哈斯德鲁巴 Hasdrubal 迦太基将领 7—501f
哈斯德鲁巴 Hasdrubal 迦太基将领 7—502a
哈斯金斯 Haskins, Charles Homer 美国教育家 7—503e
哈斯卡拉运动 Haskala 犹太人社会、文化运动 7—503c
哈斯科沃 Khaskovo 保加利亚城镇 9—258c
哈斯勒 Hassler, Hans Leo 德国作曲家 7—505b
哈斯蒙王朝 Hasmonean DYNASTY 古犹太王朝 7—503f
哈苏纳 Hassuna 美索不达米亚古城 7—505b
哈塔尔 hartal 锡兰大罢工 7—493b

哈塔克 Hartack, Bill 美国赛马骑师 7—493b
哈塔米 Khatami, Muhammad 伊朗总统 9—258d
哈塔伊 Hatay 土耳其省份 7—507b
哈特 Hart 英格兰区名 7—492b
哈特 Harte, Bret 美国作家 7—493c
哈特 Hart, Charles 英国演员 7—492c
哈特 Hart, Charley 美国匪徒 7—492c
哈特 Hart, Lorenz 美国歌词作者 7—492d
哈特 Hart, Marvin 美国拳击运动员 7—492d
哈特 Hart, Moss 美国剧作家 7—492e
哈特 Hart, Nancy 美国革命英雄 7—492e
哈特 Hart, William S. 美国演员 7—493a
哈特尔-埃迪纳 Khatr-Eddine, Mohammed 摩洛哥作家 9—258e
哈特尔浦 Hartlepool 英格兰海港 7—494b
哈特菲尔德 Hatfield 英格兰城镇 7—508b
哈特菲尔德家族和麦科伊家族 Hatfield and McCoy FAMILIES 美国两个敌对家族 7—508c
哈特福德 Hartford 美国城镇 7—493e
哈特福德才子 Hartford wit 美国诗人团体 7—494a
哈特福德会议 Hartford Convention 美国历史 7—494a
哈特河 Heart River 美国河流 7—543b
哈特河 Hutt River 新西兰河流 8—271e
哈特莱本 Hartleben, Otto Erich 德国作家 7—494b
哈特兰 Hartline, Haldan Keffer 美国生理学家 7—495a
哈特勒斯 Hāthras 印度城市 7—508f
哈特勒斯角 Hatteras, Cape 美国海角 7—509f
哈特勒斯深海平原 Hatteras Abyssal Plain 大西洋海底平原 7—509f
哈特立伯 Hartlib, Samuel 英格兰教育家 7—494f
哈特利 Hartley (town, Zimbabwe) 津巴布韦城镇 7—494c
哈特利 Hartley, David 英国医生、哲学家 7—494c
哈特利 Hartley, L(eslie) P(oles) 英国小说家 7—494d
哈特利 Hartley, Marsden 美国画家 7—494e
哈特利(小) Hartley, David, THE YOUNGER 英国政治家、发明家 7—494d
哈特曼 Hartmann, (Carl) Sadakichi 美国艺术评论家 7—495e
哈特曼 Hartmann, (Karl Robert) Eduard von 德国哲学家 7—495b
哈特曼 Hartmann, Nicolai 德国哲学家 7—495d
哈特曼·封·奥厄 Hartmann VON AUE 德国诗人 7—495a
哈特纳普氏病 Hartnup disease 疾病 7—495e
哈特韦尔 Hartwell, Leland H. 美国科学家 7—496b
哈特谢普苏特 Hatshepsut 古埃及女王 7—509b
哈特兄弟 Hart, Heinrich; and Hart, Julius 德国作家 7—492c
哈梯语 Hattic language 赫梯新王国语言 7—509f
哈提比 Khatibi, Abdelkebir 摩洛哥小说家 9—258d
哈提夫 hātif 阿拉伯传说 7—509a
哈廷顿侯爵 Hartington, Spencer Compton Cavendish, marquess of 英国政治家 7—494b
哈廷顿侯爵 Hartington, William Cavendish, marquess of 英国首相 7—494b
哈廷根 Hattingen 德国城市 7—510b
哈通 Hartung, Hans 法国画家 7—496a
哈图萨 Hattusa 古赫梯城市 7—510c
哈图萨 Khattusas 古赫梯城市 9—258f
哈图西利斯 Hattusilis 赫梯国王名 7—510c
哈图西利斯三世 Hattusilis III 赫梯国王 7—510d
哈图西利斯一世 Hattusilis I 赫梯国王 7—510c
哈托尔 Hathor 古埃及女神 7—508e
哈托一世 Hatto I 德意志美因茨大主教 7—510b
哈瓦利吉派 Khārijite 伊斯兰教派别 9—257a
哈瓦那 Havana 古巴首都 7—516d
哈瓦那 La Habana 古巴省份 9—422f
哈瓦什河 Hawash River (Ethiopia) 埃塞俄比亚河流 7—524a
哈瓦苏湖城 Lake Havasu City 美国风景区 9—455d
哈佤人 Hkawa (people) 缅甸、中国民族 8—106e
哈威奇 Harwich 美国城镇 7—500c
哈威亚湖 Hawea Lake 新西兰湖泊 7—524a
哈韦尔 Havel, Václav 捷克作家、总统 7—519a
哈韦尔莫 Haavelmo, Trygve (Magnus) 挪威经济学家 7—396c
哈韦拉 Hawera 新西兰城镇 7—524b
哈维 Harvey, Fred 美国餐馆经营者 7—498b
哈维 Harvey, Gabriel 英国作家 7—498c
哈维 Harvey, Hayward A(ugustus) 美国发明家 7—498c
哈维 Harvey, Sir John Martin 英国演员 7—498d
哈维 Harvey, Neil 澳大利亚板球运动员 7—498e
哈维 Harvey, William 英国医生 7—498e
哈维科 Haavikko, Paavo 芬兰作家 7—396c
哈维兰陨石坑 Haviland Crater 美国陨石坑 7—519e
哈维若夫 Havířov 捷克城镇 7—519e
哈文特 Havant 英格兰自治市 7—518f
哈西 Ḥasi, Tel 巴勒斯坦遗址 7—503a
哈西德派 Hasidean 犹太教派 7—503b
哈西德主义 Ḥasidism 犹太教派 7—503b
哈西德主义 Ḥasidism 犹太宗教运动 7—503b
哈西鲁迈勒 Hassi R'Mel 阿尔及利亚城镇 7—505b
哈西迈斯欧德 Hassi Messaoud 阿尔及利亚油田 7—505a
哈希姆派 Hāshimīyah 伊斯兰教派 7—502e
哈希姆系 Hāshimite 穆罕默德族裔 7—502d
哈谢克 Hašek, Jaroslav 捷克作家 7—502c
哈亚人 Haya 东非民族 7—529c
哈扬·武鲁克 Hayam Wuruk 爪哇统治者 7—529f
哈耶克 Hayek, Friedrich von 英国经济学家 7—532b
哈伊·本·设里拉 Hai ben Sherira 犹太教塔木德学者 7—409a
哈伊勒 Ḥā'il 沙特阿拉伯城镇 7—410f
哈伊马角 Ra's al-Khaymah 阿联酋成员国 14—156c
哈泽德 Hazard 美国城市 7—535a
哈泽斯莱乌 Haderslev 丹麦城市 7—401a
哈泽泰 Hazeltine, Alan 美国工程师、物理学家 7—535c
哈增布希 Hartzenbusch, Juan Eugenio 西班牙戏剧家 7—496c
哈扎尔汗 Khaz'al Khan 伊朗部族领袖 9—259a
哈扎尔人 Khazar 民族 9—259a
哈扎拉人 Ḥazāra 阿富汗蒙古血统民族 7—535a
哈兹里特 Hazlitt, William 英国作家 7—535d
铪(Hf) hafnium 化学元素 7—405a
哈巴狗 pug 狗品种 14—18c
哈达 kha-btags 中国藏族、蒙古族礼物 9—252a
孩体瑾 hei tiki 毛利人饰物 7—563f
海 Hay, Francis 苏格兰贵族 7—528d
海 Hay, Sir Gilbert 苏格兰翻译家 7—528d
海 Hay, Lucy 英国历史人物 7—528f
海 Hay, Oliver Perry 美国古生物学家 7—528f
海岸 coast 地理学 4—312a
海岸角 Cape Coast 加纳城镇 3—419f
海岸阶地 marine terrace 地质学 10—514c
海岸警卫队 coast guard 武装力量 4—312b
海岸警卫队妇女预备队 Coast Guard Women's Reserve 美国军队组织 4—312c
海岸炮 coastal artillery 武器 4—312e
海岸山脉 Coast Mountains 北美山脉 4—312c
海岸山脉 Coast Ranges (North America) 北美山脉 4—312d
海螯虾 sea crayfish 甲壳动物 15—164c
海百合 sea lily 无脊椎动物 15—166a
海百合类 crinoid 无脊椎动物 5—17e
海豹 seal 哺乳动物 15—170f
海豹皮船 kayak 赛艇 9—203f
海北友松 Kaihō Yūshō 日本画家 9—135a

海贝尔 Heiberg, Johan Ludvig 丹麦作家 7—564b
海贝尔 Heiberg, Johanne Luise 丹麦演员 7—564b
海贝尔 Heiberg, Peter Andreas 丹麦作家 7—564c
海贝格 Heiberg, Gunnar (Edvard Rode) 挪威剧作家 7—564a
海贝壳 seashell 软体动物 15—173a
海鞭 sea whip 珊瑚 15—169b
海滨马格达莱纳 Magdalena del Mar 秘鲁城市 10—379b
海滨山黧豆 beach pea (*Lathyrus maritimus*, sometimes *L. japonicus*) 植物 2—301e
海波因特 High Point 美国城市 8—75a
海布 Cheb 捷克城镇 4—97f
海布兰迪 Gerbrandy, Pieter Sjoerds 荷兰首相 7—86d
海部俊树 Kaifu Toshiki 日本首相 9—134f
海槽 oceanic trough 地质学 12—329b
海城 Haicheng 中国城市 7—409c
海醋栗 sea gooseberry 无脊椎动物 15—164f
海达 Heda, Willem Claesz(oon) 荷兰画家 7—554a
海达尔 Ḥaydar, Shaykh 波斯萨非王朝开创者 7—530e
海达人 Haida 印第安人 7—409e
海带属 Laminaria 植物学 9—466a
海胆 echinoid 棘皮动物 5—522e
海胆 urchin 棘皮动物 17—413e
海胆掌 sea-urchin cactus 植物 15—168f
海盗 buccaneer 美洲海盗 3—218b
"海盗"号探测器 Viking 美国航天器 17—560b
海盗行为 piracy 暴力行动 13—320b
海盗鱼 poacher 鱼类 13—382b
海盗蛛 pirate spider 蛛科动物 13—321c
海得 hide 英国历史 8—71e
海得拉巴 Hyderābād 巴基斯坦城市 8—278f
海得拉巴 Hyderābād 印度城市 8—278d
海得拉巴 Hyderābād 印度土邦 8—278d
海德 Head, Edith 美国服装设计师 7—538a
海德 Hyde, Charles Cheney 美国法学家 8—277d
海德 Hyde, Douglas 爱尔兰总统 8—277d
海德 Hyde, Edward 英国政治家 8—277e
海德 Hyde, Henry Baldwin 美国商人 8—277e
海德 Hyde, Henry 英国政治家 8—277e
海德 Hyde, Lawrence 英国政治家 8—277f
海德 Hyde, Sir Nicholas 英格兰首席法官 8—277f
海德堡 Heidelberg 德国城市 7—564f
海德堡大学 Heidelberg, University of 德国大学 7—565a
《海德堡教理问答》 Heidelberg Catechism 基督教文献 7—565a
海德堡浪漫派 Heidelberg Romantics 德国诗派 7—565c
海德堡人 Homo heidelbergensis 人类学 8—147d
海德堡下颌骨 Heidelberg jaw 人类学 7—565b
海德贝里 Hedberg, Olle 瑞典小说家 7—554c
海德尔·阿里 Hyder Ali 印度统治者 8—278c
海德格尔 Heidegger, Martin 德国哲学家 7—564c
海德公园 Hyde Park 伦敦公园 8—278a
海德里希 Heydrich, Reinhard (Tristan Eugen) 德国纳粹官员 8—66c
海德马克 Hedmark 挪威郡名 7—555a
海德门 Hyndman, Henry Mayers 英国马克思主义者 8—290c
海德帕克 Hyde Park 美国城镇 8—278d
海德维格 Hedvig (queen of Poland) 波兰王后 7—555b
海登 Haydon, Benjamin Robert 英国画家、作家 7—532a
海登 Heiden, Eric (Arthur) 美国速滑运动员 7—565c
海登 Hayden, Ferdinand Vandiveer 美国地质学家 7—530e
海登 Heyden, Jan van der 荷兰画家 8—66c
海登 Hayden, Melissa 加拿大芭蕾舞演员 7—530f
海登 Hayden, Sophia 美国建筑师 7—531a
海登海姆 Heidenheim 德国城市 7—565c
海登斯塔姆 Heidenstam, (Carl Gustaf) Verner von 瑞典作家 7—565c
海底电缆 undersea cable 通信 17—340a
海底断裂带 submarine fracture zone 地质学 16—299f
海底高原 oceanic plateau 地质学 12—328f
海底滑塌 submarine slump 地质学 16—300a
海底扩张假说 seafloor spreading hypothesis 地质学 15—169e
海底扇 submarine fan 地质学 16—299e
海底深沟 submarine gap 地质学 16—300a
海底生物 benthos 生态学 2—392c
海底峡谷 submarine canyon 地质学 16—299b
海地 Haiti 西印度群岛国家 7—413e
海地混合语 Haitian Creole 加勒比海岛语言 7—414e
海地角 Cap-Haïtien 海地共和国城市 3—418d
海淀 Haidian 中国北京市辖区 7—409e
海定 Hedin, Sven Anders 瑞典探险家 7—554f
海冬青 sea holly (algae) 藻类 15—165a
海都 Kaidu 蒙古可汗 9—134c
海顿 Hayton 小亚美尼亚国王 7—534c
海顿 Haydn, Joseph 奥地利作曲家 7—531b
海顿 Haydn, Michael 奥地利作曲家 7—532a
海顿-罗比 Huyton-with-Roby 英格兰地名 8—275d
海蛾鱼 dragonfish 鱼类 5—411d
海厄利亚 Hialeah 美国城市 8—68c
海厄曼斯 Heijermans, Herman 荷兰作家 7—566a
海厄特 Hyatt, Alpheus 美国动物学家 8—276f
海厄特 Hyatt, Anna Vaughn 美国雕塑家 8—277a
海厄特 Hyatt, John Wesley 美国发明家 8—277a
海恩 Gheyn, Matthias van den 佛兰德斯音乐家 7—112c
海恩 Heyn, Piet 荷兰海军上将 8—66f
海恩 Hayne, Paul Hamilton 美国诗人 7—533d
海恩 Hayne, Robert Young 美国政治家 7—533e
海恩德伯恩 Hyndburn 英格兰自治市 8—290c
海恩尼斯 Hyannis 美国村庄 8—276f
海恩斯 Haines 美国城市 7—412d
海恩斯 Haynes, Elwood 美国制造商 7—533f
海恩斯 Haines, Jackson 美国演员 7—412d
海尔 Geel 荷兰首相 7—43c
海尔 Hel 北欧神名 7—571c
海尔 Geer, Dirk Jan de 比利时城市 7—43d
海尔 Hale, George Ellery 美国天文学家 7—419a
海尔 Geyl, Pieter 荷兰历史学家 7—105d
海尔布尔 Khairpur 巴基斯坦城市 9—253a
海尔布隆 Heilbronn 德国城市 7—566d
海尔采格 Herczeg, Ferenc 匈牙利作家 8—36e
海尔达尔 Heyerdahl, Thor 挪威人种学家、探险家 8—66e
海尔德 Gelder, Aert de 荷兰画家 7—47d
海尔德兰 Gelderland 荷兰省份 7—47d
海尔河组 Hell Creek Formation 地质学 7—575d
海尔季 Kharj, Al- 沙特阿拉伯绿洲 9—257b
海尔卡努斯 Hyrcanus 犹太国王 8—297b
海尔卡努斯二世 John Hyrcanus II 犹太祭司长 9—60b
海尔卡努斯一世 John Hyrcanus I 犹太祭司长 9—60b
海尔伦 Heerlen 荷兰城市 7—556c
海尔曼 Hellman, Lillian 美国剧作家 8—1e
海尔蒙德 Helmond 荷兰城市 8—4d
海尔奇茨基 Chelčický, Peter 捷克著作家 4—103f
海尔·塞拉西 Haile Selassie 埃塞俄比亚皇帝 7—411b
海尔斯特 Helst, Bartholomeus van der 荷兰画家 8—6f
海尔斯特伦 Hellström, (Erik) Gustaf 瑞典作家 8—2a
海尔塔 Hierta, Hans 瑞典政治家 8—73c
海尔天文台 Hale Observatories 天文学 7—420a
海尔望远镜 Hale Telescope 天文学 7—420a

海尔维第共和国 Helvetic Republic 瑞士历史 8—7b
海尔维乌斯·辛纳 Helvius Cinna, Gaius 罗马诗人 8—7e
海尔辛堡 Hälsingborg 瑞典港市 7—433f
海尔辛兰 Hälsingland 瑞典省份 7—434a
海尔辛兰如尼文字 Hälsinge Runes 北欧古文字 7—434a
海耳蒙特 Helmont, Jan Baptista van 比利时科学家 8—4d
海法 Haifa 以色列港市 7—409f
海番鸭 scoter 鸟类 15—150a
海防 Haiphong 越南城市 7—412f
海鲂 dory 鱼类 5—392d
海费兹 Heifetz, Jascha 美国音乐家 7—565d
海夫拉 Khafre 埃及国王 9—252e
海福德 Hayford, John Fillmore 美国工程师 7—533b
海甘蓝 sea kale (*Crambe maritima*) 植物学 15—165d
海鸽 guillemot 鸟类 7—357b
海格斯特伦 Hägerström, Axel (Anders Theodor) 瑞典哲学家 7—406c
海狗 fur seal 哺乳动物 6—528e
海狗群岛 Fur Seal Islands (Alaska, U.S.) 美国群岛 6—529b
海龟 sea turtle 爬行动物 15—168c
"海龟"号 Turtle 美国潜艇 17—294b
海果 carpoid 棘皮动物 3—478d
海河 Hai He 中国河流 7—409a
海胡桃 sea walnut (*Mnemiopsis*) 浮游动物 15—169a
海蝴蝶 sea butterfly (snail) 软体动物 15—164b
海华 bloom, marine (biology) 生物学 2—543c
海华沙 Hiawatha 北美印第安人酋长 8—68d
海华丝 Hayworth, Rita 美国演员 7—534e
海鲫 surfperch 鱼类 16—353a
海军 navy 军种 12—52d
海军都统 nauarch 古希腊海军舰队司令 12—46f
海军军官学校 naval academy 军事学校 12—50a
海军陆战队 marine 军事 10—512f
海军上将 admiral 海军军衔 1—82b
海军上将杯 Admiral's Cup 英国帆船赛 1—82d
海军上将地毯 Admiral carpet 西班牙工艺品 1—82d
海军上将供奉剧团 Admiral's Men 英国剧团 1—82d
海军上将蛱蝶 admiral 昆虫 1—82c
海军委员会 Admiralty 英国政府机构 1—82e
海卡尔 Heikal, Muhammad Hassanein 埃及新闻记者、报纸主编 7—566b
海克尔 Haeckel, Ernst 德国动物学家 7—403d
海克尔 Hecker, Isaac Thomas 美国天主教司铎 7—553b
海克拉 Hekla 冰岛火山 7—571b
海克特 Hec, Anthony 美国诗人 7—552a
海克托罗维奇 Hektorović, Petar 南斯拉夫诗人 7—571b
海口 Haikou 中国城市 7—410c
海葵 sea anemone 无脊椎动物 15—163c
海葵鱼 anemone fish 鱼类 1—338e
海蛞蝓 sea slug (snail) 腹足动物 15—167e
海拉布伦动物园 Hellabrunn Zoo 德国动物园 7—575d
海拉尔 Hailar 中国区名 7—411a
海喇叭琴 trumpet marine 乐器 17—244b
海腊斯 Hellas 火星盆地 7—575f
海兰德-汉森 Helland-Hansen, Bjørn 挪威海洋学家 7—575d
海兰帕克 Highland Park 美国密歇根州城市 8—77a
海兰帕克 Highland Park 美国伊利诺伊州城市 8—77a
海蓝宝石 aquamarine 宝石 1—426c
海勒 Heller, Joseph 美国作家 8—1c
海勒 Heller, Yom Ṭov Lipmann ben Nathan ha-Levi 犹太拉比、学者 8—1d
海雷凯地毯 Hereke carpet 土耳其工艺品 8—38d
海蕾 blastoid 古生物学 2—531a
海里弗 Hay River 加拿大城镇 7—529b
海里耶达伦 Härjedalen 瑞典省份 7—477f
海利 Hayley, William 英国诗人 7—533b
海鲢 ladyfish (*Elops saurus*) 鱼类 9—443d
海鲢类 elopiform 鱼类 6—51d
海林克斯 Geulincx, Arnold 逻辑学家 7—105b
海鳞虫 scale worm 环节动物 15—100c
海龙 halon 化合物 7—433a
海龙 pipefish 鱼类 13—318b
海鲈 sea bass 鱼类 15—163e
海绿 pimpernel 草本植物 13—305f
海绿石 glauconite 矿物 7—155d
海伦 Helen 希腊传说人物 7—572a
海伦芬 Heerenveen 荷兰城市 7—556b
海伦娜 Helena 美国阿肯色州城市 7—572b
海伦娜 Helena 美国蒙大拿州城市 7—572b
海伦娜,圣 Helena, SAINT 罗马帝国皇后 7—572c
海伦斯 Hellens, Franz 比利时作家 8—1b
海洛夫斯基 Heyrovský, Jaroslav 捷克化学家 8—67a
海洛和利安得 Hero and Leander 希腊传说人物 8—45b
海洛因 heroin 麻醉药、毒品 8—47e
海马 sea horse 鱼类 15—165a
海迈莱伊宁 Hämäläinen, Marja-Liisa 芬兰北欧两项滑雪运动员 7—436b
海曼 Hyman, Libbie Henrietta 美国动物学家 8—288f
海曼岛 Hayman Island 澳大利亚岛屿 7—533c
海曼斯 Heymans, Corneille 比利时生理学家 8—66f
海曼斯 Hymans, Paul 比利时政治家 8—288f
海猫 meerkat 哺乳动物 11—80a
海猫 mierkat 哺乳动物 11—204c
海矛 lancelet (marine animal) 海生动物 9—473a
海梅 Häme 芬兰省份 7—440a
海门林纳 Hämeenlinna 芬兰城市 7—440b
海米萨特 Khemisset 摩洛哥城镇 9—259d
海米斯穆谢特 Khamīs Mushayṭ 沙特阿拉伯城市 9—255a
海绵 sponge 多孔动物 16—39f
海绵橡胶 sponge rubber 化工 16—40d
海明威 Hemingway, Ernest (Miller) 美国作家 8—9d
海莫尔 Highmore, Joseph 英国画家 8—77b
海母鸡 sea hen 鱼类 15—165a
海姆 Heim, Albert 瑞士地质学家 7—567b
海姆 Heem, Jan Davidsz(oon) de 荷兰画家 7—555e
海姆达尔 Heimdall 北欧神祇 7—567b
海姆达尼 Hamdānī, al- 阿拉伯作家 7—439e
海姆利奇氏法 Heimlich maneuver 医学 7—567c
海姆斯凯尔克 Heemskerck, Jacob van 荷兰探险家 7—555f
海姆斯凯尔克 Heemskerck, Maerten van 荷兰画家 7—556a
海姆斯泰德 Heemstede 荷兰城市 7—556b
海南 Hainan 中国省份 7—411e
海南 Kainan 日本城市 9—135e
海南岛 Hainan Island 中国岛屿 7—412b
海南芥 sea rocket 植物学 15—167d
海难救助 salvage 海商法 14—557d
海瑙 Haynau, Julius (Jacob), Freiherr von 奥地利军人 7—533d
海讷桑德 Härnösand 瑞典港市 7—483b
海尼夫拉 Khenifra 摩洛哥城镇 9—259d
海尼施 Hainisch, Michael (Arthur Josef Jakob) 奥地利总统 7—412e
海涅 Heine, Heinrich 德国诗人 7—567d
海涅曼 Heinemann, Barbara 美国宗教领袖 7—568b
海涅曼 Heinemann, William 英国出版商 7—568b
海宁 Haining 中国城市 7—412e
海宁 Herning 中国城市 8—44e

海牛 sea cow (*Hydrodamalis gigas*) 哺乳动物 15—164c
海牛类 sirenian 哺乳动物 15—402b
海鸥 gull 鸟类 7—369a
海泡石 sepiolite 矿物 15—218c
海皮克 High Peak 英格兰区名 8—74f
海平面 sea level 海洋科学 15—165f
海蹼鸡 sea coot (duck) 鸟类 15—164c
海鞘 sea squirt 无脊椎动物 15—168a
海雀 auk 鸟类 2—55f
海雀科 Alcidae 动物学 1—189d
海群岛 Sea Islands 美国岛屿 15—165c
海瑞 Hai Rui 中国明朝官员 7—409b
海塞 Hesse, Hermann 德国作家 8—59c
海鳃 sea pen 无脊椎动物 15—166e
海三色堇 sea pansy 无脊椎动物 15—166e
海桑 Alhazen 阿拉伯数学家、物理学家 1—226b
海瑟姆 Huysum, Jan van 荷兰画家 8—275c
海森伯 Heisenberg, Werner (Karl) 德国物理学家、哲学家 7—569d
海森伯不确定性原理 Heisenberg uncertainty principle (physics) 物理学 7—570d
海山 Hai San 马来亚华人帮会 7—409c
海山 seamount 地质学 15—171b
海扇 sea fan 无脊椎动物 15—164e
海鳝 moray 鱼类 11—385d
海商法 maritime law 法律 10—517f
海上保险 marine insurance 保险 10—513d
海上避撞规程 road at sea, rules of the 海上交通国际协议 14—324a
海上测速仪 maritime log (measurement) 航海仪器 10—518c
海上力量 sea power 军事 15—167b
海上民族 Sea People 古代民族 15—167b
海上搜查 visit and search 军事行动 18—19c
海蛇 sea serpent 神话动物 15—167d
海蛇 sea snake 动物 15—167f
海参 sea cucumber 棘皮动物 15—164c
海参鱼 cucumber fish 鱼类 5—50f
"海神"导弹 Poseidon missile 美国导弹 13—457f
"海神"号 Triton 美国潜艇 17—227f
海生蠕虫 marine worm 蠕虫 10—514c
海狮 sea lion 哺乳动物 15—166b
海蚀洞 sea cave 地质学 15—164b
海蚀阶地 terrace, marine 地质学 16—554d
海市蜃楼 mirage 虚幻景象 11—271c
海鼠 sea mouse 环节动物 15—166c
海水 seawater 水 15—174b
海水深度温度自动记录仪 bathythermograph 仪器 2—279a
海斯 Hays 美国城市 7—533f
海斯 Hythe 英格兰城镇 8—298a
海斯 Hays, Arthur Garfield 美国律师 7—534a
海斯 Haise, Fred W(allace), Jr. 美国航天员 7—413d
海斯 Hayes, Helen 美国演员 7—532c
海斯 Hayes, Isaac Israel 美国医生、探险家 7—532d
海斯 Hayes, Patrick Joseph 纽约大主教 7—532e
海斯 Hayes, Rutherford B. 美国总统 7—532e
海斯 Hayes, Woody 美国体育教练 7—533a
海斯 Hays, Will H. 美国政治家 7—534a
海斯河 Hayes River 加拿大河流 7—533b
海斯曼 Heisman, John (William) 美国体育教练 7—570e
海斯曼杯 Heisman Trophy 美国大学橄榄球赛奖杯 7—570e
海损 average 海事法 2—85a
海笋 piddock 软体动物 13—292f
海索草 hyssop (*Hyssopus officinalis*) 草本植物 8—297b
海塔纳 Khatâ'na (Egypt) 埃及城市 9—258d
海苔 nori (algae) 海藻 12—237c
海滩 beach 地理学 2—300e
海滩男孩 Beach Boys, the 美国摇滚乐队 2—301d
海特 Heig, Dorothy 美国民权和妇女权利活动家 7—565e
海特 Hayter, Stanley William 英国画家 7—534b
《海特报告》 Hite Report, The 女权主义文献 8—102b
海特亨 Geertgen TOT SINT JANS 荷兰画家 7—43d
海廷克 Haitink, Bernard 荷兰音乐指挥家 7—414f
海廷战役 Ḥattīn, Battle of 中东历史 7—510a
海桐花科 Pittosporaceae 植物学 13—331b
海图 navigation chart 航海地图 12—52a
海兔 sea hare 软体动物 15—165a
海豚 dolphin 哺乳动物 5—368a
海托华 Hightower, Rosella 美国舞蹈家 8—77b
海外测量理事会 Overseas Surveys, Directorate of 英国机构 12—512a
海外退伍军人协会 Veterans of Foreign Wars (VFW) 美国组织 17—532a
海外犹太人 Diaspora 犹太民族 5—290a
海湾 bay 地理学 2—291c
海湾 gulf 地理学 7—367e
海湾桥 Bay Bridge 旧金山跨海桥 2—291f
《海湾圣诗》 Bay Psalm Book 北美殖民地出版物 2—292e
海湾石油公司 Gulf Oil Corporation 美国公司 7—368b
海湾沿岸航道 Gulf Intracoastal Waterway 美国水道 7—367f
海湾与西方工业公司 Gulf + Western Inc. 美国公司 7—367f
海湾战争综合征 Gulf War syndrome 疾病 7—368e
海王星 Neptune 天文学 12—84a
海威科姆 High Wycombe 英格兰城镇 8—75e
海韦尔·艾布·欧文·格威内德 Hywel AB OWAIN GWYNEDD 威尔士王子、诗人 8—298e
海卫二 Nereid 天文学 12—84f
海卫一 Triton 天文学 17—227e
海味 sea food 可食水生动物 15—170b
海沃德 Hayward 美国城市 7—534c
海沃德 Hayward 美国城市 7—534d
海沃德 Heyward, (Edwin) DuBose 美国小说家 8—67c
海沃西河 Hiwassee River 美国河流 8—106d
海乌姆 Chełm 原波兰省份 4—104a
海乌姆 Chełm 波兰城市 4—104b
海乌姆诺 Chełmno 波兰集中营 4—104b
海伍德 Haywood, Eliza 英国小说家 7—534d
海伍德 Heywood, Jasper 耶稣会教士 8—67d
海伍德 Heywood, John 英国剧作家 8—67e
海伍德 Heywood, Thomas 英国剧作家 8—67e
海伍德 Haywood, William D(udley) 美国劳工领袖 7—534e
海西造山带 Hercynian orogenic belt 地质学 8—36e
海峡两岸关系协会 Association for Relations across the Taiwan Strait 中国民间团体 1—564d
海峡群岛 Channel Islands 英吉利海峡群岛 4—52b
海峡群岛 Channel Islands (California, U.S.) 美国群岛 4—52c
《海峡时报》 Straits Times, The 新加坡英文晨报 16—261e
海峡问题 Straits Question 欧洲历史 16—261d
海峡殖民地 Straits Settlements 英国直辖殖民地 16—261d
海下高原 submarine plateau 地质学 16—300a
海鲜酱 hoisin sauce 食品 8—121e
海象 sea elephant (aquatic mammal) 哺乳动物 15—164e
海象 walrus (species *Odobenus rosmarus*) 大型海兽 18—85a
海啸 tsunami 海洋学 17—251c
海蝎 sea scorpion (extinct aquatic invertebrate) 古生物 15—167d
海蝎鱼 sea scorpion (fish) 鱼类 15—167d
海星 sea star 无脊椎动物 15—168c

海鸦 murre 鸟类 11—498c
海牙 Hague, The 荷兰城市 7—407d
海牙公约 Hague Convention 欧洲历史 7—407f
海牙规则 Hague Rules 海商法 7—408a
海牙画派 Hague school 荷兰画派 7—408a
《海牙协定》 Hague Agreement 荷兰-印度尼西亚条约 7—407e
海燕 storm petrel 鸟类 16—255f
海燕子 sea swallow 鸟类 15—168c
海阳 Hai Duong 越南城镇 7—409a
海洋沉积物 marine sediment 海洋地质学 10—513f
海洋地球物理学 marine geophysics 地球物理学 10—513c
海洋地质学 marine geology 地质学 10—513c
《海洋法》 Sea, Law of the 国际法 15—163b
海洋风格 marine style 克里特陶器装饰 10—514c
海洋磷光 marine phosphorescence 化学作用 10—513e
海洋气团 maritime air mass 大气科学 10—517f
海洋生物学 marine biology 生物学 10—513a
海洋生物学实验所 Marine Biological Laboratory 美国研究机构 10—513a
海洋世界 Marineland 美国海洋水族馆 10—514d
海洋水产养殖 ocean ranching 渔业 12—327e
海洋卫星 Seasat 美国人造卫星 15—173a
海洋学 oceanography 研究世界海洋的学科 12—329c
海椰子 coco de mer (species *Lodoicea maldivica*) 植物 4—324a
海因 Hine, Lewis Wickes 美国摄影家 8—89d
海因茨公司 Heinz Company 美国食品商 7—569c
海因莱因 Heinlein, Robert A(nson) 美国作家 7—568d
海因尼克 Heinicke, Samuel 德国教育家 7—568c
海因斯 Hines, Earl (Kenneth) 美国作曲家 8—89e
海因斯 Hines, Gregory 美国舞蹈家 8—89e
海因修斯 Heinsius, Anthonie 荷兰政治家 7—569b
海因修斯 Heinsius, Daniël 荷兰诗人 7—569b
海因泽 Heinse, (Johann Jakob) Wilhelm 德国作家 7—569a
海罂粟 sea poppy (plant) 草本植物 15—167b
海鹦 sea parrot 鸟类 15—166e
海于格松 Haugesund 挪威城镇 7—511c
海约翰 Hay, John (Milton) 美国政治家 7—528e
《海约翰-比诺-瓦里亚条约》 Hay-Bunau-Varilla Treaty 美国-巴拿马条约 7—529a
《海约翰-庞斯福特条约》 Hay-Pauncefote Treaty 美-英条约 7—529b
海月水母属 Aurelia 动物学 2—58b
海藻 seaweed 藻类 15—174d
海泽 Heyse, Paul Johann Ludwig von 德国作家 8—67b
海泽比 Hedeby (Danish) 丹麦古城市 7—554c
海战游戏 naumachia 古罗马模拟海战 12—47b
海之光钻石 Daryā-e Nūr 伊朗王冠宝石 5—159b
海蜘蛛 sea spider 节肢动物 15—168a
海州 Haeju 朝鲜城市 7—404a
海州常山 glory-bower 植物 7—161a
海鳟 sea trout 鱼类 15—168c
亥姆霍兹 Helmholtz, Hermann von 德国科学家 8—3a
亥通那统 Hetonaian Series 地质学 8—63d
亥维赛 Heaviside, Oliver 英国物理学家 7—547f
氦(He) helium 化学元素 7—574e
氦年代测定法 helium dating 地质年代学 7—575a
犴 elk 哺乳动物 6—46c
蚶 ark shell 软体动物 1—489f
邯郸 Handan 中国城市 7—456c
含碘食盐 iodized salt 食盐 8—429f
含硫盐类 sulfosalt 矿物学 16—323b
含米特-闪米特诸语言 Hamito-Semitic languages 亚非语系 7—444b
含生草 rose of Jericho (*Anastatica hierochuntica*) 草本植物 14—401f
含水层 aquifer 水文学 1—428b
含羞草 sensitive plant 草本植物 15—215c
含羞草类 mimosa 草本植物 11—240b
函馆 Hakodate 日本城市 7—416e
函授教育 correspondence education 教育 4—521f
函数 function 数学 6—523a
焓 enthalpy 物理学 6—88f
涵化 acculturation 人类学 1—47f
涵延 tension 文学艺术 16—546a
寒冻土 Cryosol 农业 5—42c
寒武纪 Cambrian period 地质学 3—366a
寒鸦 jackdaw (species *Corvus monedula*) 鸟类 8—503f
韩 Han 中国历史 7—450a
韩昌黎 Han Changli 中国作家 7—452c
韩城 Hancheng 中国城市 7—455c
韩德尔 Handel, George Frideric 英国作曲家 7—457a
韩非 Han Fei 中国思想家 7—452c
《韩非子》 Hanfeizi 中国古代著作集 7—459a
韩幹 Han Gan 中国画家 7—452e
韩国 Korea, South 亚洲国家 9—354f
韩国临时政府 Korean Provisional Government 韩国历史 9—358a
韩滉 Han Huang 中国画家、政治家 7—452f
韩江 Han Jiang 中国河流 7—453a
韩礼德 Halliday, M(ichael) A(lexander) K(irkwood) 英国语言学家 7—430d
韩林儿 Han Lin'er 中国农民领袖 7—453e
韩龙云 Han Yongun 朝鲜佛教领袖 7—454c
韩莎 Khansā', al- 阿拉伯诗人 9—256a
韩侂胄 Han Tuozhou 中国大臣 7—453f
韩湘 Han Xiang 中国道教人物 7—453f
韩信 Han Xin 中国古代将领 7—454b
韩愈 Han Yu 中国作家 7—454c
罕百里学派 Ḥanābilah 伊斯兰教派 7—454f
罕萨 Hunza 巴基斯坦城镇 8—263c
铪(Ha) hahnium 化学元素 7—409a
汉 Han DYNASTY 中国王朝 7—452a
汉哀帝刘欣 Han'aidi Liu Xin 中国皇帝 7—451c
汉堡 Hamburg 德国城市 7—437e
汉堡 hamburger 食品 7—439d
汉堡美术馆 Hamburg Art Gallery 德国美术馆 7—439d
汉伯里·布朗 Hanbury Brown, Robert 英国天文学家 7—455c
汉布东尼安种马 Hambletonian 马品种 7—437e
汉布东尼安种马有奖赛 Hambletonian Stake 赛马 7—437e
汉布尔顿 Hambleton 英国区名 7—437d
汉朝帝王 Han——: 中国帝王 7—450c
汉成帝刘骜 Hanchengdi Liu Ao 中国皇帝 7—451b
汉德 Hand, (Billings) Learned 美国法学家 7—456a
汉德林 Handlin, Oscar 美国历史学家 7—458d
汉迪 Handy, W. C. 美国作曲家 7—458f
汉弗莱 Humphrey, Doris 美国舞蹈家 8—250b
汉弗莱 Humphrey, Hubert H(oratio) 美国副总统 8—250d
汉弗莱 Humfrey, Pelham 美国作曲家 8—247f
汉弗莱斯 Humphreys, Joshua 美国军舰设计师 8—250e
汉弗莱斯 Humphreys, West Hughes 美国法官 8—250f
汉弗莱斯 Humphreys, William Jackson 美国物理学家 8—250f
汉弗莱斯峰 Humphreys Peak 美国山峰 8—250f
汉高祖刘邦 Hangaozu Liu Bang 中国皇帝 7—450c
汉光武帝刘秀 Hanguangwudi Liu Xiu 中国皇帝 7—451c
汉和帝刘肇 Hanhedi Liu Zhao 中国皇帝 7—451f
汉画像石 relief stone sculpture of Han dynasty 中国古代艺术 14—215e

汉江 Han Jiang 中国河流 7—453a
汉江 Han River 韩国河流 7—453f
汉景帝刘启 Hanjingdi Liu Qi 中国皇帝 7—450e
汉剧 hanju 戏剧 7—460e
汉考克 Hancock, Herbie 美国作曲家 7—455d
汉考克 Hancock, John 美国政治家 7—455d
汉考克 Hancock, Joy Brig 美国军官 7—455e
汉考克 Hancock, Thomas 英国发明家 7—455e
汉考克 Hancock, Winfield Scott 美国军人 7—455f
汉科克 Hancock 美国城市 7—455c
汉克斯 Hanks, Nancy 美国公职人员 7—460f
汉克斯 Hanks, Tom 美国电影演员 7—461a
汉口 Hankou (China) 中国武汉市区 7—460f
汉密尔顿 Hamilton, Alexander 美国政治家 7—442b
汉密尔顿 Hamilton, Alice 美国病理学家 7—442e
汉密尔顿 Hamilton, Andrew 美国法官 7—442e
汉密尔顿 Hamilton, (Anthony Walter) Patrick 英国作家 7—443b
汉密尔顿 Hamilton, Edith 美国教育家、作家 7—442e
汉密尔顿 Hamilton, Gavin 苏格兰艺术家 7—443a
汉密尔顿 Hamilton, Sir Ian (Standish Monteith) 英国军人 7—443a
汉密尔顿 Hamilton, Scott 美国花样滑冰运动员 7—443b
汉密尔顿 Hamilton, Sir William 英国外交家、考古学家 7—443c
汉密尔顿 Hamilton, Sir William, 9TH BARONET 苏格兰哲学家 7—443c
汉密尔顿 Hamilton, William Thomas 美国边疆开拓者 7—443f
汉密尔顿夫人 Hamilton, Emma, Lady 英国贵妇 7—442f
汉密尔顿-戈登 Hamilton-Gordon, George 英国首相 7—444a
汉密尔顿公爵(第二) Hamilton, William Hamilton, 2nd duke of, EARL OF CAMBRIDGE 苏格兰保王党人 7—442b
汉密尔顿侯爵(第三)和公爵(第一) Hamilton, James Hamilton, 3rd marquess and 1st duke of, EARL OF CAMBRIDGE 苏格兰保王党人 7—441f
汉密尔顿侯爵(第一) Hamilton, John Hamilton, 1st marquess of, EARL OF ARRAN, LORD AVEN 苏格兰贵族 7—441f
汉密尔顿侯爵和公爵 Hamilton, MARQUESSES AND DUKES OF 苏格兰贵族 7—441f
汉密尔顿-坦普尔-布莱克伍德 Hamilton-Temple-Blackwood, Frederick Temple 英国外交家 7—444a
汉明帝刘庄 Hanmingdi Liu Zhuang 中国皇帝 7—451d
汉姆 Hamm, Mia 美国英式足球运动员 7—444f
汉姆生 Hamsun, Knut 挪威作家 7—449e
汉穆拉比 Hammurabi 巴比伦国王 7—447f
《汉穆拉比法典》 Hammurabi, Code of 巴比伦法律 7—448b
汉纳 Hanna, Mark 美国实业家 7—461b
汉纳-巴伯拉海洋世界 Hanna-Barbera Marineland 美国水族馆 7—461c
汉纳和巴伯拉 Hanna, William (Denby); and Barbera, Joseph (Roland) 美国影片制作人 7—461c
汉内斯·哈夫斯泰因 Hannes Hafstein (Icelandic statesman and poet) 冰岛政治家、诗人 7—461d
汉尼拔 Hannibal 迦太基军人 7—461d
汉尼拔 Hannibal 美国城市 7—461e
汉宁顿 Hannington, James 英国传教士 7—461e
汉诺 Hanno 迦太基贵族 7—461f
汉诺 Hanno 迦太基探险者 7—461f
汉诺威 Hannover 德国行政区 7—462a
汉诺威 Hannover 德国城市 7—462b
汉诺威 Hanover 德意志邦国 7—462e
汉诺威 Hanover 美国城镇 7—462f
汉诺威 Hanover 美国城镇 7—462f
汉诺威 Hanover 美国村镇 7—463a
汉诺威王朝 Hanover, HOUSE OF 英国历史 7—463a
汉平帝刘衎 Hanpingdi Liu Kan 中国皇帝 7—451c
汉普登 Hampden, John 英国议会领袖 7—448c
汉普登 Hampden, Walter 美国演员 7—448d
汉普顿 Hampton 美国城市 7—448f
汉普顿 Hampton, Lionel (Leo) 美国音乐家 7—449a
汉普顿 Hampton, Wade 美国军人 7—449a
汉普顿宫 Hampton Court 英国宫殿 7—449b
汉普顿宫会议 Hampton Court Conference 英国历史 7—449b
汉普顿锚地 Hampton Roads 美国碇泊地 7—449c
汉普顿锚地会议 Hampton Roads Conference 美国历史 7—449d
汉普顿锚地战役 Hampton Roads, Battle of 美国历史 7—449d
汉普郡 Hampshire 英格兰郡名 7—448e
汉普郡埃文河 Hampshire Avon (river, England) 英格兰河流 7—448f
汉普郡绵羊 Hampshire 哺乳动物 7—448f
汉普郡猪 Hampshire 哺乳动物 7—448f
汉奇 Hantzsch, Arthur Rudolf 德国化学家 7—466c
汉卿 Han-Ch'ing 中国数学家 7—452c
汉萨姆马车 hansom cab 交通工具 7—465d
汉萨同盟 Hanseatic League 德国历史 7—463e
汉塞尔特 Henselt, Adolf von 德国音乐家 8—27f
汉森 Hansen, Alvin Harvey 美国经济学家 7—463f
汉森 Hansen, Emile Christian 丹麦植物学家 7—463f
汉森 Hanson, Howard 美国作曲家 7—465e
汉森 Hansen, H(ans) C(hristian Svane) 丹麦政治家 7—464f
汉森 Hanson, John 美国政治家 7—465f
汉森 Hansen, Jens Andersen 丹麦政治家 7—465a
汉森 Hansen, Martin (Jens) Alfred 丹麦作家 7—465a
汉森 Hansen, Peter Andreas 德国天文学家 7—465b
汉森 Hansen, William Webster 美国物理学家 7—465b
汉森氏病 Hansen's disease 疾病 7—465c
汉莎航空公司 Lufthansa 德国航空公司 10—274a
汉斯贝里 Hansberry, Lorraine 美国剧作家 7—463c
汉斯立克 Hanslick, Eduard 奥地利音乐评论家 7—465c
汉斯廷 Hansteen, Christopher 挪威天文学家 7—466b
汉斯·亚当二世 Hans Adam II, prince of Lie censtein 列支敦士登公爵 7—463b
汉松 Hansson, Ola 瑞典作家 7—466a
汉松 Hansson, Per Albin 瑞典首相 7—466a
汉塔瓦迪王国 Hanthawaddy kingdom 缅甸历史 7—466c
汉特-曼西 Khanty-Mansi 俄罗斯自治区 9—256c
汉特-曼西斯克 Khanty-Mansiysk 俄罗斯城市 9—256d
汉特人和曼西人 Khant and Mansi 西伯利亚西部民族 9—256b
汉文帝刘恒 Hanwendi Liu Heng 中国皇帝 7—450d
汉武帝刘彻 Hanwudi Liu Che 中国皇帝 7—450e
汉西 Hānsi 印度城市 7—465c
汉献帝刘协 Hanxiandi Liu Xie 中国皇帝 7—451f
汉宣帝刘询 Hanxuandi Liu Xun 中国皇帝 7—451a
汉亚 Haanja 爱沙尼亚地区 7—395d
汉阳 Hanyang (China) 中国武汉市区 7—466e
汉语 Han language 中国语言 7—453b
汉语拼音方案 Pinyin romanization 语言 13—316e
汉元帝刘奭 Hanyuandi Liu Shi 中国皇帝 7—451b
汉藏诸语言 Sino-Tibetan languages 语言 15—397e
汉章帝刘炟 Hanzhangdi Liu Da 中国皇帝 7—451e
汉昭帝刘弗陵 Hanzhaodi Liu Fuling 中国皇帝 7—451a
汉昭烈帝刘备 Hanzhaoliedi Liu Bei 中国帝王 7—466e
汉志 Hejaz 沙特阿拉伯地区 7—570f
汉志铁路 Hejaz Railway 中东铁路 7—571a
汉中 Hanzhong 中国城市 7—466f
汉钟离 Han Zhongli 中国神话人物 7—454e
汉字 Chinese character 文字 4—168f
汉字 kanji 日语文字 9—158d
汉族 Han 中国民族 7—450b
汗 Khan, Ali Akbar 印度作曲家 9—255c
汗 Khan, Fazlur R. 美国土木工程师 9—255c

汗 sweat 生理学 16—375f
汗热病 sweating sickness 疾病 16—376a
汗腾格里峰 Hantengri Feng 中国山峰 7—466b
汗腺 sweat gland 解剖学 16—375f
旱冰运动 roller-skating 体育 14—360c
旱成土 aridisol 土壤 1—471a
旱地耕作 dryland farming 农业 5—433d
旱金莲 nasturtium 植物 12—8c
旱蕨 cliffbrake 植物 4—290a
旱生植物 xerophyte 植物学 18—376a
旱獭 marmot 哺乳动物 10—526e
旱叶草 bear grass 草本植物 2—305a
旱作 dry farming 农业 5—432b
焊接 welding 金属工艺 18—175c
蔊菜 marsh cress 植物 10—538b
翰林院 Hanlin Academy 中国宫廷机构 7—461a
夯土 rammed earth 土木工程 14—140e
行会 grêmio 葡萄牙工会 7—302a
行列式 determinant 数学 5—266a
杭爱山脉 Hangayn Mountains 蒙古山脉 7—459b
杭济 Ghanzi 博茨瓦纳村庄 7—108e
杭州 Hangzhou 中国城市 7—459d
杭州湾 Hangzhou Bay 中国海湾 7—459f
绗缝 quilting 装饰艺术 14—91e
航海饼干 Seabiscuit 美国良种赛马 15—169b
航海博物馆 Mariners, Museum 美国博物馆 10—514e
航海故事 imram 爱尔兰文学 8—349b
航海条例 Navigation Acts 英国法律 12—51e
航空 aviation 航空学 2—88b
航空电子系统 avionics 航空航天 2—89f
航空耳炎 aerotitis 疾病 1—97e
航空法 air law 法律 1—144d
航空航天工程 aerospace engineering 工程 1—97b
航空航天医学 aerospace medicine 医学 1—97d
航空母舰 aircraft carrier 军舰 1—146d
航空邮件 airmail 邮政 1—147b
航空站 airport 航空 1—147e
航天飞机 space shuttle 航天器 15—561f
航天器 spacecraft 航天飞行器 15—563a
航天员 astronaut 航天 2—8a
航天站 space station 航天 15—562d
航位推算 dead reckoning 航海、航空 5—192f
蒿 wormwood 草本植物 18—339a
蚝壳介壳虫 oystershell scale (*Lepidosaphes ulmi*) 昆虫 12—527c
蚝隆头鱼 tautog 鱼类 16—498c
毫巴 millibar 计量单位 11—228f
毫米 millimetre 计量单位 11—229c
豪 Howe, Elias 美国发明家 8—200a
豪 Howe, E. W. 美国作家 8—200a
豪 Howe, Gordie 美国运动员 8—200b
豪 Howe, Irving 美国评论家、教育家 8—200b
豪 Howe, Joseph 加拿大政治家 8—200d
豪 Howe, Julia Ward 美国作家 8—200e
豪 Howe, Richard Howe, Earl, Baron Howe of Langar 英国军人 8—200e
豪 Howe, Samuel Gridley 美国教育家 8—200f
豪 Howe, William 美国发明家 8—201a
豪 Howe, William Howe, 5th Viscount 英国军人 8—201a
豪布拉肯 Houbraken, Arnold 荷兰画家 8—192c
豪布拉肯 Houbraken, Jacobus 荷兰画家 8—192c
豪达 Gouda 荷兰城市 7—227e
豪达干酪 Gouda 食品 7—227f
豪德高原 Hawd Plateau 非洲高原 7—524a
豪厄尔 Howell, James 威尔士作家 8—201c
豪厄尔(好人) Howel Dda 威尔士首长 8—201c
豪厄尔斯 Howells, William White 美国人类学家 8—201d
豪恩斯洛 Hounslow 英国大伦敦自治市 8—193e
豪尔法坎 Khawr Fakkān 阿联酋城镇 9—258f
豪尔萨巴德 Khorsabad (ancient Assyrian city) 亚述古城 9—264a
豪尔绍尼 Harsanyi, John C. 美国经济学家 7—492a
豪夫 Hauff, Wilhelm 德国作家 7—511a
豪盖 Hauge, Alfred 挪威作家 7—511b
豪格 Haug, Thorleif 挪威北欧两项滑雪运动员 7—511b
豪格维茨 Haugwitz, Christian Count (Graf) von 普鲁士外交家 7—511e
豪豪 Hauhau 新西兰毛利族宗教 7—511e
豪角 Howe, Cape 澳大利亚海角 8—200a
豪克 Hauch, Johannes Carsten 丹麦作家 7—510e
豪拉 Howrah 印度城市 8—202c
豪拉基湾 Hauraki Gulf 新西兰海湾 7—513a
豪拉尼 Hawrani, Akram al- 叙利亚政治家 7—527c
豪兰 Ḥawrān 叙利亚地区 7—527c
豪兰岛 Howland Island 太平洋珊瑚礁 8—202a
豪里 Haury, Emil W. 美国人类学家 7—513b
豪麻 haoma 植物 7—467d
豪曼 Howman, John 英国修道院长 8—202b
豪普特 Haupt, Herman 美国工程师 7—512a
豪普特曼 Hauptmann, Bruno (Richard) 美国窃贼 7—512b
豪普特曼 Hauptman, Herbert A(aron) 美国数学家 7—512a
豪萨人 Hausa 非洲民族 7—513b
豪萨-西斯凯 Xhosa-Ciskei (South Africa) 非洲历史共和国 18—377a
豪萨语 Hausa language 非洲语言 7—513d
豪萨诸邦 Hausa states 非洲历史 7—513d
豪塞尔 Hausser, Paul 德国纳粹党卫军将军、战地司令 7—514b
豪瑟尔 Hauser, Kaspar 德国青年 7—513e
豪斯 House, Edward M(andell) 美国外交家 8—194d
豪斯 Heuss, Theodor 德国总统 8—64b
豪斯菲尔德 Hounsfield, Sir Godfrey Newbold 英国工程师 8—193e
豪斯霍弗尔 Haushofer, Karl (Ernst) 德国政治学家 7—513f
豪斯曼 Housman, A(lfred) E(dward) 英国学者 8—196a
豪斯曼 Housman, Laurence 英国画家 8—196b
豪斯曼 Houseman, John 美国演员 8—195c
豪特 Hout, Jan van 荷兰学者 8—197a
豪特曼兄弟 Houtman, Cornelis and Frederik de 荷兰探险家 8—197a
豪特斯普林斯 Hot Springs (city, New Mexico) 美国城市 8—190a
豪威尔斯 Howells, William Dean 美国作家 8—201d
豪乌洞 Howe Caverns 美国岩洞群 8—201b
豪勋爵岛 Lord Howe Island 奥大利亚属地 10—219d
豪伊 Haughey, Charles James 爱尔兰总理 7—511c
豪伊杜-比豪尔 Hajdú-Bihar 匈牙利州名 7—415a
豪伊杜伯瑟尔梅尼 Hajdúböszörmény 匈牙利城镇 7—415a
豪伊杜沙格 Hajdúság 匈牙利地区 7—415b
豪伊克子爵 Howick, Charles Grey, Viscount 英国军人 8—202a
豪伊克子爵 Howick, Henry George Grey, Viscount 英国政治家 8—202a
豪猪 porcupine 啮齿动物 13—440d
壕沟之战 Ditch, Battle of the 穆斯林与麦加人之战 5—345a
嚎哭鸟 guácharo 鸟类 7—333f
好斗原田 Fighting Harada 日本职业拳击手 6—310e
好拉 houri 伊斯兰教 8—194c
好莱坞 Hollywood 美国城市 8—134b
好莱坞 Hollywood 美国洛杉矶区名 8—134a
好莱坞十人 Hollywood Ten 美国历史 8—134b
好利节 Holī 印度节日 8—125c

好人豪厄尔 Hywell THE GOOD (Welsh king) 威尔士国王 8—298e
好望角 Cape of Good Hope 南非省份 3—420f
好望角 Good Hope, Cape of 南非海岬 7—207d
好望角艾鼬 Cape polecat 哺乳动物 3—421c
好望角红宝石 Cape ruby 宝石 3—421c
好望角狐 Cape fox 哺乳动物 3—420c
好望角水牛 Cape buffalo 哺乳动物 3—419f
《好望角照相星表》 Cape Photographic Durchmusterung (CPD) 天文学 3—421c
《好望角照相星表》 CPD 天文学 4—561f
好望角祖母绿 Cape emerald 矿物 3—420b
"好友"号(查尔斯顿) Best Friend of Charleston 美国第一辆铁路机车 2—438e
郝尔氏苔藓虫 Hallopora 古生物学 7—430f
郝寿臣 Hao Shouchen 中国京剧演员 7—467b
号 horn 乐器 8—175c
号笛 hornpipe 乐器 8—178e
号角齐鸣 fanfare 音乐 6—232e
号角舞 horn dance 英国宗教舞蹈 8—175f
号子 work song 音乐 18—332f
耗减优惠 depletion allowance 经济 5—250b
浩罕 Kokand 乌兹别克斯坦城市 9—336d
诃梨朋阇耶 Haripunjaya 泰国古王国 7—477b
诃里诃罗 Harihara 印度教神祇 7—476e
诃陀瑜伽 Haṭha Yoga 印度哲学 7—508e
禾本科 Gramineae 植物学 7—244d
禾草类 grass 草本植物 7—260e
禾草学 agrostology 植物学 1—131a
禾木树 grass tree 木本植物 7—261b
合 conjunction 天文学 4—432b
合艾 Hat Yai 泰国城镇 7—506f
合并词 portmanteau word 语法 13—452e
《合并法》 Union, Act of 不列颠历史 17—345c
合唱队 chorus 音乐和戏剧 4—199f
合唱音乐 choral music 音乐 4—197c
合成氨法 synthetic ammonia process 化学 16—403c
合成代谢 anabolism 生物学 1—307c
合成金刚石 synthetic diamond 人造石 16—403c
合成酶 synthetase 酶 16—403c
合成纤维 synthetic fibre 纺织 16—403d
合成照片 photomontage 摄影术 13—265c
合川 Hechuan 中国城市 7—552d
合恩角 Horn, Cape 智利海角 8—175f
《合法货币案》 Legal Tender Cases 美国法案 9—560d
合肥 Hefei 中国城市 7—556c
合欢山 Hehuan Shan 中国山名 7—563d
合欢属 Albizia 植物学 1—184b
合伙企业 partnership 企业 13—68e
合金 alloy 冶金学 1—242f
合礼 kosher 犹太教 9—362b
《合理劳动标准法》 Fair Labor Standards Act 美国1938年法律 6—215a
合囊蕨科 Marattiaceae 植物学 10—490b
合浦 Hepu 中国城市 8—30d
合气道 aikido 防身术 1—140f
合气道 hapkido 徒手自卫术 7—467e
合取式 conjunction 逻辑学 4—432c
合山 Heshan 中国城市 8—57b
合赞 Ghāzān, Mahmūd 波斯统治者 7—110a
合趾猿 siamang (*Symphalangus syndactylus*) 哺乳动物 15—346a
合众国航空集团公司 USAir Group, Inc. 美国航空公司 17—422a
合众国际社 United Press International (UPI) 美国通讯社 17—363d
合作社 cooperative 社会、经济组织 4—485d
何巴 Hobab (biblical priest) 《圣经》人物 8—109f
何尔 Hor (Egyptian god) 埃及神名 8—172d
何尔米斯达斯, 圣 Hormisdas, SAINT 教皇 8—174d
何烈山 Mount Hareh (Egypt) 埃及城镇 11—441a
何露斯 Horus 埃及神名 8—187c
何尼 Hogni (legendary hero) 日耳曼传说人物 8—120a
何努斯 Honos 古罗马神名 8—160e
何其芳 He Qifang 中国作家 7—536f
何塞利托 Joselito 西班牙斗牛士 9—88f
《何西阿书》 Hosea, Book of 圣经文献 8—188a
何细亚 Hoshea 圣经人物 8—188a
何仙姑 He Xiangu 中国道教人物 7—537c
何香凝 He Xiangning 中国革命家、画家 7—537a
何晏 He Yan 中国哲学家 7—537d
何耶揭唎婆 Hayagrīva 藏传佛教八大明王之一 7—529e
何应钦 He Yingqin 中国国民党将领 7—537e
和服 kimono 日本饰服 9—283c
和服腰带 obi 服饰 12—320d
和歌 waka 日本诗歌 18—68a
和歌山 Wakayama 日本本州岛中部县名 18—68c
和歌山 Wakayama 日本本州和歌山县城市 18—68c
和好 Hoa Hao 越南社团 8—108e
和解 settlement 法律 15—235d
和睦时期 Good Feelings, Era of 美国历史 7—207b
和平 Hoa Binh 越南城市 8—108e
和平保卫者导弹 Peacekeeper missile 美国导弹 13—109c
和平队 Peace Corps 美国对外服务机构 13—108f
和平港 Port-de-Paix 海地港口 13—444e
"和平"号航天站 Mir 苏联航天站 11—269d
和平祭坛 Ara Pacis 罗马祭坛 1—429b
和平教会 Peace Mission 美国黑人组织的教派 13—109a
和平鸟科 Irenidae 动物学 8—445d
和平亲王 Paz, Manuel de Godoy, príncipe de la (prince of) 西班牙王室宠臣 13—106d
和平烟袋 peace pipe 美洲印第安礼仪用器物 13—109b
和平主义 pacifism 政治 12—536e
和琴 wagon 日本乐器 18—63e
和尚 heshang 佛教 8—57b
和珅 Heshen 中国清代大臣 8—57b
和声 harmony 音乐 7—482a
和辻哲郎 Watsuji Tetsurō 日本哲学家 18—145f
和田 Hotan 中国城市 8—190a
和田地毯 Khotan rug 工艺品 9—264e
和田河 Hotan He 中国河流 8—190b
和弦 chord 音乐 4—197f
"和子"句 Filioque 宗教 6—315a
河岸唑蝰 river jack (snake) 蛇 14—315f
河北 Hebei 中国省份 7—548f
河池 Hechi 中国城市 7—551f
河床 streambed 水文学 16—273a
河堤 levee 土木工程 10—44f
河鼓二 Altair 天文学 1—253f
河锅晓斋 Kawanabe Gyōsai 日本画家 9—202f
河桦 river birch (*Betula nigra*) 木本植物 14—315d
河间地带 Transoxania 突厥斯坦历史地区 17—198b
河江 Ha Giang 越南城镇 7—394c
河井宽次郎 Kawai Kanjirō 日本陶瓷家 9—202d
河口湾 estuary 河口近海水体 6—142e
河狸 beaver 哺乳动物 2—316c
河狸鼠 nutria (*Myocastor coypus*) 哺乳动物 12—306a
河流 Rivers 尼日利亚州名 14—316e
河流及河系 rivers and river systems 地理学 14—317d

河流阶地 river terrace 地质学 14—316a
河流生态系统 riverine ecosystem 生态学 14—316d
河流作用 fluvial process 地质学 6—380c
河马 hippopotamus (*Hippopotamus amphibius*) 哺乳动物 8—92c
河漫滩 floodplain 地貌学 6—363a
河姆渡文化 Hemudu culture 中国考古 8—11e
河南 Henan 中国省份 8—12a
河内 Hanoi 越南首都 7—462c
河畔弟兄会 River Brethren 宗教组织 14—315e
河上肇 Kawakami Hajime 日本理论家 9—202e
河苔草 riverweed 水生植物 14—319f
河苔草目 Podostemales 水生植物 13—385a
河套平原 Hetao Plain 中国平原 8—61c
河童 kappa 日本民间传说 9—173a
河图洛书 Hetu Luoshu 中国哲学 8—63e
河豚 puffer 鱼类 14—18a
河豚 river dolphin (*Platanistidae*) 哺乳动物 14—315e
河乌 dipper 鸟类 5—333e
河乌科 Cinclidae (bird family) 动物学 4—240d
河西走廊 Hexi Zoulang 中国地区 8—66b
河鸭 river duck 鸟类 14—315f
河源 Heyuan 中国城市 8—67c
河竹默阿弥 Kawatake Mokuami 日本作家 9—203c
曷萨拉王朝 Hoysala DYNASTY 印度王朝 8—203b
核 kernel 数学 9—241e
核磁共振 nuclear magnetic resonance (NMR) 物理学 12—288c
核蛋白 nucleoprotein 生物化学 12—291b
核冬天 nuclear winter 核战争假想 12—290c
核反应 nuclear reaction 物理学 12—288f
核反应堆 nuclear reactor 物理学 12—289a
核苷 nucleoside 生物化学 12—291c
核苷酸 nucleotide 生物化学 12—291d
核工程 nuclear engineering 工程 12—287d
核管理委员会 Nuclear Regulatory Commission (NRC) 美国机构 12—289e
核光学模型 optical model 物理学 12—436a
核果 drupe 植物果实 5—430f
核合成 nucleosynthesis 物理学 12—291c
核黄疸 kernicterus 病理现象 9—241f
核黄素 riboflavin 生物化学 14—277a
核黄素缺乏症 riboflavin deficiency 疾病 14—277b
核聚变 nuclear fusion 物理学 12—288b
核壳层模型 shell nuclear model 物理学 15—296f
核裂变 nuclear fission 物理学 12—287e
核能 nuclear energy 物理学 12—287c
核素 nuclide 物理学 12—292c
核酸 nucleic acid 生物化学 12—290e
核酸酶 nuclease 生物化学 12—290d
核糖 ribose 生物化学 14—277b
核糖核酸 RNA 生物化学 14—322d
核糖体 ribosome 生物化学 14—277b
核武器 nuclear weapon 大规模杀伤性武器 12—289f
核心家庭 nuclear family 社会学、人类学 12—287e
核医学 nuclear medicine 医学 12—288e
核子 nucleon 物理学 12—291b
荷包牡丹 bleeding heart 草本植物 2—532b
荷包牡丹科 Fumariaceae 植物学 6—522b
荷包牡丹属 Dicentra 植物学 5—294b
荷尔德林 Hölderlin, (Johann Christian) Friedrich 德国诗人 8—124e
荷尔卡王朝 Holkar DYNASTY 印度历史 8—131a
荷尔斯泰因 Holstein 德国历史地区 8—138e
荷尔斯泰因-弗里斯牛 Holstein-Friesian 奶牛品种 8—139c
荷尔斯泰因-戈托普公爵 Holstein-Gottorp, Karl Peter Ulrich, Herzog von (duke of) 俄国皇帝 8—139c
荷尔斯泰因海 Holstein Sea 地质学 8—139d
荷尔斯泰因间冰期 Holstein Interglacial Stage 地质学 8—139c
荷尔斯泰因斯堡 Holsteinsborg 格陵兰城镇 8—139d
荷兰 Holland 荷兰历史区域 8—131b
荷兰 Netherlands, The 欧洲国家 12—91e
荷兰城 Hollandia (Indonesia) 印度尼西亚城市 8—132e
荷兰东印度公司 Dutch East India Company 荷兰贸易机构 5—480a
荷兰盾 Guilder 荷兰货币 7—355f
荷兰干酪 Dutch cheese 食品 5—480a
荷兰共和国 Dutch Republic 欧洲历史国家 5—481b
荷兰归正会 Dutch Reformed Church 南非基督教会 5—481a
荷兰皇家航空公司 KLM 荷兰公司 9—318d
荷兰黄铜 Dutch metal 合金 5—480f
荷兰货船狗 Dutch barge dog 动物 5—480a
荷兰老公会 Old Catholic Church of The Netherlands 荷兰天主教 12—367a
荷兰式砌合 Dutch bond 建筑 5—480a
荷兰文学 Dutch literature 欧洲文学 5—480d
荷兰西印度公司 Dutch West India Company 荷兰贸易机构 5—481d
荷兰亚麻布 holland 纺织 8—131d
荷兰榆树病 Dutch elm disease 植物真菌病 5—480b
荷兰语 Dutch language 欧洲语言 5—480d
荷兰战争 Dutch War 法荷之战 5—481c
荷兰战争 Dutch Wars 英荷之战 5—481d
荷马 Homer 古希腊诗人 8—144e
荷马 Homer 美国城市 8—144f
荷马氏族 Homerids 古希腊氏族 8—145d
《荷马赞美诗集》 Homeric Hymns 文学 8—145c
荷人 Ho 印度民族 8—107a
荷属安的列斯 Netherlands Antilles 加勒比海岛屿 12—93b
荷属东印度群岛 Dutch East Indies 荷兰海外领地 5—480a
荷台达 Ḥudaydah, Al- 也门城市 8—220c
盉 he 中国古代酒器 7—535f
盒式磁带 cassette 录音磁带 3—503e
盒式磁带录像机 videocassette recorder 电子学 17—546e
盒式舞台布景 box set 舞台美术 3—97c
颌 jaw 解剖学 8—552c
貉 raccoon dog (*Nyctereutes procyonoides*) 哺乳动物 14—104b
鼯鼠 chinchilla rat 哺乳动物 4—167c
贺川丰彦 Kagawa Toyohiko 日本作家 9—131e
贺德勒 Hodler, Ferdinand 瑞士画家 8—113d
贺加斯 Hogarth, William 英国艺术家 8—118f
贺拉斯 Horace 古罗马诗人 8—172e
贺拉斯·弗拉库斯 Horatius Flaccus, Quintus 古罗马诗人 8—173c
贺拉斯体颂歌 Horatian ode 诗歌 8—173a
贺拉提乌斯三兄弟和库里阿提乌斯三兄弟 Horatii and Curiatii 罗马神话人物 8—173b
贺兰山 Helan Shan 中国山脉 7—571c
贺麟 He Lin 中国哲学家 7—536a
贺龙 He Long 中国元帅 7—536c
贺绿汀 He Luting 中国作曲家 7—536d
贺茂真渊 Kamo Mabuchi 日本国学派代表 9—150b
喝彩人 claque 戏剧 4—260b
赫 Heh (Egyptian religion) 埃及宗教 7—563d
赫巴特 Hebat 小亚细亚女神 7—548c
赫本 Hepburn, Audrey 美国演员 8—29e
赫本 Hepburn, Katharine 美国演员 8—29f
赫彼奈人 Hirpini 民族 8—95a
赫伯恩 Hepburn, Francis Stewart 苏格兰贵族 8—29f

赫伯恩 Hepburn, James 苏格兰贵族 8—29f
赫伯勒 Habara (India) 印度城市 7—396f
赫伯特 Herbert, Sir A(lan) P(atrick) 英国作家、政治家 8—34e
赫伯特 Herbert (of Cherbury), Edward Herbert, 1st Baron 英国哲学家、历史学家 8—34f
赫伯特 Herbert, George 英国诗人 8—35a
赫伯特 Herbert, George Edward Stanhope Molyneux 英国埃及学家 8—35a
赫伯特 Herbert, Henry Howard Molyneux 英国政治家 8—35b
赫伯特 Herbert, Victor 美国作曲家 8—35b
赫伯特 Herbert, Xavier 澳大利亚小说家 8—35c
赫伯特 Herbert, Zbigniew 波兰作家 8—35c
赫伯特河 Herbert River 澳大利亚河流 8—35d
赫伯特(拉格伦的)勋爵 Herbert (of Ragland) Edward Somerset, Lord 英国保王党成员 8—35a
赫柏 Hebe 希腊神话人物 7—548d
赫卜塞德节 Heb-Sed festival 埃及节日 7—548c
赫布里底群岛 Hebrides 苏格兰岛群 7—551c
赫布洛克 Herblock 美国漫画家 8—35e
赫策尔 Hetzer, Ludwig 瑞士再浸礼派人士 8—63f
赫岑多夫 Hötzendorf, Franz (Xaver Josef), Graf Conrad von 奥匈帝国军人 8—191d
赫茨 Heutsz, Johannes Benedictus van 荷兰军人 8—64c
赫茨 Hertz, Joseph Herman 犹太教拉比 8—54c
赫茨贝格 Hertzberg, Ewald Friedrich, Graf von 普鲁士政治家 8—54c
赫茨伯格 Herzberg, Gerhard 加拿大物理学家 8—55e
赫茨尔 Herzl, Theodor 犹太复国主义者 8—56b
赫茨尔利亚 Herzliyya 以色列城市 8—56d
赫茨米尔 Hertsmere 英格兰区名 8—53e
赫茨普龙 Hertzsprung, Ejnar 丹麦天文学家 8—54f
赫达雅特 Hedāyat, Şādeq 伊朗作家 7—554b
赫德 Hurd, Peter 美国画家 8—264c
赫德 Hart, Sir Robert 1st Baronet 英籍中国官员 7—492f
赫德岛与麦克唐纳群岛 Heard and McDonald Islands 澳大利亚海外领地 7—541b
赫德利 Hedley, William 英国发明家 7—555a
赫德森 Hudson, George 英国金融家 8—221a
赫德森 Hudson, Rock 美国电影演员 8—221c
赫德森 Hudson, Thomas 英国画家 8—221c
赫德森 Hudson, W(illiam) H(enry) 英国作家、博物学家 8—221d
赫德维格玻璃器皿 Hedwig glass 埃及玻璃制品 7—555c
赫德维希 Hedwig, Johann 德国植物学家 7—555b
赫蒂彻 Khadījah 穆罕默德的元配夫人 9—252e
赫顿 Hutton, James 苏格兰地质学家 8—271f
赫恩 Herne, James A. 美国剧作家 8—44c
赫恩 Hearn, (Patricio) Lafcadio (Tessima Carlos) 日本作家 7—541d
赫恩 Hearne, Samuel 英国探险家 7—541e
赫恩 Hearne, Thomas 英国历史学家 7—541f
赫恩贝 Herne Bay 英格兰地名 8—44c
赫尔 Hull 加拿大城市 8—230d
赫尔 Hull (England) 英格兰城市 8—230d
赫尔 Hull, Bobby 加拿大运动员 8—230e
赫尔 Hull, Cordell 美国政治家 8—231a
赫尔 Hull, Clark L(eonard) 美国心理学家 8—230e
赫尔 Hoel, Halvor (Nielsen) 挪威政治家 8—114c
赫尔 Herr, Herbert Thacker 美国工程师 8—49b
赫尔 Hull, Isaac 美国军人 8—231b
赫尔 Hull, William 美国军人 8—231c
赫尔巴特 Herbart, Johann Friedrich 德国哲学家、教育家 8—34d
赫尔岑 Herzen, Aleksandr (Ivanovich) 俄国作家 8—55f
赫尔措格 Herzog, Johann Jakob 德国神学家 8—56e
赫尔措格 Herzog, Werner 德国电影导演 8—56f
赫尔大厦 Hull House 美国社会服务所 8—231c
赫尔德 Herder, Johann Gottfried von 德国哲学家 8—36f
赫尔德(小) Held, John, Jr. 美国画家 7—571d
赫尔德伯格阶 Helderbergian Stage 地质学 7—571f
赫尔德利奇卡 Hrdlička, Aleš 美国人类学家 8—203c
赫尔德瓦尔 Hardwār 印度城市 7—473d
赫尔蒂 Hölty, Ludwig Heinrich Christoph 德国诗人 8—140b
赫尔多伊 Hardoi 印度城镇 7—473c
赫尔方德 Helphand, Alexander Israel (Lazarevitsch) 俄国社会主义者 8—5c
赫尔格森 Helgesen, Paul 丹麦人文学家 7—572e
赫尔河畔金斯顿 Kingston upon Hull 英格兰城市 9—293d
赫尔利 Hurley, Patrick J(ay) 美国外交家 8—265a
赫尔曼 Hermann, Eduard 德国语言学家 8—40f
赫尔曼 Herrmann, (Johann) Wilhelm 德国神学家 8—51a
赫尔曼 Herman, Woody 美国音乐家 8—40c
赫尔曼(赖谢瑙的) Hermann von Reichenau 德意志学者 8—40e
赫尔曼德河 Helmand River 亚洲河流 8—2a
赫尔曼·冯·萨尔扎 Hermann von Salza 德国十字军领袖 8—40e
赫尔曼·米勒公司 Herman Miller, Inc. 美国家具公司 8—40c
赫尔曼一世 Hermann I 图林根伯爵 8—40e
赫尔梅斯 Hermes, Georg 德国神学家 8—42a
赫尔门尼希尔德,圣 Hermenegild, Saint 西哥特王子 8—41b
赫尔门斯 Hermonthis 埃及古城 8—43b
赫尔蒙山 Hermon, Mount 亚洲山名 8—43a
赫尔米雷斯 Gelmírez, Diego 西班牙主教 7—48e
赫尔莫尔德(博绍的) Helmold of Bosau 德国历史学家 8—4c
赫尔内斯石碑 Helnaes Stone 丹麦石碑 8—4e
赫尔尼基人 Hernici 意大利古代民族 8—44e
赫尔珀 Helper, Hinton Rowan 美国作家 8—5b
赫尔普曼 Helpmann, Sir Robert (Murray) 澳大利亚舞蹈家 8—5c
赫尔斯 Hulls, Jonathan 英国发明家 8—231e
赫尔斯 Hulse, Russell Alan 美国物理学家 8—231f
赫尔斯顿 Helston 英格兰城镇 8—7a
赫尔斯氏病 Hers' disease 疾病 8—51a
赫尔斯坦 Helstein, Ralph 美国劳工领袖 8—7a
赫尔松 Kherson 乌克兰州名 9—259e
赫尔松 Kherson 乌克兰城市 9—259e
赫尔旺 Hirwaun 威尔士地名 8—95f
赫尔韦斯 Helwys, Thomas 英国宗教领袖 8—7f
赫尔维蒂人 Helvetii 凯尔特民族 8—7c
赫尔维乌斯·普里斯库斯 Helvidius Priscus 罗马哲学家 8—7d
赫尔西恩岛 Helsion Island (Pacific Ocean) 太平洋岛屿 8—6f
赫尔希 Hershey 美国居民区 8—52e
赫尔希 Hershey, A. D. 美国生物学家 8—52f
赫尔希 Hershey, Milton Snavely 美国企业家 8—52f
赫尔峡谷 Hells Canyon 美国峡谷 8—2a
赫尔辛格 Helsingør 丹麦城市 8—5f
赫尔辛基 Helsinki 芬兰首都 8—6a
《赫尔辛基协议》 Helsinki Accords 欧洲历史 8—6d
《赫尔辛基新闻》 Helsingen Sanomat 芬兰报纸 8—5f
赫尔兹 Herz, Henri 奥地利音乐家 8—55d
赫尔佐格 Hertzog, J(ames) B(arry) M(unnik) 南非总理 8—54d
赫尔佐克 Herzog, Chaim 以色列总统 8—56d
赫耳 Hull, Albert Wallace 美国物理学家 8—230d
赫耳玛佛洛狄忒 Hermaphroditus 希腊神话人物 8—41b
赫耳墨斯 Hermes 希腊神话人物 8—41e
赫耳墨斯秘义书 Hermetic writings 希腊文献 8—42a
赫耳墨头柱 herm 希腊宗教 8—40b
赫菲斯托斯 Hephaestus 希腊火神 8—30b
赫菲斯托斯神庙 Hephaestus, Temple of 希腊神庙 8—30c
赫格西普斯,圣 Hegesippus, Saint 希腊历史学家 7—563b

赫格希默 Hergesheimer, Joseph 美国作家 8—39d
赫-古尔贝尔 Høegh-Guldberg, Ove 丹麦政治家 8—114b
赫赫 Neheh (Egyptian religion) 埃及宗教 12—68a
赫赫人 Hehe 非洲民族 7—563d
赫基默 Herkimer 美国村庄 8—40a
赫基默 Herkimer, Nicholas 美国军人 8—40a
赫贾吉 Ḥajjāj (ibn Yūsuf ath-Thaqafī), al- 伍麦叶王朝总督 7—415e
赫卡 heka 古埃及宗教 7—571a
赫卡柏 Hecuba 希腊传说人物 7—554a
赫卡泰奥斯(米利都的) Hecataeus of Miletus 希腊作家 7—551e
赫卡忒 Hecate 希腊女神 7—551e
赫卡特海峡 Hecate Strait 加拿大海峡 7—551f
赫卡通皮洛斯 Hecatompylos 古安息人城市 7—551f
赫克 khirqah 伊斯兰教 9—260a
赫克尔 Heckel, Erich 德国画家 7—552f
赫克曼 Heckman, James J. 美国经济学家、教育家 7—553c
赫克曼 Heckmann, Otto (Hermann Leopold) 德国天文学家 7—553d
赫克瑟姆 Hexham 英格兰城镇 8—66a
赫克特 Hecht, Ben 美国作家 7—552b
赫克托耳 Hector 希腊神话人物 7—553f
赫克谢尔 Heckscher, Eli Filip 瑞典经济学家 7—553e
赫库兰尼姆 Herculaneum 意大利古城 8—35f
赫拉 Hera 希腊宗教神名 8—30f
赫拉班 Hrabanus Magnentius 法兰克大主教 8—203b
赫拉波维茨基 Khrapovitsky, Antony 俄国大主教 9—264f
赫拉岛 Hiera (island, Italy) 意大利岛屿 8—72a
赫拉德茨-克拉洛韦 Hradec Králové 捷克城镇 8—203b
赫拉夫-里内特 Graaff-Reinet (historical district, South Africa) 南非古地名 7—234f
赫拉夫-里内特 Graaff-Reinet 南非城镇 7—234f
赫拉克勒斯 Heracles 希腊-罗马神话人物 8—31d
赫拉克利德斯·本都库斯 Heracleides Ponticus 希腊哲学家 8—31b
赫拉克利特 Heracleitus 希腊哲学家 8—31b
赫拉克利翁 Heracleon 诺斯替教哲学家 8—31c
赫拉克洛纳斯 Heraclonas 拜占廷皇帝 8—32c
赫拉神殿 Heraeum 希腊神殿 8—32c
赫拉斯科夫 Kheraskov, Mikhail Matveyevich 俄国诗人 9—259d
赫拉特 Herāt 阿富汗省份 8—33b
赫拉特 Herāt 阿富汗城市 8—33c
赫拉特地毯 Herāt carpet 工艺品 8—33d
赫拉特画派 Herāt school 绘画 8—33e
赫兰尼科斯(莱斯沃斯的) Hellanicus of Lesbos 希腊历史学家 7—575e
赫勒 Heller, Robert 美国魔术师 8—1d
赫勒敦 Khaldūn, Ibn 穆斯林历史学家 9—253f
赫勒尔德港 Port Herald (Malaŵi) 马拉维城镇 13—445e
赫勒拉龙 Herrerasaurus 古生物学 8—49f
赫勒诺斯 Helenus 希腊传说人物 7—572d
赫勒斯滂 Hellespont (strait, Turkey) 土耳其海峡 8—1e
赫勒万 Ḥulwān 埃及古村落 8—232d
赫雷弗灵恩湖 Grevelingen Lake 荷兰湖泊 7—305f
赫雷罗兰 Hereroland 纳米比亚地区 8—39a
赫雷罗人 Herero 民族 8—38f
赫雷斯 Jerez de García Salinas 墨西哥城市 8—569c
赫雷斯-德拉弗龙特拉 Jerez de la Frontera 西班牙城市 8—569c
赫雷斯男爵(第四) Herries, John Maxwell, 4th Baron 苏格兰贵族 8—50b
赫雷肖夫 Herreshoff, Nathanael Greene 美国工程师 8—49f
赫楞 Hellen 希腊神话人物 7—576c
赫里福德 Hereford 英格兰城市 8—37e
赫里福德伯爵(第一) Hereford, William FitzOsbern, 1st Earl of 法国贵族 8—38a
赫里福德公爵 Hereford, Henry, Duke of 英格兰国王 8—38a
赫里福德郡 Herefordshire 英格兰单一政区 8—38c
赫里福德牛 Hereford 牛品种 8—37f
赫里福德-伍斯特 Hereford and Worcester 英格兰旧郡名 8—38a
赫里霍尔 Herihor 埃及国王 8—39d
赫里克 Herrick, James Bryan 美国医生 8—50a
赫里克 Herrick, Robert 英国诗人 8—50a
赫里曼 Herriman, George 美国漫画家 8—50c
赫里欧 Herriot, Édouard 法国总理 8—50e
赫里斯特斯 Christus, Petrus 佛兰德斯画家 4—211b
赫里索洛拉斯 Chrysoloras, Manuel 希腊学者 4—216c
赫里沃德(觉醒的) Hereward the Wake 英国历史 8—39c
赫里谢金德尔 Harishchandra 印度作家 7—477d
赫里兹地毯 Heriz carpet 伊朗工艺品 8—39f
赫理斯乐队 Hollies, the 英国五人摇滚乐队 8—133d
赫利奥波利斯 Heliopolis 古埃及城市 7—574b
赫利奥波利斯 Heliopolis (ancient Syria) 叙利亚古城 7—574b
赫利奥多罗斯(埃美萨的) Heliodorus of Emesa 希腊作家 7—573e
赫利俄斯 Helios 希腊宗教神祇 7—574b
赫列勃尼科夫 Khlebnikov, Velimir Vladimirovich 俄国诗人 9—260d
赫林 Herrin 美国城市 8—50c
赫林顿 Herrington, Arthur William Sidney 美国工程师 8—50e
赫林卡 Hlinka, Andrej 斯洛伐克自治派领袖 8—106e
赫隆达斯 Herondas (Greek poet) 希腊诗人 8—48d
赫卢 Hélou, Charles (Alexandre) 黎巴嫩总统 8—5b
赫卢赫卢韦野生动物保护区 Hluhluwe Game Reserve 南非野生动物保护区 8—106f
赫鲁恩·范·普林斯特勒 Groen van Prinsterer, Guillaume 荷兰政治家 7—317e
赫鲁利人 Heruli 民族 8—55b
赫鲁普 Hørup, Viggo 丹麦政治家 8—187b
赫鲁绍夫斯基 Hrušovský, Ivan 斯洛伐克作曲家 8—203e
赫鲁特方丹 Grootfontein 纳米比亚城镇 7—319a
赫鲁晓夫 Khrushchev, Nikita (Sergeyevich) 苏联领导人 9—264f
赫伦 Heron of Alexandria (Greek geometer) 希腊数学家 8—48d
赫伦岛 Heron Island 澳大利亚岛屿 8—48d
赫罗达斯 Herodas 希腊诗人 8—45f
赫罗纳 Gerona 西班牙省份 7—99b
赫罗纳 Gerona 西班牙城市 7—99c
赫罗斯维塔 Hrosvitha 德国诗人 8—203d
赫罗特 Groote, Geert 荷兰教士、教育家 7—318e
赫罗图 Hertzsprung-Russell diagram 天文学 8—55a
赫罗兹尼 Hrozný, Bedřich 捷克考古学家 8—203d
赫洛特里 Hlothere 肯特国王 8—106f
《赫马牧人书》 Shepherd of Hermas 基督教 15—304b
赫迈扎尼 Hamadhānī, al- 阿拉伯语言学家 7—435e
赫曼斯沃克 Hermansverk 挪威城市 8—41a
赫梅里 Hemery, David (Peter) 英国运动员 8—9a
赫梅利尼茨基 Khmelnytskyy 乌克兰州名 9—260e
赫梅利尼茨基 Khmelnytskyy 乌克兰城市 9—260f
赫梅利尼茨基 Khmelnitsky, Bohdan 哥萨克人首领 9—260e
赫门兹 Hemans, Felicia Dorothea 英国诗人 8—8a
赫米尔布尔 Hamīrpur 印度北方邦城市 7—444b
赫米尔布尔 Hamīrpur 印度喜马偕尔邦城市 7—444b
赫米斯小行星 Hermes 天文学 8—42a
赫明 Heminge, John 英国演员 8—9d
赫莫克拉特斯 Hermocrates 古希腊外交家 8—43a
赫默尔亨普斯特德 Hemel Hempstead 英格兰城镇 8—9a
赫默肯 Hemerken, Thomas 荷兰神学家 8—9a
赫姆别尔德尔 Khem-Beldyr (Russia) 俄罗斯城市 9—259d
赫纳昆剑麻 henequen (*Agave fourcroydes*) 植物 8—14a

赫尼 Henie, Sonja 美国运动员 8—15b
赫努曼格尔 Hanumāngarh 印度城市 7—466e
赫努姆 Khnum 古埃及丰产神 9—261f
赫普 Hep (Egyptian god) 埃及神名 8—29a
赫普尔怀特 Hepplewhite, George 英国家具设计师 8—30c
赫普沃思 Hepworth, Dame (Jocelyn) Barbara 英国雕刻家 8—30e
赫丘利斯 Hercules (Greco-Roman mythology) 希腊罗马神话 8—36d
赫丘利斯灯塔 Hercules, Tower of 古罗马灯塔 8—36d
赫丘利斯之杖 Hercules' club (plant) 植物 8—36e
赫塞尔里格 Hesilrige, Sir Arthur, 2ND BARONET 英国政治家 8—57c
赫塞尔廷 Heseltine, Philip 英国作曲家 8—57a
赫斯 Hess, Dame Myra 英国钢琴家 8—58f
赫斯 Hess, Moses 德国新闻工作者 8—58e
赫斯 Hoess, Rudolf Franz 纳粹党徒 8—114d
赫斯 Hess, Victor Francis 奥地利物理学家 8—59b
赫斯 Hess, Walter Rudolf 瑞士生理学家 8—59b
赫斯 Hess, (Walter Richard) Rudolf 德国纳粹领袖 8—58f
赫斯堡 Hesburgh, Theodore M(artin) 美国教育家 8—56f
赫斯顿 Heston, Willie 美国运动员 8—60f
赫斯顿 Hurston, Zora Neale 美国民俗学家 8—266c
赫斯基森 Huskisson, William 英国政治家 8—268c
赫斯科维茨 Herskovits, Melville J. 美国人类学家 8—53a
赫斯珀里得斯 Hesperides 希腊神话人物 8—58b
赫斯珀洛斯 Hesperus 希腊罗马神话 8—58d
赫斯特 Hurst, Fannie 美国作家 8—266b
赫斯特 Hearst, Patricia (Campbell) 美国赫斯报系继承人 7—542a
赫斯特 Hearst, William Randolph 美国报纸发行人 7—542b
赫斯特德 Husted, Marjorie Child 美国家政学家、实业家 8—269e
赫斯特蒙苏 Herstmonceux 英格兰乡村 8—53b
赫斯提 Hestia 希腊宗教灶神 8—60d
赫塔费 Getafe 西班牙城镇 7—104b
赫特 Hurt, Mississippi John 美国歌手 8—266c
赫特福德 Hertford 英格兰城镇教区 8—53c
赫特福德伯爵 Hertford, Edward Seymour, earl of, BARON BEAUCHAMP 英格兰贵族 8—53c
赫特福德伯爵 Hertford, Edward Seymour, earl of 英格兰摄政 8—53c
赫特福德伯爵(第六) Hertford, Richard de Clare, 6th earl of 英格兰贵族 8—53d
赫特福德郡 Hertfordshire 英格兰郡名 8—53d
赫特林 Hertling, Georg (Friedrich), Graf von 德国政治家 8—53e
赫特纳 Hettner, Alfred 德国地理学家 8—63e
赫特森 Hutson, Don 美国运动员 8—271d
赫特维希 Hertwig, Oskar (Wilhelm August) 德国胚胎学家 8—53e
赫特维希 Hertwig, Richard (Carl Wilhelm Theodor) von 德国生物学家 8—53f
赫梯人 Hittite 民族 8—105e
赫梯象形文字 Hittite hieroglyphic writing 文字 8—106a
赫梯语 Hittite language 语言 8—106b
赫托夫 Hedtoft(-Hansen), Hans (Christian) 丹麦政治家 7—555a
赫瓦尔 Hvar 克罗地亚岛屿 8—275e
赫瓦莱那 hvarenah 琐罗亚斯德教概念 8—275e
赫威赛人 Hwicce 民族 8—276c
赫维 Hervey, John 英国政治家 8—55b
赫维(伊克沃斯的) Hervey (of Ickworth), John Hervey, Baron 英国政治家 8—55b
赫维留 Hevelius, Johannes 波兰天文学家 8—64d
赫维什 Heves 匈牙利州名 8—64d
赫维湾 Hervey Bay 澳大利亚城市 8—55c
赫维西 Hevesy, George Charles de 匈牙利化学家 8—64e
赫维兹多斯拉夫 Hviezdoslav 斯洛伐克诗人 8—275f
赫沃皮茨基 Chłopicki, (Grzegorz) Józef 波兰将军 4—183d
赫西 Hersey, John (Richard) 美国作家 8—52e
赫西 Hussey, Obed 美国发明家 8—269c
赫西奥德 Hesiod 希腊诗人 8—57d
赫西基奥斯(亚历山大城的) Hesychius OF ALEXANDRIA 希腊词典作者 8—61a
赫西基乌斯(米利都) Hesychius OF MILETUS 拜占廷历史学家 8—61b
赫西奇乌斯(耶路撒冷的) Hesychius OF JERUSALEM 基督教神学家 8—61b
赫希巴赫 Herschbach, Dudley R(obert) 美国化学家 8—51a
赫希斯特公司 Hoechst Aktiengesellschaft 德国企业 8—114a
赫歇尔 Heschel, Abraham Joshua 犹太哲学家、神学家 8—57a
赫歇尔 Herschel, Caroline Lucretia 英国天文学家 8—51b
赫歇尔 Herschel, Sir John (Frederick William) 英国天文学家 8—51c
赫歇尔 Herschel, Sir William (Frederick) 英国天文学家 8—51f
赫胥黎 Huxley, Sir Andrew Fielding 英国生理学家 8—272f
赫胥黎 Huxley, Aldous (Leonard) 英国作家 8—272d
赫胥黎 Huxley, Hugh Esmor 英国分子生物学家 8—273a
赫胥黎 Huxley, Sir Julian (Sorell) 英国生物学家 8—273a
赫胥黎 Huxley, T(homas) H(enry) 英国生物学家 8—273c
赫伊津哈 Huizinga, Johan 荷兰历史学家 8—229d
赫伊斯曼 Huysman, Roelof (Dutch humanist) 荷兰人文学者 8—275a
赫泽勒 Gezelle, Guido 佛兰芒教士、诗人 7—106d
赫扎里巴克 Hazārībāg 印度城市 7—535c
赫扎里巴克野生动物保护区 Hazārībāg Wildlife Sanctuary 印度自然保护区 7—535c
赫扎努夫 Chrzanów 波兰城市 4—217a
赫哲语 Hezhen language 中国语言 8—68c
赫哲族 Hezhen 中国民族 8—68b
赫兹 hertz 计量单位 8—53f
赫兹 Hertz, Gustav (Ludwig) 德国物理学家 8—54a
赫兹 Hertz, Henrik 丹麦作家 8—54b
赫兹 Hertz, Heinrich (Rudolf) 德国物理学家 8—54b
褐鹎 brownbul 鸟类 3—195c
褐黄病 xanthosis (medicine) 疾病 18—373d
褐栎 brown oak 植物 3—194e
褐煤 brown coal 矿物 3—194d
褐煤 lignite 矿物 10—94d
褐色轰炸机 Brown Bomber, The (boxer) 美国拳击运动员 3—194d
褐衫队 Brownshirts (Nazi Germany) 纳粹德国组织 3—197f
褐蛇 brown snake 爬行动物 3—194e
褐鹈鹕 brown pelican (*Pelecanus occidentalis*) 鸟类 3—194e
褐铁矿 limonite 矿物 10—106a
褐隐士蛛 brown recluse 节肢动物 3—194e
褐藻 brown algae 藻类 3—194a
褐藻门 Phaeophyta 植物学 13—216f
褐蛛 brown spider 节肢动物 3—194f
褐鳟 brown trout (*Salmo trutta*) 鱼类 3—195a
鹤 crane 鸟类 4—567e
鹤壁 Hebi 中国城市 7—549f
鹤冈 Tsuruoka 日本城市 17—251e
鹤岗 Hegang 中国城市 7—556e
鹤立岗 Hao-li (China) 中国城市 7—467b
鹤鸵 cassowary 鸟类 3—506e
鹤鸵类 casuariiform 鸟类 3—516f
鹤望兰 bird-of-paradise flower (*Strelitzia reginae*) 草本植物 2—489d
鹤屋南北四世 Tsuruya Namboku IV 日本剧作家 17—251f
鹤形类 gruiform 动物学 7—328b
鹤嘴锄 mattock 农具 11—32e
黑瘤病 black knot 植物病害 2—513c

黑暗时代 Dark Ages 西欧历史 5—150c
黑巴蒂 Black Barty 海盗 2—510a
黑斑病 black spot 植物病害 2—516b
黑斑羚 impala (*Aepyceros melampus*) 哺乳动物 8—345a
黑帮分子 Black Hundreds 俄国政治组织成员 2—513b
黑豹党 Black Panther Party 美国黑人政党 2—514c
黑贝尔 Hebbel, (Christian) Friedrich 德国戏剧家 7—548c
黑镖客 thug 印度匪徒 17—68f
黑布拉 Hebra, Ferdinand von 奥地利医生 7—550a
黑彩陶器 black-figure pottery 希腊陶器 2—511d
黑长尾猴 grivet 哺乳动物 7—317b
黑潮 Kuroshio 太平洋洋流 9—403e
黑辰砂 metacinnabar 矿物 11—147b
黑川纪章 Kurokawa Kisho 日本建筑师 9—403a
黑刺李 blackthorn (*Prunus spinosa*) 木本植物 2—521a
黑德 Head, Bessie Emery 非洲小说家 7—537f
黑德尔 Khiḍr (Ottoman admiral) 奥斯曼帝国海军上将 9—259f
黑德尔 Khiḍr, al- 伊斯兰教传说人物 9—259f
黑德兰港 Port Hedland 澳大利亚城镇、港口 13—445d
黑电气石 schorl 矿物 15—129f
黑顶白颊林莺 blackpoll warbler 鸟类 2—520a
黑顶林莺 blackcap (*Sylvia atricapilla*) 鸟类 2—518e
黑洞 black hole 天文学 2—512e
黑短袜丑闻 Black Sox Scandal 美国棒球丑闻 2—516a
黑尔 Hare, David 英国剧作家 7—475b
黑尔 Hale, Edward Everett 美国作家 7—418f
黑尔 Hale, Horatio (Emmons) 美国人类学家 7—419b
黑尔 Hare, Sir John 英国演员 7—475c
黑尔 Hale, John Parker 美国律师、参议员 7—419c
黑尔 Hale, Lucretia Peabody 美国作家 7—419d
黑尔 Hale, Sir Matthew 英国法学家 7—419d
黑尔 Hale, Nathan 美国军人 7—419f
黑尔 Hale, Sarah Josepha 美国作家 7—419f
黑尔 Hare, William 爱尔兰杀人犯 7—475c
黑尔福德 Herford 德国城市 8—39c
黑尔戈兰 Helgoland 德国岛屿 7—572e
《黑尔戈兰-桑给巴尔条约》 Helgoland-Zanzibar Treaty 英-德条约 7—572f
黑尔·怀特 Hale White, William 英国作家 7—420b
《黑尔-霍斯-卡廷法》(1933) Hare-Hawes-Cutting Act 美国法案 7—475c
黑尔佳,圣 Helga, Saint 俄罗斯圣徒 7—572d
黑尔马施豪森的罗杰 Helmarshausen, Roger of 德意志修士 8—2c
黑尔马施豪森的罗杰 Roger of Helmarshausen 德意志修士 14—352e
黑尔曼施塔特 Hermannstadt (Romania) 罗马尼亚城市 8—41a
黑尔姆布雷希特 Helmbrecht (literary hero) 文学史诗主人公 8—2c
黑尔姆施泰特 Helmstedt 德国城市 8—4e
黑尔讷 Herne 德国城市 8—44b
黑尔什姆子爵(第一) Hailsham (of Hailsham), Douglas McGarel Hogg, 1st Viscount 英国法官、政治家 7—411d
黑尔斯 Hales, Stephen 英国植物学家 7—420d
黑尔滕 Herten 德国城市 8—53b
黑尔韦格 Hellweg 德国西部高原 8—2a
黑尔韦格 Herwegh, Georg 德国诗人 8—55d
黑尔佐格 Herzog, Isaac Halevi 犹太学者 8—56e
黑方尖碑 Black Obelisk 亚述纪念碑 2—514b
黑肺 black lung 疾病 2—513f
黑粉病 smut 禾谷类病害 15—456d
黑弗里尔 Haverhill 美国城市 7—519d
黑弗里尔热 Haverhill fever 疾病 7—519e
黑弗灵 Havering 英格兰自治市 7—519e
黑钙土 chernozem 土壤 4—126f
黑格 Heeger, Alan J. 美国化学家 7—555d
黑格 Haig, Douglas Haig, 1st Earl 英国军人 7—410a
黑格 Hägg, Gunder 瑞典运动员 7—406d
黑格 Haig, The (golfer) 美国运动员 7—410c
黑格尔 Hegel, Georg Wilhelm Friedrich 德国哲学家 7—556f
黑格尔主义 Hegelianism 哲学 7—559d
黑格隆德 Hägglund, Joel Emmanuel (radical leader) 美国激进派领袖 7—407a
黑格斯敦 Hagerstown 美国城市 7—406c
黑格斯粒子 Higgs particle 物理学 8—73f
黑寡妇 black widow 蜘蛛 2—517c
黑海 Black Sea 欧洲内陆海 2—515d
黑海鲁季 Harūj al-Aswad, al- 利比亚高原 7—496d
黑河 Hei He 中国河流 7—563e
黑河 Heihe 中国城市 7—565f
黑褐煤 black lignite 矿物 2—513f
黑喉石鵰 stonechat (species *Saxicola torquata*) 鸟类 16—250f
黑狐 black fox 哺乳动物 2—512b
黑胡椒 black pepper (*Piper nigrum*) 藤本植物 2—514d
黑胡桃 black walnut (*Juglans nigra*) 木本植物 2—517b
黑胡子 Blackbeard (pirate) 海盗 2—517d
黑桦 black birch 木本植物 2—510d
黑吉乌斯 Hegius, Alexander 德国教育家 7—563c
黑尖鲨 blacktip shark 鱼类 2—521a
黑角 Pointe-Noire 刚果港口、城镇 13—389f
黑脚人 Blackfoot 印第安人群体 2—519b
黑金刚石 carbonado 矿物 3—444f
黑金镶嵌 niello 金属工艺品制造 12—180f
黑克尔 Hecker, Friedrich (Karl Franz) 德国政治家 7—553b
黑克尔 Hecker, Johann Julius 德国神学家 7—553c
黑克尔管 heckelphone 乐器 7—553a
黑里空大号 helicon 乐器 7—573a
黑里绍 Herisau 瑞士城市 8—39e
黑栎 black oak (*Quercus velutina*) 木本植物 2—514b
黑脸歌唱团表演 minstrel show 美国戏剧 11—266f
黑脸派 Kālāmukha (Hindu ascetic) 印度教苦行者 9—138e
黑脸山魈 drill (*Mandrillus leucophaeus*) 哺乳动物 5—424d
黑林 Hering, (Karl) Ewald (Konstantin) 德国生理学家 8—39e
黑林山 Black Forest 德国山区 2—511f
黑龙江 Heilongjiang (China) 东亚河流 7—566d
黑龙江 Heilongjiang 中国省份 7—566d
黑鲈 black bass 鱼类 2—510a
黑麦 rye (*Secale cereale*) 谷类作物 14—475e
黑麦草 ryegrass 草本植物 14—476a
黑麦威士忌酒 rye whiskey 酒类 14—475f
黑鳗藤属 Stephanotis 植物学 16—220b
黑猫 black cat 哺乳动物 2—510d
黑莓 blackberry 灌木 2—517d
黑霉 black mold (plant disease) 植物病害 2—514a
黑锰矿 hausmannite 矿物 7—514b
黑弥撒 black mass 宗教活动 2—513f
黑幕揭发者 muckraker 美国作家 11—461a
黑尿热 blackwater fever 疾病 2—521c
黑啤酒 stout 酒类 16—257f
黑漆 black varnish 油漆 2—517a
黑旗乐队 Black Flag 美国乐队 2—511e
黑铅 black lead 矿物 2—513c
黑蜣 bess beetle 昆虫 2—436a
黑热病 kala-azar 疾病 9—137e
黑人邦 black state 南非黑人地区 2—516c
黑人法令 black code 美国历史 2—510d
黑人国家主义 black nationalism 美国黑人政治运动 2—514b

黑人穆斯林运动 Black Muslim movement 美国宗教与文化组织 2—514a
黑人特性运动 Negritude 文学运动 12—67c
黑人戏剧 black theatre 美国戏剧运动 2—516f
黑人英语 Ebonics 美国英语方言 5—518e
黑人娱乐电视台 Black Entertainment Television 美国多媒体集团 2—511c
黑塞哥维那 Hercegovina 波斯尼亚和黑塞哥维那一部分 8—35f
黑塞哥维那 Herzegovina 波斯尼亚和黑塞哥维那一部分 8—55f
黑色电影 film noire 电影制作的风格 6—316a
黑色火药 black powder 炸药 2—515b
黑色喜剧 black comedy 文学 2—511a
黑色星期五 Black Friday 美国历史 2—512b
黑色页岩 black shale 岩石 2—515f
黑色幽默 black humour 文学 2—513b
黑色战争 Black War 澳大利亚历史 2—517b
黑森 Hessen 德国州名 8—59f
黑森-达姆施塔特 Hesse-Darmstadt 德国前伯爵领地 8—59e
黑森-卡塞尔 Hesse-Kassel 德国前伯爵领地 8—59e
黑砂 black sand 矿物 2—515d
黑鲨 black shark 鱼类 2—516a
黑山 Karatepe 土耳其古城遗址 9—180a
黑山 Montenegro 欧洲国家 11—362d
黑山派诗人 Black Mountain poet 美国诗派成员 2—514a
黑衫党 Blackshirt 意大利法西斯组织 2—520b
黑衫队 Blackshirts (Nazi corps) 德国纳粹党卫军 2—520c
黑蛇 black snake 爬行动物 2—516a
黑石 Black Stone of Mecca 穆斯林圣物 2—516e
黑炻器 black basaltes (stoneware) 工艺品 2—510a
黑市 black market 非法交易 2—513f
黑手帮 Black Hand 美国歹徒帮伙 2—512c
黑手党 Mafia 意大利犯罪组织 10—377e
黑手社 Black Hand 欧洲历史 2—512b
黑水河 Black River 红河支流 2—515b
黑水鸡 water hen 鸟类 18—136a
黑斯 Heiss, Carol (Elizabeth) 美国花样滑冰运动员 7—570e
黑斯尔米尔 Haslemere 英格兰城镇 7—503e
黑斯廷斯 Hastings 苏格兰自治市 7—505c
黑斯廷斯 Hastings 美国城市 7—505d
黑斯廷斯 Hastings 新西兰城市 7—505d
黑斯廷斯 Hastings, Frank Abney 英国军人 7—506a
黑斯廷斯 Hastings, Warren 英国首相、驻印度总督 7—506a
黑斯廷斯 Hastings, William Hastings, Baron 英格兰外交家 7—506d
黑斯廷斯侯爵(第一) Hastings, Francis Rawdon-Hastings, 1st marquess of, 2nd earl of Moira 英国军人、殖民地官员 7—505e
黑斯廷斯战役 Hastings, Battle of 欧洲历史 7—505d
黑死病 Black Death 传染病 2—511a
黑素 melanin 生物色素 11—92e
黑素瘤 melanoma 疾病 11—92f
黑燧石 flint (mineral) 矿物 6—361c
黑太子 Black Prince, The 英国历史 2—515b
黑太子红宝石 Black Prince's ruby 英国国王王冠上宝石 2—515b
《黑檀杂志》 Ebony 美国月刊 5—519a
黑陶 black pottery 中国古陶器 2—514f
黑体 blackbody 物理学 2—518b
黑体字 black letter 书法 2—513c
黑天 Krishna 印度教神祇 9—378a
黑天诞辰节 Janmāṣṭamī 印度教节日 8—534e
黑田长政 Kuroda Nagamasa 日本名将 9—402f
黑田清隆 Kuroda Kiyotaka 日本政治家 9—402f
黑铜矿 tenorite 矿物 16—545a
黑土 black earth 土壤 2—511c
黑土带 Black Belt 美国自然地理区 2—510c
黑尾鹿 black-tailed deer 哺乳动物 2—516f
黑沃尔特河 Black Volta River 非洲河流 2—517a
黑沃里尔河 Black Warrior River 美国河流 2—517c
黑钨矿 wolframite 矿物 18—310c
黑稀金矿 euxenite 矿物 6—177c
黑藓 black moss (plant) 植物 2—514a
黑线鳕 haddock (*Melanogrammus aeglefinus*) 鱼类 7—400e
黑乡 Black Country 英格兰工业区 2—511a
黑兴根 Hechingen 德国城市 7—552a
黑猩猩 chimpanzee 哺乳动物 4—159e
黑熊 Asiatic black bear (species *Selenarctos thibetanus*) 哺乳动物 1—553f
黑鸭 black duck (*Anas rubripes*) 鸟类 2—511b
黑眼豆 black-eyed pea 植物 2—511d
黑雁 brant (*Branta bernicla*) 鸟类 3—123d
黑羊王朝 Kara Koyunlu 土库曼部族联盟 9—173e
黑曜岩 obsidian 岩石 12—323f
黑伊 Hay 澳大利亚城镇 7—528c
黑衣兄弟会 Black Friar 宗教团体 2—512b
黑衣修士剧院 Blackfriars Theatre 伦敦城内剧院 2—519e
黑鹰 Black Hawk 美国印第安人领袖 2—512c
黑鱼 blackfish 鱼类 2—519a
黑云母 biotite 矿物 2—486e
黑泽明 Kurosawa Akira 日本电影导演 9—403b
黑杖 Black Rod 英国古代官职 2—515d
黑住教 Kurozumi-kyō 日本神道教教派 9—403f
黑兹尔顿 Hazleton 美国城市 7—535d
黑子 sunspot 天文学 16—344b
嘿轩 Mokken (Japanese scholar) 日本学者 11—314d
痕量元素 trace element 生物学 17—185b
亨比泽 Hembyze, Jan van 加尔文宗领袖 8—8f
亨伯河 Humber River 加拿大河流 8—243d
亨伯河口湾 Humber, River 英格兰海湾 8—243c
亨伯里陨石坑 Henbury Craters 澳大利亚陨石坑 8—12d
亨伯桥 Humber Bridge 英格兰悬索桥 8—243c
亨伯赛德 Humberside 英格兰地区名 8—243e
亨伯特一世 Humbert I 意大利伯爵 8—243e
亨策 Henze, Hans Werner 德国作曲家 8—28f
亨茨曼 Huntsman, Benjamin 英国发明家 8—262f
亨茨维尔 Huntsville 美国得克萨斯州城市 8—262f
亨茨维尔 Huntsville 美国亚拉巴马州城市 8—262f
亨德尔 Handl, Jacob 奥地利作曲家 7—458d
亨德克 Handke, Peter 奥地利作家 7—458c
亨德里克斯 Hendrix, Jimi 美国音乐家 8—13f
亨德里克斯 Hendricks, Thomas A(ndrews) 美国政治家 8—13e
亨德森 Henderson 美国肯塔基州城市 8—12e
亨德森 Henderson 美国内华达州城市 8—12f
亨德森 Henderson 美国北卡罗来纳州城市 8—12f
亨德森 Henderson, Arthur 英国政治家 8—13a
亨德森 Henderson, Alexander 苏格兰牧师 8—12f
亨德森 Henderson, (James) Fletcher 美国音乐家 8—13c
亨德森 Henderson, Lawrence Joseph 美国生物化学家 8—13c
亨德森 Henderson, Sir Nevile Meyrick 英国政治家 8—13d
亨德森 Henderson, Thomas 苏格兰天文学家 8—13d
亨厄洛 Hengelo 荷兰城镇 8—14c
亨吉斯特和霍萨 Hengist and Horsa 英国历史人物 8—14c
亨克 Genk 比利时城市 7—64a
亨克 hank 计算单位 7—460f
亨克尔 Heinkel, Ernst Heinrich 德国飞机设计师 7—568c
亨莱恩 Henlein, Konrad 德国政治家 8—15d
亨勒 Henle, Friedrich Gustav Jacob 德国病理学家 8—15c
亨勒氏襻 loop of Henle 解剖学 10—215a

亨里克-德卡瓦略 Henrique de Carvalho (Angola) 安哥拉城镇 8—16f
亨丽埃塔·安妮(英格兰的) Henrietta Anne of England 英格兰公主 8—16e
亨丽埃塔·玛丽亚 Henrietta Maria 英格兰王后 8—16e
亨利 Henry 统治者之名 8—16f
亨利 Henry 君士坦丁堡皇帝 8—17c
亨利 Henry 葡萄牙国王 8—23e
亨利 henry 物理学 8—24d
亨利 Henry, Alice 澳大利亚记者 8—26b
亨利 Henry, Joseph 美国科学家 8—26c
亨利 Henri, Robert 美国画家 8—16c
亨利 Henry, Patrick 美国政治家 8—26f
亨利 Henry, William 英国化学家 8—27b
亨利 Henley, William Ernest 英国作家 8—15e
亨利(埃诺的) Henry of Hainautwt 君士坦丁堡皇帝 8—25a
亨利(安茹的) Henry of Anjou 英格兰国王 8—24e
亨利(奥特兰茨的) Henry of Oatlands 英国贵族 8—25b
亨利(波旁的) Henry of Bourbon 法国国王 8—24f
亨利(博林布鲁克) Henry Bolingbroke 英格兰国王 8—24e
亨利(捕鸟者) Henry the Fowler 德意志国王 8—25c
亨利(布卢瓦的) Henry of Blois 英格兰主教 8—24e
亨利(短披风) Henry Curtmantle 英格兰国王 8—24e
亨利(菲茨恩普雷斯) Henry FitzEmpress 英格兰国王 8—24e
亨利(菲茨亨利) Henry FitzHenry 英格兰国王 8—24e
亨利(佛兰德的) Henry of Flanders 君士坦丁堡皇帝 8—24f
亨利(根特的) Henry of Ghent 法国哲学家、神学家 8—24f
亨利(航海家) Henry the Navigator 葡萄牙王子 8—25d
亨利(患病者) Henry the Sufferer 卡斯蒂利亚国王 8—26a
亨利(金雀花) Henry Plantagenet 英格兰国王 8—25b
亨利(九世) Henry (IX) 约克公爵 8—20f
亨利(慷慨的) Henry the Liberal 卡斯蒂利亚国王 8—25c
亨利(慷慨好施者) Mercedes, El de las 卡斯蒂利亚国王 11—124e
亨利(兰开斯特的) Henry of Lancasterwt 英格兰国王 8—25a
亨利(纳瓦拉的) Henry of Navarre 法国国王 8—25a
亨利(胖子) Henry the Fat 纳瓦拉国王 8—25c
亨利(七世) Henry (VII) 德意志国王 8—23b
亨利(三世) Henry (III) 英格兰国王 8—18c
亨利(杀兄者) Henry the Fratricide 卡斯蒂利亚国王 8—25c
亨利(圣者) Henry, Saint 神圣罗马皇帝 8—24e
亨利(狮子) Henry the Lion 萨克森公爵 8—25d
亨利(枢机主教—国王) Henry the Cardinal-King 葡萄牙国王 8—25c
亨利(私生子) Henry the Bastard 卡斯蒂利亚国王 8—25c
亨利(特拉斯塔马拉的) Henry of Trastámara 卡斯蒂利亚国王 8—25b
亨利(无能者) Henry the Impotent 卡斯蒂利亚国王 8—25c
亨利(贤明者) Henry Beauclerc 英格兰统治者之名 8—24e
亨利(小) Henry the Younger 不伦瑞克公爵 8—26b
亨利(幼王) Henry the Young King 英格兰国王 8—26a
亨利八世 Henry VIII 神圣罗马皇帝 8—17a
亨利八世 Henry VIII 英格兰国王 8—20b
亨利堡 Henry, Fort 美国战略据点 8—26c
《亨利·德雷伯星表》 Henry Draper Catalogue 天文学 8—27c
亨利定律 Henry's law 化学 8—27d
亨利二世 Henry II Jasomirgott 奥地利公爵 8—17a
亨利二世 Henry II 不伦瑞克公爵 8—17b
亨利二世 Henry II 英格兰国王 8—17e
亨利二世 Henry II 法国国王 8—20f
亨利二世 Henry II 神圣罗马皇帝 8—21e
亨利二世 Henry II 纳瓦拉国王 8—23e
亨利二世 Henry II 巴代利亚公爵 8—23f
亨利二世 Henry II 卡斯蒂利亚国王 8—24c
"亨利"号 Hunley 美国历史 8—256f
亨利皇家赛船会 Henley Royal Regatta 体育赛事 8—15f
亨利角 Henry, Cape 美国海岬 8—26b
亨利·拉斯佩 Henry Raspe 德意志僭主 8—25b
亨利六世 Henry VI 神圣罗马皇帝 8—17a
亨利六世 Henry VI 神圣罗马皇帝 8—23a
亨利六世 Henry VI 英格兰国王 8—19d
亨利·皮蒂尔国家公园 Henri Pittier National Park 委内瑞拉公园 8—16d
亨利七世 Henry VII 英格兰国王 8—19e
亨利七世 Henry VII 神圣罗马皇帝 8—23c
亨利三世 Henry III 英格兰国王 8—18c
亨利三世 Henry III 法国国王 8—21b
亨利三世 Henry III 神圣罗马皇帝 8—22a
亨利三世 Henry III 法国国王 8—23e
亨利三世 Henry III 萨克森公爵 8—23f
亨利三世 Henry III 卡斯蒂利亚国王 8—24c
亨利森 Henryson, Robert 苏格兰诗人 8—27e
亨利山 Henry Mountains 美国山脉 8—27c
亨利十二世 Henry XII 巴伐利亚公爵 8—17b
亨利十世 Henry X 巴伐利亚公爵 8—17b
亨利四世 Henry IV 神圣罗马皇帝 8—17a
亨利四世 Henry IV 英格兰国王 8—18e
亨利四世 Henry IV 法国国王 8—21c
亨利四世 Henry IV 神圣罗马皇帝 8—22b
亨利四世 Henry IV 卡斯蒂利亚国王 8—24d
亨利四世风格 Henry IV style 法国艺术与建筑风格 8—27c
亨利·苏索 Henry Suso (German mystic) 德国神秘主义者 8—25c
《亨利王约》 Henrician Articles 波兰历史 8—16d
亨利五世 Henry V 英格兰国王 8—19a
亨利五世 Henry V 神圣罗马皇帝 8—22e
亨利希(费尔德克的) Heinrich von Veldeke 德国诗人 7—568e
亨利希(梅尔克的) Heinrich von Melk 德国诗人 7—568e
亨利希(莫龙根的) Heinrich von Morungen 德国诗人 7—568e
亨利希·尤利乌斯 Heinrich Julius 不伦瑞克公爵 7—568f
亨利一世 Henry I 英格兰国王 8—17c
亨利一世 Henry I 法兰西国王 8—20f
亨利一世 Henry I 德意志国王 8—21e
亨利一世 Henry I 海地统治者 8—23d
亨利一世 Henry I 纳瓦拉国王 8—23d
亨利一世 Henry I 卡斯蒂利亚国王 8—24b
亨利一世 Henry I 神圣罗马皇帝 8—24d
亨纳·安里恩 Henne am Rhyn, Otto 瑞士历史学家 8—15f
亨内克 Huneker, James Gibbons 美国艺术评论家 8—254b
亨内平 Hennepin, Louis 方济各会教士 8—16a
亨尼希 Hennig, Willi 德国动物学家 8—16b
亨佩尔 Hempel, Carl Gustav 美国哲学家 8—11d
亨普斯特德 Hempstead 美国城镇 8—11d
亨奇 Hench, Philip Showalter 美国医生 8—12e
亨萨克 Hunsaker, Jerome C(larke) 美国工程师 8—257a
亨森 Henson, Jim 美国演员 8—28c
亨森 Henson, Matthew Alexander 美国探险家 8—28e
亨森 Hensen, Victor 德国生理学家 8—28a
亨舍尔 Henschel, Sir (Isidor) George 英国音乐家 8—27f
亨施 Hänsch, Theodor W. 德国物理学家 7—463d
亨施克 Henschke, Alfred (Expressionist writer) 德国作家 8—27f
亨斯洛 Henslow, John Stevens 英国植物学家 8—28b
亨斯洛 Henslowe, Philip 英国剧场经理 8—28b
亨斯滕贝格 Hengstenberg, Ernst Wilhelm 德国神学家 8—14f
亨特 Hunter, Alberta 美国歌唱家 8—258e
亨特 Hunter, Catfish 美国职业棒球运动员 8—258f
亨特 Hunter, Clementine 美国民间艺术家 8—258f

亨特 Hunter-Gault, Charlayne 美国记者 8—259c
亨特 Hunter, David 美国军人 8—259a
亨特 Hunt, Henry 英国政治家 8—257d
亨特 Hunt (of Llanfair Waterdine), (Henry Cecil) John Hunt, Baron 英国军人 8—257d
亨特 Hunt, Harriot Kezia 美国医生、改革者 8—257c
亨特 Hunt, H(aroldson) L(afayette) 美国企业家 8—257b
亨特 Hunt, (James Henry) Leigh 英国作家 8—257e
亨特 Hunter, Mary (writer) 美国作家 8—259b
亨特 Hunt, Mary Hannah 美国戒酒运动领导人 8—257f
亨特 Hunt, Richard Morris 美国建筑师 8—258b
亨特 Hunt, R. Timothy 英国科学家 8—258a
亨特 Hunt, Ward 美国最高法院大法官 8—258c
亨特 Hunter, William 英国医生 8—259b
亨特 Hunt, William Holman 英国画家 8—258c
亨特 Hunt, William Morris 美国画家 8—258d
亨特-高尔特 Hunter, John 英国外科医生 8—259a
亨特河 Hunter River 澳大利亚河流 8—259d
亨特利侯爵(第一)和伯爵(第六) Huntly, George Gordon, 1st marquess and 6th earl of 苏格兰阴谋家 8—262e
亨特氏综合征 Hunter's syndrome 疾病 8—259f
亨廷登 Huntingdon 英格兰城镇 8—261f
亨廷登郡 Huntingdonshire 英格兰区名 8—261f
亨廷顿 Huntington 美国印第安纳州城市 8—261f
亨廷顿 Huntington 美国纽约州城镇 8—262a
亨廷顿 Huntington 美国西弗吉尼亚州城市 8—262a
亨廷顿 Huntington, Collis P(otter) 美国企业家 8—262b
亨廷顿 Huntington, Ellsworth 美国地理学家 8—262c
亨廷顿 Huntington, Henry E. 美国企业家、收藏家 8—262c
亨廷顿 Huntingdon, Selina Hastings, Countess of 英国宗教领袖 8—261e
亨廷顿比奇 Huntington Beach 美国城市 8—262d
亨廷顿图书馆、画廊和植物园 Huntington Library, Art Gallery, and Botanical Gardens 美国机构 8—262d
亨肖 Henshaw, James Ene 尼日利亚剧作家 8—28a
恒常性现象 constancy phenomenon (psychology) 心理学 4—449a
恒河 Ganges River 亚洲河流 7—1a
恒河鳄 gavial (*Gavialis gangeticus*) 爬行动物 7—37a
恒河猴 rhesus monkey (*Macaca mulatta*) 哺乳动物 14—260a
恒河-亚穆纳河河间地区 Ganges-Yamuna Doab 印度地区 7—1a
恒伽王朝 Gaṅga DYNASTY 印度王朝 6—576e
恒温器 thermostat 装置 17—35d
恒温箱 incubator 隔热设备 8—354a
恒温箱雉 incubator bird 鸟类 8—354b
恒温性 homeothermy 生物学 8—144e
恒温性 homoiothermy 生物学 8—148a
恒星 star 天文学 16—194f
恒星时 sidereal time 天文学 15—353a
恒星周期 sidereal period 天文学 15—353a
桁架 truss 建筑 17—245b
鸻 plover 鸟类 13—374c
鸻属 Charadrius 生物学 4—61d
鸻形类 charadriiform 鸟类 4—60e
横滨 Yokohama 日本城市 18—453a
横波 transverse wave 物理学 17—200d
横渡太平洋赛 Transpacific Race 帆船比赛 17—198b
横断山脉 Hengduan Mountains 中国山脉 8—14b
横帆 square sail 帆具 16—167d
横帆双桅船 brig 帆船 3—154f
横贯加拿大公路 Trans-Canada Highway 加拿大公路 17—193e
横光利一 Yokomitsu Riichi 日本作家 18—453b
横墙(承重)结构 cross-wall construction (architecture) 建筑 5—33b
横山大观 Yokoyama Taikan 日本画家 18—453d
横纹肌 striated muscle 解剖学 16—276f
横须贺 Yokosuka 日本海港 18—453c
衡平法 equity 法律 6—108f
衡山 Heng Mountain 中国山脉 8—14d
衡水 Hengshui 中国城市 8—14d
衡阳 Hengyang 中国城市 8—14f
吽哆教 Humch'igyo (Korean religion) 朝鲜宗教 8—245b
轰炸机 bomber 军用飞机 3—22b
弘法大师 Kōbō Daishi (Buddhist saint) 佛教圣者 9—329b
弘历 Hongli 中国清朝皇帝 8—157f
弘前 Hirosaki 日本城市 8—94c
弘仁 Hongren 中国画家 8—158c
弘一 Hongyi 中国教育家、书法家 8—159a
弘治 Hongzhi 中国皇帝年号 8—159c
红百合木 lantern tree (*Crinodendron hookeranum*) 植物 9—489c
红柏 red cedar 木本植物 14—187e
红斑 erythema 皮肤病 6—125a
红斑狼疮 lupus erythematosus 疾病 10—290c
红斑性冻疮 erythema pernio 疾病 6—125b
红斑性肢痛病 erythermalgia 血管病 6—125b
红苞凤梨 billbergia 植物 2—473c
红宝石 ruby 宝石 14—438e
红堡 Red Fort 印度城堡 14—188f
红背蛛 redback 蜘蛛 14—191b
红彩陶器 red-figure pottery 希腊陶器 14—188d
红场 Red Square 俄罗斯首都莫斯科中心广场 14—190e
红蝽 red bug 昆虫 14—187c
红大麻哈鱼 sockeye salmon (*Oncorhynchus nerka*) 鱼类 15—478f
红党 Parti Rouge 加拿大政党 13—66f
红点鲑 char 鱼类 4—59c
红点鲑属 Salvelinus 鱼类 14—558a
红电气石 rubellite 矿物 14—436b
红翻石鹬 ruddy turnstone 鸟类 14—439f
红飞袋鼠 red flyer 有袋动物 14—188f
红蝠 red bat (*Lasiurus borealis*) 蝙蝠 14—187b
红锆石 hyacinth 矿物 8—276d
红汞 Mercurochrome (antiseptic) 抗菌剂 11—126c
红狗 Red Dog 扑克牌赌戏 14—188c
红鹳 flamingo 涉禽 6—347a
红果花楸 rowan (*Sorbus aucuparia*) 木本植物 14—425f
红果石蕊 British soldiers (*Cladonia cristatella*) 植物 3—168c
红海 Red Sea 非洲东北部与阿拉伯半岛之间海域 14—190b
红海省 Bahr al-Ahmar, al- 埃及省份 2—142e
红河 Red River 越南河流 14—189e
红河猪 red river hog 哺乳动物 14—189f
红胡子 Barbarossa 德意志国王、神圣罗马帝国皇帝 2—218e
红花 safflower (*Carthamus tinctorius*) 草本植物 14—496c
红花槭 red maple (*Acer rubrum*) 木本植物 14—189b
红绘 beni-e 日本木刻版画 2—384e
红尖晶石 ruby spinel 宝石 14—439a
红角鸮 scops owl 鸟类 15—147c
红脚鹬 redshank 鸟类 14—194b
红军 Red Army 苏联武装力量 14—186d
红军村 Krasnoarmiysk 乌克兰城市 9—372b
红兰姆酒 Red Rum 英国越野赛马 14—190a
红帘石 piedmontite 矿物 13—294a
红磷铁矿 strengite 矿物 16—275c
红榴石 carbuncle 宝石 3—449e
《红楼梦》 Hongloumeng 中国文学 8—157f
红卢奇 Krasny Luch 乌克兰城市 9—373a
红毛丹 rambutan (*Nephelium lappaceum*) 木本植物 14—138d
红毛窃蠹 deathwatch beetle (*Xestobium refuvillosum*) 昆虫 5—197b
红霉素 erythromycin 药物 6—126a

红门兰属 Orchis 植物学 12—447e
红牛剧院 Red Bull Theatre 英国剧院 14—187d
《红旗》 Hongqi 中国杂志 8—158a
红旗渠 Hongqi Qu 中国水利工程 8—158b
红千层属 Callistemon 植物学 3—356b
红雀仙人掌 redbird cactus (*Pedilanthus tithymaloides*) 植物 14—191b
红色伯爵 Red Earl 威尔士贵族 14—188d
红色高棉 Khmer Rouge 柬埔寨政治集团 9—261d
"红色精灵"和"蓝色喷流" red sprites and blue jets 闪电 14—190e
红色军团 Red Army Faction 联邦德国左翼恐怖组织 14—187a
红色旅 Red Brigades 意大利极左派恐怖组织 14—187c
红色男爵 Red Baron, The 德国航空家 14—187b
红色盆地 Red Basin (China) 中国四川盆地 14—187b
红色细陶器 terra sigillata ware 古罗马陶器 16—554c
红山文化 Hongshan culture 中国新石器文化 8—158e
红杉 redwood (*Sequoia sempervirens*) 木本植物 14—195c
红杉国家公园 Sequoia National Park 美国公园 15—220d
红杉属 Sequoia 植物学 15—220c
红衫运动 Red Shirt Movement 印度国民运动 14—190c
红砷镍矿 niccolite 矿物 12—167f
红十字会和红新月会 Red Cross and Red Crescent 慈善机构 14—187f
红树林植物 mangrove 植物学 10—459b
红水河 Hongshui He 中国河流 8—158f
红隼 kestrel 鸟类 9—245a
红统 Ang Thong 泰国城镇 1—339f
红头 Kizilbash 伊朗萨非王朝历史 9—312b
红头美洲鹫 turkey vulture (*Cathartes aura*) 鸟类 17—284d
红头潜鸭 redhead (*Aythya americana*) 鸟类 14—192f
红外辐射 infrared radiation 物理 8—384e
红外套 Red Jacket 塞内卡人首长 14—189b
红外天文学 infrared astronomy 天体研究 8—384d
红外源 infrared source 天文学 8—384e
红尾黑鲨 red-tailed black shark 鱼类 14—191a
红尾鸟 redstart 鸟类 14—194c
红卫兵 Red Guards 中国历史 14—188f
红文鸟 red munia (bird) 鸟类 14—189c
红沃尔特河 Red Volta River 西非河流 14—191a
红硒铜矿 umangite 矿物 17—334e
红细胞 erythrocyte 生物学 6—125e
红细胞压积 hematocrit 医学 8—8c
红细胞增多症 polycythemia 病理现象 13—412b
红蟹 red crab 甲壳动物 14—187f
红心 hearts 牌戏 7—543f
红锌矿 zincite 矿物 18—554b
红疣 erythrasma 疾病 6—125c
红雪 red snow 生物学 14—190d
红眼病 pinkeye (veterinary medicine) 牛眼病 13—314c
红眼雀 towhee 鸟类 17—180d
红眼鱼 rudd (*Scardinius erythrophthalmus*) 鱼类 14—439d
红伊凡 Ivan THE RED 莫斯科大公 8—492b
"红衣主教" Red Eminence, The 法国政治家 14—188d
红衣主教花 cardinal flower 植物 3—453e
红衣主教雀 cardinal (*Cardinalis* [formerly *Richmondena*] *cardinalis*) 鸟类 3—453d
红衣主教鱼 cardinal fish 鱼类 3—453e
红移 red shift 天文学 14—190c
红银矿 ruby silver 矿物 14—439a
红鲉 redfish (*Sebastes marinus*) 鱼类 14—192c
红釉 flambé glaze 中国瓷釉品种 6—345f
红与黑 Rouge et Noir (card game) 牌戏 14—419b
红云 Red Cloud 美国苏人首领 14—187e
红藻 red algae 藻类 14—186c
红藻门 Rhodophyta 生物学 14—269f
红蜘蛛 red spider 动物学 14—190e
红柱石 andalusite 矿物 1—324b
红字写印 rubrication 书法或印刷 14—438d
红嘴奎利亚雀 red-billed quelea (bird) 鸟类 14—187b
宏观经济学 macroeconomics 经济学 10—363d
虹 rainbow 气象学 14—127b
虹彩玻璃 lustred glass 玻璃工艺 10—293c
虹鳉 guppy (*Lebistes reticulatus*, also *Poecilia reticulata*) 鱼类 7—377e
虹膜 iris 解剖学 8—447c
虹桥国家保护区 Rainbow Bridge National Monument 美国自然保护区 14—127c
虹吸管 siphon 器具 15—401a
虹雉 monal 鸟类 11—329b
虹鳟 rainbow trout (*Salmo gairdneri*) 鱼类 14—127c
洪堡 Homburg 德国城市 8—143e
洪堡 Humboldt, Alexander von 德国科学家、探险家 8—243f
洪堡 Humboldt, (Karl) Wilhelm, Baron (Freiherr) von 德国语言学家 8—244e
洪堡冰川 Humboldt Glacier 格陵兰冰川 8—245a
洪堡河 Humboldt River 美国河流 8—245a
洪堡洋流 Humboldt Current (Pacific Ocean) 太平洋洋流 8—245a
洪贝尔(锡尔瓦坎迪达的) Humbert OF SILVA CANDIDA 法国枢机主教 8—243f
洪承畴 Hong Chengchou 中国大臣 8—155c
洪德 Hund, Friedrich (Hermann) 德国物理学家 8—252c
洪德库特 Hondecoeter, Melchior de 荷兰画家 8—151e
洪都拉斯 Honduras 中美洲国家 8—151e
洪都拉斯湾 Honduras, Gulf of 加勒比海海湾 8—152d
洪多歌曲 cante jondo 音乐 3—410f
洪谷子 Hung-ku-tzu 中国艺术家 8—254c
洪湖 Hong Hu 中国湖泊 8—155c
洪梅尔 Hummel, Johann Nepomuk 奥地利作曲家 8—248c
洪诺留 Honorius 教皇称号 8—160a
洪诺留 Honorius 西罗马帝国皇帝 8—160d
洪诺留(二世) Honorius (II) 敌对教皇 8—160b
洪诺留二世 Honorius II 教皇 8—160b
洪诺留三世 Honorius III 教皇 8—160c
洪诺留四世 Honorius IV 教皇 8—160d
洪诺留一世 Honorius I 教皇 0 100a
洪佩尔丁克 Humperdinck, Engelbert 德国作曲家 8—249f
洪仁玕 Hong Rengan 中国太平天国领导人 8—157a
洪森 Hun Sen 柬埔寨政治人物 8—251d
洪深 Hong Shen 中国戏剧家 8—157c
洪昇 Hong Sheng 中国文学家、戏曲作家 8—157d
洪水 flood 河水泛滥 6—362d
洪斯代尔 Honesdale 美国自治镇 8—153b
洪斯吕克 Hunsrück 德国山区 8—257a
洪特霍斯特 Honthorst, Gerrit van 荷兰画家 8—160f
洪武 Hongwu (Chinese emperor) 中国皇帝年号 8—159a
洪熙 Hongxi (Chinese emperor) 中国皇帝年号 8—159a
洪秀全 Hong Xiuquan 中国太平天国领导人 8—157d
洪泽湖 Hongze Hu 中国湖泊 8—159b
魟 ray 鱼类 14—169c
鸿基 Hong Gai 越南城市 8—155c
侯宝林 Hou Baolin 中国相声演员 8—191d
《侯达比亚协议》 Ḥudaybiyah, Pact of Al- 伊斯兰教史 8—220c
侯德榜 Hou Debang 中国化学家 8—191e
侯爵 marquess 欧洲贵族称号 10—529c
侯马 Houma 中国城市 8—193c
侯马盟书 Covenant of Houma 中国考古 4—554d

侯乃尼(伊本·易司哈克) Ḥunayn ibn Isḥāq (al-Ibādī) 阿拉伯学者 8—252a
侯赛尼 Ḥusaynī, Amīn al- 耶路撒冷伊斯兰法学家 8—267e
侯赛尼 Husayni, Faysal ibn Abd al-Qadir al- 巴勒斯坦政治领袖 8—267f
侯赛因 Hussein 约旦国王 8—268e
侯赛因王朝 Ḥusaynid DYNASTY 突尼斯王朝 8—268a
侯赛因一世 Ḥusayn I 伊朗国王 8—267c
侯赛因·伊本·阿里 Ḥusayn ibn ʿAlī 汉志国王 8—267d
侯赛因·伊本·阿里 Ḥusayn ibnʿAlī, al- 什叶派英雄 8—267d
侯赛因·伊本·艾因·贝格 Hüseyin ibn Eyne Beg 奥斯曼历史 8—268b
侯苏纳 Ḥassūnah, ʿAbd al-Khāliq 埃及外交官 7—505c
侯外庐 Hou Wailu 中国历史学家 8—192a
喉 larynx 解剖学 9—502e
喉部恶性肿瘤 laryngeal cancer 疾病 9—502c
喉肛鱼 pirate perch (*Aphredoderus sayanus*) 鱼类 13—321c
喉科学 laryngology 医学 9—502e
喉盘鱼 clingfish 鱼类 4—292f
喉塞音 glottal stop 语音学 7—161c
喉炎 laryngitis 疾病 9—502d
猴 monkey 动物学 11—341d
猴㹴 affenpinscher 狗品种 1—103e
猴痘 monkeypox 疾病 11—342c
猴科 Cercopithecidae 动物学 4—9c
猴谜树 monkey puzzle tree 木本植物 11—342b
猴面包 baobab (*Adansonia digitata*) 木本植物 2—210e
猴戏图 singerie 艺术 15—393c
猴子罐 monkey pot 木本植物 11—342a
猴子乐队组陶 Affenkapelle ware 瓷塑 1—103d
骺缺血性坏死 epiphyseal ischemic necrosis (disorder) 疾病 6—101f
吼猴 howler monkey 哺乳动物 8—202a
后白河天皇 Shirakawa, Go- 日本天皇 15—322b
后滨阶地 berm 地理 2—417e
后稷 Houji 中国传说人物 8—193a
后口动物 Deuterostomia 体腔动物 5—269a
后浪漫主义音乐 Postromantic music 音乐风格 13—461b
后黎朝 Later Le DYNASTY 越南历史 9—509f
后李朝 Later Ly DYNASTY 越南历史 9—509f
后梁太祖朱晃 Houliangtaizu Zhu Huang 中国皇帝 8—193b
后鸟羽天皇 Toba, Go- 日本天皇 17—125c
后勤学 logistics 管理科学 10—191f
后鳃类 opisthobranch 海产腹足类动物 12—431f
后三条天皇 Sanjō, Go- 日本天皇 15—35a
后肾 metanephros 解剖学 11—151d
后熟 afterripening 植物学 1—113c
后堂 apse 建筑 1—423e
后堂回廊 ambulatory 宗教建筑 1—272c
后藤象二郎 Gotō Shōjirō 日本政治家 7—225d
后藤新平 Gotō Shimpei 日本政治家 7—225c
后醍醐 Daigo, Go- 日本天皇 5—111d
后天知识 a posteriori knowledge 哲学 1—1b
后土 Houtu 中国神名 8—197b
后象 afterimage 生理学 1—113c
后言 epirrhema 古希腊喜剧 6—102a
后羿 Hou Yi 中国神话人物 8—192c
后印象主义 Postimpressionism 西方绘画流派 13—460f
后周世宗柴荣 Houzhoushizong Chai Rong 中国皇帝 8—197b
厚壁组织 sclerenchyma 植物组织 15—145c
厚蛤 quahog 软体动物 14—72e
厚皮马勃目 Sclerodermatales (fungus) 真菌 15—145e
厚头啸鹟 thickhead 鸟类 17—38a
厚涂法 impasto 油画技术 8—345a
厚膝鸻 thickknee 鸟类 17—38b
候补骑士 esquire 称号 6—134c
鲎 horseshoe crab 海生节肢动物 8—183f
呼布苏古勒湖 Hübsügül Dalay (Mongolia) 蒙古湖泊 8—220a
呼肠孤病毒 reovirus 病毒 14—233b
呼杜德 ḥudūd, al- 德鲁兹教义 8—222d
呼和浩特 Hohhot 中国城市 8—121b
呼警 hue and cry 英国法律 8—222f
呼兰 Hulan 中国区名 8—230b
呼伦 Hu-lun (China) 中国城市 8—205d
呼伦贝尔草原 Hulun Buir Grassland 中国草原 8—232c
呼伦湖 Hulun Hu 中国湖泊 8—232d
呼罗珊 Khorāsān 南亚历史地区 9—263b
呼罗珊地毯 Khorāsān carpet 工艺品 9—263d
呼神派 Kūkā (religious sect) 宗教派别 9—391e
呼图白 khutbah 伊斯兰教 9—266e
呼吸 breathing 生理现象 3—135c
呼吸 respiration 生理现象 14—242b
呼吸分析器 breath analyzer 酒精含量测定仪器 3—135c
呼吸窘迫综合征 respiratory distress syndrome 病理现象 14—242e
呼吸疗法 respiratory therapy 医疗 14—242e
忽必烈汗 Khubilai Khan 中国元朝皇帝 9—265f
忽布 hop 植物 8—166f
狐 fox 哺乳动物 6—430b
狐步舞 fox-trot 舞蹈 6—432b
狐蝠 fox bat 哺乳动物 6—431f
狐蝠科 Pteropodidae 动物学 13—567b
狐猴 lemur 哺乳动物 10—5c
狐鲣 bonito (*Sarda*) 鱼类 3—32b
狐狸狗 spitz 狗品种 16—37d
狐鲨 fox shark 鱼类 6—432a
狐尾草 foxtail 草本植物 6—432f
狐鼬 taira (mammal) 哺乳动物 16—433f
弧光灯 arc lamp 电学 1—444f
弧菌 vibrio 细菌 17—534e
弧形窗 lunette 建筑 10—284d
胡安(奥地利的) Juan DE AUSTRIA 西班牙军官 9—96a
胡安·波因萨特 Poinsat, Juan 葡萄牙神学家 13—388b
胡安·德富卡海峡 Juan de Fuca Strait 北美海峡 9—96c
胡安·费尔南德斯群岛 Juan Fernández Islands 智利岛群 9—96e
胡安·何塞(奥地利的) Juan José DE AUSTRIA 西班牙首相 9—96e
胡安·卡洛斯 Juan Carlos 西班牙国王 9—96b
胡安·曼努埃尔 Juan Manuel, Don 西班牙作家 9—97a
胡安娜 Joan 卡斯蒂利亚女王 9—38c
胡安娜(疯子) Joan THE MAD 卡斯蒂利亚女王 9—41a
胡拜尔 Khubar, al- 沙特阿拉伯城市 9—265f
胡贝 Hubay, Jenö 匈牙利音乐家 8—217e
胡伯尔 Huber, Robert 德国生物化学家 8—219d
胡伯尔 Huber, Wolf 奥地利画家 8—219e
胡布利-塔尔瓦德 Hubli-Dhārwād 印度城市 8—219f
胡布迈尔 Hubmaier, Balthasar 德国宗教改革家 8—219f
胡德 Hood, John B(ell) 美国军人 8—161b
胡德 Hood, Raymond M(athewson) 美国建筑师 8—161d
胡德 Hood, Thomas 英国诗人 8—161f
胡德(惠特利的)子爵(第一) Hood (of Whitley), Samuel Hood, 1st Viscount 英国海军上将 8—161e
胡德岛 Hood Island (Galápagos Islands) 太平洋岛屿 8—162a
胡德里弗 Hood River 美国城市 8—162a
胡德山 Hood, Mount 美国山峰 8—161c
胡德山国家森林 Mount Hood National Forest 美国森林 11—441a
胡德王朝 Hūdid DYNASTY 西班牙王朝 8—220e
胡蒂卡尔帕 Juticalpa 洪都拉斯城市 9—121c
胡蒂亚帕 Jutiapa 危地马拉城市 9—121c

胡丁厄 Huddinge 瑞典城市 8—220e
胡顿 Hooton,Earnest A(lbert) 美国人类学家 8—166b
胡尔 Hoel,Sigurd 挪威小说家 8—114c
胡尔勒氏综合征 Hurler's syndrome 病理现象 8—265a
胡风 Hu Feng 中国作家 8—204d
胡佛 Hoover,Herbert (Clark) 美国总统 8—166c
胡佛 Hoover,J(ohn) Edgar 美国官员 8—166e
胡佛水坝 Hoover Dam 美国水坝 8—166f
胡佛委员会 Hoover Commission 美国机构 8—166f
胡夫 Khufu 埃及国王 9—266b
胡富夫 Hufūf,al- 沙特阿拉伯城镇 8—223d
胡格狄特里希 Hugdietrich (literature) 文学 8—223e
胡格利河 Hooghly River 印度河流 8—162e
胡格利-钦苏拉 Hooghly-Chinsura 印度城镇 8—162e
胡格诺派 Huguenot 法国基督教派 8—226f
胡根贝格 Hugenberg,Alfred 德国实业家 8—223e
胡瓌 Hu Gui 中国画家 8—204f
胡汉民 Hu Hanmin 中国政治人物 8—205a
胡胡伊 Jujuy 阿根廷省份 9—105a
胡椒 pepper (*Piper nigrum*) 植物 13—153b
胡椒薄荷 peppermint (*Mentha piperita*) 草本植物 13—154a
胡椒碱 piperine 化合物 13—319a
胡椒鹀 peppershrike 鸟类 13—154c
胡椒科 Piperaceae 植物学 13—318e
胡椒目 Piperales 植物学 13—318f
胡椒树 pepper tree (*Schinus molle*) 木本植物 13—153e
胡锦涛 Hu Jintao 中国领导人 8—205b
胡卡尔河 Júcar River 西班牙河流 9—98f
胡克 Hooker,Isabella Beecher 美国主张妇女参政者 8—163b
胡克 Hooker,Joseph 美国军人 8—163d
胡克 Hooker,Sir Joseph Dalton 英国植物学家 8—163e
胡克 Hooke,Robert 英国物理学家 8—163a
胡克 Hooker,Richard 英国神学家 8—163f
胡克 Hook,Sidney 美国教育家 8—162f
胡克 Hooker,Thomas 美洲传教士 8—164b
胡克 Hook,Theodore Edward 英国作家 8—162f
胡克 Hooker,Sir William Jackson 英国植物学家 8—164c
胡克定律 Hooke's law 物理学 8—164d
胡克起义 Hukbalahap Rebellion 菲律宾历史 8—229d
胡克斯 Hooks,Benjamin L. 美国法官、牧师 8—164e
胡拉盆地 Ḥula,ʿEmeq 以色列盆地 8—230a
胡兰 Huram 推罗国王 8—264c
胡狼 jackal 哺乳动物 8—503e
胡里卜盖 Khouribga 摩洛哥城市 9—264e
胡里人 Hurrian 民族 8—265e
胡里语 Hurrian language 语言 8—265f
胡里语楔形文字 Hurrian writing 文字 8—266a
胡利 El Juli 西班牙斗牛士 6—10d
胡利奥 Juliani,Petrus 教皇 9—107a
胡利奥 Julião,Pedro 教皇 9—107a
胡利亚莫利纳 Julia Molina (Dominican Republic) 多米尼加共和国城市 9—106a
胡鲁克 Hurok,Sol(omon Isaievich) 美国演出主办人 8—265b
胡萝卜 carrot (*Daucus carota*) 草本植物 3—484f
胡萝卜素 carotene 化合物 3—474d
胡萝卜素血症 carotenemia 病理现象 3—474d
胡马雍 Humāyūn 印度莫卧儿皇帝 8—243b
胡曼 Humann,Karl 德国考古学家 8—243a
胡蔓藤科 Loganiaceae 植物学 10—188f
胡米利亚 Jumilla 西班牙城市 9—108c
胡姆斯 Khums,Al- 利比亚城镇 9—266c
胡闹诗 nonsense verse 文学 12—229f
胡内多阿拉 Hunedoara 罗马尼亚县名 8—254a
胡内多阿拉 Hunedoara 罗马尼亚城市 8—254a
胡尼亚尼河 Hunyani River 非洲河流 8—263c
胡宁 Junín 阿根廷城市 9—112a
胡宁 Junín 秘鲁省份 9—112a
胡帕人 Hupa 民族 8—263f
胡珀 Hooper,Franklin Henry 美国《不列颠百科全书》总编辑 8—165c
胡珀 Hooper,Horace Everett 美国出版商 8—165d
胡齐斯坦 Khūzestān 伊朗地理区域 9—266f
胡奇坦 Juchitán 墨西哥城市 9—99a
胡琴 huqin 弦乐器 8—264b
胡萨克 Husak,Gustav 捷克斯洛伐克领导人 8—267b
胡萨克隧道 Hoosac Tunnel 美国隧道 8—166b
胡萨雷克·封·海因莱因 Hussarek von Heinlein,Max Hussarek,Baron (Freiherr) 奥地利首相 8—268e
胡萨托尼克河 Housatonic River 美国河流 8—194d
胡萨维克 Húsavík 冰岛城镇 8—267c
胡塞尔 Husserl,Edmund 德国哲学家 8—269a
胡塞马 Hoceima,al- (enclave,Morocco) 摩洛哥飞地 8—112b
胡塞马 Hoceima,al- 摩洛哥城市 8—112b
胡塞马 Khuzama,Al- (Morocco) 摩洛哥城市 9—266e
胡塞因 Husain,Zakir 印度总统 8—267a
胡塞因沙·阿拉丁 Ḥusayn Shāh ʿAlāʾ ad-Dīn 孟加拉统治者 8—267e
胡适 Hu Shi 中国学者 8—205d
胡斯 Goes,Hugo van der 佛兰德斯画家 7—177d
胡斯 Hus,Jan 捷克宗教改革家 8—266d
胡斯克·杜乐队 Hüsker Dü 美国乐队 8—268c
胡斯曼 Huysmans,Camille 比利时作家、首相 8—275b
胡斯派信徒 Hussite 基督教派 8—269c
胡斯托 Justo,Agustín Pedro 阿根廷总统 9—120e
胡桃 walnut 木本植物 18—83e
胡桃目 Juglandales 植物学 9—104a
胡特尔派信徒 Hutterite 基督教派 8—271f
胡滕 Hutten,Philipp von 委内瑞拉总督 8—271e
胡同 Hutong 中国街巷称谓 8—271d
胡图人 Hutu 民族 8—272d
胡颓子 oleaster (*Elaeagnus angustifolia*) 木本植物 12—372b
胡颓子科 Elaeagnaceae 植物学 6—12f
胡威诺 huayño 舞蹈 8—217d
胡韦达 Hoveyda,Amīr ʿAbbas 伊朗首相 8—197e
胡惟庸 Hu Weiyong 中国大臣 8—205e
胡、夏、赫 Hu,Sia,and Heh 埃及宗教神名 8—204d
胡须地衣 beard lichen 植物 2—305f
胡亚雷斯 Juárez,Benito (Pablo) 墨西哥总统 9—97c
胡耀邦 Hu Yaobang 中国领导人 8—205f
胡耶 Goeje,Michael Jan de 荷兰学者 7—177b
胡伊 Khoei,Abolqasem al- 宗教人士 9—261f
胡枝子 lespedeza 草本植物 10—39a
胡志明 Ho Chi Minh 越南领袖 8—107b
胡志明市 Ho Chi Minh City 越南城市 8—108a
胡志明小道 Ho Chi Minh Trail 越南战争期间的山林小路 8—108c
胡兹达尔 Khuzdār 巴基斯坦城镇 9—266e
胡子罐 Bartmannkrug 德国产陶罐 2—251c
壶 hu 中国古代酒器 8—204c
壶菌纲 Chytridiomycetes 菌类 4—232c
壶口瀑布 Hukou falls 中国瀑布 8—229f
壶藓 urn moss 植物 17—417b
葫芦 bottle gourd (*Lagenaria siceraria*) 植物 3—75b
葫芦巴 fenugreek (species *Trigonella foenum -graecum*) 草本植物 6—278a
葫芦岛 Huludao 中国城市 8—232b

葫芦科 Cucurbitaceae 植物学 5—51a
葫芦类 gourd 植物学 7—230f
葫芦瓢树 calabash tree (*Crescentia cujete*) 木本植物 3—332c
湖北 Hubei 中国省份 8—218e
湖泊 lake 地理 9—452d
湖泊生态系统 lacustrine ecosystem 生态学 9—440d
湖地狸狗 Lakeland terrier 动物 9—456c
湖鲱 lake herring 鱼类 9—455e
湖龙 Limnoscelis 古生物学 10—105a
湖南 Hunan 中国省份 8—251d
湖畔诗人 Lake poet 文学 9—455f
湖区 Lake District 英格兰风景区 9—455a
湖上住宅 Lake Dwellings 史前聚落遗迹 9—455b
湖熟文化 Hushu culture 中国青铜文化 8—268b
湖沼学 limnology 水文学 10—105a
湖州 Huzhou 中国城市 8—275d
湖鳟 lake trout (*Salvelinus namaycush*) 鱼类 9—456a
槲果 mast 食品 11—14a
槲果和坚果象甲 acorn and nut weevil 昆虫 1—56b
槲果树目 Balanopales 植物学 2—161d
槲寄生 mistletoe 木本植物 11—286f
槲寄生科 Viscaceae 植物学 18—16c
蝴蝶 butterfly 昆虫 3—292f
蝴蝶 Papillon (French criminal) 法国罪犯 13—25a
蝴蝶草 butterfly weed (*Asclepias tuberosa*) 植物 3—293c
蝴蝶魟 butterfly ray 鱼类 3—293b
蝴蝶兰 butterfly orchid 植物 3—293b
蝴蝶鱼 butterfly fish 鱼类 3—293a
虎 tiger (*Leo tigris*) 哺乳动物 17—89f
虎斑蛾 tiger moth 昆虫 17—90d
虎斑陶瓷皿 tigerware 工艺品 17—91b
虎刺掌属 Pereskia 植物学 13—163a
虎耳草 saxifrage 植物 15—95b
虎耳草科 Saxifragaceae 植物学 15—94f
虎甲 tiger beetle 昆虫 17—90c
虎鲸 grampus 哺乳动物 7—245e
虎林 Hulin 中国县名 8—230c
虎猫 margay (*Felis wiedii*) 哺乳动物 10—505b
《虎门条约》 Bogue, Treaty of 中国历史 3—1b
虎皮鹦鹉 budgerigar 鸟类 3—230b
虎皮鹦鹉 shell parakeet 鸟类 15—297a
虎钳 vise 工具 18—18a
虎鲨 bullhead shark 鱼类 3—248f
虎鲨 tiger shark (*Galeocerdo cuvieri*) 鱼类 17—90e
虎蛇 tiger snake (species *Notechis scutatus*) 爬行动物 17—90f
虎跳峡 Hutiao Xia 中国峡谷 8—271c
虎尾草属 Chloris 植物学 4—184c
虎尾兰属 Sansevieria 植物学 15—38b
虎眼石 tiger's-eye 宝石 17—91b
虎眼万年青属 Ornithogalum 植物学 12—468d
虎鱼 tigerfish 鱼类 17—91a
琥珀 amber 树脂化石 1—269d
琥珀酸 succinic acid 化合物 16—301f
琥珀玉髓玻璃制品 amberina glass 艺术玻璃器皿 1—270a
互变异构 tautomerism 化学 16—498e
互搭板 bevel siding 建筑板 2—446d
互惠 reciprocity 国际贸易 14—183e
互惠共生 mutualism 生物学 11—518f
互养作用 syntrophism 生物学 16—403e
互助会 friendly society 互助组织 6—493d
户栗郁子 D'Aquino, Iva Toguri 日裔美籍播音员 5—146a
户田 Toda 日本城市 17—128b
护符 amulet 符咒 1—304f
护国政体 Protectorate 英国政府 13—542d
护航 convoy 海上武装护卫 4—475c
护教士 Apologist 基督教著述家 1—414c
护理学 nursing 医疗保健专业 12—303f
护墙板 wainscot 室内墙面镶板 18—66b
护身符 talisman 宗教 16—445b
护身链 menat 埃及吉祥饰物 11—106d
护士 nurse 医疗保健 12—303d
护士鲨 nurse shark (*Ginglymostoma cirratum*) 鱼类 12—303e
护世天王 lokapāla 印度教、佛教 10—194b
护卫 housecarl 北欧历史 8—195a
护卫舰 frigate 军舰 6—494e
护卫灵 ka 古埃及宗教 9—123c
护照 passport 出国证件 13—80b
扈从 lictor 古罗马高官跟随人员 10—83b
扈从队 comitatus 古罗马军事组织 4—382b
扈里 Khuri, Bishara al- 黎巴嫩总统 9—266d
鹱形类 procellariiform 鸟类 13—525a
花 flower 植物学 6—374f
花斑岩 granophyre 岩石 7—255e
花斑雁 pied goose 鸟类 13—293e
花边 lace 编织艺术 9—435e
花边图册 lace pattern book 编织艺术 9—436a
花蝽 flower bug 昆虫 6—375f
花道 hanamichi 日本戏剧 7—455b
花缎 damask 织物 5—126e
花粉 pollen 植物学 13—406a
花岗闪长岩 granodiorite 岩石 7—255e
花岗岩 granite 岩石 7—254f
花岗岩化作用 granitization 地质学 7—255b
花岗岩铁路 Granite Railway 美国铁路 7—255b
花岗岩藓 granite moss 苔藓植物 7—255a
花格玻璃 latticinio glass 工艺品 9—516a
花格图案 tartan 苏格兰图案 16—486d
花红 crab apple 木本植物 4—562d
花花公子热 dandy fever 疾病 5—134a
花环花 garland flower (plant) 草本植物 7—16c
花剑 foil 击剑运动用剑 6—386c
花椒属 Zanthoxylum 植物学 18—498d
花金龟 flower chafer 昆虫 6—376a
花茎甘蓝 broccoli (*Brassica oleracea*, Italica group) 植物 3—172f
花拉子密 Khwārizmī, al- 阿拉伯数学家 9—267e
花剌子模 Khwārezm 亚洲古地名 9—267d
花剌子模沙王朝 Khwārezm-Shāh DYNASTY 突厥王朝 9—267d
花郎徒 Hwarangdo 朝鲜历史 8—276b
花莲 Hualian 中国县名 8—209d
花莲 Hualian 中国城市 8—209e
花鳞鱼 Thelodus 古生物学 17—21f
花蜜 nectar 植物蜜腺分泌物 12—63d
花瓶地毯 Vase carpet 工艺品 17—477b
花旗集团 Citigroup 美国金融服务公司 4—248a
花楸 mountain ash 木本植物 11—442f
花圈 wreath 花饰 18—342e
花荵 Jacob's ladder 植物 8—511f
花荵科 Polemoniaceae 植物学 13—399b
花沙山 Bukit Fraser 马来西亚游览胜地 3—239e
花沙山 Frasers Hill (West Malaysia) 马来西亚山脉 6—455f
花生 peanut (*Arachis hypogaea*) 豆科植物 13—111d
花生 Peanuts 漫画作品 13—111e
花石斑鱼 hind 鱼类 8—87c
花式骑术 dressage 运动 5—421d
花饰 floral decoration 装饰艺术 6—363e
花饰 garland 植物装饰品 7—15d

花鼠 chipmunk 哺乳动物 4—178b
花束 nosegay 装饰品 12—272e
花坛 parterre 园艺学 13—65b
花序 inflorescence 植物学 8—383a
花样滑冰 figure skating 体育 6—311d
花样游泳 synchronized swimming 体育项目 16—401c
花椰菜 cauliflower (*Brassica oleracea*, Botrytis group) 植物 3—535e
花椰菜形陶器 cauliflower ware 陶瓷制品 3—535f
花叶病 mosaic 植物病害 11—412c
花叶兰属 Vriesea 植物学 18—53e
花蝇 anthomyiid fly 昆虫 1—378b
花蝇 flower fly 昆虫 6—376b
花园城市 garden city 城市规划 7—11a
花园地毯 garden carpet 工艺品 7—10f
花园挂毯 garden tapestry 工艺品 7—11e
花札牌 Hanafuda 日本牌戏 7—455a
花毯鲷 catalufa 鱼类 3—520b
花烛属 Anthurium 植物学 1—380f
哗啷器 rattle 乐器 14—163f
划蝽 water boatman 昆虫 18—135c
划痕 scarification 文身 15—104e
划十字 cross, sign of the 基督教 5—31e
划艇 canoe 船 3—406b
划艇 rowboat 船 14—426b
华北平原 North China Plain 中国平原 12—251e
华彩段 cadenza 音乐 3—312f
华德 Ward, William George 伦敦印刷商 18—105c
华东师范大学 East China Normal University 中国高等学府 5—503e
华顿(夫人) Wharton, Edith 美国作家 18—218f
华恩达米 Khwāndamīr, Ghiyās ad-Dīn Muḥammad 波斯历史学家 9—267c
华尔 Ward, Frederick Townsend 美国政治冒险家 18—104a
华尔街 Wall Street 美国纽约市街名和主要金融机构所在地 18—76e
《华尔街日报》 Wall Street Journal, The 美国报纸 18—76f
华尔克 Walker, William 美国冒险家 18—75d
华尔兹 waltz 舞蹈 18—89a
华夫饼干 waffle 食品 18—61b
华夫脱党 Wafd 埃及政党 18—61a
华富里 Lop Buri 泰国城镇 10—215f
华盖 aureole 大气科学 2—58d
华盖 baldachin 建筑 2—164e
华卡 huaca 印加宗教 8—207d
华空 Houakhong (Laos) 老挝城镇 8—192c
华莱士 Wallace, Anthony F(rancis) C(larke) 美国人类学家 18—77e
华莱士 Wallace, Alfred Russel 英国人类学家 18—77b
华莱士 Wallace, George C(orley) 美国政治家 18—78b
华莱士 Wallace, Henry A(gard) 美国副总统 18—78d
华莱士 Wallace, Lewis 美国外交家、律师 18—78e
华莱士 Wallace, Sir Richard, Baronet 英国美术品收藏家 18—79a
华莱士 Wallace, (Richard Horatio) Edgar 英国小说家 18—78a
华莱士 Wallace, Sir William 苏格兰民族英雄 18—79a
华莱士堡 Wallaceburg 加拿大城镇 18—79c
华莱士夫妇 Wallace, De Witt and Lila Bell Acheson 美国《读者文摘》创办人 18—77f
华莱士氏线 Wallace's Line 动物区系假设分界线 18—79c
华莱士收藏馆 Wallace Collection 伦敦艺术博物馆 18—79b
华莱斯 Wallas, Graham 英国教育家 18—80a
华雷斯 Juárez 墨西哥城市 9—97b
华雷斯城 Ciudad Juárez (Mexico) 墨西哥城市 4—252a
华丽摇滚 glam rock 音乐 7—150d
华林 Waring, Edward 英国数学家 18—106e
华伦海特 Fahrenheit, Daniel Gabriel 德国物理学家 6—212f
华伦斯坦 Wallenstein, Albrecht Wenzel Eusebius von 波希米亚政治家 18—80d
华纳兄弟影片公司 Warner Brothers 美国电影制片公司 18—108e
华沙 Warsaw 波兰首都 18—111c
华沙公国 Warsaw, Duchy of 波兰历史 18—113c
《华沙公约》 Warsaw, Compact of 波兰历史 18—113c
华沙起义 Warsaw Uprising 波兰历史 18—114a
《华沙条约》 Warsaw Pact 国际关系 18—113f
华沙犹太区起义 Warsaw Ghetto Uprising 波兰历史 18—113e
华盛顿 Washington 英格兰城镇 18—117e
华盛顿 Washington 美国州名 18—117e
华盛顿 Washington 美国首都 18—120c
华盛顿 Washington 美国佐治亚州城市 18—124d
华盛顿 Washington 美国北卡罗来纳州城市 18—124e
华盛顿 Washington 美国宾夕法尼亚州城市 18—124e
华盛顿 Washington 美国得克萨斯州历史名城 18—124e
华盛顿 Washington, Bushrod 美国最高法院大法官 18—125a
华盛顿 Washington, Booker T(aliaferro) 美国教育学家 18—124f
华盛顿 Washington, Denzel 美国橄榄球球员 18—125b
华盛顿 Washington, Dinah 美国歌唱家 18—125c
华盛顿 Washington, George 美国总统 18—125c
华盛顿 Washington, Kenny 美国棋盘式橄榄球球员 18—130e
华盛顿(哥伦比亚特区) Washington, D.C. 美国首都 18—131b
华盛顿大教堂 Washington Cathedral 美国圣公会教堂 18—131a
华盛顿岛 Washington Island (Kiribati) 太平洋中西部岛屿 18—131c
华盛顿渡河村州立公园 Washington Crossing State Park 美国公园 18—131b
华盛顿港 Port Washington 美国社区 13—447e
华盛顿国立大教堂 Washington National Cathedral 美国圣公会教堂 18—131d
华盛顿湖运河 Lake Washington Ship Canal 美国水道 9—456b
华盛顿会议 Washington Conference 国际会议 18—131a
华盛顿纪念碑 Washington Monument 美国纪念碑 18—131c
华盛顿桥 George Washington Bridge 美国桥梁 7—78c
华盛顿山 Washington, Mount 美国山脉 18—130f
华盛顿首都国际赛 Washington, D.C. International 国际平道马赛 18—131c
《华盛顿邮报》 Washington Post, The 美国报纸 18—131e
华氏城 Pāṭaliputra (India) 印度城市 13—84b
华氏温标 Fahrenheit temperature scale 计量单位 6—213a
华特林岛 Watling Island (The Bahamas) 巴哈马群岛岛屿 18—144d
华特林岛 Watling's Island (The Bahamas) 巴哈马群岛岛屿 18—144e
华特灵大道 Watling Street 英国古罗马道路 18—144e
华托 Watteau, (Jean-)Antoine 法国18世纪画家 18—146e
华佗 Hua Tuo 中国古代名医 8—207a
华夏 Hua Xia 中国和汉族的古称 8—207a
华谢基 Washakie 美国印第安人首长 18—117a
华兴会 Huaxinghui 中国革命团体 8—217b
华严寺 Huayan Monastery 中国寺院 8—217c
华严宗 Kegon 佛教宗派 9—212d
华支睾吸虫病 clonorchiasis 疾病 4—299b
华柱 candelabrum 建筑 3—397d
华兹华斯 Wordsworth, Dorothy 英国散文作家 18—331d
华兹华斯 Wordsworth, William 英国浪漫主义诗人 18—331e
华族 kazoku 日本贵族 9—208a
哗变 mutiny 军队突然叛变 11—518a
滑板运动 skateboarding 体育项目 15—414a
滑冰 ice-skating 娱乐、运动 8—312d

滑冰 skating (sport) 体育项目 15—414b
滑冰 ICE SKATING 娱乐、运动 16—120b
滑冰航行 skate sailing 体育项目 15—414a
滑动细菌 gliding bacterium 微生物学 7—158e
滑稽动作 lazzo 戏剧 9—536a
滑稽歌剧 opera buffa 意大利音乐 12—429a
滑稽男仆 zanni 意大利喜剧角色 18—498c
滑降滑雪 downhill skiing 体育项目 5—407a
滑距骨兽 litoptern 古生物学 10—149b
滑口鱼 slipmouth 鱼类 15—433a
滑轮 pulley 机械 14—21b
滑轮组 block and tackle 机械 2—538a
滑膜组织 synovial tissue 解剖学 16—403a
滑皮银汉鱼 grunion (species *Leuresthes tenuis*) 鱼类 7—330e
滑坡 landslide 地质学 9—479c
滑蛇 smooth snake (*Coronella austriaca*) 爬行动物 15—456a
滑石 talc 矿物 16—443e
滑膛枪 musket 武器 11—511b
滑铁卢 Waterloo 加拿大城市 18—141e
滑铁卢 Waterloo 美国城市 18—141f
滑铁卢车站 Waterloo Station 英国火车站 18—142b
滑铁卢战役 Waterloo, Battle of 欧洲历史 18—141f
滑头鱼 smoothhead (fish) 鱼类 15—456a
滑翔袋鼯 glider 哺乳动物 7—158b
滑翔机 glider 无动力航空器 7—158d
滑翔结趾鼩 flying phalanger (marsupial) 哺乳动物 6—382a
滑翔运动 gliding (sport) 体育项目 7—158e
滑雪 SKIING 体育项目 16—133a
滑雪板 ski 滑雪装备 15—416f
滑雪板运动 snowboarding 体育 15—464c
滑雪橇运动 bobsledding 体育项目 2—556f
滑雪巡逻队 ski patrol 救护组织 15—417b
滑雪运动 skiing 体育项目 15—417e
滑移 slip 物理学 15—432f
滑蹠蟾属 Liopelma 动物学 10—129a
化粪池 septic tank 污水处理装置 15—219d
化合价 valence 化学 17—449b
化合物 chemical compound 化学 4—106c
化合致幻药 designer drug 药品 5—261b
化身 avatar 印度教 2—83f
化石 fossil 古生物学 6—420e
化学 chemistry 自然科学学科 4—111e
化学不育剂 chemosterilant 化合物 4—113d
化学沉淀 chemical precipitation 化学 4—109e
化学缔合 chemical association 化学 4—105d
化学镀 electroless plating 电化学 6—25a
化学发光 chemiluminescence 化学 4—111d
化学反应 chemical reaction 化学 4—109f
化学分类学 chemotaxy 生物学 4—113e
化学符号 chemical symbol 化学 4—111a
化学感受 chemoreception 生理学 4—113b
化学工程 chemical engineering 化学 4—107f
化学合成 chemical synthesis 化学 4—111a
化学计量 stoichiometry 化学 16—245c
化学键 chemical bonding 化学 4—105f
化学疗法 chemotherapy 医疗 4—113f
化学平衡 chemical equilibrium 化学 4—108f
化学式 chemical formula 化学 4—109a
化学水文学 chemical hydrology 水文学 4—109c
化学银行公司 Chemical Banking Corporation 美国持股公司 4—105e
化学元素 chemical element 化学 4—107c
化学战 chemical warfare 战争 4—111c
化学指示剂 chemical indicator 化学 4—109c
化学中间体 chemical intermediate 化学 4—109e
化油器 carburetor 机器装置 3—449e
化妆品 cosmetic 美容用品 4—529f
化装 makeup 表演艺术 10—416a
划分 partition 数学 13—68d
华国锋 Hua Guofeng 中国政治家 8—206b
华罗庚 Hua Luogeng 中国数学家 8—206d
华山 Hua Shan 中国名山 8—206f
华伦 Warren, Mercy Otis 美国诗人、剧作家 18—110c
华嵒 Hua Yan 中国画家 8—207b
画笔草 paint brush (plant) 草本植物 12—549f
画家米勒 Maler Müller 德国剧作家、画家 10—428f
画匠 limner 绘画 10—105a
画卷 scroll painting 中国绘画 15—158e
画框 picture frame 镶嵌装置 13—292d
画廊 pinacotheca 绘画作品陈列馆 13—306c
画眉 babbler 鸟类 2—108f
画眉草 love grass 草本植物 10—249d
《画品》 Huapin 中国绘画理论著作 8—216d
话鼓 talking drum 通讯工具 16—445c
桦木 birch 木本植物 2—487e
桦木科 Betulaceae 植物学 2—445d
怀阿拉 Whyalla 澳大利亚港市 18—242f
怀昂 Wyong 澳大利亚城镇 18—369d
怀奥河 Waiau River 新西兰河流 18—65a
怀奥河 Waiau River 新西兰河流 18—65b
怀伯尔 Whymper, Edward 英国登山运动员 18—243a
怀俄明 Wyoming 美国州名 18—367c
怀俄明惨案 Wyoming Massacre 屠杀北美殖民地居民事件 18—369c
怀厄莱阿莱峰 Waialeale, Mount 美国夏威夷山峰 18—64f
怀厄奈岭 Waianae Range 美国夏威夷州山脉 18—65a
怀恩 Wynne (o Lasynys), Ellis 威尔士牧师 18—367b
怀恩多特 Wyandotte 美国城市 18—364e
怀恩多特人 Wyandot (people) 北美印第安人族群联盟 18—364e
怀恩多特溶洞 Wyandotte Cave 美国印第安纳州洞穴 18—364f
《怀恩多特宪法》 Wyandotte Constitution 美国历史 18—364f
怀尔 Wyre 英格兰自治市 18—369d
怀尔德 Wilder, Billy 美国电影编剧 18—253c
怀尔德 Wilder, Douglas 美国政治人物 18—253d
怀尔德 Wilder, Gene 美国喜剧演员 18—253e
怀尔德 Wild, Jonathan 英国伦敦犯罪分子头目 18—251a
怀尔德 Wilder, Laura Ingalls 美国儿童文学作家 18—253f
怀尔德 Wilder, Thornton (Niven) 美国作家 18—254a
怀尔德曼 Wildman, Sir John 英国宣传鼓动家 18—255c
怀尔森林 Wyre Forest 英格兰区名 18—369d
怀海 Huaihai 中国高僧 8—208e
怀河 Wye, River 英国河流 18—366a
怀化 Huaihua 中国城市 8—208e
怀基基 Waikiki 美国夏威夷州游乐区 18—65e
怀卡雷莫阿纳湖 Waikaremoana, Lake 新西兰湖泊 18—65c
怀卡托 Waikato 新西兰行政区 18—65c
怀卡托河 Waikato River 新西兰河流 18—65e
怀科姆比 Wycombe 英格兰白金汉郡区名 18—365f
怀拉拉帕 Wairarapa 新西兰行政区 18—66e
怀劳河 Wairau River 新西兰河流 18—66f
怀利 Wylie, Elinor 美国诗人 18—366e
怀卢阿河 Wailua River 美国河流 18—65e
怀卢库 Wailuku 美国城市 18—65f
怀马卡里里河 Waimakariri River 新西兰河流 18—65f
怀梅阿 Waimea 美国城镇 18—66a
怀尼米港 Port Hueneme 美国城市 13—445e

怀宁 Huai-ning (China) 中国城市 8—208b
怀让 Huairang 中国高僧 8—209c
怀圣寺 Huaisheng Temple 中国伊斯兰教清真寺 8—209c
怀斯 Wise, Isaac Mayer 犹太教拉比 18—296d
怀斯 Wise, John 美洲殖民地基督教牧师 18—296e
怀斯 Wise, Robert 美国电影导演 18—296e
怀斯 Wise, Stephen Samuel 美国犹太复国主义运动领袖 18—296f
怀斯曼 Wiseman, Frederick 美国电影制作家 18—297a
怀素 Huai Su 中国书法家 8—208b
怀塔基河 Waitaki River 新西兰河流 18—66f
《怀唐伊条约》 Waitangi, Treaty of 新西兰历史 18—67a
怀特 White, Alma Bridwell 美国宗教领袖 18—228a
怀特 White, Andrew Dickson 美国教育家、外交家 18—228b
怀特 White, Byron R. 美国最高法院大法官 18—228c
怀特 White, E. B. 美国随笔作家 18—228d
怀特 White, Edward Douglass 美国最高法院大法官 18—228d
怀特 White, Ellen Gould Harmon 美国宗教领袖 18—229a
怀特 White, Edward H., II 美国航天员 18—228f
怀特 White, Gilbert 英国博物学家 18—229b
怀特 White, Helen Magill 美国教育学家 18—229c
怀特 White, John 英国画家 18—229d
怀特 White, Leslie A(lvin) 美国人类学家 18—229d
怀特 White, Minor 美国摄影家 18—229e
怀特 White, Pearl Fay 美国演员 18—230a
怀特 White, Patrick (Victor Martindale) 澳大利亚作家 18—229f
怀特 White, Stanford 美国建筑师 18—230b
怀特 White, T(erence) H(anbury) 英国小说家 18—230c
怀特 White, Theodore H(arold) 美国记者 18—230c
怀特 White, William 美国基督教圣公会主教 18—230e
怀特 White, William Allen 美国新闻工作者 18—230f
怀特 White, Walter (Francis) 美国黑人代言人 18—230d
怀特 White, William Hale 英国作家 18—231a
怀特岛 White Island 新西兰岛屿 18—232e
怀特岛 Wight, Isle of 英格兰岛郡 18—248c
怀特菲尔德 Whitefield, George 基督教圣公会传教士 18—235c
怀特菲什湾 Whitefish Bay 苏必利尔湖东南部湖湾 18—235d
怀特海 Whitehead, Alfred North 英国数学家 18—235f
怀特豪尔宫 Whitehall Palace 原英国王宫 18—235e
怀特河 White River 美国阿肯色州河流 18—233e
怀特河 White River 美国内布拉斯加州河流 18—233e
怀特黑德 Whitehead, (John) Henry (Constantine) 英国数学家 18—236b
怀特黑德 Whitehead, Robert 英国工程师 18—236b
怀特黑文 Whitehaven 英格兰港口 18—235f
怀特霍尔 Whitehall 伦敦威斯敏斯特市街道 18—235e
怀特霍斯 Whitehorse 加拿大城市 18—236c
怀特霍斯谷 Vale of White Horse 英格兰区名 17—449a
怀特罗克 White Rock 加拿大城市 18—233e
怀特洛克 Whitelocke, Bulstrode 英国律师 18—236c
怀特马塔港 Waitemata Harbour 新西兰海港 18—67c
怀特曼 Wightman, Hazel Hotchkiss 美国女子网球运动员 18—248e
怀特曼 Whiteman, Paul 美国管乐队领队 18—236d
怀特曼杯 Wightman Cup 英美女子网球赛冠军杯 18—248f
怀特普莱恩斯 White Plains 美国城市 18—233d
怀特萨尔弗斯普林斯 White Sulphur Springs 美国城市 18—234d
怀特山 White Mountains 美国山脉 18—233a
怀特斯普林斯 White Springs 美国城镇 18—234c
怀廷 Whiting 美国城市 18—237a
怀托莫 Waitomo 新西兰石灰岩洞 18—67d
怀乌库 Waiuku 新西兰城市 18—67f
怀希 Waihi 新西兰城市 18—65c
怀希基岛 Waiheke Island 新西兰火山岛 18—65c
怀亚特 Wyatt, James 英国建筑师 18—365b
怀亚特 Wyatt, John 英国机械师 18—365c
怀亚特 Wyat, Sir Thomas 英国诗人 18—364f
怀亚特(小) Wyat, Sir Thomas, THE YOUNGER 英格兰军人 18—365a
怀疑论 Skepticism 哲学 15—416b
怀玉山 Huaiyu Shan 中国山名 8—209d
怀月堂安度 Kaigetsudō Ando 日本浮世绘画家 9—135a
淮安 Huai'an 中国城市 8—208c
淮北 Huaibei 中国城市 8—208d
淮河 Huai He 中国河流 8—207e
淮军 Huai Jun 中国清末军队 8—208a
淮南 Huainan 中国城市 8—209a
淮南子 Huai-nan-tzu 中国哲学家 8—208a
《淮南子》 Huainanzi 中国哲学文献 8—209b
槐叶蘋目 Salviniales 植物学 14—558d
踝关节 ankle 解剖学 1—362a
踝节目 Condylarthra 古生物学 4—418a
坏疽 gangrene 病理现象 7—1c
坏死 necrosis 病理现象 12—63c
坏血病 scurvy 疾病 15—161e
欢乐儿童会 Enfants sans Souci 法国社团 6—76b
《欢喜市场报》 Ananda Bazar Patrika 印度报纸 1—315e
欢欣星期日 Laetare Sunday 基督教 9—444b
獾 badger 哺乳动物 2—129e
还魂草 resurrection plant 草本植物 14—245a
还原反应 reduction 化学 14—195a
还原染料 vat dye 化学 17—479c
还原主义 reductionism 哲学 14—195b
环 ring 数学 14—304c
环斑海豹 ringed seal (*Pusa* or *Phoca*, *hispida*) 哺乳动物 14—304e
环丙烷 cyclopropane 化合物、麻醉药 5—87a
环虫 segmented worm 无脊椎动物 15—188b
环蝶 morpho 昆虫 11—402e
环法自行车赛 Tour de France 体育 17—176f
环己基氨基磺酸盐 cyclamate 化学 5—84f
环己六醇 cyclohexanehexol (biochemistry) 生物化学 5—86d
环礁 atoll 地貌类型 2—31c
环节动物 annelid 动物学 1—366a
环结 girdle tie 古埃及宗教护符 7—142b
环颈鸫 ouzel (*Turdus torquatus*) 鸟类 12—510c
环颈蛇 ring-necked snake (*Diadophis punctatus*) 爬行动物 14—304d
环颈鸭 ring-necked duck (*Aythya collaris*) 水禽 14—304c
环境 environment 生物学 6—90f
环境 milieu (literary criticism) 文学评论 11—215d
环境地质学 environmental geology 地质学 6—91a
环境雕刻 environmental sculpture 艺术形式 6—91b
环境工程 environmental engineering 工程学 6—91a
环境剧场 environmental theatre 戏剧运动流派 6—91c
环境论 environmentalism 社会学 6—91c
环境生物学 environmental biology 生态学 6—91a
环美公司 Transamerica Corporation 美国公司 17—194c
环球航空公司 Trans World Airlines, Inc. (TWA) 美国公司 17—194a
"环球航运挑战者"号 Glomar Challenger 海洋钻探船 7—160e
环球信息网 World Wide Web (WWW) 计算机环球网 18—337f
环球影片公司 Universal Pictures Company 美国公司 17—376d
《环球邮报》 Globe and Mail, The 加拿大报纸 7—160b
环三亚甲基三硝胺 cyclotrimethylenetrinitramine (explosive) 炸药 5—87f
环蛇 krait 动物学 9—370b
环尾浣熊 ringtail 哺乳动物 14—304d

环尾猫 ringtailed cat 哺乳动物 14—304d
环状襞 plica circularis 解剖学 13—371b
环状硅酸盐 cyclosilicate 化合物 5—87b
环状星云 Ring Nebula 天文学 14—304c
桓谭 Huan Tan 中国思想家 8—210a
桓武天皇 Kammu 日本天皇 9—150a
寰球剧院 Globe Theatre 英国剧院 7—160c
鹮 ibis 鸟类 8—302e
鹮嘴鹬 ibisbill (*Ibidorhyncha struthersii*) 鸟类 8—302f
缓步虫 slug 软体动物 15—437f
缓步虫 tardigrade 无脊椎动物 16—481c
缓冲器 snubber 减震装置 15—465f
缓冲溶液 buffer 化学术语 3—234c
缓龙属 Bradysaurus 古生物学 3—109e
缓刑 probation 法律 13—523e
幻 maya 印度哲学 11—49e
幻觉 hallucination 心理学 7—431d
幻龙属 Nothosaurus 古生物学 12—274b
幻数 magic number 物理学 10—382a
幻想曲 fantasia 音乐作品 6—234a
幻想小说 fantasy 文学 6—234b
幻影式战斗机 Mirage 军事装备 11—271d
幻影说 Docetism 基督教异端 5—356a
换称 antonomasia 修辞方法 1—397d
换能器 transducer 能量转换器具 17—195c
换气过度 hyperventilation 病理现象 8—294a
换位 conversion 逻辑学 4—474e
换义 antanaclasis 修辞 1—374e
换喻 metonymy 辞格 11—159f
换质 obversion 逻辑学 12—324e
唤醒 arousal (psychology) 心理学 1—511d
浣熊 raccoon 哺乳动物 14—103f
浣熊类 procyonid 动物学 13—527a
荒诞不经故事 tall tale 文学 16—445d
荒诞派戏剧 Absurd, Theatre of the 戏剧 1—33b
荒漠 desert 地理学 5—259b
荒漠砾石盖层 desert pavement 地质构造 5—260c
荒漠猞猁 desert lynx 动物 5—260c
荒漠睡鼠 desert dormouse 动物 5—260b
荒漠文化群 Desert cultures 北美古代文化 5—260b
荒漠岩漆 desert varnish 地质学 5—260d
荒漠隐修 eremitic monasticism 基督教隐修方式 6—113e
荒漠自流盆地 Desert Artesian Basin (Australia) 澳大利亚盆地 5—260b
荒木贞夫 Araki Sadao 日本陆军大将 1—437b
荒尾 Arao 日本城市 1—440a
皇带鱼 oarfish (*Regalecus glesne*) 鱼类 12—315f
皇帝 emperor 君主称号 6—63b
皇宫剧院 Palais-Royal Theatre 法国剧院 12—556a
皇家艾伯特大厅 Royal Albert Hall 伦敦音乐厅 14—430a
皇家安大略博物馆 Royal Ontario Museum 加拿大艺术收藏馆 14—432c
皇家芭蕾舞团 Royal Ballet 英国芭蕾舞团 14—430d
皇家大道 Camino Real 公路 3—374e
皇家地理学会 Royal Geographical Society (RGS) 英国学术团体 14—431d
皇家法院 Royal Courts of Justice 英国法庭 14—431b
皇家谷 Vale Royal 英格兰自治市 17—449b
皇家国立剧院 Royal National Theatre 英国剧院 14—431f
皇家加拿大骑警队 Royal Canadian Mounted Police (RCMP) 加拿大警察组织 14—430f
皇家交易所 Royal Exchange 英国旧金融机构 14—431d
皇家军械博物馆 Royal Armouries 英国博物馆 14—430b
皇家空军博物馆 Royal Air Force Museum 英国国家博物馆 14—429f
皇家利明顿矿泉市 Royal Leamington Spa 英格兰城镇 14—431e
皇家罗马体 Romain du Roi 印刷字体 14—361f
皇家莎士比亚剧团 Royal Shakespeare Company 英国剧团 14—432d
皇家坦布里奇韦尔斯 Royal Tunbridge Wells (England) 英格兰自治市 14—432f
皇家天文学会 Royal Astronomical Society (RAS) 英国科学学会 14—430c
皇家温尼伯芭蕾舞团 Royal Winnipeg Ballet 加拿大芭蕾舞团 14—433a
皇家戏剧艺术学院 Royal Academy of Dramatic Art (RADA) 英国戏剧学校 14—429d
皇家学会 Royal Society 英国学会 14—432e
皇家艺术学院 Royal Academy of Arts 英国国家艺术学院 14—429d
皇家植物园 Royal Botanic Garden (India) 印度植物园 14—430e
皇家植物园 Royal Botanic Gardens (England) 英国植物园 14—430e
皇家植物园 Royal Botanic Garden 英国植物园 14—430e
皇家植物园和国家植物标本室 Royal Botanic Gardens and National Herbarium 澳大利亚植物园 14—430f
皇太极 Abahai 中国帝王 1—4f
《皇舆全览图》 Huangyu Quanlantu 中国地图册 8—216a
黄白杨 yellow poplar 木本植物 18—437a
黄斑 macula lutea 解剖学 10—364a
黄宾虹 Huang Binhong 中国画家 8—210c
黄檗宗 Ōbaku 日本佛教宗派 12—317d
黄长石 melilite 矿物 11—97a
黄巢 Huang Chao 中国农民起义领袖 8—210e
黄疸 jaundice 病理现象 8—549f
黄刀印第安人 Yellowknife 加拿大民族 18—437d
黄道 ecliptic 天文学 5—525f
黄道带 zodiac 天文学 18—561a
黄道光 zodiacal light 天文学 18—561a
黄帝 Huangdi 中国传说人物 8—213f
《黄帝内经》 Huangdi Neijing 中国医学著作 8—214b
黄粉蝶 sulfur butterfly 昆虫 16—325c
黄蜂 wasp 昆虫 18—132b
黄蜂蛾 wasp moth 昆虫 18—132e
黄富数 Huynh Phu So 越南哲学家 8—274f
黄盖鲽 dab 鱼类 5—101e
黄公望 Huang Gongwang 中国画家 8—210e
黄狗合同 yellow-dog contract 契约 18—436c
黄瓜 cucumber (*Cucumis sativus*) 攀缘植物 5—50e
黄瓜叶甲 cucumber beetle 昆虫 5—50f
黄果树瀑布 Huangguoshu Falls 中国瀑布 8—214b
黄海 Yellow Sea 中、朝间陆架浅海 18—437b
黄河 Huang He 中国河流 8—211a
黄河三角洲 Huanghe Sanjiaozhou 中国地区 8—214c
黄褐森鸫 wood thrush (bird) 鸟类 18—321c
黄花岗起义 Huanghuagang Uprising 中国历史 8—214d
黄花探 Hoang Hoa Tham (Vietnamese nationalist) 越南民族主义者 8—109a
黄花藤 canary creeper (species *Tropaeolum peregrinum*) 草本植物 3—394a
黄化病 yellows(plant disease) 植物病害 18—437f
黄桦 yellow birch (species *Betula alleghaniensis*, or *B. lutea*) 木本植物 18—436c
黄昏大嘴雀 evening grosbeak 鸟类 6—182b
黄昏鸟属 Hesperornis 古生物学 8—58c
黄假高粱 Indian grass (species *Sorghastrum nutans*) 草本植物 8—

360a
黄巾起义 Yellow Turbans 中国历史 18—437b
黄金储备 gold reserve 经济学 7—186e
黄金分割画派 Section d'Or 艺术团体 15—178d
黄金海岸 Gold Coast 非洲海岸 7—186c
黄金律 Golden Rule 《圣经》箴言 7—190c
黄金十字架演说 Cross of Gold speech 美国政治演说 5—32d
黄金时代 Golden Age 拉丁文学 7—188b
黄金世纪 Golden Age 西班牙文学 7—188b
黄金象牙雕像 chryselephantine 古代艺术品 4—215c
黄晋发 Huynh Tan Phat 越南领导人 8—274f
黄晶 citrine 矿物 4—249b
黄精 Solomon's seal 草本植物 15—499d
黄静果 Cua,Paulus 越南学者 5—46d
黄菊 Huang Ju 中国领导人 8—211f
黄君璧 Huang Junbi 中国画家 8—212a
黄葵 musk mallow (species *Hibiscus moschatus*, or H. abelmoschus) 草本植物 11—510e
黄昆 Huang Kun 中国物理学家 8—212b
黄濑户陶器 Ki Seto ware 日本陶器 9—268a
黄老之学 Huang-Lao zhi xue 中国哲学 8—214e
黄梨洲 Huang Li-chou 中国学者 8—212c
黄鹂 oriole 鸟类 12—461d
黄连山 Hoang Lien Son 越南省份 8—109a
黄连山 Hoang Lien Son (peak, Vietnam) 越南山峰 8—109b
黄鳞 yellow scales (*Xanthoria parietina*) 植物 18—437b
黄陵 Huangling 中国县名 8—214f
黄榴石 topazolite 矿物 17—156b
黄绿磷灰石 asparagus stone 宝石 1—556e
黄绿藻 yellow-green algae 植物 18—436f
黄麻 jute 草本植物 9—121a
黄麻属 Corchorus 植物学 4—501c
黄帽派 Yellow Hat sect (Tibetan Buddhism) 藏传佛教宗派 18—436f
黄莓 yellowberry 植物 18—437c
黄梅戏 Huangmeixi 中国戏曲 8—215a
黄嘌呤尿症 xanthinuria 疾病 18—373d
黄埔军校 Whampoa Military Academy 中国陆军军官学校 18—218e
黄潜蝇 frit fly 昆虫 6—497c
黄筌 Huang Quan 中国画家 8—212c
黄雀 siskin 鸟类 15—404a
黄热病 yellow fever 疾病 18—436d
黄色新闻 yellow journalism 新闻 18—436f
黄山 Huangshan 中国城市 8—215b
黄山 Huang Shan 中国名山 8—212d
黄石 Huangshi 中国城市 8—215c
黄石国家公园 Yellowstone National Park 美国国家公园 18—438a
黄石河 Yellowstone River 美国河流 18—438b
黄石湖 Yellowstone Lake 美国湖泊 18—437f
黄水仙 daffodil (*Narcissus pseudonarcissus*) 草本植物 5—106a
黄素 flavin 生物色素 6—352b
黄檀木 rosewood 木本植物 14—406a
黄体 corpus luteum 解剖学 4—520f
黄体化激素 luteinizing hormone (LH) 生物化学 10—294b
黄铁矿 pyrite 矿物 14—46f
黄庭坚 Huang Tingjian 中国诗人 8—212f
黄铜 brass 合金 3—125d
黄铜矿 chalcopyrite 矿物 4—30f
黄铜马饰品 horse brass 装饰品 8—180c
黄土 loess 土壤学 10—185b
黄土高原 Huangtu Gaoyuan 中国高原 8—215d
黄腿鹬 yellowlegs 鸟类 18—437e
黄鹀 yellowhammer (*Emberiza citrinella*) 鸟类 18—437c
黄锡矿 stannite 矿物 16—193c
黄兴 Huang Xing 中国革命家 8—213b
黄岩 Huangyan 中国城市 8—215f
黄颜木染料 fustic 天然染料 6—533f
黄杨科 Buxaceae 植物学 3—295a
黄杨木 boxwood 木材 3—99a
黄油果 butternut 木本植物 3—293e
黄玉 topaz 矿物 17—156a
黄原酸盐 xanthate 化学 18—373c
黄藻门 Xanthophyta 植物学 18—373d
黄子卿 Huang Ziqing 中国物理化学家 8—213c
黄宗羲 Huang Zongxi 中国学者 8—213c
黄宗霑 Howe, James Wong 美国电影摄影师 8—200c
黄遵宪 Huang Zunxian 中国诗人 8—213e
黄佐临 Huang Zuolin 中国戏剧家 8—213e
獚狗 spaniel 狗品种 16—4e
湟中 Huangzhong 中国县名 8—216b
煌斑岩 lamprophyre 岩石 9—468e
煌绿 brilliant green 染料 3—157e
蝗虫 short-horned grasshopper 昆虫 15—333b
蝗鸟 locust bird 鸟类 10—183a
磺胺 sulfanilamide 药物 16—317e
磺胺嘧啶 sulfadiazine 药物 16—317e
磺胺噻唑 sulfathiazole 药物 16—318b
磺胺药 sulfa drug 药物 16—317d
磺化 sulfonation 化学 16—320f
磺酸 sulfonic acid 化合物 16—323b
磺酰胺 sulfonamide 化合物 16—320b
簧风琴 harmonium 乐器 7—481f
簧片风琴 reed organ 乐器 14—196d
簧乐器 reed instrument 乐器 14—196d
灰孢目 Lycoperdales 植物学 10—308e
灰背隼 merlin (*Falco columbarius*) 鸟类 11—132d
灰背鱼 grayback 鱼类 7—267e
灰吹法 cupellation 冶金方法 5—65c
灰狗长途客运汽车公司 Greyhound Lines, Inc. 美国公司 7—307f
灰姑娘 Cinderella 文学 4—240e
灰光灯 limelight 舞台聚光灯 10—103e
灰鬼 Gray Ghost, The (racehorse) 美国赛马 7—267c
灰海豹 gray seal (*Halichoerus grypus*) 哺乳动物 7—267d
灰海鲈 graysby 鱼类 7—267f
灰红蝠 hoary bat (*Lasiurus cinereus*) 哺乳动物 8—109e
灰狐 gray fox (*Urocyon cinereoargenteus*) 哺乳动物 7—267b
灰胡桃 butternut (*Juglans cinerea*) 木本植物 3—293d
灰华洞穴 tufa cave 地质学 17—259d
灰化土 podzolic soil 土壤学 13—385c
灰桦 gray birch (*Betula populifolia*) 木本植物 7—267b
灰鲸 gray whale (*Eschrichtius robustus*, sometimes classified as *E. glaucus* or *E. gibbosus*) 哺乳动物 7—267d
灰连雀 hypocoly (*Hypocolius ampelinus*) 鸟类 8—295b
灰林鸱 poor-me-one 鸟类 13—431b
灰霉疫病 gray mold blight (plant disease) 植物疾病 7—267c
灰泥 plaster 建筑材料 13—349f
灰泥粉刷 stuccowork 建筑 16—287c
灰泥画 lime painting 绘画 10—103d
灰鸟 graybird 鸟类 7—267e
灰壤 podzol 土壤学 13—385b
灰色单色画 grisaille 绘画技法 7—315e
灰山 Kültepe 土耳其古城遗址 9—393c
灰土 spodosol 土壤学 16—38e
灰西鲱 alewife (species *Pomolobus*, or *Alosa*, *pseudoharengus*) 鱼类 1—199a

灰熊 grizzly bear 哺乳动物 7—317b
灰岩残丘 pepino hill 地质学 13—152f
灰岩参差面 lapiés 地质学 9—494f
灰岩盆地 polje 地质学 13—404e
灰雁 greylag 鸟类 7—308a
灰衣贵人 Gray Eminence, The 德国外交官 7—267b
灰沼狸 suricate (*Suricata suricatta*) 哺乳动物 16—353e
诙谐曲 scherzo 音乐 15—113f
诙谐作品 burlesque 文学 3—268b
辉长岩 gabbro 岩石 6—538b
辉碲铋矿 tetradymite 矿物 16—563c
辉沸石 stilbite 矿物 16—237a
辉风鸟 manucode 鸟类 10—476c
辉格党 Whig Party 美国历史 18—223c
辉格党和托利党 Whig and Tory 英国历史 18—223b
辉绿岩 diabase 岩石 5—282d
辉木属 Psaronius 古生物学 13—556a
辉钼矿 molybdenite 矿物 11—326a
辉砷钴矿 cobaltite 矿物 4—314a
辉石 pyroxene 矿物 14—47f
辉石岩 pyroxenite 岩石 14—48c
辉锑矿 stibnite 矿物 16—234d
辉铜矿 chalcocite 矿物 4—30d
辉银矿 argentite 矿物 1—465c
徽州 Hui-chou (China) 中国城市 8—227d
回避关系 avoidance relationship 社会学 2—91a
回避行为 avoidance behaviour 生物学 2—90f
回采 stoping 采矿 16—253f
回肠 ileum 解剖学 8—333c
回肠炎 ileitis 病理现象 8—333b
回肠造口术 ileostomy 外科手术 8—333b
回归热 relapsing fever 传染病 14—213c
回纥 Huihe 中国古代民族 8—228c
回火 tempering 冶金 16—533c
回交 backcross 生物学 2—119b
回扣 rebate 贸易 14—182a
回力球 jai alai 西班牙球戏 8—518d
回目 seder 犹太法规 15—181d
回声测深仪 echo sounder 测量器 5—523b
回声测深仪 Fathometer 仪器商标名 6—249d
回声定位 echolocation 动物生理过程 5—523c
“回声”号通信卫星 Echo 美国人造卫星 5—523b
回文 palindrome 文学 12—566b
回纹饰 fret 艺术和建筑装饰 6—485b
回旋加速器 cyclotron 物理设备 5—87f
回旋曲 rondeau 音乐曲式 14—387f
回旋曲 rondo 器乐曲 14—388b
回旋诗 roundelay 诗歌 14—420b
回忆 recall 心理学 14—182f
回忆录 memoir 文体 11—103c
回转 slalom 体育 15—425a
回族 Hui 中国民族 8—227d
茴芹 anise (*Pimpinella anisum*) 草本植物 1—359f
茴香 fennel (species *Foeniculum vulgare*) 草本植物 6—276f
茴鱼 grayling 鱼类 7—267f
蛔虫病 ascariasis 疾病 1—539f
蛔虫属 Ascaris 生物学 1—539f
鮰鱼 ictalurid 鱼类 8—317d
《汇报》 Allgemeine Zeitung 德文报纸 1—240a
汇报法官 rapporteur 法国法律 14—155c
汇丰控股有限公司 HSBC Holdings PLC 银行控股公司 8—203e
汇款单 money order 金融 11—335c
汇率 exchange rate 金融 6—189b
汇票 exchange, bill of 金融 6—188f
汇水区 catchment area 地理学 3—522e
会馆 huiguan 中国同乡会 8—228c
《会规手册》 Manual of Discipline 犹太教文献 10—476b
会合周期 synodic period 天文学 16—402f
会津若松 Aizu-wakamatsu 日本城市 1—150b
会牧书信 Pastoral Epistle (New Testament writings) 《新约全书》 13—83b
会堂 synagogue 犹太教活动场所 16—400d
会议 council 基督教 4—542b
会议 synod 基督教 16—402f
会泽安 Aizawa Yasushi 日本思想家 1—150a
会众 congregation 宗教 4—428c
绘画 painting 艺术 12—550f
绘卷 emaki 日本艺术 6—54f
桧苹果锈病 cedar-apple rust 植物病害 3—549b
贿赂 bribery 违法行为 3—148d
彗星 comet 天文学 4—380a
秽多 eta (Japanese minority) 日本民族 6—143c
秽语癖 scatologia 性偏离行为 15—106c
惠比寿 Ebisu 日本神话神名 5—517e
惠彻 Whitcher, Frances Miriam Berry 美国作家 18—227f
惠德比岛 Whidbey Island 美国岛屿 18—223a
惠迪岛 Whiddy Island 爱尔兰岛屿 18—223b
惠蒂埃 Whittier, John Greenleaf 美国作家 18—240e
惠蒂尔 Whittier 美国城市 18—240e
惠佃制 benefice 法兰克王国租田制 2—381f
惠栋 Hui Dong 中国学者 8—227e
惠顿 Wheaton 美国城市 18—220d
惠顿 Wheaton, Henry 美国海商法学家 18—220e
惠尔登 Wheldon, Sir Huw Pyrs 英国电视节目制作人 18—222e
惠更斯 Huygens, Christiaan 荷兰数学家 8—274c
惠更斯 Huygens, Constantijn 荷兰艺术家 8—274e
惠更斯原理 Huygens' principle 物理学 8—274e
惠加尔帕 Juigalpa 尼加拉瓜城市 9—104d
惠拉盖尔济 Hveragerdhi 冰岛村庄 8—275f
惠勒 Wheeler, Joseph 美国骑兵将领 18—221e
惠勒 Wheeler, John Archibald 美国物理学家 18—221d
惠勒 Wheeler, Sir (Robert Eric) Mortimer 英国考古学家 18—221e
惠勒 Wyler, William 美国电影导演 18—366d
惠勒 Wheeler, William A(lmon) 美国副总统 18—221f
惠勒 Wheeler, William Morton 美国昆虫学家 18—222a
惠勒峰 Wheeler Peak 美国新墨西哥州最高点 18—222a
《惠勒-霍华德法》 Wheeler-Howard Act 美国法律 18—222a
惠灵 Wheeling 美国城市 18—222b
惠灵顿 Wellington 澳大利亚城镇 18—179d
惠灵顿 Wellington 英格兰城镇 18—179d
惠灵顿 Wellington 新西兰北岛行政区 18—179e
惠灵顿 Wellington 新西兰首都 18—179e
惠灵顿港 Wellington Harbour (New Zealand) 新西兰海湾 18—181d
惠洛克 Wheelock, Eleazar 美国教育家 18—222b
惠洛克 Wheelock, Lucy 美国教育家 18—222c
惠涅利 Whinnery, John Roy 美国电气工程师 18—223f
惠普尔 Whipple, George H(oyt) 美国病理学家 18—224d
惠普尔 Whipple, Squire 美国土木工程师 18—224e
惠普公司 Hewlett-Packard Company 美国公司 8—65a
惠乔尔人和科拉人 Huichol and Cora 中美印第安人 8—227f
惠森迪岛 Whitsunday Island 坎伯兰群岛的最大岛屿 18—240b
惠山 Hyesan 朝鲜城市 8—287f
惠施 Hui Shi 中国哲学家 8—227e
惠斯顿 Whiston, William 英格兰圣公会牧师 18—227c
惠斯勒 Whistler, James (Abbott) McNeill 美国画家 18—226e

惠斯勒克拉夫特 Whistlecraft, William and Robert 英格兰外交家 18—226c
惠斯特 whist 纸牌游戏 18—225f
惠斯特骨牌 domino whist 游戏 5—375a
惠斯特式桥牌 bridge whist 纸牌游戏 3—152e
惠斯通 Wheatstone, Sir Charles 英国物理学家 18—220f
惠特比 Whitby 英格兰北约克郡城镇 18—227e
惠特比会议 Whitby, Synod of 宗教会议 18—227f
惠特布雷德图书奖 Whitbread Book Award 英国文学奖 18—227d
惠特尔 Whittle, Sir Frank 英国飞行员 18—241b
惠特尔西 Whittelsey, Abigail Goodrich 美国编辑 18—240d
惠特菲尔德 Whitfield, Mal 美国中距离赛跑运动员 18—236f
惠特霍恩 Whithorn 苏格兰自治市 18—237a
惠特吉夫特 Whitgift, John 坎特伯雷大主教 18—236f
惠特克 Whittaker, Charles E(vans) 美国最高法院大法官 18—240b
惠特克 Whittaker, Sir Edmund Taylor 英国数学家 18—240c
惠特克 Whitaker, Sir Frederick 新西兰总理 18—227c
惠特拉姆 Whitlam, Gough 澳大利亚政治家 18—237b
惠特里奇 Whittredge, (Thomas) Worthington 美国风景画家 18—241c
惠特利 Wheatley, John 英国工党政治家 18—220c
惠特利 Wheatley, Phillis 美国黑人诗人 18—220d
惠特利 Whately, Richard 都柏林圣公会大主教 18—219c
惠特利协议会 Whitley Council 英国劳资联合组织 18—237c
惠特洛克 Whitlock, Elizabeth 英国演员 18—237d
惠特曼 Whitman 美国马萨诸塞州城镇 18—237d
惠特曼 Whitman, Marcus 美国医学家 18—237c
惠特曼 Whitman, Sarah Helen Power 美国诗人、散文家 18—237e
惠特曼 Whitman, Walt 美国诗人 18—237f
惠特尼 Whitney, Anne 美国雕塑家 18—238d
惠特尼 Whitney, Adeline Dutton Train 美国作家 18—238d
惠特尼 Whitney, Charlotte Anita 美国主张妇女参政权者 18—238e
惠特尼 Whitney, Eli 美国发明家 18—238f
惠特尼 Whitney, Gertrude Vanderbilt 美国雕刻家 18—239b
惠特尼 Whitney, John Hay 美国富翁、运动员 18—239c
惠特尼 Whitney, Josiah Dwight 美国地质学家 18—239d
惠特尼 Whitney, Mary Watson 美国天文学家 18—239d
惠特尼 Whitney, Phyllis Ayame 美国作家 18—239e
惠特尼 Whitney, William C(ollins) 美国海军部长 18—239f
惠特尼 Whitney, William Dwight 美国语言学家 18—240a
惠特尼 Whitney, Willis Rodney 美国化学家 18—240a
惠特尼美国艺术博物馆 Whitney Museum of American Art 美国博物馆 18—240b
惠特尼山 Whitney, Mount 美国本土最高点 18—239e
惠特斯特布尔 Whitstable 英格兰肯特郡城镇 18—240b
惠特沃思 Whitworth, Sir Joseph, Baronet 英国工程师 18—241d
惠特沃思 Whitworth, Kathy 美国运动员 18—241e
惠廷顿 Whittington, Dick 英格兰商人 18—241a
惠州 Huizhou 中国城市 8—229b
喙 beak 动物学 2—303a
喙甲 billbug 昆虫 2—473d
喙鲸 beaked whale 哺乳动物 2—303c
喙头目 Rhynchocephalia 动物学 14—272b
喙形风格 beak style 巴布亚新几内亚艺术 2—303b
喙鱼 billfish 鱼类 2—473f
喙嘴龙属 Rhamphorhynchus 古生物学 14—258b
慧能 Huineng 中国高僧 8—228d
慧远 Huiyuan 中国高僧 8—229a
慧智知派 Ḥabad 犹太教派 7—396e
昏厥 fainting 病理现象 6—214d
昏迷 coma 病理现象 4—375e
婚后住所 residence 人类学 14—239e
婚书 ketubba 犹太教 9—247a
婚姻 marriage 社会学 10—530d
婚姻法 marriage law 法律 10—531a
浑仪 armillary sphere 古天文仪器 1—500e
珲春 Hunchun 中国城市 8—252b
魂魄 hun and po 道教 8—251c
魂质 leśyā 耆那教 10—41d
混沌 chaos 力学、数学 4—56a
混沌 Chaos 希腊早期宇宙论 4—55f
混汞法 patio process 冶金学 13—88e
混合 blending 纺织 2—532e
混合利底亚调式 Mixolydian mode 音乐 11—296a
混合诗 macaronic 拉丁诗体 10—327e
混合稀土金属 misch metal 合金 11—274f
混合岩 migmatite 岩石 11—206a
混积岩 peperite 地质学 13—151f
混乱时期 Troubles, Time of 俄国历史 17—237b
混凝土 concrete 建筑材料 4—413d
混凝纸 papier-mâché 经过浆状处理的纸 13—24f
混血人 Métis 加拿大历史民族 11—159e
混杂 contamination 文学 4—464e
混战球戏 mêlée 古代游戏 11—96b
活板门蛛 trap-door spider 昆虫 17—201d
活报剧 Living Newspaper 戏剧 10—163a
活动电影机 Cinématographe 电影机械 4—241c
活动雕刻 mobile 艺术 11—300b
活动顶盖写字台 rolltop desk 家具 14—361c
活动桥 movable bridge 桥 11—448e
活动台板出入口 trap 戏剧 17—201c
活度系数 activity coefficient 化学 1—61d
活佛 Phat Song (Vietnamese philosopher) 越南哲学家 13—221f
活化络合物理论 activated-complex theory 化学 1—61c
活化能 activation energy 化学 1—61c
活栎 live oak 植物 10—159d
活塞和气缸 piston and cylinder 机械 13—326f
活塞军号 flügelhorn 乐器 6—376f
活石头 living stone (plant) 植物 10—163b
活腿桌 gateleg table 家具 7—28f
活性污泥法 activated-sludge method 污水处理 1—61c
活字印刷 typography 印刷 17—309c
活组织检查 biopsy 医学 2—485d
火 fire 可燃物质燃烧 6—324f
火彩 fire 宝石闪光 6—325b
火草 fireweed (*Epilobium angustifolium*) 草本植物 6—328b
火柴 match 引火物 11—18c
火车大劫案 Great Train Robbery 英国历史 7—275d
火成岩 igneous rock 岩石 8—326f
火刺虫 fireworm 蠕虫 6—328c
火丛 burning bush 植物 3—273d
火地岛 Tierra del Fuego 南美岛群 17—89a
火地岛地域人种 Fuegian local race 美洲印第安地理人种 6—510a
火地岛区 Tierra del Fuego 阿根廷行政区 17—89b
火腹蟾蜍 fire-bellied toad 两栖动物 6—325c
火冠戴菊 firecrest 鸟类 6—327d
火花塞 spark plug 电气元件 16—8d
火花室 spark chamber 辐射探测器 16—8c
火鸡 turkey 禽类 17—284b
火鸡蚋 turkey gnat 昆虫 17—284d
火鸡舞 turkey trot 舞蹈 17—284d
火鸡鱼 turkey fish 鱼类 17—284d
火棘 firethorn 植物 6—328a
火箭 rocket 喷气推进装置 14—342d

"火箭"号 Rocket 英国最早的机车 14—343b
火箭女郎踢踏舞团 Rockettes, the 美国踢踏舞团 14—343b
火结神 Ho-musubi 日本宗教神名 8—108d
火警报警器 fire alarm 报警设施 6—325b
火炬木 torchwood(*Amyris*) 灌木或树木 17—159e
火炬仙人掌 torch cactus 植物 17—159e
火烈鸟乐团 Flamingos, the 美国乐团 6—347b
火炉 stove 设备 16—258b
火奴鲁鲁 Honolulu 美国港口 8—159e
火炮 artillery 武器 1—531c
火炮 cannon 武器 3—405b
"火炮大王" Cannon King, The 德国实业家 3—405e
火雀 fire finch 鸟类 6—326b
火绒草 edelweiss (*Leontopodium alpinum*) 植物 5—536e
火山 volcano 地质学 18—35a
火山玻璃 volcanic glass 岩石 18—34e
火山弹 bomb 地质学 3—19a
火山灰 pozzolana 水凝水泥 13—477c
火山灰年代学 tephrochronology 地质学 16—548b
火山灰锥 ash cone (volcanic deposits) 地质学 1—544b
火山活动 volcanism 地质学 18—34f
火山口湖 Crater Lake 美国深水湖 4—571c
火山砾 lapillus 地质学 9—494f
火山列岛 Volcano Islands 日本岛屿 18—37b
火山泥流 lahar 地质学 9—449e
火山穹丘 volcanic dome 地质学 18—34d
火山学 volcanology 地球科学 18—37b
火山渣 scoria 地质学 15—148a
火山渣锥 cinder cone 地质学 4—240e
火山轴线 Eje Volcánico (Mexico) 墨西哥火山山脉 6—7d
火神式自动机关炮 Vulcan automatic cannon 武器 18—54b
火绳机 matchlock 机械发火装置 11—18f
火绳枪 harquebus 武器 7—485f
火树 flamboyant tree 木本植物 6—346c
火腿 ham 食品 7—434e
火卫二 Deimos 天文学 5—214b
火卫一 Phobos 天文学 13—254c
火星 Mars 天文学 10—532b
火星全球勘探者 Mars Global Surveyor 美国航天器 10—532f
火星探路者 Mars Pathfinder 美国航天器 10—533c
火星运河 Mars, canals of 天文学 10—532e
火焰 flame 燃烧气体 6—346c
火焰喷射器 flame thrower 武器 6—346c
火药 gunpowder 炸药 7—373b
火药阴谋案 Gunpowder Plot 英国历史 7—373e
火蚁 fire ant 昆虫 6—325c
火疫病 fire blight 植物病害 6—325c
火鱼 fire-fish (fish) 鱼类 6—326c
火狱 jahannam 伊斯兰教 8—517f
火灾保险 fire insurance 保险险种 6—326c
火葬 cremation 丧葬习俗 5—4f
火柱会 Pillar of Fire 美国基督教会 13—303f
钬(Ho) holmium 化学元素 8—135c
或然论 probabilism 哲学 13—522f
或然论 syādvāda 耆那教学说 16—391b
货币 money 经济学 11—334e
货币贬值 devaluation 金融 5—270d
货币虫 nummulite 古生物学 12—299c
货币供应量 money supply 经济学 11—335c
货币数量说 quantity theory of money 经济学 14—74d
货币政策 monetary policy 经济学 11—334a
货币主义 monetarism 经济学 11—333f
货车 freight car 载运工具 6—474a
货物崇拜 cargo cult 宗教运动 3—456f
货物出门不退 caveat emptor 法律 3—541a
货物入市税 octroi 税收 12—335b
货物运输法 carriage of goods 法律 3—481c
获得性免疫缺陷综合征 acquired immune deficiency syndrome 疾病 1—57d
获得性状 acquired character 生物学 1—57d
获释奴隶 freedman 得到自由的奴隶 6—470d
获月 harvest moon 天文学 7—497e
霍埃费尔男爵 Hoëvell, Wolter Robert, Baron van 荷兰政治家 8—114d
霍巴特 Hobart 澳大利亚城市 8—110a
霍巴特 Hobart 美国城市 8—110a
霍巴特 Hobart, Garret A(ugustus) 美国政治家 8—110a
霍巴特 Hobart, John Henry 美国传教士 8—110b
霍巴特 Hobart, Percy 英国陆军军官 8—110b
霍巴特帕夏 Hobart Paşa 英国军人 8—110c
霍贝玛 Hobbema, Meindert 荷兰画家 8—110c
霍本 Hoban, James 爱尔兰建筑师 8—109f
霍比 Hobby, Oveta Culp 美国官员 8—111c
霍比 Hoby, Sir Thomas 英国外交官 8—111f
霍博肯 Hoboken 美国城市 8—111e
霍布豪斯 Hobhouse, Emily 英国改革家 8—111c
霍布豪斯 Hobhouse, Sir John Cam 英国政治家 8—111d
霍布豪斯 Hobhouse, L(eonard) T(relawny) 英国社会学家 8—111d
霍布森 Hobson, Laura Z(ametkin) 美国作家 8—111f
霍布斯 Hobbs 美国城市 8—111b
霍布斯 Hobbs, Sir John Berry 英国运动员 8—111b
霍布斯 Hobbes, Thomas 英国哲学家 8—110d
霍查 Hoxha, Enver 阿尔巴尼亚领导人 8—202c
霍城 Ho 加纳城镇 8—107a
霍达兰 Hordaland 挪威郡名 8—173c
霍德 Hoad, Lew 澳大利亚运动员 8—108f
霍德凯维奇 Chodkiewicz, Jan Karol 波兰将军 4—188a
霍德梅泽瓦沙海伊 Hódmezővásárhely 匈牙利城镇 8—113e
霍德纳盐湖 Hodna, Chott el- 阿尔及利亚湖泊 8—113f
霍德斯科 Chodsko 捷克历史地区 4—188c
霍顿 Houghton 美国城市 8—192f
霍顿 Haughton, Billy 美国骑手 7—511d
霍顿 Haughton, Percy Duncan 美国教练 7—511d
霍顿 Horton, Robert E(lmer) 美国工程师 8—187b
霍顿男爵(第一) Houghton (of Great Houghton), Richard Monckton Milnes, 1st Baron 英国诗人 8—192f
霍多维茨基 Chodowiecki, Daniel (Nikolaus) 德国版画家 4—188b
霍恩 Horne, Herman Harrell 美国教育哲学家 8—176f
霍恩 Horne, John 英国政治家 8—176f
霍恩 Horne, Lena 美国演员 8—176f
霍恩 Horne, Marilyn 美国歌唱家 8—177a
霍恩 Hone, William 英国新闻记者 8—152e
霍恩堡 Heuneburg 德国古遗址 8—64a
霍恩伯爵 Horn (af Ekebyholm), Arvid Bernhard, Greve (Count) 瑞典政治家 8—175e
霍恩博斯特尔 Hornbostel, Erich Moritz von 奥地利音乐学家 8—176e
霍恩布洛尔 Hornblower, Jonathan Carter 英国发明家 8—176d
霍恩海姆 Hohenheim, Philippus Aureolus Theophrastus Bombast von (alchemist) 瑞士医生 8—120b
霍恩洛厄家族 Hohenlohe FAMILY 德意志皇族 8—120b
霍恩洛厄-希灵斯菲斯特 Hohenlohe-Schillingsfürst, Chlodwig Karl Viktor, Fürst zu 德意志皇族 8—120d
霍恩洛厄-英格尔芬根 Hohenlohe-Ingelfingen, Friedrich Ludwig, Fürst zu 普鲁士元帅 8—120c

霍恩洛厄-英格尔芬根 Hohenlohe-Ingelfingen, Kraft, Prinz zu 普鲁士军官、军事著作家 8—120c
霍恩群岛 Horne Îslands 太平洋岛屿 8—177b
霍恩施泰因伯爵 Thun und Hohenstein, Leo, Count (Graf) von 奥地利政治家 17—70a
霍恩斯比 Hornsby, Rogers 美国运动员 8—178e
霍恩泰因 Hontheim, Johann Nikolaus von 德国历史学家、神学家 8—160f
霍恩·图克 Horne Tooke, John 英国政治家 8—177b
霍恩瓦尔特 Hohenwart, Karl Siegmund, Graf von 奥地利首相 8—120e
霍尔 Hall, Adelaide 美国爵士乐即兴演奏家 7—425a
霍尔 Hall, Asaph 美国天文学家 7—425a
霍尔 Hall, Basil 英国军官、旅行家 7—425b
霍尔 Hall, Charles Francis 美国探险家 7—425c
霍尔 Hall, Charles Martin 美国化学家 7—425c
霍尔 Hoar, Ebenezer R(ockwood) 美国政治家 8—109b
霍尔 Hall, Gus 美国政治组织者 7—426a
霍尔 Hoar, George Frisbie 美国政治家 8—109c
霍尔 Hall, G(ranville) Stanley 美国心理学家 7—425e
霍尔 Hall, James 美国作家 7—426a
霍尔 Hall, James 美国地质学家 7—426b
霍尔 Hall, Sir John 新西兰总理 7—426c
霍尔 Hall, Joseph 英国圣公会主教 7—426e
霍尔 Hall, Joyce C(lyde) 美国商人 7—426e
霍尔 Hall, John L. 美国物理学家 7—426d
霍尔 Hall, Marshall 英国生理学家 7—426f
霍尔 Hall, Sir Peter (Reginald Frederick) 英国戏剧导演 7—427a
霍尔 Hall, Radclyffe 英国作家 7—427b
霍尔 Hall, Robert 英国牧师、作家 7—427c
霍尔 Hall, Samuel 英国工程师 7—427c
霍尔 Hoare, Sir Samuel (John Gurney), 2ND BARONET 英国政治家 8—109c
霍尔巴赫 Holbach, Paul-Henri Dietrich, baron d' 法国哲学家 8—123e
霍尔拜克 Holbæk 丹麦城市 8—123e
霍尔拜因(大) Holbein, Hans, THE ELDER 德国画家 8—123f
霍尔拜因(小) Holbein, Hans, THE YOUNGER 德国画家 8—124a
霍尔堡 Holberg, Ludvig 北欧作家 8—124c
霍尔-贝利沙 Hore-Belisha (of Devonport), (Isaac) Leslie Hore-Belisha, Baron 英国大臣 8—173d
霍尔本 Holborn 英国前自治市 8—124d
霍尔丹 Haldane, Elizabeth Sanderson 苏格兰改革家 7—418a
霍尔丹 Haldane, J. B. S. 英国遗传学家 7—418a
霍尔丹 Haldane, John Scott 英国生理学家 7—418b
霍尔丹 Haldane, Richard Burdon, 1ST VISCOUNT HALDANE OF CLOAN 英国政治家 7—418c
霍尔德尔 Holder, Alfred Theophil 奥地利语言学家 8—124d
霍尔德曼 Haldeman, H(arry) R(obbins) 美国官员 7—418d
霍尔德内斯 Holderness 英格兰半岛 8—125a
霍尔蒂 Horthy, Miklós (Nagybányai) 匈牙利军人 8—186b
霍尔顿 Halton 英格兰区名 7—434d
霍尔顿 Houlton 美国城镇 8—193b
霍尔克罗夫特 Holcroft, Thomas 英国作家 8—124d
霍尔密兹德 Hormizd 波斯萨珊国王之名 8—174d
霍尔密兹德二世 Hormizd II 波斯萨珊国王 8—174d
霍尔密兹德四世 Hormizd IV 波斯萨珊国王 8—174e
霍尔密兹德一世 Hormizd I 波斯萨珊国王 8—174d
霍尔莫戈雷 Kholmogory 俄罗斯港口 9—262c
霍尔姆 Holm, Hanya 美国舞蹈家 8—134c
霍尔姆 Holm, Sven 丹麦小说家 8—134d
霍尔木兹岛 Hormuz 伊朗岛屿 8—175b
霍尔木兹甘 Hormozgān 伊朗省份 8—175b
霍尔木兹海峡 Hormuz, Strait of 波斯湾海峡 8—175c
霍尔奈 Horney, Karen 美国精神分析学家 8—178b
霍尔内曼 Hornemann, Friederich Konrad 德国探险家 8—178a
霍尔齐厄斯 Goltzius, Hendrik 荷兰画家 7—197f
霍尔-琼斯 Hall-Jones, Sir William 新西兰总理 7—427e
霍尔施泰因 Holstein, Friedrich (August) von 德国政治家 8—138f
霍尔斯顿河 Holston River 美国河流 8—139d
霍尔斯特 Holst, Gustav (Theodore) 英国作曲家 8—138b
霍尔斯特 Holste, Luc 德国古典学者 8—138d
霍尔斯特布罗 Holstebro 丹麦城市 8—138e
霍尔斯特德 Halsted, William Stewart 美国外科医生 7—434a
霍尔泰 Holtei, Karl von 德国作家 8—140a
霍尔特 Gorter, Herman 荷兰诗人 7—219e
霍尔特 Holt, Edwin B(issell) 美国心理学家 8—139d
霍尔特 Holt, Harold (Edward) 澳大利亚总理 8—139e
霍尔特 Holt, Winifred 美国福利工作者 8—139f
霍尔托巴吉 Hortobágy 匈牙利地区 8—187a
霍尔韦格 Hollweg, Theobald von Bethmann 德国政治家 8—133e
霍耳 Hall, Chester Moor 英国法学家、数学家 7—425c
霍耳 Hall, Sir James 苏格兰地质学家 7—426c
霍耳效应 Hall effect 物理学 7—427d
霍法 Hoffa, James P. 美国劳工领袖 8—115a
霍法 Hoffa, James R(iddle) 美国劳工领袖 8—115b
霍费尔 Hofer, Andreas 蒂罗尔爱国志士 8—114e
霍夫 Hof 德国城市 8—114e
霍夫 Hove 英格兰城镇 8—197c
霍夫鲍尔 Hofbauer, Saint Clement Mary 维也纳主保圣徒 8—114e
霍夫兰 Hovland, Carl I(ver) 美国心理学家 8—198a
霍夫雷 Jofre, Eder 巴西拳击手 9—43d
霍夫迈尔 Hofmeyr, Jan (Hendrik) 南非政治家 8—117f
霍夫迈斯特 Hofmeister, Sebastian 瑞士宗教改革家 8—117e
霍夫迈斯特 Hofmeister, Wilhelm (Friedrich Benedikt) 德国植物学家 8—117e
霍夫曼 Hofmann, August Wilhelm von 德国化学家 8—116f
霍夫曼 Hoffman, Daniel 美国诗人、教育家 8—115d
霍夫曼 Hoffman, Dustin 美国演员 8—115e
霍夫曼 Hoffmann, E(rnst) T(heodor) A(madeus) 德国作家、作曲家 8—116a
霍夫曼 Hoffmann, Heinrich 德国画家 8—116b
霍夫曼 Hofmann, Hans 德国画家 8—116f
霍夫曼 Hoffmann, Josef 德国建筑师 8—116c
霍夫曼 Hofmann, Josef Casimir 美国钢琴家 8—117b
霍夫曼 Hoffmann, Max 德国将军 8—116c
霍夫曼 Hoffman, Malvina 美国雕塑家 8—115f
霍夫曼 Hofmann, Melchior 德国神秘主义者 8—117b
霍夫曼 Hoffman, Paul G(ray) 美国制造商 8—115f
霍夫曼 Hoffmann, Roald 美国化学家 8—116d
霍夫曼 Hoffman, Samuel Kurtz 美国工程师 8—116a
霍夫曼·封·法勒斯莱本 Hoffmann von Fallersleben, August Heinrich 德国诗人 8—116e
霍夫曼斯塔尔 Hofmannsthal, Hugo von 奥地利作家 8—117c
霍夫曼斯瓦尔道 Hofmannswaldau, Christian Hofmann von 德国诗人 8—117e
霍夫青泽 Hofzinser, Johann Nepomuk 奥地利魔术师 8—118c
霍夫斯冰原 Hofsjökull 冰岛冰川 8—118a
霍夫斯塔特 Hofstadter, Richard 美国历史学家 8—118a
霍夫斯塔特 Hofstadter, Robert 美国物理学家 8—118b
霍夫特 Hooft, Gerardus' t 荷兰物理学家 8—162c
霍夫特 Hooft, Pieter Corneliszoon 荷兰作家 8—162d
霍弗 Hoffer, Eric 美国哲学家 8—115c
霍戈柳 Hogoleu (Caroline Islands) 加罗林群岛岛屿 8—120b
霍格 Hoge, Jane Currie Blaikie 美国福利工作者 8—119b
霍格 Hogg, Douglas McGarel, 1ST VISCOUNT HAILSHAM OF HAILSHAM 英国政治

家 8—119d
霍格 Hogg, James 苏格兰诗人 8—119e
霍格 Hogg, Quintin 英国社会改革家 8—119e
霍格 Hogg, Thomas Jefferson 英国作家 8—119f
霍格兰 Hoagland, Dennis Robert 美国植物学家 8—108f
霍格思 Hogarth, David George 英国考古学家 8—118f
霍根 Hogan, Ben 美国运动员 8—118e
霍光 Huo Guang 中国大臣 8—263d
霍赫 Hooch, Pieter de 荷兰画家 8—161b
霍亨多普 Hogendorp, Dirk van 荷兰政治家 8—119c
霍亨斯陶芬王朝 Hohenstaufen DYNASTY 德意志王朝 8—120e
霍亨索伦王朝 Hohenzollern DYNASTY 欧洲王朝 8—120f
霍华德 Howard, Bronson (Crocker) 美国剧作家 8—198b
霍华德 Howard, Catherine 英国王后 8—198c
霍华德 Howard, Charles 英国军人 8—198c
霍华德 Howard, Sir Ebenezer 英国城市规划家 8—198c
霍华德 Howard, Edward 英国制造商 8—198d
霍华德 Howard, Henry 英国贵族 8—198d
霍华德 Howard, John 英国贵族 8—198e
霍华德 Howard, John 英国慈善家 8—198e
霍华德 Howard, John Winston 澳大利亚总理 8—198e
霍华德 Howard, Leslie 英国演员、导演 8—199a
霍华德 Howard, Leland Ossian 美国昆虫学家 8—198f
霍华德 Howard, Oliver O(tis) 美国军人 8—199b
霍华德 Howard, Philip 英国贵族 8—199c
霍华德 Howard, Sir Robert 英国剧作家 8—199c
霍华德 Howard, Roy W. 美国记者 8—199d
霍华德 Howard, Sidney (Coe) 美国剧作家 8—199d
霍华德 Howard, Thomas 英国贵族 8—199f
霍华德大学 Howard University 美国大学 8—199f
霍华德家族 Howard FAMILY 英格兰家族 8—198b
霍霍巴树 jojoba (*Simmondsia chinensis*) 植物 9—76a
霍霍坎文化 Hohokam culture 北美印第安文化 8—121d
霍基蒂卡 Hokitika 新西兰城市 8—122e
霍加尔 Hoggar (plateau, Africa) 非洲高原 8—120a
霍金 Hawking, Stephen W(illiam) 英国物理学家 7—525e
霍金森 Hokinson, Helen 美国漫画家 8—122e
霍金斯 Hawkins, Coleman 美国音乐家 7—525f
霍金斯 Hawkins, Sir John 英格兰法官、作家 7—526c
霍金斯 Hawkins, Sir John 英格兰军人 7—526a
霍金斯 Hawkyns, Sir John 英格兰军人 7—527a
霍金斯 Hawkins, Sir Richard 英国海员、冒险家 7—526c
霍金斯 Hawkyns, Sir Richard 英国海员、冒险家 7—527a
霍金维尔 Hodgenville 美国城市 8—112e
霍卡诸语言 Hokan languages 语言 8—122c
霍克 Hawke (of Towton), Edward Hawke, 1st Baron 英国军人 7—525b
霍克 Hawke, Robert 澳大利亚总理 7—525c
霍克海默 Horkheimer, Max 德国哲学家 8—174c
霍克利夫 Hoccleve, Thomas 英国诗人 8—112a
霍克内 Hockney, David 英国画家 8—112d
霍克斯 Hawks, Howard (Winchester) 美国电影导演 7—526d
霍克斯堡河 Hawkesbury River 澳大利亚河流 7—525d
霍克斯堡男爵(第二) Hawkesbury, Robert Banks Jenkinson, 2nd Baron 英国首相 7—525d
霍克斯比(老) Hauksbee, Francis, THE ELDER 英国科学家 7—511f
霍克斯比(小) Hauksbee, Francis, THE YOUNGER 英国科学家 7—511f
霍克斯伯里港 Port Hawkesbury 加拿大城镇 13—445d
霍克斯穆尔 Hawksmoor, Nicholas 英国建筑师 7—526e
霍克斯沃思 Hawkesworth, John 英国作家 7—525e
霍克湾 Hawke's Bay 新西兰行政区名 7—525d
霍克伍德 Hawkwood, Sir John 英国雇佣军统领 7—527a
霍克肖 Hawkshaw, Sir John 英国工程师 7—526e
霍奎厄姆 Hoquiam 美国城市 8—172c
霍拉 hora 民间舞蹈 8—172e
霍拉伯德 Holabird, William 美国建筑师 8—123c
霍拉尔 Hollar, Wenzel 捷克版画家 8—132e
霍拉马巴德 Khorramābād 伊朗城市 9—264a
霍拉姆沙赫尔 Khorramshahr 伊朗城市 9—264a
霍拉提乌斯·科克列斯 Horatius Cocles 罗马英雄 8—173c
霍兰 Holland 美国城市 8—131c
霍兰 Holland, Henry 英国建筑师 8—131e
霍兰 Holland, Henry Edmund 新西兰劳工领袖 8—131e
霍兰 Holland, John Henry 美国数学家 8—132a
霍兰 Holland, John Philip 美国发明家 8—132c
霍兰 Holland, Sir Sidney (George) 新西兰总理 8—132c
霍兰 Holand, Thomas 英国贵族 8—123d
霍兰 Holland, Thomas 英国贵族 8—132d
霍兰 Holland, Sir (Thomas) Erskine 英国法律著作家 8—131d
霍兰地区 Holland, Parts of 英格兰旧区名 8—132c
“霍兰”号 Holland 美国潜水器 8—131c
霍兰男爵(第三) Holland (of Foxley and of Holland), Henry Richard Vassall Fox, 3rd Baron 英国政治家 8—132a
霍兰男爵(第一) Holland (of Foxley), Henry Fox, 1st Baron 英国政客 8—131f
霍兰隧道 Holland Tunnel 美国隧道 8—132d
霍勒里思 Hollerith, Herman 美国发明家 8—132e
霍勒姆 Holum, Dianne 美国速度滑冰运动员 8—140c
霍勒斯·曼学校 Horace Mann School 纽约学校 8—173a
霍利 Holley, Marietta 美国作家 8—133b
霍利 Holley, Robert William 美国生物化学家 8—133b
霍利奥克 Holyoke 美国城市 8—143c
霍利戴 Holiday, Billie 美国歌唱家 8—130b
霍利岛 Holy Island 英格兰岛屿 8—141b
霍利德 Holliday, Doc 美国赌徒、匪徒 8—133c
霍利黑德 Holyhead 威尔士港口 8—143b
霍利斯 Holles, Thomas Pelham- 英国首相 8—132f
霍利斯(伊菲尔德的) Holles (of Ifield), Denzil Holles, 1st Baron 英国政治家 8—132f
霍利斯普林斯 Holly Springs 美国城市 8—133f
霍利韦尔 Holywell 威尔士城镇 8—143d
霍利约克 Holyoake, Sir Keith Jacka 新西兰总理 8—143c
霍利约克 Holyoke, Edward 美国教育家 8—143c
霍林的狼 Howlin' Wolf 美国音乐家 8—202b
霍林希德 Holinshed, Raphael 英国历史学家 8—130f
霍隆 Ḥolon 以色列城市 8—137f
霍卢布 Holub, Emil 波希米亚博物学家 8—140b
霍乱 cholera 疾病 4—190e
霍伦 Hoorn 荷兰城市 8—165f
霍伦贝格 Heulenburg, Heulalius von 德国医生、作家 8—64a
霍伦希布 Horemheb 古埃及国王 8—173f
霍罗 horo 保加利亚舞蹈 8—179b
霍罗费努阿 Horowhenua 新西兰自治区 8—179b
霍罗格 Khorog 塔吉克斯坦城市 9—263f
霍罗克斯 Horrocks, Jeremiah 英国天文学家 8—179d
霍罗曼斯基 Choromański, Michał 波兰作家 4—199d
霍罗维茨 Horowitz, Vladimir 美国钢琴家 8—179c
霍洛 Jolo 菲律宾岛屿 9—77e
霍马 Houma 美国城市 8—193c
霍曼轨道 Hohmann orbit 航天 8—121c
霍梅尼 Khomeini, Ruhollah 伊朗宗教领袖 9—262d
霍米雅科夫 Khomyakov, Aleksey Stepanovich 俄国神学家 9—262e
霍默 Homer, Louise 美国演员 8—145a
霍默 Homer, Winslow 美国画家 8—145a
霍姆 Home, Henry (Scottish philosopher) 苏格兰哲学家 8—143e
霍姆 Home, John 苏格兰剧作家 8—143f

霍姆伯爵(第十四) Home, Alexander Frederick Douglas-Home, 14th earl of 英国首相 8—143e
霍姆伯爵(第一) Home, Alexander Home, 1st earl of 苏格兰贵族 8—143e
霍姆斯 Ḥimṣ 叙利亚城市 8—86f
霍姆斯 Holmes, Oliver Wendell 美国医生、作家 8—134e
霍姆斯 Holmes, Oliver Wendell, Jr. 美国法律史学家 8—134e
霍姆斯 Holmes, William Henry 美国考古学家 8—135b
霍姆斯特德 Homestead 美国佛罗里达州城市 8—145d
霍姆斯特德 Homestead 美国宾夕法尼亚州城镇 8—145e
霍穆尔卡 Homolka, Oscar 美国演员 8—148a
霍穆托夫 Chomutov 捷克城市 4—192b
霍瑙瑙 Honaunau 美国夏威夷岛村庄、历史遗址 8—151b
霍讷伯爵 Hoorne, Filips van Montmorency, Graaf van 荷兰政治家 8—166a
霍尼顿花边 Honiton lace 英国工艺品 8—159d
霍尼曼 Horniman, Annie (Elizabeth Fredericka) 英国剧院经理 8—178d
霍尼韦尔国际公司 Honeywell International Inc. 美国公司 8—155a
霍尼亚拉 Honiara 所罗门群岛首府 8—159d
霍宁达尔湖 Hornindals Lake 挪威湖泊 8—178d
霍佩 Hoppe, Willie 美国台球大师 8—171e
霍佩-赛勒 Hoppe-Seyler, Ernst Felix (Immanuel) 德国医生 8—171e
霍皮人 Hopi 民族 8—169a
霍皮语 Hopi language 语言 8—169c
霍珀 Hopper, Edward 美国画家 8—171e
霍普 Hope 加拿大城镇 8—167d
霍普 Hope 美国城市 8—167e
霍普 Hope, Anthony 英国作家 8—167f
霍普 Hope, A(lec) D(erwent) 澳大利亚诗人 8—167e
霍普 Hope, Bob 美国演员 8—167f
霍普 Hope, John 美国教育家 8—168a
霍普 Hope, Lugenia Burns 美国社会改革家 8—168a
霍普 Hope, Thomas 英国作家、艺术家 8—168b
霍普 Hope, Victor Alexander John 英国政治家 8—168c
霍普顿(斯特拉顿的)男爵 Hopton (of Stratton), Ralph Hopton, Baron 英格兰将领 8—172b
霍普菲尔德 Hopefield 南非城镇 8—168e
霍普金森 Hopkinson, Francis 美国律师、作家 8—171c
霍普金森 Hopkinson, John 英国物理学家 8—171c
霍普金斯 Hopkins, Sir Anthony 英国演员 8—169f
霍普金斯 Hopkins, Esek 美国军人 8—169e
霍普金斯 Hopkins, Sir Frederick Gowland 英国生物化学家 8—169f
霍普金斯 Hopkins, Gerard Manley 英国诗人 8—170a
霍普金斯 Hopkins, Harry L(loyd) 美国官员 8—170c
霍普金斯 Hopkins, Johns 美国富商 8—170e
霍普金斯 Hopkins, Mark 美国教育家 8—170f
霍普金斯 Hopkins, Mark 美国资本家 8—171a
霍普金斯 Hopkins, Samuel 美国神学家 8—171b
霍普金斯维尔 Hopkinsville 美国城市 8—171d
霍普纳 Hoppner, John 英国画家 8—171f
霍普-琼斯 Hope-Jones, Robert 美国管风琴制造商 8—168d
霍普特曼 Hauptmann, Gerhart (Johann Robert) 德国作家 7—512c
霍普特曼 Hauptmann, Moritz 德国音乐家 7—512f
霍普韦尔 Hopewell 美国城市 8—168f
霍普韦尔文化 Hopewell culture 印第安文化 8—168f
霍普韦尔文化国家历史公园 Hopewell Culture National Historical Park 美国国家纪念地 8—169a
霍普伍德渡口 Hopwood's Ferry (Australia) 澳大利亚城市 8—172c
霍普钻石 Hope diamond 宝石 8—168c
霍奇 Hodge, Charles 美国学者 8—112e
霍奇金 Hodgkin, Sir Alan (Lloyd) 英国生理学家 8—113a
霍奇金 Hodgkin, Dorothy Mary Crowfoot 英国化学家 8—113b
霍奇金 Hodgkin, Thomas 英国医生 8—113c
霍奇金氏病 Hodgkin disease 疾病 8—113c
霍奇卡尔科 Xochicalco 墨西哥古城 18—394a
霍奇米尔科 Xochimilco 墨西哥行政区 18—394b
霍奇森 Hodgson, Frances Eliza (writer) 美国作家 8—113d
霍奇森 Hodgson, Ralph 英国诗人 8—113d
霍奇斯 Hodges, Courtney Hicks 美国陆军军官 8—112f
霍奇斯 Hodges, Johnny 美国音乐家 8—113a
霍茹夫 Chorzów 波兰城市 4—200b
霍萨 Horsa (Anglo-Saxon leader) 盎格鲁-撒克逊人领袖 8—180a
霍萨尔特 Gossaert, Jan 佛兰德斯画家 7—221f
霍桑 Hawthorne, Nathaniel 美国作家 7—527f
霍桑 Hawthorne, Rose 天主教修女 7—528b
霍桑调查 Hawthorne research 社会经济实验 7—528b
霍森斯 Horsens 丹麦城市 8—183c
霍舍姆 Horsham 澳大利亚城市 8—185b
霍舍姆 Horsham 英格兰区名 8—185c
霍申加巴德 Hoshangābād 印度城市 8—188a
霍斯 Hawes, Harriet Ann Boyd 美国考古学家 7—524b
霍斯 Hawes, Josiah Johnson 美国摄影家 7—524b
霍斯 Hawes, Stephen 英国诗人 7—524c
霍斯金斯 Hoskyns, Sir Edwyn Clement, 13TH BARONET 英国《圣经》学者 8—188e
霍斯利 Horsley, John Callcott 英国画家 8—185c
霍斯利 Horsley, Sir Victor (Alexander Haden) 英国生理学家 8—185c
霍斯罗夫 Khosrow 波斯国王之名 9—264b
霍斯罗夫二世 Khosrow Ⅱ 波斯国王 9—264c
霍斯罗夫一世 Khosrow Ⅰ 波斯国王 9—264b
霍斯罗夫之春地毯 Spring of Khosrow Carpet 古波斯工艺品 16—162f
霍斯罗夫之冬地毯 Winter of Khosrow Carpet 工艺品 18—290f
霍斯梅 Hosmer, Harriet Goodhue 美国雕刻家 8—188e
霍斯舒瀑布 Horseshoe Falls 加拿大瀑布 8—184c
霍斯特 Horst, Louis 美国钢琴家、作曲家 8—185d
霍斯提利安 Hostilian 罗马皇帝 8—189d
霍斯提利乌斯 Hostilius, Tullus 传说中的罗马国王 8—189e
霍索恩 Hawthorn, John Michael 英国赛车运动员 7—527e
霍塔 jota 西班牙舞蹈 9—92b
霍特 Hort, Fenton J(ohn) A(nthony) 英国学者 8—185e
霍特里 Hawtrey, Sir Ralph (George) 英国经济学家 7—528b
霍特奇诺 Khotchino (Russia) 俄国城市 9—264e
霍滕西娅 Hortensia 罗马女杰 8—186a
霍滕修斯 Hortensius, Quintus 罗马独裁官 8—186b
霍滕修斯·霍塔卢斯 Hortensius Hortalus, Quintus 罗马演说家 8—186b
霍屯督面包 Hottentot bread (plant) 植物 8—191c
霍屯督人 Hottentot (people) 民族 8—191c
霍屯督诸语言 Hottentot languages 语言 8—191c
霍瓦内斯 Hovhaness, Alan 美国作曲家 8—197f
霍瓦人 Hova (people) 民族 8—197c
霍瓦特 Horváth, Ödön Edmund Josef von 匈牙利作家 8—187d
霍维 Hovey, Richard 美国作家 8—197e
霍维茨 Horvitz, H. Robert 美国生物学家 8—187e
霍维克 Hovick, Rose Louise 美国演员 8—198a
霍维利亚诺斯 Jovellanos, Gaspar Melchor de 西班牙作家 9—94d
霍文威普国家保护区 Hovenweep National Monument 美国自然保护区 8—197c
霍沃思 Haworth 英格兰城镇 7—527a
霍沃思 Haworth, Sir (Walter) Norman 英国化学家 7—527b

霍希亚布尔 Hoshiārpur 印度城市 8—188b
霍休斯 Hosius, Stanislaus 波兰枢机主教 8—188d
霍修斯(科尔多瓦的) Hosius OF CÓRDOBA 西班牙主教 8—188d
霍延 Goyen, Jan Josephs(zoon) van 荷兰画家 7—234a
霍耶斯韦达 Hoyerswerda 德国城市 8—202f
霍伊 Khvoy 伊朗城市 9—267b
霍伊 Hoe, Robert 美国制造商 8—114a
霍伊 Hoe, Richard March 美国发明家 8—113f
霍伊岛 Hoy 苏格兰岛屿 8—202e
霍伊尔 Hoyle, Edmond 英国作家 8—202f
霍伊尔 Hoyle, Sir Fred 英国天文学家 8—202f
霍伊克 Hawick 英国城镇 7—524c
霍伊斯勒合金 Heusler alloy 磁性合金 8—64b
豁免 dispensation 教会法 5—341c
豁免 immunity 法律 8—344b
獾加狓 okapi (*Okapia johnstoni*) 哺乳动物 12—357e

J

几丁质 chitin 化合物 4—181e
几维 kiwi 鸟类 9—311c
击板乐器 clapper 乐器 4—259f
击棍 club 原始武器 4—305c
击剑 FENCING 体育项目 16—86a
击剑 fencing 体育项目 6—272b
击弦键琴 clavichord 乐器 4—273d
饥荒 famine 爱尔兰历史 6—228e
玑子 baroque pearl 形状怪异的珍珠 2—238f
机场艺术品 Airport art 艺术品 1—148a
机床 machine tool 机器 10—348e
机动车保险 motor-vehicle insurance 保险 11—435e
机动雪橇 snowmobile 机动车 15—465c
机构 mechanism 机械 11—68e
机会成本 opportunity cost 经济学 12—434d
机器 machine 机械系统 10—347b
机器人 robot 机器 14—336d
机器拖拉机站 machine-tractor station (MTS) 苏联国营机构 10—349e
机枪 machine gun 武器 10—348b
机身 fuselage 航空器 6—532d
机体 airframe 航空器 1—147a
机械工程 mechanical engineering 工程 11—67d
机械工程和电气混合工会 Amalgamated Engineering and Electrical Union (AEEU) 英国工人组织 1—263d
机械利益 mechanical advantage 物理学 11—67c
机械论 mechanism 哲学 11—68e
机械能 mechanical energy 物理学 11—67c
机械效率 mechanical efficiency 物理学 11—67c
机械性刺激感受作用 mechanoreception 生物学 11—68f
机翼 wing 航空器 18—287d
机遇音乐 chance music 音乐 4—43a
机缘论 occasionalism 哲学 12—325d
机载警戒与控制系统 AWACS 军事 2—91f
肌病 myopathy 家畜疾病 11—525d
肌醇 inositol 化合物 8—394e
肌电描记法 electromyography 医疗测试 6—27c
肌动蛋白 actin 生物化学 1—59c
肌苷酸 inosinic acid 化合物 8—394e
肌红蛋白 myoglobin 蛋白质 11—525d
肌强直 myotonia 疾病 11—525f
肌肉 muscle 解剖学 11—501a
肌肉解剖图 écorché 绘画 5—530e
肌肉肿瘤 muscle tumour 病理学 11—501d
肌萎缩性侧索硬化 amyotrophic lateral sclerosis (ALS) 疾病 1—306b
肌炎 myositis 疾病 11—525e
肌营养不良 muscular dystrophy 疾病 11—501f
肌原纤维 myofibril 生理学 11—525c
矶崎新 Isozaki Arata 日本建筑师 8—475a
矶蟹 kelp crab 蟹 9—218e
鸡 chicken 家禽 4—146e
鸡草 chickweed 植物 4—146f
鸡肺脑炎 avian pneumoencephalitis (bird disease) 禽类疾病 2—88a
鸡冠花 cockscomb 植物 4—323f
鸡龟 chicken turtle (species *Deirochelys reticularia*) 水龟科动物 4—146f
鸡素烧 sukiyaki 日本烹调 16—315c
鸡尾鹦鹉 cockatiel 鸟类 4—321c
鸡西 Jixi 中国城市 9—36c
鸡新城疫 Newcastle disease 禽类疾病 12—147b
鸡形类 galliform 鸟类 6—560b
鸡眼 corn 皮肤病 4—510b
鸡足草 cocksfoot grass 植物 4—323f
奇蹄类 perissodactyl 哺乳动物 13—170b
唧唧鹨 peep 鸟类 13—122b
积分 integral 数学 8—403d
积分变换 integral transform 数学 8—403e
积分法 integration 数学 8—404c
积分方程 integral equation 数学 8—403e
积分器 integrator 数学仪器 8—404d
积分仪 integraph 数学仪器 8—404a
积脓 empyema 病理现象 6—66a
姬蝽 damsel bug 昆虫 5—129f
姬发 Chi Fa 中国帝王 4—138b
姬蜂 ichneumon 昆虫 8—315e
姬路 Himeji 日本城市 8—86b
姬鸮 elf owl (*Micrathene whitneyi*) 猛禽 6—35f
姬啄木鸟 piculet 鸟类 13—292e
基 Key, David M(cKendree) 美国政治活动家 9—247e
基 Key, Francis Scott 美国国歌歌词作者 9—248a
基 Key, V(aldimer) O(rlando), Jr. 美国政治学家 9—248b
基埃塔 Kieta 巴布亚新几内亚城镇 9—273f
《基安地协定》(1755) Gianti Agreement 印度尼西亚历史 7—117c
基安尼尼 Giannini, A(madeo) P(eter) 美国银行家 7—115f
基安恰诺泰尔梅 Chianciano Terme 意大利城镇 4—138d
基奥海恩 Keohane, Nannerl Overholser 美国学者、行政管理者 9—236c
基奥加湖 Kyoga Lake 乌干达湖泊 9—413e
基奥贾 Chioggia 意大利城镇 4—177e
基奥卡克 Keokuk 美国城市 9—236e
基奥卡克 Keokuk 美国印第安人政客 9—236d
基奥瓦人 Kiowa 民族 9—298a
基奥佐托 Chiozzotto (Venetian composer) 意大利作曲家 4—177f
基堡伯爵领地 Kyburg 瑞士伯爵领地 9—412f
《基本法》 Fundamental Laws 俄国法律 6—525d
基本家庭 elementary family (kinship) 社会学 6—33a
基本粒子 elementary particle 物理学 6—33a
基本相互作用 fundamental interaction 物理学 6—525b
基本英语 Basic English 英语简化形式 2—258f
基比亚 Gibeah 以色列古城 7—120b
基遍 Gibeon 古巴勒斯坦城镇 7—120b
基布多 Quibdó 哥伦比亚城市 14—89f
基布尔 Keble, John 基督教牧师、诗人 9—210b
基础代谢率 basal metabolic rate (BMR) 医学 2—255a
基础低音 ground bass 音乐 7—323b
基础小学 Grundschule 德国教育 7—329f
基茨比厄尔 Kitzbühel 奥地利城镇 9—310e

基茨比厄尔山 Kitzbühel Alps 奥地利山脉 9—310f
基大利斋日 Gedaliah, fast of 犹太教节日 7—42e
基代波河谷国家公园 Kidepo Valley National Park 乌干达国家公园 9—269d
基德 Kyd, Thomas 英国戏剧家 9—412f
基德 Kidd, William 英国海盗 9—269a
基德尔 Kidder, Alfred V(incent) 美国考古学家 9—269c
基德兰德 Kydland, Finn E. 挪威经济学家 9—413a
基德伦-韦希特 Kiderlen-Wächter, Alfred von 德国政治家 9—269d
基德明斯特 Kidderminster 英格兰城镇 9—269c
基德斯顿 Kidston, Robert 英国古植物学家 9—270f
基地组织 Qaeda, al- 伊斯兰军事组织 14—51f
基蒂霍克 Kitty Hawk 美国城镇 9—310d
基蒂克米奥特 Kitikmeot 加拿大地区 9—310a
基蒂马特 Kitimat 加拿大自治镇 9—310a
基甸 Gideon 《圣经》人物 7—123a
基甸国际 Gideons International 基督教组织 7—123a
基督奥体 mystical body of Christ 基督教 11—530a
基督刺 Christ thorn (flowering plant) 植物 4—202c
基督弟兄会 Christadelphian 美国基督教派别 4—202c
基督复临 Second Coming 基督教 15—176d
基督复临安息日会信徒 Seventh-day Adventist 新教 15—238e
基督复临归一会 United Society of Believers in Christ's Second Appearing 新教派别 17—364a
基督复临会 Advent Christian Church 美国基督教会 1—89c
基督复临派 Adventist 美国基督教派别 1—89c
基督公教会 Christian Catholic Church 美国教会 4—205c
基督会 Church of Christ 基督教保守派 4—224b
基督会 Disciples of Christ 美国基督教保守派 5—338e
基督会 Iglesia ni Kristo 宗教 8—326b
基督会世界大会 World Convention of Churches of Christ 基督教国际组织 18—334d
基督及所罗门圣殿贫穷骑士团 Poor Knights of Christ and of the Temple of Solomon 基督教军事团体 13—431a
基督降临节 Advent 基督教节日 1—89c
基督教 Christianity 宗教 4—207c
基督教妇女禁酒联合会 Woman's Christian Temperance Union (WCTU) 美国组织 18—314c
基督教公理会全国协进会 National Association of Congregational Christian Churches 美国教会机构 12—11f
基督教公理会总会 General Council of Congregational Christian Churches 美国宗教组织 7—55e
基督教合一派 Unity School of Christianity 美国宗教派别 17—374e
基督教会世界服务社 Church World Service 救济机构 4—224e
基督教教职 ministry 基督教 11—258b
基督教科学派 Christian Science 美国教派 4—206b
《基督教科学箴言报》 Christian Science Monitor, The 美国报纸 4—206e
基督教民主联盟 Christian Democratic Union (CDU) 德国政党 4—205e
基督教民主人民党 Christian Democratic People's Party 瑞士政党 4—205e
基督教女青年会 Young Women's Christian Association (YWCA) 基督教组织 18—466a
基督教青年会 Young Men's Christian Association (YMCA) 基督教组织 18—465b
基督教社会联盟 Christian Social Union (CSU) 德国政党 4—206f
基督教社会主义 Christian Socialism 政治哲学 4—207a
基督教徒种姓制度 Christian caste 印度社会 4—205b
《基督教原理》 Institutes of the Christian Religion 基督教著作 8—400d
基督教阵线 Christian Front 美国反犹太组织 4—206a
基督教正统主义 Protestant Orthodoxy 宗教 13—544a
基督肉身不朽论 Aphthartodocetism 基督教异端学说 1—409d
基督神人二性 Christ, two natures of 基督教信条 4—202b
基督圣体节 Corpus Christi, Feast of 天主教节日 4—520e
基督嗣子论 Adoptionism 基督教 1—84d
基督徒美以美会 Christian Methodist Episcopal Church 美国黑人教会 4—206a
基督一性论派 monophysite 基督教派别 11—345f
基督一志论者 Monothelite 基督教徒 11—347e
基顿 Keaton, Buster 美国演员 9—209d
基顿 Keaton, Diane 美国演员 9—209e
基多 Quito 厄瓜多尔首都 14—95f
基恩 Keene 美国城市 9—211e
基恩 Kean, Charles (John) 英国演员 9—208c
基恩 Keene, Charles Samuel 英国画家 9—211e
基恩 Kean, Edmund 英国演员 9—208d
基恩 Kean, Ellen 英国演员 9—209a
基恩 Keen, William Williams 美国医师 9—211d
基尔 Kiel 德国城市 9—271b
基尔比 Kilby, Jack 美国工程师 9—277e
基尔伯恩 Kilburn, Thomas 英国工程师 9—277c
基尔代尔 Kildare 爱尔兰集镇 9—277f
基尔代尔伯爵(第十) Kildare, Thomas Fitzgerald, 10th Earl of 爱尔兰起义领袖 9—278a
基尔代尔郡 Kildare 爱尔兰郡名 9—277f
基尔多南 Kildonan 加拿大历史地区 9—278a
基尔戈 Kilgore 美国城市 9—278a
基尔霍夫 Kirchhoff, Gustav Robert 德国物理学家 9—299d
基尔霍夫电路定则 Kirchhoff's circuit rules 电学 9—299e
基尔基尔 Kilkeel 北爱尔兰渔港 9—278f
基尔肯尼 Kilkenny 爱尔兰城市 9—279b
基尔肯尼 Kilkenny 爱尔兰郡名 9—278f
基尔库克 Kirkūk 伊拉克城市 9—304a
基尔马诺克 Kilmarnock 苏格兰城镇 9—280c
基尔梅斯 Quilmes 阿根廷行政区 14—91d
基尔默 Kilmer, (Alfred) Joyce 美国诗人 9—280d
基尔皮 Kilpi, Volter 芬兰小说家 9—280e
基尔赛斯 Kilsyth (Scotland) 苏格兰区名 9—280f
基尔特 guild 行业协会 7—354f
基尔特社会主义 Guild Socialism 政治运动 7—355e
《基尔条约》 Kiel, Treaty of 丹麦与瑞典战争和约 9—271c
基尔希纳 Kirchner, Ernst Ludwig 德国画家 9—299f
基尔希维 Kirchwey, Freda 美国编辑、出版商 9—300c
基尔运河 Kiel Canal 欧洲运河 9—271c
基费尔 Kiefer, Anselm 德国画家 9—271a
基辅 Kiev 乌克兰州名 9—273f
基辅 Kiev 乌克兰首都 9—274a
基哈德森 Gerhardsen, Einar (Henry) 挪威首相 7—87a
基吉 Chigi, Fabio 教皇 4—149c
基济岛 Kizhi Island 俄罗斯岛屿 9—311e
基加利 Kigali 卢旺达城市 9—276c
基节腺 coxal gland 动物学 4—560b
基金霍斯山口 Kicking Horse Pass 加拿大山口 9—268f
基卡普人 Kickapoo 民族 9—268e
基克拉泽斯 Cyclades 希腊州名 5—84e
基库尤人 Kikuyu 非洲民族 9—276e
基奎特 Kikwit 刚果(金)城镇 9—277a
基拉卢 Killaloe 爱尔兰城镇 9—279c
基拉尼 Killarney 爱尔兰城镇 9—279d
基拉尼省立公园 Killarney Provincial Park 加拿大公园 9—279e
基拉宁 Killanin (of Galway), Michael Morris, 3rd Baron 爱尔兰作家 9—279c
基拉韦厄 Kilauea 美国活火山 9—277a

基拉西乌斯二世 Gelasius Ⅱ 教皇 7—47a
基拉西乌斯一世,圣 Gelasius I,SAINT 教皇 7—47a
基拉伊 Kiraly,Karch 美国排球运动员 9—299a
基勒 Keeler,James (Edward) 美国天文学家 9—211b
基勒 Keeler,Wee Willie 美国棒球运动员 9—211c
基里巴斯 Kiribati 太平洋岛国 9—301a
基里蒂马蒂环礁 Kiritimati Atoll 太平洋珊瑚环礁 9—302b
基里克斯陶杯 kylix 古希腊陶器 9—413b
基里诺 Quirino 菲律宾省份 14—95b
基里维纳群岛 Kiriwina Islands 巴布亚新几内亚岛群 9—302b
基利 Kili 太平洋岛屿 9—278b
基利 Killy,Jean-Claude 法国滑雪运动员 9—280c
基利 Keely,John E(rnst) W(orrell) 美国骗子 9—211d
基利安,圣 Kilian, SAINT 传教主教 9—278b
基利格鲁 Killigrew, Thomas 英国剧作家 9—280b
基利斯 Kilis 土耳其城镇 9—278f
基列 Gilead 古巴勒斯坦地名 7—130b
基列西弗 Kiriath-sepher 巴勒斯坦古城 9—300f
基林 Killeen 美国城市 9—279f
基林努斯 Quirinus 罗马神话主神 14—95c
基林群岛 Keeling Islands (Indian Ocean) 印度洋群岛 9—211d
基龙 Edaphosaurus 古生物学 5—534d
基隆 Jilong 中国台湾城市 9—23c
基卢瓦岛 Kilwa 坦桑尼亚城邦 9—281a
基律纳 Kiruna 瑞典城市 9—305e
基罗加 Quiroga,Horacio 乌拉圭小说家 14—95d
基罗加 Quiroga,Vasco de 墨西哥女校创始人 14—95e
《基罗斯法》 Queiroz Law 巴西历史 14—85e
基洛夫 Kirov 俄罗斯州名 9—304c
基洛夫 Kirov 俄罗斯城市 9—304c
基洛夫 Kirov, Sergey Mironovich 苏联共产党领导人 9—304d
基洛夫芭蕾舞团 Kirov Ballet 俄罗斯芭蕾舞团 9—304e
基洛夫斯克 Kirovsk 俄罗斯城市 9—304f
基洛纳 Kelowna 加拿大城市 9—218d
基洛瓦巴德 Kirovabad (Azerbaijan) 阿塞拜疆城市 9—304e
基洛瓦坎 Kirovakan 亚美尼亚城市 9—304f
基洛沃格勒 Kirovograd 乌克兰州名 9—304f
基洛沃格勒 Kirovograd 乌克兰城市 9—304f
基马尔科雕刻 Key Marco carving 北美雕刻 9—248c
基抹 Chemosh 古代闪米特人神 4—113d
基姆湖 Chiemsee 德国湖泊 4—148b
基姆雷 Kimry 俄罗斯城市 9—283c
基姆希 Kimhi,David 欧洲希伯来语学者 9—282f
基姆希 Kimhi, Joseph 欧洲语法家 9—283a
基姆希 Kimhi,Moses 欧洲希伯来语语法家 9—283b
基纳 Qinā 埃及省份 14—63a
基纳 Qinā 埃及省会城市 14—63b
基纳巴卢山 Kinabalu,Mount 马来西亚山峰 9—283c
基纳巴唐岸河 Kinabatangan River 马来西亚河流 9—283d
基纳拉 Quinará 几内亚比绍西南部地区 14—92c
基纳斯顿 Kynaston,Edward 英格兰演员 9—413c
基奈峡湾国家公园 Kenai Fjords National Park 美国国家公园 9—223c
基内 Quinet,Edgar 法国诗人 14—93c
基尼阿斯 Cineas 古希腊国王顾问 4—241a
基尼利 Keneally,Thomas 澳大利亚作家 9—224e
基尼人 Kenite 古代部落 9—224f
基涅 Keene,Laura 美国演员 9—211e
基涅什马 Kineshma 俄罗斯城市 9—284d
基涅武甫 Cynewulf 诺森伯里亚诗人 5—89b
基诺 Keno 赌博 9—228a
基诺 Kino,Eusebio 耶稣会传教士 9—294d
基诺尔琴 kinnor 乐器 9—294d
基诺沙 Kenosha 美国城市 9—228b
基诺语 Jino language 中国语言 9—32d
基诺族 Jino 中国民族 9—32c
基帕冯 Citpāvan 印度种姓 4—249a
基帕里夏湾 Kiparissía,Gulf of 希腊海湾 9—298b
基平 Kipping, Frederic Stanley 英国化学家 9—298f
基普西基人 Kipsikis 非洲民族 9—298f
基奇纳 Kitchener 加拿大城市 9—309a
基切 Quiché 危地马拉省份 14—90a
基切人 Quiché 危地马拉马雅印第安人 14—90a
基切语 Quiché language 印第安语言 14—90b
基钦纳伯爵(第一) Kitchener (of Khartoum and of Broome), Horatio Herbert Kitchener,1st Earl 英国陆军元帅 9—309b
基萨拉琴 kithara 弦乐器 9—309f
基萨沃斯 Kissavos (Greece) 希腊山峰 9—307d
基塞金 Gieseking,Walter (Wilhelm) 德国钢琴家 7—123f
基塞龙山 Cithaeron 希腊山脉 4—248a
基桑加尼 Kisangani 刚果(金)城市 9—305f
基色 Gezer 以色列古地名 7—106e
基什 Gish,Dorothy 美国演员 7—144d
基什 Gish,Lillian (Diana) 美国演员 7—144d
基什 Kish 美索不达米亚古城邦 9—306b
基什法鲁迪 Kisfaludy,Károly 匈牙利戏剧家 9—306b
基什孔费莱吉哈佐 Kiskunfélegyháza 匈牙利城镇 9—307a
基什拉 Quicherat,Jules(-Étienne-Joseph) 法国历史学家、考古学家先驱 14—90c
基什内尔 Kirchner,Néstor (Carlos) 阿根廷总统 9—300b
基什尼奥夫 Kishinyov (Moldova) 摩尔多瓦城市 9—306e
基数 base 数学 2—256b
基思 Keith,Sir Arthur 英国解剖学家 9—214a
基思 Keith,Benjamin Franklin 美国歌舞剧团经理 9—214a
基思 Keith,William 美国油画家 9—214b
基斯勒 Kiesler,Frederick John 美国建筑师 9—273d
基斯利 Keighley 英格兰城镇 9—212f
基斯洛沃茨克 Kislovodsk 俄罗斯城市 9—307b
基斯马尤 Kismaayo 索马里海港 9—307b
基苏木 Kisumu 肯尼亚城市 9—308a
基塔城 Kitay-gorod 莫斯科区名 9—309a
基塔隆琴 chitarrone 乐器 4—181c
基塔伊 Kitaj,R(onald) B(rooks) 英国画家 9—308e
基特尔 Kittl,Ema(soprano) 捷克歌唱家 9—310d
基特尔袍 kittel 犹太教 9—310b
基特峰国立天文台 Kitt Peak National Observatory (KPNO) 美国天文台 9—310b
基特加 Gitega 布隆迪城镇 7—145e
基特里 Kittery 美国城镇 9—310b
基特里奇 Kittredge,George Lyman 美国文学家 9—310d
基特曼斯胡普 Keetmanshoop 纳米比亚城镇 9—212b
基特韦 Kitwe 赞比亚城镇 9—310e
基提翁 Citium 塞浦路斯城市 4—248c
基廷 Keating,Paul 澳大利亚政治家 9—209c
基瓦尼 Kewanee 美国城市 9—247c
基瓦尼斯国际 Kiwanis International 国际组织 9—311b
基威诺湾 Keweenaw Bay 美国湖湾 9—247c
基威诺系 Keweenawan System 地质学 9—247c
基韦斯特 Key West 美国城市 9—248c
基韦廷 Keewatin 加拿大行政区 9—212b
基维 Kivi,Aleksis 芬兰文学家 9—311a
基维拉 kivela 南非舞蹈音乐 9—311a
基维利斯 Civilis,Gaius Julius 罗马军官 4—256b
基翁加 Quionga 莫桑比克村庄 14—95a
基伍湖 Kivu,Lake 东非湖泊 9—311b
基西杜古 Kissidougou 几内亚城市 9—307e

基西拉 Cythera 希腊岛屿 5—95c
基西人 Kisii (people) 民族 9—306f
基西人 Kissi 民族 9—307d
基希纳乌 Chişinău 摩尔多瓦城市 4—180e
基歇尔 Kircher, Athanasius 耶稣会教士 9—299d
基谢廖夫 Kiselyov, Pavel Dmitriyevich 俄国将军 9—306a
基谢廖夫斯克 Kiselyovsk 俄罗斯城市 9—306b
基辛格 Kissinger, Henry A(lfred) 美国政治学家、国务卿 9—307e
基辛格 Kiesinger, Kurt Georg 德意志联邦总理 9—273c
基亚布雷拉 Chiabrera, Gabriello 意大利诗人 4—138d
基亚克萨里斯 Cyaxares 米底国王 5—83d
基亚拉蒙蒂 Chiaramonti, Barnaba Gregorio (pope) 教皇 4—139b
基亚罗斯塔米 Kiarostami, Abbas 伊朗导演 9—268c
基亚马 Kiama 澳大利亚城镇 9—268b
基亚瓦里 Chiavari 意大利城镇 4—139c
基要主义 fundamentalism 美国新教守旧主义 6—525d
基耶达法 Kjeldahl method 分析化学 9—312b
基耶蒂 Chieti 意大利城市 4—148d
基耶萨 Chiesa, Giacomo della (pope) 教皇 4—148d
基因 gene 遗传学 7—53d
基因流动 gene flow 遗传学 7—54c
基因型 genotype 遗传学 7—65f
基因中心 genecentre 遗传学 7—54f
基尤植物园 Kew Gardens 英国伦敦植物园 9—247b
基泽尔 Kizel 俄罗斯城市 9—311d
基质 ground substance 生物化学 7—324d
基质 matrix 地质学 11—27d
基祖瓦德纳 Kizzuwadna 安纳托利亚古王国 9—312b
基佐 Guizot, François(-pierre-Guillaume) 法国政治人物、历史学家 7—365e
基座摇椅 platform rocker 家具 13—353e
嵇康 Ji Kang 中国文学家 9—11a
畸胎 monster 疾病 11—351d
畸形学 teratology 生物学 16—548e
畸形足 clubfoot 病理学 4—305f
箕子 Kija 朝鲜国王 9—276d
嗐嘚咱 cherub 宗教 4—129a
激发 excitation 物理学 6—189c
激光唱片 compact disc (CD) 小型光盘 4—395b
激光器 laser 光学器件 9—504d
激活 activation 生理学 1—61c
激进公民联盟 Radical Civic Union (UCR) 阿根廷政党 14—112c
激进民主党 Radical Democratic Party 瑞士政党 14—112d
激进派 radical 政治 14—111b
激进派共和党人 Radical Republican 美国历史 14—112f
激进社会党 Radical-Socialist Party 法国政党 14—113a
激流划艇竞赛 wild-water racing 体育 18—252e
激流生态系统 lotic ecosystem 生态学 10—231a
激素 hormone 生物化学 8—174e
激子 exciton 物理学 6—189d
及耳 gill 计量单位 7—131a
及时行乐 carpe diem 文学 3—475e
吉 Gee, Kenneth 英国运动员 7—43b
吉安 Ji'an 中国城市 9—12f
吉安·加斯托内 Gian Gastone 托斯卡纳大公 7—115e
吉奥狄斯地毯 Ghiordes carpet 工艺品 7—112f
吉奥克 Giauque, William Francis 美国物理化学家 7—117e
吉奥梅特雷斯 Geometres, John 拜占廷诗人 7—73a
吉奥人 Gio (people) 非洲民族 7—137e
吉贝尔蒂 Ghiberti, Lorenzo 意大利雕塑家 7—112d
吉备真备 Kibi Makibi 日本遣唐史 9—268e
吉本 Gibbon, Edward 英国历史学家 7—118a
吉本 Gibbon, Lewis Grassic 苏格兰作家 7—118d
吉本斯 Gibbons, Abigail Hopper 美国社会改革家 7—118e
吉本斯 Gibbons, Cedric 美国电影美工师 7—118e
吉本斯 Gibbons, Grinling 英国装饰木雕师 7—118f
吉本斯 Gibbons, James 美国主教 7—118f
吉本斯 Gibbons, Orlando 英国作曲家 7—119a
吉本斯 Gibbons, Stella (Dorothea) 英国作家 7—119b
吉本斯诉奥格登案 Gibbons v. Ogden 美国法院案例 7—119b
吉兵卫 Kichibē (Japanese printmaker) 日本印章制造家 9—268e
吉伯 Gilbert, William 英国物理学家 7—129b
吉伯林派 Ghibelline 意大利历史 7—112c
吉伯特(拉文纳的) Guibert of Ravenna (antipope) 敌对教皇 7—353d
吉卜 Jīb, al- (Israel) 古巴勒斯坦城镇 9—20a
吉卜林 Kipling, Rudyard 英国小说家 9—298c
吉布里勒 Jibrīl 伊斯兰教教义 9—20b
吉布森 Gibson, Althea 美国女子网球运动员 7—121c
吉布森 Gibson, Bob 美国棒球运动员 7—121d
吉布森 Gibson, Charles Dana 美国画家 7—121d
吉布森 Gibson, John 英国雕刻家 7—121e
吉布森 Gibson, Josh 美国棒球运动员 7—122a
吉布森 Gibson, William Hamilton 美国插图画家、作家 7—122a
吉布森 Gibson, Wilfred Wilson 英国诗人 7—122a
吉布森港 Port Gibson 美国城市 13—445b
吉布森沙漠 Gibson Desert 澳大利亚自然保护区 7—122b
吉布斯 Gibbs, James 英国建筑师 7—119e
吉布斯 Gibbs, J(osiah) Willard 美国科学家 7—119c
吉布斯 Gibbs, William Francis 美国造船工程师 7—119f
吉布斯—杜亨方程 Gibbs - Duhem equation 化学 7—120a
吉布提 Djibouti 非洲国家 5—351a
吉布提 Djibouti 吉布提首都 5—351d
吉川英治 Yoshikawa Eiji 日本小说家 18—461b
吉达 Jiddah 沙特阿拉伯港口 9—20d
吉大港 Chittagong 孟加拉国城市 4—182b
吉德拉尔 Chitrāl 巴基斯坦城镇 4—182a
吉德勒杜尔加 Chitradurga 印度城镇 4—182a
吉登伯勒姆 Chidambaram 印度城镇 4—147e
吉丁虫 metallic wood-boring beetle 昆虫 11—148e
吉丁斯 Giddings, Franklin H(enry) 美国社会学家 7—122c
吉多(勃艮第的) Guido of Burgundy (pope) 教皇 7—354c
吉多(卡斯泰洛城的) Guido de Castellis (pope) 教皇 7—354a
吉多(卡斯泰洛城的) Guido di Città di Castello (pope) 教皇 7—354b
吉多尔 Chitor (India) 印度城镇 4—181f
吉多尔格尔 Chittaurgarh 印度城镇 4—182c
吉厄斯库特斯 gyascutus 想象中的大型四足动物 7—388d
吉尔 Gilles li Muisis 法国诗人 7—132b
吉尔 Gill, André 法国漫画家 7—131a
吉尔 Gill, (Arthur) Eric (Rowton) 英国艺术家、作家 7—131b
吉尔 Gill, Sir David 苏格兰天文学家 7—131a
吉尔 Gill, Irving John 美国建筑师 7—131d
吉尔 Gill, John 美国报纸发行人 7—131d
吉尔 Gill, Laura Drake 美国教育家 7—131e
吉尔伯特 Gilbert Crispin 英格兰《圣经》注释家 7—127d
吉尔伯特 Gilbert Foliot 英格兰主教 7—127d
吉尔伯特 Gilbert, Anne Jane Hartley 美国舞蹈家、演员、 7—127e
吉尔伯特 Gilbert, Cass 美国建筑师 7—127f
吉尔贝特 Gilberts, Guillaume des (French actor) 法国演员 7—129c
吉尔伯特 Gilbert, Grove Karl 美国地质学家 7—128a
吉尔伯特 Gilbert, Sir Humphrey 英国军人、航海家 7—128c
吉尔伯特 Gilbert, John 美国演员 7—128d
吉尔伯特 Gilbert, Sir John 英国画家 7—128d
吉尔伯特 Gilbert, Sir (Joseph) Henry 英国化学家 7—128b
吉尔伯特 Gilbert, Linda 美国社会福利工作者 7—128e

吉尔伯特 Gilbert, Rufus Henry 美国外科医生、运输专家 7—128f
吉尔伯特 Gilbert, Walter 美国分子生物学家 7—129a
吉尔伯特 Gilbert, Sir W(illiam) S(chwenk) 英国剧作家 7—128f
吉尔贝特 Guilbert, Yvette 法国歌唱家 7—354f
吉尔伯特(森普林哈姆的),圣 Gilbert of Sempringham, Saint 英格兰教士 7—127e
吉尔伯特群岛 Gilbert Islands 太平洋岛群 7—129c
吉尔布雷思夫妇 Gilbreth, Frank Bunker and Lillian Evelyn 美国工业管理家 7—129c
吉尔达斯 Gildas 英国历史学家、修士 7—129d
吉尔德 Gilder, Jeannette Leonard 美国编辑、作家 7—129e
吉尔·德·翁塔侬父子 Gil de Hontañón, Juan and Rodrigo 西班牙建筑师 7—126d
吉尔多 Gildo 摩尔人君主 7—130a
吉尔福德 Guildford 英格兰自治市 7—356a
吉尔福德 Guilford 美国城镇 7—356b
吉尔福德 Guilford, Joy Paul 美国心理学家 7—356b
吉尔福德伯爵(第二) Guilford, Frederick North, 2nd earl of 英国首相 7—356b
吉尔福德郡府战役 Guilford Court House, Battle of 美国历史 7—356c
吉尔伽美什 Gilgamesh 美索不达米亚故事人物 7—130d
吉尔古德 Gielgud, Sir (Arthur) John 英国演员、导演 7—123b
吉尔吉斯人 Kyrgyz 民族 9—416f
吉尔吉斯斯坦 Kyrgyzstan 中亚国家 9—417a
吉尔吉斯语 Kyrgyz language 语言 9—416f
吉尔吉特 Gilgit 印度北部巴基斯坦控制区城镇 7—130f
吉尔贾 Jirjā 上埃及城镇 9—34d
吉尔卡湖 Chilka Lake 印度潟湖 4—156f
吉尔克里斯特 Gilchrist, Percy (Carlyle) 英国冶金学家 7—129d
吉尔雷 Gillray, James 英国漫画家 7—133b
吉尔曼 Gilman, Alfred G. 美国药理学家 7—133f
吉尔曼 Gilman, Charlotte Anna Perkins (Stetson) 美国妇女运动理论家 7—133e
吉尔曼 Gilman, Caroline Howard 美国作家、出版商 7—133d
吉尔曼 Gilman, Daniel Coit 美国教育家 7—133f
吉尔摩 Gilmore, Patrick (Sarsfield) 美国指挥家 7—134b
吉尔默 Gilmer, Elizabeth Meriwether 美国新闻记者 7—134a
吉尔纳尔丘陵 Gīrnār Hills 印度自然地理区 7—142e
吉尔内 Girne (Cyprus) 塞浦路斯城市 7—142e
吉尔平 Gilpin, Bernard 英格兰教士 7—134b
吉尔平 Gilpin, Laura 美国摄影家 7—134c
吉尔森林国家公园 Gīr Forest National Park 印度国家公园 7—140d
吉尔山 Gīr Range 吉尔山 7—140e
吉尔斯 Giers, Nikolay Karlovich 俄罗斯政治家 7—123e
吉尔松 Gilson, Étienne(-Henry) 法国哲学家 7—134d
吉尔特尔山脉 Kīrthar Range 巴基斯坦山地 9—305d
吉尔扎伊人 Ghilzay 阿富汗民族 7—112f
吉尔真蒂 Girgenti (Sicily) 意大利城市 7—142c
吉夫阿塔伊姆 Givʿatayim 以色列城市 7—146c
吉夫特 Qifṭ 埃及农业城镇 14—60c
吉福德 Gifford, Edward W(inslow) 美国人类学家 7—124c
吉福德 Gifford, William 英国编辑、学者 7—124d
吉格洛 Guiglo 科特迪瓦城镇 7—354e
吉格马车 gig 轻便马车 7—125c
吉格默格卢尔 Chikmagalūr 印度城镇 4—150c
吉格舞 jig 舞蹈 9—21a
吉洪诺夫 Tikhonov, Nikolay Aleksandrovich 苏联总理 17—94b
吉洪诺夫 Tikhonov, Nikolay Semyonovich 苏联诗人、散文作家 17—94b
吉洪,圣 Tikhon, Saint 俄罗斯正教牧首 17—93f
吉胡提 Djhuty (Egyptian god) 埃及神名 5—350f
吉加瓦 Jigawa 尼日利亚州名 9—21b
吉杰勒 Jijel 阿尔及利亚港口 9—22b
吉杰利 Djidjelli (Algeria) 阿尔及利亚城镇 5—351e
吉卡 Ghica, Ion 罗马尼亚首相 7—112e
吉卡蒂拉 Gikatilla, Joseph 西班牙犹太教哲学家 7—126c
吉卡里拉阿帕切人 Jicarilla Apache 民族 9—20d
吉坎眉 Kyaikkami 缅甸城镇 9—412c
吉科宁 Kekkonen, Urho K(aleva) 芬兰总统 9—214d
吉孔戈罗 Gikongoro 卢旺达省份 7—126d
吉拉丹 Girardin, Émile de 法国新闻记者 7—141c
吉拉德 Girard, Stephen 美国金融家 7—141c
吉拉尔德斯 Güiraldes, Ricardo 阿根廷小说家 7—363a
吉拉尔迪 Giraldi, Giambattista 意大利小说家 7—141a
吉拉尔东 Girardon, François 法国雕刻家 7—141d
吉拉尔杜斯 Giraldus Cambrensis 英国主教、历史学家 7—141a
吉拉斯 Djilas, Milovan 南斯拉夫作家 5—351f
吉拉斯 Gillars, Mildred 二战期间美籍纳粹政府播音员 7—132a
吉莱斯(罗马的) Giles of Rome 意大利神学家 7—130c
吉莱斯皮 Gillespie, Dizzy 美国音乐家 7—132c
吉莱斯皮 Gillespie, George 苏格兰长老会领袖、作家 7—132d
吉莱斯皮 Gillespie, Mother Angela 美国宗教领袖 7—132b
吉莱斯皮 Gillespie, Thomas 苏格兰长老会牧师 7—132e
吉兰 Gīlān 伊朗省份 7—127b
吉兰达约 Ghirlandajo, Domenico 意大利画家 7—113a
吉兰丹 Kelantan 马来西亚州名 9—215a
吉朗 Geelong 澳大利亚城市 7—43c
吉勒鲁普 Gjellerup, Karl Adolph 丹麦诗人、小说家 7—146f
吉勒姆 Gillam, Bernhard 美国漫画家 7—131f
吉勒特 Gillette, William Hooker 美国剧作家、演员 7—132f
吉雷松 Giresun 土耳其城市 7—142c
吉里 Jīlī, al- 伊斯兰教神秘主义者 9—22c
吉里 Gigli, Beniamino 意大利男高音歌唱家 7—125f
吉里 Giry, (Jean-Marie-Joseph-) Arthur 法国历史学家 7—143e
吉里 Giri, Varahagiri Venkata 印度政治家、总统 7—142c
吉里迪 Gīrīdīh 印度城镇 7—142d
吉利尔斯 Gilels, Emil 苏联钢琴家 7—130b
吉利普斯 Gylippus 斯巴达将军 7—388e
吉利斯 Gilliss, James Melville 美国天文学家、海军官员 7—133a
吉利亚克人 Gilyak 西伯利亚民族 7—134e
吉利亚克语 Gilyak language 西伯利亚语言 7—134f
吉廖岛 Giglio Island 意大利岛屿 7—126a
吉列 Gillette, King Camp 美国制造商 7—132e
吉林 Jilin 中国省份 9—22c
吉林 Jilin 中国城市 9—22f
吉林大学 Jilin University 中国大学 9—23b
吉灵厄姆 Gillingham 英格兰东南部城市 7—133a
吉隆坡 Kuala Lumpur 马来西亚首都 9—386c
吉伦 Gillen, Francis James 澳大利亚人类学家 7—132a
吉伦特 Gironde 法国省份 7—143a
吉伦特 Gironde 法国河口湾 7—143b
吉伦特派 Girondin 法国政治团体 7—143b
吉罗 Giraud, Henri(-Honoré) 法国陆军官员 7—141e
吉罗代-特里奥松 Girodet-Trioson, Anne-Louis 法国画家 7—142f
吉罗迪亚 Girodias, Maurice 法国出版商 7—142f
吉洛 Gillot, Claude 法国画家、雕塑家 7—133a
吉马尔 Guimard, Hector(-Germain) 法国建筑师 7—358a
吉马尔 Guimard, (Marie-) Madeleine 法国芭蕾演员 7—358b
吉马朗埃斯 Guimarães, Bernardo (Joaquim da Silva) 巴西诗人、戏剧家 7—357f
吉马朗埃斯·罗萨 Guimarães Rosa, João 巴西小说家 7—358a
吉马朗伊什 Guimarães 葡萄牙城镇 7—357f
吉麦内兹·德·西斯内罗斯 Jiménez de Cisneros, Francisco, Cardenal (Cardinal) 天主教枢机主教 9—24a

吉梅博物馆 Guimet Museum 法国艺术馆 7—358c
吉梅拉 Guimerá, Ángel 西班牙剧作家、诗人 7—358c
吉梅塔 Jimeta 尼日利亚城镇 9—24c
吉姆河 Jim River (North Dakota-South Dakota, U.S.) 美国河流 9—23e
《吉姆·克劳法》 Jim Crow Law 美国法律 9—23e
吉姆利 Gimli 加拿大城镇 7—134f
吉姆索普 Jim Thorpe 美国自治镇 9—23e
吉纳斯特拉 Ginastera, Alberto (Evaristo) 拉丁美洲作曲家 7—135c
吉南 Guinan, Texas 美国演员 7—358d
吉尼 Gini, Corrado 意大利统计学家 7—136c
吉尼 Guiney, Louise Imogen 美国诗人、散文作家 7—361f
吉尼奥尔 Guignol 法国木偶戏角色 7—354e
吉尼斯 Guinness, Sir Alec 英国演员 7—362a
吉尼斯 Guinness, Sir Benjamin Lee, 1st Baronet 爱尔兰酿酒商 7—362c
吉尼斯有限公司 Guinness PLC 爱尔兰公司 7—362c
吉纽 Gignoux, Maurice-Irénée-Marie 法国地质学家 7—126a
吉诺卡斯特 Gjirokastër 阿尔巴尼亚城市 7—147a
吉诺维斯 Genovese, Vito 美国匪徒 7—66a
吉庞服 gipon 服装 7—140b
吉皮乌斯 Gippius, Zinaida Nikolayevna 俄罗斯诗人 7—140c
吉普 jeep 车 8—557c
吉普 Gipp, George 美国橄榄球运动员 7—140c
吉普赛人 Gypsy 民族 7—391e
吉普赛语 Romany language 与北印度-雅利安诸语言有关的语言 14—374b
吉普斯夸 Guipézcoa 西班牙省份 7—362e
吉普斯夸纳公司 Guipuzcoana, Compañía 西班牙公司 7—362f
吉普斯兰德 Gippsland 澳大利亚地区 7—140d
吉萨 Jīzah, Al- 埃及省份 9—36e
吉萨 Jīzah, Al- 埃及城市 9—36e
吉萨金字塔 Giza, Pyramids of 埃及古墓葬建筑 7—146e
吉桑 Guisan, Henri 瑞士军事领袖 7—363b
吉森 Giessen 德国行政区 7—124a
吉森 Giessen 德国城市 7—124b
吉沙尔 Kishar (Mesopotamian mythology) 美索不达米亚神话 9—306d
吉山 Kichizan 日本佛像画家 9—268e
吉绍尔甘杰 Kishorganj 孟加拉国城镇 9—306f
吉申格尔 Kishangarh 印度城市 9—306c
吉申格尔绘画 Kishangarh painting 印度画派 9—306c
吉斯伯恩 Gisborne 新西兰城市 7—144b
吉斯伯恩阶 Gisbornian Stage 地质学 7—144b
吉斯伯爵 Guise, Louis d'Armagnac, comte de (count of) 法国贵族 7—364a
吉斯德纳河 Kistna (India) 印度河流 9—308a
吉斯公爵 Guise, dukes of 法国贵族 7—363c
吉斯公爵(第二) Guise, François de Lorraine, 2^{e} duc de 法国政治阴谋家 7—363d
吉斯公爵(第三) Guise, Henri I de Lorraine, 3e duc de 法国天主教派首领 7—363e
吉斯公爵(第四) Guise, Charles de Lorraine, 4e duc de 法国贵族 7—363f
吉斯公爵(第五) Guise, Henri II de Lorraine, 5e duc de 法国贵族 7—364a
吉斯公爵(第一) Guise, Claude de Lorraine, 1er duc de 法国贵族 7—363d
吉斯卡尔·德斯坦 Giscard d'Estaing, Valéry 法国总统 7—144b
吉斯拉萨迦 Gísla saga 冰岛文学 7—144f
吉斯莱厄里 Ghislieri Antonio (pope) 教皇 7—113b
吉斯勒贝尔图 Gislebertus 法国雕刻家 7—144f
吉斯林 Quisling, Vidkun (Abraham Lauritz Jonsson) 挪威军官 14—95e
吉斯枢机主教 Guise, cardinals of 天主教 7—363b
吉斯枢机主教(第二) Guise, Louis II de Lorraine, 2e cardinal de 法国主教 7—363c
吉斯枢机主教(第三) Guise, Louis III de Lorraine, 3^{e} cardinal de 法国主教 7—363c
吉斯枢机主教(第一) Guise, Louis I de Lorraine, 1er cardinal de 法国主教 7—363c
吉斯特 Gist, Christopher 英属美洲探险家 7—145c
吉斯特 Gist, George 切罗基领导人 7—145d
吉苏尔夫二世 Gisulph II 萨莱诺君主 7—145d
吉他 guitar 乐器 7—364a
吉特巴舞 jitterbug 舞蹈 9—34e
吉特恩琴 gittern 乐器 7—145e
吉特里 Guitry, Lucien (Germain) 法国演员 7—364d
吉特里 Guitry, Sacha 法国剧作家 7—364d
吉田兼好 Yoshida Kenkō 日本诗人 18—460e
吉田茂 Yoshida Shigeru 日本首相 18—460f
吉田五十八 Yoshida Isoya 日本建筑师 18—460e
吉田哲郎 Yoshida Tetsurō 日本建筑师 18—461a
吉通·德·莫沃 Guyton de Morveau, Louis Bernard 法国化学家 7—386c
吉娃娃犬 Chihuahua 狗品种 4—149f
吉旺希 Givenchy, Hubert de 法国时装设计师 7—146d
吉希泰尔 Gicel, Johann Georg 德国神智学者 7—122b
吉祥记 tilak 印度教 17—94e
吉祥诗 maṅgal-kāvya 孟加拉、印度颂神诗 10—457b
吉祥天女 Lakṣmī 印度教女神 9—457a
吉辛 Gissing, George (Robert) 英国小说家 7—145b
吉雄河 Qishon River 以色列河流 14—69c
吉雅思·伊本·加维斯·伊本·阿萨尔特·艾赫泰勒 Ghiyāth ibn Ghawth ibn aṣ-Ṣalt al-Akhṭal 伍麦叶王朝诗人 7—113b
吉亚柯梅蒂 Giacometti, Alberto 瑞士画家、雕塑家 7—114f
吉亚尼 Giyani 南非城镇 7—146d
吉耶尔湖 Guiers, Lake 塞内加尔湖泊 7—354d
吉耶曼 Guillemin, Roger Charles Louis 美国生理学家 7—357b
吉耶讷 Guyenne 法国旧地名 7—385f
吉野作造 Yoshino Sakuzō 日本政治家 18—461b
吉约曼 Guillaumin, (Jean-Baptiste-) Armand 法国画家 7—357a
吉赞 Jīzān 沙特阿拉伯城镇 9—36f
吉藏 Jizang 中国僧人 9—36f
吉泽布雷希特 Giesebrec, (Friedrich) Wilhelm (Benjamin) von 德国历史学家 7—123e
吉札克 Dzhizak 乌兹别克斯坦城市 5—490f
吉兹亚税 jizya 伊斯兰教 9—37a
吉兹语 Geʿez language 埃塞俄比亚教堂语言 7—44a
极北居民 Hyperborean 民族 8—291d
极地反气旋 polar anticyclone 气象学 13—396c
极地气团 polar air mass 气象学 13—396c
极地生态群系 polar biome 极地生态学 13—396e
极度节俭法则 parsimony, law of (logic) 哲学 13—63a
极端爱国主义 jingoism 政治 9—29d
极端保王派 ultra 法国历史 17—333a
极端主义 Ultraism 文学运动 17—333b
极光 aurora 大气科学 2—60b
极化子 polaron 物理学 13—398b
极简抽象派艺术 minimalism 艺术 11—250f
极乐鸟 bird-of-paradise 鸟类 2—489b
极谱法 polarography 分析化学 13—397f
极权主义 totalitarianism 政治学 17—172a
极限 limit 数学 10—104c
极限运动 extreme sports 体育运动 6—199c

极小值 minimum 数学 11—251b
极星 polestar 天文学 13—399d
极移 polar motion 地球物理学 13—397b
极移 polar wandering 地球物理学 13—397c
极值 extremum 数学 6—199c
极坐标 polar coordinates 解析几何学 13—397b
即兴表演 improvisation 戏剧 8—349a
即兴创作 improvisation 音乐 8—348f
即兴刻画 graffito 考古学 7—240a
即兴曲 impromptu 钢琴曲 8—348e
即兴喜剧 commedia dell'arte 戏剧形式 4—382f
即召民兵 minuteman 美国历史 11—268d
笈多体文字 Gupta script 印度古文字 7—377f
笈多王朝 Gupta DYNASTY 印度古王朝 7—377e
急流 jet stream 气象学 9—6f
急性人 Hotspur 英国判逆者 8—191b
急诊医学 emergency medicine 医学专科 6—59d
疾病 disease 医学 5—340a
疾旋风 Whirlaway 美国良种赛马 18—224f
棘肌 spinalis muscle 解剖学 16—32a
棘林 thorn forest 植物 17—56c
棘轮 ratchet 机械装置 14—161c
棘皮动物 echinoderm 无脊椎动物 5—522c
棘鳍鱼 spiny-finned fish 鱼类 16—33e
棘球海林檎属 Echinosphaerites 古生物学 5—522e
棘球蚴病 echinococcosis 疾病 5—522c
棘鲨 spiny shark 古生物学 16—34b
棘鼠 spiny rat 啮齿动物 16—34a
棘头虫 spiny-headed worm 无脊椎动物 16—33e
集胞黏菌 cellular slime mold 菌类 3—558a
集胞黏菌纲 Acrasieae 生物学 1—57e
集成电路 integrated circuit (IC) 电子元件集合 8—404a
集达塞纳 Chitrasena 柬埔寨军人 4—182a
集合论 set theory 数学 15—232b
集合小管 collecting tubule 解剖学 4—345f
集锦曲 quodlibet 音乐 14—97a
集块岩 agglomerate 岩石 1—121b
集宁 Jining 中国区名 9—30e
集市 bazaar 公共交易场所 2—298e
集市 fair 临时性市场 6—214d
集水区 watershed 地质学 18—143a
集体安全 collective security 国际关系 4—346e
集体流动 mass flow 植物学 11—5a
集体模型 collective model 物理学 4—346d
集体农场 kibbutz 以色列集体居民点 9—268d
集体农庄 kolkhoz 苏联农业组织 9—339b
集体迫害 pogrom 政治 13—387b
集体谈判 collective bargaining 经济学 4—345f
集体无意识 collective unconscious 心理学 4—346e
集体行为 collective behaviour 心理学 4—346a
集体治疗 group therapy 心理疗法 7—325f
集体主义 collectivism 社会学 4—346e
集邮 philately 收藏 13—231b
集邮 stamp collecting 嗜好 16—187b
集约农业 intensive agriculture 农业 8—407b
集中营 concentration camp 拘留中心 4—409a
集装箱化 containerization 货运技术 4—464d
鹏 chat 鸟类 4—89b
鹏鸫 chat-thrush 鸣禽 4—89c
鹡鸰 wagtail 鸟类 18—64b
鹡鸰科 Motacillidae (bird family) 动物学 11—430c
瘠地冻原地带 Barren Grounds 加拿大冻原地区 2—242d
几何图形风格 Geometric style 古希腊艺术 7—73a
几何学 geometry 数学 7—73c
几内亚 Guinea 西非国家 7—358e
几内亚 Guinea 西非沿海地区 7—359e
几内亚比绍 Guinea-Bissau 西非国家 7—360a
几内亚高原 Guinea Highlands 非洲高原 7—361b
几内亚公司 Casa da Guiné 葡萄牙贸易公司 3—495f
几内亚公司 Guiné, Casa da (Portuguese trading house) 葡萄牙贸易公司 7—358d
几内亚谷粒 guinea grains (seeds) 种子 7—361b
几内亚龙线虫 guinea worm (*Dracunculus medinensis*) 寄生虫 7—361d
几内亚湾 Guinea, Gulf of 大西洋海湾 7—359f
几内亚洋流 Guinea Current 大西洋洋流 7—361a
己基雷琐辛 hexylresorcinol 药物 8—66c
己烯雌酚 diethylstilbestrol (DES) 合成雌激素 5—307e
挤压伤 crush injury 医学 5—40b
济南 Jinan 中国城市 9—26b
济宁 Jining 中国城市 9—30f
给水 water supply 生活 18—139a
脊神经 spinal nerve 解剖学 16—31f
脊髓 spinal cord 解剖学 16—31e
脊髓灰质炎 poliomyelitis 疾病 13—400f
脊髓灰质炎疫苗 polio vaccine 医药制剂 13—400f
脊髓空洞症 syringomyelia 疾病 16—407c
脊髓痨 tabes dorsalis 疾病 16—413e
脊髓造影术 myelography 医学 11—524a
脊索 notochord 解剖学 12—274d
脊索动物 chordate 动物学 4—198a
脊旋螺属 Lophospira 古生物学 10—217e
脊柱 vertebral column 解剖学 17—525f
脊柱侧凸 scoliosis 病理学 15—146b
脊柱剑 Dhū al-faqār 伊斯兰教神话 5—281b
脊柱裂 spina bifida 疾病 16—31d
脊柱弯曲 spinal curvature 病理学 16—31f
脊椎动物 vertebrate 动物学 17—526b
脊椎关节强硬 spondylosis 病理学 16—39e
脊椎前移 spondylolisthesis 病理学 16—39e
脊椎炎 spondylitis 病理学 16—39d
戟 halberd 武器 7—417d
麂 muntjac 偶蹄目鹿科动物 11—487f
计划生育 planned parenthood 社会学 13—343e
计量经济学 econometrics 经济分析 5—526e
计量学 metrology 测量科学 11—161c
计时赛 time trial 自行车比赛 17—100b
计算尺 slide rule 计算工具 15—431b
计算机 computer 电子机器 4—401f
计算机安全 computer security 计算机科学 4—406b
计算机病毒 computer virus 计算机科学 4—406d
计算机程序 computer program 计算机科学 4—404f
计算机程序设计语言 computer programming language 计算机科学 4—405a
计算机存储器 computer memory 计算机科学 4—403e
计算机犯罪 computer crime 计算机科学 4—403a
计算机辅助工程 computer-aided engineering (CAE) 计算机科学 4—402e
计算机辅助教学 computer-assisted instruction (CAI) 计算机科学 4—402f
计算机化轴向层面 X 射线摄影法 CAT 医学 3—518a
计算机化轴向体层摄影 computerized axial tomography 计算机科学 4—406e
计算机科学 computer science 计算机 4—405c
计算机模拟 computer simulation 计算机科学 4—406c
计算机图形学 computer graphics 计算机科学 4—403b

计算机网络 computer network 计算机科学 4—404e
计算器 calculator 机器 3—336c
计算数学 numerical analysis 数学 12—297c
计算语言学 computational linguistics 计算机科学 4—401f
记分制 mark system 英国刑罚 10—520c
记录官 recorder 法律官员 14—185a
记录语句 protocol sentence 哲学 13—546a
记数制 numeral system 数学 12—297b
记忆 memory 心理学 11—103d
记忆术 mnemonic 辅助记忆 11—298d
伎乐面具 gigaku mask 日本艺术 7—125d
纪 period 地质学 13—169b
纪伯伦 Gibran, Khalil 黎巴嫩裔美国作家 7—121b
纪德 Gide, André(-Paul-Guillaume) 法国作家 7—122c
纪贯之 Ki Tsurayuki 日本宫廷贵族 9—268a
纪君祥 Ji Junxiang 中国剧作家 9—10f
纪廉 Guillén, Jorge 西班牙诗人 7—357c
纪廉 Guillén (Batista), Nicolás 古巴诗人 7—357d
纪录电影 documentary film 电影 5—356e
纪念碑 cenotaph 纪念性建筑 3—562f
纪念节 Remembrance, Day of (Judaism) 犹太教节日 14—222b
纪实剧 Fact, Theatre of 德国戏剧运动 6—209f
纪事官 remembrancer 英国官员 14—222b
纪尧姆 Guillaume, Charles Édouard 法国物理学家 7—356f
纪尧姆(奥朗日的) Guillaume d'Orange 法国传说英雄 7—356e
纪尧姆(巴尤的) Guillaume de Baillou 法国内科医生 7—356e
纪尧姆(格里摩阿尔德的) Guillaume de Grimoard (pope) 教皇 7—356e
纪尧姆(洛里的) Guillaume de Lorris 法国作家 7—356e
纪伊半岛 Kii Peninsula 日本半岛 9—276c
纪政 Ji Zheng 中国运动员 9—11d
技工讲习所 mechanics' institute 英国-美国组织 11—68c
技巧运动 tumbling 体育 17—265f
技术 technology 科技 16—513c
技术教育 technical education 教育 16—513a
技术援助 technical assistance 国际关系 16—512f
季奥诺 Giono, Jean 法国作家 7—138a
季德洛 Didelot, Charles(-Louis) 法国舞蹈家 5—303a
季风 monsoon 气象学 11—351b
季风林 monsoon forest 生态学 11—351d
季风洋流 Monsoon Current 洋流 11—351c
季格舞 gigue 舞蹈 7—126b
季霍列茨克 Tikhoretsk 俄罗斯城市 17—94c
季霍米罗夫 Tikhomirov, Vasily Dmitrievich 俄国芭蕾舞演员 17—93e
季节 season 气候学 15—173c
季节迁徙 transhumance 社会学 17—196f
季里诺 Quirino, Elpidio 菲律宾政治领袖 14—95b
季利伊阿尼斯 Dhiliyiánnis, Theódoros 希腊首相 5—280b
季列耶夫斯基 Kireyevsky, Ivan Vasilyevich 俄国哲学家 9—300d
季洛杜 Giraudoux, (Hyppolyte-) Jean 法国作家 7—141f
季马 Jima 埃塞俄比亚城镇 9—23f
季曼岭 Timan Ridge 俄罗斯山岭 17—97f
季米特里(Ⅱ)·顿斯科伊 Dmitry (Ⅱ) Donskoy 莫斯科公爵 5—352c
季米特洛夫 Dimitrov, Georgi Mikhailovich 保加利亚共产党领袖 5—319a
季米特洛夫格勒 Dimitrovgrad 保加利亚城镇 5—319b
季米特洛夫格勒 Dimitrovgrad 俄罗斯城市 5—319b
季米特洛沃 Dimitrovo (Bulgaria) 保加利亚城镇 5—319b
季诺维也夫 Zinovyev, Grigory Yevseyevich 俄国革命家 18—556b
季审法院 quarter sessions 法律 14—79a
季索 Tiso, Jozef 斯洛伐克神职人员 17—112d
季托夫 Titov, Gherman Stepanovich 苏联航天员 17—120e
季翁塔(皮萨诺) Giunta Pisano 意大利画家 7—146b
季戊四醇四硝酸酯 PETN 有机化合物 13—207a
剂量计 dosimeter 测量仪器 5—393d
荠菜 shepherd's purse (*Capsella bursa-pastoris*) 草本植物 15—304d
济班 Dhībān (Jordan) 约旦古遗址 5—280b
济贝尔 Sybel, Heinrich von 德国历史学家 16—391c
济慈 Keats, John 英国诗人 9—209e
济金根 Sickingen, Franz von 德意志宗教改革家 15—351a
济金绍尔 Ziguinchor 塞内加尔城镇 18—551d
济莱 Zile 土耳其城镇 18—551e
济良诺夫斯克 Zyryanovsk 哈萨克斯坦城市 18—578e
济米亚托夫 Zimyatov, Nikolay 苏联越野滑雪运动员 18—553d
济贫法 Poor Law 英国法律 13—431a
济贫院 workhouse 提供就业和施舍食物的机构 18—333b
济州 Cheju 韩国城市 4—102e
济州岛 Cheju Island 韩国岛屿 4—102e
继承领地税 relief 中世纪税务 14—215b
继承人 heir 法律 7—569c
继承税 inheritance tax 税务 8—387e
继电器 relay 电磁装置 14—214d
继续教育 continuing education 教育 4—470a
祭 matsuri 日本庆典 11—28e
祭典 yajña 印度教 18—404e
祭司 cohen 犹太教教士 4—332c
祭司王约翰 Prester John 传说中的统治者 13—499b
祭司长 high priest 犹太教 8—75b
祭司职务 priesthood 宗教礼仪职务 13—507b
祭台 altar 宗教艺术 1—254c
祭坛后部装饰 retable 宗教艺术 14—245b
祭坛画 altarpiece 宗教艺术 1—254d
祭献 sacrifice 宗教 14—489e
寄居蟹 hermit crab 蟹类 8—42d
寄生甲壳动物 crustacean louse 无脊椎动物 5—40f
寄生鲇 candiru (*Vandellia cirrhosa*) 鱼类 3—397f
寄生物学 parasitology 生物学 13—39a
寄生现象 parasitism 生物学 13—38f
寄生蝇 tachinid fly 昆虫 16—417c
寄托 bailment 法律 2—149f
寄赠本 giftbook 年册或诗文集 7—125a
寂护 Śāntirakṣita 印度佛教大师 15—49b
寂静主义 Quietism 基督教灵修理论 14—90f
寂塔 dakhma 印度祆教葬俗 5—114c
蓟爵士 K.T. 苏格兰勋位 9—385f
蓟类 thistle 植物 17—41b
蓟马 thrips 昆虫 17—65e
蓟县 Ji Xian 中国县名 9—11b
蓟勋位 Thistle, The Most Ancient and Most Noble Order of the 苏格兰骑士团勋位 17—41c
暨南大学 Jinan University 中国大学 9—26f
稷 panicum 植物 13—12b
加埃塔 Gaeta 意大利港口城镇 6—544d
加埃塔公爵 Gaëte, Martin-Michel-Charles Gaudin, duc de (duke of) 法国财政大臣 6—544e
加埃沃 Giaever, Ivar 美国物理学家 7—115c
加昂 gaon 犹太教首脑的称号 7—5e
加奥 Gao 马里城镇 7—4a
加百列 Gabriel 《圣经》中天使长名字 6—541c
加贝利奇 Gabelich, Gary 美国赛车运动员 6—538d
加贝伦茨 Gabelentz, Hans Conon von der 德国语言学家 6—538c
加贝罗内斯 Gaberones (Botswana) 博茨瓦纳首都旧称 6—538e
加贝斯湾 Gabes, Gulf of 突尼斯海湾 6—538e
加比尼乌斯 Gabinius, Aulus 古罗马政治家 6—538f
加比斯 Qābis 突尼斯城镇 14—51b

加伯特 Garbett, Cyril Forster 英国大主教 7—7e
加博里欧 Gaboriau, Émile 法国侦探小说家 6—541b
加布 Gabú 几内亚比绍城镇 6—542d
加布里埃尔 Gabriel 美国奴隶 6—541c
加布里埃尔 Gabriel, Ange-Jacques 法国建筑师 6—541d
加布里埃利 Gabrieli, Andrea 意大利作曲家 6—541e
加布里埃利 Gabrieli, Giovanni 意大利作曲家 6—542a
加布里洛维奇 Gabrilowitsch, Ossip (Salomonovich) 俄国出生的美国钢琴家 6—542c
加布列莱诺人 Gabrielino 北美印第安居民集团 6—542b
加布罗沃 Gabrovo 保加利亚城镇 6—542c
加查教团 gaccha 印度耆那教派别 6—542d
加查·玛达 Gajah Mada 印度尼西亚古帝国首相 6—548d
加成反应 addition reaction 化学反应 1—73f
加达 Gadda, Carlo Emilio 意大利作家 6—542e
加达里夫 Qaḍārif, al- 苏丹城镇 14—51d
加达默尔 Gadamer, Hans-Georg 德国哲学家 6—542d
加大拉 Gadara 巴勒斯坦古城 6—542e
加代 Guadet, Marguerite-Élie 法国革命领导人 7—335f
加岱 Gade, Niels (Vilhelm) 丹麦作曲家 6—543b
加丹加 Katanga 刚果(金)历史地区 9—194d
加丹加杂岩 Katangan Complex 地质学 9—194d
加德尔 Gardel, Carlos 阿根廷歌手、演员 7—10d
加德满都 Kāthmāndu 尼泊尔首都 9—195e
加德纳 Gardiner 美国城市 7—12d
加德纳 Gardner, Alexander 美国摄影家 7—13a
加德纳 Gardner, Ava (Lavinia) 美国演员 7—13b
加德纳 Gardner, Erle Stanley 美国作家 7—13d
加德纳 Gardner, Helen 美国艺术史学家、教育家 7—13e
加德纳 Gardener, Helen Hamilton 美国作家、改革家 7—11e
加德纳 Gardner, Isabella Stewart 美国艺术品收藏家 7—13f
加德纳 Gardiner, James Garfield 加拿大政治家 7—12d
加德纳 Gardner, Percy 英国考古学家 7—14a
加德纳 Gardiner, Stephen 英格兰主教、政治家 7—12f
加德纳 Gardiner, Samuel Rawson 英国历史学家 7—12e
加德纳博物馆 Gardner Museum 美国艺术收藏馆 7—14a
加德兹 Gardeyz 阿富汗城镇 7—12d
加登 Garden, Mary 美国歌唱家 7—10e
加登城 Garden City 美国城市 7—11a
加登城 Garden City 美国居民村 7—11a
加登岛 Garden Island 澳大利亚岛屿 7—11d
加迪 Gaddi, Agnolo 意大利画家 6—542f
加迪 Gaddi, Taddeo 意大利画家 6—543a
加迪斯 Gaddis, William (Thomas) 美国小说家 6—543a
加的夫 Cardiff 威尔士城市 3—452c
加的夫巨人 Cardiff Giant 美国骗局 3—452e
加的斯 Cadiz 菲律宾港口 3—313b
加的斯 Cádiz 西班牙省份 3—313b
加的斯 Cádiz 西班牙海港 3—313b
加的斯湾 Cádiz, Bay of 大西洋小海湾 3—313d
加的斯湾 Cádiz, Gulf of 伊比利亚海湾 3—313d
加蒂诺 Gatineau 加拿大城镇 7—29e
加蒂诺河 Gatineau River 加拿大河流 7—29f
加顿 Gatton 澳大利亚城镇 7—30b
加尔 Gard 法国省份 7—10b
加尔 Gall, Franz Joseph 德国解剖学家、生理学家 6—555f
加尔巴 Galba 罗马皇帝 6—551c
加尔布雷思 Galbraith, John Kenneth 美国经济学家 6—551d
加尔达湖 Garda, Lake 意大利湖泊 7—10d
加尔达渔村 Peschiera del Garda 意大利港口村庄 13—192e
加尔迪 Gardie, Jacob Pontusson, Greve De la 瑞典政治家 7—12d
加尔迪 Gardie, Magnus Gabriel, Greve De la 瑞典政治家 7—12d
加尔蒂山脉 Galty Mountains 爱尔兰山脉 6—563e
加尔都西会 Carthusians 天主教修会 3—489f
加尔多斯 Galdós, Benito Pérez 西班牙小说家 6—551e
加尔戈东高原 Galgodon Highlands 索马里山地 6—552d
加尔各答 Calcutta 印度城市 3—337e
加尔各答大学 Calcutta, University of 印度大学 3—340d
加尔各答黑洞 Black Hole of Calcutta 印度历史 2—513a
加尔河 Gal Oya 斯里兰卡河流 6—549b
加尔赫峰 Galdhø Peak 挪威山峰 6—551e
加尔加略(-卡塔兰) Gargallo (y Catalán), Pablo 西班牙雕塑家 7—14d
加尔加诺 Gargano 意大利海岬 7—14e
加尔加斯洞穴 Gargas 法国古艺术洞穴 7—14f
加尔利 Kārli 印度村庄 9—182f
加尔默罗会 Carmelite 天主教修会 3—464c
加尔纳里安 Garnerin, André-Jacques 法国航空家 7—17a
加尔桥 Gard, Pont du 法国高架渠 7—10c
加尔塞斯 Garcés, Francisco (Tomás) 西班牙教士、探险家 7—8b
加尔桑 Garção, Pedro António Correia 葡萄牙诗人 7—8b
加尔斯温特 Galswintha 墨洛温王后 6—562d
加尔万 Galvin, George (entertainer) 英国演员 6—564f
加尔韦 Galway, Henri de Massue, MARQUIS DE RUVIGNY ET RAINEVAL 法国军人 6—565a
加尔维斯 Gálvez, José, MARQUÉS (marguess) DE LA SONORA 西班牙行政官员 6—564e
加尔维斯 Gálvez, Manuel 阿根廷作家 6—564f
加尔维斯顿 Galveston 美国城市 6—564d
加尔维斯顿湾 Galveston Bay 美国沿海小海湾 6—564e
加尔文 Calvin, John 法国基督教改革领袖 3—358f
加尔文主义 Calvinism 基督教新教 3—361c
加法尔·阿斯凯里 Jaʿfar al-ʿAskarī 伊拉克政治领袖 8—515d
加法尔帕夏 Jaʿfar Pasha 伊拉克政治领袖 8—515e
加法尔·伊本·穆罕默德 Jaʿfar ibn Muḥammad 伊斯兰教伊玛目 8—515d
加法器 adding machine 计算器 1—73a
加菲尔德 Garfield, John 美国电影、戏剧演员 7—14c
加菲尔德 Garfield, James A(bram) 美国第20任总统 7—14b
加芬库 Gafencu, Grigore 罗马尼亚外交家 6—544e
加夫里洛 Gavrilo 塞尔维亚牧首 7—37c
加夫尼 Gaffney 美国城市 6—544f
加夫萨 Qafṣah 突尼斯城镇 14—52a
加弗纳斯岛 Governors Island 美国岛屿 7—232f
加弗斯顿 Gaveston, Piers, EARL OF CORNWALL 英格兰大臣 7—37a
加富尔 Cavour, Camillo Benso, conte di (count of) 皮埃蒙特政治家 3—543a
加感 loading 通信技术 10—172a
加格恩 Gagern, Friedrich (Ludwig Balduin Karl Moritz), Freiherr von 德意志军事官员 6—545e
加格恩 Gagern, Hans Christoph, Freiherr von 德意志政治家、作家 6—545f
加格恩 Gagern, Maximilian (Joseph Ludwig), Freiherr von 德意志政治家 6—546b
加格恩 Gagern, (Wilhelm) Heinrich (August), Freiherr von 德国外交家、政治家 6—546a
加工船 factory ship 捕鲸母船 6—210c
加工硬化 work hardening 冶金 18—332e
加古川 Kakogawa 日本城市 9—137d
加贺 Kaga 日本城市 9—131a
加济阿巴德 Ghāziābād 印度城镇 7—110b
加济安泰普 Gaziantep 土耳其城市 7—40d
加济布尔 Ghāzīpur 印度城镇 7—110c
加济兰加国家公园 Kāziranga National Park 印度国家公园 9—208a
加济乌迪讷格尔 Ghāziuddinnagar (India) 印度城镇 7—110c

加加林 Gagarin, Yury Alekseyevich 苏联航天员 6—545b
加拉巴赫地毯 Karabagh rug 工艺品 9—174b
加拉巴舞 garabā 印度舞蹈 7—7a
加拉茨 Galați 罗马尼亚县名 6—550e
加拉茨 Galați 罗马尼亚县城 6—550e
加拉德特 Gallaudet, Thomas Hopkins 美国教育家 6—557b
加拉格尔和希恩 Gallagher, Ed; and Shean, Al 美国演员 6—556d
加拉哈 Galahad 传奇骑士 6—549f
《加拉罕宣言》 Karakhan Manifesto 中国-苏联关系 9—178a
加拉霍奈国家公园 Garajonay National Park 西班牙公园 7—7b
加拉加斯 Caracas 委内瑞拉共和国首都 3—434f
加拉加斯公司 Caracas Company (colonial trading company) 欧洲殖民贸易公司 3—436c
加拉蒙 Garamond, Claude 法国出版商 7—7b
加拉米安 Galamian, Ivan 美国小提琴家、教师 6—550a
加拉尼温斯 Garanhuns 巴西城市 7—7d
加拉帕戈斯地雀 Galapagos finch 鸟类 6—550a
加拉帕戈斯群岛 Galapagos Islands 太平洋厄瓜多尔岛群 6—550b
加拉人 Galla (people) 非洲民族 6—556d
加拉沙宁 Garašanin, Ilija 塞尔维亚首相 7—7d
加拉斯 Gallas, Matthias, COUNT (Graf) VON CAMPO 奥地利将军 6—556f
加拉提亚 Galatia 古安纳托利亚中部地区 6—550f
加拉希尔斯 Galashiels 英国城镇 6—550d
加拉信 Kalasin 泰国城镇 9—139a
加来 Calais 法国港口 3—333d
加来海峡 Calais, Pas de (English Channel) 欧洲水道 3—333d
加来海峡省 Pas-de-Calais 法国省份 13—70d
加莱 Gallé, Émile 法国艺术玻璃设计师 6—557c
加莱里乌斯 Galerius 罗马皇帝 6—552d
加赖加尔 Kāraikāl 印度城市 9—176f
加兰 Garland 美国城市 7—15d
加兰 Garland, (Hannibal) Hamlin 美国作家 7—15f
加兰 Garland, John 英格兰语法学家、诗人 7—16a
加兰巴国家公园 Garamba National Park 刚果(金)公园 7—7b
加兰德 Galland, Adolf 德国飞行员 6—556e
加朗 Galland, Antoine 法国学者 6—556e
加勒 Galle 斯里兰卡港市 6—557c
加勒比共同体和共同市场 Caribbean Community and Common Market (Caricom) 经济组织 3—457c
加勒比海 Caribbean Sea 大西洋西部海 3—457e
加勒比群岛 Caribbees (islands, Caribbean Sea) 加勒比海岛屿 3—457f
加勒比人 Carib 美洲印第安人 3—457a
加勒比文学 Caribbean literature 美洲文学 3—457d
加勒比洋流 Caribbean Current 大西洋洋流 3—457d
加勒比诸语言 Cariban languages 南美洲印第安语言 3—457c
加勒胡斯角形器 Gallehus Horns 金制工艺品 6—558a
加勒角 Point de Galle (Sri Lanka) 斯里兰卡港口 13—389a
加勒特 Garrett, Pat 美国执法人员 7—19b
加勒特姊妹 Garret, Mary Smith; and Garett, Emma 美国教育家 7—18f
加勒廷 Gallatin, Albert 美国政府官员 6—556f
加勒廷河 Gallatin River 美国河流 6—557a
加雷达地毯 Karadagh rug 工艺品 9—176a
加雷特 Garrett, João Baptista da Silva Leitão de Almeida, VISCONDE (viscount) DE ALMEIDA GARRETT 葡萄牙作家 7—18f
加里 Gary 美国城市 7—22a
加里 Gary, Elbert Henry 美国法学家 7—22b
加里 Gary, Romain 法国作家 7—22c
加里波第 Garibaldi, Giuseppe 意大利民族运动领袖 7—15b
加里波第山 Garibaldi, Mount 加拿大山峰 7—15c
加里东造山带 Caledonian orogenic belt 欧洲地质学 3—343a
加里金 Gallitzin, Demetrius Augustine 美国天主教司铎 6—561b
加里克 Garrick, David 英格兰演员、诗人 7—19b
加里曼丹 Kalimantan 印度尼西亚省份 9—141a
加里宁 Kalinin (Russia) 俄罗斯地名 9—141f
加里宁 Kalinin, Mikhail Ivanovich 苏联政治家 9—141f
加里宁格勒 Kaliningrad 俄罗斯州名 9—142a
加里宁格勒 Kaliningrad 俄罗斯加里宁格勒州城市 9—142b
加里宁格勒 Kaliningrad 俄罗斯莫斯科州城市 9—142c
加里普·德德 Gālib Dede 土耳其诗人 6—552e
加里萨 Garissa 肯尼亚城镇 7—15d
加里森 Garrison, William Lloyd 美国编辑 7—20b
加里斯 Garis, Howard R(oger) 美国作家 7—15c
加里斯都 Calixtus 教皇称号 3—352b
加里斯都(三世) Calixtus(Ⅲ) 敌对教皇 3—352c
加里斯都二世 Calixtus Ⅱ 教皇 3—352c
加里斯都三世 Calixtus Ⅲ 教皇 3—352d
加里斯都一世,圣 Calixtus I, SAINT 教皇 3—352c
加力燃烧室 afterburner 机械 1—113b
加利 galli 侍奉女神的祭司 6—558e
加利奥 Gallio, Junius 罗马官员 6—560f
加利波利 Gallipoli 土耳其城镇 6—561a
加利波利半岛 Gallipoli Peninsula (Turkey) 土耳其半岛 6—561a
加利波利斯 Gallipolis 美国城市 6—561a
加利·达·比比恩纳家族 Galli DA BIBIENA FAMILY 意大利艺术家家族 6—558f
加利费侯爵 Galliffet, Gaston-Alexandre-Auguste, marquis de 法国将军 6—560a
加利福尼亚 California 美国州名 3—345c
加利福尼亚标准石油公司 Standard Oil Company of California 美国公司 16—187f
加利福尼亚大学 California, University of 美国大学 3—349f
加利福尼亚高架渠 California Aqueduct 美国水利工程 3—350b
加利福尼亚桂树 California laurel (*Umbellularia californica*) 乔木 3—350c
加利福尼亚科学学会 California Academy of Sciences 美国科学机构 3—350a
加利福尼亚理工学院 California Institute of Technology 美国大学 3—350b
加利福尼亚联合石油公司 Union Oil Company of California 美国石化企业 17—348d
加利福尼亚肉豆蔻 California nutmeg (*Torreya californica*) 乔木 3—350d
加利福尼亚湾 California, Gulf of 太平洋东部海湾 3—349f
加利福尼亚洋流 California Current 海洋学 3—350b
加利福尼亚罂粟 California poppy (*Eschscholzia californica*) 植物 3—350d
加利-库尔奇 Galli-Curci, Amelita 美国歌唱家 6—558f
加利库姆海峡 Gallicum Fretum (English Channel) 英-法间狭窄水道 6—559f
加利莱伊 Galilei, Vincenzo 意大利音乐家 6—553e
加利利 Galilee 以色列古地区 6—553c
加利利 Galili, Yisrael 以色列指挥官 6—555d
加利利海 Galilee, Sea of 以色列湖泊 6—553d
加利马尔 Gallimard, Gaston 法国出版商 6—560d
加利纳 Galena 美国城市 6—552b
加利温库岛 Galiwinku 澳大利亚岛屿 6—555e
加利西亚 Galicia 东欧历史地区 6—552f
加利西亚 Galicia 西班牙自治区、历史区域 6—552f
加利西亚方言 Galician dialect 葡萄牙方言 6—553b
加利西亚进攻 Galician Offensive (World War I) 第一次世界大战史 6—553b
加利亚德舞 galliard 欧洲宫廷舞 6—559b
加利亚尼 Galiani, Ferdinando 意大利经济学家 6—552e

加利亚诺 Gagliano, Marco da 意大利作曲家 6—546b
加列戈斯 Gallegos (Freire), Rómulo 委内瑞拉总统 6—557f
加列尼 Gallieni, Joseph-Simon 法国军事官员 6—559f
加列努斯 Gallienus, Publius Licinius Egnatius 罗马皇帝 6—559f
加林沙 Garrincha 巴西足球运动员 7—20b
加龙河 Garonne River 法国河流 7—18e
加卢皮 Galuppi, Baldassare 意大利作曲家 6—563f
加卢斯 Gallus, Gaius Cornelius 罗马军人、诗人 6—562a
加卢斯 Gallus, Gaius Vibius Trebonianus 罗马皇帝 6—562a
加卢斯 Gallus, Jacobus 捷克斯洛伐克作曲家 6—562a
加卢斯 Gallus, Quintus Roscius 罗马喜剧演员 6—562b
加卢斯·凯撒 Gallus Caesar 罗马皇帝 6—562b
加鲁阿 Garoua 喀麦隆城镇 7—18e
加伦 Galen 古罗马医师、哲学家 6—552a
加伦 Galen, Clemens August, Graf von 德国主教 6—552b
加罗德 Garrod, Dorothy Annie Elizabeth 英国考古学家 7—20d
加罗法洛 Garofalo, Benvenuto do 意大利画家 7—18e
加罗林环礁 Caroline Atoll 太平洋珊瑚岛 3—472e
加罗林群岛 Caroline Islands 西太平洋群岛 3—472f
加罗丘陵 Gāro Hills 印度丘陵 7—18d
加罗斯 Garros, Pey de 法国诗人 7—20e
加洛林王朝 Carolingian DYNASTY 法兰克王朝 3—473a
加洛林王朝法规汇编 capitulary 欧洲历史 3—427f
加洛林王朝艺术 Carolingian art 欧洲艺术 3—473b
加洛林小写字体 Carolingian minuscule 书法字体 3—473d
加洛普舞 galop 欧洲舞蹈 6—562c
加洛韦 Galloway 苏格兰地区 6—561d
加马 Gama, (José) Basílio da 巴西诗人 6—565b
加马尔哈蒂 Kāmārhāti 印度城市 9—145e
加煤机 stoker 机器 16—246a
加米 jāmiʿ (Islām) 祈祷处 8—532a
加米涅夫 Kamenev, Lev Borisovich 苏联政治人物 9—148a
加米施-帕滕基兴 Garmisch-Partenkirchen 德国城镇 7—16d
加米什利 Qāmishlī, Al- 叙利亚城镇 14—53d
加冕地毯 Coronation Carpet 工艺品 4—518a
加冕典礼 coronation 典礼 4—518a
加冕事务长 lord high steward 英国荣誉职位 10—219c
加缪 Camus, Albert 法国小说家 3—384d
加拿大 Canada 美洲国家 3—386a
加拿大白鲑 cisco 鱼类 4—246c
加拿大保守党 Conservative Party of Canada 加拿大政党 4—446c
加拿大杯 Canada Cup (golf) 高尔夫球赛奖杯 3—388f
加拿大地盾 Canadian Shield 北美地盾 3—391a
加拿大帝国商业银行 Canadian Imperial Bank of Commerce 加拿大金融机构 3—389e
加拿大东区 Canada East 加拿大地区 3—388f
《加拿大法案》(1791) Canada Bill 加拿大历史 3—388e
《加拿大法案》 Canada Act 加拿大历史 3—388c
加拿大橄榄球联合会 Canadian Football League (CFL) 体育组织 3—389d
加拿大高压 Canadian high 气象学 3—389d
加拿大工人大会 Canadian Labour Congress (CLC) 加拿大工会 3—389e
加拿大公司 Canada Company 加拿大机构 3—388e
加拿大国家铁路公司 Canadian National Railway Company 加拿大铁路系统 3—390d
加拿大国庆节 Canada Day 加拿大纪念日 3—388f
加拿大航空公司 Air Canada 加拿大航空机构 1—142d
加拿大进步保守党 Progressive Conservative Party of Canada 加拿大政党 13—529c
加拿大浸礼联盟 Baptist Federation of Canada 宗教机构 2—213a
加拿大联合教会 United Church of Canada 加拿大基督教会 17—351e
加拿大联盟 Canadian Alliance 加拿大政党 3—389b
加拿大落基山 Canadian Rockies 美洲山脉 3—390f
加拿大-美国挑战杯 Canadian-American Challenge Cup 汽车比赛奖杯 3—389c
加拿大人河 Canadian River 北美河流 3—390f
加拿大圣公会 Canada, Anglican Church of 加拿大基督教会 3—388b
加拿大松节油 canada turpentine 含油树脂 3—389b
加拿大太平洋铁路公司 Canadian Pacific Railway Ltd. 加拿大铁路私营公司 3—390d
加拿大文学 Canadian literature 文学 3—389f
加拿大西区 Canada West 加拿大地区 3—389b
加拿大香脂 canada balsam 含油树脂 3—388e
加拿大学会 Institut Canadien 加拿大组织 8—400c
加拿大雁 Canada goose (species *Branta canadensis*) 鸟类 3—389a
加拿大银行 Canada, Bank of 加拿大金融机构 3—388c
加拿大紫杉 Canada yew 植物 3—389b
加拿大自由党 Liberal Party of Canada 加拿大政党 10—73b
加拿大自治领成立纪念日 Dominion Day 加拿大节日 5—374f
加那利群岛 Canary Islands 大西洋群岛 3—394b
加那利洋流 Canary Current 北大西洋洋流 3—394b
加纳 Ghana 西非古代帝国 7—107c
加纳 Ghana 西非国家 7—107d
加纳 Garner, Alan 英国作家 7—16e
加纳 Gana, Alberto Blest 智利作家 6—571a
加纳 Garner, John Nance 美国副总统 7—16f
加纳列托(小) Canaletto THE YOUNGER 意大利画家 3—392d
加纳内河 Ganane, Webi (Ethiopia and Somalia) 非洲河流 6—571b
加纳诺克 Gananoque 加拿大城镇 6—571b
加纳萨 Ganassa, Zan 意大利演员、剧团经理 6—571b
加内桑 Ganesan, Sivaji 印度电影明星 6—576c
加尼埃 Garnier, Bernard (counter-antipope) 敌对教皇 7—17f
加尼埃 Garnier, (Jean-Louis-) Charles 法国建筑师 7—17f
加尼埃 Garnier, Robert 法国剧作家 7—18b
加尼埃 Garnier, Tony 法国建筑师 7—18b
加尼奥阿 Gagnoa 科特迪瓦城镇 6—546c
加尼特 Garnett, Constance (Clara) 英国翻译家 7—17d
加尼特 Garnett, David 英国作家 7—17d
加尼特 Garnett, Edward (William) 英国评论家 7—17e
加尼特 Garnett, Henry 英格兰隐修院院长 7—17e
加尼特 Garnet, Henry Highland 美国黑人牧师 7—17c
加尼特 Garnett, Richard 英国作家 7—17f
加尼韦特-加西亚 Ganivet y García, Ángel 西班牙小说家 7—1e
加尼耶-帕热斯 Garnier-Pagès, Louis-Antoine 法国政治家 7—18c
加捻 twisting 纺织 17—303c
加诺 Garneau, François-Xavier 加拿大历史学家 7—16e
加诺 Garneau, Hector de Saint-Denys 加拿大诗人 7—16e
加蓬 Gabon 非洲国家 6—539e
加蓬河口 Gabon Estuary 加蓬河湾 6—541a
加蓬蝰蛇 Gaboon viper (*Bitis gabonica*) 非洲毒蛇 6—541a
加普 Gap 法国城市 7—6d
加普林达什维利 Gaprindashvili, Nona 苏联女子国际象棋世界冠军 7—6e
加人 Ga 加纳人 6—538a
加萨尼 Ghassān 阿拉伯古代王国 7—109a
加萨尼 Ghassaniy, Muyaka bin Haji al- 肯尼亚诗人 7—109b
加塞 Gasser, Herbert Spencer 美国生理学家 7—26a
加沙 Gaza 巴勒斯坦城市 7—39b
加沙地带 Gaza Strip 巴勒斯坦地区 7—39c
加什河 Gash River 非洲河流 7—24a
加斯 Gath 以色列古王城 7—29e
加斯 Gass, William H(oward) 美国作家 7—25e
加斯贝利 Gasperi, Alcide de 意大利总理 7—25c

加斯东(第三) Gaston III 法国伯爵 7—26d
加斯东(法兰西的) Gaston DE FRANCE 法国亲王 7—26f
加斯顿 Garstang, John 英国考古学家 7—21a
加斯凯 Gasquet, Francis (Neil) Aidan 英国教士 7—25e
加斯科涅 Gascony 法国古地名 7—23e
加斯科涅湾 Gascogne, Golfe de 欧洲海湾 7—23c
加斯科因河 Gascoyne River 澳大利亚河流 7—24a
加斯科因-塞西尔 Gascoyne-Cecil, (Edgar Algernon) Robert 英国保守党人 7—23f
加斯科因-塞西尔 Gascoyne-Cecil, James Edward Hubert 英国政治家 7—23f
加斯科因-塞西尔 Gascoyne-Cecil, Robert 英国首相 7—24a
加斯里 Guthrie 美国城市 7—382d
加斯帕里 Gasparri, Pietro 梵蒂冈枢机主教 7—24f
加斯佩 Gaspé 加拿大城镇 7—24f
加斯佩 Gaspé, Philippe Aubert de 加拿大作家 7—25a
加斯佩半岛 Gaspé Peninsula 加拿大半岛 7—25b
加斯佩西省立公园 Gaspesian Provincial Park 加拿大公园 7—25c
加斯佩洋流 Gaspé Current 大西洋洋流 7—25a
加斯普林斯基 Gasprinski, Ismail 土耳其作家 7—25c
加斯山 Gas Hills 美国山地 7—22f
加斯泰因 Gastein (Austria) 奥地利城镇 7—26a
加斯泰因河谷 Gastein Valley 奥地利河谷 7—26b
《加斯泰因条约》 Gastein, Convention of 普鲁士-奥地利条约 7—26a
加斯特芬格 Gastfenger, Polykarpus 德国医生、作家 7—26d
加斯托尼亚 Gastonia 美国城市 7—26f
加速度 acceleration 物理学 1—44a
加速度计 accelerometer 仪器 1—44e
加速运动应激反应 acceleration stress 生理学 1—44b
加塔梅拉塔 Gattamelata 骑士纪念碑 7—30b
加泰罗尼亚 Catalonia 西班牙自治区 3—519c
加泰罗尼亚文学 Catalan literature 西班牙文学 3—519a
加泰罗尼亚艺术博物馆 Catalonia Museum of Art 西班牙博物馆 3—519f
加泰罗尼亚语 Catalan language 语言 3—518f
加泰土丘 Çatalhüyük 土耳其考古遗址 3—519b
加特 Ghāt 利比亚绿洲 7—109c
加特林 Gatling, Richard Jordan 美国发明家 7—29f
加特林堡 Gatlinburg 美国城市 7—29f
加特林机枪 Gatling gun 武器 7—30a
加特契纳 Gatchina 俄罗斯城市 7—28e
加藤高明 Katō Takaaki 日本首相 9—196d
加藤弘之 Katō Hiroyuki, DANSHAKU (BARON) 日本作家 9—196c
加藤清正 Katō Kiyomasa 日本武将 9—196d
加通湖 Gatun Lake 巴拿马人工湖 7—30c
加图 Cato, Publius Valerius 古罗马诗人 3—529d
加图(大) Cato, Marcus Porcius 罗马政治家 3—529a
加图(小) Cato, Marcus Porcius 罗马贵族党领袖 3—529c
加图马 Gatooma (Zimbabwe) 津巴布韦城镇 7—30b
加瓦尔 Gaoual 几内亚城镇 7—6a
加瓦尔尼 Gavarnie 法国山村 7—36f
加瓦尔尼 Gavarni, Paul 法国画家 7—36e
加瓦齐 Gavazzi, Alessandro 意大利教会与政治改革家 7—36 f
加瓦特尔湾 Gwādar Bay 阿拉伯海海湾 7—387b
加维兰 Kid Gavilan 古巴拳击手 9—269a
加沃特舞 gavotte 舞蹈 7—37c
加乌朗加 Gaurānga (Hindu mystic) 印度教神秘主义者 7—34c
加乌乔 gaucho 南美历史 7—30d
加乌乔文学 gaucho literature 南美文学 7—30f
加西拉索·德·拉·维加 Garcilaso DE LA VEGA 西班牙诗人 7—10a
加西亚 García 统治者之名 7—8c
加西亚 García, Anastasio Somoza 尼加拉瓜总统 7—8e
加西亚 Garcia, Carlos Polestico 菲律宾总统 7—8e
加西亚 García, Manuel (Patricio Rodríguez) 西班牙声乐教师 7—8f
加西亚 García, Manuel del Popolo (Vicente) 西班牙歌唱家、作曲家 7—8f
加西亚·德·拉·韦尔塔 García de la Huerta, Vicente (Antonio) 西班牙剧作家 7—9a
加西亚二世 García II 加利西亚国王 7—8c
加西亚二世(或三世) García II (or III) 潘普洛纳(纳瓦拉)、阿拉贡国王 7—8d
加西亚·古铁雷斯 García Gutiérrez, Antonio 西班牙戏剧家 7—9a
加西亚·罗夫莱斯 García Robles, Alfonso 墨西哥外交家 7—10a
加西亚·洛尔卡 García Lorca, Federico 西班牙剧作家 7—9a
加西亚·马尔克斯 García Márquez, Gabriel 拉丁美洲作家 7—9d
加西亚·莫雷诺 García Moreno, Gabriel 厄瓜多尔总统 7—9f
加西亚三世(或四世) García III (or IV) 潘普洛纳(纳瓦拉)国王 7—8d
加西亚四世(或五世) García IV (or V) 潘普洛纳(纳瓦拉)国王 7—8e
加西亚(一世) García(I) 纳瓦拉传奇人物 7—8c
加西亚一世(或二世) García I (or II) Sanchez 潘普洛纳(纳瓦拉)国王 7—8d
加香甜酒 cordial 甜酒 4—502c
加休曼努 Kaahumanu 夏威夷皇后 9—123d
加延 Qāyen 伊朗城镇 14—55f
加演 benefit performance 演出制度 2—382b
加央 Kangar 马来西亚城镇 9—156a
加伊乌斯,圣 Gaius, SAINT 教皇 6—548d
加因萨·帕斯 Gainza Paz, Alberto 阿根廷《新闻报》主编 6—547f
加赞库卢 Gazankulu 前南非黑人邦 7—39e
加泽尔半岛 Gazelle Peninsula 巴布亚新几内亚半岛 7—40c
加扎 Gaza 莫桑比克史 7—39b
加扎勒河 Baḥr al-Ghazāl 苏丹河流 2—142f
加扎利 Ghazālī, al- 伊斯兰教义学家 7—109f
加兹登 Gadsden 美国城市 6—543e
加兹登 Gadsden, James 美国军人、外交家 6—543e
加兹登购地 Gadsden Purchase 美国-墨西哥条约 6—543f
加兹尼 Ghaznī 阿富汗城市 7—110d
加兹温 Kazvin 伊朗城市 9—208a
夹金玻璃画屏 verre églomisé 工艺品 17—523f
夹金玻璃品 Zwischengoldgläser 工艺品 18—577d
夹竹桃 oleander 木本植物 12—372a
夹竹桃科 Apocynaceae 植物学 1—411a
伽 gal 计量单位 6—549b
伽倻 Kaya 朝鲜古代部落联盟 9—203f
伽巴尔人 Gabar 伊朗民族 6—538a
伽柏 Gabor, Dennis 英国电气工程师 6—541a
伽勃 Gabo, Naum 俄罗斯雕塑家 6—539c
伽伐尼 Galvani, Luigi 意大利医生、物理学家 6—563f
伽法尔汗 Ghaffar Khan, (Khan) Abdul 普什图人领袖 7—107b
伽哈达伐拉王朝 Gāhadavāla DYNASTY 统治印度的家族 6—546c
伽勒 Galle, Johann Gottfried 德国天文学家 6—557e
伽利略 Galileo 意大利科学家 6—553f
伽利略变换 Galilean transformations 物理学 6—553c
"伽利略"号飞船 Galileo 美国航天器 6—555c
伽利略望远镜 Galilean telescope 观测仪器 6—553c
伽利略卫星 Galilean satellite 木星的大卫星 6—553b
伽罗瓦 Galois, Évariste 法国数学家 6—562b
伽马 Gama, Vasco da 葡萄牙航海家 6—565b
伽摩 Kāma 印度神话 9—144e
伽莫夫 Gamow, George 美国核物理学家 6—570d
伽倻琴 kayakeum 乐器 9—204a
伽桑狄 Gassendi, Pierre 法国数学家、哲学家 7—25f
伽色尼王朝 Ghaznavid DYNASTY 突厥人王朝 7—110c

《伽泰》 Gāthā 琐罗亚斯德教经典 7—29e
伽泰·帕拉瓦工艺 ghaṭa-pallava 印度艺术 7—109c
佳构剧 well-made play 戏剧 18—178b
佳吉列夫 Diaghilev, Sergey (Pavlovich) 俄国芭蕾舞艺术家 5—283f
佳美兰 gamelan 印度尼西亚地方管弦乐队 6—569d
佳木斯 Jiamusi 中国城市 9—12e
佳音教 Gai'wiio (religious movement) 北美洲宗教派别 6—546f
迦百农 Capernaum 以色列古城 3—425b
迦本 Gabin, Jean 法国电影演员 6—538f
迦比尔 Kabīr 印度诗人 9—125a
迦得支派 Gad 以色列人支派 6—542d
迦尔吉 Kalkin 印度教 9—142d
迦尔洵 Garshin, Vsevolod Mikhaylovich 俄罗斯作家 7—20f
迦勒底 Chaldea 古巴比伦地区 4—31a
迦勒底公教会 Chaldean Catholic Church 东仪教会 4—31a
迦勒底式礼仪 Chaldean rite 宗教礼仪 4—31b
迦勒底语 Chaldean language 语言 4—31b
迦梨陀娑 Kālidāsa 梵语诗人 9—140d
迦利 Kālī 印度教女神 9—140c
迦利布 Ghālib, Mīrzā Asadullāh Khān 印度诗人 7—107c
迦楼罗 Garuḍa 印度神话 7—21e
《迦罗迦师故事》 Kālakācāryakathā 印度耆那教 9—138c
迦玛列二世 Gamaliel II 犹太教公会主席 6—566a
迦玛列三世 Gamaliel III 《密西拿》编纂家 6—566a
迦玛列一世 Gamaliel I 犹太教学者 6—565f
迦摩缕波 Kāmarūpa 印度古代王国 9—145f
迦南 Canaan 亚洲历史地区 3—385c
迦南狗 Canaan dog 牧羊犬 3—385e
迦南铭文 Canaanite inscriptions 亚洲考古 3—385f
迦南诸语言 Canaanite languages 语言 3—385f
迦南宗教 Canaanite religion 古代宗教 3—386a
迦腻色迦 Kaniṣka 贵霜国王 9—158d
迦毗罗 Kapila 吠陀圣人 9—171f
迦苏勒文化 Ghassulian culture 巴勒斯坦史前史 7—109b
迦太基 Carthage 北非古代城市 3—489b
迦太基 Carthage 美国密苏里州城市 3—489e
迦太基 Carthage 美国伊利诺伊州城市 3—489d
迦太基战争 Carthaginian Wars 欧洲历史 3—489f
迦太基总督管区 Carthage, Exarchate of 拜占廷帝国行省 3—489e
迦约马特 Gayōmart 琐罗亚斯德教 7—39b
痂 scab 病理学 15—98f
家常读本画师 Housebook, Master of the 哥特画家 8—195a
家畜 livestock 哺乳动物 10—162c
家鸽 domestic pigeon (*Columba livia*) 鸟类 5—370a
家祭 saṃskāra 印度教 15—1f
家经 Gṛhya-sūtra 印度教 7—308b
家韭葱 houseleek 植物 8—195b
家具 furniture 家庭设备 6—530d
家麻雀 house sparrow (*Passer domesticus*) 鸟类 8—194f
家猫 domestic cat (*Felis catus*) 动物 5—369f
家牛 cattle 牛类 3—531e
家禽 fowl 饲养的禽类 6—428d
家蛇 house snake 动物 8—194e
家神 domovoy 斯拉夫神话神名 5—375e
家神 Lar 古罗马神名 9—497f
家鼠 house mouse 哺乳动物 8—194e
家庭 family 社会学 6—227d
"家庭" Family, The 基督教组织 6—228b
家庭包工制 domestic system 经济学 5—370d
家庭暴力 domestic violence 社会与法律概念 5—370f
家庭悲剧 domestic tragedy 戏剧 5—370e
家庭彩绘 Hausmalerei 工艺 7—514a
家庭法院 family court 法律机构 6—228c
家庭服务 domestic service 社会学 5—370b
家庭派 Familist 宗教派别 6—227c
家庭医学 family practice 医学 6—228d
家庭幼儿学校 dame school 幼儿教育机构 5—127d
家系 lineage 社会学 10—118f
家蝇 housefly (*Musca domestica*) 昆虫 8—195a
家长和教师联谊会 Parent-Teacher Association 美国组织 13—40e
家长和教师联谊会 PTA 美国组织 13—566b
《家族公约》 Famille, Pacte de 法国-西班牙联盟公约 6—227c
家族萨迦 family sagas (literature) 中世纪文学 6—228e
家族性黑蒙性白痴 amaurotic familial idiocy 疾病 1—267c
家族性周期性麻痹 familial periodic paralysis 疾病 6—226f
嘉宝 Garborg, Arne Evensen 挪威作家 7—8a
嘉宝 Garbo, Greta 瑞典演员 7—7f
嘉布遣会 Capuchin 天主教教会 3—433b
嘉当 Cartan, Élie-Joseph 法国数学家 3—486d
嘉当 Cartan, Henri(-Paul) 法国数学家 3—486e
嘉德爵士 K.G. 英国爵士名 9—251a
嘉德勋位 Garter, The Most Noble Order of the 英国骑士勋位 7—21b
嘉定 Gia Dinh 越南城镇 7—114d
嘉定 Jiading 中国上海市区名 9—12b
嘉靖 Jiajing 中国明朝皇帝年号 9—12d
嘉兰 Garland, Judy 美国演员 7—16b
嘉兰属 Gloriosa 植物学 7—160f
嘉陵江 Jialing Jiang 中国河流 9—12d
嘉隆 Gia Long 越南皇帝 7—114d
嘉庆 Jiaqing 中国清朝皇帝年号 9—19a
嘉绒语 Jiarong language 语言 9—19a
嘉兴 Jiaxing 中国城市 9—19b
嘉逊 Garson, Greer 美国演员 7—21a
嘉义 Jiayi 中国台湾县名 9—19d
嘉义 Jiayi 中国台湾城市 9—19e
嘉峪关 Jiayuguan 中国城市 9—19f
镓 gallium 化学元素 6—561b
荚蒾 viburnum 植物 17—534f
荚果 legume 植物 9—563e
戛纳 Cannes 法国城市 3—403a
颊骨 cheekbone 解剖学 4—100c
蛱蝶 brush-footed butterfly 昆虫 3—209a
甲 nail 解剖学 11—543b
甲氨喋呤 methotrexate 药物 11—159a
甲苯 toluene 化工原料 17—142f
甲苯磺丁脲 tolbutamide 药物 17—137e
甲兵 hoplite 古希腊步兵 8—171d
甲虫 beetle 昆虫 2—336b
甲虫形护符 scarab 古埃及宗教徽章 15—103f
甲醇 methanol 化合物 11—158b
甲酚 cresol 化工 5—7e
甲府 Kōfu 日本县城 9—332f
甲骨文 bone and shell script 中国古文字 3—27f
甲骨文 jiaguwen 中国古文字 9—12d
甲基 methyl group 化学 11—159c
甲基氯 methyl chloride 化合物 11—159c
甲基吗啡 methylmorphine 药物 11—159d
甲基溴 methyl bromide 化合物 11—159c
甲加 Karkar 叙利亚古堡 9—182c
甲腈 formonitrile 化合物 6—410a
甲壳虫乐队 Beatles, the 英国音乐团体 2—308c
甲壳动物 crustacean 无脊椎动物 5—40c
甲硫氨酸 methionine 化合物 11—158d
甲龙 Ankylosaurus 恐龙 1—362b

甲米 Krabi 泰国城市 9—369b
甲米地 Cavite 菲律宾省份 3—542f
甲米地哗变 Cavite Mutiny 菲律宾历史 3—542f
甲描育 Calbayog 菲律宾城市 3—335a
甲醛 formaldehyde 化合物 6—409a
甲烷 methane 化合物 11—158b
甲万那端 Cabanatuan 菲律宾城市 3—303f
甲氧基氯 methoxychlor 化合物 11—159b
甲胄鱼 ostracoderm 古生物学 12—493b
甲状旁腺 parathyroid gland 动物解剖学 13—39d
甲状旁腺功能减退 hypoparathyroidism 内分泌疾病 8—295d
甲状旁腺功能亢进 hyperparathyroidism 内分泌疾病 8—293c
甲状旁腺腺瘤 parathyroid adenoma 疾病 13—39c
甲状腺 thyroid gland 解剖学 17—76c
甲状腺功能减退 hypothyroidism 内分泌疾病 8—296c
甲状腺功能亢进 hyperthyroidism 内分泌疾病 8—293f
甲状腺功能试验 thyroid function test 医学 17—76b
甲状腺降钙素 thyrocalcitonin 生物化学 17—76b
甲状腺素 thyroxine 生物学 17—76e
甲状腺炎 thyroiditis 疾病 17—76e
甲状腺肿 goitre 病理现象 7—184c
甲状腺肿瘤 thyroid tumour 疾病 17—76d
贾巴尔普尔 Jabalpur 印度城市 8—501c
贾巴武 Jabavu,Davidson Don Tengo 南非政治领袖 8—501c
贾卜奈 Jabneh 巴勒斯坦古城 8—502a
贾德 Judd,Charles Hubbard 美国心理学家 9—101a
贾德 Judd,Gerrit P(armele) 美国传教士 9—101b
贾德森 Judson,Adoniram 美国语言学家 9—103a
贾德森 Judson,E. Z. C. 美国冒险家 9—103b
贾恩茨考斯韦角 Giant's Causeway 北爱尔兰海角 7—117c
贾恩卡纳 Giancana,Sam 美国黑帮歹徒 7—115e
贾尔达帕拉野生动物保护地 Jaldapāra Wild Life Sanctuary 印度野生动物保护地 8—522d
贾尔迪尼 Giardini,Felice 意大利作曲家 7—117d
贾尔冈 Jālgaon 印度城市 8—522d
贾尔纳 Chālna 孟加拉国港口 4—33c
贾法尔 Onn bin Ja'afar,Dato 马来亚政治家 12—422d
贾菲 Jaffee,Irving 美国运动员 8—515f
贾夫纳 Jaffna 斯里兰卡历史王国 8—515f
贾夫纳 Jaffna 斯里兰卡港口 8—516a
贾盖 Chāgai 巴基斯坦地名 4—25f
贾根 Jagan,Cheddi (Berret) 圭亚那政治领袖 8—516a
贾海诸语言 Jahaic languages 语言 8—517e
贾汗季 Jahāngīr 印度莫卧儿皇帝 8—517e
贾河 Dja River 非洲河流 5—350b
贾科莫·达·伦蒂尼 Giacomo da Lentini 意大利诗人 7—115a
贾科尼 Giacconi,Riccardo 意大利裔美籍物理学家 7—114e
贾科萨 Giacosa,Giuseppe 意大利剧作家 7—115b
贾可布森 Jacobsen,Josephine 美国诗人 8—512b
贾克森 Juxon,William 英格兰坎特伯雷大主教 9—122d
贾昆人 Jakun 民族 8—521e
贾拉拉巴德 Jalālābād 阿富汗城市 8—522a
贾拉勒阿巴德 Dzhalal-Abad 吉尔吉斯斯坦城市 5—490d
贾拉特 Jarratt,Devereux 美国安立甘宗教士 8—546a
贾拉伊尔画派 Jalāyirid school 巴格达细密画派 8—522c
贾拉伊尔人 Jalāyirid 民族 8—522b
贾朗达尔 Jullundur 印度城市 9—107f
贾劳恩 Jālaun 印度城镇和县 8—522b
贾勒特 Jarrett,Keith 美国音乐家 8—546d
贾雷尔 Jarrell,Randall 美国诗人 8—546b
贾利勒家族 Jalīlī family 奥斯曼帝国伊拉克人家族 8—522e
贾林戈 Jalingo 尼日利亚城镇 8—522e
贾卢伊特环礁 Jaluit Atoll 马绍尔群岛共和国岛链环礁 8—522f
贾罗 Jarrow 英格兰港口 8—546e
贾洛尔 Jālor 印度城市 8—522f
贾马勒布尔 Jamālpur 孟加拉国城市 8—524d
贾马里 Jama'are 尼日利亚城镇和世袭酋长国名 8—523a
贾马梅 Jamaame 索马里城镇 8—523a
贾玛尔扎德 Jamalzadeh,Mohammad Ali 伊朗散文作家 8—524d
贾米 Jāmī 波斯学者、诗人 8—532a
贾姆达尼 Jāmdānī 印度纺织品 8—524f
贾姆鲁德 Jamrūd 巴基斯坦城镇 8—533c
贾姆讷格尔 Jāmnagar 印度城镇 8—533b
贾姆谢德布尔 Jamshedpur 印度城镇 8—533c
贾木纳河 Jamuna (Asia) 亚洲河流 8—533d
贾帕 Jakpa,Sumalia Ndewura 非洲国王 8—521e
贾庆林 Jia Qinglin 中国领导人 9—11f
贾思勰 Jia Sixie 中国古代农书作者 9—12b
贾斯珀 Jasper 加拿大地名 8—548a
贾斯珀 Jasper 美国城市 8—548a
贾斯珀(哈特菲尔德的) Jasper of Hatfield 威尔士贵族 8—548c
贾斯珀国家公园 Jasper National Park 加拿大公园 8—548c
贾似道 Jia Sidao 中国南宋宰相 9—12a
贾特 Jāṭ 印度种姓 8—549b
贾特基语 Jatki language 语言 8—549e
贾瓦拉 Jawara,Sir Dawda Kairaba 冈比亚总统 8—553b
贾瓦切夫 Javacheff,Christo 保加利亚艺术家 8—551f
贾瓦斯基 Jaworski,Leon 美国律师 8—553e
贾维 Garvey,Marcus (Moziah) 美国黑人运动领袖 7—21f
贾维斯 Jarvis,John Wesley 纽约画家 8—547b
贾维斯岛 Jarvis Island 太平洋岛屿 8—547b
贾希兹 Jāḥiẓ,al- 伊斯兰学者 8—517f
贾亚瓦德纳 Jayewardene,J.R. 斯里兰卡总统 8—555a
贾伊洛洛 Djailolo (Indonesia) 印度尼西亚岛屿 5—350c
贾伊洛洛 Jailolo (Indonesia) 印度尼西亚城市 8—518f
贾伊瑟尔默 Jaisalmer 印度城市 8—519d
贾因蒂亚 Jaintia 印度历史土邦 8—519b
贾因蒂亚丘陵 Jaintia Hills 印度自然地理区 8—519b
钾(K) potassium 化学元素 13—461f
钾碱 potash 化合物 13—461f
钾缺乏 potassium deficiency 病理生理现象 13—462b
钾霞石 kaliophilite 矿物 9—142c
钾-氩年龄测定法 potassium-argon dating 测年法 13—462b
钾盐 sylvite 矿物 16—397a
钾盐镁矾 kainite 矿物 9—135e
钾云母 potash mica 矿物 13—461f
假柏 false cypress 植物学 6—225a
假宝石原料 paste 燧石玻璃 13—80e
假潮 seiche 气象学 15—191a
假单胞菌 pseudomonad 细菌 13—556f
假饵钓鱼 fly-tying 钓鱼方法 6—381a
假发 wig 戏装或个人装饰品 18—247f
假喉言语 pseudolaryngeal speech 食管言语 13—556f
假结核病 pseudotuberculosis 疾病 13—557d
假荆芥 catnip (*Nepeta cataria*) 草本植物 3—528f
假狂犬病 pseudorabies 动物病毒性疾病 13—557c
假柳穿鱼 bastard toadflax 草本植物 2—270e
假面剧 masque 娱乐 11—4c
假面哑剧 mumming play 戏剧 11—481c
假名 kana 日本文字 9—151e
假名 prajñapti 佛教哲学 13—483d
假名垣鲁文 Kanagaki Robun 日本小说家 9—152b
假牛繁缕目 Theligonales 植物学 17—21e
假妊娠 false pregnancy 病理现象 6—225c
假设演绎法 hypothetico-deductive method 哲学 8—296b
假升麻 goatsbeard (species *Aruncus dioicus* or *A. sylvester*) 草本植物

7—170a
假声 falsetto 声乐 6—225f
假施瓦格氏蜓属 Pseudoschwagerina 古生物学 13—557c
假释 parole 刑法 13—60e
假太阳鸟 false sunbird 二种鸟的俗称 6—225d
假体 prosthesis 医学 13—540f
假吸血蝠 false vampire bat 哺乳动物 6—225e
假象 pseudomorph 矿物学 13—557a
假性黄疸 artificial jaundice 疾病 1—530f
假性甲状旁腺功能减退 pseudohypoparathyroidism 疾病 13—556e
假性球麻痹 pseudobulbar palsy 疾病 13—556d
假熊猴属 Notharctus 古生物学 12—274a
假血友病 B pseudohemophilia B 疾病 13—556e
假牙 denture 牙科学 5—248d
假叶树 butcher's broom 植物 3—288f
假种皮 aril 植物学 1—472b
斝 jia 中国古代酒器 9—11e
榎本武扬 Enomoto Takeaki 日本政治家 6—86a
价电子 valence electron 电子学 17—449c
价格 price 经济学 13—503c
价格歧视 price discrimination 经济学 13—504f
价格维持 price maintenance 经济学 13—505a
价值学 axiology 哲学 2—93c
驾洛 Karak (Korean tribal league) 古代朝鲜部落联盟 9—177e
驾驭 driving and coaching 马术 5—425e
架上绘画 easel painting 绘画 5—501d
假日 parhelion 大气科学 13—41c
嫁接 graft 园艺学 7—240b
嫁妆 dowry 结婚习俗 5—407e
尖笔 stylus 书写工具 16—294b
尖顶杯 steeple cup 金属制品 16—208c
尖顶饰 finial 建筑装饰 6—319d
尖拱窗 lancet window 建筑 9—473c
尖喙鸟 sharpbill (*Oxyruncus cristatus*) 鸟类 15—283a
尖晶石 spinel 矿物 16—32a
尖塔 steeple 建筑 16—208c
尖头 cusp 建筑 5—77c
尖头并指(趾)畸形 acrocephalosyndactyly 医学 1—58a
尖头草螽 cone-headed grasshopper 昆虫 4—418e
尖吻浣熊 olingo 哺乳动物 12—374d
尖牙 cuspid 解剖学 5—77c
坚齿鱼目 Pycnodontiformes 古生物学 14—41e
坚打谷地 Kinta Valley 马来西亚谷地 9—297e
坚德布尔 Chāndpur 孟加拉国河港 4—45b
坚固城堡 Gaillard, Château 法国城堡 6—547a
坚果 nut 植物果实 12—305b
坚果象甲 nut weevil 昆虫 12—305c
坚外壳虫属 Deiphon 古生物学 5—214c
坚振礼 confirmation 基督教 4—421e
坚殖腺类 pycnogonid 动物学 14—41e
间苯二酚 resorcinol 酚类有机化合物 14—241f
间奏曲 intermezzo 音乐 8—410c
肩 shoulder 解剖学 15—337a
肩胛骨 scapula 解剖学 15—103e
监察官 censor 古罗马官员 3—563d
监护权和婚姻 wardship and marriage 封建法律用语 18—105f
监护人 guardian 法律 7—343c
监护征赋制 encomienda 西班牙法律制度 6—70b
监狱 prison 监禁罪犯场所 13—519f
兼并 annexation 法律 1—366d
兼并 merger 商业 11—129d
菅原道真 Sugawara Michizane 日本汉学家 16—310b
犍陀罗 Gandhāra 巴基斯坦历史地区 6—571f
犍陀罗艺术 Gandhāra art 佛教艺术 6—571f
鲣鸟 booby (*Sula*) 热带海鸟 3—36e
茧 cocoon 生物学 4—324f
茧蜂 braconid 昆虫 3—105b
柬埔寨 Cambodia 亚洲国家 3—364b
柬埔寨语 Cambodian language 语言 3—365b
检波 detection 电子学 5—265c
检察机关 procuracy 政府机构 13—526f
检察院 ministère public 法国法律机构 11—258a
检非违使 Kebiishi 日本警察官 9—210b
检审法院 audiencia 中世纪政府机构 2—45e
检疫 quarantine 病理学 14—77b
减充血药 decongestant 药物 5—203f
减轻情节 extenuating circumstance 法律 6—197e
减轻责任 diminished responsibility 法律 5—318e
减数分裂 meiosis 细胞学 11—87a
减速运动伤 deceleration injury 冲击性损伤 5—202a
减刑 commutation 法律 4—393c
减压病 decompression sickness 疾病 5—203e
减压舱 decompression chamber (medical device) 医疗设备 5—203e
减振器 shock absorber 机械工艺学 15—328a
减重短程高速汽车赛 drag racing 汽车运动 5—410d
减重高速汽车 hot rod 汽车 8—189e
剪刀 scissors 工具 15—145a
剪股颖 bent grass 草本植物 2—390e
剪切波 shear wave 物理学 15—290e
剪切模量 shear modulus 物理学 15—290d
剪切应力 shear stress 物理学 15—290e
剪秋罗属 Lychnis 植物学 10—308c
剪式椅 scissors chair 家具 15—145b
剪水鹱 shearwater 鸟类 15—291c
剪影 silhouette 工艺美术 15—368d
剪纸 paper-cut 中国民间工艺品 13—23f
剪纸装饰术 decoupage 艺术 5—204c
睑内翻 entropion 眼病 6—90a
睑皮松垂症 blepharochalasis 眼病 2—533c
睑外翻 ectropion 眼病 5—532c
睑下垂 ptosis 眼病 14—3a
睑腺炎 hordeolum (medicine) 眼病 8—173d
睑炎 blepharitis 眼病 2—533b
简 Jane 美国地下诊所 8—533f
简 Jane SEYMOUR 英国王后 8—534a
简并气体 degenerate gas 物理学 5—211d
简牍 jiandu 中国古代书写材料 9—13d
简化曲棍球 shinty 体育 15—319d
《简明不列颠百科全书》 Concise Encyclopædia Britannica 百科全书 4—412b
简斯维尔 Janesville 美国城市 8—534b
简谐运动 simple harmonic motion 物理学 15—384b
简易审判 summary jurisdiction 英美法律 16—332f
碱 alkali 化合物 1—231d
碱 base 化合物 2—256b
碱金属 alkali metal 化学元素 1—232a
碱石灰 soda lime 混合物 15—482e
碱土金属 alkaline-earth metal 化学元素 1—232b
碱性长石 alkali feldspar 矿物 1—231f
碱性辉长岩 essexite 岩石 6—137c
碱性磷酸酶 alkaline phosphatase 生物化学 1—232b
碱性氧气转炉炼钢法 basic oxygen process (BOP) 炼钢方法 2—259a
碱液 lye 化工 10—309f
碱中毒 alkalosis 病理学 1—232f
翦伯赞 Jian Bozan 中国历史学家 9—13b

见 darshan 印度教 5—153d
间谍活动 espionage 非法情报活动 6—133d
间谍小说 spy story 文学 16—166d
间接凸印 indirect relief printing 印刷术 8—368f
间歇泉 geyser 地质学 7—105f
间歇泉 Geysir 冰岛间歇泉 7—106b
间歇训练 interval training 体育训练方法 8—424b
饯别酒杯 stirrup cup 器皿 16—242a
建安七子 Seven Writers of the Jian'an Period 中国历史文人 15—238a
建部贤弘 Takebe Katahiro 日本数学家 16—441d
建国五基 Five Principles (Indonesian history) 印度尼西亚历史 6—341e
建设团结党 United Development Party 印度尼西亚政党 17—351f
建文 Jianwen 中国明朝皇帝年号 9—18d
建溪 Jian Xi 中国河流 9—13e
建窑 Jian Kiln 中国宋代瓷窑 9—13d
建窑器皿 Chien ware 中国器皿 4—148c
建造 construction 建筑学 4—460f
建州三卫 three garrisons in Jianzhou 中国历史 17—63e
建筑师协作事务所 Architects Collaborative, The (TAC) 建筑师组织 1—452a
建筑学 architecture 工程学 1—452a
剑齿虎 sabre-toothed cat 古生物学 14—484f
剑道 kendo 日本击剑方式 9—224c
剑杆织机 rapier loom 纺织 14—155a
剑龙 Stegosaurus 古生物学 16—210e
剑虻 stiletto fly 昆虫 16—237a
剑桥 Cambridge 加拿大城市 3—366d
剑桥 Cambridge 英格兰城市 3—366d
剑桥 Cambridge 美国马里兰州城市 3—367b
剑桥 Cambridge 美国马萨诸塞州城市 3—367c
剑桥柏拉图派 Cambridge Platonists 英国哲学团体 3—368c
剑桥大学 Cambridge, University of 英国高等学府 3—367e
《剑桥纲领》 Cambridge Platform 基督教文献 3—368c
剑桥郡 Cambridgeshire 英格兰郡名 3—368d
剑桥评论家 Cambridge critics 英国文艺评论家 3—368b
剑桥旗 Cambridge Flag 北美殖民地旗帜 3—368c
《剑桥协定》 Cambridge Agreement 英国历史 3—368b
剑滩 Sword Beach 第二次世界大战历史 16—390a
剑尾鱼 swordtail (*Xiphophorus helleri*) 鱼类 16—391a
剑吻鲨 goblin shark 鱼类 7—171a
剑舞 sword dance 民间舞蹈 16—390d
剑鱼 swordfish (*Xiphias gladius*) 鱼类 16—390f
剑鱼座30 30 Doradus 天文学 17—40d
剑鱼座S S Doradus 天文学 14—478a
健康 health 生理学 7—539e
健康保险 health insurance 社会保险 7—540b
健美运动 body building 体育 2—563a
健蛰虫 tentacle worm 动物 16—547a
渐新马属 Mesohippus 古生物学 11—140a
渐新世 Oligocene Epoch 地质学 12—373e
渐增反复 incremental repetition 诗歌 8—353f
谏义里 Kediri 印度尼西亚县名 9—210f
谏义里 Kediri 印度尼西亚城市 9—210f
谏早 Isahaya 日本城市 8—458e
腱 tendon 解剖学 16—538d
腱膜 aponeurosis 解剖学 1—414d
腱炎 tendinitis 病理学 16—538b
鉴 jian 中国古代水器 9—13b
鉴真 Jianzhen 中国唐代僧人 9—18d
键 key 机械器件 9—247e
键合 bonding 化学 3—26f
键合异构 linkage isomerism 化学 10—123e
键盘乐器 clavier 乐器 4—273f
键盘乐器 keyboard instrument 乐器 9—248d
僭主 tyrant 希腊统治者 17—310d
箭 arrow (weapon) 武器 1—515f
箭齿兽属 Toxodon 古生物学 17—182d
箭虫 arrowworm 无脊椎动物 1—516f
箭毒 curare 化合物 5—66e
箭毒蛙 arrow-poison frog 两栖动物 1—516a
箭十字党 Arrow Cross Party 匈牙利法西斯组织 1—516a
箭石 belemnoid 古生物学 2—351d
江别 Ebetsu 日本城市 5—517d
江布尔 Dzhambul 哈萨克斯坦州名 5—490d
江布尔 Dzhambul 哈萨克斯坦城市 5—490e
江布尔 Jaunpur 印度城镇 8—550a
《江格尔》 Jiangge'er 蒙古族史诗 9—16b
江汉 Kōkan (Japanese painter) 日本画家 9—336d
江户 Edo 日本城市 5—547e
江户时代 Edo period (Japanese history) 日本历史 5—547e
江华岛 Kanghwa Island 韩国岛屿 9—157c
江界 Kanggye 朝鲜城市 9—157c
江亢虎 Jiang Kanghu 中国政治人物 9—14c
江陵 Jiangling 中国县名 9—16c
江陵 Kangnŭng 韩国城市 9—157c
江门 Jiangmen 中国城市 9—16d
江南 Kōnan 日本城市 9—344b
江南机器制造总局 Jiangnan Arsenal 中国清代军用企业 9—16e
江南丘陵 Jiangnan Qiuling 中国丘陵 9—16f
江崎玲於奈 Esaki, Leo 日本物理学家 6—126e
江青 Jiang Qing 中国政治人物 9—14f
江苏 Jiangsu 中国省份 9—16f
江藤新平 Etō Shimpei 日本政治家 6—152c
江西 Jiangxi 中国省份 9—17d
江西苏维埃 Jiangxi Soviet 中国历史 9—18a
江鳕 burbot (*Lota lota*) 淡水鱼 3—257e
江淹 Jiang Yan 中国文学家 9—15c
江阴 Jiangyin 中国城市 9—18b
江油 Jiangyou 中国城市 9—18c
江原 Kangwŏn 朝鲜道名 9—157e
江原 Kangwŏn 韩国道名 9—157f
江泽民 Jiang Zemin 中国领导人 0 16d
江孜 Gyangzê 中国县名 7—388c
将军 general 军衔 7—55b
将军 strategus 军衔 16—265d
将棋 shogi 日本象棋 15—329c
姜 ginger (*Zingiber officinale*) 草本植物 7—135e
姜饼装饰 gingerbread 建筑 7—136b
姜饼棕榈果 doum nut 植物 5—403d
姜村 Dschang 喀麦隆城镇 5—433f
姜罐 ginger jar 瓷器 7—136a
姜花 ginger lily 草本植物 7—136a
姜黄 turmeric (*Curcuma longa*) 草本植物 17—289b
姜姜布雷岛 Jangjangbure (The Gambia) 冈比亚河岛屿 8—534d
姜科 Zingiberaceae 植物学 18—554f
姜夔 Jiang Kui 中国南宋词人 9—14d
姜目 Zingiberales 植物学 18—555a
姜片虫病 fasciolopsiasis 寄生虫病 6—245b
姜亚纲 Zingiberidae 植物学 18—555d
姜汁啤酒 ginger beer 饮料 7—135f
豇豆 cowpea 植物 4—558e
浆果 berry 植物学 2—430b
浆果鹃属 Arbutus 植物学 1—444e

浆细胞性骨髓 plasma cell myeloma 疾病 13—349b
橿原 Kashihara 日本城市 9—191b
鳉鱼 killifish 鱼类 9—280a
疆南星属 Arum 植物学 1—535a
讲道 derasha 犹太教 5—251e
讲坛 bema 建筑 2—373d
奖牌 medal 工艺制品 11—69e
桨帆船 galley 靠桨推进的远洋船 6—558c
桨轮 paddle wheel 船推进装置 12—539a
桨吻鲟 paddlefish 鱼类 12—539b
蒋鼎文 Jiang Dingwen 中国将领 9—13f
蒋海澄 Chiang Hai-ch'eng 中国诗人 4—138e
蒋介石 Jiang Jieshi 中国政治人物 9—13f
蒋经国 Jiang Jingguo 中国政治人物 9—14b
蒋廷黻 Jiang Tingfu 中国历史学家 9—15b
蒋兆和 Jiang Zhaohe 中国画家 9—16a
降钙素 calcitonin 激素 3—335d
降落伞 parachute 航空装置 13—30e
降神会 séance 神秘学 15—171c
降水 precipitation 气象学 13—489a
酱汁 sauce 食品 15—81b
交比 cross ratio 数学 5—32e
交叉节奏 cross-rhythm 音乐 5—32f
交叉平行线影法 cross-hatching (drawing) 绘画技法 5—32d
交错从表 cross-cousin 人类学 5—32b
交代矿床 replacement deposit 矿床学 14—233f
交代作用 metasomatic replacement 矿物学 11—153b
交点 node 天文学 12—223e
交沸石 harmotome 矿物 7—482c
交鬼 necromancy 巫术 12—63c
交互式多媒体 interactive multimedia 电子系统 8—407f
交换婚姻 exchange marriage 社会学 6—189a
交换律 commutative law 数学 4—393d
交换系数 austausch coefficient 物理学 2—61a
交流电 alternating current 物理学 1—255b
交替进行 hocket 音乐 8—112c
交替圣歌 antiphon 音乐 1—393e
交通管理 traffic control 交通 17—189f
交响曲 symphony 音乐 16—399f
交响诗 symphonic poem 音乐 16—399e
交响协奏曲 sinfonia concertante 音乐 15—390e
交响乐团 symphony orchestra 音乐 16—400c
交易会 trade fair 贸易 17—187e
交易券 trading stamp 商业 17—189b
交战状态 belligerency 国际法 2—365f
交织 entrelacement 文学 6—90a
交织字母 monogram 书法 11—344e
交趾支那 Cochinchina 越南地区 4—319e
交嘴雀 crossbill 鸟类 5—33b
郊地 umland 地理学 17—337c
郊狼 Coyote 民间传说 4—560c
浇铸 casting 工业技术 3—512d
胶版复印 hectograph 印刷 7—553e
胶合板 plywood 复合板材 13—379f
胶结作用 cementation 地质学 3—561c
胶粒 micelle 物理化学 11—178b
胶黏剂 adhesive 化学 1—77e
胶乳 latex 化学 9—510f
胶体 colloid 物理学 4—351d
胶印 offset printing 印刷 12—344c
胶原 collagen 蛋白质 4—345e
胶子 gluon 物理学 7—165b
椒江 Jiaojiang 中国区名 9—18e
椒盐卷饼 pretzel 食品 13—500f
焦秉贞 Jiao Bingzhen 中国画家 9—18e
焦虫 piroplasmid 原生动物 13—322c
焦达纳格布尔 Chota Nāgpur 印度高原 4—200e
焦德雷尔班克实验站 Jodrell Bank Experimental Station 英国天文学机构 9—43a
焦尔达诺 Giordano, Luca 意大利画家 7—138b
焦尔达诺 Giordano, Umberto 意大利作曲家 7—138c
焦尔哈德 Jorhāt 印度县城 9—87e
焦耳 joule 计量单位 9—92f
焦耳 Joule, James Prescott 英国物理学家 9—92f
焦耳定律 Joule's law 电学 9—93a
焦耳-汤姆孙效应 Joule-Thomson effect 物理学 9—93a
焦夫 Jawf, al- 沙特阿拉伯城镇、绿洲 8—553c
焦夫 Jawf, al- 也门绿洲 8—553c
焦格瀑布 Jog Falls 印度瀑布 9—43e
焦硅酸盐 pyrosilicate 矿物 14—47f
焦基 Giuochi 意大利画家 7—146b
焦孔多 Giocondo, Fra Giovanni 意大利建筑师 7—137e
焦利蒂 Giolitti, Giovanni 意大利首相 7—137f
焦沥青 pyrobitumen 烃类物质 14—47a
焦磷酸四乙酯 tetraethyl pyrophosphate 化合物 16—563d
焦虑 anxiety 医学 1—402b
焦石英 lechatelierite 矿物 9—550c
焦炭 coke 煤炭产品 4—336c
焦糖 caramel 食品 3—437b
焦特布尔 Jodhpur 印度城市 9—42e
焦亚-德尔科莱 Gioia del Colle 意大利城镇 7—137f
焦油 tar 化工 16—477b
焦作 Jiaozuo 中国城市 9—18f
蕉鹃 turaco 鸟类 17—275f
蕉麻 abaca (*Musa textilis*) 草本植物 1—3f
蕉森莺 bananaquit (*Coereba flaveola*) 鸟类 2—189d
蕉叶贝属 Leptodus 古生物学 10—32e
礁湖星云 Lagoon Nebula 天文学 9—448b
鹪鹩 wren 鸟类 18—343b
鹪鹩鸫 wrenthrush (*Zeledonia coronata*) 鸟类 18—344d
鹪鹩科 Troglodytidae (bird family) 动物学 17—230c
鹪鹩雀鹛 wrentit (species *Chamaea fasciata*) 鸟类 18—344e
鹪鹩莺 wren-warbler 鸟类 18—344a
鹪莺 prinia 鸟类 13—516d
嚼虱 chewing louse 昆虫 4—136f
嚼烟 chewing tobacco 烟草 4—137a
角 horn 动物学 8—175c
角蠋蛾 regal moth 昆虫 14—201f
角杯 drinking horn 酒器 5—425c
角草 hornwort 植物 8—179a
角叉菜 Irish moss (*Chondrus crispus*) 藻类 8—447f
角蝉 treehopper 昆虫 17—208d
角齿藓 horn-tooth moss 植物 8—176a
角蛋白 keratin 生物学 9—239c
角动量 angular momentum 物理学 1—353f
角斗士 gladiator 古罗马历史 7—148f
角豆树 carob (*Ceratonia siliqua*) 豆科乔木 3—471c
角蛤属 Goniophora 古生物学 7—205c
角胡麻 unicorn plant 草本植物 17—342f
角化病 keratosis 疾病 9—239e
角茴香科 Hypecoaceae 植物学 8—290e
角甲藻属 Ceratium 生物学 4—9a
角蝰属 Cerastes 动物学 4—8f
角砾岩 breccia 岩石 3—135d
角龙 ceratopsian 古生物学 4—9b
角马 gnu 哺乳动物 7—168e

角膜 cornea 解剖学 4—511d
角膜放射状切开术 radial keratotomy 外科手术 14—110c
角膜炎 keratitis 疾病 9—239d
角鲨 horned shark 鱼类 8—177f
角珊瑚 horn coral 古生物学 8—175f
角闪岩 amphibolite 岩石 1—298a
角闪岩相 amphibolite facies 岩石学 1—298a
角速度 angular velocity 物理学 1—354a
角帖书 hornbook 儿童识字祈祷书 8—176d
角尾蜂 horntail 昆虫 8—178f
角蜥 horned toad 动物 8—178a
角藓 horned liverwort 植物 8—177c
角响尾蛇 horned rattlesnake 动物 8—177f
角鸮 horned owl 鸟类 8—177d
角形竖琴 angular harp 乐器 1—353e
角宿一 Spica 天文学 16—25e
角岩相 hornfels facies 岩石学 8—178c
角银矿 cerargyrite 矿物 4—8f
角蝇 horn fly (*Haematobia irritans*) 害虫 8—176a
角质海绵 horny sponge 动物 8—179a
角嘴海雀 puffin 鸟类 14—18b
绞盘 capstan 机械装置 3—432c
绞杀榕 strangler fig 木本植物 16—262e
绞痛 colic 病理学 4—344e
绞刑 hanging 刑罚 7—459b
铰刀 reamer 切削刀具 14—181c
矫形外科 orthopedics 医学 12—474f
皎漂 Kyaukpyu 缅甸城镇 9—412e
皎施 Kyaukse 缅甸城镇 9—412e
脚轮矮床 trundle bed 家具 17—244e
脚气病 beriberi 疾病 2—407c
脚手架 scaffold 建筑 15—99d
脚踏车 velocipede 交通工具 17—495a
脚镯 anklet 珠宝装饰 1—362a
搅乳海 churning of the milky ocean 印度教神话 4—230d
搅乳器 churn 机器 4—230c
叫鹤 seriema 鸟类 15—226a
叫鸭 screamer 鸟类 15—155d
校对 proofreading 出版 13—534c
校勘 textual criticism 编辑出版 17—7e
轿式马车 chaise 车 4—29a
轿子 litter 交通工具 10—149d
教法根源学 uṣūl al-fiqh 伊斯兰教法制度 17—425b
教法学 fiqh 伊斯兰教法制度 6—324c
教父 Church Father 基督教早期人物 4—223f
教父 Father of the Church 基督教早期人物 6—249c
教父 godfather 基督教入教者的监护人 7—173e
教父(教母) godparent 基督教入教者的监护人 7—175e
教父著作 patristic literature 基督徒著作 13—91c
教皇 pope 罗马主教的专称 13—432c
教皇国 Papal States 教皇领土 13—21a
教皇体系 papacy 天主教中央统辖体系 13—18c
教皇永无谬误论 papal infallibility 天主教教义 13—20f
教皇诏书 bull 罗马教廷文件 3—245e
教皇自动诏书 motu proprio 天主教教会文件 11—438a
教会 church 基督教 4—222f
教会保留地 Clergy Reserves 加拿大历史 4—286a
教会调式 church mode 音乐 4—224a
教会法 canon law 基督教法律 3—407b
《教会法大全》 Corpus Juris Canonici 天主教教法汇编 4—520f
《教会法典》 Codex Juris Canonici 教会法典汇编 4—326e
教会法院 ecclesiastical court 宗教当局司法机构 5—520d
教会分裂 schism 基督教 15—117c
教会教育 parochial education 宗教教育 13—60b
教会节期 church year 基督教节令和节日 4—224e
教会军 Church Army 英国教会组织 4—223f
教会人员特权 clergy, benefit of 宗教特权 4—285f
教会斯拉夫语 Church Slavonic language (liturgical language) 语言 4—224d
教会纹章 ecclesiastical heraldry 基督教纹章 5—520f
教会辖地 Church States 意大利历史地区 4—224d
教会议会 consistory 天主教 4—447a
教会与国家 church and state 基督教 4—223c
教会奏鸣曲 church sonata 音乐 4—224d
教会奏鸣曲 sonata da chiesa 音乐 15—508c
教理问答 catechism 宗教教育 3—522f
教理学校 catechetical school 教育 3—522f
教练机 trainer 军事 17—191e
教令 decretal 天主教 5—204d
教母 godmother 基督教入教者的监护人 7—174f
教牧人员救济委员会 Church Commissioners 英国教会组织 4—223f
教派神道 Kyōha Shintō 日本宗教组织 9—413f
教区 diocese 基督教主教辖区 5—325b
《教士公民组织法》 Civil Constitution of the Clergy 法国历史 4—253b
教士宪章 Priests' Charter 瑞士历史 13—508d
教堂 church 基督教建筑 4—222f
教堂地下室 crypt 建筑 5—42d
教堂门环 sanctuary knocker 教堂装饰品 15—23f
教堂门廊 galilee 建筑 6—553d
教堂司事 sexton 教会职员 15—245b
教堂音乐 church music 音乐 4—224b
教廷大使 nuncio 梵蒂冈教廷代表 12—300d
教廷使节 legate 天主教 9—560f
教团印第安人 Mission Indians 民族 11—278d
教务评议会 presbytery 教务管理机构 13—495e
教学 teaching 教育学 16—510c
教学机械 teaching machine 教育 16—510e
教育剧 Lehrstück 戏剧 9—565b
教育小说 Bildungsroman 文学 2—472b
教育小说 education novel 文学 5—548a
教育心理学 educational psychology 教育学 5—548a
《教育修正案第九条》 Title IX 美国《联邦教育修正案》的条款 17—119d
教育制度 educational system 教育 5—548b
酵母菌 yeast 生物学 18—434a
酵母属 Saccharomyces 生物学 14—486a
阶乘 factorial 数学 6—210b
阶段 maqām 伊斯兰教苏非派教语 10—485e
阶名唱法 solmization 音乐 15—497d
阶梯形琢型 step cut 宝石工艺 16—219f
阶形山墙 crow step (architecture) 建筑 5—35c
疖 boil 疾病 3—6c
结巴 stammering 语言障碍 16—186f
接触法 contact process 化学 4—464c
接触镜片 contact lens 眼科学 4—464b
接地 ground 电学 7—323b
接骨木 elder 植物 6—16c
接合 conjugation 有性生殖过程 4—432b
接合贝属 Composita 古生物学 4—399d
接合菌纲 Zygomycetes 生物学 18—578b
接近理论 contiguity, theory of 心理学 4—466a
接力赛跑 relay race 体育 14—214e
接龙 Play and Pay (card game) 纸牌游戏 13—365d
接头 joint 木工 9—74f

接种 inoculation 医疗操作 8—394c
秸秆 straw 植物 16—272c
揭发者 delator 古罗马告密者 5—218a
揭阳 Jieyang 中国城市 9—20e
街坊文教馆 neighbourhood house 社会服务机构 12—69a
街坊文教馆 settlement house 社会服务机构 15—235f
街头影片 street film 德国电影 16—274a
节 knot 计量单位 9—324e
节颈鱼 arthrodire 古生物学 1—527c
节理 joint 地质学 9—75b
节礼日 Boxing Day 节日 3—98f
节律特征 prosodic feature (phonetics) 语音学 13—539b
节拍 metre 音乐 11—160d
节拍器 metronome 音乐仪器 11—161d
节期中祝日 ḥol ha-moʿed 犹太教节日 8—123c
节日 feast 宗教、农业、文化纪念日 6—257f
节日 holiday 宗教、世俗纪念日 8—125e
节日季后赛 Fiesta Bowl 美国大学橄榄球赛 6—308e
节食 dieting 营养学 5—307e
节叶门 Articulatae (botany) 植物学 1—529f
节育 birth control 社会学 2—493e
节约法令 sumptuary law 法律 16—334e
节杖 caduceus 希腊神话 3—314e
节杖 sceptre 统治者权威象征 15—107c
节肢动物 arthropod 无脊椎动物 1—527c
节肢介体病毒 arbovirus 微生物学 1—444a
节奏 rhythm 音乐 14—273b
节奏 rhythm 诗 14—273d
节奏程式 rhythmic mode 音乐 14—274b
节奏与布鲁斯 rhythm and blues 音乐 14—273f
《劫波经》 Kalpa-sūtra 印度教手册 9—144a
《劫波经》 Kalpa-sūtra 印度耆那教经典 9—144a
劫持 hijacking 法律 8—77e
杰巴 Jebba 尼日利亚城镇 8—557a
杰巴尔 Djebar, Assia 阿尔及利亚作家 5—350c
杰拜勒舍迈尔 Jabal Shammar 沙特阿拉伯地区 8—501a
杰贝勒河 Baḥr al-Jabal 尼罗河一段 2—143a
杰布 Jebb, John 英国政治、宗教和社会改革家 8—557a
杰德堡 Jedburgh 苏格兰自治市 8—557b
杰德夫拉 Djedefre 埃及法老 5—350d
杰德拉布尔 Chatrapur 印度城镇 4—91e
杰迪代 Jadida, el- 摩洛哥城市 8—514e
杰尔 Győr 匈牙利城镇 7—391a
杰尔巴岛 Jarbah 突尼斯岛屿 8—545b
杰尔拜古里 Jalpaiguri 印度城市 8—522f
杰尔宾特 Derbent 俄罗斯城市 5—251f
杰尔查文 Derzhavin, Gavrila Romanovich 俄国诗人 5—256b
杰尔莫 Jarmo 伊拉克史前考古遗址 8—545e
杰尔莫堡 Qalat Jarmo (Iraq) 伊朗考古遗址 14—52f
杰尔-莫雄-肖普朗 Győr-Moson-Sopron 匈牙利州名 7—391b
杰尔若纽夫 Dzier żoniów 波兰城市 5—490f
杰法拉 Jifārah, Al- 非洲平原 9—20f
杰斐逊 Jefferson, Arthur Stanley (screen comedian) 美国演员 8—557e
杰斐逊 Jefferson, Joseph 美国演员 8—557f
杰斐逊 Jefferson, Martha 美国总统夫人 8—558a
杰斐逊 Jefferson, Thomas 美国总统 8—558b
杰斐逊(瞎子莱蒙) Jefferson, Blind Lemon 美国乡村歌手、吉他手 8—557e
杰斐逊城 Jefferson City 美国密苏里州首府 8—561b
杰斐逊飞机 Jefferson Airplane, the 美国乐队 8—561a
杰斐逊共和党党员 Jeffersonian Republican 早期美国政党党员 8—561d
杰斐逊河 Jefferson River 美国河流 8—561c
杰斐逊纪念堂 Jefferson Memorial 美国华盛顿市纪念馆 8—561c
杰斐逊维尔 Jeffersonville 美国城市 8—561d
杰斐逊要塞国家纪念地 Fort Jefferson National Monument 美国城堡 6—413e
杰夫代特·帕夏 Cevdet Paşa, Ahmed 土耳其政治家 4—19b
杰弗里 Geoffrey 统治者之名 7—70b
杰弗里 Geoffrey 布列塔尼公爵 7—70d
杰弗里 Jeffrey, Edward Charles 美国植物学家 8—561d
杰弗里 Jeffrey, Francis Jeffrey, Lord 苏格兰法官 8—561e
杰弗里(蒙默思的) Geoffrey of Monmouth 英格兰编年史家 7—70d
杰弗里(维拉杜安的) Geoffrey of Villehardouin 法国将军、编年史家 7—70e
杰弗里二世 Geoffrey II 法国安茹伯爵 7—70b
杰弗里斯 Jeffreys, Sir Harold 英国天文学家 8—561f
杰弗里斯 Jeffries, James Jackson 美国拳击运动员 8—562b
杰弗里斯 Jefferies, (John) Richard 英国博物学家 8—557c
杰弗里斯男爵 Jeffreys (of Wem), George Jeffreys, 1st Baron 英格兰法官 8—561f
杰弗里四世 Geoffrey IV 布列塔尼公爵 7—70c
杰弗里四世 Geoffrey IV 法国安茹伯爵 7—70c
杰弗斯 Jeffers, (John) Robinson 美国诗人 8—557d
杰格布卜 Jaghbūb, al- 利比亚绿洲 8—516e
杰格德尔布尔 Jagdalpur 印度城市 8—516c
杰汉·沙阿 Jahān Shāh 阿塞拜疆黑羊王朝国王 8—517e
杰赫拉 Jahra, al- 科威特城镇和地区 8—518c
杰赫勒姆 Jhelum 巴基斯坦城镇 9—10d
杰赫勒姆河 Jhelum River 巴基斯坦河流 9—10d
杰济拉 Jazīrah, al- 美索不达米亚地区 8—555b
杰济拉省 Jazīrah, al- 苏丹地区 8—555c
杰焦战役 Jājau, Battle of 印度历史 8—519d
杰凯尔 Jekyll, Gertrude 英国园林建筑师 8—563a
杰克里人 Jekri (people) 尼日利亚民族 8—562f
杰克林 Jackling, Daniel Cowan 美国冶金学家 8—504a
杰克·伦敦 London, Jack 美国小说家 10—203d
杰克斯-布莱克 Jex-Blake, Sophia Louisa 英国女医师 9—9f
杰克兔 jackrabbit 哺乳动物 8—504b
杰克逊 Jackson 美国怀俄明州城市 8—504b
杰克逊 Jackson 美国密西西比州城市 8—504b
杰克逊 Jackson 美国密歇根州城市 8—504b
杰克逊 Jackson 美国田纳西州城市 8—504d
杰克逊 Jackson, Andrew 美国总统 8—504e
杰克逊 Jackson, A. V. Williams 美国语言学者 8—504d
杰克逊 Jackson, Charles Thomas 美国化学家 8—505d
杰克逊 Jackson, Glenda 英国演员 8—505e
杰克逊 Jackson, Henry (boxer) 美国拳击运动员 8—505f
杰克逊 Jackson, Howell E. 美国律师、最高法院大法官 8—505f
杰克逊 Jackson, Helen Hunt 美国诗人、小说家 8—505f
杰克逊 Jackson, Janet 美国歌手 8—506a
杰克逊 Jackson, Jesse 美国民权运动领袖 8—506b
杰克逊 Jackson, John Hughlings 英国神经病学家 8—506d
杰克逊 Jackson, Mahalia 美国歌唱家 8—506d
杰克逊 Jackson, Maynard 美国政治人物 8—506e
杰克逊 Jackson, Mercy Ruggles Bisbe 美国医生 8—506f
杰克逊 Jackson, Peter 澳大利亚拳击运动员 8—507a
杰克逊 Jackson, Reggie 美国棒球运动员 8—507a
杰克逊 Jackson, Robert H(oughwout) 美国最高法院大法官 8—507b
杰克逊 Jackson, Sheldon 美国基督教长老会牧师 8—507c
杰克逊 Jackson, Shirley (Hardie) 美国小说家 8—507c
杰克逊 Jackson, Shoeless Joe 美国棒球运动员 8—507d
杰克逊 Jackson, Thomas Jonathan 美国将军 8—507e
杰克逊 Jackson, William 英国作曲家 8—508a

杰克逊 Jackson, William Henry 美国摄影家 8—508b
杰克逊洞国家保护区 Jackson Hole National Monument 美国野生动物保护区 8—508b
杰克逊港 Port Jackson 澳大利亚港口 13—445e
杰克逊氏癫痫 jacksonian epilepsy 病理现象 8—508b
杰克逊维尔 Jacksonville 美国阿肯色州城市 8—508c
杰克逊维尔 Jacksonville 美国佛罗里达州城市 8—508c
杰克逊维尔 Jacksonville 美国北卡罗来纳州城市 8—508d
杰克逊维尔 Jacksonville 美国俄勒冈州城市 8—508d
杰克逊维尔 Jacksonville 美国伊利诺伊州城市 8—508d
杰拉 Gela 意大利古代城市 7—46c
杰拉德(克雷莫纳的) Gerard of Cremona 欧洲学者 7—85f
杰拉尔顿 Geraldton 澳大利亚城镇 7—85b
杰拉尔混合语 língua-geral 巴西语言 10—122c
杰拉里叛乱 Jelālī Revolts 土耳其历史 8—563a
杰勒德 Gerard, John 英国植物学家 7—86b
杰勒德(威尔士的) Gerald of Wales 威尔士历史学家 7—85b
杰勒法 Djelfa 阿尔及利亚城镇 5—350e
杰里德 Jarīd(Tunisia) 突尼斯地区 8—545d
杰里德盐湖 Jarīd, Shaṭṭ, Al- 突尼斯湖泊 8—545d
杰里科 Jericho 以色列占领区城镇 8—569c
杰利科 Jellicoe, John Rushworth Jellicoe, 1st Earl 英国海军元帅 8—563d
杰利内克 Jellinek, Adolf 犹太教拉比 8—563e
杰利内克 Jellinek, Elvin M(orton) 美国生理学家 8—563e
杰罗尔德 Jerrold, Douglas William 英国剧作家 8—570c
杰罗尔德 Gerould, Katharine Elizabeth Fullerton 美国作家 7—99f
杰罗姆 Jerome, Chauncey 美国发明家 8—570b
杰罗姆 Jerome, Jerome K(lapka) 英国小说家 8—570c
杰罗尼莫 Geronimo 印第安人领袖 7—99d
杰洛西剧团 Gelosi, Compagnia dei 意大利戏剧团体 7—48f
杰马 Jemaa 尼日利亚城镇 8—565a
杰马勒布尔 Jamālpur 印度城镇 8—524d
杰马勒帕夏 Cemal Paşa 土耳其军官 3—561a
杰马耶勒家族 Gemayel family 黎巴嫩马龙派家族 7—49d
杰曼 German, Sir Edward 英国作曲家 7—88f
杰曼努斯(欧塞尔的),圣 Germanus of Auxerre, Saint 法国大主教 7—94f
杰曼努斯一世,圣 Germanus I, Saint 希腊神学家 7—94e
杰梅卡湾 Jamaica Bay 美国港湾 8—524a
杰米多夫家族 Demidov family 俄罗斯家族 5—234e
杰米尼亚尼 Geminiani, Francesco 意大利音乐家 7—50b
杰米森 Jemison, Mary 美洲印第安人俘虏 8—565a
杰米斯顿 Germiston 南非城市 7—98f
杰米斯图斯·普莱桑 Gemistus Plethon, George 拜占廷哲学家 7—50d
杰明 Jermyn, Henry 英格兰宠臣 8—569e
杰姆 El-Djem (Tunisia) 突尼斯地名 6—10b
杰姆 Jamm, Al- (Tunisia) 突尼斯地名 8—532b
杰纳布河 Chenāb River 印度河流 4—119f
杰纳赫 Jonah, Rabbi (Hebrew grammarian) 希伯来语法学家 9—78d
杰纳西河 Genesee River 美国河流 7—58a
杰纳西阶 Genesee Stage 地质学 7—58b
杰内 Djenné 马里城市 5—350e
杰内修斯 Genesius, Joseph 拜占廷学者 7—58c
杰尼 genie (spirit) 精灵 7—63e
杰尼瓦 Geneva 美国城镇 7—62a
杰宁 Janīn 巴勒斯坦城镇 8—534d
杰诺伦山洞 Jenolan Caves 澳大利亚名胜 8—567b
杰诺韦西 Genovesi, Antonio 意大利哲学家、经济学家 7—66b
杰钦 Děčín 捷克城市 5—203a
杰日尼奥夫 Dezhnyov, Semyon Ivanov 俄罗斯探险家 5—277e
杰日尼奥夫海角 Dezhnyov, Cape 俄罗斯海角 5—277e
杰塞尔 Jessel, Sir George 英格兰法学家 9—4f
杰塞尔 Jessel, George (Albert) 美国演员 9—5a
杰什布尔帕特 Jashpur Pāts 印度自然地理区 8—547c
杰士卡 Žižka, Jan, Count (Hrabě) 波希米亚军事统帅 18—560a
杰苏阿尔多 Gesualdo, Don Carlo, principe (prince) di Venosa 意大利作曲家 7—103f
杰索尔 Jessore 孟加拉国城市 9—5c
杰瓦迪丘陵 Javādi Hills 印度山地 8—551f
杰维斯 Jervis, John Bloomfield 美国工程师 9—4c
杰维斯(坎特伯雷的) Gervase of Canterbury 英格兰修士、历史学家 7—101d
杰维斯岛 Jervis Island (Galápagos Islands) 太平洋岛屿 9—4d
杰维斯湾 Jervis Bay 澳大利亚海湾 9—4c
杰文斯 Jevons, William Stanley 英国逻辑学家 9—7c
《杰乌利诺停战协定》 Deulino, Truce of 俄-波协定 5—268a
杰伊 Jay, John 美国缔造者之一 8—554a
杰伊巴萨 Chaibāsā 印度城镇 4—27d
杰伊汉河 Ceyhan River 土耳其河流 4—19c
《杰伊条约》 Jay Treaty 美国历史 8—554c
杰兹卡兹甘 Dzhezkazgan 哈萨克斯坦城市 5—490e
拮抗作用 antagonism 医学 1—374c
洁净礼 purification 社会学 14—32e
洁净室 clean room 防尘工作场所 4—276d
结 knot 捆扎技术 9—323e
结肠 colon 解剖学 4—357d
结肠炎 colitis 疾病 4—345d
结肠造口术 colostomy 外科手术 4—365c
结肠直肠癌 colorectal cancer 疾病 4—364d
结缔组织 connective tissue 组织学 4—436c
结构论 construction theory (logical positivism) 哲学 4—460f
结构主义 structuralism 人类学 16—282f
结构主义 structuralism 语言学派别 16—283a
结合律 associative law 数学 2—1a
结合能 binding energy 物理学 2—476d
结核病 tuberculosis (TB) 疾病 17—255a
结核菌素试验 tuberculin test 医学 17—255a
结核性脊椎炎 tuberculous spondylitis 病理现象 17—255f
结节龙属 Nodosaurus 古生物学 12—223f
结节性动脉周围炎 periarteritis nodosa (vascular disease) 病理现象 13—167b
结节性多动脉炎 polyarteritis nodosa 疾病 13—411a
结晶岩 crystalline rock 岩石 5—44f
结缕草属 Zoysia 植物学 18—569e
结膜黄斑 pinguecula 解剖学 13—313a
结膜炎 conjunctivitis 病理现象 4—432c
结舌 tongue-tie 医学 17—151d
《结社法案》 Combination Acts 英国法令 4—377b
结绳纪事 quipu 印加人记数工具 14—95a
结束礼 siyyum 犹太教 15—411a
结网 netting 纺织业 12—94c
结趾鼰 phalanger 哺乳动物 13—217e
结尾诗节 envoi 诗歌 6—91d
桔槔 shaduf 灌溉工具 15—253b
桔梗 balloonflower (species *Platycodon grandiflorum*) 植物学 2—178e
桔梗目 Campanulales 植物学 3—378b
桔井 Krâchéh 柬埔寨城镇 9—369b
捷尔茨 Terts, Abram 俄罗斯作家 16—558a
捷尔茨 Tertz, Abram 俄罗斯作家 16—558b
捷尔诺波尔 Ternopol 乌克兰州名 16—553d
捷尔诺波尔 Ternopol 乌克兰城市 16—553d
捷尔任斯基 Dzerzhinsky, Feliks Edmundovich 苏联领导人 5—490c

捷尔任斯克 Dzerzhinsk 俄罗斯城市 5—490c
捷克布杰约维采 České Budějovice 捷克城市 4—17a
捷克弟兄福音会 Evangelical Church of Czech Brethren 捷克基督教会 6—178a
捷克共和国 Czech Republic 中欧国家 5—97f
捷克-摩拉维亚高地 Českomoravská Vysočina 捷克高地 4—17a
捷克斯洛伐克 Czechoslovakia 欧洲历史国家 5—99d
捷克斯洛伐克教会 Czechoslovak Hussite Church 捷克斯洛伐克民族教会组织 5—99c
捷克斯洛伐克正教会 Orthodox Church of Czechoslovakia 东正教 12—473f
捷克文学 Czech literature 文学 5—97a
捷克语 Czech language 语言 5—96f
捷列克河 Terek River 俄罗斯河流 16—549d
捷列什科娃 Tereshkova, Valentina 苏联航天员 16—550d
捷斯 Thiès 塞内加尔城镇 17—39a
睫状肌 ciliaris muscle 生理学 4—237e
截击机 interceptor 军用飞机 8—408b
截面 cross section 核物理学 5—33a
截瘫 paraplegia 病理现象 13—38d
羯陵伽 Kaliṅga 印度地区 9—141f
羯提计耶 Kārttikeya (Hindu god) 印度教神 9—188f
解放巴勒斯坦民主人民阵线 Popular Democratic Front for the Liberation of Palestine (PDFLP) 巴勒斯坦政治组织 13—436f
解放巴勒斯坦人民阵线 Popular Front for the Liberation of Palestine (PFLP) 巴勒斯坦政治组织 13—437b
《解放日报》 Liberation Daily 中国报纸 10—74e
解放神学 liberation theology 天主教运动 10—74f
解放协会 Liberation, Union of 俄国政治团体 10—74d
《解放宣言》 Emancipation Manifesto 俄皇解放农奴法令 6—55a
《解放宣言》 Emancipation Proclamation 林肯解放美国奴隶法令 6—55b
解放战争 Liberation, War of 中国历史 10—74d
《解放者》 Liberator, The 美国期刊 10—75b
解放者 Liberator (U.S. aircraft) 美国轰炸机 10—75b
解构 deconstruction 法国文学批评学派 5—204a
解经学 exegesis 探讨《圣经》的学问 6—191a
解经原则 hermeneutics 宗教 8—41c
解经准则 middot 犹太教 11—200f
解理 cleavage 地质学 4—277e
解剖学 anatomy 医学 1—320a
解酸药 antacid 药物 1—374a
解脱 moksha 印度教 11—314e
解析几何 analytic geometry 数学 1—313a
解罪 absolution 基督教 1—30e
介电常数 dielectric constant 物理学 5—305c
介壳虫 scale insect 昆虫 15—100b
介壳灰岩 coquina 石灰岩 4—496c
介壳灰岩蛤 coquina clam 软体动物 4—496c
介兰 Guérin, Camille 法国细菌学家 7—349e
介入文学 littérature engagée 文学 10—149d
介形虫 mussel shrimp 甲壳动物 11—512f
介子 meson 亚原子微粒 11—140c
戒酒协会 Alcoholics Anonymous (AA) 社会组织 1—190f
戒酒运动 temperance movement 社会运动 16—532e
戒日王 Harṣa 印度皇帝 7—491f
芥 mustard 草本植物 11—515d
芥川龙之介 Akutagawa Ryūnosuke 日本作家 1—159d
界 loka 印度教 10—194b
界面 interface 物质相分界面 8—408e
疥疮 scabies 皮肤病 15—98f
借记卡 debit card 金融 5—197e
堺 Sakai 日本城市 14—533d
堺利彦 Sakai Toshihiko 日本共产党创始人 14—533e
今日与明日作家 Van Nu en Straks circle 作家群 17—462a
今世 ʻolam ha-ze 犹太教术语 12—365c
今治 Imabari 日本城市 8—340e
金(Au) gold 化学元素 7—185d
金 Jin DYNASTY 中国王朝 9—24e
金 King, B.B. 美国吉他手 9—285c
金 King, Clarence 美国地质学家 9—285f
金 King, Carol Weiss 美国律师 9—285e
金 King, Ernest Joseph 美国海军上将 9—286a
金 King, Frank 美国漫画家 9—286b
金 King, Franklin Hiram 美国农业科学家 9—286b
金 King, Gregory 英国系谱学家 9—286c
金 King, Henry 英国诗人、圣公会主教 9—286c
金 Küng, Hans 瑞士天主教神学家 9—397a
金 King, Martin Luther, Jr. 美国黑人牧师 9—286d
金 King, Rufus 美国政治家 9—287f
金 King, W.L. Mackenzie 加拿大总理 9—288b
金 King, Stephen 美国小说家 9—288a
金 King, William (Maori chief) 毛利人首领 9—288d
金 King, William Rufus de Vane 美国政治家 9—288d
金(夫人) King, Billie Jean 美国网球运动员 9—285d
金杯 golden cup (*Hunnemannia fumariifolia*) 草本植物 7—189b
金杯赛 Gold Cup 美国摩托艇比赛 7—186d
金贝 Kimbe 巴布亚新几内亚港口 9—282c
金本位制 gold standard 货币制度 7—187b
金碧山 Jinbi Shan 中国山名 9—27a
金碧山水 jinbi shan shui 中国绘画 9—27a
金边 Phnom Penh 柬埔寨首都 13—253f
金伯利 Kimberley 澳大利亚高原地区 9—282c
金伯利 Kimberley 加拿大城市 9—282c
金伯利 Kimberley 南非城市 9—282d
金伯利岩 kimberlite 岩石 9—282d
金博尔顿男爵 Kimbolton, Edward Montagu, Baron 英国军事将领 9—282e
金仓鼠 golden hamster (*Mesocricetus auratus*) 哺乳动物 7—189f
金策 Kimch'aek 朝鲜城市 9—282e
金昌 Jinchang 中国城市 9—27b
金翅科 Carduelidae 动物学 3—455e
金翅雀 goldfinch 鸟类 7—191e
金春禅凤 Komparu Zempō 日本能剧演员 9—343e
金春禅竹 Komparu Zenchiku 日本能剧演员 9—343e
金茨伯格 Ginzberg, Louis 美国学者 7—137c
金大健 Kim Dae-gŏn 朝鲜天主教司铎 9—281b
金大中 Kim Dae Jung 韩国总统 9—281c
金岛 King Island 澳大利亚岛屿 9—289b
金德 Jīnd 印度城市 9—27d
金德莱布 Kinderlieb, Heinrich 德国作家 9—284b
金德讷格尔 Chandernagore 印度城市 4—44a
金滴虫 chrysomonad 原生动物 4—216d
金迪 Kindī, Yaʻqūb ibn Isḥāq aṣ-Ṣabāḥ, al- 伊朗伊斯兰教哲学家 9—284b
金迪奥 Quindío 哥伦比亚省份 14—93a
金迪沃罗巴克运动 Jindyworobak movement 澳大利亚文学运动 9—27d
金迪亚 Kindia 几内亚城镇 9—284c
金雕 golden eagle (*Aquila chrysaetos*) 鸟类 7—189b
金蝶兰属 Oncidium 植物学 12—416f
金杜 Kindu 刚果(金)城市 9—284c
金盖莱 Kinguélé 加蓬地名 9—293e
金刚乘 Vajrayāna 佛教宗派 17—446a
金刚杵 vajra 藏传佛教法器 17—445f
《金刚经》 Diamond Sūtra 佛教经典 5—287a

金刚砂 Carborundum 化合物 3—449c
金刚砂 emery 岩石 6—60b
金刚石 diamond 矿物 5—286b
金刚手 Vajrapāṇi 佛教神话菩萨 17—445f
金刚瑜伽母 Vajrayoginī 佛教女神 17—446b
金格罗伊 Kingaroy 澳大利亚城镇 9—290a
金冠戴菊 goldcrest 鸟类 7—188a
金光教 Konkō-kyō 日本教派 9—346f
金龟子 scarab beetle 昆虫 15—104a
金果 Kingo, Thomas 丹麦诗人 9—290f
金合欢 acacia 木本植物 1—39d
金衡制 troy weight 货币学 17—239d
金弘道 Kim Hong-do 朝鲜画家 9—281d
金红石 rutile 矿物 14—470d
金华 Jinhua 中国城市 9—30d
金汇兑本位制 gold-exchange standard 货币制度 7—186d
金鸡菊 tickseed 植物 17—86b
金鸡纳树属 Cinchona 植物学 4—239f
金鸡纳素 cinchonine 生物碱 4—239f
金吉 Kingi, Wiremu 新西兰毛利族首长 9—290d
金贾 Jinja 乌干达城镇 9—31b
金橘 kumquat 植物 9—395f
金卡丁伯爵(第十二) Kincardine, James Bruce, 12th Earl of 英国政治家 9—283e
金卡丁-迪赛德 Kincardine and Deeside 苏格兰区名 9—283e
金卡丁郡 Kincardineshire 苏格兰郡名 9—283f
金凯德 Kincaid, Jamaica 美国作家 9—283d
金克尔 Kinkel, Gottfried 德国诗人 9—294a
金-克兰委员会 King-Crane Commission 国际政治 9—288f
金克森姆 Kincsem 欧洲赛马 9—284a
金拉米 Gin Rummy 纸牌游戏 7—135c
金兰 Cam Ranh 越南城市 3—363a
金兰湾 Cam Ranh Bay 越南海湾 3—363a
金莲花 globeflower 草本植物 7—160c
金莲木科 Ochnaceae 植物学 12—331d
金链花 golden chain 木本植物 7—189a
金陵八家 Jinling Bajia 中国画家 9—31d
金路易 louis d'or (monetary unit) 法国古货币名 10—242a
金缕地 Cloth of Gold, Field of 法国历史 4—300b
金缕梅 witch hazel 落叶灌木 18—298e
金缕梅科 Hamamelidaceae 植物学 7—436c
金缕梅目 Hamamelidales 植物学 7—437e
金缕梅亚纲 Hamamelidae 植物学 7—437e
金绿宝石 chrysoberyl 宝石 4—216a
金绿猫眼石 cymophane 宝石 5—89a
金罗斯 Kinross 苏格兰地区 9—295a
金罗斯郡 Kinrossshire 苏格兰历史郡 9—295a
金马刺战役 Golden Spurs, Battle of the 欧洲历史 7—190d
金马伦高原 Cameron Highlands 马来西亚游览区 3—372f
金曼 Kingman 美国城市 9—290f
金曼礁 Kingman Reef 太平洋岛屿 9—290f
金猫 golden cat 哺乳动物 7—188f
金毛鼹 golden mole 哺乳动物 7—190b
金玫瑰 golden rose 工艺品 7—190c
金门 Jinmen 中国县名 9—31d
金门岛 Chin-men Tao (China) 中国岛屿 4—160e
金门岛 Jinmen Dao 中国岛屿 9—31e
金门高地国家公园 Golden Gate Highlands National Park 南非公园 7—189f
金门海峡 Golden Gate 美国海峡 7—189d
金门桥 Golden Gate Bridge 美国吊桥 7—189e
金目鱼 goldeye 鱼类 7—191c
金牧场 King Ranch 美国牧场 9—289c
金纳迪乌斯(马赛的) Gennadius OF MARSEILLES 法国学者 7—64c
金纳迪乌斯(诺夫哥罗德的) Gennadius OF NOVGOROD 俄罗斯大主教 7—64d
金纳迪乌斯二世(斯科拉里奥斯) Gennadios II SCHOLARIOS 希腊正教神学家 7—64b
金纳迪乌斯一世(君士坦丁堡的),圣 Gennadius I OF CONSTANTINOPLE, SAINT 拜占廷基督教神学家 7—64c
金纳斯利 Kinnersley, Ebenezer 美国科学家 9—294c
金牛犊 golden calf 基督教 7—188e
金牛-利特罗月谷 Taurus-Littrow Valley "阿波罗"17号登月着陆点 16—497e
金牛山遗址 Jinniushan site 考古学 9—32b
金牛座 Taurus 天文学 16—497d
金牛座T型星 T Tauri star 天文学 16—412b
金牛座α Alpha Tauri 天文学 1—250c
金诺克 Kinnock, Neil (Gordon) 英国政治人物 9—294c
金瓯半岛 Ca Mau Peninsula 越南半岛 3—303a
金皮 Gympie 澳大利亚城市 7—390e
金瓶掣签 Jinping cheqian 藏传佛教制度 9—32f
《金瓶梅》 Jinpingmei 中国明代小说 9—33a
金齐 Kinzie, Juliette Augusta Magill 美国拓荒者、作家 9—297f
金钱松 golden larch (*Pseudolarix amabilis*) 木本植物 7—190b
金枪鱼 tuna 鱼类 17—267c
金泉 Kimch'ŏn 韩国城市 9—282f
金雀 verdin 鸟类 17—513a
金雀花 broom 植物 3—185f
金雀花 Plantagenet, Edmund 英格兰贵族 13—345d
金雀花王室 Plantagenet, HOUSE OF 英格兰王室 13—345c
金日成 Kim Il-sung 朝鲜领袖 9—281e
《金融时报》 Financial Times 英国报纸 6—317d
金融市场 money market 金融 11—335a
金塞尔 Kinsale 爱尔兰城镇 9—295b
金塞拉 Kinsella, Thomas 爱尔兰诗人 9—295b
金色道钉国家历史遗迹 Golden Spike National Historic Site 美国纪念碑 7—190d
金色啸鹟 golden whistler 鸟类 7—190e
金沙江 Jinsha Jiang 中国河流 9—33b
金沙萨 Kinshasa 刚果(金)首都 9—295c
金山 Jin Shan 中国演员 9—25b
金山卫 Jinshanwei 中国城镇 9—33c
金善宝 Jin Shanbao 中国农学家 9—25c
金少山 Jin Shaoshan 中国京剧演员 9—25e
金十字英勇勋章 Distinguished Service Order 英国勋章 5—343f
金十字英勇勋章获得者 D.S.O. 英国勋章得主 5—434a
金手套拳击赛 Golden Gloves 体育 7—189f
金属 metal 材料科学 11—147d
金属废料 scrap metal 报废金属 15—155b
金属化作用 metalation 化学过程 11—148c
金属击鸣乐器 metallophone 乐器 11—149c
金属尖笔 metal point 绘画用具 11—148a
金属间化合物 intermetallic compound 化合物 8—410c
金属键 metallic bond 化学 11—148c
金属镌刻 metal cut 艺术 11—147f
金属疲劳 metal fatigue 材料力学 11—148a
金属饰环 torque 首饰 17—164e
金属羰基化合物 metal carbonyl 化合物 11—147e
金属纤维 metallic fibre 纺织原料 11—148d
金属制品 metalwork 工艺品 11—150c
金属自由电子模型 free-electron model of metals 固体物理学 6—468d
金数 golden number 历法 7—190b
金水母属 Chrysaora 动物学 4—215b
金丝蝴蝶 Saint-Andrew's-cross (*Ascyrum hypericoides*) 植物 14—

506c
金丝雀 canary (species *Serinus canaria*) 鸟类 3—392f
金丝桃 Saint-John's-wort 植物 14—515f
金丝燕 swiftlet 鸟类 16—384c
金丝蛛 golden silk spider 昆虫 7—190d
金斯 Jeans, Sir James (Hopwood) 英国物理学家 8—556f
金斯堡 Ginsberg, Allen 美国诗人 7—136e
金斯波特 Kingsport 美国城市 9—292e
金斯伯格 Ginsburg, Ruth Bader 美国法官 7—137a
金斯敦 Kingston 牙买加首都 9—293a
金斯敦 Kingstown 美国城镇 9—293e
金斯顿 Kingston 澳大利亚城镇 9—292e
金斯顿 Kingston 加拿大城市 9—292f
金斯顿 Kingston 美国纽约州城市 9—293b
金斯顿 Kingston 美国村庄 9—293c
金斯顿 Kinston 澳大利亚城镇 9—297d
金斯顿女王大学 Queen's University at Kingston 加拿大大学 14—84d
金斯峰 Kings Peak 美国山峰 9—292a
金斯福德·史密斯 Kingsford Smith, Sir Charles Edward 澳大利亚飞行员 9—292b
金斯河谷国家公园 Kings Canyon National Park 美国风景区 9—291c
金斯利 Kingsley, Charles 英国牧师 9—292c
金斯利 Kingsley, Henry 英国小说家 9—292d
金斯利 Kingsley, Mary Henrietta 英国旅行家 9—292d
金斯林 King's Lynn 英格兰城镇 9—291e
金斯林-西诺福克 King's Lynn and West Norfolk 英格兰自治市 9—291f
金斯山战役 Kings Mountain, Battle of 美国独立战争 9—291f
金斯维尔 Kingsville 美国城市 9—293e
金斯伍德 Kingswood 英格兰城镇 9—293e
金斯县 Kings County 美国县名 9—291d
金寺 Golden Temple (Sikh temple) 印度锡克教寺庙 7—190d
金穗草 goldentop (species *Lamarckia aurea*) 草本植物 7—191b
金塔纳 Quintana, Manuel José 西班牙诗人 14—94b
金塔纳罗奥 Quintana Roo 墨西哥州名 14—94c
金太祖完颜旻 Jintaizu Wanyan Min 中国金朝皇帝 9—33e
金滩 Gold Beach 二战诺曼底登陆中五个目标海滩中的一个 7—186b
金特 Günther 德意志国王 7—374d
金特 Günther, Ignaz 德国雕刻家 7—374e
金特 Günther, Johann Christian 德国诗人 7—374f
金特罗兄弟 Quintero, Serafín and Joaquín Álvarez (Spanish dramatists) 西班牙戏剧家 14—94d
金湾 King Sound 澳大利亚海湾 9—289f
金文 Bronze Inscription 中国文字 3—181e
金西 Kinsey, Alfred Charles 美国动物学家 9—295c
金县 Chin-hsien (China) 中国地名 4—160e
金相学 metallography 化学 11—149a
金香木 champac (*Michelia champaca*) 乔木 4—39f
金星 Venus 天文学 17—509d
"金星"号探测器 Venera 苏联行星探测器系列 17—498b
金眼鲷 alfonsino 鱼类 1—215f
金眼鸭 goldeneye 鸟类 7—190e
金羊毛勋位 Golden Fleece, The Order of the 欧洲骑士勋位 7—189d
金叶 gold leaf 工艺品 7—186e
金怡濂 Jin Yilian 中国工程院院士 9—26a
金银纯度印记 hallmark 制品合格标记 7—430e
金银细丝工艺品 filigree 珠宝饰物 6—314f
金雍 Kan Oum (Vietnamese leader) 越南泰族头人 9—151e
金雍 Kham Um (Tai chief) 越南泰族头人 9—254e
金泳三 Kim Young Sam 韩国总统 9—282a
金鱼 goldfish (*Carassius auratus*) 鱼类 7—191f
金元外交 Dollar Diplomacy 美国外交政策 5—366a
金岳霖 Jin Yuelin 中国哲学家 9—26a
金云母 phlogopite 矿物 13—253d
金载圭 Kim Jae Kyu 韩国军官 9—281f
金藻 golden algae 藻类植物 7—188c
金藻门 Chrysophyta 生物学 4—216e
金泽 Kanazawa 日本城市 9—153a
金帐汗国 Golden Horde 蒙古汗国 7—190a
金正日 Kim Chong Il 朝鲜领导人 9—281a
金正喜 Kim Chŏng-hui 朝鲜书法家 9—281a
金脂鲤 dorado (*Salminus maxillosus*) 鱼类 5—387e
金制品 goldwork 工艺品 7—195a
金钟柏 American arborvitae (species *Thuja occidentalis*) 针叶乔木 1—275d
金钟花 golden bell (plant) 植物 7—188d
金州 Jinzhou 中国区名 9—34a
金兹布尔格 Ginzburg, Natalia 意大利作家 7—137c
金字塔 pyramid 墓葬建筑 14—45a
《金字塔报》 Ahram, Al- 埃及报纸 1—137f
金字塔式台球 pyramids 体育 14—45c
金字塔文 Pyramid Texts 古埃及宗教文献 14—45c
金字塔战役 Pyramids, Battle of the 埃及历史 14—45d
金字体书法 chrysography 书法 4—216b
津 Tsu 日本城市 17—250e
津巴布韦 Zimbabwe 非洲南部国家 18—551f
津巴布韦遗迹 Zimbabwe 非洲石头建筑废墟 18—553b
津德 Zinder, Norton David 美国生物学家 18—554d
津德尔 Zinder 尼日尔城市 18—554c
津恩 Zinn, Walter Henry 美国核物理学家 18—555f
津吉尔利许于克 Zincirli Höyük 土耳其考古遗址 18—554b
津加雷利 Zingarelli, Nicola Antonio 意大利作曲家 18—554d
津内曼 Zinnemann, Fred 美国电影导演 18—555f
津轻海峡 Tsugaru Strait 太平洋海峡 17—250f
津山 Tsuyama 日本城市 17—252c
津市 Jinshi 中国城市 9—33d
津苏 Zinsou, Émile Derlin 达荷美政治家 18—556d
津贴制度 Bounty System 美国历史 3—83c
筋骨草 bugleweed 植物 3—236e
紧身健美装 corset 服装 4—523a
紧士裤 jeans 服装 8—556e
紧性 compactness 数学 4—395c
堇菜目 Violales 植物学 18—3e
堇菜属 Viola 植物学 18—3c
堇青石 cordierite 矿物 4—502d
锦标赛 tournament 体育 17—178e
锦带花属 Weigela 植物学 18—169b
锦绘 nishiki-e 日本美术作品 12—202d
锦江 Kŭm River 韩国河流 9—394a
锦葵 mallow 植物 10—434a
锦葵科 Malvaceae 植物学 10—438e
锦葵目 Malvales 植物学 10—439a
锦鳚 gunnel 鱼类 7—373a
锦绣式花圃 broderie 法国园林艺术 3—174a
锦州 Jinzhou 中国城市 9—34a
谨斋 Kunjae (Korean painter) 朝鲜画家 9—397e
槿麻 kenaf (species *Hibiscus cannabinus*) 植物 9—223b
进步党 Progressive Party (U.S.,1912) 美国政党(1912) 13—529f
进步党 Progressive Party 美国政党(1924) 13—530a
进步党 Progressive Party 美国政党(1948) 13—530a
进步联邦党 Progressive Federal Party 南非政党 13—529e
进步联盟 Alliance for Progress 国际经济发展计划 1—240d

进步民主党 Progressive Democrats 爱尔兰政党 13—529d
进步同盟 Progressive Bloc 俄国政治联盟 13—529c
进攻性行为 aggressive behaviour 心理学 1—121e
进化 evolution 生物学理论 6—185d
进前 aliyah 犹太教 1—231c
进行曲 march 音乐 10—495d
近点角 anomaly 天文学 1—368c
近东 Near East 地理区域 12—57f
近畿 Kinki 日本地区 9—294a
近交 inbreeding 亲缘关系交配 8—350b
近距导航系统 short-range navigation 近距导航仪 15—333d
近距支援飞机 close support aircraft 强击机 4—299f
近邻同盟 amphictyony 古希腊历史 1—298b
近视 myopia 视力缺陷 11—525e
近似音 approximant 语音学 1—422d
近松门左卫门 Chikamatsu Monzaemon 日本剧作家 4—150a
近体诗 modern-style poetry 文学 11—305a
近卫文麿 Konoe Fumimaro 日本首相 9—347a
近音词误用 malapropism 写作手法 10—421c
晋 Jin DYNASTY 中国王朝 9—24f
晋城 Jincheng 中国城市 9—27c
晋祠 Jin Memorial Hall 中国古代建筑群 9—25a
晋江 Jin Jiang 中国河流 9—24f
晋江 Jinjiang 中国城市 9—31c
晋武帝司马炎 Jinwudi Sima Yan 中国皇帝 9—33f
晋州 Chinju 韩国城市 4—176b
浸礼会总协议会 Baptist General Conference 美国宗教组织 2—213a
浸礼宗信徒 Baptist 基督教教派信徒 2—212d
浸泡足病 immersion foot 足损伤病 8—343b
靳辅 Jin Fu 中国清代名臣 9—24f
禁忌食品 terefah 犹太教教规 16—549d
禁戒派 Encratite 基督教派别 6—70c
禁酒党 Prohibition Party 美国政党 13—530c
禁酒令 prohibition 法律 13—530b
禁令 injunction 法律 8—388c
《禁书目录》 Index Librorum Prohibitorum 天主教 8—357c
禁卫军 Janissary 奥斯曼帝国精锐部队 8—534d
禁卫军 Praetorian Guard 罗马皇帝的御林军 13—478d
禁线 forbidden lines 物理学 6—399c
禁运 embargo 经济法 6—56b
《禁运法案》 Embargo Act 美国法案 6—56d
禁运品 contraband 战争中禁运货物 4—470d
禁止发言规则 gag rule 美国历史 6—545a
《禁止核试验条约》 Nuclear Test-Ban Treaty 国际协定 12—289f
《禁止淫秽出版物法》 Obscene Publications Act 英国法规 12—323a
禁制 yama 印度宗教哲学 18—408f
缙绅会议 zemsky sobor 俄国会议 18—507b
茎 stem 植物学 16—216b
京阪神工业区 Keihanshin Industrial Zone 日本工业区 9—213a
京滨工业区 Keihin Industrial Zone 日本工业区 9—213b
京茨堡 Ginzburg, Vitaly Lazarevich 苏联物理学家 7—137d
京都 Kyōto 日本城市 9—414c
京都 Kyōto 日本府名 9—414c
京都大学 Kyōto University 日本大学 9—416d
京格莱布德 Chingleput 印度城镇 4—176a
京杭运河 Beijing-Hangzhou Canal (China) 中国运河 2—344e
京畿道 Kyŏnggi 韩国道名 9—414a
京九铁路 Jing Jiu Railway 中国铁路 9—28b
京剧 Peking opera 中国戏剧 13—126e
京烧 Kyō-yaki 日本彩陶 9—413e
京戏 jingxi 中国戏剧 9—30b
京叶工业区 Keiyō Industrial Zone 日本工业区 9—214b
京语 Gin language 亚洲语言 7—135a
京兆尹 eparch 拜占廷政府官员 6—94b
京兹堡 Günzburg, David, Baron 俄国犹太学者 7—375c
京兹堡 Günzburg, Horace, Baron 俄国商人、慈善家 7—375d
京兹堡 Günzburg, Joseph (Yozel), Baron 俄国犹太慈善家、金融家 7—375e
京族 Gin 中国民族 7—134f
泾河 Jing He 中国河流 9—27f
泾源 Jingyuan 中国县名 9—30d
经 sūtra 宗教文献 16—363a
经度 longitude (geography) 地理学 10—210f
经互会 Comecon 国际经济组织 4—378e
《经集》 Suttanipāta 佛教文献 16—363b
经籍 scripture 宗教圣书 15—157f
经济地质学 economic geology 地质学 5—528a
经济发展 economic development 经济学 5—527c
经济法则 economy, law of (logic) 哲学 5—530e
经济合作与发展组织 Economic Co-operation and Development, Organisation for (OECD) 国际组织 5—527b
经济互助委员会 Mutual Economic Assistance, Council for (CMEA) 国际组织 11—518d
经济及社会理事会 Economic and Social Council (ECOSOC) 联合国机构 5—527a
经济计划 economic planning 经济学 5—528d
经济恐慌 panic 经济学 13—12a
经济区域化 economic regionalism 经济 5—529b
经济衰退 recession 经济学 14—183b
经济特区 special economic zone (SEZ) 中国经济区 16—11a
经济稳定器 economic stabilizer 经济学 5—529c
经济学 economics 社会科学 5—530a
《经济学家》 Economist, The 英国杂志 5—530d
经济预测 economic forecasting 经济学 5—527e
经济增长 economic growth 经济学 5—528a
经济战 economic warfare 经济学 5—529f
经济指标 economic indicator 经济学 5—528d
经济制度 economic system 经济学 5—529c
经济周期 business cycle 经济学 3—284e
经绝期 menopause 生理学 11—117d
经量部 Sautrāntika 古印度佛教部派 15—86d
经络 meridians and collaterals 中医 11—130e
经前综合征 premenstrual syndrome (PMS) 生理学 13—493c
经团联 Keidanren 日本社团 9—212f
经纬仪 theodolite 测量仪器 17—23f
经文歌 motet 声乐作品体裁 11—430d
经文护符匣 phylactery 犹太教器具 13—270c
经文楣铭 mezuzah 犹太教 11—172e
经学 study of Confucian classics 中国儒家经典 16—288c
经验主义 Empiricism 哲学 6—64c
经院哲学 Scholasticism 哲学 15—127b
经藏 Sutta Piṭaka 佛教文献 16—363b
荆浩 Jing Hao 中国画家 9—27d
荆棘冠冕 Thorns, Crown of 宗教圣物 17—57a
荆江 Jing Jiang 中国河流 9—28a
荆门 Jingmen 中国城市 9—29c
惊厥 convulsion 病理现象 4—475e
惊跳反应 startle reaction 心理学 16—199e
晶洞 geode 矿物 7—69f
晶粒 grain 金属微晶 7—243c
晶砂党 Clear Grits 加拿大政党 4—277a
晶体 crystal 物理学 5—43f
晶体管 transistor 电子学 17—196f
晶体镶嵌珐琅工艺 en résille 装饰艺术 6—67a

晶质玻璃 crystal (glass) 玻璃 5—44d
晶质铀矿 uraninite 矿物 17—408d
晶轴 axis 晶体学 2—93f
晶状体 lens 解剖学 10—13e
晶状体后纤维组织增生 retrolental fibroplasia 疾病 14—247c
晶状体脱位 lens dislocation 眼科疾病 10—14b
腈 nitrile 化合物 12—204a
精氨酸 arginine 生物化学 1—465e
精诚兄弟会 Ikhwān aṣ-Ṣafā' 秘密宗教团体 8—331e
精简指令集计算 RISC 电子计算技术 14—312c
精灵 elf 日耳曼民间故事 6—35e
精灵 fairy 民间传说中超自然存在物 6—216f
精密时计 chronometer 计时装置 4—214c
精囊 seminal vesicle 解剖学 15—204f
精囊炎 vesiculitis 疾病 17—528b
精气论 pneumatism 医学理论 13—380f
精确主义 precisionism 绘画 13—489b
精神 mind 哲学 11—243f
精神病 psychosis 疾病 13—564e
精神病学 psychiatry 医学 13—560b
精神错乱 insanity 法律 8—396c
精神发育迟缓 mental retardation 功能病 11—120d
精神分裂症 schizophrenia 精神障碍 15—118a
精神分析 psychoanalysis 心理学 13—560c
精神神经症 psychoneurosis 精神障碍 13—563d
精神外科 psychosurgery 医学 13—565c
精神卫生 mental hygiene 医学 11—119d
精神药理学 psychopharmacology 医学 13—564a
精神运动性发作 psychomotor seizure 病理现象 13—563c
精神障碍 mental disorder 疾病 11—119b
精算师 actuary 保险业 1—62c
精索 spermatic cord 解剖学 16—22d
精陶 faience fine 陶器 6—213f
精卫 Jingwei 中国神话人物 9—30b
精细结构 fine structure 光谱学 6—318c
精选 beneficiation 选矿 2—382a
精液 semen 生物化学 15—204a
精油 essential oil 植物香精 6—135c
精致绣品 orphrey 工艺品 12—471b
精子 sperm 生理学 16—22a
精子发生 spermatogenesis 生理学 16—22d
鲸 whale 哺乳动物 18—217b
鲸蜡 spermaceti 化工 16—22c
鲸蜡醇 cetyl alcohol 化合物 4—18f
鲸蜡油 sperm oil 化工 16—22a
鲸类 cetacean 水生哺乳动物 4—17f
鲸鸟 whalebird 鸟类 18—218a
鲸鲨 whale shark (species *Rhincodon typus*) 鱼类 18—217f
鲸头鹳 whale-headed stork 鸟类 18—217f
鲸湾 Whales, Bay of 南极洲海湾 18—218a
鲸湾港 Walvis Bay 南部非洲港口城镇 18—89a
鲸须 whalebone 须鲸口中的角质薄片 18—218a
鲸油 whale oil 化工 18—217f
鲸鱼座 *o* Omicron Ceti (star) 天文学 12—415a
鲸鱼座 UV 型星 UV Ceti star 天文学 17—434d
井伏鳟二 Ibuse Masuji 日本小说家 8—310a
井冈山 Jinggang Shan 中国山地 9—28e
井冈山 Jinggangshan 中国城市 9—28f
井架 derrick 机械装置 5—255a
井里汶 Cirebon 印度尼西亚城市 4—245d
《井里汶协定》 Cheribon Agreement (Indonesian history) 印度尼西亚历史 4—125c
井上馨 Inoue Kaoru, Kōshaku (Marquess) 日本大臣 8—394f
井上圆了 Inoue Enryō 日本哲学家 8—394e
井上哲次郎 Inoue Tetsujirō 日本哲学家 8—395a
井田 ching-t'ien 中国古代土地制度 4—175f
井田 jingtian 中国古代土地制度 9—30b
井田制 well-field system 中国古代土地制度 18—177f
井伊直弼 Ii Naosuke 日本政治家 8—329c
井原西鹤 Ihara Saikaku 日本诗人 8—329a
肼 hydrazine 化合物 8—281b
颈 neck 解剖学 12—62e
颈动脉 carotid artery 生理学 3—474e
颈箍式项圈 choker 工艺品 4—190a
颈卵器 archegonium 植物学 1—447f
颈饰 bulla 装饰性垂饰 3—247a
颈椎病 cervical spondylosis 疾病 4—15e
景德镇 Jingdezhen 中国城市 9—28b
景观画 veduta 绘画 17—487e
景洪 Jinghong 中国城市 9—29a
景教 Jingjiao 宗教 9—29b
景颇语 Jingpo language 中国民族语言 9—30a
景颇族 Jingpo 中国民族 9—29e
景泰 Jingtai 中国明朝皇帝年号 9—30b
景泰蓝 cloisonné 中国工艺品 4—298b
景天 sedum 植物 15—184e
景天科 Crassulaceae 植物学 4—570f
警报信号 alarm signal 动物传递信息手段 1—167a
警察 police 治安、执法机构 13—399f
警察地带 Police Zone 纳米比亚地区 13—400c
警察权力 police power 美国法律 13—400b
警戒机制 aposematic mechanism 生物学 1—415a
警句 aphorism 文学表述 1—408e
警句诗 epigram 诗形式 6—100a
警卫官 sergeant at arms 保安官员 15—223f
《警务报》 Police Gazette, The 英国报纸 13—400b
径流量 runoff 水文学 14—450c
净化 catharsis 文艺评论 3—524e
净礼 ablution 宗教礼俗 1—25e
净琉璃 jōruri 日本说唱形式 9—88a
净身池 mikvah 犹太教 11—210c
净土 Sukhāvatī 佛教 16—314e
净土宗 Jōdo 日本佛教派别 9—42f
净土宗 Pure Land Buddhism 东亚佛教派别 14—32a
胫骨 tibia 解剖学 17—84f
竞技场 hippodrome 古希腊运动场 8—92a
竞叫桥牌 auction bridge 纸牌游戏 2—45a
竞偶场 lek 动物求偶场地 10—1b
竞人 Jieng (people) 民族 9—20e
竞争 competition 生态学 4—398b
竞争排斥原理 competitive exclusion, principle of 生物学 4—398c
竞走 walking 田径竞赛项目 18—75f
敬诗 rispetto 诗歌 14—312f
敬畏节日 yamim nora'im 犹太教 18—412e
敬先节 Parentalia 古罗马宗教节日 13—40e
敬语形式 honorific 语法形式 8—159f
静电沉淀 electrostatic precipitation 电学方法 6—31e
静电感应 electrostatic induction 电学 6—31e
静电计 electrometer 仪表 6—26f
静冈 Shizuoka 日本城市 15—327a
静力学 statics 物理学 16—201e
静脉 vein 血管 17—491a
静脉窦 venous sinus 解剖学 17—507c
静脉曲张 varicose vein 生理病变 17—473d
静脉血栓形成 phlebothrombosis 病理状态 13—253a
静脉炎 phlebitis 病理现象 13—253a

静态雕刻 stabile 抽象雕刻 16—174f
静湾石器工艺 Stillbay industry 南非考古学 16—237f
静物画 still-life painting 绘画 16—237e
静修 Hesychasm 基督教 8—60f
静止环 stationary rings (gymnastics) 体操器械 16—201f
静止环 still rings (gymnastics) 体操器械 16—237f
静坐示威 sit-in 社会抗议 15—405c
镜 mirror 光学 11—273e
镜泊湖 Jingpo Hu 中国湖泊 9—29f
镜像核 mirror nucleus 物理学 11—274b
究竟实体 niṣprapañca 佛教哲学理论 12—202f
鸠鸽科 Columbidae 动物学 4—369c
鸠摩罗 Kumāra(Hindu god) 印度教神祇 9—394c
鸠摩罗什 Kumārajīva 中国佛教学者 9—394c
鸠山一郎 Hatoyama Ichirō 日本首相 7—509a
九八年一代 '98,Generation of 西班牙文学家 12—197a
九谷瓷器 Kutani ware 日本瓷器 9—406e
九华山 Jiuhua Shan 中国山名 9—34f
九江 Jiujiang 中国城市 9—35b
九连棋 Nine Men's Morris 游戏 12—196a
九岭山 Jiuling Shan 中国山地 9—35d
九·六城 Seis de Septiembre (Argentina) 阿根廷城市 15—192c
九龙 Cuu Long 越南省份 5—80f
九龙半岛 Jiulong Bandao 中国半岛 9—35d
九龙江 Jiulong Jiang 中国河流 9—35d
九三学社 September Third Society 中国政党 15—219c
《九十五条论纲》 Ninety-five Theses 德国宗教史 12—197a
九十英里海滩 Ninety Mile Beach 新西兰游览区 12—197c
"九一八"事变 September Eighteenth Incident 日本侵略中国事件 15—218f
九月 September 历法 15—218f
九月大屠杀 September Massacres 法国历史 15—219b
九寨沟 Jiuzhaigou 中国风景区 9—35f
《九章算术》 Jiuzhang Suanshu 中国古代数学著作 9—36a
九州岛 Kyushu 日本岛屿 9—418a
九柱地滚球 ninepins 体育 12—196c
久尔贝勒 Diourbel 塞内加尔城镇 5—331a
久尔久 Giurgiu 罗马尼亚县名 7—146b
久尔久 Giurgiu 罗马尼亚城市 7—146b
久古河 Diougou River (western Africa) 非洲河流 5—331a
久留米 Kurume 日本城市 9—404e
久鲁 Churu 印度县城 4—231a
久洛费海尔瓦尔 Gyulafehérvár (Romania) 罗马尼亚县城 7—393f
久米正雄 Kume Masao 日本小说家 9—395d
久隅守景 Kusumi Morikage 日本画家 9—406a
灸疗法 moxa treatment 医学 11—449f
韭葱 leek (species *Allium porrum*) 植物 9—558a
酒店 public house 英国酒馆 14—5b
酒馆 tavern 售酒堂饮场所 16—499b
酒柜 cellarette 家具 3—557a
酒精 grain alcohol 化合物 7—243d
酒精饮料 alcoholic beverage 酒类 1—190e
酒精中毒 alcoholism 医学 1—191a
酒井抱一 Sakai Hōitsu 日本画家 14—533d
酒井田家族 Sakaida FAMILY 日本陶工家族 14—533f
酒泉 Jiuquan 中国城市 9—35e
酒神节 Bacchanalia 希腊罗马宗教节日 2—113f
酒神赞歌 dithyramb 古希腊歌曲 5—345a
酒石酸 tartaric acid 化合物 16—486f
酒坛 oinochoe 古希腊陶器 12—356a
酒田 Sakata 日本城市 14—534c
旧奥斯科尔 Stary Oskol 俄罗斯城市 16—199f
旧大陆猴 Old World monkey 哺乳动物 12—369b
旧德里 Old Delhi 印度城市 12—367d
旧费斯富尔 Old Faithful 美国间歇泉 12—367f
旧河 Old River (Belize) 伯利兹河流 12—368d
旧金山 San Francisco 美国城市 15—8d
旧金山-奥克兰海湾桥 San Francisco-Oakland Bay Bridge 美国海湾桥 15—11f
旧金山会议 San Francisco Conference 国际会议 15—11d
旧卡斯蒂利亚 Old Castile 西班牙历史地名 12—366f
旧礼仪派 Old Believer 俄国宗教 12—366d
旧鲁萨 Staraya Russa 俄罗斯城市 16—196f
《旧罗马圣咏》 Old Roman chant 基督教教仪曲调汇编 12—368d
旧马尔达 Old Mālda (India) 印度城镇 12—367f
旧皮质 archipallium 解剖学 1—451e
旧圣彼得教堂 Old Saint Peter'sBasilica 罗马教堂 12—368e
旧石器时代 Paleolithic Period 人类古代文化阶段 12—561b
旧危地马拉 Antigua Guatemala 危地马拉城市 1—387d
旧喜剧 Old Comedy 古希腊戏剧 12—367c
旧艺术 Ars Antiqua 法国音乐 1—517e
《旧约》 Old Testament 《圣经》的一部分 12—368f
旧扎戈拉 Stara Zagora 保加利亚城镇 16—196e
臼杵 Usuki 日本城市 17—425b
臼和杵 mortar and pestle 器具 11—408d
厩蝇 stable fly (*Stomoxys calcitrans*) 昆虫 16—175c
救恩 salvation 宗教 14—557e
救国委员会 Public Safety, Committee of 法国大革命政治机构 14—10a
救火车 fire engine 消防设备 6—325d
救济 relief 社会福利 14—215b
救济学校 almonry school 英国慈善学校 1—247c
救济院 almshouse 美国公共收容机构 1—247f
救生艇 lifeboat 船舶 10—90c
救世军 Salvation Army 国际基督教组织 14—557f
《救世主》 Heliand 古撒克逊史诗 7—572f
救赎 redemption 基督教教义 14—192a
舅甥关系 avunculate 社会学 2—91e
居德布兰达尔河 Gudbrandsdalslågen (river, Norway) 挪威河流 7—347d
居德布兰河谷 Gudbrands Valley 挪威谷地 7—347d
居德瀑布 Gull Falls 冰岛瀑布 7—369d
居尔 Gurs 法国集中营 7—379c
居尔布兰松 Gulbransson, Olaf 德国画家 7—367d
居尔皮普 Curepipe 毛里求斯城镇 5—67c
居雷尔 Curel, François de 法国剧作家 5—67c
居里 curie 放射性物质计量单位 5—67f
居里 Curie, Irène (physicist) 法国物理化学家 5—67f
居里 Curie, Pierre 法国物理化学家 5—68d
居里点 Curie point 物理学 5—69a
居里夫人 Curie, Marie 法国物理学家 5—68a
居里克 Guericke, Otto von 德国物理学家、工程师 7—349c
居鲁士 Cyrus 波斯国王名 5—94b
居鲁士(小) Cyrus THE YOUNGER 波斯王子 5—94c
居鲁士二世 Cyrus II 波斯国王 5—94b
居鲁士一世 Cyrus I 波斯国王 5—94b
居蒙 Cumont, Franz(-Valéry-Marie) 比利时考古学家 5—60e
居米什哈内 Gümüşhane 土耳其城市 7—371d
居米斯帕拉 Gümüşpala, Ragıp 土耳其将军、正义党创始人 7—371d
居纳尔松 Gunnarsson, Gunnar 冰岛小说家 7—372f
居内梅 Guynemer, Georges-Marie 法国飞行员 7—385f
居纽 Cugnot, Nicolas-Joseph 法国军事工程师 5—52d
居斯特罗 Güstrow 德国城市 7—382a
居特斯洛 Gütersloh 德国城市 7—382d
居维利埃 Cuvilliés, François de, THE ELDER 巴伐利亚建筑师 5—81e

居维叶 Cuvier, Georges, Baron 法国动物学家、政治家 5—81a
居伊 Guy 佛兰德伯爵 7—384c
居伊 Guy 法国斯波莱托公爵 7—384c
居伊 Cui, César (Antonovich) 俄国作曲家 5—52d
居伊(肖利亚克的) Guy DE CHAULIAC (medieval surgeon) 法国外科医生 7—384d
居伊昂(夫人) Guyon, Jeanne-Marie Bouvier de La Motte, (MADAME DU CHESNOY) 法国奥秘神学家 7—386a
居伊-布拉谢 Guy-Blaché, Alice 美国导演 7—384f
居伊二世 Guy II 法国斯波莱托公爵 7—384d
居庸关 Juyong Guan 中国长城关口 9—122e
鉤杜父鱼 miller's-thumb 鱼类 11—227f
鉤鱼 gudgeon (species *Gobio gobio*) 鱼类 7—347f
菊池宽 Kikuchi Kan 日本戏剧家 9—276d
菊粉廓清率 inulin clearance 肾功能测试 8—426d
菊蒿 tansy 草本植物 16—469d
菊花石雕 chrysanthemum-marble carving 石雕工艺品 4—214f
菊科 Compositae (plant family) 植物学 4—399e
菊目 Asterales 植物学 2—3b
菊苣 chicory (species *Cichorium intybus*) 植物 4—147d
菊石类 ammonoid 古生物学 1—293d
菊属 Chrysanthemum 植物学 4—214e
菊头桔梗 sheep's bit (*Jasione montana*) 草本植物 15—292f
菊芋 Jerusalem artichoke (*Helianthus tuberosus*) 植物 9—4a
菊竹清训 Kikutake Kiyonori 日本建筑师 9—276e
锔(Cm) curium 化学元素 5—69c
橘 tangerine (*Citrus reticulata deliciosa*) 木本植物 16—463f
橘属 Citrus 植物学 4—249f
橘子战争(1801) Oranges, War of the 法西之间战争 12—443b
咀嚼 chewing 生理学 4—136e
枸橼 citron (*Citrus medica*) 植物 4—249e
枸橼酸乙胺嗪 diethylcarbamazine 药物 5—307d
矩阵 matrix 数学 11—26f
举母 Koromo (Japan) 日本城市 9—360b
举手教派 Ringatu 毛利人宗教派别 14—304d
举重 weight lifting 体育项目 18—169d
榉属 Zelkova 植物学 18—506f
巨柏 giant arborvitae (*Thuja plicata*) 木本植物 7—116c
巨蚕蛾 giant silkworm moth 昆虫 7—117a
巨大荨麻疹 giant urticaria (disorder) 疾病 7—117a
巨非洲水鼩鼱 giant African water shrew 哺乳动物 7—116c
巨蝮 bushmaster (species *Lachesis muta*) 毒蛇 3—283e
巨港 Palembang 印度尼西亚城市 12—558f
巨骨舌鱼 pirarucu (*Arapaima gigas*) 鱼类 13—321b
巨匠造物主 Demiurge 哲学 5—235c
巨结肠 megacolon 病理现象 11—80c
巨爵 krater 古希腊容器 9—373b
巨然 Juran 中国画家 9—115f
巨人 giant 神话人物 7—116b
"巨人"号机车 Big Boy 美国巨型机车 2—467b
巨人山 Giant Mountains 欧洲山脉 7—116e
巨人症 gigantism 疾病 7—125e
巨杉 big tree (*Sequoiadendron giganteum*) 木本植物 2—468c
巨舌症 macroglossia 病理现象 10—363e
巨神经纤维 giant nerve fibre 动物解剖学 7—116f
巨石工程 cyclopean masonry 防御工事 5—86f
巨石阵 Stonehenge 英国考古 16—251c
巨势金冈 Kose Kanaoka 日本世俗画家 9—362a
巨噬细胞系统 macrophage system 生理学 10—363f
巨头鲸 pilot whale 鲸鱼 13—304e
巨头鹊鸭 bufflehead (*Bucephala albeola*) 鸟类 3—234e
巨头螈属 Cacops 古生物学 3—310f
巨蜥 megalosaur 古生物学 11—80e
巨蜥 monitor lizard 爬行动物 11—340e
巨蜥属 Varanus 动物学 17—471c
巨细胞病毒 cytomegalovirus (CMV) 病毒 5—95f
巨细胞性假结核病 giant-cell thyroiditis 病理理象 7—116e
巨蟹 giant crab (*Macrocheira kaempferi*) 甲壳动物 7—116e
巨蟹座 Cancer 天文学 3—396d
巨星 giant star 天文学 7—117a
巨星乐队 Big Star 美国乐队 2—467f
巨型独角兽 giant unicorn (extinct rhinoceros) 古生物学 7—117a
巨型计算机 supercomputer 计算机科学 16—344e
巨引源 Great Attractor 天文学 7—269b
巨猿属 Gigantopithecus 古生物学 7—125f
巨藻属 Macrocystis 生物学 10—363d
巨柱式 colossal order 建筑学 4—364f
巨嘴鸟 toucan 鸟类 17—174a
句法 syntax 语法 16—403a
句子演算 sentential calculus (logic) 逻辑学 15—216a
拒服兵役者 conscientious objector 世界历史 4—443b
具 yantra 宗教 18—423d
具刺魔蜥 thorny devil (lizard) 动物 17—57d
具角罂粟 horned poppy 植物 8—177e
具体 concrete 哲学 4—414a
具体音乐 musique concrète 音乐作曲技术 11—510c
具志坚用高 Gushiken, Yoko 日本拳击运动员 7—379f
俱吠罗 Kubera 印度教财神 9—387d
俱乐部运动 club movement 美国社会运动 4—305e
俱利摩 Kūrma 印度教 9—402e
俱舍宗 Kusha 日本佛教派别 9—405b
剧场 theatre 建筑 17—17f
剧场之争 theatres, war of the 英国历史 17—19a
据誓断讼 compurgation 英国法律 4—401e
距角 elongation 天文学 6—51d
惧狼 dire wolf (species *Canis dirus*) 古生物学 5—335f
惧龙属 Albertosaurus 古生物学 1—182d
飓风 hurricane 气象学 8—266a
"飓风"式飞机 Hurricane 英国战斗机 8—266a
锯 saw 工具 15—92c
锯齿 denticle 化石 5—248a
锯盖鱼 robalo (fish) 鱼类 14—325a
锯鹱 prion 鸟类 13—518d
锯喙鸭 sawbill (duck) 鸟类 15—93d
锯鳞蝰 saw-scaled viper (*Echis carinatus*) 毒蛇 15—92f
锯木厂 sawmill 工厂 15—94a
锯木天牛 wood-boring beetle 昆虫 18—319e
锯鲨 saw shark 鱼类 15—93a
锯鳐 sawfish 鱼类 15—93d
聚氨基甲酸酯 polyurethane 化合物 13—418c
聚苯乙烯 polystyrene 化合物 13—417e
聚变 fusion 核物理学 6—533a
聚变反应堆 fusion reactor 核反应装置 6—533a
聚丙烯腈 polyacrylonitrile 化合物 13—410e
聚醋酸乙烯酯 polyvinyl acetate 化合物 13—418d
聚砜 polysulfone 化合物 13—417f
聚氟乙烯 polyvinyl fluoride 化合物 13—418f
聚光灯 spotlight 灯具 16—160a
聚硅氧烷 polysiloxane 化合物 13—417e
聚合 polymerization 化学反应 13—414c
聚合草 comfrey 植物 4—380e
聚合酶链反应 polymerase chain reaction (PCR) DNA片段复制技术 13—414b
聚合水 orthowater 化学 12—476b
聚合水 polywater 化学 13—418f
聚合物 polymer 化合物 13—413e

聚焦 focusing 眼的调节功能 6—384a
聚氯乙烯 polyvinyl chloride (PVC) 化合物 13—418e
聚醚 polyether 化合物 13—412d
聚三氟氯乙烯 polychlorotrifluoroethylene 化合物 13—411f
聚斯迈尔 Süssmayr, Franz Xaver 奥地利作曲家 16—361d
聚四氟乙烯 polytetrafluoroethylene (PTFE) 化合物 13—418a
聚谈会 tertulia 西班牙文学沙龙 16—558a
聚糖 glycan 生物化学 7—165e
聚特芬 Zutphen 荷兰城市 18—576b
聚烯烃 polyolefin 化合物 13—415f
聚乙烯醇 polyvinyl alcohol 化合物 13—418d
聚酯 polyester 化合物 13—412c
鹃鵙 cuckoo-shrike 鸟类 5—49f
鹃鵙科 Campephagidae 动物学 3—382a
鹃鸡 cuckoo roller (*Leptosomus discolor*) 鸟类 5—49e
鹃唾虫 cuckoo spit insect 昆虫 5—50a
鹃形类 cuculiform 鸟类 5—50b
卷柏 spike moss 蕨类植物 16—30d
卷柏属 Selaginella 植物学 15—195b
卷草纹条饰 rinceau 建筑装饰 14—303c
卷顶病 curly top 植物病害 5—70b
卷菊石属 Tropites 古生物学 17—235a
卷毛狗 poodle 狗品种 13—430b
卷舌音 retroflex 语音学 14—247b
卷筒卷宗 Pipe Rolls 英格兰历史资料 13—318b
卷尾 drongo 鸟类 5—426f
卷尾猴科 Cebidae 动物学 3—547b
卷尾浣熊 kinkajou (species *Potos flavus*) 动物 9—293f
卷象 leaf-rolling weevil 昆虫 9—542f
卷须 tendril 植物器官 16—538d
卷叶蛾 leaf roller moth 昆虫 9—542e
卷叶饰 crocket 建筑装饰 5—22a
卷嘴蛎属 Gryphaea 古生物学 7—331c
绢蝶 parnassian butterfly 昆虫 13—59b
绢云母 sericite 矿物 15—226a
决 gcod 佛教密法 7—40f
决策理论 decision theory 统计学 5—203b
决定论 determinism 哲学 5—266e
决定子 determinant 遗传物质 5—266a
决斗 duel 审判方法 5—447a
诀别词 good-night 歌谣 7—207e
角色 role 社会学 14—359a
角色歌曲 chanson à personnages 法国中世纪对话体歌曲 4—53a
觉罗塔格山 Jueluotag Shan 中国山脉 9—103e
觉囊派 Jo-nang-pa 中国藏传佛教派别 9—37c
觉猷 Kakuyū (Japanese priest) 日本教士 9—137e
绝对反应速率理论 absolute reaction rates, theory of (chemistry) 物理化学 1—30d
绝对零度 absolute zero 热力学 1—30d
绝对命令 categorical imperative 哲学 3—523b
绝对唯心主义 Absolute Idealism 哲学 1—30c
绝罚 excommunication 教会制裁形式 6—189e
绝灭 extinction 生物学 6—198a
绝热过程 adiabatic process 热力学 1—78c
绝热去磁 adiabatic demagnetization 物理学 1—78b
绝育 sterilization 避孕措施 16—225d
绝缘体 insulator 物理学 8—402c
掘土派成员 Digger 英格兰主张平分土地者 5—313a
掘穴 burrowing 动物行动方式 3—276a
掘足类 tusk shell 海生贝类 17—295c
蕨 fern 植物 6—287e
蕨 Warabi 日本城市 18—102e
蕨类植物 pteridophyte 植物 13—566f
蕨藓 fern moss 植物 6—288b
爵 jue 中国古代酒器 9—103c
爵床科 Acanthaceae 植物学 1—42a
爵床叶饰 acanthus 建筑装饰 1—42c
爵士舞 jazz dance 舞蹈 8—555f
爵士摇滚乐 jazz-rock 音乐 8—556a
爵士乐 jazz 音乐 8—555d
爵士乐诗 jazz poetry 诗歌 8—556a
蹶鼠 birch mouse 啮齿目动物 2—488a
攫禽 raptor 鸟类 14—155d
军备控制 arms control 军事 1—503c
军曹鱼 cobia (species *Rachycentron canadum*) 鱼类 4—316d
军刀 sword 兵器 16—389e
军笛 fife 乐器 6—309a
军阀 warlord 中国近代史 18—107b
军法 military law 法律 11—217c
军法官 kaziasker 奥斯曼帝国官员 9—207e
军工复合体 military-industrial complex 军事、工业 11—217b
军功勋章 Merit, Legion of 美国勋章 11—131d
军号 bugle 管乐器 3—236c
军机处 junjichu 中国清代政务机构 9—113a
军舰 Man o' War 美国赛马 10—445b
军舰鸟 frigate bird 海鸟 6—495a
军区 theme 拜占廷军事单位 17—22a
军区总督 ban 匈牙利历史 2—188b
军人同盟 Military League 希腊军官组织 11—218a
军事法庭 court-martial 军事法律 4—549f
军事工程学 military engineering 工程学 11—216c
军事管制法 martial law 法律 10—544f
军事建制单位 military unit 军事组织 11—218b
军事警察 Carabiniere 意大利国家警察 3—433f
军事训练 drill 军事 5—424e
军团 legion 军事学 9—561f
军械库展览会 Armory Show 美国艺术展览 1—501f
军用桥 military bridge 桥梁 11—216a
军政府 military government 军管机构 11—217a
均变论 uniformitarianism 地质学 17—344c
均密石英岩 novaculite 沉积岩 12—278c
均势 power, balance of 国际关系 13—473f
均田 chün-t'ien 中国古代土地制度 4—221e
均田制 equal-field system 中国古代土地制度 6—106a
均相反应 homogeneous reaction 化学反应 8—148a
均质化 homogenization 工艺过程 8—148a
君权神授 divine right of kings 维护专制统治学说 5—346f
君士坦丁 Constantine 阿尔及利亚城市 4—454a
君士坦丁 Constantine 统治者之名 4—450b
君士坦丁 Constantine 罗马皇帝 4—453e
君士坦丁八世 Constantine VIII 拜占廷皇帝 4—450f
君士坦丁巴西利卡 Basilica of Constantine (Rome) 罗马的大会堂 2—262b
君士坦丁堡 Constantinople (Turkey) 土耳其城市 4—454f
君士坦丁堡会议 Constantinople, Council of 基督教会议 4—454f
君士坦丁堡会议 Constantinople, Council of 基督教会议 4—455a
君士坦丁堡会议 Constantinople, Council of 基督教会议 4—455a
君士坦丁堡会议 Constantinople, Council of 基督教会议 4—455b
君士坦丁堡牧首区 Patriarchate of Constantinople 希腊正教 13—90d
君士坦丁堡普世牧首区 Ecumenical Patriarchate of Constantinople 东正教首位教会 5—533f
《君士坦丁堡协定》 Constantinople Agreement 第一次世界大战秘密协定 4—455b
君士坦丁大帝 Constantine THE GREAT 罗马皇帝 4—454c
君士坦丁大公 Constantine, VELIKY KNYAZ ("Grand Prince" or "Duke")

沙皇保罗一世之子 4—454b
君士坦丁二世 Constantine (II) 敌对教皇 4—451d
君士坦丁二世 Constantine II 罗马皇帝 4—453d
《君士坦丁惠赐书》 Constantine, Donation of 文件 4—454d
君士坦丁九世(莫诺马库斯) Constantine IX Monomachus 拜占廷皇帝 4—450f
君士坦丁凯旋门 Constantine, Arch of 意大利罗马建筑 4—454d
君士坦丁六世 Constantine VI 拜占廷皇帝 4—450c
君士坦丁七世(波菲罗格尼图斯) Constantine VII Porphyrogenitus 拜占廷皇帝 4—450d
君士坦丁三世 Constantine III 拜占廷皇帝 4—450b
君士坦丁十世(杜卡斯) Constantine X Ducas 拜占廷皇帝 4—451a
君士坦丁十一世(拉斯卡里斯) Constantine (XI) Lascaris 拜占廷皇帝 4—451a
君士坦丁十一(或十二)世(帕莱奥洛古斯) Constantine XI (or XII) Palaeologus 拜占廷皇帝 4—451b
君士坦丁四世 Constantine IV 拜占廷皇帝 4—450b
君士坦丁五世(科普罗尼姆斯) Constantine V Copronymus 拜占廷皇帝 4—450c
君士坦丁一世 Constantine I 罗马皇帝 4—451d
君士坦斯二世(波戈纳图斯) Constans II POGONATUS 拜占廷皇帝 4—449b
君士坦斯一世 Constans I 罗马皇帝 4—449b
君士坦提乌斯 Constantius 罗马皇帝名 4—455c
君士坦提乌斯 Constantius, Flavius Claudius 罗马皇帝 4—455e
君士坦提乌斯二世 Constantius II 罗马皇帝 4—455d
君士坦提乌斯三世 Constantius III 罗马皇帝 4—455e
君士坦提乌斯一世(克洛卢斯) Constantius I Chlorus 罗马皇帝 4—455c
君泰金 Güntekin, Reşat Nuri 土耳其小说家 7—374b
君王诗体 rhyme royal 七行诗节 14—271f
君岳 Kungaku (Japanese painter) 日本画家 9—397b
君主制 monarchy 国家制度 11—329d
《君子协定》 Gentlemen's Agreement 美国-日本协定 7—68f
钧窑 Jun kiln 中国宋代瓷窑 9—108f
莙达菜 chard 植物 4—62d
菌根 mycorrhiza 生物学 11—523d
菌核 sclerotium 生物学 15—145f
菌血症 bacteremia 医学症状 2—125a
郡 shire 英国行政单位 15—323a
郡(县) county 行政区划 4—545c
郡山 Kōriyama 日本城市 9—359a
郡守 tetrarch 古希腊罗马官衔 16—564f
郡县制 prefectures and counties, system of 中国古代行政制度 13—491f
郡长 sheriff 英国官员 15—307b
郡政厅 County Hall 英国建筑 4—545e

K

咖啡 coffee 食品 4—330b
咖啡馆 café 餐饮业 3—321c
咖啡锈病 coffee rust 植物病害 4—330c
咖啡因 caffeine 化合物 3—321f
喀巴拉 Kabbala 犹太教 9—124f
喀博达思鼓 kobdas 萨满教魔鼓 9—328c
喀布尔 Kabul 阿富汗首都 9—125f
喀布尔河 Kābul River 亚洲河流 9—126b
喀尔巴阡地槽 Carpathian Geosyncline 地质学 3—475c
喀尔巴阡-罗塞尼亚公教会 Carpatho-Rusin Catholic Church 东仪天主教会 3—475e
喀尔巴阡山 Podkarpackie 波兰省份 13—384c
喀尔巴阡山脉 Carpathian Mountains 欧洲山脉 3—475d
喀尔喀人 Khalkha 民族 9—254d
喀耳刻 Circe 希腊传说 4—244a
喀拉海 Kara Sea 北冰洋海名 9—173f
喀拉汗国 Karakitai 中国西部古王国 9—178b
喀拉吉地毯 Karaje rug 工艺品 9—177c
喀拉喀托 Krakatoa 印度尼西亚火山 9—370c
喀拉喀托信风 Krakatoa winds 气候学 9—370e
喀拉拉邦 Kerala 印度邦名 9—238f
喀拉拉平原 Kerala Plains 印度平原 9—239b
喀喇汗王朝 Qarakhanid dynasty 伊莱克汗王朝 14—53f
喀喇昆仑山 Karakoram Range 亚洲山脉 9—178c
喀喇昆仑山公路 Karakoram Highway 亚洲公路 9—178c
喀琅施塔得 Kronshtadt 俄罗斯军港 9—381a
喀琅施塔得 Kronstadt (Romania) 罗马尼亚县名 9—381b
喀琅施塔得叛乱 Kronshtadt Rebellion 苏联历史 9—381b
喀里多尼亚 Caledonia 不列颠北部地区古称 3—342f
喀里多尼亚运河 Caledonian Canal 苏格兰水道 3—343a
喀利格拉加动物群 Kali Glagah Fauna 古生物学 9—140d
喀利河 Kāli (India) 印度河流 9—140d
喀罗尼亚 Chaeronea 古希腊城镇 4—25a
喀迈拉 Chimera 希腊神话 4—158e
喀麦隆 Cameroon 非洲国家 3—373a
喀麦隆火山 Cameroon, Mount 非洲火山 3—374b
喀戎 Chiron 希腊神话 4—179e
喀山 Kazan 俄罗斯城市 9—206f
喀什 Kashi 中国城市 9—190e
喀什地毯 Kashgar rug 工艺品 9—190e
喀斯喀特山脉 Cascade Range 北美洲山脉 3—497f
喀斯喀特隧道 Cascade Tunnel 美国最长铁路隧道 3—498a
喀斯特 karst 地质学 9—188b
喀提林 Catiline 罗马贵族 3—528d
喀土穆 Khartoum 苏丹城市 9—257e
喀土穆之围 Khartoum, Siege of 苏丹历史 9—257f
喀瓦德一世 Kavadh I 波斯萨珊帝国国王 9—201a
喀西特人 Kassite 古代民族 9—193c
喀新风 khamsin 气象学 9—255b
喀亚尔 khyāl 印度民间舞蹈剧 9—267e
卡 calorie 物理学 3—357e
卡埃迪 Kaédi 毛里塔尼亚城镇 9—129b
卡埃塔尼家族 Caetani family 意大利贵族世家 3—321b
卡埃塔诺 Caetano, Marcelo José das Neves Alves 葡萄牙总理 3—321c
卡安 Cain, Henri-Louis (French actor) 法国演员 3—326a
卡昂 Caen 法国城市 3—315f
卡奥尔 Cahors 法国城镇 3—323f
卡奥科兰 Kaokoland 纳米比亚地区 9—170f
卡巴 Kabba 尼日利亚城镇 9—124e
卡巴比什人 Kabābīsh 民族 9—123e
卡巴尔 cabal 秘密组织 3—303c
卡巴尔达-巴尔卡里亚 Kabardino-Balkariya 俄罗斯的共和国 9—124b
卡巴尔达语 Kabardian language 语言 9—124a
卡巴哈尔-门多萨 Carvajal y Mendoza, Luisa de 天主教信徒 3—492e
卡巴莱 cabaret 餐馆 3—304a
卡巴莱塔 cabaletta 音乐 3—303d
卡巴雷加瀑布 Kabarega Falls 乌干达瀑布 9—124d
卡巴列夫斯基 Kabalevsky, Dmitry 俄罗斯作曲家 9—124a
卡巴尼斯 Cabanis, Pierre-Jean-Georges 法国哲学家 3—304a
卡巴微生物 kappa organism 生物 9—173b
卡巴西拉斯 Cabasilas, Nicholas 希腊正教在俗神学家 3—304d
卡巴西拉斯 Cabasilas, Nilus 希腊神学家 3—304d
卡贝 Cabet, Étienne 法国社会主义者 3—305b
卡贝德卢 Cabedelo 巴西城市 3—305a

卡贝尔 Cabell, James Branch 美国作家 3—305a
卡贝略港 Puerto Cabello 委内瑞拉港口城市 14—15d
卡奔塔利亚湾 Carpentaria, Gulf of 澳大利亚海湾 3—475f
卡本代尔 Carbondale 美国宾夕法尼亚州城市 3—445c
卡本代尔 Carbondale 美国伊利诺伊州城市 3—445c
卡比尔人 Kabyle 民族 9—126c
卡比里 Cabeiri 古代神话 3—305a
卡比利亚 Kabylie 阿尔及利亚地区 9—126d
卡比亚 Kabia (Indonesia) 印度尼西亚岛屿 9—125a
卡毕拉 Kabila, Laurent 刚果民主共和国总统 9—125a
卡宾 carbene 化学 3—440e
卡宾达 Cabinda 安哥拉北部飞地 3—305e
卡宾枪 carbine 武器 3—442b
卡波 Carbo, Gaius Papirius 罗马政治家 3—442b
卡波 Carbo, Gnaeus Papirius 罗马将军 3—442b
卡波艾拉 capoeira 巴西舞蹈 3—428e
卡波迪蒙特瓷器 Capodimonte porcelain 那不勒斯瓷器 3—428c
卡波迪蒙特国家博物馆和美术馆 Capodimonte, National Museum and Gallery of 意大利那不勒斯艺术博物馆 3—428c
卡波迪斯特里亚 Capodistria (Slovenia) 斯洛文尼亚海港 3—428e
卡波季斯特里亚斯 Kapodístrias, Ioánnis Antónios, Count (Komis) 希腊政治家 9—172c
卡波克拉蒂斯派 Carpocratian 基督教派别 3—478c
卡波雷托战役 Caporetto, Battle of 第一次世界大战历史 3—429a
卡波尼 Capponi, Gino, Marchese 意大利历史学家 3—430a
卡波特 Capote, Truman 美国小说家 3—429a
卡波西氏肉瘤 Kaposi sarcoma 疾病 9—172f
卡伯尔沃格 Kabelvåg 挪威村镇 9—124f
卡伯特 Cabot, George 美国联邦党领袖 3—307e
卡伯特 Cabot, John 欧洲航海家 3—307e
卡伯特 Cabot, Sebastian 英国航海家 3—307f
卡伯特海峡 Cabot Strait 加拿大海峡 3—308a
卡伯特家族 Cabot FAMILY 美国家族 3—307d
卡伯特森 Culbertson, Ely 美国桥牌权威 5—53e
卡勃里奥尔 cabriole 芭蕾舞蹈动作 3—309a
卡博什 Caboche, Simon 法国政客 3—307b
卡布尔彻 Caboolture 澳大利亚城镇 3—307c
卡布拉巴萨 Cabora Bassa 莫桑比克水电设施 3—307c
卡布拉尔 Cabral, Amílcar 几内亚政治家 3—308b
卡布拉尔 Cabral, Pedro Álvares 葡萄牙航海家 3—308b
卡布拉尔·德梅卢·内图 Cabral de Melo Neto, João 巴西诗人 3—308d
卡布里尼 Cabrini, Saint Frances Xavier 美国天主教徒 3—309a
卡布里亚斯 Chabrias 雇佣军人 4—21f
卡布罗尔 Cabrol, Fernand 天主教隐修士 3—309d
卡布斯 Qābūs ibn Saʿīd 阿曼苏丹 14—51c
卡布韦 Kabwe 赞比亚城镇 9—126b
卡布韦人 Kabwe man 民族 9—126b
卡车司机工会 Teamsters Union 美国工会组织 16—511f
卡彻马克文化 Kachemak culture 阿拉斯加早期文化 9—126f
卡茨 Katz, Sir Bernard 英国生理学家 9—198b
卡茨 Cats, Jacob 荷兰作家 3—530a
卡茨基尔三角洲 Catskill Delta 美国地理 3—530c
卡茨基尔山脉 Catskill Mountains 美国山脉 3—530d
卡茨基尔野牲饲养场 Catskill Game Farm, Inc. 美国私人动物园 3—530c
卡达尔 Kadár, Ján 捷克斯洛伐克导演 9—127d
卡达尔 Kádár, János 匈牙利总理 9—127d
卡达尔人 Kadar 民族 9—127c
卡达尔索-巴斯克斯 Cadalso y Vázquez, José de 西班牙作家 3—311f
卡达雷 Kadare, Ismail 阿尔巴尼亚小说家 9—127f
卡达里派 Qadarīyah 伊斯兰教 14—51d
卡达·莫斯托 Ca'da Mosto, Alvise 威尼斯探险家 3—303a
卡达桑人 Kadazan (people) 民族 9—128a
卡达耶夫 Katayev, Valentin (Petrovich) 苏联小说家 9—194f
卡达耶夫 Katayev, Yevgeny Petrovich 苏联作家 9—195a
卡代罗 Cadalo 敌对教皇 3—311e
卡丹 Cardin, Pierre 法国女装设计师 3—453b
卡丹巴家族 Kadamba FAMILY 印度古王朝 9—127c
卡德尔 Ghadr 锡克族政党 7—107a
卡德尔 Kardelj, Edvard 南斯拉夫政治家 9—180f
卡德利尔舞 quadrille 舞蹈 14—72b
卡德曼 Cadman, Charles Wakefield 美国作曲家 3—313e
卡德摩斯 Cadmus 希腊神话 3—314b
卡德纳斯 Cárdenas 古巴城市 3—451e
卡德纳斯 Cárdenas, Bartolomé de 西班牙画家 3—451e
卡德纳斯 Cárdenas (del Río), Lázaro 墨西哥总统 3—451e
卡德韦尔 Cardwell (of Ellerbeck), Edward Cardwell, Viscount 英国政治家 3—455e
卡德沃拉 Caedwalla 西撒克逊国王 3—315d
卡德沃朗 Cadwallon 不列颠国王 3—314f
卡德沃思 Cudworth, Ralph 英格兰神学家、伦理学家 5—51d
卡登-班德罗夫斯基 Kaden-Bandrowski, Juliusz 波兰小说家 9—128b
卡迪 qadi 伊斯兰教法执行官 14—51f
卡迪根 Cardigan 威尔士城镇 3—452e
卡迪根伯爵(第七) Cardigan, James Thomas Brudenell, 7th Earl of, BARON BRUDENELL OF STONTON 英国将军 3—452e
卡迪根郡 Cardiganshire 威尔士郡名 3—453a
卡迪根湾 Cardigan Bay 威尔士港湾 3—452f
卡迪拉克 Cadillac 美国城市 3—313a
卡迪里教团 Qādirīyah 伊斯兰教派别 14—51f
卡迪里苏丹国 Kathiri sultanate 阿拉伯半岛国家 9—195e
卡迪瑞 Kaḍiri 印度尼西亚古王国 9—128c
卡迪什 Kaddish 犹太教 9—128b
卡迪亚克 Cadillac, Antoine Laumet de La Mothe 法国军人、探险家 3—313a
卡的普南 Katipunan 菲律宾民族主义组织 9—196b
卡蒂埃 Cartier, Sir George Étienne, BARONET 加拿大政治家 3—489f
卡蒂埃 Cartier, Jacques 法国海员 3—490a
卡蒂埃-布勒松 Cartier-Bresson, Henri 法国摄影家 3—490b
卡蒂奥拉 Katiola 科特迪瓦城镇 9—196a
卡蒂布·切莱比 Kâtip Çelebi 土耳其历史学家 9—196a
卡蒂亨克岛 Cuttyhunk (island, Massachusetts, U.S.) 美国岛屿 5—80f
卡蒂曼杜 Cartimandua 不列颠古代王国女王 3—490e
卡蒂人 Chatti 日耳曼部落 4—92d
卡叠什 Kadesh 叙利亚古城 9—128b
卡叠什战役 Kadesh, Battle of 叙利亚历史 9—128c
卡丁车运动 karting 体育 9—188d
卡杜纳 Kaduna 尼日利亚州名 9—128e
卡杜纳 Kaduna 尼日利亚城市 9—128f
卡杜纳河 Kaduna River 尼日利亚河流 9—129a
卡顿 Catton, (Charles) Bruce 美国新闻工作者 3—532b
卡顿斯维尔 Catonsville 美国村庄 3—529e
卡顿-汤普森 Caton-Thompson, Gertrude 英国考古学家 3—529d
卡多尔公爵 Cadore, Jean-Baptiste Nompère de Champagny, duc de (duke of) 法国政治家 3—314e
卡多尔纳 Cadorna, Luigi 意大利将军 3—314e
卡多根 Cadogan, William Cadogan, 1st Earl 英国军人 3—314d
卡多马 Kadoma 津巴布韦城镇 9—128d
卡多人 Caddo 北美印第安人 3—312c
卡多索 Cardoso, Fernando Henrique 巴西总统 3—455a
卡多佐 Cardozo, Benjamin Nathan 美国法学家 3—455b

卡恩 Cahan, Abraham 美国记者 3—323c
卡恩 Kahn, Albert 美国建筑师 9—132d
卡恩 Kahn, Florence Prag 美国公职人员 9—132e
卡恩 Kahn, Gustave 法国诗人 9—132f
卡恩 Kahn, Herman 美国物理学家 9—132f
卡恩 Kahn, Louis I(sadore) 美国建筑师 9—133a
卡恩 Kahn, Otto Hermann 美国银行家 9—133b
卡恩 Kahn, Reuben Leon 美国免疫学家 9—133c
卡恩 Kahn, Robert Elliot 美国工程师 9—133d
卡恩格瓦尼 KaNgwane 南非黑人邦居住地 9—157e
卡恩韦勒 Kahnweiler, Daniel-Henry 法国艺术品商人 9—133e
卡尔 Carr, Emily 加拿大画家 3—478e
卡尔 Carr, E(dward) H(allett) 英国政治学家 3—478d
卡尔 Kahr, Gustav, Ritter von 德国政治家 9—133f
卡尔 Carr, John Dickson 美国侦探小说作家 3—478f
卡尔 Carr, Sir Robert 英格兰贵族 3—478f
卡尔巴拉 Karbalā' 伊拉克城市 9—180d
卡尔巴拉战役 Karbalā', Battle of 伊拉克历史 9—180e
卡尔贝山 Carbet Mountains 加勒比海火山 3—442a
卡尔波 Carpeaux, Jean-Baptiste 法国雕刻家 3—475e
卡尔波夫 Karpov, Anatoly Yevgenyevich 苏联国际象棋大师 9—187a
卡尔布 Kalb, Johann 德国军官 9—139a
卡尔达诺 Cardano, Girolamo 意大利医生 3—451c
卡尔达什-达赖尼亚 Caldas da Rainha 葡萄牙城镇 3—340f
卡尔达斯 Caldas 哥伦比亚省份 3—340e
卡尔德达尔 Calderdale 英格兰自治市 3—341c
卡尔德龙 Calderón, Sila María 波多黎各总督 3—341d
卡尔德隆 Calderón, Rodrigo, Conde (count) de Oliva, Marqués (marquess) de Siete Iglesias 西班牙王室宠臣 3—341c
卡尔德隆 Calderón, Serafín Estébanez 西班牙作家 3—341d
卡尔德隆·德·拉·巴尔卡 Calderón de la Barca, Pedro 西班牙剧作家 3—341e
卡尔德纳尔 Cardenal, Ernesto 尼加拉瓜诗人 3—451d
《卡尔迪斯条约》 Cardis, Treaty of 俄国与瑞典条约 3—454f
卡尔蒂妮 Kartini, Raden Adjeng, (Lady) 印度尼西亚社会名人 9—188e
卡尔东·德维亚尔伯爵 Carton de Wiart, Henri(-Victor), Comte (Count) 比利时政治家 3—491a
卡尔杜齐 Carducci, Giosuè 意大利诗人 3—455d
卡尔杜奇 Carducci, Vincenzo 意大利画家 3—455e
卡尔顿 Carleton, Guy 英国政治家 3—459e
卡尔顿 Carlton, Steve 美国棒球运动员 3—463a
卡尔顿 Carleton, William 爱尔兰作家 3—459f
卡尔顿山 Carleton, Mount 加拿大山脉 3—459e
卡尔顿王府写字台 Carlton House table 家具 3—463a
卡尔顿维尔 Carletonville 南非城镇 3—460a
卡尔夫 Kalf, Willem 荷兰画家 9—140a
卡尔弗城 Culver City 美国城市 5—57c
卡尔弗尔特 Karlfeldt, Erik Axel 瑞典诗人 9—182e
卡尔弗特 Calvert, Cecilius 英国政治家 3—358f
卡尔弗特 Calvert, Charles 英国政治家 3—358f
卡尔弗特 Calvert, George 英国政治家 3—358f
卡尔弗特 Calvert, Leonard 马里兰殖民地总督 3—358f
卡尔弗韦尔 Culverwel, Nathanael 英格兰哲学家 5—57d
卡尔古利 Kalgoorlie 澳大利亚城镇 9—140b
卡尔洪 Calhoun 美国城市 3—344d
卡尔霍恩 Calhoun, John C(aldwell) 美国政治家 3—344d
卡尔基米什 Carchemish 罗马古代城邦 3—450b
卡尔吉王朝 Khaljī dynasty 印度王朝 9—254c
卡尔季察 Kardhítsa 希腊城镇 9—181a
卡尔加里 Calgary 加拿大城市 3—344b
卡尔金斯 Calkins, Mary Whiton 美国哲学家、心理学家 3—352e
卡尔卡斯 Calchas 希腊神话 3—335b
卡尔卡松 Carcassonne 法国城镇 3—449f
卡尔卡维查斯 Karkavítsas, Andréas 希腊小说家 9—182c
卡尔科孔狄利斯 Chalcocondyles, Laonicus 拜占廷历史学家 4—30e
卡尔克布雷纳 Kalkbrenner, Frédéric 法国钢琴家 9—142d
卡尔孔狄利斯 Chalcondyles, Demetrius 希腊导师 4—30f
卡尔勒 Karle, Jerome 美国晶体学家 9—182d
卡尔利诺 Carlino (Florentine painter) 意大利画家 3—460b
卡尔罗斯 Culross 苏格兰自治市 5—54e
卡尔洛瓦茨 Karlovac 克罗地亚城市 9—183a
卡尔洛维茨 Karlowitz (Serbia) 塞尔维亚城镇 9—183b
《卡尔洛维茨条约》 Carlowitz, Treaty of 欧洲历史事件 3—462a
卡尔马 Kalmar 瑞典省份 9—143a
卡尔马 Kalmar 瑞典城市 9—143a
卡尔马 Karmah 苏丹市镇 9—184c
卡尔·马克思城 Karl-Marx-Stadt (Germany) 德国城市 9—182d
卡尔·马克思峰 Karl Marx Peak 塔吉克斯坦山峰 9—182d
卡尔马联合 Kalmar Union 北欧历史 9—143b
卡尔马特派 Qarmatian 伊斯兰教派别 14—54a
卡尔马战争 Kalmar War 丹麦和瑞典战争 9—143b
卡尔迈勒 Karmal, Babrak 阿富汗总统 9—184d
卡尔迈勒山 Carmel, Mount 以色列山脉 3—464b
卡尔曼 Coloman 匈牙利国王 4—354f
卡尔梅基亚 Kalmykia 俄罗斯的共和国 9—143e
卡尔梅克人 Kalmyk 民族 9—143d
卡尔梅特 Calmette, Albert (Léon Charles) 法国细菌学家 3—357a
卡尔米埃勒 Karmi'el 以色列城镇 9—185a
卡尔莫纳 Carmona, António Oscar de Fragoso 葡萄牙总统 3—465a
卡尔纳克 Carnac 法国村庄 3—465b
卡尔纳克 Karnak 埃及古都遗址 9—185a
卡尔内 Carné, Marcel 法国电影导演 3—466c
卡尔尼克山脉 Carnic Alps 欧洲山脉 3—467f
卡尔尼施山 Karnische Alpen (Austria-Italy) 欧洲山脉 9—186d
卡尔诺基·冯·克勒什帕塔克 Kálnoky von Köröspatak, Gusztav Siegmund, Count (Graf) 奥匈帝国政治家 9—143f
卡尔帕乔 Carpaccio, Vittore 意大利画家 3—475a
卡尔帕索斯 Kárpathos 希腊岛屿 9—187a
卡尔佩珀起义 Culpeper's Rebellion 北美殖民地人民起义 5—54d
卡尔皮 Carpi 意大利城镇 3—478c
卡尔皮 Carpi, Jacopo Berengario da 意大利解剖学家 3—478c
卡尔皮尼 Carpini, Giovanni da Pian del (Franciscan author) 方济各会修士 3—478c
卡尔普雷奈德 Calprenède, Gaultier de Coste, seigneur deLa 法国作家 3—358a
卡尔奇 Carchi 厄瓜多尔省份 3—450c
卡尔萨温娜 Karsavina, Tamara (Platonovna) 英国芭蕾舞演员 9—187e
卡尔-桑德斯 Carr-Saunders, Sir Alexander (Morris) 英国社会学家 3—478f
卡尔森 Carlson, Chester F. 美国物理学家 3—462e
卡尔森 Carlson, Evans (Fordyce) 美国军官 3—462f
卡尔沙教团 Khālsā 印度锡克教派别 9—254e
卡尔舍亚卡 Karşiyaka 土耳其城镇 9—188b
卡尔施塔特 Karlstadt (Croatia) 克罗地亚城市 9—183f
卡尔施塔特 Karlstadt, Andreas Rudolf Bodenstein von 德意志神学家 9—183f
卡尔十六世古斯塔夫 Carl XVI Gustaf 瑞典国王 3—459e
卡尔斯 Kars 土耳其城市 9—187d
卡尔斯巴德 Carlsbad (Czech Republic) 捷克共和国城市 3—462b
卡尔斯巴德 Carlsbad 美国加利福尼亚州城市 3—462b

卡尔斯巴德 Carlsbad 美国新墨西哥州城市 3—462c
卡尔斯巴德 Karlsbad(Czech Republic) 捷克城市 9—183b
卡尔斯巴德洞窟国家公园 Carlsbad Caverns National Park 美国公园 3—462d
《卡尔斯巴德决议》 Carlsbad Decrees 德意志历史 3—462d
卡尔斯堡 Karlsburg(Romania) 罗马尼亚县城 9—183c
卡尔斯伯格海岭 Carlsberg Ridge 印度洋海底山岭 3—462e
卡尔斯克鲁纳 Karlskrona 瑞典城镇 9—183c
卡尔斯库加 Karlskoga 瑞典城镇 9—183c
卡尔斯鲁厄 Karlsruhe 德国行政专区 9—183c
卡尔斯鲁厄 Karlsruhe 德国城市 9—183e
卡尔斯塔德 Karlstad 瑞典城市 9—183e
卡尔松 Carlsson, Arvid 瑞典药理学家 3—463a
卡尔塔尼塞塔 Caltanissetta 意大利城市 3—358a
卡尔滕布鲁纳 Kaltenbrunner, Ernst 奥地利纳粹党人 9—144a
卡尔瓦多斯 Calvados 法国省份 3—358e
卡尔韦 Calvé, Emma 法国女高音歌唱家 3—358e
卡尔维纳 Karviná 捷克共和国城市 9—189c
卡尔维诺 Calvino, Italo 意大利小说家 3—362b
卡尔文 Calvin, Melvin 美国生物化学家 3—361b
卡尔沃斯 Kálvos, Andréas Ioannídis 希腊诗人 9—144d
卡尔沃主义 Calvo Doctrine 国际法 3—362c
卡尔西登 Chalcedon 土耳其古城镇 4—29f
卡尔西迪字母 Chalcidian alphabet 希腊字母 4—30c
卡尔西顿会议 Chalcedon, Council of 基督教 4—29f
卡尔希 Karshi 乌兹别克斯坦城市 9—188a
卡尔扎比吉 Calzabigi, Ranieri 意大利诗人 3—362e
卡尔扎伊 Karzai, Hamid 阿富汗总统 9—189c
卡伐勒 Caballé, Montserrat 西班牙高音歌唱家 3—303d
卡法吉沃罗马约利卡陶器 Caffaggiolo maiolica 意大利陶器 3—321d
卡法罗 Caffaro DI CASCHIFELLONE 热那亚军人 3—321f
卡菲埃里家族 Caffiéri FAMILY 法国雕刻和金工世家 3—322a
卡菲尔人 Kaffir 非洲民族 9—129f
卡菲尔语 Kaffir language 语言 9—129f
卡菲尔战争 Kaffir Wars 南非历史 9—129f
卡菲克卢本岛 Kaffeklubben Island 北冰洋岛屿 9—129e
卡菲里斯坦 Kāfiristān(Afghanistan) 阿富汗地区 9—129f
卡菲利 Caerphilly 威尔士要塞 3—316f
卡菲氏综合征 Caffey's syndrome 病理现象 3—322a
卡芬雅克 Cavaignac, Louis-Eugène 法国将军 3—537a
卡夫 Kāf, Al- 突尼斯城镇 9—130c
卡夫 Karve,(Maharishi) Dhondo Keshav 印度教育家 9—189b
卡夫卡 Kafka, Franz 捷克德语小说家 9—129f
卡夫卡夫 Kawkaw(Mali) 马里城镇 9—203c
卡夫拉 Cabra 西班牙城市 3—308a
卡夫雷拉 Cabrera, Manuel Estrada 危地马拉总统 3—308d
卡夫雷拉 Cabrera(y Griñó), Ramón 西班牙将领 3—308e
卡夫雷拉·因凡特 Cabrera Infante, Guillermo 古巴小说家 3—308f
卡夫里略 Cabrillo, Juan Rodríguez 欧洲探险家 3—309a
卡夫食品公司 Kraft Foods Inc. 美国公司 9—369e
卡夫泽人 Kafzeh 以色列出土人骨遗存 9—130f
卡弗 Carver, George Washington 美国农业化学家 3—493a
卡弗 Carver, John 新英格兰总督 3—493c
卡弗 Carver, Jonathan 北美洲早期探险家 3—493c
卡弗 Carver, Robert 苏格兰作曲家 3—493e
卡弗 Carver, Raymond(Clevie) 美国短篇小说家 3—493d
卡弗拉里亚 Kaffraria 非洲殖民地名称 9—129f
卡弗利耶 Cavelier, René-Robert(French explorer) 法国探险家 3—541b
卡弗坦长袍 caftan 服装 3—322c
卡弗椅 Carver chair 家具 3—493f
卡富埃 Kafue 赞比亚城镇 9—130e
卡富埃国家公园 Kafue National Park 赞比亚公园 9—130e
卡富埃河 Kafue River 非洲河流 9—130f
卡富尔 Kāfūr, Abū al-Misk 埃及统治者 9—130f
卡盖拉河 Kagera River 非洲河流 9—131e
卡冈诺维奇 Kaganovich, Lazar Moiseyevich 苏联共产党领导人 9—131b
卡刚果 Kakongo 非洲历史国家 9—137d
卡格-埃勒特 Karg-Elert, Sigfrid 德国作曲家 9—181e
卡格尼 Cagney, James 美国演员 3—323b
卡格瓦 Kagwa, Sir Apolo 非洲布干达首相 9—132b
卡瓜斯 Caguas 波多黎各城镇 3—323c
卡瓜苏 Caaguazú 巴拉圭省份 3—303b
卡哈尔 Cajal, Santiago Ramón y 西班牙组织学家 3—330d
卡哈马卡 Cajamarca 秘鲁省份 3—330e
卡哈马卡 Cajamarca 秘鲁省会城市 3—330e
卡哈那莫库 Kahanamoku, Duke Paoa 美国运动员 9—132b
卡汗 Kahun 古埃及小镇 9—134a
卡赫拉曼马拉什 Kahramanmaraş 土耳其城市 9—133f
卡胡卢伊 Kahului 美国城市 9—134a
卡惠拉人 Cahuilla 印第安人 3—323f
卡霍巴 Cahaba 美国村庄 3—323c
卡基纳达 Kākināda 印度城镇 9—137c
卡季米尔-佩里埃 Casimir-Périer, Jean(-Paul-Pierre) 法国政治家 3—500f
卡季耶夫卡 Kadijevka(Ukraine) 乌克兰城市 9—128c
卡加姆 Kagame,(Abbé) Alexis 卢旺达诗人 9—131a
卡加延-德奥罗 Cagayan de Oro 菲律宾城市 3—322d
卡加延河 Cagayan River 菲律宾河流 3—322d
卡加延苏禄 Cagayan Sulu 菲律宾岛屿 3—322d
卡杰拉霍 Khajurāho 印度古城 9—253b
卡捷港 Port-Cartier 加拿大城镇 13—444d
卡介苗 BCG vaccine 疫苗 2—300c
卡津 Kazin, Alfred 美国文学评论家 9—207e
卡津人 Cajun 法裔加拿大人的后裔 3—331b
卡卡杜国家公园 Kakadu National Park 澳大利亚地区 9—137a
卡卡梅加 Kakamega 肯尼亚城镇 9—137a
卡卡塔 Kakata 利比里亚城市 9—137b
卡卡啄羊鹦鹉 kaka 鸟类 9—137a
卡凯 Caca(Roman deity) 古罗马宗教 3—309d
卡科斯与卡凯 Cacus and Caca 古罗马宗教 3—311e
卡克蒂奥人 Caquetío 委内瑞拉印第安民族 3—433e
卡克拉河 Ghāghara River 亚洲河流 7—107c
卡克奇克尔人 Cakchiquel 马雅印第安民族 3—331b
卡克奇克尔语 Cakchiquel language 马雅语言 3—331c
卡克斯顿 Caxton, William 英国印刷商 3—543f
卡克塔 Caquetá 哥伦比亚省份 3—433d
卡孔达 Caconda 安哥拉城镇 3—310e
卡库佩 Caacupé 巴拉圭城市 3—303b
卡拉 Calah 亚述古城 3—333b
卡拉 Carrà, Carlo 意大利画家 3—479a
卡拉奥拉 Calahorra 西班牙城镇 3—333c
卡拉奥斯曼奥卢 Karaosmanoğlu, Yakup Kadri 土耳其作家 9—179e
卡拉巴尔 Calabar 尼日利亚港口 3—332b
卡拉巴略山 Caraballo Mountains 菲律宾山脉 3—433e
卡拉比克 Karabük 土耳其城镇 9—174b
卡拉博加兹戈尔湾 Kara-Bogaz-Gol Gulf 土库曼斯坦水湾 9—173e
卡拉布里亚 Calabria 意大利区名 3—332e
卡拉布里亚阶 Calabrian Stage 地质学 3—333b
卡拉代尼赞雷格利西 Karadenizereğlisi(Turkey) 土耳其县城 9—176a
卡拉代尼兹海峡 Karadeniz Boğazi(Turkey) 土耳其海峡 9—176a

卡拉德克·德拉夏洛泰 Caradeuc de la Chalotais, Louis-René de 法国行政官员 3—436e
卡拉顿 Caradon 英格兰区名 3—436e
卡拉多克统 Caradoc Series 地质学 3—436e
卡拉尔卡 Calarcá 哥伦比亚城市 3—334c
卡拉法 Carafa, Gian Pietro 教皇 3—436f
卡拉干达 Karaganda 哈萨克斯坦州名 9—176d
卡拉干达 Karaganda 哈萨克斯坦城市 9—176e
卡拉格兹 Karagöz 土耳其戏剧 9—176e
卡拉哈里大羚羊国家公园 Kalahari Gemsbok National Park 南非国家公园 9—138b
卡拉哈里沙漠 Kalahari 非洲沙漠地区 9—138a
卡拉汉 Callahan, Harry (Morey) 美国摄影家 3—353c
卡拉汉 Callaghan, (Leonard) James 英国首相 3—353a
卡拉汉 Callaghan, Morley (Edward) 加拿大小说家 3—353b
卡拉吉 Karajī, al- 数学家、工程师 9—177d
卡拉季奇 Karadžić, Vuk Stefanović 塞尔维亚语言学者 9—176c
卡拉加人 Karaga (people) 西伯利亚南部民族 9—176d
卡拉迦列 Caragiale, Costache 罗马尼亚演员 3—436f
卡拉迦列 Caragiale, Ion Luca 罗马尼亚剧作家 3—437a
卡拉卡尔帕克斯坦 Karakalpakstan 乌兹别克斯坦的共和国 9—177e
卡拉卡拉 Caracalla 罗马皇帝 3—434b
卡拉卡拉大浴场 Caracalla, Baths of 古罗马公共浴场 3—434e
卡拉卡拉鹰 caracara 猛禽 3—434f
卡拉卡乌阿 Kalakaua 夏威夷王 9—138c
卡拉凯特 Caraquet 加拿大渔港 3—437d
卡拉科尔 Caracol 马雅古城 3—436d
卡拉科尔 Karakol 吉尔吉斯斯坦城市 9—178b
卡拉克 Karak, Al- 约旦城镇 9—177e
卡拉库尔绵羊 Karakul 绵羊品种 9—178e
卡拉库姆沙漠 Karakum Desert 土库曼斯坦沙漠 9—178f
卡拉库姆运河 Karakum Canal 土库曼斯坦水道 9—178f
卡拉库塞 Karaköse (Turkey) 土耳其省份 9—178e
卡拉拉 Carrara 意大利城市 3—480b
卡拉拉家族 Carrara FAMILY 意大利中世纪家族 3—480c
卡拉利斯 Caralis (Roman city, Sardinia) 古罗马城市 3—437b
卡拉马 Calama 智利城市 3—333e
卡拉马塔湾 Kalamáta, Gulf of (Greece) 希腊海湾 9—138d
卡拉马西阿诺斯舞 kalamatianos 希腊链舞 9—138d
卡拉马祖 Kalamazoo 美国城市 9—138e
卡拉迈 Kalámai 希腊港口 9—138d
卡拉曼利斯 Karamanlis, Konstantinos 希腊政治家 9—179a
卡拉米 Calamy, Edmund 英格兰神学家 3—334b
卡拉棉群岛 Calamian Group 菲律宾群岛 3—333e
卡拉莫琼人 Karamojong 非洲民族 9—179c
卡拉姆津 Karamzin, Nikolay Mikhaylovich 俄国作家 9—179c
卡拉姆芦笔 qalam 古代芦笔 14—52d
卡拉·穆斯塔法帕夏 Kara Mustafa Paşa, Merzifonlu 奥斯曼首席大臣 9—173f
卡拉派 Karaism 犹太教教派 9—177a
卡拉齐 Carracci, Agostino 意大利画家 3—479b
卡拉齐 Carracci, Annibale 意大利画家 3—479b
卡拉齐 Carracci, Lodovico 意大利画家 3—479e
卡拉奇 Karāchi 巴基斯坦城市 9—174c
卡拉恰耶夫-切尔克西亚 Karachayevo-Cherkesiya 俄罗斯的共和国 9—174b
卡拉乔尔杰 Karadjordje 塞尔维亚领袖 9—176a
卡拉乔尔杰王朝 Karadjordjević DYNASTY 塞尔维亚王朝 9—176b
卡拉乔洛 Caracciolo, Francesco, DUCA (duke) DI BRIENZA 意大利那不勒斯海军舰队司令 3—436c
卡拉丘里王朝 Kalacuri DYNASTY 印度王朝 9—137f
卡拉人 Kala (people) 民族 9—137e
卡拉桑斯 Calasanz, Saint Joseph 西班牙天主教司铎 3—334d
卡拉施马车 calash 马车 3—334e
卡拉什尼科夫 1947 型步枪 Kalashnikov Model 1947 (Soviet rifle) 苏联步枪 9—138f
卡拉什-塞维林 Caraş-Severin 罗马尼亚县名 3—437e
卡拉斯 Calas, Jean 法国胡格诺派教徒 3—334c
卡拉斯 Callas, Maria 女高音歌唱家 3—353f
卡拉斯基利亚 Carrasquilla, Tomás 哥伦比亚小说家 3—480d
卡拉塔库斯 Caratacus 不列颠部族国王 3—437f
卡拉塔斯卡潟湖 Caratasca Lagoon 洪都拉斯潟湖 3—437f
卡拉特拉瓦 Calatrava, Santiago 西班牙建筑师 3—334f
卡拉特拉瓦骑士团 Calatrava, Order of 西班牙军事、宗教集团 3—334e
卡拉瓦卡 Caravaca 西班牙城市 3—438b
卡拉瓦乔 Caravaggio 意大利画家 3—438b
卡拉万克山脉 Karawanken 欧洲山脉 9—180d
卡拉韦 Caraway, Hattie Ophelia 美国政治家 3—439c
卡拉维洛夫 Karavelov, Lyuben Stoychev 保加利亚作家 9—180c
卡拉维因 Qarawīyīn 摩洛哥大学 14—53f
卡拉温 Qalā'ūn 埃及马木路克苏丹 14—52f
卡拉温大清真寺 Qalā'ūn Mosque 埃及开罗市建筑群 14—53a
卡拉沃索 Cálabozo 委内瑞拉城市 3—332e
卡拉沃沃 Carabobo 委内瑞拉州名 3—433f
卡拉沃沃战役 Carabobo, Battle of 拉丁美洲独立战争 3—434a
卡拉西奥多里 Carathéodory, Constantin 德国数学家 3—438a
卡拉西王朝 Karası DYNASTY 土库曼人王朝 9—179e
卡拉雅人 Carajá 南美印第安民族 3—437a
卡拉扬 Karajan, Herbert von 管弦乐指挥家 9—177a
卡拉伊 Kállay, Miklós 匈牙利政治家 9—142f
卡腊套山 Karatau 哈萨克斯坦山脉 9—179f
卡莱蒂-布鲁尼 Caletti-Bruni, Pier Francesco (Italian composer) 意大利作曲家 3—344a
卡莱尔 Carlisle 英格兰城市 3—460c
卡莱尔 Carlisle 美国自治镇 3—460c
卡莱尔 Carlisle, John G(riffin) 美国政府官员 3—460d
卡莱尔 Carlile, Richard 英国记者 3—460a
卡莱尔 Carlyle, Thomas 苏格兰散文作家 3—463b
卡莱尔伯爵(第三) Carlisle, Charles Howard, 3rd earl of 英国首席大臣 3—460d
卡莱尔伯爵夫人 Carlisle, Lucy Hay, countess of 英国阴谋家 3—460e
卡莱尔委员会 Carlisle Commission 英国历史 3—460e
卡莱克西科 Calexico 美国城市 3—344a
卡莱米 Kalemi 刚果(金)城镇 9—139e
卡莱皮诺 Calepino, Ambrogio 意大利词典编纂者 3—344a
卡莱斯和泽特斯 Calais and Zetes 希腊神话 3—333e
卡莱斯亚阶 Calaisian Substage 地质学 3—333e
卡莱伊斯 Kallérgis, Dimítrios 希腊政治家 9—142f
卡赖斯卡基斯 Karaïskákis, Geórgios 希腊绿林好汉 9—176f
卡兰 Cāraṇ 印度教种姓 3—437b
卡兰博瀑布 Kalambo Falls 非洲瀑布 9—138e
卡兰达里教团 Qalandarīyah 伊斯兰教派别 14—52f
卡兰达什 Caran d'Ache 法国讽刺画家 3—437c
卡兰津人 Kalenjin 东非民族 9—139f
卡兰卡瓦人 Karankawa 北美印第安人 9—179d
卡兰萨 Carranza, Bartolomé de 天主教神学家 3—479f
卡兰萨 Carranza, Venustiano 墨西哥总统 3—480a
《卡郎提奥法典》 Kalantiyaw, Code of 菲律宾法典 9—138f
卡劳帕帕 Kalaupapa 美国夏威夷州半岛 9—139a
卡劳修斯 Carausius, Marcus Aurelius Mausaeus 罗马军官 3—438b
卡勒 Karrer, Paul 瑞士化学家 9—187b
《卡勒帕公约》 Halepa, Pact of 土耳其-希腊条约 7—420d
卡勒平原 Curragh, The 爱尔兰丘陵地 5—70c

《卡勒瓦拉》 Kalevala 芬兰民族史诗 9—139f
卡勒维斯 Kalvis 波罗的海地区宗教 9—144d
卡雷 Carrhae (ancient Mesopotamian city) 古罗马城市 3—481b
卡雷尔 Carrel, Alexis 法国外科医师 3—480e
卡雷尔-达金氏液 Carrel-Dakin fluid 防腐液 3—480e
卡雷拉 Carrera, José Miguel 智利总统 3—481a
卡雷拉 Carrera, Rafael 危地马拉独裁者 3—481b
卡雷梅 Carême, Marie-Antoine 法国名厨 3—455f
卡雷尼奥·德米兰达 Carreño de Miranda, Juan 西班牙画家 3—480f
卡雷尼奥港 Puerto Carreño 哥伦比亚城市 14—15e
卡雷山 Karre Mountains 中非共和国山脉 9—187b
卡雷神庙 Maison-Carrée 法国古罗马神庙 10—412a
卡雷斯 Chares 雅典将军 4—63e
卡雷斯 Chares of Lindos 古希腊雕刻家 4—63e
卡雷战役 Carrhae, Battle of 罗马历史 3—481b
卡累利阿 Karelia 俄罗斯的共和国 9—181a
卡累利阿地峡 Karelian Isthmus 北欧地峡 9—181c
卡累利阿语 Karelian language 北欧语言 9—181c
卡里 Cary, (Arthur) Joyce (Lunel) 英国小说家 3—494c
卡里 Cary, Annie Louise 美国歌剧演员 3—494a
卡里 Cary, Elisabeth Luther 美国艺术和文学评论家 3—494b
卡里 Cary, Henry Francis 英国翻译家 3—494c
卡里 Cary, Lucius 英格兰贵族 3—494d
卡里埃 Carrière, Eugène 法国画家 3—483a
卡里埃 Carrier, Jean-Baptiste 法国大革命激进派 3—482e
卡里埃-贝勒斯 Carrier-Belleuse, Albert(-Ernest) 法国雕刻家 3—482f
卡里奥·德·拉班德拉 Carrío de Lavandera, Alonso 西班牙殖民政府官员 3—483e
卡里奥塔基斯 Kariotákis, Kóstas 希腊诗人 9—182b
卡里巴 Kariba 津巴布韦城镇 9—181e
卡里巴湖 Kariba, Lake 非洲湖泊 9—181e
卡里巴水坝 Kariba Dam 非洲水坝 9—181f
卡里贝尔特 Charibert 墨洛温王朝统治者之名 4—64d
卡里贝尔特二世 Charibert II 阿基坦国王 4—64d
卡里贝尔特一世 Charibert I 法兰克国王 4—64d
卡里布 Caribou 美国城市 3—458b
卡里布山 Cariboo Mountains 加拿大山脉 3—457f
卡里布小道 Cariboo Road 加拿大小径 3—458a
卡里德莫斯 Charidemus 古希腊雇佣军头目 4—64d
卡里尔 Carrier, Willis Haviland 美国发明家 3—482f
卡里姐妹 Cary, Alice; and Cary, Phoebe 美国诗人 3—494a
卡里卡里 Kurri Kurri 澳大利亚城镇 9—403f
卡里克 Carrick 英格兰区名 3—481f
卡里克 Carrick (Scotland) 苏格兰区名 3—482a
卡里克伯爵 Carrick, John Stewart, earl of 苏格兰国王 3—482a
卡里克弗格斯 Carrickfergus 北爱尔兰城镇 3—482a
卡里克麦克罗斯花边 Carrickmacross 工艺品 3—482b
卡里略 Carrillo, Julián 墨西哥作曲家 3—483b
卡里略 Carrillo, Santiago 西班牙共产党总书记 3—483b
卡里略-索托马约 Carrillo y Sotomayor, Luis 西班牙诗人 3—483d
卡里姆汗·桑德 Karīm Khān Zand (Moḥammad) 伊朗统治者 9—182a
卡里努斯 Carinus 罗马皇帝 3—459c
卡里诺 Carreño, (Maria) Teresa 委内瑞拉钢琴家 3—480e
卡里斯布鲁克 Carisbrooke 英格兰地名 3—459d
卡里同 Chariton 希腊小说家 4—65b
卡里翁氏病 Carrión's disease 疾病 3—484a
卡里西米 Carissimi, Giacomo 意大利作曲家 3—459d
卡里辛比山 Karisimbi, Mount 非洲山峰 9—182c
卡里亚 Caria 安纳托利亚古行政区 3—457a
卡里亚夫陨石坑 Kaali järv Craters 爱沙尼亚陨石坑 9—123d
卡里亚人 Kharia 印度民族 9—256f
卡里亚语 Carian language 古代语言 3—457a
卡立格特绘画 Kālīghāṭ painting 印度水彩画风格 9—140e
卡利 Cali 哥伦比亚城市 3—344f
卡利埃尔 Callières, François de 法国外交家 3—354f
卡利班甘 Kalibangan 印度古遗址 9—140d
卡利德谷 Callide Valley 澳大利亚谷地 3—354f
卡利登河 Caledon River 非洲河流 3—342f
卡利敦 Calydon 希腊古城市 3—362c
卡利俄珀 Calliope 希腊神话 3—355f
卡利恩 Caerleon 威尔士城镇 3—316c
卡利古拉 Caligula 罗马皇帝 3—350f
卡利卡特 Calicut (India) 印度城市 3—345c
卡利克拉特 Callicrates 雅典建筑师 3—354d
卡利马科斯 Callimachus 希腊雕刻家 3—355c
卡利马科斯 Callimachus 希腊诗人 3—355d
卡利姆诺斯 Kálimnos 希腊岛屿 9—141e
卡利尼 Carlini, Armando 意大利哲学家 3—460b
卡利尼库斯(赫利奥波利斯的) Callinicus of Heliopolis 希腊火药发明者 3—355e
卡利诺斯 Callinus 希腊诗人 3—355f
卡利普索 calypso 特立尼达民歌 3—362d
卡利什 Kalisz 波兰旧省份 9—142c
卡利什 Kalisz 波兰城市 9—142d
卡利斯 Calais 美国城市 3—333d
卡利斯基 Kalisky, René 比利时作家 9—142c
卡利斯提尼斯 Callisthenes of Olynthus 希腊历史学家 3—356b
卡利斯图斯一世 Callistus 希腊正教牧首 3—356d
卡利斯托 Callisto 希腊神话 3—356c
卡利斯托加 Calistoga 美国城市 3—352b
卡利亚里 Cagliari 意大利城市 3—323a
卡利亚斯 Callias 古雅典军事家 3—354d
卡利亚斯 Callias 古雅典外交家 3—354d
卡廖斯特罗伯爵 Cagliostro, Alessandro, Count (count) di 意大利骗子 3—323a
卡列尔人 Carrier 印第安民族 3—482c
卡列金 Kaledin, Aleksey Maksimovich 俄罗斯帝国军官 9—139d
卡列拉 Carriera, Rosalba (Giovanna) 意大利画家 3—482f
卡列拉人 Kariera 澳大利亚民族 9—181f
卡列斯 Calles, Plutarco Elías 墨西哥军政领导人 3—354b
卡列塔伯爵(第六) Calheta, Luiz de Vasconcelos e Sousa, 6th Count of (conde de) 葡萄牙宠臣 3—344d
卡林 Kaline, Al 美国棒球运动员 9—141e
卡林顿 Carrington (of Upton), Peter Alexander Rupert Carington, 6th Baron, Baron Carrington of Bulcot Lodge 英国政治家 3—483d
卡林顿 Carrington, Richard Christopher 英国天文学家 3—483e
卡林娜 Karina, Anna 丹麦演员 9—182a
卡林维尔 Carlinville 美国城市 3—460b
卡林西亚 Carinthia (Austria) 奥地利州名 3—459c
卡柳梅特城 Calumet City 美国城市 3—358c
卡柳梅特区 Calumet District 美国工业区 3—358c
卡龙·德·博马舍 Caron de Beaumarchais, Pierre-Augustin 法国作家 3—473f
卡龙德莱特男爵 Carondelet, (Francisco Luis) Hector, baron de 西班牙总督 3—474a
卡龙加 Karonga 马拉维城镇 9—187a
卡隆 Charon 希腊神话 4—84a
卡隆 Caron, Antoine 法国画家 3—473e
卡卢加 Kaluga 俄罗斯州名 9—144b
卡卢加 Kaluga 俄罗斯城市 9—144c
卡卢卢希 Kalulushi 赞比亚城镇 9—144c
卡卢萨人 Calusa 民族 3—358d
卡卢什 Kalush 乌克兰城市 9—144c

卡卢特勒 Kalutara 斯里兰卡城镇 9—144d
卡鲁 Karroo 南非地理区域 9—187c
卡鲁 Carew, Sir George 英国军人 3—456a
卡鲁 Carew, Rod 美国棒球运动员 3—456a
卡鲁 Carew, Thomas 英格兰诗人 3—456a
卡鲁阿鲁 Caruaru 巴西城市 3—492a
卡鲁济 Karuzi 布隆迪城镇 9—189b
卡鲁帕诺 Carúpano 委内瑞拉城市 3—492b
卡鲁奇 Carrucci, Jacopo 佛罗伦萨画家 3—485b
卡鲁斯 Carus 罗马皇帝 3—492b
卡鲁斯 Carus, Titus Lucretius 罗马诗人、哲学家 3—492c
卡鲁索 Caruso, Enrico 意大利歌唱家 3—492c
卡鲁系 Karroo System 地质学 9—187c
卡路里盆地 Caloris 水星上盆地 3—357f
卡吕普索 Calypso 希腊神话 3—362d
卡律布狄斯 Charybdis (in Greek mythology) 希腊神话 4—87b
卡伦 Cullen, Countee 美国诗人 5—54a
卡伦 Cullen, Paul 爱尔兰大主教 5—54b
卡伦 Cullen, William 苏格兰医生 5—54b
卡伦德 Callander 苏格兰自治市 3—353d
卡伦德 Callendar, H(ugh) L(ongbourne) 英国物理学家 3—354b
卡伦德效应 Callendar effect 大气科学 3—354b
卡伦河 Kārūn River 伊朗河流 9—188f
卡罗 Caro, Annibale 罗马抒情诗人 3—471b
卡罗 Caro, Sir Anthony 英国雕刻家 3—471b
卡罗伯特(安茹的) Carobert OF ANJOU (king of Hungary) 匈牙利国王 3—471d
卡罗尔 Carroll, Anna Ella 美国作家 3—484a
卡罗尔 Carroll, Charles 美国爱国领袖 3—484b
卡罗尔 Carroll, Earl 美国戏剧导演 3—484b
卡罗尔 Carroll, John 美国天主教主教 3—484c
卡罗尔 Carroll, Lewis 英国数学家、作家 3—484c
卡罗尔 Carol, Martine 法国电影演员 3—472a
卡罗尔 Carroll, Vinnette 美国剧作家、舞台剧导演和演员 3—484e
卡罗尔顿 Carrollton 美国城市 3—484f
卡罗尔二世 Carol II 罗马尼亚国王 3—471e
卡罗尔舞 carole 舞蹈 3—472a
卡罗尔一世 Carol I 罗马尼亚国王 3—471d
卡罗拉 Carora 委内瑞拉城市 3—474b
卡罗兰 Carolan, Terence 爱尔兰音乐家 3—472a
卡罗利纳 Carolina 波多黎各城镇 3—472b
卡罗琳(勃兰登堡-安斯巴赫的) Caroline OF BRANDENBURG-ANSBACH 英国王后 3—472c
卡罗琳(不伦瑞克-吕讷堡的) Caroline OF BRUNSWICK-LÜNEBURG 英国王后 3—472d
卡罗琳夜鹰 chuck-will's-widow (species *Caprimulgus carolinensis*) 鸟类 4—219b
卡罗姆台球 carom billiards 球戏 3—473e
卡罗尼河 Caroni River 特立尼达和多巴哥河流 3—474a
卡罗尼河 Caroní River 委内瑞拉河流 3—474b
卡罗萨 Carossa, Hans 德国作家 3—474b
卡罗瑟斯 Carothers, Wallace Hume 美国化学家 3—474e
卡罗式照相法 calotype 摄影术 3—358a
卡罗托 Caroto, Gian Francesco 意大利画家 3—474f
卡罗维发利 Karlovy Vary 捷克城市 9—183a
卡罗伊 Károlyi, Mihály, Gróf 匈牙利政治家 9—186f
卡洛 Carlow 爱尔兰郡名 3—462a
卡洛 Carlow 爱尔兰城市 3—462a
卡洛 Kahlo (de Rivera), Frida 墨西哥画家 9—132c
卡洛 Callot, Jacques 法国铜版画家 3—356d
卡洛 Karo, Joseph ben Ephraim 犹太教律法编纂家 9—186e
卡洛奥坎 Caloocan 菲律宾城市 3—357c
卡洛登战役 Culloden, Battle of 英国历史 5—54c
卡洛夫 Karloff, Boris 英国演员 9—183a
卡洛福泰 Carloforte 意大利城镇 3—461a
卡洛曼 Carloman 统治者名称 3—461a
卡洛曼 Carloman 德意志、北意大利国王 3—461b
卡洛曼 Carloman 法兰克国王 3—461c
卡洛曼 Carloman 法兰克亲王 3—461b
卡洛曼 Carloman 法兰西国王 3—461b
卡洛纳 Calonne, Charles-Alexandre de 法国国务活动家 3—357b
卡洛斯 Carlos, DON 贵族 3—461d
卡洛斯(奥地利的) Carlos DE AUSTRIA 阿斯图里亚斯王子 3—461c
卡洛斯·路易斯(波旁的) Carlos Luis DE BORBÓN, COUNT (conde) DE MONTEMOLÍN 西班牙贵族 3—461d
卡洛斯·马利亚 Carlos María DE LOS DOLORES DE BORBÓN Y AUSTRIA-ESTE, DUKE (duque) DE MADRID 西班牙贵族 3—461d
卡洛斯·马利亚·伊西德罗(波旁的) Carlos María Isidro DE BORBÓN, COUNT (conde) DE MOLINA 西班牙王子 3—461e
卡洛塔 Carlota 墨西哥皇后 3—461f
卡洛韦 Calloway, Cab 美国爵士乐作曲家 3—356e
卡洛伊 Kállay, Benjamin 奥匈帝国政治家 9—142e
卡马 Khama, Sir Seretse 博茨瓦纳总统 9—254f
卡马尔多利会 Camaldolese 天主教本笃会 3—363b
卡马尔格 Camargue 法国地区 3—363d
卡马圭 Camagüey 古巴省份 3—363a
卡马圭 Camagüey 古巴城市 3—363b
卡马河 Kama River 俄罗斯河流 9—144f
卡马河畔切尔内 Naberezhnye Chelny 俄罗斯城市 11—533e
卡马卡埃哈 Kamakaeha, Liliu 夏威夷王后 9—145a
卡马拉季 Kamaraj, Kumaraswami 印度政治家 9—145d
卡马兰 Kamarān 也门岛屿 9—145e
卡马雷西陶器 Kamáres ware 古希腊陶器 9—145e
卡马尼奥拉服 carmagnole 服装式样 3—463d
卡马乔 Camacho, Manuel Ávila (President of Mexico) 墨西哥总统 3—363a
卡马三世 Khama III 南部非洲酋长 9—254e
卡马森 Carmarthen 威尔士区名 3—463e
卡马森 Carmarthen 威尔士城镇 3—463e
卡马森侯爵 Carmarthen, Thomas Osborne, Marquess of 英格兰政治家 3—463f
卡马森郡 Carmarthenshire 威尔士郡名 3—463f
卡马斯雨期 Kamasian Pluvial Stage 地质学 9—145f
卡马朱河 Kamazhu He 中国河流 9—145f
卡玛戈 Camargo, Marie(-Anne de Cupis de) 法国芭蕾舞演员 3—363c
卡迈克尔 Carmichael, Hoagy 美国钢琴家 3—464d
卡迈克尔 Carmichael, Leonard 美国心理学家 3—464e
卡曼 Carman, (William) Bliss 加拿大诗人 3—463d
卡梅尔 Carmel 美国城市 3—464b
卡梅拉里乌斯 Camerarius, Joachim 德国古典学者 3—371f
卡梅拉里乌斯 Camerarius, Rudolph Jacob 德国植物学家 3—372a
卡梅拉塔会社 Camerata 意大利诗人与音乐家团体 3—372a
卡梅伦 Cameron, Duncan 苏格兰商人 3—372b
卡梅伦 Cameron, Julia Margaret 英国摄影家 3—372c
卡梅伦 Cameron, Richard 苏格兰教士 3—372d
卡梅伦 Cameron, Simon 美国参议员 3—372e
卡梅伦 Cameron, Verney Lovett 欧洲探险家 3—372e
卡梅伦(洛奇尔的) Cameron (of Lochiel), Sir Ewen 苏格兰高地部落首领 3—372b
卡梅伦派 Cameronian 苏格兰基督教派别 3—373a
卡梅申 Kamyshin 俄罗斯城市 9—151c
卡美拉琼帽 kamelaukion 头饰 9—147f
卡门 Kármán, Theodore von 美国工程学家 9—184d
卡门培尔干酪 Camembert cheese 食品 3—371a
卡门谢克 Kamenshek, Dorothy 美国运动员 9—148c

卡蒙斯 Camões, Luís (Vaz) de 葡萄牙民族诗人 3—374f
卡米 Camus, Marcel 法国电影导演 3—385b
卡米哈米哈 Kamehameha 夏威夷国王名 9—146e
卡米哈米哈二世 Kamehameha Ⅱ 夏威夷国王 9—147a
卡米哈米哈三世 Kamehameha Ⅲ 夏威夷国王 9—147b
卡米哈米哈四世 Kamehameha Ⅳ 夏威夷国王 9—147c
卡米哈米哈五世 Kamehameha Ⅴ 夏威夷国王 9—147e
卡米哈米哈一世 Kamehameha Ⅰ 夏威夷国王 9—146e
卡米拉 Camilla 古罗马神话人物 3—374c
卡米勒 Kāmil, al-Malik al- 阿尤布王朝苏丹 9—149a
卡米勒 Kāmil, Muṣṭafā 埃及民族主义者 9—149a
卡米勒帕夏 Kâmil Paşa, Mehmed 土耳其首席大臣 9—149b
卡米卢斯 Camillus, Marcus Furius 罗马军人 3—374c
卡米纳 Kamina 刚果(金)城镇 9—149b
卡米纳柳尤 Kaminaljuyú 危地马拉文化遗址 9—149b
卡米尼斯蒂奎亚河 Kaministiquia River 加拿大河流 9—149c
卡米撒派 Camisard 法国新教教徒 3—374e
卡缅涅茨-波多利斯基 Kamenets-Podolsky (*oblast*, Ukraine) 乌克兰州名 9—147f
卡缅涅茨-波多利斯基 Kamenets-Podolsky 乌克兰城市 9—147f
卡缅斯科耶 Kamenskoye (Ukraine) 乌克兰城市 9—148d
卡缅斯克-沙赫京斯基 Kamensk-Shakhtinsky 俄罗斯城市 9—148d
卡明斯 Cummins, Albert Baird 美国律师、州长 5—60c
卡明斯 Cummings, Bruce Frederick 英国作家 5—60b
卡明斯 Cummins, George David 美国归正圣公会创始人 5—60d
卡明斯 Cummins, Maria Susanna 美国作家 5—60d
卡明斯卡 Kaminska, Ida 演员 9—149d
卡莫拉 Camorra 意大利帮会 3—375b
卡莫纳 Carmona (Angola) 安哥拉省份 3—465a
卡莫纳 Carmona 西班牙城镇 3—465a
卡莫斯 Kamose 埃及国王 9—150c
卡默勒 Kammerer, Paul 奥地利生物学家 9—149f
卡默洛特 Camelot 亚瑟王传奇地名 3—371a
卡姆 Karm, Dun 马耳他民族诗人 9—184a
卡姆岛 Karm Island 挪威岛屿 9—184a
卡姆登 Camden 澳大利亚城镇 3—368e
卡姆登 Camden 英格兰自治市 3—368e
卡姆登 Camden 美国阿肯色州城市 3—368f
卡姆登 Camden 美国新泽西州城市 3—368f
卡姆登 Camden 美国南卡罗来纳州城市 3—369a
卡姆登 Camden, Charles Pratt, 1st Earl, Viscount Bayham of Bayham Abbey, Baron Camden of Camden Place 英国法学家 3—369b
卡姆登 Camden, William 英国古物收藏家 3—369e
卡姆登侯爵、伯爵和男爵 Camden, Marquess, Earl, and Baron 英国普拉特家族名 3—369b
卡姆登侯爵(第一) Camden, John Jeffreys Pratt, 1st Marquess, 2nd Earl Camden, Earl of the County of Brecknock, Viscount Bayham of Bayham Abbey, Baron Camden of Camden Place 英国驻爱尔兰总督 3—369c
卡姆登战役 Camden, Battle of 美国独立战争 3—369b
卡姆登镇小组 Camden Town Group 英国画家团体 3—369f
卡姆罗斯 Camrose 加拿大城市 3—384c
卡姆诺克 Cumnock 苏格兰城市 5—60d
卡姆诺克-杜恩瓦利 Cumnock and Doon Valley 苏格兰区名 5—60e
卡姆帕纳 Campaña, Pedro (Flemish painter) 佛兰德斯画家 3—377a
卡姆萨克 Kamsack 加拿大城镇 9—151c
卡穆河 Camú River 多米尼加共和国河流 3—384c
卡那封 Caernarvon 威尔士城镇 3—316c
卡那封伯爵(第四) Carnarvon, Henry Howard Molyneux Herbert, 4th earl of 英国政治家 3—465f
卡那封伯爵(第五) Carnarvon, George Edward Stanhope Molyneux Herbert, 5th earl of 英国埃及学家 3—465e
卡那封郡 Caernarvonshire 威尔士郡名 3—316d
卡那封岭 Carnarvon Range 澳大利亚高地 3—466a
卡那封峡谷 Carnarvon Gorge 澳大利亚峡谷 3—466a
卡纳波依化石 Kanapoi fossil 人科化石 9—152d
卡纳布 Kanab 美国城市 9—152a
卡纳蒂克 Carnatic (India) 印度地区 3—466a
卡纳蒂克音乐 Carnatic music 印度音乐 3—466a
卡纳蒂克战争 Carnatic Wars 印度历史 3—466b
卡纳尔 Canal, Giovanni Antonio (painter) 意大利画家 3—392a
卡纳加岛 Kanaga Island 美国岛屿 9—152a
卡纳卡 Kanaka 澳大利亚雇工 9—152c
卡纳拉语 Kanarese language 印度语言 9—152e
卡纳莱托 Canaletto 意大利画家 3—392c
卡纳里奥人 Canario (people) 民族 3—392d
卡纳里斯 Kanáris, Konstantínos 希腊政治家 9—152e
卡纳里斯 Canaris, Wilhelm (Franz) 德国海军上将 3—392d
卡纳利 Canali, Isabella 意大利演员 3—392d
卡纳普 Carnap, Rudolf 逻辑实证学派创始人 3—465c
卡纳塞基 Carnesecchi, Pietro 意大利人文学者 3—467f
卡纳斯塔 Canasta 牌戏 3—395b
卡纳斯特拉山 Canastra Mountains 巴西山脉 3—395b
卡纳塔克 Karnātaka 印度邦名 9—185d
卡纳塔克 Karnātaka 印度语言区 9—186a
卡纳塔克高原 Karnātaka Plateau 印度高原 9—186b
卡纳塔克海岸 Karnātaka Coast 印度沿海低地 9—186a
卡纳塔克湖 Kanatak Lake 美国湖泊 9—152f
卡纳塔寺庙建筑 Karnatic temple architecture 印度南部建筑形式 9—186b
卡纳维拉尔角 Canaveral, Cape 美国城市 3—395c
卡南加 Kananga 刚果(金)城市 9—152d
卡讷克 Kanık, Orhan Veli 土耳其诗人 9—158a
卡内 Kanye 博茨瓦纳村庄 9—170d
卡内 Kane, Sheikh Hamidou 非洲作家 9—155c
卡内奥赫 Kaneohe 美国城镇 9—155d
卡内奥赫湾 Kaneohe Bay 美国海湾 9—155e
卡内蒂 Canetti, Elias 小说家 3—400b
卡内基 Carnegie, Andrew 美国实业家 3—466e
卡内基 Carnegie, Dale 美国演说家 3—467d
卡内基音乐厅 Carnegie Hall 美国纽约市音乐厅 3—467d
卡内拉 Carnera, Primo 意大利拳击运动员 3—467e
卡内洛内斯 Canelones 乌拉圭城市 3—400b
卡内洛人 Canelo 南美印第安民族 3—400a
卡内姆-博尔努 Kanem-Bornu 非洲古帝国 9—155d
卡内帕诺瓦 Canepanova, Pietro 教皇 3—400b
卡嫩城 Canon City 美国城市 3—407b
卡尼 Kearney 美国城市 9—209b
卡尼 Kearny, Stephen Watts 美国军官 9—209b
卡尼奥拉 Carniola 斯洛文尼亚地区 3—468a
卡尼巴达姆 Kanibadam 塔吉克斯坦城市 9—158a
卡尼茨 Canitz, Friedrich Rudolf, Freiherr von (baron of) 德国宫廷诗人 3—401f
卡尼夫 Caniff, Milton (Arthur) 美国连环画家 3—401c
卡尼阶 Karnian Stage 地质学 9—186d
卡尼曼 Kahneman, Daniel 美国心理学家 9—133d
卡尼修斯,圣 Canisius, Saint Peter 天主教教义师 3—401f
卡尼亚皮斯科河 Caniapiscau River 加拿大河流 3—401c
卡涅阿德斯 Carneades 希腊哲学家 3—466e
卡宁 Kanin, Garson 美国作家、导演 9—158b
卡宁半岛 Kanin Peninsula 俄罗斯半岛 9—158c
卡农 canon 音乐 3—407a
卡农图姆 Carnuntum 古罗马军营 3—471b
卡努尔 Kurnool 印度城市 9—402e
卡努里人 Kanuri 非洲民族 9—170c

卡努西翁 Canusium (ancient town, Italy) 意大利古城镇 3—415b
卡诺 Kano 尼日利亚州名 9—159b
卡诺 Kano 尼日利亚城市 9—159d
卡诺 Cano, Alonso 西班牙画家 3—405f
卡诺 Carnot, Lazare 法国政治家 3—470b
卡诺 Cano, Melchor 天主教神学家 3—406a
卡诺 Carnot, Sadi 法国工程师 3—470d
卡诺 Carnot, Sadi 法国总统 3—470e
卡诺阿斯 Canoas 巴西城市 3—406b
卡诺萨 Canossa 意大利城堡 3—408e
卡诺萨迪普利亚 Canosa di Puglia 意大利城镇 3—408e
卡诺瓦 Canova, Antonio, MARCHESE (marquess) D'ISCHIA 意大利雕刻家 3—408f
卡诺瓦河 Kanawha River 美国河流 9—152f
卡诺瓦斯·德尔·卡斯蒂略 Cánovas del Castillo, Antonio 西班牙政治家 3—409d
卡诺循环 Carnot cycle 物理学 3—470f
卡帕 Capa, Robert 匈牙利摄影家 3—418e
卡帕阿 Kapaa 美国城市 9—171e
卡帕布兰卡 Capablanca, José Raúl 古巴国际象棋大师 3—418f
卡帕多西亚 Cappadocia 安纳托利亚古代行政区 3—429c
卡潘诺里 Capannori 意大利市镇 3—419c
卡潘潘甘人 Kapampangan (people) 菲律宾民族 9—171f
卡庞捷 Carpentier, Georges 法国拳击运动员 3—477c
卡佩尔 Capel, Arthur 英国政治家 3—424e
卡佩尔 Cappel, Louis 基督教神学家 3—429f
卡佩尔战争 Kappel Wars 瑞士宗教战争 9—173c
卡佩拉 Capella, Martianus Minneus Felix 迦太基律师 3—424e
卡佩拉里 Cappellari, Bartolomeo Alberto (pope) 教皇 3—429f
卡佩拉努斯 Capellanus, Andreas 法国作家 3—424f
卡佩勒堡 Fort Qu'Appelle 加拿大城镇 6—415a
卡佩勒河 Qu'Appelle River 加拿大河流 14—77a
卡佩伦男爵 Capellen, Godert Alexander Gerard Philip, baron van der 荷属东印度群岛总督 3—424f
卡佩洛 Capello, Bianca 威尼斯贵族女子 3—424f
卡佩纳 Capena 意大利古城 3—425a
卡佩王朝 Capetian DYNASTY 中世纪法兰西王朝 3—425b
卡彭 Capone, Al 美国歹徒 3—428f
卡彭特 Carpenter, Edward 英国作家 3—476b
卡彭特 Carpenter, Harlean (American actress) 美国演员 3—476c
卡彭特 Carpenter, John Alden 美国作曲家 3—476c
卡彭特 Carpenter, Mary 英国慈善家 3—476e
卡彭特 Carpenter, M(alcolm) Scott 美国宇航员 3—476d
卡彭铁尔 Carpentier (y Valmont), Alejo 古巴小说家 3—477b
卡皮 Carpi, Ugo da 意大利版画家 3—478c
卡皮察 Kapitsa, Pyotr Leonidovich 苏联物理学家 9—172b
卡皮蒂岛 Kapiti Island 新西兰岛屿 9—172a
卡皮林火山国家保护区 Capulin Volcano National Monument 美国国家保护区 3—433c
卡皮塔诺 Capitano 意大利喜剧角色 3—427b
卡皮特尔里夫国家公园 Capitol Reef National Park 美国国家公园 3—427e
卡皮托 Capito, Wolfgang Fabricius 欧洲人文学家 3—427c
卡皮托利尼博物馆 Capitoline Museums 罗马艺术陈列馆 3—427f
卡普 Capp, Al 美国漫画家 3—429c
卡普 Kapp, Wolfgang 普鲁士政治家 9—173a
卡普阿 Capua 古代意大利城市 3—432f
卡普阿 Capua 意大利城镇 3—433a
卡普阿斯河 Kapuas River 印度尼西亚河流 9—173d
卡普安纳 Capuana, Luigi 意大利评论家 3—433a
卡普德拉马德莱娜 Cap-de-la Madeleine 加拿大城市 3—418c
卡普芬贝格 Kapfenberg 奥地利城市 9—171f
卡普格雷夫 Capgrave, John 英国历史学家 3—425d
卡普拉 Capra, Frank 美国电影导演 3—430a
卡普拉拉 Caprara, Giovanni Battista 意大利教廷外交家 3—430b
卡普拉亚岛 Capraia Island 意大利岛屿 3—430b
卡普兰 Kaplan, Mordecai Menahem 犹太教拉比 9—172c
卡普雷奥吕 Capréolus, Jean 基督教学者 3—430c
卡普雷拉岛 Caprera Island 意大利岛屿 3—430c
卡普里岛 Capri, Island of 意大利岛屿 3—430d
卡普里维 Caprivi, (Georg) Leo, Graf von 德国军事家 3—431f
卡普里维地带 Caprivi Strip 纳米比亚地区 3—432a
卡普罗利 Caproli, Carlo 意大利作曲家 3—432b
卡普尼 Kapuni 新西兰油田 9—173d
卡普萨石器工艺 Capsian industry 北非文化遗存 3—432b
卡普斯卡辛 Kapuskasing 加拿大城镇 9—173e
卡普苏卡斯 Kapsukas (Lithuania) 立陶宛城市 9—173c
卡普坦 Kapteyn, Jacobus Cornelius 荷兰天文学家 9—173c
卡齐尔 Katzir, Ephraim 以色列总统 9—198c
卡齐米日 Casimir 波兰国王、公爵之名 3—500b
卡齐米日二世 Casimir II 波兰统治者 3—500c
卡齐米日三世 Casimir III 波兰国王 3—500c
卡齐米日四世 Casimir IV 波兰国王 3—500e
卡齐米日一世 Casimir I 波兰公爵 3—500b
卡齐纳 Katsina 尼日利亚州名 9—196f
卡齐纳 Katsina 尼日利亚城镇 9—197a
卡其布 khaki 织物 9—253e
卡奇纳 kachina 印第安宗教 9—127b
卡奇湾 Kachchh, Gulf of 阿拉伯海海湾 9—126e
卡奇沼泽地 Kachchh, Rann of 南亚地理区 9—126e
卡契尼 Caccini, Giulio 意大利歌唱家 3—309e
卡恰 caccia 意大利音乐 3—309e
卡钳 caliper 测量工具 3—351a
卡戎 Chiron 天文学 4—179f
卡荣语 Koyong language 越南语言 9—368c
卡萨 Kassa (Ethiopian emperor) 埃塞俄比亚皇帝 9—192d
卡萨 Kassa (Ethiopian emperor) 埃塞俄比亚皇帝 9—192d
卡萨 Casa, Giovanni Della 意大利主教、诗人 3—495f
卡萨布兰卡 Casablanca 摩洛哥港口 3—496a
卡萨布兰卡会议 Casablanca Conference 第二次世界大战史 3—496c
卡萨尔 Casal, Julián del 古巴诗人 3—496e
卡萨尔斯 Casals, Pablo 西班牙大提琴家 3—496e
卡萨格兰德 Casa Grande 美国城市 3—496a
卡萨格兰德遗址国家保护区 Casa Grande Ruins National Monument 美国遗址保护区 3—496a
卡萨拉 Kassalā 苏丹传统地区 9—192e
卡萨拉 Kassalā 苏丹城镇 9—192f
卡萨莱蒙费拉托 Casale Monferrato 意大利城镇 3—496e
卡萨芒斯 Casamance 塞内加尔区名 3—497a
卡萨芒斯河 Casamance River 西非河流 3—497a
卡萨纳雷 Casanare 哥伦比亚省份 3—497b
卡萨诺瓦 Casanova, Giovanni Giacomo 意大利教士、作家 3—497b
卡萨帕 Caazapá 巴拉圭省份 3—303b
卡萨帕 Caazapá 巴拉圭城镇 3—303c
卡萨人 Khāsā (people) 南亚民族 9—258a
卡萨斯 Casas, Bartolomé de Las 西班牙历史学家 3—497c
卡萨特 Cassatt, Mary 美国油画家 3—502f
卡萨特金 Kasatkin, Ivan Dmitrovich (Orthodox saint) 东正教圣者 9—189e
卡萨武布 Kasavubu, Joseph 政治家 9—189e
卡塞比尔 Käsebier, Gertrude 美国摄影师 9—190b
卡塞尔 Kassel 德国行政区 9—193a
卡塞尔 Kassel 德国城市 9—193b
卡塞尔 Cassel, (Karl) Gustav 瑞典经济学家 3—503c

卡塞尔瓷器 Cassel porcelain 德国瓷器 3—503c
卡塞格林反射望远镜 Cassegrain reflector 仪器 3—503b
卡塞拉 Casella, Alfredo 意大利作曲家 3—498d
卡塞拉颜料公司 Cassella Farbewerke Mainkur Aktiengesellschaft 德国化工公司 3—503d
卡塞雷斯 Cáceres 西班牙省份 3—309f
卡塞雷斯 Cáceres 西班牙城市 3—310a
卡塞利奥 Casserius, Julius 意大利解剖学家 3—503d
卡塞林 Qaṣrayn, Al- 突尼斯城镇 14—54f
卡塞塔 Caserta 意大利城市 3—499a
《卡赛尔·赛义德条约》 Kasser Said, Treaty of 法国-突尼斯条约 9—193c
《卡赛尔·赛义德条约》(1881) Qaṣr as-Saʿīd, Al-, Treaty of 法国-突尼斯条约 14—54e
卡赛姆 Qāsim, ʿAbd al-Karīm 伊拉克军官 14—54d
卡桑德尔 Cassandre 法国美术家 3—502e
卡桑德拉 Cassandra 希腊神话 3—502e
卡桑德拉 Kassándra 希腊地峡 9—192f
卡桑杰 Kasanje 非洲历史王国 9—189d
卡森 Carson, David 美国平面造型设计师 3—485b
卡森 Carson (of Duncairn), Edward Henry Carson, Baron 英国律师 3—485c
卡森 Carson, Kit 美国印第安事务官 3—485d
卡森 Carson, Rachel (Louise) 美国生物学家 3—485e
卡森 Cassin, René(-Samuel) 英国律师 3—504c
卡森河 Carson River 美国河流 3—485f
卡森市 Carson City 美国城市 3—485e
卡山得 Cassander 马其顿国王 3—502d
卡尚 Kāshān 伊朗城市 9—190c
卡尚地毯 Kāshān carpet 伊朗工艺品 9—190c
卡绍 Kaschau (Slovakia) 斯洛伐克城市 9—190a
卡舍尔 Cashel 爱尔兰城镇 3—499e
卡施尼茨 Kaschnitz, Marie Luise 德国诗人 9—190a
卡什 Cash, W. J. 美国作家 3—499c
卡什 Karsh, Yousuf 加拿大摄影家 9—187f
卡什加地毯 Qashqāʾī rug 工艺品 14—54b
卡舒埃鲁-迪-伊塔佩米林 Cachoeiro de Itapemirim 巴西城市 3—310c
卡斯 Cases, Emmanuel(-Augustin-Dieudonné-Joseph), Count (comte) de Las 法国历史学家 3—499b
卡斯 Cass, Lewis 美国陆军军官 3—502c
卡斯 Casse, Pierre-Emmanuel-Albert, Baron Du 法国军事史学家 3—503b
卡斯鲍姆 Kassebaum, Nancy Landon 美国参议员 9—192f
卡斯蒂 Casti, Giovanni Battista 意大利诗人 3—510a
卡斯蒂格里奥尼 Castiglioni, Francesco Saverio (pope) 教皇 3—510d
卡斯蒂格里奥尼 Castiglioni, Goffredo (pope) 教皇 3—510d
卡斯蒂利奥内 Castiglione, Baldassare 意大利外交官 3—510a
卡斯蒂利亚 Castile 西班牙地区 3—510e
卡斯蒂利亚 Castilla, Ramón 秘鲁军人 3—511f
卡斯蒂利亚方言 Castilian dialect 西班牙方言 3—511e
卡斯蒂利亚和莱昂 Castile and León 西班牙自治区 3—511b
卡斯蒂利亚-拉曼查 Castile-La Mancha 西班牙自治区 3—511a
卡斯蒂廖内 Castiglione, Giovanni Benedetto 意大利画家 3—510b
卡斯蒂廖内公爵 Castiglione, Pierre-François-Charles Augereau, duc de (duke of) 法国军官 3—510d
卡斯蒂列霍 Castillejo, Cristóbal de 西班牙诗人 3—512a
卡斯蒂略 Castillo, Ana 美国作家 3—512a
卡斯蒂略 Castilho, António Feliciano de 西班牙作家 3—511d
卡斯蒂略 Castillo, Michel del 西班牙裔小说家 3—512b
卡斯蒂略·索洛萨诺 Castillo Solorzano, Alonso de 西班牙小说家 3—512c
卡斯蒂永战役 Castillon, Battle of 英法百年战争 3—512c
卡斯尔巴 Castlebar 爱尔兰城镇 3—513d
卡斯尔敦 Castletown 不列颠古都 3—514b
卡斯尔夫妇 Castle, Vernon and Irene 美国舞蹈家 3—513a
卡斯尔角 Castle Point 英格兰区名 3—513c
卡斯尔雷 Castlereagh 北爱尔兰区名 3—513e
卡斯尔雷子爵 Castlereagh, Robert Stewart, Viscount 英国外相 3—513e
卡斯尔梅恩 Castlemaine 澳大利亚城市 3—513d
卡斯尔梅恩阶 Castlemainian Stage 地质学 3—513e
卡斯尔梅恩女伯爵 Castlemaine, Barbara Palmer, countess of 英国贵族 3—513d
卡斯尔山起事 Castle Hill Rising 澳大利亚历史 3—513c
卡斯格温特 Cas-gwent (Wales) 威尔士集镇 3—495f
卡斯喀人 Kaska 古安纳托利亚民族 9—191f
卡斯卡斯基亚 Kaskaskia 美国村落 9—192a
卡斯卡斯基亚河 Kaskaskia River 美国河流 9—192a
卡斯凯什 Cascais 葡萄牙城镇 3—498a
卡斯隆 Caslon, William 英国铸字工人 3—501e
卡斯帕罗夫 Kasparov, Gary 苏联国际象棋大师 9—192a
卡斯佩勒 Kasperle 木偶戏主角 9—192b
卡斯珀 Casper 美国城市 3—501f
卡斯珀松 Caspersson, Torbjörn Oskar 瑞典细胞学家 3—502a
卡斯普罗维奇 Kasprowicz, Jan 波兰诗人 9—192c
卡斯塔雷斯 Carstares, William 苏格兰牧师 3—486a
卡斯塔利亚泉 Castalia 诗歌 3—507c
卡斯塔莫努 Kastamonu 土耳其城市 9—193d
卡斯塔尼奥 Castagno, Andrea del 意大利画家 3—507a
卡斯泰尔 Castel, Charles-Irénée 法国时事评论家 3—508c
卡斯泰尔诺沃-泰代斯科 Castelnuovo-Tedesco, Mario 意大利作曲家 3—509c
卡斯泰尔韦特拉诺 Castelvetrano 意大利城镇 3—509f
卡斯泰洛城 Città di Castello 意大利城镇 4—249f
卡斯泰洛里宗 Kastellórizon 希腊岛屿 9—193e
卡斯特 Custer, George Armstrong 美国骑兵军官 5—77e
卡斯特 Custer 美国城市 5—77e
卡斯特尔 Castres 法国城镇 3—514f
卡斯特尔伯爵 Castres, Jacques d'Armagnac, comte de (count of) 法国贵族 3—515a
卡斯特尔罗索 Castelrosso (Greece) 希腊岛屿 3—509f
卡斯特尔诺 Castelnau, Michel de, SIEUR (sire) DE LA MAUVISSIÈRE 法国外交家 3—509b
卡斯特尔韦特罗 Castelvetro, Lodovico 意大利文学评论家 3—509f
卡斯特拉尔-里波尔 Castelar y Ripoll, Emilio 西班牙政治家 3—508d
卡斯特拉卡尼 Castracani, Castruccio 雇佣兵队长 3—514e
卡斯特勒 Kastler, Alfred 法国物理学家 9—193e
卡斯特里 Castries 圣卢西亚城镇 3—515a
卡斯特里奥蒂 Kastrioti, George 阿尔巴尼亚英雄 9—194b
卡斯特里奥塔 Castriota, George 阿尔巴尼亚民族英雄 3—515b
卡斯特利翁 Castellón 西班牙省份 3—509a
卡斯特利翁-德拉普拉纳 Castellón de la Plana 西班牙城市 3—509a
卡斯特利亚诺斯 Castellanos, Rosario 墨西哥小说家、评论家和外交家 3—508f
卡斯特伦 Castrén, Matthias Alexander 芬兰民族主义者 3—514e
卡斯特罗 Castro 智利城镇 3—515b
卡斯特罗 Castro(y Quesada), Américo 西班牙语言学家 3—515b
卡斯特罗 Castro, Cipriano 委内瑞拉独裁者 3—515c
卡斯特罗 Castro, Eugénio de 葡萄牙诗人 3—515d
卡斯特罗 Castro, Fidel 古巴总理 3—515e
卡斯特罗 Castro, Inês de 葡萄牙国王情妇 3—516c

卡斯特罗 Castro, João de 葡萄牙海军军官 3—516c
卡斯特罗 Castro, Rosalía de 西班牙作家 3—516d
卡斯特罗·阿尔维斯 Castro Alves, Antônio de 巴西诗人 3—516d
卡斯特罗-贝尔维斯 Castro y Bellvís, Guillén de 西班牙剧作家 3—516e
卡斯特罗普-劳克塞尔 Castrop-Rauxel 德国城市 3—516e
卡斯特洛·布兰科 Castelo Branco, Camilo 葡萄牙小说家 3—509d
卡斯特洛·梅略尔 Castelo Melhor, Luiz de Vasconcelos e Sousa, 3° conde de (3rd count of), 6° CONDE (6th count) DA CALHETA 葡萄牙王室宠臣 3—509e
卡斯特州立公园 Custer State Park 美国南达科他州西南部一地区 5—77f
卡斯滕 Carstens, Asmus Jacob 德国肖像画家 3—486a
卡斯藤士峰 Carstensz, Mount (Indonesia) 印度尼西亚山峰 3—486b
卡斯廷 Castine 美国城镇 3—512d
卡斯托耳与波鲁克斯 Castor and Pollux (Roman deities) 罗马神话 3—514b
卡斯托里亚 Kastoría 希腊城镇 9—194a
卡松古 Kasungu 马拉维城镇 9—194b
卡苏尔 Kasūr 巴基斯坦城市 9—194b
卡索·安德拉德 Caso y Andrade, Alfonso 墨西哥考古学者 3—501f
卡索邦 Casaubon, Isaac 法国神学家 3—497d
卡塔丁山 Katahdin, Mount 美国山峰 9—194d
卡塔尔 Qatar 阿拉伯半岛国家 14—54f
卡塔尔久 Catargiu, Lascăr 罗马尼亚政治家 3—521f
卡塔戈 Cartago 哥斯达黎加城市 3—486d
卡塔古姆 Katagum 尼日利亚城镇 9—194d
卡塔赫纳 Cartagena 哥伦比亚城市 3—486b
卡塔赫纳 Cartagena 西班牙城市 3—486c
卡塔卡利舞 kathākali 印度古典舞蹈 9—195b
卡塔克舞 kathak 印度古典舞蹈 9—195b
卡塔库尔干 Kattakurgan 乌兹别克斯坦城市 9—197e
卡塔利娜岛 Catalina Island 美国加利福尼亚岛屿 3—519c
卡塔罗 Cattaro (Montenegro) 黑山共和国城镇 3—531a
卡塔罗湾 Cattaro, Bocche di (Montenegro) 黑山共和国海湾 3—531a
卡塔马卡 Catamarca 阿根廷省份 3—521a
卡塔马卡 Catamarca 阿根廷城市 3—521a
卡塔内奥 Cattaneo, Carlo 意大利政论家 3—531a
卡塔尼亚 Catania 意大利城市 3—521c
卡塔尼亚湾 Catania, Gulf of 意大利海湾 3—521d
卡塔通博河 Catatumbo River 哥伦比亚河流 3—522b
卡泰布 Kateb Yacine 阿尔及利亚剧作家 9—195a
卡泰里尼 Kateríni 希腊城镇 9—195b
卡坦杜瓦 Catanduva 巴西城市 3—521b
卡坦端内斯 Catanduanes 菲律宾岛屿 3—521b
卡坦宁 Katanning 澳大利亚城镇 9—194e
卡坦扎罗 Catanzaro 意大利城市 3—521d
卡特 Carter, Betty 美国爵士乐歌手 3—487c
卡特 Catt, Carrie Chapman 美国女权运动领导人 3—530e
卡特 Carter, Elizabeth 英国诗人 3—487d
卡特 Carter, Elliot (Cook, Jr.) 美国作曲家 3—487e
卡特 Carter, Howard 英国考古学家 3—487f
卡特 Carter, Jimmy 美国总统 3—488a
卡特 Carter, Maybelle 美国吉他手 3—488d
卡特 Carte, Richard D'Oyly 英国演出经理 3—486e
卡特彼勒公司 Caterpillar Inc. 美国制造商 3—523f
卡特尔 cartel 经济学 3—487a
卡特尔 Cattell, James McKeen 美国心理学家 3—531a
卡特尔 Cattell, Raymond B(ernard) 美国心理学家 3—531c
卡特加特海峡 Kattegat 丹麦海峡 9—197e
卡特家族 Carter FAMILY 美国音乐家族 3—487b
卡特科夫 Katkov, Mikhail Nikiforovich 俄国新闻工作者 9—196b
卡特克 Katyk (Ukraine) 乌克兰城市 9—198a
卡特赖特 Cartwright, Alexander Joy 棒球规则编订人 3—491d
卡特赖特 Cartwright, Edmund 英国发明家 3—491d
卡特赖特 Cartwright, John 英国改革鼓吹者 3—491e
卡特赖特 Cartwright, Peter 美国牧师 3—491f
卡特赖特 Cartwright, Sir Richard John 加拿大政治家 3—491f
卡特勒 Cutler, Manasseh 北美牧师 5—79c
卡特勒博讷 Quatre Bornes 毛里求斯城镇 14—81a
卡特雷特 Carteret, John 英国政治家 3—488f
卡特里特 Carteret, Sir George, BARONET 英国政治人物 3—488e
卡特利兰属 cattleya 植物学 3—532b
卡特利努斯 Catelinus 教皇 3—523e
卡特林 Catlin, George 美国画家 3—528e
卡特琳·德·美第奇 Catherine DE MÉDICIS 法国王后 3—526b
卡特鲁 Catroux, Georges 法国将军 3—529f
卡特伦 Catron, John 美国最高法院大法官 3—529e
卡特迈国家公园和自然保护区 Katmai National Park and Preserve 美国国家公园 9—196b
卡特那 Katna 叙利亚古城 9—196c
卡特韦克 Katwijk 荷兰城市 9—197e
卡特维尔诸语言 Kartvelian languages 南高加索语言 9—188f
卡提阿瓦半岛 Kāthiāwār Peninsula 印度半岛 9—195d
卡提尔 Kartēr 伊朗琐罗亚斯德教祭司 9—188d
卡廷屠杀案 Katyn Massacre 波兰历史 9—198a
卡通巴 Katoomba 澳大利亚城镇 9—196e
卡图卢斯 Catulus, Gaius Lutatius 罗马统帅 3—533a
卡图卢斯 Catullus, Gaius Valerius 罗马诗人 3—532c
卡图卢斯 Catulus, Quintus Lutatius 罗马将军、作家 3—533a
卡图卢斯 Catulus, Quintus Lutatius 罗马政治家 3—533b
卡图维勒尼人 Catuvellauni 古不列颠部落 3—533b
卡托巴人 Catawba 北美印第安民族 3—522b
《卡托-康布雷齐和约》 Cateau-Cambrésis, Peace of 欧洲历史 3—522e
卡托利科斯 catholicos 基督教首脑称号 3—528c
卡托切角 Catoche, Cape 墨西哥地岬 3—529d
卡托维兹 Katowice 波兰旧省份 9—196f
卡托维兹 Katowice 波兰城镇 9—196f
卡托维茨 Kattowitz (Poland) 波兰城镇 9—197e
卡瓦德蒂雷尼 Cava de' Tirreni 意大利城镇 3—536f
卡瓦蒂纳 cavatina 音乐 3—539a
卡瓦尔卡塞莱 Cavalcaselle, Giovanni Battista 意大利美术史家 3—537d
卡瓦尔坎蒂 Cavalcanti, Alberto 巴西电影导演 3—537c
卡瓦尔坎蒂 Cavalcanti, Guido 意大利诗人 3—537d
卡瓦菲 Cavafy, Constantine 希腊诗人 3—536f
卡瓦菲斯 Kaváfis, Konstantínos Pétrou 希腊作家 9—201b
卡瓦酒 kava 饮料 9—201a
卡瓦拉 Kavála 希腊城镇 9—201b
卡瓦拉蒂 Kavaratti 印度城镇 9—201e
卡瓦拉河 Cavalla River 西非河流 3—538c
卡瓦利 Cavalli, (Pier) Francesco 意大利作曲家 3—538c
卡瓦利河 Cavally River (western Africa) 西非河流 3—538f
卡瓦利尼 Cavallini, Pietro 罗马画家 3—538e
卡瓦利耶 Cavalier, Jean 法国宗教领袖 3—537e
卡瓦利耶(阿尔皮诺的) Cavaliere D'ARPINO 意大利画家 3—538a
卡瓦列雷 Cavaliere, Emilio del 意大利作曲家 3—537f
卡瓦列雷·迪·坎迪亚 Cavaliere di Candia, Mario (singer) 意大利歌唱家 3—538b
卡瓦列里 Cavalieri, (Francesco) Bonaventura 意大利数学家 3—538b
卡瓦列罗 Caballero, Fernán 西班牙小说家 3—303e
卡瓦列罗 Caballero, Francisco Largo 西班牙总理 3—303f

卡瓦柳 Carvalho, Sebastião de (Portuguese leader) 葡萄牙领袖 3—492f
卡瓦鲁斯 Cabarrus, François, conde de (count of) 西班牙经济学家 3—304c
卡瓦洛蒂 Cavallotti, Felice (Carlo Emmanuele) 意大利新闻记者 3—538f
卡瓦纳 Kavanagh, Patrick 爱尔兰诗人 9—201d
卡瓦尼列斯 Cabanilles, Juan Bautista José 西班牙管风琴家 3—303f
卡瓦尼亚斯 Cabañas 萨尔瓦多省份 3—303f
卡瓦人 Kawa (people) 缅甸、中国民族 9—202a
卡瓦耶-科尔 Cavaillé-Coll, Aristide 法国管风琴制作家 3—537b
卡瓦伊夫人 Kawaíb 南美印第安人 9—202e
卡瓦伊古安 Cabaiguán 古巴城市 3—303c
卡万戈 Kavango 纳米比亚地理区 9—201d
卡韦萨·德巴卡 Cabeza de Vaca, Álvar Núñez (Spanish explorer) 西班牙探险家 3—305b
卡韦松 Cabezón, Antonio de 西班牙作曲家 3—305b
卡韦伊哈伊 Kawaihae 美国夏威夷州深水港 9—202e
卡维恩 Kavieng 巴布亚新几内亚港口 9—201e
卡维尔 Cavell, Edith (Louisa) 英国护士 3—541b
卡维尔盐漠 Kavīr Desert 伊朗盐碱地 9—201f
卡维马斯 Cabimas 委内瑞拉城市 3—305d
卡温顿 Covington 美国城市 4—556c
卡文迪什 Cavendish 加拿大农村社区 3—541d
卡文迪什 Cavendish 英国惠斯特牌手 3—541c
卡文迪什 Cavendish, George 英国作家 3—541d
卡文迪什 Cavendish, Henry 英国物理学家 3—541e
卡文迪什 Cavendish, Lord Frederick Charles 英国政治家 3—541d
卡文迪什 Cavendish, Spencer Compton 英国政治家 3—542c
卡文迪什 Cavendish, Thomas 英国航海家 3—542c
卡文迪什 Cavendish, William 英国首相 3—542d
卡文迪什实验 Cavendish experiment 物理学 3—542d
卡文郡 Cavan 爱尔兰郡名 3—539a
卡翁达 Kaunda, Kenneth 赞比亚政治家 9—199d
卡翁德人 Kaonde 非洲民族 9—171d
卡沃萨湖群 Kawartha Lakes 加拿大湖泊 9—203a
卡乌卡乌台地 Kaukauveld 非洲台地 9—199b
卡武拉 Kawoela (Indonesia) 印度尼西亚岛屿 9—203d
卡西 Kāshī, al- 数学家、天文学家 9—191a
卡西安 Cassian, Saint John 基督教修士 3—504a
卡西奥多鲁斯 Cassiodorus 古罗马历史学家 3—505b
卡西迪 Cassidy, Butch 美国不法分子 3—504b
卡西基亚雷 Casiquiare 委内瑞拉河道 3—501c
卡西雷尔 Cassirer, Ernst 德国犹太哲学家 3—505c
卡西尼 Cassini, Gian Domenico 法国天文学家 3—504d
卡西尼 Cassini, Jacques 法国天文学家 3—504e
卡西尼(蒂里的) Cassini de Thury, César-François 法国天文学家 3—504f
卡西尼伯爵 Cassini, (Jacques-) Dominique, comte de (count of) 法国天文学家 3—504c
卡西尼定律 Cassini's laws 天文学 3—504f
卡西诺 casino 赌场 3—501a
卡西诺 Cassino 意大利城镇 3—505a
卡西诺牌戏 Casino 游戏 3—501b
卡西丘陵 Khāsi Hills 印度地理区 9—258b
卡西人 Khāsi 印度民族 9—258b
卡西斯 Khasis (Semitic god) 闪米特神祇 9—258c
卡西维劳努斯 Cassivellaunus 不列颠酋长 3—506b
卡西亚内米西 Caccianemici, Gherardo (pope) 教皇 3—309e
卡西语 Khāsi language 印度语言 9—258c
卡希纳 Cascina 意大利城镇 3—498a
卡希亚斯 Caxias 巴西城市 3—543e
卡希亚斯公爵 Caxias, Luiz Alves de Lima e Silva, duque de (duke of) 巴西政治家 3—543e
卡希亚斯公爵城 Duque de Caxias 巴西城市 5—468e
卡谢夫 Kacew, Romain 法国小说家 9—126e
卡谢乌 Cacheu 几内亚比绍城镇 3—310c
卡修斯 Dio Cassius 罗马行政官、历史学家 5—325b
卡修斯 Cassius, Gaius 暗杀凯撒的刺客 3—505e
卡修斯 Cassius, Gaius Avidius 罗马皇帝 3—505f
卡修斯·隆吉努斯 Cassius Longinus, Gaius 刺客 3—505f
卡修斯·隆吉努斯 Cassius Longinus, Gaius 罗马法学家 3—506a
卡修斯·隆吉努斯 Cassius Longinus, Quintus 罗马高官 3—506a
卡修斯·维塞列努斯 Cassius Vecellinus, Spurius 罗马执政官 3—506b
卡雅泽拉斯 Cajàzeiras 巴西城市 3—330f
卡亚俄 Callao 秘鲁海港 3—353d
卡亚尔 kayāl 音乐 9—204a
卡亚努斯 Kajanus, Robert 芬兰指挥家 9—136f
卡亚帕人 Cayapa 厄瓜多尔印第安人 3—544b
卡宴 Cayenne 法属圭亚那首府 3—544b
卡宴辣椒粉 cayenne pepper 香料 3—544c
卡扬人 Kayan 婆罗洲民族 9—204a
卡耶 Caillié, René-Auguste 法国探险家 3—325d
卡耶博特 Caillebotte, Gustave 法国画家 3—325b
卡耶塔 Caieta (Italy) 意大利城镇 3—325a
卡耶坦 Cajetan 天主教神学家 3—330f
卡耶坦(蒂埃内的),圣 Cajetan of Thiene, Saint 天主教人士 3—331a
卡耶伊 Cayey 波多黎各城镇 3—544c
卡伊 Kayes 马里城镇 9—204d
卡伊罗利 Cairoli, Benedetto 意大利政治家 3—329e
卡伊群岛 Kai Islands 印度尼西亚群岛 9—134b
卡伊塔人 Cáhita 北美印第安部落 3—323d
卡因 Khayin (Semitic god) 闪米特神祇 9—259a
卡因吉湖 Kainji Lake 尼日尔水库 9—135e
卡尤加人 Cayuga 北美印第安人 3—545d
卡尤加统 Cayugan Series 地质学 3—545d
卡尤塞马 cayuse 北美野马 3—545e
卡约 Cayo (Belize) 伯利兹城市 3—545c
卡约 Caillaux, Joseph (-Marie-Auguste) 法国政治家 3—325a
卡约里 Cajori, Florian 美国教育家、数学家 3—331a
卡赞 Kazan, Elia 美国导演 9—207a
卡赞勒克 Kazanlŭk 保加利亚城镇 9—207b
卡赞扎基斯 Kazantzákis, Níkos 希腊作家 9—207b
卡泽赫 Kazeh (Tanzania) 坦桑尼亚城镇 9—207c
卡泽伦 Kāzerūn 伊朗城镇 9—207d
卡泽诺维亚阶 Cazenovian stage 地质学 3—545f
卡曾贝 Kazembe 中非隆达族国家 9—207d
卡曾斯 Cousins, Norman 美国作家 4—551f
卡曾斯 Cousins, Robin 英国花样滑冰运动员 4—552a
卡曾斯 Cousins, Samuel 英国画家 4—552a
卡扎德絮 Casadesus, Robert 法国钢琴家 3—496d
卡扎菲 Qaddafi, Muammar al- 利比亚领导人 14—51d
卡扎科夫 Kazakov, Yury 苏联小说家 9—206d
卡扎乌雷 Kazaure 尼日利亚城镇 9—207c
卡札尔王朝 Qājār dynasty 伊朗王朝 14—52c
卡兹顿 Cardston 加拿大城镇 3—455c
开 karat 金计量单位 9—179f
开伯尔山口 Khyber Pass 南亚山口 9—267f
开城 Kaesŏng 朝鲜城市 9—129c
开大肌 dilator muscle 解剖学 5—315e
开尔文 Kelvin 计量单位 9—219a
开尔文 Kelvin (of Largs), William Thomson, Baron 英国科学家 9—219b
开发银行 development bank 金融 5—271b

开放大学 Open University 英国大学 12—428c
开放源代码软件 open-source software 计算机软件 12—428a
开封 Kaifeng 中国城市 9—134d
开封犹太人 Kaifeng Jew 民族 9—134e
《开皇律》 Kaihuang lü 中国隋代法典 9—135b
开间 bay 建筑 2—291d
开立姆地毯 kilim 工艺品 9—278b
开罗 Cairo 埃及首都 3—327b
开罗 Cairo 美国城市 3—329d
开罗地毯 Cairene rug 埃及工艺品 3—326e
开罗会议 Cairo Conferences 第二次世界大战史 3—329e
开曼海沟 Cayman Trench 加勒比海海槽 3—545c
开曼群岛 Cayman Islands 加勒比海英国殖民地 3—545a
开默林·昂内斯 Kamerlingh Onnes, Heike 荷兰物理学家 9—148d
开姆尼茨 Chemnitz 德国城市 4—113a
开普边境战争 Cape Frontier Wars 南非历史 3—420d
开普地域人种 Capoid local race 非洲人种 3—428e
开普敦 Cape Town 南非城市 3—421c
开普菲尔河 Cape Fear River 美国河流 3—420b
开普吉拉多 Cape Girardeau 美国城市 3—420d
开普科勒尔 Cape Coral 美国城市 3—420b
开普科洛德人 Cape Coloured (people) 南非民族 3—420b
开普勒 Kepler, Johannes 德国天文学家 9—236f
开普勒望远镜 Keplerian telescope 仪器 9—238b
开普勒新星 Kepler's Nova 天文学 9—238c
开普勒行星运动定律 Kepler's laws of planetary motion 天文学 9—238b
开普梅 Cape May 美国城市 3—420e
开普平原 Cape Flats 南非平原 3—420c
开普省 Cape Province (South Africa) 南非省份 3—421c
开普省 Kaapprovinsie (South Africa) 南非省份 9—123d
开普远人 Telanthropus capensis 考古学 16—522b
开普殖民地 Cape Colony 南非英国殖民地 3—420a
开塞利 Kayseri 土耳其城市 9—204d
开赛河 Kasai River 非洲河流 9—189d
开脱礼 ḥaliṭẓa 犹太教典礼 7—424f
开胃菜 antipasto 食品 1—393b
开胃食品 appetizer 食品 1—418d
开悟 Satori 日本佛教禅宗用语 15—78c
开阳 Mizar 天文学 11—297d
开远 Kaiyuan 中国城市 9—136e
锎(Cf) californium 化学元素 3—350e
凯 Cayes (Haiti) 海地城镇 3—544c
凯 Kaye, Danny 美国演员 9—204b
凯 Kaye, Nora 美国演员 9—204c
凯 Kay, John 英国工程师 9—203d
凯 Kay, Ulysses (Simpson) 美国作曲家 9—203e
凯阿 Kéa 希腊岛屿 9—208c
凯阿布勒姆 Kyabram 澳大利亚城镇 9—412c
凯比尔堡 Ksar el-Kebir 摩洛哥城市 9—385d
凯比尔港 Mers el-Kebir 阿尔及利亚港口 11—135d
凯比河 Kebbi River (Nigeria) 尼日利亚河流 9—210b
凯布 Keb (Egyptian god) 埃及神祇 9—210b
凯布尔 Cable, George W(ashington) 美国作家 3—306f
凯布讷山 Kebnekaise 瑞典山脉 9—210c
凯彻尔 Ketchel, Stanley 美国拳击运动员 9—245d
凯茨比 Catesby, Robert 英格兰火药阴谋策划者 3—524a
凯达 Kheda 印度城市 9—259c
凯德 Cade, Jack 英格兰叛乱首领 3—312e
凯德伯里 Cadbury, George 英国社会改革家 3—311f
凯德蒙 Caedmon 古英语基督教诗人 3—315c
《凯德蒙手稿》 Caedmon manuscript 古英语《圣经》释义 3—315d
凯蒂 Ceṭṭi 印度种姓集团 4—18e
凯厄米希河 Kiamichi River 美国河流 9—268b
凯厄斯 Caius, John 英国人文主义者 3—330d
凯厄图尔瀑布 Kaieteur Falls 圭亚那瀑布 9—134c
凯恩 Kane, Elisha Kent 美国医生 9—155b
凯恩 Kane, John 美国画家 9—155b
凯恩 Kern, Johann Conrad 瑞士外交家 9—241d
凯恩 Cain, James M(allahan) 美国小说家 3—326a
凯恩 Caine, Sir Michael 英国电影演员 3—326b
凯恩 Caine, Sir (Thomas Henry) Hall 英国小说家 3—326b
凯恩顿 Kyneton 澳大利亚城镇 9—413d
凯恩戈姆山 Cairngorm Mountains 不列颠群岛最高山 3—327a
凯恩㹴狗 cairn terrier 狗品种 3—326f
凯恩斯 Cairns 澳大利亚港口 3—327a
凯恩斯 Keynes, John Maynard 英国经济学家 9—249b
凯恩斯 Keynes, John Neville 英国哲学家 9—250b
凯恩斯 Keynes, Richard Darwin 英国生理学家 9—250c
凯尔 Ker 古希腊宗教 9—238f
凯尔 Kell, Joseph 英国文学家 9—215b
凯尔 Kael, Pauline 美国电影评论家 9—129b
凯尔采 Kielce 波兰旧省份 9—271d
凯尔采 Kielce 波兰城市 9—271d
凯尔德 Caird, Edward 英国哲学家 3—326d
凯尔德 Caird, John 英国神学家 3—326e
凯尔恩斯 Cairnes, John Elliott 爱尔兰古典经济学家 3—326f
凯尔盖朗甘蓝 Kerguelen cabbage (species *Pringlea antiscorbutica*) 植物 9—240b
凯尔盖朗群岛 Kerguelen Islands 印度洋群岛 9—240c
凯尔爵士 Ker, Sir Robert 英格兰贵族 9—238f
凯尔-卡里克 Kyle and Carrick 苏格兰区名 9—413b
凯尔克拉德 Kerkrade 荷兰城镇 9—240d
凯尔森 Kelsen, Hans 美国法学家 9—218e
凯尔斯 Kells (Ireland) 爱尔兰城镇 9—217c
《凯尔斯书》 Kells, Book of 福音书 9—217c
凯尔索 Cherso (Croatia) 克罗地亚岛屿 4—128d
凯尔索 Kelso 苏格兰城市 9—218f
凯尔泰什 Kertész, André 美国新闻摄影记者 9—243e
凯尔泰斯 Kertész, Imre 匈牙利作家 9—244a
凯尔特教会 Celtic Church 不列颠早期基督教会 3—559e
凯尔特人 Celt 古代印欧民族 3—558f
凯尔特文学 Celtic literature 古代文学 3—560b
凯尔特伊比利亚 Celtiberia 西班牙地区 3—559d
凯尔特-伊比利亚语 Celto-Iberian language 欧洲语言 3—561a
凯尔特诸语言 Celtic languages 西欧语言 3—559e
凯尔特宗教 Celtic religion 古代宗教 3—560d
凯尔万 Quervain, Marcel Roland de 瑞士冰川学家 14—87d
凯尔维尔石碑 Kylver Stone 瑞典古代北欧字母石碑 9—413c
凯尔西 Quercy 法国历史文化区 14—86f
凯尔西 Kelsey, Henry 英国探险家 9—218f
凯法利尼亚 Cephallenia 希腊岛屿 4—6f
凯菲 Keffi 尼日利亚城镇 9—212c
凯菲索多托斯(大) Cephisodotus THE ELDER 古希腊雕刻家 4—8c
凯格勒 Kegalle 斯里兰卡城镇 9—212d
凯格温 Keigwin, Richard 英国海军军官 9—213a
凯霍加福尔斯 Cuyahoga Falls 美国城市 5—81f
凯霍加河 Cuyahoga River 美国河流 5—81f
凯基利乌斯 Caecilius, Statius 罗马喜剧诗人 3—315b
凯基利乌斯(卡拉克特的) Caecilius OF CALACTE 希腊修辞学家 3—315a
凯基纳·阿列安努斯 Caecina Alienus, Aulus 罗马将军 3—315b
凯凯塔苏瓦克 Qeqertarsuaq 格陵兰(丹)岛屿 14—56a
凯克里节 Kekri 古代芬兰宗教节日 9—214e
凯克洛普斯 Cecrops 古希腊传说中国王 3—548e
凯克奇人 Kekchí 民族 9—214d

凯克天文台 Keck Observatory 夏威夷岛的天文台 9—210d

凯库拉岭 Kaikoura Range 新西兰山名 9—135c

凯库勒 Kekule von Stradonitz,(Friedrich) August 化学家 9—214e

凯拉 Queyras 法国吉尔河大阿尔卑斯流域 14—89b

凯拉姆 Kalām 伊斯兰教思辨教义学 9—138d

凯莱 Cayley,Arthur 英国数学家 3—544c

凯莱 Cayley,Sir George 英国空气动力学家 3—544e

凯勒 Keller,Ferdinand 瑞士考古学家 9—215c

凯勒 Keller,Gottfried 瑞士德语小说家 9—215d

凯勒 Kellar,Harry 美国魔术师 9—215b

凯勒 Keller,Helen (Adams) 美国作家 9—215e

凯勒卜河 Kalb River,Al- 黎巴黎河流 9—139b

凯勒曼 Kellermann,Bernhard 德国作家 9—215f

凯勒斯 Kellas,Eliza 美国教育家 9—215b

凯里 Kaili 中国城市 9—135c

凯里 Carey,George (Leonard) 坎特伯雷大主教 3—456b

凯里 Carey,Henry 英格兰诗人 3—456c

凯里 Carey,Henry C(harles) 美国经济学家 3—456c

凯里 Carey,Ron 美国劳工领袖 3—456d

凯里 Carey,William 英国传教士 3—456d

凯里奥格 Ceiriog (Welsh lyricist) 威尔士抒情诗人 3—550d

凯里奥格 Ceiriog,Eos (Welsh poet) 威尔士诗人 3—550d

凯里奥特斯 Kyriotes,John 拜占廷诗人 9—417e

凯里厄 Kerrier 英格兰区名 9—243a

凯里郡 Kerry 爱尔兰郡名 9—243a

凯里蓝色㹴狗 Kerry blue terrier 狗品种 9—243c

凯里尼亚 Kyrenia 塞浦路斯城市 9—416e

凯里尼亚山脉 Kyrenia Mountains 塞浦路斯山脉 9—416e

凯里斯堡 Careysburg 利比里亚城市 3—456f

凯利 Kelly,Ellsworth 美国画家 9—217c

凯利 Kelly,Emmett (Lee) 美国马戏团小丑 9—217c

凯利 Kelley,Florence 美国社会改革家 9—216a

凯利 Kelly,Gene 美国舞蹈家、演员、导演 9—217d

凯利 Kelly,Grace 美国演员 9—217e

凯利 Kelly,George (Edward) 美国剧作家 9—217e

凯利 Kelly,Hugh 英国剧作家 9—217f

凯利 Kelly,John B. 美国赛艇运动员 9—218a

凯利 Kelly,Ned 澳大利亚绿林好汉 9—218a

凯利 Kelly,Walt 美国连环画画家 9—218b

凯利 Kelly,William 美国铁器制造商 9—218b

凯利乌斯·鲁富斯 Caelius Rufus,Marcus 罗马政治家 3—315e

凯隆堡 Kalundborg 丹麦城市 9—144c

凯卢阿-科纳 Kailua - Kona 美国游览区 9—135d

凯卢阿-拉尼凯 Kailua - Lanikai 美国居民社区 9—135d

凯鲁阿尔 Kéroualle,Louise-Renée de 英王查理的法国情妇 9—242c

凯鲁阿内 Kérouané 几内亚城镇 9—242c

凯鲁比尼 Cherubini,(Maria) Luigi (Carlo Zenobio Salvatore) 法国作曲家 4—129b

凯鲁万 Qayrawān,Al- 突尼斯城镇 14—55f

凯鲁亚克 Kerouac,Jack 美国诗人 9—242b

凯路米特 calumet 美洲印第安文化 3—358c

凯吕斯 Caylus,Anne-Claude-Philippe de Tubières,comte de (count of) 法国考古学家 3—544f

凯罗尔 Cayrol,Jean(-Raphaël-Marie-Noël) 法国作家 3—545c

凯洛夫 Kairov,Ivan Andreyevich 苏联教育家 9—135f

凯洛格 Kellogg 美国城市 9—216c

凯洛格 Kellogg,Clara Louise 美国歌剧演员 9—216c

凯洛格 Kellogg,Frank B(illings) 美国国务卿 9—216e

凯洛格 Kellogg,John Harvey 美国医师 9—216f

凯洛格 Kellogg,Louise Phelps 美国历史学家 9—216f

凯洛格 Kellogg,W(ill) K(eith) 美国工业家、慈善家 9—217a

《凯洛格-白里安公约》 Kellogg-Briand Pact 国际公约 9—217a

凯洛格公司 Kellogg Company 美国公司 9—217b

凯马尔 Kemal,(Mehmed) Namık 土耳其作家 9—220d

凯马特公司 K mart Corporation 美国连锁商店 9—123a

凯麦尼 Kemeny,Zoltan 瑞士雕刻家 9—222a

凯曼贾琴 kamanjā 乐器 9—145c

凯梅尼 Kemény,Zsigmord,Báró (Baron) 匈牙利小说家 9—222b

凯门鳄 caiman 爬行动物 3—325d

凯门蜥 caiman lizard (*Dracaena*) 爬行动物 3—325e

凯米 Kemi 芬兰城市 9—222c

凯米奥浮雕宝石 cameo 宝石 3—371b

凯米河 Kemi River 芬兰河流 9—222d

凯末尔 Kemal,Mustafa (Turkish statesman) 土耳其政治家 9—220d

凯末尔 Kemal,Yashar 土耳其小说家 9—220e

凯末尔帕夏扎德 Kemalpaşazâde 奥斯曼帝国历史学家 9—220f

凯姆斯勋爵 Kames,Henry Home,Lord 苏格兰律师 9—148e

凯穆纳 Kemmuna (Malta) 马耳他岛屿 9—222d

凯纳德萨 Kenadsa 阿尔及利亚城镇 9—223a

凯纳侯爵 Quesne, Abraham Duquesne, marquis du 法国海军军官 14—87e

《凯纳甲湖条约》 Küçük Kaynarca,Treaty of 俄国-土耳其条约 9—388e

凯南 Kennan,George F(rost) 美国外交家、历史学家 9—225b

凯内马 Kenema 塞拉利昂城镇 9—224f

凯尼恩 Kenyon,Dame Kathleen (Mary) 英国考古学家 9—236c

凯尼福克河 Caney Fork River 美国河流 3—400d

凯涅厄斯 Caeneus 希腊神话 3—316a

凯诺 Queneau,Raymond 法国作家 14—86b

凯诺拉 Kenora 加拿大城镇 9—228a

凯帕拉港 Kaipara Harbour 新西兰港湾 9—135f

凯佩尔 Keppel (of Elvedon),Augustus Keppel,Viscount,Baron Elden 英国海军上将、政治家 9—238d

凯佩斯 Kepes,Gyorgy 美国画家 9—236f

凯普 Cape,(Herbert) Jonathan 英国出版商 3—419c

凯普费尔 Kämpfer,Engelbert 德意志旅行家 9—150f

凯普勒 Keppler,Joseph 美国杂志创办人 9—238e

凯齐拉哈比 Kezilahabi,Euphrase 坦桑尼亚小说家 9—251a

凯奇 Cage,John 美国先锋派作曲家 3—322d

凯奇 Ketch, Jack 英格兰刽子手 9—245d

凯奇凯梅特 Kecskemét 匈牙利城镇 9—210d

凯奇坎 Ketchikan 美国城市 9—245d

凯撒 Caesar,Crispus 罗马统治者 3—317a

凯撒 Caesar,Drusus 罗马执政官 3—317a

凯撒 Caesar,Gaius 罗马皇帝奥古斯都的外孙 3—317a

凯撒 Caesar,Germanicus 罗马将军 3—317a

凯撒 Caesar,Julius 罗马独裁者、政治家 3—317a

凯撒·奥古斯都 Caesar Augustus (Roman emperor) 罗马皇帝 3—320c

凯撒草 Caesar weed (plant) 草本植物 3—320c

凯撒里亚 Caesarea (ancient Mauretania) 毛里塔尼亚古海港 3—320c

凯撒里亚 Caesarea 巴勒斯坦古港口 3—320c

凯撒里亚卡帕多西亚 Caesarea Cappadociae (Turkey) 土耳其城市 3—320e

凯撒利乌斯(阿尔勒的),圣 Caesarius of Arles,Saint 基督教传教士 3—320f

凯撒利乌斯(海斯特尔巴赫的) Caesarius of Heisterbach 德国传教士 3—320f

凯撒斯劳滕 Kaiserslautern 德国城市 9—136b

凯塞林 Kesselring,Albert 德国陆军元帅 9—244e

凯瑟 Cather,Willa (Sibert) 美国小说家 3—525a

凯瑟琳 Katherine 澳大利亚城镇 9—195d

凯瑟琳(阿拉贡的) Catherine of Aragon 英格兰王后 3—526e

凯瑟琳(博洛尼亚的),圣 Catherine of Bologna,Saint 意大利神学家 3—527a

凯瑟琳(布拉干萨的) Catherine of Braganza 英格兰王后 3—527a
凯瑟琳(霍华德) Catherine Howard 英格兰王后 3—526d
凯瑟琳(帕尔) Catherine Parr 英格兰王后 3—527c
凯瑟琳,圣 Catherine,Saint 意大利神学家 3—526b
凯瑟琳(热那亚的),圣 Catherine of Genoa,Saint 奥秘神学家 3—527a
凯瑟琳(瑞典的),圣 Catherine of Sweden,Saint 隐修院院长 3—527b
凯瑟琳(锡耶纳的),圣 Catherine of Siena,Saint 天主教修士 3—527b
凯瑟琳(亚历山大的),圣 Catherine of Alexandria,Saint 基督教殉教士 3—526e
凯瑟琳奥古斯塔河 Kaiserin Augusta River(New Guinea) 新几内亚河流 9—136b
凯什兰 Koechlin,Charles 法国作曲家 9—332b
凯斯 Keyes,Alan 美国政治人物 9—248f
凯斯 Case,Steve 美国企业家 3—498a
凯斯(泽布吕赫的和多佛的) Keyes(of Zeebrugge and of Dover),Roger John Brownlow Keyes,1st Baron 英国海军将领 9—249a
凯斯蒂文(南、北区) Kesteven,Parts of 英格兰行政区 9—244f
凯斯狗 Keeshond 狗品种 9—212a
凯斯门特 Casement,Sir Roger 英国公职人员 3—498e
凯斯内尔 Quesnel, Pasquier 法兰西天主教神学家 14—87f
凯斯内斯 Caithness 苏格兰历史郡 3—330b
凯斯特勒 Koestler,Arthur 英国小说家 9—332c
凯斯特纳 Kästner,Erich 德国作家 9—193f
凯斯图蒂斯 Kęstutis 立陶宛大公 9—245b
凯索姆 Keesom,Willem Hendrik 荷兰物理学家 9—212a
凯塔 Keta 加纳城镇 9—245c
凯塔 Keita,Modibo 马里总统 9—213d
凯塔 Keita,Salif 马里足球运动员 9—213f
凯塔亚 Kaitaia 新西兰城市 9—136d
凯泰 Cailletet,Louis-Paul 法国物理学家 3—325c
凯坦加塔 Kaitangata 新西兰城市 9—136d
凯特 Keith,James(Francis Edward) 苏格兰军事领袖 9—214a
凯特 Ket,Robert 英格兰凯特起义领导人 9—245c
凯特尔 Quetelet,(Lambert) Adolphe(Jacques) 比利时数学家、天文学家、社会学家 14—88a
凯特尔 Keitel,Wilhelm 德国陆军元帅 9—213f
凯特勒 Ketteler,Wilhelm Emmanuel,Freiherr von(baron of) 天主教社会改革家 9—246b
凯特林 Kettering 英格兰城镇 9—246b
凯特林 Kettering 美国城市 9—246c
凯特林 Kettering, Charles F(ranklin) 美国工程师 9—246c
凯特人 Ket 西伯利亚民族 9—245b
凯瓦连 Caibarién 古巴城市 3—324f
凯文,圣 Kevin,Saint 爱尔兰基督教教士 9—247b
凯沃 Kawa 古埃及殖民地 9—202a
凯西 Casey,William J. 美国中央情报局局长 3—499b
凯西克 Keswick 英格兰城镇 9—245b
凯希洛夫斯基 Kieślowski,Krzysztof 波兰导演 9—273e
凯-夏特沃斯 Kay-Shuttleworth,Sir James(Phillips) 英国医生 9—203e
凯兴斯泰纳 Kerschensteiner,Georg 德国教育理论家 9—243d
凯休 Kehew,Mary Morton Kimball 美国改革家 9—212e
凯旋门 Arc de Triomphe 法国巴黎纪念碑 1—444f
凯旋门 triumphal arch 建筑 17—228c
凯旋门大奖赛 Prix de l'Arc de Triomphe 国际马赛 13—522c
凯旋式 triumph 古罗马史 17—228b
凯伊 Key,Ellen(Karolina Sofia) 瑞典男女平等主义者 9—247f
凯泽 Kaiser,Georg 德国戏剧家 9—135f
凯泽 Keyser,Hendrick de 荷兰雕刻家 9—250d
凯泽 Kaiser,Henry J(ohn) 美国实业家 9—136a
凯泽 Keiser,Reinhard 德国作曲家 9—213d
凯泽 Keyser,Thomas de 荷兰建筑师 9—250e
凯泽尔 Kayser,Heinrich(Gustav Johannes) 德国物理学家 9—204d
凯泽林 Keyserling,Hermann Alexander,Graf von(Count of) 德国社会哲学家 9—250f
楷书 kaishu 中国汉字书体 9—136c
"勘测者"号探测器 Surveyor 美国空间探测器 16—358e
勘查 inquest 法律 8—395d
勘探 prospecting 寻找矿床 13—539f
堪察加 Kamchatka 俄罗斯州名 9—146c
堪察加半岛 Kamchatka Peninsula 俄罗斯半岛 9—146c
堪察加彼得罗巴甫洛夫斯克 Petropavlovsk-Kamchatsky 俄罗斯港口 13—212d
堪察加河 Kamchatka River 俄罗斯河流 9—146d
堪察加人 Kamchadal 堪察加半岛民族 9—146b
堪培拉 Canberra 澳大利亚首都 3—395c
堪萨冰期 Kansan Glacial Stage 地质学 9—160f
堪萨斯 Kansas 美国州名 9—161a
堪萨斯城 Kansas City 美国堪萨斯州城市 9—163d
堪萨斯城 Kansas City 美国密苏里州城市 9—163f
堪萨斯城爵士乐风格 Kansas City style 美国音乐 9—164b
《堪萨斯城明星报》 Kansas City Star 美国报纸 9—164a
堪萨斯城群 Kansas City Group 地质学 9—164a
堪萨斯河 Kansas River 美国河流 9—164c
《堪萨斯-内布拉斯加法案》 Kansas-Nebraska Act 美国历史 9—164b
堪萨斯内战 Bleeding Kansas 美国历史 2—532b
戡乱委员会 Troubles,Council of 尼德兰历史 17—237a
坎巴人 Kamba 非洲民族 9—145f
坎班 Kamban,Gudmundur(Jonsson Hallgrimsson) 冰岛作家 9—146a
坎贝 Cambay 印度城镇 3—363f
坎贝尔 Campbell,Alexander 美国教士 3—379a
坎贝尔 Campbell,Archibald 英国贵族 3—379b
坎贝尔 Campbell,Sir Colin 英国军人 3—379b
坎贝尔 Campbell,Donald Malcolm 英国赛车驾驶员 3—379b
坎贝尔 Campbell,Douglas Houghton 美国植物学家 3—379c
坎贝尔 Campbell,E. Simms 美国黑人漫画家 3—379d
坎贝尔 Campbell,Henry 英国首相 3—379d
坎贝尔 Campbell,John 英格兰贵族 3—379d
坎贝尔 Campbell,Joseph 美国作家 3—379f
坎贝尔 Campbell,John Archibald 美国最高法院大法官 3—379d
坎贝尔 Campbell,John McLeod 苏格兰神学家 3—379e
坎贝尔 Campbell,John W. 美国科幻小说作家 3—379f
坎贝尔 Campbell,Kim 加拿大政治家 3—380a
坎贝尔 Campbell,Robert 加拿大贸易商 3—380b
坎贝尔 Campbell,Roy 诗人 3—380c
坎贝尔 Campbell,Thomas 苏格兰诗人 3—380c
坎贝尔 Campbell,William Ellsworth 美国魔术家 3—380d
坎贝尔 Campbell,William Wallace 美国天文学家 3—380d
坎贝尔 Campbell,William Wilfred 加拿大诗人 3—380e
坎贝尔-班纳曼 Campbell-Bannerman,Sir Henry 英国首相 3—380f
坎贝尔岛 Campbell Island 新西兰火山岛 3—381a
坎贝尔敦 Campbelltown 澳大利亚城市 3—381d
坎贝尔敦 Campbeltown 苏格兰海港 3—381d
坎贝尔顿 Campbellton 加拿大城市 3—381c
坎贝尔夫人 Campbell,Mrs. Patrick 英国演员 3—380b
坎贝尔罐头汤公司 Campbell Soup Company 美国公司 3—381b
坎贝尔里弗 Campbell River 加拿大自治镇 3—381b
坎贝尔山 Campbell Hill 美国山峰 3—381a
坎贝尔斯维尔 Campbellsville 美国城市 3—381c
坎贝湾 Cambay,Gulf of 印度海湾 3—363f
坎比奥 Cambio,Arnolfo di(Italian sculptor and architect) 意大利建筑师 3—364a

坎波巴索 Campobasso 意大利城市 3—383e
坎波贝洛岛 Campobello Island 加拿大岛屿 3—383e
坎波伯爵 Campo, Matthias Gallas, Graf von (count of) 奥地利将军 3—383c
《坎波城条约》 Medina del Campo, Treaty of 西班牙-英格兰条约 11—78a
《坎波福尔米奥条约》 Campo Formio, Treaty of 法国-奥地利条约 3—383c
坎波斯 Campos, Arsenio Martínez (Spanish general and politician) 西班牙将军 3—383f
坎波斯兄弟 Campos, Haroldo de and Augusto de 巴西诗人 3—383f
坎波亚莫尔-坎波索里奥 Campoamor y Campoosorio, Ramón de 西班牙诗人 3—383d
坎伯兰 Cumberland 英格兰旧郡名 5—57f
坎伯兰 Cumberland 美国城市 5—58b
坎伯兰 Cumberland, Richard 英国剧作家 5—58c
坎伯兰 Cumberland, Richard 英国神学家 5—58c
坎伯兰高原 Cumberland Plateau 美国高原 5—59b
坎伯兰公爵 Cumberland, Ernest Augustus, duke of 汉诺威国王 5—58b
坎伯兰公爵 Cumberland, William Augustus, duke of 英国将军 5—58e
坎伯兰公路 Cumberland Road 美国公路 5—59c
坎伯兰豪斯 Cumberland House 加拿大古地名 5—59a
坎伯兰河 Cumberland River 美国河流 5—59b
坎伯兰群岛 Cumberland Islands 澳大利亚群岛 5—59a
坎伯兰山口 Cumberland Gap 美国东部山口 5—58f
坎伯兰式摔跤 Cumberland wrestling 体育 5—59d
坎伯兰湾 Cumberland Sound 加拿大海湾 5—59c
坎伯兰峡谷 Cumberland Narrows 美国峡谷 5—59a
坎伯兰长老会 Cumberland Presbyterian Church 美国基督教会 5—59b
坎伯诺尔德 Cumbernauld 苏格兰城镇 5—59d
坎伯诺尔德-基尔赛斯 Cumbernauld and Kilsyth 苏格兰区名 5—59e
坎博尔达 Kambalda 澳大利亚城镇 9—146a
坎布里奇伯爵 Cambridge, Edmund of Langley, Earl of 英格兰王子 3—367c
坎布里奇伯爵 Cambridge, James Hamilton, Earl of 苏格兰保皇党人 3—367c
坎布里奇伯爵 Cambridge, William Hamilton, Earl of 苏格兰保皇党人 3—367d
坎布里奇伯爵、侯爵及公爵 Cambridge, EARLS, MARQUESSES, AND DUKES OF 英国贵族名 3—367c
坎布里奇公爵(第二) Cambridge, George William Frederick Charles, 2nd Duke of 英国陆军元帅 3—367d
坎布里奇公爵(第一) Cambridge, Adolphus Frederick, 1st Duke of 英国陆军元帅 3—367d
坎布里奇侯爵和公爵 Cambridge, George Augustus, Marquess and Duke of 英国国王 3—367d
坎布里亚 Cumbria 英格兰郡名 5—59f
坎达武 Kadavu 斐济岛屿 9—128a
坎大哈 Kandahār 阿富汗城市 9—153d
坎代 Katay Don Sasorith 老挝民族主义者 9—194e
坎代拉 Candela (Outeriño), Felix 墨西哥建筑师 3—397c
坎德尔 Kandel, Eric 美国神经生物学家 9—153f
坎德拉 candela 计量单位 3—397c
坎德勒 Candler, Asa Griggs 美国商人 3—398c
坎德勒 Kändler, Johann Joachim 雕刻家 9—154f
坎蒂加 cantiga 音乐 3—412b
坎蒂莱纳 cantilena 音乐 3—412b
坎东布雷 candomblé 巴西宗教 3—399a
坎顿 Canton, John 英国物理学家 3—414a
坎顿岛 Kanton Atoll 基里巴斯岛屿 9—170a
坎儿井 qanāt 供水系统 14—53d
坎菲尔德 Canfield, Cass 美国出版家 3—400d
坎戈 Kango 加蓬城镇 9—157d
坎格里 Kangri (Turkey) 土耳其城市 9—157d
坎加鲁岛 Kangaroo Island 澳大利亚海岛 9—156d
坎加斯-德纳塞阿 Cangas de Narcea 西班牙城市 3—400e
坎杰拉雨期 Kanjeran Pluvial Stage 地质学 9—158d
坎卡基 Kankakee 美国城市 9—158e
坎卡基河 Kankakee River 美国河流 9—158e
坎克林 Kankrin, Egor Frantsevich, Graf (Count) 俄国大臣 9—158e
坎昆 Cancún 墨西哥城市 3—397a
坎拉翁 Canlaon 菲律宾城市 3—402c
坎拉翁山 Canlaon, Mount 菲律宾活火山 3—402c
坎利夫(赫德利的) Cunliffe (of Headley), Walter Cunliffe, 1st Baron 英国银行家 5—62c
坎卢普斯 Kamloops 加拿大城市 9—149e
坎曼 Khammam 印度城市 9—255b
坎纳达语 Kannada language 印度语言 9—158f
坎纳达语文学 Kannada literature 印度文学 9—159a
坎纳雷焦 Cannaregio, Andrea di (composer) 意大利作曲家 3—402f
坎纳诺尔 Cannanore 印度城市 3—402f
坎尼扎罗 Cannizzaro, Stanislao 意大利化学家 3—405a
坎尼战役 Cannae, Battle of 布匿战争 3—402e
坎宁 Canyon 美国城市 3—416b
坎宁 Canning, Charles John Canning, Earl 印度总督 3—403f
坎宁 Canning, George 英国首相 3—404a
坎宁 Canning, Stratford (British diplomat) 英国外交家 3—404f
坎宁安 Cunningham, Alexander 苏格兰贵族 5—62d
坎宁安 Cunningham, Allan 苏格兰诗人 5—62e
坎宁安 Cunningham, Andrew Browne 英国海军军官 5—62f
坎宁安 Cunningham, Sir Alan Gordon 英国陆军军官 5—62c
坎宁安 Cunningham, Glenn 美国运动员 5—63a
坎宁安 Cunningham, Imogen 美国摄影家 5—63b
坎宁安 Cunningham, Kate Richards O'Hare 美国社会主义者、改革家 5—63c
坎宁安 Cunningham, Laurie 英国足球运动员 5—63e
坎宁安 Cunningham, Merce 美国舞蹈演员 5—63e
坎宁安 Cunningham, William 苏格兰阴谋家 5—63f
坎宁安 Cunningham, William 英国经济学家、牧师 5—64a
坎宁兰兹国家公园 Canyonlands National Park 美国国家公园 3—416c
坎宁盆地 Canning Basin 澳大利亚盆地 3—404f
坎农 Cannon, Annie Jump 美国天文学家 3—405b
坎农 Cannon, Harriet Starr 美国宗教领袖 3—405c
坎农 Cannon, James 美国牧师 3—405d
坎农 Cannon, Joseph Gurney 美国政治家 3—405d
坎农 Cannon, Walter Bradford 美国神经病学家 3—405e
坎诺克蔡斯 Cannock Chase 英格兰区名 3—405b
《坎诺普斯法令》 Canopus, Decree of 古埃及法令 3—408c
坎帕拉 Kampala 乌干达首都 9—150d
坎帕内拉 Campanella, Roy 美国棒球运动员 3—377a
坎帕尼 Campani, Giuseppe 意大利光学仪器制造者 3—377c
坎帕尼亚 Campania 意大利南部区名 3—377d
坎帕尼亚-迪罗马 Campagna di Roma 意大利平原 3—376e
坎帕斯皮河 Campaspe River 澳大利亚河流 3—379a
坎佩尔 Quimper 法国城镇 14—92a
坎佩尔彩陶 Quimper faience 法国锡釉陶器 14—92b
坎佩基奥 Campeggio, Lorenzo 意大利枢机主教 3—381f
坎佩切 Campeche 墨西哥州名 3—381d
坎佩切 Campeche 墨西哥城市 3—381e
坎佩切湾 Campeche, Bay of 墨西哥湾小海湾 3—381f
坎彭 Kampen 荷兰城市 9—150e

坎彭 Campen, Jacob van 荷兰建筑师 3—382a
坎皮达诺 Campidano 意大利平原 3—382b
坎皮恩 Campion, Saint Edmund 英格兰耶稣会士 3—383b
坎皮恩 Campion, Thomas 英国作曲家 3—383b
坎皮纳斯 Campinas 巴西城市 3—382d
坎普 Camp, Walter Chauncey 美国体育界人士 3—376a
坎普尔 Kānpur 印度县城 9—160e
坎普里科恩-邦克群岛 Capricorn-Bunker Group 澳大利亚珊瑚礁岛 3—430e
坎普斯 Campos 巴西城市 3—383e
坎普斯-杜若尔当 Campos do Jordão 巴西城市 3—383f
坎奇尔鼷鹿 kanchil 哺乳动物 9—153b
坎萨人 Kansa 北美印第安民族 9—160e
坎斯克 Kansk 俄罗斯城市 9—164d
坎索海峡 Canso, Strait of 加拿大海峡 3—409f
坎塔布里人 Cantabri 古代伊比利亚部落 3—409f
坎塔布连山 Cantabrian Mountains 西班牙山脉 3—410b
坎塔夫里亚 Cantabria 西班牙省份 3—410a
坎塔夫里亚 Cantabria 西班牙历史地区 3—409f
坎塔拉剑麻 cantala (*Agave cantala*) 植物 3—410c
坎塔斯航空公司 Qantas Airways Limited 澳大利亚公司 14—53e
坎特 Kanter, Rosabeth Moss 美国社会科学工作者 9—167c
坎特伯雷 Canterbury 新西兰地名 3—411e
坎特伯雷 Canterbury 英格兰城市 3—411b
坎特伯雷大主教 Canterbury, archbishop of 英国大主教 3—411e
坎特伯雷会议及约克会议 Canterbury and York, Convocations of 英国基督教会议 3—411f
坎特伯雷平原 Canterbury Plains 新西兰低地 3—411f
坎特龙 Cantillon, Richard 爱尔兰经济学家 3—413b
坎特卢普的圣多马 Cantelupe, Saint Thomas de 英格兰教士、改革家 3—411a
坎提尔 Qantîr (Egypt) 古埃及城市 14—53f
坎廷弗拉斯 Cantinflas 拉丁美洲电影演员 3—413b
坎图 Cantù 意大利城镇 3—415a
坎托 Cantor, Eddie 美国喜剧演员 3—414d
坎托罗维奇 Kantorowicz, Hermann 德国学者 9—170b
坎托罗维奇 Kantorovich, Leonid Vitalyevich 苏联经济学家 9—170a
坎维岛 Canvey Island 英格兰岛屿 3—416b
坎雄戈 Canchungo 几内亚比绍城镇 3—396f
坎佐纳 canzona 音乐 3—416c
坎佐内里 Canzoneri, Tony 美国职业拳击手 3—416d
坎佐内特 canzonet 声乐 3—416e
砍林鸟 woodhewer (bird) 鸟类 18—323b
砍林鸟科 Dendrocolaptidae 动物学 5—242a
砍砸器工艺 Chopper chopping-tool industry 史前石器工艺 4—196f
康 Cão, Diogo 葡萄牙航海家 3—416e
康巴塞雷斯 Cambacérès, Jean-Jacques-Régis de, DUC (duke) DE PARME 法国政治家 3—363e
康柏计算机公司 Compaq Computer Corporation 美国计算机制造商 4—396a
康邦 Cambon, Joseph 法国财政官 3—365b
康邦 Cambon, Jules 法国外交家 3—365c
康邦 Cambon, Paul 法国外交家 3—365d
康贝尔 Cambert, Robert 法国作曲家 3—364a
康搏伊 Conboy, Sara Agnes McLaughlin 美国劳工领袖 4—408e
康布雷 Cambrai 法国城镇 3—365e
康布雷联盟 Cambrai, League of 欧洲历史 3—365f
《康布雷条约》 Cambrai, Treaty of 欧洲历史 3—365f
康布雷战役 Cambrai, Battle of 第一次世界大战史 3—365e
康德 Kant, Immanuel 哲学家 9—164d
康德尔 Condell, Henry 英国演员 4—415c
康德拉捷夫 Kondratev, Nikolay D(mitriyevich) 俄国经济学家 9—344e
康德镇 Vila do Conde 葡萄牙城镇 17—560d
康德主义 Kantianism 哲学 9—167d
康登 Condon, Edward U(hler) 美国物理学家 4—416f
康登和格林 Comden, Betty; and Green, Adolf 美国音乐喜剧作家 4—378d
康迪 Kandi 贝宁城镇 9—154b
康蒂 Conti, Niccolò dei 威尼斯商人 4—465f
康定 Kangding 中国县名 9—157a
康定斯基 Kandinsky, Wassily 画家 9—154b
康杜尔梅尔 Condulmer, Gabriele (pope) 教皇 4—418a
康多尔 Candolle, Alphonse(-Louis-Pierre) Pyrame de 瑞士植物学家 3—398d
康多尔 Candolle, Augustin Pyrame de 瑞士植物学家 3—398e
康厄安群岛 Kangean Islands 印度尼西亚岛群 9—157b
康恩 Conn CÉTCHATHACH 爱尔兰国王 4—433a
康菲石油公司 Conoco Phillips 美国公司 4—438b
康弗斯 Converse, Frederick Shepherd 美国作曲家 4—474d
康福德 Cornford, Frances (Crofts) 英国诗人 4—514f
康福思 Cornforth, Sir John Warcup 澳大利亚化学家 4—515a
康福特 Comfort, Alex 英国老年学家 4—380e
康格多山 Kangto Shan 中国山峰 9—157d
康格尔顿 Congleton 英格兰自治市 4—424e
康格里夫 Congreve, Richard 英国哲学家 4—429e
康格里夫 Congreve, William 英国剧作家 4—429e
康格里夫 Congreve, Sir William, 2ND BARONET 英国炮兵军官 4—430a
康华里 Cornwallis, Charles Cornwallis, 1st Marquessand 2nd Earl 英国军人、政治家 4—516b
《康华里法规》 Cornwallis Code 英属印度行政法规 4—516d
康吉弗兰 Conjeeveram (India) 印度城镇 4—432b
康吉鳗 conger eel 鱼类 4—424d
康加尔王朝 Kangarid DYNASTY 伊朗王朝 9—156b
康加里国家公园 Congaree National Park 美国国家公园 4—423c
康加里河 Congaree River 美国河流 4—423c
康茄舞 conga 舞蹈 4—423b
康捷米尔 Kantemir, Antiokh Dmitriyevich 俄国政治家 9—167a
康捷米尔 Kantemir, Dmitry (Konstantinovich) 政治家 9—167b
康康 Kankan 几内亚城镇 9—158e
康康·穆萨 Kankan Mūsā (Mali emperor) 马里皇帝 9—158e
康康舞 cancan 舞蹈 3—395e
康科德 Concord 美国加利福尼亚州城市 4—412c
康科德 Concord 美国马萨诸塞州城镇 4—412d
康科德 Concord 美国新罕布什尔州城市 4—412e
康科德 Concord 美国北卡罗来纳州城市 4—412f
康科德四轮马车 Concord coach 美国驿站马车 4—413a
康科德战役 Concord, Battle of 美国历史 4—412f
康科迪亚 Concordia 阿根廷城市 4—413c
康科迪亚伯爵 Concordia, Giovanni Pico della Mirandola, conte di 意大利学者 4—413d
康科迪娅 Concordia 罗马女神 4—413c
康克林 Conklin, Edwin Grant 美国生物学家 4—432f
康克林 Conkling, Roscoe 美国政治家 4—432f
康拉德 Conrad 德意志国王 4—439b
康拉德 Conrad 德意志国王 4—439d
康拉德 Conrad 德意志国王 4—440a
康拉德 Conrad 洛林公爵 4—440b
康拉德 Conrad, Frank 美国电气工程师 4—440c
康拉德 Conrad, Joseph 英国小说家 4—440d
康拉德 Konrad VON MARBURG 德意志异端裁判官 9—347d
康拉德(红色的) Conrad THE RED 洛林公爵 4—440b
康拉德(小) Conrad THE YOUNGER 德意志君主 4—440b
康拉德(小) Conrad, Charles, Jr. 美国航天员 4—440b
康拉德二世 Conrad II 德意志国王 4—439c

康拉德·封·维尔茨堡 Konrad von Würzburg 中古高地德语诗人 9—347e
康拉德·冯·赫岑多夫 Conrad von Hötzendorf, Franz (Xaver Josef), Graf (Count) 奥匈帝国军事家 4—441b
康拉德三世 Conrad Ⅲ 德意志国王 4—439d
康拉德四世 Conrad Ⅳ 德意志国王 4—439f
康拉德五世 Conrad Ⅴ 德意志君主 4—440a
康拉德一世 Conrad Ⅰ 德意志国王 4—439b
康拉丁 Conradin 德意志君主 4—441c
康林纽斯 Corineus 传说人物 4—506d
康罗贝尔 Canrobert (town, Algeria) 阿尔及利亚城镇 3—409e
康罗贝尔 Canrobert, (François-) Certain 法国军人 3—409e
康罗伊 Conroy, Jack 美国作家 4—441e
康茂德 Commodus 罗马皇帝 4—387b
康蒙斯 Commons, John R. 美国经济学家 4—389d
康纳 Connor, Ralph 加拿大长老会牧师 4—438a
康纳科佩 cornucopia 装饰花纹 4—515e
康纳勒哈斯(-曼德斯) Canalejas (y Méndez), José 西班牙政治家 3—392b
康纳里 Connery, Sir Sean 苏格兰演员 4—437d
康纳斯 Connors, Jimmy 美国网球运动员 4—438a
康纳斯维尔 Connersville 美国城市 4—437d
康乃馨 carnation (*Dianthus caryophyllus*) 草本植物 3—466b
康奈尔 Cornell, Ezra 美国企业家 4—513c
康奈尔大学 Cornell University 美国大学 4—513e
康奈山 Conner, Mount 澳大利亚突岩 4—437c
康内利 Connelly, Cornelia (Augusta) 天主教女隐修院院长 4—436f
康内利 Connelly, Marc 美国剧作家 4—437a
康尼奥特 Conneaut 美国城市 4—433d
康尼奥特阶 Conneaut Stage 地质学 4—433d
康尼布兰造山运动 Kanimblan orogeny 地质学 9—158b
康尼马拉 Connemara 爱尔兰行政区 4—437b
康尼马拉马 Connemara 马品种 4—437c
康尼努斯家族 Comnenus family 拜占廷皇族 4—393e
康涅狄格 Connecticut 美国州名 4—433e
康涅狄格才子 Connecticut wit (poets) 美国文学团体成员 4—436c
康涅狄格河 Connecticut River 美国河流 4—436b
康诺利 Connolly, Cyril (Vernon) 英国评论家 4—437e
康诺利 Connolly, James 爱尔兰工会领导人 4—437e
康诺利 Connolly, Maureen Catherine 美国女子网球运动员 4—437f
康诺特 Connaught 爱尔兰古国名 4—433c
康诺特和斯特拉森公爵 Connaught and Strathearn, Arthur William Patrick Albert, duke of 加拿大总督 4—433c
康帕内拉 Campanella, Tommaso 欧洲哲学家 3—377a
康帕尼奥拉 Campagnola, Domenico 意大利油画家 3—376e
康帕尼奥拉 Campagnola, Giulio 意大利油画家 3—376f
康皮 Campi, Giulio 意大利画家 3—382b
康平 Campin, Robert 佛兰德斯画家 3—382b
康普顿 Compton 美国城市 4—400f
康普顿 Compton, Arthur Holly 美国物理学家 4—400f
康普顿 Compton, Henry 英国主教 4—401a
康普顿 Compton, Karl Taylor 美国物理学家 4—401a
康普顿 Compton, Spencer 英国贵族 4—401b
《康普顿百科全书及事实索引》 Compton's Encyclopedia and Fact-Index 百科全书 4—401d
康普顿-伯内特夫人 Compton-Burnett, Dame I(vy) 英国作家 4—401b
康普顿效应 Compton effect 物理学 4—401c
康普拉 Campra, André 法国歌剧作家 3—384a
《康普鲁顿合参本圣经》 Complutensian Polyglot Bible 基督教经典 4—399d
康切罗斯 concheros 墨西哥舞蹈 4—411e
康萨尔维 Consalvi, Ercole 意大利教廷政治家 4—441f
康塞普申湾 Conception Bay 大西洋海湾 4—410a
康塞普西翁 Concepción 智利城市 4—409c
康塞普西翁 Concepción 巴拉圭省份 4—409d
康塞普西翁 Concepción 巴拉圭城市 4—409e
康塞普西翁-德拉贝加 Concepción de la Vega (Dominican Republic) 多米尼加共和国城市 4—409e
康瑟尔布拉夫斯 Council Bluffs 美国城市 4—542c
康瑟尔格罗夫 Council Grove 美国城市 4—542d
康生 Kang Sheng 中国政治人物 9—155e
康斯太布尔 Constable, John 英国画家 4—448c
康斯坦察 Constanța 罗马尼亚县名 4—449e
康斯坦察 Constanța 罗马尼亚城市 4—449e
康斯坦茨 Konstanz 德国城市 9—347f
康斯坦茨湖 Constance, Lake 欧洲湖泊 4—449a
康斯坦茨会议 Constance, Council of 天主教会议 4—448f
康斯坦蒂亚 Constantia 塞浦路斯古城 4—450a
康斯坦蒂亚 Constantia 南非居住区 4—450a
康斯坦丁 Constantine 教皇 4—451d
康斯坦丁 Constantine, Learie (Nicholas), Baron Constantine of Maraval and Nelson 特立尼达官员、板球运动员 4—454d
康斯坦丁(非洲人) Constantine the African 中世纪医学家、学者 4—454c
康斯坦丁二世 Constantine Ⅱ 希腊国王 4—451c
康斯坦丁二世 Constantine Ⅱ 苏格兰国王 4—453f
康斯坦丁诺夫卡 Konstantinovka 乌克兰城市 9—347f
康斯坦丁三世 Constantine Ⅲ 苏格兰国王 4—453f
康斯坦丁-西尔瓦努斯 Constantine-Silvanus 亚美尼亚宗教领导人 4—454f
康斯坦丁一世 Constantine Ⅰ 希腊国王 4—451b
康斯坦丁一世 Constantine Ⅰ 苏格兰国王 4—453e
康斯特布尔 Constable, Archibald 苏格兰出版商 4—448c
康斯托克 Comstock, Anthony 美国改革家 4—407a
康斯托克 Comstock, John Henry 美国教育家 4—407c
康斯托克(夫人) Comstock, Anna Botsford 美国画家 4—407a
《康斯托克法》 Comstock Act 美国法案 4—407d
康斯托克银矿 Comstock Lode 美国银矿 4—407e
康苏斯 Consus 古代意大利宗教神灵 4—464b
康索尔导航系统 consol 导航 4—447b
康索特 consort 音乐 4—447e
康塔基昂 kontakion 拜占廷诗体 9—348a
康塔勒 Cantal 法国省份 3—410b
康塔罗斯酒杯 kantharos 古希腊陶器 9—167c
康塔塔 cantata 音乐 3—410d
康特 Caunt, Benjamin 英国拳击运动员 3—536c
康特 Canth, Minna 芬兰小说家 3—411f
康特吕伯 Canteloube (de Malaret), (Marie-) Joseph 法国作曲家 3—410f
康提 Kandy 斯里兰卡早期王国 9—155a
康提 Kandy 斯里兰卡城镇 9—155a
"康-提基"号 Kon-Tiki 航海木筏 9—344a
康铜 constantan 合金 4—450a
康图奇 Contucci, Andrea 意大利建筑师 4—473f
康托尔 Cantor, Georg (Ferdinand Ludwig Philipp) 德国数学家 3—414e
康托尔 Cantor, Moritz Benedikt 德国数学史家 3—414f
康万戈阶 Conewango Stage 地质学 4—419c
康威 Conwy 英国威尔士城镇 4—476e
康韦 Conway 美国城市 4—475e
康韦 Conway, Henry Seymour 英国军事指挥官 4—475e
康韦 Conway, Jill Ker 美国学者 4—475f
康韦 Conway, Moncure Daniel 美国牧师、作家 4—476a

康韦 Conway,Thomas 美国将军 4—476b
康韦(阿灵顿的) Conway (of Allington),William Martin Conway Boron 美国登山运动员 4—476c
康韦尔 Cornwell,David John Moore 英国作家 4—516e
康韦尔 Conwell,Russell Herman 美国律师、著作家 4—476c
康沃尔 Cornwall 加拿大城市 4—515e
康沃尔 Cornwall 英格兰郡名 4—515f
康沃尔伯爵 Cornwall,Piers Gaveston,Earl of 英国贵族 4—516a
康沃尔伯爵 Cornwall,Richard,Earl of 罗马帝国皇帝 4—516b
康沃尔公爵领地 Cornwall,duchy of 英国贵族领地 4—516a
康沃尔语 Cornish language 英格兰西南部语言 4—515b
康沃尔语文学 Cornish literature 英国文学 4—515c
康沃利斯岛 Cornwallis Island 加拿大西北地区岛屿 4—516e
康熙 Kangxi (Chinese emperor) 中国皇帝年号 9—157f
《康熙南巡图》 Kangxi Nanxuntu 中国清代画作 9—157f
康有为 Kang Youwei 中国学者 9—155f
抗爆值 antiknock rating 汽油 1—388a
抗辩 demurrer 法律 5—241a
抗磁性 diamagnetism 物理学 5—286a
抗代谢物 antimetabolite 生物化学 1—388f
抗胆碱酯酶药 anticholinesterase 药物 1—383d
抗毒素 antitoxin 生物化学 1—395a
抗坏血酸 ascorbic acid 化合物 1—543b
抗拉强度 tensile strength 物理学 16—545f
抗凝血药 anticoagulant 药物 1—384d
抗生素 antibiotic 化合物 1—382f
抗体 antibody 生物化学 1—383a
抗微生物因子 antimicrobial agent 生物化学 1—388f
抗血清 antiserum 生物化学 1—394e
抗压强度试验 compressive strength test 物理学 4—400d
抗氧化剂 antioxidant 化合物 1—393a
抗议派 Remonstrant 荷兰基督教会派别 14—222f
抗抑郁药 antidepressant 药物 1—384e
抗原 antigen 生物化学 1—385b
抗真菌剂 antimycotic 生物化学 1—390b
抗租斗争 Antirent War 美国历史 1—394d
抗组织胺药 antihistamine 药物 1—387e
钪(Sc) scandium 化学元素 15—102e
考爱岛 Kauai 美国火山岛 9—198d
考波利坎 Caupolicán 马普切人首长 3—536c
考波什堡 Kaposvár 匈牙利城镇 9—172f
考布里奇 Cowbridge 威尔士城镇 4—557c
考茨基 Kautsky,Karl 德国政治家 9—200f
考德 Cawdor 苏格兰村庄 3—543d
考德雷 Cowdray (of Midhurst),Weetman Dickinson Pearson,1st Viscount 英国工程师、政治家 4—557c
考德威尔 Caldwell,Erskine 美国作家 3—342c
考德威尔 Caldwell,Sarah 美国歌剧指挥 3—342d
考德威尔 Caldwell,Taylor 美国作家 3—342e
考迪尼岔路口 Caudine Forks 意大利山口 3—535b
考底利耶 Kauṭilya 印度政治家 9—200e
考恩斯维尔 Cowansville 加拿大城镇 4—556e
考尔 Cowl,Jane 美国剧作家、演员 4—558a
考尔巴赫 Kaulbach,Wilhelm von 德国画家 9—199c
考尔德 Calder,Alexander (Stirling) 美国雕刻家 3—341a
考尔德科特 Caldecott,Randolph 英国艺术家 3—340f
考尔德科特奖章 Caldecott Medal 美国儿童美术奖 3—340f
考尔德伦 Calderone,Mary Steichen 美国医师、作家 3—342a
考尔迪科特 Caldicott,Helen Broinowski 美国医师 3—342b
考尔洛曹 Karloca (Serbia) 塞尔维亚城镇 9—182f
考尔斯 Cowles,Henry Chandler 美国植物学家 4—558c
考尔斯家族 Cowles FAMILY 美国出版业家族 4—558b
考夫博伊伦 Kaufbeuren 德国城市 9—198d
考夫曼 Kaufman,Denis Arkadyevich 苏联导演 9—198f
考夫曼 Kaufman,George S(imon) 美国剧作家 9—198f
考夫曼 Kaufmann,Konstantin Petrovich 俄罗斯帝国将军 9—199a
考夫曼 Kauffmann,(Maria Anna Catharina) Angelica 瑞士画家 9—198d
考格利瓷器 Caughley ware 英国瓷器 3—535c
《考工记》 Kaogongji 中国科技专著 9—170e
考古年代表 archaeological time scale 考古学 1—446f
考古学 archaeology 研究人类遗物的科学 1—446f
考核 residencia 西班牙考察官员制度 14—239f
考津齐 Kazinczy,Ferenc 匈牙利文人 9—207f
考卡 Cauca 哥伦比亚省份 3—533b
考卡河 Cauca River 哥伦比亚河流 3—533c
考卡山谷 Valle del Cauca 哥伦比亚省份 17—454c
考考斯卡 Kokoschka,Oskar 奥地利画家 9—337a
考克 Koch,Martin 瑞典小说家 9—330b
考克饶夫 Cockcroft,Sir John Douglas 英国物理学家 4—322b
考克斯 Cox,Jacob Dolson 美国政治领袖 4—559d
考克斯 Cox,James M(iddleton) 美国报纸发行人 4—559e
考克斯 Cox,Kenyon 美国画家、评论家 4—559f
考克斯 Cox,Sir Percy (Zachariah) 英国外交家 4—559f
考克斯 Cox,Richard 英国主教 4—560a
考克斯 Cox,William Trevor 爱尔兰作家 4—560b
考克西失业请愿军 Coxey's Army 美国历史 4—560b
考拉 Cowra 澳大利亚城镇 4—559c
考拉克 Kaolack 塞内加尔城镇 9—171a
考拉纳莫达 Kaura Namoda 尼日利亚城镇 9—200c
考里松 kauri pine (*Agathis australis*) 木本植物 9—200d
考利 Cowley,Abraham 英国诗人、作家 4—558c
考利 Cowley,Malcolm 美国文学评论家 4—558d
考洛尼亚 Caulonia 意大利古城 3—536b
考洛乔 Kalocsa 匈牙利城镇 9—144a
考姆艾哈迈尔 Kawm al-Aḥmar (Egypt) 埃及历史遗址 9—203d
考姆翁布 Kawm Umbū 埃及城镇 9—203d
考纳斯 Kaunas 立陶宛城镇 9—199c
考尼茨 Kaunitz,Wenzel Anton von 奥地利首相 9—200b
考彭斯战役 Cowpens,Battle of 美国历史 4—558e
考珀伯爵(第一) Cowper,William Cowper,1st Earl 英格兰律师 4—559b
考珀氏腺 Cowper's gland 解剖学 4—559b
考普 Cope,Jack 南非作家 4—488b
考普斯 Kops,Bernard 英国剧作家 9—351e
考沙克 Kassák,Lajos 匈牙利作家 9—192d
考绍 Kassa (Slovakia) 斯洛伐克城市 9—192d
考斯 Cowes 英格兰地名 4—557e
考陶尔德艺术馆 Courtauld Institute Galleries 英国博物馆、学校 4—550a
考特(夫人) Court,Margaret 澳大利亚女子网球运动员 4—549c
考特纳 Käutner,Helmut 德国演员 9—200e
考特尼 Courtney (of Penwith),Leonard Henry Courtney,Baron 英国政治家 4—550e
考特尼奇 Courtneidge,Dame Cicely 英国演员 4—550e
考托河 Cauto River 古巴河流 3—536e
考托瑙 Katona,József 匈牙利律师 9—196e
考瓦路比亚 Covarrubias,Miguel 墨西哥画家、人类学者 4—554a
考维尔 Cowell,Henry (Dixon) 美国作曲家 4—557d
考文垂 Coventry 英格兰城市 4—555a
考文垂 Coventry 美国城镇 4—555a
考文垂 Coventry,Sir John 英国政治家 4—555c
考文垂 Coventry (of Aylesborough),Thomas Coventry,1st Baron 英国法学家 4—555c
考文垂 Coventry,Sir William 英国政治家 4—555d

考乌特莫克 Cuauhtémoc 阿兹特克印第安人皇帝 5—46f
考西耶赫王朝 Kāʻūsīyeh DYNASTY 巴文德王朝 9—200d
考伊克奥乌利 Kauikeaouli (Hawaiian king) 夏威夷国王 9—199b
烤 roasting 烹饪方法 14—324f
烤饼 scone 食品 15—146d
烤蛤 clambake 食品 4—258f
烤盘干酪 fondue neuchâteloise 瑞士名菜 6—392a
烤肉 barbecue 食品 2—219c
靠椅 confidante 家具 4—421b
苛性钾 caustic potash 化合物 3—536e
苛性钠 caustic soda 化合物 3—536e
呵叻 Khorat (Thailand) 泰国城市 9—263f
呵叻高原 Khorat Plateau 泰国高原 9—263f
珂勒惠支 Kollwitz, Käthe 德国版画家 9—339f
珂罗版印刷法 collotype 印刷 4—352a
珂珀树 copal tree 木本植物 4—487c
珂珀脂 copal 树脂 4—487c
柯珋琁照相法 collodion process 摄影术 4—351d
柯布伦茨 Coblentz, William W(eber) 美国物理学家 4—316e
柯慈 Coetzee, J. M. 南非小说家 4—329d
柯蒂斯 Curtis, Benjamin R(obbins) 美国最高法院大法官 5—72c
柯蒂斯 Curtis, Charles 美国副总统 5—72d
柯蒂斯 Curtis, Charles Gordon 美国发明家 5—72d
柯蒂斯 Curtis, Cyrus Hermann Kotzschmar 美国出版商 5—72e
柯蒂斯 Curtiss, Glenn (Hammond) 美国工程师 5—73a
柯蒂斯 Curtis, George William 美国作家 5—72e
柯蒂斯 Curtis, Lionel George 英国政府官员 5—72f
柯蒂斯 Curtiz, Michael 美国导演 5—73c
柯蒂斯杯 Curtis Cup 高尔夫球赛奖杯 5—73a
柯恩斯 Khons 古埃及宗教月神 9—263a
柯尔贝尔 Colbert, Charles 法国政治家 4—337d
柯尔贝尔 Colbert, Jean-Baptiste 法国财政总监 4—337d
柯尔贝尔 Colbert, Jean-Baptiste, MARQUIS DE SEIGNELAY 法国国务大臣 4—338b
柯尔贝尔针绣花边 point Colbert 工艺品 13—388e
柯尔比 Kirby, Rollin 美国漫画家 9—299b
柯尔比 Kirby, William 加拿大作家 9—299b
柯尔比-史密斯 Kirby-Smith, E. 美国将领 9—299c
柯尔达 Korda, Sir Alexander 英国电影导演 9—352d
柯尔克利斯 Kirklees 英格兰自治市 9—303d
柯尔克孜语 Kirgiz language 语言 9—300e
柯尔克孜族 Kirgiz 中国民族 9—300d
柯尔律治 Coleridge, (David) Hartley 英国诗人 4—342e
柯尔律治 Coleridge, Sara 英国翻译家 4—343c
柯尔律治 Coleridge, Samuel Taylor 英国诗人 4—342f
柯尔莫哥洛夫 Kolmogorov, Andrey Nikolayevich 苏联数学家 9—340b
《柯尔·尼德里》 Kol Nidre 犹太教祈祷曲 9—337d
柯尔斯坦 Kirstein, Lincoln 美国舞蹈界权威 9—305c
柯尔索 Corso, Gregory 美国诗人 4—523f
柯菲 covid 古代长度单位 4—555f
柯合巴 cohoba 药物 4—334d
柯亨 Cohen, Hermann 德国哲学家 4—332e
柯胡特 Kohut, Alexander 美国犹太教学者 9—335d
柯金蒂洛赫 Kirkintilloch 苏格兰城镇 9—303b
柯卡尔迪(格兰吉的) Kirkcaldy (of Grange), Sir William 苏格兰军人 9—302e
柯卡斯 Kirkus, Virginia 美国评论家、作家 9—304a
柯科迪 Kirkcaldy 苏格兰区名 9—302d
柯科迪 Kirkcaldy 苏格兰城镇 9—302d
柯克 Cocker, Edward 英国作者 4—322c
柯克 Coke, Sir Edward 英国法学家 4—336d
柯克 Kirk, Sir John 苏格兰医生 9—302c
柯克 Kirk, Norman Eric 新西兰总理 9—302d
柯克兰 Kirkland, Joseph 美国小说家 9—303b
柯克兰 Kirkland, Lane 美国工会领袖 9—303b
柯克兰 Kirkland, Samuel 美国牧师 9—303c
柯克兰莱克 Kirkland Lake 加拿大城镇 9—303c
柯克曼 Kirkman, Jacob 英国乐器制造家 9—303d
柯克帕特里克 Kirkpatrick, Jeane 美国政治人物 9—303e
柯克帕特里克 Kirkpatrick, Ralph (Leonard) 美国音乐学家 9—303f
柯克山岭 Kirk Range 马拉维高原 9—302d
柯克斯维尔 Kirksville 美国城市 9—303f
柯克沃尔 Kirkwall 苏格兰城市 9—304b
柯克伍德空隙 Kirkwood gaps 天文学 9—304b
柯库布里 Kirkcudbright 苏格兰地名 9—303a
柯库布里郡 Kirkcudbrightshire 苏格兰历史郡 9—302f
柯勒 Kohler, Josef 德国法学家 9—334d
柯勒 Kohler, Kaufmann 美国神学家 9—334d
柯勒乔 Correggio 意大利画家 4—521a
柯勒乔家族 Correggio FAMILY 意大利家族 4—521c
柯里 Currie, Sir Arthur William 加拿大司令官 5—71a
柯里 Currie, Sir Donald 英国船主、政治家 5—71a
柯里 Curry, Haskell Brooks 美国数学家、教育家 5—71c
柯里 Curry, John 英国花样滑冰运动员 5—71d
柯里 Curry, John Steuart 美国画家 5—71d
柯里尔 Collier, Jeremy 英格兰主教 4—348e
柯里尔和艾夫斯 Currier, Nathaniel; and Ives, James Merritt 美国石版画家 5—71b
柯里小子 Curry, Kid 美国歹徒 5—71e
柯里佐夫 Koltsov, Aleksey Vasilyevich 俄国诗人 9—341c
柯立芝 Coolidge, (John) Calvin 美国总统 4—481c
柯利 Curley, James M(ichael) 美国政治家 5—69f
柯林斯 Collins, Anthony 英国自然神论者 4—349d
柯林斯 Collins, Eileen 美国宇航员 4—349e
柯林斯 Collins, Tom 澳大利亚作家 4—350d
柯林特 Corinth, Lovis 德国画家 4—507e
柯伦 Curran, John Philpot 爱尔兰律师、政治家 5—70c
柯伦泰 Kollontay, Aleksandra Mikhaylovna 俄国革命家 9—339e
柯伦特河 Current River 美国河流 5—70f
柯罗 Corot, (Jean-Baptiste-) Camille 法国画家 4—518e
柯罗连科 Korolenko, Vladimir Galaktionovich 俄国小说家 9—359f
柯姆 Curme, George O(liver) 美国语法学家 5—70b
柯南道尔 Doyle, Sir Arthur Conan 英国作家 5—408a
柯尼斯堡 Königsberg (Russia) 俄罗斯城市 9—346a
柯尼斯堡阿尔贝图斯大学 Königsberg, Albertus University of 普鲁士高等学府 9—346a
柯尼希 Koenig, Marie-Pierre(-Joseph-François) 法国陆军军官 9—332b
柯尼希格雷茨 Königgrätz (Czech Republic) 捷克城镇 9—345f
柯尼希湖 Königssee 德国湖泊 9—346c
柯尼希斯马克伯爵 Königsmark, Philipp Christoph, Count (Graf) von 德国贵族 9—346c
柯尼希斯马克女伯爵 Königsmark, MariaAurora, Countess (Gräfin) von 萨克森选侯的情妇 9—346b
柯尼希斯温特 Königswinter 德国城市 9—346c
柯珀 Cowper, William 英国诗人 4—558f
柯普 Kopp, Hermann Franz Moritz 德国化学家 9—350c
柯普律吕·法齐尔·艾哈迈德帕夏 Köprülü Fazıl Ahmed Paşa 奥斯曼帝国首相 9—350f
柯普律吕·法齐尔·穆斯塔法帕夏 Köprülü Fazıl Mustafa Paşa 奥斯曼帝国首相 9—351b
柯普律吕·穆罕默德帕夏 Köprülü Mehmed Paşa 奥斯曼帝国首相 9—351c
柯普律吕扎德 Köprülüzade 土耳其政治家 9—351e

柯秋宾斯基 Kotsyubinsky, Mikhaylo (Mikhaylovich) 乌克兰小说家 9—366a
柯萨 Cossa, Baldassare 敌对教皇 4—532a
柯萨科夫氏综合征 Korsakoff syndrome 疾病 9—360c
柯石英 coesite 矿物 4—329c
柯斯丘什科 Kościuszko, Tadeusz (Andrzej Bonawentura) 波兰将军 9—361d
柯特利亚列夫斯基 Kotlyarevsky, Ivan (Petrovich) 乌克兰作家 9—365b
柯廷 Curtin, John (Joseph) 澳大利亚总理 5—72b
柯瓦列夫斯卡娅 Kovalevskaya, Sofya (Vasilyevna) 俄国数学家 9—367f
柯宛 Kirwan, Richard 爱尔兰化学家 9—305e
柯温 Curwen, John 英国音乐教育家 5—74f
柯伍德山 Curwood, Mount 美国山峰 5—75a
柯西 Cauchy, Augustin-Louis, Baron 法国数学家 3—534f
柯西金 Kosygin, Aleksey Nikolayevich 苏联政治家 9—364a
柯伊伯 Kuiper, Gerard Peter 美国天文学家 9—391a
柯伊伯带 Kuiper belt 天文学 9—391b
柯伊伯机载天文台 Kuiper Airborne Observatory 天文观测飞机 9—391b
科 Coo (Greece) 希腊岛屿 4—477a
科阿莫 Coamo 波多黎各城镇 4—311f
科阿特佩克 Coatepeque 危地马拉城市 4—312f
科阿韦拉 Coahuila 墨西哥州名 4—310e
科埃略 Coello, Alonso Sánchez 西班牙画家 4—328d
科埃略 Coello, Claudio 西班牙画家 4—328d
科昂-塔努吉 Cohen-Tannoudji, Claude 法国物理学家 4—333a
科奥劳岭 Koolau Range 美国山岭 9—349c
科巴 Cobar 澳大利亚城镇 4—314b
科巴姆 Cobham, Sir Alan (John) 英国飞行员 4—316d
科堡 Coburg 德国城市 4—317d
科堡半岛 Cobourg Peninsula 澳大利亚半岛 4—316e
科鲍兹琴 koboz 乐器 9—329c
科贝赫 Cobergher, Wenceslas 佛兰芒建筑师 4—316c
科贝特 Corbett, James J(ohn) 美国拳击运动员 4—499f
科贝特 Cobbett, William 英格兰新闻记者 4—314f
科本 Köppen, Wladimir (Peter) 德国气象学家 9—350d
科本茨尔 Cobenzl, (Johann) Ludwig (Joseph), Grafvon (count of) 奥地利外交官 4—316a
科本茨尔 Cobenzl, (Johann) Philipp, Craf von (count of) 奥地利政治家 4—316b
科比 Corby 英格兰城镇 4—501b
科比埃尔 Corbière, Tristan 法国诗人 4—500b
科比纳耶 Corbinaye, Rose-Perrine le Roy de la 法国演员 4—500d
科比特国家公园 Corbett National Park 印度国家公园 4—500a
科比西埃 Corbusier, Le 瑞士建筑师 4—500e
科波 Copeau, Jacques 法国演员 4—488b
科波拉 Coppola, Francis Ford 美国电影导演 4—494a
科伯恩 Cockburn, Sir Alexander James Edmund, 10TH BARONET 英国法官 4—321e
科伯恩 Coburn, Alvin Langdon 英国摄影家 4—317e
科伯克河谷国家公园 Kobuk Valley National Park 美国国家公园 9—329c
科布 Cobb, Frank I(rving) 美国记者 4—314b
科布 Cobb, Howell 美国政治家 4—314c
科布 Cobb, Irvin S(hrewsbury) 美国新闻记者 4—314c
科布 Cobb, John 美国家具工匠 4—314d
科布 Cobb, John Rhodes 英国赛车运动员 4—314e
科布 Cobb, Ty 美国棒球运动员 4—314e
科布登 Cobden, Richard 英国政治家 4—315d
科布登-桑德森 Cobden-Sanderson, Thomas James 英国图书设计及装帧家 4—315f
科布多 Hovd 蒙古城镇 8—197c
科布伦茨 Koblenz 德国行政专区 9—328e
科布伦茨 Koblenz 德国城市 9—329a
科布洛 Corbulo, Gnaeus Domitius 罗马将军 4—500d
科策布 Kotzebue 美国城市 9—366c
科策布 Kotzebue, August (Friedrich Ferdinand) von 德国剧作家 9—366c
科策布 Kotzebue, Otto von 俄罗斯军官 9—366d
科茨 Coates, Florence Van Leer Earle Nicholson 美国诗人 4—313a
科茨 Coates, Joseph Gordon 新西兰总理 4—313a
科茨地 Coats Land 南极洲地区 4—313d
科茨沃尔德 Cotswold 英格兰区名 4—537b
科茨沃尔兹 Cotswolds 英格兰山脉 4—537c
科达古 Kodagu (India) 印度县名 9—331d
科达伦 Coeur d'Alene 美国城市 4—329f
科达伦湖 Coeur d'Alene Lake 美国湖泊 4—330a
科达伦山 Coeur d'Alene Mountains 美国山脉 4—330a
科达氏木目 Cordaitales 古生物学 4—501e
科达伊 Kodály, Zoltán 匈牙利作曲家 9—331e
科达伊洛·达马塔 Cordeiro da Matta, Joaquim Dias 非洲诗人 4—502a
科黛 Corday, Charlotte 法国贵族 4—501f
科德 cord 计量单位 4—501c
科德 Cord, Errett Lobban 美国汽车制造商 4—501d
科德角 Cod, Cape 美国半岛 4—325e
科德角印第安人 Cape Indians (people) 北美印第安民族 3—420e
科德角运河 Cape Cod Canal 美国人工水道 3—420a
科德雷亚努 Codreanu, Corneliu (Zelea) 罗马尼亚政治鼓动家 4—327c
科德利埃俱乐部 Cordeliers, Club of the 法国历史 4—502a
科德林顿 Codrington, R(obert) H(enry) 英国人类学家 4—327c
科德罗斯 Codrus 传说中的雅典国王 4—327d
科德穆瓦 Cordemoy, (Louis-)Géraud de 法国历史学家 4—502b
科德韦尔 Caldwell 美国城市 3—342b
科德韦尔 Caldwell 美国自治镇 3—342c
科迪 Cody 美国城市 4—327e
科迪 Cody, William F(rederick) 美国陆军侦察员 4—327e
科迪勒拉 cordillera 平行大山系地形 4—502e
科迪勒拉地槽 Cordilleran Geosyncline 美洲地质构造 4—502e
科迪勒拉新火山 Neo-Volcánica, Cordillera 墨西哥火山 12—77e
科迪亚克 Kodiak 美国城市 9—332a
科迪亚克熊 Kodiak bear (*Ursus arctos middendorffi*) 动物 9—332a
科蒂 Coty, François(-Marie-Joseph-Spoturno) 法国商人 4—540b
科蒂 Coty, René(-Jules-Gustave) 法国总统 4—540b
科蒂安山脉 Cottian Alps 欧洲山脉 4—538a
科蒂尼奥 Coutinho, Afrânio 巴西作家、文学评论家 4—552f
科蒂纽 Coutinho, Manuel de Sousa 葡萄牙历史 4—552f
科蒂荣舞 cotillion 舞蹈 4—536c
科蒂乌斯 Cottius 利古里亚部落国王 4—538b
科丁顿 Coddington, William 新英格兰殖民地总督 4—326a
科顿 Cotton, Sir Arthur Thomas 英国灌溉工程师 4—538e
科顿 Cotton, Charles 英国诗人 4—538e
科顿 Cotton, John 新英格兰基督教领袖 4—538f
科顿 Cotton, Sir (Thomas) Henry 英国高尔夫球运动员 4—538f
科顿准男爵(第一) Cotton, Sir Robert Bruce, 1ST BARONET 英国收藏家 4—538f
科多尔 Côte-d'Or 法国省份 4—536a
科多尔 Côte-d'Or, Prieur de la 法国军事工程师 4—536b
科多马努斯 Codommanus 波斯国王 4—326f
科多纳家族 Codona FAMILY 马戏表演家族 4—326f
科恩 Cohen, Albert 美国犯罪学家 4—332c
科恩 Cohen, Ernst Julius 荷兰化学家 4—332d
科恩 Cohn, Edwin Joseph 美国生物化学家 4—333d

科恩 Cohn, Ferdinand (Julius) 德国博物学家 4—333e
科恩 Cone, Fairfax M(astick) 美国商人 4—418d
科恩 Kohn, Fritz Nathan 奥地利戏剧导演 9—335c
科恩 Cohn, Harry 美国电影巨头 4—334b
科恩 Coen, Jan Pieterszoon 荷属东印度总督 4—329a
科恩 Cohen, Leonard 加拿大歌手、歌曲作者 4—332e
科恩 Cohen, Stanley 美国生物化学家 4—332f
科恩 Kohn, Walter 美国物理学家 9—335c
科恩伯格 Kornberg, Arthur 美国生物化学家 9—359c
科恩伯里子爵 Cornbury, Henry Hyde, Viscount 英国政治家 4—511d
科恩布利特 Kornblit, Aleksandr 俄国戏剧导演 9—359c
科恩戈尔德 Korngold, Erich Wolfgang 美国作曲家 9—359e
科恩海姆 Cohnheim, Julius Friedrich 德国病理学家 4—334b
科恩海特 Coornhert, Dirck Volckertszoon 荷兰诗人、翻译家 4—486e
科恩姐妹 Cone, Claribel; and Cone, Etta 美国艺术收藏家 4—418c
科恩群岛 Corn Islands 尼加拉瓜群岛 4—510d
科恩兄弟诉弗吉尼亚州案 Cohens v. Virginia 美国法院案件 4—333b
科尔 Kohl, Helmut 德国总理 9—334b
科尔 Coeur, Jacques 法国富商 4—329e
科尔 Cole, Johnnetta 美国人类学家、教育家 4—339f
科尔 Kold, Kristen Mikkelsen 丹麦教育家 9—338d
科尔 Cole, Natalie 美国歌手 4—340a
科尔 Cole, Nat King 美国音乐家 4—340a
科尔 Cole, Thomas 美国画家 4—340b
科尔巴思 Colbath, Jeremiah Jones 美国副总统 4—337c
科尔贝 Kolbe, Hermann 德国化学家 9—338b
科尔贝 Corbeil, William of 坎特伯雷大主教 4—499d
科尔贝-埃索讷 Corbeil-Essonnes 法国城镇 4—499d
科尔贝格 Kolberg(Poland) 波兰城镇 9—338c
科尔比 Colby, Frank Moore 百科全书编辑 4—338c
科尔比 Kolbe, Saint Maksymilian Maria 天主教司铎 9—338b
科尔宾 Corbin, Margaret 美国独立战争英雄 4—500c
科尔波特瓷器 Coalport porcelain 英国瓷器 4—311e
科尔伯恩港 Port Colborne 加拿大城市 13—444d
科尔伯特 Colbert, Claudette 美国演员 4—337d
科布布鲁克 Colebrook, Leonard 英国医学家 4—340c
科布布鲁克代尔桥 Coalbrookdale Bridge 英国桥梁 4—311d
科尔布鲁克-卡梅伦考察团 Colebrook-Cameron Commission 英国考察团 4—340d
科尔布特 Korbut, Olga Valentinovna 苏联体操运动员 9—352b
科尔察 Korçë 阿尔巴尼亚城市 9—352b
科尔德斯特里姆 Coldstream 苏格兰小自治市 4—339f
科尔德威 Koldewey, Robert 德国考古学家 9—338e
科尔迪茨堡 Colditz Castle 德国战俘营 4—339e
科尔迪岛 Caldey Island 威尔士岛屿 3—342a
科尔蒂 Corti, Luigi, Count (Conte) 意大利外交家 4—525d
科尔蒂纳丹佩佐 Cortina d'Ampezzo 意大利城镇 4—525f
科尔顿 Colton, Gardner Quincy 美国麻醉学家 4—366f
科尔多贝斯 Cordobés, El 西班牙斗牛士 4—504a
科尔多凡 Kordofan 苏丹地区 9—352f
科尔多凡诸语言 Kordofanian languages 苏丹语言 9—353a
科尔多瓦 Córdoba 阿根廷省份 4—502f
科尔多瓦 Córdoba 阿根廷城市 4—502f
科尔多瓦 Córdoba 哥伦比亚省份 4—503b
科尔多瓦 Córdoba 墨西哥城市 4—503c
科尔多瓦 Córdoba 西班牙省份 4—503c
科尔多瓦 Córdoba 西班牙城市 4—503c
科尔多瓦 Cordova 美国城市 4—504c
科尔多瓦 Córdoba, Gonzalo Fernández de 美国城市 4—503f
科尔多瓦清真寺-大教堂 Córdoba, Mosque-Cathedral of 西班牙教堂 4—503f
《科尔多瓦星表》 Córdoba Durchmusterung (CD) 天文学 4—504a
科尔多维罗 Cordovero, Moses ben Jacob 犹太教拉比 4—504d
科尔法克斯 Colfax, Schuyler 美国副总统 4—344d
科尔凡蒂 Korfanty, Wojciech 波兰政治领袖 9—358c
科尔凡蒂线 Korfanty Line 波兰历史 9—358d
科尔夫球 korfball 体育 9—358e
科尔盖特-帕尔莫利夫公司 Colgate-Palmolive Company 美国公司 4—344e
科尔古耶夫岛 Kolguyev Island 俄罗斯岛屿 9—338f
科尔哈泽 Kohlhase, Hans 德国商人 9—335a
科尔基诺 Korkino 俄罗斯城市 9—359a
科尔基斯 Colchis 高加索南部古地理区 4—338e
科尔基斯低地 Colchis Lowland (Georgia) 格鲁吉亚低地平原 4—338f
科尔科瓦杜山 Corcovado, Mount 巴西山峰 4—501c
科尔库人 Korku 民族 9—359a
科尔莱奥内 Corleone 意大利城市 4—509c
科尔劳施 Kohlrausch, Friedrich Wilhelm Georg 德国物理学家 9—335b
科尔雷恩 Coleraine 北爱尔兰城镇 4—342e
科尔马 Colmar 法国城镇 4—352e
科尔曼 Coleman, James S(amuel) 美国社会学家 4—340e
科尔曼 Coleman, Ornette 美国萨克斯管演奏家 4—340f
科尔曼 Colman, Ronald 美国电影演员 4—352d
科尔曼(老) Colman, George, THE ELDER 英国喜剧作家 4—352b
科尔曼(林迪斯凡的),圣 Colman OF LINDISFARNE, SAINT 爱尔兰教士 4—352a
科尔曼(小) Colman, George, THE YOUNGER 英国剧作家 4—352c
科尔纳罗 Cornaro, Caterina 威尼斯贵族 4—511c
科尔内管 cornett 乐器 4—514e
科尔内留斯,圣 Cornelius, SAINT 教皇 4—512f
科尔内托 Corneto (Italy) 意大利城镇 4—514e
科尔尼 Cornu, Paul 法国工程师 4—515d
科尔尼洛夫 Kornilov, Lavr Georgiyevich 俄罗斯帝国将军 9—359e
科尔努图斯 Cornutus, Lucius Annaeus 罗马哲学家 4—515e
科尔佩珀 Colepeper (of Thoresway), John Colepeper, 1st Baron 英格兰政治家 4—342d
科尔奇诺伊 Korchnoi, Viktor 苏联国际象棋大师 9—352c
科尔切斯特 Colchester 苏格兰自治市、区 4—338c
科尔沁草原 Horqin Grassland 中国草原 8—179d
科尔丘拉 Korčula 克罗地亚岛屿 9—352c
科尔萨科夫 Korsakov 俄罗斯城市 9—360d
科尔松 Colson, Jean-Claude-Gilles (French playwright) 法国剧作家 4—366d
科尔特 Colter, John 美国探险家 4—366e
科尔特·范·德·林登 Cort van der Linden, Pieter 荷兰政治家 4—524a
科尔特兰 Coltrane, John (William) 美国作曲家 4—367a
科尔特斯 Cortés, Hernán, MARQUÉS DEL VALLE DE OAXACA 西班牙殖民者 4—524d
科尔特斯港 Puerto Cortés 洪都拉斯港市 14—15e
科尔特斯海 Cortés, Sea of (Pacific Ocean) 墨西哥西北部海湾 4—525c
科尔托 Cortot, Alfred-Denis 音乐指挥家、教师 4—526d
科尔托纳 Cortona 意大利城市 4—526c
科尔托纳 Cortona, Luca da 意大利画家 4—526d
科尔托纳 Cortona, Pietro da 意大利艺术家 4—526d
科尔维努斯 Corvinus, Matthias 匈牙利国王 4—527f
科尔温 Colwyn 威尔士地名 4—375c
科尔温贝 Colwyn Bay 威尔士城市 4—375c
科尔武 Corvo, Baron 英国作家 4—527f
科尔武岛 Corvo Island 葡萄牙火山岛 4—527f

科尔西尼家族 Corsini FAMILY 佛罗伦萨贵族世家 4—523f
科尔希达 Kolkhida 格鲁吉亚平原 9—339a
科耳班 Colburn, Irving Wightman 美国发明家 4—338b
科耳特 Colt, Samuel 美国枪械制造商 4—366e
科菲维尔 Coffeyville 美国城市 4—330f
科芬 Coffin, Henry Sloane 美国教育家 4—331a
科芬 Coffin, Levi 美国废奴主义者 4—331b
科芬 Coffin, Robert P(eter) Tristram 美国诗人 4—331b
科夫 Cobh 爱尔兰海军基地 4—316c
科夫堡 Corfe Castle 英格兰城堡 4—505e
科夫卡 Koffka, Kurt 德国心理学家 9—332d
科夫罗夫 Kovrov 俄罗斯城市 9—368b
科夫诺 Kovno (Lithuania) 立陶宛城镇 9—368b
科夫斯港 Coffs Harbour 澳大利亚港口 4—331c
科弗达尔 Coverdale, Miles 英格兰埃克塞特主教 4—555d
科孚 Corfu 希腊州名 4—505f
《科孚宣言》 Corfu Declaration 巴尔干历史 4—506b
科福里杜亚 Koforidua 加纳城镇 9—332f
科福伊德 Kofoid, Charles Atwood 美国动物学家 9—332e
科格尔尼恰努 Kogălniceanu, Mihail 罗马尼亚政治家 9—333a
科根 Coggan, (Frederick) Donald, Baron 英国神学家 4—331d
科哈拉山 Kohala Mountains 美国夏威夷山脉 9—333f
科哈诺夫斯基 Kochanowski, Jan 波兰诗人 9—330d
科哈特 Kohāt 巴基斯坦城镇 9—334a
科哈西特 Cohasset 美国城镇 4—332b
科汉 Cohan, George M(ichael) 美国演员 4—332a
科赫 Koch, (Heinrich Hermann) Robert 德国细菌学家 9—330b
科赫 Koch, Ilsa 德国战争罪犯 9—329f
科赫 Koch, Rudolf 德国书法家 9—330c
科赫巴 Kokhba, Bar 犹太领袖 9—336f
科赫德斯 Cojedes 委内瑞拉城市 4—336b
科赫尔 Kocher, Emil Theodor 瑞士外科医师 9—330f
科赫姆 Cochem 德国城市 4—319c
科赫特拉耶尔韦 Kohtla-Järve 爱沙尼亚城市 9—335c
科胡特佩克 Cojutepeque 萨尔瓦多城市 4—336c
科霍夫斯基 Kochowski, Wespazjan 波兰诗人 9—331c
科霍戈 Korhogo 科特迪瓦城镇 9—358f
科霍斯 Cohoes 美国城市 4—334d
科基拉维尔 Coquilhatville 刚果(金)城市 4—496b
科吉 Kogi 尼日利亚州名 9—333b
科济耶山脉 Cozie, Alpi (France – Italy) 欧洲山脉 4—561c
科贾埃利 Kocaeli 土耳其省份 9—329e
科杰尼采 Kozienice 波兰城镇 9—368e
科金博 Coquimbo 智利区名 4—496b
科金博 Coquimbo 智利城市 4—496c
科举 keju 中国封建考试选拔制度 9—214d
科凯迈基河 Kokemäen River 芬兰河流 9—336e
科科 Koko 尼日利亚城镇 9—336f
科科河 Coco River 洪都拉斯河流 4—324b
科科角 Koko Head 美国海角 9—336f
科科拉 Kokkola 芬兰城市 9—336f
科科伦艺术馆 Corcoran Gallery of Art 美国博物馆 4—501c
科科莫 Kokomo 美国县城 9—337a
科科努科人 Coconuco 南美印第安人部落 4—324d
科科斯岛 Cocos Island 哥斯达黎加岛屿 4—324f
科科斯群岛 Cocos Islands 澳大利亚海外领地 4—324f
科克 Cork 爱尔兰城市 4—508e
科克 Kock, Charles-Paul de 法国作家 9—331c
科克 Koch, Frederick Henry 美国民间戏剧之父 9—329f
科克 Koch, Kenneth 美国教师、作家 9—330a
科克 Coke, Thomas 英国教士 4—336e
科克本港 Cockburn Harbour 西印度群岛港口、村落 4—321f
科克本湾 Cockburn Sound 澳大利亚海湾 4—321f
科克伯爵(第一) Cork, Richard Boyle, 1st Earl of 英格兰殖民者 4—509b
科克郡 Cork 爱尔兰郡名 4—508e
科克拉乌斯 Cochlaeus, Johannes 德国人文学家 4—320b
科克兰 Coquelin, Benoît-Constant 法国演员 4—495f
科克里尔 Cockerill, William 英国出生的发明家 4—322d
科克伦 Cochran, Sir Charles Blake 英国戏剧演出人 4—320c
科克伦 Cochran, Eddie 美国摇滚乐歌手 4—320d
科克伦 Cochrane, Elizabeth 美国新闻记者 4—320f
科克伦 Cochran, Jacqueline 美国飞行员 4—320d
科克伦 Cochrane, Thomas (British admiral) 英国海军上将 4—320f
科克伦 Cochran, Welker 美国台球运动员 4—320e
科克茅斯 Cockermouth 英格兰城镇 4—322d
科克皮特地区 Cockpit Country 牙买加地区 4—323c
科克切塔夫 Kokchetav 哈萨克斯坦城市 9—336e
科克三世 Kok III, Adam 南非早期国家领袖 9—336b
科克斯巴扎尔 Cox's Bāzār 孟加拉国城镇 4—560c
科克斯科姆山 Cockscomb Range 伯利兹山脉 4—323f
科克斯珀岛 Cockspur Island 美国岛屿 4—323f
科克托 Cocteau, Jean 法国诗人 4—325b
科拉 Cora (Italy) 意大利城镇 4—496e
科拉半岛 Kola Peninsula 俄罗斯海角 9—337f
科拉蒂纳 Colatina 巴西城市 4—337c
科拉尔 Kollár, Ján 斯洛伐克诗人 9—339b
科拉古 choragus 古希腊戏剧 4—197b
科拉克 Colac 澳大利亚城市 4—337c
科拉(里恩佐的) Cola DI RIENZO 意大利民众领袖 4—337a
科拉利 Coralli, Jean 法国舞蹈家 4—499b
科拉罗夫格勒 Kolarovgrad (city, Bulgaria) 保加利亚城市 9—338a
科拉姆 Colum, Padraic 美国诗人 4—367d
科拉纳 Khorana, Har Gobind 美国生物化学家 9—263b
科拉琴 kora 乐器 9—351f
科拉人 Cora (people) 民族 4—496e
科拉托 Corato 意大利城镇 4—499d
科拉伊斯 Koraïs, Adamántios 希腊文学家 9—351f
科拉鼬 kolinsky 哺乳动物 9—339a
科莱(夫人) Colet, Louise 法国诗人 4—343e
科莱恩 Colijn, Hendrikus 荷兰政治家 4—345a
科莱尔湖 Colair Lake (India) 印度湖泊 4—337c
科莱克 Kollek, Teddy 以色列政治人物 9—339d
科莱利 Corelli, Arcangelo 意大利小提琴家、作曲家 4—505b
科莱特 Collett, Glenna 挪威作家 4—348b
科莱特 Colette, (Sidonie-Gabrielle) 法国作家 4—343f
科莱特(夫人) Collett, Camilla 挪威小说家 4—348a
科莱特,圣 Colette, SAINT 天主教女隐修院院长 4—344b
科兰 Colines, Simon de 法国印刷商 4—345c
科兰古侯爵 Caulaincourt, Armand(-Augustin-Louis), marquis de, DUC (duke) DE VICENCE 法国将军 3—535d
科兰·缪塞 Colin MUSET 法国诗人 4—345c
科兰太因河 Courantyne River 南美洲河流 4—547c
科勒 Koller, Carl 美国医师 9—339d
科勒尔盖布尔斯 Coral Gables 美国城市 4—498a
科勒里 Caullery, Maurice(-Jules-Gaston-Corneille) 法国生物学家 3—536a
科勒里奇-泰勒 Coleridge-Taylor, Samuel 英国作曲家 4—343c
科勒斯集团公司 Corus Group, PLC 国际钢铁、金属制品生产商 4—527c
科雷尔 Correr, Angelo (pope) 教皇 4—521e
科雷马河 Kolyma River 俄罗斯河流 9—341d
科雷马山地 Kolyma Upland 俄罗斯山地 9—341d
科雷希多岛 Corregidor Island 菲律宾岛屿 4—521d
科雷亚 Correa, Charles 印度建筑师 4—521a
科雷亚·加尔绍 Correia Garção, Pedro António 葡萄牙诗人 4—

521e
科雷兹 Corrèze 法国省份 4—522b
科里 Cori 意大利城镇 4—506b
科里 Corey, Elias James 美国化学家 4—505d
科里奥拉努斯 Coriolanus, Gnaeus Marcius 罗马传说人物 4—508a
科里奥利 Coriolis, Gustave-Gaspard 法国工程师 4—508b
科里奥利力 Coriolis force 物理学 4—508c
科里班特 Corybant 神 4—528a
科里登 Corydon 美国城镇 4—528b
科里夫妇 Cori, Carl; and Cori, Gerty 美国生物化学家 4—506c
科里弗顿 Corriverton 圭亚那城镇 4—522f
科里根 Corrigan, Sir Dominic John, Baronet 爱尔兰医师 4—522d
科里根-马圭尔 Corrigan-Maguire, Mairéad 北爱尔兰社会工作者 4—522e
科里利 Corelli, Marie 英国作家 4—505d
科里洛斯 Choerilus 希腊叙事诗人 4—188e
科里洛斯 Choerilus 雅典悲剧诗人 4—188e
科里氏病 Cori's disease 疾病 4—508e
科里亚克 Koryak 俄罗斯的共和国 9—361a
科里亚克人 Koryak 俄罗斯民族 9—361a
科利 Koli 印度种姓 9—339a
科利茨 Collitz, Hermann 美国语言学家 4—351b
科利尔 Collier, Arthur 英格兰神学家 4—348d
《科利尔百科全书》 Collier's Encyclopedia 美国百科全书 4—348f
科利马 Colima 墨西哥州名 4—345b
科利马 Colima 墨西哥城市 4—345c
科利牧羊狗 collie 狗品种 4—348c
科利尼 Coligny, Gaspard II de, seigneur (lord) de Châtillon 法国海军上将 4—344f
科利普斯 Corippus, Flavius Cresconius 拉丁语诗人 4—508d
科利奇帕克 College Park 美国城市 4—347f
科利奇站 College Station 美国城市 4—347f
科利丘吉诺 Kolchugino (Russian S. F. S. R.) 俄罗斯城市 9—338d
科利特 Colet, John 英格兰神学家 4—343d
科连特斯 Corrientes 阿根廷省份 4—522b
科连特斯 Corrientes 阿根廷城市 4—522c
科连特斯角 Corrientes, Cape 墨西哥海岬 4—522c
科林 Conlin, Bernard (U.S. actor) 美国演员 4—433a
科林斯 Corinth 希腊城市 4—506e
科林斯 Corinth 美国城市 4—507b
科林斯 Korinthos 希腊州名 9—358f
科林斯 Collings, Jesse 英国政治家 4—349a
科林斯 Collins, Janet 美国芭蕾舞演员 4—349f
科林斯 Collins, Marva 美国教育家 4—350a
科林斯 Collins, Michael 爱尔兰英雄 4—350b
科林斯 Collins, Michael 美国航天员 4—350c
科林斯 Collins, William 英国诗人 4—350e
科林斯 Collins, (William) Wilkie 英国神秘小说大师 4—350d
科林斯堡 Fort Collins 美国城市 6—413b
科林斯地峡 Corinth, Isthmus of 希腊地峡 4—507c
科林斯同盟 Corinth, League of 古希腊历史 4—507e
科林斯维尔 Collinsville 美国城市 4—350f
科林斯运河 Corinth Canal 希腊河道 4—507f
科林斯柱式 Corinthian order 建筑学 4—507f
科林托 Corinto 尼加拉瓜港口 4—508a
科林伍德 Collingwood, Cuthbert Collingwood, 1st Baron 英国海军司令 4—349b
科林伍德 Collingwood, R(obin) G(eorge) 英国历史学家 4—349c
科林兄弟 Colling, Robert; and Colling, Charles 英国牲畜饲养家 4—349a
科琳娜 Corinna 希腊诗人 4—506e
科灵 Kolding 丹麦城市 9—338e
科隆 Cologne 德国城市 4—353a
科隆 Colón 古巴城市 4—357d
科隆 Colón 巴拿马城市 4—357d
科隆 Köln 德国行政区 9—340c
科隆 Colón, Diego 西印度群岛总督 4—357e
科隆-贝沙尔 Colomb-Béchar (Algeria) 阿尔及利亚城镇 4—355a
科隆比纳 Columbine 戏剧人物 4—369f
科隆博 Colombo, Joseph A., Sr. 美国罪犯 4—357a
科隆博 Colombo, Matteo Realdo 意大利解剖学家 4—357b
科隆布 Colombes 法国巴黎郊区 4—355b
科隆布 Colombe, Michel 法国雕刻家 4—355a
科隆大学 Cologne, University of 德国大学 4—354e
科隆动物园 Cologne Zoological Garden, AG 德国动物园 4—354f
科隆纳 Colonna, Oddone (pope) 教皇 4—359c
科隆纳家族 Colonna family 罗马贵族世家 4—359b
科隆娜 Colonna, Vittoria 意大利诗人 4—359c
科隆群岛 Colón, Archipiélago de (Ecuador) 厄瓜多尔群岛 4—357e
科隆香水 cologne 香水 4—354e
科卢梅拉 Columella, Lucius Junius Moderatus 罗马军人 4—375a
科卢韦齐 Kolwezi 刚果(金)城市 9—341c
科伦巴 Corumbá 巴西城市 4—526f
科伦巴,圣 Columba, Saint 传教士 4—367d
科伦坡 Colombo 斯里兰卡首都 4—356e
科伦坡计划 Colombo Plan 国际经济计划 4—357c
科伦斯 Correns, Carl Erich 德国植物学家 4—521e
科伦索 Colenso, John 基督教主教 4—341b
科伦泰河 Kolenté River (Sierra Leone, Guinea) 非洲河流 9—338f
科罗 Coro 委内瑞拉城市 4—516e
科罗多 Corrado di Suburra 教皇 4—520f
科罗尔 Koror 太平洋岛屿 9—360b
科罗拉 Corrora (Caroline Islands) 加罗林岛屿 4—522f
科罗拉多 Colorado 美国州名 4—360c
科罗拉多高原 Colorado Plateau 美国高原 4—363b
科罗拉多国家保护区 Colorado National Monument 美国保护区 4—363a
科罗拉多河 Colorado River 北美河流 4—363c
科罗拉多河 Colorado River 美国河流 4—363e
科罗拉多河 Colorado River 阿根廷河流 4—363e
科罗拉多马铃薯甲虫 Colorado potato beetle (species *Leptinotarsa decemlineata*) 昆虫 4—363b
科罗拉多蜱热 Colorado tick fever 疾病 4—363f
科罗拉多人 Colorado 厄瓜多尔印第安人 4—360b
科罗拉多沙漠 Colorado Desert 美国沙漠 4—363a
科罗拉多斯普林斯 Colorado Springs 美国城市 4—363e
科罗廖夫 Korolyov 俄罗斯城市 9—359f
科罗廖夫 Korolyov, Sergey Pavlovich 苏联航天器设计家 9—360a
科罗曼德尔半岛 Coromandel Peninsula 新西兰半岛 4—516f
科罗曼德尔海岸 Coromandel Coast 印度平原 4—516f
科罗纳 Corona 美国城市 4—517a
科罗纳多 Coronado 美国城市 4—517d
科罗纳多 Coronado, Francisco Vázquez de 西班牙探险家 4—517d
科罗纳多湾 Coronado Bay 太平洋海湾 4—517e
科罗纳赫挽歌 coronach 凯尔特人诗歌 4—517d
科罗内尔 Coronel 智利城市 4—518b
科罗内尔 Coronel, María Fernández (Spanish mystic) 西班牙神秘主义者 4—518b
科罗萨尔 Corozal 伯利兹城镇 4—519a
科罗舍茨 Korošec, Anton 斯洛文尼亚政治领袖 9—360b
科罗斯坚 Korosten 乌克兰城市 9—360c
科罗瓦 Corowa 澳大利亚城镇 4—519a
科洛·德布瓦 Collot d'Herbois, Jean-Marie 法国激进民主派成员 4—351f
科洛德人 Coloured 南非民族 4—366c

科洛迪 Collodi, C. 意大利作家 4—351c
科洛丰 Colophon 古希腊城市 4—359f
科洛夫拉特(-利布斯泰因斯基) Kolowrat(-Liebsteinsky), (Franz) Anton, Graf von 奥地利政治家 9—341a
科洛科特罗尼斯 Kolokotrónis, Theódoros 希腊爱国者 9—340e
科洛梅亚 Kolomyya 乌克兰城市 9—341a
科洛明斯科耶 Kolomenskoye 莫斯科地名 9—340f
科洛姆 Colomb, Philip Howard 英国海军军官 4—355a
科洛姆纳 Kolomna 俄罗斯城市 9—341a
科洛尼尔国家历史公园 Colonial National Historical Park 美国公园 4—358a
科洛舞 kolo 巴尔干集体舞 9—340d
科洛西莫 Colosimo, James 美国罪犯 4—364f
科马蒂河 Komati River 非洲河流 9—342b
科马尔诺 Komárno 斯洛伐克城镇 9—341e
科马吉尼 Commagene 近东历史地区 4—382d
科马克 Cormack, Allan MacLeod 美国物理学家 4—509d
科马罗夫 Komarov, Vladimir Mikhaylovich 苏联航天员 9—342a
科马罗夫植物研究所 Komarov Botanical Institute 俄罗斯植物研究中心 9—342a
科马罗姆-埃斯泰尔戈姆 Komárom-Esztergom 匈牙利州名 9—341f
科马穆尔运河 Kommamur Canal 印度运河 9—343a
科马纳 Comana 土耳其古城 4—375f
科马内奇 Comăneci, Nadia 罗马尼亚体操运动员 4—376b
科马亚瓜 Comayagua 洪都拉斯城市 4—376b
科玛尔 Camār 印度种姓 3—363b
科曼多尔群岛 Komandor Islands 俄罗斯岛群 9—341e
科曼切人 Comanche 北美印第安部落 4—375f
科梅索 commesso 艺术 4—385e
科蒙多尔牧羊狗 komondor 狗品种 9—343d
科米 Komi 俄罗斯的共和国 9—342c
科米-彼尔米亚克俄罗 Komi-Permyak 俄罗斯州名 9—342e
科米诺 Comino 地中海岛屿 4—382a
科米人 Komi 民族 9—342c
科米萨尔热夫斯基 Komisarjevsky, Theodore 俄国戏剧导演 9—342e
科米萨尔热夫斯卡娅 Komissarzhevskaya, Vera Fyodorovna, COUNTESS (Grafinya) MURAVYOVA 俄国演员 9—342f
科米索 Comiso 意大利城镇 4—382a
科米塔斯 Komitas 亚美尼亚音乐学家 9—343a
科米坦 Comitán 墨西哥城市 4—382b
科明尼斯 Commynes, Philippe de 佛兰德政治家 4—393d
科摩林角 Comorin, Cape 印度海角 4—394c
科摩罗 Comoros 非洲国家 4—394c
科莫 Como 意大利城市 4—393f
科莫埃国家公园 Komoé National Park 科特迪瓦国家公园 9—343c
科莫埃河 Komoé River 西非河流 9—343d
科莫迪亚努斯 Commodianus 基督教诗人 4—386c
科莫蒂尼 Komotiní 希腊城镇 9—343d
科莫多 Komodo 印度尼西亚岛屿 9—343b
科莫多龙 Komodo dragon (*Varanus komodoensis*) 爬行动物 9—343b
科莫恩 Komorn (Slovakia) 斯洛伐克城镇 9—343d
科莫湖 Como, Lake 意大利湖泊 4—394a
科莫陶 Komotau (Czech Republic) 捷克城市 9—343d
科姆斯托克 Comstock, Elizabeth Leslie Rous 美国社会改革家 4—407c
科穆纳尔斯克 Kommunarsk 乌克兰城市 9—343b
科纳 Kona (Hawaii, U.S.) 美国居民社区 9—344b
科纳布鲁克 Corner Brook 加拿大城市 4—514a
科纳彻 Conacher, Lionel (Pretoria) 加拿大体育家 4—408b
科纳尔斯基 Konarski, Stanisław 波兰教育改革家 9—344c
科纳克里 Conakry 几内亚首都 4—408c
科纳芒统 Conemaugh Series 地质学 4—419a
科南特 Conant, James B(ryant) 美国教育家 4—408d
科内尔 Cornell, Eric A. 美国物理学家 4—513c
科内尔 Cornell, Joseph 美国艺术家 4—513d
科内尔 Cornell, Katharine 美国演员 4—513d
科内利乌斯 Cornelius, Peter 德国作曲家 4—513a
科内利乌斯 Cornelius, Peter von 德国画家 4—513b
科内利亚诺 Conegliano 意大利城镇 4—419a
科内利亚诺 Conegliano, Emanuele (librettist) 意大利作家 4—419a
科内斯托加大货车 Conestoga wagon 马拉货车 4—419b
科内斯托加人 Conestoga (people) 北美印第安人 4—419b
科尼 Coni (Italy) 意大利城市 4—430b
科尼艾兰 Coney Island 美国岛屿 4—419c
科尼比尔 Conibear, Hiram Boardman 美国赛艇教练 4—430c
科尼比尔 Conybeare, William Daniel 英国地质学家、古生物学家 4—476f
科尼什摔跤 Cornish wrestling 体育 4—515c
科尼亚 Konya 土耳其城市 9—348c
科尼亚地毯 Konya carpet 工艺品 9—348d
科尼亚克 Cognac 法国城镇 4—331e
科尼亚克阶 Coniacian Stage 地质学 4—430b
科尼亚克酒 cognac 法国白兰地 4—331e
科尼亚提斯 Choniates, Michael 拜占廷人文主义学者 4—195a
科尼亚提斯 Choniates, Nicetas 拜占廷政治家 4—195a
科涅茨波尔斯基 Koniecpolski, Stanisław 波兰军事领袖 9—345e
科涅夫 Konev, Ivan Stepanovich 苏联将领 9—344f
科涅利亚 Cornelia 罗马贵族 4—512f
科宁 Corning 美国城市 4—515b
科宁 Konin 波兰旧省份 9—346d
科宁 Konin 波兰城市 9—346d
科宁厄姆 Conyngham, Gustavus 美国海军军官 4—477a
科宁克 Koninck, Philips 荷兰画家 9—346d
科宁克斯洛 Coninxloo, Gillis van 佛兰德斯画家 4—432a
科农 Conon 雅典海军统帅 4—438e
科农 Conon 教皇 4—438e
科农(萨摩斯的) Conon OF SAMOS 希腊数学家、天文学家 4—438e
科诺普尼茨卡 Konopnicka, Maria 波兰小说家 9—347c
科诺托普 Konotop 乌克兰城市 9—347c
科诺瓦洛夫 Konovalov, Aleksandr Ivanovich 俄国政治人物 9—347c
科诺伊人 Conoy 美国印第安人 4—438f
科帕尔贝里 Kopparberg 瑞典旧省份 9—350d
科帕卡巴纳 Copacabana 巴西区名 4—487b
科帕沃于尔 Kópavogur 冰岛城镇 9—350a
科潘 Copán 洪都拉斯古城 4—487c
科佩 Coppée, François 法国诗人 4—491e
科佩尔 Koper 斯洛文尼亚海港 9—350a
科佩斯 Koppers, Wilhelm 德国人类学家 9—350e
科佩特山脉 Kopet-Dag Range 亚洲山脉 9—350b
科佩伊斯克 Kopeysk 俄罗斯城市 9—350c
科皮施 Kopisch, August 德国画家 9—350c
科皮亚波 Copiapó 智利城市 4—490e
科平 Coppin, Fanny Jackson 美国教育家、传教士 4—493f
科珀德 Coppard, A(lfred) E(dgar) 英国作家 4—491d
科珀曼河 Coppermine River 加拿大河流 4—493d
科珀斯克里斯蒂 Corpus Christi 美国城市 4—520d
科珀斯克里斯蒂湾 Corpus Christi Bay 美国小湾 4—520e
科普 Cope, Edward Drinker 美国古生物学家 4—487f
科普费尔 Köpfel, Wolfgang 德国宗教改革家 9—350c
科普兰 Copeland 英格兰区名 4—488c
科普兰 Copland, Aaron 美国作曲家 4—490e

科普兰 Copeland, Charles Townsend 美国新闻工作者 4—488d
科普利 Copley, John Singleton 美国画家 4—491c
科普日夫尼采 Kopřivnice 捷克城镇 9—350f
科普特公教会 Coptic Catholic Church 天主教会 4—494d
科普特圣咏 Coptic chant 音乐 4—494e
科普特艺术 Coptic art 艺术 4—494d
科普特语 Coptic language 语言 4—494e
科普特语文献 Coptic literature 文学 4—494f
科普特正教会 Coptic Orthodox Church 埃及基督教会 4—494f
科普托斯 Coptos (Egypt) 埃及城镇 4—495a
科普托斯 Koptos (Egypt) 埃及城镇 9—351e
科齐巴 Koziba, Bar 犹太领袖 9—368e
科齐乌斯 Cocceius, Johannes 荷兰神学家 4—318f
科齐亚努斯 Cocceianus, Cassius Dio (Roman historian) 古罗马历史 4—318f
科奇人 Koch 民族 9—329e
科奇斯 Cochise 美国印第安人酋长 4—319f
科奇斯文化 Cochise culture 北美印第安古文化 4—320a
科恰班巴 Cochabamba 玻利维亚城市 4—319b
科切拉谷地 Coachella Valley 美国谷地 4—310b
科钦 Cochin 印度港口 4—319d
科丘·贝伊 Koçu Bey 土耳其改革家 9—331c
科日布斯基 Korzybski, Alfred (Habdank Skarbek) 美国科学家 9—361c
科萨 Cossa, Francesco del 意大利画家 4—532a
科萨拉 Kosala 印度古王国 9—361c
科萨马洛阿潘 Cosamaloapan 墨西哥城市 4—528f
科萨奇-克维特卡 Kosach-Kvitka, Larisa Petrovna 乌克兰诗人 9—361c
科萨人 Xhosa 非洲民族 18—376f
科萨语 Xhosa language 非洲语言 18—377a
科塞尔 Kossel, Albrecht 德国生物化学家 9—363c
科森扎 Cosenza 意大利城市 4—528f
科沙林 Koszalin 波兰城市 9—364b
科尚(小) Cochin, Charles-Nicolas, THE YOUNGER 法国画家 4—319d
科斯 Causses 法国石灰岩高原 3—536d
科斯 Cos 希腊岛屿 4—528e
科斯 Koss, Johann Olav 挪威速滑运动员 9—363b
科斯 Coase, Ronald 美国经济学家 4—312a
科斯巴 Kosba, Simeon bar 犹太领袖 9—361d
科斯蒂利亚 Costilla, Miguel Hidalgo y (father of Mexican independence) 墨西哥领导人 4—534f
科斯蒂洛 Costello, Lou 美国艺术家 4—534e
科斯格雷夫 Cosgrave, Liam 爱尔兰政治家、总理 4—528f
科斯格雷夫 Cosgrave, William Thomas 爱尔兰政治家、总统 4—529a
科斯拉伊 Kosrae 密克罗尼西亚岛屿 9—363b
科斯罗埃斯 Chosroes 波斯国王之名 4—200e
科斯马蒂工艺 Cosmati work 镶嵌技术 4—529e
科斯马斯 Cosmas 埃及地理学家、商人 4—529d
科斯马斯和达米安,圣 Cosmas and Damian, SAINTS 基督教殉教士 4—529e
科斯皮夸 Cospicua 马耳他城镇 4—531f
科斯塔 Costa, Gabriel da 犹太哲学家 4—532d
科斯塔 Costa, Isaäc da 荷兰作家 4—532d
科斯塔 Costa, Lorenzo 意大利画家 4—532e
科斯塔 Costa, Lúcio 巴西建筑师 4—532e
科斯塔·阿莱格里 Costa Alegre, Caetano da 非洲黑人作家 4—532f
科斯塔-加夫拉斯 Costa-Gavras 法国导演 4—533a
科斯塔梅萨 Costa Mesa 美国城市 4—533a
科斯塔诺人 Costanoan 美国印第安人 4—534c
科斯坦 Costain, Thomas B(ertram) 美国小说家 4—534b
科斯特 Coster, Charles (-Théodore-Henri) de 比利时小说家 4—534e
科斯特 Coster, Laurens Janszoon 荷兰印刷术发明家 4—534e
科斯特里科夫 Kostrikov, Sergey Mironovich 苏联共产党领导人 9—363e
科斯特罗马 Kostroma 俄罗斯州名 9—363f
科斯特罗马 Kostroma 俄罗斯城市 9—363f
科斯特罗维茨基 Kostrowitzki, Wilhelm Apollinaris de 法国诗人 9—363f
科斯特洛 Costello, Elvis 英国歌手 4—534c
科斯特洛 Costello, John A(loysius) 爱尔兰总理 4—534d
科斯特曼斯维尔 Costermansville 刚果(金)城市 4—534f
科斯托拉尼 Kosztolányi, Dezsö 匈牙利诗人 9—364c
科苏梅尔岛 Cozumel 加勒比海岛屿 4—561c
科苏特 Kossuth, Lajos 匈牙利政治改革家 9—363c
科索瓦人 Kosova (people) 肯尼亚民族 9—362e
科索沃 Kosovo 塞尔维亚地名 9—362e
科索沃战役 Kosovo, Battle of 巴尔干半岛 1389 年战争 9—363a
科索沃战役 Kosovo, Battle of 巴尔干半岛 1448 年战争 9—363a
科塔 Kota 印度县城 9—364d
科塔尔 Kothar 古西闪米特人神祇 9—364f
科塔尔管 curtal 乐器 5—72a
科塔家族 Cotta FAMILY 德国出版商家族 4—537c
科塔科塔 Kota Kota (Malaŵi) 马拉维城镇 9—364f
科塔人 Kota 印度土著 9—364d
科塔萨尔 Cortazar 墨西哥城市 4—524b
科塔萨尔 Cortázar, Julio 阿根廷小说家 4—524b
科坦 Cotán, Juan Sánchez 西班牙画家 4—535a
科唐坦 Cotentin, Anne-Hilarion de 法国海军上将 4—536b
科特 Kotte 斯里兰卡历史王国 9—366b
科特 Kotte 斯里兰卡城镇 9—366b
科特 Cort, Henry 英国制造商 4—524a
科特 Cotte, Robert de 法国建筑师 4—537e
科特布里奇 Coatbridge 苏格兰城镇 4—312f
科特布斯 Cottbus 德国城市 4—537e
科特迪瓦 Côte d'Ivoire 西非国家 4—535b
科特卡 Kotka 芬兰城市 9—365a
科特拉斯 Kotlas 俄罗斯城市 9—365a
科特赖克 Kortrijk 比利时城市 9—360e
科特赖克战役 Kortrijk, Battle of 欧洲历史 9—360f
科特兰 Cortland 美国城市 4—526b
科特雷耳 Cottrell, Frederick Gardner 美国教育家 4—540a
科特罗曼王朝 Kotromanić DYNASTY 欧洲历史 9—365f
科特曼 Cotman, John Sell 英国画家 4—536d
科特纳 Kortner, Fritz 德国演员 9—360d
科特尼 Courtenay 加拿大城市 4—550c
科特圣吕克 Côte-Saint-Luc 加拿大城市 4—536b
科滕 Cotten, Joseph 美国演员 4—537f
科提恩 Courteen, Sir William 英国商人、船主 4—550a
科廷顿 Cottington (of Hanworth), Francis Cottington, Baron 英国财政大臣、大使 4—538a
科图斯 Cotys 色雷斯女神 4—540c
科图伊 Cotuí 多米尼加共和国城市 4—540b
科托多尼亚纳国家公园 Coto Doñana National Park 西班牙公园 4—536e
科托尔 Kotor 黑山城镇 9—365d
科托尔湾 Kotor, Gulf of 黑山海湾 9—365e
科托伦戈,圣 Cottolengo, Saint Giuseppe (Benedetto) 天主教圣者 4—538c
科托努 Cotonou 贝宁港市 4—537a
科托帕希 Cotopaxi 厄瓜多尔火山峰 4—537b
科托什 Kotosh 秘鲁考古遗址 9—365f
科瓦东加 Covadonga 西班牙村庄 4—553e
科瓦风格 korwar style 雕刻艺术 9—360f

科瓦利斯 Corvallis 美国城市 4—527c
科瓦列夫斯基 Kovalevsky, Aleksandr Onufriyevich 俄国比较胚胎学创始人 9—368a
科瓦斯纳 Covasna 罗马尼亚县名 4—554a
科瓦泰 Kołłątaj, Hugo 波兰政治活动家 9—339c
科万 Cobán 危地马拉城市 4—314a
科威特 Kuwait 亚洲国家 9—408b
科威特 Kuwait 科威特首都 9—409c
科维良 Covilhã 葡萄牙城市 4—555f
科维努斯 Corvinus, Jakob 德国作家 4—527f
科温 Corwin, Edward Samuel 美国政治学家 4—527f
科温 Corwin, Thomas 美国政治家 4—528a
科文特加登 Covent Garden 英国广场 4—554f
科沃布热格 Kołobrzeg 波兰城镇 9—340e
科沃德 Coward, Sir Noël (Peirce) 英国剧作家 4—556e
科西阿斯科峰 Kosciusko, Mount 澳大利亚山峰 9—361d
科西嘉 Corsica 法国大区 4—523a
科西嘉民族解放阵线 Corsican National Liberation Front 科西嘉政治组织 4—523e
科西莫 Cosimo 意大利大公爵之名 4—529b
科西莫(老) Cosimo THE ELDER (Florentine ruler) 意大利统治者 4—529d
科西莫二世 Cosimo Ⅱ 托斯卡纳大公 4—529c
科西莫三世 Cosimo Ⅲ 托斯卡纳大公 4—529d
科西莫一世 Cosimo Ⅰ 佛罗伦萨、托斯卡纳公爵 4—529b
科西齐莱 Kgositsile, Keorapetse 南非诗人 9—251f
科西沃尔加 Cocibolca 尼加拉瓜古城 4—320f
《科希采条例》 Koszyce, Pact of 波兰历史 9—364c
科希策 Košice 斯洛伐克城市 9—362d
科希策政府 Košice government 捷克斯洛伐克历史 9—362d
科希马 Kohīma 印度城镇 9—334a
科希斯坦 Kohistān 亚洲多山地区 9—334a
科歇 Cochet, Henri 法国网球运动员 4—319c
科雄 Cauchon, Pierre 法国主教 3—534d
科学 science 反映客观规律的知识体系 15—142c
科学博物馆 Science, Museum of 美国博物馆 15—142c
科学博物馆 Science Museum 英国博物馆 15—142f
科学城 Akademgorodok 俄罗斯科学院 1—152b
科学工业博物馆 Science and Industry, Museum of 美国博物馆 15—142c
科学和世界事务会议 Conference on Science and World Affairs 国际会议 4—420c
科学幻想小说 science fiction 文学 15—142e
科学基督会 Church of Christ, Scientist 宗教派别 4—224c
科学家派 científico 墨西哥历史 4—236e
科学理论 scientific theory 系统性概念化结构 15—143d
科学论派 Scientology 美国宗教-科学运动 15—143e
《科学美国人》 Scientific American 美国杂志 15—143c
科学史博物馆 History of Science, Museum of the 牛津大学机构 8—101b
科学史博物馆 Storia della Scienza, Museo di 意大利仪器、地图收藏馆 16—255a
科学统一运动 Unity of Science movement 哲学 17—374e
科学院山 Akademiya Nauk Range 塔吉克斯坦山脉 1—152b
科学院湾 Academy Bay 加拉帕戈斯群岛海湾 1—41c
科学院总植物园 Main Botanical Garden of the Academy of Sciences 俄罗斯植物园 10—407a
科亚特利库埃 Coatlicue 阿兹特克人女神 4—313c
科伊艾克 Coihaique 智利城市 4—334f
科伊杜 Koidu 塞拉利昂城镇 9—335d
科伊夫帽 coif 帽 4—334f
科伊科伊人 Khoikhoin 非洲民族 9—262a
科伊科伊诸语言 Khoikhoin languages 语言 9—262b
科伊帕萨盐沼 Coipasa, Salar de 玻利维亚盐沼 4—336a
科伊桑诸语言 Khoisan languages 语言 9—262b
科伊特 Coiter, Volcher 荷兰医师 4—336b
科伊瓦岛 Coiba Island 巴拿马岛屿 4—334e
科-依-诺尔钻石 Koh-i-noor 英国女王王冠钻石 9—333e
科因 Coín 西班牙城市 4—335c
科英布拉 Coimbra 葡萄牙城市 4—335b
科英布拉公爵 Coimbra, Pedro, 1° duque de 葡萄牙摄政王 4—335c
科尤库克河 Koyukuk River 北美河流 9—368c
科约阿坎 Coyoacán 墨西哥区名 4—560c
科泽科德 Kozhikode 印度城市 9—368d
科泽卢赫 Koželuch, Leopold (Anton) 捷克作曲家 9—368d
科曾斯 Cozens, Alexander 英国画家 4—561b
科曾斯 Cozzens, James Gould 美国小说家 4—561c
科曾斯 Cozens, John Robert 英国画家 4—561b
科扎尼 Kozáni 希腊城市 9—368c
科兹列夫 Kozyrev, Nikolay Aleksandrovich 苏联天文学家 9—368e
科兹洛夫 Kozlov (Russia) 俄罗斯城市 9—368e
钶 columbium 化学元素 4—370c
颏兰属 Maxillaria 植物学 11—43c
颏形掌 chin cactus 植物 4—160d
磕头 ketou 中国旧时礼仪 9—246a
蝌蚪 tadpole 水生幼体 16—420c
蝌蚪虾 tadpole shrimp 动物 16—420c
壳 test 动物外骨骼 16—560a
壳层原子模型 shell atomic model 物理学 15—295f
壳房贝 Conchidium 古生物学 4—411e
壳硬蛋白 sclerotin 生物化学 15—145f
咳嗽 cough 生理反应 4—541c
可比价值 comparable worth 经济学术语 4—396d
可变电阻器 rheostat 电学 14—260a
可待因 codeine 药物 4—326b
可的松 cortisone 药物 4—526b
可卡因 cocaine 药物 4—318e
可可 cacao (*Theobroma cacao*) 乔木 3—309d
可可比奇 Cocoa Beach 美国城市 4—324b
可可粉 cocoa 食品 4—324b
可可碱 theobromine 药物 17—23b
可可-罗克莱奇 Cocoa-Rockledge 美国城市 4—324c
可可油 theobroma oil 植物脂肪 17—23b
可可脂 cocoa butter 植物脂肪 4—324c
可口可乐公司 Coca-Cola Company, The 美国公司 4—318c
可乐果 kola nut 木本植物坚果 9—337e
可乐果属 Cola 植物学 4—336f
可逆性 reversibility 热力学 14—251e
可溶性硅酸钠 soluble glass 化合物 15—501d
可翁仁贺 Kaō Ninga 日本画家 9—170e
可亚 Kréa Henri 阿尔及利亚诗人、戏剧家、小说家 9—373f
可证实原则 verifiability principle 哲学 17—515d
可支配的收入 disposable income 经济学 5—342d
克 gram 计量单位 7—244a
克贝尔 Koerber, Ernest von 奥地利首相 9—332c
克德沙 qedesha 神娼 14—56a
克恩 Kern, Jerome (David) 美国作曲家 9—241c
克恩滕 Kärnten 奥地利州名 9—186d
克尔 Kerr, Deborah 美国演员 9—242c
克尔 Kerr, Jean 美国作家 9—242d
克尔 Kerll, Johann Caspar von 德国作曲家 9—240d
克尔 Kerr, Sir John Graham 英国胚胎学家 9—242e
克尔 Kerr, Roy P(atrick) 新西兰数学家 9—242f
克尔白 Ka'bah 麦加大清真寺 9—123e
克尔电光效应 Kerr electro-optic effect 物理学 9—242f

克尔冈 Khargon 印度城镇 9—256f
克尔贾利 Kŭrdzhali 保加利亚城镇 9—401f
克尔恺郭尔 Kierkegaard, Søren 丹麦宗教哲学家 9—271f
克尔科诺谢山 Krkonoše (mountains, Czech Republic) 捷克山脉 9—379d
克尔克 Krk 克罗地亚岛屿 9—379c
克尔克拉雷利 Kırklareli 土耳其城市 9—303d
克尔克林氏瓣 Kerckring, valve of (anatomy) 解剖学 9—239f
克尔莱札 Krleža, Miroslav 南斯拉夫小说家 9—379d
克尔罗伊特 Kölreuter, Josef Gottlieb 德国植物学家 9—341b
克尔曼 Kermān 伊朗省份 9—240e
克尔曼地毯 Kermān carpet 伊朗工艺品 9—241a
克尔曼沙阿 Kermanshah (Iran) 伊朗城市 9—241c
克尔纳 Kerner, Justinus Andreas Christian 德国诗人 9—241e
克尔纳 Körner, (Karl) Theodor 德国诗人 9—359c
克尔纳 Körner, Theodor 奥地利总统 9—359d
克尔切伊 Kölcsey, Ferenc 匈牙利诗人 9—338d
克尔塞夫尼 Karlsefni, Thorfinn (Icelandic explorer) 冰岛探险家 9—183c
克尔谢希尔 Kırşehir 土耳其城市 9—305a
克尔谢希尔地毯 Kirshehr rug 工艺品 9—305b
克夫拉赫 Köflach 奥地利城镇 9—332e
克格 Køge 丹麦城市 9—333b
克格勃 KGB 苏联安全机构 9—251a
克格尔河 Ghaggar River 印度河流 7—107b
克霍基亚 Cahokia 美国村庄 3—323e
克基拉 Corcyra (Greece) 希腊岛屿 4—501c
克基拉 Kérkira (Greece) 希腊岛屿 9—240d
克基拉迈莱纳 Corcyra Melaina (Croatia) 克罗地亚岛屿 4—501c
克吉伦 Kjellén, Rudolf 瑞典政治学家 9—312c
克拉 carat 计量单位 3—437e
克拉半岛 Kra Peninsula (Southeast Asia) 东南亚半岛 9—369a
克拉邦德 Klabund 表现主义诗人 9—312c
克拉布特里 Crabtree, Lotta 美国演员 4—563e
克拉德诺 Kladno 捷克城市 9—312d
克拉地峡 Kra, Isthmus of 亚洲地峡 9—369a
克拉蒂 Cratty, Mabel 美国社会工作者 4—572b
克拉多克 Craddock, Charles Egbert 美国作家 4—564b
克拉夫 Clough, Arthur Hugh 英国诗人 4—303e
克拉夫 Clough, Anne Jemima 英国教育家 4—303d
克拉夫丘克 Kravchuk, Leonid 乌克兰总统 9—373f
克拉夫特 Kraft, Adam 雕刻家 0—009d
克拉夫特-埃宾 Krafft-Ebing, Richard, Freiherr von 德裔精神病学家 9—369d
克拉弗豪斯 Claverhouse, John Graham of 苏格兰军人 4—273d
克拉格 Krag, Jens Otto 丹麦首相 9—370a
克拉格斯 Craggs, James 英国政客 4—564c
克拉格斯 Klages, Ludwig 德国心理学家 9—312e
克拉根福 Klagenfurt 奥地利城市 9—312e
克拉古耶瓦茨 Kragujevac 塞尔维亚城市 9—370a
克拉科夫 Kraków 波兰城市 9—370e
克拉科夫共和国 Cracow, Republic of 波兰自由市 4—564a
克拉科夫先锋运动 Awangarda Krakowska 波兰文学 2—92b
克拉科夫鞋 crakow 鞋 4—566b
克拉克 Clark, Abraham 美国爱国主义者 4—263d
克拉克 Clarke, Sir Andrew 英国工程师 4—266c
克拉克 Clarke, (Sir) Arthur C. 英国作家 4—266d
克拉克 Clark, Alvan Graham 美国天文学家 4—263e
克拉克 Clarke, Alexander Ross 英国大地测量学家 4—266c
克拉克 Clark, Champ 美国众议院议长 4—263e
克拉克 Clarke, Charles Cowden 英国评论家 4—266e
克拉克 Clerk, Sir Dugald 英国工程师 4—286b
克拉克 Clark, Eugenie 美国鱼类学家 4—263f
克拉克 Clarke, Edward Daniel 英国矿物学家 4—266f
克拉克 Clark, Francis Edward 美国传教士 4—264a
克拉克 Clark, George Rogers 美国军事领袖 4—264a
克拉克 Clark, Helen 新西兰总理 4—264c
克拉克 Clark, James 苏格兰赛车运动员 4—264d
克拉克 Clark, Joe 加拿大总理 4—264d
克拉克 Clark, John Bates 美国经济学家 4—264e
克拉克 Clarke, James Freeman 美国神学家 4—267b
克拉克 Clarke, John H(essin) 美国最高法院大法官 4—267c
克拉克 Clark, John Maurice 美国经济学家 4—264f
克拉克 Clark, John Pepper 尼日利亚抒情诗人 4—265a
克拉克 Clarke, Kenny 美国鼓演奏家 4—267d
克拉克 Clark (of Saltwood), Kenneth Mackenzie Clark, Baron 英国艺术史家 4—265a
克拉克 Clark, Marguerite 美国演员 4—265c
克拉克 Clarke, Martha 美国舞蹈演员、编导 4—267e
克拉克 Clarke, Marcus (Andrew Hislop) 澳大利亚作家 4—267d
克拉克 Clarke, Mary Frances 美国宗教领袖、教育家 4—267f
克拉克 Clark, Mark (Wayne) 美国陆军将领 4—265c
克拉克 Clarke, Rebecca Sophia 美国儿童文学作家 4—267f
克拉克 Clarke, Samuel 英格兰神学家 4—268a
克拉克 Clark, Septima Poinsette 美国教育家、民权活动家 4—265d
克拉克 Clark, Tom C. 美国司法部长 4—265e
克拉克 Clark, William 美国探险家 4—266a
克拉克 Clark, Walter van Tilburg 美国小说家 4—265f
克拉克顿文化期工艺 Clactonian industry 石片-石器工艺 4—257b
克拉克河 Clark Fork 美国河流 4—266c
克拉克和波特 Clarke, Helen Archibald; and Porter, Charlotte Endymion 美国作家 4—267a
克拉克洪 Kluckhohn, Clyde K(ay) M(aben) 美国人类学家 9—319c
克拉克湖国家公园和自然保护区 Lake Clark National Park and Preserve 美国自然保护区 9—455a
克拉克空军基地 Clark Air Base 菲律宾前美军基地 4—266b
克拉克曼南 Clackmannan 苏格兰区名 4—257a
克拉克森 Clarkson, Thomas 废奴主义者 4—268c
克拉克氏羚 Clark's gazelle (antelope) 哺乳动物 4—268b
克拉克斯堡 Clarksburg 美国城市 4—268b
克拉克斯代尔 Clarksdale 美国城市 4—268c
克拉克斯顿 Claxton, Laurence 英格兰教派领袖 4—274b
克拉克斯维尔 Clarksville 美国城市 4—268d
克拉克西 Craxi, Bettino 意大利政治家 4—573d
克拉肯韦尔 Clerkenwell 英格兰地区 4—286c
克拉雷(阿西西的),圣 Clare of Assisi, Saint 女修道院院长 4—260d
克拉里恩断裂带 Clarion Fracture Zone 海洋地质学 4—263c
克拉里恩河 Clarion River 美国河流 4—263d
克拉列维奇 Kraljević, Marko 塞尔维亚国王 9—371a
克拉列沃 Kraljevo 塞尔维亚城市 9—371a
克拉林 Clarín (pen name) 西班牙作家 4—263a
克拉伦登伯爵 Clarendon, earls of 英格兰贵族 4—262a
克拉伦登伯爵(第二) Clarendon, Henry Hyde, 2nd earl of 英格兰政治家 4—262c
克拉伦登伯爵(第四) Clarendon, George William Frederick Villiers, 4th earl of 英国外交大臣 4—262d
克拉伦登伯爵(第一) Clarendon, Edward Hyde, 1st earl of 英格兰政治家 4—262a
《克拉伦登法典》 Clarendon Code 英格兰法律 4—262f
克拉伦登阶 Clarendonian Stage 地质学 4—263a
《克拉伦登条例》 Clarendon, Assize of 英国法令 4—262e
《克拉伦登宪法》 Clarendon, Constitutions of 英国历史 4—262f
克拉伦斯公爵 Clarence, dukes of 英格兰贵族 4—261d
克拉伦斯公爵 Clarence, George Plantagenet, duke of 英格兰贵族 4—261e

克拉伦斯公爵 Clarence, Lionel of Antwerp, duke of 爱尔兰总督 4—261d
克拉伦斯公爵 Clarence, Prince William Henry, duke of 大不列颠和爱尔兰国王 4—261f
克拉伦斯公爵 Clarence, Thomas Plantagenet, duke of 爱尔兰总督 4—261d
克拉伦斯河 Clarence River 澳大利亚河流 4—261f
克拉伦斯河 Clarence River 新西兰河流 4—261f
克拉伦斯马车 clarence 四轮马车 4—261d
克拉伦斯统 Clarence Series 地质学 4—261f
克拉马斯福尔斯 Klamath Falls 美国城市 9—313a
克拉马斯河 Klamath River 美国河流 9—313a
克拉马斯山 Klamath Mountains 美国山脉 9—313a
克拉马特人 Klamath 北美印第安部落 9—313a
克拉马托尔斯克 Kramatorsk 乌克兰城市 9—371b
克拉玛依 Karamay 中国城市 9—179b
克拉末 Kramers, Hendrik Anthony 荷兰物理学家 9—371d
克拉默 Klammer, Franz 奥地利滑雪运动员 9—313b
克拉默 Kramer, Josef 纳粹集中营长官 9—371c
克拉默 Cramer, Johann Baptist 德国钢琴家 4—566c
克拉默法则 Cramer's rule 数学 4—566c
克拉姆 Cram, Donald J(ames) 美国化学家 4—566b
克拉姆 Crumb, George (Henry) 美国作曲家 5—39a
克拉姆 Cram, Ralph Adams 美国建筑师 4—566b
克拉姆尼克 Kramnik, Vladimir 俄罗斯国际象棋大师 9—371d
克拉纳赫(老) Cranach, Lucas, THE ELDER 德国画家 4—566e
克拉帕 Clapp, Cornelia Maria 美国动物学家、教育家 4—259e
克拉帕雷德 Claparède, Édouard 瑞士心理学家 4—259d
克拉皮纳化石遗存 Krapina remains 南斯拉夫出土人骨化石 9—371e
克拉珀顿 Clapperton, Hugh 探险家 4—260a
克拉珀姆派 Clapham Sect 基督教派 4—259e
克拉普罗特 Klaproth, Heinrich Julius 德国东方学家、探险家 9—313c
克拉普罗特 Klaproth, Martin Heinrich 德国化学家 9—313c
克拉普斯 Craps 游戏 4—570b
克拉普西 Crapsey, Adelaide 美国诗人 4—570b
克拉斯 Claes, Ernest (André Jozef) 比利时小说家 4—257d
克拉斯 Claesz, Pieter 荷兰画家 4—257d
克拉斯费尔德夫妇 Klarsfeld, Beate and Serge 法国政治活动家 9—313d
克拉斯诺达尔 Krasnodar 俄罗斯边疆区 9—372b
克拉斯诺达尔 Krasnodar 俄罗斯城市 9—372c
克拉斯诺顿 Krasnodon 乌克兰城市 9—372c
克拉斯诺夫 Krasnov, Pyotr Nikolayevich 俄国军官 9—372d
克拉斯诺戈尔斯克 Krasnogorsk 俄罗斯城市 9—372c
克拉斯诺卡姆斯克 Krasnokamsk 俄罗斯城市 9—372d
克拉斯诺图林斯克 Krasnoturinsk 俄罗斯城市 9—372d
克拉斯诺沃茨克 Krasnovodsk (*oblast*, Turkmenistan) 土库曼斯坦州名 9—372e
克拉斯诺亚尔斯克 Krasnoyarsk 俄罗斯区名 9—372e
克拉斯诺亚尔斯克 Krasnoyarsk 俄罗斯城市 9—372f
克拉斯诺耶塞洛 Krasnoye Selo 俄罗斯区名 9—372f
克拉苏 Crassus, Lucius Licinius 罗马法学家 4—571a
克拉苏 Crassus, Marcus Licinius 罗马政治家 4—571b
克拉苏·狄维斯·穆齐阿努斯 Crassus Dives Mucianus, Publius Licinius 罗马政治家 4—571c
克拉泰夫阿斯 Crateuas 希腊药理学家、艺术家 4—572a
克拉特罗斯 Craterus 马其顿将军 4—571e
克拉特斯 Crates 希腊演员、作家 4—571e
克拉特斯(底比斯的) Crates OF THEBES 希腊哲学家 4—571f
克拉特斯(马卢斯的) Crates OF MALLUS 希腊哲学家 4—571e
克拉提诺斯 Cratinus 希腊诗人 4—572a
克拉通 craton 地质学 4—572a
克拉图 Crato 巴西城市 4—572a
克拉韦里尼亚 Craveirinha, José 东非作家 4—572c
克拉维棍 claves 乐器 4—273d
克拉维霍 Clavijo, Ruy González de (Spanish diplomat) 西班牙外交家 4—273f
克拉维霍-法哈尔多 Clavijo y Fajardo, José 西班牙博物学家 4—273f
克拉西茨基 Krasicki, Ignacy 波兰诗人 9—371f
克拉肖 Crashaw, Richard 英格兰诗人 4—570f
克拉谢夫斯基 Kraszewski, Józef Ignacy 波兰小说家 9—373a
克拉辛斯基 Krasiński, Zygmunt, Count (Hrabia) 波兰诗人 9—371f
克拉约瓦 Craiova 罗马尼亚城市 4—565f
克拉佐曼纳 Clazomenae 古希腊城市 4—276d
克莱 Kle 利比里亚城镇 9—313f
克莱 Clay, Cassius Marcellus 美国反奴隶制领袖 4—274c
克莱 Clay, Cassius Marcellus (boxer) 美国拳击运动员 4—274d
克莱 Clay, Henry 美国政治家 4—274d
克莱 Klaj, Johann 德国诗人 9—312f
克莱 Clay, Lucius D(uBignon) 美国陆军将领 4—275a
克莱安西斯 Cleanthes 斯多葛派哲学家 4—276f
克莱奥丰 Cleophon 雅典政治家 4—285a
克莱奥弗拉德斯画匠 Cleophrades Painter 希腊陶瓶画匠 4—285a
克莱奥梅尼三世 Cleomenes III 斯巴达国王 4—284a
克莱奥梅尼一世 Cleomenes I 斯巴达国王 4—283f
克莱贝尔 Kléber, Jean-Baptiste 法国将军 9—313f
克莱本 Claiborne, William 美洲殖民地商人 4—257e
克莱伯 Kleiber, Erich 奥地利指挥家 9—314d
克莱布斯 Klebs, Edwin 德国医师 9—314a
克莱德班克 Clydebank 苏格兰区名 4—308e
克莱德河 Clyde, River 苏格兰河流 4—308c
克莱德男爵 Clyde (of Clydesdale), Colin Campbell, Baron 英国军人 4—308d
克莱顿 Clayton 美国城市 4—275e
克莱顿 Clayton, John Middleton 美国官员 4—275e
《克莱顿-布尔沃条约》 Clayton-Bulwer Treaty 美英协议 4—276b
《克莱顿反托拉斯法》 Clayton Antitrust Act 美国法律 4—275f
克莱恩 Crane, (Harold) Hart 美国诗人 4—568d
克莱恩 Crane, Stephen 美国小说家 4—568e
克莱恩(夫人) Klein, Melanie 英国精神分析心理学家 9—315b
克莱尔 Clare 爱尔兰郡名 4—260c
克莱尔 Clare 澳大利亚城镇 4—260c
克莱尔 Clare, Ada 美国作家、演员 4—260e
克莱尔 Clare, John 英国浪漫诗人 4—260e
克莱尔 Clair, René 法国电影导演 4—257f
克莱尔 Clare, Richard de 英格兰贵族 4—261b
克莱尔伯爵(第一) Clare, John Fitzgibbon, 1st earl of 爱尔兰大法官 4—261a
克莱尔动物园 Clères Zoological Park 法国动物园 4—285d
克莱尔侯爵 Clare, Thomas Pelham-Holles, marquess of 英国首相 4—261b
克莱尔蒙特 Claremont 美国加利福尼亚州城市 4—261b
克莱尔莫尔 Claremore 美国俄克拉何马州城市 4—261c
克莱尔沃 Clairvaux 法国村庄 4—258b
克莱夫 Cleve, Per Teodor 瑞典化学家 4—287b
克莱夫特歌谣 Klephtic ballad 土耳其文学 9—316c
克莱芙 Clive, Kitty 英国女演员 4—295d
克莱克斯多普 Klerksdorp 南非城镇 9—316e
克莱兰 Cleland, James 英国作家 4—279d
克莱兰 Cleland, John 英国小说家 4—279d
克莱朗博 Clérambault, Louis-Nicholas 法国作曲家 4—285c
克莱里休诗体 clerihew 诗歌形式 4—286b
克莱龙 Clairon, Mlle 法国演员 4—258b

克莱马克斯 Climax 美国城镇 4—292d
克莱曼蒂 Clementi, Muzio 英国作曲家 4—283b
克莱门蒂斯 Clementis, Vladimír 斯洛伐克律师 4—283e
克莱门蒂娅 Clementia 古罗马宗教女神 4—283c
克莱门斯 Clemens, Jacobus 作曲家 4—280b
克莱门斯 Clemens, Roger 美国职业棒球球员 4—280b
克莱门斯 Clemens, Samuel Langhorne 美国作家 4—280c
克莱门斯 Clemens, Titus Flavius 基督教神学家 4—280c
克莱门特 Clemente, Roberto 美国棒球运动员 4—283a
克莱门汀 Clementine 美国月球探测器 4—283c
克莱蒙费朗 Clermont-Ferrand 法国城市 4—286d
克莱蒙会议 Clermont, Council of 欧洲历史 4—286d
克莱蒙-加诺 Clermont-Ganneau, Charles 法国考古学家 4—286e
"克莱蒙特"号 Clermont 美国蒸汽机船 4—286c
克莱莫 Clemo, Jack 英国诗人 4—283f
克莱姆 Klem, Bill 美国棒球裁判员 9—316a
克莱姆 Klemm, Gustav Friedrich 德国人类学家 9—316b
克莱姆佩特 Clampett, Robert 美国动画片导演 4—258f
克莱佩达 Klaipėda 立陶宛城市 9—312f
克莱佩达争端 Klaipėda dispute 欧洲历史 9—312f
克莱斯勒 Kreisler, Fritz 小提琴家 9—374f
克莱斯勒 Chrysler, Walter P(ercy) 美国汽车公司创始人 4—215d
克莱斯勒大厦 Chrysler Building 纽约摩天大厦 4—215e
克莱斯勒汽车公司 Chrysler Corporation 美国汽车公司 4—215e
克莱斯特 Kleist, (Bernd) Heinrich (Wilhelm) von 德国剧作家 9—315e
克莱斯特 Kleist, Ewald Christian von 德国抒情诗人 9—315d
克莱斯特 Kleist, E(wald) Georg von 普鲁士行政长官 9—315d
克莱斯特 Kleist, Paul Ludwig (Ewald) von 德国将军 9—315f
克莱图斯,圣 Cletus, Saint (pope) 教皇 4—287a
克莱托马科斯 Cleitomachus 希腊哲学家 4—279c
克莱沃 Kleve 德国城市 9—316f
克莱武 Clive, Robert, 1st Baron Clive of Plassey 英国军事家 4—295e
克莱因 Klein, A.M. 加拿大诗人 9—314e
克莱因 Klein, Calvin (Richard) 美国时装设计师 9—314f
克莱因 Klein, Felix 德国数学家 9—314f
克莱因 Klein, Lawrence Robert 美国经济学家 9—315a
克莱因 Cline, Maggie 美国歌手 4—292e
克莱因 Cline, Patsy 美国乡村歌手 4—292f
克莱因瓶 Klein bottle 拓扑学 9—315c
克莱因斯 Clynes, John Robert 英国工党创始人 4—309a
克莱兹代尔 Clydesdale 苏格兰区名 4—308e
克莱兹代尔马 Clydesdale 马品种 4—308f
克赖顿 Crichton, James 苏格兰演说家、学者 5—11b
克赖顿 Creighton, James Edwin 美国哲学家 5—4d
克赖尔 Crile, George Washington 美国外科医师 5—12b
克赖尔斯海姆 Crailsheim 德国城市 4—565f
克赖斯基 Kreisky, Bruno 奥地利总理 9—374e
克赖斯特彻奇 Christchurch 新西兰城市 4—202d
克赖斯特彻奇 Christchurch 英格兰自治市 4—202d
克赖斯特彻奇博物馆 Christchurch Mansion 博物馆 4—202e
克兰 Kerang 澳大利亚城镇 9—239c
克兰 Crane, Caroline Julia Bartlett 美国牧师 4—568c
克兰 Kline, Franz 美国画家 9—317b
克兰 Crane, Walter 英国画家 4—569a
克兰伯恩子爵 Cranborne, Robert Cecil, Viscount 英格兰政治家 4—567c
克兰布鲁克 Cranbrook 加拿大城市 4—567c
克兰布鲁克伯爵(第一) Cranbrook, Gathorne Gathorne-Hardy, 1st earl of 英国政治家 4—567c
克兰迪人 Querand 民族 14—86e
克兰顿 Clanton 美国城市 4—259c
克兰多尔 Crandall, Prudence 美国教师 4—567d
克兰菲尔德 Cranfield, Lionel 英国贵族 4—569c
克兰费尔特氏综合征 Klinefelter's syndrome 疾病 9—317c
克兰福德 Cranford 美国城镇 4—569c
克兰凯 Krancke, Theodor 德国军官 9—371e
克兰康奈尔伯爵 Clanconnell, Turlough Luineach O'Neill, earl of 爱尔兰蒂龙族长 4—259b
克兰科 Cranko, John 南非舞蹈家 4—569e
克兰里卡德侯爵和伯爵(第五) Clanricarde, Ulick de Burgh, marquess and 5th earl of 英格兰贵族 4—259c
克兰麦 Cranmer, Thomas 坎特伯雷大主教 4—569f
克兰莫里斯子爵 Clanmaurice, Henry Charles Keith Petty-Fitzmaurice, Viscount 爱尔兰贵族 4—259b
克兰尼 Clanny, William Reid 英国内科医生 4—259b
克兰斯顿 Cranston 美国城市 4—570c
克兰托尔 Crantor 希腊哲学家 4—570c
克兰沃 Clanvowe, Sir Thomas 英国宫廷诗人 4—259d
克朗 Klang (Malaysia) 马来西亚城镇 9—313b
克朗 Krone, Julie 美国赛马骑手 9—380e
克朗波因特 Crown Point 美国镇区 5—36f
克朗代克河 Klondike River 加拿大河流 9—318e
克朗号 crumhorn 乐器 5—39b
克朗麦克诺伊斯 Clonmacnoise 爱尔兰教堂遗址 4—299a
克朗梅尔 Clonmel 爱尔兰自治市 4—299b
克朗普顿 Crompton, Rookes Evelyn Bell 英国发明家 5—24f
克朗普顿 Crompton, Samuel 英国发明家 5—25a
克劳 Crowe, Sir Eyre (Alexamder Barby Wichart) 英国外交家 5—35e
克劳贝格 Clauberg, Johann 德国哲学家 4—270b
克劳德 Claude, Albert 美国细胞学家 4—270d
克劳德 Claude, Georges 法国工程师 4—270e
克劳狄 Claudius 罗马皇帝 4—271d
克劳狄安 Claudian 古典传统诗人 4—271c
克劳狄(哥特库斯) Claudius Gothicus 罗马皇帝 4—271f
克劳狄(失明的) Claudius Caecus, Appius 罗马政治家 4—272a
克劳狄·托勒玫 Claudius Ptolemaeus 埃及数学家 4—272b
克劳狄王朝 Claudian dynasty 古罗马王朝 4—271d
克劳狄乌斯 Claudius, Matthias 德国诗人 4—271f
克劳狄乌斯·马梅提努斯 Claudius Mamertinus 罗马官员 4—272b
克劳狄乌斯·纳马提安努斯 Claudius Namatianus, Rutilius 罗马诗人 4—272b
克劳狄乌斯·普尔喀 Claudius Pulcher, Appius 罗马政治家 4—272b
克劳狄乌斯·普尔喀 Claudius Pulcher, Publius 罗马执政官 4—272c
克劳狄乌斯·萨比努斯·因雷基伦西斯 Claudius Sabinus Inregillensis, Appius 古罗马最显贵家族奠基者 4—272c
克劳福德 Crawford, F(rancis) Marion 美国小说家 4—572e
克劳福德 Crawford, Isabella Valancy 加拿大诗人 4—572f
克劳福德 Crawford, Thomas 美国雕刻家 4—573a
克劳福德 Crawford, William H(arris) 美国政府官员 4—573b
克劳福特 Crowfoot 印第安酋长 5—35e
克劳福兹维尔 Crawfordsville 美国城市 4—573c
克劳馥 Crawford, Joan 美国演员 4—572f
克劳利 Crawley 英格兰城镇 4—573c
克劳利 Crowley, Robert 英格兰基督教社会主义者 5—35f
克劳奇河畔伯纳姆 Burnham-on-Crouch 英格兰城镇 3—273c
克劳人 Crow 北美印第安民族 5—35a
克劳塞维茨 Clausewitz, Carl (Philipp Gottlieb) von 普鲁士大将军 4—272c
克劳瑟 Crowther, Samuel (Adjai) 非洲传教士 5—37b
克劳森 Claussen, Sophus 丹麦诗人 4—273a
克劳斯 Kraus, Karl 奥地利新闻工作者 9—373c
克劳斯 Klaus, Karl Karlovich 俄国化学家 9—313e

克劳斯 Crouse, Russel (American playwright) 美国戏剧家 5—34f
克劳斯-伯尔特 Kraus-Boelté, Maria 美国教育家 9—373d
克劳斯修士 Klaus, Brother 瑞士民间英雄 9—313e
克劳苏拉 clausula 音乐 4—273b
克劳修斯 Clausius, Rudolf (Julius Emanuel) 德国数学物理学家 4—272f
克劳伊泽尔 Creuzer, Georg Friedrich 德国古典学者 5—10a
克劳泽 Krause, Karl Christian Friedrich 德意志哲学家 9—373e
克勒 Köhler, Georges J.F. 德国免疫学家 9—334c
克勒 Köhler, Thomas 德国运动员 9—334e
克勒 Köhler, Wolfgang 德国心理学家 9—334e
克勒奥庇斯 Cleobis 德意志神话 4—283f
克勒格布尔 Kharagpur 印度城市 9—256e
克勒克卡莱 Kırıkkale 土耳其城镇 9—301f
克勒拉希 Călăraşi 罗马尼亚县名 3—334b
克勒拉希 Călăraşi 罗马尼亚城市 3—334c
克勒曼 Kellermann, François-Christophe, DUC (duke) DE VALMY 法国将军 9—216a
克勒曼 Clurman, Harold 美国戏剧导演 4—307b
克勒默 Kroemer, Herbert 物理学家 9—380b
克勒斯尔 Klesl, Melchior 奥地利政治家 9—316e
克勒松 Cresson, Edith 法国总理 5—8c
克勒索 Creusot, Le (France) 法国城镇 5—9f
克勒兹 Creuse 法国省份 5—9f
克雷 Cray, Seymour R. 美国电子工程师 4—573d
克雷比永 Crébillon, Claude-Prosper Jolyot, sieur de 法国小说家 5—1d
克雷比永 Crébillon, Prosper Jolyot, sieur de 法国戏剧家 5—1e
克雷布 Crabbe, George 英国作家 4—563c
克雷布斯 Krebs, Edwin G. 美国生物化学家 9—374a
克雷布斯 Krebs, Sir Hans Adolf 英国生物化学家 9—374b
克雷布斯 Krebs, Johann Ludwig 德国作曲家 9—374c
克雷布斯氏循环 Krebs cycle (biochemistry) 生物化学 9—374c
克雷策尔 Kretzer, Max 德国作家 9—376d
克雷德尔山 Cradle Mountain 澳大利亚山峰 4—564b
克雷迪顿 Crediton 英格兰城镇 5—2c
克雷蒂安 Chrétien, Jean 加拿大律师 4—201f
克雷蒂安·德·特罗亚 Chrétien DE TROYES 法国诗人 4—202a
克雷费尔德 Krefeld 德国城市 9—374d
克雷夫科尔 Crèvecoeur, Michel-Guillaume-Saint-Jean de 美国作家、博物学家 5—10c
克雷格 Craig, Edward Gordon 英国演员、演出人 4—564d
克雷格 Craig, James 美国冰球运动员 4—565c
克雷格 Craig, James 英国政治家 4—565c
克雷格 Craig, Sir James (Henry) 英国军人 4—565c
克雷基侯爵 Créquy, Charles I de Blanchefort, marquisde, PRINCE DE POIX, DUC DE, (duke of) LESDIGUIÈRES 法国元帅 5—6f
克雷基骑士 Créquy, François, chevalier de (knight of), MARQUIS DE MARINES 法国元帅 5—6f
克雷吉 Craigie, Sir William Alexander 苏格兰词典编纂家 4—565e
克雷加文 Craigavon 北爱尔兰区、自治市 4—565d
克雷加文 Craigavon 北爱尔兰自治市 4—565d
克雷加文子爵(第一) Craigavon, James Craig, 1st Viscount 爱尔兰军人 4—565d
克雷洛夫 Krylov, Ivan Andreyevich 俄国寓言作家 9—385b
克雷马 Crema 意大利城镇 5—4e
克雷玛齐 Crémazie, Octave 加拿大诗人 5—5c
克雷芒 Clement 天主教教皇、敌对教皇 4—280c
克雷芒(八世) Clement (VIII) 敌对教皇 4—281e
克雷芒(七世) Clement (VII) 敌对教皇 4—281b
克雷芒(三世) Clement (III) 敌对教皇 4—280d
克雷芒(亚历山大的),圣 Clement OF ALEXANDRIA, SAINT 基督教护教士 4—282e
克雷芒八世 Clement VIII 教皇 4—281e
克雷芒二世 Clement II 教皇 4—280d
克雷芒九世 Clement IX 教皇 4—281f
克雷芒六世 Clement VI 教皇 4—281b
克雷芒七世 Clement VII 教皇 4—281c
《克雷芒前书》 Clement, First Letter of 克雷芒一世著作 4—282f
克雷芒三世 Clement III 教皇 4—280e
克雷芒十二世 Clement XII 教皇 4—282c
克雷芒十三世 Clement XIII 教皇 4—282c
克雷芒十世 Clement X 教皇 4—282a
克雷芒十四世 Clement XIV 教皇 4—282d
克雷芒十一世 Clement XI 教皇 4—282a
克雷芒四世 Clement IV 教皇 4—280e
克雷芒通谕 Unigenitus 教皇通谕 17—344f
克雷芒五世 Clement V 教皇 4—280f
克雷芒一世,圣 Clement I, SAINT 教皇 4—280c
克雷米厄 Crémieux, (Isaac-) Adolphe 法国政治家 5—5d
克雷莫纳 Cremona, (Antonio) Luigi (Gaudenzio Giuseppe) 意大利数学家 5—5f
克雷莫纳 Cremona 意大利城市 5—5f
克雷默 Kramer, Dame Leonie Judith 澳大利亚文学家 9—371c
克雷默 Cremer, Gerard de 佛兰德制图学家 5—5d
克雷默 Kramer, Jack 美国网球运动员 9—371b
克雷默 Kramer, Stanley 美国电影制片人 9—371c
克雷姆斯 Krems 奥地利城市 9—375b
克雷姆西尔 Kremsier (Czech Republic) 捷克城市 9—375c
克雷佩林 Kraepelin, Emil 德国精神病学家 9—369c
克雷普斯 Kreps, Juanita Morris 美国经济学家 9—375e
克雷奇默 Kretschmer, Ernst 德国精神病学家 9—376b
克雷奇默 Kretschmer, Paul 语言学家 9—376c
克雷桑 Cressent, Charles 法国家具制作大师 5—8b
克雷申蒂家族 Crescentii FAMILY 罗马贵族世家 5—7e
克雷斯 Kress, S. H. 美国艺术品收藏家 9—376a
克雷斯蒂安 Chrestien, Florent 法国诗人 4—201e
克雷斯卡斯 Crescas, Ḥasdai ben Abraham 西班牙哲学家 5—7c
克雷斯纳 Krasner, Lee 美国画家 9—372a
克雷斯皮 Crespi, Daniele 意大利画家 5—7f
克雷斯皮 Crespi, Giovanni Battista 伦巴第画家 5—8a
克雷斯皮 Crespi, Giuseppe Maria 意大利画家 5—8a
克雷斯韦尔绝壁 Creswell Crags 英格兰峡谷 5—8f
克雷塔罗 Querétaro 墨西哥州名 14—87a
克雷塔罗 Querétaro 墨西哥城市 14—87a
克雷特 Cret, Paul Phillippe 美国建筑师 5—8f
克雷韦-米凯维丘斯 Krėve-Mickievičius, Vincas 立陶宛诗人 9—377b
克雷文 Craven 英格兰区名 4—572c
克雷文 Craven, Frank 美国演员、导演 4—572d
克雷文 Craven, William Craven, Earl of 英格兰廷臣 4—572d
克雷西勒斯 Cresilas 希腊雕刻家 5—7e
克雷西战役 Crécy, Battle of 英法历史事件 5—1e
克雷伊 Creil 法国城镇 5—4d
克雷伊茨 Creutz, Gustav Philip, Greve 瑞典诗人 5—9f
克里 Kerry, John 美国参议员 9—243b
克里昂 Cleon 雅典民主派领袖 4—284b
克里奥尔马 Criollo 南美小型马 5—17f
克里奥尔人 Creole 民族 5—6b
克里奥尔语 creole 语言 5—6c
克里巴奇牌戏 Cribbage 游戏 5—10f
克里比 Kribi 喀麦隆港口 9—377b
克里布 Cribb, Tom 英国徒手拳击家 5—10f
克里登斯清水复兴 Creedence Clearwater Revival 美国摇滚乐队 5—2f
克里蒂乌斯和内西奥特斯 Critius and Nesiotes 希腊雕刻师 5—

19c
克里尔 Creel, George (Edward) 美国新闻工作者 5—3d
克里格尔 Krieger, Johann Philipp 德国作曲家 9—377c
克里赫 Krige, (Mattheus) Uys 南非戏剧家 9—377d
克里克 Crick, Francis Harry Compton 英国生物物理学家 5—11c
克里克莱德 Cricklade 英格兰城镇 5—12b
克里克人 Creek 北美印第安部落 5—3a
克里克战争 Creek War 美国历史事件 5—3d
克里勒 Crerar, Henry Duncan Graham 加拿大陆军军官 5—7a
克里勒 Crerar, John 美国企业家、慈善家 5—7b
克里利 Creeley, Robert (White) 美国诗人 5—3e
克里米乔 Crimmitschau 德国城市 5—17e
克里米亚 Crimea 乌克兰行政区域 5—13e
克里米亚半岛 Crimean Peninsula 乌克兰半岛 5—13f
克里米亚汗国 Crimea, khanate of the 乌克兰古国名 5—13f
克里米亚天体物理台 Crimean Astrophysical Observatory 乌克兰天文台 5—13f
克里米亚战争 Crimean War 欧洲历史事件 5—14a
克里默 Cremer, Sir (William) Randal 英国工人领袖 5—5d
克里姆 Krim, Mathilde 美国医学研究人员 9—377e
克里姆尔瀑布 Krimmler Waterfall 奥地利瀑布 9—377f
克里姆林 kremlin 俄国城堡 9—375a
克里姆希尔特 Kriemhild 欧洲传说人物 9—377c
克里木特 Klimt, Gustav 奥地利画家 9—316f
克里平 Crippen, Robert Laurel 美国航天员 5—18a
克里普尔克里克 Cripple Creek 美国城市 5—18b
克里普斯 Cripps, Sir (Richard) Stafford 英国政治家 5—18b
克里普岩 KREEP 月面熔岩 9—374c
克里人 Cree 加拿大印第安民族 5—2d
克里斯 Cleese, John 英国喜剧演员 4—278a
克里斯蒂 Christie, Dame Agatha (Mary Clarissa) 英国作家 4—208b
克里斯蒂 Christy, Edwin P. 美国演员 4—211c
克里斯蒂 Christie, Julie 英国电影演员 4—208c
克里斯蒂安 Christian 统治者之名 4—203a
克里斯蒂安 Christian 德意志公爵 4—203a
克里斯蒂安(小) Christian THE YOUNGER 德意志公爵 4—204f
克里斯蒂安八世 Christian Ⅷ 丹麦国王 4—204c
克里斯蒂安二世 Christian Ⅱ 丹麦、挪威国王 4—203c
克里斯蒂安九世 Christian Ⅸ 丹麦国王 4—204d
克里斯蒂安六世 Christian Ⅵ 丹麦、挪威国王 4—204b
克里斯蒂安尼亚 Christiania (Norway) 挪威城市 4—207c
克里斯蒂安尼亚 Kristiania (Norway) 挪威城市 9—378f
克里斯蒂安七世 Christian Ⅶ 丹麦、挪威国王 4—204c
克里斯蒂安三世 Christian Ⅲ 丹麦、挪威国王 4—203e
克里斯蒂安桑 Kristiansand 挪威城镇 9—378f
克里斯蒂安十世 Christian Ⅹ 丹麦国王 4—204e
克里斯蒂安斯塔德 Kristianstad 瑞典旧省份 9—379a
克里斯蒂安斯塔德 Kristianstad 瑞典城市 9—379a
克里斯蒂安四世 Christian Ⅳ 丹麦、挪威国王 4—203f
克里斯蒂安松 Kristiansund 挪威城镇 9—379a
克里斯蒂安五世 Christian Ⅴ 丹麦、挪威国王 4—204b
克里斯蒂安一世 Christian Ⅰ 丹麦、挪威国王 4—203b
克里斯蒂公司 Christie's International PLC 英国拍卖公司 4—208d
克里斯蒂洛 Cristillo, Louis Francis 美国喜剧演员 5—18e
克里斯蒂娜 Christina 瑞典女王 4—208f
克里斯蒂娜·德·皮桑 Christine DE PISAN 法国诗人 4—209a
克里斯蒂娜港 Kristinehamn 瑞典城镇 9—379a
克里斯蒂亚 Cristea, Miron 罗马尼亚牧首 5—18e
克里斯顿 Creston, Paul 美国作曲家 5—8e
克里斯勒农场战役 Crysler's Farm, Battle of 美英历史事件 5—43e
克里斯皮 Crispi, Francesco 意大利政治家 5—18c
克里斯平和克里斯皮尼安,圣 Crispin and Crispinian, SAINTS 基督教二圣人 5—18d
克里斯普斯 Crispus 君士坦丁大帝长子 5—18d
克里斯琴 Christian, Charlie 美国爵士乐吉他演奏家 4—204f
克里斯琴 Christian, Fletcher 水手 4—205a
克里斯琴斯特德 Christiansted 美属维尔京地名 4—208a
克里斯塔尔市 Crystal City 美国县城 5—44d
克里斯坦森 Christensen, Harold 美国舞蹈演员 4—202e
克里斯坦森 Christensen, Lew (Farr) 美国舞蹈演员 4—202f
克里斯坦森 Christensen, Willam 美国舞蹈演员 4—202f
克里斯特曼·格维兹门松 Kristmann Gudmundsson (Icelandic novelist) 冰岛小说家 9—379b
克里斯滕森 Kristensen, (Aage) Tom 丹麦诗人 9—378e
克里斯滕森 Kristensen, Knud 丹麦政治家 9—378d
克里斯托 Christo 保加利亚艺术家 4—210b
克里斯托费尔 Christopher, COUNT OF OLDENBURG 奥尔登堡伯爵 4—211a
克里斯托夫 Christophe, Henry 海地总统 4—210c
克里斯托弗 Christopher 统治者之名 4—210f
克里斯托弗 Christopher 敌对教皇 4—211a
克里斯托弗(巴伐利亚的) Christopher OF BAVARIA 丹麦国王 4—210f
克里斯托弗,圣 Christopher, SAINT 基督教圣徒 4—211a
克里斯托弗三世 Christopher Ⅲ 丹麦国王 4—210f
克里斯托福里 Cristofori, Bartolomeo (di Francesco) 意大利拨弦键琴制造家 5—18f
克里斯托福罗·菲尼 Cristoforo Fini, Tommaso di 意大利画家 5—19a
克里斯托瓦尔 Cristoval (Solomon Islands) 所罗门群岛岛屿 5—19a
克里索斯托,圣约翰 Chrysostom, Saint John 君士坦丁堡大主教 4—216f
克里坦登 Crittenden, John J. 美国政治家 5—19d
《克里坦登妥协案》 Crittenden Compromise 美国历史 5—19e
克里特 Crete 希腊岛屿 5—9c
克里特海 Crete, Sea of 希腊海域 5—9d
克里托布洛斯 Critobulos Michael 拜占廷历史学家 5—19c
克里托劳斯 Critolaus 希腊哲学家 5—19d
克里韦利 Crivelli, Carlo 意大利画家 5—19e
克里维 Creevey, Thomas 英国政客、官吏 5—4c
克里沃罗格 Krivoy Rog 乌克兰城市 9—379b
克里西波斯 Chrysippus 古希腊哲学家 4—215d
克里西斯湖 Chrissie, Lake 南非淡水湖 4—202b
克里西乌马 Criciúma 巴西城市 5—11c
克里希纳 Krishna 印度县名 9—378b
克里希纳河 Krishna River 印度河流 9—378c
克里希纳讷格尔 Krishnanagar 印度县城 9—378c
克里雅河 Keriya He 中国河流 9—240c
克里赞德尔 Chrysander, Karl Franz Friedrich 德国音乐历史学家 4—214d
克里扎尼奇 Križanić, Juraj 天主教司铎 9—379b
克力司吉 Kresge, S.S. 美国商人 9—375f
克力司吉公司 Kresge Co. 美国公司 9—376a
克利 Klee, Paul 瑞士画家 9—314b
克利俄 Clio 希腊女神 4—294d
克利尔沃特 Clearwater 美国城市 4—277b
克利夫 Cliff, Jimmy 牙买加歌手、歌曲作家 4—289e
克利夫顿 Clifton 美国新泽西州城市 4—291a
克利夫顿 Clifton 美国亚利桑那州城市 4—291a
克利夫兰 Cleveland 英格兰郡名 4—287b
克利夫兰 Cleveland 美国俄亥俄州城市 4—287c
克利夫兰 Cleveland 美国田纳西州城市 4—287e
克利夫兰 Cleveland, Emeline Horton 美国教授 4—287f
克利夫兰 Cleveland, Grover 美国律师 4—288a
克利夫兰 Cleveland, Horace William Shaler 美国园林建筑师 4—288b

克利夫兰 Cleveland,John 英国诗人 4—288c
克利夫兰伯爵 Cleveland,Thomas Wentworth,earl of 英国保王党人 4—288d
克利夫兰海茨 Cleveland Heights 美国城市 4—288e
克利夫兰栗色马 Cleveland Bay 马品种 4—288d
克利夫兰女公爵 Cleveland, Barbara Villiers, duchess of, COUNTESS OF SOUTHAMPTON, BARONESS NONSUCH 英格兰贵族 4—287f
克利夫兰水族馆 Cleveland Aquarium 美国水族馆 4—288d
克利夫兰艺术博物馆 Cleveland Museum of Art 美国博物馆 4—288e
克利夫特 Clift,Montgomery 美国演员 4—290f
克利弗 Cleaver,(Leroy) Eldridge 美国黑人 4—277f
克利福德 Clifford,Sir Hugh Charles 英国小说家 4—290b
克利福德 Clifford,John 基督教牧师 4—290c
克利福德 Clifford,Nathan 美国最高法院大法官 4—290d
克利福德 Clifford,William Kingdon 英国数学家 4—290e
克利福德(查德利的) Clifford (of Chudleigh),Thomas Clifford,1st Baron 英国政治家 4—290d
克利克 Kölliker,Rudolf Albert von 瑞士胚胎学家 9—339e
克利里 Cleary,Beverly 美国儿童文学作家 4—277d
克利马内 Quelimane 莫桑比克城镇 14—86a
克利珀顿岛 Clipperton Island 东太平洋环礁 4—295b
克利珀顿断裂带 Clipperton Fracture Zone 地质学 4—295a
克利青 Klitzing,Klaus von 德国物理学家 9—318c
克利塞罗,圣 Clitherow,Saint Margaret 英格兰天主教徒 4—295b
克利斯平原 Chryse Planitia 火星地区 4—215b
克利斯提尼(西锡安的) Cleisthenes OF SICYON 古希腊僭主 4—279a
克利斯提尼(雅典的) Cleisthenes OF ATHENS 雅典政治家 4—278d
克利斯托瓦尔 Cristóbal 巴拿马港口 5—18e
克利索普斯 Cleethorpes 英格兰城市 4—278b
克利提亚斯 Cleitias 雅典陶瓶画匠 4—279b
克利通诺河 Clitunno River 意大利河流 4—295d
克利希 Clichy 法国巴黎工业区 4—289a
克列茨瓦尔德 Kreutzwald,F(riedrich) Reinhold 爱沙尼亚医生 9—377a
克列尔 Crelle,August Leopold 德国数学家、工程师 5—4d
克列夫 Cleef,Joos van (Flemish painter) 佛兰德斯画家 4—278a
克列夫 Cleve,Joos van 佛兰德斯画家 4—287b
克列孟梭 Clemenceau,Georges 法国政治家 4—279e
克列缅丘格 Kremenchug 乌克兰城市 9—375a
克列斯 Keres,Paul 爱沙尼亚国际象棋大师 9—240a
克林 Klin 俄罗斯城市 9—317a
克林 Kleene,Stephen Cole 美国数学家 9—314d
克林达乔夫卡 Krindachyovka (Ukraine) 乌克兰城市 9—378a
克林顿 Clinton 美国艾奥瓦州城市 4—293c
克林顿 Clinton 美国马萨诸塞州城镇 4—293d
克林顿 Clinton 美国村庄 4—293d
克林顿 Clinton,DeWitt 美国政界领袖 4—293d
克林顿 Clinton,George 美国军人 4—293f
克林顿 Clinton,Sir Henry 美国独立战争英军司令 4—294a
克林顿 Clinton,William 美国总统 4—294a
克林格尔 Klinger,Friedrich Maximilian von 德国剧作家 9—317d
克林格尔 Klinger,Max 德国画家 9—317e
克林彭 Krimpen,Jan van 荷兰邮票设计家 9—377f
克林奇河 Clinch River 美国河流 4—292e
克林特 Klint,Kaare 丹麦建筑师 9—318a
克灵曼斯峰 Clingmans Dome 美国山峰 4—293a
克柳切夫火山 Klyuchvskaya Volcano 俄罗斯活火山 9—319f
克柳切夫斯基 Klyuchevsky, Vasily Osipovich 俄国历史学家 9—319f
克龙涅 Cronjé,Pieter Arnoldus 南非将领 5—29a
克龙斯塔德 Kroonstad 南非城镇 9—381c
克龙斯塔姆 Kronstam,Henning 丹麦舞蹈家 9—381b
克龙斯泰特 Cronstedt,Axel Fredrik 瑞典矿物学家 5—29a
克娄巴特拉方尖碑 Cleopatra's Needle 古埃及石碑 4—285a
克娄巴特拉七世 Cleopatra VII THEA PHILOPATOR 埃及王后 4—284c
克娄巴特拉一世(西拉) Cleopatra I SYRA 埃及女王 4—284b
克卢埃 Clouet, François 法国画家 4—303c
克卢埃 Clouet,Jean 肖像画家 4—303d
克卢蒂 Cloete,(Edward Fairly) Stuart (Graham) 南非小说家 4—298b
克卢格 Klug, Aaron 英国化学家 9—319d
克卢格 Kluge,(Hans) Günther von 德国陆军元帅 9—319e
克卢克 Kluck,(Heinrich Rudolph) Alexander von 德国将军 9—319c
克卢尼 Clooney,Rosemary 美国歌手 4—299c
克卢尼斯-罗斯家族 Clunies-Ross FAMILY 英国移民 4—306b
克卢日 Cluj 罗马尼亚县名 4—305f
克卢日-纳波卡 Cluj-Napoca 罗马尼亚城市 4—306a
克卢萨河 Clutha River 新西兰河流 4—308b
克卢萨-中部奥塔戈 Clutha-Central Otago 新西兰行政区 4—308a
克卢莎里舞 căluşari 罗马尼亚宗教舞蹈 3—358e
克卢什 Queluz 葡萄牙城镇 14—86a
克卢西乌姆 Clusium 意大利古代城镇 4—307d
克卢伊德 Clwyd 威尔士郡名 4—308c
克卢伊德河 Clwyd,River 威尔士河流 4—308c
克虏伯 Krupp,Alfred 德国实业家 9—383d
克虏伯·冯·波伦·翁德·哈尔巴黑 Krupp von Bohlen und Halbach, Alfried 德国实业家 9—384b
克虏伯·冯·波伦·翁德·哈尔巴黑 Krupp von Bohlen und Halbach, Gustav 德国外交家 9—384d
克虏伯公司 Krupp AG 德国公司 9—383f
克鲁 Crewe 英格兰城镇 5—10d
克鲁安国家公园和自然保护地 Kluane National Park and Reserve 加拿大国家公园 9—319b
克鲁采尔 Kreutzer,Rodolphe 法国作曲家 9—376f
克鲁岑 Crutzen,Paul 荷兰化学家 5—41a
克鲁登湾村 Cruden Bay 苏格兰度假村 5—38c
克鲁格 Kruger,Barbara 美国艺术家 9—382e
克鲁格 Kruger,Paul 南非政治家 9—382f
克鲁格 Krueger,Walter 美国军官 9—382d
克鲁格电报 Kruger telegram 南非历史 9—383b
克鲁格国家公园 Kruger National Park 南非国家公园 9—383b
克鲁格斯多普 Krugersdorp 南非城镇 9—383c
克鲁津什腾 Krusenstern,Adam Johann 俄国海军军官 9—385a
克鲁克 Crook,George 美国陆军军官 5—29e
克鲁克斯 Crookes,Sir William 英国化学家、物理学家 5—29f
克鲁克香克 Cruikshank,George 英国画家 5—38d
克鲁米里 Kroumirie 突尼斯山区 9—382b
克鲁姆 Krum 保加利亚汗 9—383c
克鲁姆巴赫 Krumbacher,Karl 德国学者 9—383c
克鲁-楠特威奇 Crewe and Nantwich 英格兰自治市 5—10d
克鲁努贝里 Kronoberg 瑞典省份 9—381a
克鲁帕 Krupa,Gene 美国摇摆乐鼓手 9—383d
克鲁泡特金 Kropotkin 俄罗斯城市 9—381c
克鲁泡特金 Kropotkin,Peter 俄国地理学家 9—381d
克鲁普斯卡娅 Krupskaya, Nadezhda Konstantinovna 俄国革命家 9—384e
克鲁奇 Krutch,Joseph Wood 美国博物学家 9—385a
克鲁奇科夫斯基 Kruczkowski,Leon 波兰小说家 9—382c
克鲁人 Kru 民族 9—382b
克鲁萨 Crousaz,Jean-Pierre de 瑞士神学家、哲学家 5—34f
克鲁塞斯 Cruces 古巴城市 5—37c
克鲁赛罗 Cruzeiro 巴西城市 5—41e
克鲁森施特恩角国家保护区 Cape Krusenstern National Monument 美国保护区 3—420e

克鲁什内山脉 Krušné hory (Europe) 欧洲山脉 9—385a
克鲁斯 Cruz, Celia 古巴裔美国歌手 5—41b
克鲁斯 Crus, Lucius Cornelius Lentulus 罗马政治家 5—39b
克鲁斯 Cruz, Sor Juana Inés de la 墨西哥诗人、修女 5—41c
克鲁斯琴 crwth 乐器 5—41e
克鲁斯-索萨 Cruz e Sousa, João da 巴西诗人 5—41d
克鲁瓦 Croix 法国城镇 5—23c
克鲁瓦西侯爵 Croissy, Charles Colbert, marquis de 法国外交大臣 5—23b
克鲁西乌斯 Clusius, Carolus (Latin) 法国植物学家 4—307f
克吕登纳(夫人) Krüdener, Barbara Juliane, Freifrau von 俄国神秘主义者 9—382d
克吕弗 Clüver, Philipp 德国地理学家 4—308b
克吕格 Kreuger, Ivar 瑞典金融家 9—376d
克吕格尔 Crüger, Johannes 德国作曲家 5—38c
克吕尼 Cluny 法国城镇 4—306c
克吕尼博物馆 Cluny Museum 法国博物馆 4—306e
克吕尼狭条凸纹花边 Cluny guipure 工艺品 4—306d
克吕塞 Crucé, Émeric 法国作家 5—37c
克吕泰涅斯特拉 Clytemnestra 希腊传说 4—309a
克吕韦尔 Klüver, Heinrich 美国心理学家 9—319e
克律韦耶 Cruveilhier, Jean 法国病理学家 5—41a
克伦佩雷尔 Klemperer, Otto 德国指挥家 9—316b
克伦人 Karen 民族 9—181d
克伦斯基 Kerensky, Aleksandr Fyodorovich 俄国社会革命党人 9—239f
克伦斯基进攻 Kerensky Offensive (World War I) 第一次世界大战史 9—240a
克伦威尔 Cromwell, Henry 爱尔兰统治者 5—25b
克伦威尔 Cromwell, Oliver 英格兰军人、政治家 5—25b
克伦威尔 Cromwell, Richard 英格兰政治家 5—28b
克伦威尔 Cromwell, Thomas, EARL OF ESSEX, BARON CROMWELL OF OKEHAM 英格兰政治家 5—28c
克伦威尔椅 Cromwellian chair 家具 5—28e
克伦泽 Klenze, Leo von 德国建筑师 9—316c
克伦诸语言 Karen languages 东南亚语言 9—181d
克罗 Cros, (Émile-Hortensius-) Charles 法国发明家、诗人 5—30e
克罗巴特里克山 Croagh Patrick 爱尔兰山峰 5—20a
克罗伯 Kroeber, A. L. 美国人类学家 9—380a
克罗伯勒 Crowborough 英格兰城镇 5—35d
克罗地亚 Croatia 巴尔干半岛国家 5—20b
克罗地亚文学 Croatian literature 文学 5—21a
克罗地亚语 Croatian language (South Slavic language) 语言 5—21a
克罗尔 Krall, Diana 加拿大音乐家 9—371a
克罗夫茨 Crofts, Freeman Wills 爱尔兰小说家 5—23a
克罗夫茨 Crofts, James 英国贵族 5—23a
克罗夫特 Croft, William 英国管风琴家、作曲家 5—23a
克罗根 Croghan, George 美国商人 5—23a
克罗克 Krock, Arthur B. 美国政论家 9—379f
克罗克 Crocker, Charles 美国商人、银行家 5—21e
克罗克 Croker, John Wilson 英国政治家、作家 5—23d
克罗克 Crocker, Lucretia 美国教育家 5—21f
克罗克 Kroc, Ray 美国餐馆老板 9—379e
克罗克 Croker, Thomas Crofton 爱尔兰古文物收藏家 5—23e
克罗克岛 Croker Island 澳大利亚岛屿 5—23f
克罗克福德 Crockford, William 英国商人 5—22c
克罗克马尔 Krochmal, Nachman 犹太教学者 9—379f
克罗克特 Crockett, Davy 美国政治家 5—22b
克罗克特 Crockett, Samuel Rutherford 苏格兰小说家 5—22c
克罗兰 Crowland 英格兰堂区 5—35f
克罗勒-穆勒国家博物馆 Kröller-Müller State Museum 荷兰博物馆 9—380d
克罗利 Croly, Herbert David 美国作家 5—23f
克罗利 Croly, Jane Cunningham 美国记者 5—23f
克罗马农人 Cro-Magnon 古代智人群体 5—19f
克罗梅日什 Kroměříž 捷克城市 9—380e
克罗默伯爵(第一) Cromer, Evelyn Baring, 1st Earl of, VISCOUNT ERRINGTON OF HEXHAM, VISCOUNT CROMER, BARON CROMER OF CROMER 英国行政官员、外交家 5—24c
克罗默蒂 Cromarty 苏格兰海港 5—24a
克罗姆 Crome, John 英国画家 5—24b
克罗姆德莱 Kromdraai 南非考古遗址 9—380e
克罗姆兰克 Crommelynck, Fernand 比利时剧作家 5—24f
克罗纳卡 Cronaca, Il 意大利建筑师 5—28e
克罗内克 Kronecker, Leopold 德国数学家 9—380f
克罗宁 Cronin, A. J. 苏格兰小说家、医生 5—28e
克罗宁 Cronin, James Watson 美国核物理学家 5—28f
克罗宁与坦迪 Cronyn, Hume; and Tandy, Jessica 美国夫妇演员 5—29c
克罗诺基自然保护区 Kronotsky Nature Reserve 俄罗斯自然保护区 9—381a
克罗齐 Croce, Benedetto 意大利哲学家 5—21c
克罗齐 Croce, Giovanni 意大利作曲家 5—21d
克罗塞特 Crossett 美国城市 5—33d
克罗瑟斯 Crothers, Rachel 美国剧作家 5—34c
克罗森炻器 Kreussen stoneware 德国盐釉炻器 9—376e
克罗斯 Cross, Hardy 美国土木工程学教授 5—31d
克罗斯 Cross, Mary Ann (novelist) 英国作家 5—31d
克罗斯 Queiroz, Rachel de 巴西小说家 14—85c
克罗斯比 Crosby, Bing 美国歌唱家 5—30f
克罗斯比 Crosby, Fanny 美国赞美诗作家 5—31a
克罗斯比 Crosby, Harry 美国诗人 5—31b
克罗斯河 Cross River 西非河流 5—32f
克罗斯河州 Cross River 尼日利亚州名 5—32f
克罗斯内斯特山口 Crowsnest Pass 加拿大山隘 5—37b
克罗斯诺 Krosno 波兰旧省份 9—381f
克罗斯诺 Krosno 波兰城市 9—381f
克罗斯子爵(第一) Cross (of Broughton-in-Furness), Richard Assheton Cross, 1st Viscount 英国政治家 5—31d
克罗托 Kroto, Sir Harold W. 英国化学家 9—382a
克罗托内 Crotone 意大利城镇 5—34e
克罗伊 Krogh, August 丹麦生理学家 9—380c
克罗伊茨伯格 Kreutzberg, Harald 德国现代舞演员 9—376e
克罗伊茨菲尔德-雅各布二氏病 Creutzfeldt-Jakob disease 疾病 5—10a
克罗伊茨纳赫 Kreuznach (Germany) 德国城市 9—377b
克罗伊登 Croydon 英格兰自治市 5—37b
克罗伊斯 Croesus 吕底亚国王 5—22f
克罗泽群岛 Crozet Islands 南印度洋群岛 5—37c
克洛卜施托克 Klopstock, Friedrich Gottlieb 德国诗人 9—319a
克洛岱尔 Claudel, Camille(-Rosalie) 法国雕刻家 4—270e
克洛岱尔 Claudel, Paul(-Louis-Charles-Marie) 法国诗人 4—271a
克洛德(法国的) Claude OF FRANCE 法国王后 4—270c
克洛狄乌斯·阿尔比努斯 Clodius Albinus (Roman general) 罗马将军 4—297f
克洛狄乌斯·普尔喀 Clodius Pulcher, Publius 罗马政客 4—297f
克洛狄亚 Clodia 罗马美女 4—297e
克洛迪昂 Clodion 法国雕刻家 4—297e
克洛迪奥 Chlodio 墨洛温王朝创始人 4—183d
克洛多梅尔 Clodomir 墨洛温国王 4—298a
克洛夫斯基 Klafsky, Katharina 匈牙利歌唱家 9—312d
克洛罗斯 Chloros (Greece) 希腊城市 4—185f
克洛诺斯 Cronus 希腊古宗教男性神 5—29b
克洛诺维茨 Klonowic, Sebastian (Fabian) 波兰诗人 9—318f
克洛普考 Klapka, György 匈牙利军人 9—313b
克洛斯 Close, Chuck 德国地质学家 4—299e

克洛斯 Cloos, Hans 美国画家 4—299d
克洛斯 Kloos, Willem (Johan Theodoor) 荷兰诗人 9—318f
克洛斯男爵 Cloots, Jean-Baptiste du Val-de-Grâce, Baron de 法国激进民主派 4—299d
克洛斯特新堡 Klosterneuburg 奥地利城市 9—319b
克洛塔尔 Chlotar 墨洛温国王名 4—186b
克洛塔尔二世 Chlotar II 墨洛温国王 4—186b
克洛塔尔三世 Chlotar III 墨洛温国王 4—186c
克洛塔尔四世 Chlotar IV 墨洛温国王 4—186d
克洛塔尔一世 Chlotar I 墨洛温国王 4—186b
克洛提尔达,圣 Clotilda, SAINT 法兰克王后 4—300b
克洛维 Clovis 墨洛温王朝统治者之名 4—304d
克洛维奥 Clovio, Giulio 意大利细密画画家 4—304c
克洛维二世 Clovis II 墨洛温王朝国王 4—304e
克洛维三世 Clovis III 墨洛温王朝国王 4—304e
克洛维斯 Clovis 美国城市 4—304e
克洛维斯文化遗存 Clovis complex 古代文化 4—304f
克洛维一世 Clovis I 墨洛温王朝创立者 4—304d
克洛泽尔伯爵 Clauzel, Bertrand, Comte 法国元帅 4—273b
克马德克海沟 Kermadec Trench 南太平洋海沟 9—240e
克马德克群岛 Kermadec Islands 南太平洋火山群岛 9—240e
克麦罗沃 Kemerovo 俄罗斯州名 9—222c
克麦罗沃 Kemerovo 俄罗斯城市 9—222c
克姆克华帛 kimkhwāb 印度锦缎 9—283b
克姆尼茨 Chemnitz, Martin 德意志神学家 4—113a
克穆诸语言 Khmuic languages 东南亚语言 9—261e
克纳佩兹布什 Knappertsbusch, Hans 德国指挥家 9—320b
克奈赛 Knesset 以色列议会 9—320f
克讷克 Kinik (Turkey) 土耳其城镇 9—293f
克内贝尔 Knebel, Karl Ludwig von 德国诗人 9—320c
克内尔 Quesnel 加拿大城镇 14—87f
克内尔 Körner, Wilhelm 德国有机化学家 9—359d
克尼夫斯夫洛福什 Knivsflåfoss (Norway) 挪威瀑布 9—323a
克尼福森 Knyphausen, Wilhelm, Freiherr von 德意志军人 9—327a
克尼格雷茨战役 Königgrätz, Battle of 普鲁士、奥地利历史 9—346a
克尼佩尔-契诃娃 Knipper-Chekhova, Olga (Leonardovna) 俄国演员 9—322d
克尼亚人 Kenyah 东南亚民族 9—235c
克努特 Canute 统治者之名 3—415b
克努特 Canute 英格兰、丹麦、挪威国王 3—415f
克努特(二世) Canute (II) 英格兰、丹麦国王 3—415f
克努特(圣) Canute, SAINT 丹麦国王 3—415f
克努特(一世) Canute (I) 英格兰、丹麦、挪威国王 3—415d
克努特二世 Canute II 英格兰、丹麦、挪威国王 3—415c
克努特六世 Canute VI 丹麦国王 3—415c
克努特三世 Canute III 英格兰、丹麦国王 3—415c
克努特四世 Canute IV 丹麦国王 3—415c
克诺夫 Knopf, Alfred A. 美国出版商 9—323a
克诺罗佐夫 Knorozov, Yury Valentinovich 俄国语言学家 9—323b
克诺珀斯 Canopus 古埃及城市 3—408b
克诺珀斯坛 Canopic jar 古埃及葬仪用具 3—408a
克诺索斯 Knossos 希腊古城 9—323c
克佩尔湾 Keppel Bay 太平洋海湾 9—238e
克佩勒人 Kpelle 西非民族 9—368f
克钦人 Kachin 亚洲民族 9—126f
克钦山区 Kachin Hills 缅甸高地 9—127a
克丘亚人 Quechua 南美印第安人 14—82e
克丘亚诸语言 Quechuan languages 南美西部地区民族语言 14—82f
克热内克 Krenek, Ernst 美国作曲家 9—375c
克萨尔特南戈 Quetzaltenango 危地马拉省会 14—88e
克塞姆苏丹 Kösem Sultan 奥斯曼苏丹皇后 9—362a
克桑西 Xánthi 希腊城市 18—373d
克什米尔 Kashmir (India-Pakistan) 印度-巴基斯坦地理区 9—191c
克什米尔谷 Kashmir, Vale of 印度谷地 9—191c
克什米尔披巾 kashmir shawl 服饰 9—191d
克什米尔湿婆派 Kashmir Śaivism 印度宗教派别 9—191d
克什米尔语 Kashmiri language 亚洲语言 9—191e
克斯林 Köslin (Poland) 波兰城市 9—362e
克塔 iqṭāʿ 伊斯兰教国家的赐给土地 8—438c
克塔克 Cuttack 印度城镇 5—80b
克特勒 Ketterle, Wolfgang 美国物理学家 9—246d
克特卢姆 Kötlum, Jóhannes Jónasson úr (Icelandic poet) 冰岛诗人 9—365b
克特西比乌斯 Ctesibius OF ALEXANDRIA 希腊物理学家、发明家 5—46c
克特西亚斯 Ctesias 希腊医生、历史学家 5—46b
克滕 Köthen 德国城市 9—364f
克瓦兰 Kvaran, Einar Hjörleifsson 冰岛新闻记者 9—410c
克瓦西尔 Kvasir 古斯堪的纳维亚神话 9—410c
克瓦诸语言 Kwa languages 西非语言 9—410d
克万 Kwan, Michelle 美国花样滑冰运动员 9—410f
克万茨 Quantz, Johann Joachim 德国音乐家 14—76d
克维德 Quidde, Ludwig 德国历史学家、和平主义者 14—90e
克维多-比列加斯 Quevedo y Villegas, Francisco Gómez de 西班牙诗人、语言大师 14—89a
克维克林斯卡 Ćwiklińska, Mieczyslawa 波兰喜剧演员 5—83a
克沃兹科 Kłodzko 波兰城市 9—318e
克谢尔 Köchel, Ludwig (Alois Ferdinand), Rittervon 奥地利学者 9—330e
克谢辛斯卡 Kschessinska, Mathilde 俄罗斯芭蕾舞演员 9—385d
克伊波 Kuyper, Abraham 荷兰神学家 9—409e
克伊普 Cuyp, Aelbert Jacobsz(oon) 荷兰画家 5—82a
克伊普 Cuyp, Jacob Gerritsz(oon) 荷兰画家 5—82b
克孜尔石窟 Kizil caves 中国佛教石窟 9—311f
克孜勒 Kyzyl 俄罗斯城市 9—418c
克孜勒奥尔达 Kzyl-Orda 哈萨克斯坦州名 9—418e
克孜勒河 Kızıl River 土耳其河流 9—312a
克孜勒基亚 Kyzyl-Kiya 吉尔吉斯斯坦城市 9—418c
克孜勒库姆 Kyzylkum 中亚沙漠 9—418e
克孜勒群岛 Kızıl Adalar 土耳其岛屿 9—311e
刻赤 Kerch 乌克兰城市 9—239e
刻刀 graver (printmaking) 雕刻工具 7—264a
刻法洛斯 Cephalus 希腊、罗马文学人物 4—8b
刻花 bright-cut 雕刻方法 3—156c
刻花玻璃 cut glass 装饰玻璃工艺品 5—78e
刻片工艺 cut-card work 装饰技术 5—78d
刻瑞斯 Ceres 古罗马女神 4—10f
刻丝 kesi 中国工艺品 9—244d
刻拓版画 scratchboard 美术技法 15—155c
客观主义 objectivism 艺术或文学理论 12—320f
《客籍法和镇压叛乱法》(1798) Alien and Sedition Acts 美国法律 1—228c
客籍民 metic 古希腊历史 11—159d
客家 Hakka 中国汉族支系 7—416b
客家方言 Kan-Hakka dialect 汉语方言 9—151e
客西马尼园 Gethsemane 耶路撒冷花园 7—104c
客栈 inn 小旅馆 8—389e
氪(Kr) krypton 化学元素 9—385b
肯 Ken, Thomas 英国赞美诗作家 9—223a
肯布尔 Kemble, Adelaide 英国歌唱家 9—220f
肯布尔 Kemble, Charles 英国剧院经理 9—221a
肯布尔 Kemble, Elizabeth (actress) 英国演员 9—221b
肯布尔 Kemble, Fanny 英国剧作家 9—221b

肯布尔 Kemble, George Stephen 英国演员、剧院经理 9—221d
肯布尔 Kemble, Henry Stephen 英国演员 9—221d
肯布尔 Kemble, John Philip 英国演员、经理 9—221e
肯布尔 Kemble, Roger 英国演员、剧院经理 9—222a
肯布尔 Kemble, Sarah (English actress) 英国演员 9—222a
肯布尔(夫人) Kemble, Elizabeth 英国演员 9—221b
肯布尔(夫人) Kemble, Maria Theresa 英国歌唱家 9—221f
肯布尔(夫人) Kemble, Priscilla 英国演员 9—221f
肯达里 Kendari 印度尼西亚城镇 9—224a
肯德 Kander, Lizzie Black 美国福利工作者 9—154a
肯德尔 Kendal 英格兰城镇 9—223c
肯德尔 Kendall, Edward Calvin 美国化学家 9—223e
肯德尔 Kendall, Henry 澳大利亚诗人 9—223f
肯德尔 Kendall, Henry Way 美国核物理学家 9—223f
肯德尔夫妇 Kendal, Dame Margaret; and William Hunter (Grimston) 英国演员 9—223d
肯德尔女公爵 Kendal, Ehrengarde Melusina, Duchess of 英王情妇 9—223c
肯德鲁 Kendrew, John Cowdery 英国生物化学家 9—224d
肯德人 Kindah 民族 9—284a
肯德瓦 Khandwa 印度城镇 9—255f
肯蒂格尔恩，圣 Kentigern, Saint 大隐修院院长 9—229f
肯定前件假言推理和否定后件假言推理 modus ponens and modus tollens 逻辑学 11—308b
肯顿 Kenton, Stan 美国作曲家 9—230a
肯明斯 Cummings, E.E. 美国诗人、画家 5—60b
肯穆尔子爵(第六) Kenmure, William Gordon, 6th Viscount 苏格兰历史人物 9—225a
肯纳邦克波特 Kennebunkport 美国城镇 9—225c
肯纳贝克河 Kennebec River 美国河流 9—225c
肯纳出使 Kenner mission 美国历史 9—227c
肯纳德 Cunard, Sir Samuel, 1st Baronet 英国商人、船主 5—61a
肯纳威克 Kennewick 美国城市 9—227f
肯内斯，圣 Kenneth, Saint 爱尔兰大隐修院院长 9—227e
肯尼迪 Kennedy, Anthony M(cLeod) 美国最高法院大法官 9—225d
肯尼迪 Kennedy, Edward M(oore) 美国参议员 9—225d
肯尼迪 Kennedy, John F(itzgerald) 美国总统 9—225f
肯尼迪 Kennedy, John P(endleton) 美国小说家 9—226d
肯尼迪 Kennedy, Joseph P(atrick) 美国商人 9—226e
肯尼迪 Kennedy, Robert F(rancis) 美国司法部长 9—227a
肯尼迪 Kennedy, Walter 苏格兰诗人 9—227b
肯尼迪海峡 Kennedy Channel 北冰洋水道 9—227b
肯尼思二世 Kenneth II 苏格兰人和皮克特人联合国王 9—227e
肯尼思三世 Kenneth III 苏格兰国王 9—227e
肯尼思一世 Kenneth I 苏格兰国王 9—227d
肯尼特 Kennet 英格兰区名 9—227d
肯尼亚 Kenya 非洲国家 9—233e
肯尼亚非洲民族联盟 Kenya African National Union (KANU) 肯尼亚政党 9—235b
肯尼亚山 Kenya, Mount 肯尼亚火山 9—235a
肯涅利 Kennelly, Arthur Edwin 美国电气工程师 9—227c
肯涅利-亥维赛层 Kennelly-Heaviside layer 电离层 9—227c
肯诺造山运动 Kenoran orogeny 地质学 9—228b
肯帕德 Khambhāt (India) 印度城镇 9—255a
肯彭兰(地区) Kempenland 比利时高原 9—222e
肯珀内尔 Kempeneer, Pieter de 佛兰德斯宗教画家 9—222e
肯普 Kempe, John 英格兰政治家 9—222d
肯普 Kempe, Margery 英国宗教神秘主义者 9—222e
肯普夫 Kempff, Wilhelm 德国钢琴家 9—222f
肯普隆格 Cîmpulung 罗马尼亚市镇 4—239e
肯普滕 Kempten 德国城市 9—222f
肯普西 Kempsey 澳大利亚城镇 9—222f
肯塞特 Kensett, John Frederick 美国风景画家 9—228c
肯塔尔 Quental, Antero Tarquínio de 葡萄牙诗人 14—86c
肯塔基 Kentucky 美国州名 9—230b
肯塔基大赛 Kentucky Derby 美国传统马赛 9—233c
肯塔基河 Kentucky River 美国河流 9—233e
肯塔基湖 Kentucky Lake 美国人工湖 9—233d
《肯塔基决议》 Kentucky Resolution 美国历史 9—233e
肯塔基咖啡树 Kentucky coffee tree (species *Gymnocladus dioica*) 木本植物 9—233b
肯套 Kentau 哈萨克斯坦城市 9—229f
肯特 Kent 英格兰王国 9—228e
肯特 Kent 英格兰郡名 9—228f
肯特 Kent 美国城市 9—229a
肯特 Kent, James 美国法学家 9—229b
肯特 Kent, Rockwell 美国画家 9—229c
肯特 Kent, William 英国画家 9—229d
肯特堡 Fort Kent 美国城镇 6—413f
肯特伯爵 Kent, Odo, earl of 征服者威廉异母兄弟 9—229c
肯特伯爵(第三) Kent, Thomas Holland, 3rd earl of 王室事务总管 9—229d
肯特伯爵(第一) Kent, Edmund Plantagenet, 1st earl of 英格兰国王之弟 9—229a
肯特洞 Kent's Cavern 英格兰大洞穴 9—230a
肯特修女 Kent, Nun of 英格兰预言家 9—229c
肯特与斯特拉森公爵 Kent and Strathern, Edward Augustus, duke of 英国陆军元帅 9—229e
肯辛顿公园 Kensington Gardens 英国公园 9—228d
肯辛顿宫 Kensington Palace 英国皇家宫殿 9—228d
肯辛顿-切尔西 Kensington and Chelsea 英格兰自治市 9—228d
肯辛顿石碑 Kensington Stone 北美石碑 9—228e
肯雅塔 Kenyatta, Jomo 肯尼亚总理、总统 9—235c
垦丁国家公园 Kending National Park 中国台湾国家公园 9—224a
空 emptiness 神秘主义哲学、宗教名词 6—66a
空谷阶 Kungurian Stage 地质学 9—397c
空海 Kūkai 日本佛教高僧 9—391e
空化 cavitation 物理学 3—542f
空间 space 物理学 15—560b
空间电荷 space charge 电学 15—560b
空间定向障碍 spatial disorientation 病理生理现象 16—9e
空间群 space group 结晶学 15—560f
空间收缩 space contraction 物理学 15—560c
空间知觉 space perception 动物意识 15—561d
空晶石 chiastolite 矿物 4—139c
空军 air force 军种 1—143d
空军军官学校 air force academy 军官学校 1—144b
空气 air 气体混合物 1—142b
空气动力学 aerodynamics 物理学 1—96b
空气栓塞 air embolism 疾病 1—143d
空气弹簧 air spring 机械 1—145e
空气调节 air-conditioning 采暖通风 1—142d
空气透视法 aerial perspective 绘画、制图技术 1—95f
空手道 karate 日本技击法 9—179f
空速表 airspeed indicator 航空仪器 1—148d
空头市场 bear market 商业 2—305b
空位 vacancy 结晶学 17—439f
空域 air space 国际法 1—145d
空中花园 Hanging Gardens of Babylon 古巴比伦遗址 7—459c
空中交通管制 air-traffic control 航空法 1—145e
空中劫持 skyjacking 非法夺取飞行中的飞机或其他飞行器 15—423f
空中客车工业公司 Airbus Industrie 欧洲企业 1—146b
“空中列车” Skytrain (U.S. aircraft) 美国飞机 15—424d
空中照相 aerial photography 摄影 1—96a

空中转 tour en l'air 舞蹈 17—177a
空中作战 air warfare 空中军事行动 1—145e
箜篌 konghou 乐器 9—345c
孔布 Combes,(Justin-Louis-)Émile 法国政治家 4—376f
孔达拉 Koundara 几内亚城镇 9—367a
孔达洛 caṇḍāla 印度社会等级 3—397b
孔代亲王 Condé, PRINCES OF 法国贵族 4—414b
孔代亲王(第八) Condé, Louis-Joseph, 8e prince de (8th prince of), DUC (duke) DE BOURBON 法国王族 4—415b
孔代亲王(第二) Condé, Henri I de Bourbon, 2e prince de (2nd prince of) 法国王族 4—414d
孔代亲王(第九) Condé, Louis-Henri-Joseph, 9e prince de (9th prince of), DUC (duke) DE BOURBON 法国王族 4—415c
孔代亲王(第六) Condé, Louis III, 6e prince de (6th prince of), DUC (duke) DE BOURBON 法国王族 4—415a
孔代亲王(第七) Condé, Louis-Henri, 7e prince de (7th prince of), DUC (duke) DE BOURBON 法国首相 4—415a
孔代亲王(第三) Condé, Henri II de Bourbon, 3e prince de (3rd prince of) 法国王族 4—414d
孔代亲王(第四) Condé, Louis II de Bourbon, 4e prince de (4th prince of) 法国将军 4—414e
孔代亲王(第五) Condé, Henri-Jules de Bourbon, 5e prince de (5th prince of) 法国王族 4—414f
孔代亲王(第一) Condé, Louis I de Bourbon, 1er prince de (1st prince of) 法国军事首领 4—414c
孔德 Comte, Auguste 法国哲学家 4—407e
孔德人 Khond 印度民族 9—262f
孔狄亚克 Condillac, Étienne Bonnot de 法国哲学家 4—415f
孔迪亚瓦 Kundiawa 巴布亚新几内亚城镇 9—396f
孔蒂 Conti, Gregory (antipope) 敌对教皇 4—465e
孔蒂亲王 Conti, PRINCES OF 法国贵族 4—465b
孔蒂亲王 Conti, Armand I de Bourbon, prince de 法国王族 4—465c
孔蒂亲王 Conti, François de Bourbon, prince de 法国王族 4—465b
孔蒂亲王 Conti, François-Louis de Bourbon, prince de 法国王族 4—465c
孔蒂亲王 Conti, Louis-Armand I de Bourbon, prince de 法国王族 4—465c
孔蒂亲王 Conti, Louis-Armand II de Bourbon, prince de 法国王族 4—465d
孔蒂亲王 Conti, Louis-François de Bourbon, prince de 法国王族 4—465d
孔蒂亲王 Conti, Louis-François-Joseph de Bourbon, prince de 法国王族 4—465e
孔杜克图斯 conductus 音乐 4—417f
孔多尔坎基 Condorcanqui, José Gabriel 印加革命者 4—417a
孔多塞 Condorcet, Marie-Jean-Antoine-Nicolas de Caritat, marquis de 法国数学家、革命家 4—417a
孔府 Kongfu 中国历史古迹 9—345c
孔戈尼亚斯 Congonhas 巴西城镇 4—428b
孔伋 K'ung Chi 中国哲学家 9—397b
孔季利斯 Kondílis, Geórgios 希腊将军 9—344d
孔径 aperture 光学 1—408a
孔敬 Khon Kaen 泰国城镇 9—262f
孔卡 Conca, Sebastiano 意大利画家 4—408f
孔库雷河 Konkouré River 几内亚河流 9—346f
孔拉尔 Conrart, Valentin 法国学者 4—441d
孔庙 Kongmiao 中国历史古迹 9—345d
孔帕尼 Compagni, Dino 佛罗伦萨官员 4—395d
孔佩尔 Compère, Loyset 佛兰芒作曲家 4—397f
孔奇尼 Concini, Concino, MARQUIS D'ANCRE 意大利冒险家 4—412a
孔乔斯河 Conchos River 墨西哥河流 4—411f
孔丘 Kong Qiu 中国哲学家 9—345a
孔雀 peacock 鸟类 13—110a
孔雀宝座 Peacock Throne 印度著名宝物 13—110d
孔雀帝国 Mauryan empire 古印度国家 11—41c
《孔雀东南飞》 Kongque Dongnan Fei 中国文学作品 9—345e
孔雀绿 malachite green 染料 10—419b
孔雀石 malachite 矿物 10—419a
孔雀松 peacock pine 木本植物 13—110d
孔雀缨鳃蚕 peacock worm 海产蠕虫 13—110d
孔尚任 Kong Shangren 中国清代文学家 9—345a
孔斯坦塞 Constance 西西里女王 4—448e
孔斯特 Kunst, Jaap 荷兰民族音乐学家 9—398f
孔斯峡湾 Kongs Fjord 北冰洋水湾 9—345e
孔索人 Konso 民族 9—347e
孔塔-弗内森 Comtat-Venaissin 法国旧省份 4—407e
孔塔戈拉 Kontagora 尼日利亚城镇 9—348a
孔塔里尼家族 Contarini FAMILY 威尼斯显贵家族 4—464e
孔泰 Conté, Nicolas-Jacques 法国发明家 4—464e
孔泰笔 conté crayon 文具 4—464f
孔特雷拉斯 Contreras (Mexico) 墨西哥区名 4—472c
孔特雷拉斯战役 Contreras, Battle of 美国历史 4—472c
孔脱 Kundt, August (Adolph Eduard Eberhard) 德国物理学家 9—396f
孔西德朗 Considérant, Victor-Prosper 法国社会主义者 4—446f
孔西延斯 Conscience, Hendrik 比利时小说家 4—443a
孔祥熙 Kong Xiangxi 中国银行家 9—345b
孔泽维奇 Kontsevich, Maxim 俄罗斯数学家 9—348b
孔子 Confucius 中国古代思想家、教育家 4—422e
孔子鸟 Confuciusornis 中国化石 4—423a
孔子哲学 Philosophy of Confucius, the 中国哲学 13—246d
孔嘴贝 Rhynchotrema 地质学 14—272b
恐怖海峡乐队 Dire Straits 英国摇滚乐队 5—335e
恐怖片 horror film 电影 8—179e
恐怖统治 Terror, Reign of 法国历史 16—556b
恐怖小说 horror story 文学 8—179f
恐怖症 phobia 焦虑障碍 13—254b
恐怖主义 terrorism 政治 16—556c
恐颌猪属 Dinohyus 古生物学 5—324a
恐龙 dinosaur 古生物学 5—324b
恐鸟 moa 绝灭鸟类 11—299b
恐鸟属 Dinornis 古生物学 5—324b
恐水病 hydrophobia (disease) 疾病 8—286b
恐鱼属 Dinichthys 古生物学 5—323b
控告 impleader (law) 法律 8—347e
控诉状 complaint 法律 4—398d
控制经济 command economy 经济学 4—382d
控制理论 control theory 数学 4—473c
控制论 cybernetics 控制理论 5—83e
控制系统 control system 自动化 4—472d
口 mouth 解剖学 11—448c
口吃 stuttering 语言障碍 16—292c
口疮性口炎 aphthous stomatitis 疾病 1—409e
口袋选区 pocket borough 英国选举区 13—383b
口技 ventriloquism 发声技巧 17—508c
口径 calibre 武器测量单位 3—345a
口腔癌 oral cancer 疾病 12—440f
口腔溃疡 canker sore 疾病 3—402b
口腔外科学 oral surgery 医学 12—441b
口琴 harmonica 乐器 7—481f
口授教理 catechesis (theology) 神学 3—522f
口述记录机 dictating machine 语言复制设备 5—300e
口蹄疫 foot-and-mouth disease (FMD) 牲畜疾病 6—396e
口头约定 stipulatio 罗马法 16—240d
口香糖 chewing gum 食品 4—136e
口育鱼 mouthbreeder 鱼类 11—448d

口欲期 oral stage 精神分析 12—441a
口髭 mustache 上唇的须 11—514e
叩壁蜥 chuckwalla (species *Sauromalus obesus*) 爬行动物 4—219c
叩头虫 click beetle 昆虫 4—289b
叩诊 percussion 诊断手段 13—159d
扣甲 snapping beetle 昆虫 15—459b
扣形饰品 buckle 饰物 3—224a
扣押 seizure (law) 法律 15—194d
扣押财产通知 garnishment 法律 7—18d
扣押财物 distress 法律 5—343f
扣押令 attachment 美国法律 2—37e
寇谦之 Kou Qianzhi 中国北魏道士 9—366e
寇松 Curzon, Mary Victoria Leiter 印度总督夫人 5—75c
寇松侯爵 Curzon (of Kedleston), George Nathaniel Curzon, Marquess, Viscount Scarsdale, Baron Ravensdale 英国政治家 5—75a
寇松线 Curzon Line 苏波分界线 5—75d
枯草热 hay fever 疾病 7—529b
枯川 Kosen (Japanese Communist leader) 日本共产党领袖 9—362b
哭墙 Wailing Wall (Judaism) 犹太教圣地 18—65e
堀口舍己 Horiguchi Sutemi 日本建筑师 8—173f
堀田正俊 Hotta Masatoshi 日本政治家 8—191b
堀田正睦 Hotta Masayoshi 日本政治家 8—191b
骷髅虾 skeleton shrimp 甲壳动物 15—415b
苦 dukkha 佛教 5—452f
苦艾酒 absinthe 酒类 1—30b
苦橄岩 picrite 岩石 13—291f
苦根 bitterroot (*Lewisia rediviva*) 植物 2—504d
苦力 coolie 亚洲劳工 4—482b
苦路十四处 Cross, Stations of the 天主教 5—31e
苦木科 Simaroubaceae 植物学 15—379b
苦难的简 Calamity Jane 美国传奇女性 3—333f
苦难会士 Passionist 天主教修会成员 13—79f
苦苹果 bitter apple 植物 2—504a
苦苣苔科 Gesneriaceae 植物学 7—102d
苦泉微体化石 Bitter Springs microfossils 古生物学 2—504a
苦甜藤 bittersweet 植物 2—504f
苦娃达 couvade 风俗 4—553c
苦味酒 bitters 酒类 2—504e
苦味酸 picric acid 化合物 13—291e
苦行 tapas 印度教 16—474e
苦行主义 asceticism 宗教 1—540c
库阿特利 Kuwatli, Shukri al- 叙利亚政治家 9—409d
库埃 Coué, Émile 法国药剂师 4—541b
库埃纳瓦卡 Cuernavaca 墨西哥城市 5—52b
库埃提苏丹国 Qu'aiti sultanate 也门历史国家 14—73b
库埃瓦 Cueva (de Garoza), Juan de la 西班牙剧作家 5—52c
库安德烈 Coindre, André 法国教士 4—336a
库奥皮奥 Kuopio 芬兰城市 9—399c
库巴 Kuba 非洲历史王国 9—387a
库巴 Kuba 阿塞拜疆城市 9—387a
库巴巴 Kubaba 叙利亚女神 9—387c
库巴地毯 Kuba carpet 工艺品 9—387a
库巴人 Kuba 民族 9—386f
库巴唐 Cubatão 巴西城市 5—48e
库班戈河 Kubango River (Africa) 非洲河流 9—387c
库班河 Kuban River 俄罗斯河流 9—387c
库班河畔斯拉维扬斯克 Slavyansk-na-Kubani 俄罗斯城市 15—429d
库贝利克 Kubelík, Rafael (Jeronym) 瑞士指挥家 9—387c
库比福勒化石遗存 Koobi Fora remains 肯尼亚人科化石 9—348f
库比契克 Kubitschek, Juscelino 巴西总统 9—387f
库宾 Kubin, Alfred 奥地利艺术家 9—387e
库波维 Kubovy, Aryeh Leon 以色列外交家 9—387f
库伯兰 Couperin, François 法国作曲家 4—546b
库伯兰 Couperin, Louis 法国作曲家 4—546c
库伯佩迪 Coober Pedy 澳大利亚城镇 4—477b
库勃里克 Kubrick, Stanley 美国电影导演 9—387f
库布人 Kubu 印度尼西亚民族 9—388a
库藏交换 depot trade 商业 5—250d
库车 Kuqa 中国县名 9—399f
库茨 Kuts, Vladimir 苏联运动员 9—407d
库存单位 SKU 库存产品编码 15—422c
库德 Cooder, Ry 美国吉他手、歌手 4—477b
库德姆卡尔 Kudymkar 俄罗斯城市 9—389c
库迪尔卡 Kudirka, Vincas 立陶宛医生 9—388f
库蒂拉 Couturat, Louis(-Alexandre) 法国哲学家 4—553a
库东 Couthon, Georges 法国雅各宾派领导人 4—552e
库都鲁 kudurru 美索不达米亚界石 9—389b
库杜古 Koudougou 布基纳法索城镇 9—366e
库恩 Kun, Béla 匈牙利共产党领导人 9—396b
库恩 Coon, Carleton (Stevens) 美国人类学家 4—482e
库恩 Kuhn, (Franz Felix) Adalbert 德国语言学家 9—390a
库恩 Kuhn, Maggie 美国社会激进主义者 9—390a
库恩 Kuhn, Richard 德国生物化学家 9—390b
库恩 Kuhn, Thomas S. 美国科学史学家 9—390c
库恩 Kuhn, Walt 美国画家 9—390d
库恩切夫 Kunchev, Vasil Ivanov 保加利亚牧师 9—396d
库尔 Chur 瑞士州首府 4—222e
库尔 kul 印度家庭单位 9—392a
库尔 Court, Antoine 基督教新教牧师 4—549b
库尔帮乐队 Kool and the Gang 美国乐队 9—349b
库尔贝 Courbet, Gustave 法国画家 4—547c
库尔伯瓦 Courbevoie 法国工业区 4—547e
库尔布里思 Coolbrith, Ina Donna 美国诗人 4—480f
库尔布斯基 Kurbsky, Andrey Mikhaylovich, Knyaz (Prince) 俄国军事统帅 9—400e
库尔茨 Kurz, Hermann 德国作家 9—404f
库尔德地毯 Kurdish rug 工艺品 9—401c
库尔·德·热伯兰 Court de Gébelin, Antoine 法国学者 4—549e
库尔德人 Kurd 亚洲民族 9—401a
库尔德斯坦 Kordestān 伊朗地区 9—352e
库尔德斯坦 Kurdistan 亚洲地区 9—401d
库尔德语 Kurdish language 亚洲语言 9—401c
库尔干 Kurgan 俄罗斯州名 9—402b
库尔干 Kurgan 俄罗斯城市 9—402b
库尔干秋别 Kurgan-Tyube 塔吉克斯坦州名 9—402c
库尔干秋别 Kurgan-Tyube 塔吉克斯坦城市 9—402c
库尔干文化 Kurgan culture 欧洲古代文化 9—402b
库尔加迪 Coolgardie 澳大利亚城镇 4—481c
库尔兰 Courland 欧洲历史地区 4—548b
库尔兰潟湖 Courland Lagoon 波罗的海海湾 4—548c
库尔勒 Korla 中国城市 9—359b
库尔曼 Culmann, Carl 瑞士工程师 5—54d
库尔纳 Khulna 孟加拉国城市 9—266c
库尔南 Cournand, André F(rédéric) 美国医师、生理学家 4—548c
库尔诺 Cournot, Antoine-Augustin 法国经济学家 4—548d
库尔恰托夫 Kurchatov, Igor Vasilyevich 苏联核物理学家 9—400f
库尔斯克 Kursk 俄罗斯州名 9—404a
库尔斯克 Kursk 俄罗斯城市 9—404a
库尔斯克湾 Kursky Zaliv (Europe) 欧洲潟湖 9—404c
库尔斯克战役 Kursk, Battle of 第二次世界大战史 9—404b
库尔泰亚-德阿尔杰什 Curtea de Argeş 罗马尼亚城镇 5—72b
库尔特尼 Courtenay, William 坎特伯雷大主教 4—550c
库尔提乌斯 Curtius, Ernst 德国考古学家 5—73b
库尔提乌斯 Curtius, Georg 德国语言学者 5—73b

库尔提乌斯 Curtius, Julius 德国政治家 5—73c
库尔提乌斯 Curtius, Marcus 罗马传奇英雄 5—73c
《库尔威奇和奥尔温》 Kulhwch and Olwen 威尔士文学 9—392f
库尔泽梅 Kurzeme 拉脱维亚地区 9—404f
库尔佐拉 Curzola (Croatia) 克罗地亚岛屿 5—75a
库法克斯 Koufax, Sandy 美国职业棒球运动员 9—366f
库法字体 Kūfic script 伊斯兰风格字母书写体 9—389d
库费 Kūfah 伊拉克城市 9—389d
库夫拉绿洲 Kufrah, Al- 利比亚绿洲群 9—389e
库夫施泰因 Kufstein 奥地利城镇 9—389e
库格林 Coughlin, Charles E(dward) 美国天主教士、政治家 4—541c
库根 Coogan, Jackie 美国演员 4—477c
库哈斯 Koolhaas, Rem 荷兰建筑师 9—349d
库霍恩男爵 Coehoorn, Menno, baron van 荷兰军官 4—328b
库基人 Kuki 亚洲民族 9—391f
库克 Cooke, Alistair 美国记者 4—479f
库克 Kook, Abraham Isaac 犹太教神秘主义者 9—349a
库克 Cook, Arthur James 英国工人领袖 4—477d
库克 Cook, Frederick Albert 美国医生、探险家 4—477e
库克 Cook, George Cram 美国小说家 4—477e
库克 Cook, James 英国海军上校 4—477f
库克 Cook, Sir Joseph 澳大利亚总理 4—478c
库克 Cooke, Jay 美国金融家 4—480a
库克 Cooke, Rose Terry 美国诗人、作家 4—480a
库克 Cooke, Sam 美国歌手、词曲作家 4—480b
库克 Cook, Thomas 英国商人 4—478e
库克 Cooke, Sir William Fothergill 英国发明家 4—480c
库克敦 Cooktown 澳大利亚港镇 4—480d
库克海峡 cook Strait 新西兰海峡 4—479d
库克罗普斯 Cyclops 希腊传说 5—87a
库克南瀑布 Kukenaam Falls 南美瀑布 9—391f
库克群岛 Cook Islands 新西兰自治领地 4—478f
库克山 Cook, Mount 新西兰最高峰 4—478d
库克山国家公园 Mount Cook National Park 新西兰公园 11—440e
库克斯敦 Cookstown 北爱尔兰城镇 4—480d
库克斯港 Cuxhaven 德国港市 5—81f
库克湾 Cook Inlet 北太平洋小湾 4—478f
库克维尔 Cookeville 美国城市 4—480c
库克沃西 Cookworthy, William 英国制造商 4—480e
库库诺尔 Koko Nor (China) 中国湖泊 9—337a
库库塔 Cúcuta 哥伦比亚城市 5—51b
库库泰尼-特里波利耶文化 Cucuteni-Tripolye culture 欧洲古代文化 5—51b
库拉 kula 交易制度 9—392b
库拉河 Kura River 亚洲河流 9—400b
库拉金 Kurakin, Boris Ivanovich, Knyaz (Prince) 俄国外交家 9—400b
库拉科娃 Kulakova, Galina 苏联滑雪运动员 9—392c
库拉索岛 Curaçao 荷属安的列斯群岛岛屿 5—66e
库拉特 Kurath, Hans 美国语言学家 9—400d
库莱布拉水道 Culebra Cut (Panama) 巴拿马水道 5—53f
库莱夫拉岛 Culebra Island 波多黎各岛屿 5—53f
库朗 Courant, Richard 美国数学家 4—547b
库朗特舞 courante 舞蹈 4—547b
库雷热 Courrèges, André 法国女装设计师 4—548d
库雷沃维奇 Kuryłowicz, Jerzy 波兰历史语言学家 9—404e
库里阿提乌斯三兄弟 Curiatii 罗马民间传说 5—67f
库里埃 Courier, Paul-Louis 法国学者 4—547f
库里奥 Curio, Gaius Scribonius 罗马政治家 5—69b
库里奥 Curio, Gaius Scribonius 罗马政治家、演说家 5—69b
库里蒂巴 Curitiba 巴西城市 5—69c
库里科 Curicó 智利城市 5—67f
库里亚 curia 古罗马政治区划 5—67c
库里亚 curia 欧洲历史 5—67d
库里亚穆里亚 Khurīyā Murīyā 阿曼群岛 9—266d
库利 Cooley, Charles Horton 美国社会学家 4—481a
库利 Cooley, Denton A(rthur) 美国外科医师 4—481b
库利昂岛 Culion Island 菲律宾岛屿 5—54a
库利吉 Coolidge, William D(avid) 美国工程师 4—482a
库利科罗 Koulikoro 马里城镇 9—366f
库利科沃战役 Kulikovo, Battle of 俄国历史 9—393a
库利那制 Kulinism 印度种姓制度 9—393a
库利南钻石 Cullinan diamond 宝石 5—54c
库利奇 Coolidge, Elizabeth Penn Sprague 美国慈善家 4—481d
库利奇 Coolidge, Julian Lowell 美国数学家 4—481e
库利奇 Coolidge, Martha 美国电影制片人 4—481f
库利奇 Coolidge, William Augustus Brevoort 英格兰历史学家 4—481f
库利氏贫血 Cooley's anemia 病理学 4—481b
库利亚布 Kulyab 塔吉克斯坦城市 9—393f
库利亚坎 Culiacán 墨西哥城市 5—53f
库列巴基 Kulebaki 俄罗斯城市 9—392e
库列绍夫 Kuleshov, Lev Vladimirovich 苏联电影理论家 9—392e
库林 Kulin 波斯尼亚总督 9—393a
库林丘陵 Cuillin Hills 苏格兰山群 5—53b
库龙巴人 Kurumba 印度民族 9—404d
库隆 Coulon, Johnnyk 美国职业拳击手 4—542a
库隆角国家公园 Ujung-Kulon National Park 印度尼西亚国家公园 17—324f
库卢克语 Kurukh language 印度语言 9—404d
库鲁 Kourou 法属圭亚那城镇 9—367c
库鲁病 kuru 疾病 9—404c
库鲁克人 Kurukh (people) 印度民族 9—404d
库鲁马 Kourouma, Ahmadou 非洲小说家 9—367d
库鲁曼 Kuruman 南非城镇 9—404d
库鲁内格勒 Kurunegala 斯里兰卡城镇 9—404e
库鲁恰伊河 Kuruçay (river, Asia) 亚洲河流 9—404c
库鲁萨 Kouroussa 几内亚城镇 9—367e
库仑 coulomb 计量单位 4—541e
库仑 Coulomb, Charles-Augustin de 法国物理学家 4—541e
库仑法 coulometry 化学 4—542a
库仑力 Coulomb force 物理学 4—541e
库伦 Niislel Khureheh (Mongolia) 蒙古首都乌兰巴托旧称 12—190d
库伦达草原 Kulunda Steppe 西伯利亚低地 9—393f
库洛米耶公爵 Coulommiers, Henri II d'Orléans, duc de (duke of) 法国反叛者 4—542a
库马 Cooma 澳大利亚城镇 4—482d
库马拉斯瓦米 Coomaraswamy, Ananda Kentish 印度史学家 4—482d
库马拉通加 Kumaratunga, Chandrika Bandaranaike 斯里兰卡总统 9—394d
库马-马内奇洼地 Kuma-Manych Depression 俄罗斯洼地 9—394a
库马纳 Cumaná 委内瑞拉城市 5—57e
库马纳戈托 Cumanagoto 委内瑞拉印第安人 5—57f
库马努斯湾 Cumanus, Sinus (Mediterranean Sea) 意大利海湾 5—57f
库马诺沃 Kumanovo 马其顿城市 9—394c
库马西 Kumasi 加纳城市 9—394e
库迈 Cumae 意大利古城 5—57d
库麦里 Kumayri 亚美尼亚城市 9—395a
库曼人 Cuman 土耳其游牧民族 5—57e
库曼人 Kuman 突厥部落 9—394c
库蒙祖罗斯 Koumoundhoúros, Aléxandros 希腊政治家 9—367a
库米拉 Comilla 孟加拉国城镇 4—381f

库莫 Kumo 尼日利亚城镇 9—395f
库默尔 Kummer, Ernst Eduard 德国数学家 9—395e
库姆 Qom 伊朗城市 14—70d
库姆 Combe, William 英国作家 4—376e
库姆拉山 Comeragh Mountains 爱尔兰山脉 4—379f
库姆兰 Qumrān 亚洲考古遗址 14—96e
库那克萨战役 Cunaxa, Battle of 中东历史 5—61b
库纳巴拉布兰 Coonabarabran 澳大利亚城镇 4—482e
库纳人 Cuna 巴拿马印第安人 5—61a
库奈特拉 Qunayṭirah, Al- 叙利亚省份 14—96f
库南伯尔 Coonamble 澳大利亚城镇 4—482f
库瑙 Kuhnau, Johann 德国作曲家 9—390e
库内奥 Cuneo 意大利城市 5—62a
库内内 Kunene, Mazisi (Raymond) 南非诗人 9—397a
库内内河 Kunene River 非洲河流 9—397a
库尼 Cooney, Loretta 美国演员 4—482f
库尼伯特，圣 Cunibert, Saint 科隆主教 5—62b
库尼亚 Cunha, Euclides (Rodrigues Pimenta) da 巴西作家 5—62b
库尼耶岛 Kunie Island (New Caledonia) 新喀利多尼亚岛屿 9—397c
库宁 Kooning, Willem de (painter) 美国画家 9—349f
库诺 Cuno, Wilhelm (Carl Josef) 德国政治家 5—64a
库诺贝利努斯 Cunobelinus 不列颠地区统治者 5—64a
库诺氏木科 Cunoniaceae 植物学 5—64b
库诺斯克法莱 Cynoscephalae 希腊山脉 5—89f
库欧科 Cuoco, Vincenzo 意大利史学家 5—64c
库佩勒斯 Couperus, Louis Marie Anne 荷兰小说家 4—546d
库珀 Cupar 苏格兰城市 5—65b
库珀 Cooper, Anthony Ashley 英国工业改革家 4—483b
库珀 Cooper, Sir Astley Paston, 1st Baronet 英国外科医师 4—483b
库珀 Couper, Archibald Scott 苏格兰化学家 4—546a
库珀 Cooper, Cynthia 美国篮球运动员 4—483c
库珀 Küpper, Christian Emil Marie (Dutch painter) 荷兰画家 9—399f
库珀 Cooper, Dame Gladys 英国演员 4—483e
库珀 Cooper, Gary 美国演员 4—483c
库珀 Cooper, James Fenimore 美国作家 4—483f
库珀 Cooper, John M(ontgomery) 美国人种学家 4—484a
库珀 Cooper, Kent 美国记者 4—484c
库珀 Cooper, L(eroy) Gordon, Jr. 美国航天员 4—484c
库珀 Cooper, Leon N. 美国物理学家 4—484d
库珀 Cooper, Peter 美国发明家、慈善家 4—484e
库珀 Cooper, Samuel 英国画家 4—484f
库珀 Cooper, Susan Augusta Fenimore 美国作家、慈善家 4—485b
库珀 Cooper, Sarah Brown Ingersoll 美国教育家 4—485a
库珀 Cooper, Thomas 英国主教 4—485b
库珀 Cooper, Thomas 英国作家 4—485c
库珀河 Cooper Creek 澳大利亚间歇河 4—485c
库珀盆地 Cooper Basin 澳大利亚洼地 4—485c
库珀斯敦 Cooperstown 美国村庄 4—485f
库珀学院 Cooper Union 美国学院 4—485d
库普 Coup, W(illiam) C(ameron) 美国马戏团经理 4—545f
库普弗细胞 Kupffer cell 细胞学 9—399e
库普卡 Kupka, František 法国画家 9—399e
库普林 Kuprin, Aleksandr Ivanovich 俄国小说家 9—399f
库普曼斯 Koopmans, Tjalling C(harles) 美国经济学家 9—349f
库齐库斯 Cyzicus 古希腊城镇 5—96c
库奇比哈尔 Cooch Behār 印度城镇 4—477b
库奇金统 Coutchiching Series 地质学 4—552d
库奇马 Kuchma, Leonid Danylovych 乌克兰政治人物 9—388d
库奇普迪舞 kuchipudi 印度古典舞蹈 9—388c
库奇亚格兰德 Cuchilla Grande 乌拉圭丘陵带 5—49b
库钦人 Kutchin 北美印第安人 9—407a
库琼巴语 Kuchumba language 语言 9—388e
库丘林 Cú Chulainn 古爱尔兰文学故事人物 5—46d
库瑞涅 Cyrene 希腊神话仙女 5—93b
库萨河 Coosa River 美国河流 4—486f
库塞埃 Kusaie (Caroline Islands) 加罗林群岛 9—405a
库塞维茨基 Koussevitzky, Serge 美国指挥家 9—367e
库桑科斯基 Kuusankoski 芬兰城镇 9—408a
库施 Cush 努比亚古地名 5—75f
库施特诸语言 Cushitic languages 闪含语系语族之一 5—76e
库施王朝 Cushite dynasty 埃及王朝 5—76d
库什 Kusch, Polykarp 美国物理学家 9—405a
库什蒂亚 Kushtia 孟加拉国城市 9—405e
库什克河 Kushk River 亚洲河流 9—405e
库什曼 Cushman, Charlotte Saunders 美国戏剧演员 5—76e
库什曼 Cushman, Joseph Augustine 美国古生物学家 5—76f
库什曼 Cushman, Vera Charlotte Scott 美国社会工作者 5—77a
库什瓦 Kushva 俄罗斯城市 9—405e
库舒克 Kushukh 月神 9—405e
库思伯特，圣 Cuthbert, Saint 基督教隐修院院长 5—79a
库斯 Coues, Elliott 美国鸟类学家 4—541b
库斯贝 Coos Bay 美国城市 4—486e
库斯科 Cuzco 秘鲁省份 5—82c
库斯科 Cuzco 秘鲁城市 5—82d
库斯科娃 Kuskova, Yekaterina Dmitriyevna 俄国政论作家 9—405f
库斯塔奈 Kustanay 哈萨克斯坦州名 9—405f
库斯塔奈 Kustanay 哈萨克斯坦城市 9—406a
库斯提 Kūstī 苏丹城镇 9—406a
库斯图 Coustou, Guillaume 法国雕刻家 4—552c
库斯托 Cousteau, Jacques-Yves 法国海军军官 4—552b
库斯托扎战役 Custoza, battles of 意大利历史 5—78c
库苏古尔湖 Hövsgöl Lake 蒙古湖泊 8—198b
库塔曼德拉 Cootamundra 澳大利亚城镇 4—487a
库塔伊西 Kutaisi 格鲁吉亚城市 9—406d
库泰 Koetai (Indonesia) 印度尼西亚河流 9—332d
库泰 Kutai (Indonesia) 印度尼西亚河流 9—406d
库汤格Ⅰ峰 Kutang I (mountain, Nepal) 尼泊尔山峰 9—406e
库唐斯 Coutances 法国城镇 4—552d
库特 Kūt, Al- 伊拉克城镇 9—406b
库特 Coote, Sir Eyre 英国军人 4—487b
库特赖 Courtrai (Belgium) 比利时城市 4—550f
库特赖战役 Courtrai, Battle of (1302) 欧洲历史 4—550f
库特林 Courteline, Georges 法国作家 4—550b
库特纳霍拉 Kutná Hora 捷克城市 9—407c
库特内国家公园 Kootenay National Park 加拿大国家公园 9—350a
库特内河 Kootenay River 北美河流 9—350a
库特内人 Kutenai 民族 9—407b
库图尔 Couture, Thomas 法国画家 4—553b
库图瓦 Courtois, Bernard 法国化学家 4—550f
库图佐夫 Kutuzov, Mikhail Illarionovich, Prince (Knyaz) 俄国陆军司令官 9—407d
库万阶 Couvinian Stage 地质学 4—553e
库西 Coucy 法国村庄 4—541a
库西 Cousy, Bob 美国篮球运动员 4—552d
库西 Courci, John de 盎格鲁-诺曼征服者 4—547e
库西奥湖 Cusio, Lago (Italy) 意大利湖泊 5—77b
库西宁 Kuusinen, Otto V. 芬兰共产党缔造者 9—408a
库西山 Koussi, Mount 非洲火山 9—367f
库谢维茨基 Kusevitzky, Sergey Aleksandrovich 美国指挥家 9—405b
库欣 Cushing, Frank Hamilton 美国民族志学者 5—75f
库欣 Cushing, William 美国法学家 5—76b

库欣 Cushing, William Barker 美国海军军官 5—76b
库兴 Cushing, Harvey Williams 美国外科医生 5—76a
库兴氏综合征 Cushing's syndrome 疾病 5—76c
库亚巴 Cuiabá 巴西城市 5—53a
库亚巴河 Cuiabá River 巴西河流 5—53a
库亚瓦滨海 Kujawsko-Pomorskie 波兰省份 9—391d
库亚维亚 Kujavia 波兰低地 9—391c
库耶霍夜鹰 cuejo (bird) 鸟类 5—51f
库依卡 cueca 南美民间舞蹈 5—51e
库尤尼河 Cuyuni River 南美河流 5—82b
库约 Cuyo 阿根廷历史地区 5—82a
库赞 Cousin, Victor 法国哲学家 4—551c
库赞(老) Cousin, Jean, THE ELDER 法国画家 4—551b
库赞(小) Cousin, Jean, THE YOUNGER 法国画家 4—551c
库赞-蒙托邦 Cousin-Montauban, Charles-Guillaume-Marie-Apollinaire-Antoine, COMTE (count) DE PALIKAO 法国将军 4—551e
库扎 Cuza, Alexandru Ion 罗马尼亚大公 5—82b
库朱瓦克 Kuujjuaq 加拿大行政区 9—407f
库兹涅茨 Kuznets, Simon (Smith) 美国经济学家 9—409f
库兹涅茨克 Kuznetsk (Russia) 俄罗斯城市 9—410a
库兹涅茨克煤田 Kuznetsk Coal Basin 俄罗斯煤田 9—410a
库兹涅佐夫 Kuznetsov, Anatoly Vasilyevich 苏联作家 9—410b
库兹涅佐夫 Kuznetsov, Vasily Vasilyevich 苏联外交家 9—410c
库左尼 Cuzzoni, Francesca 意大利歌唱家 5—82f
锛 kurchatovium 化学元素 9—401a
裤子 trousers 服装 17—237c
酷詹姆斯 LL Cool J 美国说唱歌手 10—167c
夸 qa 计量单位 14—51b
夸察夸尔科斯 Coatzacoalcos 墨西哥城市 4—313d
夸德 quad 计量单位 14—71d
夸德拉图斯 Quadratus, SAINT 基督教护教士 14—72a
夸尔斯 Quarles, Francis 英国宗教诗人 14—78e
夸父 Kuafu 中国神话人物 9—386c
夸胡高原 Kwahu Plateau 加纳高原 9—410e
夸贾林环礁 Kwajalein Atoll 马绍尔群岛共和国环礁 9—410e
夸克 quark 亚原子粒子 14—78a
夸扣特尔人 Kwakiutl 北美印第安人 9—410f
夸夸 Qwaqwa 南非非独立黑人邦 14—99c
夸拉 Kwara 尼日利亚州名 9—411c
夸莱克 Kwolek, Stephanie 美国化学家 9—412b
夸里 Quare, Daniel 英国钟表制造家 14—77f
夸伦吉 Quarenghi, Giacomo Antonio Domenico 意大利建筑师、画家 14—77f
夸美纽斯 Comenius, John Amos 捷克教育改革家 4—379b
夸纳赫 Quanah (Comanche leader) 美国科曼切人领袖 14—74a
夸佩尔 Coypel, Antoine 法国画家 4—560e
夸佩尔 Coypel, Charles-Antoine 法国画家 4—560f
夸佩尔 Coypel, Noël 法国画家 4—561a
夸齐莫多 Quasimodo, Salvatore 意大利诗人、翻译家 14—80c
夸瑟沃 Coysevox, Antoine 法国雕刻家 4—561a
夸饰主义 culteranismo 西班牙文学 5—54e
夸斯兰论文集 Tractatus Coislinianus 文学 17—186c
夸特马 quarter horse 赛马 14—79a
夸特马赛 quarter-horse racing 体育 14—79a
夸脱 quart 计量单位 14—79a
夸希奥科病 kwashiorkor 疾病 9—411d
夸张 hyperbole 文学 8—291b
夸张方式 Ercles vein 表达方式 6—112e
夸祖卢 KwaZulu 南非前黑人邦 9—411e
夸祖卢/纳塔尔 KwaZulu/Natal 南非省份 9—411e
跨栏跑 hurdling 体育项目 8—264e
跨行 enjambment 诗歌 6—84b
跨行业联合企业 conglomerate 商业 4—425a
会计 accounting 金融 1—47c
会计计算机 accounting machine 计算机科学 1—47d
块滑石 steatite 矿物 16—206e
块茎 tuber 植物学 17—255a
块菌 truffle 菌类 17—240f
块体坡移 mass wasting 地质学 11—6f
块体移动 mass movement 地质学 11—5c
块铜矾 antlerite 矿物 1—395c
快步 trot 马赛步法 17—235c
快步马赛 trotting 马赛 17—236f
快帆船 clipper ship 帆船 4—294f
快活节 Hilaria 罗马宗教节日 8—78e
快兰卡里织品 qalamkārī textile 彩绘织物 14—52e
快乐派 Khorram-dīnān 伊斯兰教 9—263f
快乐小分队/新秩序乐队 Joy Division/New Order 英国摇滚乐队 9—95a
快马邮递 Pony Express 美国历史 13—430a
快门 shutter 摄影 15—345a
快庆 Kaikei 日本雕刻家 9—135b
快速书写法 Speedwriting 速记系统 16—18a
快子 tachyon 物理学 16—418b
筷子 chopsticks 餐具 4—197a
宽·阿派旺 Khuang Aphaiwong 泰国政治家 9—265e
宽德贝莱 KwaNdebele 南非黑人邦 9—411a
宽钝虫属 Bathyuriscus 古生物学 2—279a
宽多河 Kwando River 非洲河流 9—411a
宽耳蝠 barbastelle (*Barbastella*) 哺乳动物 2—219b
宽发盖海百合 Platycrinites 古生物学 13—364c
宽和教会派 Broad Church 英国教派 3—171b
宽和派 latitudinarian 基督教 9—515b
宽肩黾蝽 broad-shouldered water strider (insect) 昆虫 3—171c
宽角羚 broad-horned antelope 动物 3—171c
宽角螺属 Platyceras 古生物学 13—364c
宽口陶器人 Beaker folk 欧洲古代民族 2—303d
宽蛇 adder 爬行动物 1—72e
宽叶羽衣甘蓝 collard (*Brassica oleracea*, Acephala group) 植物学 4—345e
宽扎河 Kwanza River 安哥拉河流 9—411b
宽政改革 Kansei reforms 日本历史 9—164c
宽嘴鱼 tomtate 鱼类 17—146c
髋 hip 解剖学 8—90d
匡特 Quant, Mary 英国女装设计师 14—74b
匡扎节 Kwanzaa 非洲裔美国人节日 9—411c
狂暴武士 berserker 欧洲古代传说 2—431a
狂飙突进 Sturm und Drang 德国文学运动 16—291c
狂欢节 carnival 节日 3—468a
狂欢节 Fasching 德语国家天主教徒庆祝活动 6—245a
狂欢节歌曲 carnival song 意大利音乐 3—468b
狂闹剧 extravaganza 文学、音乐作品 6—199b
狂犬病 rabies 急性病毒性传染病 14—103b
狂言 kyōgen 日本戏剧 9—413f
鵟 buzzard 猛禽 3—296f
鵟类 buteo 猛禽类 3—289c
旷野宫殿 desert palace 倭马亚王朝行宫 5—260c
旷野教父 Desert Fathers 基督教隐士 5—260b
旷野隐修 idiorrhythmic monasticism 基督教 8—323a
矿工猫 miner's cat 哺乳动物 11—247a
矿井瓦斯 mine gas 有害气体 11—246a
矿瘤 nodule 矿床学 12—224a
矿脉 vein 矿床学 17—491a
矿泉疗养地 spa 疗养地 15—559e
矿泉水 mineral water 饮料 11—246e
矿石 ore 矿床学 12—451d

矿水城 Mineralnye Vody 俄罗斯城镇 11—246f
矿物 mineral 固体物质 11—246d
矿物燃料 fossil fuel 矿产 6—421a
矿物学 mineralogy 地质学 11—246f
矿物油 mineral oil 石油副产品 11—246e
矿业公会 Real Cuerpo de Minería 西属美洲殖民地矿业主同业公会 14—179c
框档种仁 quandong nut 植物学 14—74a
框架建筑 framed building 建造 6—435e
框架设计 frame design 装饰艺术 6—435c
框架竖琴 frame harp 乐器 6—435d
框形结构故事 frame story 文学 6—435e
眶上隆凸 supraorbital ridge (anatomy) 解剖学 16—349a
盔伯劳 helmet-shrike 鸟类 8—2f
盔甲 armour 保护服装 1—501f
窥基 Kuiji 中国佛教唯实宗创始人 9—390f
窥视者汤姆 peeping tom 性行为 13—122c
窥阴癖 voyeurism 性行为 18—52e
奎采奥湖 Cuitzeo, Lake 墨西哥湖泊 5—53d
奎达 Quetta 巴基斯坦城市 14—88c
奎达欣 Qodashim 犹太教口传律法 14—70d
奎德林堡 Quedlinburg 德国城市 14—83a
奎蒂科省立公园 Quetico Provincial Park 加拿大荒野公园 14—88b
奎多 Quidor, John 美国画家 14—90e
奎尔 Quayle, Dan 美国政治人物 14—81c
奎尔帕特岛 Quelpart Island (South Korea) 韩国岛屿 14—86a
奎尔恰 Quercia, Jacopo della 意大利雕刻家 14—86f
奎卡特克人 Cuicatec 中美洲印第安人 5—53a
奎奎 Kwekwe 津巴布韦城市 9—412b
奎拉帕 Cuilapa 危地马拉城市 5—53b
奎勒 Queler, Eve 美国指挥家 14—85f
奎勒-库奇 Quiller-Couch, Sir Arthur Thomas 英国诗人 14—91b
奎里多 Querido, Israël 荷兰小说家 14—87b
奎里斯 Quiris 罗马公民 14—95d
奎利亚雀 quelea (*Quelea quelea*) 鸟类 14—85e
奎隆 Quilon 印度城镇 14—91e
奎卢河 Kouilou River 非洲河流 9—366f
奎纳克林 quinacrine 药物 14—92c
奎纳纳 Kwinana 澳大利亚城镇 9—412b
奎内河 Khwae Noi River 泰国河流 9—267c
奎尼丁 quinidine 生物碱 14—93d
奎尼人 Kweni(people) 民族 9—412b
奎宁 quinine 生物碱 14—93e
奎松 Quezon (y Molina), Manuel (Luis) 菲律宾政治家 14—89b
奎松市 Quezon City 菲律宾城市 14—89d
奎特拉瓦克 Cuitláhuac 南美阿兹特克人皇帝 5—53d
奎屯 Kuytun 中国城市 9—409e
奎托 Kuito 安哥拉城镇 9—391c
奎心图案地毯 medallion carpet 工艺品 11—70a
奎因 Queen, Ellery 美国小说家 14—83b
奎因 Quin, James 英国演员 14—92b
奎因 Quine, Willard Van Orman 美国逻辑学家 14—93b
喹啉 quinoline 有机化合物 14—93f
魁北克 Quebec 加拿大省份 14—81d
魁北克 Quebec 加拿大城市 14—82b
魁北克党 Parti Québécois 加拿大政党 13—66d
《魁北克法案》 Quebec Act 英国议会通过的法案 14—82d
魁北克会议 Quebec Conferences 第二次世界大战史 14—82e
魁北克集团 Bloc Québécois 加拿大政党 2—537a
魁北克战役 Quebec, Battle of 美洲历史 14—82c
魁北克战役 Quebec, Battle of 美国历史 14—82d
魁尔 Quayle, Sir Anthony 英国演员 14—81b
魁奈 Quesnay, François 法国经济学家 14—87d
魁扎尔科亚特尔 Quetzalcóatl 古墨西哥神祇 14—88d
蝰蛇 viper 爬行动物 18—5a
蝰鱼 viperfish 鱼类 18—5b
傀儡戏 puppetry 木偶戏 14—30a
溃疡 ulcer 病理现象 17—329a
溃疡病 canker 植物病害 3—402b
坤甸 Pontianak 印度尼西亚城市 13—428e
昆巴 Kumba 喀麦隆城镇 9—395b
昆比 Kumbi 西非古城 9—395d
昆比 Quimby, Harriet 美国飞行员 14—91f
昆比 Quimby, Phineas Parkhurst 美国精神疗法专家 14—92a
昆比恩 Queanbeyan 澳大利亚城市 14—81d
昆比萨利赫 Koumbi Saleh (western African site) 马里古城 9—367a
昆比尤特 Coon Butte (meteor crater, Arizona) 美国亚利桑那州陨石坑 4—482e
昆布兰 Cwmbrân 威尔士城镇 5—83a
昆采维奇 Kuncewicz(owa), Maria 波兰小说家 9—396c
昆虫 insect 昆虫学 8—396d
昆虫学 entomology 动物学 6—89b
昆德拉 Kundera, Milan 捷克小说家 9—396e
昆迪纳马卡 Cundinamarca 哥伦比亚省份 5—61b
昆蒂湾 Quinte, Bay of 加拿大安大略湖湖湾 14—94c
昆顿 Quinton, Amelia Stone 美国印第安人改革组织者 14—94f
昆古尔 Kungur 俄罗斯城市 9—397c
昆卡 Cuenca 厄瓜多尔城市 5—51f
昆卡 Cuenca 西班牙省份 5—51f
昆卡 Cuenca 西班牙城市 5—52a
昆卡地毯 Cuenca carpet 工艺品 5—52a
昆栏树目 Trochodendrales 植物 17—229d
昆仑山 Kunlun Shan 中国山脉 9—397e
昆明 Kunming 中国城市 9—398a
昆明池 K'un-ming Ch'ih (China) 中国湖泊 9—396c
昆明夷 Kunming Yi 中国古代民族 9—398c
昆内尔 Quennell, Sir Peter (Courtney) 英国翻译家 14—86c
昆曲 kunqu 中国剧种 9—398d
昆山 Con Son 越南城镇 4—408b
昆山 Kunshan 中国城市 9—398e
昆士兰 Queensland 澳大利亚州名 14—84e
昆斯 Queens 美国纽约市行政区 14—84b
昆斯伯里侯爵规则 Marquess of Queensberry rules 拳击规则 10—529d
昆斯敦 Queenstown 澳大利亚城镇 14—85c
昆斯敦 Queenstown 南非城镇 14—85c
昆斯顿高地战役 Queenston Heights, Battle of 美国-加拿大战役 14—85b
昆斯顿三角洲 Queenston Delta 地质学 14—85b
昆嵩 Kon Tum 越南城市 9—344b
昆陶尔 Kuntaur 冈比亚城镇 9—399b
昆特里尔 Quantrill, William C. 美国历史人物 14—74d
昆特罗 Quintero, José (Benjamin) 美国导演 14—94c
昆提卢斯 Quintillus, Marcus Aurelius Claudius 罗马皇帝 14—94e
昆体良 Quintilian 古罗马修辞学家 14—94d
昆图斯(士麦那的) Quintus, SMYRNAEUS 希腊诗人 14—95a
昆西 Quincy 美国马萨诸塞州城市 14—92f
昆西 Quincy 美国伊利诺伊州城市 14—92f
昆西计划 Quincy Plan 儿童教育方法 14—93a
髡残 Kuncan 中国画家 9—396c
醌 quinone 有机化合物 14—94a
捆扎 seizing 捆绑方法 15—194c
扩散 diffusion 物理学 5—312b
扩散室 diffusion chamber 辐射探测装置 5—312b

扩展的 ASCII 码 ASCII 美国信息交换标准码 1—541e
括约肌 sphincter muscle 解剖学 16—24f
阔鼻猴 platyrrhine 哺乳动物 13—364e
阔边帽 sombrero 帽 15—504e
阔边女帽 poke bonnet 服饰 13—393b
阔齿龙属 Diadectes 古生物学 5—283c
阔德城 Quad Cities 美国工业联合体 14—71e
阔嘴鸟 broadbill 鸟类 3—171c
廓尔喀 Gurkha 尼泊尔城镇 7—378e
廓尔喀刀蛇 kukri snake 爬行动物 9—392a

L

垃圾处理系统 refuse disposal system 环境保护 14—201c
垃圾填埋 sanitary landfill 环境保护 15—34e
垃圾箱画派 Ashcan School 美国现实主义画家 1—546a
拉阿尔 La Halle, Adam de (poet) 法国诗人 9—423a
拉阿尔普 La Harpe, Frédéric-César de 瑞士政治家 9—423a
拉阿尔普 La Harpe, Jean-François de 法国文学批评家 9—423a
拉埃内克 Laënnec, René-Théophile-Hyacinthe 法国医生 9—444b
拉昂 Laon 法国城镇 9—492e
拉奥 Rau, Sir Benegal Narsing 印度法学家 14—165a
拉奥 Rao, P. V. Narasimha 印度总理 14—153a
拉奥 Rao, Raja 印度作家 14—153c
拉奥孔 Laocoön 希腊传说人物 9—492b
拉奥罗塔瓦 La Orotava 西班牙城镇 9—424b
拉奥罗亚 La Oroya 秘鲁城市 9—424c
拉·巴-奥默节 Lag ba-ʿOmer 犹太教节日 9—446c
拉巴比 Lahbabi, Mohammed Aziz 摩洛哥作家 9—449f
拉巴布琴 rabāb 乐器 14—100e
拉巴德一世 Rabad I 犹太历史学家 14—100e
拉巴迪 Labadie, Jean de 法兰西神学家 9—429c
拉巴尔纳斯二世 Labarnas II 赫梯国王 9—430a
拉巴尔纳斯一世 Labarnas I 赫梯国王 9—430a
拉巴斯 La Paz 玻利维亚首都 9—424c
拉巴斯 La Paz 洪都拉斯城镇 9—424e
拉巴斯 La Paz 墨西哥城市 9—424e
拉巴特 Rabat 马耳他城镇 14—100f
拉巴特 Rabat 摩洛哥首都 14—101a
拉巴托领 rabato 服饰 14—101b
拉班 Laban, Rudolf 舞蹈理论家 9—429d
拉班·巴梭马 Rabban bar Sauma (ecclesiastic) 景教东方助祭长 14—101c
拉班努 Rabanus Maurus 基督教神学家 14—100f
拉班舞谱 Labanotation 舞蹈记录法 9—429f
拉斑玄武岩 tholeiite 矿物 17—42a
拉包尔 Rabaul 巴布亚新几内亚城镇 14—101c
拉贝 Labé 几内亚城镇 9—430a
拉贝 Labé, Louise 法国诗人 9—430b
拉贝 Raabe, Wilhelm 德国作家 14—100c
拉贝阿利维洛 Rabéarivelo, Jean-Joseph 马达加斯加作家 14—102c
拉贝奥 Labeo, Marcus Antistius 古罗马法学家 9—430c
拉贝河畔王宫镇 Dvůr Králové nad Labem 捷克城市 5—484f
拉贝河畔乌斯季 Ústí nad Labem 捷克城市 17—424f
拉贝加 La Vega 多米尼加共和国城市 9—429a
拉贝里乌斯 Laberius, Decimus 罗马剧作家 9—430d
拉贝马南雅拉 Rabemananjara, Jacques 马达加斯加政治家、剧作家 14—102f
拉本塔 La Venta 墨西哥古代居民区 9—429a
拉比 rabbi 犹太人宗教导师 14—101c
拉比 Rabi, Isidor Isaac 犹太人宗教导师 14—102f
拉比大会 Rabbinical Assembly, The 犹太教派别组织 14—101e
拉比旦 Rabutin, Roger de 法国浪子 14—103f
拉比赫·祖拜尔 Rābiḥ az-Zubayr 穆斯林军事首脑 14—103c
拉比什 Labiche, Eugène-Marin 法国剧作家 9—430e
拉比特 Rabbit, William 老挝首相 14—102b
拉比犹太教 Rabbinic Judaism 犹太教 14—101e
拉彼达卡瓦达斯 La Piedad Cavadas 墨西哥城市 9—425a
拉彼鲁兹 La Pérouse, Jean-François de Galaup, Count (comte) de 法国航海家 9—424e
拉彼鲁兹海峡 La Perouse Strait 亚洲水道 9—425a
拉宾 Rabin, Yitzhak 以色列总理 14—103c
拉宾斯克 Labinsk 俄罗斯城市 9—430f
拉波波特 Rappoport, Solomon Zanvel (Jewish writer) 犹太作家 14—155c
拉波布琴 rabob (musical instrument) 乐器 14—103e
拉伯克 Lubbock 美国城市 10—263e
拉伯雷 Rabelais, François 法国作家、牧师 14—102d
拉博 Rabaut, Paul 基督教牧师、宗教改革家 14—101c
拉博勒-埃斯库布拉克 La Baule-Escoublac 法国名胜区 9—419a
拉博里 Labori, Fernand-Gustave-Gaston 法国律师 9—431b
拉卜楞 Blabrang 中国甘肃城镇 2—508f
拉布 Raab (Hungary) 匈牙利城市 14—100c
拉布 Rab 克罗地亚岛屿 14—100d
拉布安 Labuan 马来西亚岛屿 9—434b
拉布尔多内 La Bourdonnais, Bertrand-François Mahé, Count (comte) de 法国军人 9—419a
拉布拉 Rabbula 埃德萨基督教主教 14—102c
拉布拉多 Labrador 加拿大地名 9—433d
拉布拉多茶 Labrador tea (species *Ledum groenlandicum*) 木本植物 9—433f
拉布拉多城 Labrador City 加拿大城市 9—433d
拉布拉多海 Labrador Sea 大西洋水域 9—433e
拉布拉多洋流 Labrador Current 大西洋洋流 9—433d
拉布拉凯 Lablache, Luigi 意大利歌唱家 9—430f
拉布雷亚沥青坑 La Brea Tar Pits 美国化石坑 9—419b
拉布楞寺 Labuleng Monastery 中国佛寺 9—419c
拉布廖拉 Labriola, Antonio 意大利哲学家 9—434a
拉布鲁斯特 Labrouste, Henri 法国建筑师 9—434b
拉布吕尼 Labrunie, Gérard 法国诗人 9—434b
拉布吕耶尔 La Bruyère, Jean de 法国讽刺道德学家 9—419b
拉布歇雷 Labouchere, Henry Du Pré 英国政治家 9—431c
拉采尔 Ratzel, Friedrich 德国地理学家 14—164d
拉岑霍费尔 Ratzenhofer, Gustav 奥地利军人、进化论者 14—164e
拉长石 labradorite 矿物 9—433f
拉冲 Lachung 印度村庄 9—437a
拉床 broaching machine 机床 3—171b
拉达尔 Raddall, Thomas Head 英国小说家 14—109c
拉达克 Ladākh 印度地区 9—440e
拉达克 Radak (Hebrew grammarian) 希伯来语学者 14—108a
拉达克里希南 Radhakrishnan, Sarvepalli 印度学者、总统 14—110b
拉达克山 Ladākh Range 亚洲山系 9—440f
拉代西拉德 Désirade, La 加勒比海岛屿 5—261c
拉德 Ladd, Alan (Walbridge) 美国电影演员 9—440f
拉德 Rudd, Steele 澳大利亚小说家、剧作家 14—439d
拉德布鲁赫 Radbruch, Gustav 德国法学家 14—108f
拉德茨基 Radetzky, Joseph, Count (Graf) 奥地利军事改革家 14—109f
拉德贡达 Radegunda, Saint 法国墨洛温王后 14—109d
拉德克利夫 Radcliffe, Ann 英国小说家 14—109a
拉德克利夫 Radcliffe, Thomas 英格兰外交家 14—109b
拉德克利夫 Ratclyffe, Thomas 英格兰外交家 14—161d
拉德克利夫-布朗 Radcliffe-Brown, A(lfred) R(eginald) 英国社会人类学家 14—109b
拉德洛 Ludlow 英格兰城镇 10—272e
拉德洛 Ludlow 美国城镇 10—272f

拉德洛夫 Radlov, Vasily (Vasilyevich) 德国学者、俄国政府顾问 14—119b
拉德洛统 Ludlow Series 地质学 10—273a
拉德纳 Lardner, Ring 美国作家 9—499a
拉德诺夏尔 Radnorshire 威尔士区名 14—119c
拉德温斯 Radewyns, Florentius 天主教神学家 14—110a
拉狄克 Radek, Karl (Bernhardovich) 共产国际早期领导人 14—109d
拉迪波 Ladipo, Duro 尼日利亚戏剧家 9—442b
拉迪盖 Radiguet, Raymond 法国小说家、诗人 14—113a
拉迪克地毯 Lâdik carpet 工艺品 9—441e
拉迪诺人 Ladino 中美洲民族 9—442a
拉迪诺语 Ladino language 犹太西班牙语 9—442a
拉迪奇 Radić, Stjepan 克罗地亚农民领袖 14—111b
拉迪斯拉斯 Ladislas 统治者之名 9—442b
拉迪斯拉斯 Ladislas 那不勒斯国王 9—442d
拉迪斯拉斯四世 Ladislas IV 匈牙利国王 9—442c
拉迪斯拉斯五世 Ladislas V 匈牙利、波希米亚国王 9—442d
拉迪斯拉斯一世 Ladislas I 匈牙利国王 9—442b
拉迪松 Radisson, Pierre Esprit 法国探险家、毛皮商 14—118d
拉蒂博尔 Ratibor (Poland) 波兰城镇 14—162c
拉蒂格 Lartigue, Jacques-Henri (-Charles-Auguste) 法国画家、摄影家 9—502b
拉蒂根 Rattigan, Sir Terence (Mervyn) 英国剧作家 14—163f
拉蒂克 La Tuque 加拿大城镇 9—428f
拉蒂默 Latimer, Hugh 英国基督教改革家 9—511c
拉蒂默子爵 Latimer (of Danby), Thomas Osborne, Viscount 英国政治家 9 511d
拉蒂纳 Latina 意大利城市 9—514d
拉蒂尼 Latini, Brunetto 意大利学者 9—514e
拉蒂斯邦 Ratisbon (Germany) 德国城市 14—163a
拉蒂乌姆 Latium (Italy) 意大利区名 9—515c
拉丁阿威罗伊主义 Latin Averroism 基督教学说 9—513a
拉丁顿 Ludington 美国城市 10—272e
拉丁-法利希诸语言 Latin-Faliscan languages 语言 9—513a
拉丁阶 Ladinian Stage 地质学 9—441f
拉丁节 Feriae Latinae 古罗马宗教节日 6—284f
拉丁美洲 Latin America 罗曼语美洲诸国 9—511f
拉丁美洲基督教工团主义者联合会 Confederación Latinoamericana de Sindicalistas Cristianos (Clasc) 拉丁美洲工人组织 4—419d
拉丁美洲文学 Latin-American literature 美洲文学 9—512d
拉丁美洲一体化协会 Latin-American Integration Association 国际经济组织 9—512c
拉丁姆 Latium 意大利古地区 9—515b
拉丁努斯 Latinus 罗马传说人物 9—514e
拉丁人 Latin 拉丁姆地区古民族 9—511d
拉丁人的权利 jus Latii 罗马公民权利 9—117c
拉丁同盟 Latin League 罗马史 9—513c
《拉丁文词典》 Thesaurus Linguae Latinae 辞书 17—35f
拉丁文学 Latin literature 文学 9—513c
拉丁语 Latin language 语言 9—513a
拉丁字母 Latin alphabet 文字 9—511e
拉顿 Raton 美国城市 14—163d
拉多飞地 Lado Enclave 中部非洲地区 9—442e
拉多加湖 Ladoga, Lake 欧洲湖泊 9—442f
拉多姆 Radom 原波兰省份 14—119c
拉多姆 Radom 波兰城市 14—119c
拉多维茨 Radowitz, Joseph Maria von 普鲁士外交家 14—119e
拉俄墨东 Laomedon 希腊神话人物 9—492d
拉恩 Larne 北爱尔兰城镇 9—501a
拉恩河 Larne River 北爱尔兰河流 9—501b
拉尔巴格 Ralbag 犹太学者 14—132f
拉尔博 Larbaud, Valery-Nicolas 法国作家 9—498d
拉尔夫(科吉舍尔的) Ralph of Coggeshall 英格兰编年史家 14—133f
拉尔戈·卡瓦列罗 Largo Caballero, Francisco 西班牙总理 9—499e
拉尔卡科尔人 Larka Kol (people) 印度民族 9—500d
拉尔卡纳 Lārkāna 巴基斯坦城镇 9—500d
拉尔平原 Rahr Plains 印度恒河下游平原 14—124a
拉尔萨 Larsa 伊拉克古城 9—501f
拉尔什山口 Larche, Col de (French) 法国山隘 9—499a
拉尔泰 Lartet, Édouard Armand Isidore Hippolyte 法国地质学家、考古学家 9—502a
拉尔修 Laërtius, Diogenes 希腊历史学家 9—444b
拉伐尔 Laval, François de Montmorency 加拿大天主教主教 9—525b
拉伐尔大学 Laval University 加拿大大学 9—525d
拉法吉 La Farge, John 美国画家 9—420a
拉法吉 La Farge, Oliver (Hazard Perry) 美国人类学家 9—420c
拉法里纳 La Farina, Giuseppe 意大利革命家、作家 9—420c
拉法耶蒂顾问城 Conselheiro Lafaiete 巴西城市 4—444d
拉法耶特 La Fayette, Gilbert Motier de 法国元帅 9—420d
拉法耶特(夫人) La Fayette, Marie-Madeleine (Pioche de la Vergne), comtesse de 法国作家 9—420e
拉法耶特侯爵 Lafayette, Marie-Joseph-Paul-Yves-Roch-Gilbert du Motier, marquis de 法国贵族 9—444e
拉芳登 La Fontaine 法国芭蕾舞演员 9—421d
拉菲 Raffi 亚美尼亚小说家 14—121b
拉菲达派 Rāfiḍah 伊斯兰教派别 14—121f
拉菲内斯克 Rafinesque, Constantine Samuel 博物学家 14—122a
拉菲特 Laffite, Jean 美洲海盗 9—445a
拉菲特 Laffitte, Jacques 法国银行家、政治家 9—445c
拉菲特 Laffitte, Pierre 法国哲学家 9—445c
拉菲亚 Lafia 尼日利亚城镇 9—445d
拉菲亚吉 Lafiagi 尼日利亚城镇 9—445e
拉斐尔 Raphael 《圣经》、《古兰经》天使长 14—154b
拉斐尔 Raphael 意大利画家、建筑大师 14—154d
拉斐特 Lafayette 美国路易斯安那州城市 9—444d
拉斐特 Lafayette 美国印第安纳州城市 9—444d
拉芬 Ruffin, Edmund 美国土壤化学之父 14—443b
拉芬 Ruffin, Josephine St. Pierre 美国社区领袖 14—443c
拉芬斯堡 Ravensburg 德国城市 14—167e
拉丰泰因 Lafontaine, Henri-Marie 比利时国际法学家 9—445e
拉封丹 La Fontaine, Jean de 法国寓言诗人 9—421d
拉封丹 LaFontaine, Sir Louis Hippolyte, Baronet 加拿大政治家 9—445f
拉冯 Lavon, Pinhas 以色列政治人物 9—527f
拉夫 Raaff, Anton 德国歌唱家 14—100c
拉夫 Raff, Joachim 德国作曲家 14—121b
拉夫 Rahv, Philip 美国评论家 14—124a
拉夫伯勒 Loughborough 英格兰地名 10—233a
拉夫金 Lufkin 美国城市 10—274a
拉夫兰 Loveland 美国城市 10—250f
拉夫里翁 Lávrion (Greece) 希腊城镇 9—528a
拉夫罗夫 Lavrov, Pyotr (Lavrovich) 俄国哲学家 9—528a
拉夫桑贾尼 Rafsanjani, Hashemi 伊朗总统 14—122a
拉夫运河 Love Canal 美国环境问题 10—249c
拉弗 Laver, Rod(ney George) 澳大利亚网球运动员 9—526b
拉弗尔和霍兰男爵(第一) Lovel and Holland, John Perceval, 1st Baron 英国政治家 10—250d
拉弗格 Laforgue, Jules 法国诗人 9—446b
拉弗莱什 La Flesche, Francis 美国人种学家 9—420e
拉弗莱什 La Flesche, Susette 美国作家 9—420f
拉弗雷内 La Fresnaye, Roger de 法国画家 9—422a
拉福格 Lafforgue, Laurent 法国数学家 9—445d
拉福莱特 La Follette, Robert M(arion) 美国政治家 9—421a

拉福雷 Laforet (Díaz), Carmen 西班牙小说家 9—446a
拉福斯 La Fosse, Charles de 法国画家 9—421f
拉戈斯 Lagos, Ricardo 智利总统 9—448f
拉格比 Rugby 英格兰城镇、自治市 14—444e
拉格尔克维斯特 Lagerkvist, Pär (Fabian) 瑞典作家 9—446e
拉格尔斯 Ruggles, Carl 美国作曲家 14—445b
拉格尔斯-布赖斯 Ruggles-Brise, Sir Evelyn (John) 英国监狱改革者 14—445c
拉格兰奇 La Grange 美国城市 9—422c
拉格朗日 Lagrange, Joseph-Louis, Count (comte) del'Empire 法国数学家 9—448f
拉格朗日 Lagrange, Marie-Joseph 法国神学家 9—449b
拉格朗日点 Lagrangian point 天文学 9—449c
拉格朗日函数 Lagrangian function 物理学 9—449b
拉格伦男爵(第一) Somerset, 1st Baron 英国陆军元帅 14—122e
拉格洛夫 Lagerlöf, Selma (Ottiliana Lovisa) 瑞典小说家 9—446f
拉格什 Lagash 古苏美尔都城 9—446c
拉各斯 Lagos 尼日利亚州名 9—448b
拉各斯 Lagos 尼日利亚港口、城市 9—448c
拉古莱特 La Goulette (Tunisia) 突尼斯城镇 9—422c
拉古玛 La Guma, Alex 南非作家 9—422e
拉古纳比奇 Laguna Beach 美国城市 9—449c
拉古纳区 Laguna District 墨西哥地区 9—449d
拉古南动物园 Ragunan Zoological Gardens 印度尼西亚动植物园 14—123b
拉古萨 Ragusa 意大利城市 14—123b
拉古萨 Ragusa (Croatia) 克罗地亚城市、港口 14—123c
拉瓜迪亚 La Guardia, Fiorello H(enry) 美国政治家 9—422d
拉瓜伊拉 La Guaira 委内瑞拉城市 9—422c
拉哈布拉 La Habra 美国城市 9—422f
拉哈河 Laja River 墨西哥河流 9—452b
“拉”号探险船 Ra 纸莎草探险小船 14—100b
拉合尔 Lahore 巴基斯坦城市 9—450b
拉合尔博物馆 Lahore Museum 巴基斯坦博物馆 9—450c
拉赫蒂 Lahti 芬兰城市 9—450d
拉赫季 Laḥij 也门城镇 9—449f
拉赫玛尼诺夫 Rachmaninoff, Sergey (Vasilyevich) 作曲家 14—105e
拉赫曼 Lachmann, Karl (Konrad Friedrich Wilhelm) 德国校勘学家 9—436f
拉赫曼 Rahman, Mujibur 孟加拉国总统 14—123e
拉赫曼 Ismail bin Dato ʻAbdul Rahman, Tun 马来亚政治家 8—470a
拉赫曼 Rahman, Tunku Abdul (prime minister of Malaysia) 马来西亚总理 14—123f
拉赫曼 Rahman, Tuanku Abdul (Malayan ruler) 马来亚统治者 14—123f
拉赫曼(东古) Abdul Rahman Putra Alhaj, Tunku (Prince) 马来西亚总理 1—15d
拉赫曼(端古) Abdul Rahman, Tuanku (King) 马来西亚国王 1—15d
拉赫穆和拉哈穆 Lahmu and Lahamu 美索不达米亚的神祇 9—450a
拉赫斯 Lachs, Manfred 波兰作家、外交家 9—437a
拉亨达语 Lahnda language 巴基斯坦语言 9—450b
拉洪 Lāhūn, al- 埃及古村落遗址 9—451a
拉洪塔 La Junta 美国城市 9—423c
拉祜语 Lahu language 中国民族语言 9—450e
拉祜族 Lahu 中国民族 9—450e
拉基火山 Laki 冰岛火山 9—456f
拉季舍夫 Radishchev, Aleksandr Nikolayevich 俄国作家 14—118c
拉济维乌家族 Radziwiłł family 波兰-立陶宛王公家族 14—119f
拉加 Raga (island, Vanuatu) 瓦鲁阿图火山岛 14—122d
拉加 raga 音乐 14—122d
拉加利索尼埃侯爵 La Galissonière, Roland-Michel Barrin, marquis de 新法兰西总督 9—422b
拉贾·阿里·哈吉·宾·拉贾·阿赫玛德 Raja Ali Haji bin Raja Amhad 布吉-马来亲王 14—129d
拉贾戈巴拉查理 Rajagopalachari, Chakravarti 印度政治家、总督 14—129d
拉贾蒙德里 Rājahmundry 印度城市 14—129d
拉贾斯坦 Rājasthān 印度邦名 14—129f
拉贾斯坦草原 Rājasthān Steppe 印度荒原 14—130b
拉贾斯坦绘画 Rājasthānī painting 印度细密画 14—130c
拉贾斯坦木偶 Rājasthānī puppet 印度木偶 14—130e
拉贾斯坦诸语言 Rājasthānī languages 印度-雅利安语、方言 14—130c
拉贾伊 Raja'i, Mohammad Ali 伊朗政治人物 14—129e
拉焦里 Rājauri 印度县名 14—130f
拉杰巴莱耶姆 Rājapālaiyam 印度城市 14—129f
拉杰布达纳 Rājputāna 印度古邦 14—131c
拉杰德夫 Redjedef 埃及国王 14—193c
拉杰格尔 Rājgarh 印度城镇 14—131a
拉杰果德 Rājkot 印度城镇 14—131a
拉杰吉尔丘陵 Rājgīr Hills 印度自然地理区 14—131a
拉杰默哈尔 Rājmahāl 印度古城镇 14—131b
拉杰南德冈 Rāj-Nāndgaon 印度城市 14—129c
拉杰普特绘画 Rājput painting 印度艺术 14—131c
拉杰普特人 Rājput 印度父系氏族 14—131b
拉杰沙希 Rājshāhi 孟加拉国城市 14—131d
拉金 Larkin, Philip (Arthur) 英国诗人 9—500d
拉卡 Raqqah, Ar- 叙利亚城镇 14—155d
拉卡比陶器 lakabi ware 伊斯兰工艺品 9—452c
拉卡尔普雷奈德 La Calprenède, Gaultier de Coste, Seigneur de 法国作家 9—419d
拉卡纳尔 Lakanal, Joseph 法国教育家 9—452d
拉卡陶器 Raqqah ware 穆斯林陶器 14—155e
拉卡伊 Lacaille, Nicolas Louis de 法国天文学家 9—435b
拉凯阿河 Rakaia River 新西兰河流 14—131e
拉凯斯 Laches 雅典贵族 9—436e
拉凯塔 Lacaita, Sir James 意大利政治家 9—435b
拉凯特管 rackett 乐器 14—108a
拉坎敦人 Lacandón 马雅印第安人 9—435c
拉康 Racan, Honorat de Bueil, seigneur de 法国诗人 14—103f
拉康 Lacan, Jacques (Marie Émile) 法国精神分析家 9—435c
拉康潘 Campine, la (region, Belgium) 比利时地区 3—382e
拉科代尔 Lacordaire, Henri 法国天主教教士 9—437d
拉科夫斯基 Rakovski, Georgi Sava 保加利亚作家 14—132c
拉科夫斯基 Rakovsky, Khristian Georgiyevich 保加利亚革命家 14—132d
拉科鲁尼亚 Coruña, La 西班牙省份 4—526f
拉科鲁尼亚 Coruña, La 西班牙城市 4—526f
拉科尼亚 Laconia 希腊历史地区 9—437c
拉科尼亚湾 Laconia, Gulf of 希腊海湾 9—437d
拉科齐二世 Rákóczi, Ferenc, II 特兰西瓦尼亚公爵 14—131f
拉科齐二世 Rákóczi, György, II 特兰西瓦尼亚公爵 14—132a
拉科齐一世 Rákóczi, Ferenc, I 匈牙利贵族 14—131e
拉科齐一世 Rákóczi, György, I 特兰西瓦尼亚公爵 14—132a
拉科斯特 Lacoste, Rene 法国网球运动员 9—437e
拉科西 Rákosi Mátyás 匈牙利共产党统治者 14—132b
拉克 Lacq 法国村庄 9—437e
拉克 Lack, David Lambert 英国鸟类学家 9—437b
拉克-达尔格瓦诸语言 Lakk-Dargwa languages 高加索语言 9—456f
拉克代夫、米尼科伊和阿明迪维群岛 Laccadive, Minicoy, and Amīndīvi Islands (India) 印度岛群 9—435e
拉克雷泰尔 Lacretelle, Jacques de 法国小说家 9—438e

拉克雷泰尔(小) Lacretelle, Jean-Charles-Dominique de, THE YOUNGER 法国历史学家 9—438f
拉克鲁斯港 Puerto La Cruz 委内瑞拉城市 14—15f
拉克鲁瓦 Lacroix, (François-Antoine-) Alfred 法国矿物学家 9—438f
拉克伦河 Lachlan River 澳大利亚河流 9—436f
拉克罗斯 La Crosse 美国城市 9—420a
拉克洛 Laclos, Pierre(-Ambroise-François) Choderlos de 法国军人、作家 9—437c
拉克沙群岛 Lakshadweep 印度中央直辖区 9—456f
拉克斯代拉萨迦 Laxdaela saga 冰岛文学 9—534a
拉克斯内斯 Laxness, Halldór 冰岛小说家 9—534a
拉克塔留斯山战役 Mons Lactarius, Battle of 意大利历史 11—350e
拉克坦提乌斯 Lactantius 基督教护教士 9—439f
拉克万纳 Lackawanna 美国城市 9—437b
拉孔达明 La Condamine, Charles-Marie de 法国博物学家 9—420a
拉奎拉 L'Aquila 意大利城市 9—497e
拉拉歌 counting-out rhyme 儿童歌谣 4—544a
拉拉米造山运动 Laramide orogeny 地质学 9—498b
拉拉穆里人 Rarámuri (people) 墨西哥印第安人 14—155f
拉拉人 Lala 尼日利亚民族 9—457b
拉腊 Lara 委内瑞拉州名 9—497f
拉腊 Lara, Brian 西印度群岛板球运动员 9—497f
拉腊 Larra (y Sánchez de Castro), Mariano José de 西班牙作家 9—501d
拉腊什 Larache 摩洛哥港市 9—498a
拉廊 Ranong 泰国城镇 14—152a
拉朗德 Lalande, Jérôme 法国天文学家 9—457b
拉勒米 Laramie 美国城市 9—498c
拉勒米河 Laramie River 美国河流 9—498c
拉勒米山 Laramie Mountains 美国山脉 9—498c
拉雷 Larrey, Dominique-Jean, Baron 法国军医 9—501e
拉雷多 Laredo 美国城市 9—499b
拉雷斯坦 Laristan 伊朗地区 9—500b
拉雷塔 Larreta, Enrique Rodríguez 阿根廷小说家 9—501e
拉雷韦耶尔-勒波 La Révellière-Lépeaux, Louis-Marie de 法国政治人物 9—425c
拉里奥哈 La Rioja 阿根廷省份 9—425c
拉里奥哈 La Rioja 阿根廷城市 9—425d
拉里奥哈 La Rioja 西班牙自治区 9—425d
拉里奥湖 Lario (lake, Italy) 意大利湖泊 9—499f
拉里奥诺夫 Larionov, Mikhail Fyodorovich 法国画家 9—499f
拉里夫 La Rive, Auguste-Arthur de 瑞士物理学家 9—425e
拉里萨 Larissa 希腊城镇 9—500a
拉里坦河 Raritan River 美国河流 14—156a
拉里维 Larivey, Pierre de 法国剧作家 9—500b
拉里乌斯湖 Larius, Lacus (Italy) 意大利湖泊 9—500b
拉利贝拉 Lalībela 埃塞俄比亚宗教中心 9—457c
拉利伯爵 Lally, Thomas-Arthur, comte de (count of) 法国军人 9—458a
拉利伯塔德 La Libertad 秘鲁省份 9—423c
拉利伯塔德 La Libertad 萨尔瓦多城市 9—423d
拉利克 Lalique, René 法国珠宝商 9—457d
拉利内阿 La Línea 西班牙城镇 9—423d
拉链 zipper 滑动紧固件 18—558b
拉龙日湖 Ronge, Lac la 加拿大湖泊 14—388f
拉卢维耶尔 La Louvière 比利时城镇 9—423d
拉鲁斯 Larousse, Pierre(-Athanase) 法国辞书编著家 9—501c
《拉鲁斯百科大词典》 Grand Dictionnaire encyclopédique Larousse 法国百科全书 7—249d
拉鲁斯出版社 Larousse 法国出版社 9—501b
拉吕 La Rue, Pierre de 佛兰德斯作曲家 9—426f
拉罗 Lalo, Édouard(-Victor-Antoine) 法国作曲家 9—458a
拉罗克 La Rocque, Jean-François de 法国探险家 9—426e
拉罗马纳 La Romana 多米尼加共和国城市 9—426e
拉罗米吉耶尔 Laromiguière, Pierre 法国哲学家 9—501b
拉罗什(夫人) La Roche, Sophie von 德国作家 9—425f
拉罗什富科(公爵) La Rochefoucauld, François VI, Duke (duc) de 法国作家 9—426b
拉罗什富科家族 La Rochefoucauld FAMILY 法国贵族 9—426a
拉罗什富科-利昂库尔(公爵) La Rochefoucauld-Liancourt, François-Alexandre-Frédéric, Duke (duc) de 法国教育家 9—426c
拉罗汤加岛 Rarotonga 南太平洋岛屿 14—156b
拉罗谢尔 La Rochelle 法国港市 9—426c
拉洛夫 Ralov, Kirsten 丹麦舞蹈家 14—133e
拉马迪 Ramādī, ar- 伊拉克城市 14—135a
拉马迪埃 Ramadier, Paul 法国总理 14—135b
拉马丁 Lamartine, Alphonse de 法国诗人、政治家 9—460a
拉马尔 Lamar 美国城市 9—458d
拉马尔 Lamar, Joseph R(ucker) 美国最高法院大法官 9—458f
拉马尔 Lamar, Lucius Q (uintus) C(incinnatus) 美国法理学家、最高法院大法官 9—459a
拉马尔 Lamar, Mirabeau Buonaparte 得克萨斯共和国总统 9—459a
拉马尔莫拉 La Marmora, Alfonso Ferrero 意大利军人、政治家 9—423e
拉马克 Lamarck, Jean-Baptiste(-Pierre-Antoine) de Monet, chevalier de (knight of) 法国生物学家 9—459b
拉马克斯 Raemaekers, Louis 荷兰漫画家 14—120f
拉马略·奥尔蒂冈 Ramalho Ortigão, José Duarte 葡萄牙新闻记者 14—135d
拉马齐尼 Ramazzini, Bernardino 意大利医学家 14—137d
拉马桥 Rama's Bridge (India and Sri Lanka) 印度和斯里兰卡间沙洲 14—136f
拉马人 Lama (People) 多哥民族 9—458d
拉马什 La Marche, Olivier de 勃艮第历史学家、诗人 9—423e
拉马什图 Lamashtu 美索不达米亚神祇 9—460c
拉马斯 Lamas, Carlos Saavedra 阿根廷法学家 9—460c
拉马坦萨 La Matanza 阿根廷行政区 9—423f
拉马特甘 Ramat Gan 以色列城市 14—136f
拉马赞王朝 Ramazan DYNASTY 土库曼王朝 14—137d
拉马兹无痛分娩法 Lamaze 产科学 9—460c
拉玛 Rama 暹罗国王谥号 14—134e
拉玛 Lamarr, Hedy 奥地利演员 9—460a
拉玛八世 Rama VIII 暹罗国王 14—135a
拉玛二世 Rama II 暹罗国王 14—134f
拉玛九世 Rama IX 泰国国王 14—135a
拉玛六世 Rama VI 暹罗国王 14—135a
拉玛七世 Rama VII 暹罗国王 14—135a
拉玛三世 Rama III 暹罗国王 14—134f
拉玛四世 Rama IV 暹罗国王 14—135a
拉玛铁菩提一世 Ramathibodi I 大城王国国王 14—137a
拉玛五世 Rama V 暹罗国王 14—135a
拉玛一世 Rama I 暹罗国王 14—134e
拉曼 Raman, Sir Chandrasekhara Venkata 印度物理学家 14—135d
拉曼查 La Mancha 西班牙高原 9—423d
拉曼纽扬 Ramanujan, Srinivasa 印度数学家 14—136c
拉曼效应 Raman effect 光学 14—135e
拉梅 Ramé, Maria Louise 英国作家 14—138e
拉梅内 Lamennais, (Hugues-) Félicité(-Robert de) 法国政治著作家 9—463f
拉梅斯沃勒姆 Rāmeswaram 印度岛屿 14—139c
拉梅特 Lameth, Alexandre(-Theodore-Victor), comte de (count of) 法国贵族 9—464c
拉美特利 La Mettrie, Julien Offroy de 法国医生、哲学家 9—423f
拉美西姆 Ramesseum 埃及国王陵庙 14—139c

拉美西斯 Ramses 埃及国王之名 14—143b
拉美西斯八世 Ramses Ⅷ 埃及国王 14—144c
拉美西斯二世 Ramses Ⅱ 埃及国王 14—143b
拉美西斯九世 Ramses Ⅸ 埃及国王 14—144d
拉美西斯六世 Ramses Ⅵ 埃及国王 14—144b
拉美西斯七世 Ramses Ⅶ 埃及国王 14—144c
拉美西斯三世 Ramses Ⅲ 埃及国王 14—143e
拉美西斯十世 Ramses Ⅹ 埃及国王 14—144d
拉美西斯十一世 Ramses Ⅺ 埃及国王 14—144e
拉美西斯四世 Ramses Ⅳ 埃及国王 14—144a
拉美西斯五世 Ramses Ⅴ 埃及国王 14—144b
拉美西斯一世 Ramses Ⅰ 埃及国王 14—143b
拉蒙·贝伦格尔 Ramon Berenguer 巴塞罗那伯爵之名 14—140f
拉蒙·贝伦格尔二世 Ramon Berenguer Ⅱ 巴塞罗那伯爵 14—141a
拉蒙·贝伦格尔三世 Ramon Berenguer Ⅲ 巴塞罗那伯爵 14—141a
拉蒙·贝伦格尔四世 Ramon Berenguer Ⅳ 巴塞罗那伯爵 14—141b
拉蒙·贝伦格尔一世 Ramon Berenguer Ⅰ 巴塞罗那伯爵 14—140f
拉蒙-卡哈尔 Ramón y Cajal, Santiago 西班牙组织学家 14—141b
拉蒙塔涅-博勒加尔 Lamontagne-Beauregard, Blanche 加拿大诗人 9—466d
拉蒙特 Lamont, Johann von 德国天文学家 9—466b
拉蒙特 Lamont, Thomas William 美国金融家 9—466c
拉弥亚 Lamia 希腊神话女妖 9—464d
拉米罗 Ramiro 统治者之名 14—140a
拉米罗二世 Ramiro Ⅱ 阿拉贡国王 14—140b
拉米罗二世 Ramiro Ⅱ 莱昂和阿斯图里亚斯国王 14—140b
拉米罗一世 Ramiro Ⅰ 阿拉贡国王 14—140b
拉米斯 Ramus, Petrus 法国哲学家、修辞学家 14—145b
拉米亚 Lamía 希腊城市 9—464d
拉米亚战争 Lamian War 希腊历史 9—465e
拉米伊战役 Ramillies, Battle of 西班牙王位继承战争 14—140a
拉米纸牌游戏 rummy 牌戏 14—448a
拉密堡 Fort-Lamy (Chad) 乍得首都旧名 6—413f
拉缅斯科耶 Ramenskoye 俄罗斯城市 14—139c
拉明顿高原 Lamington Plateau 澳大利亚高原 9—466a
拉缪 Ramuz, Charles-Ferdinand 瑞士小说家 14—145c
拉摩 Lha-mo 藏传佛教八大明王之一 10—55c
拉摩里西尔 Lamoricière, Christophe-Louis-Leon Juchault de 法国军人 9—466d
拉莫 Rameau, Jean-Philippe 法国作曲家 14—138e
拉莫 Ramo, Simon 美国工程师 14—140e
拉莫尔 Larmor, Sir Joseph 爱尔兰物理学家 9—500f
拉莫斯 Ramos, Fidel 菲律宾总统 14—141c
拉莫特·勒瓦耶 La Mothe Le Vayer, François de 法国思想家 9—424a
拉默纳特布勒姆 Rāmanāthapuram 印度城镇 14—136a
拉姆 Ram, Jagjivan 印度政治家 14—134a
拉姆安拉 Rām Allāh 巴勒斯坦城镇 14—134b
拉姆波拉 Rampolla, Mariano 意大利天主教神职人员 14—141f
拉姆福德 Rumford 美国城镇 14—447f
拉姆拉 Ramla 以色列城市 14—140d
拉姆·莫恩·罗伊 Ram Mohun Roy (Indian reformer) 印度改革者 14—134c
拉姆莫恩·罗伊 Rammohan Roy (Indian reformer) 印度改革者 14—140e
拉姆尼谷 Rhymney Valley 威尔士拉摩根郡区名 14—272a
拉姆尼沼泽 Romney Marsh 英吉利海峡沿岸平地 14—386f
拉姆珀斯统 Lampasan Series 地质学 9—467f
拉姆齐 Ramsay, Allan 苏格兰诗人 14—142a
拉姆齐 Ramsay, Allan 英国画家 14—142c
拉姆齐 Ramsey, (Arthur) Michael, Baron Ramsey of Canterbury 圣公会坎特伯雷大主教 14—144f
拉姆齐 Ramsay, Bertram Home 英国海军军官 14—142d
拉姆齐 Ramsay, Fox Maule 英国政治家 14—142f
拉姆齐 Ramsay, James Andrew Broun 印度总督 14—142f
拉姆齐 Ramsey, Norman Foster 美国物理学家 14—145a
拉姆齐 Ramsay, Sir William 英国化学家 14—142f
拉姆斯登 Ramsden, Jesse 英国精密工具设计制造家 14—143a
拉姆斯盖特 Ramsgate 英国城镇 14—145a
拉姆西 Ramsey 英格兰堂区、城镇 14—144e
拉姆西 Romsey 英格兰教区、城镇 14—387a
拉穆 Lamu 肯尼亚城镇 9—469a
拉穆河 Ramu River 巴布亚新几内亚河流 14—145b
拉穆斯 Ramos, Graciliano 巴西小说家 14—141d
拉穆特人 Lamut (people) 西伯利亚北部居民 9—469a
拉那德 Ranade, Mahadev Govind 印度历史学家、法官 14—145e
拉纳 Rana 挪威地理区域 14—145d
拉纳 Lannes, Jean, duc (duke) de Montebello 法国元帅 9—487b
拉纳 Rahner, Karl 挪威地理区域 14—123f
拉纳卡 Larnaca 塞浦路斯城市 9—500f
拉纳克 Lanark 苏格兰城镇 9—469e
拉纳克 Ranak 犹太哲学家 14—145f
拉纳克伯爵 Lanark, William Hamilton, Earl of 苏格兰保王派 9—469f
拉纳克郡 Lanarkshire 苏格兰历史郡 9—469f
拉奈 Lanai 美国岛屿 9—469e
拉奈伏 Ranaivo, Flavien 抒情诗人 14—145e
拉瑙湖 Lanao, Lake 菲律宾湖泊 9—469e
拉内拉赫 Ranelagh 英国伦敦切尔西区前旅游胜地 14—149c
拉内利 Llanelli 威尔士城镇 10—168c
拉内利 Llanelli 威尔士自治市 10—168c
拉尼尔 Lanier, Nicholas 英国作曲家 9—486d
拉尼尔 Lanier, Sidney 美国音乐家、诗人 9—486d
拉尼凯 Lanikai (Hawaii, U.S.) 美国社区 9—486f
拉涅罗 Raniero (pope) 教皇 14—150e
拉努 La Noue, François de 法国军人 9—424b
拉诺斯 Llanos 南美洲平原 10—168d
拉帕茨基 Rapacki, Adam 波兰社会主义者、经济学家 14—153d
拉帕尔马 La Palma 西班牙岛屿 9—424c
拉帕汉诺克河 Rappahannock River 美国河流 14—155b
拉帕洛 Rapallo 意大利城市 14—153e
拉帕努伊岛 Rapa Nui 智利岛屿 14—153d
拉帕伊 Lapai 尼日利亚城镇 9—494d
拉潘帕 La Pampa 阿根廷省份 9—424c
拉庞特诗体 rhupunt 威尔士文学 14—271c
拉佩林堡 Fort Laperrine (Algeria) 阿尔及利亚城镇旧名 6—413f
拉彭贝格 Lappenberg, Johann Martin 德国历史学家 9—496b
拉彭兰塔 Lappeenranta 芬兰城市 9—496b
拉皮 Lappi 芬兰省份 9—496c
拉皮德城 Rapid City 美国城市 14—154f
拉皮尔 Rapier, James T. 美国种植园主、劳工组织者 14—155a
拉皮省 Lapin lääni (Finland) 芬兰省份 9—494f
拉皮塔文化 Lapita culture 大洋洲岛屿文化 9—495a
拉普 RAPP 苏联作家组织 14—155b
拉普 Rapp, George 美国禁欲主义者 14—155b
拉普阿运动 Lapua Movement 芬兰法西斯主义运动 9—497b
拉普捷夫海 Laptev Sea 北冰洋边缘海 9—497a
拉普拉普 Lapu-Lapu 菲律宾城市 9—497b
拉普拉斯 Laplace, Pierre-Simon, marquis de 法国数学家 9—495b
拉普拉斯变换 Laplace transform 数学 9—495c
拉普拉斯方程 Laplace's equation 数学 9—495c
拉普拉塔 La Plata 阿根廷城市 9—425a
拉普拉塔河 La Plata River 波多黎各河流 9—425b
拉普拉塔河 Plata, Río de la 南美河口湾 13—351a
拉普拉塔总督辖区 Río de la Plata, Viceroyalty of the 中南美洲历史

区域 14—308f
拉普兰 Lapland 北欧地区 9—495d
拉普兰 Lapland (province, Finland) 芬兰省份 9—495e
拉普兰 Lappland 瑞典历史省份 9—496d
拉普兰自然保护区 Laplandsky Nature Reserve 北欧自然保护区 9—495e
拉普人 Lapp 北欧土著居民 9—495e
拉普沃思 Lapworth, Charles 英国地质学家 9—497d
拉普语 Lapp language 北欧语言 9—496a
拉齐 Rāzī, ar- 伊斯兰哲学家、医师 14—174a
拉齐 Rāzī, ar- (Muslim theologian) 穆斯林神学家 14—174b
拉齐奥 Lazio 意大利区名 9—535f
拉齐布日 Racibórz 波兰城镇 14—106d
拉齐尔 Lazear, Jesse William 美国医生 9—535f
拉奇普特·雷依 Lajpat Rai, Lala 印度作家、政治家 9—452c
拉让河 Rajang River 马来西亚河流 14—129e
拉日利埃 Largillière, Nicolas de 法国画家 9—499d
拉日什 Lajes 葡萄牙城镇 9—452b
拉日斯 Lajes 巴西城市 9—452b
拉若 Largeau (Chad) 乍得城镇 9—499d
拉撒路 Lazarus 《圣经》人物 9—535c
拉撒路 Lazarus, Moritz 犹太哲学家 9—535e
拉萨 Lhasa 中国城市 10—55c
拉萨尔 La Salle 加拿大城市 9—427a
拉萨尔 La Salle 美国城市 9—427a
拉萨尔 La Sale, Antoine de 法国作家 9—426f
拉萨尔 Lassalle, Ferdinand 德国社会主义者 9—506e
拉萨尔 La Salle, René-Robert Cavelier, sieur de 法国探险家 9—427b
拉萨狗 Lhasa apso 狗品种 10—55e
拉萨河 Lhasa He 中国河流 10—55f
拉萨勒 La Salle, Saint Jean-Baptiste de 法国教育家 9—427b
拉萨姆 Rassam, Hormuzd 伊拉克亚述学家 14—159c
拉塞达埃蒙 Lacedaemon (Greece) 希腊古城 9—436b
拉塞尔 Russell 新西兰城镇 14—456f
拉塞尔 Russell, Bill 美国篮球运动员 14—457c
拉塞尔 Russell (of Killowen), Charles Russell, Baron 英格兰法官 14—457d
拉塞尔 Russell, Charles Taze 美国宗教领袖 14—457e
拉塞尔 Russell, Francis 英国贵族 14—457f
拉塞尔 Russell, George William 爱尔兰诗人 14—457f
拉塞尔 Russell, John Scott 英国土木工程师 14—458e
拉塞尔 Russell, Ken 英国电影导演 14—458e
拉塞尔 Russell, Lillian 美国演员 14—458f
拉塞尔 Russell, Morgan 美国画家 14—459a
拉塞尔 Russell, Pee Wee 美国演奏家 14—459b
拉塞尔 Russell, Rosalind 美国演员 14—459c
拉塞尔 Lassell, William 英国天文学家 9—507b
拉塞尔洞窟国家保护区 Russell Cave National Monument 美国亚拉巴马州大山洞 14—459d
拉塞雷纳 La Serena 智利城市 9—427d
拉塞佩德伯爵 Lacépède, (Bernard-Germain-) Étienne de La Ville-sur-Illon, comte de (count of) 法国博物学家 9—436b
拉塞瓦 La Ceiba 洪都拉斯城市 9—419d
拉瑟弗德 Rutherfurd, Lewis Morris 美国天体物理学家 14—470b
拉瑟福德 Rutherford 美国自治镇 14—468c
拉瑟福德 Rutherford, Dame Margaret 英国演员 14—469e
拉瑟福德 Rutherford, Mark 英国作家 14—469f
拉森峰 Lassen Peak 美国山峰 9—507c
拉森陆缘冰架 Larsen Ice Shelf 南极冰架 9—501f
拉绍德封 Chaux-de-Fonds, La 瑞士西部城镇 4—96d
拉伸 drawing 纺织 5—416e
拉施塔特和巴登条约 Rastatt and Baden, treaties of 神圣罗马帝国-法国和约 14—159e
拉什 Rush, Benjamin 美国医师、改革家 14—454b
拉什 Rush, Richard 美国政治家 14—454d
拉什 Rush, William 美国雕刻家 14—454d
拉什巴 Rashba 西班牙拉比 14—157a
《拉什-巴戈特协定》 Rush-Bagot Agreement 美国历史 14—454e
拉什巴兹 Rashbaz 西班牙神学家 14—157a
拉什迪 Rushdie, Salman 英籍印度小说家 14—454e
拉什顿 Rashidun 哈里发 14—157d
拉什克利夫 Rushcliffe 英格兰自治市 14—454e
拉什利 Lashley, Karl S(pencer) 美国心理学家 9—505f
拉什莫尔 Rushmoor 英格兰自治市 14—454f
拉什莫尔山 Rushmore, Mount (South Dakota, U.S.) 美国山脉 14—455a
拉什莫尔山国家纪念碑 Mount Rushmore National Memorial 美国纪念碑 11—441e
拉什努 Rashnu 琐罗亚斯德教神祇 14—157e
拉什特 Rasht 伊朗城市 14—157e
拉什沃思 Rushworth, John 英国历史学家 14—455a
拉思本 Rathbun, Mary Jane 美国海洋动物学家 14—161f
拉思伯恩 Rathbone, Basil 英国演员 14—161f
拉斯阿尔普哈拉斯 Las Alpujarras 西班牙多山地区 9—502e
拉斯巴卡斯 Las Vacas (Mexico) 墨西哥城市 9—503f
拉斯贝拉 Las Bela 巴基斯坦县名 9—502f
拉斯彼德拉斯 Las Piedras 乌拉圭城市 9—503f
拉斯基 Laski, Harold J(oseph) 英国政治学家 9—506d
拉斯卡拉歌剧院 La Scala 意大利歌剧院 9—427c
拉斯卡里斯 Lascaris, Constantine 拜占廷帝国时期语法家 9—504b
拉斯卡里斯 Lascaris, John 希腊学者 9—504c
拉斯·卡萨斯 Las Casas, Bartolomé de 西班牙史学家 9—502f
拉斯卡斯 Las Cases, Emmanuel (-Augustin-Dieudonné-Joseph), comte de 法国历史学家 9—503c
拉斯科布 Raskob, John Jakob 美国金融家 14—158b
拉斯科洞穴 Lascaux Grotto 法国史前艺术遗址 9—504c
拉斯克 Lasker, Albert (Davis) 美国慈善家 9—506a
拉斯克 Lasker, Eduard 普鲁士政治家 9—506b
拉斯克 Lasker, Emanuel 德国象棋大师 9—506b
拉斯克 Rask, Rasmus (Kristian) 丹麦语言学家 14—158a
拉斯克鲁塞斯 Las Cruces 美国城市 9—503c
拉斯克-许勒 Lasker-Schüler, Else 德国作家 9—506c
拉斯朗-马桑科姆 Lasseran-Massencôme, Blaise de 法国军人 9—507c
拉斯利拉 rāslīlā 印度民间舞剧 14—158c
拉斯马里斯马斯沼泽 Las Marismas 西班牙沼地 9—503d
拉斯穆桑代姆 Ra's Muṣandam (Oman) 阿曼半岛 14—156d
拉斯穆森 Rasmussen, Halfdan 丹麦诗人 14—158c
拉斯穆森 Rasmussen, Knud Johan Victor 丹麦人种学家 14—158d
拉斯纳瓦斯的阿方索 Las Navas, El de 卡斯蒂利亚国王 9—503d
拉斯纳瓦斯的阿方索 Navas, El de Las 卡斯蒂利亚国王 12—50f
拉斯帕尔马斯 Las Palmas 西班牙省份 9—503d
拉斯帕尔马斯 Las Palmas 西班牙城市 9—503e
拉斯佩 Raspe, Henry 德国僭主 14—159a
拉斯佩 Raspe, Rudolf Erich 德国学者、冒险家 14—159a
拉斯佩尼亚斯 Las Peñas (Mexico) 墨西哥港口 9—503e
拉斯佩齐亚 La Spezia 意大利城市 9—427d
拉斯佩耶斯指数 Laspeyres index 经济学 9—506e
拉斯普廷 Rasputin, Grigory Yefimovich 沙皇宠臣 14—159a
拉斯塔法里教徒 Rastafarian 政治-宗教运动 14—159d
拉斯泰尔 Rastell, William 英国出版商、律师 14—159f
拉斯坦努拉 Ras Tanura 沙特阿拉伯港口 14—156d
拉斯特曼 Lastman, Pieter 荷兰画家 9—508e

拉斯特山湖 Last Mountain Lake 加拿大湖泊 9—508b
拉斯滕堡暗杀密谋 Rastenburg Assassination Plot 德国历史 14—159f
拉斯廷 Rustin, Bayard 美国黑人民权活动家 14—466f
拉斯图纳斯 Las Tunas 古巴省份 9—503f
拉斯韦尔 Lasswell, Harold D(wight) 美国政治学家 9—507e
拉斯韦加斯 Las Vegas 美国内华达州城市 9—503f
拉斯韦加斯 Las Vegas 美国新墨西哥州城市 9—504b
拉斯乌尔德斯山谷 Las Hurdes 西班牙地区 9—503d
拉斯夏马拉 Ras Shamra 叙利亚文化遗址 14—156d
拉苏弗里耶尔 La Soufriere 瓜德罗普岛火山 9—427d
拉苏勒王朝 Rasūlid DYNASTY 埃及王朝 14—160a
拉苏瓦山 Lassois, Mont 法国古城遗址 9—507e
拉索 Lasso, Orlando di 佛兰德斯作曲家 9—507d
拉塔基亚 Latakia 叙利亚城市 9—509a
拉塔昆加 Latacunga 厄瓜多尔城市 9—509a
拉塔纳会 Ratana church 新西兰毛利人宗教组织 14—161b
拉塔齐 Rattazzi, Urbano 意大利律师 14—163e
拉塔耶 La Taille, Jean de 法国作家 9—427e
拉泰科雷 Latécoère, Pierre 法国飞机制造者 9—509c
拉坦诺 La Tène 瑞士凯尔特人文化遗址 9—427e
拉特 Lāt, al- 阿拉伯女神 9—508f
拉特尔 Lateur, Frank 比利时作家 9—510e
拉特尔·德·塔西尼 Lattre de Tassigny, Jean de 法国军官 9—516c
拉特克 Rathke, Martin H(einrich) 德国解剖学家 14—162b
拉特克 Ratke, Wolfgang 德国教育改革家 14—163b
拉特拉姆努斯 Ratramnus 基督教神学家 14—163d
拉特兰 Rutland 英格兰莱斯特郡区名 14—470f
拉特兰 Rutland 美国佛蒙特州城市 14—471a
拉特兰公爵(第七) Rutland, John James Robert Manners, 7th Duke of 英国政治家 14—471a
拉特兰会议 Lateran Council 天主教会议 9—510c
《拉特兰条约》 Lateran Treaty 天主教史 9—510d
拉特雷穆瓦耶 La Trémoille, Georges de 法国权臣 9—428e
拉特雷穆瓦耶家族 La Trémoille FAMILY 法兰西贵族 9—428c
拉特雷耶 Latreille, Pierre-André 法国动物学家 9—515d
拉特利奇 Rutledge, John 美国议员 14—471b
拉特利奇 Rutledge, Wiley B(lount), Jr. 美国大法官 14—471c
拉特罗布 Latrobe, Benjamin (Henry) 美国建筑师 9—515d
拉特罗布河 La Trobe River 澳大利亚河流 9—428e
拉特罗布河谷 Latrobe Valley 澳大利亚河谷 9—515f
拉特纳普勒 Ratnapura 斯里兰卡城镇 14—163d
拉特瑙 Rathenau, Emil 德国实业家 14—162a
拉特瑙 Rathenau, Walther 德国政治家、工业家 14—162b
拉特尼娜 Latynina, Larisa Semyonovna 苏联体操运动员 9—517e
拉特斯 Lattes, C(ésare) M(ansueto) G(iulio) 巴西物理学家 9—516a
拉提 Ratti, Ambrogio Damiano Achille (pope) 教皇 14—163f
拉铁摩尔 Lattimore, Owen 美国汉学家 9—516a
拉铁摩尔 Lattimore, Richmond 美国诗人、翻译家 9—516b
拉图尔 La Tour, Charles (Turgis de Saint-Étienne de) 法国殖民者 9—428a
拉图尔 La Tour, Georges de 法国画家 9—428a
拉图尔 La Tour, Maurice-Quentin de 法国画家 9—428c
拉推号 sackbut 乐器 14—487d
拉托纳 Latona (Greek mythology) 希腊神话 9—515c
拉脱维亚 Latvia 欧洲国家 9—516d
拉脱维亚文学 Latvian literature 欧洲文学 9—517b
拉脱维亚语 Latvian language 欧洲语言 9—517a
拉瓦尔 Laval, Carl Gustaf Patrik de 瑞典科学家 9—525b
拉瓦尔品第 Rāwalpindi 巴基斯坦城市 14—168a
拉瓦格 Laoag 菲律宾城市 9—492a
拉瓦卡港 Port Lavaca 美国城市 13—446a
拉瓦勒 Laval 加拿大城市 9—525a
拉瓦勒 Laval 法国城镇 9—525a
拉瓦利埃颈饰 lavaliere 服饰 9—525e
拉瓦利埃女公爵 La Vallière, Louise-Françoise de La Baume le Blanc, duchesse de 法国国王情妇 9—428f
拉瓦人 Lawa (people) 缅甸、中国民族 9—529c
拉瓦特尔 Lavater, Johann Kaspar 瑞士作家 9—525e
拉瓦锡 Lavoisier, Antoine-Laurent 法国化学家 9—526e
拉瓦耶哈 Lavalleja 乌拉圭省份 9—525e
拉威尔 Ravel, (Joseph-) Maurice 法国作曲家 14—166a
拉韦朗 Laveran, (Charles-Louis-) Alphonse 法国病理学家 9—526c
拉韦朗德里 La Vérendrye, Pierre Gaultier de Varennes, sieur de (sire of) 加拿大探险家 9—429b
拉韦勒 Lavelle, Louis 法国哲学家 9—525f
拉韦纳 Ravenna 意大利城市 14—166f
拉韦松-莫利安 Ravaisson-Mollien, Jean-Gaspard-Félix Lacher 法国哲学家 14—165e
拉维达岛 Rábida Island 太平洋岛屿 14—103a
拉维多利亚 La Victoria 秘鲁区名 9—429c
拉维河 Rāvi River 印度、巴基斯坦河流 14—168a
拉维尼乌姆 Lavinium 意大利古城 9—526d
拉维日里 Lavigerie, Charles(-Martial-Allemand) 法国枢机主教 9—526d
拉文斯布吕克 Ravensbrück 德国纳粹集中营 14—167d
拉翁唐 La Hontan, Louis-Armand de Lom d'Arce, baron de 法国军人、作家 9—423b
拉乌尔 Raoult, François-Marie 法国化学家 14—153d
拉乌雷尔 Laurel, José Paciano 菲律宾总统 9—521c
拉乌尼翁 La Unión 萨尔瓦多城市 9—428f
拉西 Lacy, Franz Moritz, Count (Graf) von 奥地利元帅 9—440e
拉希 Rashi 犹太教评论家 14—157a
拉希 Rasch, Albertina 美国舞蹈家 14—156f
拉希德 Rashīd (Egypt) 埃及城镇 14—157b
拉希德 Rashīd, ar- 摩洛哥阿拉维王朝创建者 14—157b
拉希德丁 Rashīd ad-Dīn 伊斯兰教领袖 14—157c
拉希德丁 Rashīd ad-Dīn 波斯政治家、历史学家 14—157c
拉希德·里达 Rashīd Riḍā, (Muḥammad) 叙利亚学者 14—157d
拉希迪耶 Rachidia, Er- 摩洛哥城镇 14—105e
拉希姆亚尔汗 Rahīmyār Khān 巴基斯坦城镇 14—123e
拉希纳 Lahina (Sikh Gurū) 锡克教古鲁 9—450a
拉喜特拉库塔王朝 Rāṣṭrakūṭa DYNASTY 印度教王朝 14—160a
拉夏洛泰 La Chalotais, Louis-René de Caradeuc de 法国官员 9—419e
拉肖塞 La Chaussée, Pierre-Claude Nivelle de 法国剧作家 9—419f
拉歇尔小姐 Rachel, Mademoiselle 法国演员 14—105c
拉歇兹 Lachaise, Gaston 美国雕刻家 9—436c
拉谢塔尔迪侯爵 La Chétardie, Jacques-Joachim Trotti, Marquis de 法国外交家 9—419f
拉辛 Racine 美国城市 14—106d
拉辛 Racine, Jean(-Baptiste) 法国戏剧诗人 14—106e
拉辛 Razin, Stenka 俄国哥萨克领袖 14—174b
拉欣 Lachine 加拿大城市 9—436e
拉欣 Rašín, Alois 捷克政治家 14—157f
拉亚松森 Asunción, La 委内瑞拉城市 2—10e
拉耶 Laie 美国城镇 9—451c
拉伊 Rye 英格兰城镇 14—475b
拉伊 Rye 美国纽约州城市 14—475d
拉伊博利尼 Raibolini, Francesco di Marco di Giacomo 意大利艺术家 14—124b
拉伊代尔 Ryedale 英格兰约克郡区名 14—475f
拉伊多内 Laidoner, Johan 爱沙尼亚军人 9—451c
拉伊尔 La Hire, Laurent de 法国画家 9—423b
拉伊金 Laigin (Ireland) 爱尔兰省份 9—451d

拉伊金 Raikin, Arkady Isaakovich 苏联喜剧演员 14—124e
拉伊蒙迪 Raimondi, Marcantonio 意大利铜版画大师 14—125c
拉伊纳尔迪 Rainaldi, Carlo 意大利建筑师 14—126f
拉伊纳尔迪 Rainaldi, Girolamo 意大利建筑师 14—127a
拉伊人 Rai 尼泊尔土著部落 14—124b
拉伊瓦尔特瓶 Lājvard ware 伊朗工艺品 9—452c
拉扎克 Abdul Razak bin Hussein, Tun Haji 马来西亚总理 1—15e
拉扎勒斯 Lazarus, Emma 美国作家 9—535d
拉扎勒斯(小) Lazarus, Fred, Jr. 美国商人 9—535d
拉扎列夫 Lazarev, Pyotr Petrovich 苏联物理学家 9—535b
拉扎斯菲尔德 Lazarsfeld, Paul Felix 美国社会学家 9—535b
拉兹格勒 Razgrad 保加利亚城镇 14—174a
拉兹马拉 Razmara, Ali 伊朗政府官员 14—174d
拉兹语 Laz language 语言 9—535a
喇叭虫属 Stentor 原生动物学 16—219f
喇叭角石属 Lituites 古生物学 10—152e
喇叭螺 trumpet 腹足动物 17—243d
喇叭鸟 trumpeter 鸟类 17—244c
喇嘛 lama 藏传佛教高僧 9—458d
喇嘛教 Lamaism 藏传佛教 9—458d
腊埃提亚 Raetia 古罗马行省 14—121a
腊玛古猿属 Ramapithecus 古生物学 14—136e
腊斯克 Rusk, (David) Dean 美国国务卿 14—455b
蜡 wax 半透明塑性物质 18—150d
蜡瓣花 winter hazel 木本植物 18—290e
蜡蝉 plant hopper 昆虫 13—345b
蜡翅鸟 waxwing 鸟类 18—151e
蜡膏 petrolatum 石油产品 13—210d
蜡画法 encaustic painting 绘画技法 6—68e
蜡色涂 rō-iro 日本漆工艺 14—322e
蜡塑 wax sculpture 艺术 18—151a
蜡质植物 waxplant 多种具蜡质植物统称 18—151d
蜡烛 candle 照明 3—398a
蜡烛鱼 candlefish 鱼类 3—398b
蜡嘴鸟 waxbill 鸟类 18—151b
辣根 horseradish (*Armoracia lapathifolia*) 植物 8—183d
辣根树 horseradish tree 植物 8—183e
辣椒 chili pepper 调味品 4—156f
辣椒 pepper 植物 13—153b
辣椒草 peppergrass 草本植物 13—153f
辣椒粉 paprika 调味品 13—26d
辣椒素 capsaicin 化合物 3—432b
辣虾酱 sambal 调味品 14—562d
辣匝禄会会士 Lazarist (religious society) 天主教组织 9—535b
来访者中心式心理治疗 client-centred psychotherapy 心理学 4—289d
来福枪鸟 riflebird 鸟类 14—296f
来福枪手鸟 rifleman 鸟类 14—296f
来航 Leghorn (Italy) 意大利城市 9—561f
来山得 Lysander 古希腊军事领袖 10—317e
莱 lai 诗歌体裁 9—451b
莱 Lay, Elzy 美国匪徒 9—534c
莱昂 Leon 西班牙古王国 10—19a
莱昂 León 墨西哥城市 10—19b
莱昂 León 尼加拉瓜城市 10—19b
莱昂 León 西班牙省份 10—19c
莱昂 León 西班牙城市 10—19c
莱昂 Lyon, Amy 英国将军纳尔逊的情妇 10—315e
莱昂 León, Juan Ponce de 西班牙探险家 10—19c
莱昂 León, Luis de 西班牙诗人 10—19d
莱昂 Lyon, Mary (Mason) 美国教育家 10—315f
莱昂(莫德纳的) Leon of Modena 意大利拉比、作家 10—19c
莱昂蒂尼 Leontini 古希腊城市 10—27c
莱昂内尔(安特卫普的) Lionel of Antwerp 英格兰贵族 10—128e
莱昂斯 Lyons, Joseph Aloysius 澳大利亚总理 10—316d
莱昂提乌斯(拜占廷的) Leontius of Byzantium 拜占廷神学家 10—27d
莱奥 Léaud, Jean-Pierre 法国电影演员 9—546f
莱奥 Leo, Leonardo (Ortensio Salvatore de) 意大利作曲家 10—18d
莱奥本 Leoben 奥地利城镇 10—18e
莱奥波尔德 Leopold, Carl Gustaf af 瑞典宫廷诗人 10—30a
莱奥卡雷斯 Leochares 希腊雕刻家 10—18e
莱奥纳多·达·芬奇 Leonardo da Vinci 佛罗伦萨艺术家、科学家 10—19f
莱奥纳多·达·芬奇科学技术博物馆 Leonardo da Vinci Museum of Science and Technology 意大利博物馆 10—26a
莱奥纳尔迪 Leonardi, Piero 意大利地质学家 10—19e
莱奥纳尔多(比萨的) Leonardo Pisano 意大利数学家 10—25d
莱奥南 Léonin 法国作曲家 10—26e
莱奥内 Leone, Giovanni 伊斯兰学者 10—26b
莱奥尼 Leoni, Leone 佛罗伦萨雕刻家 10—26c
莱奥尼 Leoni, Pompeo 意大利雕刻家 10—26c
莱奥尼达斯 Leonidas 斯巴达国王 10—26d
莱奥尼达斯(塔兰托姆的) Leonidas of Tarentum 希腊诗人 10—26d
莱奥帕尔迪 Leopardi, Giacomo 意大利诗人、哲学家 10—28c
莱奥提基德斯 Leotychides 斯巴达国王 10—30c
莱奥维希尔德 Leovigild 西班牙国王 10—30c
莱巴赫 Laibach (Slovenia) 斯洛文尼亚首都 9—451b
莱巴赫会议 Laibach, Congress of 欧洲历史 9—451b
莱巴赫杉属 Lebachia 古生物学 9—547d
莱巴嫩 Lebanon 美国康涅狄格州城镇 9—548e
莱巴嫩 Lebanon 美国密苏里州城市 9—548e
莱巴嫩 Lebanon 美国宾夕法尼亚州城市 9—548f
莱巴嫩 Lebanon 美国田纳西州城市 9—548f
莱邦博山 Lebombo Mountains 非洲山脉 9—549e
莱比锡 Leipzig 德国城市 9—569b
莱比锡大学 Leipzig, University of 德国大学 9—569d
莱比锡动物园 Leipzig Zoological Garden 德国动物园 9—569e
莱比锡战役 Leipzig, Battle of 拿破仑战争 9—569d
莱波尔特 Leipoldt, C(hristiaan Frederik) Louis 南非医生、作家 9—569a
莱博昂普罗旺斯 Les Baux-en-Provence 法国村庄 10—35d
莱博瓦 Lebowa 南非原黑人邦 9—549f
莱博瓦戈莫 Lebowakgomo 南非城镇 9—550a
莱博维茨 Leibovitz, Annie 美国摄影师 9—566c
莱布 Lebu 智利城市 9—550c
莱布尔 Leibl, Wilhelm 德国画家 9—565e
莱布尼兹 Leibniz, Gottfried Wilhelm 德国哲学家、数学家 9—565f
莱城 Lae 巴布亚新几内亚港口 9—443f
莱德 Ladd, George Trumbull 美国心理学家 9—441a
莱德贝特 Ledbetter, Huddie William (musician) 美国音乐家 9—552e
莱德伯格 Lederberg, Joshua 美国遗传学家 9—552f
莱德-富兰克林 Ladd-Franklin, Christine 美国科学家 9—441b
莱德曼 Lederman, Leon Max 美国物理学家 9—553a
莱德维尔 Leadville 美国城市 9—541c
莱登 Leyden (The Netherlands) 荷兰城市 10—54e
莱登 Leyden, Lucas van 荷兰画家 10—54e
莱迪吉耶尔公爵 Lesdiguières, François de Bonne, duc de (duke of) 法国统帅 10—36f
莱迪史密斯 Ladysmith 南非城镇 9—443f
莱迪亚德 Ledyard, John 美国探险家 9—553d
莱蒂西亚 Leticia 哥伦比亚城市 10—42a
莱杜斯 Laetus, Julius Pomponius 意大利人文主义者 9—444c
莱顿 Leiden 荷兰城市 9—567c
莱顿 Layton, Irving (Peter) 加拿大诗人 9—534f

莱顿 Leighton, Margaret 英国演员 9—568b
莱顿 Leighton, Robert 苏格兰牧师 9—568c
莱顿(施特列顿的) Leighton (of Stretton), Frederic Leighton, Baron 英国画家 9—568b
莱顿瓶 Leyden jar 电学 10—54e
莱多公路 Ledo Road (Burma) 缅甸公路 9—553b
莱恩 Lane, Sir Allen 英国出版商 9—479e
莱恩 Lane, Alfred Church 美国地质学家 9—479e
莱恩 Laing, Alexander Gordon 苏格兰探险家 9—451e
莱恩 Laine, Dame Cleo 英国歌手、演员 9—451d
莱恩 Lane, Franklin K(night) 美国政治家 9—479f
莱恩 Lane, Harriet 美国代理第一夫人 9—479f
莱恩 Lane, Sir Hugh Percy 爱尔兰艺术品商人 9—480a
莱恩 Lang, John Dunmore 澳大利亚作家 9—481a
莱恩 Lane, Jonathan Homer 美国物理学家 9—480b
莱恩 Lehn, Jean-Marie 法国化学家 9—565a
莱恩 Laing, R(onald) D(avid) 英国精神病学家 9—451e
莱恩群岛 Line Islands 太平洋岛屿 10—118e
莱尔 Lisle 美国村庄 10—138f
莱尔德 Laird, Macgregor 苏格兰探险家 9—451f
莱尔多·德·特哈达 Lerdo de Tejada, Sebastián 墨西哥总统 10—33d
莱尔罗克斯 Lerroux, Alejandro 西班牙政治家 10—35b
莱尔马公爵 Lerma, Francisco Gómez de Sandoval y Rojas, duque de (duke of) 西班牙政治家 10—33f
莱尔马河 Lerma River 墨西哥河流 10—33f
莱尔米特 L'Hermite, Tristan 法国作家 10—56a
莱尔内特-荷勒尼亚 Lernet-Holenia, Alexander 奥地利戏剧家 10—34f
莱尔山 Lyell, Mount 澳大利亚矿区 10—311a
莱佛士 Raffles, Sir Stamford 英国行政官员 14—121c
莱夫卡山 Lévka Mountains 希腊山脉 10—48e
莱夫卡斯 Leucas 希腊岛屿 10—42d
莱夫科萨 Lefkoşa (Cyprus) 塞浦路斯城市 9—559b
莱夫里哈 Lebrija 西班牙城市 9—550a
莱夫尼 Levnî, Abdülcelil 奥斯曼画家 10—48f
莱弗·埃里克松(幸运者) Leif Eriksson THE LUCKY 挪威探险家 9—567e
莱弗托夫 Levertov, Denise 美国诗人 10—46a
莱歌 lay 诗歌体裁 9—534b
莱格 Legge, William 英国政治家 9—561e
莱格伦齐 Legrenzi, Giovanni 意大利作曲家 9—563c
莱格尼察 Legnica 波兰旧省份 9—563b
莱格尼察 Legnica 波兰城市 9—563b
莱格特 Leggett, Anthony J. 英国物理学家 9—561e
莱古亚-萨尔塞多 Leguía y Salcedo, Augusto Bernardino 秘鲁总统 9—563d
莱哈尔 Lehár, Franz 匈牙利作曲家 9—563f
莱海纳 Lahaina 美国城市 9—449d
莱赫米王朝 Lakhmid DYNASTY 阿拉伯王朝 9—456e
莱赫纳 Lehna (Sikh Gurū) 锡克教古鲁 9—565b
莱洪 Lechoń, Jan 波兰诗人 9—550e
莱基 Lecky, William Edward Hartpole 爱尔兰历史学家 9—550f
莱基托斯陶瓶 lekythos 希腊陶器 10—1d
莱加列 Legaré, Hugh Swinton 美国政治家 9—560e
莱加斯皮 Legaspi 菲律宾城市 9—560e
莱加斯皮 Legazpi, Miguel López de 西班牙探险家 9—560f
莱-卡-佩三氏综合征 Legg-Calvé-Perthes syndrome 疾病 9—561e
莱凯 Les Cayes 海地城镇 10—35e
《莱康普顿宪法》 Lecompton Constitution 美国历史 9—551e
莱科 Lecco 意大利城镇 9—550c
莱克 Lake, Simon 美国发明家 9—454d
莱克查尔斯 Lake Charles 美国城市 9—454f
莱克城 Lake City 美国城市 9—455a
莱克福里斯特 Lake Forest 美国城市 9—455d
莱克赫斯特 Lakehurst 美国城镇 9—456b
莱克黑德 Lakehead (city, Ontario, Canada) 加拿大城市 9—456b
莱克杰尼瓦 Lake Geneva 美国城市 9—455d
莱克兰 Lakeland 美国城市 9—456b
莱克岭 Lake Ridge (North America) 北美山岭 9—455f
莱克路易斯 Lake Louise 加拿大村庄 9—455e
莱克普拉西德 Lake Placid 美国村庄 9—455f
莱克斯恩特伦斯 Lakes Entrance 澳大利亚城市 9—456c
莱克威尔士 Lake Wales 美国城市 9—456a
莱克维尤 Lakeview 美国城市 9—456d
莱克伍德 Lakewood 美国新泽西州城镇 9—456d
莱克伍德 Lakewood 美国俄亥俄州城市 9—456d
莱克希特诸语言 Lekhitic languages 欧洲语言 10—1c
莱克子爵(第一) Lake (of Delhi and of Aston Clinton), Gerard Lake, 1st Viscount 英国军人 9—454d
莱肯姆比琴 likembe 乐器 10—96a
莱莱韦尔 Lelewel, Joachim 波兰历史学家 10—2a
莱兰大隐修院 Lérins, Abbey of 法国隐修院 10—33e
莱勒 Lalor, Mother Teresa 美国宗教领袖 9—458c
莱勒 Lalor, Peter 澳大利亚矿工暴动首领 9—458c
莱里达 Lérida 西班牙省份 10—33d
莱里达 Lérida 西班牙城市 10—33e
莱里斯 Leiris, Michel 法国作家 9—569e
莱里亚 Leiria 葡萄牙城镇 9—569e
莱利 Lely, Sir Peter 英国画家 10—2c
莱利斯塔德 Lelystad 荷兰城市 10—2d
莱利乌斯 Laelius, Gaius 罗马军人、政治家 9—444a
莱利乌斯(小) Laelius Sapiens, Gaius, THE YOUNGER 罗马军人、政治家 9—444a
莱利乌斯氏兰属 Laelia 植物学 9—443f
莱罗斯岛 Léros 希腊岛屿 10—34f
莱马 Laima 波罗的海宗教神名 9—451d
莱马 Lima 美国城市 10—101d
莱曼 Lehmann, John 英国作家 9—564c
莱曼 Lehmann, (Peter Martin) Orla 丹麦政治家 9—564d
莱曼 Lehmann, Rosamond (Nina) 英国小说家 9—564e
莱曼岛 Lemain Island (The Gambia) 冈比亚岛屿 10—2e
莱芒湖 Léman, Lac (Europe) 欧洲湖泊 10—3b
莱蒙 Lemmon, Jack 美国演员 10—4b
莱蒙特 Reymont, Władysław Stanisław 波兰作家 14—255a
莱蒙托夫 Lermontov, Mikhail (Yuryevich) 俄国作家 10—34a
莱米吉乌斯(兰斯的),圣 Remigius OF REIMS, SAINT 兰斯基督教主教 14—222b
莱明斯特 Leominster 美国城市 10—18f
莱姆 Lem, Stanislaw 波兰科幻小说家 10—2d
莱姆病 Lyme disease 疾病 10—311d
莱姆布鲁克 Lehmbruck, Wilhelm 德国艺术家 9—564f
莱姆豪斯 Limehouse 英格兰地区 10—103d
莱姆里吉斯 Lyme Regis 英格兰区名 10—311e
莱姆斯特 Leominster 英格兰城镇 10—18f
莱纳 Leiner, Benjamin (boxer) 美国运动员 9—568d
莱瑙 Lenau, Nikolaus 奥地利诗人 10—6a
莱尼斯 Rainis 拉脱维亚诗人、戏剧家 14—128c
莱尼亚尼 Legnani, Pierina 意大利芭蕾舞演员 9—563a
莱尼亚诺 Legnano 意大利城市 9—563b
莱诺克斯 Lenox 美国城镇 10—13b
莱诺铸排机 Linotype 印刷 10—125d
《莱普提涅斯法》 Leptines, Law of 雅典法律 10—32b
莱普提斯 Leptis 古非洲城镇 10—32c
莱奇沃思 Letchworth 英格兰城镇 10—41e
莱切 Lecce 意大利城市 9—550c

莱热 Léger, Fernand 法国画家 9—561c
莱热 Léger, Marie-René-Auguste-Alexis Saint-Léger 法国诗人 9—561e
莱萨马·利马 Lezama Lima, José 古巴作家 10—55b
莱塞 Loesser, Frank (Henry) 美国作曲家 10—186c
莱施-奈恩二氏综合征 Lesch-Nyhan syndrome 疾病 10—36d
莱什诺 Leszno 原波兰省份 10—41e
莱什诺 Leszno 波兰城镇 10—41e
莱什琴斯基 Leszczyński, Stanisław (king of Poland) 波兰国王 10—41e
莱思罗普 Lathrop, Julia Clifford 美国社会福利工作者 9—511b
莱思罗普 Lathrop, Mother Alphonsa 美国作家、修女 9—511a
莱斯布里奇 Lethbridge 加拿大城市 10—41e
莱斯河 Lesse River 比利时河流 10—39c
莱斯卡兹 Lescaze, William 美国建筑师 10—36d
莱斯科 Lescot, Pierre 法国建筑师 10—36e
莱斯勒 Leisler, Jacob 美国民兵首领 9—570b
莱斯利 Leslie, Alexander 苏格兰军队指挥官 10—37e
莱斯利 Leslie, John 苏格兰主教 10—37e
莱斯利 Leslie, Sir John 苏格兰物理学家 10—37e
莱斯皮纳斯 Lespinasse, Julie de 法国文学沙龙主人 10—39b
莱斯特 Leicester 英格兰城市 9—566d
莱斯特 Lestres, Alonié de 加拿大历史学家 10—41c
莱斯特 Leyster, Judith 荷兰画家 10—54f
莱斯特伯爵 Leicester, EARLS OF 英国贵族 9—566e
莱斯特伯爵 Leicester, Robert Dudley, earl of, BARON DENBIGH 英国贵族 9—566e
莱斯特伯爵 Leicester, Simon de Montfort, earl of 法国贵族 9—566e
莱斯特伯爵(第一) Leicester, Robert Sidney, 1st earl of 英国政治家 9—566f
莱斯特郡 Leicestershire 英格兰郡名 9—566f
莱斯特兰奇 L'Estrange, Sir Roger 英国新闻记者 10—41b
莱斯沃斯 Lesbos 希腊岛屿 10—36c
莱斯谢蒂基 Leszetycki, Teodor 波兰钢琴家 10—41e
莱索托 Lesotho 非洲国家 10—38a
莱特 Leyte 菲律宾岛屿 10—54f
莱特 Light, Francis 英国军人 10—93b
莱特湾战役 Leyte Gulf, Battle of 第二次世界大战史 10—55a
莱特兄弟 Wright, Wilbur and Orville 美国飞机发明家 18—347b
莱托-福尔贝克 Lettow-Vorbeck, Paul von 德国军人 10—42c
莱托里化石 Laetolil remains 古人类学 9—444c
莱瓦尔德 Lewald, Fanny 德国作家 10—49e
莱瓦尼卡 Lewanika 南非国王 10—49f
莱瓦索 Levassor, Émile 法国发明家 10—44e
莱万多夫斯基 Lewandowski, Louis 犹太作曲家 10—49f
莱韦尔廷 Levertin, Oscar Ivar 瑞典诗人 10—46a
莱维 Lévis 加拿大城市 10—48a
莱维 Levi, Carlo 意大利作家 10—46c
莱维 Levi, Primo 意大利犹太裔作家 10—46d
莱维 Lévy, Paul(-Pierre) 法国数学家 10—49d
莱维-布吕尔 Lévy-Bruhl, Lucien 法国哲学家 10—49d
莱维敦 Levittown (New Jersey, U.S.) 美国新泽西州社区 10—48e
莱维敦 Levittown 美国纽约州社区 10—48e
莱维敦 Levittown 美国宾夕法尼亚州社区 10—48e
莱维-鲁西二氏综合征 Levy-Roussy syndrome 疾病 10—49e
莱维-蒙塔尔奇尼 Levi-Montalcini, Rita 美国、意大利神经学家 10—46f
莱维纳斯 Lévinas, Emmanuel 法国哲学家 10—47c
莱维-斯特劳斯 Lévi-Strauss, Claude 法国社会人类学家 10—47a
莱维塔 Levita, Elijah Bokher 意大利语法学家 10—48a
莱维特 Levitt, Helen 美国摄影家 10—48d
莱文 Leeuwen, Denys van 佛兰德神学家 9—558c
莱文 Levine, Jack 美国画家 10—47e
莱文 Levine, James 美国音乐家 10—47f
莱文 Levin, Meyer 美国作家 10—47c
莱文顿 Leventon, Alla 俄国演员 10—45d
莱文森 Levinson, Salmon Oliver 美国法学家 10—47f
莱文沃思 Leavenworth 美国城市 9—547b
莱翁卡瓦洛 Leoncavallo, Ruggero 意大利作曲家 10—26a
莱翁一世 Levon I 亚美尼亚国王 10—49b
莱沃库森 Leverkusen 德国城市 10—46a
莱武卡 Levuka 斐济城市 10—49b
莱西纳 Lesina (Croatia) 克罗地亚岛屿 10—37c
莱希 Leahy, Frank 美国橄榄球教练 9—543e
莱希 Leahy, William D(aniel) 美国军人 9—543f
莱希哈特 Leichhardt, (Friedrich Wilhelm) Ludwig 探险家和博物学家 9—567a
莱希米安 Leśmian, Bolesław 波兰诗人 10—37e
莱希涅夫斯基 Leśniewski, Stanisław 波兰逻辑学家 10—37f
莱辛 Lessing, Doris (May) 英国作家 10—40a
莱辛 Lessing, Gotthold Ephraim 德国剧作家 10—40b
莱辛顿勋爵 Lethington, Sir Richard Maitland, Lord 苏格兰诗人 10—41f
莱雄角什港 Leixões, Port of 葡萄牙港口 10—1a
莱亚德 Layard, Sir Austen Henry 英国考古学家 9—534e
莱亚尔 Leal, Juan de Nisa Valdés 西班牙艺术家 9—544e
莱亚尔普尔 Lyallpur (Pakistan) 巴基斯坦城市 10—307c
莱亚门 Layamon 中古英语诗人 9—534d
莱伊 Laye, Camara 非洲作家 9—534f
莱伊 Ley, Robert 非洲作家 10—54e
莱伊什港 Portlaoise 爱尔兰郡首府 13—452d
莱伊什郡 Laoighis 爱尔兰郡名 9—492c
莱因德纸草书 Rhind papyrus 古埃及数学文献 14—261d
莱因哈特 Reinhardt, Ad 美国画家 14—210f
莱因哈特 Reinhardt, Django 吉他演奏家 14—211a
莱因哈特 Rinehart, Mary Roberts 美国小说家 14—303f
莱因肯斯 Reinkens, Joseph Hubert 德国历史学家 14—211e
莱因斯 Reines, Frederick 美国物理学家 14—210d
莱茵板岩山脉 Rhenish Slate Mountains (Germany) 德国中莱茵高地山脉 14—259f
莱茵豪森 Rheinhausen 德国城市 14—259d
莱茵河 Rhine River 西欧河流 14—261f
莱茵黑森-普法尔茨 Rheinhessen-Pfalz 德国行政区 14—259d
莱茵兰 Rhineland 西欧地区 14—262b
莱茵兰德 Rhinelander 美国城市 14—263d
莱茵兰-帕拉蒂纳特 Rhineland-Palatinate 德国州名 14—262e
莱茵兰-普法尔茨 Rheinland-Pfalz (Germany) 德国州名 14—259e
莱茵联盟 Rhine, Confederation of the 欧洲历史 14—261e
莱茵领地伯爵短裤 rhinegraves 衣服 14—262b
莱茵瀑布 Rhine Falls 中欧莱茵河瀑布 14—261e
莱茵石 rhinestone 玻璃、水晶宝石 14—263d
莱泽堡 Letzeburg (city, Luxembourg) 卢森堡城市 10—42d
莱泽维茨 Leisewitz, Johann Anton 德国剧作家 9—569f
梾木 dogwood 木本植物 5—362a
铼(Re) rhenium 化学元素 14—259f
赖阿特阿 Raiatea 南太平洋背风群岛最大岛 14—124b
赖氨酸 lysine 化学 10—318d
赖奥斯利 Wriothesley, Henry 英国贵族 18—348d
赖奥斯利 Wriothesley, Thomas 英国国务大臣 18—348d
赖白里 Leadbelly 美国歌手 9—541b
赖伯雷利 Rāe Bareli 印度城镇 14—120c
赖布尔 Raipur 印度城市 14—128e
赖城 Rayy 伊朗古城遗址 14—173f
赖城陶瓷 Rayy ware 伊朗陶瓷 14—173f
赖德 Ryde 英格兰地名 14—475a
赖德 Ryder, Albert Pinkham 美国油画家 14—475a

赖德 Ride, Sally 美国航天员 14—291b
赖德杯 Ryder Cup 英-美高尔夫球团体赛 14—475b
赖德律-洛兰 Ledru-Rollin, Alexandre-Auguste 法国律师、政治家 9—553d
赖丁 Riding, Laura 美国诗人 14—291f
赖恩迪尔湖 Reindeer Lake 加拿大湖泊 14—210b
赖恩哈特 Reinhardt, Max 戏剧导演 14—211b
赖恩海姆 Reinheim 德国村庄 14—211e
赖尔 Lyell, Sir Charles, Baronet 苏格兰地质学家 10—309f
赖尔 Ryle, Gilbert 英国哲学家 14—476c
赖尔 Ryle, Sir Martin 英国射电天文学家 14—476d
赖尔森 Ryerson, (Adolphus) Egerton 加拿大教育家 14—476a
赖伐尔 Laval, Pierre 法国政治人物 9—525c
赖盖特和班斯特德 Reigate and Banstead 英格兰自治市 14—208f
赖格尔 Raigarh 印度历史地区 14—124c
赖格尔 Raigarh 印度城市 14—124d
赖根杰 Raiganj 印度城市 14—124c
赖久尔 Raichūr 印度城市 14—124c
赖克尔 Rijkel, Denys van 基督教神学家 14—299f
赖克斯岛 Rikers Island 美国岛屿 14—300a
赖利 Riley, Bridget 英国画家 14—300e
赖利 Riley, Charles Valentine 美国昆虫学家 14—300e
赖利 Riley, James Whitcomb 美国诗人 14—300f
赖利 Reilly, Sidney (George) 英国间谍 14—209a
赖马尔 Raimar, Freimund 德国诗人 14—125c
赖马鲁斯 Reimarus, Hermann Samuel 哲学家 14—209b
赖买丹月 Ramaḍān 伊斯兰教教历九月 14—135a
赖麦锡 Ramusio, Giovanni Battista 意大利地理学家 14—145c
赖默 Rymer, Thomas 英国文学评论家 14—476f
赖纳 Reiner, Fritz 美国指挥家 14—210d
赖纳尔德(达瑟尔的) Rainald of Dassel 德意志政治家 14—126e
赖讷 Rheine 德国城市 14—259d
赖内克 Reinecke, Carl (Heinrich Carsten) 德国钢琴家 14—210c
赖尼植物 Rhynie plants 古生物学 14—272c
赖奇 Reitsch, Hanna 德国飞行员 14—212f
赖萨德 Resad, Mehmed (Ottoman sultan) 奥斯曼苏丹 14—238e
赖森 Raisen 印度城市 14—129a
赖斯 Rice, Alice (Caldwell) Hegan 美国小说家 14—279c
赖斯 Rice, Condoleezza 美国国务卿 14—279c
赖斯 Rice, Dan 美国马戏演员 14—279e
赖斯 Rice, Elmer 美国剧作家 14—279f
赖斯 Rice, (Henry) Grantland 美国体育专栏作家 14—279f
赖斯 Reis, Johann Philipp 德国物理学家 14—212a
赖斯 Rice, Thomas Dartmouth 美国演员 14—280a
赖斯 Reiss, Winold 美国艺术家 14—212d
赖斯布雷克 Rysbrack, John Michael 英国雕刻家 14—477a
赖斯布鲁克 Ruysbroeck, Jan van 佛兰芒奥秘修行家 14—471f
赖斯布鲁克 Ruysbroeck, Willem van 法国探险家 14—472a
赖斯顿 Reston, James 美国专栏作家 14—244a
赖斯克 Reiske, Johann Jakob 阿拉伯文学学者 14—212b
赖斯纳 Reisner, George Andrew 美国考古学者 14—212c
赖斯韦克 Rijswijk 荷兰城市 14—300a
赖特 Wright, Sir Almroth Edward 英国细菌学家 18—345f
赖特 Wright, Archibald Lee 美国拳击运动员 18—346a
赖特 Wright, Benjamin 美国工程师 18—346a
赖特 Wright, Frances 美国社会改革家 18—346b
赖特 Wright, Frank Lloyd 美国建筑师 18—346c
赖特 Wright, Joseph 英国画家 18—346f
赖特 Wright, Judith (Arundell) 澳大利亚诗人 18—346f
赖特 Wright, Laura Maria Sheldon 美国传教士 18—347a
赖特 Wright, Mickey 美国高尔夫球运动员 18—347b
赖特 Wright, Quincy 美国政治学家 18—347e
赖特 Wright, Richard 美国小说家 18—347f
赖特 Wright, Sewall 美国遗传学家 18—348b
赖特 Wright, Warren 美国金融家 18—348c
赖特(小) Wright, James C(laude), Jr. 美国政治家 18—346e
赖特氏效应 Sewall Wright effect 遗传学 15—243d
赖特综合征 Reiter syndrome 疾病 14—212e
赖希 Reich, Wilhelm 维也纳心理学家 14—207a
赖希德帕夏 Reşid Paşa, Mustafa 奥斯曼大臣 14—239d
赖希施塔特公爵 Reichstadt, Napoléon-François-Charles-Joseph Bonaparte, Herzog von 拿破仑(二世) 14—207f
赖希施泰因 Reichstein, Tadeus 瑞士化学家 14—208a
赖夏洛姆 Ra-Shalom 天文学 14—100b
赖肖尔 Reischauer, Edwin O(ldfather) 美国历史学家 14—212a
赖谢瑙 Reichenau 德国温特湖小岛 14—207b
赖谢瑙 Reichenau, Walther von 德国陆军元帅 14—207c
赖辛堡 Castle Rising 英格兰堂区 3—513d
赖兴巴赫 Reichenbach (Poland) 波兰城市 14—207c
赖兴巴赫 Reichenbach, Hans 德国哲学家、教育家 14—207d
赖兴巴赫瀑布 Reichenbach Falls 瑞士瀑布 14—207d
赖兴贝格 Reichenberg (Czech Republic) 捷克城市 14—207d
赖伊 Lie, Trygve (Halvdan) 联合国秘书长 10—84b
赖因伯格 Rheinberger, Joseph (Gabriel) 德国作曲家 14—259c
赖因哈德 Reinhard, Hans 苏黎世政治家 14—210f
赖因马尔·封·哈格瑙 Reinmar von Hagenau 德国诗人 14—211f
赖因斯多尔夫 Leinsdorf, Erich 美国音乐家 9—568e
濑户 Seto 日本城市 15—233f
濑户大桥 Seto Great Bridge 日本本州与四国间大桥 15—234a
濑户黑陶器 Seto-guro ware 日本陶器 15—234a
濑户内 Setouchi 日本工业区 15—234d
濑户内海 Inland Sea 日本内海 8—389c
濑户陶器 Seto ware 日本陶器 15—234a
兰 Lang, Andrew 苏格兰学者 9—480c
兰 Lang, (Alexander) Matheson 英国戏剧家 9—481a
兰 Lang, Jack 澳大利亚总理 9—480e
兰(兰贝斯的) Lang (of Lambeth), (William) Cosmo Gordon Lang, Baron 基督教牧师 9—480d
兰巴雷内 Lambaréné 加蓬城市 9—461e
兰巴人 Lamba 多哥民族 9—461b
兰巴耶克 Lambayeque 秘鲁省份 9—461e
兰贝尔 Lambert, Franz 法国改革家 9—462b
兰贝斯 Lambeth 英国自治市 9—463a
兰贝斯代尔夫特陶器 Lambeth delftware 工艺品 9—463b
兰贝斯会议 Lambeth Conference 基督教 9—463a
兰贝斯四条款 Lambeth Quadrilateral 基督教 9—463b
兰贝斯走步舞 Lambeth walk 舞蹈 9—463c
兰贝特(赫施费尔德的) Lambert of Hersfeld 德国历史学家 9—462a
兰贝特(斯波莱托的) Lambert of Spoleto 意大利国王 9—462b
兰波 Rimbaud, (Jean-Nicolas-) Arthur 法国诗人、冒险家 14—301f
兰波特 Langport 英格兰城镇 9—484c
兰伯顿 Lumberton 美国城市 10—280b
兰伯特 Lambert, Constant 英国作曲家 9—462b
兰伯特 Lambert, Gerard Barnes 美国商人 9—462c
兰伯特 Lambert, John 英国将领 9—462d
兰伯特 Lambert, Piggy 美国篮球教练 9—462e
兰伯特芭蕾舞团 Ballet Rambert 英国艺术团 2—176e
兰伯特夫人 Rambert, Dame Marie 英国导演 14—137e
兰伯特共形投影 Lambert conformal projection 制图学 9—462f
兰博 Lambeau, Curly 美国橄榄球教练 9—461f
兰博尔迪尼 Ramboldini, Vittorino del 意大利教育家 14—138b
兰布顿 Lambton, John George 英国政治家 9—463e
兰布尔 Rāmpur 印度城市 14—142a
兰布尔博阿利亚 Rampur Boalia (Bangladesh) 孟加拉国城市 14—142a

兰布尔吉亚尔氏鞭毛虫 Giardia lamblia 寄生性原生动物 7—117d
兰布尔兄弟 Limburg, Pol, Herman, and Jehanequin de 佛兰德斯画家 10—102f
兰彻斯特 Lanchester, Frederick William 英国制造商 9—473c
兰茨胡特 Landshut 德国城市 9—479a
兰达 Landa, Diego de 西班牙教士 9—475b
兰达夫 Llandaff 威尔士城市 10—167f
兰代 Lindet, Jean-Baptiste-Robert 法国革命家 10—117b
兰代洛统 Llandeilan Series 地质学 10—167f
兰道 Landau 德国城市 9—475c
兰道 Landau, Ezekiel 波兰犹太拉比 9—475d
兰德 Lander 美国城市 9—475f
兰德 Rand, Ayn 美国作家 14—146f
兰德 Land, Edwin Herbert 美国发明家、物理学家 9—473f
兰德 Lander, Harald 丹麦舞蹈演员 9—475f
兰德 Rand, Paul 美国美术设计师 14—147a
兰德 Lander, Richard Lemon 英国探险家 9—476a
兰德 Rand, Sally 美国演员 14—147b
兰德堡 Randburg 南非城镇 14—147f
兰德尔 Langdell, Christopher Columbus 美国教育家 9—481d
兰德尔 Randall, John Herman, Jr. 美国哲学家 14—147d
兰德尔 Randall, Samuel J(ackson) 美国众议员 14—147e
兰德尔-麦基弗 Randall-MacIver, David 美国考古学家 14—147f
兰德方丹 Randfontein 南非城镇 14—148a
《兰德勒姆-格里芬法案》 Landrum-Griffin Act 美国法律 9—478b
兰德里 Landry, Tom 美国橄榄球教练 9—478c
兰德林多德韦尔斯 Llandrindod Wells 威尔士城镇 10—168b
兰德-麦克纳利公司 Rand McNally and Company 美国公司 14—147d
《兰德每日邮报》 Rand Daily Mail 原南非报纸 14—147c
兰德施泰纳 Landsteiner, Karl 美国免疫学家 9—479c
兰德斯塔德 Randstad 荷兰大都会区 14—149b
兰登 Landon, Alfred M(ossman) 美国政治人物 9—477f
兰登 Landen, John 英国数学家 9—475f
兰登 Landon, Letitia Elizabeth 英国作家 9—477f
兰迪 Lundy 英格兰岛屿 10—283f
兰迪德诺 Llandudno 威尔士海滨胜地 10—168b
兰迪尼 Landini, Francesco 意大利作曲家 9—477a
兰迪斯 Landis, Kenesaw Mountain 美国法官 9—477b
兰杜马人 Landuma 几内亚民族 9—479d
兰顿 Langton, Stephen 英格兰枢机主教 9—484e
兰顿 Langton, Walter 英国政治人物 9—484f
兰多 Lando 教皇 9—477e
兰多 Landor, Walter Savage 英国作家 9—478a
兰多夫斯卡 Landowska, Wanda (Louise) 波兰出生的音乐家 9—478a
兰多维利统 Llandovery Series 地质学 10—168a
兰弗兰科 Lanfranco, Giovanni 意大利画家 9—480c
兰弗朗克 Lanfranc 坎特伯雷大主教 9—480b
兰盖 Ringuet 加拿大小说家 14—305d
兰盖 Linguet, Simon-Nicolas-Henri 法国新闻工作者 10—122c
兰盖夫尼 Llangefni 威尔士城镇 10—168c
兰盖维奇 Langiewicz, Marian (Melchior) 波兰军人 9—483c
兰戈伦 Llangollen 威尔士城镇 10—168c
兰戈人 Lango 乌干达民族 9—484c
兰格 Lange, Christian Lous 挪威国际和平倡导者 9—481e
兰格 Lange, Dorothea 美国摄影家 9—482a
兰格 Langer, Susanne K(nauth) 美国哲学家、教育家 9—482e
兰根 Langen, Eugen 德国工程师 9—482d
兰河 Lahn River 德国河流 9—450a
兰花 orchid 草本植物 12—447c
兰霍恩 Langhorne, John 英国诗人 9—483b
兰吉特辛吉·维伯哈吉 Ranjitsinhji Vibhaji, Sir, Maharaja Jam Saheb of Nawānagar 印度板球运动员 14—150f
兰吉·希罗厄 Rangi Hiroa, Te 新西兰人类学家 14—150c
兰季特·辛格 Ranjit Singh 印度国王 14—150e
兰加马蒂 Rāngāmāti 孟加拉国城镇 14—149c
兰金 Rankin, Jeannette 美国议员 14—151e
兰金 Rankine, William John Macquorn 苏格兰工程师、物理学家 14—151f
兰金循环 Rankine cycle 物理学 14—151f
兰卡瓜 Rancagua 智利区城市 14—145f
兰开斯特 Lancaster 英格兰城市 9—470b
兰开斯特 Lancaster 美国加利福尼亚州城市 9—470c
兰开斯特 Lancaster 美国俄亥俄州城市 9—470c
兰开斯特 Lancaster 美国宾夕法尼亚州城市 9—470d
兰开斯特 Lancaster 美国南卡罗来纳州城市 9—470d
兰开斯特 Lancaster, Burt 美国演员 9—471b
兰开斯特 Lancaster, Sir James 英国商人 9—471c
兰开斯特 Lancaster, Joseph 英国出生的教育家 9—471d
兰开斯特 Lancaster, Sir Osbert 英国画家、作家 9—471e
兰开斯特伯爵(第二) Lancaster, Thomas, 2nd Earl of 英国贵族 9—470e
兰开斯特伯爵(第三) Lancaster, Henry, 3rd Earl of 英国贵族 9—470f
兰开斯特伯爵(第一) Lancaster, Edmund, 1st Earl of 英国贵族 9—470e
兰开斯特伯爵和公爵 Lancaster, EARLS AND DUKES OF 英国贵族 9—470e
兰开斯特公爵 Lancaster, John of Gaunt, Duke of 英国贵族 9—471a
兰开斯特公爵(第一)和伯爵(第四) Lancaster, Henry, 1st Duke and 4th Earl of 英国军人、外交家 9—471a
兰开斯特海峡 Lancaster Sound 加拿大海峡 9—471f
兰开斯特王室 Lancaster, HOUSE OF 英国王室 9—471a
兰开夏 Lancashire 英格兰郡名 9—470a
兰凯特管 ranket (musical instrument) 乐器 14—151d
兰坎亨 Ramkhamhaeng 暹罗速古台国王 14—140c
兰克 Rank, Baron 英国工业家、电影制片人 14—150f
兰克 Ranke, Leopold von 德国历史学家 14—151c
兰克 Rank, Otto 奥地利心理学家 14—151a
兰克斯特 Lankester, Sir Edwin Ray 英国动物学家 9—486f
兰利 Langley 加拿大城市 9—483f
兰利 Langley, Samuel Pierpont 美国天文学家、工程师 9—483f
兰利的埃德蒙 Langley, Edmund of 英国贵族 9—483f
兰罗特 Lönnrot, Elias 芬兰民俗学者 10—213f
兰曼 Lanman, Charles Rockwell 美国梵语学者 9—487a
兰明低地暴乱 Lambing Flat Riots 澳大利亚历史 9—463c
兰姆 Lamb, Charles 英国作家 9—460e
兰姆 Lamb, Sir Horace 英国数学家 9—460f
兰姆 Lamb, Mary Ann 英国作家 9—461a
兰姆 Lamb, Sydney M(acDonald) 美国语言学家 9—461a
兰姆(小) Lamb, Willis Eugene, Jr. 美国物理学家 9—461b
兰讷斯 Randers 丹麦城市 14—147f
兰尼埃三世 Rainier III 摩纳哥公国统治者 14—128a
兰尼米德 Runnymede 英格兰区、市 14—450b
兰诺赫 Rannoch 苏格兰地理区 14—152a
兰佩杜萨 Lampedusa, Giuseppe Tomasi di (Italian author) 意大利作家 9—467f
兰佩杜萨岛 Lampedusa Island 意大利岛屿 9—467f
兰毗尼 Lumbinī 尼泊尔佛教圣地 10—280c
兰普雷茨 Lamprecht, Karl Gottfried 德国历史学家 9—468c
兰普曼 Lampman, Archibald 加拿大诗人 9—468a
兰奇安尼 Lanciani, Rodolfo Amadeo 意大利考古学家 9—473d
兰奇西 Lancisi, Giovanni Maria 意大利医学家 9—473e
兰契 Rānchi 印度城镇 14—146c

兰恰诺 Lanciano 意大利城镇 9—473d
兰乔格兰德国家公园 Rancho Grande National Park (Venezuela) 委内瑞拉国家公园 14—146d
兰乔-库卡蒙加 Rancho Cucamonga 美国城市 14—146c
兰乔拉布尔阶 Rancholabrean stage 地质学 14—146d
兰萨库斯 Lampsacus 希腊古城 9—468e
兰萨罗特岛 Lanzarote 西班牙岛屿 9—490f
兰塞姆 Ransome, Arthur (Michell) 美国诗人 14—152c
兰塞姆 Ransom, John Crowe 英国小说家 14—152b
兰氏龙属 Lambeosaurus 古生物学 9—461f
兰属 Cymbidium 植物学 5—88f
兰斯 Reims 法国城市 14—209c
兰斯伯里 Lansbury, Angela 美国演员 9—487c
兰斯伯里 Lansbury, George 英国政治人物 9—487d
兰斯大教堂 Reims Cathedral 法国建筑 14—209d
《兰斯-杜埃圣经》 Reims-Douai Bible 天主教《圣经》 14—209e
《兰斯-杜埃圣经》 Rheims-Douay Bible 天主教《圣经》 14—259c
兰斯顿 Langston, John Mercer 美国教育家、外交家 9—484d
兰斯多恩侯爵(第五) Lansdowne, Henry Charles Keith Petty-Fitzmaurice, 5th marquess of 英国外交家 9—487e
兰斯多恩侯爵(第一) Lansdowne, William Petty-Fitzmaurice, 1st marquess of 英国政治家 9—487f
兰斯基 Lansky, Meyer 美国犯罪集团首脑 9—488e
兰斯克鲁纳 Landskrona 瑞典城镇 9—479b
兰斯塔 Landstad, Magnus Brostrup 挪威诗人 9—479c
兰斯组 Lance Formation 地质学 9—472d
兰特 rand 南非货币单位 14—146e
兰特里 Langtry, Lillie 英国演员 9—484f
兰特里森特 Llantrisant 威尔士城镇 10—168e
兰特威特马哲 Llantwit Major 威尔士城镇 10—168f
兰图尔 Rantoul 美国伊利诺伊州村庄 14—152c
兰托弗特 Langtoft, Peter 英格兰历史学家 9—484e
兰维恩统 Llanvirn Series 地质学 10—168f
兰西尔 Ransier, Alonzo J. 美国众议员 14—152a
兰西尔 Landseer, Sir Edwin (Henry) 英国画家、雕刻家 9—479a
兰溪 Lanxi 中国城市 9—490c
兰仙人掌 orchid cactus 双子叶植物 12—447e
兰辛 Lansing 美国城市 9—488b
兰学 rangaku 日本术语 14—149c
兰屿 Lanyu 中国岛屿 9—490d
兰泽尔 Lansel, Peider 瑞士诗人 9—488a
兰扎 Lanza, Giovanni 意大利政治家 9—490e
兰州 Lanzhou 中国城市 9—490f
兰州大学 Lanzhou University 中国大学 9—491b
兰兹 Lantz, Walter 美国动画电影制片人 9—490b
兰兹角 Land's End 英格兰半岛 9—478c
栏杆 balustrade 建筑 2—185b
阑尾 appendix 解剖学 1—417f
阑尾炎 appendicitis 疾病 1—417f
蓝岸 Côte d'Azur 法国文化大区 4—535a
蓝宝石 sapphire 宝石 15—57e
蓝背鱼 blueback 鱼类 2—549d
蓝采和 Lan Caihe 道教神名 9—469a
蓝草音乐 bluegrass 美国音乐风格 2—550e
蓝地 blue ground 岩石 2—548b
蓝点颏 bluethroat (*Erithacus svecicus* or *Luscinia svecica*) 鸟类 2—551e
蓝蝶 blue butterfly 昆虫 2—547b
蓝干酪 blue cheese 食品 2—547c
蓝胡子 Bluebeard 故事人物 2—549d
蓝花参 tuftybell 草本植物 17—259e
蓝花楹 jacaranda 木本植物 8—502d
蓝晶石 kyanite 矿物 9—412d
蓝鲸 blue whale (*Balaenoptera*, or *Sibbaldus*, *musculus*) 哺乳动物 2—549c
蓝菌 cyanobacterium 原核生物 5—83c
蓝鹪莺 blue wren (bird) 鸟类 2—549d
蓝磷灰石 moroxite 矿物 11—402b
蓝岭 Blue Ridge 美国山脉 2—548f
蓝岭公路 Blue Ridge Parkway 美国公路 2—549a
蓝绿藻 blue-green algae 原核生物 2—547e
蓝牛 nilgai (*Boselaphus tragocamelus*) 哺乳动物 12—194b
《蓝皮书》 Blue Book, The 名人录 2—547a
蓝苹 Lan P'ing 中国政治人物 9—469b
蓝鸲 bluebird 鸟类 2—550a
蓝鳃鱼 bluegill (*Lepomis macrochirus*) 鱼类 2—550d
蓝色法规 blue law 美国历史 2—548b
蓝色花 blue flower, the 文学 2—547e
蓝色牛仔裤 blue jeans (apparel) 服装 2—548b
蓝鲨 blue shark (*Prionace glauca*) 鱼类 2—549b
蓝山 Blue Mountains 牙买加山脉 2—548c
蓝山 Blue Mountains 美国山脉 2—548c
蓝山山脉 Blue Mountains 澳大利亚山脉 2—548b
蓝衫团 Blue Shirt 爱尔兰法西斯组织 2—549b
蓝闪石 glaucophane 矿物 7—155d
蓝闪石片岩相 glaucophane schist facies 地质学 7—155e
蓝饰雀 cordon bleu 鸟类 4—504c
蓝绶带陪审团 blue-ribbon jury 司法 2—548e
蓝松鸦 blue jay 鸟类 2—548b
蓝天公司 Coop Himmelblau 建筑师事务所 4—483a
蓝田 Lantian 中国县名 9—489f
蓝田关口 Lantian Pass 中国关隘 9—490b
蓝田人 Lantian man 古人类学 9—490a
蓝铁矿 vivianite 矿物 18—28a
蓝铜矿 azurite 矿物 2—104e
蓝袜 Bluestocking 英国妇女团体 2—551d
蓝细尾鹪莺 bluecap 鸟类 2—550b
蓝蟹 blue crab 甲壳类动物 2—547c
蓝辛 Lansing, Robert 美国政治家 9—488c
《蓝辛-石井协定》 Lansing-Ishii Agreement 美-日互换照会 9—488d
蓝眼草 blue-eyed grass 草本植物 2—547d
蓝衣学校 blue coat school 教育 2—547c
蓝荫鼎 Lan Yinding 中国画家 9—469c
蓝婴综合征 blue baby syndrome 疾病 2—547a
蓝瑛 Lan Ying 中国画家 9—469c
蓝针插属 Brunonia 草本植物 3—207f
蓝钟花 bluebell 植物 2—549e
蓝嘴鸟 bluebill (duck) 鸟类 2—550a
澜沧 Lan Xang 老挝王国 9—469c
澜沧江 Lancang Jiang 中国河流 9—469f
篮球 BASKETBALL 体育项目 16—59a
篮球运动 basketball 体育 2—263e
镧 lanthanum 化学元素 9—489e
镧系收缩 lanthanide contraction 化学 9—489d
镧系元素 lanthanide element (chemistry) 化学元素 9—489e
缆绳 cable 绞合绳 3—306a
缆绳形柱 salomónica 建筑 14—551c
榄仁 pili nut 植物种仁 13—303c
榄仁树属 Terminalia 植物学 16—552a
懒猴 loris 哺乳动物 10—222f
懒熊 sloth bear (*Melursus ursinus*) 哺乳动物 15—435c
郎静山 Lang Jingshan 中国摄影家 9—480f
郎平 Lang Ping 中国排球运动员 9—481c
郎世宁 Castiglione, Guiseppe 意大利天主教修士、画家 3—510c
狼 wolf 哺乳动物 18—306e

狼毒 wolfsbane (plant) 草本植物 18—310c
狼鲱 wolf herring (*Chirocentrus dorab*) 鱼类 18—307f
狼獾 wolverine 哺乳动物 18—312b
狼林山脉 Nangnim Mountains 朝鲜山脉 11—554d
狼人 werewolf 欧洲民间传说 18—190d
狼蛇 wolf snake 爬行动物 18—308a
狼尾草属 Pennisetum 植物学 13—142c
狼鳚 wolffish 鱼类 18—309c
狼营阶 Wolfcampian Stage 地质学 18—308c
狼蛛 wolf spider 节肢动物 18—308a
琅勃拉邦 Louangphrabang 老挝城镇 10—232b
琅南塔 Louang Namtha 老挝城镇 10—232b
廊 gallery 建筑学 6—558b
廊坊 Langfang 中国城市 9—483a
廊开 Nong Khai 泰国城镇 12—228d
廊沙赖战役 Nong Sa Rai, Battle of 东南亚历史 12—228e
朗 Long, Crawford Williamson 美国外科医生 10—205f
朗 Long, George Washington de 美国探险家 10—206a
朗 Long, Huey (Pierce) 美国政治家 10—206a
朗巴尔亲王夫人 Lamballe, Marie-Thérèse-Louise de Savoie-Carignan, Princess de 法国贵族 9—461c
朗班 Ramban (Jewish scholar) 犹太学者 14—137e
朗贝尔蒙 Lambermont, August, Baron 比利时政治家 9—461f
朗贝萨 Lambessa 阿尔及利亚村庄 9—462f
朗伯 lambert 计量单位 9—462a
朗伯 Lambert, Johann Heinrich 瑞士-德国科学家、哲学家 9—462d
朗布尔 Rangpur 孟加拉国城市 14—150d
朗布兰奇 Long Branch 美国城市 10—206d
朗布隆 Romblon 菲律宾岛屿、城镇 14—374d
朗布耶侯爵夫人 Rambouillet, Catherine de Vivonne, marquise de 法国文学赞助人 14—138c
朗布依埃 Rambouillet 法国城镇 14—138b
朗布依埃绵羊 Rambouillet 绵羊品种 14—138c
朗达 Rhondda 威尔士乡镇、区 14—270a
朗达-西农-塔夫 Rhondda Cynon Taff 威尔士自治市 14—270b
朗达子爵(第一) Rhondda (of Llanwern), David Alfred Thomas, 1st Viscount 英国实业家 14—270c
朗道 Landau, Lev Davidovich 苏联物理学家 9—475d
朗德 Landes 法国森林区 9—476b
朗德 Landes 法国省份 9—476b
朗德 Round, Henry Joseph 英国电子工程师 14—419e
朗登 London, Artur (Gerard) 捷克斯洛伐克官员 10—203b
朗顿 Longden, Johnny 美国骑手 10—209b
朗顿庄园瓷器 Longton Hall porcelain 英国瓷器 10—212c
朗多 Lando DI SEZZE (pope) 教皇 9—477f
朗多尼亚 Rondônia 巴西州名 14—388c
朗厄兰岛 Langeland 丹麦岛屿 9—482d
朗方 L'Enfant, Pierre-Charles 美国工程师、建筑师 10—6e
朗费罗 Longfellow, Henry Wadsworth 美国诗人 10—209c
朗福德伯爵 Rumford, Sir Benjamin Thompson, Graf von (Count of) 英国物理学家 14—448a
朗福德伯爵(第六) Longford, Edward Arthur Henry Pakenham, 6th earl of 英国戏剧家 10—209e
朗福德郡 Longford 爱尔兰郡名 10—209e
朗盖尔 Longair, Malcolm Sim 苏格兰天文学家 10—208f
朗戈斯 Longus 古希腊作家 10—212f
朗格 Lange, Antoni 波兰作家 9—481e
朗格 Lang, Fritz 美国电影导演 9—480d
朗格 Lange, Friedrich Albert 德国哲学家 9—482b
朗格 Lang, Matthäus 德国政治家 9—481b
朗格 Lange, Oskar Ryszard 经济学家 9—482c
朗格冰原 Langjökull 冰岛冰川 9—483d
朗格多克 Languedoc 法国历史文化区 9—485f
朗格多克-鲁西永 Languedoc-Roussillon 法国大区 9—486b
朗格多克语 Languedoc language 法国语言 9—486b
朗格多克运河 Languedoc Canal (France) 法国运河 9—486b
朗格尔 Langer, František 捷克医生、作家 9—482e
朗格尔山 Wrangell Mountains 美国山脉 18—342c
朗格尔-圣伊莱亚斯国家公园和自然保护区 Wrangell-Saint Elias National Park and Preserve 美国公园和保护区 18—342d
朗格兰 Langland, William 英国诗人 9—483e
朗格朗 Lenglen, Suzanne 法国网球运动员 10—6f
朗格勒 Langres 法国城镇 9—484c
朗格卢瓦 Langlois, Charles-Victor 法国学者 9—484b
朗荷恩 Langhorne, Nancy Witcher 英国政客 9—483c
朗吉努斯 Longinus 古希腊文学评论家 10—210e
朗加宝 Longabaugh, Harry 美国匪徒 10—208f
朗科恩 Runcorn 英格兰城镇 14—448f
朗科恩 Runcorn, Stanley Keith 英国地球物理学家 14—448f
朗克雷 Lancret, Nicolas 法国画家 9—473e
朗克洛 Lenclos, Ninon de 法国名妓 10—6c
朗雷扎克 Lanrezac, Charles(-Louis-Marie) 法国军人 9—487c
朗蒙特 Longmont 美国城市 10—211c
朗明德系 Longmyndian 地质学 10—211c
朗缪尔 Langmuir, Irving 美国物理化学家 9—484b
朗姆酒 rum 酒 14—447b
朗姆酒叛乱 Rum Rebellion 澳大利亚历史 14—447d
朗纳尔·洛德布罗克 Ragnar Lothbrok 北欧海盗英雄 14—122f
朗诺 Lon Nol 柬埔寨军人、政治家 10—197b
朗帕尔 Rampal, Jean-Pierre(-Louis) 法国长笛演奏家 14—141d
朗热 Langey, Guillaume du Bellay, seigneur de (lord of) 法国将军 9—483a
朗塞 Rancé, Armand-Jean Le Bouthillier de 法兰西天主教神职人员 14—145f
朗塞斯顿 Launceston 澳大利亚城市 9—519f
朗丝黛耳 Lonsdale, Dame Kathleen 英国晶体学家 10—214b
朗斯 Lens 法国城镇 10—13c
朗斯代尔 Lonsdale, Frederick Leonard 英国剧作家 10—214a
朗斯代尔 Lonsdale, Gordon Arnold 苏联间谍 10—214b
朗斯代尔 Lonsdale, William 英国地质学家 10—214c
朗斯代尔奖带 Lonsdale Belt 体育 10—214c
朗斯顿 Launceston 英格兰城镇 9—520a
朗斯河 Rance River 法国河流 14—145f
朗斯洛 Lancelot 英国传奇骑士 9—473a
朗斯特里特 Longstreet, James 美国军人 10—212b
朗诵唱 Sprechstimme 音乐 16—161c
朗特里 Rowntree, B(enjamin) Seebohm 英国社会学家、慈善家 14—428a
朗韦尔 Longwell, Chester R. 美国地质学家 10—213a
朗维尤 Longview 美国得克萨斯州城市 10—213a
朗维尤 Longview 美国华盛顿州城市 10—213a
朗沃思 Longworth, Alice Roosevelt 美国政治家 10—213b
朗伍德植物园 Longwood Gardens 美国植物园 10—213b
朗香 Longchamp, William 英格兰政治家 10—209b
朗伊 Lange, David (Russell) 新西兰总理 9—481f
朗伊蒂基河 Rangitikei River 新西兰北岛河流 14—150d
朗伊塔塔河 Rangitata River 新西兰南岛河流 14—150c
朗兹 Lowndes, Marie Adelaide 英国小说家 10—256d
浪 furlong 英制旧长度单位 6—529e
浪荡文学派 scapigliatura 意大利文学运动 15—103c
浪漫主义 Romanticism 思想状态 14—373c
浪漫主义芭蕾舞 Romantic ballet 芭蕾舞 14—373c
浪人 rōnin 日本武士 14—389a
浪蚀台 wave-cut platform 地质学 18—148e
劳 Law, (Andrew) Bonar 英国首相 9—528a
劳 Law, Edward 印度总督 9—528c

劳 Law,John 苏格兰货币改革家 9—528c
劳 Law,William 英国作家 9—528d
劳埃德 Lloyd,Clive 西印度群岛板球运动员 10—169b
劳埃德 Lloyd,Earl 美国篮球运动员 10—169b
劳埃德 Lloyd,Harold 美国电影演员 10—169c
劳埃德 Lloyd,Henry Demarest 美国新闻记者 10—169d
劳埃德 Lloyd,(John) Selwyn (Brooke) 英国政治家 10—169e
劳埃德 Lloyd,Marie 英国杂耍艺人 10—169e
劳埃德 TSB 集团 Lloyds TSB Group PLC 英国商业银行 10—170e
劳埃德保险社 Lloyd's of London 英国公司 10—170f
劳埃德船级社 Lloyd's Register of Shipping 英国船级学会 10—171a
劳埃德公司 Corporation of Lloyd's 保险公司 4—519f
劳埃德-韦伯 Lloyd Webber,Sir Andrew 英国作曲家 10—170d
劳达 lauda 意大利诗歌体裁 9—517f
劳德 Lauder,Estée 美国企业家 9—518a
劳德 Lauder,Sir Harry (MacLennan) 苏格兰演员 9—518b
劳德 Laud,William 英国圣公会坎特伯雷大主教 9—517f
劳德 Lauder,William 苏格兰伪文制造者 9—518c
劳德代尔 Lauderdale (Scotland) 苏格兰地区 9—518c
劳德代尔堡 Fort Lauderdale 美国城市 6—413f
劳德代尔伯爵(第八) Lauderdale,James Maitland,8th earl of 苏格兰政治家 9—518c
劳德代尔公爵 Lauderdale,John Maitland,duke of 英国大臣 9—518d
劳登 Loudoun (Scotland) 苏格兰区名 10—232f
劳登 Loudon,John Claudius 苏格兰园艺师 10—232f
劳登巴赫 Laudenbach,Pierre-Jules-Louis 法国演员 9—518a
劳登氏草属 Loudonia 植物学 10—232f
劳迪塞亚 Laodicea 亚洲古城 9—492b
劳东 Laudon,Gideon Ernest,Freiherr von (baron of) 奥地利元帅 9—518e
劳东男爵 Loudon,Gideon Ernst,Freiherr von(baron of) 奥地利元帅 10—232e
劳动(劳动力) labour 经济学 9—431d
劳动法 labour law 法律 9—432e
劳动分工 labour,division of 经济学 9—431e
劳动解放社 Labour,Liberation of 俄国组织 9—432b
劳动经济学 labour economics 经济学 9—432d
劳动骑士团 Knights of Labor 美国劳工组织 9—322a
劳动时间 labour,hours of 经济学 9—432a
劳顿 Lawton 美国城市 9—533d
劳顿 Laughton,Charles 美国电影演员 9—519d
劳厄 Laue,Max (Theodor Felix) von 德国物理学家 9—518e
劳厄衍射图样 Laue diffraction pattern 物理学 9—518f
劳恩堡 Lauenburg 原德意志公国 9—518f
劳恩伯格 Leuenberger,Niklaus 瑞士农民起义领袖 10—43d
劳夫林 Laughlin,Robert B. 美国物理学家 9—519d
劳弗 Laufer,Berthold 美国人类学家 9—519a
劳工节 Labor Day 国际节日 9—430f
劳工联合会联盟 Federation of Labour Exchanges (FBT) 法国劳工组织联盟 6—263d
劳合·乔治 Lloyd George,David 英国首相 10—169f
劳赫鲁德·加西亚 Laugerud García,Kjell Eugenio 危地马拉总统 9—519a
劳济茨诸语言 Lusatian languages 欧洲语言 10—292a
劳肯 Lauchen,Georg Joachim von 奥地利天文学家 9—517e
劳拉 Laura 文学人物 9—520b
劳拉纳 Laurana,Francesco 意大利雕刻家 9—520f
劳拉纳 Laurana,Luciano 意大利建筑师 9—521a
劳莱和哈代 Laurel,Stan;and Hardy,Oliver 美国演员 9—521d
劳勒 Lawler,Ray(mond Evenor) 澳大利亚演员 9—529e
劳雷尔 Laurel 美国马里兰州城市 9—521b
劳雷尔 Laurel 美国密西西比州城市 9—521b
劳里 Lowry,(Clarence) Malcolm 英国小说家 10—256e
劳里 Lowry,Laurence Stephen 英国画家 10—256d
劳里厄姆 Laurium 希腊城镇 9—523d
劳里科查湖 Lauricocha,Lake 秘鲁湖泊 9—523a
劳里亚 Lauria,Ruggiero di 意大利军人 9—522f
劳伦 Lauren,Ralph 美国时装设计师 9—521e
劳伦蒂乌斯 Laurentius 敌对教皇 9—522e
劳伦蒂乌斯(坎特伯雷的),圣 Laurentius of Canterbury, Saint 英国圣公会坎特伯雷大主教 9—522e
劳伦琴海槽 Laurentian Trough 北美冰槽 9—522d
劳伦琴山脉 Laurentian Mountains 加拿大山地 9—522d
劳伦斯 Lawrence 美国堪萨斯州城市 9—530a
劳伦斯 Lawrence 美国马萨诸塞州城市 9—530a
劳伦斯 Lawrence of Canterbury, Saint 英国圣公会坎特伯雷大主教 9—530c
劳伦斯 Lawrence, Abbott 美国商人 9—530c
劳伦斯 Lawrence(of the Punjab and of Grately), John Laird Mair Lawrence, 1st Baron 印度总督 9—531e
劳伦斯 Lawrance,Charles Lanier 美国航空工程师 9—529f
劳伦斯 Lawrence,D(avid) H(erbert) 英国作家 9—530d
劳伦斯 Lawrence, Ernest Orlando 美国物理学家 9—530f
劳伦斯 Lawrence,Frederick William 英国政治家 9—531a
劳伦斯 Lawrence,Gertrude 英国演员 9—531a
劳伦斯 Laurens,Henry 美国政治家 9—522b
劳伦斯 Lawrence,Sir Henry Montgomery 英国军人 9—531c
劳伦斯 Lawrence,Jacob 美国画家 9—531c
劳伦斯 Lawrence,James 美国军人 9—531d
劳伦斯 Laurence,(Jean) Margaret 加拿大作家 9—521f
劳伦斯 Lawrence,Mary Wells 美国实业家 9—531f
劳伦斯 Lawrence,Stringer 英国军人 9—532a
劳伦斯 Lawrence,Sir Thomas 英国画家 9—532c
劳伦斯 Lawrence,T(homas) E(dward) 英国战略家 9—532a
劳伦斯,圣 Lawrence,Saint 古罗马基督教殉道者 9—530b
劳伦斯(布林迪西的),圣 Lawrence of Brindisi, Saint 天主教教义师 9—530b
劳伦太德冰盖 Laurentide Ice Sheet 北美冰盖 9—522d
劳马 Rauma 芬兰城市 14—165b
劳群岛 Lau Group 斐济岛屿 9—517e
劳森 Lawson,Andrew Cowper 美国地质学家 9—533a
劳森 Lawson, Edward Levy- (English newspaperman) 英国报业主 9—533b
劳森 Lawson,Henry (Archibald) 澳大利亚作家 9—533b
劳森 Lawson,John Howard 美国剧作家 9—533c
劳森 Lawson,(Victor) Fremont 美国报纸发行人 9—533b
劳申伯格 Rauschenberg,Robert 美国画家 14—165b
劳斯 Louth 爱尔兰郡名 10—247d
劳斯 Rous,(Francis) Peyton 美国病理学家 14—420e
劳斯 Lawes,Henry 英国作曲家 9—529c
劳斯 Lawes,Sir John Bennet,1st Baronet 英国农学家 9—529c
劳斯 Lawes,Lewis Edward 美国刑罚学家 9—529d
劳斯 Lawes,William 英国作曲家 9—529d
劳斯莱斯公司 Rolls-Royce PLC 英国公司 14—361b
劳塔罗 Lautaro 智利印第安人领袖 9—524a
劳特布尔 Lauterbur,Paul 美国化学家 9—524b
劳特布伦嫩 Lauterbrunnen 瑞士城镇 9—524b
劳特岛 Laut Island 印度尼西亚岛屿 9—524a
劳托卡 Lautoka 斐济城市 9—524c
劳勿 Raub 马来西亚城市 14—165a
劳西茨山 Lausitzer Gebirge (eastern Europe) 欧洲山脉 9—524a
劳兴布施 Rauschenbusch,Walter 神学教授 14—165d
劳亚古大陆 Laurasia 地质学 9—521a
劳伊斯 Lauis (Switzerland) 瑞士城镇 9—519e

劳役偿债制 peonage 劳役形式 13—150e
劳资关系 industrial relations 经济 8—377c
《劳资关系报告与揭露法案》 Labor-Management Reporting and Disclosure Act (1959) (U.S. law) 美国法律 9—431a
《劳资关系法案》 Labor-Management Relations Act (1947) (U.S. law) 美国法律 9—431a
崂山 Lao Mountain 中国山脉 9—491e
铹(Lr) lawrencium 化学元素 9—532d
老波因特康弗特 Old Point Comfort 美国海岬 12—368c
老成土 ultisol 土壤类型 17—332f
老丑妇 hag 欧洲民间传说 7—405c
老窗户采光权 ancient lights 英国法律 1—323a
老大党 GOP (United States) 美国政党 7—211a
老大党 Grand Old Party (United States) 美国政党 7—251b
老大哥鲑 tyee 鱼类 17—305b
老第三纪 Paleogene period 地质学 12—559f
老鸽舍剧院 Vieux-Colombier, Theatre of the 法国剧院 17—557b
老公会 Old Catholic church 基督教 12—366f
老骨头 Old Bones (racehorse) 赛马 12—366e
老鹳草 geranium 草本植物 7—85d
老河口 Laohekou 中国城市 9—492c
老红砂岩 Old Red Sandstone 地质学 12—368d
老虎花 tiger-flower 植物 17—90c
老觊觎王位者 Old Pretender, the 英国历史 12—368c
老街 Lao Cai 越南城镇 9—491d
老君 Lao-chün 中国哲学家 9—491d
老君庙 Laojunmiao 中国城镇 9—492d
老卡拉巴尔 Old Calabar (Nigeria) 尼日利亚城镇 12—366f
老流派 Escola Velha 西班牙戏剧流派 6—129a
老年 old age 生理学 12—366b
老年科学和老年医学 gerontology and geriatrics 医学科学 7—99e
老年人 senior citizen 60岁或65岁以上的人 15—213a
老年性痴呆 senile dementia 病理学 15—212f
老年性聋 presbycusis 生理学 13—494e
老年医学 geriatrics 医学 7—87b
老人河 Oldman River 加拿大河流 12—371b
老人星 Canopus 天文学 3—408c
老人椅 grandfather chair 家具 7—253c
老人掌 old-man cactus 植物 12—367f
老舍 Lao She 中国作家 9—491e
老视 presbyopia 生理学 13—494e
老维克剧团 Old Vic 英国剧团 12—369a
老挝 Laos 亚洲国家 9—492f
老挝伊沙拉 Lao Issara 老挝政治运动 9—491d
老挝语 Lao language 东南亚语言 9—491d
老英格兰牧羊狗 Old English sheep dog 狗品种 12—367e
老鹰乐队 Eagles, the 美国乐队 5—494a
老子 Laozi 中国哲学家 9—494a
《老子》 Laozi 道家经典 9—494c
铑(Rh) rhodium 化学元素 14—268f
酪氨酸 tyrosine 生物化学 17—312b
酪蛋白画 casein painting 绘画 3—498c
酪乳 buttermilk 饮料 3—293c
酪蝇 skipper 昆虫 15—421a
叻武里 Ratchaburi 泰国城镇 14—161c
乐果 dimethoate 杀虫剂 5—318c
乐交 Lac Giao (Vietnam) 越南城市 9—435b
乐浪 Nangnang 古朝鲜郡名 11—554c
乐山 Leshan 中国城市 10—36f
乐山大佛 Leshan dafo 中国古代佛像 10—37b
乐园 paradise 宗教 13—31b
勒阿佛尔 Le Havre 法国城镇 9—537d
勒巴厄乌斯,圣 Lebbaeus, SAINT 圣徒 9—549a
勒班陀战役 Lepanto, Battle of 欧亚历史事件 10—30d
勒邦 Le Bon, Gustave 法国社会心理学家 9—536c
勒邦 Lebon, Philippe 法国化学家 9—549f
勒贝尔 Le Bel, Joseph-Achille 法国化学家 9—536b
勒贝格 Lebesgue, Henri-Léon 法国数学家 9—549b
勒贝格积分 Lebesgue integral 数学 9—549c
勒波尔 Port, le 法国海港 13—443d
勒波夫斯基 Lepofsky, Manford (U.S. author) 美国作家 10—31e
勒波特 Le Pautre, Antoine 法国建筑师 9—538f
勒伯夫 Leboeuf, Edmond 法国元帅 9—549e
勒布 Loeb, Jacques 美国生物学家 10—184f
勒布朗 Le Brun, Charles 法国画家 9—536c
勒布朗 Lebrun, Charles-François, DUC (duke) DE PLAISANCE, PRINCE DE L' EMPIRE 法国政治家 9—550b
勒布伦 Lebrun, Albert 法国总统 9—550a
勒达 Leda 希腊传说人物 9—552d
勒代斯库 Rădescu, Nicolae 罗马尼亚军官、政治人物 14—109f
勒德布尔 Ledebour, Georg 德国政治家 9—552e
勒德拉姆 Ratlām 印度中央邦城镇 14—163c
勒德洛 Ludlow, Edmund 英国政治家 10—272f
勒德纳吉里 Ratnāgiri 印度城镇 14—163c
勒丁顿 Ludington, Sybil 美国独立战争英雄 10—272e
勒杜 Ledoux, Claude-Nicolas 法国建筑师 9—553b
勒顿 Lurton, Horace H(armon) 美国最高法院大法官 10—291d
勒法努 Le Fanu, Sheridan 爱尔兰作家 9—537c
勒菲埃尔 Lefuel, Hector-Martin 法国建筑师 9—559c
勒菲弗尔·戴塔普尔 Lefèvre d'Étaples, Jacques 法国人文学家 9—559b
勒费弗尔 Lefèbvre, Anne 法国作家 9—558e
勒费弗尔 Lefebvre, Georges 法国历史学家 9—558f
勒费弗尔 Lefebvre, Marcel(-François) 法国大主教 9—559a
勒费弗尔 Lefebvre, (Pierre-) François-Joseph, DUC (duke) DE DANTZIG 法国元帅 9—558f
勒夫 Love, Augustus Edward Hough 英国地球物理学家 10—249c
勒夫勒 Loeffler, Charles Martin (Tornow) 美国作曲家 10—185a
勒夫勒 Löffler, Friedrich August Johannes 德国细菌学家 10—187a
勒弗尔阶 Reuveran Stage 地质学 14—249f
勒格罗 Legros, Alphonse 英国画家 9—563d
勒根 Lurgan 北爱尔兰城镇 10—291a
勒加利安纳 Le Gallienne, Eva 美国演员 9—537d
勒姜人 Rejang 印度尼西亚明古鲁省的部落 14—213a
勒卡雷 Le Carré, John 英国作家 9—536d
勒科克 Lecocq, (Alexandre) Charles 法国作曲家 9—551e
勒科克·德·布瓦博德朗 Lecoq de Boisbaudran, Paul-Émile 法国化学家 9—552a
勒克莱尔 Leclerc, Charles(-Victor-Emmanuel) 法国将军 9—551b
勒克莱尔 Leclerc, Georges-Louis (French naturalist) 法国博物学家 9—551c
勒克莱尔 Leclerc, Jean 圣经学者 9—551d
勒克莱尔 Leclerc, Jacques-Philippe 圣经学者 9—551c
勒克莱尔 LeClercq, Tanaquil 美国演员 9—551d
勒克莱尔(大) Leclair, Jean-Marie, THE ELDER 法国作曲家 9—551a
勒克朗谢 Leclanché, Georges 法国工程师 9—551b
勒克勒索 Le Creusot 法国城镇 9—537a
勒克曼 Luckman, Sid 美国橄榄球运动员 10—270b
勒克瑙 Lucknow 印度城市 10—270c
《勒克瑙协定》 Lucknow Pact 印度历史 10—270d
勒克斯 lux 计量单位 10—302f
勒孔特·德·李勒 Leconte de Lisle, Charles-Marie-René 法国诗人 9—551e
勒库弗勒 Lecouvreur, Adrienne 法国演员 9—552a
勒利德布尔 Lalitpur 印度城镇 9—457f
勒利德布尔 Lalitpur 尼泊尔城镇 9—458a

勒卢赫 Lelouch, Claude 法国电影导演 10—2b
勒卢瓦尔 Leloir, Luis Federico 阿根廷生物化学家 10—2b
勒鲁 Leroux, Gaston 法国小说家 10—35a
勒马斯 Lemass, Sean F(rancis) 爱尔兰总理 10—3b
勒马松 Le Maçon, Robert 法国大法官 9—538a
勒曼 Lehmann, Johann Gottlob 德国地质学家 9—564b
勒曼 Lehmann, Lilli 德国歌唱家 9—564c
勒曼 Lehmann, Lotte 德国歌唱家 9—564d
勒芒 Le Mans 法国城市 9—538a
勒芒耐力大奖赛 Le Mans Grand Prix d'Endurance 汽车赛 9—538c
勒梅尔·德·贝尔热 Lemaire de Belges, Jean 瓦隆诗人、历史学家 10—2e
勒梅斯特尔 Le Maistre, Antoine 法国神学家 9—538a
勒梅斯特尔·德萨西 Le Maistre de Sacy, Isaac-Louis 法国神学家 9—538a
勒梅特 Lemaître, (François-Élie-) Jules 法国剧作家 10—3a
勒梅特 Lemaître, Georges 比利时天文学家 10—2f
勒梅西埃 Lemercier, Jacques 法国建筑师 10—3d
勒蒙 LeMond, Greg 美国自行车运动员 10—5a
勒蒙尼耶 Lemonnier, (Antoine-Louis-) Camille 比利时作家 10—5a
勒米尔蒙 Remiremont 法国城镇 14—222d
勒莫安 Lemoyne, Jean-Baptiste 法国雕刻家 10—5b
勒莫安·德·边维尔 Le Moyne de Bienville, Jean-Baptiste 法国探险家 9—538c
勒莫安·迪贝维尔 Le Moyne d'Iberville, Pierre 法国军人、探险家 9—538d
勒默尔酒杯 Römer 酒器 14—385b
勒默西埃 Lemercier, (Louise-Jean) Népomucène 法国剧作家 10—3e
勒姆 Röhm, Ernst 德国军官 14—356b
勒姆尼库沃尔恰 Rîmnicu Vîlcea 罗马尼亚县城 14—302d
勒拿河 Lena River 俄罗斯河流 10—5e
勒纳 Lerner, Alan Jay 美国歌剧作者 10—34d
勒纳 Lerner, Abba P. 美国经济学家 10—34c
勒纳 Lenard, Philipp 德国物理学家 10—5f
勒纳尔 Renard, Charles 法国军事工程师 14—226d
勒纳尔 Renard, Jules 法国作家 14—226d
勒纳尔 Renart, Jean 法国诗人 14—226f
勒南 Renan, (Joseph-) Ernest 法国历史学家、神学家 14—226c
勒南兄弟 Le Nain, Antoine, Louis, and Mathieu 法国画家 9—538d
勒内(法兰西的) Renée of France 宗教改革人物 14—228a
勒内一世 René I 法国贵族 14—227e
勒尼奥 Regnault, Henri-Victor 法国化学家、物理学家 14—205c
勒尼奥伯爵 Regnault de Saint Jean d'Angély, Michel-Louis-Étienne, Comte 法国行政官 14—205d
勒尼亚尔 Regnard, Jean-François 法国戏剧家 14—205b
勒努瓦 Lenoir, (Jean-Joseph-) Étienne 法国发明家 10—12f
勒努维耶 Renouvier, Charles-Bernard 法国哲学家 14—232a
勒诺多 Renaudot, Théophraste 法国医生、新闻业之父 14—227a
勒诺尔芒 Lenormant, François 法国亚述学家 10—13b
勒诺尔芒 Lenormand, Henri-René 法国戏剧家 10—12f
勒诺尔芒 Lenormand, Louis-Sebastien 法国航空家 10—13a
勒诺特尔 Le Nôtre, André 法国园林建筑师 9—538e
勒庞 Le Pen, Jean-Marie 法国民族主义者 9—538f
勒蓬廷山脉 Lepontine Alps 欧洲山脉 10—31e
勒皮 Le Puy 法国城市 9—539b
勒普顿 Lupton, Thomas Goff 英国雕版画家 10—290c
勒普拉 Le Play, (Pierre-Guillaume-) Frédéric 法国社会学家 9—539a
勒琴斯 Lutyens, Sir Edwin (Landseer) 英国建筑师 10—302a
勒让德 Legendre, Adrien-Marie 法国数学家 9—561b
勒热夫 Rzhev 俄国城市 14—477f
勒热纳 Le Jeune, Claude 法国作曲家 9—537f
勒热纳 Lejeune, Louis-François, Baron 法国将军、石版画家 10—1b
勒萨日 Lesage, Alain-René 法国作家 10—35f
勒萨日 Lesage, Jean 加拿大政治家 10—36a
勒沙普利埃 Le Chapelier, Jean 法国政治家 9—536e
勒舍婆那陀 Ṛṣabhanātha 印度耆那教始祖 14—434c
勒斯滕堡 Rustenburg 南非城镇 14—466d
勒索 extortion 法律 6—198b
勒泰利耶 Le Tellier, François-Michel 法国政治家 9—539d
勒泰利耶 Le Tellier, Michel 法国政治家 9—539d
勒忒 Lethe 希腊神话 10—41f
勒图凯-巴黎普拉日 Le Touquet-Paris-Plage 法国城镇 9—539e
勒托 Leto 古典神话 10—42a
勒瓦娄哇文化期打制石片技术 Levalloisian stone-flaking technique 人类学 10—44d
勒瓦卢瓦-佩雷 Levallois -Perret 法国城市 10—44c
勒威 Loewe, Frederick 德国作曲家 10—186e
勒威 Loewe, (Johann) Carl (Gottfried) 美国作曲家 10—186e
勒威克 Lerwick 苏格兰城镇 10—35c
勒威耶 Le Verrier, Urbain-Jean-Joseph 法国天文学家 9—539f
勒韦迪 Reverdy, Pierre 法国诗人、道德家 14—251b
勒维 Loewi, Otto 美国药理学家 10—186f
勒维 Loewy, Salomon 奥地利作曲家 10—187a
勒维克 Lévesque, René 加拿大政治家 10—46b
勒维特 Leavitt, Henrietta Swan 美国天文学家 9—547c
勒温 Lewin, Kurt 美国心理学家 10—50c
勒夏忒列 Le Chatelier, Henry-Louis 法国化学家 9—536f
勒辛 Rössing 纳米比亚铀矿 14—410f
勒叙厄 Le Sueur, Eustache 法国画家 9—539d
勒絮尔 Lesueur, Jean-François 法国作曲家 10—41c
勒伊肯 Luyken, Jan 荷兰诗人 10—305d
勒伊特 Ruyter, Michiel Adriaanszoon de 荷兰海军舰队司令 14—472b
雷 thunder 气象学 17—70b
雷 Rais, Gilles de 法国元帅 14—128e
雷 Retz, Gilles de 法国元帅 14—247e
雷 Rae, John 美国经济学家、医生、教师 14—120a
雷 Rae, John 苏格兰医生、探险家 14—120b
雷 Ray, Jean 比利时小说家 14—169f
雷 Ray, John 英格兰博物学家、生物学家 14—170a
雷 Ray, James Earl 美国抢劫犯 14—169e
雷 Ray, Man 美国摄影家、画家 14—170b
雷 Ray, Nicholas 美国电影编剧、导演 14—170e
雷阿尔 real 巴西货币单位 14—178b
雷巴奇耶 Rybachye 吉尔吉斯斯坦城市 14—474d
雷暴 thunderstorm 气象学 17—70f
雷贝克琴 rebec 乐器 14—182b
雷贝洛 Rebelo, Jorge 非洲诗人、律师 14—182c
雷宾斯克 Rybinsk 俄罗斯城市 14—474d
雷宾斯克水库 Rybinsk Reservoir 俄罗斯伏尔加河水库 14—474e
雷伯 Reber, Grote 英国天文学家、无线电工程师 14—182c
雷伯恩 Raeburn, Sir Henry 苏格兰画家 14—120d
雷伯恩 Rayburn, Sam 美国众议员 14—171d
雷布查人 Lepchā 亚洲民族 10—30e
雷布曼 Rebmann, Johannes 传教士、探险家 14—182d
雷布尼克 Rybnik 波兰城市 14—474e
雷达 radar 电子学 14—108a
雷岛 Ré Island 法国比斯开湾岛屿 14—175b
雷德贝里 Rydberg, Viktor 瑞典作家 14—474f
雷德布拉夫 Red Bluff 美国城市 14—187b
雷德布里奇 Redbridge 英格兰自治市 14—191c
雷德迪尔 Red Deer 加拿大城市 14—188b
雷德迪尔河 Red Deer River 加拿大河流 14—188c
雷德尔 Redl, Alfred 奥地利军事情报首脑 14—193c

雷德尔 Raeder, Erich 德国海军总司令 14—120e
雷德菲尔德 Redfield, Robert 美国文化人类学家 14—192b
雷德福 Redford, (Charles) Robert 美国演员 14—192d
雷德格雷夫 Redgrave, Sir Michael (Scudamore) 英国戏剧、电影演员 14—192e
雷德格雷夫 Redgrave, Vanessa 美国演员 14—192e
雷德河 Red River 美国河流 14—189e
雷德河移民区 Red River Settlement 加拿大移民定居点 14—190a
雷德河印第安战争 Red River Indian War 美国历史 14—189f
雷德河战役 Red River Campaign 美国南北战争史 14—189f
雷德克劳德 Red Cloud 美国城市 14—187f
雷德克利夫 Redcliffe 澳大利亚城市 14—191e
雷德兰兹 Redlands 美国城市 14—193d
雷德利希 Redlich, Joseph 奥地利政治家、历史学家 14—193d
雷德罗克河 Red Rock River 美国河流 14—190a
雷德蒙 Redmond 美国华盛顿州城市 14—193e
雷德蒙 Redmond 美国俄勒冈州城市 14—193e
雷德蒙 Redmond, John (Edward) 爱尔兰民族主义党领袖 14—193e
雷德沃尔德 Raedwald 东英吉利国王 14—120e
雷德伍德城 Redwood City 美国城市 14—195d
雷德伍德国家公园 Redwood National Park 美国国家公园 14—195d
雷登 Rheden 荷兰城市 14—259a
雷迪 Reidy, Affonso (Eduardo) 巴西建筑师 14—208f
雷迪 Reddie, Cecil 英国教育改革家 14—191e
雷迪 Redi, Francesco 意大利医师、诗人 14—192f
雷迪奇 Redditch 英格兰区名 14—191f
雷蒂 Réti, Richard 匈牙利国际象棋大师 14—245e
雷蒂夫 Retief, Piet 布尔人领袖 14—246b
雷蒂孔山 Rhätikon Mountains 欧洲雷提亚山脉山群 14—258d
雷蒂库斯 Rheticus, Georg Joachim 天文学家、数学家 14—260b
雷蒂罗公园 Retiro Park 西班牙公园 14—246d
雷电崇拜 thunder cult 史前信仰及习俗 17—70d
雷电华影片公司 RKO Radio Pictures, Inc. 美国电影制片厂 14—322c
雷电式战斗机 Thunderbolt (U.S. aircraft) 军用飞机 17—70e
雷丁 Reading 英国城镇 14—176e
雷丁 Reading 美国宾夕法尼亚州城市 14—176f
雷丁 Redding 英国城镇 14—191e
雷丁 Reding, Aloys 瑞士政治家、军事统帅 14—193a
雷丁 Reding, Ital 瑞士政治家 14—193a
雷丁 Redding, Otis 美国歌手 14—191f
雷丁 Radin, Paul 美国人类学家 14—113b
雷丁公司 Reading Company 美国公司 14—177b
雷东 Redon, Odilon 法国画家 14—193f
雷东多比奇 Redondo Beach 美国城市 14—194b
雷恩 Rennes 法国城市 14—230b
雷恩 Wren, Sir Christopher 英国建筑师 18—343d
雷恩 Raine, Kathleen 英国女诗人、评论家 14—127e
雷恩 Renn, Ludwig 德国小说家 14—229e
雷恩巴罗 Rainborow, Thomas 英格兰军人 14—127a
雷恩彩陶 Rennes faience 法国陶器 14—230c
雷恩奎斯特 Rehnquist, William 美国最高法院大法官 14—206e
雷恩斯 Rains, Claude 美国演员 14—128c
雷恩沃特 Rainwater, James 美国物理学家 14—128d
雷夫尔斯托克 Revelstoke 加拿大城市 14—250e
雷夫尔斯托克山国家公园 Mount Revelstoke National Park 加拿大公园 11—441e
雷夫逊 Revson, Charles H(askeell) 美国商人 14—253e
雷盖 reggae 音乐舞蹈 14—203d
雷戈·卡瓦尔坎蒂 Rêgo Cavalcanti, José Lins do 巴西作家 14—206a
雷格尔 Reger, Max 德国作曲家 14—203c
雷格拉 Regla 古巴城市 14—205a
雷格泰姆 ragtime 音乐 14—123a
雷根斯堡 Regensburg 德国城市 14—202f
雷公 Leigong 中国神话 9—568d
雷古卢斯 Regulus, Marcus Atilius 罗马将军、政治家 14—206c
雷管 detonator 起爆装置 5—267b
雷圭元 Lei Guiyuan 中国工艺美术家 9—565d
雷赫托宁 Lehtonen, Joel 芬兰小说家 9—565b
雷亨巴赫 Reichenbach, Georg von 德国天文仪器制造家 14—207c
雷霍博特 Rehoboth 纳米比亚城镇 14—206f
雷霍沃特 Reḥovot 以色列城市 14—207a
雷吉奥 Régio, José 葡萄牙诗人 14—204b
雷吉诺 Regino von Prüm 德国编年史家 14—204b
雷吉斯坦 Rīgestān 阿富汗干旱高原区 14—298a
雷加尔管风琴 regal 乐器 14—201e
雷贾伊扎德·马哈茂德·艾克雷姆 Recaizade Mahmud Ekrem (Turkish author) 土耳其作家 14—182e
雷焦艾米利亚 Reggio nell'Emilia 意大利城市 14—203f
雷焦公爵 Reggio, Nicolas-Charles Oudinot, duc de (duke of) 乌迪诺公爵 14—203e
雷焦卡拉布里亚 Reggio di Calabria 意大利城市 14—203e
雷金纳德 Reginald of Châtillon 安条克公爵 14—204a
雷卡米耶夫人 Récamier, (Jeanne-Françoise) Julie(-Adélaïde), dame de 法国沙龙主人 14—182f
雷科德 Recorde, Robert 英国医生、数学家 14—185a
雷克灵豪森 Recklinghausen 德国城市 14—183f
雷克灵豪森 Recklinghausen, Friedrich Daniel von 德国病理学家 14—184a
雷克吕斯 Reclus, (Jean-Jacques-) Élisée 法国地理学家 14—184a
雷克纳 Requena 西班牙城市 14—238b
雷克瑟姆 Wrexham 威尔士郡级市 18—345e
雷克瑟姆 Wrexham 威尔士城镇 18—345f
雷克森斯-苏尼加 Requesens y Zúñiga, Luis de 西班牙驻尼德兰总督 14—238c
雷克斯 Raikes, Robert 英国新闻记者、慈善家 14—124d
雷克斯堡 Rexburg 美国城市 14—254c
雷克斯罗思 Rexroth, Kenneth 美国画家、作家、诗人 14—254d
雷克斯猫 Rex cat 猫品种 14—254c
雷克托 Recto, Claro Mayo 菲律宾政治家 14—185f
雷克雅未克 Reykjavík 冰岛首都 14—255a
雷夸伊文化 Recuay 南美古代文化 14—186b
雷兰德 Rejlander, Oscar G(ustav) 瑞典画家、摄影家 14—213a
雷勒斯 Reles, Abe 美国凶手、黑帮匪徒 14—214f
雷利 Raleigh, Sir Walter 英国探险家、作家 14—133a
雷利 Raleigh, Sir Walter (Alexander) 苏格兰作家 14—133c
雷利兹阶 Relizian Stage 地质学 14—216b
雷列耶夫 Ryleyev, Kondraty Fyodorovich 俄国诗人 14—476e
雷龙属 Brontosaurus 古生物学 3—180e
雷马 Rema 波兰学者 14—216c
雷马根 Remagen 德国城市 14—216c
雷马克 Remak (Hebrew grammarian) 希伯来语法家 14—216c
雷马克 Remarque, Erich Maria 德国小说家 14—216e
雷马克 Remak, Robert 德国胚胎学家、神经病学家 14—216c
雷芒多 Raimundo, Don 西班牙神职人员 14—125e
雷蒙 Raymond 统治者之名 14—172a
雷蒙 Raymond 安条克公爵 14—172a
雷蒙(普瓦捷的) Raymond of Poitiers 安条克公爵 14—172e
雷蒙(圣吉尔的) Raymond of Saint-Gilles 图卢兹伯爵 14—172e
雷蒙德 Raymond, Alex(ander Gillespie) 美国连环漫画家 14—172e
雷蒙德 Raymond, Henry Jarvis 美国新闻记者、政治家 14—172e
雷蒙德(佩尼亚福特的), 圣 Raymond of Peñafort, Saint 多明我会修

士 14—172d
雷蒙德特雷斯 Raymond Terrace 澳大利亚城镇 14—173a
雷蒙六世 Raymond VI 图卢兹伯爵 14—172c
雷蒙七世 Raymond VII 图卢兹伯爵 14—172c
雷蒙三世 Raymond III 特里波利十字军团伯爵 14—172d
雷蒙四世 Raymond IV 图卢兹伯爵、普罗旺斯侯爵 14—172b
雷蒙一世 Raymond I 图卢兹伯爵 14—172d
雷明顿 Remington,Eliphalet 美国发明家 14—222c
雷明顿 Remington,Frederic 美国画家、雕刻家 14—222c
雷姆 rem 计量单位 14—216b
雷姆森 Remsen,Ira 美国化学家 14—223a
雷姆沙伊德 Remscheid 德国城市 14—223a
雷穆斯 Remus (Roman mythology) 传说中的罗马城建立者 14—223b
雷纳 Renner,Karl 奥地利总理 14—230a
雷纳 Rainer,Yvonne 美国舞蹈编导 14—127e
雷纳尔神父 Raynal, Guillaume-Thomas, abbé de 法国作家、宣传家 14—173a
雷纳努斯 Rhenanus,Beatus 德国人文主义者 14—259e
雷纳图斯 Renatus,Flavius Vegetius 罗马军事著作者 14—226f
雷乃 Resnais,Alain 法国电影导演 14—241a
雷尼 Reni,Guido 意大利画家 14—228e
雷尼 Reaney,James Crerar 加拿大诗人、剧作家 14—181c
雷尼 Rainey,Joseph Hayne 美国黑人众议员 14—127f
雷尼 Rainey,Ma 美国黑人歌唱家 14—128a
雷尼尔山 Rainier,Mount 美国喀斯喀特山脉 14—128b
雷尼尔山国家公园 Mount Rainier National Park 美国公园 11—441e
雷尼湖 Rainy Lake 北美湖泊 14—128e
雷尼耶 Régnier,Henri(-François-Joseph) de 法国诗人 14—205e
雷尼耶 Régnier,Mathurin 法国讽刺诗人 14—205f
雷鸟 ptarmigan 鸟类 13—566c
雷鸟 thunderbird 印第安人神话 17—70d
雷努阿尔 Raynouard,François-Juste-Marie 法国戏剧家、罗曼语语言学家 14—173b
雷诺 Reno 美国城市 14—230e
雷诺 Leino,Eino 芬兰作家 9—568e
雷诺 Renault,Louis 法国法学家、教育家 14—227c
雷诺 Renault,Louis 法国汽车制造商 14—227c
雷诺 Reno,Janet 美国律师、政府官员 14—230f
雷诺 Reynolds,Mary Ellen 美国女演员 14—255f
雷诺 Reynolds,Osborne 英国工程师、物理学家 14—255f
雷诺 Reynaud,Paul 法国政治家 14—255c
雷诺阿 Renoir,Jean 法国电影导演、画家 14—231a
雷诺阿 Renoir,Pierre-Auguste 法国画家 14—231c
雷诺·德·蒙托邦 Renaud DE MONTAUBAN 法国传说英雄 14—226f
雷诺汽车公司 Renault 法国公司 14—227b
雷诺萨 Reynosa 墨西哥城市 14—256c
雷诺氏病 Raynaud's disease 妇女病 14—173b
雷诺数 Reynolds number 物理学 14—256b
雷诺特 Renault,Mary 南非小说家 14—227d
雷诺兹 Reynolds,Albert 爱尔兰总理 14—255d
雷诺兹 Reynolds,Sir Joshua 英国画家 14—255d
雷诺兹 Reynolds,Walter 坎特伯雷大主教 14—256a
雷诺兹烟草控股公司 Reynolds Tobacco Holdings 美国公司 14—256b
雷普顿 Repton 英格兰堂区 14—236f
雷普顿 Repton,Humphry 英国园林设计师、风景画家 14—237a
雷齐乌斯 Retzius,Magnus Gustaf 瑞典解剖学家、人类学家 14—247f
雷乔蒙塔努斯 Regiomontanus 德国天文学家、数学家 14—204c
雷日科夫 Ryzhkov,Nikolay 苏联总理 14—477c
雷赛布 Lesseps,Ferdinand(-Marie),Viscount (vicomte) de 法国外交家 10—39c
雷森迪 Resende 巴西城市 14—238f
雷森迪 Resende,Garcia de 葡萄牙诗人、编年史家 14—239a
雷申山口 Reschenscheideck (Italy) 意大利山口 14—238e
雷神 Thunderer 宗教天神 17—70e
雷神式火箭 Thor rocket 航天器运载火箭 17—54b
雷石东 Redstone,Sumner 美国传媒公司决策人 14—194e
雷士贝属 Resserella 古生物学 14—243a
雷兽 brontothere 古生物学 3—180f
雷兽 titanothere 古生物学 17—115d
雷斯达尔 Ruisdael,Jacob (Isaakszoon) van 荷兰画家 14—446a
雷斯达尔 Ruysdael,Salomon van 荷兰画家 14—472a
雷斯蒂夫 Restif,Nicolas-Edme 法国小说家 14—243d
雷斯顿 Reston 美国弗吉尼亚州城市社区 14—243f
雷斯克 Reszke,Jean de 波兰男高音歌唱家 14—245b
雷斯皮吉 Respighi,Ottorino 意大利作曲家 14—241f
雷斯枢机主教 Retz,Jean-François-Paul de Gondi,cardinalde 投石党运动的法国贵族叛乱领袖之一 14—247e
雷斯特尔夫人 Restell,Madame 美国施堕胎术者、避孕用品供应者 14—243c
雷斯托梅尔 Restormel 英格兰自治市 14—244b
雷塔卢莱乌 Retalhuleu 危地马拉城市 14—245d
雷特尔 Rethel,Alfred 德国画家 14—245d
雷特氏综合征 Rett syndrome 疾病 14—247d
雷提亚-罗曼语诸方言 Raeto-Romance dialects 欧洲语言 14—121a
雷提亚山脉 Rhaetian Alps 欧洲山脉 14—257d
雷提亚语 Raetian language 古雷提亚人语言 14—121a
雷提亚语诸方言 Rhaetian dialects 欧洲语言 14—257e
雷瓦 Rewa 印度城镇 14—254b
雷瓦尔 Reval (Estonia) 爱沙尼亚首都 14—249f
雷瓦河 Rewa River 斐济河流 14—254c
雷瓦里 Rewāri 印度城市 14—254c
雷维厄斯 Revius,Jacobus 荷兰基督教诗人 14—251f
雷维尔 Revell,Viljo 芬兰建筑师 14—250c
雷维尔斯 Revels,Hiram R(hoades) 美国教士、教育家 14—250c
雷维亚希赫多群岛 Revillagigedo Islands 太平洋群岛 14—251f
雷文 Raven,Simon (Arthur Noël) 英国小说家、剧作家 14—166e
雷文故事 Raven cycle 口头传说 14—166f
雷文斯克罗夫特 Ravenscroft, George 英国玻璃制造商 14—167e
雷文斯克罗夫特 Ravenscroft,Thomas 英国作曲家 14—167f
雷文特洛乌伯爵 Reventlow,Christian Ditlev Frederik,Count (Lensgreve) 丹麦官员 14—250f
雷乌斯 Reus 西班牙城市 14—248f
雷武埃尔塔斯 Revueltas,José 墨西哥小说家 14—254a
雷武埃尔塔斯 Revueltas, Silvestre 墨西哥作曲家 14—254a
雷西姆农 Réthimnon 希腊州首府、港口 14—245e
雷西纳 Resina (Italy) 意大利城镇 14—240b
雷西斯滕西亚 Resistencia 阿根廷省会 14—240e
雷西瓦 Lysva 俄罗斯城市 10—319b
雷西亚山口 Resia Pass 欧洲山口 14—239d
雷希察 Reşiţa 罗马尼亚城市 14—240f
雷锡昂公司 Raytheon Company 美国公司 14—173e
雷亚尔城 Ciudad Real 西班牙省份 4—252b
雷亚尔城 Ciudad Real 西班牙城市 4—252c
雷亚尔城 Vila Real 葡萄牙城镇 17—560e
雷亚尔港 Puerto Real 西班牙城镇 14—16c
雷亚尔山脉 Real,Cordillera 玻利维亚山系 14—178b
雷耶斯 Reyes,Alfonso 墨西哥作家、外交官 14—254e
雷耶斯(普列托) Reyes (Prieto),Rafael 哥伦比亚探险家、总统 14—254f
雷耶斯·巴索阿尔托 Reyes Basoalto,Neftalí Ricardo (writer) 智利诗人 14—254f

雷伊 Ray, Charlotte E. 美国律师 14—169e
雷伊 Rey, Jacobus Hercules de la 布尔人领袖 14—254d
雷伊 Ray, Satyajit 印度电影导演 14—170f
雷扎耶 Reẓā'īyeh (Iran) 伊朗城市 14—257a
雷州半岛 Leizhou Bandao 中国半岛 10—1a
镭(Ra) radium 化学元素 14—118e
罍 lei 酒器 9—565c
垒固 Loi-kaw 缅甸城镇 10—192f
垒球 softball 体育项目 15—485e
累犯(行为) recidivism 法律 14—183d
累范特风 levanter 气象学 10—44e
累进税 progressive tax 经济学 13—530a
累普济乌斯 Lepsius, Karl Richard 德国埃及学家 10—32a
累退税 regressive tax 经济学 14—206a
累西腓 Recife 巴西城市 14—183d
肋骨 rib 解剖学 14—274f
肋木属 Pleuromeia 古生物学 13—370d
肋球藻属 Pleurococcus 植物学 13—370c
泪管与泪腺 tear duct and gland 解剖学 16—512b
泪囊炎 dacryocystitis 疾病 5—103f
类鼻疽 melioidosis 传染病 11—97c
类比 analogy 推理方法 1—310a
类比 qiyas 伊斯兰教法学 14—70c
类病毒 viroid 病毒结构 18—14d
类毒素 toxoid 细菌毒素 17—182d
类风湿性关节炎 rheumatoid arthritis 疾病 14—261b
类固醇 steroid 化合物 16—227e
类固醇激素 steroid hormone 化合物 16—228a
类胡萝卜素 carotenoid 生物色素 3—474d
类黄酮 flavonoid 生物色素 6—352c
类人猿 ape 灵长类动物 1—407d
类人猿亚目 Anthropoidea 动物学 1—380b
类肉瘤病 sarcoidosis 疾病 15—63c
类石 lithops 植物 10—147e
类蜀黍 teosinte (*Zea mexicana* or *Euchlaena mexicana*) 草本植物 16—547d
类星体 quasar 天文学 14—80a
类型论 types, theory of 逻辑学 17—307d
类型名 type name 戏剧 17—307c
类型学 typology 分类方法 17—309e
类叶升麻 baneberry 草本植物 2—196d
类异戊二烯 isoprenoid 有机物 8—473c
棱齿龙属 Hypsilophodon 古生物学 8—296e
棱镜 prism 光学器件 13—519d
楞次定律 Lenz's law 电磁学 10—15c
楞高语 Rengao language 越南语言 14—228c
《楞伽阿跋多罗宝经》 kāvatāra-sūtra 佛教经典 9—486f
冷冻 freezing 食品保鲜法 6—472e
冷冻手术 cryosurgery 医疗技术 5—42c
冷发射 cold emission (physics) 物理学 4—339a
冷港战役 Cold Harbor, battles of 美国历史 4—339a
冷湖 Lenghu 中国城镇 10—6f
冷静爵士乐 cool jazz 音乐 4—480e
冷凝器 condenser 冷却装置 4—415e
冷球蛋白血症 cryoglobulinemia 病理状态 5—42b
冷泉三郎 Reizei Saburō (Japanese painter) 日本画家 14—213a
冷却系统 cooling system 机械设备 4—482b
冷杉 fir 木本植物 6—324c
冷杉香脂 balsam of fir 香脂 2—181d
冷水花属 Pilea 草本植物 13—302c
冷水江 Lengshuijiang 中国城市 10—7a
冷血性 cold-bloodedness 动物学 4—338f
冷阴症 frigidity 心理学、性学 6—495b
冷战 Cold War 国际政治 4—339a
厘金 lijin 中国清代税种 10—95f
厘米 centimetre 计量单位 3—565b
狸藻 bladderwort 植物 2—522e
离岸流 rip current 流体动力学 14—310e
离合器 clutch 机器部件 4—307f
离合诗 acrostic 文学 1—58e
离婚 divorce 法律 5—348a
离婚书 get 犹太教文件 7—103f
离解 dissociation 化学 5—343c
《离骚》 Lisao 中国文学 10—134f
离心泵 centrifugal pump 机器设备 4—5c
离心机 centrifuge 机械装置 4—5d
离心力 centrifugal force 物理学 4—5b
离子 ion 物理学 8—430b
离子对 ion pair 化学、物理学 8—430f
离子键 ionic bond 化学 8—432d
离子交换反应 ion-exchange reaction 化学 8—430c
离子交换容量 ion-exchange capacity 化学 8—430b
离子交换树脂 ion-exchange resin 有机化合物 8—430e
梨 pear 木本植物 13—112b
梨车人 Licchavi 印度古代部族 10—81e
梨浆虫病 piroplasmosis (animal disease) 家畜疾病 13—322c
梨俱吠陀 Rigveda 印度教古经籍 14—299d
梨形琢型 drop cut 钻石雕琢工艺 5—427a
梨园 liyuan 中国戏曲 10—165f
梨园戏 liyuanxi 中国戏曲 10—165f
梨子地 nashiji 日本工艺 12—5c
犁 plow 农具 13—374d
犁鼻器 vomeronasal organ (anatomy) 解剖学 18—47a
犁头鳐 guitarfish 鱼类 7—364c
鹂莺 superb warbler (bird) 鸟类 16—344e
黎 Loei 泰国城镇 10—185b
黎巴嫩 Lebanon 亚洲国家 9—547d
黎巴嫩山 Lebanon Mountains 地中海山脉 9—548f
黎刹 Rizal (y Alonso), José 菲律宾爱国志士、医生 14—321c
黎刹崇拜 Rizalist cult 菲律宾民族宗教 14—322a
黎刹市 Rizal City (Philippines) 菲律宾城市 14—322a
黎朝 Le DYNASTY (Vietnamese history) 越南王朝 9—536b
黎德寿 Le Duc Tho 越南政治家 9—537b
黎峨 Rigault de Genouilly, Charles 法国海军上将 14—297f
黎凡特 Levant 地理学 10—44d
黎锦熙 Li Jinxi 中国语言文字学家 10—60a
黎里 Lyly, John 英国作家 10—311b
黎利 Le Loi 越南皇帝 9—537f
黎曼 Riemann, (Georg Friedrich) Bernhard 德国数学家 14—294a
黎曼几何 Riemannian geometry 几何学 14—294d
黎曼ζ函数 Riemann zeta function 数学 14—294c
黎明俪歌 alba 音乐 1—172b
黎塞留 Richelieu, Armand-Jean du Plessis, cardinaet duc de 法国大臣 14—285e
黎塞留公爵 Richelieu, Armand-Emmanuel du Plessis, duke (duc) de 法国贵族、军人 14—285d
黎塞留公爵 Richelieu, Louis-François-Armand du Plessis, duc de (duke of) 法国贵族、军人、政治家 14—285f
黎塞留河 Richelieu River 加拿大河流 14—286a
黎塞留河畔圣让 Saint-Jean-sur-Richelieu 加拿大城市 14—514c
黎圣宗 Le Thanh Tong 越南皇帝 9—539e
黎施潘 Richepin, Jean 法国诗人、戏剧家 14—286b
黎笋 Le Duan 越南政治家 9—537b
黎太祖 Le Thai To (Vietnamese emperor) 越南皇帝 9—539e
黎文悦 Le Van Duyet 越南政治家 9—539f
黎文中 Le Van Trung (Vietnamese religious leader) 越南宗教领袖

9—539f
黎逸 Roi Et 泰国城镇 14—356f
黎语 Li language 中国语言 10—61c
黎元洪 Li Yuanhong 中国北洋政府总统 10—66b
黎族 Li 中国民族 10—56e
藜 goosefoot 草本植物 7—210f
藜芦属 Veratrum 植物学 17—511a
礼 li 中国儒家的社会道德规范 10—57b
礼拜 salat 伊斯兰教礼仪 14—538e
礼拜式戏剧 liturgical drama 戏剧 10—152f
礼拜仪式音乐 liturgical music 宗教音乐 10—153b
《礼记》 Liji 中国儒家经典 10—95d
礼节 etiquette 社会学 6—152a
"礼炮"号航天站 Salyut 苏联航天站系列 14—558e
礼品交换 gift exchange 社会风俗 7—124e
礼萨 Rezā 波斯画家 14—256d
礼萨·巴列维 Reza Shah Pahlavi 伊朗国王 14—256e
礼俗性残毁 mutilation, ritual 风俗 11—518a
礼仪交换 ceremonial exchange 社会学 4—10f
礼仪沐浴 ritual bath 宗教或巫术仪式 14—314e
礼仪文学 courtesy literature 文学 4—550c
礼舟 Bucentaur 威尼斯共和国大帆船 3—218d
李 plum 木本植物 13—375b
李 Lee, Ann 宗教领袖 9—553e
李 Lee, Arthur 美国外交官 9—553e
李 Lee, Darid M. 美国物理学家 9—553f
李 Lee, Gypsy Rose 美国演员 9—554a
李 Lee, Harper 美国作家 9—554b
李 Lee, Henry 美国军人 9—554b
李 Lee, John Clifford Hodges 美国军人 9—554d
李 Lie, Jonas (Lauritz Idemil) 挪威小说家 10—83f
李 Lee, Ivy Ledbetter 美国公共关系工作者 9—554c
李 Lee, Laurie 英国作家 9—554d
李 Lee, Mary Ann 美国芭蕾舞演员 9—554e
李 Lee, Manfred B. 美国作家 9—554e
李 Lie, (Marius) Sophus 挪威数学家 10—84a
李 Lee, Nathaniel 英国剧作家 9—554e
李 Lee, Richard Henry 美国政治家 9—554f
李 Lee, Robert E. 美国军人 9—555a
李 Lee, Spike 美国电影导演 9—555c
李 Lee, Vernon 英国作家 9—555e
李 Lee, William 英国发明家 9—555e
李-阿思本舰队 Lay-Osborn flotilla 中国历史 9—534d
李昂 Li Ang 中国皇帝 10—57b
李翱 Li Ao 中国哲学家、诗人 10—57b
李奥 Lyot, Bernard(-Ferdinand) 法国天文学家 10—316e
李白 Li Bai 中国诗人 10—57c
李贲 Ly Bon 越南皇帝 10—307b
李比希 Liebig, Justus, Freiherr von (baron of) 德国化学家 10—84e
李必达 Lepidus, Marcus Aemilius 古罗马政治家 10—31d
李必达 Lepidus, Marcus Aemilius 古罗马元老 10—31d
李必达 Lepidus, Marcus Aemilius 古罗马政治家 10—31d
李冰 Li Bing 中国古代水利专家 10—57d
李卜克内西 Liebknecht, Karl 德国社会民主党人 10—85a
李卜克内西 Liebknecht, Wilhelm 德国社会主义者 10—85c
李卜曼 Liebermann, Max 德国画家 10—84d
李长春 Li Changchun 中国领导人 10—57d
李朝 Ly DYNASTY (Vietnamese history) 越南历史 10—307a
李朝 Yi DYNASTY 越南历史 18—444e
李朝风格 Yi style 朝鲜古代艺术风格 18—445c
李成 Li Cheng 中国画家 10—57f
李承晚 Rhee, Syngman 韩国总统 14—259a
李达 Li Da 中国哲学家 10—58a
李大钊 Li Dazhao 中国共产主义运动先驱 10—58c
李德奈尔 Lidner, Bengt 瑞典诗人 10—83f
李登辉 Li Denghui 中国政治人物 10—58d
李调查团 Lee Commission 印度历史 9—556a
李顿 Lytton, Sir Henry Alfred 英国喜剧演员 10—319f
李顿(克内伯沃斯的) Lytton (of Knebworth), Edward George Earle Bulwer-Lytton, 1st Baron 英国政治家、诗人 10—319c
李顿伯爵(第二) Lytton, Victor Alexander George Robert Bulwer-Lytton, 2nd Earl of 英国殖民官员 10—319f
李顿伯爵(第一) Lytton, (Edward) Robert Bulwer-Lytton, 1st Earl of 英国外交家 10—319e
李顿调查团 Lytton Commission 国际联盟史 10—320a
李顿男爵和伯爵 Lytton, BARONS AND EARLS 英国贵族之名 10—319c
李-恩菲尔德步枪 Lee-Enfield rifle 武器 9—556a
李尔 Lear 文学作品人物 9—545c
李耳 Li Erh 中国哲学家 10—58f
李夫西 Livesay, Dorothy 加拿大诗人 10—162c
李芾甘 Li Fei-kan 中国作家 10—58f
李干 prune 水果干 13—551e
李公麟 Li Gonglin 中国画家 10—58f
李固 Li Gu 中国东汉大臣、学者 10—59a
李光耀 Lee Kuan Yew 新加坡政治家 9—556a
李国鼎 Li Guoding 中国财经专家 10—59b
李贺 Li He 中国诗人 10—59b
李赫特 Richter, Sviatoslav 苏联钢琴家 14—288f
李鸿章 Li Hongzhang 中国清末大臣 10—59c
李后主 Li Hou-chu 中国诗人、皇帝 10—59e
李惠堂 Li Huitang 中国足球运动员 10—59e
李济 Li Ji 中国考古学家 10—59f
李嘉图 Ricardo, David 英国经济学家 14—277d
李诫 Li Jie 中国建筑学家 10—60a
李进忠 Li Jinzhong 中国明代宦官 10—60c
李凯原理 Riecke's principle 地质学 14—292f
李衎 Li Kan 中国画家 10—60c
李科克 Leacock, Stephen (Butler) 加拿大作家 9—540b
李可夫 Rykov, Aleksey Ivanovich 俄国革命家 14—476b
李可染 Li Keran 中国画家 10—60d
李克用 Li Keyong 中国唐代河东军首领 10—60f
李苦禅 Li Kuchan 中国画家 10—61a
李悝 Li Kui 中国战国政治家 10—61b
李适 Li Kuo 中国皇帝 10—61c
李岚清 Li Lanqing 中国国务院副总理 10—61d
李立三 Li Lisan 中国共产党早期领导人 10—62e
李利恩克龙 Liliencron, Detlev, Baron (Freiherr) von 德国作家 10—98a
李林甫 Li Linfu 中国唐代大臣 10—62e
李隆基 Li Longji 中国唐代皇帝 10—62a
李洛 Lillo, George 英国剧作家 10—99e
李洛埃 LeRoy, Mervyn 美国电影导演 10—35b
李梅 LeMay, Curtis E(merson) 美国军人 10—3c
李密 Li Mi 中国农民起义军领袖 10—62a
李曩霄 Li Nang-hsiao 中国皇帝 10—62a
李宁 Li Ning 中国体操运动员 10—62a
李鹏 Li Peng 中国人大常委会委员长 10—62c
李普曼 Lipmann, Fritz Albert 美国生物化学家 10—130e
李普曼 Lippmann, Gabriel 法国物理学家 10—131f
李普曼 Lippmann, Walter 美国新闻评论家、作家 10—132a
李普曼 Lippmann, Yom-Tob 犹太学者 10—132b
李奇微 Ridgway, Matthew B. 美国陆军军官 14—291d
李清照 Li Qingzhao 中国宋代诗人 10—62e
李瑞环 Li Ruihuan 中国政协主席 10—62f
李森科 Lysenko, Trofim Denisovich 苏联生物学家 10—317f
李善兰 Li Shanlan 中国数学家 10—63b

李商隐 Li Shangyin 中国唐代诗人 10—63a
李上佐 Yi Sang-cha 朝鲜画家 18—445b
李少君 Li Shaojun 中国西汉方士 10—63c
李时珍 Li Shizhen 中国明代医药学家 10—63d
李世民 Li Shimin 中国唐代皇帝 10—63d
李叔同 Li Shutong 中国近代教育家 10—63e
李属 Prunus 植物学 13—551f
李舜臣 Yi Sun-shin 朝鲜民族英雄 18—445d
李思训 Li Sixun 中国唐代画家 10—64b
李斯 Li Si 中国秦代政治家 10—63e
李斯特 Liszt, Franz 匈牙利钢琴演奏家、作曲家 10—140f
李斯特 List, (Georg) Friedrich 美国经济学家 10—139e
李四光 Li Siguang 中国地质学家 10—63f
李嵩 Li Song 中国宋代画家 10—64d
李太白 Li T'ai-po 中国唐代诗人 10—64f
李泰国 Lay, Horatio Nelson 英国外交官 9—534c
李唐 Li Tang 中国宋代画家 10—64f
李特沃斯 Litwos 波兰作家 10—153e
李铁拐 Li Tieguai 中国神话中的道教人物 10—65a
李霆 Yi Chŏng 朝鲜画家 18—444f
李维 Livy 古罗马历史学家 10—165c
李维诺夫 Litvinov, Maksim Maksimovich 苏联外交家 10—153d
李维乌斯·安得罗尼库斯 Livius Andronicus, Lucius 罗马史诗、戏剧的创始人 10—164f
李沃夫 Lvov, Georgy Yevgenyevich, Prince (Knyaz) 俄国政治家 10—306e
李希霍芬 Richthofen, Ferdinand Paul Wilhelm, Freiherr von 德国地理学家、地质学家 14—289a
李锡尼 Licinius 罗马皇帝 10—82e
李先念 Li Xiannian 中国领导人 10—65b
李秀成 Li Xiucheng 中国太平天国将领 10—65e
李冶 Li Ye 中国金元时期数学家 10—65f
李寅文 Yi In-mun 朝鲜画家 18—445a
李邕 Li Yong 中国唐代书法家 10—65f
李煜 Li Yu 中国五代词人、皇帝 10—66a
李渊 Li Yuan 中国唐代皇帝 10—66b
李元昊 Li Yuanhao 中国皇帝 10—66b
李远哲 Lee, Yuan T(seh) 美国化学家 9—555f
李泽冈环 Liesegang ring 物理化学 10—87e
李真 Li Zhen 中国唐代画家 10—66c
李政道 Lee, Tsung-Dao 美国物理学家 9—555c
李治 Li Zhi (Chinese emperor) 中国唐代皇帝 10—66e
李贽 Li Zhi 中国明代思想家 10—66d
李卓皓 Li Zhuohao 中国生物化学家 10—66e
李自成 Li Zicheng 中国明代农民起义领袖 10—66e
李宗仁 Li Zongren 中国国民党将领 10—66f
里阿诺斯 Rhianus 希腊诗人、学者 14—261d
里安农 Rhiannon 威尔士宗教女神 14—261d
里昂 Lyon 法国城市 10—315c
里昂 Lyonnais 法国历史地区 10—316b
里昂彩陶 Lyon faience 法国陶器 10—316a
里昂的高乃依 Lyon, Corneille de 法国画家 10—315e
里昂会议 Lyon, councils of 天主教普世会议 10—315e
里昂乃斯 Lyonnesse (ancient Scotland) 苏格兰历史地区 10—316c
里昂乃斯 Lyonnesse 英国神话 10—316c
里昂涅 Leone, Sergio 意大利电影导演 10—26b
里昂屠夫 Butcher of Lyon (Nazi leader) 纳粹首领 3—288e
里奥阿查 Ríohacha 哥伦比亚城市 14—310d
里奥班巴 Riobamba 厄瓜多尔城市 14—310c
里奥布朗库 Rio Branco 巴西城市 14—305e
《里奥布朗库法》 Rio Branco Law 巴西法律 14—305f
里奥德奥罗 Río de Oro 西撒哈拉南部地区 14—309a
里奥格兰德 Rio Grande 巴西城市 14—309d
里奥格兰德航空公司 Varig 巴西公司 17—473e
里奥加耶戈斯 Río Gallegos 阿根廷城市 14—309c
里奥克拉罗 Rio Claro 巴西城市 14—305f
里奥夸尔托 Río Cuarto 阿根廷城市 14—306a
里奥内格罗 Río Negro 阿根廷省份 14—310b
里奥汀托矿 Riotinto Mines 西班牙铜矿 14—310e
里巴斯 Ribas, Óscar (Bento) 安哥拉民俗学家 14—275b
里巴特 Ribāṭ (Morocco) 摩洛哥首都 14—275c
里保 Ribaut, Jean 法国探险家、殖民者 14—275c
里贝克 Riebeeck, Jan (Anthoniszoon) van 荷兰探险家 14—292e
里贝拉 Ribera, José de 西班牙画家 14—276e
里贝朗普雷图 Ribeirão Prêto 巴西城市 14—276c
里贝罗 Ribeiro, Aquilino (Gomes) 葡萄牙小说家 14—276c
里贝罗 Ribeiro, Bernardim 葡萄牙诗人、外交官 14—276d
里贝罗·科托 Ribeiro Couto, Rui 巴西诗人 14—276d
里本瀑布 Ribbon Fall 美国内华达山瀑布 14—275e
里比多 libido 心理学 10—77b
里宾特洛甫 Ribbentrop, Joachim von 德国外交家 14—275c
里伯 Ribe 丹麦城市 14—276c
里伯斯金 Libeskind, Daniel 美籍波兰建筑师 10—77a
里博 Ribot, Alexandre(-Felix-Joseph) 法国政治家 14—277b
里博 Ribot, Théodule-Armand 法国心理学家 14—277c
里博维莱 Ribeauvillé 法国城镇 14—276c
里布尔河 Ribble, River 英格兰河流 14—275e
里布尔河谷 Ribble Valley 英格兰区名 14—275e
里敕尔 Ritschl, Albrecht 基督教神学家 14—313e
里茨 Ritz, César 法国商人 14—314f
里得雷 Ridley, Nicholas 英格兰主教 14—292b
里德 Ried 奥地利城市 14—292f
里德 Ridder, Alfons de (Flemish novelist) 比利时佛兰芒语小说家 14—291a
里德 Reade, Charles 英国作家 14—176b
里德 Reed, Sir Carol 英国电影导演 14—195e
里德 Reid, Forrest 爱尔兰小说家 14—208b
里德 Reid, Sir George Houston 澳大利亚总理 14—208b
里德 Read, Sir Herbert 英国诗人 14—176a
里德 Reid, Harry Fielding 美国地震学家、冰川学家 14—208c
里德 Reed, John 美国诗人 14—195f
里德 Read, Opie (Percival) 美国新闻工作者、小说家 14—176b
里德 Reed, Stanley F(orman) 美国最高法院大法官 14—196a
里德 Reid, Thomas 苏格兰哲学家 14—208c
里德 Reed, Thomas B(rackett) 美国共和党领袖 14—196a
里德 Reed, Walter 美国细菌学家 14—196b
里德 Reid, Whitelaw 美国外交家 14—208e
里德伯 Rydberg, Johannes Robert 瑞典物理学家 14—474e
里德伯常量 Rydberg constant 原子物理学 14—475a
里德尔氏甲状腺炎 Riedel thyroiditis 疾病 14—293a
里德卡-克里夫兰 Redcar and Cleveland 英格兰自治市 14—191d
里德勒 Ridler, Anne (Barbara) 英国诗人、剧作家 14—292a
里德利 Ridley, Henry Nicholas 英国植物学家 14—292a
里丁侯爵(第一) Reading, Rufus Daniel Isaacs, 1st Marquess of 英国外交家 14—177a
里顿豪斯 Rittenhouse, David 美国天文学家、发明家 14—314c
里多尔菲 Ridolfi, Roberto 佛罗伦萨阴谋家 14—292c
里多运河 Rideau Canal 加拿大运河 14—291c
里恩 Rehan, Ada 美国演员 14—206d
里恩 Lean, Sir David 英国电影导演 9—544e
里恩 Rhyn, Otto Henne am 瑞士历史学家 14—272a
里恩佐 Rienzo, Cola di 意大利民众领袖 14—294f
里尔 Lille 法国城市 10—98e
里尔 Rhyl 威尔士城镇 14—271d
里尔 Riel, Louis 加拿大梅蒂人领袖 14—293e
里尔 Riehl, Wilhelm Heinrich 德国记者、历史学家 14—293e

里尔第一大学、第二大学、第三大学 Lille I, II, and III, Universities of 法国大学 10—99a
里尔富特湖 Reelfoot Lake 美国湖泊 14—197b
里尔花边 Lille lace 编织工艺品 10—99a
里尔克 Rilke, Rainer Maria 奥地利诗人 14—301a
里尔琴 lyre 乐器 10—316f
里尔舞 reel 舞蹈 14—197b
里法 Rifāʿ, Ar- 巴林城市 14—296a
里法尔 Lifar, Serge 法国舞蹈家、编导 10—88b
里法伊教团 Rifāʿīyah 伊斯兰教派别 14—296b
里芬施塔尔 Riefenstahl, Leni 德国电影演员 14—293a
里夫 RIF (Talmudic scholar) 研究《塔木德》的学者 14—295e
里夫 Rive, Richard 南非作家、教师 14—315c
里夫 Reeve, Tapping 美国法学家 14—197c
里夫比约 Rifbjerg, Klaus (Thorvald) 丹麦诗人 14—296b
里夫人 Rif 摩洛哥柏柏尔诸部落 14—295e
里夫山脉 Rif 摩洛哥山脉 14—295e
里夫斯 Reeves, William Pember 新西兰政治家 14—197d
里夫战争 Rif War 西班牙历史 14—295f
里弗顿 Riverton 美国城市 14—319e
里弗福里斯特 River Forest 美国村庄 14—315f
里弗赖纳 Riverina 澳大利亚地区 14—316d
里弗鲁日 River Rouge 美国城市 14—315f
里弗赛德 Riverside 美国城市 14—319c
里弗斯 Rivers, Larry 美国画家 14—317a
里弗斯 Rivers, Thomas Milton 美国病毒学家 14—317b
里弗斯 Rivers, W(illiam) H(alse) R(ivers) 英国医学心理学家、人类学家 14—317c
里弗斯伯爵(第二) Rivers, Anthony Woodville, 2nd Earl 英格兰贵族 14—316e
里弗斯伯爵(第一) Rivers, Richard Woodville, 1st Earl 英格兰贵族 14—317b
里弗斯利化石 Riversleigh fossils 澳大利亚化石 14—319d
里冈 Reagon, Bernice Johnson 美国音乐家 14—178a
里戈 Rigaud, Hyacinthe 法国肖像画家 14—297d
里戈顿舞 rigaudon 法国民间舞蹈 14—297e
里戈尔 Rigord 法国编年史家 14—299c
里格 league 计量单位 9—543d
里格 Rigg, Dame Diana 英国舞名剧演员 14—298b
里格 Rieger, František Ladislav 捷克政治家 14—293c
里格 Riegger, Wallingford 美国作曲家 14—293d
里格登 Rigdon, Sidney 美国摩门教信徒 14—298a
里格利(小) Wrigley, William, Jr. 美国口香糖生产商 18—348c
里根 Reagan, Ronald W(ilson) 美国总统 14—177c
里根特公园 Regent's Park 英国伦敦公园 14—203b
里海 Caspian Sea 世界最大内陆海 3—502b
里海沿岸低地 Caspian Depression 里海北端地区 3—502a
里基 Rickey, Branch (Wesley) 美国棒球队总经理 14—290c
里加 Riga 拉脱维亚城市 14—297b
里加湾 Riga, Gulf of 波罗的海大海湾 14—297d
里甲 li-chia 中国历史 10—58a
里甲 lijia 中国历史 10—95e
里贾纳 Regina 加拿大城市 14—204a
里金山 Wrekin, The 英格兰什罗普郡区名 18—343b
里卡 Ricca, Paul 美国黑帮分子 14—277f
里卡多 Ricardo (Leite), Cassiano 巴西诗人、记者 14—277d
里凯德邦雷波 Riquet de Bonrepos, Pierre-Paul, Baron 法国政府官员、工程师 14—312a
里科弗 Rickover, Hyman G(eorge) 美国海军将领 14—290e
里克蒂 Riqueti, André-Boniface-Louis 法国军人 14—312b
里克蒂 Riqueti, Honoré-Gabriel (French politician) 法国政治家 14—312b
里克蒂 Riqueti, Victor 法国政治经济学家 14—312b
里克尔 Ricoeur, Paul 法国哲学家、历史学家 14—290f
里克哈姆 Rikham (Hebrew grammarian) 希伯来语法学家 14—300a
里克森堡 Fort Rixon 津巴布韦村庄 6—415b
里克斯达格 Riksdag 瑞典等级议会 14—300c
里克特 Richter, Burton 美国物理学家、地震学家 14—288c
里克特 Richter, Charles Francis 美国物理学家 14—288c
里克特 Richter, Conrad Michael 美国小说家 14—288d
里肯巴克 Rickenbacker, Edward Vernon 美国飞行员、实业家 14—289e
里拉 lira 意大利货币单位 10—134b
里拉 Rila 保加利亚最高山岭 14—300c
里拉修道院 Rila Monastery 保加利亚修道院和文化遗址 14—300d
里里 Iri 韩国城市 8—445f
《里里伯利若》 Lilli burlero 英国歌谣 10—99b
里马克 Rímac 秘鲁区名 14—301e
里曼 Riemann, (Karl Wilhelm Julius) Hugo 德国音乐学家 14—294c
里门施奈德 Riemenschneider, Tilman 德国雕刻家 14—294e
里米尼 Rimini 意大利城镇 14—302c
里米尼会议 Rimini, Council of 基督教会议 14—302d
里墨尔 rímur 冰岛文学 14—303c
里姆 Ream, Vinnie 美国雕塑家 14—181b
里姆斯基 Rimniksky, Aleksandr Vasilyevich Suvorov, Graf (Count) 俄国军事统帅 14—302e
里姆斯基-科萨科夫 Rimsky-Korsakov, Nikolay (Andreyevich) 俄国作曲家、编辑 14—302e
里穆斯基 Rimouski 加拿大城市 14—302e
里纳尔多(塞尼的) Rinaldo DEI SEGNI 教皇 14—303c
里诺特梅图斯 Rhinotmetus 拜占廷皇帝 14—264a
里帕布利肯河 Republican River 美国河流 14—238a
里佩尔达公爵 Riperdá, Juan Guillermo Riperdá, duque de 荷兰政治冒险家 14—311a
里彭 Ripon 英格兰城市 14—311c
里彭 Ripon 美国城市 14—311d
里彭伯爵(第一) Ripon, Frederick John Robinson, 1st Earl of 英国首相 14—311d
里彭伯爵和侯爵 Ripon, EARL AND MARQUESSES OF 英国贵族鲁宾逊家族之名 14—311d
里彭侯爵(第一) Ripon, George Frederick Samuel Robinson, 1st Marquess of 英国政治家、印度总督 14—311e
里普利 Ripley, George 美国记者、改革者 14—311b
里普利 Ripley, Robert LeRoy 美国漫画家 14—311b
里普利 Ripley, W(illiam) Z(ebina) 美国经济学家 14—311c
里普希茨 Lipchitz, Jacques 法国雕刻家 10—129f
里奇 Ricci, Saint Catherine dei 意大利神学家 14—277f
里奇 Rich, Claudius James 意大利神学家 14—280c
里奇 Ritchie (of Dundee), Charles Thomson Ritchie, 1st Baron 英国政治家 14—313c
里奇 Rich, John 英国演员、剧院经理 14—280d
里奇 Richer, Jean 意大利神学家 14—286c
里奇 Ricci, Ruggiero 美国小提琴家 14—278c
里奇 Rich, Robert 英国殖民官员 14—280f
里奇(莱斯的) Rich (of Leighs), Richard Rich, 1st Baron 英国大法官 14—280e
里奇奥 Riccio, David 苏格兰女王秘书 14—279a
里奇伯勒 Richborough 英格兰古港口遗址 14—285c
里奇尔 Ritschl, F(riedrich) W(ilhelm) 德国古典学者 14—313f
里奇夫人 Rich, Lady Penelope 英国贵妇 14—280e
里奇-库尔巴斯特罗 Ricci-Curbastro, Gregorio 意大利数学家 14—278d
里奇兰 Richland 美国城市 14—286e

里奇勒 Richler, Mordecai 加拿大小说家 14—286f
里奇蒙伯爵 Richmond, Arthur, earl of 英格兰亲王 14—287f
里奇蒙伯爵 Richmond, Henry Tudor, earl of 布列塔尼公爵 14—287f
里奇蒙伯爵 Richmond, John of Gaunt, earl of 法国军官 14—287e
里奇蒙伯爵 Richmond, John of Montfort, earl of 英格兰国王 14—287f
里奇蒙伯爵和公爵 Richmond, EARLS AND DUKES OF 英国封爵贵族 14—287e
里奇蒙公爵(第三) Richmond, Charles Lennox, 3rd duke of 英国政治家 14—288a
里奇蒙公爵(第一) Richmond, Charles Lennox, 1st Duke of 英格兰贵族 14—287f
里奇蒙和伦诺克斯公爵夫人 Richmond and Lennox, Frances Teresa Stuart, duchess of 英王查理二世情妇 14—288a
里奇韦陶瓷 Ridgway ware 英国陶瓷 14—291e
里奇伍德 Ridgewood 美国新泽西州居民村 14—291d
里乔 Riccio, Andrea 意大利雕刻家、金工 14—278e
里萨 Riesa 德国城市 14—294f
里萨拉尔达 Risaralda 哥伦比亚省份 14—312b
里什蒙 Richemont, Arthur, constable de 法国统帅 14—286a
里士满 Richmond 澳大利亚新南威尔士州城镇 14—287a
里士满 Richmond 澳大利亚塔斯马尼亚岛城镇 14—287a
里士满 Richmond 英国城市 14—287b
里士满 Richmond 美国加利福尼亚州城市 14—287b
里士满 Richmond 美国印第安纳州城市 14—287c
里士满 Richmond 美国肯塔基州城市 14—287c
里士满 Richmond 美国纽约州城市 14—287c
里士满 Richmond 美国弗吉尼亚州城市 14—287d
里士满河 Richmond River 澳大利亚河流 14—288b
里士满阶 Richmondian Stage 地质学 14—288b
里士满希尔 Richmondshire 英格兰区名 14—288c
里氏震级 Richter scale 地震强度量级 14—289a
里思(斯通黑文的) Reith (of Stonehaven), John Charles Walsham Reith, 1st Baron 英国商人 14—212e
里斯 Rhys, Ernest Percival 英国文学家 14—272f
里斯 Riesz, Frigyes 匈牙利数学家 14—295b
里斯 Rhys, Jean 西印度群岛女小说家 14—273a
里斯 Riis, Jacob A(ugust) 美国新闻记者 14—299d
里斯 Reese, Lizette Woodworth 美国诗人 14—197c
里斯 Rhys, Siôn Dafydd 威尔士医生、语法学家 14—273b
里斯本 Lisbon 葡萄牙行政区 10—134f
里斯本 Lisboa 葡萄牙首都 10—134f
里斯本大学 Lisbon, University of 葡萄牙大学 10—137f
里斯冰期 Riss Glacial Stage 地质学 14—312f
里斯蒂奇 Ristić, Jovan 塞尔维亚政治家、首相 14—313a
里斯曼 Riesman, David 美国社会学家 14—295a
里斯托里 Ristori, Adelaide 意大利演员 14—313b
里斯-玉木间冰期 Riss-Würm Interglacial Stage 地质学 14—313a
里特 Ritter, Johann Wilhelm 德国物理学家 14—314e
里特 Ritt, Martin 美国电影导演 14—314b
里特尔 Ritter, Carl 德国地理学家 14—314c
里特弗尔德 Rietveld, Gerrit Thomas 荷兰建筑师 14—295c
里托拉 Ritola, Ville 芬兰长跑运动员 14—313d
里托奈罗 ritornello 音乐 14—313d
里瓦达维亚 Rivadavia, Bernardino 阿根廷总统 14—314f
里瓦达维亚海军准将城 Comodoro Rivadavia 阿根廷城市 4—394b
里瓦尔塔 Ribalta, Francisco 西班牙画家 14—275a
里瓦罗尔伯爵 Rivarol, Antoine Rivaroli, Count (comte) de 法国政论家 14—315b
里瓦斯 Rivas 尼加拉瓜城市 14—315b
里瓦斯公爵 Rivas, Angel de Saavedra (Ramírez de Baquendano), Duke (duque) de 西班牙作家 14—315c
里韦 Rivet, Paul 法国人种学家 14—319f
里韦拉 Rivera 乌拉圭城市 14—316a
里韦拉 Rivera, José Eustasio 哥伦比亚诗人 14—316c
里韦亚属 Rivea 植物学 14—315d
里维埃尔 Rivière, Jacques 法国作家 14—320b
里维埃拉 Riviera 法、意地中海沿岸地区 14—320a
里维尔 Revere 美国城市 14—251c
里维尔 Revere, Paul 美国民间英雄 14—251c
里维拉 Rivera, Diego 墨西哥画家 14—316a
里维耶尔-迪卢 Rivière-du-Loup 加拿大城市 14—320d
里窝那 Livorno 意大利城市 10—165b
里沃 Rievaulx 英格兰隐修院遗址 14—295d
里沃利 Rivoli 意大利城镇 14—320e
里沃利公爵 Rivoli, André Masséna, duc de (duke of) 法国将领 14—320e
里乌谷 Lliw Valley 威尔士区名 10—169a
里西梅尔 Ricimer 罗马将军 14—289c
里西姆纳 Rhithymna 希腊城市 14—264c
里希迈基 Riihimäki 芬兰城市 14—299d
里希特 Richter, Hans 匈牙利指挥家 14—288e
里希特尔 Richter, Johann Paul Friedrich 德国小说家 14—288f
里希特霍芬 Richthofen, Manfred, Freiherr von 德国飞行员 14—289b
里希耶 Richier, Germaine 法国雕刻家 14—286e
里巷猫 alley cat 哺乳动物 1—239f
里歇 Richet, Charles (Robert) 法国生理学家 14—286d
里雄莱锡安 Rishon LeZiyyon 以色列城市 14—312d
里雅地毯 rya rug 工艺品 14—473e
里亚布申斯基家族 Ryabushinsky FAMILY 俄国实业家家族 14—473f
里亚德 Riyād, Maḥmūd 埃及外交家 14—320f
里亚德 Riyād, Muḥammad ʿAbd al-Munʿim 埃及军官 14—320f
里亚尔 rial 伊朗、阿曼和也门的货币单位 14—274c
里亚尔 riyal 沙特阿拉伯和卡塔尔的货币单位 14—321b
里耶卡 Rijeka 克罗地亚城市 14—299e
里伊 Rie, Lucie, Dame 英国陶瓷艺术家 14—292c
里永 Riom 法国城镇 14—310d
里约 Rio (Brazil) 巴西城市 14—305e
里约热内卢 Rio de Janeiro 巴西州名 14—306a
里约热内卢 Rio de Janeiro 巴西城市 14—306b
《里约热内卢议定书》 Rio de Janeiro, Protocol of 南美洲历史 14—308e
里约热内卢植物园 Rio de Janeiro Botanical Garden 巴西植物园 14—308f
里泽 Rize 土耳其城市 14—322a
里兹波特 Reedsport 美国城市 14—197a
里兹兰 Rhuddlan 威尔士社区 14—271b
里兹内尔 Riesener, Jean-Henri 法国家具工匠 14—294f
里兹平原 Reeds, Plain of 越南平原 14—196f
俚语 slang 语言学 15—425c
理 li 中国古代哲学 10—57a
理查 Richard 统治者之名 14—280f
理查 Richard 罗马人的国王 14—282a
理查(好人) Richard THE GOOD 诺曼底公爵 14—282d
理查(狮心王) Richard COEUR DE LION 英格兰国王 14—282b
理查(四世) Richard (IV) 英格兰国王 14—282b
理查(韦瑟谢德的) Richard OF WETHERSHED 坎特伯雷大主教 14—282d
理查(无畏者) Richard THE FEARLESS 诺曼底公爵 14—282d
理查(伊利的) Richard OF ELY 英格兰主教 14—282c
理查德 Richard, Cliff 英国歌手 14—282d
理查德(圣维克托的) Richard OF SAINT VICTOR 法国天主教神学家 14—282d

理查德(奇切斯特的),圣 Richard of Chichester, Saint 英格兰主教 14—282c
理查德·威奇 Richard Wyche 英格兰主教 14—282d
理查二世 Richard Ⅱ 英格兰国王 14—281c
理查二世 Richard Ⅱ 英格兰国王 14—282b
理查三世 Richard Ⅲ 英格兰国王 14—281d
理查三世 Richard Ⅲ 英格兰国王 14—282b
理查森 Richardson 美国城市 14—283d
理查森 Richardson, Benjamin 英国玻璃制造商 14—283e
理查森 Richardson, Dorothy M(iller) 英国小说家 14—283e
理查森 Richardson, Henry Handel 澳大利亚作家 14—283f
理查森 Richardson, Henry Hobson 美国建筑师 14—283f
理查森 Richardson, John 历史小说作家 14—284b
理查森 Richardson, Sir John 苏格兰军医、博物学家 14—284b
理查森 Richardson, Lewis Fry 英国物理学家、心理学家 14—284c
理查森 Richardson, Robert C. 美国物理学家 14—284e
理查森 Richardson, Sir Ralph (David) 英国戏剧、电影演员 14—284d
理查森 Richardson, Samuel 英国小说家 14—284f
理查森 Richardson, Tony 英国导演 14—285a
理查森山脉 Richardson Mountains 加拿大落基山脉山系 14—285c
理查森数 Richardson number 气象学 14—285c
理查孙 Richardson, Sir Owen Willans 英国物理学家 14—284d
理查一世 Richard Ⅰ 英格兰国王 14—280f
理查一世 Richard Ⅰ 英格兰国王 14—282a
理查兹 Richards, Audrey I(sabel) 英国社会人类学家 14—282e
理查兹 Richards, Dickinson Woodruff 美国生理学家 14—282e
理查兹 Richards, Sir Gordon 英国骑手 14—283a
理查兹 Richards, I(vor) A(rmstrong) 英国诗人 14—283a
理查兹 Richards, Theodore William 美国化学家 14—283b
理查兹 Richards, Sir Viv 西印度群岛板球运动员 14—283b
理查兹 Richards, Sir William Buell 加拿大政治家 14—283c
理查兹 Richards, William 美国传教士 14—283c
理查兹(夫人) Richards, Ellen Swallow 美国化学家 14—282f
理发 hairdressing 修剪、整理头发 7—413c
理发店四重唱 barbershop quartet singing 音乐 2—220d
理发师 barber 服务行业 2—219e
理藩院 Lifan Yuan 中国清代政府机构 10—88b
理卡德 Rickard, Tex 美国赌场主 14—289d
理想类型 ideal type 社会学 8—321c
理想气体 ideal gas (physics) 物理学 8—321b
理想溶液 ideal solution 化学 8—321b
理想语言 ideal language 分析哲学 8—321b
理性 reason 哲学 14—181e
锂(Li) lithium 化学元素 10—146d
锂辉石 spodumene 矿物 16—38f
锂剂 lithium 药物 10—146f
锂云母 lepidolite 矿物 10—30f
鲤鱼 carp (species *Cyprinus carpio*) 鱼类 3—474f
澧水 Li Shui 中国河流 10—63e
醴陵 Liling 中国城市 10—98b
鳢 snakehead 鱼类 15—458f
力 force 物理学 6—399f
力矩 force, moment of a 物理学 6—400c
力矩 moment of a force 物理学 11—326d
力偶 couple 力学 4—546e
力线 force, line of 物理学 6—400b
力学 mechanics 物理学 11—67f
力学时 dynamical time 天体力学 5—488c
《历代志》 Chronicles, books of the 《圣经·旧约》 4—213e
历法 calendar 天文学 3—343b
历时语言学 diachronic linguistics 语言学 5—283c
历史 history 社会科学 8—99b
历史编纂学 historiography 历史学 8—98f
历史地理学 historical geography 地理学 8—98c
历史剧 chronicle play 说教性史剧 4—213d
历史排他主义 historical particularism (anthropology) 人类学 8—98f
历史批评 historical criticism 文学 8—98c
历史小说 historical novel 文学 8—98e
历史学派 historical school of economics 经济学 8—98f
历史语言学 historical linguistics 语言学 8—98d
历书 almanac 天文学 1—244f
历书时 Ephemeris Time (ET) 天文学 6—95b
立川 Tachikawa 日本城市 16—417b
立祷词 amidah 犹太教 1—288e
立法机关调查权 legislative investigative powers 法律 9—562e
立法团 Corps Législatif 法国立法机构 4—520c
立法议会 Legislative Assembly 法国历史 9—562e
立方晶系 isometric system 晶体学 8—472e
立花 rikka 日本插花 14—300a
立克次 Ricketts, Howard T(aylor) 美国病理学家 14—290a
立克次氏体 rickettsia 微生物 14—290a
立绒 velvet 纺织 17—495d
立式钢琴 upright piano 乐器 17—405f
立陶宛 Lithuania 欧洲国家 10—147e
立陶宛、波兰和俄罗斯犹太工人总联盟 General Union of Jewish Workers in Lithuania, Poland, and Russia 俄国政治运动 7—57e
立陶宛大公国 Lithuania, grand duchy of 欧洲历史 10—148c
立陶宛文学 Lithuanian literature 文学 10—148f
立陶宛语 Lithuanian language 语言 10—148e
立体电影 3-D 电影 17—63b
立体拼花大玻璃 gemmail 玻璃画 7—50c
立体声系统 stereophonic sound system 音响设备 16—225c
立体主义 Cubism 视觉艺术 5—48e
立窝尼亚高地 Litvonian Highland (Latvia) 拉脱维亚高地 10—153e
立宪会议 Constituent Assembly 苏俄民选机构 4—456b
立宪联邦党 Constitutional Union Party 美国政党 4—460e
立宪民主党 Constitutional Democratic Party (Russia) 俄国政党 4—460e
立宪民主党人 Kadet 俄国政党 9—128c
立宪政友会 Rikken Seiyūkai 日本政党 14—300c
立正佼成会 Risshō-Kōsei-kai 日本佛教教团 14—313a
立柱卷顶座钟 pillar and scroll shelf clock 钟表 13—303f
丽都桥 Rialto Bridge 意大利威尼斯桥名 14—274d
丽江 Lijiang 中国城市 10—95f
丽金龟 shining leaf chafer 昆虫 15—317c
丽水 Yŏsu 韩国城市 18—461c
丽蝇 blow fly 昆虫 2—545e
丽鱼 cichlid 鱼类 4—234f
利 artha 印度教 1—527a
利安得 Leander (Greek mythology) 希腊神话人物 9—545a
利奥 Leo 统治者之名 10—15c
利奥 Leo, Heinrich 普鲁士历史学家 10—18d
利奥(非洲的) Leo Africanus 伊斯兰学者 10—18c
利奥(哈扎尔人) Leo the Khazar 拜占廷皇帝 10—18d
利奥(亚美尼亚人) Leo the Armenian 拜占廷皇帝 10—18c
利奥(伊索里亚人) Leo the Isaurian 拜占廷皇帝 10—18c
利奥(智者) Leo the Wise 拜占廷皇帝 10—18d
利奥八世 Leo Ⅷ 教皇 10—16f
利奥波德 Leopold 统治者之名 10—28e
利奥波德 Leopold, Jan Hendrik 荷兰诗人 10—30a
利奥波德二世 Leopold Ⅱ 比利时国王 10—29a
利奥波德二世 Leopold Ⅱ 神圣罗马帝国皇帝 10—29e

利奥波德二世 Leopold II 意大利托斯卡纳大公 10—29f
利奥波德二世湖 Leopold II, Lake (Africa) 非洲湖泊 10—30a
利奥波德国王岭 King Leopold Ranges 澳大利亚山系 9—289b
利奥波德(小)和洛布 Leopold, Nathan F(reudenthal), Jr.; and Loeb, Richard A. 美国匪徒 10—30b
利奥波德三世 Leopold III 比利时国王 10—29c
利奥波德维尔 Léopoldville 刚果(金)城市 10—30c
利奥波德一世 Leopold I 普鲁士元帅 10—28e
利奥波德一世 Leopold I 比利时国王 10—28f
利奥波德一世 Leopold I 神圣罗马帝国皇帝 10—29c
利奥·迪·巴尼奥尔斯 Leo de Bagnols 犹太学者 10—18c
利奥二世 Leo II 东罗马帝国皇帝 10—15d
利奥二世,圣 Leo II, Saint 教皇 10—16d
利奥弗里克 Leofric 英国历史 10—18f
利奥九世,圣 Leo IX, Saint 教皇 10—17a
利奥六世 Leo VI 拜占廷皇帝 10—16a
利奥六世 Leo VI 教皇 10—16f
利奥纳 Lionne, Hugues de 法国外交大臣 10—128e
利奥诺文斯 Leonowens, Anna Harriette 英国作家 10—27b
利奥七世 Leo VII 教皇 10—16f
利奥三世 Leo III 拜占廷皇帝 10—15d
利奥三世,圣 Leo III, Saint 教皇 10—16d
利奥十二世 Leo XII 教皇 10—17f
利奥十三世 Leo XIII 教皇 10—18a
利奥十世 Leo X 教皇 10—17c
利奥十一世 Leo XI 教皇 10—17e
利奥四世 Leo IV 拜占廷皇帝 10—15f
利奥四世,圣 Leo IV, Saint 教皇 10—16e
利奥塔尔 Liotard, Jean-Étienne 瑞士画家 10—129a
利奥塔尔 Lyotard, Jean-François 法国哲学家 10—316e
利奥泰 Lyautey, Louis-Hubert-Gonzalve 法国政治家、军人 10—307c
利奥泰港 port-Lyautey (Morocco) 摩洛哥港口 13—446b
利奥体诗 leonine verse 拉丁语、法语诗体 10—26f
利奥五世 Leo V 教皇帝 10—16a
利奥五世 Leo V 拜占廷皇帝 10—16e
利奥一世 Leo I 东罗马帝国皇帝 10—15d
利奥一世,圣 Leo I, Saint 教皇 10—16b
利巴 Lipa 菲律宾城市 10—129d
利巴尼奥斯 Libanius 希腊修辞学家 10—71f
利巴威斯 Libavius, Andreas 德国化学家 10—72a
利包 Libau (Latvia) 拉脱维亚城市 10—72a
利堡 Fort Lee 美国自治镇 6—414a
利贝尔与利贝拉 Liber and Libera 古罗马神名 10—72b
利贝拉莱 Liberale da Verona 意大利画家 10—73d
利贝雷茨 Liberec 捷克城市 10—75b
利贝里乌斯 Liberius 教皇 10—76b
利贝罗 Ribeyro, Julio Ramón 拉丁美洲短篇小说大师之一 14—277a
利比 Lippi, Filippino 意大利画家 10—131c
利比 Lippi, Fra Filippo 佛罗伦萨画家 10—131d
利比 Libby, Willard Frank 美国化学家 10—72a
利比蒂娜 Libitina 古罗马女神 10—77c
利比里亚 Liberia 非洲国家 10—75c
利比亚 Libya 非洲国家 10—80b
利比亚猫 Caffre cat (species *Felis libyca*) 哺乳动物 3—322b
利比亚沙漠 Libyan Desert 非洲沙漠 10—81d
利波尔德 Lippold, Richard 美国雕刻家 10—132b
利伯 Lieber, Francis 美国政治哲学家、法学家 10—84c
利伯 Lieber, Thomas 瑞士宗教领袖 10—84d
利伯蒂维尔 Libertyville 美国伊利诺伊州村庄 10—76f
利伯勒 Liebler, Thomas 瑞士宗教领袖 10—85e
利伯勒尔 Liberal 美国城市 10—72c
利伯维尔 Libreville 加蓬首都 10—80a
利布尔讷 Libourne 法国城镇 10—77c
利车卡尔(寻求曲) ricercare 音乐 14—280c
利茨 Lietz, Hermann 德国教育改革家 10—87f
利茨曼 Lietzmann, Hans 德国基督教历史学家 10—87f
利达 Lida 白俄罗斯城市 10—83b
利达 Lydda (Israel) 以色列城市 10—309d
利德 Lead 美国城市 9—540c
利德 lied 歌曲 10—86d
利德 Lydd 美国城市 10—309d
利德尔 Liddell, Henry George 英国词典编纂家 10—83b
利德尔·哈特 Liddell Hart, Sir Basil (Henry) 英国军事史学家、战略家 10—83c
利德盖特 Lydgate, John 英国诗人 10—309d
利德曼 Lidman, Sara 瑞典作家 10—83e
利德斯河谷 Liddesdale 英国谷地 10—83d
利德雪平 Lidköping 瑞典城镇 10—83e
利登 Liddon, Henry Parry 英国神学家 10—83d
利迪 Leidy, Joseph 美国动物学家 9—567d
利迪策 Lidice 捷克村庄 10—83d
利底亚调式 Lydian mode 宗教音乐 10—309f
利读和利写 readerly and writerly 文学 14—176d
利顿工业公司 Litton Industries, Inc. 美国公司 10—152c
利多卡因 lidocaine 化合物 10—83f
利恩茨 Lienz 奥地利城镇 10—87d
利尔 Lier 比利时城市 10—87e
利尔 Llyr 凯尔特神话人物 10—171b
利尔 Lear, Edward 英国画家 9—545c
利尔 Lear, William P(owell) 美国企业家 9—545d
利尔伯恩 Lilburne, John 英国平均派领袖 10—96f
利尔蒙特 Learmont, Thomas 苏格兰诗人 9—545e
利菲河 Liffey, River 爱尔兰河流 10—90e
利芬斯 Lievens, Jan 荷兰画家 10—88a
利弗 Lever, Charles James 爱尔兰作家 10—45e
利弗夫人美术馆 Lady Lever Art Gallery 英国美术馆 9—443b
利弗美术馆 Lever Art Gallery 英国美术馆 10—45f
利弗莫尔 Livermore 美国城市 10—160e
利弗莫尔 Livermore, Mary Ashton Rice 美国女权主义者 10—160f
利富岛 Lifou, Île 法国岛屿 10—90f
利盖蒂 Ligeti, György 匈牙利作曲家 10—91e
利戈节 Līgo feast 波罗的海地区宗教节日 10—94f
利戈里奥 Ligorio, Pirro 意大利建筑师 10—94f
利格尼茨 Liegnitz (Poland) 波兰城市 10—87b
利格特集团公司 Liggett Group Inc. 美国公司 10—91e
利根川 Tone River 日本河流 17—147f
利根川进 Tonegawa Susumu 日本分子生物学家 17—147f
利古奥里 Liguori, Saint Alfonso Maria de' 意大利神学家 10—95a
利古里亚 Liguria 意大利西北部地区 10—95a
利古里亚共和国 Ligurian Republic 欧洲历史 10—95c
利古里亚海 Ligurian Sea 地中海海湾 10—95c
利古里亚人 Ligurian 欧洲古代民族 10—95b
利古里亚语 Ligurian language 欧洲古代语言 10—95c
利哈伊 Lehi 美国城市 9—564a
利哈伊谷铁路公司 Lehigh Valley Railroad Company 美国企业 9—564a
利河 Lea, River 英国河流 9—540a
利胡埃 Lihue 美国城市 10—95d
利华兄弟公司 Lever Brothers 英国公司 10—45f
利华休姆(西部群岛的) Leverhulme (of The Western Isles), William Hesketh Lever, 1st Viscount, Baron Leverhulme of Bolton-le-Moors 英国企业家 10—45f
利霍利霍 Liholiho 夏威夷国王 10—95d
利霍利霍 Liholiho, Alexander 夏威夷国王 10—95d

利基 Leakey, L(ouis) S(eymour) B(azett) 英国人类学家 9—543f
利基 Leakey, Mary Douglas 人类学家 9—544b
利基 Leakey, Richard (Erskine Frere) 肯尼亚人类学家 9—544c
利己主义 egoism 哲学 5—558d
利甲人 Rechabite 古代以色列教派派别 14—183c
利金河 Licking River 美国河流 10—82f
利卡斯特兰属 Lycaste 植物学 10—307f
利卡塔 Licata 意大利城镇 10—81d
利卡西 Likasi 刚果(金)城市 10—95f
利考尼亚 Lycaonia 古安纳托利亚地区 10—307e
利科夫龙(哈尔基斯的) Lycophron of Chalcis 古希腊诗人、学者 10—309a
利科马岛 Likoma Island 马拉维岛屿 10—96b
利克里克 Leigh Creek 澳大利亚城镇 9—567f
利克苏斯 Lixus 摩洛哥古代遗址 10—165d
利克特 Likert, Rensis 美国社会科学家 10—96a
利克天文台 Lick Observatory 美国大型高山天文台 10—82e
利口酒 aquavit 饮料 1—427c
利库德集团 Likud 以色列政治联盟 10—96b
利库尔戈斯 Lycurgus 斯巴达立法者 10—309b
利库尔戈斯 Lycurgus 雅典政治家 10—309c
利拉尔 Lilar, Suzanne 比利时作家 10—96e
利拉·玛丽·柯伯 Koerber, Leila Marie (American actress) 美国演员 9—332c
利拉琴 lira 乐器 10—134c
利兰 Leland, Charles Godfrey 美国作家 10—1d
利兰 Leland, Henry Martyn 美国工程师 10—1e
利兰 Leland, John 英国文物工作者 10—1f
利兰丁战争 Lelantine War 希腊历史 10—2a
利勒博讷 Lillebonne 法国城镇 10—99a
利勒哈默尔 Lillehammer 挪威城镇 10—99b
利里河 Liri River 意大利河流 10—134e
利利 Lillie, Frank Rattray 美国动物学家 10—99d
利利 Lily, William 英国学者、语法学家 10—100a
利连撒尔 Lilienthal, David E. 美国商人、官员 10—98a
利林塔尔 Lilienthal, Otto 德国航空工程师 10—98b
利留卡拉尼 Liliuokalani 夏威夷群岛女王 10—98d
利隆圭 Lilongwe 马拉维城市 10—99e
利隆圭平原 Lilongwe Plain 马拉维平原 10—99f
利马 Lima 秘鲁省份 10—100c
利马 Lima 秘鲁首都 10—100c
利马 Lima, Jorge de 巴西作家 10—101e
利马 Lima, Manuel dos Santos 安哥拉作家 10—101e
利马·巴雷托 Lima Barreto, Afonso Henriques de 巴西作家 10—101f
利马豆 lima bean 植物 10—101f
利-马洛里 Leigh-Mallory, Trafford 英国军官 9—568a
利马萨瓦 Limasawa 菲律宾岛屿 10—102a
利马圣马科斯国家重点大学 San Marcos of Lima, Main National University of 秘鲁大学 15—16a
利马索尔 Limassol 塞浦路斯城市 10—102a
利马瓦迪 Limavady 北爱尔兰城镇 10—102b
利玛窦 Ricci, Matteo 意大利耶稣会传教士 14—278a
利曼·封·赞德尔斯 Liman von Sanders, Otto 德国将军 10—101f
利曼岩洞 Lehman Caves 美国石灰石洞穴群 9—564b
利梅拉 Limeira 巴西城市 10—103d
利门湾 Limmen Bight 澳大利亚海湾 10—104f
利蒙 Limón 哥斯达黎加省份 10—105e
利蒙 Limón 哥斯达黎加城市 10—105e
利蒙 Limón, José (Arcadio) 美国舞蹈家 10—105e
利蒙湾 Limón, Bahía 巴拿马港湾 10—105e
利眠宁 chlordiazepoxide 药物 4—183f
利明顿矿泉市 Leamington Spa (England) 英格兰城市 9—544e
利摩日 Limoges 法国城市 10—105b
利摩日瓷器 Limoges ware 法国瓷器 10—105d
利摩日画珐琅 Limoges painted enamel 法国工艺品 10—105c
利莫赞 Limosin, Léonard 法国画家 10—106b
利默里克 Limerick 爱尔兰城市 10—103f
利默里克伯爵(第二) Limerick, Thomas Dongan, 2nd earl of 英国殖民地总督 10—104a
利默里克花边 Limerick lace 织物 10—104a
利默里克郡 Limerick 爱尔兰郡名 10—103e
利姆诺斯 Lemnos 希腊岛屿 10—4c
利姆水道 Limfjorden 丹麦海峡 10—104b
利穆赞 Limousin 法国大区 10—106c
利纳克尔 Linacre, Thomas 英国医生、学者 10—109b
利纳雷斯 Linares 智利城市 10—109c
利纳雷斯 Linares 西班牙城镇 10—109c
利尿药 diuretic 药物 5—345e
利涅 Ligne, Charles-Joseph, prince de 比利时军官、文人 10—94c
利努斯,圣 Linus, Saint 教皇 10—127a
利诺 Leno, Dan 英国演员 10—12e
利诺萨岛 Linosa Island 意大利岛屿 10—125d
利诺斯 Linus 希腊神话 10—126f
利帕尔间隔 Lipalian interval 地质学 10—129d
利帕里群岛 Lipari Islands (Italy) 意大利岛屿 10—129e
利佩茨克 Lipetsk 俄罗斯州名 10—130a
利佩茨克 Lipetsk 俄罗斯城市 10—130a
利皮施 Lippisch, Alexander M(artin) 美国空气动力学家 10—131f
利皮扎马 Lipizzaner 马品种 10—130d
利珀 Lippe 德国历史 10—131a
利珀河 Lippe River 德国河流 10—131b
利珀希 Lippershey, Hans 荷兰发明家 10—131c
利普顿 Lipton, Seymour 美国雕刻家 10—133a
利普顿 Lipton, Sir Thomas Johnstone, 1st Baronet 英国商人 10—133b
利普塞特 Lipset, Seymour Martin 美国社会学家、政治学家 10—132e
利普施塔特 Lippstadt 德国城市 10—132d
利普斯 Lipps, Theodor 德国心理学家 10—132c
利普斯科姆 Lipscomb, Gene 美国橄榄球运动员 10—132d
利普斯科姆 Lipscomb, William Nunn, Jr. 美国物理化学家 10—132e
利普西乌斯 Lipsius, Richard Adelbert 德国神学家 10—133a
利普修斯 Lipsius, Justus 佛兰芒人文学者 10—132f
利奇 Leech, John 英国漫画家 9—557b
利奇菲尔德 Lichfield 英格兰城市 10—82b
利奇菲尔德 Litchfield 美国城镇 10—142b
利奇菲尔德 Litchfield, Paul W(eeks) 美国实业家 10—142c
利润 profit 经济学 13—528b
利润分享 profit sharing 经济学 13—528b
利萨 Lissa (Croatia) 克罗地亚岛屿 10—139b
利萨 Lisa, Manuel 美国商人 10—134e
利萨尔迪 Lizardi, José Joaquín Fernández de 墨西哥编辑、作家 10—167a
利萨如图形 Lissajous figure 数学 10—139b
利瑟 Lisse 荷兰城市 10—139c
利什曼病 leishmaniasis 传染病 9—570a
利思戈 Lithgow, William 苏格兰作家 10—146c
利斯 Leith 苏格兰港口 9—570c
利斯本 Lisburn 北爱尔兰区名 10—138a
利斯本 Lisburn 北爱尔兰城镇 10—138a
利斯顿 Liston, Sonny 美国拳击运动员 10—140c
利斯戈 Lithgow 澳大利亚城市 10—146c
利斯基 Liski 俄罗斯城市 10—138e
利斯莫尔 Lismore 澳大利亚城市 10—138f
利斯莫尔 Lismore 爱尔兰城镇 10—138f

利斯莫尔 Lismore 苏格兰岛屿 10—139a
《利斯莫尔教长集》 Lismore, The Book of the Dean of 苏格兰和爱尔兰文学 10—139a
利斯佩克托尔 Lispector, Clarice 巴西作家 10—139a
利斯塔 Lista (y Aragón), Alberto 西班牙作家 10—139f
利斯塔尔 Liestal 瑞士乡村 10—87e
利斯特 Lister, Joseph, Baron Lister, of Lyme Regis 英国医学家 10—140a
利斯特 Lister, Joseph Jackson 英国光学家 10—140b
利斯特 Lister, Samuel Cunliffe 英国发明家 10—140b
利斯特氏菌病 listeriosis 疾病 10—140b
利斯沃亚 Lisboa, António Francisco 巴西雕刻家 10—134f
利他林 Ritalin 药物 14—313c
利他主义 altruism 伦理学理论 1—258a
利塔尼河 Līṭānī River 黎巴嫩河流 10—142b
利特尔 Little, Royal 美国商人 10—149e
利特尔顿 Littleton 美国城市 10—152a
利特尔顿 Lyttelton 新西兰城镇 10—319b
利特尔顿 Littleton, Mark (U.S. author) 美国作家 10—152a
利特尔顿 Littleton, Sir Thomas 英国法学家 10—152a
利特尔顿(弗兰克雷的) Lyttelton (of Frankley), George Lyttelton, 1st Baron 英国政治家 10—319b
利特尔伍德 Littlewood, Joan (Maud) 英国戏剧导演 10—152b
利特克 Litke, Fyodor Petrovich, Count (Graf) 俄国探险家 10—149a
利特雷 Littré, (Maximilien-)Paul-Émile 法国语言学家 10—152d
利特里姆 Leitrim 爱尔兰郡名 9—570f
利特维诺夫 Litvínov 捷克工业区 10—153c
利韦里亚 Liberia 哥斯达黎加城市 10—75c
利维 Levy, David 以色列政治家 10—49c
利维 Levy, Edward (English newspaperman) 英国报业主 10—49c
利维 Levy, Joseph Moses 英国报业主 10—49c
利维-劳森 Levy-Lawson, Edward (English newspaperman) 英国报业主 10—49e
利维牛仔裤 Levi's (apparel) 服装 10—48a
利维斯 Leavis, F.R. 英国文学评论家 9—547b
利维·斯特劳斯公司 Levi Strauss & Co. 美国公司 10—47b
利维亚 Llivia 西班牙城镇 10—169a
利维娅·德鲁西拉 Livia Drusilla 罗马史 10—162e
利末 Levi (Apostle of Jesus) 《圣经》人物 10—46c
《利未记》 Leviticus 《圣经》篇章 10—48c
利未人 Levite 古代以色列人支派 10—48c
利文伯爵(第一) Leven, Alexander Leslie, 1st Earl of, Lord Balgonie 苏格兰军人 10—45b
利文湖 Leven, Loch 苏格兰湖泊 10—45b
利文斯 Livings, Henry 英国剧作家 10—163c
利文斯敦 Livingstone 赞比亚城镇 10—164b
利文斯敦 Livingstone, David 苏格兰探险家 10—164b
利文斯敦瀑布 Livingstone Falls 刚果河瀑布 10—164e
利文斯顿 Livingston 苏格兰城镇 10—163d
利文斯顿 Livingston 美国城市 10—163d
利文斯顿 Livingston, Edward 美国政治家 10—163d
利文斯顿 Livingston, Henry Brockholst 美国最高法院大法官 10—163e
利文斯顿 Livingston, Robert 美国律师、政治家 10—163f
利文斯顿 Livingston, Robert R. 美国政治家 10—163f
利文斯顿 Livingston, William 美国州长 10—164a
利文斯通 Livingstone, Sir Richard Winn 英国学者 10—164d
利翁内特 Lyonnet, Pierre 荷兰博物学家 10—316c
利翁湾 Lion, Gulf of 地中海海湾 10—128c
利沃夫 Lviv 乌克兰州名 10—306d
利沃夫 Lviv 乌克兰城市 10—306d
利沃夫 Lwoff, André 法国生物学家 10—306f
利沃尼亚 Livonia 欧洲地区 10—164f
利沃尼亚 Livonia 美国城市 10—165a
利沃尼亚战争 Livonian War 欧洲历史 10—165a
利乌多尔芬王朝 Liudolfing dynasty 德国历史 10—158c
利乌多尔夫 Liudolf 士瓦本公爵 10—158b
利乌特普兰德(克雷莫纳的) Liutprand of Cremona 伦巴第外交家、主教 10—159a
利物浦 Liverpool 加拿大城镇 10—161b
利物浦 Liverpool 英国城市 10—161b
利物浦伯爵(第二) Liverpool, Robert Banks Jenkinson, 2nd Earl of, Baron Hawkesbury of Hawkesbury 英国首相 10—161d
利物浦伯爵(第一) Liverpool, Charles Jenkinson, 1st Earl of, Baron Hawkesbury of Hawkesbury 英国政治家 10—161c
利物浦瓷器 Liverpool porcelain 英国软质瓷器 10—161e
利物浦街车站 Liverpool Street Station 英国伦敦火车站 10—161e
利物浦精陶 Liverpool delft 英国锡釉陶器 10—161d
利西波斯 Lysippus 古希腊雕刻家 10—318d
利西昌斯克 Lisichansk 乌克兰城市 10—138d
利西茨基 Lissitzky, El 俄国画家 10—139c
利西格拉泰纪念亭 Lysicrates, Choragic Monument of 古希腊建筑 10—318c
利西马科斯 Lysimachus 马其顿国王 10—318c
利希滕贝格 Lichtenberg 德国市区 10—82b
利希滕贝格 Lichtenberg, Georg Christoph 德国物理学家、作家 10—82c
利希滕斯坦 Lichtenstein, Roy 美国画家 10—82c
利息 interest 金融 8—408c
利雪 Lisieux 法国城镇 10—138d
利血平 reserpine 药物 14—239a
利雅得 Riyāḍ, ar- 沙特阿拉伯省份 14—320e
利雅得 Riyadh 沙特阿拉伯首都 14—321a
利亚 Leah 《圣经》人物 9—543e
利亚德河 Liard River 加拿大河流 10—71e
利亚多夫 Lyadov, Anatoly 俄国作曲家 10—307b
利亚格特·阿里汗 Liaquat Ali Khan 巴基斯坦总理 10—71d
利亚普切夫 Liapchev, Andrei 保加利亚政治家 10—71c
利耶帕亚 Liepāja 拉脱维亚城市 10—87d
利益集团 interest group 政治学 8—408d
利永 Liyong, Taban lo 乌干达作家 10—165e
利用题解教科书的自学 programmed learning 教育方法 13—529a
利泽德半岛 Lizard Peninsula 英国半岛 10—166f
利兹 Leeds 英格兰城市 9—557d
利兹公爵(第一) Leeds, Thomas Osborne, 1st Duke of, Marquess of Carmarthen, Earl of Danby, Viscount Latimer of Danby, Viscount Osborne of Dunblane, Baron Osborne of Kiveton 英国政治家 9—557f
沥青 asphalt 化合物 1—557c
沥青 bitumen 化合物 2—505a
沥青 pitch 化合物 13—327d
沥青地砖 asphalt tile 建筑材料 1—557d
沥青湖 pitch lake 地质学 13—327d
沥青砂 tar sand 地质学 16—477c
沥青岩 asphaltite 矿物 1—557d
沥青铀矿 pitchblende 矿物 13—327e
枥木 Tochigi 日本县名 17—127d
隶农 colonus 佃农 4—359d
隶书 lishu 中国汉字书体 10—138a
栎树 oak 木本植物 12—314d
郦道元 Li Daoyuan 中国地理学家 10—58b
荔枝 litchi (*Litchi chinensis*) 木本植物 10—142d
莉莉 Lillie, Beatrice (Gladys) 英国演员 10—99c
《莉莉-玛莲》 Lili Marleen 德国歌曲 10—97a
鬲 li 中国古代炊具 10—57a
栗 chestnut 木本植物 4—134a
栗栎 chestnut oak 木本植物 4—134c

栗色猞猁 bay lynx 哺乳动物 2—292b
栗色羊驼 guanaco (*Lama guanacoe*) 哺乳动物 7—337f
栗鸮 bay owl (species *Phodilus badius*) 鸟类 2—292d
栗疫病 chestnut blight 植物病害 4—134c
砾石 gravel 岩石学 7—263f
砾石砍砸器 pebble chopper 工具 13—116c
砾岩 conglomerate 岩石 4—424e
蛎鹬 oystercatcher 鸟类 12—527b
笠冈 Kasaoka 日本城市 9—189e
粒级标准 grade scale 沉积学 7—238d
粒面细工 granulation 珠宝制作工艺 7—257a
粒细胞缺乏症 agranulocytosis 传染病 1—127b
粒玄岩 dolerite(petrology) 岩石 5—364b
粒雪 firn 冰川学 6—328d
粒子 particle (high-energy physics) 高能物理学 13—67c
粒子加速器 particle accelerator 物理学研究设备 13—67c
粒子数布居反转 population inversion 物理学 13—439a
傈僳语 Lisu language 中国民族语言 10—140e
傈僳族 Lisu 中国民族 10—140d
痢疾 dysentery 传染病 5—489a
溧阳 Liyang 中国城市 10—165d
连 company 军事单位 4—395e
连苯三酚 pyrogallol 有机化合物 14—47b
连发步枪 repeating rifle 武器 14—233c
连分数 continued fraction 数学 4—469a
连杆机构 linkage 机械 10—123d
连歌 renga 日本诗体 14—228c
连拱廊 arcade 建筑 1—445a
连横 Lian Heng 中国史学家 10—67c
连环画 comic strip 绘画 4—380f
连环会 Linked Ring 英国摄影家协会 10—123f
连接酶 ligase 化学 10—91c
连结成分 connective 逻辑学 4—436c
连科兰 Lenkoran 阿塞拜疆城市 10—12b
连翘 forsythia 植物 6—413a
连锁群 linkage group 遗传学 10—123e
连锁商店 chain store 商业 4—28d
连通性 connectedness 数学 4—433d
连香树 katsura tree (*Cercidiphyllum japonicum*) 木本植物 9—197c
连续 continuity 数学 4—470a
连续航行 continuous voyage 国际法 4—470b
连续性长篇小说 roman-fleuve 文学 14—363f
连云港 Lianyungang 中国城市 10—69c
连载作品 serial 文学 15—225e
连战 Lian Zhan 中国政治人物 10—67d
帘幔 curtain 室内装饰织物 5—71f
莲 lotus 植物 10—231e
莲花生 Padmasambhava 印度佛教密宗僧人 12—540c
莲目 Nelumbonales 植物学 12—72f
莲妮亚 Lenya, Lotte 奥地利演员 10—15a
莲如 Rennyo 日本佛教领袖 14—230e
涟虫 hooded shrimp 甲壳动物 8—162b
涟漪蝽 ripple bug 昆虫 14—311f
梿枷 flail 古代农具 6—345c
联邦 Commonwealth 国家联盟 4—389d
联邦 commonwealth 政治实体 4—390b
联邦安全 Federal Security Service (FSB) 俄罗斯安全机构 6—261e
联邦参议院 Bundesrat 德国议会上院 3—251f
联邦储备系统 Federal Reserve System 美国金融机构 6—261c
联邦储蓄保险公司 Federal Deposit Insurance Corporation (FDIC) 美国保险公司 6—261a
联邦党 Federalist Party 美国早期政党 6—263b
联邦调查局 Federal Bureau of Investigation (FBI) 美国政府机构 6—260c
联邦派同盟 Union League 美国历史 17—346a
联邦区 Federal District 墨西哥区名 6—261b
联邦式 Federal style 美国建筑风格 6—261f
联邦戏剧计划 Federal Theatre Project 美国政府计划 6—262a
联邦宪法法院 Federal Constitutional Court 德国法院 6—260e
联邦艺术计划 Federal Art Project 美国政府计划 6—260c
联邦议院 Bundestag 德国议会下院 3—252a
联邦运动会 Commonwealth Games 体育 4—390b
联邦制 federalism 政治组织模式 6—262a
《联邦主义者文集》 Federalist, The 美国政论文集 6—263a
联邦作家计划 Federal Writers' Project 美国政府计划 6—262a
联苯 biphenyl 芳烃 2—487a
联苯胺 benzidine 有机化合物 2—396d
联合 Rengō 日本工会组织 14—228d
联合东印度公司 United East India Company 荷兰贸易公司 17—351f
《联合法》 Union, Act of 英格兰历史 17—345c
联合飞机公司 United Aircraft Corporation 美国公司 17—349f
联合服务公司 United Service Organizations, Inc. (USO) 美国社会服务组织 17—363f
联合福音信义会 United Evangelical Lutheran Church 美国基督教会 17—351f
联合工业协议会 Joint Industrial Council 英国工人协会 9—75c
联合国 United Nations (UN) 国际组织 17—356e
联合国大会 General Assembly 联合国机构 7—55d
联合国儿童基金会 United Nations Children's Fund 联合国机构 17—361b
联合国儿童紧急援助基金会 UNICEF 联合国机构 17—342b
联合国工业发展组织 United Nations Industrial Development Organization (UNIDO) 联合国机构 17—362d
联合国韩国重建局 United Nations Korean Reconstruction Agency (UNKRA) 联合国机构 17—362f
联合国环境规划署 United Nations Environment Programme (UNEP) 联合国机构 17—362d
联合国环境和发展会议 United Nations Conference on Environment and Development (UNCED) 国际会议 17—361f
联合国货币及金融会议 United Nations Monetary and Financial Conference 国际会议 17—362f
联合国教育、科学及文化组织 United Nations Educational, Scientific and Cultural Organization (UNESCO) 联合国机构 17—362b
联合国近东巴勒斯坦难民救济工程处 United Nations Relief and Works Agency for Palestine Refugees in the Near East (UNRWA) 联合国机构 17—363a
联合国开发计划署 United Nations Development Programme (UNDP) 联合国机构 17—362b
联合国粮食及农业组织 Food and Agriculture Organization (FAO) 联合国机构 6—394e
联合国贸易和发展会议 United Nations Conference on Trade and Development (UNCTAD) 联合国大会常设机构 17—362a
(联合国)秘书长 secretary-general 联合国主要行政长官 15—178c
(联合国)秘书处 Secretariat 联合国机构 15—177f
联合国难民事务高级专员办事处 United Nations High Commissioner for Refugees, Office of the (UNHCR) 联合国机构 17—362d
联合国人口基金 United Nations Population Fund (UNFPA) 联合国信托基金 17—362f
联合国善后救济总署 United Nations Relief and Rehabilitation Administration (UNRRA) 国际组织 17—363a
联合国社会发展研究所 United Nations Research Institute for Social Development (UNRISD) 联合国机构 17—363b
联合国训练研究所 United Nations Institute for Training and Research

(UNITAR) 联合国机构 17—362e
联合国资本发展基金 United Nations Capital Development Fund (UNCDF) 联合国机构 17—361b
联合果品公司 United Fruit Company 美国公司 17—352d
联合航空公司 United Airlines, Inc. 美国国际航空公司 17—349f
联合会杯 Federation Cup 世界女子网球赛优胜奖 6—263d
联合基督教会 United Church of Christ 美国新教派别 17—351e
联合技术公司 United Technologies Corporation 美国公司 17—374c
联合剧团 Uniti, Compagnia degli 意大利演员团体 17—374d
联合利华公司 Unilever 跨国公司 17—344f
联合群岛 Union Group (southwestern Pacific Ocean) 新西兰群岛 17—345f
联合商标公司 United Brands Company 美国公司 17—351d
联合石油公司 Unocal Corporation 美国石油化工企业 17—402c
联合收割机 combine 农业机械 4—378a
联合诉讼和控告 joinder and impleader 法律 9—74c
联合太平洋铁路公司 Union Pacific Railroad Company 美国铁路公司 17—348d
联合碳化物公司 Union Carbide Corporation 美国公司 17—345d
联合铁路公司 Consolidated Rail Corporation 美国公司 4—447c
联合王国国旗 Union Jack 英国国旗 17—345f
联合卫理公会 United Methodist Church 美国新教教会 17—356b
联合-西格纳尔公司 Allied-Signal Inc. 美国公司 1—241a
联合长老会 United Presbyterian Church 苏格兰基督教会 17—363c
联机服务系统 online system 计算机科学 12—422a
联觉 synesthesia 心理学 16—402d
联盟国家 Allied Powers 世界大战史 1—240f
"联盟"号飞船 Soyuz 苏联航天器 15—559b
联盟诗人 Confederation group 加拿大文学 4—420a
联体双胎 conjoined twin 医学 4—432b
联铁 Conrail 美国公司 4—441d
联想 association 心理学 1—563f
联想测验 association test 心理学 1—564f
联想学习 associative learning 动物行为 2—1a
联艺公司 United Artists Corporation 美国电影公司 17—351a
联轴器 coupling 机械器件 4—546f
联轴器 shaft coupling 机器装置 15—254a
联珠法 anadiplosis 修辞方法 1—308d
廉价惊险小说 penny dreadful 英国文学 13—146b
廉价惊险小说 shilling shocker 小说 15—314f
廉价市场 Bon Marché 法国百货公司 3—23a
廉价小说 dime novel 美国廉价平装冒险小说 5—318a
镰孢霉萎蔫病 Fusarium wilt 植物病害 6—532b
镰仓 Kamakura 日本城市 9—145a
镰仓雕 Kamakura-bori 日本漆工艺品 9—145b
镰仓时代 Kamakura period 日本历史 9—145c
镰刀 sickle 农具 15—351b
镰鱼 Moorish idol (*Zanclus canescens*) 鱼类 11—381e
镰状细胞性贫血 sickle-cell anemia 疾病 15—351b
镰嘴管舌鸟 iiwi (*Vestiaria coccinea*) 鸣禽 8—329e
镰嘴鸟 scythebill 鸟类 15—162d
练习曲 étude 音乐 6—154a
炼金术 alchemy 伪科学 1—188c
炼金药 elixir 古代炼金物质 6—41d
炼狱 purgatory 天主教教义 14—32b
恋诗歌手 minnesinger 德国诗人-音乐家 11—259d
恋童癖 pedophilia 性偏离行为 13—120c
恋物癖 fetishism 心理变态、性偏离 6—297f
链 chain 机械 4—27d
链杆菌热 streptobacillary fever 传染病 16—275d
链接 catenation 化学 3—523f
链霉菌属 Streptomyces 细菌学 16—275f
链霉素 streptomycin 药物 16—275f
链球菌 streptococcus 菌种 16—275e
链珊瑚 Halysites 古生物学 7—434d
链式反应 chain reaction 物理学 4—28c
链状硅酸盐 inosilicate 化合物 8—394d
链状闪电 chain lightning 气象学 4—28a
楝科 Meliaceae 植物学 11—96f
良姜 shellflower 植物学 15—298f
良宽 Ryōkan 日本禅僧、诗人、书法家 14—477a
良心 conscience 心理学 4—442f
良性天疱疮 benign pemphigus (medicine) 疾病 2—385a
良渚文化 Liangzhu culture 中国新石器文化 10—69b
凉钵 psykter 古希腊陶器 13—565f
凉棚 arbor 建筑 1—443e
凉亭 kiosk 建筑 9—298a
凉亭鸟 bowerbird 鸟类 3—94c
凉鞋 sandal 鞋 15—26b
梁 beam 建筑 2—303e
梁 lintel (architecture) 建筑 10—126b
梁辰鱼 Liang Chenyu 中国明代戏曲家 10—67e
梁冀 Liang Ji 中国东汉大臣 10—67e
梁楷 Liang Kai 中国宋代画家 10—67e
梁龙 Diplodocus 古生物学 5—331f
梁启超 Liang Qichao 中国学者、思想家 10—68a
梁实秋 Liang Shiqiu 中国作家、学者 10—68b
梁漱溟 Liang Shuming 中国哲学家 10—68d
梁思成 Liang Sicheng 中国建筑学家 10—68d
梁思永 Liang Siyong 中国考古学家 10—68f
梁武帝萧衍 Liangwudi Xiao Yan 中国南朝皇帝 10—69a
梁赞 Ryazan 俄罗斯公国 14—474c
梁赞 Ryazan 俄罗斯州名 14—474c
梁赞 Ryazan 俄罗斯城市 14—474d
梁柱体系 post-and-lintel system 建筑学 13—459d
椋鸟 starling 鸟类 16—198d
椋鸟科 Sturnidae 鸟类 16—291e
量步购地 Walking Purchase 北美殖民地历史 18—76b
量规 gauge 计量工具 7—31f
量角器 protractor 仪器 13—547e
量热计 calorimeter 仪器 3—357f
量水堰 weir 水利 18—172d
两 tael 中国重量单位 16—421b
两班 yangban 朝鲜社会等级 18—419e
两板贝属 Dielasma 古生物学 5—305b
两步舞 two-step 舞蹈 17—303f
两部神道 Ryōbu Shintō 日本神道教 14—477a
两党制 two-party system 政治学 17—303d
《两个世界评论》 Revue des Deux Mondes 法国期刊 14—254a
两极细胞 bipolar cell 神经细胞 2—487b
两姐妹镇 Dos Hermanas 西班牙城镇 5—392f
两面论 double-aspect theory (philosophy) 哲学 5—398a
两难故事 dilemma tale 非洲文学 5—315f
两栖类 amphibian 动物学 1—297a
两栖鲵 amphiuma 两栖动物 1—299f
两栖战 amphibious warfare 军事 1—297d
两西西里王国 Two Sicilies, Kingdom of the 意大利历史 17—303f
两项运动 biathlon 冬季体育运动 2—456f
两形 biform 神话人物 2—466c
两性现象 bisexuality 生物学 2—495b
两伊战争 Iran-Iraq War 伊朗、伊拉克之间的战争 8—441a
两院制 bicameral system 政治体制 2—460d
亮氨酸 leucine 氨基酸 10—42e
亮度 brightness 物理学 3—156d
量 pramāṇa 印度哲学 13—483f

量词逻辑 logic of quantifiers 逻辑学 10—191a
量词逻辑 quantifiers, logic of (formal logic) 逻辑学 14—74c
量纲分析 dimensional analysis 物理学、工程学 5—318b
量化 quantification 逻辑学 14—74b
量子 quantum 物理学 14—74e
量子场论 quantum field theory 物理学 14—75f
量子电动力学 quantum electrodynamics (QED) 物理学 14—75e
量子计算机 quantum computer 计算机科学 14—75a
量子力学 quantum mechanics 数学、物理学 14—76b
量子色动力学 quantum chromodynamics (QCD) 物理学 14—74f
量子数 quantum number 物理学 14—76d
辽 Liao DYNASTY 中国王朝 10—69e
辽东半岛 Liaodong Bandao 中国半岛 10—70c
辽河 Liao He 中国河流 10—69f
辽宁 Liaoning 中国省份 10—70d
辽太祖耶律亿 Liaotaizu Yelü Yi 中国皇帝 10—71a
辽天祚帝耶律延禧 Liaotianzuodi Yelü Yanxi 中国皇帝 10—71a
辽阳 Liaoyang 中国城市 10—71b
辽源 Liaoyuan 中国城市 10—71c
疗热草 feverwort 草本植物 6—300b
疗肾野豌豆 kidney vetch (*Anthyllis vulneraria*) 草本植物 9—270e
《聊斋志异》 Liaozhaizhiyi 中国清代文言短篇小说集 10—71c
廖内 Riau 印度尼西亚省份 14—274e
寮语 Laotian language 亚洲语言 9—494a
燎原大火 wildland fire 自然灾害 18—254c
鹩哥 mynah 鸟类 11—524f
鹩鹛 wren-babbler 鸟类 18—344a
了结债务协议 composition 法律 4—400a
钌(Ru) ruthenium 化学元素 14—468b
蓼目 Polygonales 植物学 13—413b
廖仲恺 Liao Zhongkai 中国革命家 10—70b
列昂捷夫 Leontyev, Konstantin Nikolayevich 俄国作家 10—27d
列昂捷夫 Leontief, Wassily 美国经济学家 10—27b
列昂尼多夫 Leonidov, Leonid Mironovich 苏联演员 10—26e
列昂诺夫 Leonov, Aleksey Arkhipovich 苏联航天员 10—26f
列昂诺夫 Leonov, Leonid Maksimovich 苏联作家 10—27a
列奥米尔 Réaumur, René-Antoine Ferchault de 法国昆虫学家 14—181f
列别捷夫 Lebedev, Pyotr Nikolayevich 俄国物理学家 9—549a
列别捷夫 Lebedev, Sergey Vasilyevich 俄国化学家 9—549a
列宾 Repin, Ilya Yefimovich 俄国画家 14—233e
列城 Leh 印度城镇 9—563f
列当 broomrape 草本植物 3—186b
列蒂 Rieti 意大利城市 14—295c
列队毛虫 processionary caterpillar 昆虫 13—525f
列队行进 procession 天主教礼仪 13—525d
列夫达 Revda 俄罗斯城市 14—249f
列夫斯基 Levski, Vasil 保加利亚革命者 10—49b
列克星敦 Lexington 美国马萨诸塞州城镇 10—54a
列克星敦 Lexington 美国密苏里州城市 10—54b
列克星敦 Lexington 美国弗吉尼亚州城市 10—54b
列克星敦 Lexington 美国肯塔基州城市 10—54c
列克星敦和康科德战役 Lexington and Concord, Battles of 美国历史 10—54d
列肯 Lekain 法国演员 10—1b
列米佐夫 Remizov, Aleksey Mikhaylovich 俄国作家 14—222e
列那狐 Reynard THE Fox 文学人物 14—255b
列宁 Lenin, Vladimir Ilich 苏联领导人 10—7c
列宁峰 Lenin Peak 中亚山峰 10—11b
列宁伏尔加-波罗的海航道 Lenin Volga-Baltic Waterway 俄罗斯水道 10—11c
列宁格勒 Leningrad (city and *oblast*, Russia) 俄罗斯城市 10—11c
列宁格勒事件 Leningrad Affair 苏联历史 10—11d
列宁格勒之围 Leningrad, Siege of 苏联历史 10—11c
"列宁"号 Lenin 苏联破冰船 10—7a
列宁纳巴德 Leninabad 塔吉克斯坦城市 10—11c
列宁纳坎 Leninakan (Armenia) 亚美尼亚城市 10—11c
列宁诺戈尔斯克 Leninogorsk 哈萨克斯坦城市 10—11f
列宁斯克-库兹涅茨基 Leninsk-Kuznetsky 俄罗斯城市 10—12b
列宁图书馆 Lenin Library 俄罗斯国家图书馆 10—11a
列宁勋章 Lenin, Order of 苏联勋章 10—7b
列宁遗嘱 Lenin's Testament 苏联历史 10—11f
列宁主义 Leninism 共产主义理论 10—11e
列奇察 Rechitsa 白俄罗斯城市 14—183c
列日 Liège 比利时省份 10—86e
列日 Liège 比利时城市 10—86f
列舍夫斯基 Reshevsky, Samuel Herman 美国国际象棋大师 14—239c
列氏温标 Réaumur temperature scale 温度计 14—182a
列斯科夫 Leskov, Nikolay Semyonovich 俄国小说家 10—37d
列索西比尔斯克 Lesosibirsk 俄罗斯城市 10—38a
列托语 Lettish language 波罗的海地区语言 10—42b
《列王纪》 Kings, books of 《圣经》 9—291a
列维 Lévi, Sylvain 法国东方学家 10—46d
列维(本·格尔绍姆) Levi ben Gershom 法国犹太学者 10—46e
列维茨基 Levitsky, Ivan 乌克兰小说家 10—48d
列维涅 Lhevinne, Josef 俄国钢琴家 10—56a
列维-齐维塔 Levi-Civita, Tullio 意大利数学家 10—46e
列文 Levene, Phoebus (Aaron Theodor) 美国化学家 10—45c
列文虎克 Leeuwenhoek, Antonie van 荷兰科学家 9—558c
列希 leshy 斯拉夫神话中妖精 10—37c
列希蒂兹基 Leschetizky, Theodor 波兰音乐家 10—36d
列线图 alignment chart (applied mathematics) 数学 1—229e
列御寇 Lieh Yü-k'ou 中国战国思想家 10—87b
列扎诺夫 Rezanov, Nikolay Petrovich 俄国外交家 14—257a
列支敦士登 Liechtenstein 欧洲国家 10—85e
列兹金卡舞 lezginka 舞蹈 10—55c
列子 Liezi 中国战国思想家 10—88a
《列子》 Liezi 中国道家文献 10—88a
劣地 badland 地质学 2—130b
烈普宁 Repnin, Nikolay Vasilyevich, Knyaz (Prince) 俄国外交家 14—234a
烈性酒 spirit 酒精饮料 16—35c
鴷形类 piciform 鸟类 13—289a
猎豹 cheetah (*Acinonyx jubatus*) 哺乳动物 4—100f
猎兵 chasseur 法国装甲部队 4—88d
猎蝽 assassin bug 昆虫 1—559f
猎狗现场追猎选拔赛 field trial 猎狗之间的比赛 6—306e
猎狐 fox hunting 打猎活动 6—432a
猎狐㹴狗 fox terrier 狗品种 6—432a
猎狐狗 foxhound 狗品种 6—432e
猎户座 Orion 天文学 12—461f
猎户座大星云 Orion Nebula 天文学 12—462a
猎户座α Alpha Orionis 天文学 1—250b
猎獾狗 dachshund 狗品种 5—103b
猎浣熊狗 coonhound 狗品种 4—482f
猎鸥 jaeger 鸟类 8—515a
猎枪 shotgun 武器 15—336e
猎犬座α Alpha Canum Venaticorum 天文学 1—249f
猎人赫恩 Herne THE HUNTER 英国民间传说人物 8—44b
猎人小屋 Hunters' Lodges 美加秘密组织 8—259e
猎水獭狗 otterhound 狗品种 12—500c
猎头俗 headhunting 人类学 7—538e
猎蛛 hunting spider 蛛形纲动物 8—261e
猎蛛蛛 spider-hunting spider 动物 16—29b
裂变材料 fissile material 核物理学 6—336e

裂变产物 fission product 核物理学 6—336f
裂变径迹测年法 fission-track dating 测定年龄方法 6—337a
裂缝藓 slit moss 藓类植物 15—433f
裂谷 Rift Valley (Africa) 东非大裂谷 14—296f
裂谷 rift valley 地形 14—296f
裂谷热 Rift Valley fever 动物病毒性传染病 14—297a
裂合酶 lyase 生理学 10—307c
裂化 cracking 石油炼制过程 4—563f
裂口鲨 Cladoselache 古生物学 4—257c
裂体腔动物 schizocoelomate 无脊椎动物 15—117f
裂头虫属 Crepicephalus 古生物学 5—6e
鬣齿兽属 Hyaenodon 古生物学 8—276e
鬣狗 hyena 哺乳动物 8—287c
鬣鳞蜥 iguana 动物学 8—328c
鬣鳞蜥类 iguanid 动物学 8—328e
鬣鳞蜥属 Uta 动物学 17—425d
鬣蜥 agama 爬行动物 1—114f
鬣蜥科 Agamidae 动物学 1—115c
鬣羊 aoudad (*Ammotragus lervia*) 哺乳动物 1—404e
邻苯二甲酸 phthalic acid 化合物 13—269c
邻氯青霉素 cloxacillin 药物 4—305b
林白 Lindbergh, Charles A. 美国飞行员 10—116a
林堡 Limburg 比利时省份 10—102e
林堡 Limburg 荷兰省份 10—102f
林堡干酪 Limburger 食品 10—103a
林堡公国 Limburg 欧洲历史 10—102d
林贝 Limbe 喀麦隆港口 10—102b
林彪 Lin Biao 中国军事家 10—107b
林波波河 Limpopo River 非洲河流 10—106f
林伯渠 Lin Boqu 中国政治家 10—107d
林布人 Limbu 尼泊尔土著部落 10—102d
林鸱 potoo 鸟类 13—464c
林茨 Linz 奥地利城市 10—127c
林茨-多纳维茨法 L-D process 炼钢法 9—419a
林茨纲领 Linz program 欧洲历史 10—127d
林达尔 Lindahl, Erik Robert 瑞典经济学家 10—115e
林袋鼠 forester 哺乳动物 6—406d
林戴胜 wood hoopoe 鸟类 18—320c
林丹 Legdan (Mongol chief) 蒙古汗名 9—561a
林丹 Lindane 化工 10—115f
林丹汗 Ligdan Khan 蒙古大汗 10—91c
林道 Lindau 德国城市 10—116f
林德 Linde, Carl (Paul Gottfried) von 德国工程师 10—116d
林德 Lind, James 英国医生 10—115d
林德 Lind, Jenny 瑞典歌唱家 10—115e
林德布拉德 Lindblad, Bertil 瑞典天文学家 10—116d
林德夫妇 Lynd, Robert (Staughton); and Lynd, Helen 美国社会学家 10—314c
林德格伦 Lindgren, Astrid 瑞典儿童读作作家 10—117b
林德格伦 Lindegren, Erik (Johan) 瑞典诗人 10—116e
林德格伦 Lindgren, Waldemar 美国地质学家 10—117c
林德利 Lindley, John 英国植物学家 10—117d
林德利 Lindley, William 英国工程师 10—117e
林德曼 Lindemann, (Carl Louis) Ferdinand von 德国数学家 10—116e
林德曼岛 Lindeman Island 澳大利亚岛屿 10—116e
林登 Linden 圭亚那城市 10—116f
林登 Linden, Pieter Cort van der 荷兰政治家 10—117a
林登塔尔 Lindenthal, Gustav 美国工程师 10—117a
林迪斯芳 Lindisfarne (England) 英格兰岛屿 10—117d
林迪斯芳福音书 Lindisfarne Gospels 基督教文献 10—117d
林地诸文化 Woodland cultures 北美洲东部史前文化 18—324a
林董 Hayashi Tadasu, Count (Hakushaku) 日本外交家 7—530d
林都斯 Lindos 罗得岛城镇 10—117e
林顿 Linton, Ralph 美国人类学家 10—126c
林顿 Linton, William James 英国木刻家 10—126d
林顿-林茅斯 Lynton and Lynmouth 英格兰城镇 10—314f
林恩 Lynn 美国城市 10—314e
林恩运河 Lynn Canal 美国水道 10—314f
林风眠 Lin Fengmian 中国画家 10—107e
林芙美子 Hayashi Fumiko 日本小说家 7—530a
林伽 liṅga 印度教 10—121d
林伽派 Liṅgāyat 印度教教派 10—121d
林戈 Ringo, Johnny 美国歹徒 14—305b
林鸽 wood pigeon (speices *Columba palumbus*) 鸟类 18—320e
林格氏液 Ringer's solution 医学 14—304e
林贡斯人 Lingones 欧洲民族 10—122b
林龟 wood turtle (*Clemmys insculpta*) 龟类 18—321c
林黑文牡蛎 lynnhaven 软体动物 10—314f
林吉特 ringgit 马亚西亚货币单位 14—304f
林加延湾 Lingayen Gulf 菲律宾海湾 10—121e
林鵙科 Prionopidae (bird family) 动物学 13—519a
林蕨 wood fern 草本植物 18—320a
林克飞行练习器 Link Trainer 航空学 10—123d
林克莱特 Linklater, Eric (Robert) 苏格兰作家 10—123f
林肯 Lincoln 英国城市 10—109e
林肯 Lincoln 美国伊利诺伊州城市 10—109e
林肯 Lincoln 美国内布拉斯加州城市 10—109f
林肯 Lincoln, Abraham 美国总统 10—110a
林肯 Lincoln, Benjamin 美国军人 10—114e
林肯 Lincoln, Robert Todd 美国政治家 10—114f
林肯-道格拉斯辩论 Lincoln-Douglas Debates 美国历史 10—115a
林肯港 Port Lincoln 澳大利亚城市 13—446a
林肯公园动物园 Lincoln Park Zoo 美国动物园 10—115c
林肯纪念堂 Lincoln Memorial 美国建筑 10—115b
林肯郡 Lincolnshire 英格兰郡名 10—115c
林肯隧道 Lincoln Tunnel 交通 10—115c
林肯营 Abraham Lincoln Battalion 历史事件 1—28a
林莱克 Lynn Lake 加拿大矿区 10—314f
林兰英 Lin Lanying 中国物理学家 10—108a
林狸 linsang 哺乳动物 10—125f
林利斯戈 Linlithgow 苏格兰城市 10—124a
林利斯戈侯爵(第二) Linlithgow, Victor Alexander John Hope, 2nd Marquess of 英国政治家 10—124a
林林兄弟 Ringling Brothers 美国马戏家族 14—304f
林羚 sitatunga (*Tragelaphus spekei*) 哺乳动物 15—406a
林罗山 Hayashi Razan 日本学者 7—530a
林茅斯 Lynmouth (England) 英格兰城镇 10—314e
林木线 timberline 林业 17—98a
林纳德·斯金纳德乐队 Lynyrd Skynyrd 美国摇滚乐队 10—315b
林奈 Linnaeus, Carolus 瑞典植物学家 10—124c
林奈环形山 Linné 天文学 10—124e
林南科斯基 Linnankoski, Johannes 芬兰小说家、演说家、独立运动战士 10—124e
林内巴赫灯 Linnebach lantern 剧院照明装置 10—124f
林奇 Lynch, Benito 阿根廷作家 10—313e
林奇 Lynch, John (Mary) 爱尔兰总理 10—313f
林奇 Lynch, John R(oy) 美国政治家 10—314a
林奇堡 Lynchburg 美国城市 10—314a
林巧稚 Lin Qiaozhi 中国妇产科专家 10—108b
林区居民联欢大会 bushmen's carnival 澳大利亚牧人竞技会 3—283f
林赛 Lindsay 加拿大城镇 10—117f
林赛 Lindsey 盎格鲁-撒克逊人王国 10—118c
林赛 Lindsey, Ben B. 美国法官 10—118c
林赛 Lyndsay, Sir David 苏格兰诗人 10—314d

林赛 Lindsay, Norman (Alfred William) 澳大利亚作家、画家 10—118a
林赛 Lindsay, Vachel 美国诗人 10—118a
林赛和克劳斯 Lindsay, Howard; and Crouse, Russel 美国剧作家 10—117f
林蛇 mangrove snake 爬行动物 10—459c
林纾 Lin Shu 中国翻译家 10—108c
林鼠 wood rat 哺乳动物 18—320f
林斯 Lins 巴西城市 10—125e
林斯 Lins, Osman 巴西小说家 10—125e
林斯·多·雷戈·卡瓦尔坎蒂 Lins do Rego Cavalcanti, José 巴西小说家 10—125f
林索登 Linschoten, Jan Huyghen van 荷兰探险家 10—126a
林特 Linth, Hans Conrad Escher von der 瑞士科学家、政治家 10—126c
林跳鼠 jumping mouse 哺乳动物 9—108d
林蛙 Wood frog (*Rana sylvatica*) 两栖动物 18—320b
林务官蛾 forester moth 昆虫 6—406e
林铣十郎 Hayashi Senjūrō 日本首相 7—530b
林鸮 wood owl 鸟类 18—320d
林小鼠 wood mouse 哺乳动物 18—320d
林雪平 Linköping 瑞典城市 10—124a
《林芽椰蒂协定》 Linggadjati Agreement 印度尼西亚历史 10—121e
林岩鹨 dunnock 鸟类 5—464e
林燕 woodswallow 鸟类 18—324f
林洋港 Lin Yanggang 中国台湾省政治家 10—108e
林邑 Lin-yi (ancient Indochinese kingdom) 亚洲古国 10—108e
林荫大道 boulevard 城市规划 3—80f
林莺 woodwarbler 鸟类 18—325b
林莺科 Parulidae 动物学 13—69e
林璎 Lin, Maya 美国建筑师 10—107a
林语堂 Lin Yutang 中国作家、学者 10—108f
林鸳鸯 wood duck (*Aix sponsa*) 鸟类 18—319e
林则徐 Lin Zexu 中国清末爱国政治家 10—109a
林芝 Nyingchi 中国地区、县名 12—310a
林子平 Hayashi Shihei 日本军事学家 7—530c
临边昏暗 limb darkening 天文学 10—102b
临川 Linchuan 中国城市 10—109c
临床心理学 clinical psychology 心理学 4—293a
临汾 Linfen 中国城市 10—121a
临桂 Lin-kuei (China) 中国城市 10—108a
临海 Linhai 中国城市 10—123b
临河 Linhe 中国城市 10—123c
临济宗 Rinzai 日本禅宗支派 14—305e
临界点 critical point 物理学 5—19b
临界角 critical angle 光学 5—19a
临界质量 critical mass 核物理学 5—19b
临朐 Linqu 中国城市 10—125d
临时记号 accidental 音乐 1—45e
临时支撑 shoring 建筑 15—332f
临时执政 interrex 古罗马史 8—423a
临潼 Lintong 中国市辖区 10—126e
临夏 Linxia 中国城市 10—127a
临沂 Linyi 中国城市 10—127b
临终病人安养所 hospice 社会学 8—189a
临终之歌 marwysgafn 威尔士宗教长诗 10—552f
临淄 Linzi 中国市辖区 10—127d
淋巴结 lymph node 解剖学 10—312b
淋巴瘤 lymphoma 疾病 10—313e
淋巴瘤性甲状腺肿 struma lymphomatosa (endocrine disorder) 疾病 16—283d
淋巴水肿 lymphedema 疾病 10—313a
淋巴网状细胞瘤 lymphoreticuloma 疾病 10—313e
淋巴细胞 lymphocyte 白细胞 10—313a
淋巴系统 lymphatic system 解剖学 10—312c
淋巴小结 lymph nodule 解剖学 10—312b
淋巴液 lymph 生理学 10—311e
淋巴组织 lymphoid tissue 解剖学 10—313d
磷(P) phosphorus 化学元素 13—260b
磷光 phosphorescence 物理学 13—259d
磷光体 phosphor 发光物质 13—259d
磷化氢 hydrogen phosphide (gas) 化合物 8—284b
磷灰石 apatite 矿物 1—407a
磷块岩 phosphorite 岩石 13—260a
磷蜡蝉 lanternfly (*Lanternaria phosphorea*) 昆虫 9—489d
磷铝锂石 amblygonite 矿物 1—270c
磷铝石 variscite 矿物 17—473f
磷氯铅矿 pyromorphite 矿物 14—47e
磷锰锂矿 lithiophilite 矿物 10—146d
磷青铜 phosphor bronze 铜锡合金 13—259d
磷缺乏 phosphorus deficiency 病理生理现象 13—260e
磷酸(H_3PO_4) phosphoric acid 化合物 13—259f
磷酸二脂酶抑制剂 PDE-5 inhibitor 药物 13—107d
磷酸化 phosphorylation 化学术语 13—260f
磷酸三丁酯 tributyl phosphate 化学 17—215b
磷酸盐矿物 phosphate mineral 矿物 13—257f
磷酸盐岩 phosphate rock 岩石 13—259b
磷酸盐(酯) phosphate 化合物 13—257f
磷铁锂矿 triphylite 矿物 17—224b
磷虾 krill 甲壳动物 9—377d
磷循环 phosphorus cycle 生物学 13—260e
磷钇矿 xenotime 矿物 18—376a
磷脂 phospholipid 生物化学 13—259c
鳞 scale 动物学 15—99f
鳞翅目昆虫 lepidopteran 动物学 10—31a
鳞茎 bulb 植物 3—240a
鳞茎腐烂病 bulb rot 植物疾病 3—240c
鳞绿泥石 leptochlorite 矿物 10—32c
鳞毛蕨 shield fern 植物学 15—312a
鳞木属 Lepidodendron 古生物学 10—30e
鳞皮病 psorosis 植物疾病 13—559e
鳞石英 tridymite 矿物 17—217e
鳞尾松鼠 scaletail 哺乳动物 15—100d
鳞子木属 Leptospermum 植物学 10—33b
淋病 gonorrhea 疾病 7—205d
淋滤 leaching 地质学 9—540b
淋溶土 alfisol 土壤学 1—215e
膦(PH_3) phosphine 化合物 13—259b
伶猴 titi 哺乳动物 17—116b
灵 tama 日本宗教 16—449a
灵薄狱 limbo 天主教神学 10—102c
灵厄里克 Ringerike 挪威地理区域 14—304e
灵歌 spiritual 音乐 16—35d
灵魂 soul 宗教、哲学概念 15—526a
灵魂乐队 De La Soul 美国说唱乐乐队 5—189e
灵柩台 catafalque 丧葬建筑 3—518f
灵克宾 Ringkøbing 丹麦州名 14—304f
灵轮 Merkava 犹太教 11—131f
灵猫 civet 哺乳动物 4—252d
灵猫 viverrid 哺乳动物 18—27d
灵媒 medium 神秘学 11—78f
灵巧炸弹 smart bomb 武器 15—440d
灵渠 Ling Qu 中国古运河 10—121c
灵萨克 Ringsaker 挪威城镇 14—304d
灵猩 greyhound 狗品种 7—307d

灵猩 Greyhound 赛马 7—307f
灵体会 spiritual assembly 巴哈教组织 16—35f
灵屋 tamaya 日本神道教 16—450d
灵应牌 Ouija board 神秘学 12—506e
灵友会 Reiyū-kai 日本宗教组织 14—212f
灵乐 soul music 美国黑人音乐 15—526c
灵长类 primate 动物学 13—509c
灵智学 anthroposophy 哲学 1—380f
玲珑瓷 linglong ware 中国陶瓷 10—121f
铃铛花 bellwort 植物学 2—369b
铃鼓 tambourine 乐器 16—451b
铃兰 lily of the valley (*Convallaria majalis*) 草本植物 10—100b
铃鹿 Suzuka 日本城市 16—366c
铃木春信 Suzuki Harunobu 日本浮世绘艺术家 16—366e
铃木大拙 Suzuki, D(aisetsu) T(eitarō) 日本佛教学者 16—366c
铃木贯太郎 Suzuki Kantarō 日本首相 16—366f
铃木善幸 Suzuki Zenkō 日本首相 16—366f
铃木文治 Suzuki Bunji 日本工人运动组织者 16—366d
铃木一郎 Suzuki, Ichiro 日本棒球运动员 16—366c
铃木正三 Suzuki Shōsan 日本佛教禅师 16—366f
凌家卫岛 Langkawi Island 马来西亚岛屿 9—483d
凌霄 trumpet creeper 植物 17—243f
陵墓 mausoleum 墓葬建筑 11—41c
菱 water chestnut 草本植物 18—135d
菱川师宣 Hishikawa Moronobu 日本艺术家 8—96d
菱沸石 chabazite 矿物 4—21d
菱蝗 grouse locust 昆虫 7—326f
菱镁矿 magnesite 矿物 10—386b
菱锰矿 rhodochrosite 矿物 14—269a
菱锶矿 strontianite 矿物 16—281e
菱田春草 Hishida Shunsō 日本画家 8—96d
菱铁矿 siderite 矿物 15—353a
菱锌矿 smithsonite 矿物 15—453d
菱锌矿黄铜 calamine brass 铜锌合金 3—333f
菱形花纹装饰 diaper 建筑表面装饰 5—288f
聆听 samāʿ 伊斯兰教苏非教派用语 14—559e
翎笔 calamus (writing implement) 书写工具 3—334b
羚类 antelope 动物学 1—376e
羚羊 gazelle 哺乳动物 7—40a
“羚羊”号 Ariel 人造地球卫星 1—471e
零点能 zero-point energy 物理学 18—512e
零式飞机 Zero 日本战斗机 18—512d
零售 retailing 商业 14—245c
岭谷地区 Ridge and Valley 美国自然地理区 14—291c
岭南画派 Lingnan school 中国画派 10—121f
领半足鹎 collared hemipode (bird) 鸟类 4—345f
领鞭虫 choanoflagellate 原生动物 4—186f
领鹑 plains wanderer 鸟类 13—339e
领地 fief 欧洲封建社会封地 6—304d
领海 territorial waters 国际法 16—556a
领路狗 guide dog 导盲犬 7—353f
领事 consul 国家任命的驻外政府官员 4—461b
领域 territory 生态学 16—556b
领域性行为 territorial behaviour 动物学 16—555f
领主 donatário 葡属殖民领地首脑 5—377a
领主法院 manorial court 中世纪法律 10—470b
领主自留地产 demesne 英国封建法律 5—233c
令状 warrant 法律 18—109a
令状 writ 法律 18—348e
溜冰鞋 skate 体育用品 15—414a
刘安 Liu An 中国哲学家 10—153e
刘骜 Liu Ao 中国皇帝 10—153e
刘邦 Liu Bang 中国皇帝 10—153e
刘备 Liu Bei 中国皇帝 10—153e
刘别谦 Lubitsch, Ernst 美国电影导演 10—264e
刘秉忠 Liu Bingzhong 中国元代政治家 10—153e
刘伯承 Liu Bocheng 中国军事家 10—153f
刘彻 Liu Che 中国皇帝 10—154b
刘炟 Liu Da 中国皇帝 10—154b
刘鹗 Liu E 中国清末小说家 10—154b
刘弗陵 Liu Fuling 中国皇帝 10—154c
刘海粟 Liu Haisu 中国画家 10—154d
刘恒 Liu Heng 中国皇帝 10—154f
刘洪 Liu Hong 中国汉代天文学家 10—154f
刘华清 Liu Huaqing 中国军事家 10—155a
刘徽 Liu Hui 中国魏晋时期数学家 10—155c
刘家峡水电站 Liujiaxia Hydroelectric Station 中国水电站 10—158c
刘瑾 Liu Jin 中国明代宦官 10—155d
刘开渠 Liu Kaiqu 中国雕塑家 10—155e
刘衎 Liu Kan 中国皇帝 10—155f
刘坤一 Liu Kunyi 中国清末将领 10—155f
刘启 Liu Qi 中国皇帝 10—156a
刘少奇 Liu Shaoqi 中国领导人 10—156a
刘奭 Liu Shi 中国皇帝 10—156e
刘松年 Liu Songnian 中国宋代画家 10—156e
刘维尔 Liouville, Joseph 法国数学家 10—129b
刘翔 Liu Xiang 中国田径运动员 10—157a
刘向 Liu Xiang 中国汉代学者 10—156f
刘协 Liu Xie 中国皇帝 10—157b
刘勰 Liu Xie 中国南朝文学理论家 10—157b
刘欣 Liu Xin 中国皇帝 10—157c
刘秀 Liu Xiu 中国皇帝 10—157c
刘询 Liu Xun 中国皇帝 10—157c
刘易舍姆 Lewisham 英格兰自治市 10—53d
刘易斯 Lewes 英格兰地区 10—50a
刘易斯 Lewes 英格兰城镇 10—50a
刘易斯 Lewes 美国城市 10—50a
刘易斯 Lewis, Alun 威尔士诗人 10—50d
刘易斯 Lewis, Sir Arthur 英国经济学家 10—50e
刘易斯 Lewis, C. Day 英国诗人 10—50e
刘易斯 Lewis, C(larence) I(rving) 美国哲学家 10—50e
刘易斯 Lewis, C. S. 英国学者、作家 10—50f
刘易斯 Lewis, David Kellogg 美国哲学家 10—51a
刘易斯 Lewis, Edward B. 美国遗传学家 10—51b
刘易斯 Lewes, George Henry 英国哲学家 10—50b
刘易斯 Lewis, (Harry) Sinclair 美国小说家 10—52d
刘易斯 Lewis, Isaac Newton 美国军人、发明家 10—51c
刘易斯 Lewis, Jerry 美国喜剧演员 10—51d
刘易斯 Lewis, John (Aaron) 美国音乐家 10—51d
刘易斯 Lewis, John L(lewellyn) 美国劳工领袖 10—51e
刘易斯 Lewis, Lennox 英国拳击运动员 10—51f
刘易斯 Lewis, Meade 美国音乐家 10—52b
刘易斯 Lewis, Meriwether 美国探险家 10—52c
刘易斯 Lewis, Matthew Gregory 英国作家 10—52a
刘易斯 Lewis, (Percy) Wyndham 英国艺术家、作家 10—52e
刘易斯(格林·柯提) Lewis Glyn Cothi 威尔士游吟诗人 10—50d
刘易斯堡 Lewisburg 美国城市 10—53c
刘易斯敦 Lewistown 美国城镇 10—53f
刘易斯顿 Lewiston 美国爱达荷州城市 10—53e
刘易斯顿 Lewiston 美国缅因州城市 10—53f
刘易斯-哈里斯 Lewis and Harris 苏格兰岛屿 10—53b
刘易斯和克拉克远征 Lewis and Clark Expedition 美国历史 10—53a
刘易斯-克拉克洞穴 Lewis and Clark Caverns 美国洞穴 10—52f
刘易斯岭 Lewis Range 北美洲山岭 10—53c

刘易斯杂岩 Lewisian Complex 地质学 10—53d
刘禹锡 Liu Yuxi 中国唐代文学家 10—157e
刘渊 Liu Yuan 中国十六国时期统治者 10—157c
刘元 Liu Yuan 中国元代雕塑家 10—157d
刘肇 Liu Zhao 中国皇帝 10—157f
刘知几 Liu Zhiji 中国唐代历史学家 10—157f
刘庄 Liu Zhuang 中国皇帝 10—158a
留基伯 Leucippus 古希腊哲学家 10—42e
留克特拉战役 Leuctra, Battle of 希腊历史 10—43d
留兰香 spearmint (species *Mentha spicata*) 草本植物 16—11a
留里克 Rurik 斯堪的纳维亚人领袖 14—452b
留里克王朝 Rurik DYNASTY 中世纪俄国统治者 14—452b
留萌 Rumoi 日本城市 14—448b
留尼汪 Réunion 法国海外省 14—248c
留声机 Gramophone 电器 7—245d
留声机 phonograph 电器 13—256f
留音 suspension 音乐 16—360d
留院隐修 cenobitic monasticism 宗教 3—562e
留置权 lien 法律 10—87b
流变 flow 物理学 6—374f
流便尼 Reubeni, David 犹太冒险家 14—248a
流便支派 Reuben 犹太人祖先 14—248a
流产 abortion 病理现象 1—27a
流程图 flowchart 步骤程序图表 6—374f
流出 fayḍ 伊斯兰哲学 6—256a
流动货船 tramp steamer 运输工具 17—192f
流动劳工 migrant labour 经济学 11—206e
流动图书馆 bookmobile 图书馆 3—38c
流动性偏好 liquidity preference 经济学 10—134b
流珥 Reuel (biblical priest) 《圣经》人物 14—248c
流放地 penal colony 惩罚罪犯的地区 13—134f
流放和放逐 exile and banishment 刑罚 6—192f
流控技术 fluidics 自动控制技术 6—377e
流浪 vagrancy 社会学 17—443b
流浪汉小说 picaresque novel 文学 13—283d
流浪主教 episcopus vagans 基督教 6—103a
流氓无产阶级 Lumpenproletariat 社会集团 10—282a
流明 lumen 光学 10—280c
流沙 quicksand 地质学 14—90d
流石 flowstone 地质学 6—376d
流数 fluxion 数学 6—380e
流苏花边 macramé 工艺制品 10—362d
流苏树 fringe tree 木本植物 6—495e
流苏松鸡 ruffed grouse 鸟类 14—443b
流苏鹬 ruff (*Philomachus pugnax*) 鸟类 14—442f
流体 fluid 物理学 6—376f
流体力学 fluid mechanics 物理学 6—377c
流亡者 émigré 法国历史 6—60c
流纹岩 rhyolite 岩石 14—272e
流线型化 streamlining 空气动力学 16—273b
流星 meteor 天文学 11—155a
流星花 shooting star 草本植物 15—331f
流星体 meteoroid 天文学 11—157d
流星雨 meteor shower 天文学 11—155d
流星陨石坑 Meteor Crater 美国陨石坑 11—155b
流行 epidemic 病理学 6—99a
流行病学 epidemiology 医学 6—99b
流行抒情曲 pop ballad 音乐 13—431f
流行小说 fashionable novel 文学 6—245d
流行性感冒 influenza 疾病 8—383c
流行性关节红斑 erythema arthriticum epidemicum 传染病 6—125b
流行性腮腺炎 mumps 传染病 11—481d
流行性胸肌痛 pleurodynia 传染病 13—370d
流形 manifold 数学 10—461b
流血星期日 Bloody Sunday 俄国历史 2—543a
流血星期日 Bloody Sunday 英国历史 2—543b
流溢说 emanationism 哲学、神学理论 6—55a
流音 liquid 语音学 10—133e
流域 drainage basin 地理学 5—412d
琉科忒亚 Leucothea 希腊神话女神 10—43b
琉璃河遗址 Liulihe site 中国古代遗址 10—158d
琉璃苣 borage (*Borago officinalis*) 草本植物 3—43c
琉球海沟 Ryukyu Trench 日本琉球群岛东缘深海沟 14—477c
琉球群岛 Ryukyu Islands 日本岛屿 14—477b
硫(S) sulfur 化学元素 16—323f
硫胺素 thiamine 维生素 17—37d
硫醇 thiol 化学 17—39f
硫代硫酸钠 hyposulfite of soda 化合物 8—295e
硫镉矿 greenockite 矿物 7—294f
硫汞柳酸钠 Merthiolate (antiseptic) 防腐剂 11—136d
硫钴矿 linnaeite 矿物 10—124b
硫化 vulcanization 化学 18—54c
硫化浮雕 sulphides (glass) 水晶玻璃制品 16—328e
硫化氢 hydrogen Sulfide 化合物 8—284b
硫化染料 sulfur dye 染料 16—325c
硫化物 sulfide 化合物 16—318c
硫化物矿物 sulfide mineral 矿物 16—318c
硫黄岛 Iwo Jima 日本岛屿 8—496f
硫磺 brimstone 化学元素 3—157f
硫柳汞 thimerosal 药物 17—39d
硫脲 thiourea 化合物 17—40a
硫砷铜矿 enargite 矿物 6—68e
硫属元素 chalcogen 化学元素 4—30f
硫酸(H_2SO_4) sulfuric acid 化工 16—325e
硫酸氢 hydrogen sulfate 化合物 8—284b
硫酸盐(酯) sulfate 化合物 16—317f
硫酸盐化 sulfation 化学 16—318b
硫酸盐矿物 sulfate mineral 矿物学 16—318a
硫酸盐制浆法 kraft process 造纸方法 9—369f
硫锑铜银矿 polybasite 矿物 13—411a
硫铜银矿 stromeyerite 矿物 16—280e
硫细菌 sulfur bacterium 微生物 16—325b
硫循环 sulfur cycle 生态学 16—325c
硫银锗矿 argyrodite 矿物 1—469a
硫质喷气孔 solfatara 地质学 15—495d
硫唑嘌呤 azathioprine 药物 2—99f
榴弹 grenade 武器 7—302f
榴辉岩 eclogite 岩石 5—526a
榴莲 durian (*Durio zibethinus*) 木本植物 5—473e
榴霰弹 shrapnel 弹药 15—338b
瘤蝽 ambush bug 昆虫 1—272d
瘤牛 zebu (cattle) 印度牛品种 18—505b
瘤足动物 oncopod 动物学 12—417b
柳 willow 木本植物 18—271e
柳比莫夫 Lyubimov, Yury Petrovich 苏联戏剧导演 10—320e
柳别尔齐 Lyubertsy 俄罗斯城市 10—320e
柳穿鱼 toadflax 草本植物 17—124f
柳公权 Liu Gongquan 中国唐代书法家 10—154c
柳江 Liu Jiang 中国河流 10—155d
柳栎 willow oak 木本植物 18—272a
柳属 Salix 植物学 14—546e
柳树图案 Willow pattern 工艺美术 18—272b
柳条边 Willow Palisade 中国历史 18—272b
柳条编制品 wickerwork 家具 18—243e
柳叶菜科 Onagraceae 植物学 12—416b
柳叶菜属 Epilobium 植物学 6—101a

《柳叶刀》 Lancet,The 英国医学杂志 9—473b
柳永 Liu Yong 中国宋代诗人 10—157c
柳州 Liuzhou 中国城市 10—159b
柳宗元 Liu Zongyuan 中国唐代文学家 10—158a
锍 matte 化学 11—29e
六朝 Six Dynasties 中国历史 15—409d
六法 Six Principles 中国艺术理论 15—409f
六分仪 sextant 仪器 15—245a
六角晶系 hexagonal system 结晶学 8—65f
六角形手风琴 concertina 乐器 4—410c
六角芝水 Rokkaku Shisui 日本漆器大师 14—357f
六六诗体 sestina 诗体 15—232a
六氯铂酸 hexachloroplatinic acid 化学 8—65d
六氯化苯 benzene hexachloride (BHC) 化合物 2—396c
六面体陨铁 hexahedrite 陨石 8—65f
六年制中学 realschule 德国教育 14—181b
六派哲学 Six Schools 印度哲学 15—410a
六盘山 Liupan Shan 中国山脉 10—158e
六盘水 Liupanshui 中国城市 10—158f
六人团 Six,Les 法国作曲家小组 15—409c
六人制橄榄球 six-man football 体育项目 15—409e
六日赛 six-day race 体育项目 15—409d
六三小组 Gruppo 63 意大利文学团体 7—331a
六文本合参 Hexapla 《圣经·旧约》文本 8—66a
六线鱼 greenling 鱼类 7—294e
六音步诗行 hexameter 文学 8—66a
六音音列 hexachord 音乐 8—65d
六月 June 历法 9—110a
六月甲虫 June beetle 昆虫 9—110a
六月进攻(1917) June Offensive 第一次世界大战史 9—110b
六月一日海战 First of June,Battle of the 法英海战 6—329b
鹨 pipit 鸟类 13—319b
鹨莺 songlark 鸟类 15—514e
龙 dragon 传说怪兽 5—411a
龙 long 中国神话动物 10—205f
龙䲢 weever 鱼类 18—166b
龙伯格 Romberg,Sigmund 美国作曲家 14—374c
龙布陵岛 Lomblen Island 印度尼西亚岛屿 10—196b
龙川 Long Xuyen 越南城市 10—208e
龙达 Ronda 西班牙城市 14—387e
龙达讷国家公园 Rondane National Park 挪威自然保护区 14—007f
龙达讷山 Rondane 挪威山脉 14—387f
龙胆 gentian 草本植物 7—66f
龙胆目 Gentianales 植物学 7—67b
龙格 Runge,Friedlieb Ferdinand 德国化学家 14—449d
龙骨 keel 船体部件 9—210f
龙蒿 tarragon (*Artemisia dracunculus*) 草本植物 16—485d
龙卷 tornado 气象学 17—161e
龙口海峡 Bocas del Dragón (Caribbean Sea) 加勒比海海峡 2—557c
龙口泽兰 dragon's-mouth (*Arethusa bulbosa*) 植物 5—412a
龙门石窟 Longmen caves 中国石窟 10—211b
龙目 Lombok 印度尼西亚岛屿 10—196b
龙脑香科 Dipterocarpaceae 植物学 5—335b
龙讷比 Ronneby 瑞典城镇 14—389b
龙尼 Ronne,Finn 美国作家 14—389a
龙尼陆缘冰 Ronne Ice Shelf 南极威尔海浮冰体 14—389b
龙骑兵 dragoon 军事 5—412b
龙泉窑 Longquan kiln 中国瓷窑 10—211e
龙萨 Ronsard,Pierre de 法国诗人 14—389c
龙塞斯瓦列斯 Roncesvalles 西班牙村庄 14—387e
龙山文化 Longshan culture 中国文化 10—211f
龙舌兰酒 pulque 墨西哥啤酒 14—22b
龙舌兰酒 tequila 酒精饮料 16—548d
龙舌兰科 Agavaceae 植物学 1—118b
龙虱 predaceous diving beetle 昆虫 13—489e
龙树 Nāgārjuna 印度佛教哲学家 11—539a
龙毯 dragon rug 库巴工艺品 5—411b
龙头花 dragonhead 植物 5—411f
龙头鱼 Bombay duck (*Harpodon nehereus*) 鱼类 3—22b
龙溪 Longxi (China) 中国城市 10—213c
龙虾 lobster 节肢动物 10—173d
龙虾笼 lobster pot 捕虾工具 10—174a
龙涎香 ambergris 香料 1—270a
龙线虫 dragon worm 无脊椎动物 5—411d
龙血树脂 dragon's blood 树脂 5—412a
龙血树属 Dracaena 植物学 5—408d
龙牙草 agrimony 草木植物 1—129f
龙岩 Longyan 中国城市 10—213e
龙眼 longan (*Euphoria longana*) 木本植物 10—209a
龙云 Long Yun 中国军人 10—208e
龙爪兰属 Dactylorhiza 植物学 5—104a
泷泽马琴 Takizawa Bakin 日本作家 16—441f
聋 deafness 病理现象 5—194b
隆巴德 Lombard,Carole 美国演员 10—195b
隆巴迪 Lombardi,Vince 美国橄榄球教练 10—195c
隆巴多 Lombardo,Guy (Albert) 美国音乐家 10—195d
隆巴尔多 Lombardo,Pietro 威尼斯雕刻家 10—195e
隆比 Lombi 刚果(金)城市 10—196b
隆波克 Lompoc 美国城市 10—197a
隆达帝国 Lunda empire 非洲历史 10—283d
隆达人 Lunda 非洲民族 10—283c
隆德 Lund 瑞典城市 10—283b
隆德贝里 Lundeberg,Christian 瑞典政治家 10—283e
隆德莱 Rondelet,Guillaume 法国博物学家、医师 14—388b
隆德里纳 Londrina 巴西城市 10—205d
隆盖纳 Longhena,Baldassare 威尼斯建筑师 10—210a
隆哥蒙塔努斯 Longomontanus,Christian 丹麦天文学家 10—211e
隆格维尔公爵 Longueville,Henri II d'Orléans,duc de (duke of) 法国历史人物 10—212e
隆格维尔公爵夫人 Longueville,Anne-Geneviève de Bourbon-Condé,duchesse de 法国历史人物 10—212d
隆格伊 Longueuil 加拿大城市 10—212d
隆王温古河 Lungwebungu River 非洲河流 10—286c
隆吉 Longhi,Alessandro 威尼斯画家 10—210c
隆吉 Longhi,Pietro 威尼斯画家 10—210c
隆吉努斯 Longinus,Gaius Cassius 罗马度支官 10—210f
隆吉努斯 Longinus,Quintus Cassius 罗马官员 10—210f
隆卡利 Roncalli,Angelo Giuseppe 教皇 14—387e
隆莱 Lunglei 印度城镇 10—286c
隆勒索涅 Lons-le-Saunier 法国城镇 10—214a
隆美尔 Rommel,Erwin (Johannes Eugen) 德国元帅 14—386c
隆鸟 Aepyornis 古生物学 1—95d
隆起 uplift 地质学 17—404f
隆钦热绛巴 Klong-chen rab-'byamspa 中国藏传佛教法师 9—318f
隆庆 Longqing 中国皇帝 10—211e
隆人 Rong (people) 亚洲民族 14—388c
隆瑞莫 Longjumeau,Andrew of (French diplomat to Central Asia) 法国外交官 10—211a
隆瑞莫 Longumeau,Andrew of (French diplomat to Central Asia) 法国外交官 10—212f
隆瑞莫 Lonjumel,Andrew of (French diplomat to Central Asia) 法国外交官 10—213f
隆萨 Lunsar 塞拉利昂城镇 10—286f
隆头鱼 wrasse 鱼类 18—342d

隆维 Longwy 法国城镇 10—213c
隆兴寺 Longxing Monastery 中国佛寺 10—213d
垄断 monopoly 经济学 11—346c
垄断竞争 monopolistic competition 经济学 11—346b
楼顶房屋 penthouse 建筑 13—149e
楼梯 staircase 建筑 16—182c
楼梯端柱 newel 建筑 12—148b
楼梯藓 stair-step moss (*Hylocomium splendens*) 植物 16—182b
楼陀罗 Rudra 印度宗教神名 14—442d
耧斗菜 columbine 植物 4—370a
蝼蛄 mole cricket 昆虫 11—317d
镂空边饰工艺 opus interassile 工艺 12—439b
漏 āsrāva 佛教哲学 1—558f
漏斗虫 chonotrich 原生动物 4—195d
漏斗网蛛 funnel-web spider 蜘蛛 6—527f
漏斗胸 pectus excavatum 先天性缺陷 13—118e
漏斗蛛 funnel weaver 蜘蛛 6—527e
漏壶 clepsydra 水钟 4—285c
卢 Loo 牌戏 10—214d
卢阿拉巴河 Lualaba River 刚果(金)河流 10—262d
卢阿普拉河 Luapula River 非洲河流 10—263b
卢埃格尔 Lueger, Karl 奥地利政治家 10—273e
卢埃林 Llewellyn, Richard 威尔士作家 10—169a
卢埃林(阿普·格鲁菲德) Llywelyn AP GRUFFUDD 威尔士邦主 10—171c
卢埃林(阿普·约尔沃思) Llywelyn AP IORWERTH 威尔士邦主 10—171c
卢埃林·伊·格林 Llywelyn y Glyn 威尔士诗人 10—171d
卢埃纳人 Luena (people) 非洲民族 10—273f
卢埃纳人 Lwena (people) 非洲民族 10—306f
卢安瓜国家公园 Luangwa National Park 赞比亚国家公园 10—262f
卢安瓜河 Luangwa River 非洲河流 10—262f
卢安果王国 Loango, Kingdom of 非洲古国 10—172a
卢安夏 Luanshya 赞比亚城镇 10—263a
卢奥人 Luo 肯尼亚民族 10—287b
卢巴-隆达诸邦 Luba-Lunda states 非洲历史 10—263d
卢巴人 Luba 刚果(金)民族 10—263c
卢班戈 Lubango 安哥拉城市 10—263e
卢贝 Loubet, Émile(-François) 法国总统 10—232c
卢贝茨基 Lubecki, Ksawery Drucki 波兰政治家 10—264b
卢贝克 Lubec 美国城镇 10—263f
卢本巴文化期工艺 Lupemban industry 人类学 10—289d
卢本巴希 Lubumbashi 刚果(金)城市 10—266c
卢比 rupee 印度、巴基斯坦、斯里兰卡货币单位 14—450e
卢比 rupiah 印度尼西亚货币单位 14—451b
卢比亚纳 Lubiana (Slovenia) 斯洛文尼亚首都 10—264d
卢宾 Lubin, David 美国农业改良家 10—264d
卢博莫 Loubomo 刚果(布)城镇 10—232d
卢布 ruble 俄罗斯货币单位 14—438b
卢布尔雅那 Ljubljana 斯洛文尼亚首都 10—167b
卢布林 Lubelskie 波兰省份 10—264b
卢布林 Lublin 波兰城市 10—265a
《卢布林联合》 Lublin, Union of 欧洲历史 10—265b
卢布内 Lubny 乌克兰城市 10—265c
卢查纳伯爵 Luchana, Baldomero Espartero, Count (conde) de 西班牙政治家 10—269b
卢彻来府邸 Rucellai, Palazzo 建筑 14—439a
卢茨克 Lutsk 乌克兰城市 10—301e
卢德 Lod 以色列城市 10—183b
卢德 Llwyd, Morgan 威尔士作家 10—171b
卢德米拉,圣 Ludmila, SAINT 斯拉夫殉教者 10—273b
卢德派 Luddite 英国历史 10—272a
卢迪亚纳 Ludhiāna 印度城市 10—272d
卢顿 Luton 英格兰区名 10—301d
卢尔 Llull, Ramon 加泰罗尼亚神学家 10—171a
卢尔德 Lourdes 法国城镇 10—246e
卢尔号 lur 乐器 10—290e
卢尔人 Lur 伊朗民族 10—290e
卢菲拉河 Lufira River 刚果河流 10—274a
卢浮宫博物馆 Louvre Museum 法国博物馆 10—248d
卢伽尔扎吉西 Lugalzagesi 美索不达米亚统治者 10—274b
卢甘斯克 Luhansk 乌克兰州名 10—277a
卢甘斯克 Luhansk 乌克兰城市 10—277b
卢港 Looe 英格兰城镇 10—214d
卢戈 Lugo 西班牙省份 10—275e
卢戈 Lugo 意大利城镇 10—275e
卢戈 Lugo 西班牙城市 10—275f
卢戈尔氏液 Lugol's solution 医学 10—276a
卢戈日 Lugoj 罗马尼亚城市 10—276a
卢戈希 Lugosi, Bela 美国电影演员 10—276b
卢格巴拉人 Lugbara 非洲民族 10—275b
卢格杜南西斯 Lugdunensis 古罗马行省 10—275b
卢格尔手枪 Luger pistol 武器 10—275d
卢贡内斯 Lugones, Leopoldo 阿根廷诗人 10—276a
卢沟桥 Lugouqiao 中国古建筑 10—276d
卢沟桥事变 Marco Polo Bridge Incident 中国抗日战争史 10—498b
卢古鲁人 Luguru 坦桑尼亚民族 10—276e
卢古斯 Lugus 凯尔特神名 10—276e
卢海耶 Luḥayyah, Al- 也门城镇 10—277b
卢汉 Luján 阿根廷城市 10—278a
卢汉 Luhan, Mabel Dodge 美国作家 10—277a
卢赫雅人 Luhya 肯尼亚民族 10—277c
卢加 Louga 塞内加尔城镇 10—233a
卢加德 Lugard, F.D. 英国殖民官员 10—274e
卢加尔班达 Lugalbanda 苏美尔文学 10—274b
卢加鲁斯 Luggarus (Switzerland) 瑞士城市 10—275e
卢加诺 Lugano 瑞士城镇 10—274d
卢加诺湖 Lugano, Lake 欧洲湖泊 10—274d
卢嘉锡 Lu Jiaxi 中国物理化学家 10—260a
卢金 Lukin, Lionel 英国工程师 10—278f
卢卡 Lucca 意大利城市 10—267e
卢卡(科尔托纳的) Luca DA CORTONA 意大利画家 10—266e
卢卡共和国 Lucca, Republic of 欧洲历史 10—268a
卢卡里斯 Lucaris, Cyril 君士坦丁堡牧首 10—267a
卢卡尼亚 Lucania 意大利古地区 10—267a
卢卡奇 Lukács, György 匈牙利哲学家 10—278a
卢卡申科 Lukashenka, Alyaksandr Hrygorevich 白俄罗斯总统 10—278d
卢卡斯 Lucas, George 美国电影导演 10—267c
卢卡斯(小) Lucas, Robert E., Jr. 美国经济学家 10—267d
卢坎 Lucan 古罗马诗人 10—266e
卢考特山 Lookout Mountain 美国山岭 10—214e
卢考特山战役 Lookout Mountain, Battle of 美国历史 10—214e
卢克 Luque 巴拉圭城市 10—290d
卢克莱修 Lucretius 古罗马诗人、哲学家 10—270e
卢克雷蒂娅 Lucretia 古罗马传说人物 10—270d
卢克斯 Luks, George (Benjamin) 美国画家 10—278f
卢克索 Luxor 埃及市镇 10—305a
卢肯伯爵(第三) Lucan, George Charles Bingham, 3rd Earl of 英国元帅 10—266f
卢库加 Lukuga 刚果(金)城镇 10—279a
卢库加河 Lukuga River 刚果(金)河流 10—279a
卢库卢斯 Lucullus, Lucius Licinius 古罗马执政官 10—271d
卢拉·达席尔瓦 Lula da Silva, Luiz Inácio 巴西总统 10—279b
卢雷岩洞 Luray Caverns 美国洞穴 10—290f

卢里亚 Luria, Isaac ben Solomon 犹太教喀巴拉派创始人 10—291b
卢里亚 Luria, Salvador (Edward) 美国生物学家 10—291c
卢利 Luli 腓尼基国王 10—279c
卢利 Lully, Raymond (Catalan mystic) 加泰罗尼亚神秘主义者 10—280a
卢隆加河 Lulonga River 刚果(金)河流 10—280a
卢卢比人 Lullubi 伊朗古民族 10—279d
卢美特 Lumet, Sidney 美国电影导演 10—280c
卢蒙巴 Lumumba, Patrice (Hemery) 刚果(金)总理 10—282b
卢穆特 Lumut 马来西亚港市 10—282d
卢纳 Luna, Álvaro de 卡斯蒂利亚王室总管 10—282e
卢纳察尔斯基 Lunacharsky, Anatoly Vasilyevich 俄国作家 10—282f
卢嫩堡 Lunenburg 加拿大城镇 10—284d
卢尼河 Lūni 印度河流 10—286e
卢佩斯库 Lupescu, Magda 罗马尼亚冒险家 10—289e
卢皮诺家族 Lupino FAMILY 英国戏剧家族 10—290a
卢普河 Loup River 美国河流 10—246e
卢普区 Loop, The 美国芝加哥商业区 10—215a
卢普斯 Lupus (English ecclesiastic) 英国大主教 10—290c
卢齐卡 Ružička, Leopold (Stephen) 瑞士化学家 14—472c
卢齐利乌斯 Lucilius, Gaius 古罗马作家 10—269f
卢奇安 Lucian 古希腊作家 10—269b
卢日尼采河 Lužnice River 欧洲河流 10—306a
卢日山 Lužické Hory (central Europe) 捷克山脉 10—306a
卢萨蒂亚 Lusatia 欧洲地区 10—291f
卢萨蒂亚山 Lusatian Mountains 捷克山群 10—292a
卢萨卡 Lusaka 赞比亚首都 10—291e
卢塞蒂 Luisetti, Hank 美国篮球运动员 10—277f
卢塞恩 Lucerne 瑞士州名 10—268e
卢塞恩 Lucerne 瑞士城市 10—268e
卢塞恩湖 Lucerne, Lake 瑞士湖泊 10—269a
卢塞纳 Lucena 菲律宾城市 10—268d
卢瑟福 Rutherford, Ernest, BARON RUTHERFORD OF NELSON, OF CAMBRIDGE 英国核物理学家 14—468d
卢瑟福原子模型 Rutherford atomic model 物理学 14—470a
卢瑟诉鲍登案 Luther v. Borden 美国法院案例 10—300d
卢森堡 Luxembourg 比利时省份 10—302f
卢森堡 Luxembourg 欧洲国家 10—303a
卢森堡 Luxembourg 卢森堡首都 10—304a
卢森堡 Luxemburg, Rosa 德国革命家 10—304d
卢森堡公爵 Luxembourg, François-Henri de Montmorency-Bouteville, duc de 法国军人 10—304c
卢森堡国家博物馆 Luxembourg National Museum 卢森堡博物馆 10—304d
卢森堡语 Luxemburgian language 德语方言 10—304f
卢斯 Luce, Clare Boothe 美国剧作家 10—268a
卢斯 Luce, Henry R. 美国出版家 10—268b
卢斯 Luce, Stephen Bleecker 美国教育家 10—268d
卢斯特瑙 Lustenau 奥地利城镇 10—293b
卢梭 Rousseau, Henri 法国画家 14—420f
卢梭 Rousseau, Jean-Baptiste 法国戏剧家、诗人 14—421a
卢梭 Rousseau, Jean-Jacques 法国哲学家 14—421b
卢梭 Rousseau, (Pierre-Étienne-) Théodore 法国画家 14—424a
卢泰尔堡 Loutherbourg, Philip James de 英国画家 10—247d
卢泰愚 Roh Tae Woo 韩国总统 14—355c
卢特菲·赛义德 Luṭfī as-Sayyid, Aḥmad 埃及新闻工作者 10—294d
卢特夫·阿里汗·桑德 Loṭf ʿAlī Khān Zand 伊朗统治者 10—229e
卢特荒漠 Lūt Desert 伊朗沙漠 10—293f
卢特普兰德 Liutprand 伦巴第国王 10—159a
卢图利 Lutuli, Albert (John Mvumbi) 南非非洲人国民大会主席 10—301f
卢托斯瓦夫斯基 Lutosławski, Witold 波兰作曲家 10—301d
卢瓦尔 Loire 法国省份 10—193c
卢瓦尔河 Loire River 法国河流 10—193d
卢瓦尔河地区 Pays de la Loire 法国地区 13—106b
卢瓦尔河畔圣伯努瓦 Saint-Benoît-sur-Loire 法国卢瓦雷省村庄 14—507d
卢瓦尔-谢尔 Loir-et-Cher 法国省份 10—193a
卢瓦河 Loir River 法国河流 10—193b
卢瓦侯爵 Louvois, François-Michel Le Tellier, marquis de 法国大臣 10—248b
卢瓦勒人 Luvale 非洲民族 10—302c
卢瓦雷 Loiret 法国省份 10—193e
卢瓦齐 Loisy, Alfred Firmin 法国圣经学者 10—193e
卢万 Louvain 比利时城市 10—247e
卢万公教大学 Louvain, Catholic University of 比利时大学 10—247e
卢旺达 Rwanda 非洲国家 14—472e
卢旺达-乌隆迪 Ruanda-Urundi 比利时统治的东非两处土地 14—435a
卢旺达语 Rwanda language 班图族语言 14—473d
卢韦 Louvet (de Couvray), Jean-Baptiste 法国作家 10—248a
卢维 Louÿs, Pierre 法国小说家、诗人 10—249a
卢维人 Luwian 古安纳托利亚民族 10—302d
卢维语 Luwian language 古安纳托利亚语言 10—302e
卢沃奇·亨 Llywarch Hen 威尔士文学 10—171b
卢武阿河 Luvua River 刚果(金)河流 10—302d
卢武铉 Roh Moo Hyun 韩国总统 14—355b
卢西 Lussy, Melchior 瑞士天主教活动家 10—293a
卢西安(安提阿的),圣 Lucian OF ANTIOCH, SAINT 基督教神学家、殉教士 10—269c
卢西多尔 Lucidor (Swedish poet) 瑞典诗人 10—269e
卢西努斯 Luscinus, Gaius Fabricius 古罗马政治家 10—292b
“卢西塔尼亚”号 Lusitania 英国海轮 10—293a
卢西塔尼亚人 Lusitani 伊比利亚半岛民族 10—292f
卢西特 Lucite 化工 10—270a
卢西乌斯二世 Lucius II 教皇 10—270a
卢西乌斯三世 Lucius III 教皇 10—270b
卢西乌斯一世,圣 Lucius I, SAINT 教皇 10—270a
卢西亚诺 Luciano, Lucky 美国匪徒 10—269d
卢谢丘陵 Lushai Hills (India) 印度丘陵 10—292b
卢谢人 Lushai 印度民族 10—292b
卢雅人 Luyia (people) 肯尼亚民族 10—305d
卢伊尼 Luini, Bernardino 伦巴第画家 10—277d
卢伊塞诺人 Luiseño 北美印第安人 10—277e
卢伊特波尔德 Luitpold 巴伐利亚摄政王 10—278a
卢扎托 Luzzatto, Moshe Ḥayyim 犹太教神秘哲学家 10—306c
卢扎托 Luzzatto, Samuel David 犹太作家、学者 10—306c
芦笛 chalumeau 乐器 4—33d
芦荟属 Aloe 植物学 1—248d
芦鳗 reedfish 鱼类 14—196e
芦木属 Calamites 古植物学 3—333f
芦屋 Ashiya 日本城市 1—548b
芦竹 giant reed (*Arundo donax*) 草本植物 7—116f
芦状凤梨属 Neoglaziovia 植物学 12—78c
庐陵 Luling (China) 中国城市 10—279d
庐山 Lu Shan 中国名山 10—260f
庐山会议 Lushan Plenum 中国历史 10—292b
庐州 Lu-chou (China) 中国城市 10—259a
炉 furnace 热装置 6—529e
炉边椅 inglenook 家具 8—386b
炉用陶器 Hafner ware 德国釉陶 7—404e
炉油 furnace oil 燃料 6—529f

泸州 Luzhou 中国城市 10—305e
胪滨 Lupin (China) 中国城市旧称 10—289f
鸬鹚 cormorant 鸟类 4—509e
鈩 rutherfordium 化学元素 14—470b
颅缝骨化症 craniosynostosis 疾病 4—569d
颅骨崇拜 skull cult 原始人习俗 15—422e
颅相学 phrenology 神秘学 13—268d
颅咽管瘤 craniopharyngioma 疾病 4—569d
鲈形类 perciform 鱼类 13—158c
鲈鱼 perch 鱼类 13—157d
卤化氰 cyanogen halide 化合物 5—83c
卤化物矿物 halide mineral 矿物 7—423a
卤水 brine 盐水 3—158b
卤素 halogen 化学元素 7—432f
鲁 Lu 中国西周诸侯国 10—258e
鲁 Roux, Jacques 天主教司铎 14—425a
鲁 Roux, (Pierre-Paul-)Émile 法国细菌学家 14—425a
鲁 Roux, Wilhelm 德国动物学家 14—425b
鲁阿哈国家公园 Ruaha National Park 坦桑尼亚公园 14—434e
鲁阿卡纳 Ruacana 非洲水利工程 14—434d
鲁阿佩胡山 Ruapehu, Mount 新西兰活火山 14—435a
鲁埃 Rouher, Eugène 法国国务活动家 14—419c
鲁埃达 Rueda, Lope de 西班牙戏剧家 14—442e
鲁埃格 Rouergue 法国旧省份 14—419b
鲁安-诺兰达 Rouyn-Noranda 加拿大城市 14—425c
鲁昂 Rouen 法国城市 14—418e
鲁昂陶瓷器 Rouen ware 法国彩陶、瓷器 14—418f
鲁奥 Rouault, Georges(-Henri) 法国画家、陶艺家 14—418a
鲁奥河 Ruo River 非洲河流 14—450d
鲁贝 Roubaix 法国城镇 14—418c
鲁本斯 Rubens, Peter Paul 佛兰德画家 14—436c
鲁本斯主义者 Rubenist 欧洲画家、批评家 14—436c
鲁比孔河 Rubicon 意大利河流 14—437b
鲁比利亚克 Roubiliac, Louis-François 英国雕刻家 14—418c
鲁比尼 Rubini, Giovanni Battista 意大利歌唱家 14—437c
鲁比亚 Rubbia, Carlo 意大利物理学家 14—435d
鲁别日诺耶 Rubezhnoye 乌克兰城市 14—436f
鲁宾氏试验 Rubin's test 医疗 14—437d
鲁宾斯坦 Rubinstein, Artur 钢琴演奏家 14—437f
鲁宾斯坦 Rubinstein, Anton Grigoryevich 俄国作曲家、钢琴家 14—437e
鲁宾斯坦 Rubinstein, Helena 美国慈善家、制造商 14—438a
鲁宾斯坦 Rubinstein, Ida 舞蹈家 14—438a
鲁宾逊 Robinson, Boardman 美国画家 14—333c
鲁宾逊 Robinson, Brooks (Calbert), Jr. 美国棒球运动员 14—333d
鲁宾逊 Robinson, Edward 圣经学家 14—333d
鲁宾逊 Robinson, Edward G. 美国电影演员 14—333d
鲁宾逊 Robinson, (Esmé Stuart) Lennox 爱尔兰剧作家、戏剧导演 14—335c
鲁宾逊 Robinson, Frank 美国棒球运动员 14—333f
鲁宾逊 Robinson, Frederick John 英国首相 14—333f
鲁宾逊 Robinson, George Frederick Samuel 英国政治家 14—334a
鲁宾逊 Robinson, George Geoffrey (editor) 英国记者 14—334a
鲁宾逊 Robinson, Henry Crabb 英国文人 14—334a
鲁宾逊 Robinson, Sir Hercules (George Robert) 英国殖民地总督 14—334d
鲁宾逊 Robinson, Harriet Jane Hanson 美国作家 14—334a
鲁宾逊 Robinson, Henry Peach 英国摄影家 14—334b
鲁宾逊 Robinson, Henry Wheeler 基督教神学家 14—334c
鲁宾逊 Robinson, Jackie 美国黑人棒球运动员 14—334e
鲁宾逊 Robinson, John 英格兰牧师 14—335a
鲁宾逊 Robinson, James Harvey 美国历史学家 14—334f
鲁宾逊 Robinson, Joseph T(aylor) 美国律师 14—335b
鲁宾逊 Robinson, Joan (Violet) 英国经济学家 14—335a
鲁宾逊 Robinson, Max 美国电视记者 14—335d
鲁宾逊 Robinson, Rubye 美国民权活动家 14—335f
鲁宾逊 Robinson, Robert (Henry) 英国记者、广播员 14—335e
鲁宾逊 Robinson, Sugar Ray 美国拳击运动员 14—336a
鲁宾逊 Robinson, William 英国园林设计师 14—336b
鲁宾逊 Robinson, William Heath 英国漫画家 14—336b
鲁勃廖夫 Rublyov, Andrey 俄国画家 14—438c
鲁卜哈利沙漠 Rubʿ al-Khali 阿拉伯半岛南部沙漠 14—435b
鲁布纳拉扬河 Rūpnārāyan River 印度河流 14—451c
鲁布讷加尔 Rūpnagar (India) 印度城市 14—451c
鲁布斯卡 Lubuskie 波兰省份 10—266d
鲁布佐夫斯克 Rubtsovsk 俄罗斯城市 14—438e
鲁达基 Rūdakī 波斯文诗人 14—439c
鲁达希隆斯卡 Ruda Śląska 波兰城市 14—439c
鲁道菲氏鳁鲸 Rudolphi's rorqual 哺乳动物 14—442c
鲁道夫 Rudolf 统治者之名 14—440c
鲁道夫 Rudolf 法国国王 14—440e
鲁道夫 Rudolf 德意志僭王 14—440e
鲁道夫 Rudolf 神圣罗马帝国皇帝 14—441b
鲁道夫 Rudolf, ARCHDUKE AND CROWN PRINCE OF AUSTRIA 奥匈帝国皇储 14—441c
鲁道夫 Rudolph, Paul (Marvin) 美国建筑师 14—441f
鲁道夫 Rodolph, Utto 苏丹著作家 14—349e
鲁道夫 Rudolph, Wilma 美国运动员 14—442a
鲁道夫(埃姆斯的) Rudolf VON EMS 中古高地德语诗人 14—441d
鲁道夫(哈布斯堡的) Rudolf OF HABSBURG 德意志国王 14—441d
鲁道夫(莱茵费尔登的) Rudolf OF RHEINFELDEN 德意志僭王 14—441d
鲁道夫(士瓦本的) Rudolf OF SWABIA 德意志僭王 14—441d
鲁道夫二世 Rudolf II 勃艮第国王 14—440d
鲁道夫二世 Rudolf II 神圣罗马帝国皇帝 14—441a
鲁道夫湖 Rudolf, Lake 东非湖泊 14—441e
鲁道夫三世 Rudolf III 勃艮第国王 14—440d
《鲁道夫星表》 Rudolphine Tables 天文学 14—442c
鲁道夫一世 Rudolf I 勃艮第国王 14—440d
鲁道夫一世 Rudolf I 德意志国王 14—440f
鲁德 Ruud, Birger 挪威运动员 14—471d
鲁德内 Rudny 哈萨克斯坦城市 14—440c
鲁德尔 Rudel, Julius 美国指挥家 14—440a
鲁德尼茨基 Rudnicki, Adolf 波兰小说家 14—440b
鲁德普特 Roodepoort 南非城市 14—389f
鲁登道夫 Ludendorff, Erich 普鲁士将军 10—272a
鲁迪尼侯爵 Rudinì, Antonio Starabba, marchese di 意大利政治家、首相 14—440b
鲁尔 Ruhr 德国河流、工业区 14—445e
鲁尔福 Rulfo, Juan (Perez) 墨西哥小说家 14—447a
鲁尔河畔米尔海姆 Mülheim an der Ruhr 德国城市 11—475a
鲁尔集团 RAG Aktiengesellschaft 德国煤业公司 14—122c
鲁尔克 Rourke, Constance Mayfield 美国历史学家 14—420d
鲁尔蒙德 Roermond 荷兰城市 14—351f
鲁菲吉河 Rufiji River 坦桑尼亚河流 14—443e
鲁菲尼 Ruffini, Paolo 意大利数学家、医生 14—443d
鲁菲尼氏终柱 Ruffini ending 解剖学 14—443d
鲁菲努斯 Rufinus 东罗马帝国大臣 14—443e
鲁菲努斯 Rufinus, Tyrannius 罗马基督教教士 14—443f
鲁弗鲁瓦 Rouvroy, Louis de 法国军人、作家 14—425a
鲁福 Ruffo, Fabrizio 罗马枢机主教、政客 14—443d
鲁富斯 Rufus, Lucius Verginius 罗马总督 14—443f
鲁富斯 Rufus, Marcus Caelius 罗马政治家 14—444a
鲁富斯 Rufus, Publius Sulpicius 罗马演说家 14—444a
鲁亨盖里 Ruhengeri 卢旺达省份 14—445d
鲁吉人 Rugi 日耳曼部落 14—445d

鲁凯语 Rukai language 中国台湾省土著民族语言 14—446e
鲁凯泽 Rukeyser, Muriel 美国诗人 14—446f
鲁凯族 Rukai 中国台湾省土著民族 14—446d
鲁夸湖 Rukwa, Lake 坦桑尼亚湖泊 14—447a
鲁莱斯 Roulers (Belgium) 比利时城市 14—419d
鲁梅利亚 Rumelia 欧洲历史地区 14—447f
鲁米 Jalāl ad-Dīn ar-Rūmī 波斯诗人 8—521f
鲁勉采夫 Rumyantsev, Nikolay Petrovich, Graf (Count) 俄国政治家 14—448c
鲁勉采夫 Rumyantsev, Pyotr Aleksandrovich, Count (Graf) Zadunaysky 俄国陆军将领 14—448d
鲁莫尔 Rumor, Mariano 意大利天主教民主党领袖 14—448b
鲁默特 Reumert, Poul (Hagen) 丹麦舞台剧、电影明星 14—248c
鲁内贝里 Runeberg, Johan Ludvig 芬兰诗人 14—449c
鲁尼 Rooney, Mickey 美国电影演员 14—390f
鲁尼恩 Runyon, (Alfred) Damon 美国记者 14—450d
鲁帕岛 Rupat Island 印度尼西亚岛屿 14—450e
鲁佩特 Rupert 德意志国王 14—450f
鲁珀尔阶 Rupelian Stage 地质学 14—450e
鲁珀特堡 Fort-Rupert 加拿大村庄 6—415b
鲁珀特豪斯 Rupert House (Canada) 加拿大村庄 14—451b
鲁珀特河 Rupert River 加拿大河流 14—451b
鲁珀特兰德 Rupert's Land 加拿大历史地区 14—451b
鲁珀特亲王 Rupert, Prince 英国军人 14—450f
鲁珀特王子地 Prince Rupert's Land (Canada) 加拿大历史地区 13—515b
鲁珀特王子港 Prince Rupert 加拿大城市 13—515a
鲁普 Rupp, Adolph (Frederick) 美国大学篮球队教练 14—451c
鲁热维奇 Różewicz, Tadeusz 波兰诗人、剧作家 14—434b
鲁日·德·李尔 Rouget de Lisle, Claude-Joseph 法国国歌作者 14—419b
鲁萨 Roosa, Stuart Allen 美国航天员 14—391a
鲁萨尔卡 rusalka 斯拉夫神话 14—452f
鲁塞 Ruse 保加利亚城市 14—452f
鲁塞尔 Roussel, Albert(-Charles-Paul-Marie) 法国作曲家 14—424b
鲁瑟 Reuther, Walter (Philip) 美国劳工领袖 14—249e
鲁瑟拉勒 Roeselare 比利时城市 14—352a
鲁思 Ruth, Babe 美国棒球运动员 14—467d
鲁思文 Ruthven, John 苏格兰伯爵 14—470c
鲁思文 Ruthven, Patrick Ruthven, 3rd Lord 苏格兰新教分子 14—470c
鲁思文(埃特里克的)勋爵 Ruthven (of Ettrick), Patrick Ruthven, Lord 英军司令官 14—470c
鲁思·伊丽莎白·戴维丝 Davis, Ruth Elizabeth (American actress) 美国演员 5—177c
鲁斯卡 Ruska, Ernst (August Friedrich) 德国工程师 14—455b
鲁斯塔维 Rustavi 格鲁吉亚城市 14—466d
鲁斯塔维里 Rustaveli, Shota 格鲁吉亚诗人 14—466c
鲁斯泰梅 Rustamid kingdom 阿尔及利亚古伊斯兰国 14—466c
鲁斯韦尔十字碑 Ruthwell Cross 苏格兰人工制品 14—470c
鲁特 Root, Elihu 美国律师 14—396a
鲁特 Root, John Wellborn 美国建筑师 14—396c
《鲁特-高平协定》 Root-Takahira Agreement 美日协定 14—396c
鲁提利乌斯·克劳狄乌斯·纳马提安努斯 Rutilius Claudius Namatianus 罗马诗人 14—470e
鲁瓦 Roy, Gabrielle 加拿大法语小说家 14—429a
鲁瓦 Roy, (Joseph) Camille 加拿大评论家、文学史家 14—429a
鲁瓦耶-科拉尔 Royer-Collard, Pierre-Paul 法国政治家、哲学家 14—433e
鲁韦斯 Ruways, ar- 阿联酋工业联合体所在地 14—471e
鲁维埃 Rouvier, Maurice 法国国务活动家 14—424f
鲁文佐里国家公园 Ruwenzori National Park 乌干达国家公园 14—471f
鲁文佐里山脉 Ruwenzori Range 乌干达、刚果(金)界山 14—471f
鲁沃迪普利亚 Ruvo di Puglia 意大利城镇 14—471e
鲁伍马河 Ruvuma River 非洲河流 14—471e
鲁武布河 Ruvubu River 布隆迪河流 14—471e
鲁西 Lucy, Richard de 英国法官 10—271e
鲁西-莱维二氏综合征 Roussy-Levy syndrome (medicine) 疾病 14—424e
鲁西永 Roussillon 法国大区 14—424c
鲁迅 Lu Xun 中国文学家 10—261e
鲁迅纪念馆 Lu Xun Memorial 中国博物馆 10—262a
鲁伊斯 Ruiz, Juan 西班牙诗人 14—446b
鲁伊斯 Ruiz, José Martínez 西班牙文学评论家 14—446b
鲁伊斯·德·阿拉尔孔 Ruiz de Alarcón (y Mendoza), Juan 墨西哥戏剧家 14—446d
鲁伊斯雪山 Ruiz, Mount 哥伦比亚活火山 14—446c
镥(Lu) lutetium 化学 10—294c
陆地卫星 Landsat 航天器 9—478c
陆费逵 Lu-fei K'uei 中国出版家 10—259c
陆龟 tortoise 爬行动物 17—168b
陆机 Lu Ji 中国西晋文学家 10—259e
陆九渊 Lu Jiuyuan 中国宋代哲学家 10—260c
陆军 army 军种 1—505c
陆军妇女队 Women's Army Corps (WAC) 美国陆军单位 18—315d
陆军、海军和空军院校 military, naval, and air academies 军事院校 11—215e
陆军上尉 captain 军官 3—432d
陆栖动植物育养箱 terrarium 建筑 16—555a
陆桥 land bridge 地质学 9—474a
陆荣廷 Lu Rongting 中国军人 10—260e
陆上行动 terrestrial locomotion 动物学 16—555d
陆探微 Lu Tanwei 中国南朝画家 10—261d
陆象山 Lu Hsiang-shan 中国宋代哲学家 10—259a
陆修静 Lu Xiujing 中国南朝道士 10—261e
陆游 Lu You 中国南宋诗人 10—262b
录心派 Psychiana 美国教派 13—560a
录音 sound recording 应用物理学 15—529a
鹿 deer 哺乳动物 5—205f
鹿儿岛 Kagoshima 日本城市 9—131f
鹿港 Lugang 中国台湾省城镇 10—274b
鹿虎 deer tiger 哺乳动物 5—206d
鹿角 staghead 植物病害 16—180e
鹿角甲虫 pinching bug 昆虫 13—307b
鹿角蕨 staghorn fern 植物 16—180f
鹿肉 venison 食品 17—506b
鹿食草 hellebore 草本植物 7—576a
鹿食兰 helleborine 草本植物 7—576b
鹿鼠 deer mouse 哺乳动物 5—206d
鹿特丹 Rotterdam 荷兰城市 14—417b
鹿特丹 Rotterdam 美国纽约州城镇 14—417d
鹿特丹动物园 Royal Rotterdam Zoological Garden Foundation 荷兰动物园 14—432c
鹿屋 Kanoya 日本城市 9—160d
鹿眼树 buckeye 木本植物 3—222d
鹿寨战役 Fallen Timbers, Battle of 美国历史 6—223c
鹿沼 Kanuma 日本城市 9—170c
绿林好汉 bushranger 澳大利亚土匪 3—284b
禄田制 Sadki Na grades 泰国土地制度 14—493a
禄星 Lu Hsing 中国神话 10—259e
《路得记》 Ruth, Book of 《圣经·旧约》 14—467f
路德 Luther, Hans 德国政治家 10—294e
路德 Luther, Martin 德国宗教领袖 10—294f
路德维希 Ludwig, Carl F. W. 德国生理学家 10—273b

路德维希 Ludwig, Emil 德国传记作家 10—273c
路德维希 Ludwig, Otto 德国小说作家 10—273d
路德维希堡 Ludwigsburg 德国城市 10—273e
路德维希港 Ludwigshafen 德国城市 10—273e
路环岛 Luhuan Island 中国岛屿 10—277c
路济弗尔 Lucifer 古罗马神话 10—269e
路济弗尔 Lucifer 萨丁地区主教 10—269e
《路加福音》 Luke, Gospel According to 基督教文献 10—278f
路加,圣 Luke, SAINT 圣经人物 10—278d
路加斯·范·莱登 Lucas VAN LEYDEN 北欧文艺复兴时期画家 10—267b
路路阿堡 Luluabourg 刚果(金)城市 10—280a
路面 pavement 土木工程 13—102a
路特阶 Lutetian Stage 地质学 10—294c
路透 Reuter, Paul Julius, Baron (Freiherr) von 路透社创办人 14—249c
路透社 Reuters 英国通讯社 14—249d
路易 Louis 统治者之名 10—233b
路易 Louis 荷兰国王 10—239c
路易 Louis 那不勒斯国王 10—239e
路易 Louis 法国国王 10—239e
路易 Louis 西班牙国王 10—239f
路易 louis 法国古金币 10—239f
路易 Louis of Nevers 佛兰德伯爵 10—242a
路易 Louis, Victor 法国建筑师 10—240f
路易(巴伐利亚人) Louis THE BAVARIAN 神圣罗马帝国皇帝 10—240b
路易(大君主) Louis THE GRAND MONARCH 法国国王 10—240c
路易(儿童) Louis THE CHILD 东法兰克国王 10—240b
路易(法兰西的) Louis DE FRANCE 法国贵族 10—240a
路易(固执者) Louis THE STUBBORN 法国国王 10—240d
路易(海外归来的) Louis d' OUTREMER 法兰西国王 10—240a
路易(口吃者) Louis LE BÈGUE 法兰西国王 10—240a
路易(口吃者) Louis THE STAMMERER 法兰西国王 10—240d
路易(懒王) Louis LE FAINÉANT 法国国王 10—240a
路易(拿骚的) Louis OF NASSAU 尼德兰贵族 10—240a
路易(胖子) Louis THE FAT 法国国王 10—240c
路易(虔诚者) Louis THE DEBONAIR 神圣罗马皇帝皇帝 10—240c
路易(虔诚者) Louis THE PIOUS 神圣罗马皇帝皇帝 10—240d
路易(日耳曼人) Louis THE GERMAN 东法兰克国王 10—240c
路易(善良的) Louis THE GOOD 波旁公爵 10—240c
路易(深受爱戴者) Louis THE WELL-BELOVED 法国国王 10—240d
路易(圣) Louis, SAINT 法国国王 10—240a
路易(狮心) Louis COEUR-DE-LION 法国国王 10—240a
路易(狮子) Louis THE LION 法国国王 10—240c
路易(十七) Louis (XVII) 法国挂名国王 10—237e
路易(塔兰托的) Louis OF TARANTO 那不勒斯国王 10—240b
路易(瞎子) Louis THE BLIND 神圣罗马皇帝皇帝 10—240b
路易(小) Louis THE YOUNGER 东法兰克分封王 10—240d
路易(正义者) Louis THE JUST 法国国王 10—240c
路易八世 Louis VIII 法国国王 10—234f
路易-查理 Louis-Charles DE FRANCE 法国国王 10—242a
路易大帝 Louis THE GREAT 匈牙利国王、法国国王 10—240c
路易二世 Louis II 安茹公爵 10—233c
路易二世 Louis II 巴伐利亚国王 10—233f
路易二世 Louis II 东法兰克国王 10—238a
路易二世 Louis II 法兰国国王 10—234c
路易二世 Louis II 佛兰德伯爵 10—234b
路易二世 Louis II 神圣罗马帝国皇帝 10—238f
路易二世 Louis II 匈牙利国王 10—239d
路易-菲力普 Louis-Philippe 法国国王 10—242b
路易港 Port Louis 毛里求斯首都 13—446a
路易九世 Louis IX 法国国王 10—235a
路易六世 Louis VI 法国国王 10—234e
路易-拿破仑 Louis-Napoléon 法国皇帝 10—242a
路易七世 Louis VII 法国国王 10—234e
路易三世 Louis III 安茹公爵 10—233c
路易三世 Louis III 巴伐利亚国王 10—234a
路易三世 Louis III 东法兰克分封王 10—238c
路易三世 Louis III 法兰国国王 10—234c
路易三世 Louis III 神圣罗马帝国皇帝 10—239a
路易十八 Louis XVIII 法国国王 10—237f
路易十二 Louis XII 法国国王 10—236a
路易十六 Louis XVI 法国国王 10—237c
路易十六风格 Louis XVI style 艺术 10—241f
路易十三 Louis XIII 法国国王 10—236c
路易十三风格 Louis XIII style 艺术 10—241a
路易十世 Louis X 法国国王 10—235d
路易十四 Louis XIV 法国国王 10—236d
路易十四风格 Louis XIV style 艺术 10—241a
路易十五 Louis XV 法国国王 10—236f
路易十五风格 Louis XV style 艺术 10—241e
路易十一 Louis XI 法国国王 10—235e
路易丝(萨伏依的) Louise OF SAVOY 法国政治家 10—242c
路易斯 Louis 葡萄牙国王 10—239e
路易斯 Lewis, G(ilbert) N(ewton) 美国化学家 10—51c
路易斯 Louis, Joe 美国拳击运动员 10—240d
路易斯 Louis, Morris 美国画家 10—240e
路易斯(佩雷拉·德·索萨) Luís (Pereira de Sousa), Washington 巴西总统 10—277d
路易斯安那 Louisiana 美国州名 10—242d
路易斯安那购地 Louisiana Purchase 美国历史 10—245f
路易斯安那混合语 Louisiana Creole 美国语言 10—245f
路易斯堡 Louisbourg 加拿大城镇 10—242c
路易斯阶 Luisian Stage 地质学 10—277f
路易斯理论 Lewis theory 化学 10—53c
路易斯气 lewisite 化学 10—53e
路易斯维尔 Louisville 美国城市 10—246c
路易四世 Louis IV 法国国王 10—234d
路易四世 Louis IV 东法兰克国王 10—238d
路易四世 Louis IV 神圣罗马帝国皇帝 10—239a
路易五世 Louis V 法国国王 10—234d
路易西亚德群岛 Louisiade Archipelago 巴布亚新几内亚岛屿 10—242d
路易一世 Louis I 安茹公爵 10—233b
路易一世 Louis I 巴伐利亚公爵 10—233d
路易一世 Louis I 巴伐利亚国王 10—233d
路易一世 Louis I 佛兰德伯爵 10—234b
路易一世 Louis I 神圣罗马帝国皇帝 10—238d
路易一世 Louis I 匈牙利国王 10—239c
鲑 bluefish (*Pomatomus saltatrix*) 鱼类 2—550c
潞安 Lu-an (China) 中国城市 10—258f
潞西 Luxi 中国城市 10—305a
鹭 heron 鸟类 8—48b
鹭管鱼 snipefish 鱼类 15—461c
鹭鹤 kagu (*Rhynochetus jubatus*) 鸟类 9—132a
麓原 pediment 地质学 13—120a
露 dew 气象学 5—275a
露地耕作制 open-field system 欧洲农业 12—427d
露兜树目 Pandanales 木本植物 13—9a
露脊鲸 right whale 哺乳动物 14—298e
露莓 dewberry 植物 5—275d
露面宝光 heiligenschein (physics) 物理学 7—566d
露明木架构造 half-timber work 建筑学 7—421e
露丝 Loos, Anita 美国作家 10—215c
露天采矿 open-pit mining 采矿 12—427f

露天采矿 opencast mining 采矿 12—428c
露天开采 surface mining 采矿 16—351e
露尾甲 sap beetle 昆虫 15—56a
露西 Lucy, Sir Thomas 英国乡绅 10—271f
露西,圣 Lucy, Saint 基督教殉教者 10—271d
露西尔·莱苏尔 LeSueur, Lucille (American actress) 美国演员 10—41d
露阴癖 exhibitionism 性偏离 6—192f
露珠草 enchanter's nightshade 草本植物 6—69c
驴 donkey 马科动物 5—384a
驴兰 donkey orchid 植物 5—384b
驴蹄草 marsh marigold (*Caltha palustris*) 草本植物 10—538e
吕埃-马迈松 Rueil-Malmaison 法国城市 14—442e
吕贝克 Lübeck 德国城市 10—263f
吕伯 Lüber, Thomas 瑞士宗教领袖 10—264d
吕不韦 Lü Buwei 中国战国时期政治家 10—258f
吕布克 Lübke, Heinrich 德国总统 10—264f
吕布兰 Leblanc, Nicolas 法国化学家 9—549d
吕岑战役 Lützen, Battle of 欧洲历史 10—302b
吕措 Lützow, Adolf, Freiherr von 普鲁士军人 10—302c
吕德 Rude, François 法国雕刻家 14—439f
吕德里茨 Lüderitz 纳米比亚城镇 10—272c
吕德斯海姆 Rüdesheim 德国城镇 14—440a
吕登沙伊德 Lüdenscheid 德国城市 10—272c
吕底亚 Lydia 古安纳托利亚地区 10—309e
吕底亚语 Lydian language 古安约托利亚语言 10—309f
吕蒂希 Lüttich (city, Belgium) 比利时城市 10—301f
吕洞宾 Lü Dongbin 中国道教仙人 10—259a
吕尔萨 Lurçat, Jean 法国画家 10—291a
吕伐登 Leeuwarden 荷兰城市 9—558b
吕菲斯克 Rufisque 塞内加尔城镇 14—443f
吕凤子 Lü Fengzi 中国画家 10—259d
吕根 Rügen 德国岛屿 14—445a
吕后 Lühou 中国汉代皇后 10—277c
吕济尼昂家族 Lusignan family 法国家族 10—292d
吕骥 Lü Ji 中国音乐家 10—259f
吕卡翁 Lycaon 希腊神话 10—307e
吕克斯(大) Ruckers, Hans the Elder 佛兰芒乐器制造家 14—439b
吕克特 Rückert, Friedrich 德国诗人 14—439b
吕刻昂 Lyceum 古希腊学园 10—308a
吕勒奥 Luleå 瑞典港市 10—279c
吕勒河 Lule River 瑞典河流 10—279b
吕里 Lully, Jean-Baptiste 法国作曲家 10—279e
吕利耶尔 Rulhière, Claude-Carloman de 法国作家 14—447b
吕梁山 Lüliang Shan 中国山脉 10—279c
吕米埃兄弟 Lumière, Auguste and Louis 法国发明家 10—280d
吕南 Lynen, Feodor 德国生物化学家 10—314e
吕讷堡 Lüneburg 德国行政区 10—284b
吕讷堡 Lüneburg 德国城市 10—284c
吕讷堡荒原 Lüneburger Heath 德国地区 10—284c
吕内维尔 Lunéville 法国城镇 10—284e
吕内维尔彩陶 Lunéville faience 法国陶瓷 10—284e
吕嫩 Lünen 德国城市 10—284c
吕宁 Luening, Otto 美国音乐家 10—273f
吕沛林 Lü P'ei-lin 中国哲学家 10—260d
吕佩尔 Rüppell, (Wilhelm Peter) Eduard (Simon) 德国博物学家、探险家 14—451d
吕热-波 Lugné-Poe, Aurélien-François-Marie 法国演员 10—275e
吕容 Lugeon, Maurice 瑞士地质学家 10—275d
吕塞尔斯海姆 Rüsselsheim 德国城市 14—459e
吕叔湘 Lü Shuxiang 中国语言学家 10—261b
吕宋 Luzon 菲律宾岛屿 10—306b
吕宋海峡 Luzon Strait 菲律宾海峡 10—306c
吕特伯夫 Rutebeuf 法国诗人 14—467b
吕维尼侯爵 Ruvigny, Henri de Massue, marquis de 法国军人 14—471e
吕西阿斯 Lysias 古希腊演说词作家 10—318b
吕西斯(塔兰托姆的) Lysis of Tarentum 古希腊哲学家 10—318f
吕西亚 Lycia 土耳其古地区 10—308d
吕西亚语 Lycian language 土耳其古语言 10—308d
吕西亚字母 Lycian alphabet 土耳其古文字 10—308d
吕谢尔 Luchaire, Achille 法国历史学家 10—269a
吕嵒 Lü Yen (Chinese mythology) 中国道教仙人 10—262b
吕伊纳公爵 Luynes, Charles d'Albert, Duke de 法国政治家 10—305e
吕祖 Lü Tsu (Chinese mythology) 中国道教仙人 10—261e
旅大 Lü-ta (China) 中国城市 10—261d
旅大 Lüda (China) 中国城市 10—272a
旅鸽 passenger pigeon (*Ectopistes migratorius*) 绝灭候鸟 13—77a
旅馆 hotel 供住宿的商业性设施 8—190c
旅人蕉 traveler's tree (species *Ravenala madagascariensis*) 植物 17—203d
旅人蕉科 Strelitziaceae 植物学 16—275b
旅鼠 lemming 哺乳动物 10—3f
旅顺 Lüshun 中国大连市辖区 10—292c
旅行图书馆 traveling library 文化 17—203e
旅行推销员问题 traveling salesman problem 数学 17—203e
"旅行者"号试验机 Voyager 美国飞机 18—52c
"旅行者"号探测器 Voyager 美国太空探测器 18—52d
旅游杯赛 Tourist Trophy races 体育 17—178a
铝(Al) aluminum 化学元素 1—258d
铝青铜 aluminum bronze 冶金学 1—259a
铝热剂 Thermit 化学 17—33d
铝铁硅钙壳 duricrust 土壤学 5—473f
铝土矿 bauxite 矿石 2—288b
履螺 slipper shell 腹足类动物 15—433c
履行 performance 法律 13—165b
履行职责令 mandamus 英国法律 10—452a
律法书卷 Sefer Torah 犹太教 15—186f
律法学校 Talmud Torah 犹太教 16—448e
律管 Lü pipes 中国音乐 10—260d
律师 lawyer 法律 9—533d
律师联合会 Advocates, Faculty of 苏格兰法律 1—90f
律师协会 bar association 行业团体 2—214a
律师学院 Inns of Court 英国律师协会 8—393e
律藏 Vinaya Piṭaka 佛教经典 17—567d
律宗 Ritsu 佛教派别 14—314b
绿霸鹟 pewee 鸟类 13—215a
绿胞藻 chloromonad 原生动物 4—185b
绿背纸币运动 Greenback movement 美国历史 7—290c
绿伯劳 shrike-vireo 鸟类 15—340a
绿脆云母 clintonite 矿物 4—294d
绿带会运动 Ribbonism 爱尔兰秘密结社运动 14—276b
绿党 Green Party 爱尔兰共和国政党 7—289d
绿党 Greens, the 欧洲政党 7—295c
绿岛 Lü Dao 中国岛屿 10—259a
绿兜帽兰 greenhood 草本植物 7—292e
绿谷 Green Glen (Scotland) 苏格兰城市 7—289b
绿谷狗 Groenendael 狗品种 7—317e
绿金翅雀 greenfinch 鸟类 7—292d
绿鹃 vireo 鸟类 18—6c
绿帘角闪岩相 epidote-amphibolite facies 岩石学 6—99f
绿帘石 epidote 矿物 6—99e
绿泥石 chlorite 矿物 4—184d
绿皮树 palo verde 木本植物 12—574d

绿片岩相 greenschist facies 地质学 7—295d
绿绒蒿属 Meconopsis 植物学 11—69d
绿色和平组织 Greenpeace 国际环保组织 7—295b
绿色剧场 green theatre 园林 7—290a
绿色系列色料 famille verte 中国彩瓷色系 6—227d
绿山 Akhḍar Mountains 利比亚山脉 1—154c
绿山 Zielona Góra 波兰城市 18—550e
绿蛇 green snake 爬行动物 7—289f
绿松石 turquoise 矿物 17—293d
绿铜锌矿 aurichalcite 矿物 2—58f
绿头鸭 mallard (*Anas platyrhyncos*) 水禽 10—432c
绿蛙 green frog (*Rana clamitans melanota*) 水栖动物 7—289a
绿仙 pixie 英格兰民间传说 13—335a
绿心木 greenheart (*Ocotea rodiaei*) 木本植物 7—292e
绿咬鹃 quetzal 鸟类 14—88d
绿叶鸟 leafbird 鸟类 9—542f
绿叶鸟科 Chloropseidae 动物学 4—185e
绿茵挂毯 menues verdure 工艺品 11—121d
绿茵挂毯 verdure tapestry 工艺品 17—513d
绿玉髓 chrysoprase 矿物 4—216e
绿藻 green algae 浮游植物 7—288b
绿藻门 Chlorophyta 植物学 4—185d
绿洲 oasis 地质学 12—316a
绿柱石 beryl 矿物 2—434d
绿嘴地鹃 malcoha 鸟类 10—426d
氯(Cl) chlorine 化学元素 4—184a
氯苯 chlorobenzene 化合物 4—184e
氯苯吡胺 chlorpheniramine 药物 4—186a
氯苯酚 chlorophenol 化合物 4—185c
氯丙嗪 chlorpromazine 药物 4—186a
氯铂酸 chloroplatinic acid (chemistry) 化合物 4—185e
氯代甲烷 chloromethane (chemical compound) 化合物 4—185b
氯丹 chlordane 化合物 4—183f
氯丁橡胶 neoprene 化合物 12—78f
氯仿 chloroform 化合物 4—185a
氯氟烃 chlorofluorocarbon (CFC) 化合物 4—184f
氯胍 chloroguanide 药物 4—185b
氯化铵(NH_4Cl) ammonium chloride 化合物 1—293c
氯化汞(I) mercury (I) chloride 化合物 11—127c
氯化苦 chloropicrin 化合物 4—185d
氯化钠(NaCl) sodium chloride 化合物 15—484a
氯化氢 hydrogen chloride 化合物 8—283d
氯化松节油 Strobane 化合物 16—279a
氯化乙烯 ethylene chloride 化合物 6—151f
氯喹 chloroquine 药物 4—185e
氯霉素 chloramphenicol 抗生素 4—183e
氯缺乏 chlorine deficiency 生理学 4—184c
氯铜矿 atacamite 矿物 2—12b
氯乙烷 ethyl chloride 化合物 6—151d
氯乙烯 chloroethylene 化合物 4—184f
滤器 filter 摄像装置 6—316e
滤食 filter feeding 动物摄食方法 6—316e
孪歌 gymel 音乐 7—389a
孪晶现象 twinning 结晶学 17—303b
孪生花 twinflower (*Linnaea borealis*) 植物 17—302f
栾树 goldenrain tree (*Koelreuteria paniculata*) 木本植物 7—190f
滦河 Luan He 中国河流 10—262d
滦平 Luanping 中国城市 10—263a
銮湖 Luang Lake 泰国湖泊 10—262f
銮披汶·颂堪 Phibunsongkhram, Luang 泰国元帅、首相 13—226a
卵 egg 生物学 5—556b
卵巢 ovary 解剖学 12—510e
卵巢癌 ovarian cancer 疾病 12—510d
卵管 oviduct (anatomy) 解剖学 12—513b
卵黄 yolk 胚胎学 18—454a
卵菌纲 Oomycetes 植物 12—424d
卵裂 cleavage 胚胎学 4—277e
卵磷脂 lecithin 生物化学 9—550e
卵生 oviparity 生物学 12—513e
卵生顶游米诺鱼 egg-laying topminnow (fish) 鱼类 5—556f
卵牙 egg tooth 解剖学 5—556f
卵子 ovum 生理学 12—514c
卵子发生 oogenesis 生理学 12—424c
乱伦 incest 社会学 8—351d
乱子草 muhly 草本植物 11—471b
掠灰蝶 harvester 昆虫 7—498a
掠鸟龙 Ornitholestes 古生物学 12—468e
掠水鸥 skimmer 鸟类 15—418d
抡摔 Schwingen 体育 15—141c
伦巴第 Lombard 意大利区名 10—195b
伦巴第 Lombardy 意大利区名 10—196a
伦巴第联盟 Lombard League 意大利历史 10—195c
伦巴第人 Lombard 欧洲民族 10—195a
伦巴第铁王冠 Iron Crown of Lombardy 圣物 8—450e
伦巴赫 Lenbach, Franz von 德国画家 10—6b
伦巴舞 rumba 舞蹈 14—447d
伦拜克 Rumbek 苏丹城镇 14—447e
伦贝格 Lemberg (Ukraine) 乌克兰城市 10—3d
伦伯姆 Lönnbohm, Armas Eino Leopold (Finnish poet) 芬兰诗人 10—213f
伦勃朗 Rembrandt Harmenszoon van Rijn 荷兰画家 14—217a
伦布瓦人 Lumbwa (people) 非洲民族 10—280c
伦茨 Lenz, Jakob Michael Reinhold 德国诗人、剧作家 10—15b
伦茨堡 Rendsburg 德国城镇 14—227d
伦茨堡彩陶 Rendsburg faience 德国陶器 14—227e
伦道夫 Randolph 美国城镇 14—148a
伦道夫 Randolph, A(sa) Philip 美国工会活动家 14—148a
伦道夫 Randolph, Edward 英国皇家代理人 14—148e
伦道夫 Randolph, Edmund Jennings 美国律师 14—148c
伦道夫 Randolph, John 美国政治领袖 14—148e
伦道夫 Randolph, Peyton 美国政治家 14—149a
伦道夫 Randolph, Thomas (military commander) 苏格兰贵族 14—149a
伦道夫 Randolph, Thomas 英国诗人、剧作家 14—149a
伦德克维斯特 Lundkvist, Artur 瑞典诗人 10—283e
伦德莱尔舞 ländler 舞蹈 9—477c
伦德施泰特 Rundstedt, Gerd von 德国陆军元帅 14—449a
伦迪 Lundy, Benjamin 美国出版商 10—284a
伦迪河 Lundi River 津巴布韦河流 10—283e
伦迪小路战役 Lundy's Lane, Battle of 美国历史 10—284a
伦蒂尼 Lentini, Giacomo da (Italian poet) 意大利诗人 10—14f
伦杜 Rundu 纳米比亚市镇 14—449c
伦敦 London 英国首都 10—197c
伦敦 London 加拿大城市 10—203b
伦敦 London, Fritz Wolfgang 美国物理学家 10—203c
伦敦博物馆 Museum of London 英国博物馆 11—503c
伦敦城 London, City of 英国自治体 10—203c
伦敦大火 Great Fire of London 英国历史 7—272a
伦敦大瘟疫 Great Plague of London 英格兰历史 7—273e
伦敦大学 London, University of 英国大学 10—204a
伦敦德里 Londonderry 北爱尔兰前郡名 10—205c
伦敦德里 Londonderry 北爱尔兰城市 10—205c
伦敦德里侯爵(第二) Londonderry, Robert Stewart, 2nd marquess of 爱尔兰政治家 10—205d
伦敦东区 East End 英国伦敦传统区域 5—504b
伦敦动物园 London Zoo 英国动物园 10—205b

伦敦弗吉尼亚公司 Virginia Company of London 英国公司 18—13f
伦敦公司 London Company 英国贸易公司 10—204e
伦敦海军会议 London Naval Conference 英国历史 10—205a
伦敦集团 London group 英国艺术家组织 10—204f
伦敦警察厅 Scotland Yard 伦敦警察总部 15—151c
伦敦兰心剧院 Lyceum Theatre 英国伦敦剧场 10—308b
伦敦佬语言 cockneyism 写作语言 4—323c
伦敦码头工人罢工 London Dock Strike 英国历史 10—204f
伦敦黏土 London Clay 地质学 10—204d
伦敦桥 London Bridge 英国泰晤士河桥梁 10—204c
伦敦桥 London Bridge 儿童游戏 10—204d
伦敦桥车站 London Bridge Station 英国伦敦火车站 10—204d
伦敦塔 London, Tower of 英国建筑 10—203f
伦敦西区 West End 英国伦敦地区 18—197d
《伦敦新闻画报》 Illustrated London News 英国画刊 8—338d
伦敦证券交易所 London Stock Exchange 英国交易所 10—205b
伦敦职业拳击比赛规则 London Prize Ring rules 体育 10—205a
伦顿 Renton 美国华盛顿州城市 14—232d
伦恩 Lunn, Sir Arnold (Henry Moore) 英国滑雪运动员 10—286e
伦弗鲁 Renfrew 苏格兰区名 14—228a
伦弗鲁 Renfrew 苏格兰小城市 14—228b
伦弗鲁 Renfrewshire 苏格兰旧郡名 14—228b
伦盖伊火山 Ol Doinyo Lengai 坦桑尼亚火山 12—364b
伦格-巴奇 Renger-Patzsch, Albert 德国摄影家 14—228d
伦格伦 Lenngren, Anna Maria 瑞典诗人 10—12c
伦河 Lune, River 英格兰河流 10—284b
伦吉家族 Lunghi FAMILY 意大利建筑师家族 10—286b
伦卡人 Lenca 中美印第安人 10—6c
伦可夫 Ruhmkorff, Heinrich Daniel 德国机械师 14—445e
伦克姆 Renkum 荷兰城市 14—228f
伦理学 ethics 哲学 6—145f
伦理学相对主义 ethical relativism 伦理学观点 6—145d
伦马克 Renmark 澳大利亚城镇 14—229a
伦纳德 Leonard, Benny 美国拳击运动员 10—19d
伦纳德阶 Leonardian Stage 地质学 10—19e
伦内尔 Rennell, James 英国地理学家 14—229f
伦内尔岛 Rennell Island 太平洋所罗门群岛环礁 14—230a
伦内普 Lennep, Jacob van 荷兰作家 10—12b
伦尼 Rennie, John 苏格兰土木工程师 14—230d
伦尼-莱纳佩人 Lenni Lenape (people) 北美印第安人 10—12c
伦诺科 Lennoaceae 植物学 10—12c
伦诺克斯 Lennox, Charlotte 英国小说家 10—12d
伦诺克斯 Lennox, Charles Lennox, 1st Duke of 英国贵族 10—12d
伦诺克斯 Lenox, James 美国慈善家 10—13c
伦诺克斯伯爵夫人 Lennox, Margaret Douglas, Countess of 英国贵族 10—12e
伦帕河 Lempa River 中美洲河流 10—5c
伦皮拉港 Puerto Lempira 洪都拉斯城镇 14—16a
伦琴 roentgen 计量单位 14—351d
伦琴 Roentgen, Abraham 德国细木工匠、设计师 14—351d
伦琴 Roentgen, David 法国家具师 14—351d
伦琴 Röntgen, Wilhelm Conrad 德国物理学家 14—389d
伦琴射线管 roentgen tube 电子学 14—351e
伦斯福德 Lunceford, Jimmie 美国音乐家 10—283b
伦斯勒 Rensselaer 美国纽约州城市 14—232c
伦斯特 Leinster 爱尔兰省份 9—568f
《伦斯特集》 Leinster, The Book of 爱尔兰文学 9—568f
伦索尔 Lenthall, William 英国政治家 10—14d
伦特夫妇 Lunt, Alfred; and Fontanne, Lynn 美国夫妻演出队 10—286f
伦图卢斯 Lentulus, Publius Cornelius 古罗马政治家 10—14f
伦图卢斯·克鲁斯 Lentulus Crus, Lucius Cornelius 古罗马政治家 10—14f
伦图卢斯·斯平特 Lentulus Spinther, Publius Cornelius 古罗马政治家 10—14f
伦威克 Renwick, James 苏格兰基督教殉教者 14—232e
伦威克(小) Renwick, James, (Jr.) 美国建筑师 14—232f
《伦维尔协定》 Renville Agreement 荷兰-印度尼西亚协定 14—232d
伦西 Runcie, Robert 坎特伯雷大主教 14—448f
伦肖兄弟 Renshaw, William; and Renshaw, Ernest 英格兰网球运动员 14—232b
《论语》 Lunyu 中国儒家经典 10—287b
沧龙 mosasaur 绝灭的蜥蜴 11—413a
轮 chakra 印度教修炼秘术 4—29e
轮 wheel 机械部件 18—221a
《轮唱歌》 round 音乐 14—419e
轮虫 rotifer 无脊椎动物 14—416c
轮回 saṃsāra 印度哲学 15—1e
轮垦农业 shifting agriculture 农业 15—312c
轮流对白 stichomythia 古希腊戏剧 16—234e
轮盘赌 Roulette 赌博方式 14—419d
轮式装载机 tractor loader 机械 17—186e
轮胎 tire 车辆部件 17—109c
轮线螺属 Trochonema 古生物学 17—229e
轮演剧目剧院 repertory theatre 戏剧 14—233d
轮椅 bath chair 有轮的椅子 2—277b
轮藻 stonewort 藻类 16—252f
轮藻纲 Charophyceae 植物学 4—84c
轮轴 wheel and axle 机械部件 18—221b
轮转凹版印刷 rotogravure printing 印刷 14—416d
轮转印刷机 rotary press 印刷机 14—413d
轮作 crop rotation 农耕方法 5—30b
论辩文 apology 文学 1—414c
《论藏》 Abhidhamma Piṭaka 佛教著作 1—23c
《论衡》 Lunheng 中国汉代哲学著作 10—286d
《论教皇的权力与至高地位》 Treatise on the Power and Primacy of the Pope 宗教文本 17—205a
论争诗 tenson 法国文学 16—546a
论证 argument 逻辑 1—467f
罗 Roe, Sir Alliott Verdon 英国飞机设计师 14—350d
罗 Rowe, Nicholas 英国作家 14—426b
罗 Roe, Sir Thomas 英格兰外交家 14—350d
罗阿讷 Roanne 法国城镇 14—324d
罗阿坦 Roatán 洪都拉斯省会 14—324f
罗安达 Luanda 安哥拉首都 10—262d
罗昂 Rohan, Benjamin de 法国胡格诺派领袖 14—355e
罗昂 Rohan, Charles de 法国将军 14—355e
罗昂公爵 Rohan, Henri, duc de 法国军人、著作家 14—355e
罗昂家族 Rohan FAMILY 欧洲大贵族世家 14—355e
罗昂-蒙巴宗 Rohan-Montbazon, Marie de 法国公爵 14—355f
罗昂亲王 Rohan, Louis-René-Édouard, prince de 枢机主教 14—355f
罗巴尔 Ropar 印度城市 14—396d
罗巴克 Roebuck, John 英国医生、化学家 14—351c
罗巴切夫斯基 Lobachevsky, Nikolay Ivanovich 俄国数学家 10—172b
罗巴切夫斯基几何 Lobachevskian geometry 数学 10—172b
罗巴兹 Robards, Jason 美国戏剧和电影演员 14—325a
罗贝尔 Robert, Hubert 法国画家 14—328e
罗贝尔(弗里斯人) Robert THE FRISIAN 佛兰德公爵 14—328d
罗贝尔(虔诚者) Robert THE PIOUS 法国国王 14—328d
罗贝尔(强者) Robert THE STRONG 法国卡佩王朝诸王祖先 14—328d
罗贝尔(日内瓦的) Robert OF GENEVA (antipope) 敌对教皇 14—328b

罗贝尔(托里尼的) Robert de Torigni 诺曼编年史家 14—327f
罗贝尔(耶路撒冷人) Robert the Jerusalemite 佛兰德公爵 14—328d
罗贝尔(莫莱姆的),圣 Robert of Molesme, Saint 法兰西本笃会会士 14—328c
罗贝尔二世 Robert Ⅱ 佛兰德伯爵 14—326f
罗贝尔二世 Robert Ⅱ 法国国王 14—327a
罗贝尔二世 Robert Ⅱ 诺曼底公爵 14—327b
罗贝尔;罗伯特 Robert 统治者之名 14—326c
罗贝尔-乌丹 Robert-Houdin, Jean-Eugène 法国魔术师 14—329a
罗贝尔一世 Robert Ⅰ 佛兰德伯爵 14—326e
罗贝尔一世 Robert Ⅰ 法国国王 14—326f
罗贝尔一世 Robert Ⅰ 诺曼底公爵 14—327b
罗贝基-布里凯蒂 Robecchi-Bricchetti, Luigi 意大利探险家 14—326b
罗贝瓦尔 Roberval, Gilles Personne de 法国数学家 14—331d
罗贝瓦尔 Roberval, Jean-François de La Rocque, sieur de 法国殖民者 14—331d
罗贝瓦尔天平 Roberval balance 商业衡器 14—331e
罗贝瓦勒 Roberval 加拿大城市 14—331c
罗本岛 Robben Island 南非岛屿 14—325c
罗本古拉 Lobengula 南非恩德贝勒国王 10—173c
罗比 Roby (England) 英格兰地名 14—337a
罗比 Robey, Sir George 英国演员 14—332c
罗比亚 Robbia, Andrea Della 佛罗伦萨雕刻家 14—325e
罗比亚 Robbia, Giovanni Della 佛罗伦萨雕刻家 14—325e
罗比亚 Robbia, Luca Della 佛罗伦萨雕刻家 14—325f
罗宾·古德费洛 Robin Goodfellow 英格兰民间传说 14—332f
罗宾汉 Robin Hood 英国民谣传奇英雄 14—332f
罗宾森 Robinson, Sir Robert 英国化学家 14—335e
罗宾斯 Robins, Benjamin 英国数学家 14—333b
罗宾斯 Robbins, Frederick Chapman 美国病毒学家 14—325f
罗宾斯 Robbins, Jerome 美国舞蹈家 14—325f
罗宾斯 Robbins (of Clare Market), Lionel Charles Robbins, Baron 英国经济学家 14—326b
罗宾逊 Robinson, Bill 美国舞蹈家 14—333b
罗宾逊 Robinson, Edwin Arlington 美国诗人 14—333e
罗宾逊 Robinson, Mary 爱尔兰律师 14—335c
罗波那 Rāvaṇa 印度教神话 14—165f
罗伯茨 Roberts, Bartholomew 英国海盗船船长 14—329b
罗伯茨 Roberts, Sir Charles G(eorge) D(ouglas) 加拿大诗人、作家 14—329c
罗伯茨 Roberts, Elizabeth Madox 美国南方小说家 14—329d
罗伯茨 Roberts (of Kandahar, Pretoria, and Waterford), Frederick Sleigh Roberts, 1st Earl, Viscount St. Pierre 英国陆军元帅 14—329e
罗伯茨 Roberts, Sir Gilbert 英国工程师 14—329e
罗伯茨 Roberts, Isaac 英国天文学家 14—329f
罗伯茨 Roberts, Joseph Jenkins 利比里亚总统 14—330a
罗伯茨 Roberts, Kate 威尔士语小说家 14—330b
罗伯茨 Roberts, Kenneth (Lewis) 美国记者 14—330b
罗伯茨 Roberts, Owen (Josephus) 美国最高法院大法官 14—330c
罗伯茨 Roberts, Richard 英国发明家 14—330d
罗伯茨(小) Roberts, John G., Jr. 美国首席大法官 14—330a
罗伯茨港 Robertsport 利比里亚城镇、渔港 14—331c
罗伯茨角 Point Roberts 美国村庄 13—389d
罗伯-格里耶 Robbe-Grillet, Alain 法国作家 14—325b
罗伯斯比尔 Robespierre, Maximilien-François-Marie-Isidore de 法国雅各宾派领袖 14—332a
罗伯特 Robert 诺曼人冒险家 14—326c
罗伯特 Robert 拉丁皇帝 14—326e
罗伯特 Robert 统治者之名 14—327a
罗伯特 Robert, Henry Martyn 美国陆军军官 14—328e
罗伯特 Robert, Shaaban 斯瓦希里语作家 14—328f
罗伯特(安茹的) Robert of Anjou 那不勒斯国王 14—328a
罗伯特(贝列斯梅的) Robert of Bellême, 3rd earl of Shropshire or Shrewsbury 诺曼人权贵 14—328a
罗伯特(布鲁斯的) Robert the Bruce 苏格兰国王 14—328c
罗伯特(格洛斯特的) Robert of Gloucester 中古英语编年史学家 14—328b
罗伯特(科特尼的) Robert of Courtenay 君士坦丁堡皇帝 14—328b
罗伯特(欧特维尔的) Robert de Hauteville 阿普利亚公爵 14—327f
罗伯特(瑞米耶日的) Robert of Jumièges 伦敦主教 14—328b
罗伯特(智者) Robert the Wise 那不勒斯国王 14—328e
罗伯特(总管) Robert the Steward 苏格兰国王 14—328d
罗伯特二世 Robert Ⅱ 苏格兰国王 14—327d
罗伯特·圭斯卡德 Robert Guiscard 阿普利亚公爵 14—328a
罗伯特三世 Robert Ⅲ 苏格兰国王 14—327e
罗伯特一世 Robert Ⅰ 苏格兰国王 14—327c
罗伯逊 Robertson, Alice Mary 美国教育家 14—330d
罗伯逊 Robertson, Sir Dennis Holme 英国经济学家 14—330f
罗伯逊 Robertson, Ethel Florence Lindesay 澳大利亚作家 14—331a
罗伯逊 Robertson, Marjorie 英国演员 14—331a
罗伯逊 Robertson, Margaret Shafto (English actress-manager) 英国演员 14—331a
罗伯逊 Robeson, Paul (Bustill) 美国歌唱家、黑人社会活动家 14—331f
罗伯逊 Robertson, Thomas William 英国剧作家 14—331a
罗伯逊 Robertson, William 苏格兰历史学家 14—331b
罗伯逊 Robertson, Sir William Robert 英国陆军元帅 14—331c
罗伯逊海峡 Robeson Channel 北美海峡 14—331f
罗伯兹-奥斯汀 Roberts-Austen, Sir William Chandler 英国冶金学家 14—330d
罗勃蒂 Roberti, Ercole (Grandi d' Antonio) de' 意大利画家 14—329a
罗布莱斯 Roblès, Emmanuel 法国小说家 14—336c
罗布林 Roebling, John Augustus 美国土木工程师 14—351a
罗布林 Roebling, Washington Augustus 美国土木工程师 14—351b
罗布林卡 Nor-bu-gling-ka 中国园林 12—231c
罗布·罗伊 Rob Roy 苏格兰高地歹徒 14—324f
罗布泊 Lop Nor 中国湖泊 10—215f
罗布森 Robson, Dame Flora (McKenzie) 英国演员 14—336f
罗布森山 Robson, Mount 加拿大落基山脉最高峰 14—336f
罗常培 Luo Changpei 中国语言学家 10—287c
罗彻斯特伯爵(第二) Rochester, John Wilmot, 2nd earl of 英国宫廷才子 14—339d
罗彻斯特伯爵(第一) Rochester, Henry Wilmot, 1st Earl of 英国保王党将领 14—339c
罗彻斯特伯爵(第一) Rochester, Lawrence Hyde, 1st earl of 英格兰政治家 14—339f
罗彻斯特伯爵和子爵 Rochester, earls and viscounts of 英格兰封爵贵族 14—339c
罗彻斯特子爵 Rochester, Robert Carr, Viscount 英格兰贵族 14—339c
罗丹 Rodin, Auguste 法国雕刻家 14—348e
罗得 Rhodes 希腊罗得岛城市、州首府 14—267b
罗得贝尔 Rodbell, Martin 美国生物化学家 14—345f
罗得岛 Rhode Island 美国州名 14—264d
罗得岛 Rhode Island 美国岛屿 14—267a
罗得岛 Rhodes 希腊岛屿 14—267c
《罗得岛海洋法》 Rhodian Sea Law 拜占廷法律 14—268e
罗得岛巨像 Rhodes, Colossus of 青铜铸像 14—267f
罗得岛设计学院 Rhode Island School of Design 美国大学 14—267a
罗得里格斯·莫内加尔 Rodríguez Monegal, Emir 乌拉圭出生的文学评论家 14—350b
罗得斯 Rhodes, Cecil (John) 南非金融家 14—267d

罗得斯奖学金 Rhodes scholarship 教育资助金 14—268c
罗得西亚和尼亚萨兰联邦 Rhodesia and Nyasaland, Federation of 非洲历史上的联邦 14—268d
罗得西亚脊毛狗 Rhodesian ridgeback 狗品种 14—268d
罗得西亚人 Rhodesian man 人类学 14—268d
罗德 Rhodes, Alexandre de 法国天主教耶稣会教士 14—267d
罗德 Rod, Édouard 瑞士法语作家 14—345f
罗德 Rodd, Kylie Tennant 奥地利著作家 14—346c
罗德贝尔图斯 Rodbertus, Johann Karl 普鲁士经济学家 14—346a
罗德城 Road Town 英属维尔京群岛城市 14—324b
罗德津斯基 Rodzinsky, Artur 美国指挥家 14—350c
罗德里戈 Roderick 西班牙国王 14—348a
罗德里戈 Rodrigo, Joaquín 西班牙作曲家 14—349f
罗德里戈城 Ciudad Rodrigo 西班牙城市 4—252c
罗德里格斯 Rodriguez, Lorenzo 墨西哥建筑师 14—350a
罗德里格斯·阿尔维斯 Rodrigues Alves, Francisco de Paula 巴西总统 14—349f
罗德里格斯岛 Rodrigues Island 毛里求斯属地 14—349f
罗德里格斯·洛博 Rodrigues Lobo, Francisco 葡萄牙诗人 14—350a
罗德里克(奥康纳) Roderic O'Connor 爱尔兰国王 14—348a
罗德曼 Rodman, Thomas Jackson 美国发明家 14—349b
罗德纳山 Rodna Massif 罗马尼亚山脉 14—349b
罗德尼 Rodney, Caesar 美国政治家 14—349c
罗德尼 Rodney (of Stoke-Rodney), George Brydges Rodney, 1st Baron 英格兰海军上将 14—349c
罗德宁娜 Rodnina, Irina (Konstantinovna) 苏联运动员 14—349d
罗德兹 Rodez 法国城镇 14—348b
罗登巴赫 Rodenbach, Albrecht 佛兰芒作家 14—346c
罗登巴赫 Rodenbach, Georges(-Raymond-Constantin) 比利时诗人 14—346e
罗地岛 Roti Island 印度尼西亚岛屿 14—416b
罗蒂 Rorty, Richard (McKay) 美国哲学家 14—398c
罗顿-黑斯廷斯 Rawdon-Hastings, Francis 英国殖民行政长官 14—168c
罗多 Rodó, José Enrique 乌拉圭出生的哲学家 14—349d
罗多彼山脉 Rhodope Mountains 欧洲山脉 14—269e
罗多斯托 Rodosto (Turkey) 土耳其城市 14—349e
罗厄诺克 Roanoke 美国城市 14—324d
罗厄诺克岛 Roanoke Island 美国岛屿 14—324e
罗厄诺克河 Roanoke River 美国河流 14—324e
罗恩 Rowan, Andrew Summers 美国陆军军官 14—425f
罗恩 Roon, Albrecht Theodor Emil, Graf von 普鲁士军官 14—390e
罗恩 Rowan, Carl 美国新闻记者 14—426a
罗尔 Rolle, Richard 英格兰神学家 14—360a
罗尔丹 Roldán, Pedro 西班牙雕刻家 14—358e
罗尔多斯·阿吉莱拉 Roldós Aguilera, Jaime 厄瓜多尔总统 14—359a
罗尔夫 Rolf (duke of Normandy) 海盗、诺曼底公国创始人 14—359b
罗尔夫 Rolfe, Frederick William 英国作家、怪人 14—359b
罗尔夫 Rolfe, John 弗吉利亚殖民官员 14—359c
罗尔夫斯 Rohlfs, (Friedrich) Gerhard 德国探险家 14—356a
罗尔青 Lortzing, Albert 德国作曲家 10—224a
罗尔沙赫 Rorschach, Hermann 瑞士精神病学家 14—398a
罗尔斯 Rawls, Betsy 美国高尔夫球运动员 14—169b
罗尔斯 Rolls, Charles Stewart 英国汽车驾驶员、飞行员、汽车制造商 14—361a
罗尔斯 Rawls, John 美国哲学家 14—169b
罗尔斯顿-珀瑞纳公司 Ralston Purina Company 美国公司 14—133f
罗尔斯特兰德彩陶 Rörstrand faience 瑞典陶器 14—398c
罗尔瓦格 Rölvaag, O(le) E(dvart) 美国小说家 14—361d
罗非鱼属 Tilapia 鱼类 17—94f
罗夫诺 Rivne 乌克兰州名 14—320d
罗夫诺 Rivne 乌克兰城市 14—320e
罗弗敦群岛 Lofoten 挪威岛屿 10—187b
罗干 Luo Gan 中国领导人 10—287d
罗贡水坝 Rogun Dam 塔吉克斯坦大型水坝 14—355b
罗贯中 Luo Guanzhong 中国元末明初小说家 10—287f
罗哈 Roha (Ethiopia) 埃塞俄比亚古王朝都城、朝圣中心 14—355d
罗哈斯 Roxas 菲律宾城市 14—428d
罗哈斯 Rojas, Fernando de 西班牙作家 14—357a
罗哈斯 Roxas (y Acuna), Manuel 菲律宾政治领袖、总统 14—428d
罗哈斯 Rojas, Manuel (Sepúlveda) 智利小说家 14—357a
罗哈斯·比良德兰多 Rojas Villandrando, Agustín de 西班牙演员、作家 14—357c
罗哈斯·皮尼利亚 Rojas Pinilla, Gustavo 哥伦比亚独裁者 14—357b
罗哈斯·索里利亚 Rojas Zorrilla, Francisco de 西班牙戏剧家 14—357c
罗海姆 Róheim, Géza 美国精神分析学家 14—355f
罗汉柏 false arborvitae (*Thujopsis dolabrata*) 木本植物 6—224f
罗汉松 yellowwood 木本植物 18—438c
罗汉松科 Podocarpaceae 植物学 13—384e
罗怙那陀·室罗摩尼 Raghunātha Śiromaṇi 印度哲学家 14—122e
罗基卡纳 Rokycana, Jan 波希米亚教会大主教 14—358a
罗基坦斯基 Rokitansky, Karl, Freiherr von 奥地利病理学家 14—357e
罗加兰 Rogaland 挪威郡名 14—352b
罗家伦 Luo Jialun 中国文史学家 10—287f
罗杰 Roger 统治者之名 14—352b
罗杰 Roger 诺曼人统治者 14—352c
罗杰 Roger 阿普利亚公爵 14—352c
罗杰(博尔萨) Roger Borsa 阿普利亚公爵 14—352e
罗杰(霍夫登的) Roger of Hoveden 英格兰编年史家 14—352e
罗杰(劳里亚的) Roger of Lauria 意大利海军上将 14—352f
罗杰(蓬泰韦克的) Roger of Pont l'Évêque 约克大主教 14—352f
罗杰二世 Roger II 西西里大伯爵 14—352d
罗杰斯 Rogers 美国城市 14—353a
罗杰斯 Rogers, Bruce 美国活版印刷师 14—353a
罗杰斯 Rogers, Carl R(ansom) 美国心理学家 14—353b
罗杰斯 Rogers, Edith Nourse 美国政府工作者 14—353c
罗杰斯 Rogers, Ginger 美国演员 14—353d
罗杰斯 Rogers, Harriet Burbank 美国教育家 14—353d
罗杰斯 Rogers, Henry Darwin 美国地质学家 14—353e
罗杰斯 Rodgers, Jimmie 美国歌手 14—348b
罗杰斯 Rogers, John 宗教改革家 14—353e
罗杰斯 Rogers, John 英格兰君主国派领袖 14—353f
罗杰斯 Rogers, Mary Joseph 美国天主教传教士 14—354a
罗杰斯 Rodgers, Richard 美国作曲家 14—348c
罗杰斯 Rogers, Robert 美国军人 14—354a
罗杰斯 Rogers, Samuel 英国诗人 14—354b
罗杰斯 Rogers, Will 美国作家 14—354c
罗杰斯 Rogers, William 英国教育改革家 14—354d
罗杰斯 Rogers, Woodes 英国私掠船船长 14—354e
罗杰斯山口 Rogers Pass 加拿大山口 14—354f
罗杰·辛普森岛 Roger Simpson Island (Kiribati) 基里巴斯岛屿 14—353a
罗杰一世 Roger I 西西里伯爵 14—352c
罗金厄姆侯爵(第二) Rockingham, Charles Watson-Wentworth, 2nd marquess of 英国首相 14—343e
罗金厄姆陶瓷器 Rockingham ware 英格兰陶、瓷器 14—343f
罗津 Najin 朝鲜城市 11—545f

罗经 compass 航海 4—397d
罗卡尔 Rocard, Michel (Louis Leon) 法国政治家 14—337d
罗卡角 Roca, Cape 葡萄牙海角 14—337b
罗卡人 Rokanese (people) 印度尼西亚民族 14—357e
罗卡人 Rokka (people) 印度尼西亚民族 14—357f
罗卡韦马车 rockaway 四轮马车 14—341d
罗卡耶 rocaille 建筑及装饰艺术风格 14—337b
罗科尔 Rockall 苏格兰岛屿 14—341d
罗科索夫斯基 Rokossovsky, Konstantin Konstantinovich 苏联军事将领 14—358a
罗克 Rocque, François de la 法国法西斯分子 14—345b
罗克 Roark, Helen Newington Wills Moody 美国运动员 14—324f
罗克艾兰 Rock Island 美国城市 14—341a
罗克艾兰铁路公司 Rock Island Railroad 美国公司 14—341a
罗克渡口战役 Rorke's Drift, Battle of 南非祖鲁战争 14—397f
罗克尔河 Rokel River 塞拉利昂河流 14—357e
罗克福德 Rockford 美国城市 14—343c
罗克福尔干酪 Roquefort 法国干酪 14—397e
罗克福克党 Locofoco Party 美国党派 10—181a
罗克汉普顿 Rockhampton 澳大利亚城市 14—343d
罗克河 Rock River 美国河流 14—341b
罗克莱奇 Rockledge (Florida, U.S.) 美国城市 14—344a
罗克兰 Rockland 美国城市 14—344a
罗克鲁瓦 Rocroi 法国城镇 14—345c
罗克鲁瓦战役 Rocroi, Battle of 法国历史 14—345c
罗克尼 Rockne, Knute (Kenneth) 美国橄榄球教练 14—344a
罗克桑娜 Roxana 亚历山大大帝王妃 14—428d
罗克石碑 Rök Stone 瑞典纪念石碑 14—357d
罗克斯堡 Roxburgh 苏格兰历史郡 14—428e
罗克斯堡 Roxburgh 苏格兰地区 14—428f
罗克斯伯里 Roxbury 美国波士顿市住宅区 14—428f
罗克斯普林斯 Rock Springs 美国城市 14—341c
罗克韦尔 Rockwell, Norman 美国画家 14—344b
罗克韦尔国际公司 Rockwell International Corporation 美国公司 14—344c
罗克维尔 Rockville 美国城市 14—344b
罗克希尔 Rock Hill 美国城市 14—340f
罗克西音乐乐队 Roxy Music 英国艺术摇滚乐队 14—428f
罗拉 Rolla 美国城市 14—359d
罗拉德派 Lollard 英国历史 10—194d
罗赖马 Roraima 巴西州名 14—397f
罗赖马山 Roraima, Mount 南美山脉 14—397f
罗兰 Rolin, Dominique 比利时小说家 14—359c
罗兰 Rowland, F. Sherwood 美国化学家 14—427b
罗兰 Rowland, Henry Augustus 美国物理学家 14—427c
罗兰 Roland (de La Platière), Jean-Marie 法国工业科学家 14—358c
罗兰 Loren, Sophia 意大利电影演员 10—220c
罗兰导航系统 loran 航空、航海导航系统 10—218c
罗兰迪亚 Rolândia 巴西城市 14—358e
罗兰夫人 Roland (de La Platière), Jeanne-Marie 法国政治家 14—358d
罗兰·霍尔斯特-范德斯哈尔克 Roland Holst-van der Schalk, Henriëtte Goverdina Anna 荷兰诗人 14—358e
罗兰森 Rowlandson, Mary 英裔美国殖民地作家 14—427c
罗兰森 Rowlandson, Thomas 英国画家 14—427d
罗兰氏树属 Rollinia 植物学 14—359f
《罗兰之歌》 Chanson de Roland, La 古法语史诗 4—53c
罗勒 basil (*Ocimum* basilicum) 草本植物 2—260e
罗雷尔 Rohrer, Heinrich 瑞士物理学家 14—356e
罗里(奥康纳) Rory O'Connor 爱尔兰国王 14—398d
罗利 Raleigh 美国城市 14—132f
罗利 Rowley, William 英国剧作家 14—427e
罗林爵士 Rowling, Sir Wallace Edward 新西兰教育家 14—428a
罗林森 Rawlinson, Sir Henry Creswicke 英国东方学家 14—168f
罗林斯 Rawlins 美国城市 14—168f
罗林斯 Rawlings, Jerry J. 加纳军政领袖 14—168d
罗林斯 Rawlings, Marjorie Kinnan 美国小说家 14—168e
罗林斯 Rollins, Sonny 美国音乐家 14—360f
罗琳 Rowling, J. K. 英国作家 14—427f
罗伦齐尼 Lorenzini, Carlo 意大利作家 10—222a
罗伦佐(高贵的) Lorenzo the Magnificent 意大利政治家 10—222b
罗伦佐图书馆 Laurentian Library 意大利图书馆 9—522c
罗罗 Lolo (people) 民族 10—194e
罗洛 Rollo 斯堪的纳维亚海盗 14—361a
罗马 Roma 澳大利亚城镇 14—361e
罗马 Rome 意大利首都 14—374d
罗马 Rome 美国佐治亚州城市 14—384d
罗马 Rome 美国纽约州城市 14—384d
罗马大奖 Grand Prix de Rome 法国艺术奖学金 7—251d
罗马大学 Rome, University of 意大利大学 14—385a
罗马帝国 Roman Empire 以罗马为中心的古老国家 14—363f
《罗马帝王纪》 Augustan History 古罗马皇帝传记集 2—49e
罗马法 Roman law 古罗马帝国法律 14—364a
罗马副将 legate 罗马共和国军事统帅 9—560e
罗马公路系统 Roman road system 地中海地区交通网 14—367a
罗马公民权 civitas 古罗马 4—256c
罗马共和国 Roman Republic 法国在罗马城建的国家 14—365b
罗马共和国与罗马帝国 Roman Republic and Empire 古罗马历史 14—365b
罗马古笛 tibia 乐器 17—85a
《罗马观察家报》 Osservatore romano, L' 意大利报纸 12—487e
罗马广场 Roman Forum 古罗马广场 14—364a
罗马国立博物馆 Roman National Museum 意大利博物馆 14—364e
罗马国王 Rome, Napoléon, king of 奥地利君主 14—384f
罗马和平 Pax Romana 古罗马历史 13—105a
罗马-荷兰法 Roman-Dutch law 法律 14—363d
罗马教廷机构 Roman Curia 天主教 14—363b
罗马历 Roman republican calendar 历法 14—366f
罗马尼亚 Romania 东南欧国家 14—368f
罗马尼亚公教会 Roman Catholic Church of Romania 东仪天主教会 14—362c
罗马尼亚文学 Romanian literature 文学 14—370d
罗马尼亚语 Romanian language 语言 14—370c
罗马尼亚正教会 Romanian Orthodox Church 正教会 14—371d
罗马努斯 Romanus 教皇 14—374b
罗马诺 Romano 教皇 14—371f
罗马诺 Romano, Ezzelino III da (Italian noble) 意大利贵族 14—371f
罗马诺 Romano, Giulio 意大利艺术家 14—371f
罗马诺 Romano, Giulio 意大利音乐家 14—372a
罗马七丘 Seven Hills of Rome 古罗马城城址 15—237a
罗马骑士 eques 古罗马骑兵队员、阶层 6—108a
《罗马人传奇》 Gesta Romanorum 拉丁语文学 7—103a
罗马氏族 gens 人类学 7—66e
罗马式艺术 Romanesque art 艺术 14—368d
罗马数字 Roman numeral 计数符号 14—364e
罗马体 roman 印刷字体 14—362b
《罗马条约》 Rome, Treaties of 欧洲历史 14—384f
罗马字母 Roman alphabet 字母 14—362c
罗马字体 roman script 书写体 14—367c
罗马宗教 Roman religion 罗马人宗教信仰 14—364e
罗曼 Roman 罗马尼亚城市 14—362a
罗曼 Romains, Jules 法国小说家 14—361f
罗曼采罗 romancero 西班牙民间谣曲 14—368c

罗曼·罗兰 Rolland, Romain 法国小说家 14—359d
罗曼尼诺 Romanino, Il 意大利画家 14—371f
罗曼努斯二世 Romanus II 拜占廷皇帝 14—374a
罗曼努斯;罗马努斯 Romanus 统治者之名 14—373f
罗曼努斯三世 Romanus III Argyrus 14—374a
罗曼努斯四世 Romanus IV Diogenes 拜占廷皇帝 14—374a
罗曼努斯一世(莱卡佩努斯) Romanus I Lecapenus 拜占廷皇帝 14—373f
罗曼诺夫 Romanov, Fyodor Nikitich 莫斯科主教 14—373a
罗曼诺夫王朝 Romanov dynasty 俄国统治者 14—372a
罗曼什海沟 Romanche Gap 大西洋赤道附近海底洼地 14—368d
罗曼什语 Romansh language 罗曼语属 14—373c
罗曼诸语言 Romance languages 语言学 14—367e
罗梅罗 Romero, Francisco 西班牙斗牛士 14—386a
罗梅罗 Romero, José Rubén 墨西哥小说家 14—386b
罗梅罗家族 Romero family 西班牙吉他演奏家家族 14—386a
罗蒙诺索夫 Lomonosov 俄罗斯城镇 10—196e
罗蒙诺索夫 Lomonosov, Mikhail Vasilyevich 俄国诗人、科学家 10—196e
罗蒙诺索夫海岭 Lomonosov Ridge 北冰洋海底山脉 10—197a
罗米利 Romilly, Sir Samuel 英国法律改革家 14—386b
《罗密欧与朱丽叶》 Romeo and Juliet 莎士比亚作品 14—385a
罗摩 Rāma 印度教神灵 14—134d
《罗摩功行录》 Rāmcaritmānas 梵文叙事诗 14—138e
罗摩克里希纳 Ramakrishna 印度教名人 14—135b
罗摩克里希纳教会 Ramakrishna Mission 印度宗教团体 14—135d
罗摩那大仙 Ramana Maharshi 印度教哲学家、瑜伽师 14—135f
罗摩难陀 Rāmānanda 印度哲学家 14—136a
罗摩奴阇 Rāmānuja 印度教神学家、哲学家 14—136b
罗摩提陀 Ramatirtha 印度教名人 14—137a
《罗摩衍那》 Rāmāyaṇa 印度史诗 14—137b
罗默 Romer, Alfred Sherwood 美国古生物学家 14—385b
罗默 Rohmer, Eric 法国作家、电影导演 14—356c
罗默 Rømer, Ole (Christensen) 丹麦天文学家 14—385f
罗默 Rohmer, Sax 英国作家 14—356d
罗姆·达斯 Rām Dās 印度锡克教祖师 14—134b
罗姆·拉伊派 Rām Rāiyā 印度锡克教教派 14—134c
罗姆内 Romny 乌克兰城市 14—387a
罗姆尼 Romney 美国城市 14—386e
罗姆尼 Romney, George 英国画家 14—386e
罗姆尼伯爵 Romney, Henry Sidney, earl of 英格兰政治家 14—386f
罗姆·辛格 Ram Singh 印度锡克教哲学家 14—134c
罗慕路斯·奥古斯图卢斯 Romulus Augustulus 西罗马帝国皇帝 14—387e
罗慕路斯与雷穆斯 Romulus and Remus 传说人物 14—387c
罗慕洛 Romulo, Carlos P(eña) 菲律宾将军 14—387b
罗穆埃尔德(拉韦纳的),圣 Romuald of Ravenna, Saint 本笃会独修派创始人 14—387a
罗纳-普朗克公司 Rhône-Poulenc SA 法国公司 14—270e
罗讷 Rhône 法国省份 14—270d
罗讷-阿尔卑斯 Rhône-Alpes 法国大区 14—270d
罗讷河 Rhône River 欧洲河流 14—270f
罗讷河口省 Bouches-du-Rhône 法国省份 3—76e
罗讷河葡萄酒 Rhône wine 法国红葡萄酒 14—271a
罗盘方位图 rhumb chart 航海图 14—271c
罗盘图 compass chart 航海 4—397f
罗珀 Roper, Elmo (Burns, Jr.) 美国民意测验者 14—397b
罗珀河 Roper River 澳大利亚河流 14—397c
罗普申 Ropshin, V. (Russian novelist) 俄国小说家 14—397d
罗普斯 Rops, Félicien 比利时画家 14—397c
罗奇 Roach, Hal 美国电影导演 14—323b
罗奇 Roche, Kevin 美国籍建筑师 14—338a
罗奇 Roach, Max 美国爵士乐鼓手 14—323c
罗奇代尔 Rochdale 英格兰城镇、自治市 14—337f
罗奇福德 Rochford 英格兰区名 14—340a
罗恰 Rocha 乌拉圭城市 14—337d
罗切斯特 Rochester 英格兰城市 14—338e
罗切斯特 Rochester 美国明尼苏达州城市 14—339a
罗切斯特 Rochester 美国新罕布什尔州城市 14—339b
罗切斯特 Rochester 美国纽约州城市 14—339b
罗琴科 Rodchenko, Aleksandr (Mikhailovich) 苏联画家 14—346c
罗热 Roget, Peter Mark 英国医生、语言学家 14—354f
罗日耶 Rogier, Charles Latour 比利时政治家 14—355a
罗荣桓 Luo Ronghuan 中国军事家 10—288b
罗萨 Rosa, João Guimarães 巴西著作家 14—398d
罗萨 Rosa, Salvator 意大利画家 14—398e
罗萨里奥 Rosario 阿根廷城市 14—399c
罗萨斯 Rosas, Juan Manuel de 阿根廷军事领导人 14—399e
罗塞 Roset, Michel 瑞士政界人物 14—405d
罗塞蒂 Rossetti, Christina 英国诗人 14—409d
罗塞蒂 Rossetti, Dante Gabriel 英国画家、诗人 14—409f
罗塞蒂 Rossetti, Gabriele 意大利诗人、革命家 14—410c
罗塞蒂 Rossetti, William Michael 英国艺术评论家 14—410d
罗塞恩达尔 Rossendale 英格兰区、自治市 14—409d
罗塞尔与罗塞尔帕克 Roselle and Roselle Park 美国城镇 14—403c
罗塞里尼 Rossellini, Roberto 意大利导演 14—409a
罗塞利诺 Rossellino, Antonio 意大利雕刻家 14—409b
罗塞利诺 Rossellino, Bernardo 意大利建筑师、雕刻家 14—409c
罗塞尼亚公教会 Ruthenian Catholic Church 宗教教会 14—468a
罗塞尼亚人 Ruthenian 民族 14—467f
罗塞尼亚语 Ruthenian language 语言 14—468b
罗塞塔 Rosetta 埃及城镇 14—405d
罗塞塔石碑 Rosetta Stone 古埃及石碑 14—405e
罗赛斯 Rosyth 苏格兰城镇、海军基地 14—412f
罗瑟 Rother 英格兰郡名 14—414e
罗瑟勒姆 Rotherham 英格兰自治市 14—414e
罗瑟米尔子爵(第一) Rothermere (of Hemsted), Harold Sidney Harmsworth, 1st Viscount 英国报业主 14—414f
罗森 Rawson 阿根廷城市 14—169b
罗森(夫人) Rowson, Susanna 美国演员、教育家 14—428c
罗森巴赫 Rosenbach, A(braham) S(imon) W(olf) 美国手稿收藏家、书商 14—403f
罗森堡 Rosenberg, Harold 美国作家、教育家 14—404b
罗森堡 Rosenberg, Isaac 英国诗人、画家 14—404b
罗森堡夫妇 Rosenberg, Julius and Ethel 美国文职官员 14—404c
罗森贝格 Rosenberg, Alfred 德国纳粹主义理论家 14—403f
罗森伯格 Rosenberg, William Samuel (U.S. theatre figure) 美国戏剧人物 14—404c
罗森布施 Rosenbusch, Karl Heinrich Ferdinand 德国地质学家 14—404c
罗森茨维格 Rosenzweig, Franz 德国犹太教神学家 14—404e
罗森达尔 Roosendaal 荷兰城市 14—391b
罗森菲尔德 Rosenfeld, Otto (psychologist) 奥地利心理学家 14—404d
罗森费尔德 Rosenfeld, Lev Borisovich 苏联政府官员 14—404d
罗森海姆 Rosenheim 德国城市 14—404d
罗森沃德 Rosenwald, Julius 美国商人、慈善家 14—404d
罗沙 Rocha, Glauber 巴西电影导演 14—337e
罗刹 rakshasa 印度教神话 14—132e
罗莎峰 Monte Rosa 欧洲山脉 11—360f
罗莎蒙德 Rosamond 英王情妇 14—399c
罗尚博伯爵 Rochambeau, Jean-Baptiste-Donatien de Vimeur, comte de 法国将领 14—337f

罗什 Rosh 犹太学者 14—406a
罗什福尔 Rochefort 法国城镇、港口 14—338c
罗什福尔 Rochefort, Victor-Henri, MARQUIS DE ROCHE-FORT-LUCAY 法国记者 14—338c
罗什富科 Rochefoucauld, François Ⅵ, Duke (duc) de La (writer) 法国作家 14—338e
罗什富科家族 Rochefoucauld, La, FAMILY 法国贵族家族 14—338e
罗什蒙 Rochemont, Charles Pictet de 瑞士政治家 14—338e
罗氏龙 Romeria 古生物学 14—386a
罗思柴尔德 Rothschild, Louis-Georges 法国政治领袖 14—416a
罗思柴尔德 Rothschild (of Tring), Lionel Walter Rothschild, 2nd Baron 英国动物学家、收藏家 14—415f
罗思柴尔德家族 Rothschild FAMILY 欧洲银行世家 14—415a
罗思科 Rothko, Mark 美国画家 14—415a
罗思坦 Rothstein, Arnold 美国大赌徒、私酒犯 14—416a
罗斯 Rowse, A(lfred) L(eslie) 英国历史学家、作家 14—428b
罗斯 Rose, Billy 美国剧团经理、作曲家 14—400f
罗斯 Ross, Sir David 苏格兰道德哲学家 14—406f
罗斯 Rose, Ernestine 美国改革家、女权主义者 14—401a
罗斯 Ross, Edward A. 美国社会学奠基人、作家 14—407a
罗斯 Roth, Henry 美国教师、机械师、作家 14—413f
罗斯 Rose, Hugh Henry, BARON STRATHNAIRN OFSTRATHAIRN AND OF JHÄNST 英国陆军元帅 14—401c
罗斯 Ross, Harold W. 美国报刊编辑 14—407b
罗斯 Ross, John 美国印第安人酋长 14—407d
罗斯 Ross, Sir John 英国海军军官 14—407e
罗斯 Ross, Sir James Clark 英国海军军官 14—407c
罗斯 Ross, Martin (19th-20th-century Irish novelist) 爱尔兰小说家 14—407e
罗斯 Rose, Pete 美国棒球运动员 14—401d
罗斯 Roth, Philip 美国小说家 14—414b
罗斯 Ross, Sir Ronald 英国细菌学家 14—407f
罗斯 Rosse, William Parsons, 3rd earl of 爱尔兰天文学家 14—409a
罗斯(夫人) Ross, Betsy 美国裁缝 14—406e
罗斯(夫人) Ross, Nellie Tayloe 美国州长 14—407e
罗斯堡 Roseburg 美国俄勒冈州城市 14—402f
罗斯比 Rossby, Carl-Gustaf Arvid 瑞典-美国气象学家 14—408e
罗斯比波 Rossby wave 气象学 14—408f
罗斯伯里 Rosebery 澳大利亚城镇 14—402e
罗斯伯里堡 Fort Rosebery (Zambia) 赞比亚城镇 6—415b
罗斯伯里伯爵(第五) Rosebery, Archibald Philip Primrose, 5th earl of 英国首相 14—402e
罗斯丹 Rostand, Edmond 法国戏剧家 14—411f
罗斯岛 Ross Island 巴哈马岛屿 14—408d
罗斯福 Roosevelt, Franklin D(elano) 美国总统 14—391c
罗斯福 Roosevelt, Theodore 美国总统 14—395a
罗斯福(夫人) Roosevelt, (Anna) Eleanor 罗斯福总统夫人 14—391b
罗斯福岛 Roosevelt Island 南极洲罗斯属地 14—395c
罗斯福岛 Roosevelt Island 美国伊斯特河岛屿 14—395c
罗斯海 Ross Sea 南极洲海域 14—408d
罗斯基勒 Roskilde 丹麦城市 14—406c
罗斯金 Ruskin, John 英国作家、艺术家 14—455c
罗斯康芒 Roscommon 爱尔兰郡名 14—400a
罗斯康芒 Roscommon 爱尔兰集镇 14—400b
罗斯克兰斯 Rosecrans, William S(tarke) 美国战略家 14—402f
罗斯-克罗默蒂 Ross and Cromarty 苏格兰旧郡名 14—408a
罗斯-克罗默蒂 Ross and Cromarty 苏格兰区名 14—408b
罗斯兰 Rossland 加拿大城市 14—411d
罗斯陆缘冰 Ross Ice Shelf 南太平洋罗斯海浮动冰原 14—408c
罗斯米德男爵(第一) Rosmead, Hercules (George Robert) Robinson, 1st Baron 英国殖民总督 14—406d
罗斯米尼-塞尔巴蒂 Rosmini-Serbati, Antonio 意大利宗教哲学家 14—406d
罗斯人 Rus 欧洲古代民族 14—452e
罗斯氏海豹 Ross seal (*Ommatophoca rossi*) 哺乳动物 14—408e
罗斯索恩 Rawsthorne, Alan 英国作曲家 14—169c
罗斯特罗波维奇 Rostropovich, Mstislav (Leopoldovich) 苏联指挥家 14—412e
罗斯托夫 Rostov 俄罗斯州名 14—412b
罗斯托夫 Rostov 俄罗斯城市 14—412c
罗斯托夫采夫 Rostovtsev, Iakov Ivanovich 俄国出生的考古学家 14—412d
罗斯托夫采夫 Rostovtzeff, Michael Ivanovich 俄国职业军人 14—412d
罗斯托克 Rostock 德国城市 14—412a
罗斯托普钦伯爵 Rostopchin, Fyodor Vasilyevich, Graf 俄国军官、政治家 14—412b
罗斯韦尔 Roswell 美国城市 14—412e
罗斯维尔 Roseville 美国城市 14—405f
罗斯沃尔 Rosewall, Ken 澳大利亚网球运动员 14—406a
罗斯西 Rothesay 苏格兰城镇 14—414f
罗宋汤 borsch 食品 3—57a
罗素 Russell, Bertrand 英国思想家 14—457a
罗素 Russell, Henry Norris 美国天文学家 14—457f
罗素 Russell (of Kingston Russell), John Russell, 1st Earl 英国首相 14—458c
罗素 Russell, William Russell, Lord 英格兰辉格党政治家 14—459d
罗素家族 Russell FAMILY 英格兰辉格党家族 14—456f
罗诉韦德案 Roe v. Wade 美国最高法院案例 14—350f
罗索 Roseau 多米尼加联邦首都 14—402d
罗索 Rosso 毛里塔尼亚城镇 14—411d
罗索 Rosso, Giovanni Battista di Jacopo 意大利画家 14—411d
罗索 Rosso, Medardo 意大利雕刻家 14—411e
罗塔岛 Rota 西太平洋美国火山岛 14—413b
罗塔尔山 Rothaar Hills 德国山区 14—414c
罗塔克 Rohtak 印度城市 14—356f
罗塔琴 rotta 弦乐器 14—417a
罗特 Roth, Joseph 新闻记者、小说家 14—414b
罗特 Rothe, Richard 基督教神学家 14—414d
罗特布拉特爵士 Rotblat, Sir Joseph 英国物理学家 14—413e
罗特尔王 Rother, König 日耳曼传奇人物 14—414e
罗特克 Roethke, Theodore 美国诗人 14—352a
罗特鲁 Rotrou, Jean de 法国剧作家 14—417a
罗特米 Rotimi, Ola 尼日利亚学者 14—416d
罗特内斯特岛 Rottnest Island 澳大利亚岛屿 14—417d
罗特韦尔狗 Rottweiler 狗品种 14—417e
罗图马 Rotuma 斐济属地 14—417e
罗托鲁阿 Rotorua 新西兰城市 14—416f
罗托鲁阿湖 Rotorua, Lake 新西兰湖泊 14—416f
罗陀 Rādhā 印度教神话 14—110a
罗瓦涅米 Rovaniemi 芬兰省会 14—425d
罗威尔 Rowell, Newton Wesley 加拿大政治家 14—426c
罗韦雷托 Rovereto 意大利城镇 14—425e
罗韦尼基 Rovenky 乌克兰城市 14—425e
罗维戈 Rovigo 意大利城市 14—425f
罗维雷 Rovere, Francesco della (pope) 教皇 14—425e
罗维特 Louvet, Jean 比利时剧作家 10—248a
罗西尼 Rossini, Gioacchino (Antonio) 意大利作曲家 14—410f
罗西乌斯 Roscius 罗马喜剧演员 14—400a
罗希尔坎德 Rohilkhand 印度冲积低地 14—356a
罗夏测验 Rorschach Test 心理学 14—398b
罗霄山 Luoxiao Shan 中国山名 10—289a
罗歇 Roger, Pierre (pope) 教皇 14—352f
罗谢耳盐 Rochelle salt 化合物 14—338e

罗亚·巴斯托斯 Roa Bastos, Augusto 巴拉圭小说家 14—322f
罗亚尔岛 Isle Royale 美国岛屿 8—469c
罗亚尔(夫人) Royall, Anne Newport 美国旅行家 14—433b
罗亚尔港 Port Royal 牙买加港口城镇 13—447a
罗亚尔港 Port Royal (Nova Scotia) 加拿大城镇 13—447a
罗亚尔欧克 Royal Oak 美国城市 14—432c
罗耶里奇 Roerich, Nicholas 俄国舞台设计师 14—351f
罗伊 Roy, Manabendra Nath 印度共产党领袖 14—429b
罗伊 Roy, Ram Mohun 印度宗教哲学家、社会改革家 14—429c
罗伊斯 Reuss 德国历史公国 14—248f
罗伊斯 Royce, Sir (Frederick) Henry 英国企业家 14—433c
罗伊斯 Royce, Josiah 美国哲学家 14—433d
罗伊斯顿子爵 Royston, Philip Yorke, Viscount 英国大法官 14—433f
罗伊斯特 Royster, Vermont (Connecticut) 美国新闻工作者 14—433e
罗伊特 Reuter, Ernst 德国共产党人、社会民主党领袖 14—249a
罗伊特 Reuter, Fritz 德国小说家 14—249b
罗伊特林根 Reutlingen 德国城市 14—249e
罗伊希林 Reuchlin, Johannes 德国人文主义者 14—248b
罗意斯(马里亚克的),圣 Marillac, Saint Louise de 法国天主教修士 10—512a
罗勇 Rayong 泰国城镇 14—173d
罗泽尔 Rozelle, Pete 美国橄榄球联盟主任 14—434a
罗泽格尔 Rosegger, Peter 奥地利作家 14—403b
罗泽迈尔 Rosemeyer, Bernd 德国汽车运动员 14—403e
罗扎诺夫 Rozanov, Vasily Vasilyevich 俄罗斯作家 14—433f
罗振玉 Luo Zhenyu 中国古文字学家 10—288d
罗兹 Łódź 波兰城市 10—184e
罗兹 Łódź 原波兰省份 10—184e
罗兹 Łódzkie 波兰省份 10—184e
罗兹 Rhodes, James Ford 美国商人、历史学家 14—268b
罗兹 Rhodes, Lawrence 美国舞蹈演员 14—268b
罗兹 Rhodes, Wilfred R. 英格兰板球运动员 14—268c
罗兹托切 Roztocze 波兰丘陵地带 14—434b
罗兹维 Rozwi 非洲卡兰加帝国 14—434b
萝卜 radish (*Raphanus sativus*) 草本植物 14—118b
萝芙木属 Rauwolfia 木本植物 14—165d
萝玛 lauma 波罗的海地区女神 9—519e
萝藦科 Asclepiadaceae 植物学 1—542a
萝丝(利马的),圣 Rose of Lima, Saint 秘鲁主保圣人 14—400f
逻各斯 logos 古希腊哲学、神学用语 10—192b
逻辑 logic 哲学 10—190b
逻辑关系 logical relation 哲学 10—191c
逻辑实证主义 Logical Positivism 哲学 10—191b
逻辑斯谛系统 logistic system (philosophy) 哲学 10—191f
逻辑原子论 Logical Atomism 哲学 10—191a
逻辑主义 logicism 数学 10—191e
锣 gong 乐器 7—203c
骡 mule 哺乳动物 11—474e
骡鹿 mule deer (species *Odocoileus hemionus*) 哺乳动物 11—474f
螺 snail 软体动物 15—457c
螺钿 shell inlaying 中国漆器 15—296d
螺钿漆工艺 raden 日本工艺 14—109e
螺钿漆器 burgauté (lacquer ware) 工艺品 3—260a
螺钿漆器工艺 laque burgauté 工艺 9—497d
螺菌属 Spirillum 菌 16—35b
螺菌性鼠咬热 spirillary rat-bite fever 传染病 16—35b
螺毛虫 spirotrich 原生动物 16—36f
螺母 nut 紧固件 12—305b
螺栓 bolt 紧固件 3—16f
螺丝刀 screwdriver 工具 15—156b
螺纹件 screw 机械构件 15—155f
螺线 spiral 数学 16—34c
螺线管 solenoid 电学 15—495b
螺旋孢子虫属 Helicosporidium 原生动物 7—573d
螺旋测微器 micrometer 测量仪器 11—193c
螺旋桨 propeller 飞机或船只的推进装置 13—535d
螺旋体 spirochete 细菌 16—36d
螺旋藓 screw moss 藓类植物 15—156b
螺旋状柱子 barley-sugar column (architecture) 建筑学 2—232b
裸鼻鸱 owlet frogmouth 鸟类 12—517f
裸鼻雀 tanager 鸟类 16—456c
裸甲藻属 Gymnodinium 生物学 7—389d
裸颈鹳 jabiru (species *Jabiru mycteria*) 鸟类 8—501e
裸口虫 gymnostome 原生动物 7—390c
裸眉鸫 asity 鸟类 1—554f
裸眉鸫科 Philepittidae 鸟类 13—232d
裸鳃类 nudibranch 海洋动物 12—292d
裸体主义 nudism 行为方式 12—292e
裸童 putto 艺术 14—39c
裸尾鼩猬 moonrat 哺乳动物 11—378c
裸子植物 gymnosperm 植物学 7—389d
瘰疬 scrofula 结核病 15—158d
瘰鳞蛇 wart snake 爬行动物 18—114b
洛 Lowe, Doug 英国田径运动员 10—253b
洛 Low, Sir David (Alexander Cecil) 英国记者、漫画家 10—252a
洛 Low, Sir Hugh 英国官员 10—252b
洛 Lowe, Sir Hudson 英国军人 10—253b
洛 Lowe, Robert 英国政治家 10—253b
洛 Low, Seth 美国教育家 10—252c
洛(夫人) Low, Juliette Gordon 美国女童子军创建者 10—252b
洛阿河 Loa River 智利河流 10—171e
洛巴策 Lobatse 博茨瓦纳城镇 10—172e
洛巴诺夫-罗斯托夫斯基 Lobanov-Rostovsky, Aleksey Borisovich, Knyaz 俄国外交家 10—172d
洛巴托 Lobato, José Bento Monteiro 巴西作家 10—172e
洛班巴 Lobamba 斯威士兰乡村 10—172d
洛贝尔 L'Obel, Matthias de 法国植物学家 10—173a
洛比人 Lobi 非洲民族 10—173c
洛博 Lobo, Francisco Rodrigues 葡萄牙诗人 10—173c
洛布 Loeb, Richard A. 美国匪徒 10—185a
洛采 Lotze, Rudolf Hermann 德国哲学家 10—232a
洛代 Lodi 美国城市 10—184c
洛登 Lowden, Frank Orren 美国政治家 10—253a
洛登河 Loddon River 澳大利亚河流 10—183c
洛登外衣 loden coat 服装 10—183c
洛迪 Lodi 意大利城镇 10—184b
《洛迪和约》 Lodi, Peace of 意大利历史 10—184d
洛迪战役 Lodi, Battle of 意大利历史 10—184d
洛蒂 Loti, Pierre 法国小说家 10—230f
洛蒂西乌斯·色孔多斯 Lotichius Secundus, Petrus 德国诗人 10—231a
洛东江 Naktong River 韩国河流 11—547c
洛厄尔 Lowell 美国城市 10—253c
洛尔 Lorre, Peter 美国电影演员 10—223f
洛尔卡 Lorca 西班牙城镇 10—218e
洛尔卡 Lorca, Federico García 西班牙作家 10—218f
洛尔施 Lorsch 德国村庄 10—224a
洛夫克拉夫特 Lovecraft, H(oward) P(hillips) 美国作家 10—250a
洛夫莱斯 Lovelace, Richard 英国诗人 10—250e
洛夫莱斯伯爵夫人 Lovelace, Augusta Ada King, countess of 英国数学家 10—250d
洛夫洛克 Lovelock, Jack 新西兰田径运动员 10—251d
洛夫乔伊 Lovejoy, Arthur O(ncken) 美国哲学家 10—250b
洛夫乔伊 Lovejoy, Elijah P(arish) 美国新闻编辑 10—250c

洛夫特许斯 Lofthuus, Christian Jensen 挪威政革运动领导人 10—187c
洛夫廷 Lofting, Hugh 美国作家 10—187d
洛弗 Lover, Samuel 英国作家、画家 10—251e
洛弗尔(小) Lovell, James A(rthur), Jr. 美国航天员 10—251c
洛弗尔子爵 Lovell, Francis Lovell, Viscount 英国政治家 10—251b
洛高 Logau, Friedrich, Freiherr von 德国诗人 10—189d
洛格 Logue, Christopher 英国诗人 10—192c
洛格罗尼奥 Logroño 原西班牙省份 10—192c
洛格罗尼奥 Logroño 西班牙城市 10—192c
洛根 Lågen 挪威东南部河流 9—446d
洛根 Lågen 挪威中南部河流 9—446e
洛根 Logan 美国犹他州城市 10—188a
洛根 Logan 美国西弗吉尼亚州城市 10—188a
洛根 Logan, Harvey 美国匪徒 10—188a
洛根 Logan, James 英属美洲政治家 10—188a
洛根 Logan, James 北美印第安人领袖 10—188b
洛根 Logan, Joshua 美国导演、作家 10—188c
洛根 Logan, John A(lexander) 美国军人 10—188b
洛根 Logan, Sir William Edmond 加拿大地质学家 10—188d
洛根莓 loganberry (*Rubus loganobaccus*) 植物 10—188e
洛根山 Logan, Mount 加拿大山峰 10—188d
洛贡河 Logone River 乍得河流 10—192a
洛哈 Loja 厄瓜多尔省份 10—193f
洛哈 Loja 厄瓜多尔城市 10—194a
洛哈伯 Lochaber 苏格兰区名 10—175b
洛哈尔什 Lochalsh (Scotland) 苏格兰区名 10—175b
洛赫 Loch (of Drylaw), Henry Brougham Loch, 1st Baron 英国军人 10—175a
洛赫吉尔普黑德 Lochgilphead 苏格兰度假胜地 10—175c
洛赫雷 Loughrea 爱尔兰城镇 10—233b
洛赫梅本 Lochmaben 苏格兰自治市 10—175c
洛赫纳 Lochner, Stefan 德国画家 10—175d
洛赫纳加山 Lochnagar 苏格兰山名 10—175d
洛亨格林 Lohengrin 德国传说 10—192e
洛基 Loki 北欧神话人物 10—194c
洛基尔 Lockyer, Sir Joseph Norman 英国天文学家 10—181a
洛迦诺 Locarno 瑞士城镇 10—174c
《洛迦诺公约》 Locarno, Pact of 欧洲历史 10—174d
洛卡泰利 Locatelli, Pietro 意大利音乐家 10—174e
洛科贾 Lokoja 尼日利亚城镇 10—194c
洛可可艺术风格 Rococo style 欧洲艺术风格 14—345a
洛克 Locke, Alain (LeRoy) 美国教育家 10—176e
洛克 Locke, Bobby 南非高尔夫运动员 10—176f
洛克 Locke, David Ross 美国作家 10—177a
洛克 Locke, John 英国哲学家 10—177a
洛克 Locke, Matthew 英国作曲家 10—180a
洛克波特 Lockport 美国城市 10—180e
洛克菲勒 Rockefeller, David 美国银行家、慈善家 14—341d
洛克菲勒 Rockefeller, John D(avison) 美国实业家、慈善家 14—341d
洛克菲勒 Rockefeller, Laurance S(pelman) 美国资本家、慈善家 14—342a
洛克菲勒 Rockefeller, Nelson Aldrich 美国副总统 14—342a
洛克菲勒 Rockefeller, William 美国金融家、企业家 14—342b
洛克菲勒 Rockefeller, Winthrop 美国政治家、慈善家 14—342c
洛克菲勒(小) Rockefeller, John D(avison), Jr. 美国慈善家 14—341f
洛克菲勒大学 Rockefeller University 美国大学 14—342d
洛克菲勒第三 Rockefeller, John D(avison), III 美国慈善家 14—341f
洛克菲勒中心 Rockefeller Center 美国纽约市摩天大楼 14—342c
洛克港 Lock Haven 美国城市 10—176e
洛克哈特 Lockhart, John Gibson 英国作家 10—180a
洛克里伊壁犀斐里 Locri Epizephyrii 意大利古城 10—182b
洛克伦 Lokeren 比利时城市 10—194b
洛克马里亚凯 Locmariaquer 法国村庄 10—181a
洛克斯顿 Loxton 澳大利亚城镇 10—257a
洛克伍德(夫人) Lockwood, Belva Ann 美国女权运动者 10—180f
洛克希德-马丁公司 Lockheed Martin Corporation 美国航空航天公司 10—180c
洛拉莱 Loralai 巴基斯坦城镇 10—218c
洛拉维特兰人 Luorawetlan (people) 俄罗斯民族 10—289a
洛拉维特兰诸语言 Luorawetlan languages 俄罗斯语言 10—289a
洛兰 Lorrain, Claude (painter) 法国画家 10—223b
洛兰岛 Lolland 丹麦岛屿 10—194d
洛朗 Laurent, Auguste 法国化学家 9—522c
洛朗 Laurent, François 比利时法学家、历史学家 9—522c
洛朗森 Laurencin, Marie 法国画家 9—522a
洛朗斯 Laurens, Henri 法国雕刻家 9—522a
洛勒莱 Lorelei 德国莱茵河中的回音岩 10—220b
洛雷丹 Loredan, Pietro 威尼斯贵族 10—220b
洛雷恩 Lorain 美国城市 10—218b
洛雷纳 Lorena 巴西城市 10—220d
洛雷斯坦 Lorestān 伊朗省份 10—222c
洛雷斯坦青铜器 Luristan Bronze 考古学 10—291c
洛雷托 Loreto 意大利城镇 10—222c
洛雷托 Loreto 秘鲁省份 10—222d
洛雷因 Lorain, John 美国农业作家 10—218b
洛里埃 Laurier, Sir Wilfrid 加拿大总理 9—523a
洛里昂 Lorient 法国城镇 10—222e
洛里默 Lorimer, George Horace 美国报纸编辑 10—222f
洛里斯 Loris, Heinrich 瑞士音乐家 10—223a
洛里斯-梅利柯夫 Loris-Melikov, Mikhail Tariyelovich, Graf (Count) 俄国政治家 10—223a
洛里亚尔公司 Lorillard Company 美国烟草公司 10—222e
洛林 Lorraine 法国大区 10—223d
洛林枢机主教 Lorraine, CARDINALS OF 法国主教家系 10—223e
洛林枢机主教(第二) Lorraine, Charles de Lorraine, 2nd cardinal (2^{e} cardinal) de 法国枢机主教 10—223f
洛林枢机主教(第一) Lorraine, Jean de Lorraine, 1st cardinal (1er cardinal) de 法国枢机主教 10—223e
洛伦采蒂 Lorenzetti, Ambrogio 意大利画家 10—221e
洛伦采蒂 Lorenzetti, Pietro 意大利画家 10—221e
洛伦茨 Lorentz, Pare 美国电影导演 10—220f
洛伦茨 Lorenz, Konrad 奥地利动物学家 10—221b
洛伦高 Lorengau 巴布亚新几内亚城镇 10—220d
洛伦索-马贵斯 Lourenço Marques (city and province, Mozambique) 莫桑比克城市 10—246f
洛伦索-马贵斯湾 Lourenço Marques, Baía de (Mozambique) 莫桑比克海湾 10—246f
洛伦特 Lorant, Stefan 美国作家 10—218d
洛伦兹 Lorentz, Hendrik Antoon 荷兰物理学家 10—220e
洛伦兹变换 Lorentz transformations 物理学 10—221b
洛伦兹-斐兹杰惹收缩 Lorentz-FitzGerald contraction 物理学 10—221a
洛伦佐修士 Lorenzo MONACO 意大利画家 10—222b
洛马克斯 Lomax, Alan 美国音乐家 10—194f
洛马米河 Lomami River 刚果(金)河流 10—194e
洛马山 Loma Mountains 塞拉利昂山脉 10—194e
洛马水坝 Lomaum Dam 安哥拉水坝 10—194f
洛马斯德萨莫拉 Lomas de Zamora 阿根廷城市 10—194e
洛梅尼·德布里安 Loménie de Brienne, Étienne-Charles de 法国主教、政治家 10—196d
洛美 Lomé 多哥首都 10—196c
洛蒙德湖 Lomond, Loch 苏格兰湖泊 10—196e

洛米 Lomi, Orazio (Baroque painter) 意大利画家 10—196d
洛佩·德·维加 Lope de Vega 西班牙作家 10—216a
洛佩斯 Lopes, Baltasar 佛得角诗人 10—216a
洛佩斯 López, Carlos Antonio 巴拉圭独裁者 10—216d
洛佩斯 Lopes, Fernão 葡萄牙历史学家 10—216a
洛佩斯 López, Francisco Solano 巴拉圭独裁者 10—216e
洛佩斯 Lopes, Manuel 佛得角诗人 10—216c
洛佩斯·奥尔特加 López Ortega, Domingo (bullfighter) 西班牙斗牛士 10—217b
洛佩斯·贝拉尔德 López Velarde, Ramón 墨西哥诗人 10—217d
洛佩斯·波蒂略(-帕切科) López Portillo (y Pacheco), José 墨西哥总统 10—217b
洛佩斯·德·阿亚拉 López de Ayala, Pedro 西班牙诗人、史官 10—216f
洛佩斯·德·莱加斯皮 López de Legazpi, Miguel (Spanish explorer) 西班牙探险家 10—216f
洛佩斯·德·门多萨 López de Mendoza, Iñigo, marqués de Santillana 西班牙人文学者 10—217a
洛佩斯-富恩特斯 López y Fuentes, Gregorio 墨西哥小说家 10—217d
洛佩斯·雷加 López Rega, José 阿根廷政客 10—217c
洛佩斯·马特奥斯 López Mateos, Adolfo 墨西哥总统 10—217a
洛佩斯·米切尔森 López Michelsen, Alfonso 哥伦比亚总统 10—217a
洛皮塔尔 L'Hospital, Michel de 法国政治家 10—56c
洛普欣娜 Lopukhina, Yevdokiya Fyodorovna (tsarina) 俄国沙皇之妻 10—218a
洛齐 Lóczy, Lajos 匈牙利地质学家 10—183a
洛齐人 Lozi 非洲民族 10—258c
洛奇 Lodge, Henry Cabot 美国参议员 10—183d
洛奇 Lodge, Henry Cabot 美国参议员、外交家 10—183e
洛奇 Lodge, Sir Oliver Joseph 英国物理学家 10—184a
洛奇 Lodge, Thomas 英国诗人、作家 10—184a
洛桑 Lausanne 瑞士城市 9—523d
洛桑会议 Lausanne Conference 国际会议 9—523f
《洛桑条约》 Lausanne, Treaty of 国际条约 9—523f
洛色林 Roscelin 法国哲学家、神学家 14—399f
洛杉矶 Los Angeles 美国城市 10—224c
洛杉矶动物园 Los Angeles Zoo, The 美国动物园 10—227f
《洛杉矶时报》 Los Angeles Times 美国报纸 10—227e
洛杉矶县立艺术博物馆 Los Angeles County Museum of Art 美国博物馆 10—227d
洛施 Losch, Maria Magdalene von (German actress) 德国演员 10—228d
洛什 Loches 法国城镇 10—175c
洛斯 Loos, Adolf 奥地利建筑师 10—215b
洛斯 Lowes, John Livingston 美国学者 10—255f
洛斯阿拉莫斯 Los Alamos 美国城市 10—224b
洛斯安赫莱斯 Los Angeles 智利城市 10—224c
洛斯巴尔瓦塞斯侯爵 Balbases, Ambrogio di Filippo Spinola, Marquess (Marqués) de los 西班牙军人 2—162e
洛斯巴尼奥斯 Los Baños 菲律宾城镇 10—227f
洛斯多斯卡米诺斯 Los Dos Caminos 委内瑞拉城市 10—228a
洛斯基 Lossky, Nikolay Onufriyevich 俄国哲学家 10—229a
洛斯科普水库自然保护地 Loskop Dam Nature Reserve 南非自然保护区 10—228f
洛斯拉戈斯 Los Lagos 智利区名 10—228b
洛斯里奥斯 Los Ríos 厄瓜多尔省份 10—228c
洛斯莫奇斯 Los Mochis 墨西哥城市 10—228c
洛斯皮吉瓜奥斯 Los Pijiguaos 委内瑞拉矿区 10—228c
洛斯群岛 Los Islands 几内亚岛屿 10—228a
洛斯桑托斯 Los Santos 巴拿马省份 10—228d
洛斯特克斯 Los Teques 委内瑞拉城市 10—228d
洛斯特威西尔 Lostwithiel 英格兰城镇 10—229c
洛斯图斯特拉斯 Los Tuxtlas (Mexico) 墨西哥城市 10—228d
洛斯托夫特 Lowestoft 英格兰地区 10—256a
洛斯托夫特瓷器 Lowestoft porcelain 英格兰瓷器 10—256a
洛塔 Lota 智利矿区 10—229e
洛塔尔二世(或三世) Lothair II (or III) 神圣罗马帝国皇帝 10—230c
洛泰尔 Lothair 统治者之名 10—229f
洛泰尔 Lothair 法国国王 10—229f
洛泰尔(二世) Lothair (II) 法兰克分封王 10—230b
洛泰尔(塞尼的) Lothair of Segni (pope) 教皇 10—230e
洛泰尔二世 Lothair II 意大利国王 10—230e
洛泰尔一世 Lothair I 法兰克皇帝 10—230a
洛特 Lot 法国省份 10—229c
洛特 Lhote, André 法国画家 10—56d
洛特 Lot, Ferdinand 法国历史学家 10—229d
洛特河 Lot River 法国河流 10—229e
洛特-加龙 Lot-et-Garonne 法国省份 10—229d
洛特·卡米哈米哈 Lot Kamehameha (Hawaiian king) 夏威夷国王 10—229e
洛特雷亚蒙伯爵 Lautréamont, Comte de 法国作家 9—524c
洛提王朝 Lodī dynasty 印度王朝 10—184c
洛图科人 Lotuko 苏丹南部民族 10—231d
洛托 lotto (game) 博彩 10—231c
洛托 Lotto, Lorenzo 意大利画家 10—231c
洛托地毯 Lotto carpet 土耳其工艺品 10—231d
洛瓦特勋爵(第十一) Lovat, Simon Fraser, 11th Lord 苏格兰詹姆斯党人 10—249b
洛威尔 Lowell, Amy 美国作家 10—253d
洛威尔 Lowell, A(bbott) Lawrence 美国教育家 10—253c
洛威尔 Lowell, Francis Cabot 美国商人 10—253e
洛威尔 Lowell, James Russell 美国诗人 10—253e
洛威尔 Lowell, Percival 美国天文学家 10—254c
洛威尔(夫人) Lowell, Josephine Shaw 美国社会改革家 10—254b
洛威尔(小) Lowell, Robert (Traill Spence), Jr. 美国诗人 10—254d
洛韦 Lovek 柬埔寨古都 10—250d
洛维杜人 Lovedu 南非民族 10—250b
洛维尔 Lovell, Sir (Alfred Charles) Bernard 英国天文学家 10—250f
洛维奇 Lovech 保加利亚城镇 10—250a
洛维特 Lovett, William 英国宪章运动领袖 10—251e
洛文 Lowin, John 英国演员 10—256c
洛西 Losey, Joseph (Walton) 美国电影导演 10—228e
洛西茅斯 Lossiemouth 苏格兰度假胜地 10—228f
洛希极限 Roche limit 天文学 14—338b
洛锡安 Lothian 苏格兰旧省份 10—230e
洛锡安 Lothian 苏格兰行政区 10—230e
洛喜密脱 Loschmidt, Joseph 德国化学家 10—228d
洛亚蒂群岛 Loyalty Islands 法国岛屿 10—257f
洛阳 Luoyang 中国城市 10—289b
洛阳桥 Luoyang Bridge 中国宋代大型石梁桥 10—289d
洛伊 Looy, Jacobus van 荷兰作家、画家 10—215e
洛伊 Loew, Marcus 美国电影业者 10—186d
洛伊 Loy, Mina 英国诗人 10—257b
洛伊 Loy, Myrna 美国电影演员 10—257b
洛伊 Loewy, Raymond 美国工业设计家 10—186f
洛伊 Lowie, Robert H(arry) 美国人类学家 10—256b
洛伊策 Leutze, Emanuel Gottlieb 美国画家 10—44c
洛伊德 Loyd, Sam 美国智力游戏设计者 10—257f
洛伊夫 Roiphe, Anne 美国女权主义者和作家 14—356f
洛伊卡特 Leuckart, (Karl Georg Friedrich) Rudolf 德国动物学家 10—43a

洛伊萨河 Loíza River 波多黎各河流 10—193f
洛邑 Luoyi 中国周朝都城 10—289d
洛-约翰松 Lo-Johansson, Ivar 瑞典作家 10—171d
洛赞伯爵和公爵 Lauzun, Antonin-Nompar de Caumont, comteet duc de 法国军人 9—524d
洛赞公爵 Lauzun, Armand-Louis de Gontaut, duc de (duke of) 法国军人 9—524e
洛泽尔 Lozère 法国省份 10—258c
洛子峰 Lhotse 亚洲山峰 10—56e
骆马 vicuña (*Lama*, or *Vicugna*, *vicugna*) 哺乳动物 17—545e
骆驼 camel 哺乳动物 3—370a
骆驼毛 camel hair 纤维 3—370d
骆驼蓬碱 harmine 药物 7—480c
骆玉笙 Luo Yusheng 中国曲艺演员 10—288c
络合物 complex 化学 4—399b
络新妇 silk spider 节肢动物 15—372c
珞巴族 Lhoba 中国民族 10—56a
珞巴族语言 Lhoba languages 中国语言 10—56b
落潮 ebb tide 海洋学 5—515d
落袋台球 pocket billiards 体育项目 13—383b
落地钟 longcase clock 钟表 10—209a
落基山 Rocky Mount 美国城市 14—344d
落基山斑疹热 Rocky Mountain spotted fever 传染病 14—344e
落基山地沟 Rocky Mountain Trench 北美地沟 14—344f
落基山国家公园 Rocky Mountain National Park 美国国家公园 14—344d
落基山脉 Rocky Mountains 北美山脉 14—344f
落葵科 Basellaceae 植物学 2—257d
落柿舍 Rakushisha 日本诗人 14—132f
落水洞 sinkhole 地质学 15—396a
落选者沙龙 Salon des Refusés 法国艺术展览 14—551f
落叶林 deciduous forest 植被 5—202f
落叶松 larch 植物 9—498e
漯河 Luohe 中国城市 10—288f

M

妈祖 Mazu 中国民间传说女神 11—58a
麻痹 palsy (disease) 疾病 12—575c
麻痹性痴呆 paresis 疾病 13—40e
麻城 Macheng 中国城市 10—346a
麻蹉 Matsya 印度教神 11—29b
麻风 leprosy 疾病 10—31f
麻葛 magus 波斯宗教祭祀氏族 10—396a
麻黄碱 ephedrine 药物 6—95a
麻黄属 Ephedra 植物学 6—95a
麻鳽 bittern 鸟类 2—504c
麻将 mah-jongg 游戏 10—396b
麻胶版画 linocut 绘画 10—125a
麻壳龟 pitted shell turtle (*Carettochelys insculpta*) 爬行动物 13—331b
麻粒岩相 granulite facies 地质学 7—257b
麻喏巴歇帝国 Majapahit empire 印度尼西亚王国 10—413b
麻纱 dimity 纺织品 5—319c
麻省理工学院 Massachusetts Institute of Technology (MIT) 美国大学 11—10f
麻蝇 flesh fly 昆虫 6—357d
麻扎塔格山 Mazartag Shan 中国山脉 11—56d
麻疹 measles 疾病 11—64a
麻醉品 narcotic 药物 11—575d
麻醉学 anesthesiology 医学 1—338f
麻醉药 anesthetic 药物 1—339a
蔴坡 Muar 马来西亚港口 11—459f
蟆口鸱 morepork 鸟类 11—390d
马 horse (*Equus caballus*) 哺乳动物 8—180a
马-阿鲁塞 maa-alused 爱沙尼亚宗教传说精灵 10—323c
马埃 Mahe 印度城镇 10—400d
马埃岛 Mahé Island 塞舌尔岛屿 10—400d
马埃斯特腊山 Maestra, Sierra 古巴山脉 10—376e
马埃斯图 Maeztu (y Whitney), Ramiro de 西班牙新闻记者 10—377c
马安 Maʿān 约旦城镇 10—323d
马鞍山 Ma'anshan 中国城市 10—323d
马奥 Mao 多米尼加共和国城市 10—480c
马奥雷 Mahoré 印度洋岛屿 10—404a
马奥尼 Mahoney, Mary 美国护士 10—403f
马坝人 Maba man 中国旧石器时代人类化石 10—324e
马背叼羊 buzkashī 亚洲体育比赛 3—296d
马比尼 Mabini, Apolinario 菲律宾革命理论家 10—324f
《马比诺吉昂》 Mabinogion 威尔士故事集 10—325a
马比荣 Mabillon, Jean 法国学者、史学家 10—324f
马比斯 Mabuse, Jan 佛兰德斯画家 10—325b
马鞭 coachwhip (plant) 植物 4—310c
马鞭草科 Verbenaceae 植物学 17—511b
马鞭草属 Verbena 植物学 17—511a
马鞭蛇 coachwhip (Masticophis, sometimes *Coluber*, *flagellum*) 爬行动物 4—310c
马伯里 Marbury, Elizabeth 美国戏剧演员 10—492d
马伯里诉麦迪逊案 Marbury v. Madison 美国法律 10—492e
马布尔 Marble, Alice 美国网球运动员 10—491d
马布尔黑德 Marblehead 美国城镇 10—492a
马布拉卡 Magburaka 塞拉利昂城镇 10—379a
马布利 Mabley, Moms 美国喜剧演员 10—325a
马布特 Marbut, Curtis Fletcher 美国地质学家、土壤学权威 10—492f
马策伊克 Maetsuyker, Joan 荷属东印度总督 10—377b
马查多 Machado, Bernardino Luis 葡萄牙总统 10—344d
马查多(鲁伊斯) Machado (y Ruiz), Antonio 西班牙诗人、剧作家 10—344d
马查多(鲁伊斯) Machado (y Ruiz), Manuel 西班牙诗人、剧作家 10—344e
马查多·德·阿西斯 Machado de Assis, Joaquim Maria 巴西诗人、小说家 10—344f
马查多-莫拉莱斯 Machado y Morales, Gerardo 古巴英雄 10—344f
马查拉 Machala 厄瓜多尔城市 10—345a
马柴厄斯 Machias 美国城镇 10—346b
马厂遗址 Machang site 中国古代文化遗址 10—345b
马车赛 chariot racing 古代竞技比赛项目 4—65a
马辰 Banjarmasin 印度尼西亚城市 2—203a
马齿苋 purslane 植物 14—34c
马齿苋科 Portulacaceae 植物学 13—456f
马传染性贫血 equine infectious anemia (EIA) 马疾病 6—108d
马达加斯加 Madagascar 非洲岛国 10—364e
马达加斯加长尾灵猫 fossa (*Cryptoprocta ferox*) 哺乳动物 6—420b
马达加斯加共和国 Malagasy Republic 非洲岛国 10—419e
马达加斯加狐猴 sifaka 哺乳动物 15—359e
马达加斯加猬 tenrec 哺乳动物 16—545b
马达加斯加诸语言 Malagasy languages 澳斯特罗尼西亚语言 10—419e
马达莱纳岛 Maddalena Island 意大利岛屿 10—366b
马达莱纳山口 Maddalena Pass 欧洲山口 10—366b
马达里亚加-罗霍 Madariaga y Rojo, Salvador de 西班牙作家 10—366a
马代巴 Ma'dabā 约旦城镇 10—364d
马代尔纳 Maderna, Bruno 德国作曲家 10—367c
马代尔诺 Maderno, Carlo 意大利建筑师 10—367c

马代拉河 Madeira River 南美河流 10—366f
马黛茶 maté 饮料 11—18f
马当 Madang 巴布亚新几内亚港口 10—365f
马刀嘴鸟 sabrebill (bird) 鸟类 14—485b
马德拉卡 Madderakka 拉普人信奉的女神 10—366c
马德拉葡萄酒 Madeira 葡萄牙酒 10—366c
马德拉群岛 Madeira Islands 葡萄牙群岛 10—366d
马德拉沙 madrasah 穆斯林教育机构 10—371c
马德拉斯 Madras (India) 印度邦名 10—371a
马德拉斯 Madras 印度城市 10—371b
马德拉斯大学 Madras, University of 印度大学 10—371c
马德莱娜教堂 Madeleine 法国教堂 10—367a
马德勒 Mädler, Johann Heinrich von 德国天文学家 10—370d
马德雷德迪奥斯 Madre de Dios 秘鲁省份 10—371d
马德雷德迪奥斯河 Madre de Dios River 南美河流 10—371d
马德雷湖 Madre, Laguna 美国湖泊 10—371d
马德雷山脉 Sierra Madre 墨西哥山脉 15—358e
马德里 Madrid 西班牙区名 10—371e
马德里 Madrid 西班牙首都 10—371e
马德里公园 Parque de Madrid (Spain) 西班牙公园 13—60f
马德里康普鲁顿大学 Madrid, Complutensian University of 西班牙大学 10—374a
马德里刻本 Madrid Codex 马雅文化 10—374c
《马德里条约》 Madrid, Treaty of 欧洲历史 10—374b
马德罗 Madero, Francisco (Indalécio) 墨西哥总统 10—367d
马德普拉塔 Mar del Plata 阿根廷城市 10—486d
马德斯泰 Mardersteig, Giovanni 意大利活版印刷专家 10—500f
马德望 Bătdâmbâng 柬埔寨城镇 2—274c
马德维格 Madvig, Johan Nicolai 丹麦学者 10—375c
马德休斯 Mathesius, Vilém 捷克语言学家 11—23d
马镫 stirrup 骑马用具 16—241f
马迪基泽拉-曼德拉 Madikizela-Mandela Winnie 南非黑人活动家 10—368f
马迪曼 Muddiman, Henry 英国新闻记者 11—462b
马迪纳特哈布 Madīnat Habu 埃及古代陵庙 10—369c
马迪纳伊萨 Madīnah Īsā 巴林城镇 10—369a
马迪人 Madi 非洲民族 10—368f
马蒂 Martí (y Pérez), José Julián 古巴诗人 10—544c
马蒂奥利 Mattioli, Pietro Andrea Gregorio 意大利医生、植物学家 11—32d
马蒂厄 Mathieu, Claude-Louis 法国天文学家、数学家 11—24c
马蒂尔达 Matilda 神圣罗马帝国皇后 11—24f
马蒂尔达(佛兰德的) Matilda of Flanders 英格兰王后 11—25b
马蒂格 Martigues 法国城镇 10—545b
马蒂尼 Martini, Francesco Maurizio di Giorgio 意大利画家 10—549e
马蒂尼 Martini, Giovanni Battista 意大利作曲家、音乐理论家 10—549e
马蒂尼亚克子爵 Martignac, Jean-Baptiste-Sylvère Gay, vicomte de 法国政治家 10—545a
马蒂努 Martinů, Bohuslav 捷克作曲家 10—551a
马蒂诺 Martineau, Harriet 英国散文家 10—548e
马蒂诺 Martineau, James 英国神学家、哲学家 10—548f
马蒂斯 Matisse, Henri(-Émile-Benoît) 法国画家 11—25b
马蒂松 Matthisson, Friedrich von 德国诗人 11—32d
马蒂亚森 Mathiassen, Therkel 丹麦考古学家、民族学家 11—24c
马蒂亚斯 Matthias 神圣罗马帝国皇帝 11—32a
马蒂亚斯-德加尔韦斯 Matías de Gálvez (Guatemala) 危地马拉港口 11—24f
马蒂亚斯二世 Matthias II 神圣罗马帝国皇帝 11—32c
马丁 Martin 统治者之名 10—545b
马丁 Martin 阿拉贡国王 10—545e
马丁 Martin, Anne Henrietta 美国女权主义者 10—546c
马丁 Martin, A(rcher) J(ohn) P(orter) 英国生物化学家 10—546b
马丁 Martin, Billy 美国棒球运动员 10—546d
马丁 Martin, (Bon-Louis-) Henri 法国历史学家 10—546f
马丁 Martyn, Edward 爱尔兰戏剧家 10—551e
马丁 Martin, Frank 瑞士作曲家 10—546e
马丁 Martin, Gregory 天主教圣经学者 10—546f
马丁 Martin, Glenn L(uther) 美国飞机发明家 10—546e
马丁 Martin, Homer Dodge 美国画家 10—547a
马丁 Martin, Joseph William, Jr. 美国共和党国会领袖 10—547a
马丁 Martin, Luther 美国律师 10—547c
马丁 Martin, Lillien Jane 美国心理学家 10—547b
马丁 Martin, Maria 美国画家 10—547d
马丁 Martin, Mary (Virginia) 美国歌唱家、演员 10—547e
马丁 Martin, Paul 加拿大总理 10—547e
马丁 Martin, Pierre-Émile 法国工程师 10—547f
马丁 Martin, Steve 美国喜剧演员 10—548a
马丁(二世) Martin (II) 教皇名号 10—545b
马丁(三世) Martin (III) 教皇名号 10—545c
马丁(图尔的),圣 Martin of Tours, Saint 法国主保圣人 10—546a
马丁·杜·加尔 Martin du Gard, Roger 法国小说家 10—548b
马丁二世 Martin II 阿拉贡国王 10—545e
马丁-哈维 Martin-Harvey, Sir John 英国演员、制片人 10—548c
马丁·加西亚岛 Martín García Island 阿根廷岛屿 10—548c
马丁家族 Martin family 法国漆器艺术家族 10—546a
马丁·路德·金日 Martin Luther King, Jr., Day 美国假日 10—548c
马丁-玛丽埃塔公司 Martin Marietta Corporation 美国公司 10—548d
马丁纳弗兰卡 Martina Franca 意大利城镇 10—548e
马丁内斯 Martinez 美国城市 10—548f
马丁内斯 Martínez, Pedro 多米尼加棒球运动员 10—549a
马丁内斯 Martínez, Rafael Arévalo 危地马拉作家 10—549a
马丁内斯·埃斯特拉达 Martínez Estrada, Ezequiel 阿根廷作家 10—549b
马丁内斯·德·拉·罗萨 Martínez de la Rosa (Berdejo Gómez y Arroyo), Francisco de Paula 西班牙戏剧家、诗人 10—549b
马丁内斯·坎波斯 Martínez Campos, Arsenio 西班牙将军、政治家 10—549a
马丁内斯·鲁伊斯 Martínez Ruiz, José 西班牙文学评论家 10—549c
马丁内斯·蒙塔涅斯 Martínez Montañés, Juan (de) 西班牙雕塑家 10—549c
马丁内斯·西埃拉 Martínez Sierra, Gregorio 西班牙诗人、剧作家 10—549d
马丁努齐 Martinuzzi, György 匈牙利政治家 10—551b
马丁努斯 Martinus Gosia 意大利法学家 10—551b
马丁漆 vernis Martin 装潢用品 17—522a
马丁-桑托斯 Martín-Santos, Luis 西班牙精神病专家 10—548d
马丁斯 Martins, Peter 丹麦舞蹈家、编导 10—550e
马丁斯堡 Martinsburg 美国城市 10—550f
马丁斯费里 Martins Ferry 美国城市 10—550e
马丁四世 Martin IV 教皇 10—545c
马丁松 Martinson, Harry (Edmund) 瑞典小说家、诗人 10—550f
马丁松 Martinson, Moa 瑞典小说家 10—550f
马丁五世 Martin V 教皇 10—545c
马丁一世 Martin I 西西里国王 10—545e
马丁一世,圣 Martin I, Saint 教皇 10—545b
马东氏蕨科 Matoniaceae 植物学 11—26c
马兜铃 birthwort 植物 2—494c
马兜铃目 Aristolochiales 植物学 1—474e
马都拉 Madura 印度尼西亚岛屿 10—374e
马都拉人 Madurese 印度尼西亚土著居民 10—375b
马都拉语 Madurese language 印度尼西亚语言 10—375b
马都拉足 Madura foot 疾病 10—374f

马杜赖 Madurai 印度城市 10—375a
马端临 Ma Duanlin 中国宋元之际史学家 10—321b
马顿 Mattoon 美国城市 11—32e
马顿 Marten, Henry 英格兰法官 10—543f
马顿斯 Martens, Fyodor Fyodorovich 俄国法学家、外交官 10—543f
马多(欧文·格威内德的) Madog ab Owain Gwynedd 威尔士传说人物 10—370d
马多克斯 Madox, Thomas 英国历史学家 10—371a
马多尼奥斯 Mardonius 波斯武将 10—501b
马多涅 Madonie, Le 意大利山脉 10—370e
马恩 Man 科特迪瓦城镇 10—443e
马恩 Marne 法国省份 10—527a
马恩 Marne, Prieur de la 法国政治家 10—527b
马恩岛 Man, Isle of 英国岛屿 10—444a
马恩岛猫 Manx 猫品种 10—478e
马恩河 Marne River 法国河流 10—527c
马恩河畔沙隆 Châlons-sur-Marne 法国城市 4—33c
马恩拉瓦莱 Marne-la-Vallée 法国城镇 10—527c
马尔 Marl 德国城市 10—522f
马尔 Mull 苏格兰岛屿 11—475b
马尔 Marr, Nikolay Yakovlevich 俄罗斯语言学家 10—530b
马尔 Meagher, Thomas Francis 爱尔兰革命领袖 11—62d
马尔堡 Malbork 波兰城市 10—426c
马尔堡 Marburg 德国城市 10—492b
马尔堡 Marburg (Slovenia) 斯洛文尼亚城镇 10—492c
马尔堡菲利普斯大学 Marburg, Philipps University of 德国大学 10—492d
马尔堡会谈 Marburg, Colloquy of 欧洲宗教历史 10—492c
马尔贝克 Marbeck, John 英国作曲家 10—490d
马尔伯爵 Mar, earls of 苏格兰贵族家族 10—486b
马尔伯爵(第二和第十九) Mar, John Erskine, 2nd (and 19th) Earl of 苏格兰政治家 10—486c
马尔伯爵(第六) Mar, John Erskine, 6th Earl of 苏格兰贵族 10—486c
马尔伯爵(第一和第十八) Mar, John Erskine, 1st (and 18th) Earl of 苏格兰贵族 10—486b
马尔伯勒 Marlborough 美国城市 10—523b
马尔伯勒 Marlborough 新西兰行政区 10—523b
马尔伯勒公爵 Marlborough, John Churchill, 1st Duke of, Marquess of Blandford, Earl of Marlborough, Baron Churchill of Sandridge, Lord Churchill of Eyemouth, Reichsfürst (Imperial Prince) 英国将军 10—523c
马尔伯勒公爵夫人 Marlborough, Sarah Jennings, Duchess of 英国贵族 10—524a
马尔博男爵 Marbot, Jean-Baptiste-Antoine-Marcelin, baron de 法国将军 10—492b
马尔达 Mālda 印度城镇 10—427b
马尔达尔斯瀑布 Mardalsfossen 挪威瀑布 10—500e
马尔代夫 Maldives 印度洋岛国 10—427c
马尔代特人 Mardaïte 叙利亚民族 10—500e
马尔丹 Mardān 巴基斯坦城镇 10—500f
马尔登 Muldoon, Robert 新西兰总理 11—474d
马尔登 Muldoon, William 美国摔跤运动员 11—474e
《马尔登战役》 Battle of Maldon, The 古英语诗 2—282f
马尔迪赫圆丘 Mardīkh, Tall (Syria) 叙利亚古城 10—501a
马尔蒂尼 Martini, Simone 意大利画家 10—549e
马尔丁 Mardin 土耳其城市 10—501a
马尔杜克 Marduk 美索不达米亚神灵 10—501c
马尔杜克-阿帕尔-伊迪纳二世 Marduk-apal-iddina II (king of Babylonia) 巴比伦王国国王 10—501c
马尔多纳多 Maldonado 乌拉圭城镇 10—428a
马尔多纳多港 Puerto Maldonado 秘鲁城市 14—16a
马尔方氏综合征 Marfan's syndrome 疾病 10—502f
马尔盖 Margai, Sir Milton (Augustus Striery) 塞拉利昂总理 10—503a
马尔冈 Margão (India) 印度城市 10—503b
马尔格雷夫伯爵(第三) Mulgrave, John Sheffield, 3rd Earl of 英国政治家、作家 11—474f
马尔古尼奥斯 Margunios, Maximus 希腊正教主教 10—506b
马尔吉兰 Margilan 乌兹别克斯坦城市 10—505d
马尔吉洛曼 Marghiloman, Alexandru 罗马尼亚政治家 10—505c
马尔卡 Marca 索马里城市 10—493a
马尔卡斯特 Mulcaster, Richard 英国教育家 11—474c
马尔凯 Marche 意大利区名 10—497c
马尔凯西(夫人) Marchesi de Castrone, Mathilde 德国歌唱家、教师 10—497e
马尔坎托尼奥 Marcantonio 意大利雕版工人 10—493d
马尔科(克拉列维奇) Marko Kraljević 塞尔维亚国王 10—521f
马尔科夫尼科夫 Markovnikov, Vladimir Vasilyevich 俄国有机化学家 10—522c
马尔科夫尼科夫规律 Markovnikov rule 有机化学 10—522d
马尔科姆 Malcolm 苏格兰国王称谓 10—426e
马尔科姆·艾克斯 Malcolm X 美国黑人领袖 10—426f
马尔科姆二世 Malcolm II 苏格兰国王 10—426e
马尔科姆三世 Malcolm III 苏格兰国王 10—426e
马尔科姆四世 Malcolm IV 苏格兰国王 10—426f
马尔科姆一世 Malcolm I 苏格兰国王 10—426e
马尔科维奇 Marković, Svetozar 塞尔维亚政论作家 10—522b
马尔可夫 Markov, Andrey Andreyevich 俄国数学家 10—521f
马尔可夫过程 Markov process 数学 10—522a
马尔克 Marc, Franz 德国画家 10—492f
马尔克斯 Márquez, Gabriel García 哥伦比亚作家 10—530a
马尔克斯 Marqués, René 波多黎各作家 10—529a
马尔肯 Marken 荷兰岛屿、城市 10—520d
马尔库斯 Malchus (Neoplatonist philosopher) 新柏拉图主义哲学家 10—426d
马尔兰特 Maerlant, Jacob van 荷兰诗人 10—376b
马尔雷迪 Mulready, William 英国画家 11—478c
马尔罗 Malraux, André(-Georges) 法国作家、政治家 10—436a
马尔罗尼 Mulroney, Brian 加拿大政治家 11—478c
马尔马拉海 Marmara, Sea of 土耳其内海 10—525d
马尔马人 Marma 孟加拉国民族 10—525c
马尔梅迪 Malmédy 比利时城市 10—434b
马尔蒙 Marmont, Auguste-Frédéric-Louis Viesse de, duc (duke) de Raguse 法国元帅 10—525e
马尔默 Malmö 瑞典城市 10—434c
马尔默胡斯 Malmöhus 原瑞典省份 10—434d
马尔佩斯国家保护区 El Malpais National Monument 美国自然地理区 6—10e
马尔皮基 Malpighi, Marcello 意大利生物学家、医生 10—435e
马尔皮吉氏体 malpighian body (anatomy) 解剖学 10—435f
马尔皮吉氏小管 malpighian tubule 昆虫解剖学 10—435f
马尔普格 Marpurg, Friedrich Wilhelm 德国作曲家 10—528f
马尔普拉凯战役 Malplaquet, Battle of 欧洲历史 10—436a
马尔普雷莱特论战 Marprelate Controversy 英格兰历史 10—528e
马尔齐亚 Marzia, Maria Anna (singer) 意大利歌唱家 10—567b
马尔奇 March, Ausias 西班牙诗人 10—496b
马尔切夫斯基 Malczewski, Antoni 波兰诗人 10—427a
马尔切罗 Marcello, Benedetto 意大利作曲家、作家 10—495a
马尔切纳岛 Marchena Island 东太平洋岛屿 10—497e
马尔·撒母耳 Mar Samuel (Jewish scholar) 犹太学者 10—486e
马尔萨拉 Marsala 意大利城镇 10—533e
马尔萨什洛克 Marsaxlokk 马耳他村庄 10—533f
马尔萨斯 Malthus, Thomas Robert 英国经济学家 10—438a
马尔塞布 Malesherbes, Chrétien Guillaume de Lamoignon de 法国律师 10—428f
马尔塞林努斯,圣 Marcellinus, Saint 教皇 10—495a

马尔塞鲁斯二世 Marcellus II 教皇 10—495b
马尔塞鲁斯一世,圣 Marcellus I,Saint 教皇 10—495b
马尔山脉 Mar,Serra do 巴西高原东部大悬崖 10—486d
马尔尚 Marchand,Jean-Baptiste 法国军人、探险家 10—497a
马尔尚 Marchand,Marie-Françoise (French actress) 法国演员 10—497a
马尔施纳 Marschner,Heinrich August 德国作曲家 10—534a
马尔什 Marche 法国省份 10—497c
马尔斯 Mars 古罗马神祇 10—532a
马尔斯曼 Marsman,Hendrik 荷兰诗人、评论家 10—542b
马尔梭 Marceau(-Desgraviers),François-Séverin 法国将军 10—493d
马尔索 Marceau,Marcel 法国哑剧演员 10—493d
马尔特-布戎 Malte-Brun,Conrad 法国作家 10—437f
马尔托夫 Martov,L. 俄国社会民主工党孟什维克首领 10—551d
马尔托斯 Martos 西班牙城市 10—551d
马尔瓦 Mālwa 印度省份 10—439f
马尔瓦高原 Mālwa Plateau 印度高原 10—440b
马尔瓦绘画 Mālwa painting 印度画派 10—440a
马尔瓦平原 Mālwa Plains 印度平原 10—440b
马尔韦尔动物园 Marwell Zoological Park 英格兰动物园 10—552f
马尔维 Malvy,Louis-Jean 法国政治家 10—439f
马尔西人 Marsi 意大利古代民族 10—541e
《马耳伐纳协定》 Malvana,Convention of 葡萄牙和斯里兰卡历史 10—439d
马耳他 Malta 地中海岛屿、国家 10—436f
马耳他狗 Maltese 狗品种 10—437f
马耳他花边 Maltese lace 编织工艺品 10—437f
马耳他骑士团 Knights of Malta 军事医疗团体 9—322a
马耳他热 Malta fever 疾病 10—437e
马耳他语 Maltese language 马其他岛语言 10—437f
马菲星系 I 和 II Maffei I and II 天文学 10—377d
马菲亚岛 Mafia Island 坦桑尼亚岛屿 10—377f
马费伊侯爵 Maffei,Francesco Scipione,marchese di 意大利戏剧家 10—377d
马夫拉 Mafra 葡萄牙城镇 10—378a
马夫罗科扎托斯 Mavrokordátos,Aléxandros 希腊政治家 11—42a
马弗京 Mafikeng 南非城镇 10—378a
马嘎尔尼 Macartney,George Macartney,Earl 英国使节 10—328c
马盖特 Margate 英格兰城镇 10—505a
马盖特鱼 margate 鱼类 10—505b
马甘格 Magangué 哥伦比亚城市 10—378d
马戈 Mago 迦太基将军 10—394e
马戈斯文化期工艺 Magosian industry 石器工艺 10—394f
马哥利奥斯 Margoliouth,David Samuel 英国学者 10—506a
马格达莱纳 Magdalena 哥伦比亚省份 10—379a
马格达莱纳 Magdalena 墨西哥区名 10—379a
马格达莱纳河 Magdalena River 哥伦比亚河流 10—379b
马格达伦群岛 Magdalen Islands 加拿大群岛 10—379a
马格德堡 Magdeburg 德国城市 10—379e
马格德林文化 Magdalenian culture 欧洲旧石器时代 10—379c
马格尔顿 Muggleton,Lodowick 英格兰基督教领袖 11—464f
马格尔莫斯文化期工艺 Maglemosian industry 北欧史前文化 10—382f
马格机枪 MAG machine gun 武器 10—378a
马格拉夫 Marggraf,Andreas Sigismund 德国化学家 10—505c
马格朗 Magelang 印度尼西亚城市 10—379f
马格里布 Maghreb 北非地区 10—381a
马格里布字体 maghrebi script 阿拉伯语字体 10—381b
马格里特 Magritte,René(-François-Ghislain) 比利时画家 10—395c
马格姆 Margam 威尔士地区 10—503a
马格纳斯效应 Magnus effect 物理学 10—394d
马格内蒂克岛 Magnetic Island 澳大利亚群岛 10—389a
马格内斯 Magnes,Judah Leon 美国犹太教领袖 10—385f
马格内西亚(迈安德河流域) Magnesia ad Maeandrum 古爱奥尼亚城市 10—386a
马格内西亚(锡皮卢斯山地区) Magnesia ad Sipylum 古吕底亚城市 10—386a
马格嫩提乌斯 Magnentius 西罗马僭位皇帝 10—385e
马格尼托哥尔斯克 Magnitogorsk 俄罗斯城市 10—392c
马格尼耶 Maghnia 阿尔及利亚城镇 10—381a
马格努斯 Magnus 统治者之名 10—393d
马格努斯 Magnus,Johannes 瑞典大主教 10—394c
马格努斯 Magnus,Olaus 瑞典历史学家、大主教 10—394c
马格努斯二世·埃里克松 Magnus II Eriksson 瑞典国王 10—394b
马格努斯二世·哈拉尔逊 Magnus II Haraldsson 挪威国王 10—393e
马格努斯六世 Magnus VI 挪威国王 10—394a
马格努斯·马克西穆斯 Magnus Maximus 罗马皇帝 10—394d
马格努斯七世·埃里克松 Magnus VII Eriksson 瑞典国王 10—394a
马格努斯三世 Magnus III 挪威国王 10—393e
马格努斯四世 Magnus IV 挪威国王 10—393f
马格努斯五世·埃林松 Magnus V Erlingsson 挪威国王 10—393f
马格努斯一世 Magnus I 瑞典国王 10—394b
马格努斯一世·奥拉夫松 Magnus I Olafsson 挪威国王 10—393d
马格努松 Magnússon,Árni 斯堪的纳维亚语言学家 10—394d
马格努松 Magnússon,Jón 冰岛作家 10—394e
马格诺利亚 Magnolia 美国城市 10—392e
马蛤 gaper clam 软体动物 7—6e
马更些岛 Mackenzie Island (Caroline Islands) 西太平洋岛屿 10—353d
马更些河 Mackenzie River 澳大利亚河流 10—353e
马更些河 Mackenzie River 加拿大河流 10—353e
马更些山脉 Mackenzie Mountains 加拿大山脉 10—353d
马古萨 Mağusa (Cyprus) 塞浦路斯港口 10—396a
《马关条约》 Shimonoseki,Treaty of 中日不平等条约 15—316d
马圭 Magwe 缅甸城镇 10—396a
马圭纤维 maguey 植物纤维 10—395f
马国贤 Ripa,Matheo 意大利传教士 14—310f
马哈 Mácha,Karel Hynek 捷克诗人 10—344c
马哈巴德 Mahābād 伊朗城市 10—396d
马哈蒂尔·宾·穆罕默德 Mahathir bin Mohamad 马来西亚总理 10—398f
马哈尔 Mahar 印度种姓 10—398c
马哈尔 Mahal,Taj 美国歌手 10—397c
马哈福兹 Mahfouz,Naguib 埃及作家 10—400f
马哈坎河 Mahakam River 印度尼西亚河流 10—397c
马哈拉尼港 Bandar Maharani (Malaysia) 马来西亚港市 2—192f
马哈拉佩 Mahalapye 博茨瓦纳村庄 10—397d
马哈拉施特拉 Mahārāshtra 印度邦名 10—398d
马哈茂德 Mahmud 统治者之名 10—402d
马哈茂德 Maḥmūd 伽色尼王国苏丹 10—402f
马哈茂德·阿卜杜勒巴基 Mahmud Abdülbâkî 土耳其诗人 10—403c
马哈茂德二世 Mahmud II 奥斯曼苏丹 10—403a
马哈茂德·穆扎法尔·沙阿 Mahmud Muzaffar Shah 廖内群岛、林加群岛苏丹 10—403c
马哈茂德·奈迪姆帕夏 Mahmud Nedim Paşa 奥斯曼帝国外交官 10—403c
马哈茂德·沙阿 Mahmud Shah 马六甲苏丹 10—402f
马哈茂德一世 Mahmud I 奥斯曼苏丹 10—402f
马哈奇卡拉 Makhachkala 俄罗斯城市 10—416e
马哈沙拉堪 Maha Sarakham 泰国城镇 10—396d
马哈瓦里制 maḥalwārī system 英属印度田赋制度 10—397e
马哈韦利河 Mahaweli Ganga 斯里兰卡河流 10—399d
马海毛 mohair 动物纤维 11—310e

马汉 Mahan, Alfred Thayer 美国海军军官、历史学家 10—397e
马汉 Mahan, Larry E. 美国牛仔 10—398a
马赫 Mach, Ernst 奥地利物理学家 10—344a
马赫布卜讷格尔 Mahbūbnagar 印度城镇 10—399e
马赫迪 mahdī 伊斯兰教末世学救世主 10—399f
马赫迪 Mahdī, al- 苏丹宗教领导人 10—400a
马赫迪派 Mahdist 马赫迪追随者 10—400b
马赫迪耶 Mahdīyah, al- 突尼斯城镇 10—400c
马赫里苏丹国 Mahra Sultanate 阿拉伯半岛历史国家 10—404a
马赫什瑜伽师 Mahesh Yogi, Maharishi 印度教名流 10—400e
马赫数 Mach number 物理学 10—344c
马赫原理 Mach's principle 宇宙学假说 10—349f
马亨德拉 Mahendra 尼泊尔国王 10—400e
马亨德拉瓦尔曼 Mahendravarman (king of Chenla) 真腊国王 10—400e
马洪 Mahone, William 美国将军、政治家 10—403e
马洪勋爵 Mahon, Charles Stanhope, Lord 英国政治家、科学家 10—403e
马洪子爵 Mahon, Philip Henry Stanhope, Viscount 英国政治家 10—403e
马呼吸道病 equine respiratory disease 马疾病 6—108d
马霍卡 Majorca 西班牙岛屿 10—414b
马基拉岛 Makira (Solomon Islands) 所罗门群岛岛屿 10—417a
马基努尔夫 Maginulfo (antipope) 敌对教皇 10—382e
马基群落 macchie (Mediterranean vegetation) 植物学 10—333a
马基斯群岛 Marquises, Îles (French Polynesia) 法属波利尼西亚火山岛 10—530b
马基特哈伯勒 Market Harborough 英格兰城镇 10—521a
马基乌斯 Marcius, Ancus (Roman king) 罗马国王 10—498b
马基雅弗利 Machiavelli, Niccolò 意大利作家、政治家 10—346c
马吉德 maggid 犹太教巡回传教士 10—380e
马吉亚纳 Maghiāna 巴基斯坦城市 10—381a
马季亚德王朝 Mazyadid DYNASTY 穆斯林阿拉伯人王朝 11—58c
马祭 aśvamedha 印度宗教典礼 2—10f
马加比 Maccabeus, Jonathan 犹太将军 10—331d
马加比 Maccabeus, Judas 犹太领导人 10—331d
马加比家族 Maccabees 犹太教祭司长家族 10—330f
马加比运动会 Maccabiah Games 体育 10—331e
《马加比传》 Maccabees, The Books of the 《圣经》文献 10—331b
马加丹 Magadan 俄罗斯州名 10—378b
马加丹 Magadan 俄罗斯港市 10—378b
马加迪湖 Magadi, Lake 肯尼亚湖泊 10—378c
马家窑遗址 Majiayao site 中国文化遗址 10—413d
马嘉人 Magar 亚洲民族 10—378e
马江 Ma River 越南河流 10—321d
马焦雷湖 Maggiore, Lake 意大利湖泊 10—380f
马焦雷镇 Borgo Maggiore 圣马力诺共和国城镇 3—51b
马金环礁 Makin Atoll (Kiribati) 基里巴斯岛屿 10—417a
马京达瑙人 Magindanao 菲律宾民族 10—382c
马卡布鲁 Marcabru 法国诗人、音乐家 10—493c
马卡迪卡迪 Makgadikgadi 博茨瓦纳盐碱滩 10—416e
马卡蒂 Makati 菲律宾城市 10—415f
马卡尔 makar 苏格兰诗派 10—415b
马卡-雷利 Marca-Relli, Conrad 美国画家 10—493a
马卡里奥斯三世 Makarios III 塞浦路斯主教、总统 10—415c
马卡里乌斯 Macarius 俄国都主教 10—327c
马卡里乌斯(埃及人) Macarius THE EGYPTIAN 埃及隐修士 10—327d
马卡里乌斯(布尔加科夫) Macarius BULGAKOV 俄国主教 10—327d
马卡里乌斯(马格尼西亚的) Macarius MAGNES 东正教主教、教义论辩家 10—327d
马卡连科 Makarenko, Anton Semyonovich 苏联教育家 10—415b
马卡鲁峰 Makālu 亚洲山峰 10—415a
马卡罗夫 Makarov, Stepan Osipovich 俄国海军司令 10—415d
马卡罗尼艺术 macaroni 人类早期艺术形式 10—327e
马卡罗娃 Makarova, Nataliya (Romanovna) 苏联芭蕾舞演员 10—415d
马卡姆 Markham, Beryl 英国飞行员、作家 10—521c
马卡姆 Markham, Edwin 美国诗人、演说家 10—521d
马卡纳卢阿 Makanalua (Hawaii, U.S.) 美国夏威夷州半岛 10—415a
马卡帕 Macapá 巴西城市 10—326f
马卡帕加尔 Macapagal, Diosdado 菲律宾总统 10—327a
马卡潘斯盖 Makapansgat 南非山谷 10—415a
马卡斯 Macas 厄瓜多尔城镇 10—328d
马卡泰阿岛 Makatea 法属波利尼西亚岛屿 10—415e
马-卡-泰-梅-谢-基亚-基亚克 Ma-ka-tai-me-she-kia-kiak (Sauk and Fox Indian leader) 美国印第安人领袖 10—321b
马凯巴 Makeba, Miriam 南非歌唱家 10—415f
马凯特 Marquette 美国城市 10—529f
马科库 Makokou 加蓬城镇 10—417c
马科曼尼人 Marcomanni 日耳曼部落 10—498c
马科姆 Macomb 美国城市 10—360e
马科鲨 mako shark 鱼类 10—417b
马科斯 Marcos, Ferdinand E. 菲律宾总统 10—499a
马科斯(尼萨的) Marcos DE NIZA 天主教方济各会修士 10—499d
马科维茨 Markowitz, Harry M. 美国财政学家 10—522d
马可(隐士) Mark, THE HERMIT 基督教神学论辩家 10—519f
马可,圣 Mark, SAINT 教皇 10—519f
马可(传福音的),圣 Mark (THE EVANGELIST), SAINT 基督教圣者 10—519e
马可·安东尼 Marc Anthony 罗马执政者 10—493a
马可·奥勒利乌斯 Marcus Aurelius 罗马皇帝 10—500a
马可·波罗 Polo, Marco 威尼斯商人、冒险家、旅行家 13—409a
马可·波罗桥 Marco Polo Bridge 中国桥梁 10—498b
《马可福音》 Mark, The Gospel According to 《圣经·新约》 10—520b
马可尼 Marconi, Guglielmo 意大利物理学家 10—498c
马可·尤利乌斯·亚基帕 Marcus Julius Agrippa 犹太国王 10—500c
马克 mark 德国货币单位 10—519d
马克 Macke, August 德国画家 10—351d
马克 Mark, Mary Ellen 美国摄影师 10—520a
马克·冯·莱贝里希 Mack von Leiberich, Karl, Freiherr 奥地利将军 10—350e
马克拉柯夫 Maklakov, Vasily Alekseyevich 俄国政治家 10—417a
马克劳林 Maclaurin, Colin 英格兰数学家 10—356e
马克里地毯 Makri rug 土耳其工艺品 10—417e
马克里努斯 Macrinus 古罗马皇帝 10—363a
马克利乌斯 Markelius, Sven (Gottfrid) 瑞典建筑师 10—520c
马克罗比乌斯 Macrobius, Ambrosius Theodosius 古罗马学者 10—363d
马克米 Makemie, Francis 北美洲殖民地宗教领袖 10—416a
马克姆河 Markham River 巴布亚新几内亚河流 10—521e
马克尼 Makeni 塞拉利昂城镇 10—416a
马克沁 Maxim, Hudson 美国发明家 11—43e
马克沁 Maxim, Hiram Percy 美国发明家、制造商 11—43d
马克沁 Maxim, Sir Hiram (Stevens) 美国发明家 11—43d
马克沁机枪 Maxim machine gun 武器 11—43f
马克萨斯群岛 Marquesas Islands 法属波利尼西亚岛屿 10—529b
马克森提 Maxentius, Marcus Aurelius Valerius 罗马皇帝 11—43b
马克森提巴西利卡 Maxentius, Basilica of 罗马古建筑 11—43b
马克思 Marx, Karl (Heinrich) 德国哲学家、经济学家 10—553a
马克思主义 Marxism 哲学 10—556c
马克斯 Max, Adolphe 比利时政治家 11—42e
马克斯 Marx, Roberto Burle 巴西建筑师 10—555f
马克斯 Marx, Wilhelm 德国政治家 10—555f
马克斯·普朗克科学促进会 Max Planck Society for the Advancement of

Science 德国科学研究机构 11—42f
马克斯韦尔 Maxwell,Elsa 美国作家、主持人 11—46f
马克斯韦尔 Maxwell,Gavin 苏格兰作家、博物学家 11—47a
马克斯兄弟 Marx BROTHERS 美国喜剧团体 10—556a
马克斯与斯潘塞公司 Marks & Spencer P.L.C. 英国公司 10—522e
马克图勒 Maqtūl,al- 波斯神秘主义者 10—486a
马克西克斯舞 maxixe 巴西舞蹈 11—46e
马克西玛下水道 Cloaca Maxima 古罗马下水道 4—296c
马克西米安 Maximian 罗马皇帝 11—43f
马克西米连 Maximilian 统治者之名 11—44a
马克西米连 Maximilian 神圣罗马帝国皇帝 11—45d
马克西米连 Maximilian 墨西哥皇帝 11—45d
马克西米连 Maximilian 德国首相 11—45f
马克西米连二世 Maximilian Ⅱ 巴伐利亚国王 11—44e
马克西米连二世 Maximilian Ⅱ 神圣罗马帝国皇帝 11—45c
马克西米连二世·埃马努埃尔 Maximilian Ⅱ Emanuel 巴伐利亚选侯 11—44b
马克西米连三世·约瑟夫 Maximilian Ⅲ Joseph 巴伐利亚选侯 11—44f
马克西米连一世 Maximilian Ⅰ 巴伐利亚公爵 11—44a
马克西米连一世 Maximilian Ⅰ 巴伐利亚选侯、国王 11—44c
马克西米连一世 Maximilian Ⅰ 奥地利大公、神圣罗马帝国皇帝 11—44f
马克西米努斯 Maximinus 罗马皇帝 11—45f
马克西米努斯 Maximinus,Galerius Valerius 罗马皇帝 11—46a
马克西米亚努斯 Maximianus,Gaius Galerius Valerius 罗马皇帝 11—44a
马克西穆斯 Maximus,Magnus 罗马皇帝 11—46d
马克西穆斯 Maximus,Petronius 西罗马皇帝 11—46d
马克西穆斯 Maximus,Valerius 罗马历史学家 11—46e
马克西穆斯(希腊人) Maximus THE GREEK 希腊正教修士 11—46c
马克西穆斯(以弗所的) Maximus OF EPHESUS 新柏拉图主义哲学家、巫师 11—46b
马克西穆斯(忏悔者),圣 Maximus THE CONFESSOR,SAINT 拜占廷基督教神学家 11—46b
马克耶夫卡 Makeyevka 乌克兰城市 10—416d
马肯森 Mackensen,August von 德国元帅 10—352b
马孔 Mâcon 法国城镇 10—360f
马孔德人 Makonde 非洲民族 10—417c
马库尔迪 Makurdi 尼日利亚城镇 10—418a
马库姆巴教 Macumba 非洲-巴西宗教 10—364a
马库人 Makú 南美印第安人 10—417f
马库斯 Marcus,(Harold) Stanley 美国商人 10—499f
马库斯 Marcus,Rudolph A. 美国化学家 10—499d
马库斯 Marcus,Siegfried 奥地利发明家 10—499e
马库斯岛 Marcus Island (Japan) 日本岛屿 10—500c
马库泽 Marcuse,Herbert 美国政治哲学家 10—500c
马夸语 Makua language 语言 10—417f
马奎拉多拉 maquiladora 外商组装工厂 10—486a
马奎斯 Marquis,Don 美国记者、诗人 10—530a
马奎特 Marquette,Jacques 法国天主教传教士、探险家 10—529f
马昆德 Marquand,J(ohn) P(hillips) 美国小说家 10—528f
马拉 Mala (Solomon Islands) 所罗门群岛岛屿 10—418a
马拉 Marat,Jean-Paul 法国政治家 10—488f
马拉巴尔海岸 Malabar Coast 印度西海岸南部 10—418a
马拉巴公教会 Malabarese Catholic Church 印度天主教会 10—418b
马拉巴派 Malabar Christians 印度基督教团体 10—418a
马拉博 Malabo 赤道几内亚城市 10—418c
马拉迪 Maradi 尼日尔城镇 10—487c
马拉蒂 Maratta,Carlo 意大利画家 10—490a
马拉蒂亚 Malatya 土耳其城市 10—422e
马拉多纳 Maradona,Diego Armando 阿根廷足球运动员 10—487c
马拉费尔特 Magherafelt 北爱尔兰城镇 10—381a
马拉盖 Marāgheh 伊朗城镇 10—487e
马拉加 Málaga 西班牙省份 10—419d
马拉加 Málaga 西班牙省会 10—419d
马拉加葡萄酒 Málaga 西班牙酒 10—419e
马拉喀什 Marrakech 摩洛哥城市 10—530c
马拉卡尔 Malakāl 苏丹城镇 10—419f
马拉开波 Maracaibo 委内瑞拉城市 10—487b
马拉开波湖 Maracaibo,Lake 加勒比海水湾 10—487b
马拉凯 Maracay 委内瑞拉城市 10—487c
马拉科夫 Malakoff 法国城镇 10—419f
马拉科夫公爵 Malakoff,Aimable-Jean-Jacques Pélissier,duc de (duke of) 法国元帅 10—419f
马拉克贝勒 Malakbel 西闪米特人崇拜之神 10—419f
马拉库拉 Malakula 瓦努阿图岛屿 10—420a
马拉拉斯 Malalas,John 拜占廷编年史学家 10—420a
马拉硫磷 Malathion 杀虫剂 10—422d
马拉梅 Mallarmé,François-René-Auguste 法国革命家 10—432d
马拉梅 Mallarmé,Stéphane 法国诗人 10—432d
马拉默德 Malamud,Bernard 美国小说家 10—420b
马拉穆列什 Maramureş 罗马尼亚县名 10—488a
马拉瑙人 Maranao 菲律宾民族 10—488b
马拉尼翁河 Marañón River 秘鲁河流 10—488d
马拉诺 Marrano 西班牙历史 10—530d
马拉帕尔泰 Malaparte,Curzio 意大利作家 10—421b
马拉奇,圣 Malachy,SAINT 爱尔兰大主教 10—419c
马拉若岛 Marajó Island 巴西冲积岛 10—488a
马拉山脉 Marrah,Mountains 苏丹山脉 10—530b
马拉斯皮纳家族 Malaspina FAMILY 意大利家族 10—422b
马拉松 marathon 体育项目 10—489d
马拉松石油公司 Marathon Oil Company 美国公司 10—489f
马拉松造山运动 Marathon orogeny 地质学 10—490a
马拉松战役 Marathon,Battle of 古希腊历史 10—489e
马拉塔联盟 Marāṭhā confederacy 印度历史 10—489c
马拉塔人 Marāṭhā 印度民族 10—489b
马拉塔语 Marāṭhī language 印度语言 10—489d
马拉塔战争 Marāṭhā Wars 英国与印度历史 10—489c
马拉泰斯塔 Malatesta,Enrico 意大利无政府主义者 10—422c
马拉泰斯塔 Malatesta,Sigismondo Pandolfo 意大利封建领主 10—422d
马拉泰斯塔家族 Malatesta FAMILY 意大利家族 10—422b
马拉特 Marlatt,Abby Lillian 美国教育家 10—522f
马拉维 Malaŵi 非洲国家 10—422e
马拉维 Marawi 菲律宾城市 10—490c
马拉维湖 Malaŵi, Lake (East Africa) 非洲湖泊 10—423e
马拉维联盟 Maravi Confederacy 非洲历史 10—490c
马拉维人 Maravi 非洲民族 10—490c
马拉雅拉姆语 Malayalam language 印度语言 10—424d
马拉战车 chariot 马车 4—64f
马腊尼昂 Maranhão 巴西州名 10—488c
马来半岛 Malay Peninsula 东南亚半岛 10—424c
马来獾 teledu 哺乳动物 16—522e
马来群岛 Malay Archipelago 东南亚岛群 10—424a
马来人 Malay 东南亚民族 10—423e
马来酸 maleic acid 化工 10—428d
马来太阳熊 Malayan sun bear 哺乳动物 10—424f
马来体诗 pantoum 诗歌 13—17a
马来西亚 Malaysia 东南亚国家 10—424f
马来亚白手长臂猿 Malayan lar 灵长目动物 10—424e
马来亚快船 prau 船 13—486b
马来亚人民抗日军 Malayan People's Anti-Japanese Army (MPAJA) 马来西亚历史 10—424e

马来亚危机 Malayan Emergency 马亚西亚历史 10—424d
马来野牛 seladang 哺乳动物 15—195b
《马来由史话》 Sejarah Melayu 马六甲苏丹国历史著作 15—194d
马来语 Malay language 东南亚语言 10—424a
马莱 Malet, Claude-François de 法国将军 10—429a
马莱伯 Malherbe, François de 法国诗人 10—429b
马莱博湖 Malebo Pool 非洲湖泊 10—428a
马莱尔布 Malherbe, Daniel François 南非作家 10—429b
马莱冈 Mālegaon 印度城镇 10—428c
马莱-斯蒂文 Mallet-Stevens, Robert 法国建筑师 10—433d
马莱塔 Malaita 所罗门群岛火山岛 10—419e
马莱特 Mullett, Alfred B(ult) 美国建筑师 11—477f
马莱西特人 Malecite 北美印第安人 10—428c
马莱-约里斯 Mallet-Joris, Françoise 比利时作家 10—433c
马兰 Malan, Daniel F(rançois) 南非政治家 10—420b
马兰 Malan, François Stephanus 南非政治家 10—420d
马兰巴 Maramba (town, Zambia) 赞比亚城镇 10—488a
马兰比吉河 Murrumbidgee River 澳大利亚河流 11—498f
马兰德拉斯 Marandellas (town, Zimbabwe) 津巴布韦城镇 10—488b
马兰卡公教会 Malankarese Catholic Church 印度东派天主教会 10—421a
马兰热 Malanje 安哥拉城镇 10—420f
马兰维尔 Maranville, Rabbit 美国棒球运动员 10—488e
马兰扎诺 Maranzano, Salvatore 美国匪徒 10—488e
马朗 Maran 犹太学者 10—488b
马朗根风格 malanggan style 南太平洋诸岛雕刻艺术 10—420e
马勒 Mahler, Alma 奥地利作曲家古斯塔夫之妻 10—401d
马勒 Mahler, Gustav 奥地利作曲家 10—401e
马勒 Muller, Hermann Joseph 美国遗传学家 11—475f
马勒 Malle, Louis 法国电影导演 10—433a
马勒伯朗士 Malebranche, Nicolas 法国神学家 10—428a
马勒诉俄勒冈州 Muller v. State of Oregon 美国法院案例 11—477d
马雷 Mary 土库曼斯坦州名 10—563a
马雷 Mary 土库曼斯坦城市 10—563a
马雷 Marey, Étienne-Jules 法国生理学家 10—502f
马雷 Marées, Hans von 德国画家 10—502a
马雷 Maret, Hugues-Bernard, DUC (duke) DE BASSANO 法国外交家 10—502e
马雷 Marais, Jean 法国演员 10—487e
马雷 Marais, Marin 法国作曲家 10—487f
马雷查尔 Marechal, Leopoldo 阿根廷作家 10—501e
马雷岛 Maré, Île 法属新喀里多尼亚岛屿 10—501e
马雷剧团 Marais Theatre 法国剧团 10—487f
马雷马 Maremma 意大利地理区域 10—502b
马雷纳牡蛎 marennes 牡蛎品种 10—502c
马雷特 Marett, Robert R(anulph) 英国社会人类学家 10—502e
马雷夏尔 Maréchal, Pierre-Sylvain 法国诗人、政论家 10—501f
马类 equine 马科哺乳动物 6—108c
马类锥虫病 dourine 动物疾病 5—403f
马累 Male 马尔代夫首都 10—428a
马黎诺里 Marignolli, Giovanni dei 意大利圣方济各会会士 10—511c
马礼逊 Morrison, Robert 基督教传教士、翻译家 11—406e
马里 Moray 苏格兰郡名 11—385c
马里 Mali 非洲国家 10—429e
马里 Mali 非洲历史帝国 10—429d
马里 Mali 几内亚城镇 10—429e
马里 Mari 叙利亚古城遗址 10—506c
马里 Mari El 俄罗斯的共和国 10—506d
马里埃特 Mariette, Auguste(-Ferdinand-François) 法国考古学家 10—511a
马里安纳 Mariana, Juan de 西班牙历史学家 10—508a
马里安纳斯·斯科图斯 Marianus Scotus 爱尔兰编年史学家 10—508d
马里奥 Mario, Giovanni Matteo 意大利歌唱家 10—516a
马里巴 Mareeba 澳大利亚城镇 10—502a
马里贝里陶瓷器 Marieberg pottery 瑞典陶瓷器 10—510d
马里波桑人 Mariposan (California Indians) 北美印第安人 10—517a
马里伯勒 Maryborough 澳大利亚昆士兰州城市 10—564a
马里伯勒 Maryborough 澳大利亚维多利亚州城市 10—564a
马里伯勒 Maryborough (Ireland) 爱尔兰城市 10—564a
马里博 Maribo 丹麦城市 10—509a
马里博尔 Maribor 斯洛文尼亚城镇 10—509a
马里卜 Ma'rib 也门城镇 10—508f
马里查河 Maritsa River 保加利亚河流 10—518c
马里查河战役 Maritsa River, Battle of the 巴尔干半岛历史 10—518d
马里茨 Maritz, Salomon Gerhardus 南非将军、反叛者 10—518d
马里恩 Marion 美国亚拉巴马州城市 10—516b
马里恩 Marion 美国印第安纳州城市 10—516b
马里恩 Marion 美国俄亥俄州城市 10—516c
马里恩 Marion, Francis 美国将领 10—516d
马里恩岛 Marion Island 南非岛屿 10—516d
马里克沙 Malik-Shāh 塞尔柱王朝苏丹 10—431b
马里兰 Maryland 美国州名 10—564a
马里雷教 Pai Marire (religio-military cult) 毛利人宗教 12—547d
马里利亚 Marília 巴西城市 10—512a
马里联邦 Mali Federation 非洲历史 10—430e
马里纳 Marina 墨西哥印第安人公主 10—512d
马里纳 Marina (island, Vanuatu) 瓦努阿图岛屿 10—512e
马里纳 Marriner, Neville 英国小提琴家、教师 10—531d
马里内蒂 Marinetti, Filippo Tommaso (Emilio) 法国散文家、戏剧家 10—514f
马里内特 Marinette 美国城市 10—514e
马里尼 Marigny, Enguerrand de 法国宫廷侍从 10—511d
马里尼 Marini, Marino 意大利艺术家 10—515a
马里尼德王朝 Marīnid DYNASTY 柏柏尔人王朝 10—515b
马里尼亚克 Marignac, Jean-Charles-Galinard de 瑞士化学家 10—511b
马里尼亚诺战役 Marignano, Battle of 欧洲历史 10—511b
马里努斯 Marinus 教皇称号 10—515f
马里努斯 Marinus, Rabbi (Hebrew grammarian) 希伯来语法学家 10—515f
马里努斯二世 Marinus II 教皇 10—515f
马里努斯一世 Marinus I 教皇 10—515f
马里诺 Marino 意大利城镇 10—515d
马里诺 Marino, Giambattista 意大利诗人 10—515d
马里诺 Marinot, Maurice 法国画家 10—515e
马里诺主义 Marinism 意大利文学 10—515c
马里人 Mari 欧洲民族 10—506c
马里沙尔 Marichal, Juan Antonio 多米尼加棒球运动员 10—509a
马里斯 Maris, Jacob 荷兰画家 10—517a
马里斯 Maris, Matthijs 荷兰画家 10—517b
马里斯 Maris, Roger 美国棒球运动员 10—517b
马里索 Marisol 美国雕刻家 10—517c
马里湾 Moray Firth 北海海湾 11—386a
马里沃 Marivaux, Pierre (Carlet de Chamblain de) 法国戏剧家、小说家 10—519a
马里乌波尔 Mariupol 乌克兰城市 10—518e
马里乌斯 Marius, Simon 德国天文学家 10—519a
马里乌斯·塞尔维乌斯·洪诺拉图斯 Marius Servius Honoratus (Latin grammarian) 古罗马语法家 10—519a
马里亚姆波列 Marijampolė 立陶宛城市 10—511e

马里亚纳 Mariana 巴西城市 10—508a
马里亚纳海沟 Mariana Trench 太平洋海沟 10—508c
马里亚纳群岛 Mariana Islands 西太平洋岛屿 10—508b
马里亚瑙 Marianao 古巴城市 10—508c
马里亚奇 mariachi 墨西哥乐队 10—507f
马里亚特 Marryat, Frederick 英国海军军官 10—531f
马里亚特吉 Mariátegui, José Carlos 秘鲁政治领袖 10—508e
马里一世 Marie I (adventurer) 法国冒险家 10—509b
马里语 Mari language 俄罗斯马里共和国语言 10—506e
马力 horsepower 功率单位 8—183c
马立克学派 Mālikīyah 伊斯兰教学派 10—431c
马立克(伊本·艾奈斯) Mālik ibn Anas 穆斯林教法学家 10—431b
马立克·札希尔·鲁克尼·艾丁·拜巴尔斯 Malik aẓ-Ẓāhir Rukn ad-Dīn Baybars al-Bunduqdārī, al- 马木留克王朝苏丹 10—431b
马利 Mallee 澳大利亚地区 10—433b
马利安 Mariamne 犹太教、基督教传说人物 10—507f
马利奥特 Marriott, J(ohn) Willard 美国商人 10—531e
马利布 Malibu 美国城市 10—430f
马利布兰 Malibran, Maria 西班牙歌唱家 10—430f
马利丹 Maritain, Jacques 法国天主教哲学家 10—517d
马利根 Mulligan, Gerry 美国作曲家 11—477f
马利根河 Mulligan River 澳大利亚河流 11—478a
马利筋绒 milkweed floss 种籽纤维 11—220c
马利筋叶甲 milkweed beetle (species *Chrysochus cobaltinus*) 昆虫 11—220b
马利克 Malik, Adam 印度尼西亚政治家 10—431a
马利克·纳西尔·萨拉哈丁·优素福一世 Malik an-Nāṣir Ṣalāḥ ad-Dīn Yūsuf I, al- (Muslim sultan) 阿尤布王朝苏丹 10—431a
马利肯 Mulliken, Robert Sanderson 美国化学家、物理学家 11—478a
马利内勒舞 marinera (Peruvian folk dance) 秘鲁舞蹈 10—514e
马利诺夫斯基 Malinovsky, Rodion Yakovlevich 苏联元帅 10—431d
马利皮埃罗 Malipiero, Gian Francesco 意大利作曲家 10—432a
马利亚 Mary 耶稣之母 10—561c
马利亚(修女) María de Jesús, Sister (Spanish mystic) 西班牙神秘主义者 10—507a
马利亚(抹大拉的),圣 Mary Magdalene, Saint 耶稣门徒 10—563a
马利亚会 Mary, Society of 法国天主教修会 10—563e
马利亚会会士 Marist Father 天主教马利亚会成员 10—517d
马利亚会修士 Marianist 法国天主教修士 10—508c
马利亚论 Mariology 天主教神学 10—516a
马利亚小兄弟会修士 Marist Brother 天主教小兄弟会成员 10—517d
马栗 horse chestnut 植物 8—180c
马连良 Ma Lianliang 中国京剧演员 10—321b
马列维奇 Malevich, Kazimir (Severinovich) 俄国画家 10—429b
马列亚 Mallea, Eduardo 阿根廷作家 10—433b
马林 Malines (Belgium) 比利时城市 10—431c
马林 Marín, Francisco de Paula 西班牙园艺学家 10—512c
马林 Marin, John 美国画家 10—512c
马林 Marín, Luis Muñoz (Puerto Rican statesman) 波多黎各政治家 10—512d
马林巴德 Marienbad (Czech Republic) 捷克城镇 10—510e
马林巴琴 marimba 乐器 10—512b
马林堡 Marienburg (Poland) 波兰城市 10—510e
马林杜克 Marinduque 菲律宾省份 10—512e
马林加 Maringá 巴西城市 10—515a
马林科夫 Malenkov, Georgy Maksimilianovich 苏联领导人 10—428d
马林科维奇 Marinković, Vojislav 南斯拉夫政治家 10—515c
马林克人 Malinke 西非民族 10—431c
马林-米德兰银行公司 Marine Midland Banks, Inc. 美国公司 10—513d
马林纳托斯 Marinatos, Spyridon (Nikolaou) 希腊考古学家 10—512e
马林诺夫斯基 Malinowski, Bronisław (Kasper) 英国人类学家 10—431d
马林塔尔 Mariental 纳米比亚城镇 10—510f
马铃薯 potato (*Solanum tuberosum*) 植物学 13—462c
马铃薯甲虫 potato beetle (*Lema trilineata*) 昆虫 13—462d
马铃薯叶甲 potato bug 昆虫 13—462e
马羚 roan antelope (*Hippotragus equinus*) 偶蹄牛科动物 14—324c
马六甲 Melaka 马来西亚城镇、港口 11—90c
马六甲海峡 Malacca, Strait of 亚洲海峡 10—418d
马六甲苏丹国 Malacca, sultanate of 马来半岛王朝 10—418f
马龙 Malone, Karl 美国篮球运动员 10—435a
马龙德拉 Marondera 津巴布韦城镇 10—527e
马龙派教会 Maronite Church 东仪天主教会 10—527f
马隆 Malone, Dumas 美国历史学家 10—434f
马隆 Malone, Edmond 英国学者 10—435a
马隆贝湖 Malombe, Lake 马拉维湖泊 10—434f
马卢尔河 Malheur River 美国河流 10—429d
马卢拉 Maʿlula 叙利亚村庄 10—438d
马鲁阿 Maroua 喀麦隆城镇 10—528e
马鲁古 Maluku (Indonesian islands) 印度尼西亚岛屿 10—438b
马鲁古 Maluku 印度尼西亚省份 10—438c
马鲁古海 Maluku, Laut (Pacific Ocean) 西太平洋海域 10—438d
马鲁基多尔 Maroochydore 澳大利亚城镇 10—528a
马鲁利奇 Marulić, Marko 克罗地亚道德哲学家 10—552a
马鲁奇尼人 Marrucini 欧洲古代民族 10—531f
马鲁斯塔利 Marusthali 印度沙丘地区 10—552b
马鲁特 Mārūt (Islāmic myth) 伊斯兰教神话 10—552c
马鲁特 Marut, Ret (U.S. author) 美国作家 10—552c
马陆 millipede 节肢动物 11—229d
马吕 Malus, Étienne-Louis 法国物理学家 10—438e
马略 Marius, Gaius 古罗马将军、执政官 10—518e
马略卡 Mallorca (island, Spain) 西班牙岛屿 10—433e
马略特 Mariotte, Edme 法国物理学家、植物生理学家 10—516e
马略特定律 Mariotte's law (physics) 物理学 10—516f
马伦戈战役 Marengo, Battle of 欧洲历史 10—502b
马伦齐奥 Marenzio, Luca 意大利作曲家 10—502c
马罗 Marot, Clément 法国诗人 10—528a
马罗 Marot, Daniel 荷兰建筑师 10—528b
马罗 Marot, Helen 美国作家 10—528c
马罗 Marot, Jean 法国建筑师、雕刻家 10—528d
马罗博杜斯 Maroboduus 马科曼尼人国王 10—527d
马罗多-拉米二氏综合征 Maroteaux-Lamy syndrome 疾病 10—528d
马罗尼河 Maroni River 南美河流 10—527e
马罗韦讷河 Marowijne River (South America) 南美河流 10—528e
马洛 Marlow 英格兰堂区、城镇 10—524c
马洛 Marlowe, Christopher 英国诗人、剧作家 10—524d
马洛 Marlowe, Julia 美国演员 10—525c
马洛岛 Malo 瓦努阿图岛屿 10—434e
马洛蒂山 Maloti Mountains 莱索托山脉 10—435d
马洛礼 Malory, Sir Thomas 英国作家 10—435b
马洛里 Mallory, George 英国探险家 10—433e
马洛里 Mallory, Molla 挪威网球运动员 10—433f
马洛洛斯 Malolos 菲律宾城镇 10—434f
马洛齐人 Malozi (people) 非洲民族 10—435e
马洛温 Mallowan, Sir Max (Edgar Lucien) 英国考古学家 10—434b
马马罗内克 Mamaroneck 美国村庄 10—440c
马迈松 Malmaison (France) 法国城市 10—434b
马麦丁人 Mamertini 意大利雇佣兵 10—440e
马毛 horsehair 动物学 8—182f

马梅利 Mameli, Goffredo 意大利诗人 10—440e
马梅卢科 mameluco 巴西印第安人与白人的混血后裔 10—440e
马梅提努斯 Mamertinus, Claudius 古罗马官员 10—440f
马梅亚 Mamaea, Julia 罗马贵族 10—440c
马蒙 Ma'mūn, al- 阿拔斯王朝国王 10—443d
马蒙泰尔 Marmontel, Jean-François 法国诗人、剧作家 10—525f
马鸣 Aśvaghoṣa 印度诗人 2—10f
马莫尔 Mármol, José (Pedro Crisólogo) 阿根廷诗人、小说家 10—525e
马莫雷河 Mamoré River 玻利维亚河流 10—443b
马默勒布勒姆 Māmallapuram (India) 印度城市 10—440c
马默里 Mammeri, Mouloud 阿尔及利亚作家 10—442e
马默斯洞穴国家公园 Mammoth Cave National Park 美国肯塔基州公园 10—443a
马姆斯伯里 Malmesbury 英格兰城镇 10—434c
马木 Mamou 几内亚城镇 10—443b
马木路克 Mamlūk 中世纪穆斯林王朝的奴隶军队 10—440f
马穆德 Mahmoud 赛马名 10—402d
马穆利安 Mamoulian, Rouben 美国导演 10—443b
马穆鲁克 Mameluke (Asian political class) 伊斯兰王朝历史 10—440e
马那 mana 宗教 10—445c
马那瓜 Managua 尼加拉瓜首都 10—445d
马那瓜湖 Managua, Lake 尼加拉瓜湖泊 10—445e
马纳 Mana 圭亚那城镇 10—445b
马纳 Mannai 伊朗古国名 10—467b
马纳蒂 Manatí 波多黎各城镇 10—447c
马纳尔岛 Mannar Island 斯里兰卡岛屿 10—467b
马纳尔湾 Mannar, Gulf of 印度洋海湾 10—467b
马纳卡拉 Manakara 马达加斯加城镇 10—445f
马纳考 Manukau 新西兰城市 10—477f
马纳拉 Manala 芬兰神话 10—446a
马纳普里湖 Manapouri, Lake 新西兰湖泊 10—446c
马纳萨斯 Manassas 美国城市 10—446e
马纳萨斯战役 Manassas, battles of (American Civil War) 美国历史 10—446f
马纳塞斯 Manasses, Constantine 拜占廷学者 10—447b
马纳斯卢Ⅰ峰 Manāslu I 尼泊尔山脉 10—446e
马纳斯野生动物保护地 Manās Wild Life Sanctuary 印度野生动物保护区 10—446e
马纳瓦图河 Manawatu River 新西兰河流 10—447e
马纳瓦图-旺阿努伊 Manawatu-Wanganui 新西兰区名 10—447e
马奈 Manet, Édouard 法国画家 10—456b
马南南·麦克里尔 Manannán mac Lir 爱尔兰神话 10—446c
马南扎里 Mananjary 马达加斯加城镇 10—446c
马脑炎 equine encephalitis 马疾病 6—108c
马瑙斯 Manaus 巴西城市 10—447c
马内奇洼地 Manych Depression (Russia) 俄罗斯洼地 10—479a
马尼卡人 Manyika 非洲民族 10—479a
马尼克斯 Marnix, Philips van, HEER (lord) VAN SINT ALDEGONDE 荷兰神学家 10—527d
马尼夸根河 Manicouagan River 加拿大河流 10—461a
马尼拉 Manila 菲律宾首都 10—461c
马尼拉大帆船 Manila galleon 西班牙船只 10—463b
马尼拉湾 Manila Bay 菲律宾海湾 10—462f
马尼拉湾战役 Manila Bay, Battle of 美西战争 10—463a
马尼利乌斯 Manilius, Marcus 古罗马诗人 10—463b
马尼尼 Manini 西班牙园艺学家 10—463c
马尼萨 Manisa 土耳其城市 10—463f
马尼萨莱斯 Manizales 哥伦比亚城市 10—464f
马尼塞斯陶器 Manises ware 西班牙陶器 10—463f
马尼斯蒂 Manistee 美国城市 10—464a
马尼图林群岛 Manitoulin Islands 北美休伦湖群岛 10—464e
马尼托巴 Manitoba 加拿大省份 10—464a
马尼托巴湖 Manitoba, Lake 加拿大湖泊 10—464e
马尼托沃克 Manitowoc 美国城市 10—464e
马尼亚拉湖 Manyara, Lake 坦桑尼亚湖泊 10—478f
马尼亚斯科 Magnasco, Alessandro 意大利画家 10—385e
马宁 Manin, Daniele 意大利政治领导人 10—463c
马宁卡人 Maninka (people) 西非民族 10—463c
马纽 Maniu, Iuliu 罗马尼亚首相 10—464f
马努阿群岛 Manua Islands 美属萨摩亚岛屿 10—476b
马努埃尔 Manuel, Niklaus 瑞士画家、军人 10—477b
马努蒂乌斯 Manutius, Aldus, THE ELDER 意大利印刷、出版商 10—478c
马努蒂乌斯 Manutius, Paulus 意大利印刷商 10—478d
马努蒂乌斯(小) Manutius, Aldus, THE YOUNGER 意大利出版商 10—478c
马努齐奥家族 Manuzio FAMILY 意大利印刷商家族 10—478e
马努萨 Manuza (African emperor) 非洲皇帝 10—478e
马努斯岛 Manus Island 巴布亚新几内亚岛屿 10—478b
马诺埃罗·朱迪欧 Manoello Giudeo 希伯来诗人 10—469e
马诺哈尔 Manohar 印度画家 10—469e
马诺河 Mano River 非洲河流 10—469e
马诺来特 Manolete 西班牙斗牛士 10—469f
马诺洛 Manolo (bullfighter) 西班牙斗牛士 10—469f
马皮米盆地 Mapimí Basin 墨西哥凹地 10—484c
马皮瓦·卢塔 Mahpiua Luta (Sioux Indian chief) 北美印第安人领袖 10—404a
马匹展览 horse show 马匹和马术展示 8—182f
马平 Ma-p'ing (China) 中国城市 10—321d
马普 Map, Walter 英国牛津大主教 10—484b
马普切人 Mapuche 南美印第安人 10—485d
马普托 Maputo 莫桑比克首都 10—485d
马普托河 Maputo River 莫桑比克河流 10—485e
马齐乌斯 Martius, Karl Friedrich Philipp von 德国植物学家 10—551c
马其顿 Macedonia 希腊古代王国 10—339d
马其顿 Macedonia 巴尔干半岛地区 10—339f
马其顿 Macedonia 希腊地区 10—340c
马其顿 Macedonia 巴尔干半岛国家 10—340e
马其顿 Macedonicus, Lucius Aemilius Paullus 罗马将军 10—341d
马其顿内部革命组织 Internal Macedonian Revolutionary Organization (IMRO) 马其顿秘密组织 8—410e
马其顿尼 Macedonius 君士坦丁堡主教 10—341d
马其顿尼主义 Macedonianism 基督教异端 10—341d
马其顿文学 Macedonian literature 文学 10—341a
马其顿语 Macedonian language 语言 10—341a
马其顿战争 Macedonian Wars 古罗马史 10—341c
马其诺 Maginot, André(-Louis-René) 法国政治家 10—382c
马其诺防线 Maginot Line 法国防线 10—382d
马奇 March, Fredric 美国演员 10—496c
马奇 March, Francis Andrew 美国语言学家 10—496b
马奇 Mudge, Thomas 英国制表师 11—462d
马奇伯爵 March, EARLS OF 苏格兰贵族家族 10—495e
马奇伯爵 March, EARLS OF 英格兰贵族家族 10—495f
马奇伯爵 March, Alexander Stewart, Earl of 苏格兰贵族 10—495f
马奇伯爵 March, Edward, Earl of 苏格兰贵族 10—496b
马奇伯爵(第二) March, Patrick Dunbar, 2nd Earl of 苏格兰贵族 10—495e
马奇伯爵(第二) March, Roger Mortimer, 2nd Earl of 苏格兰贵族 10—496a
马奇伯爵(第五) March, Edmund Mortimer, 5th Earl of 苏格兰贵族 10—496a
马奇伯爵(第一) March, Roger Mortimer, 1st Earl of 英格兰贵族 10—495f

马奇蒙特伯爵(第一) Marchmont, Patrick Hume, 1st earl of 苏格兰新教徒 10—497f
马奇温洛克 Much Wenlock 英格兰城镇 11—460e
马钱子属 Strychnos 植物学 16—284c
马切拉塔 Macerata 意大利城市 10—342a
马丘比丘 Machu Picchu 秘鲁印加人古城 10—349f
马球 polo 古老的马术运动 13—408b
马让迪 Magendie, François 法国生理学家 10—380d
马热基艾 Mazeikiai 立陶宛城镇 11—57a
马任加 Mahajanga 马达加斯加城镇 10—397b
马荣火山 Mayon Volcano 菲律宾活火山 11—54a
马若雷尔 Majorelle, Louis 法国家具设计师 10—414c
马撒葡萄园 Martha's Vineyard 美国岛屿 10—544b
马萨 Massa 意大利城市 11—6f
马萨卡 Masaka 乌干达城镇 10—568a
马萨卡利人 Maxakali 南美印第安人 11—43a
马萨里克 Masaryk, Jan (Garrigue) 捷克斯洛伐克政治家、外交家 10—569d
马萨里克 Masaryk, Tomáš (Garrigue) 捷克斯洛伐克主要缔造者、总统 10—569d
马萨利斯一家 Marsalis family 美国爵士乐家庭 10—533e
马萨利亚 Massalia (France) 法国城市 11—11b
马萨林 Mazarin, Jules, Cardinal 法兰西首相 11—56b
马萨尼埃洛 Masaniello 意大利平民起义领袖 10—569c
马萨乔 Masaccio 意大利画家 10—567b
马萨索伊特 Massasoit 万帕诺亚格印第安人酋长 11—11c
马萨特克人 Mazatec 墨西哥印第安人 11—56e
马萨特兰 Mazatlán 墨西哥港口 11—56e
马萨特南戈 Mazatenango 危地马拉城镇 11—56e
马萨亚 Masaya 尼加拉瓜城市 10—569f
马萨瓦 Massawa (Ethiopia) 埃塞俄比亚城市 11—11c
马萨诸塞 Massachusetts 美国州名 11—7a
马萨诸塞人 Massachuset 北美印第安人 11—7a
马萨诸塞湾 Massachusetts Bay 北大西洋小海湾 11—10e
马萨诸塞湾殖民地 Massachusetts Bay Colony 美国历史 11—10f
马塞 Marcel, Gabriel(-Honoré) 法国哲学家、剧作家 10—493f
马塞多 Macedo, José Agostinho de 葡萄牙诗人 10—339d
马塞里亚 Masseria, Joe 美国犯罪集团首脑 11—11f
马塞卢 Maseru 莱索托首都 10—570b
马塞卢斯 Marcellus, Marcus Claudius 罗马名将 10—495c
马塞卢斯 Marcellus, Marcus Claudius 罗马贵族党首领 10—495c
马塞卢斯 Marcellus, Marcus Claudius 罗马贵族 10—495c
马塞卢斯剧院 Marcellus, Theatre of 意大利剧院 10—495d
马塞纳 Massena 美国城镇 11—11c
马塞纳 Masséna, André, DUC (duke) DE RIVOLI, PRINCE D'ESSLING 法国将领 11—11d
马塞约 Maceió 巴西城市 10—341e
马赛 Marseille 法国城市 10—534d
马赛 Marcel, Étienne 法国中产阶级领袖 10—493d
马赛安博塞利禁猎区 Masai Amboseli Game Reserve (Kenya) 肯尼亚公园 10—568a
马赛彩陶 Marseille faience 法国锡釉陶器 10—537a
马赛克 mosaic 艺术 11—411f
马赛克镶砌 mosaic pavement 艺术 11—412e
马赛克韵 mosaic rhyme 诗歌 11—412e
《马赛曲》 Marseillaise, La 法国国歌 10—534b
马赛人 Masai 东非游牧民族 10—567f
马三保 Ma San-pao 中国明代航海家 10—321d
马瑟 Mather, Cotton 美国宗教领导人 11—22e
马瑟 Mather, Increase 美国公理会牧师、教育家 11—22f
马瑟 Mather, Richard 基督教公理宗牧师 11—23c
马瑟尔布鲁克 Muswellbrook 澳大利亚城镇 11—516a
马瑟尔谢尔河 Musselshell River 美国河流 11—512f
马瑟洛德地区 Mother Lode Country 美国地区 11—431c
马瑟韦尔 Motherwell, Robert 美国画家 11—431d
马瑟韦尔-威肖 Motherwell and Whishaw 苏格兰城市 11—431f
马森塔 Macenta 几内亚城镇 10—342a
马沙姆(男爵夫人) Masham, Abigail, BARONESS MASHAM OF OTES 英格兰女王宠臣 10—570b
马山 Masan 韩国城市 10—569b
马尚加纳-聪加 Matshangana-Tsonga (South Africa) 南非非独立黑人区 11—27e
马尚加纳兰德 Machanganaland (South Africa) 南非非独立黑人区 10—345c
马尚男爵(第一) Masham (of Swinton), Samuel Cunliffe Lister, 1st Baron 英国发明家 10—570c
马绍 Matthau, Walter 美国演员 11—30c
马绍尔群岛 Marshall Islands 太平洋中部国家 10—541a
马绍纳兰 Mashonaland 津巴布韦地区 10—570d
马师曾 Ma Shizeng 中国粤剧演员 10—321e
马什 Marsh, Sir Edward Howard 英国文学家、收藏家 10—537e
马什 Marsh, George Perkins 美国外交家、学者 10—537e
马什 Marsh, Ngaio 新西兰作家 10—537f
马什 Marsh, Othniel Charles 美国古生物学家 10—538a
马什 Marsh, Reginald 美国画家 10—538a
马什腊法赫 Mashrafah, Al- (Syria) 叙利亚古城 10—570d
马什里克 Mashriq 亚非地区 10—570d
马术 horsemanship 体育项目 8—183b
马思聪 Ma Sicong 中国音乐家 10—321e
马斯 Maes, Nicolaes 荷兰画家 10—376b
马斯巴特 Masbate 菲律宾岛屿、城镇 10—569a
马斯伯乐 Maspero, Gaston(-Camille-Charles) 法国埃及学家 11—4b
马斯德瓦尔兰属 Masdevallia 植物学 10—569d
马斯登 Marsden, William 英国历史学家 10—534a
马斯顿 Marston, John 英国戏剧家 10—542b
马斯顿荒原之战 Marston Moor, Battle of 英国历史 10—542c
马斯尔肖尔斯 Muscle Shoals 美国河流 11—501d
马斯格雷夫 Musgrave, Samuel 英国古典学者、医师 11—503e
马斯格雷夫 Musgrave, Story 美国航天员、医生 11—503f
马斯格雷夫 Musgrave, Thea 英国作曲家 11—504a
马斯格雷夫岭 Musgrave Ranges 澳大利亚丘陵 11—504b
马斯河 Maas River (Europe) 欧洲河流 10—323f
马斯基根 Muskegon 美国城市 11—511a
马斯基林 Maskelyne, Nevil 英国天文学家 11—1f
马斯基林 Maskelyne, John Nevil 英国魔术师 11—1e
马斯吉德苏莱曼 Masjed Soleymān 伊朗城镇 11—1a
马斯金格姆河 Muskingum River 美国河流 11—511c
马斯喀特 Muscat 阿曼城镇 11—500d
马斯卡林海底高原 Mascarene Plateau (Indian Ocean) 印度洋海底高原 10—569c
马斯卡尼 Mascagni, Pietro 意大利作曲家 10—569a
马斯卡廷 Muscatine 美国城市 11—500e
马斯科吉 Muskogee 美国城市 11—511c
马斯科卡湖群 Muskoka Lakes 加拿大湖泊 11—511d
马斯克林群岛 Mascarene Islands 印度洋岛屿 10—569b
马斯拉图尔战役与格拉沃洛特战役 Mars-la-Tour and Gravelotte, Battles of 普法战争史 10—533a
马斯洛 Maslow, Abraham H(arold) 美国心理学家、哲学家 11—2a
马斯内 Massenet, Jules(-Émile-Frédéric) 法国作曲家 11—11e
马斯特顿 Masterton 新西兰城市 11—15a
马斯特里赫特 Maastricht 荷兰城市 10—324a
马斯特里赫特阶 Maestrichtian Stage 地质学 10—376f
马斯特罗亚尼 Mastroianni, Marcello 意大利电影演员 11—16a
马斯特森 Masterson, Bat 美国赌徒、记者 11—14f
马斯特斯 Masters, Edgar Lee 美国诗人、小说家 11—14c

马斯特斯和约翰逊 Masters, William H(owell); and Johnson, Virginia E(shelman) 美国性学研究专家 11—14e
马斯文戈 Masvingo 津巴布韦城镇 11—16f
马松 Masson, André 法国画家 11—13d
马松 Masson, Frédéric 法国历史学家 11—13e
马苏里 Mussoorie 印度城市 11—513f
马苏里亚恩湖区 Masurian Lakeland 波兰湖区 11—16e
马所拉本 Masoretic text 犹太教《圣经》希伯来文本 11—4b
马索·狄·班科 Maso di Banco 佛罗伦萨画家 11—2b
马索利诺 Masolino 意大利画家 11—2c
马塔 Matta, Joaquim Dias Cordeiro da (Angolan writer) 安哥拉作家 11—29d
马塔贝莱兰 Matabeleland 津巴布韦传统地区 11—17a
马塔贝勒人 Matabele (people) 非洲民族 11—16f
马塔迪 Matadi 刚果(金)城市 11—17b
马塔加尔帕 Matagalpa 尼加拉瓜城市 11—17d
马塔科人 Mataco 南美印第安人 11—17b
马塔兰 Mataram 印度尼西亚历史王国 11—18b
马塔兰 Mataram 印度尼西亚城市 11—18b
马塔罗 Mataró 西班牙城镇 11—18c
马塔莫罗斯 Matamoros 墨西哥普埃布拉州城市 11—17e
马塔莫罗斯 Matamoros 墨西哥塔毛利帕斯州城市 11—17e
马塔讷 Matane 加拿大城市 11—17f
马塔帕 Matapa 南部非洲帝国 11—18a
马塔佩迪亚河谷 Matapédia Valley 加拿大河谷 11—18a
马塔伊 Maathai, Wangari 肯尼亚环保活动家 10—324c
马太 Matthay, Tobias 英国钢琴家、教师 11—30d
马太(巴萨拉布) Matthew Basarab 瓦拉几亚大公 11—31a
马太(传教者),圣 Matthew (the Evangelist), Saint 基督教使徒 11—30f
《马太福音》 Matthew, Gospel According to 《圣经·新约》 11—31a
马泰 Matthes, François-Emile 美国地质学家、地形学家 11—30e
马泰奥 Matteo di Pasti 意大利雕刻家 11—29f
马泰奥蒂 Matteotti, Giacomo 意大利社会党领袖 11—29f
马泰尔 Martel, Édouard-Alfred 法国地理学家、洞穴学专家 10—543d
马泰拉 Matera 意大利城市 11—19a
马泰乌奇 Matteucci, Pellegrino 意大利探险家 11—30c
马坦巴 Matamba 非洲姆本杜人王国 11—17e
马坦萨斯 Matanzas 古巴省份 11—17f
马坦萨斯 Matanzas 古巴城市 11—17f
马坦泽斯堡国家保护区 Fort Matanzas National Monument 美国史迹保护区 6—414d
马唐 crabgrass 植物 4—563d
马陶拉河 Mataura River 新西兰河流 11—18c
马特 Matter, Herbert 美国广告设计家、摄影家 11—30b
马特峰 Matterhorn 欧洲山峰 11—30b
马特拉 Maṭraḥ 阿曼城镇 11—26e
马特莱 Matale 斯里兰卡城镇 11—17d
马特劳山脉 Mátra Mountains 匈牙利山脉 11—26e
马特勒 Matara 斯里兰卡城镇 11—18b
马特鲁 Maṭrūḥ 埃及省份 11—27d
马特鲁 Marsā Maṭrūḥ 埃及城市 10—533e
马特洛克 Matlock 英格兰城镇 11—25e
马特诺音波琴 ondes martenot 乐器 12—417d
马特森 Mattheson, Johann 德国作曲家、学者 11—30e
马特森 Matson, Randy 美国铅球运动员 11—27e
马特瓦拉 Matehuala 墨西哥城市 11—19a
马特维耶夫 Matveyev, Artamon Sergeyevich 俄国外交家、政治家 11—33b
马特乌斯 Matthäus, Lothar 德国足球运动员 11—30d
马特希基扎 Matshikiza, Todd 南非新闻工作者、音乐家 11—27e
马滕斯 Martens, Georg Friedrich von 德国法学家 10—544a
马提尼 Martini, Arturo 意大利雕刻家 10—549d
马提尼克 Martinique 法国海外省 10—550a
马提雅尔 Martial 古罗马铭辞诗人 10—544d
马提亚 Matthias 统治者之名 11—31f
马提亚,圣 Matthias, Saint 基督教使徒 11—32c
马提亚一世 Matthias I 匈牙利国王 11—32b
马蹄蝠 horseshoe bat 动物 8—183e
马蹄金属 Dichondra 植物学 5—294d
马蹄螺 top shell 动物 17—155f
马蹄铁 horseshoe 金属材料 8—183e
马蹄虾 horseshoe shrimp 甲壳动物 8—184d
马头星云 Horsehead Nebula 天文学 8—183a
马图-盖里 Madhu-keri (India) 印度县名 10—368a
马图拉 Mathura 印度城镇 11—24d
马图拉钻石 Matura diamond 宝石 11—32e
马图里迪 Māturīdī, Abū Manṣūr Muḥammad al- 穆斯林神学家 11—32e
马图里迪学派 Māturīdīyah 伊斯兰教派别 11—32f
马图林 Maturín 委内瑞拉城市 11—32f
马图林 Maturin, Charles Robert 爱尔兰剧作家、小说家 11—32f
马图特 Matute, Ana María 西班牙作家 11—33a
马托波山 Matopo Hills 津巴布韦丘陵 11—26c
马托格罗索 Mato Grosso 巴西州名 11—25e
马托格罗索高原 Mato Grosso Plateau 巴西高原 11—26b
马托斯 Matos, Luis Palés 波多黎各诗人 11—26d
马托斯·格拉 Matos Guerra, Gregório de 巴西诗人 11—26d
马托西纽什 Matosinhos 葡萄牙城镇 11—26d
马托亚卡 Matoaka (Powhatan Indian princess) 印第安部落首领之女 11—26b
马瓦尔迪 Māwardī, al- 穆斯林法学家 11—42c
马瓦霍夫斯基 Małachowski, Stanisław 波兰政治家 10—419b
马王堆 Ma-wang-tui 中国西汉墓葬 10—322a
马王堆汉墓 Mawangdui Hanmu 中国西汉墓葬 11—42b
马威德尔 Marwedel, Emma Jacobina Christiana 美国教育家 10—552e
马韦尔 Marvell, Andrew 英国诗人 10—552c
马尾藻海 Sargasso Sea 北大西洋中海域 15—65d
马尾藻属 Sargassum 藻类植物 15—65e
马瘟 perdesiekte 马疾病 13—161a
马瘟 equine plague 马疾病 6—108d
马文 Marvin, Lee 美国电影演员 10—552d
马翁 Mahón 西班牙城市 10—403d
马翁 Maun 博茨瓦纳村庄 11—34f
马翁港 Puerto de Mahón (Spain) 西班牙城市 14—15f
马乌宾 Ma-ubin 缅甸城镇 10—322a
马乌陡崖 Mau Escarpment 肯尼亚陡崖 11—33c
马乌莱 Maule 智利区名 11—34e
马武拉 Mavura 非洲皇帝 11—42a
马西 Massey, Raymond (Hart) 美国演员、导演 11—12b
马西 Marcy, William L(earned) 美国政治家 10—500d
马西埃·恩圭马·比约戈 Macías Nguema Biyogo (Equatorial Guinea) 赤道几内亚岛屿 10—350b
马西安 Marcian 东罗马皇帝 10—497f
马西昂派 Marcionite 基督教派别 10—498a
马西拉 Maṣīrah 阿曼岛屿 11—1a
马西利安西斯 Massiliensis, Johannes 基督教修士 11—12e
马西利乌斯(帕多瓦的) Marsilius of Padua 意大利政治哲学家 10—542a
马西隆 Massillon 美国城市 11—12e
马西姆风格 Massim style 雕刻艺术 11—12f
马西纳 Macina 马里地区 10—350b
马西娜 Masina, Giulietta 意大利电影演员 10—570f
马西尼萨 Masinissa 努米底亚王国统治者 11—1a

马西山 Marcy, Mount 美国山名 10—500d
马西斯 Massys, Quentin 佛兰德斯画家 11—13e
马西亚 Macià, Francesc 西班牙政治家 10—350a
马西亚克亲王 Marcillac, François, prince de (writer) 法国作家 10—498a
马西亚诺 Marciano, Rocky 美国拳击运动员 10—497f
马西亚斯画匠 Marsyas Painter 古希腊画匠 10—543c
马西亚斯·约楚姆松 Matthías Jochumsson (Icelandic writer) 冰岛作家 11—32c
马希尔 Māhir, Aḥmad 埃及法学家、首相 10—401c
马希尔帕夏 Māhir Pasha, Ālī 埃及总理 10—401c
马希坎人 Mahican 北美印第安人 10—401a
马戏 circus 娱乐 4—245a
马夏画派 Ma-Xia school 中国宋代画派 10—322a
马先蒿 lousewort 植物 10—247c
马肖 Machaut, Guillaume de 法国诗人、音乐家 10—345c
马歇 Marchais, Georges(-René-Louis) 法国政治家 10—496f
马歇尔 Marshall 美国城市 10—539a
马歇尔 Marshall, Alfred 英国经济学家 10—539b
马歇尔 Marshall, Clara 美国医生 10—539b
马歇尔 Marshall, David Saul 新加坡政治家、律师 10—539c
马歇尔 Marshall, George Catlett 美国陆军上将、国务卿 10—539d
马歇尔 Marshall, John 美国最高法院大法官 10—539e
马歇尔 Marshall, Sir John Hubert 英国考古学家 10—540b
马歇尔 Marshall, Sir John Ross 新西兰总理 10—540c
马歇尔 Marshall, Louis 美国律师 10—540c
马歇尔 Marshall, Penny 美国喜剧演员 10—540d
马歇尔 Marshall, Stephen 基督教长老会牧师 10—540d
马歇尔 Marshall, Thurgood 美国最高法院大法官 10—540e
马歇尔 Marshall, Thomas R(iley) 美国副总统 10—540e
马歇尔·菲尔德公司 Marshall Field & Co. 美国百货商店 10—541a
马歇尔计划 Marshall Plan 欧洲历史 10—541d
马歇尔调处 Marshall Mission 中国历史 10—541c
马谢尔 Machel, Samora 莫桑比克总统 10—345e
马辛 Massine, Léonide 苏联舞蹈演员 11—13a
马辛杰 Massinger, Philip 英国剧作家 11—13c
马修 Mathew, Theobald 爱尔兰天主教司铎 11—23d
马修 Matthew, William Diller 美国古生物学家 11—31b
马修岛 Matthew Island 新喀里多尼亚岛屿 11—31c
马修森 Mathewson, Christy 美国棒球运动员 11—24a
马修斯 Mathews, Charles 英国演员 11—23e
马修斯 Mathews, Charles James 英国作家、演员 11—23f
马修斯 Matthews, (James) Brander 美国散文作家、戏剧评论家 11—31d
马修斯 Matthews, Mother Bernardina 美国宗教领袖 11—31c
马修斯 Mathews, Shailer 美国宗教领袖 11—24a
马修斯 Matthews, Stanley 美国最高法院大法官 11—31e
马修斯 Matthews, Sir Stanley 英国足球运动员 11—31f
马修斯·达格拉卡 Mateus da Graça, José Vieira 安哥拉作家 11—21c
马雅可夫斯基 Mayakovsky, Vladimir Vladimirovich 俄国诗人 11—50a
马雅历 Mayan calendar 中美洲古历法 11—50d
马雅潘 Mayapán 马雅古城址 11—50f
马雅人 Maya 中美洲印第安人 11—49c
马雅山 Maya Mountains 伯利兹山脉 11—49f
马雅象形文字 Mayan hieroglyphic writing 中美洲文字 11—50e
马雅诸语言 Maya languages 中美洲语言 11—49e
马亚尔 Maillart, Robert 瑞士工程师 10—405f
马亚圭斯 Mayagüez 波多黎各城市 11—49f
马亚诺 Maiano, Benedetto da 意大利雕塑家 10—404b
马耶布瓦侯爵 Maillebois, Nicolas Desmarets, Marquis de 法国部长 10—406a
马耶讷 Mayenne 法国省份 11—51c
马耶讷公爵 Mayenne, Charles de Lorraine, duc de 法国神圣联盟领袖 11—51d
马耶讷河 Mayenne River 法国河流 11—51e
马伊达内克 Majdanek 德国纳粹集中营 10—413c
马伊丹佩克 Majdanpek 塞尔维亚城镇 10—413d
马伊恩东贝湖 Mai-Ndombe, Lake 刚果(金)湖泊 10—404b
马伊科国家公园 Maiko National Park 刚果(金)公园 10—405b
马伊纳 Maina 希腊半岛 10—407c
马伊-内勒 Mailly-Nesle, Marie-Anne de 英格兰画家 10—406c
马伊斯群岛 Maíz, Islas del (Nicaragua) 尼加拉瓜岛屿 10—413a
马伊塔尼 Maitani, Lorenzo 意大利建筑师、雕刻家 10—412c
马寅初 Ma Yinchu 中国经济学家 10—322b
马英九 Ma Yingjiu 中国国民党主席 10—322d
马缨丹属 Lantana 植物学 9—488f
马永 Mahillon, Victor-Charles 比利时音乐学者 10—401b
马永巴 Mayumba 加蓬城镇 11—55d
马尤岛 Maio Island 佛得角岛屿 10—411e
马友友 Ma, Yo-Yo 华裔美籍大提琴家 10—321a
马援 Ma Yuan 中国汉代将领 10—322d
马远 Ma Yuan 中国宋代画家 10—322e
马约尔 Maillol, Aristide 法国雕塑家 10—406a
马约翰 Ma Yuehan 中国体育教育家 10—323a
马约里安 Majorian 西罗马皇帝 10—414d
马约利卡陶器 majolica 意大利锡釉陶器 10—413e
马约人 Mayo 墨西哥印第安人 11—52f
马约特 Mayotte 印度洋岛屿 11—54d
马赞达兰 Māzandarān 伊朗历史地区 11—55e
马泽尔 Maazel, Lorin 美国指挥家、小提琴家 10—324d
马泽利格 Matzeliger, Jan Ernst 荷兰发明家 11—33b
马泽帕 Mazepa, Ivan Stepanovich 俄罗斯领导人 11—57b
马泽伊 Mazzei, Philip 意大利医师、商人 11—58d
马扎尔人 Magyar (people) 欧洲民族 10—396b
马扎甘 Mazagan (Morocco) 摩洛哥省份 11—55e
马扎拉-德尔瓦洛 Mazara del Vallo 意大利城镇 11—56b
马扎里沙里夫 Mazār-e Sharīf 阿富汗城镇 11—56a
马扎鲁尼河 Mazaruni River 圭亚那河流 11—56d
马真塔 Magenta 意大利城镇 10—380e
马志尼 Mazzini, Giuseppe 意大利革命家 11—58d
马致远 Ma Zhiyuan 中国元代杂剧作家、散曲家 10—323b
马朱罗 Majuro 马绍尔群岛环礁 10—414e
马朱哲 Mājūj (Islāmic myth) 伊斯兰神话 10—414e
马自达汽车公司 Mazda Motor Corporation 日本汽车制造商 11—56f
马祖 Mazu 中国唐代禅师 11—58a
马祖尔 Masur, Kurt 德国指挥家 11—16e
马祖卡舞 mazurka 波兰民间舞 11—58b
马祖列岛 Mazu Islands 中国岛屿 11—58a
马醉木属 Pieris 植物学 13—295d
马佐夫舍 Mazowieckie 波兰省份 11—57e
马佐夫舍地区托马舒夫 Tomaszów Mazowiecki 波兰城市 17—143c
马佐哈峡 Macocha Gorge 捷克旅游胜地 10—360e
马佐维亚 Mazovia 波兰低地 11—57c
马佐维亚低地 Mazovian Lowland 波兰谷地 11—57c
马佐维耶茨基 Mazowiecki, Tadeusz 波兰新闻工作者 11—57d
吗啡 morphine 止痛药 11—402d
吗哪 manna 《圣经》 10—467a
玛瑞脂 mastic 树脂 11—15a
玛柏 Mab 英国民间传说仙后 10—324e
玛查 Macha 凯尔特宗教的战争女神 10—344c
玛蒂尔达(卡诺萨的) Matilda of Canossa 托斯卡纳伯爵 11—25a

玛窦(巴齐奥的) Matteo (Serafini) da Bascio 意大利修道士 11—29e
玛窦(巴齐奥的) Bascio, Matteo da 嘉布遣会创建人 2—256a
玛尔巴 Mar-pa 中国佛教密法修行师 10—486e
玛尔格特王后 Margot, Queen 纳瓦拉王后 10—506b
玛尔科娃 Markova, Dame Alicia 英国舞蹈家 10—522b
玛法木错 Mafa Mucuo (China) 中国湖泊 10—377c
玛格丽塔 Margherita (Somalia) 索马里城镇 10—505c
玛格丽塔岛 Margarita Island 委内瑞拉岛屿 10—505a
玛格丽塔山 Margherita Peak 东非山峰 10—505c
玛格丽特 Margaret 统治者之名 10—503b
玛格丽特 Margaret 苏格兰女王 10—503d
玛格丽特(安茹的) Margaret of Anjou 英格兰王后 10—503f
玛格丽特(昂古莱姆的) Margaret of Angoulême 法国王后 10—503e
玛格丽特(奥地利的) Margaret of Austria 哈布斯堡王朝统治者 10—504a
玛格丽特(大嘴) Margaret Maultasch 苏格兰女伯爵 10—503e
玛格丽特(蒂罗尔的) Margaret of Tirol 蒂罗尔女伯爵 10—504e
玛格丽特(都铎) Margaret Tudor 苏格兰王后 10—504e
玛格丽特(法国的) Margaret of France 纳瓦拉国王 10—504b
玛格丽特(纳瓦拉的) Margaret of Navarre 法国王后 10—504c
玛格丽特(帕尔马的) Margaret of Parma 哈布斯堡王朝女摄政 10—504c
玛格丽特(普罗旺斯的) Margaret of Provence 法国王后 10—504d
玛格丽特(瓦卢瓦的) Margaret of Valois 纳瓦拉王后 10—504e
玛格丽特(安提阿的),圣 Margaret of Antioch, Saint 基督教女殉教士 10—504a
玛格丽特(苏格兰的),圣 Margaret of Scotland, Saint 苏格兰王后 10—504d
玛格丽特二世 Margrethe II 丹麦女王 10—506b
玛格丽特峰 Marguerite, Pic (East Africa) 东非山峰 10—506b
玛格丽特一世 Margaret I 丹麦、挪威、瑞典摄政 10—503b
玛各 Magog 宗教神话 10—394f
《玛赫佐尔》 mahzor 犹太教祈祷书 10—404b
玛卡梅 maqāmah 阿拉伯文学 10—485f
玛凯达 Makeda 阿拉伯半岛赛伯伊王国统治者 10—416a
玛拉 Mara, Gertrud Elisabeth 德国歌唱家 10—486f
《玛拉基书》 Malachi, The Book of 《圣经·旧约》 10—418f
玛琅 Malang 印度尼西亚城市 10—420e
玛丽 Mary 统治者之名 10—562a
玛丽 Mary 勃艮第女公爵 10—562a
玛丽 Mary 苏格兰女王 10—562d
玛丽 Marie, Pierre 法国神经病学家 10—509e
玛丽(奥兰治的) Mary of Orange 荷兰摄政者 10—563d
玛丽(勃艮第的) Mary of Burgundy 勃艮第女公爵 10—563b
玛丽(道成肉身的) Mary of the Incarnation 法国奥秘神学家 10—563d
玛丽(都铎) Mary Tudor 英格兰公主 10—563e
玛丽(法兰西的) Marie de France 法国诗人 10—509b
玛丽(吉斯的) Mary of Guise 苏格兰摄政者 10—563b
玛丽(洛林的) Mary of Lorraine 苏格兰摄政者 10—563b
玛丽(摩德纳的) Mary of Modena 英格兰王后 10—563c
玛丽(苏格兰女王) Mary Queen of Scots 苏格兰女王 10—563e
玛丽(泰克的) Mary of Teck 英国王后 10—563d
玛丽埃塔 Marietta 美国佐治亚州城市 10—510f
玛丽埃塔 Marietta 美国俄亥俄州城市 10—511a
玛丽-安托瓦内特 Marie-Antoinette 法国王后 10—509f
玛丽昂 Marion, Frances 美国电影编剧 10—516c
玛丽·奥古斯塔·戴维 Davey, Marie Augusta 美国演员 5—167f
玛丽伯德地 Marie Byrd Land 南极洲地区 10—510a
玛丽·德·美第奇 Marie de Médicis 法国王后 10—509c
玛丽二世 Mary II 英格兰女王 10—562c
玛丽港 Mariehamn 芬兰城市 10—510e
玛丽·格雷戈里玻璃 Mary Gregory glass 美国玻璃制品 10—563e
玛丽-加朗特岛 Marie-Galante 加勒比海岛屿 10—510b
玛丽-凯瑟琳 Mary Kathleen 澳大利亚地区 10—564a
玛丽·莱什琴斯卡 Marie(-Catherine) Leszczyńska 法国王后 10—509d
玛丽勒本板球俱乐部 Marylebone Cricket Club 英国体育机构 10—566f
玛丽-路易丝 Marie-Louise 法国皇后 10—510b
玛丽斯维尔 Marysville 美国城市 10—567a
玛丽-泰蕾莎(奥地利的) Marie-Thérèse of Austria 法国王后 10—510c
玛丽维尔 Maryville 美国密苏里州城市 10—567a
玛丽维尔 Maryville 美国田纳西州城市 10—567a
玛丽亚采尔 Mariazell 奥地利城镇 10—508f
玛丽亚岛 Maria Island 澳大利亚岛屿 10—507b
玛丽亚二世 Maria II 葡萄牙女王 10—506f
玛丽亚·卡罗莱娜 Maria Carolina 意大利女王 10—507a
玛丽亚·克里斯蒂娜(博尔翁的) María Cristina de Borbón 西班牙王后 10—507a
玛丽亚·克里斯蒂娜(哈布斯堡-洛雷纳的) María Cristina de Habsburgo-Lorena 西班牙王后 10—507b
玛丽亚斯河 Marias River 美国河流 10—508e
玛丽亚斯群岛 Marías Islands 墨西哥群岛 10—508d
玛丽亚·斯泰拉 Maria Stella 意大利政治冒险家 10—507c
玛丽亚·特蕾西亚 Maria Theresa 奥地利女大公、匈牙利和波西米亚女王 10—507d
玛丽亚·特立尼达·桑切斯 María Trinidad Sánchez 多米尼亚共和国省份 10—507f
玛丽亚温泉镇 Mariánské Lázně 捷克城镇 10—508d
玛丽亚一世 Maria I 葡萄牙女王 10—506f
玛丽亚镇 Villa María 阿根廷城市 17—562e
玛丽一世 Mary I 英格兰女王 10—562a
玛丽一世至二世 Mary I-II 葡萄牙女王 10—562d
玛拿西·本·以色列 Manasseh ben Israel 阿姆斯特丹人希伯来学者 10—447a
《玛拿西祷言》 Manasseh, Prayer of 外典 10—447a
玛拿西支派 Manasseh 犹太人祖先 10—446f
《玛纳斯》 Manas 中国柯尔克孜族史诗 10—446c
玛瑙 agate 矿物 1—117b
玛瑙化石地层国家保护区 Agate Fossil Beds National Monument 美国国家保护区 1—117d
玛瑙纹饰陶器 agateware 18世纪陶器 1—117d
玛尼亚 Marnia (Algeria) 阿尔及利亚城镇 10—527d
玛尼亚尼 Magnani, Anna 意大利演员 10—385c
玛旁雍错 Mapam Lake 中国淡水湖 10—484c
玛普 Mapu, Abraham 立陶宛作家 10—485c
玛莎和范德拉斯演唱组 Martha and the Vandellas 美国灵乐流行组合 10—544a
玛师列克·阿尔德赫尔 mashriq al-adhkār 巴哈教派教堂 10—570e
玛士撒拉 Methuselah 《圣经》人物 11—159b
玛斯 Maass, Clara 古巴裔美国护士 10—324a
玛他提亚 Mattathias 犹太祭司 11—29d
玛塔·哈里 Mata Hari 荷兰舞女、名妓 11—16f
玛希斯 Mathis, June 美国编剧 11—24c
玛息阿 Marsyas 希腊传说人物 10—543b
玛亚特 Maʿat 埃及女神 10—324b
玛泽瓦 matzeva 犹太教 11—33c
玛兹达 Mazdā (Zoroastrian god) 琐罗亚斯德教神祇 11—56f
玛兹达教 Mazdakism 二元宗教 11—57a
码 gauge 计量单位 7—32b
埋藏物 treasure trove 法律 17—204d
买办 comprador 中国历史 4—400c
买麻藤科 Gnetaceae 植物学 7—167e

买麻藤目 Gnetales 植物学 7—167f
买卖圣物神职 simony 基督教 15—384b
买卖特权 option (stock) 股票交易 12—438c
买主独家垄断 monopsony 经济学 11—346f
迈 May, Karl (Friedrich) 德国作家 11—48d
迈阿迪 Maʿādī, al- 埃及古遗址 10—323c
迈阿密 Miami 美国佛罗里达州城市 11—174f
迈阿密 Miami 美国俄克拉何马州城市 11—175a
迈阿密海洋馆 Miami Seaquarium 美国海洋馆 11—175d
迈阿密河 Miami River 美国河流 11—175d
迈阿密人 Miami 北美印第安人 11—174e
迈阿密滩 Miami Beach 美国城市 11—175b
《迈阿密先驱报》 Miami Herald, The 美国报纸 11—175c
迈埃尔·黑尔姆布雷希特 Meier Helmbrecht 叙事诗 11—85c
迈安德河 Maeander River (Turkey) 土耳其河流 10—375d
迈巴赫 Maybach, Wilhelm 德国工程师、实业家 11—51a
迈布里奇 Muybridge, Eadweard 英国摄影家 11—519d
迈杜古里 Maiduguri 尼日利亚城市 10—404d
迈杜人 Maidu 加利福尼亚印第安人 10—404d
迈恩布里 Mainpurī 印度城镇 10—411b
迈恩黑德 Minehead 英格兰堂区 11—246b
迈恩霍夫 Meinhof, Carl 德国学者 11—86d
迈尔 Mayr, Ernst 美国生物学家 11—55a
迈尔 Mayr, (Johannes) Simon 意大利作曲家 11—55b
迈尔 Meyer, Kuno 德国语言学者、编辑 11—170f
迈尔 Meyer, Viktor 德国化学家 11—171c
迈尔 Mayer, Werner (composer) 德国作曲家 11—52a
迈尔(罗腾堡的) Meir of Rothenburg 德意志犹太教拉比、学者 11—87c
迈尔海峡 Maelstrøm 挪威海峡 10—376a
迈尔霍夫 Meyerhof, Otto 德国生物化学家 11—171e
迈尔季 Marj, Al- 利比亚城镇 10—519c
迈尔季欧云 Marj ʿUyūn 黎巴嫩城镇 10—519d
迈尔库里 Mercouri, Melina 希腊演员、政治活动家 11—126b
迈尔-吕布克 Meyer-Lübke, Wilhelm 欧洲语言学家 11—171d
迈尔奈普塔 Merneptah 埃及国王 11—133c
迈尔斯 Myers, F(rederic) W(illiam) H(enry) 英国诗人、评论家 11—524b
迈尔斯堡 Fort Myers 美国城市 6—414e
迈尔斯城 Miles City 美国城市 11—214a
迈尔斯诉美国案 Myers v. United States 美国法院案例 11—524b
迈尔万二世 Marwān II 伍麦叶王朝哈里发 10—552e
迈尔万一世·伊本·哈凯姆 Marwān I ibn al-Hakam 伍麦叶王朝哈里发 10—552d
迈尔尤特 Maryūṭ (Egypt) 埃及城市 10—567a
迈尔祖格 Marzūq 利比亚绿洲 10—567b
迈格迪西 Maqdisī, al- 阿拉伯旅行家 10—486a
迈格拉岭 Maikala Range 印度山脉 10—405b
迈加比佐斯 Megabyzus 古代波斯武将 11—80b
迈加洛波利斯 Megalopolis 希腊居民区 11—80e
迈杰尔达河 Majardah, Wadi 突尼斯河流 10—413c
迈科普 Maykop 俄罗斯城市 11—52d
迈克蒂亚 Maiquetía 委内瑞拉城市 10—411e
迈克尔 Michael 统治者之名 11—178c
迈克尔八世·帕里奥洛加斯 Michael VIII Palaeologus 拜占廷皇帝 11—179c
迈克尔二世 Michael II 拜占廷皇帝 11—178c
迈克尔九世·帕里奥洛加斯 Michael IX Palaeologus 拜占廷皇帝 11—179e
迈克尔六世·斯特拉提奥提卡斯 Michael VI Stratioticus 拜占廷皇帝 11—179a
迈克尔七世·杜卡斯 Michael VII Ducas 拜占廷皇帝 11—179b
迈克尔三世 Michael III 拜占廷皇帝 11—178e
迈克尔森 Mikkelsen, Ejnar 丹麦探险家、作家 11—209d
迈克尔四世 Michael IV 拜占廷皇帝 11—178f
迈克尔五世·卡拉法提斯 Michael V Calaphates 拜占廷皇帝 11—178f
迈克尔·辛诺特 Sinnott, Michael 美国导演 15—396c
迈克尔一世·兰伽柏 Michael I Rhangabe 拜占廷皇帝 11—178c
迈克耳孙 Michelson, A(lbert) A(braham) 美国物理学家 11—186c
迈克耳孙-莫雷实验 Michelson-Morley experiment 物理学 11—186e
迈克·芬克 Mike Fink (folklore hero) 民间故事英雄 11—208f
迈克里地毯 Mekri carpet 工艺品 11—90b
迈兰拉 Merenre 埃及国王 11—128f
迈勒吉尔盐湖 Melrhir, Chott 阿尔及利亚湖泊 11—100c
迈雷 Mairet, Jean 法国戏剧家 10—411e
迈立开江 Mali River 缅甸河流 10—430f
迈利战役 Mylae, Battle of 罗马历史 11—524e
迈罗尼斯 Maironis 立陶宛诗人 10—411f
迈门辛 Mymensingh 孟加拉国城市 11—524f
迈蒙 Maimon, Salomon 犹太哲学家 10—406d
迈蒙尼德 Maimonides, Moses 犹太哲学家、法学家、医生 10—406e
迈蒙·伊本·凯斯·艾厄沙 Maymūn ibn Qays al-Aʿshā 阿拉伯诗人 11—52e
迈纳萨拉 Maïnassara, Ibrahim Baré 尼日尔总统 10—407c
迈内克 Meinecke, Friedrich 德国历史学家 11—86d
迈尼普斯 Menippus 希腊哲学家 11—115c
迈尼特湖 Mainit, Lake 菲律宾湖泊 10—411a
迈宁根 Meiningen 德国城市 11—86e
迈宁根剧团 Meiningen Company 德国戏剧团体 11—86e
迈农 Meinong, Alexius 奥地利哲学家、心理学家 11—86f
迈诺 Minor, Virginia Louisa 美国妇女选举权活动家 11—264b
迈诺诉哈珀塞特 Minor v. Happersett 美国最高法院案例 11—264d
迈诺特 Minot 美国城市 11—265e
迈诺特 Minot, George Richards 美国医师 11—265f
迈普战役 Maipú, Battle of 南美洲历史 10—411e
迈森 Meissen 德国城市 11—88a
迈森 Meissen, Heinrich von 德国歌唱家 11—88a
迈森瓷器 Meissen porcelain 英国瓷器 11—88b
迈斯纳 Meissner, Alexander 奥地利工程师 11—88c
迈斯纳氏小体 Meissner corpuscle 生理学 11—88d
迈斯纳效应 Meissner effect 物理学 11—88d
迈斯特尔 Maistre, Casimir-Léon 法国探险家 10—412a
迈斯特尔 Maistre, Joseph de 法国伦理学家 10—412b
迈索尔 Mysore 印度城市 11—528f
迈索尔战争 Mysore Wars 英国历史 11—529a
迈索尔之虎 Tiger of Mysore 印度迈索尔的苏丹 17—90e
迈索隆吉翁 Mesolóngion 希腊城市 11—140b
迈塔克萨斯 Metaxas, Ioannis 希腊将军、政治家 11—154a
迈塔特龙 Metatron 犹太教神话 11—154a
迈泰奥拉 Metéora 希腊隐修院 11—155f
迈特纳 Meitner, Lise 奥地利物理学家 11—89c
迈沃岛 Maéwo 瓦努阿图岛屿 10—377c
迈西角 Maisí, Cape 古巴海角 10—412a
迈锡尼 Mycenae 史前希腊城市 11—522d
迈锡尼希腊语 Mycenaean language 语言 11—523b
迈耶 Meyer, Adolf 美国精神病学家 11—170c
迈耶 Meyer, Annie Florance Nathan 美国作家 11—170d
迈耶 Meyer, Conrad Ferdinand 瑞士作家 11—170e
迈耶 Meyer, Eugene 美国报纸发行人 11—170e
迈耶 Mayer, Johann Tobias 德国天文学家 11—51e
迈耶 Meyer, Lucy Jane Rider 美国社会工作者、教育家 11—171a
迈耶 Meyer, Ray 美国篮球教练 11—171c
迈耶 Meier, Richard (Alan) 美国建筑师 11—85c

《迈耶百科词典》 Meyers Enzyklopädisches Lexikon 德国百科全书 11—172a
迈耶尔 Meyer,(Julius) Lothar 德国化学家 11—170f
迈耶霍尔德 Meyerhold, Vsevolod Yemilyevich 俄国戏剧演出人 11—171f
迈耶林 Mayerling 奥地利村庄 11—52a
迈耶松 Meyerson, Émile 法国化学家、科学哲学家 11—172b
迈伊斯蒂 Megiste (Greece) 希腊岛屿 11—81f
迈因 Maʿīn 也门古代王国 10—407a
迈因纳 Miner, Jack 加拿大博物学家、作家 11—246b
迈因纳 Miner, Myrtilla 美国教育家 11—246c
麦阿里 Maʿarrī, al- 阿拉伯诗人 10—323f
麦比乌斯 Möbius, August Ferdinand 德国数学家、理论天文学家 11—300e
麦比乌斯带 Möbius strip 数学 11—300f
麦草 wheatgrass 草本植物 18—220b
麦长蝽 chinch bug (species *Blissus leucopterus*) 昆虫 4—167a
麦德林 Medellín 哥伦比亚城市 11—70f
麦德维杰夫 Medvedev, Roy (Aleksandrovich) 苏联历史学家 11—79c
麦德维杰夫 Medvedev, Zhores Aleksandrovich 苏联生物学家 11—79d
麦迪逊 Madison 美国印第安纳州城市 10—369d
麦迪逊 Madison 美国新泽西州城镇 10—369d
麦迪逊 Madison 美国南达科他州城镇 10—369d
麦迪逊 Madison 美国威斯康星州城市 10—369e
麦迪逊 Madison, James 美国总统 10—369f
麦迪逊广场公园 Madison Square Garden 美国纽约室内运动场 10—370b
麦迪逊河 Madison River 美国河流 10—370b
麦迪亚 Médéa 阿尔及利亚城镇 11—70f
麦地那 Medina 英格兰区名 11—76f
麦地那 Medina 沙特阿拉伯城市 11—76f
麦地那河 Medina, River 英格兰河流 11—78a
麦地那龙线虫 Dracunculus medinensis 无脊椎动物 5—409b
麦地那龙线虫 Medina worm 无脊椎动物 11—78b
《麦地那宪章》 Medina, Constitution of 伊斯兰历史文献 11—78a
麦独孤 McDougall, William 美国心理学家 10—338f
麦蛾 gelechiid moth 昆虫 7—47e
麦尔基派 Melchite 基督教派别 11—95e
麦戈文 McGovern, George S(tanley) 美国参议员 10—343c
麦格劳 McGraw, John (Joseph) 美国棒球运动员、球队经理 10—343c
麦格劳蒂 McGroarty, Sister Julia 美国宗教领袖 10—343d
麦格雷戈 MacGregor, Robert 苏格兰亡命徒 10—343d
麦格赛赛 Magsaysay, Ramon 菲律宾总统 10—395e
麦圭尔 McGuire, Al 美国篮球教练 10—343f
麦华绘画 Mewār painting 印度画派 11—164e
麦鸡 lapwing 鸟类 9—497c
麦积山石窟 Maijishan caves 中国佛教石窟 10—405a
麦基弗 MacIver, David Randall- (archaeologist) 美国考古学家、人类学家 10—350c
麦基弗 MacIver, Robert Morrison 美国社会学家 10—350c
麦基诺城 Mackinaw City 美国城市 10—354e
麦基诺岛 Mackinac Island 美国岛屿 10—354d
麦基诺桥 Mackinac Bridge 美国桥梁 10—354d
麦基诺水道 Mackinac, Straits of 美国密歇根水道 10—354c
麦基诺鳟 Mackinaw trout 鱼类 10—354e
麦基斯波特 McKeesport 美国城市 10—351d
麦基塔尔会修士 Mechitarist 天主教会成员 11—69a
麦基洗德 Melchizedek 《旧约》人物 11—95f
麦基洗德祭司 Melchizedek priesthood 摩门教 11—96a
麦吉 McGhee, Brownie 美国音乐家 10—342d
麦吉 McGee, Thomas D'Arcy 加拿大作家 10—342c
麦吉 McGee, William John 美国地质学家、考古学家 10—342d
麦吉尔 McGill, James 加拿大政治家 10—342e
麦吉尔 McGill, Ralph (Emerson) 美国记者 10—342e
麦吉尔大学 McGill University 加拿大大学 10—342f
麦吉利夫雷 McGillivray, Alexander 北美印第安人领袖 10—343a
麦吉利卡迪 McGillicuddy, Cornelius Alexander (baseball manager) 美国棒球队经理 10—342f
麦吉利卡迪山 Macgillycuddy's Reeks 爱尔兰山脉 10—343b
麦加 Mecca 沙特阿拉伯城市 11—66b
麦加菲 McGuffey, William Holmes 美国教育家 10—343e
麦加克勒斯 Megacles 雅典滨海派首领 11—80b
麦加拉 Megara 希腊历史居民区 11—81b
麦加拉哲学学派 Megarian school 哲学 11—81b
麦加斯梯尼 Megasthenes 古希腊历史学家、外交家 11—81c
麦角病 ergot 植物病害 6—115a
麦角酰二乙胺 LSD 药物 10—258d
麦角甾醇 ergosterol 化合物 6—115a
麦金 McKim, Charles Follen 美国建筑师 10—354b
麦金 McKim, Ruby 美国图案设计师 10—354c
麦金德 Mackinder, Sir Halford John 英国政治地理学家 10—354f
麦金利 McKinley, Ida 美国总统 W.麦金利之妻 10—355a
麦金利 McKinley, John 美国最高法院大法官 10—355b
麦金利 McGinley, Phyllis 美国诗人 10—343b
麦金利 McKinley, William 美国总统 10—355c
麦金利山 McKinley, Mount 美国山脉 10—355b
麦金利山国家公园 Mount McKinley National Park (Alaska, U.S.) 美国公园 11—441c
麦金尼斯 MacInnes, Helen Clark 美国小说家 10—358c
麦金尼斯 McGinnes, James Anthony (circus impresario) 美国杂技团经理 10—343c
麦金尼斯 MacInnes, Tom 加拿大作家 10—350b
麦金农 MacKinnon, Catharine A. 美国女权主义者 10—355d
麦金农 Mackinnon, Roderick 美国医生 10—355e
麦金太尔 McIntire, Samuel 美国建筑师、手工艺师 10—350c
麦金托什 Macintosh, Charles 苏格兰化学家 10—350b
麦金托什 Mackintosh, Charles Rennie 苏格兰建筑师 10—355f
麦金托什 Mackintosh, Elizabeth 苏格兰作家 10—356a
麦金托什雨衣 mackintosh 防水外套 10—355f
麦酒店密谋案 Rye House Plot 英国历史 14—475f
麦卡德尔案 McCardle, Ex Parte 美国法律案例 10—331f
麦卡德尔氏病 McArdle's disease 疾病 10—327c
麦卡蒂 McCarty, Maclyn 美国生物学家 10—332f
麦卡杜 McAdoo, William G(ibbs) 美国政治家 10—326c
麦卡尔平 MacAlpin, Kenneth 苏格兰国王 10—326f
麦卡拉 McCalla, Val 英国出版商 10—331e
麦卡莱 McCarey, (Thomas) Leo 美国电影导演 10—332a
麦卡莱斯特 McAlester 美国城市 10—326e
麦卡勒斯 McCullers, Carson 美国小说家 10—335d
麦卡利斯 McAleese, Mary 爱尔兰总统 10—326d
麦卡利斯特 McAllister, (Samuel) Ward 美国律师 10—326f
麦卡伦 McAllen 美国城市 10—326e
麦卡洛克 McCulloch, Hugh 美国金融家 10—335e
麦卡洛克 McCulloch, Sir James 澳大利亚政治家 10—335e
麦卡洛克 McCulloch, John R(amsay) 英国经济学家 10—335f
麦卡洛克诉马里兰州案 McCulloch v. Maryland 美国法院案例 10—335f
麦卡琴 McCutcheon, John T(inney) 美国漫画家 10—336a
麦卡锡 MacCarthy, Sir Desmond (Charles Otto) 英国新闻记者 10—332a
麦卡锡 McCarthy, Eugene J(oseph) 美国参议员 10—332b
麦卡锡 M'Carthy, Justin 爱尔兰历史学家 10—332d
麦卡锡 McCarthy, Joseph R(aymond) 美国参议员 10—332b

麦卡锡 McCarthy, Mary (Therese) 美国小说家、评论家 10—332d
麦卡锡岛 MacCarthy Island 冈比亚河岛屿 10—332e
麦凯 Mackay 澳大利亚城市 10—350f
麦凯 McKay, Claude 美国作家 10—351a
麦凯 Mackay, Clarence Hungerford 美国慈善家 10—350f
麦凯 McKay, Donald 美国工程师 10—351b
麦凯 McKay, David O(man) 美国摩门教布道家 10—351a
麦凯 MacKaye, (James Morrison) Steele 美国剧作家、演员 10—351c
麦凯 MacKaye, Percy 美国作家 10—351b
麦凯 McCay, Winsor 美国动画影片先驱 10—332f
麦凯格 MacCaig, Norman (Alexander) 苏格兰诗人 10—331e
麦凯伦 McKellen, Sir Ian (Murray) 英国演员 10—351e
麦康伯 Macomber, Mary Lizzie 美国画家 10—360e
麦康内尔 McConnell, Francis John 美国美以美会主教 10—334b
麦考莱 Macaulay, Dame (Emilie) Rose 英国小说家、游记作家 10—329f
麦考莱 McAuley, James Phillip 澳大利亚诗人 10—329e
麦考利 Macaulay, Catharine 英国历史学家 10—329e
麦考利 McAuley, Catherine Elizabeth 英国天主教慈恩姊妹会创立者 10—329c
麦考利(罗思利的) Macaulay (of Rothley), Thomas Babington Macaulay, Baron 英国政治家、著作家 10—329c
麦考利夫 McAuliffe, Anthony C(lement) 美国将军 10—329f
麦考利夫 McAuliffe, Christa Corrigan 美国教师、"挑战者"号航天飞机机组成员 10—330a
麦考密克 McCormick, Cyrus Hall 美国工业家、发明家 10—334d
麦考密克 McCormick, Robert R(utherford) 美国报纸编辑、发行人 10—334f
麦科尔 MacColl, Ewan 英国歌唱家、歌曲作家 10—334b
麦科马克 McCormack, John 爱尔兰歌唱家 10—334c
麦科马克 McCormack, John W(illiam) 美国政治家 10—334c
麦科伊 McCoy, (Charles) Kid 美国拳击运动员 10—334f
麦科伊家族 McCoy FAMILY 美国家族 10—334f
麦克 Mack, Connie 美国棒球领队 10—350d
麦克阿瑟 MacArthur, Douglas 美国将军 10—327f
麦克阿瑟 Macarthur, John 澳大利亚农业经营者 10—328b
麦克阿瑟河 McArthur River 澳大利亚河流 10—328c
麦克布赖德 McBride, Mary Margaret 美国记者、播音员 10—330d
麦克布赖德 McBride, Patricia 美国芭蕾舞演员 10—330e
麦克布赖德 McBride, Sir Richard 加拿大政治家 10—330e
麦克布赖德 MacBride, Seán 爱尔兰政治家 10—330f
麦克丹尼尔 McDaniel, Hattie 美国演员 10—336b
麦克道威尔 MacDowell, Edward (Alexander) 美国作曲家 10—339a
麦克德莫特 McDermott, Terry 美国滑冰运动员 10—336c
麦克迪尔米德 MacDiarmid, Alan G. 美国化学家 10—336c
麦克迪尔米德 MacDiarmid, Hugh 苏格兰诗人 10—336d
麦克迪维特 McDivitt, James A(lton) 美国航天员 10—336e
麦克杜格尔 McDougall, William 加拿大政治家 10—338e
麦克多纳 MacDonagh, Donagh 爱尔兰诗人、剧作家 10—336f
麦克多诺 Macdonough, Thomas 美国军官 10—338d
麦克尔 Macaire 法国史诗人物 10—326c
麦克尔斯菲尔德 Macclesfield 英国城市 10—333c
麦克法登 McFadden, Daniel L. 美国经济学家 10—342b
麦克法夸尔 Macfarquhar, Colin 苏格兰印刷商 10—342c
麦克法特 McPhatter, Clyde 美国歌手 10—361a
麦克弗森 McPherson 美国城市 10—361c
麦克弗森 McPherson, Aimee Semple 美国宗教领袖 10—361c
麦克弗森 Macpherson, Sir David (Lewis) 加拿大政治家、铁路承包商 10—361d
麦克弗森 Macpherson, James 苏格兰诗人 10—361e
麦克弗森 McPherson, James B(irdseye) 美国将领 10—361f
麦克弗森 Macpherson, (Jean) Jay 加拿大诗人 10—361f
麦克弗森岭 McPherson Range 澳大利亚山脉 10—362a
麦克亨利 McHenry, Robert 美国百科全书编纂者 10—346a
麦克亨利堡国家纪念地和历史圣地 Fort McHenry Natioinal Monument and Historic Shrine 美国历史纪念地 6—414b
麦克拉克伦 McLachlan, Alexander 加拿大诗人 10—356b
麦克拉伦 McLaren, Bruce (Leslie) 新西兰赛车驾驶员 10—356b
麦克拉伦 Maclaren, Charles 苏格兰新闻记者、主编 10—356c
麦克拉伦 McLaren, Daniel (circus clown) 英国小丑 10—356c
麦克莱恩 McLean, Alice Throckmorton 美国社会服务组织者 10—356e
麦克莱恩 Maclean, Donald (Duart) 英国间谍 10—356f
麦克莱恩 Maclean, George 西非海岸角行政会议主席 10—356f
麦克莱恩 McLean, John 美国法学家 10—357a
麦克莱恩 Mac Lane, Saunders 美国数学家 10—325d
麦克莱恩 MacLaine, Shirley 美国电影演员 10—356c
《麦克莱恩杂志》 Maclean's 加拿大杂志 10—357b
麦克莱伦 McClellan, George B(rinton) 美国将军 10—333a
麦克朗 McClung, Clarence E(rwin) 美国动物学家 10—333f
麦克劳德 Macleod (town, Alberta, Canada) 加拿大城镇 10—357e
麦克劳德 Macleod, J(ohn) J(ames) R(ickard) 苏格兰生理学家 10—357e
麦克劳德 Macleod, Mary 苏格兰盖尔语诗人 10—358f
麦克劳德 MacLeod, Margaretha Geertruida 荷兰舞蹈家 10—358f
麦克劳德 Macleod, Norman 苏格兰基督教长老会牧师 10—358a
麦克劳德堡 Fort Macleod 加拿大城镇 6—414c
麦克劳克林 McLaughlin, John 英国音乐家 10—356d
麦克劳林 McLaughlin, Charles 爱尔兰演员 10—356d
麦克雷 McRae, Carmen 美国爵士乐歌唱家 10—362c
麦克雷 McCrae, Hugh (Raymond) 澳大利亚诗人 10—335a
麦克雷 McCrea, Jane 美国殖民时期人物 10—335a
麦克雷 McCrea, Joel (Albert) 美国电影演员 10—335b
麦克雷 Machray, Robert 加拿大大主教 10—349f
麦克雷诺兹 McReynolds, James (Clark) 美国最高法院大法官 10—362f
麦克里迪 MacCready, Paul Beattie 美国空气动力学家 10—335c
麦克里迪 Macready, William Charles 英国演员 10—362d
麦克利里 MacLeary, Donald (Whyte) 苏格兰舞蹈演员 10—357b
麦克利什 MacLeish, Archibald 美国诗人 10—357b
麦克利斯 Maclise, Daniel 爱尔兰历史画家 10—358b
麦克利亚莫瓦 MacLiammóir, Micheál 爱尔兰演员 10—358a
麦克林 Macklin, Charles 爱尔兰演员 10—356a
麦克林托克 McClintock, Barbara 美国遗传学家 10—333d
麦克林托克 McClintock, Sir Francis Leopold 英国军官、探险家 10—333d
麦克卢尔 McClure, Sir Robert John Le Mesurier 爱尔兰探险家 10—334a
麦克卢尔 Maclure, William 美国地质学家 10—358d
麦克卢尔海峡 M'Clure Strait 北冰洋海峡 10—334a
麦克卢汉 McLuhan, (Herbert) Marshall 加拿大教育家 10—358c
麦克伦南 MacLennan, Hugh 加拿大小说家 10—357d
麦克伦南 McLennan, John Ferguson 苏格兰律师、民族学家 10—357d
麦克洛茨基 McCloskey, John 美国枢机主教 10—333e
麦克洛伊 McCloy, John J(ay) 美国外交家、律师 10—333e
麦克马洪 McMahon, Sir William 澳大利亚政治家 10—358e
麦克马洪伯爵 Mac-Mahon, Marie-Edme-Patrice-Maurice, comte de 法国元帅、总统 10—325f
麦克马洪线 McMahon Line 中英历史 10—358f
麦克马伦 McMullen, Curtis 美国数学家 10—359f
麦克马纳斯 McManus, Rachel Louise 美国护士 10—358f
麦克马斯特 McMaster, John Bach 美国历史学家 10—359a
麦克梅因 McMein, Neysa 美国画家 10—359b

麦克米林 McMillin,Bo 美国橄榄球运动员 10—359f
麦克米伦 McMillan,Edwin Mattison 美国核物理学家 10—359c
麦克米伦 Macmillan,Harold 英国政治家 10—359d
麦克米伦兄弟 Macmillan,Daniel;and Macmillan Alexander 苏格兰出版商 10—359b
麦克默多 Mackmurdo,Arthur Heygate 英国建筑师 10—356b
麦克默多湾 McMurdo Sound 南极洲海湾 10—360a
麦克默里 McMurray (town,Alberta,Canada) 加拿大城镇 10—360a
麦克默里堡 Fort McMurray 加拿大城镇 6—414d
麦克默罗 MacMurrough,Dermot (Irish king) 爱尔兰国王 10—360a
麦克纳 McKenna,Joseph 美国最高法院大法官 10—351f
麦克纳 McKenna,Reginald 英国政治家 10—351f
麦克纳 McKenna,Siobhan 爱尔兰演员 10—352a
麦克纳马拉 McNamara,Robert S(trange) 美国政治家 10—360b
麦克纳坦 Macnaghten,Sir William Hay,BARONET 英国外交家 10—360a
麦克尼尔 McNeill,William H(ardy) 美国历史学家 10—360d
麦克尼斯 MacNeice,Louis 英国诗人 10—360c
麦克佩斯 Macbeth 苏格兰国王 10—330c
麦克斯韦 Maxwell,James Clerk 英国数学家、物理学家 11—47a
麦克斯韦-玻耳兹曼分布律 Maxwell-Boltzmann distribution law 化学 11—48a
麦克斯韦尔(特雷格尔斯的) Maxwell (of Terregles),Sir John 苏格兰贵族 11—48a
麦克斯韦方程组 Maxwell's equations 物理学 11—48c
麦克斯韦精灵 Maxwell's demon 物理学 11—48c
麦克斯韦山脉 Maxwell Montes 金星山脉 11—48b
麦克坦岛 Mactan Island 菲律宾岛屿 10—363f
麦克唐纳 Macdonald,Flora 苏格兰英雄 10—336f
麦克唐纳 Macdonald,George 英国小说家、诗人 10—337a
麦克唐纳 Macdonald,Sir John (Alexander) 加拿大总理 10—337c
麦克唐纳 MacDonald,(James) Ramsay 英国首相 10—337d
麦克唐纳 Macdonald,Sir James Ronald Leslie 英国工程师 10—337b
麦克唐纳 Macdonald,John Sandfield 加拿大省长 10—337d
麦克唐纳 Macdonald,Jacques(-Étienne-Joseph)-Alexandre,DUC (duke) DE TARENTE 法国元帅 10—337a
麦克唐纳 Macdonald,Ross 英国推理小说家 10—337e
麦克唐纳-道格拉斯公司 McDonnell Douglas Corporation 美国飞机制造公司 10—338c
麦克唐纳-赖特 Macdonald-Wright,Stanton 美国画家、教师 10—338a
麦克唐纳天文台 McDonald Observatory 美国天文台 10—337f
麦克唐奈尔 MacDonnell,Randal 爱尔兰贵族 10—338b
麦克唐奈尔 MacDonnell,Sorley Boy 爱尔兰首长 10—338b
麦克唐奈山脉 MacDonnell Ranges 澳大利亚山脉 10—338d
麦克亚当 McAdam,John Loudon 苏格兰发明家 10—326a
麦克尤恩 McEwen,Sir John 澳大利亚总理 10—342b
麦肯 Macken,Walter 爱尔兰作家 10—351e
麦肯罗 McEnroe,John 美国网球运动员 10—341f
麦肯齐 Mackenzie,Alexander 加拿大总理 10—352c
麦肯齐 Mackenzie,Sir Alexander 加拿大探险家 10—352c
麦肯齐 Mackenzie,Sir Alexander Campbell 苏格兰作曲家 10—352d
麦肯齐 Mackenzie,Charles Frederick 英属中非主教 10—352d
麦肯齐 Mackenzie,(Sir Edward Montague) Compton 英国作家 10—352d
麦肯齐 Mackenzie,Henry 英国作家 10—352f
麦肯齐 Mackenzie,John 英国基督教教士 10—353a
麦肯齐 Mackenzie,Sir James 英国心脏病学家 10—352f
麦肯齐 McKenzie,Sir John 新西兰政治家 10—353a
麦肯齐 Mackenzie,Sir Morell 英国医师 10—353b
麦肯齐 McKenzie,Robert (Trelford) 英国政治学家 10—353b
麦肯齐 Mackenzie,Sir Thomas 新西兰总理 10—353c
麦肯齐 Mackenzie,William Lyon 加拿大记者、政治宣传家 10—353c
麦肯齐(罗斯霍的) Mackenzie (of Rosehaugh),Sir George 苏格兰律师 10—352e
麦库尔 MacCool,Finn 爱尔兰传说 10—334c
麦夸里 Macquarie,Lachlan 英属殖民地总督 10—362a
麦夸里岛 Macquarie Island 澳大利亚岛屿 10—362c
麦夸里港 Port Macquarie 澳大利亚城镇 13—446b
麦夸里港湾 Macquarie Harbour 澳大利亚海湾 10—362b
麦夸里湖 Macquarie,Lake 澳大利亚湖泊 10—362b
麦夸里氏松 macquarie pine 木本植物 10—362c
麦奎尔 McGwire,Mark 美国棒球运动员 10—343f
麦拉玛提教团 Malāmatīyah 伊斯兰教苏非派教团 10—420a
麦勒卡特 Melqart 古代腓尼基人神话 11—100c
麦粒肿 sty 疾病 16—293e
麦罗埃 Meroe 古代库施城市 11—133e
麦罗埃语 Meroitic language 语言 11—133e
麦纳麦 Manama 巴林首都 10—446a
麦帕克林 mepacrine (drug) 药物 11—122c
麦奇生 Murchison,Sir Roderick Impey 英国地质学家 11—492a
麦钱特·泰勒斯学校 Merchant Taylors' School 英格兰学校 11—125c
麦丘恩-奥尔布赖特二氏综合征 McCune-Albright syndrome 病理现象 10—335f
麦什德 Meshed 伊朗城市 11—139a
麦氏卢尔氏螺属 Maclurites 古生物学 10—358d
麦斯吉德 masjid 穆斯林礼拜场所 11—1b
麦斯欧迪 Masʿūdī,al- 阿拉伯历史学家、旅行家 11—16b
麦西尼 Messene 希腊古城 11—143f
麦西尼亚 Messenia 希腊古地名 11—144a
麦西尼亚湾 Messenia,Gulf of 伊奥尼亚海湾 11—144b
麦西尼亚战争 Messenian Wars 古希腊历史 11—144b
麦西亚 Mercia 英格兰古代王国 11—125c
麦芽 malt 谷物产品 10—436d
麦芽糖酶 maltase 酶 10—437e
麦哲伦 Magellan,Ferdinand 葡萄牙航海家、探险家 10—379f
麦哲伦海峡 Magellan,Strait of 南美海峡 10—380c
麦哲伦云 Magellanic Cloud 天文学 10—380c
麦哲伦-智利南极区 Magallanes y La Antarctica Chilena 智利区名 10—378c
卖淫 prostitution 社会学 13—541c
脉搏 pulse 生理学 14—22d
脉翅类昆虫 neuropteran 昆虫 12—98b
脉冲星 pulsar 天文学 14—22b
《脉经》 Maijing 中医文献 10—404f
脉矿 lode 地质学 10—183c
鳗 eel 鱼类 5—554a
鳗草 eelgrass 水生植物 5—554b
鳗鲡类 anguilliform 硬骨鱼类 1—353c
鳗螈 siren 两栖动物 15—402a
满天星 baby's breath 草本植物 2—113b
满文 Man character 中国文字 10—444c
满语 Man language 中国语言 10—444e
满洲国 Manchuguo 中国历史 10—451a
满洲里 Manzhouli 中国城市 10—479c
满洲事变 Manchurian Incident 中国历史 10—451b
满族 Man 中国民族 10—443e
螨 mite 无脊椎动物 11—290c
曼 Mann,Heinrich 德国小说家 10—465f
曼 Mann,Horace 美国教育家 10—465f
曼 Mann,Thomas 德国小说家 10—466b
曼 Mann,Tom 英国劳工领袖 10—466f

曼 Mun, Thomas 英国经济学家 11—481f
曼波舞 mambo 古巴舞蹈 10—440d
曼伯拉莫河 Mamberamo River 印度尼西亚河流 10—440d
曼布尔 Maimbourg, Louis 法国历史学家 10—406d
曼彻斯特 Manchester 英国城市 10—448a
曼彻斯特 Manchester 美国康涅狄格州城镇 10—450c
曼彻斯特 Manchester 美国新罕布什尔州城市 10—450c
曼彻斯特 Manchester 美国佛蒙特州城镇 10—450d
曼彻斯特伯爵(第二) Manchester, Edward Montagu, 2nd earl of 英国将军 10—450d
曼彻斯特㹴狗 Manchester terrier 狗品种 10—450e
曼彻斯特通海运河 Manchester Ship Canal 英国水道 10—450e
曼达尔戈壁 Mandalgovĭ 蒙古城镇 10—451f
曼达拉山脉 Mandara Mountains 非洲山脉 10—452c
曼达派 Mandaeanism 中东宗教 10—451b
曼达韦 Mandaue 菲律宾城市 10—453a
曼怛罗 mantra 印度教、佛教咒语 10—475f
曼丹 Mandan 美国城市 10—452b
曼丹人 Mandan 北美印第安人 10—452a
曼德海峡 Mandeb, Strait of 红海海峡 10—453c
曼德拉 Mandela, Nelson 南非总统 10—453d
曼德莱恩 Mundelein 美国村庄 11—483c
曼德莱恩 Mundelein, George William 美国天主教枢机主教 11—483d
曼德勒 Mandalay 缅甸城市 10—451d
曼德列斯 Menderes, Adnan 土耳其政治家 11—110c
曼德人 Mande 西非民族 10—453b
曼德维尔 Mandeville, Bernand de 荷兰作家 10—454a
曼德维尔 Mandeville, Geoffrey de 荷兰作家 10—454b
曼德维尔 Mandeville, Sir John 英国作家 10—454b
曼德维尔子爵 Mandeville, Edward Montagu, Viscount 英国将军 10—454b
曼德诸语言 Mande languages 非洲语言 10—453b
曼迪雅 mandyas 东正教服饰 10—455f
曼蒂凯拉山脉 Mantiqueira Mountains 巴西山脉 10—475c
曼丁哥人 Mandingo (people) 西非民族 10—454d
曼杜 Māndu 印度城市 10—455d
曼杜拉 Mandurah 澳大利亚城镇 10—455e
曼杜里亚 Manduria 意大利城镇 10—455e
曼多加尔赫 Mandogarh (India) 印度城市 10—454d
曼多拉琴 mandora 乐器 10—454e
曼多林琴 mandolin 乐器 10—454d
曼恩 Maine 法国历史大区 10—407d
曼恩伯爵 Mun, (Adrien-) Albert (-Marie), comte de 法国基督教领袖 11—481e
曼恩·德·比朗 Maine de Biran, Marie-François-Pierre 法国政治家、哲学家 10—410e
曼恩公爵 Maine, Louis-Auguste de Bourbon, duc du 法国贵族 10—410e
曼恩河 Maine River 法国河流 10—411a
曼恩-卢瓦尔 Maine-et-Loire 法国省份 10—410f
曼法鲁蒂 Manfalūṭī, Muṣṭafā Luṭfī al- 埃及作家 10—456e
曼弗雷迪 Manfred 西西里国王 10—457a
曼弗雷多尼亚 Manfredonia 意大利城镇 10—457a
曼冈 Mangang 印度村庄 10—457f
曼戈阿拉 Mangoaela, Z(akea) D(olphin) 南索托作家、民俗学家 10—458e
曼戈切 Mangochi 马拉维城镇 10—458f
曼格拉水坝 Mangla Dam 巴基斯坦土石坝 10—458d
曼格什拉克 Mangyshlak 哈萨克斯坦州名 10—459e
曼根 Mangan, James Clarence 爱尔兰诗人 10—457c
曼谷 Bangkok 泰国首都 2—198d
曼哈顿 Manhattan 美国堪萨斯州城市 10—459f
曼哈顿 Manhattan 美国纽约市区名 10—459f
曼哈顿工程 Manhattan Project 美国原子弹工程 10—460a
曼海姆 Mannheim 德国城市 10—468c
曼海姆 Mannheim, Karl 德国社会学家 10—468d
曼海姆乐派 Mannheim school 德国音乐流派 10—468d
曼基勒 Mankiller, Wilma Pearl 美国印第安人活动家 10—465d
曼加斯·科洛拉达斯 Mangas Coloradas 北美阿帕切人首领 10—458a
曼杰利什塔姆 Mandelstam, Osip (Emilyevich) 苏联诗人 10—453f
曼凯托 Mankato 美国城市 10—465b
曼凯维奇 Mankiewicz, Herman (Jacob) 美国电影剧作家、记者 10—465b
曼凯维奇 Mankiewicz, Joseph (Leo) 美国电影导演 10—465c
曼克斯语 Manx language 英国已消亡的语言 10—478f
曼雷萨 Manresa 西班牙城镇 10—470f
曼里克 Manrique, Gómez 西班牙军人、政治家 10—470f
曼里克 Manrique, Jorge 西班牙军人、作家 10—471a
曼利 Manley, Michael 牙买加总理 10—465e
曼利 Manley, Mary de la Riviere 英国作家 10—465d
曼利谢尔 Mannlicher, Ferdinand, Ritter von 奥地利轻武器设计师 10—469c
曼密苹果 mammee apple (*Mammea americana*) 植物 10—442d
曼纳 Manner, Eeva Liisa 芬兰诗人、剧作家 10—467b
曼纳 Manners, John 英国军事官员 10—467f
曼纳林 Mannerheim, Carl Gustaf (Emil) 芬兰总统 10—467c
曼纳斯 Manners, John James Robert 英国政治家 10—467f
曼内斯 Mannes, Leopold (Damrosch) 美国音乐家、摄影技术人员 10—468a
曼内斯 Mannes, Marya 美国作家 10—468b
曼内托 Manetho 古埃及祭司 10—456e
曼尼克斯 Mannix, Daniel 澳大利亚大主教 10—469c
曼尼普尔 Manipur 印度邦名 10—463d
曼尼普尔人 Manipuri (people) 印度民族 10—463e
曼尼普里 manipuri 印度舞蹈 10—463e
曼尼亚吉塔 Mānyakheṭa 印度古城遗址 10—478f
曼涅里克二世 Menelik II 埃塞俄比亚皇帝 11—112d
曼宁 Maning, Frederick 新西兰作家、法官 10—463c
曼宁 Manning, Henry Edward 英国大主教 10—468f
曼宁 Manning, James 美国浸礼会教士、教育家 10—468f
曼宁 Manning, Marie 美国记者 10—469a
曼宁 Manning, Olivia 英国作家 10—469b
曼宁 Mannyng (of Brunne), Robert 英国诗人 10—469d
曼纽利托 Manuelito 纳瓦霍印第安人领袖 10—477d
曼努埃尔 Manuel 统治者之名 10—476c
曼努埃尔二世 Manuel II 葡萄牙国王 10—477a
曼努埃尔二世·帕里奥洛古斯 Manuel II Palaeologus 拜占廷皇帝、军人 10—476d
曼努埃尔式 Manueline 葡萄牙建筑风格 10—477c
曼努埃尔一世 Manuel I 葡萄牙国王 10—476f
曼努埃尔一世·康尼努斯 Manuel I Comnenus 拜占廷皇帝、军事领袖 10—476c
曼诺多图斯(尼科墨迪亚的) Menodotus of Nicomedia 哲学家 11—116f
曼普鲁西人 Mamprusi 加纳民族 10—443d
曼齐刻尔特战役(1071) Manzikert, Battle of 拜占廷历史 10—479e
曼齐尼 Manzini 斯威士兰城镇 10—479f
曼奇尼 Mancini, Pasquale Stanislao 意大利复兴运动领袖 10—451b
曼萨 Mansa 赞比亚城镇 10—471a
曼萨·穆萨 Mansa Mūsā (emperor of Mali) 马里皇帝 10—471a
曼萨纳尔安置中心 Manzanar Relocation Center 美国历史 10—479b
曼萨尼约 Manzanillo 古巴城市 10—479c

曼萨尼约 Manzanillo 墨西哥城市 10—479c
曼塞尔 Mansel, Henry Longueville 英国哲学家、神学家 10—471d
曼塞赫拉 Mānsehra 巴基斯坦县城 10—471d
曼森 Manson, Sir Patrick 英国寄生虫学家 10—473c
曼沙达尔 manṣabdār 印度莫卧儿帝国官员 10—471a
曼施泰因 Manstein, Erich von 德国陆军元帅 10—473c
曼斯 Mance, Sir Henry Christopher 英国科学家 10—447e
曼斯布里奇 Mansbridge, Albert 英国教育家 10—471c
曼斯菲尔德 Mansfield 英国城镇 10—471e
曼斯菲尔德 Mansfield 美国康涅狄格州城镇 10—472a
曼斯菲尔德 Mansfield 美国俄亥俄州城市 10—472a
曼斯菲尔德 Mansfield, Katherine 英国作家 10—472b
曼斯菲尔德 Mansfield, Michael J(oseph) 美国政治家 10—472c
曼斯菲尔德 Mansfield, Sir Peter 英国物理学家 10—472c
曼斯菲尔德 Mansfeld, (Peter) Ernst, Graf von (count of) 信奉天主教的雇佣军人 10—471e
曼斯菲尔德 Mansfield, Richard 美国演员 10—472d
曼斯菲尔德(夫人) Mansfield, Arabella 美国教育家 10—472a
曼斯菲尔德伯爵 Mansfield, William Murray, 1st Earl of 英国首席法官 10—472e
曼斯菲尔德山 Mansfield, Mount 美国山峰 10—472c
曼斯菲尔德子爵 Mansfield, William Cavendish, Viscount 英国军事司令官 10—472e
曼苏尔 Manṣūr 印度画家 10—473d
曼苏尔 Manṣūr, al- 阿拔斯王朝哈里发 10—473f
曼苏尔 Manṣūr, Abū ʿĀmir al- 西班牙科尔多瓦伍麦叶王朝统治者 10—473e
曼苏尔 Manṣūr, Abū Yūsuf Yaʿqūb al- 西班牙、北非穆明王朝统治者 10—473e
曼苏尔堡 Ḥiṣn Manṣūr (Turkey) 土耳其城市 8—96e
曼苏尔堡 Hüsnümansur (Turkey) 土耳其城市 8—268d
曼苏拉 Manṣūrah, al- 埃及城市 10—474a
曼塔 Manta 厄瓜多尔城市 10—474a
曼泰 Manti 美国城市 10—474f
曼特城 Ciudad Mante 墨西哥城市 4—252a
曼特尔 Mantell, Gideon Algernon 英国医生、地质学家 10—474d
曼特尔 Mantle, Mickey (Charles) 美国棒球运动员 10—475e
曼特尼亚 Mantegna, Andrea 意大利艺术家 10—474b
曼特农侯爵夫人 Maintenon, Françoise d'Aubigné, marquise de 法国王后 10—411b
曼提尼亚 Mantineia 希腊古城 10—475b
曼桐 Mindon 缅甸国王 11—245d
曼图亚 Mantua 意大利城市 10—475f
曼图亚之围 Mantua, Siege of 欧洲历史 10—476a
曼荼罗 mandala 印度教与佛教 10—451c
曼陀菲尔 Manteuffel, Edwin (Hans Karl), Freiherr von 普鲁士陆军元帅 10—474d
曼陀菲尔 Manteuffel, Hasso, Freiherr von 德国军事战略家 10—474e
曼陀罗 jimsonweed (*Datura stramonium*) 草本植物 9—24d
曼陀罗属 Datura 植物学 5—162f
曼西 Muncie 美国城市 11—482f
曼西人 Mansi (people) 西伯利亚西部民族 10—473b
曼希普 Manship, Paul 美国雕刻家 10—473a
曼祖 Manzù, Giacomo 意大利雕刻家 10—480a
曼佐尼 Manzoni, Alessandro 意大利诗人 10—479f
蔓长春花 periwinkle 草本植物 13—171c
蔓虎刺 partridgeberry (*Mitchella repens*) 植物学 13—69c
蔓生铁杉 creeping hemlock 灌木 5—4b
蔓仙人掌 vine cactus (plant) 植物 17—568f
蔓越橘 cranberry 水果 4—567a
慢步 walk 马术 18—73f
慢跑 jogging 体育运动 9—43f
慢跑步 canter 马术 3—411b
慢缺肢蜥 slowworm (lizard) 蜥蜴 15—437e
慢性疲劳综合征 chronic fatigue syndrome (CFS) 疾病 4—213c
慢性肉芽肿性疾病 chronic granulomatous disease 疾病 4—213d
《漫步者》 Rambler, The 18世纪英格兰杂志 14—138a
漫画 cartoon 绘画 3—491a
漫谈录 table talk 文学 16—414f
芒阿雷瓦群岛 Mangareva Islands (French Polynesia) 法属波利尼西亚岛屿 10—458a
芒贝图人 Mangbetu 中非民族 10—458b
芒代尔 Mandel, Georges 法国政治领袖 10—453c
芒戴 Munday, Anthony 英国剧作家 11—483b
芒德 Mende 法国城镇 11—107d
芒德尔 Mundell, Robert A(lexander) 加拿大经济学家 11—483d
芒德市墩群国家纪念地 Mound City Group National Monument (Ohio, U.S.) 美国国家公园 11—439f
芒德维尔考古公园 Moundville Archaeological Park 美国印第安人遗址 11—440a
芒福德 Mumford, Lewis 美国建筑评论家 11—481b
芒戈 Mango 多哥城镇 10—458d
芒戈人 Mongo 非洲民族 11—336b
芒戈，圣 Mungo, SAINT 基督教传教士 11—483f
芒古 Mongu 赞比亚城镇 11—339f
芒加赖人 Manggarai 印度尼西亚民族 10—458c
芒罗 Munro, H. H. 苏格兰作家 11—486a
芒人 Muong 越南少数民族 11—488e
芒萨尔 Mansart, François 法国建筑师 10—471b
芒萨尔 Mansart, Jules Hardouin- 法国建筑师、设计师 10—471c
芒什 Manche 法国省份 10—447f
芒属 Miscanthus 植物学 11—274d
芒斯特 Munster 爱尔兰省份 11—487b
芒特艾萨 Mount Isa 澳大利亚城市 11—441c
芒特巴克 Mount Barker 澳大利亚城镇 11—440c
芒特达尔文 Mount Darwin 津巴布韦城镇 11—440e
芒特迪瑟特岛 Mount Desert Island 美国岛屿 11—440e
芒特弗农 Mount Vernon 美国伊利诺伊州城市 11—442a
芒特弗农 Mount Vernon 美国纽约州城市 11—442a
芒特弗农 Mount Vernon 美国俄亥俄州城市 11—442a
芒特弗农 Mount Vernon 华盛顿的家乡 11—442b
芒特甘比尔 Mount Gambier 澳大利亚城市 11—440f
芒特哈根 Mount Hagen 巴布亚新几内亚城镇 11—441a
芒特霍利 Mount Holly 美国城镇 11—441a
芒特霍普湾 Mount Hope Bay 美国海湾 11—441b
芒特卡梅尔 Mount Carmel 美国村镇 11—440d
芒特克莱门斯 Mount Clemens 美国城市 11—440d
芒特摩根 Mount Morgan 澳大利亚城镇 11—441c
芒特普莱森特 Mount Pleasant 美国艾奥瓦州城市 11—441d
芒特普莱森特 Mount Pleasant 美国密歇根州城市 11—441d
芒特普莱森特 Mount Pleasant 美国南卡罗来纳州城镇 11—441d
芒廷阿什 Mountain Ash 威尔士城镇 11—442f
芒廷梅多斯惨案 Mountain Meadows massacre 美国历史 11—445a
芒廷维尤 Mountain View 美国城市 11—445b
芒通 Menton 法国城镇 11—121b
芒温库苏莫 Mangunkusumo, Tjipto 印度尼西亚民族主义领袖 10—459d
芒西 Munsey, Frank Andrew 美国出版商 11—486d
芒硝 mirabilite 矿物 11—270f
芒兹维尔 Moundsville 美国城市 11—439f
杧果 mango (*Mangifera indica*) 植物 10—458d
盲 blindness 病理现象 2—535c
盲肠 cecum 解剖学 3—548e
盲点 blind spot 生理学 2—535b
盲哈里 Blind Harry 苏格兰诗人 2—535a

盲鳗 hagfish 鱼形原始脊椎动物 7—406d
盲蛇 blind snake 爬行动物 2—535a
盲蛇蜥 blindworm (*Anguis fragilis*) 爬行动物 2—535c
盲鱼 blind fish 鱼类 2—535a
茫崖 Mangya 中国城镇 10—459e
牻牛儿苗目 Geraniales 植物学 7—85b
莽吉柿 mangosteen (*Garcinia mangostana*) 木本植物 10—458f
莽骑兵 Rough Rider 美国志愿骑兵团 14—419b
莽瑞体 Tabinshwehti 缅甸国王 16—413f
莽应龙 Bayinnaung 缅甸国王 2—296e
莽原战役 Wilderness, Battle of the 美国历史 18—254b
蟒 python 爬行动物 14—50e
蟒类 boid 动物学 3—6a
猫白血病 feline leukemia 猫科动物疾病 6—267f
猫猴 cobego (mammal) 哺乳动物 4—316a
猫呼吸道病 feline respiratory disease 猫疾病 6—268b
猫叫综合征 cri-du-chat syndrome 病理现象 5—10e
猫科动物 cat 动物学 3—517e
猫鸟 catbird 鸟类 3—522c
猫头鹰罐 Eulenkrüg 德国彩陶罐 6—159e
猫瘟热 feline distemper 猫疾病 6—267f
猫眼石 cat's-eye 宝石 3—530b
猫眼状闪光 chatoyance 矿物学 4—91d
猫爪花 pussy-toes 草本植物 14—36f
毛 hair 生物学 7—413a
毛鼻袋熊 wombat 哺乳动物 18—314f
毛笔画 brush drawing 绘画技法 3—208f
毛赤铜矿 chalcotrichite 矿物 4—31a
毛虫 caterpillar 昆虫 3—523f
毛达奇 Madách, Imre 匈牙利诗人 10—364d
毛掸虫 feather-duster worm 蠕虫 6—258e
毛淡棉 Moulmein 缅甸城镇 11—439c
毛德皇后地 Queen Maud Land 南极洲地区 14—84a
毛德皇后山 Queen Maud Mountains 南极洲山地 14—84b
毛滴虫 trichomonad 寄生虫 17—216d
毛滴虫病 trichomoniasis 疾病 17—216e
毛尔草坪 Mall, The 美国首都华盛顿的一段开阔地 10—432c
毛矾石 alunogen 矿物 1—259d
毛沸石 erionite 矿物 6—119a
毛葛 poplin 布 13—433e
毛茛 buttercup 草本植物 3—292b
毛茛科 Ranunculaceae 草本植物 14—152d
毛茛目 Ranunculales 植物学 14—152e
毛公鼎 Maogong Tripod 中国青铜器 10—482a
毛海豹 hair seal 哺乳动物 7—413c
毛赫 Mauch, Karl 德国探险家 11—33d
毛菌纲 Trichomycetes 真菌 17—216f
毛科 Makó 匈牙利城市 10—417b
毛克山脉 Maoke Mountains 印度尼西亚山脉 10—482a
毛口虫 trichostome 动物 17—216f
毛拉 Moura 澳大利亚城镇 11—447a
毛拉 mullah 伊斯兰教称谓 11—475c
毛拉(-蒙塔内) Maura (y Montaner), Antonio 西班牙政治家 11—36e
毛拉维教团 Mawlawīyah 伊斯兰教苏非派教团 11—42d
毛里求斯 Mauritius 印度洋岛国 11—39d
毛里求斯大麻 Mauritius hemp (*Furcraea gigantea*) 草本植物 11—40c
毛里塔尼亚 Mauretania 古代北非地区 11—36f
毛里塔尼亚 Mauritania 非洲国家 11—38e
"毛里塔尼亚"号 Mauretania 船名 11—37a
毛利人 Maori 新西兰民族 10—482d
《毛利人代表权法案》 Maori Representation Act 新西兰历史 10—483d
毛利氏 Mōri FAMILY 日本家族 11—395a
毛利语 Maori language 大洋洲语言 10—483c
毛鳞鱼 capelin (*Mallotus villosus*) 鱼类 3—424e
毛鲁斯·塞尔维乌斯·洪诺拉图斯 Maurus Servius Honoratus 罗马作家 11—41a
毛罗什河 Maros River (Romania) 罗马尼亚河流 10—528a
毛罗什瓦沙尔海伊 Marosvásárhely (Romania) 罗马尼亚县城 10—528a
毛毛雨 drizzle 气象学 5—425f
毛帽藓 hair-cap moss 植物 7—413b
毛蠓 moth fly 昆虫 11—430f
毛姆 Maugham, Robin 英国小说家、剧作家 11—34b
毛姆 Maugham, W. Somerset 英国小说家、剧作家 11—34b
毛南语 Maonan language 中国语言 10—482c
毛南族 Maonan 中国民族 10—482b
毛皮 fur 动物毛皮 6—528a
毛皮 pelage 哺乳动物有毛的表层 13—127f
毛奇 Moltke, Helmuth von 德国将军 11—325a
毛奇 Moltke, Helmuth (Johannes Ludwig) von 德国将军 11—325c
毛蕊花 mullein 草本植物 11—475c
毛瑟枪 Mauser rifle 武器 11—41c
毛石工程 rubble masonry 土木工程 14—436a
毛刷 brush 器具 3—208e
毛丝鼠 chinchilla 哺乳动物 4—167b
毛特豪森 Mauthausen 奥地利纳粹集中营 11—41e
毛特纳 Mauthner, Fritz 德国哲学家、作家 11—41f
毛头少年和戴假发者 Pipiolo and Pelucón 智利政治派别 13—319a
毛头星 feather star 无脊椎动物 6—258f
毛猬 gymnure 哺乳动物 7—390e
毛蚊 March fly 昆虫 10—496e
毛沃 Mauve, Anton 荷兰画家 11—41f
毛乌素沙地 Mu Us Desert 中国大沙区 11—459d
毛乌素沙漠 Maowusu Shamo (China) 中国大沙区 10—483e
毛细现象 capillarity 物理学 3—425e
毛细线虫 hairworm 动物 7—413d
毛细血管 capillary 解剖学 3—425f
毛蕈甲 hairy fungus beetle 昆虫 7—413d
毛叶番荔枝 cherimoya (genus *Annona cherimola*) 木本植物 4—125c
毛伊岛 Maui 美国火山岛 11—34d
毛伊拉特 Mailáth, János, Gróf (Count) 匈牙利作家 10—405d
毛泽东 Mao Zedong 中国领导人、革命家、军事家 10—481a
毛泽东思想 Mao Zedong Thought 中国革命思想体系 10—481f
矛 spear 武器 16—10a
矛兵 rapparee 爱尔兰民族主义者 14—155c
矛头蛇 fer-de-lance 爬行动物 6—278c
矛牙野猪 javelin 哺乳动物 8—552c
矛蚁 driver ant 昆虫 5—425e
茅盾 Mao Dun 中国作家 10—480c
茅膏菜科 Droseraceae 植物学 5—427b
茅膏菜科 sundew family 植物学 16—341c
茅茅运动 Mau Mau 肯尼亚政治运动 11—33c
茅崎 Chigasaki 日本城市 4—149a
茅台 Maotai 中国城镇 10—483d
茅以升 Mao Yisheng 中国桥梁工程学家 10—480e
牦牛 yak (species *Bos grunniens*) 哺乳动物 18—405a
锚 anchor 船用工具 1—322d
昴星团 Pleiades 天文学 13—368a
昴宿增十二 Pleione 天文学 13—368c
铆钉 rivet 穿钉或销栓 14—319f
茂名 Maoming 中国城市 10—482a

茂尼 Muni, Paul 美国戏剧、电影演员 11—483f
茂物 Bogor 印度尼西亚城市 2—568e
冒号分类法 Colon Classification 图书馆学 4—357f
冒纳凯阿峰 Mauna Kea 美国火山 11—34f
冒纳凯阿天文台 Mauna Kea Observatory 美国天文台 11—34f
冒纳罗亚 Mauna Loa 美国火山 11—35b
冒险故事 gest 文学 7—103a
冒险商公司 Merchant Adventurers 英国公司 11—125b
冒险湾松 adventure bay pine 木本植物 1—89f
冒险乐队 Ventures, the 美国乐队 17—508e
贸易差额 trade, balance of 经济 17—187a
贸易理事会 Trade, Board of 英格兰政府机构 17—187b
贸易署 Contratación, Casa de 西班牙历史 4—472b
贸易鼠 trade rat 哺乳动物 17—187f
贸易条件 trade, terms of 经济 17—187b
贸易条款 commerce clause 美国宪法 4—384e
贸易协定 trade agreement 经济 17—187c
帽 hat 服饰 7—506d
帽贝 limpet 软体动物 10—106d
帽猴 bonnet monkey (species *Macaca radiata*) 哺乳动物 3—33e
帽花结 cockade 服饰 4—321a
帽针 hatpin 服饰 7—509b
《玫瑰传奇》 Roman de la Rose 法国文学 14—363d
玫瑰经 rosary 宗教虔修方式 14—399d
玫瑰剧院 Rose Theatre 伦敦剧场 14—402b
玫瑰茄 roselle (*Hibiscus sabdariffa*) 草本植物 14—403b
玫瑰热 rose fever 疾病 14—401f
玫瑰十字会 Rosicrucian 秘密社团 14—406b
玫瑰碗橄榄球赛 Rose Bowl 美国橄榄球赛 14—401e
玫瑰鹦鹉 rosella 鸟类 14—403b
玫瑰油 attar of roses 香精油 2—38e
玫瑰战争 Roses, Wars of the 英国历史 14—405b
玫红尖晶石 balas ruby 宝石 2—162a
枚方 Hirakata 日本城市 8—93c
眉嵴 browridge 解剖学 3—198b
眉兰属 Ophrys 植物学 12—431a
眉谬 Maymyo 缅甸城镇 11—52e
眉山 Meishan 中国城市 11—87f
莓鲈 crappie 鱼类 4—570c
梅 May, Phil 英国讽刺画家 11—48e
梅 May, Thomas 英国作家 11—48e
梅奥 Mayo 爱尔兰郡名 11—53a
梅奥 Mayo, (George) Elton 美国心理学家 11—53e
梅奥 Mayow, John 英格兰化学家、生理学家 11—54f
梅奥 Mayo, Mary Anne Bryant 美国农民组织者 11—53f
梅奥伯爵(第六) Mayo, Richard Southwell Bourke, 6th earl of 爱尔兰政治家 11—53f
梅奥尔 Mayall, John 英国音乐人 11—50c
梅奥家族 Mayo FAMILY 美国医学世家 11—53a
梅贝克 Maybeck, Bernard (Ralph) 美国建筑师 11—51b
梅采希内 Metsähine (Finnish god) 芬兰宗教神祇 11—162a
梅察达 Masada 以色列古堡 10—567d
梅察达遗址 Horvot Mezada (Israel) 以色列古堡 8—187f
梅达 Mehta, Sir Pherozeshah 印度政治领袖 11—83f
梅达沃 Medawar, Sir Peter B(rian) 英国动物学家 11—70c
梅代尔帕德 Medelpad 瑞典省份 11—71a
梅德福 Medford 美国马萨诸塞州城市 11—71b
梅德福 Medford 美国俄勒冈州城市 11—71b
梅德宁 Madanīyīn 突尼斯城镇 10—365f
梅德斯通 Maidstone 英格兰自治市 10—404c
梅德韦 Medway (England) 英格兰区名 11—79e
梅德韦河畔罗切斯特 Rochester upon Medway 英格兰地区、自治市 14—340a
梅德沃尔 Medwall, Henry 第一部英语剧本的作者 11—79e
梅登黑德 Maidenhead 英格兰城镇 10—404c
梅迪尔 Medill, Joseph 美国编辑、出版商 11—76e
梅迪纳 Medina, Bartolomé de 西班牙神学家 11—77f
梅迪纳西多尼亚公爵 Medina-Sidonia, Alonso Pérez de Guzmán, duke (duque) de 西班牙舰队司令 11—78a
梅迪契 Medici, Alessandro de' (grand duke of Tuscany) 托斯卡纳大公 11—74b
梅迪契 Medici, Alessandro Ottaviano de' 教皇 11—74b
梅迪契 Medici, Cosimo de' 意大利统治者 11—74c
梅迪契 Medici, Cosimo de' (grand duke of Tuscany) 托斯卡纳大公 11—74d
梅迪契 Medici, Ferdinando de' (grand duke of Tuscany) 托斯卡纳大公 11—74d
梅迪契 Medici, Francesco de' (grand duke of Tuscany) 托斯卡纳大公 11—74d
梅迪契 Medici, Gian Gastone de' (grand duke of Tuscany) 托斯卡纳大公 11—74d
梅迪契 Medici, Giovanni Angelo de' (pope) 教皇 11—74d
梅迪契 Medici, Giovanni de' 教皇 11—74e
梅迪契 Medici, Giovanni de' 意大利领导人 11—74e
梅迪契 Medici, Giuliano de' 佛罗伦萨统治者 11—74e
梅迪契 Medici, Giulio de' (pope) 教皇 11—74f
梅迪契 Medici, Ippolito de' 意大利主教 11—74f
梅迪契 Medici, Lorenzino de' 意大利作者、行刺者 11—74f
梅迪契 Medici, Lorenzo de' 意大利政治家 11—75a
梅迪契 Medici, Lorenzo di Piero de', DUCA (duke) DI URBINO 意大利统治者 11—75c
梅迪契 Medici, Piero di Cosimo de' 意大利统治者 11—75d
梅迪契 Medici, Piero di Lorenzo de' 意大利统治者 11—75d
梅迪契别墅 Medici, Villa 罗马古建筑 11—75e
梅迪契瓷器 Medici porcelain 欧洲瓷器 11—75f
梅迪契家族 Medici FAMILY 意大利家族 11—73a
梅迪契-罗伦佐图书馆 Medicean-Laurentian Library 意大利图书馆 11—72f
梅迪契小教堂 Medici Chapel 意大利教堂 11—75e
梅迪辛博山脉 Medicine Bow Mountains 美国山脉 11—76b
梅迪辛哈特 Medicine Hat 加拿大城市 11—76c
梅迪辛洛奇 Medicine Lodge 美国城市 11—76c
梅迪亚什 Mediaş 罗马尼亚城市 11—71c
梅毒 syphilis 疾病 16—403f
梅毒性脑膜脑炎 syphilitic meningoencephalitis (disease) 疾病 16—404b
梅多克 Médoc 法国葡萄酒产区 11—78f
梅多斯 Meadows, Earle 美国跳高运动员 11—62c
梅厄 Meir, Golda 以色列总理 11—87c
梅厄森 Myerson, Goldie 以色列创建者 11—524c
梅恩 Maine, Sir Henry (James Sumner) 英国法学家、历史学家 10—410d
梅恩 Mayne, Cuthbert 英格兰天主教徒 11—52e
梅恩兰岛 Mainland 苏格兰岛屿 10—411b
梅尔巴(夫人) Melba, Dame Nellie 澳大利亚歌唱家 11—93b
梅尔本子爵(第二) Melbourne (of Kilmore), William Lamb, 2nd Viscount 英国首相 11—95d
梅尔达 Merta 印度城镇 11—136b
梅尔顿 Melton 英格兰自治市 11—100e
梅尔菲 Melfi 意大利城镇 11—96e
梅尔夫 Merv 中亚细亚古城 11—137c
梅尔基斯 Merkys, Antanas 立陶宛政治家 11—132a
梅尔济丰鲁·卡拉·穆斯塔法帕夏 Merzifonlu Kara Mustafa Paşa (Ottoman grand vizier) 奥斯曼首席大臣 11—137f
梅尔卡丹特 Mercadante, (Giuseppe) Saverio (Raffaele) 意大利作曲家、教师 11—123a

梅尔卡拉 Mercāra 印度城镇 11—123d
梅尔克 Melk 奥地利城镇 11—97e
梅尔克公爵 Mercoeur, Philippe-Emmanuel de Lorraine, duc de 法国贵族 11—126a
梅尔库里乌斯 Mercurius 教皇 11—126c
梅尔库姆男爵(第一) Melcombe, George Bubb Dodington, 1st Baron 英国政客 11—96a
梅尔勒·德·奥比内 Merle d'Aubigné, Jean-Henri 瑞士新教牧师 11—132a
梅尔罗斯 Melrose 苏格兰城市 11—100c
梅尔齐纳 Mielziner, Jo 美国舞台设计师 11—204a
梅尔斯 Meres, Francis 英国作家 11—129a
梅尔斯 Meersch, Jean-André van der 比利时军事领袖 11—80a
梅尔特诺默瀑布 Multnomah Falls 美国瀑布 11—481a
梅尔万·谢里阿尔·伊拉尼 Merwan Sheriar Irani (Indian religious leader) 印度宗教领导人 11—137d
梅尔维尔 Melville, Andrew 苏格兰基督教学者 11—100f
梅尔维尔 Melville, George Wallace 美国探险家 11—100f
梅尔维尔 Melville, Herman 美国小说家、诗人 11—101b
梅尔维尔 Melville, James 苏格兰基督教改革家 11—101d
梅尔维尔 Melville, Jean-Pierre 法国电影导演 11—101e
梅尔维尔岛 Melville Island 澳大利亚岛屿 11—101e
梅尔维尔岛 Melville Island 加拿大岛屿 11—101f
梅尔维尔海峡 Melville Sound (Arctic Ocean) 北冰洋海峡 11—101f
梅尔维尔子爵(第一) Melville (of Melville), Henry Dundas, 1st Viscount, Baron Dunira 英国政客 11—101a
梅尔维尔子爵海峡 Viscount Melville Sound 北冰洋海峡 18—17f
梅尔西埃 Mercier, Louis-Sébastien 法国戏剧作家 11—125f
梅尔希奥 Melchior, Johann Peter 德国陶瓷雕刻家 11—95d
梅尔辛 Mersin 土耳其城市 11—136a
梅菲尔德 Mayfield 美国城市 11—52a
梅芙 Medb 爱尔兰神话 11—70e
梅甘法 Megan's law 美国法律 11—80f
梅戈格 Magog 加拿大城市 10—394f
梅格列尔语 Megrelian language 黑海沿岸地区语言 11—81f
梅格斯 Meigs, Montgomery C(unningham) 美国工程师、建筑师 11—85d
梅赫丁茨 Mehedinţi 罗马尼亚县名 11—81f
梅赫尔·巴巴 Meher Baba 印度宗教名人 11—82a
梅赫伦 Mechelen 比利时城市 11—69a
梅赫伦 Meegeren, Han van 荷兰画家 11—79e
梅花草属 Parnassia 植物学 13—59a
梅花鹿 sika (species *Cervus nippon*) 哺乳动物 15—364c
梅花雀 avadavat (species *Amandava*, or *Estrilda*, *amandava*) 鸟类 2—82d
梅花雀科 Estrildidae 动物学 6—142b
梅季希 Mytishchi 俄罗斯城市 11—531b
梅济耶尔 Mézières (France) 法国城市 11—172d
梅加拉亚 Meghālaya 印度邦名 11—81d
梅杰 Major, John 英国首相 10—414a
梅坎博 Mékambo 加蓬城镇 11—89f
梅克尔 Meckel, Johann Friedrich 德国解剖学家 11—69b
梅克伦堡 Mecklenburg 德国历史地区 11—69b
梅克伦堡-西波美拉尼亚 Mecklenburg-West Pomerania 德国州名 11—69d
梅克纳河 Meghna River 孟加拉国河流 11—81e
梅克内斯 Meknès 摩洛哥城市 11—89f
梅克西亚 Mexia, Ynes Enriquetta Julietta 美国植物采集者 11—164f
梅肯 Macon 美国城市 10—360f
梅肯 Macon, Nathaniel 美国国会领袖 10—361a
梅拉 Mela, Pomponius 罗马作家 11—90c
梅拉伦湖 Malar, Lake 瑞典湖泊 10—421c
梅拉诺 Merano 意大利城市 11—122f
梅兰 Merlin, Antoine-Christophe 法国革命家 11—132d
梅兰伯爵 Merlin, Philippe-Antoine, Comte 法国法学家 11—132e
梅兰芳 Mei Lanfang 中国京剧艺术家 11—84c
梅兰希顿 Melanchthon, Philipp 德国神学家、人文学家 11—90f
梅勒 Mailer, Norman 美国小说家 10—405e
梅勒蒂乌斯(安提阿的),圣 Meletius of Antioch, Saint 安提阿主教 11—96d
梅勒蒂乌斯(利科波利斯的) Meletius of Lycopolis 埃及主教 11—96e
梅勒梅克河 Meramec River 美国河流 11—122f
梅勒提奥斯·佩加斯 Meletios Pegas 希腊正教牧首 11—96c
梅雷迪思 Meredith, Mary Gladys 英国作家 11—128d
梅雷迪斯 Meredith, James 美国民权运动参与者 11—128d
梅雷迪斯 Meredith, Owen 英国外交家 11—128e
梅雷迪斯 Meredith, (Oliver) Burgess 美国演员、导演 11—128a
梅雷迪斯 Meredith, Ted 美国田径运动员 11—128e
梅雷迪斯 Meredith, William 美国诗人 11—128e
梅雷莱斯 Meireles, Cecília 巴西诗人、教师 11—87e
梅里 Merry, Ann Brunton 美国演员 11—135c
梅里 Meri, Lennart 爱沙尼亚总统 11—129e
梅里 Meri, Veijo 芬兰小说家、戏剧家 11—129f
梅里爱 Méliès, Georges 法国电影实验家 11—96f
梅里安 Meriam, Junius L(athrop) 美国教育家 11—129f
梅里安 Merian, Matthäus 德国画家、书商 11—130a
梅里昂尼德 Meirionnydd 威尔士历史地区 11—87e
梅里达 Mérida 墨西哥城市 11—130b
梅里达 Mérida 西班牙城镇 11—130b
梅里达 Mérida 委内瑞拉州名 11—130b
梅里达 Mérida 委内瑞拉城市 11—130c
梅里达 Mérida, Carlos 危地马拉美术家 11—130c
梅里德辛河 Marais des Cygnes River 美国河流 10—487f
梅里登 Meriden 美国城市 11—130d
梅里蒂 Meriti (Brazil) 巴西城市 11—131e
梅里厄姆-韦伯斯特词典 Merriam-Webster dictionary 美国词典 11—134c
梅里尔 Merrill, Charles E(dward) 美国投资银行家 11—134e
梅里尔 Merrill, James 美国诗人 11—134f
梅里尔-林奇公司 Merrill Lynch & Co., Inc. 美国金融公司 11—135a
梅里菲尔德 Merrifield, Bruce 美国生物化学家、教育家 11—134e
梅里克 Merrick, David 美国戏剧演出人 11—134d
梅里克 Merrick, Joseph Carey 英国畸形人 11—134e
梅里马克河 Merrimack River 美国河流 11—135b
"梅里麦克"号和"莫尼特"号之战 Merrimack and Monitor, Battle of 美国历史 11—135b
梅里曼 Merriman, John X(avier) 南非政治家、总理 11—135b
梅里曼案 Merryman, Ex Parte 美国法律案例 11—135d
梅里美 Mérimée, Prosper 法国戏剧家、历史学家 11—130e
梅里纳人 Merina 马达加斯加民族 11—131a
梅里奇河 Meriç (Europe) 欧洲河流 11—130a
梅里特 Meritt, Anna Lea 美国艺术家 11—131e
梅里特公路 Merritt Parkway 美国公路 11—135c
梅里翁 Méryon, Charles 法国版画家 11—137e
梅里西 Merisi, Michelangelo (painter) 意大利画家 11—131d
梅里亚姆 Merriam, Clinton Hart 美国生物学家 11—134b
梅利利亚 Melilla 西班牙城镇 11—97a
梅利利亚战争 Melilla, War of 西班牙历史 11—97c
梅利纳 Méline, Félix-Jules 法国政治家、总理 11—97c
梅利特斯(坎特伯雷的),圣 Mellitus of Canterbury, Saint 英国主教 11—98a
梅利托波尔 Melitopol 乌克兰城市 11—97e

梅利乌斯 Maelius, Spurius 古罗马平民 10—376a
梅笠草 pipsissewa 草本植物 13—319d
梅列克斯 Melekess (Russia) 俄罗斯城市 11—96c
梅列日科夫斯基 Merezhkovsky, Dmitry Sergeyevich 俄国诗人、小说家 11—129b
梅林 Mehring, Franz 德国新闻记者、历史学家 11—83e
梅林坎普 Mellencamp, John 美国歌唱家、歌曲作家 11—97f
梅灵 Mering, Joseph, Freiherr von 德国医师、生理学家 11—131b
梅岭关 Meilingguan 中国关隘 11—86b
梅龙 Meron 以色列居民点 11—133f
梅隆 Mellon, Andrew W. 美国金融家、慈善家 11—98a
梅隆国民公司 Mellon National Corporation 美国公司 11—98c
梅隆内 Meloney, Marie Mattingly 美国新闻记者、编辑 11—99e
梅隆银行 Mellon Bank 美国银行 11—98c
梅鲁 Meru 肯尼亚城镇 11—137c
梅鲁火山 Meru, Mount 坦桑尼亚火山 11—137c
梅伦德斯·巴尔德斯 Meléndez Valdés, Juan 西班牙诗人、政治家 11—96c
梅洛 Melo 乌拉圭城市 11—98d
梅洛 Merlo 阿根廷城市 11—132f
梅洛 Melo, Francisco Manuel de 葡萄牙军人 11—98d
梅洛里亚 Meloria 意大利岩石岛 11—99f
梅洛-庞蒂 Merleau-Ponty, Maurice 法国哲学家、文学家 11—132b
梅洛佐 Melozzo da Forlì 意大利画家 11—100a
梅马内 Meymaneh 阿富汗城镇 11—172c
梅曼 Maiman, Theodore H. 美国物理学家 10—406c
梅梅尔 Memel (Lithuania) 立陶宛城市 11—102d
梅梅尔争端 Memel dispute 欧洲历史 11—102d
梅米 Memmi, Albert 突尼斯小说家 11—102f
梅明格 Memminger, Christopher G(ustavus) 美国财政部长 11—103a
梅明根 Memmingen 德国城市 11—103a
梅姆灵 Memling, Hans 佛兰德斯画家 11—102e
梅纳 Mena, Juan de 西班牙诗人 11—105b
梅纳(-梅德拉诺) Mena (y Medrano), Pedro de 西班牙雕刻家 11—105b
梅纳贝 Menabé 非洲历史王国 11—105c
梅纳德 Menard, John Willis 美国国会议员 11—106b
梅纳德 Ménard, Louis-Nicolas 法国作家 11—106c
梅纳尔 Maynard, François 法国诗人 11—52e
梅纳赫姆·本·萨鲁克 Menahem ben Saruq 西班牙词典编纂家、诗人 11—105e
梅纳日 Ménage, Gilles 法国学者、文人 11—105e
梅纳西瓷器 Mennecy porcelain 法国软质瓷器 11—115f
梅奈海峡 Menai Strait 爱尔兰海海峡 11—105f
梅奈桥 Menai Bridge 英国桥梁 11—105f
梅南窦 Menander Protector 拜占廷历史学家 11—106b
梅内尔 Meynell, Sir Francis (Meredith Wilfrid) 英国图书设计家 11—172c
梅内尔夫人 Meynell, Alice (Christiana Gertrude) 英国诗人、散文作家 11—172c
梅内姆 Menem, Carlos Saúl 阿根廷总统 11—112e
梅嫩德斯·德·阿维莱斯 Menéndez de Avilés, Pedro 西班牙水手 11—112f
梅嫩德斯-佩拉约 Menéndez y Pelayo, Marcelino 西班牙评论家、历史学家 11—113a
梅嫩德斯·皮达尔 Menéndez Pidal, Ramón 西班牙学者 11—113a
梅尼尔氏病 Ménière's disease 疾病 11—114e
梅宁迪湖区 Menindee Lakes 澳大利亚水库 11—114e
梅纽因 Menuhin, Sir Yehudi 美国小提琴大师 11—121e
梅农 Menon, V(engalil) K(rishnan) Krishna 印度民族主义者 11—117b
梅农盖 Menongue 安哥拉城镇 11—117c
梅努斯 Maynooth 爱尔兰村庄 11—52f
梅诺蒂 Menotti, Gian Carlo 意大利作曲家 11—117e
梅诺卡 Minorca 西班牙岛屿 11—264d
梅诺米尼 Menominee 美国城市 11—117b
梅诺米尼人 Menominee 北美印第安人 11—117a
梅瓶 mei ping 中国青瓷花瓶 11—84e
梅珀尔 Meppel 荷兰城市 11—122e
梅普尔克里克 Maple Creek 加拿大城镇 10—484f
梅齐埃尔 Mézières, Philippe de 法国贵族、作家 11—172e
梅齐亚 Mazia, Daniel 美国细胞生物学家 11—57c
梅其 Metge, Bernat 西班牙诗人、散文家 11—157f
梅奇尼科夫 Metchnikoff, Élie 俄国动物学家、微生物学家 11—154c
梅琴 Machen, Arthur 威尔士作家 10—345f
梅琴 Machen, John Gresham 美国神学家 10—345f
梅清 Mei Qing 中国清代画家 11—84e
梅曲 Metsu, Gabriel 荷兰画家 11—162a
梅日杜列琴斯克 Mezhdurechensk 俄罗斯城市 11—172d
梅瑞狄斯 Meredith, George 英国小说家、诗人 11—128a
梅萨 Mesa 美国城市 11—137f
梅萨 Maesa, Julia 古罗马贵族 10—376c
梅萨比岭 Mesabi Range 美国铁矿 11—138c
梅萨比人 Messapii 意大利古代民族 11—143f
梅萨比语 Messapic language 印欧语言 11—143f
梅萨比字母 Messapic alphabet 意大利文字 11—143f
梅萨拉·科尔维努斯 Messalla Corvinus, Marcus Valerius 罗马贵族 11—143e
梅萨利·哈吉 Messali Hadj, Ahmed 阿尔及利亚领袖 11—143d
梅萨利纳·瓦莱里娅 Messalina Valeria 罗马皇后 11—143d
梅萨热 Messager, André(-Charles-Prosper) 法国指挥家、作曲家 11—143c
梅萨热 Messager, Charles 法国作家 11—143d
梅塞德斯 Mercedes 阿根廷城市 11—124d
梅塞德斯 Mercedes 乌拉圭城市 11—124d
梅塞尔森 Meselson, Matthew Stanley 美国分子生物学家 11—138e
梅塞纳 Mesene 古代安息国属国 11—138f
梅塞纳斯 Maecenas, Gaius (Cilnius) 古罗马外交家 10—375d
梅塞施米特 Messerschmitt, Willy 德国飞机设计家 11—144b
梅瑟蒂德菲尔 Merthyr Tydfil 威尔士城镇 11—136d
梅森 Mason, Charlotte 美国慈善家 11—2d
梅森 Mason, Daniel Gregory 美国作曲家 11—2e
梅森 Mason, George 美国爱国者、政治家 11—2f
梅森 Mason, James 英国演员 11—3a
梅森 Mason, James Murray 美国参议员 11—3a
梅森 Mason, John Mitchell 美国牧师、教育家 11—3b
梅森 Mason, Lowell 美国作曲家 11—3b
梅森 Mason, Max 美国数学物理学家 11—3c
梅森 Mersenne, Marin 法国数学家、自然哲学家 11—135e
梅森城 Mason City 美国城市 11—3d
梅森-狄克森线 Mason and Dixon Line 美国历史 11—3c
梅森陶瓷器 Mason ware 英国陶瓷器皿 11—3d
梅尚 Mechain, Pierre(-François-André) 法国天文学家、水文学家 11—67b
梅施克 Meschke, Michael 瑞典木偶戏演出人 11—138d
梅什科 Mieszko 波兰统治者之名 11—205a
梅什科二世 Mieszko II Lambert 波兰国王 11—205a
梅什科三世 Mieszko III 波兰国王 11—205a
梅什科一世 Mieszko I 波兰皮亚斯特王朝大公 11—205a
梅斯 Metz 法国城镇 11—163f
梅斯 Mace, James 英国拳击运动员 10—339c
梅斯 Mays, Willie (Howard) 美国棒球运动员 11—55c
梅斯蒂索 mestizo 混血儿 11—146a
梅斯菲尔德 Masefield, John 英国诗人 10—569d
梅斯基特 Mesquite 美国城市 11—143b

梅斯卡莱罗人 Mescalero 新墨西哥民族 11—138c
梅斯罗布,圣 Mesrob, SAINT 亚美尼亚神学家、语言学家 11—143c
梅斯梅尔 Mesmer, Franz Anton 德国医生 11—139c
梅斯梅尔 Messmer, Otto 美国动画家 11—145d
梅斯纳 Messner, Reinhold 意大利登山运动员 11—145e
梅斯塔 Mesta, Perle 美国外交家 11—145f
梅斯塔河 Mesta River (Greece) 希腊河流 11—146a
梅斯特雷 Mestre 意大利威尼斯西北郊区 11—146a
梅斯脱维奇 Meštrović, Ivan 美国雕刻家 11—146a
梅斯维尔 Maysville 美国城市 11—55c
梅斯维尔阶 Maysvillian stage 地质年代学 11—55d
梅索尼埃 Meissonier, Juste-Aurèle 法国金饰工艺家、建筑师 11—88f
梅索尼埃 Meissonier, (Jean-Louis-) Ernest 法国油画家和插图画家 11—88e
梅塔 Meta 哥伦比亚省份 11—146c
梅塔 mettā (Pāli) 佛教 11—162b
梅塔 Mehta, Zubin 印度音乐家 11—83f
梅塔芬 Metaphen (disinfectant) 化合物 11—151d
梅塔河 Meta River 美洲河流 11—146c
梅塔蓬图姆 Metapontum 意大利古城市 11—153b
梅塔斯塔齐奥 Metastasio, Pietro 意大利诗人、歌剧歌词作家 11—153d
梅泰人 Meithei 印度民族 11—89b
梅陶罗河 Metauro River 意大利河流 11—154a
梅特 Meit, Conrat 佛兰德斯雕刻家 11—89a
梅特尔 Metel, François Le 法国戏剧家 11—154d
梅特卡夫 Metcalfe (of Fern Hill), Charles T(heophilus) Metcalfe, Baron 英属印度官员 11—154b
梅特克 Mietek (Polish Communist leader) 波兰共产党领袖 11—205b
梅特腊卡王朝 Maitraka DYNASTY 印度王朝 10—412f
梅特兰 Maitland 澳大利亚城市 10—412c
梅特兰 Maitland, Frederic William 英国法学家 10—412d
梅特兰 Maitland, James (Scottish economist) 苏格兰经济学家 10—412d
梅特兰 Maitland, John 苏格兰政治家 10—412d
梅特兰 Maitland (of Thirlestane), John Maitland, 1st Lord 苏格兰大法官 10—412d
梅特兰 Maitland, Sir Richard, LORD LETHINGTON 苏格兰诗人 10—412e
梅特兰(莱辛顿的) Maitland (of Lethington), William 苏格兰政治家 10—412f
梅特林克 Maeterlinck, Maurice 比利时剧作家、诗人 10—377a
梅特卢斯 Metellus, Lucius Caecilius 罗马将军 11—154d
梅特卢斯(克里特的) Metellus Creticus, Quintus Caecilius 罗马将军 11—154e
梅特卢斯(马其顿的) Metellus Macedonicus, Quintus Caecilius 罗马将军、政治家 11—154e
梅特卢斯(努米底亚的) Metellus Numidicus, Quintus Caecilius 罗马将军 11—154f
梅特卢斯·庇护 Metellus Pius, Quintus Caecilius 罗马将军 11—154f
梅特卢斯·庇护·希皮奥 Metellus Pius Scipio, Quintus Caecilius 罗马政治家 11—154f
梅特卢斯·塞莱尔 Metellus Celer, Quintus Caecilius 罗马政治家 11—154e
梅特罗 Métraux, Alfred 瑞士人类学家 11—160a
梅特罗法内斯·克里托波洛斯 Metrophanes Kritopoulos 希腊正教牧首 11—161d
梅特涅 Metternich, Klemens, Fürst von 奥地利政治家、外交大臣 11—162b
梅托齐特斯 Metochites, Theodore 拜占廷首相 11—159e
梅文鼎 Mei Wending 中国清代数学家、天文学家 11—84f
梅伍德 Maywood, Augusta 美国芭蕾舞演员 11—55d
梅西 Massey, (Charles) Vincent 加拿大政治家 11—12b
梅西 Massey, William Ferguson 新西兰总理 11—12c
梅西(夫人) Macy, Anne Sullivan 美国教师 10—364b
梅西埃 Mercier, Honoré 加拿大政治家 11—125e
梅西昂 Messiaen, Olivier 法国作曲家、管风琴家 11—144c
梅西伯爵 Mercy, Claudius Florimund, Graf von 奥地利陆军元帅 11—127e
梅西·达让托 Mercy d'Argenteau, Florimund, Graf 奥地利外交家 11—127f
梅西公司 Macy and Company, Inc. 美国大型百货公司 10—364b
梅西科默 Messikomer, Jakob 瑞士农民、考古学家 11—145a
梅西男爵 Mercy, Franz, Freiherr von 奥地利、巴伐利亚陆军元帅 11—127f
梅西耶 Mercier, Désiré-Joseph 比利时教育家 11—125d
梅西叶 Messier, Charles 法国天文学家 11—144f
《梅西叶星表》 Messier catalog(M) 天文学 11—145a
梅县 Meixian (China) 中国城市梅州旧称 11—89d
梅象 plum curculio (*Conotrachelus nenuphar*) 昆虫 13—375d
梅肖韦古墓 Maeshowe barrow 苏格兰史前坟墓 10—376c
梅休 Mayhew, Henry 英国新闻记者 11—52c
梅休 Mayhew, Jonathan 美国传教士 11—52d
梅休因 Methuen (of Corsham), Paul Sanford Methuen, 3rd Baron 英国指挥官 11—159b
梅尧臣 Mei Yaochen 中国北宋诗人 11—84f
梅耶 Meillet, Antoine 法国语言学家 11—86b
梅耶 Mayer, Louis B(urt) 美国电影业巨头 11—51e
梅耶贝尔 Meyerbeer, Giacomo 德国作曲家 11—171d
梅耶尔 Meyer, (Marie-) Paul(-Hyacinthe) 法国语言学家 11—171b
梅耶夫人 Mayer, Maria Goeppert 德国物理学家 11—51f
梅伊尔 Meïr 犹太教拉比、学者 11—87b
梅衣属 Parmelia 生物学 13—58d
梅贻琦 Mei Yiqi 中国教育家 11—85a
梅因纳斯 Meinesz, Felix Andries Vening (Dutch geodesist) 荷兰地球物理学家 11—86d
梅于尔 Méhul, Étienne-Nicolas 法国作曲家 11—84b
梅原龙三郎 Umehara Ryūzaburō 日本画家 17—337b
梅泽堡 Merseburg 德国城市 11—135e
梅扎马火山灰层 Mazama Ash 地质学 11—55e
梅州 Meizhou 中国城市 11—89d
梅佐乔尔诺 Mezzogiorno 意大利地区 11—172f
媒染染料 mordant dye 化合物 11—386c
湄公河 Mekong River 东南亚河流 11—90a
湄南河 Maenam (river, Thailand) 泰国河流 10—376b
煤 coal 矿物 4—310e
煤袋 Coalsack 天文学 4—311f
煤核 coal ball 地质学 4—311b
煤焦油 coal tar 化合物 4—311c
煤馏油 coal oil (fuel) 燃料 4—311c
煤气 coal gas 化合物 4—311b
煤绒菌属 Fuligo 微生物学 6—517f
煤污病斑 sooty mold 植物病害 15—517b
煤油 kerosine 燃料 9—242a
煤油灯 kerosine lamp 灯具 9—242a
酶 enzyme 生物化学 6—91e
酶分析 enzyme analysis 生物化学 6—92b
酶原 zymogen 生物化学 18—578d
镅(Am) americium 化学元素 1—285e
霉 mildew 生物学 11—213e
霉 mold 生物学 11—315d
霉草目 Triuridales 植物学 17—228f
《每日电讯报》 Daily Telegraph, The 英国报纸 5—112b
《每日镜报》 Daily Mirror 英国报纸 5—112a

《每日快报》 Daily Express 英国报纸 5—111f
《每日新闻》 Mainichi shimbun 日本报纸 10—411a
《每日新闻报》 Dagens Nyheter 瑞典报纸 5—106e
《每日邮报》 Daily Mail 英国报纸 5—112a
美呗 Bibai 日本城市 2—457a
美狄亚 Medea 希腊神话 11—70e
美荻 My Tho 越南城市 11—520e
美第奇 Medici, Caterina de'(queen of France) 法国王后 11—74c
美第奇 Médicis, Catherine de (queen of France) 法国王后 11—76e
美第奇 Médicis, Marie de (queen of France) 法国王后 11—76e
美第奇 Medici, Maria de'(queen of France) 法国王后 11—75d
美都姆 Maydūm 埃及古遗址 11—51c
美多迪乌斯,圣 Methodius, SAINT 基督教神学家 11—159a
美多迪乌斯一世 Methodius I, SAINT 希腊正教牧首 11—159a
美恩 Men 月神 11—105a
美孚公司 Mobil Corporation 原美国石油化工公司 11—300a
美国 United States 北美洲国家 17—364a
美国芭蕾舞剧院 American Ballet Theatre 美国艺术团体 1—276a
美国芭蕾舞团 American Ballet 美国艺术团体 1—276a
《美国百科全书》 Encyclopedia Americana, The 大型百科全书 6—71f
美国棒球联盟 American League 美国和加拿大体育机构 1—281b
美国保护协会 American Protective Association (APA) 美国政治组织 1—282f
美国保守浸礼协进会 Conservative Baptist Association of America 美国基督教组织 4—445e
美国波兰民族公教会 Polish National Catholic Church of America 美国宗教组织 13—402a
美国稠李 chokecherry (*Prunus virginiana*) 植物 4—190a
美国传教协会 American Missionary Association (AMA) 美国民权组织 1—282b
美国大学妇女协会 American Association of University Women (AAUW) 美国妇女组织 1—275f
美国大学女生联谊会 sorority 美国学生组织 15—523a
美国大学生联谊会和大学女生联谊会 fraternity and sorority 美国学生组织 6—456a
美国党 American Party 美国政党 1—282e
美国地方法院 United States District Court 美国法院 17—371c
美国地名委员会 Geographic Names, Board on (BGN) 美国政府机构 7—71c
美国第一委员会 America First Committee 美国历史 1—275a
美国电话电报公司 American Telephone & Telegraph Company (AT&T) 美国公司 1—284c
美国电影协会 Motion Picture Association of America (MPAA) 美国电影公司组织 11—433c
美国独立纪念日 Independence Day 美国历史 8—356f
美国独立战争 United States War of Independence 美国历史 17—373c
美国独木舟 pirogue 船只 13—322b
美国儿童局 United States Children's Bureau 美国联邦机构 17—370d
美国反奴隶制协会 American Anti-Slavery Society 美国历史 1—275c
美国福音信义会 American Evangelical Lutheran Church 美国基督教组织 1—277e
美国福音信义会 Evangelical Lutheran Church in America (ELCA) 美国基督教组织 6—178b
美国妇女局 United States Women's Bureau 美国联邦机构 17—374a
美国妇女选举权协会 American Woman Suffrage Association (AWSA) 美国政治组织 1—284f
美国橄榄球联盟 American Football League (AFL) 美国体育组织 1—278f
美国钢铁工人联合会 United Steelworkers of America (USWA) 美国工会 17—374b
美国钢铁公司 United States Steel Corporation 美国公司 17—373a
美国革命 American Revolution 美国历史 1—283b
美国革命女儿 Daughters of the American Revolution (DAR) 美国组织 5—164f
美国革命战争 Revolutionary War, American 美国历史 14—253c
美国公开赛 United States Open Championship 高尔夫球比赛 17—372f
美国公民自由联盟 American Civil Liberties Union (ACLU) 美国社会组织 1—276e
美国公谊服务委员会 American Friends Service Committee (AFSC) 美国和加拿大基督教组织 1—279a
美国广播公司 American Broadcasting Company (ABC) 美国公司 1—276d
美国归正会 Reformed Church in America 美国教会 14—199d
美国国会 Congress of the United States 美国政治 4—429a
美国国会大厦 Capitol, United States 美国建筑 3—427d
美国国会荣誉勋章 Congressional Medal of Honor 美国军事 4—429d
美国国家植物园 United States National Arboretum 美国园林 17—372a
美国海岸警卫队 United States Coast Guard, The (USCG) 美国军种 17—370e
美国海岸警卫队军官学校 United States Coast Guard Academy 美国高等学府 17—370f
美国海军 United States Navy, The (USN) 美国军种 17—372d
美国海军军官学校 United States Naval Academy 美国高等学府 17—372b
美国海军陆战队 United States Marine Corps, The (USMC) 美国军种 17—371c
美国海军天文台 United States Naval Observatory (USNO) 美国天文机构 17—372c
美国航空公司 American Airlines, Inc. 美国航空集团 1—275b
美国黑人英语 African American English (AAE) 英语的一种变体 1—109a
美国花马 Pinto 马品种 13—316b
美国化 Americanization 社会学 1—285a
美国计划生育联合会 Planned Parenthood Federation of America 美国社会组织 13—343f
美国进出口银行 Export-Import Bank of the United States (EXIMBANK) 美国金融机构 6—195f
美国浸礼协进会 American Baptist Association 美国宗教团体 1—276b
美国浸礼宣教协进会 Baptist Missionary Association of America 美国基督教组织 2—213a
美国军事上诉法院 United States Court of Appeals for the Armed Forces 17—371b
美国卡车司机、汽车司机、仓库工人和佣工国际工人兄弟会 International Brotherhood of Teamsters, Chauffeurs, Warehousemen and Helpers of America 美国工会组织 8—413d
美国科学促进协会 American Association for the Advancement of Science 美国科学家协会 1—275e
美国空军 United States Air Force, The (USAF) 美国军种 17—369f
美国空军军官学校 United States Air Force Academy 美国高等学府 17—370b
美国夸特马 American Quarter horse 马品种 1—282f
美国篮球协会 American Basketball Association (ABA) 美国体育组织 1—276c
美国劳工党 American Labor Party (ALP) 美国政党 1—281a
美国劳工联合会-产业工会联合会(劳联-产联) American Federation of Labor-Congress of Industrial Organizations (AFL-CIO) 美国工人组织

1—278b
美国联邦索赔法院 United States Court of Federal Claims 美国法院 17—371b
美国联合矿工工会 United Mine Workers of America (UMWA) 美国工会 17—356d
美国联合汽车工人工会 UAW 美国工人组织 17—316b
美国联合汽车、航天和农机工人国际工会 United Automobile, Aerospace and Agricultural Implement Workers of America: International Union 美国产业工会 17—351c
美国联合犹太会堂 United Synagogue of America (USA) 宗教组织 17—374c
美国陆军 United States Army, The 美国军种 17—370c
美国陆军军官学校 United States Military Academy 美国高等学府 17—371e
美国铝公司 Aluminum Company of America (Alcoa) 美国公司 1—259b
美国律师协会 American Bar Association (ABA) 美国律师组织 1—276c
美国穆斯林教团 American Muslim Mission 美国宗教组织 1—282e
美国南北战争 American Civil War 美国历史 1—277a
美国南部 South, the 美国地理 15—531e
美国农业社团联合会 American Farm Bureau Federation 美国农民组织 1—278a
美国女子业余锦标赛 United States Women's Amateur Championship 高尔夫球比赛 17—374a
美国皮毛公司 American Fur Company 美国企业 1—279a
美国平等权利协会 American Equal Rights Association (AERA) 美国社会组织 1—277e
美国骑乘马 American Saddlebred horse 马品种 1—283c
美国汽车公司 American Motors Corporation (AMC) 美国汽业制造公司 1—282c
美国全国妇女选举权协会 National American Woman Suffrage Association (NAWSA) 美国女权组织 12—10f
美国全国基督教协进会 National Council of the Churches of Christ in the U.S.A. 美国教会 12—14a
美国全国浸礼联会 National Baptist Convention of America 美国黑人教会组织 12—12b
美国人文科学基金会 National Endowment for the Humanities (NEH) 美国政府独立机构 12—14e
美国人争取民主行动组织 Americans for Democratic Action (ADA) 美国政治组织 1—285b
美国商标公司 American Brands, Inc. 美国公司 1—276d
美国商船学校 United States Merchant Marine Academy 美国高等学府 17—371d
美国上诉法院 United States Court of Appeals 美国法院 17—370f
美国圣公会 Protestant Episcopal Church 美国教会 13—543e
美国圣经学会 American Bible Society (ABS) 美国宗教组织 1—276d
美国石竹 sweet William (*Dianthus barbatus*) 植物 16—380b
美国式簧风琴 melodeon 乐器 11—98e
美国司法会议 Judicial Conference of the United States 法律 9—102b
美国诉奈特公司案 United States v. E.C.Knight Company 美国法院案例 17—373c
美国铁路捷运公司 American Railway Express Company 美国公司 1—283a
美国退伍军人协会 American Legion 美国军人组织 1—281b
美国退休人员协会 American Association of Retired Persons (AARP) 美国非营利性组织 1—275e
美国网球公开赛 United States Open Tennis Championships 国际网球比赛 17—372f
美国文学 American literature 文学 1—281c
美国文艺复兴 American Renaissance 美国文学 1—283a
美国无线电公司 Radio Corporation of America 美国公司 14—114a
美国五旬节真神会 Pentecostal Church of God of America, Inc. 美国基督教组织 13—148f
美国西部 West, THE 美国地理区域 18—193e
美国希伯来会众协进会 American Hebrew Congregations, Union of 美国犹太教组织 1—279a
《美国新闻与世界报道》 U.S. News & World Report 美国杂志 17—421f
《美国信使》 American Mercury 美国期刊 1—282b
美国信义会 Lutheran Church in America (LCA) 美国基督教组织 10—300e
美国业余锦标赛 United States Amateur Championship 美国高尔夫球赛 17—370c
美国业余体育联盟 Amateur Athletic Union of the United States (AAU) 美国体育组织 1—266f
美国医学协会 American Medical Association (AMA) 美国医师组织 1—282a
美国移民分地遗迹 Homestead National Monument of America 美国历史 8—145f
美国义勇军 Volunteers of America 美国组织 18—46b
美国艺术和科学学会 American Academy of Arts and Sciences 美国学术组织 1—275b
美国艺术基金会 National Endowment for the Arts (NEA) 美国政府独立机构 12—14d
美国银行 United States, Bank of the 美国金融机构 17—369c
美国印第安人运动 American Indian Movement (AIM) 美国民权组织 1—280f
《美国英语词典》 American Dictionary of the English Language, An 美国辞书 1—277d
《美国英语词典(按历史原则编订)》 Dictionary of American English on Historical Principles, A (DAE) 美国辞书 5—302a
美国影视博物馆 American Museum of the Moving Image 美国博物馆 1—282d
美国邮政编码 ZIP Code 邮政制度 18—558a
《美国语词典》 Dictionary of Americanisms, A 美国辞书 5—302a
美国援外合作社 CARE 国际性救济组织 3—455f
美国运通公司 American Express Company 美国运输公司 1—277e
美国哲学学会 American Philosophical Society 美国学术团体 1—282e
美国证券交易所 American Stock Exchange (AMEX) 美国金融机构 1—284c
美国之音 Voice of America (VOA) 美国传媒 18—33e
美国职业高尔夫球协会 Professional Golfers' Association of America (PGA) 美国体育组织 13—528a
美国殖民协会 American Colonization Society 美国废奴主义者组织 1—277c
美国制罐公司 American Can Company 美国公司 1—276e
美国中西部的地区主义 Midwestern Regionalism 美国文学运动 11—203c
美国州县市雇员联合会 American Federation of State, County and Municipal Employees (AFSCME) 美国社会组织 1—278f
美国自然历史博物馆 American Museum of Natural History 美国博物馆 1—282d
美国自由福音会 Evangelical Free Church of America 美国基督教组织 6—178b
美国最高法院 Supreme Court of the United States 美国法律 16—349e
美果榄 sapote (*Calocarpum mammosum*) 木本植物 15—57c
《美猴王》 Monkey 中国古典小说 11—341f
美湖 Handsome Lake (Seneca Indian chief) 印第安人领袖 7—458e
美湖崇拜 Handsome Lake cult 印第安人宗教 7—458e
美惠女神 Grace 希腊女神 7—237b

美吉多 Megiddo 巴勒斯坦古镇 11—81e
美拉尼西亚 Melanesia 太平洋群岛 11—91c
美拉尼西亚地理人种 Melanesian geographic race 人类学 11—92c
美拉尼西亚混杂语 Melanesian Pidgin 大洋洲语言 11—92e
美拉尼西亚诸语言 Melanesian languages 大洋洲语言 11—92d
美莱大屠杀 My Lai Massacre 越南战争 11—520e
美乐号 mellophone 乐器 11—98d
美丽大百合 mariposa lily 草本植物 10—516f
《美丽的澳大利亚,前进》 Advance Australia Fair 澳大利亚国歌 1—89b
美利坚大学 American University 美国大学 1—284f
美利坚高地 American Highland 南极洲地区 1—279b
美利坚合众国浸礼会 American Baptist Churches in the U.S.A. 美国基督教组织 1—276b
《美利坚合众国宪法》 Constitution of the United States of America 美国法律 4—459d
美利坚合众国信义协进会 Lutheran Council in the United States of America (LCUSA) 美国基督教组织 10—301a
美利坚赛 American round 射箭比赛 1—283b
美利坚信义会 American Lutheran Church 美国基督教组织 1—282a
美利奴绵羊 Merino 哺乳动物 11—131c
美利托(萨迪斯的) Melito OF SARDIS 希腊主教 11—97d
美联社 Associated Press (AP) 美国通讯社 1—563d
美鳞鱼属 Leptolepis 古生物学 10—32f
美名大师 baʿal shem 犹太教称号 2—106d
美名大师托夫 Baʿal Shem Ṭov 犹太教哈西德派创始人 2—106e
美尼斯 Menes 埃及国王 11—113b
美尼斯 Mēness 波罗的海各国宗教的月神 11—113c
美浓部达吉 Minobe Tatsukichi 日本法学家 11—263f
美人蕉科 Cannaceae 植物学 3—402d
美人鱼 mermaid 民间传说 11—132f
美人鱼酒店 Mermaid Tavern 伦敦俱乐部 11—133b
美柔汀法 mezzotint 艺术 11—173c
美沙酮 methadone 药物 11—157f
美声唱法 bel canto 歌剧演唱风格 2—348e
美声裸鼻雀 euphonia 鸟类 6—162c
美属萨摩亚群岛 American Samoa 太平洋美属岛屿 1—283d
美属维尔京群岛 Virgin Islands of the United States 加勒比海美属岛屿 18—8d
美术 fine art 艺术 6—318a
美术博物馆 Fine Arts, Museum of 美国文化中心 6—318a
美术博物馆 Fine Arts, Museum of 委内瑞拉博物馆 6—318a
美术风格 Beaux-Arts style (architecture) 建筑 2—316c
美术宫 Fine Arts, Palace of 墨西哥文化中心 6—318b
美术学校 Beaux-Arts, École des 法国学校 2—316b
美术学院 art, academy of 视觉艺术学院 1—521c
美术学院陈列馆 Academy, Gallery of the 佛罗伦萨博物馆 1—41c
美索不达米亚 Mesopotamia 亚洲历史地区 11—140d
美索不达米亚 Mesopotamia 阿根廷地理区域 11—141b
美索不达米亚神话 Mesopotamian mythology 亚洲文化 11—141c
美索不达米亚宗教 Mesopotamian religion 亚洲宗教 11—141e
美西螈 axolotl (*Ambystoma*, or *Siredon*, *mexicanum*) 两栖动物 2—94b
美西战争 Spanish-American War 世界历史 16—5a
美心蛤属 Venericardia 古生物学 17—498c
美须兰属 Calopogon 植物学 3—357c
美学 aesthetics 艺术哲学 1—100a
美叶树 beauty leaf (*Calophyllum inophyllum*) 木本植物 2—315c
美因茨 Mainz 德国城市 10—411d
美因-多瑙运河 Main-Danube Canal 德国水道 10—407a
美因河 Main River 德国河流 10—407c
美因河畔法兰克福 Frankfurt am Main 德国城市 6—449b
《美哉加拿大》 O Canada 加拿大国歌 12—314a
美洲 Americas 大陆 1—285c
美洲矮种马 Americas, pony of the 马品种 1—285c
美洲豹 jaguar (*Leo onca*) 哺乳动物 8—517c
美洲杯 America's Cup 国际帆船竞赛 1—285d
美洲茶属 Ceanothus 植物学 3—546d
美洲常春藤 American ivy 草本植物 1—281a
美洲赤鹿 wapiti (species *Cervus canadensis*) 哺乳动物 18—99e
美洲大沙漠 Great American Desert 北美洲半干旱地域 7—268f
美洲俄罗斯正教和希腊公教教会 Russian Orthodox Greek Catholic Church of America 东正教自治教会 14—464e
美洲狗鱼蛙 pickerel frog (*Rana palustris*) 两栖动物 13—289e
美洲国家组织 American States, Organization of (OAS) 国际组织 1—284a
美洲猝 elk, American 哺乳动物 6—46c
美洲旱獭 woodchuck (*Marmota monax*) 哺乳动物 18—321f
美洲黑栎树皮 quercitron bark 染色物质 14—86f
美洲黑熊 black bear (species *Ursus americanus*) 哺乳动物 2—510b
美洲开发银行 Inter-American Development Bank (IADB) 国际组织 8—407e
美洲拉比大会 Rabbinical Council of America 犹太教组织 14—101e
美洲梅锥象甲 American plum weevil 昆虫 1—282f
美洲摩尔人科学神庙 Moorish Science Temple of America 伊斯兰教派 11—381e
美洲尼格罗人 American Negro 美洲民族 1—282e
美洲鲵 hellbender (*Cryptobranchus alleganiensis*) 两栖动物 7—575f
美洲区域工人组织 Organización Regional Interamericana de Trabajadores (ORIT) 拉丁美洲劳工组织 12—458c
美洲山核桃 pecan (*Carya illinoensis*) 木本植物 13—116e
美洲山榄属 Bumelia 植物学 3—251a
美洲狮 puma (*Felis concolor*) 哺乳动物 14—22f
美洲斯皮扎雀 dickcissel (*Spiza americana*) 鸟类 5—294e
美洲土人 Native American 土著民族 12—39f
美洲驼 llama (*Lama glama*) 哺乳动物 10—167d
美洲鸵鸟 rhea 鸟类 14—258f
美洲熊 American bear 哺乳动物 1—276c
美洲野牛 bison (*Bison bison*) 哺乳动物 2—502c
美洲夜鹰 nighthawk 鸟类 12—188e
美洲银行公司 Bank of America Corporation 美国持股公司 2—204d
美洲银行国民信托储蓄会 America NT & SA, Bank of 美国金融机构 1—275a
美洲印第安地理人种 American Indian geographical race 人类学 1—280c
美洲印第安人 American Indian 美洲土著民族 1—279b
美洲印第安诸语言 American Indian languages 美洲语言 1—280c
美洲鹦鹉 conure 鸟类 4—473f
美洲犹太会堂协进会 Synagogue Council of America 犹太人组织 16—400e
美洲犹太教神学院 Jewish Theological Seminary of America (JTSA) 美国犹太教学术中心 9—9e
美洲有色地域人种 American Coloured local race 人类学 1—277d
美洲越橘 huckleberry 木本植物 8—220b
美洲正教会 Orthodox Church in America 北美宗教教会 12—473e
美洲正统犹太教会众联合会 Orthodox Jewish Congregations of America, Union of 犹太教联合机构 12—474b
美洲锥虫病 American trypanosomiasis 疾病 1—284f
美洲紫杉 American yew (species *Taxus canadensis*) 木本植物 1—285a
镁 magnesium 化学 10—386c
镁电气石 dravite 矿物 5—416a
镁橄榄石-铁橄榄石系列 forsterite-fayalite series 矿物系列 6—

412d
镁黄长石 åkermanite 矿物 1—154b
镁碱沸石 ferrierite 矿物 6—292e
镁铝矾 pickeringite 矿物 13—290d
镁铝榴石 pyrope 宝石 14—47f
镁钠闪石 magnesioriebeckite 矿物 10—386b
镁缺乏 magnesium deficiency 病理现象 10—386e
镁铁橄榄石 hortonolite 矿物 8—187b
镁铁矿 magnesioferrite 矿物 10—386b
镁铁闪石 cummingtonite 矿物 5—60c
镁铁质岩 mafic rock 岩石 10—377f
镁硬绿泥石 sismondine 矿物 15—404e
门 door 建筑 5—386d
门巴语 Monba language 中国语言 11—330f
门巴族 Monba 中国民族 11—330e
门采尔 Menzel, Adolf (Friedrich Erdmann) von 德国画家 11—122a
门楚 Menchú, Rigoberta 危地马拉人权活动家 11—106d
门代尔·莫海尔·塞法里姆 Mendele Moykher Sforim 俄国犹太作家 11—107f
门德尔 Mendel, Lafayette Benedict 美国生物化学家 11—107e
门德尔松 Mendelsohn, Erich 德国建筑师 11—108d
门德尔松 Mendelssohn, Fanny 德国钢琴家、作曲家 11—108e
门德尔松 Mendelssohn, Felix 德国钢琴家、指挥家 11—108f
门德尔松 Mendelssohn, Moses 德国哲学家、评论家 11—109e
门德拉 Mandla 印度城市 10—454d
门德雷斯河 Menderes River 土耳其河流 11—110c
门德人 Mende 塞拉利昂民族 11—107b
门德斯 Méndez, Aparicio 乌拉圭律师、法学家 11—110f
门德索尔 Mandasor 印度城市 10—452f
门登霍尔 Mendenhall, Thomas Corwin 美国物理学家、气象学家 11—110b
门登霍尔冰川 Mendenhall Glacier 美国冰川 11—110b
门迪 Mandi 印度城市 10—454c
门迪 Mendi 巴布亚新几内亚城市 11—110f
门迪普 Mendip 英格兰区名 11—111a
门迪普丘陵 Mendip Hills 英国丘陵 11—111b
门迪亚 Mandya 印度城市 10—455f
门蒂兰塔 Mäntyranta, Eero 芬兰滑雪运动员 10—476a
门多萨 Mendoza 阿根廷省份 11—111c
门多萨 Mendoza 阿根廷城市 11—111d
门多萨 Mendoza, Antonio de 新西班牙总督 11—111f
门多萨 Mendoza, Daniel 英国拳击运动员 11—112a
门多萨 Mendoza, Iñigo López de, marqués de Santillana 西班牙诗人 11—112a
门多萨 Mendoza, Pedro de 西班牙军人、探险家 11—112a
门多萨 Mendoza, Pedro González de 西班牙红衣主教 11—112b
门多萨阶 Mendocian Stage 地质学 11—111b
门多西诺断裂带 Mendocino Fracture Zone 东太平洋海底断裂带 11—111b
门弗雷梅戈格湖 Memphremagog, Lake 美洲湖泊 11—105a
门格尔 Menger, Carl 奥地利经济学家 11—114a
门格勒 Mengele, Josef 德国奥斯威辛灭绝营医师 11—113f
门格洛尔 Mangalore 印度城镇 10—457b
门格斯图·海尔·马里亚姆 Mengistu Haile Mariam 埃塞俄比亚国家元首 11—114a
门赫尔贝赫 Mengelberg, (Josef) Willem 荷兰交响乐指挥 11—113e
门户开放政策 Open Door policy 美国对华政策 12—427b
门捷列夫 Mendeleyev, Dmitry Ivanovich 俄国化学家 11—108b
门静脉 portal vein 解剖学 13—448a
门卡乌拉 Menkaure 埃及国王 11—115d
门肯 Menken, Adah Isaacs 美国演员、诗人 11—115e
门肯 Mencken, H.L. 美国评论家、新闻记者 11—107a
门廊 porch 建筑 13—440b
门廊(有圆柱的) portico 建筑 13—451d
门罗 Monroe 美国路易斯安那州城市 11—349a
门罗 Monroe 美国密歇根州城市 11—349a
门罗 Monroe, Bill 美国音乐家 11—349a
门罗 Monroe, Harriet 美国杂志创办人、主编 11—349b
门罗 Monroe, James 美国总统 11—349c
门罗家族 Monro FAMILY 苏格兰医生世家 11—348e
门罗维尔 Monroeville 美国自治镇 11—350b
门罗主义 Monroe Doctrine 美国政治 11—350a
门洛帕克 Menlo Park 美国加利福尼亚州城市 11—115e
门洛帕克 Menlo Park 美国新泽西州社区 11—115e
门奈赫莫斯 Menaechmus 希腊数学家 11—105d
门宁 Mennin, Peter 美国作曲家、教育家 11—116a
门宁格家族 Menninger FAMILY 美国医师世家 11—116a
门农 Memnon 希腊神话人物 11—103b
门诺·西门 Menno Simonsz(oon) 荷兰牧师 11—116c
门诺宗信徒 Mennonite 基督教派别 11—116d
门派 sampradāya 印度教 15—1c
门神 Menshen 中国神话神名 11—118b
门泰斯王朝 Menteşe DYNASTY 土库曼王朝 11—120f
门特赫德 Mandhata (India) 印度朝圣地 10—454c
门图荷太普二世 Mentuhotep II 埃及国王 11—121c
门托 Mentor 美国城市 11—121c
门兴格拉德巴赫 Mönchengladbach 德国城市 11—331b
门真 Kadoma 日本城市 9—128d
钔(Md) mendelevium 化学元素 11—108a
虻 horse fly 昆虫 8—180c
虻圆尾鹱 gadfly petrel 鸟类 6—543c
萌发 germination 植物学 7—98f
萌生林 coppice 生态学 4—493f
蒙 Hmong 中国民族 8—107a
蒙巴顿 Mountbatten, Louis Alexander 英国海军上将 11—446d
蒙巴顿 Mountbatten (of Burma), Louis Mountbatten, 1st Earl 英国政治家 11—446d
蒙巴顿 Mountbatten, Philip 英国王子 11—446f
蒙巴萨 Mombasa 肯尼亚港口 11—326d
蒙贝利亚尔 Montbéliard 法国城镇 11—359f
蒙彼利埃 Montpelier 美国城市 11—370d
蒙彼利埃 Montpellier 法国城市 11—370e
蒙彼利埃彩陶 Montpellier faience 法国彩陶 11—370f
蒙彼利埃第一大学、第二大学、第三大学 Montpellier I, II, and III, Universities of 法国大学 11—370f
蒙波斯人 Mompox 南美古代民族 11—327b
蒙博杜勋爵 Monboddo, James Burnett, Lord 苏格兰法理学家、人类学家 11—331a
蒙博托 Mobutu Sese Seko 扎伊尔总统 11—301a
蒙博托湖 Mobutu Sese Seko, Lake (eastern Africa) 非洲湖泊 11—301d
蒙博托尼罗河 Mobutu Nile (Uganda) 乌干达河流 11—301a
蒙城 Mon 印度城镇 11—327c
蒙达战役 Munda, Battle of 罗马历史 11—483b
蒙达诸民族 Muṇḍā 印度民族 11—483a
蒙达诸语言 Muṇḍā languages 印度语言 11—483a
蒙大拿 Montana 美国州名 11—356f
蒙代尔 Mondale, Walter F(rederick) 美国律师 11—331f
蒙岛 Môn, Ynys (Wales) 威尔士岛屿 11—327d
蒙得维的亚 Montevideo 乌拉圭省份 11—365c
蒙得维的亚 Montevideo 乌拉圭首都 11—365d
《蒙得维的亚公约》 Montevideo Convention 美洲历史 11—365e
蒙德 Mond, Ludwig 英国化学家、实业家 11—331f
蒙德古河 Mondego River 葡萄牙河流 11—332a
蒙德阶 Montian Stage 地质学 11—369a

蒙德里安 Mondrian, Piet 荷兰画家 11—332c
蒙德马桑 Mont-de-Marsan 法国城镇 11—352a
蒙迪诺 Mondino DE' Luzzi 意大利医生、解剖学家 11—332b
蒙蒂 Monti, Eugenio 意大利大雪橇运动员 11—368f
蒙蒂 Monti, Vincenzo 意大利诗人 11—369a
蒙蒂菲奥里 Montefiore, Claude Joseph Goldsmid 英国神学家 11—361f
蒙蒂利亚 Montilla 西班牙城市 11—369d
蒙蒂尼 Montini, Giovanni Battista 教皇 11—369d
蒙蒂茹 Montijo 葡萄牙城镇 11—369c
蒙蒂塞利 Monticelli, Adolphe(-Joseph-Thomas) 法国画家 11—369b
蒙蒂塞洛 Monticello 美国城市 11—369c
蒙蒂斯克拉鲁斯 Montes Claros 巴西城市 11—363c
蒙蒂兹 Montez, Lola 爱尔兰冒险家、舞蹈家 11—365e
蒙杜 Moundou 乍得城市 11—439f
蒙杜鲁库人 Mundurukú 南美印第安人 11—483e
蒙多涅多 Mondoñedo 西班牙城市 11—332b
蒙多维 Mondovì 意大利城镇 11—332b
蒙法尔科内 Monfalcone 意大利城镇 11—335c
蒙费拉 Montferrat 意大利历史地区 11—366c
蒙福德 Mountford, Ces 新西兰橄榄球运动员 11—446f
蒙福尔,圣 Montfort, Saint Louis-Marie Grignion de 法国天主教司铎 11—366e
蒙福孔 Montfaucon, Bernard de 法国学者 11—366c
蒙福特-德莱莫斯 Monforte de Lemos 西班牙城市 11—335d
蒙戈尔费埃(兄弟) Montgolfier, Joseph-Michel and Jacques-Étienne 法国飞行员 11—367b
蒙哥 Möngke 蒙古统治者 11—335f
蒙哥马利 Montgomery 美国县名 11—367e
蒙哥马利 Montgomery 威尔士城镇 11—367f
蒙哥马利 Montgomery (Pakistan) 巴基斯坦城市 11—367e
蒙哥马利 Montgomerie, Alexander 苏格兰诗人 11—367d
蒙哥马利 Montgomery, James 苏格兰诗人、新闻记者 11—368b
蒙哥马利 Montgomery, Lucy Maud 加拿大小说家 11—368b
蒙哥马利(阿拉曼的) Montgomery (of Alamein, of Hindhead), Bernard Law Montgomery, 1st Viscount 英国陆军元帅 11—367f
蒙哥马利郡 Montgomeryshire 威尔士历史郡 11—368c
蒙哥马利·沃德公司 Montgomery Ward & Co. 美国公司 11—368b
蒙河 Mun River 泰国河流 11—481f
蒙吉贝洛 Mongibello (volcano, Sicily) 意大利火山 11—335f
蒙吉尔 Monghyr 印度城镇 11—335f
蒙卡尔姆 Montcalm (de Saint-Véran), Louis-Joseph de Montcalm-Grozon, marquis de 法国将军 11—360a
蒙卡列里 Moncalieri 意大利城镇 11—331b
蒙卡奇 Munkács (Ukraine) 乌克兰城市 11—485c
蒙科比耶 Montcorbier, François de (French poet) 法国诗人 11—360b
蒙克 Munch, Edvard 挪威画家 11—482b
蒙克 Monck, George 英国将军 11—331c
蒙克 Munk, Kaj 丹麦剧作家 11—485b
蒙克 Monk, Maria 美国故事编造者 11—340f
蒙克 Monk, Meredith 美国表演艺术家 11—341a
蒙克 Munch, Peter Andreas 挪威历史学家 11—482e
蒙克 Munch, Peter Rochegune 丹麦历史学家 11—482e
蒙克 Monk, Thelonious (Sphere) 美国钢琴家、作曲家 11—341b
蒙克(巴利特拉蒙的) Monck (of Ballytrammon), Sir Charles Stanley, 4th Viscount 加拿大总督 11—331c
蒙克顿 Moncton 加拿大城市 11—331e
蒙克洛瓦 Monclova 墨西哥城市 11—331e
蒙库 Mongkut 暹罗国王 11—336a
蒙拉德 Monrad, Ditlev Gothard 丹麦教士、政治家 11—348d
蒙拉德 Monrad, Marcus Jakob 挪威哲学家 11—348e
蒙雷阿莱 Monreale 意大利城镇 11—348e
蒙吕克 Monluc, Blaise de Lasseran-Massencôme, Seigneur de 法国元帅 11—342e
蒙吕松 Montluçon 法国城镇 11—369d
蒙罗维亚 Monrovia 利比里亚首都 11—350b
蒙马尼 Montmagny 加拿大城市 11—369d
蒙茅斯 Monmouth 美国城市 11—342e
蒙茅斯 Monmouth 威尔士城镇 11—342e
蒙茅斯公爵 Monmouth, James Scott, Duke of, Duke of Buccleuch, Earl of Doncaster, Earl of Dalkeith, Baron Scott of Tindale, Lord Scott of Whitchester and Eskdale 英格兰反叛者 11—342f
蒙茅斯郡 Monmouthshire 威尔士郡名 11—343b
蒙茅斯郡府战役 Monmouth Court House, Battle of 美国历史 11—343a
蒙昧时代 jāhilīyah 伊斯兰教 8—517f
蒙莫朗西 Montmorency, Filips van 神圣罗马帝国宫廷侍从 11—370b
蒙莫朗西-昂古莱姆女公爵 Montmorency et Angoulême, Diane de France, Duchess de 法国女公爵 11—370b
蒙莫朗西-布特维尔 Montmorency-Bouteville, François-Henri de 法国将领 11—370b
蒙莫朗西公爵 Montmorency, Anne, duc de 法国陆军统帅 11—369e
蒙莫朗西公爵 Montmorency, François, Duke (duc) de 法国政治家 11—369f
蒙莫朗西公爵 Montmorency, Henri I, Duke (duc) de 法国政治家 11—370a
蒙莫朗西公爵 Montmorency, Henri II, Duke (duc) de 法国政治家 11—370a
蒙莫朗西男爵 Montmorency, Mathieu II, baron de 法国贵族 11—369e
蒙莫朗西男爵和公爵 Montmorency, BARONS AND DUKES OF 法国贵族家族 11—369e
蒙莫朗西瀑布 Montmorency Falls 加拿大瀑布 11—370b
蒙庞西耶公爵夫人 Montpensier, Anne-Marie-Louise d'Orléans, Duchesse de 法国王族 11—371a
蒙乔伊勋爵(第八) Mountjoy, Charles Blount, 8th Lord 英格兰军人 11—446f
蒙切戈尔斯克 Monchegorsk 俄罗斯城镇 11—331b
蒙青格尔 Munzinger, Werner 瑞士语言学家、探险家 11—488c
蒙热内夫尔山口 Montgenèvre Pass 法国山脉山口 11—367b
蒙日 Monge, Gaspard 法国数学家 11—335d
蒙萨拉特 Monsarrat, Nicholas 英国小说家 11—350f
蒙塞拉特 Montserrat 加勒比海岛屿 11—374a
蒙塞拉特山 Montserrat 西班牙山脉 11—374a
蒙森 Mommsen, (Christian Matthias) Theodor 德国历史学家、作家 11—326f
蒙森 Monson, Sir William 英国海军军官 11—351b
蒙斯 Mons 比利时城市 11—350d
蒙斯特勒莱 Monstrelet, Enguerrand de 法国历史学家 11—351e
蒙塔尔沃 Montalvo, Juan 厄瓜多尔散文家 11—356e
蒙塔丰河谷 Montafon Valley 奥地利河谷 11—352c
蒙塔格纳德人 Montagnard 印度支那山区民族 11—353c
蒙塔格奈人与纳斯卡皮人 Montagnais and Naskapi 北美印第安人 11—352f
蒙塔古 Montagu, Charles 英国政治家 11—353e
蒙塔古 Montagu, Edwin Samuel 英国政治家 11—353e
蒙塔古 Montagu, John 英格兰将军 11—353f
蒙塔古 Montagu, Lady Mary Wortley 英国作家 11—353f
蒙塔古 Montagu, (Montague Francis) Ashley 美国人类学家 11—353d
蒙塔古 Montagu, Richard 英格兰主教 11—354c
蒙塔古 Montacute, Thomas de 英格兰军官 11—352c
蒙塔古 Montagu, Thomas de 英格兰军官 11—354c

蒙塔古夫人 Montagu, Elizabeth 英国知识界名流 11—353f
蒙塔古公爵(第一) Montagu, Ralph Montagu, 1st duke of 英国小说家、廷臣 11—354b
蒙塔古侯爵 Montagu, John Neville, marquess of 英格兰军官 11—353f
蒙塔古家族 Montagu FAMILY 英格兰贵族家族 11—353d
蒙塔莱 Montale, Eugenio 意大利诗人、翻译家 11—356c
蒙塔朗贝尔 Montalembert, Marc-René, marquis de 法国将领、军事工程师 11—356e
蒙塔朗贝尔伯爵 Montalembert, Charles(-Forbes-René), comte de 法国演说家、政治家 11—356d
蒙塔纳 Montana 保加利亚城镇 11—359b
蒙塔尼亚 Montagna, Bartolommeo 意大利画家 11—352e
蒙塔尼亚纳 Montagnana 意大利城镇 11—353a
蒙塔尼亚纳 Montagnana, Antonio 意大利歌唱家 11—353b
蒙塔尼亚纳 Montagnana, Domenico 意大利乐器制作家 11—353b
蒙塔涅斯 Montañés, Juan (de) Martínez 西班牙雕刻家 11—359c
蒙台梭利 Montessori, Maria 意大利教育家 11—363f
蒙太 Montet, Pierre 法国埃及学家 11—364c
蒙太费尔特罗家族 Montefeltro FAMILY 意大利贵族世家 11—361f
蒙太奇 montage 电影艺术 11—352d
蒙泰古 Mountagu, Edward 英格兰海军上将 11—442c
蒙泰卡蒂尼-泰尔梅 Montecatini Terme 意大利城镇 11—361a
蒙泰克莱 Montéclair, Michel (Pinolet) de 法国作曲家 11—361b
蒙泰克里斯托岛 Montecristo Island 意大利岛屿 11—361e
蒙泰朗 Montherlant, Henry(-Marie-Joseph-Millon) de 法国小说家、剧作家 11—368e
蒙泰利马尔 Montélimar 法国城镇 11—362b
蒙泰梅侯爵 Monthermer, Ralph Montagu, Marquess of 英国贵族 11—368f
蒙泰圣安杰洛 Monte Sant'Angelo 意大利城市 11—361a
蒙唐 Montand, Yves 法国演员 11—359b
蒙陶克人 Montauk 美国印第安人 11—359e
蒙特 Mont 古埃及宗教之神 11—351f
蒙特 Munthe, Axel Martin Fredrik 瑞典作家、内科医生 11—487f
蒙特 Montt, Manuel 智利总统 11—374d
蒙特 Monte, Philippe de 荷兰作曲家 11—360c
蒙特 Monteux, Pierre 指挥家 11—364c
蒙特 Montt, Pedro 智利总统 11—374e
蒙特 Mount, William Sidney 美国画家 11—440a
蒙特贝洛公爵 Montebello, Jean Lannes, duc de (duke of) 法国元帅 11—361a
蒙特贝洛群岛 Monte Bello Islands 澳大利亚群岛 11—360e
蒙特布兰奇公爵 Montblanch, Martín, duque de (duke of) 阿拉贡国王 11—359f
蒙特多里 Montdory 法国演员 11—360b
蒙特斐奥雷 Montefiore, Sir Moses (Haim) 英国慈善家 11—362a
蒙特港 Puerto Montt 智利地区首府、省会 14—16a
蒙特哥贝 Montego Bay 牙买加城市 11—362b
蒙特格拉斯·德·加尔内林 Montgelas de Garnerin, Maximilian Joseph, Graf von 德国政治家 11—367a
蒙特卡洛 Monte-Carlo 摩纳哥行政区 11—360e
蒙特卡洛俄罗斯芭蕾舞团 Ballet Russe de Monte Carlo 演出团体 2—176f
蒙特克莱 Montclair 美国城镇 11—360b
蒙特克里斯蒂 Montecristi 多米尼加共和国省份 11—361c
蒙特克里斯蒂 Montecristi 多米尼加共和国城市 11—361c
蒙特库科利 Montecuccoli, Raimondo 奥地利陆军元帅 11—361e
蒙特勒 Montreux 瑞士城镇 11—373e
蒙特勒伊 Montreuil 法国城镇 11—373e
蒙特雷 Monterey 美国城市 11—363a
蒙特雷 Monterrey 墨西哥城市 11—363b
蒙特雷海底峡谷 Monterey Canyon 太平洋海底峡谷 11—363a
蒙特雷杰克干酪 Monterey Jack 食品 11—363b
蒙特雷山国家公园 Cumbres de Monterrey National Park 墨西哥公园 5—59f
蒙特里根丘陵 Monteregian Hills 加拿大山岗 11—363a
蒙特里亚 Montería 哥伦比亚城市 11—363b
蒙特利尔 Montreal 加拿大城市 11—371b
蒙特利尔美术馆 Montreal Museum of Fine Arts 加拿大美术馆 11—373d
蒙特利尔派 Montreal group 加拿大诗人团体 11—373d
蒙特利尔水族馆 Montreal Aquarium 加拿大水族馆 11—373c
蒙特利尔植物园 Montreal Botanical Garden 加拿大植物园 11—373c
蒙特利乌斯 Montelius, Oscar 瑞典考古学家 11—362c
蒙特鲁日 Montrouge 法国城镇 11—374a
蒙特罗·洛巴托 Monteiro Lobato, José Bento 巴西作家、出版家 11—362b
蒙特罗斯 Montrose 苏格兰海港 11—373e
蒙特罗斯 Montrose 美国城市 11—373f
蒙特罗斯伯爵(第五)和侯爵(第一) Montrose, James Graham, 5th Earl and 1st Marquess of 苏格兰将领 11—373f
蒙特马约 Montemayor, Jorge de 葡萄牙作家 11—362c
蒙特莫林伯爵 Montemolín, Carlos Luis de Borbón, Count (count) de 西班牙贵族 11—362c
蒙特圣朱利亚诺 Monte San Giuliano (Sicily) 意大利城镇 11—361a
蒙特斯庞侯爵夫人 Montespan, Françoise-Athénaïs de Roche-chouart, marquise de (marchioness of) 路易十四情妇 11—363c
蒙特威尔地 Monteverdi, Claudio 意大利作曲家 11—364d
蒙提萨罗 Monticello 美国弗吉尼亚州建筑物 11—369c
蒙提祖马堡国家保护区 Montezuma Castle National Monument 美国公园 11—366b
蒙提祖马二世 Montezuma II 阿兹特克皇帝 11—365f
蒙田 Montaigne, Michel (Eyquem) de 法国作家、哲学家 11—354d
蒙恬 Meng Tian 中国秦代将领 11—113e
蒙头斗篷 cowl 宗教服饰 4—557f
蒙图法-里维拉·马埃斯特雷 Montúfar y Rivera Maestre, Lorenzo 中美洲政治家、历史学家 11—374e
蒙托邦 Montauban 法国城镇 11—359e
蒙托西耶公爵 Montausier, Charles de Saint-Maure, duc de 法国陆军军官、文人 11—359f
蒙托亚 Montoya, Carlos 美国音乐家 11—370d
蒙脱石 montmorillonite 矿物 11—370b
蒙希 Munch, Charles 指挥家 11—482a
蒙希克山脉 Monchique Mountains 葡萄牙山脉 11—331c
蒙育瓦 Monywa 缅甸城镇 11—375a
蒙扎 Monza 意大利城市 11—375a
蒙自 Mengzi 中国县名 11—114c
盟约 foedus 古罗马史 6—384c
盟约神学 covenant theology 基督教神学 4—554e
鹲 tropic bird 鸟类 17—234c
猛犸象 mammoth (genus *Mammuthus*) 古生物学 10—442f
猛禽 bird of prey 鸟类 2—489e
蒙古 Mongolia 中亚国家 11—337b
蒙古包 yurt 帐篷 18—484c
蒙古地理人种 Mongoloid geographic race 亚洲人种 11—339d
蒙古高原 Mongolian Plateau 中亚高原 11—339c
蒙古人 Mongol 亚洲民族 11—336b
蒙古人民共和国 Mongolian People's Republic 中亚国家 11—339c
蒙古文 Mongolian character 蒙古族拼音文字 11—338d
蒙古文学 Mongolian literature 文学 11—338e
蒙古型痴呆 mongolism (chromosomal disorder) 疾病 11—339d
蒙古野驴 kulan 哺乳动物 9—392d
蒙古野猫 manul (mammal) 哺乳动物 10—478a

蒙古语 Mongol language 亚洲语言 11—337b
蒙古诸语言 Mongolian languages 亚洲语言 11—338e
蒙古眦褶 Mongolian eye fold 解剖学 11—338d
蒙古族 Mongol 中国少数民族 11—336f
蒙古族语 Mongolian nationality, language of 中国蒙古族语言 11—338f
锰(Mn) manganese 化学元素 10—457d
锰白云石 kutnohorite 矿物 9—407c
锰钙辉石 johannsenite 矿物 9—46a
锰橄榄石 tephroite 矿物 16—548c
锰铝榴石 spessartine 宝石 16—23d
锰缺乏 manganese deficiency 病理生理现象 10—457f
锰铁矿 jacobsite 矿物 8—512c
锰土 wad 矿石 18—59d
锰硬绿泥石 ottrelite 矿物 12—503d
锰黝帘石 thulite 矿物 17—69d
獴 mongoose 哺乳动物 11—339e
孟驳 Hsinbyushin 缅甸国王 8—204b
孟戴斯 Mendès, Catulle 法国诗人、剧作家 11—110d
孟戴斯-弗朗斯 Mendès-France, Pierre 法国总理 11—110e
孟德尔 Mendel, Gregor (Johann) 奥地利遗传学家 11—107d
孟德尔主义 Mendelism 遗传学 11—108c
孟德高维诺 Montecorvino, Giovanni da 意大利天主教传教士 11—361c
孟德斯 Mendes, Murilo 巴西诗人、外交官 11—110d
孟德斯鸠 Montesquieu, Charles-Louis de Secondat, baron de La Brède et de 法国政治哲学家 11—363d
孟恩诉伊利诺伊州案 Munn v. Illinois 美国法院案例 11—485c
孟菲斯 Memphis 美国城市 11—104f
孟菲斯王朝 Memphite DYNASTY 埃及历史 11—105a
孟菲斯种族暴动 Memphis Race Riot 美国历史 11—105a
孟斐斯 Memphis 古埃及王国都城 11—104d
孟福尔 Montfort, Simon de 法国十字军首领 11—366e
孟福尔 Montfort, Simon de 英格兰叛乱领袖 11—366f
孟福尔家族 Montfort FAMILY 欧洲家族 11—366c
孟-高棉诸语言 Mon-Khmer languages 亚洲语言 11—327d
孟浩然 Meng Haoran 中国唐代诗人 11—113d
孟既 Bagyidaw 缅甸国王 2—139d
孟加拉 Bengal 印度次大陆历史地区 2—383d
孟加拉分省 Bengal, Partition of 印度次大陆历史区划 2—383e
孟加拉国 Bangladesh 亚洲国家 2—200b
孟加拉苹果 bel fruit (species *Aegle marmelos*) 水果 2—348f
孟加拉湾 Bengal, Bay of 印度洋东北部海湾 2—383e
孟加拉亚洲学会 Asiatic Society of Bengal 学术团体 1—554a
孟加拉语 Bengali language 亚洲语言 2—383f
孟加拉语文学 Bengali literature 文学 2—383f
孟卡尔和纳吉尔 Munkar and Nakīr 伊斯兰教 11—485c
孟莱 Mangrai 兰那国王 10—459a
孟买 Bombay 印度城市 3—20a
孟买大学 Bombay, University of 印度大学 3—22a
孟奇克-史蒂文森 Menchik-Stevenson, Vera Francevna 英国国际象棋大师 11—106d
孟人 Mon 亚洲民族 11—327c
孟塞尔色系 Munsell colour system 光学 11—486c
孟山都公司 Monsanto Company 美国化学公司 11—350e
孟什维克 Menshevik 俄国政党 11—118c
孟斯 Mengs, Anton Raphael 波希米亚画家 11—114b
孟他努斯 Montanus 基督教异端领袖 11—359d
孟他努斯主义 Montanism 基督教异端 11—359c
孟王国 Mon kingdom 缅甸古王国 11—327e
孟希·阿卜杜拉·宾·阿卜杜尔·卡迪尔 Munshi Abdullah bin Abdul Kadir 马来亚作家、教师 11—486f
孟席斯 Menzies, Sir Robert Gordon 澳大利亚政治家 11—122b
孟席斯 Menzies, William Cameron 美国布景设计师 11—122c
孟语 Mon language 亚洲语言 11—327f
孟云 Bodawpaya 缅甸国王 2—560e
孟子 Mencius 中国战国时期思想家 11—106e
《孟子》 Mencius 中国儒家经典 11—107a
梦 dream 心理学、生理学 5—417b
梦庵 Muan 日本诗人 11—459f
梦幻 aisling 文学 1—149a
梦幻 dream vision (allegorical tale) 文学 5—417f
梦露 Monroe, Marilyn 美国演员 11—349e
《梦溪笔谈》 Dream Stream Essays 中国古代科技文献 5—417f
梦想期 Dreaming, the 澳大利亚土著神话 5—417f
梦淫妖 incubus 中世纪欧洲传说 8—354b
梦游症 sleepwalking 行为障碍 15—430d
梦喻 dream allegory 文学 5—417e
咪唑 imidazole 化合物 8—342b
弥达斯 Midas 古希腊传说人物 11—197e
弥尔顿 Milton, John 英国诗人 11—233d
弥基洛 Megillah 犹太教经卷 11—81f
弥迦书 Micah, Book of 《旧约》 11—178a
《弥兰陀王问经》 Milinda-panha 佛教名著 11—215e
弥勒 Maitreya 佛教未来佛 10—413a
弥勒 Müller, Erwin Wilhelm 美国物理学家 11—475d
弥勒 Müller, Johannes Peter 德国哲学家 11—476b
弥楼山 Meru, Mount 印度神话 11—137c
弥曼差派 Mimamsa 印度哲学 11—237e
弥漫性躯体血管角质瘤 angiokeratoma corporis diffusum 疾病 1—344f
弥米尔 Mimir 古斯堪的纳维亚神话 11—240b
弥诺斯 Minos 希腊神话神名 11—265e
弥诺陶洛斯 Minotaur 希腊神话怪物名 11—266a
弥撒 mass 天主教礼仪 11—4d
弥撒曲 mass 宗教音乐 11—4e
弥撒书 missal 天主教著作 11—277a
弥赛亚 messiah 犹太教 11—144e
弥生文化 Yayoi culture 日本史前文化 18—430d
弥湿罗婆罗门 Maithil Brahman 印度种姓 10—412c
迷齿螈 labyrinthodont 古生物 9—434f
迷迭香 rosemary (*Rosmarinus officinalis*) 木本植物 14—403d
迷宫 labyrinth 建筑 9—434c
迷路炎 labyrinthitis 疾病 9—434f
迷器鱼 labyrinth fish 鱼类 9—434e
迷惘的一代 Lost Generation 美国文学 10—229b
迷信 superstition 思想 16—347d
迷走神经 vagus nerve 解剖学 17—443c
猕猴 macaque 哺乳动物 10—327a
猕猴桃 kiwi (*Actinidia chinensis*) 水果 9—311d
谜语 riddle 游戏 14—291a
谜语机 Enigma 德国密码装置 6—84b
醚 ether 化合物 6—145b
麋羚 hartebeest 哺乳动物 7—493d
米 metre 计量单位 11—160b
米阿斯 Miass 俄罗斯城市 11—177a
米安瓦利 Miānwāli 巴基斯坦城市 11—175e
米巴拉格西 Me-baragesi (Mesopotamian ruler) 巴比伦国王 11—60f
米彻尔 Mitscher, Marc A(ndrew) 美国海军军官 11—293a
米彻姆 Mitchum, Robert 美国电影演员 11—290b
米达尔 Myrdal, Alva Reimer 瑞典外交家 11—526a
米达尔 Myrdal, (Karl) Gunnar 瑞典经济学家 11—526b
米达斯 Midas 弗里吉亚国王 11—197e
米德 Meade, George G(ordon) 美国陆军军官 11—61d
米德 Mead, George Herbert 美国哲学家 11—61a

米德 Meade, James Edward 英国经济学家 11—61e
米德 Mead, Margaret 美国人类学家 11—61b
米德 Mead, Richard 英国内科医生 11—61c
米德尔堡 Middelburg 荷兰城市 11—197f
米德尔伯里 Middlebury 美国城镇 11—199d
米德尔敦 Middletown 美国康涅狄格州城市 11—200e
米德尔敦 Middletown 美国纽约州城市 11—200e
米德尔敦 Middletown 美国俄亥俄州城市 11—200e
米德尔敦 Middletown 美国罗得岛州城镇 11—200f
米德尔顿 Middleton, Arthur 美国政治家 11—200a
米德尔顿 Myddelton, Sir Hugh, 1st Baronet 英国议会议员 11—523e
米德尔顿 Middleton, Thomas 英国剧作家 11—200c
米德尔顿 Middleton, T(homas) F(anshaw) 英国传教士 11—200c
米德尔顿伯爵(第二) Middleton, Charles Middleton, 2nd earl of 英国政治家 11—200b
米德尔顿伯爵(第一) Middleton, John Middleton, 1st earl of 苏格兰保王党人 11—200c
米德尔塞克斯 Middlesex 英格兰郡名 11—199e
米德尔塞克斯伯爵(第一) Middlesex, Lionel Cranfield, 1st earl of 英格兰大臣 11—200a
米德尔斯伯勒 Middlesboro 美国城市 11—199e
米德尔斯伯勒 Middlesbrough 英格兰区名 11—199e
米德费 Midfaʿi, Jamil al- 伊拉克首相、政治家 11—201a
米德哈特帕夏 Midhat Paşa 奥斯曼帝国大臣 11—201e
米德湖 Mead, Lake 美国湖泊 11—61a
米德加尔德 Midgard 斯堪的纳维亚神话 11—201a
米德拉西 Midrash 犹太教 11—202f
米德兰 Midland 加拿大城镇 11—202a
米德兰 Midland 美国密歇根州城市 11—202a
米德兰 Midland 美国得克萨斯州城市 11—202b
米德·劳伦斯 Mead Lawrence, Andrea 美国高山滑雪运动员 11—61d
米德纳布尔 Midnapore 印度城镇 11—202e
米德韦斯特城 Midwest City 美国居民区 11—203c
米德维尔 Meadville 美国城市 11—62c
米狄亚斯画家 Meidias Painter 古希腊陶瓶画家 11—85b
米迪 Midi 法国文化区 11—201e
米迪比利牛斯 Midi-Pyrénées 法国西南部大区 11—201f
米迪运河 Midi Canal 法国运河 11—201f
米底 Media 伊朗古代国家 11—71c
米底人 Mede 印欧民族 11—70e
米蒂利尼 Mytilene 希腊城镇 11—531b
米蒂利尼 Mitilíni (island, Greece) 希腊岛屿 11—291f
米蒂亚罗 Mitiaro 太平洋岛屿 11—291f
米甸人 Midianite 民族 11—202a
米恩 Meighen, Arthur 加拿大保守党领袖 11—85d
米尔 mir 俄国农户自治公社 11—269d
米尔 Mill, Hugh Robert 英国地理学家、气象学家 11—220e
米尔班克 Milbank 美国城市 11—213d
米尔贝尔 Mirbel, Charles-François Brisseau de 法国植物学家 11—272f
米尔本 Millburn 美国城镇 11—224a
米尔博 Mirbeau, Octave(-Henri-Marie) 法国作家 11—272e
米尔布尔哈斯 Mīrpur Khās 巴基斯坦城镇 11—273d
米尔茨楚施拉格 Mürzzuschlag 奥地利城镇 11—499d
米尔达尔斯冰原 Mýrdalsjökull 冰岛冰川 11—526c
米尔·达马德 Mīr Dāmād 伊斯兰教哲学家 11—269e
米尔德纳玻璃制品 Mildner glass 工艺品 11—213e
米尔登霍尔 Mildenhall 英格兰城镇 11—213e
米尔迪拉 Mildura 澳大利亚城市 11—213f
米尔顿 Milton 美国城镇 11—233c
米尔顿凯恩斯 Milton Keynes 英格兰城镇 11—236e
米尔恩 Milne, A(lan) A(lexander) 英国作家 11—230f
米尔恩 Milne, Edward Arthur 英国数学家、天体物理学家 11—231a
米尔恩 Milne, John 英国地震学家 11—231a
米尔恩斯 Milnes, Richard Monckton 英国诗人 11—231e
米尔恩湾 Milne Bay 太平洋海湾 11—231b
米尔福德 Milford 美国康涅狄格州城市 11—214e
米尔福德 Milford 美国特拉华州城市 11—214e
米尔福德港 Milford Haven 威尔士港口 11—214e
米尔福德·黑文侯爵(第一) Milford Haven, Louis Alexander Mountbatten, 1st marquess of 英国海军元帅 11—214e
米尔福德湾 Milford Sound 新西兰海湾 11—214f
米尔盖 Milngavie 苏格兰城市 11—231e
米尔豪森 Mühlhausen 德国城市 11—471b
米尔豪森 Mülhausen (France) 法国城市 11—475a
米尔·伽法 Mīr Jaʿfar 孟加拉统治者 11—269f
米尔克 Milk, Harvey 美国政治人物 11—219c
米尔克河 Milk River 北美河流 11—219e
米尔肯 Milken, Michael R. 美国金融家 11—219e
米尔纳 Milner (of Saint James's and Cape Town), Alfred Milner, Viscount 英国殖民地行政长官 11—231c
米尔热 Murger, (Louis-)Henri 法国小说家 11—494e
米尔·赛伊德·阿里 Mīr Sayyid ʿAlī 波斯画家 11—269f
米尔斯 Mills, Bertram (Wagstaff) 英国马戏主办人 11—229e
米尔斯 Mills, Caleb 美国教育家 11—229f
米尔斯 Mills, Charles Wright 美国社会学家 11—230a
米尔斯 Mills, Florence 美国歌唱家、舞蹈家 11—230b
米尔斯 Mears, Helen Farnsworth 美国雕塑家 11—63f
米尔斯 Mills, Martin 英国作家 11—230b
米尔斯 Mills, Susan Lincoln Tolman 美国传教士、教育家 11—230c
米尔斯 Mills, William Corless 美国博物馆馆长 11—230d
米尔斯十字 Mills cross 射电望远镜 11—230e
米尔斯坦 Milstein, César 阿根廷免疫学家 11—232e
米尔斯坦 Milstein, Nathan 美国小提琴家 11—232f
米尔提亚德斯,圣 Miltiades, Saint 教皇 11—232f
米尔维尔 Millville 美国城市 11—230e
米尔扎布尔-温迪亚杰尔 Mirzāpur-Vindhyāchal 印度城市 11—274c
米尔扎·侯赛因·阿里·努尔 Ḥusayn ʿAlī Nūrī, Mīrzā 巴哈教派创始者 8—267d
米尔扎丘尔 Mirzachul (Uzbekistan) 乌兹别克斯坦城市 11—274c
米饭席 rijsttafel 印度尼西亚食谱 14—299f
米非司酮 Mifepristone 药物 11—205b
米芾 Mi Fu 中国宋代画家 11—174b
米高梅影片公司 Metro-Goldwyn-Mayer, Inc. (MGM) 美国电影公司 11—161b
米高扬 Mikoyan, Anastas Ivanovich 苏联政治家 11—209f
米戈内 Mignone, Emilio Fermin 阿根廷律师 11—206c
米格尔 Michael 葡萄牙国王 11—179f
米格设计局 MiG 俄罗斯航空航天设计局 11—205d
米格战斗机 MiG 苏联战斗机 11—205f
米哈尔·维希尼奥维茨基 Michael Wiśniowiecki 波兰国王 11—179e
米哈拉布 mihrab 伊斯兰教建筑形式 11—208d
米哈拉凯 Mihalache, Ion 罗马尼亚政治家 11—208c
米哈那 miḥnah 伊斯兰教审判所 11—208d
米哈伊 Michael 罗马尼亚国王 11—180a
米哈伊 Michael 罗马尼亚国王 11—180c
米哈伊尔 Michael 俄国沙皇 11—180b
米哈伊洛夫格勒 Mikhaylovgrad 保加利亚城镇 11—209a
米哈伊洛夫卡 Mikhaylovka 俄罗斯城市 11—209a
米哈伊洛三世 Michael III 塞尔维亚大公 11—180c
米哈伊洛维奇 Mihajlović, Dragoljub 南斯拉夫军官 11—208b
米海洛夫斯基 Mikhaylovsky, Nikolay Konstantinovich 俄国文学评论家 11—209a

米赫万德 Mīrkhwānd 波斯历史学家 11—273a
米湖 Mývatn 冰岛湖泊 11—531c
米吉肯达人 Mijikenda (people) 非洲民族 11—208d
米迦勒 Michael 《圣经》、《古兰经》中的天使长之一 11—178b
米迦勒节 Michaelmas 基督教节日 11—180e
米卡埃尔·塞胡尔 Mikael Sehul 埃塞俄比亚贵族 11—208e
米卡萨腊 Meekatharra 澳大利亚城镇 11—79f
米卡伊来 Mīkāl 伊斯兰教天使 11—208e
米开朗琪罗 Michelangelo 意大利艺术家 11—181d
米开罗佐 Michelozzo 意大利建筑师 11—186a
米凯兰杰利 Michelangeli, Arturo Benedetti 意大利钢琴家 11—181d
米凯利 Mikkeli 芬兰省份 11—209d
米凯利 Mikkeli 芬兰城市 11—209d
米坎 Mikan, George (Lawrence) 美国篮球运动员 11—208e
米康 Micon 古希腊画家、雕刻家 11—191d
米科诺斯岛 Míkonos 爱琴海岛屿 11—209f
米科瓦伊奇克 Mikołajczyk, Stanisław 波兰政治家 11—209e
米克尔 Meikle, Andrew 苏格兰谷物脱粒机发明者 11—86a
米克尔森 Michelsen (Peter) Christian (Hersleb Kjerschow) 挪威政治家、首相 11—186c
米克拉斯 Miklas, Wilhelm 奥地利总统 11—209e
米克马克人 Micmac 加拿大印第安人 11—191c
米克沙特 Mikszáth, Kálmán 匈牙利小说家 11—210b
米克斯 Mix, Tom 美国电影演员 11—295f
米克特兰特库特利 Mictlantecuhtli 中美洲宗教神祇 11—197a
米孔 Mikon (Greek painter) 希腊画家 11—209f
米库利奇-拉代基 Mikulicz-Radecki, Johannes von 波兰外科医生 11—210b
米拉 Myra 土耳其城镇 11—526a
米拉 Milla, Roger 喀麦隆足球运动员 11—223b
米拉贝洛湾 Mirabéllo, Gulf of 爱琴海深水湾 11—270f
米拉波伯爵 Mirabeau, Honoré-Gabriel Riqueti, comte de 法国政治家、演说家 11—270c
米拉波侯爵 Mirabeau, Victor Riqueti, marquis de 法国政治经济学家 11—270f
米拉波子爵 Mirabeau, André-Boniface-Louis Riqueti, vicomte de 法国大革命初期反动头目 11—270c
米拉弗洛雷斯 Miraflores 秘鲁城市 11—271c
米拉蒙 Miramón, Miguel 墨西哥军人、政治家 11—271f
米拉日巴 Mi-la ras-pa 中国藏传佛教名僧 11—174d
米拉斯地毯 Melas carpet 土耳其工艺品 11—93a
米拉佐 Milazzo 意大利城镇 11—213d
米莱 Millay, Edna St. Vincent 美国诗人、剧作家 11—223e
米兰 Milan 意大利城市 11—210c
米兰 Milan 美国村庄 11—213a
米兰 Milán, Luis 西班牙作曲家 11—213b
米兰博 Mirambo 中非军阀 11—271f
米兰彩陶 Milan faience 意大利陶器 11—213c
《米兰敕令》 Milan, Edict of 罗马帝国历史 11—213b
米兰达 Miranda 委内瑞拉州名 11—272a
米兰达 Miranda, Bartolomé de 西班牙神学家 11—272b
米兰达 Miranda, Francisco de 委内瑞拉革命家 11—272b
米兰达-德埃布罗 Miranda de Ebro 西班牙城市 11—272c
米兰达诉亚利桑那州案 Miranda v. Arizona 美国法院案例 11—272c
米兰大学 Milan, University of 意大利大学 11—213b
米兰多拉 Mirandola 意大利城镇 11—272e
米兰多拉 Mirandola, Giovanni Pico della 意大利学者 11—272e
米兰花边 Milanese lace 工艺品 11—213c
米兰三世(或一世) Milan Ⅲ(or Ⅰ) 塞尔维亚大公 11—213a
米兰四世(或二世) Milan Ⅳ(or Ⅱ) 塞尔维亚大公 11—213a
米老鼠 Mickey Mouse 卡通角色 11—191a
米勒 Miller, Arthur 美国剧作家 11—225c
米勒 Miller, Alice Duer 美国作家 11—225c
米勒 Miller, (Alton) Glenn 美国作曲家、长号演奏家 11—225f
米勒 Miller, David Hunter 美国律师 11—225e
米勒 Mueller, Sir Ferdinand von 澳大利亚植物学家 11—463e
米勒 Müller, Friedrich 德国剧作家 11—475e
米勒 Müller, (Friedrich) Max 德国学者 11—476f
米勒 Müller, Georg Elias 德国心理学家 11—475e
米勒 Miller, Harriet Mann 美国儿童文学作家 11—225f
米勒 Müller, Hermann 德国政治家 11—475f
米勒 Miller, Hugh 苏格兰地质学家 11—226b
米勒 Miller, Henry (Valentine) 美国作家 11—226a
米勒 Millet, Jean-François 法国画家 11—228c
米勒 Millet, Jean-François 法国画家 11—228c
米勒 Miller, Joaquin 美国诗人、记者 11—226c
米勒 Müller, Johannes von 瑞士历史学家 11—476d
米勒 Miller, Jonathan (Wolfe) 英国演员、导演 11—226e
米勒 Müller, Karl Otfried 德国学者 11—476e
米勒 Millett, Kate 美国女权主义者、作家 11—228e
米勒 Müller, Lucas (painter) 德国画家 11—476e
米勒 Miller, Marilyn 美国演员 11—226f
米勒 Miller, Merton H(oward) 美国经济学家 11—226f
米勒 Miller, Neal E(lgar) 美国心理学家 11—227a
米勒 Müller, Otto 德国画家 11—476f
米勒 Müller, Paul Hermann 瑞士化学家 11—477a
米勒 Miller, Samuel Freeman 美国最高法院大法官 11—227b
米勒 Müller, Sophus Otto 丹麦古生物学家 11—477c
米勒 Miller, William 美国基督教派别领导人 11—227d
米勒 Müller, Wilhelm 德国诗人 11—477d
米勒兰 Millerand, Alexandre 法国律师 11—227e
米勒氏拟态 Müllerian mimicry 生物学 11—477e
米勒斯 Milles, Carl 瑞典雕刻家 11—228a
米雷 Muret, Marc-Antoine de 法国学者 11—494c
米雷费尔特 Mierevelt, Michiel Janszoon van 荷兰画家 11—204b
米里 Miri 东马来西亚港口 11—272f
米里斯(老) Mieris, Frans van, the Elder 荷兰画家 11—204b
米利茨(克罗梅日什的) Milíč (of Kroměříž), John 波希米亚神学家 11—215c
米利德 Milid 土耳其古城 11—215d
米利都 Miletus 安纳托利亚古城 11—214c
米利都传奇 Milesian tale 文学 11—214c
米利根案(1866) Milligan, Ex Parte 美国法院案例 11—228f
米利奇维尔 Milledgeville 美国城市 11—224b
米利森特 Millicent 澳大利亚城镇 11—228f
米利亚纳 Miliana 阿尔及利亚城镇 11—215b
米列斯库 Milescu, Nicolae 罗马尼亚作家、学者 11—214b
米林 Millin, Sarah Gertrude 南非作家 11—229c
米林湖 Mirim Lagoon 南美湖泊 11—273a
米留可夫 Milyukov, Pavel Nikolayevich 俄国历史学家、政治家 11—237b
米留斯·埃里克森 Mylius-Erichsen, Ludwig 丹麦探险家 11—524f
米柳亭 Milyutin, Dmitry Alekseyevich, Count (Graf) 俄国军官、政治家 11—237d
米柳亭 Milyutin, Nikolay Alekseyevich 俄国政治家 11—237d
米隆 Myron 希腊雕刻家 11—527d
米卢斯 Mulhouse 法国城镇 11—475a
米伦 Mürren 瑞士村庄 11—498e
米伦(克罗顿的) Milon of Croton 希腊运动员 11—231f
米罗 Miró (Ferrer), Gabriel 西班牙作家 11—273b
米罗 Miró, Joan 加泰罗尼亚画家 11—273b
米罗达巴拉丹二世 Merodach-Baladan Ⅱ 巴比伦尼亚国王 11—133d
米洛 Milo, Titus Annius 罗马政治家 11—231e

米洛的维纳斯 Venus de Milo 雕塑 17—509f
米洛舍维奇 Milošević, Slobodan 塞尔维亚民族主义领导人 11—232a
米洛什 Miloš 塞尔维亚农民革命家 11—231f
米洛斯 Melos 希腊岛屿 11—99f
米洛斯拉夫斯卡娅 Miloslavskaya, Mariya Ilinichna 俄国皇后 11—232c
米洛瓦诺维奇 Milovanović, Milovan 塞尔维亚首相 11—232e
米姆奈尔摩斯 Mimnermus 希腊诗人 11—240b
米拿现 Menahem 以色列国王 11—105e
米纳 mina 计量单位 11—241d
米纳蒂特兰 Minatitlán 墨西哥城市 11—243c
米纳哈萨 Minahasa 印度尼西亚地区 11—241e
米纳哈萨人 Minahasan 印度尼西亚民族 11—241e
米纳那陀 Mīnanātha (Indian guru) 印度宗教领袖 11—242e
米纳人 Mina 印度民族 11—241c
米纳斯 Minas 乌拉圭城市 11—243a
米纳斯吉拉斯 Minas Gerais 巴西州名 11—243a
米纳斯湾 Minas Basin 加拿大水湾 11—243a
米纳衣陶瓷 minai ware 伊斯兰陶瓷 11—241e
米奈尔 Minnaert, Marcel Gilles Jozef 佛兰芒天文学家、太阳物理学家 11—258f
米南德 Menander 希腊剧作家 11—106a
米南德 Menander 印度的希腊人国王 11—106b
米南卡保人 Minangkabau 印度尼西亚民族 11—242e
米尼 Meany, George 美国劳工领袖 11—63e
米尼奥 Minho 葡萄牙省份 11—250d
米尼奥拉 Mineola 美国村庄 11—246b
米尼赫 Münnich, Burkhard Christoph, Count (Graf) von 俄国陆军元帅 11—485d
米尼赫伯爵 Minikh, Burkhard Christoph, Graf von (count of) 俄国陆军元帅 11—250f
米尼劳斯 Menelaus OF ALEXANDRIA 希腊数学家 11—112c
米尼塔里人 Minitari (people) 美洲印第安人 11—258c
米尼翁 Mignon, Abraham 德国画家 11—206c
米尼亚尔 Mignard, Pierre 法国画家 11—206b
米涅 Mignet, François 法国历史学家、档案学家 11—206b
米涅 Migne, Jacques-Paul 法国出版家 11—206b
米宁 Minin, Nikita (Russian patriarch) 俄罗斯正教会牧首 11—251c
米纽伊特 Minuit, Peter 荷兰总督 11—268b
米努夫 Minūfiyah, Al 下埃及省份 11—268b
米诺 Mino DA FIESOLE 意大利雕刻家 11—263d
米诺斯文化 Minoan civilization 考古学 11—263d
米诺鱼 minnow 鱼类 11—263b
米齐瓦 Mitsiwa 埃塞俄比亚城市 11—293b
米其林公司 Michelin 法国公司 11—185e
米奇尔 Michiel, Vitale II 威尼斯执政官 11—187a
米奇利 Midgley, Thomas, Jr. 美国工程师、化学家 11—201d
米恰尔(色路拉里乌斯) Michael CERULARIUS 希腊正教会教士 11—180d
米切尔 Mitchell 美国城市 11—288a
米切尔 Mitchell, Arthur 美国舞蹈家 11—288a
米切尔 Mitchell, Charles E(dwin) 美国银行家 11—288b
米切尔 Mitchell, Edgar D(ean) 美国航天员 11—288b
米切尔 Mitchell, James Leslie (novelist) 苏格兰小说家 11—288c
米切尔 Mitchell, Joan 美国画家 11—288c
米切尔 Mitchell, John Newton 美国司法部长 11—288d
米切尔 Mitchell, John Thomas Whitehead 英国领导人 11—288e
米切尔 Mitchell, Lucy Myers Wright 考古学家 11—288e
米切尔 Mitchell, Maggie 美国演员 11—288f
米切尔 Mitchell, Margaret 美国作家 11—289a
米切尔 Mitchell, Maria 美国天文学家 11—289b
米切尔 Mitchell, Peter Dennis 英国化学家 11—289c
米切尔 Mitchell, R.J. 英国飞机设计师 11—289c
米切尔 Mitchell, S. Weir 美国医生、作家 11—289d
米切尔 Mitchell, Sir Thomas Livingstone 澳大利亚官员 11—289e
米切尔 Mitchell, Wesley C. 美国经济学家 11—289f
米切尔 Mitchell, William 美国陆军军官 11—289f
米切尔 Mitchell, W.O. 加拿大作家 11—289e
米切尔峰 Mitchell, Mount 美国山峰 11—289c
米切尔河 Mitchell River 澳大利亚河流 11—290b
米切纳 Michener, James A(lbert) 美国小说家 11—186f
米钦斯基 Miciński, Tadeusz 波兰作家、诗人、剧作家 11—191a
米丘林 Michurin, Ivan Vladimirovich 俄罗斯园艺学家 11—190f
米丘林斯克 Michurinsk 俄罗斯城市 11—190f
米却肯 Michoacán 墨西哥州名 11—190e
米塞努姆 Misenum 意大利港口 11—275a
米塞-佐克人 Mixe-Zoquean 墨西哥印第安人 11—296a
米塞-佐克诸语言 Mixe-Zoque languages 墨西哥语言 11—295f
米色陶器 creamware 陶器 4—574e
米沙沃卡 Mishawaka 美国城市 11—275b
米沙鄢群岛 Visayas 菲律宾岛群 18—16a
米沙鄢人 Visayan 菲律宾民族 18—16a
米绍 Misau 尼日利亚城镇 11—274c
米绍 Michaux, Henri 法国诗人、画家 11—180f
米舍尔 Miescher, Johann Friedrich 瑞士学者 11—204f
米申 Mission 美国城市 11—278b
米申纳里岭战役 Missionary Ridge, Battle of 美国历史 11—278e
米什 Miche, Jean-Claude 法国天主教传教士 11—181a
米什科尔茨 Miskolc 匈牙利城镇 11—276c
米什莱 Michelet, Jules 法国历史学家 11—185d
米什米人 Mishmi 印度民族 11—275f
米丝廷盖特 Mistinguett 法国喜剧演员 11—286e
米思勋爵(第一) Meath, Hugh de Lacy, 1st Lord of 爱尔兰法官 11—66a
米斯 Mus, Paul 法国学者 11—499e
米斯蒂火山 Misti Volcano 秘鲁火山 11—286e
米斯蒂克 Mystic 美国乡村 11—529f
米斯基托海岸 Miskito Coast (Nicaragua) 尼加拉瓜海岸 11—276c
米斯基托人 Miskito 尼加拉瓜印第安人 11—276c
米斯郡 Meath 爱尔兰郡名 11—65f
米斯塔西尼湖 Mistassini Lake 加拿大湖泊 11—286e
米斯特克人 Mixtec 墨西哥印第安人 11—296b
米斯特拉尔 Mistral, Frédéric 法国诗人 11—287a
米斯特拉尔 Mistral, Gabriela 智利诗人 11—287c
米苏尔岛 Misool Island 印度尼西亚岛屿 11—276d
米苏拉 Missoula 美国城市 11—282f
米苏拉塔 Miṣrātah 利比亚城镇 11—276e
米索雷群岛 Misore Islands (Indonesia) 印度尼西亚岛屿 11—276e
米塔格-列夫勒 Mittag-Leffler, Magnus Gösta 瑞典数学家 11—294d
米塔科姆 Metacom 美洲万帕诺亚格印第安首长 11—147b
米太亚得(大) Miltiades THE ELDER 雅典政治家 11—233a
米太亚得(小) Miltiades THE YOUNGER 雅典将军 11—233a
米坦尼 Mitanni 印度-伊朗人帝国 11—287f
米陶 Mitau (Latvia) 拉脱维亚城市 11—288a
米特尔兰运河 Mittelland Canal 德国水道 11—294e
米特福德 Mitford, Jessica (Lucy) 美国作家、新闻记者 11—290d
米特福德 Mitford, Mary Russell 英国剧作家、诗人 11—290e
米特福德 Mitford, Nancy 英国作家 11—290e
米特拉 Mitla 墨西哥考古遗址 11—291f
米特拉达梯 Mithradates 统治者之名 11—291a
米特拉达梯二世 Mithradates II 安息国王 11—291a
米特拉达梯六世 Mithradates VI EUPATOR 本都王国国王 11—291b

米特拉达梯一世 Mithradates I 安息国王 11—291a
米特雷 Mitre, Bartolomé 阿根廷政治家、军人 11—292d
米特罗普洛斯 Mitropoulos, Dimitri 希腊指挥家 11—292f
米特迈尔 Mittermaier, Rosi 德国高山滑雪运动员 11—294f
米特纳盖德派 Mitnagged 犹太教派别 11—292a
米滕瓦尔德 Mittenwald 德国村庄 11—294f
米突里蒂斯 metrētēs 古希腊计量单位 11—160e
米瓦特 Mivart, Saint George Jackson 英国生物学家 11—295d
米沃克人 Miwok 加利福尼亚印第安人 11—295e
米沃什 Miłosz, Czesław 美国作家、翻译家 11—232d
米西奥内斯 Misiones 阿根廷省份 11—276b
米西马岛 Misima Island 巴布亚新几内亚火山岛 11—276b
米西奈曲调 Mi-Sinai tune 音乐 11—174d
米西索加 Mississauga 加拿大城市 11—278e
米西索加响尾蛇 massasauga (*Sistrurus catenatus*) 爬行动物 11—11b
米夏埃利斯 Michaelis, Georg 德国政治家 11—180d
米夏埃利斯-门滕二氏假说 Michaelis-Menten hypothesis 生物化学 11—180e
米肖 Michaux, André 法国植物学家 11—180f
米歇尔 Michel, (Clémence-) Louise 法国无政府主义者 11—181c
米歇尔 Michel, Hartmut 德国生物化学家 11—181b
米歇尔 Michell, John 英国地质学家、天文学家 11—186a
米歇尔-莱维 Michel-Lévy, Auguste 法国矿物学家 11—181c
米歇尔斯 Michels, Robert 意大利社会学家、经济学家 11—186b
米修 Micheaux, Oscar 美国制片人、导演 11—181a
米亚尔代 Millardet, Pierre-Marie-Alexis 法国植物学家 11—223d
米亚尼战役 Miāni, Battle of 信德-英国战争 11—175d
米亚乌利斯 Miaoulis, Andreas Vokos 希腊爱国志士 11—177a
米耶尔库雷亚丘克 Miercurea-Ciuc 罗马尼亚城市 11—204b
米耶雷斯 Mieres 西班牙城镇 11—204b
米约 Millau 法国城镇 11—223e
米约 Milhaud, Darius 法国作曲家 11—214f
米约尔尼尔 Mjollnir 古斯堪的纳维亚神话 11—298b
米约萨湖 Mjøsa, Lake 挪威湖泊 11—298c
米泽 Yonezawa 日本城市 18—454d
米泽斯 Mises, Ludwig (Edler) von 美国经济学家 11—275a
米泽斯 Mises, Richard von 美国数学家 11—275a
米制 metric system 度量衡制 11—160f
米兹 Meads, Colin Earl 新西兰橄榄球运动员 11—62c
米兹腊希 Mizraḥi 犹太宗教运动 11—297f
米子 Yonago 日本城市 18—454c
米佐拉姆 Mizoram 印度邦名 11—297e
米佐丘陵 Mizo Hills 印度山地 11—297d
米佐人 Mizo 印度民族 11—297d
米佐塔基斯 Mitsotakis, Konstantinos 希腊总理 11—293c
泌尿生殖系统畸形 urogenital malformation 生理器官缺陷 17—417d
泌尿学 urology 医学 17—417e
泌乳 lactation 生物学 9—440a
泌酸细胞 oxyntic cell (anatomy) 解剖学 12—525c
宓羲 Mi Hsi 中国神话人物 11—174d
秘传宗教 mystery religion 古希腊-罗马宗教 11—529c
秘库 genizah 犹太教 7—64a
秘密出版物 samizdat 苏联出版 14—563b
《秘密会坦陀罗》 Guhyasamāja-tantra 佛教经典 7—352d
秘密投票 Australian ballot 政治学 2—67a
密藏花属 Eucryphia 植物学 6—156e
密茨凯维奇 Mickiewicz, Adam (Bernard) 波兰诗人 11—191a
密德兰银行 Midland Bank PLC 原英国银行 11—202b
密度 density 物理学 5—247b
密多罗 Mitra 印度教神 11—292b
密尔斯 Mills, Robert 美国建筑师 11—230b
密尔沃基 Milwaukee 美国城市 11—236f
密尔沃基海渊 Milwaukee Depth 大西洋海沟最深处 11—237a
密尔沃基铁路公司 Milwaukee Road 美国铁路 11—237b
密尔沃基县立动物园 Milwaukee County Zoo 美国动物园 11—237a
《密尔沃基新闻报》 Milwaukee Journal, The 美国报纸 11—237a
密耳弥冬 Myrmidon 希腊传说中的居民 11—527d
密克罗尼西亚 Micronesia 西太平洋岛屿 11—193c
密克罗尼西亚 Micronesia 西太平洋共和国 11—193e
密克罗尼西亚地理人种 Micronesian geographic race 西南太平洋人种 11—194b
密克罗尼西亚诸语言 Micronesian languages 语言 11—194b
密拉 Mylar 聚酯商品名 11—524e
密拉特 Meerut 印度城镇 11—80a
密莱司 Millais, Sir John Everett, 1st Baronet 英国油画家、插图画家 11—223b
密勒 Miller, Oskar von 德国电气工程师 11—227b
密勒指数 Miller indices 晶体学 11—227e
密立根 Millikan, Robert Andrews 美国物理学家 11—229a
密立根油滴实验 Millikan oil-drop experiment 物理实验 11—229b
密利车 mlechchha 古印度非雅利安人名称 11—298c
密列奥赛法隆战役 Myriocephalon, Battle of 突厥历史 11—527b
密罗·跋伊 Mīrā Bāī 印度教修行者、诗人 11—270a
密码 cipher 保密通信 4—243b
密码术 cryptology 保密通信 5—43b
密涅瓦 Minerva 罗马女神 11—247a
密切利希 Mitscherlich, Eilhardt 德国化学家 11—293b
密史脱拉风 mistral 气象学 11—287a
密斯·范·德·罗厄 Mies van der Rohe, Ludwig 美国建筑师 11—204c
密苏里 Missouri 美国州名 11—283a
密苏里法 Missouri Plan 美国法官挑选法 11—286c
"密苏里"号 Missouri 美国战舰 11—285e
密苏里河 Missouri River 美国河流 11—286c
密苏里狐步马 Missouri fox-trotting horse 马品种 11—286b
密苏里葫芦 Missouri gourd 藤本植物 11—286b
密苏里人 Missouri 已绝灭的北美印第安部落 11—283a
密苏里太平洋铁路公司 Missouri Pacific Railroad Company 美国公司 11—286b
《密苏里妥协案》 Missouri Compromise 美国历史 11—285f
密苏里植物园 Missouri Botanical Garden 美国植物园 11—285f
密穗桔梗属 Sphenoclea 植物学 16—24d
密特拉教 Mithraism 波斯宗教 11—291d
密特拉神 Mithra 印度-伊朗神话光明之神 11—290f
密特朗 Mitterrand, François 法国总统 11—295a
密铁拉 Meiktila 缅甸城镇 11—86b
密陀僧 litharge 矿物 10—146c
《密西拿》 Mishna 犹太教经籍 11—276a
《密西拿律法书》 Mishne Torah 犹太教著作 11—276a
密西西比 Mississippi 美国州名 11—278e
密西西比河 Mississippi River 北美河流 11—282c
密西西比河谷战役 Mississippi Valley Campaign 美国历史 11—282d
密西西比纪 Mississippian period 地质学 11—282f
密西西比骗局 Mississippi Bubble 法国历史 11—282b
密西西比文化 Mississippian culture 北美史前文化 11—282d
密细亚 Mysia 安纳托利亚历史地区 11—528f
密歇根 Michigan 美国州名 11—187a
密歇根城 Michigan City 美国城市 11—190d
密歇根大学 Michigan, University of 美国大学 11—190c
密歇根湖 Michigan, Lake 美国湖泊 11—190b
密云水库 Miyun Reservoir 中国水库 11—297c
密札 cachet, lettre de 法国历史 3—310b

密支那 Myitkyinā 缅甸城镇 11—524d
密兹瓦 mitzvah 犹太教诫条、律法 11—295c
幂级数 power series 数学 13—474c
嘧啶 pyrimidine 化合物 14—46f
蜜胺 melamine 化合物 11—90e
蜜蜂 honeybee 昆虫 8—154c
蜜蜂类 bee 生物学 2—327e
蜜獾 ratel (*Mellivora capensis*) 哺乳动物 14—161d
蜜环菌属 Armillaria 生物学 1—500d
蜜饯叉 sucket fork 餐具 16—302e
蜜树 honey tree 木本植物 8—154c
蜜熊 honey bear 哺乳动物 8—153d
蜜蚁 honey ant 昆虫 8—153d
蜜源植物 bee plant 显花植物 2—328c
蜜钟花 honey bell (*Hermannia verticillata*) 观赏植物 8—153d
眠而通 meprobamate 药物 11—122e
绵鳚 eelpout 鱼类 5—554c
绵羊 sheep 哺乳动物 15—292d
绵阳 Mianyang 中国城市 11—175e
绵枣儿 squill 植物 16—169f
棉花 cotton 植物种籽纤维 4—538c
棉花国王 King Cotton 美国历史 9—288e
棉花赛 Cotton Bowl 美国橄榄球赛 4—539a
棉花收获机 cotton harvester 机器 4—539b
棉兰 Medan 印度尼西亚城市 11—70b
棉兰老 Mindanao 菲律宾岛屿 11—244f
棉兰老海 Mindanao Sea 菲律宾海 11—245b
棉兰老海渊 Mindanao Deep (Pacific Ocean) 太平洋海沟 11—245a
棉兰老河 Mindanao River 菲律宾河流 11—245b
棉铃象甲 boll weevil (*Anthonomus grandis*) 昆虫 3—14e
棉蛉虫 cotton bollworm 昆虫 4—539a
棉鼠 cotton rat 哺乳动物 4—539c
棉尾兔 cottontail 哺乳动物 4—539e
棉屑肺 byssinosis 疾病 3—300e
棉籽 cottonseed 棉花种子 4—539c
免兵役税 scutage 封建法律 15—161f
免耕农业 till-less agriculture 耕作技术 17—96a
免疫 immunity 生物学 8—343e
免疫法 immunization 医学 8—344c
免疫球蛋白 immunoglobulin 生物化学 8—344d
免疫学 immunology 医学 8—344d
免罪罚 indulgence 天主教 8—374f
冕玻璃 crown glass 应用光学 5—36c
缅甸 Myanmar 亚洲国家 11—520e
缅甸公路 Burma Road 亚洲公路 3—269c
缅甸猫 Burmese 哺乳动物 3—269d
缅甸文学 Burmese literature 文学 3—269d
缅甸语 Burmese language 亚洲语言 3—269d
缅什科夫 Menshikov, Aleksandr Danilovich 俄国政治人物 11—118d
缅什科夫 Menshikov, Aleksandr Sergeyevich, Knyaz (Prince) 俄国军官 11—118e
缅因 Maine 美国州名 10—407d
"缅因"号战舰炸毁事件 Maine, destruction of the 美国历史 10—410c
面 face 解剖学 6—209a
面包 bread 食品 3—133e
面包果 breadfruit 乔木果实 3—134b
面包坚果 breadnut 木本植物 3—134c
面包屑软海绵 bread-crumb sponge (*Halichondria panicea*) 动物 3—133f
面包棕榈 bread palm 植物 3—134a
面粉 flour 食品 6—374c
面糊 batter 食品加工 2—281c
面具 mask 化装用具 11—1b
面盘幼虫 veliger 动物 17—494d
面神经 facial nerve 解剖学 6—209b
面食 pasta 食品 13—80c
面条 noodle 食品 12—230e
面团 dough 食品加工 5—399e
苗栗 Miaoli 中国台湾县名 11—176e
苗栗 Miaoli 中国台湾城市 11—176f
苗语 Miao language 中国语言 11—176c
苗族 Miao 中国民族 11—176a
描述伦理学 descriptive ethics 伦理学 5—258f
瞄准具 gunsight 光学器具 7—374b
秒 second 计量单位 15—176c
秒差距 parsec 天文学 13—62f
藐视法庭罪 contempt 法律 4—465a
妙带鱼 ribbonfish 妙带鱼 14—276b
《妙法莲华经》 Lotus Sūtra 佛教经籍 10—232a
庙底沟遗址 Miaodigou Site 中国文化遗址 11—176d
庙宇 temple 宗教建筑 16—533f
灭火器 fire extinguisher 消防装置 6—326a
灭火器藓 extinguisher moss 植物 6—198a
灭绝营 extermination camp 纳粹德国集中营 6—197f
灭绝种族 genocide 战争罪行 7—65d
灭业 nirjarā 印度耆那教 12—201c
民兵 militia 军事组织 11—218d
民兵式导弹 Minuteman missile 武器 11—268e
民兵运动 militia movement 美国准军事团体运动 11—218e
民粹派 Narodnik 俄国社会主义运动派别 11—576d
民都洛 Mindoro 菲律宾岛屿 11—245d
民法 civil law 法律 4—254b
民法博士协会 Doctors' Commons 英国律师教育机构 5—356c
《民法大全》 Liber Judiciorum 西哥特法典 10—72b
民防 civil defense 战时非军事防卫 4—253c
民风 folkway 社会学 6—390c
民家 Min-chia 中国白族古称 11—240e
民间传说 folklore 文化、文学 6—390a
民间会社 folk society 社会学 6—389e
民间剧团 civic theatre 艺术团体 4—253a
民间拉丁语 Vulgar Latin 语言 18—54e
民间舞蹈 folk dance 舞蹈 6—389b
民间艺术 folk art 艺术类型 6—388e
民间音乐 folk music 音乐 6—389c
民军 fyrd 英格兰古代民兵组织 6—537c
《民权法》 Civil Rights Act 美国法律 4—255a
民权运动 civil rights movement 美国群众运动 4—255b
民社党 Democratic Socialist Party 日本政党 5—237b
民事法院(普通诉讼法院) Common Pleas, Court of 英国法院 4—388e
《民数记》 Numbers 《圣经》第四卷 12—296f
民谣复兴 ballad revival 文学 2—174c
民谣摇滚 folk rock 音乐 6—389d
民意党 Narodnaya Volya 俄国革命组织 11—576d
民用波段无线电通信 citizens band radio 无线电通信系统 4—248d
民政党 Minseitō 日本政党 11—266a
民政官 aedile 古罗马官职 1—92a
民众中学 folk high school 斯堪的纳维亚教育 6—389c
民主 democracy 政治学 5—235c
民主党 Democratic Party 美国政党 5—236d
民主党 Democratic Party 南非政党 5—236d
民主集中派 Democratic Centralist 苏联党派 5—235e
民主进步党 Democratic Progressive Party (DPP) 中国台湾政党

5—237a
民主统一党 Democratic Unionist Party (DUP) 北爱尔兰政党 5—237b
民主宪政联盟 Democratic Constitutional Rally 突尼斯政党 5—235f
民主行动党 Democratic Action 委内瑞拉政党 5—235e
民主制度研究中心 Study of Democratic Institutions, Center for the 美国教育机构 16—288d
民主左翼党 Democratic Left 北爱尔兰和爱尔兰共和国政党 5—236b
《民族》 Nation, The 美国杂志 12—10b
民族集团 Bloc National 法国政治组织 2—536f
民族解放阵线 National Liberation Front 阿尔及利亚政党 12—16c
民族解放阵线 National Liberation Front (Greece) 希腊军事、政治组织 12—16e
民族解放阵线 National Liberation Front (NLF) 越南政治团体 12—16e
民族解放阵线-民族人民解放军 EAM-ELAS 希腊军事、政治组织 5—494e
民族觉醒党 National Awakening Party (PKB) 印度尼西亚政党 12—12a
民族人民解放军 ELAS (National Popular Liberation Army; Greece) 希腊军事、政治组织 6—13e
民族人民解放军(希腊) National Popular Liberation Army (Greece) 希腊抵抗组织 12—35b
《民族圣约》 National Covenant 苏格兰宗教史 12—14b
民族音乐学 ethnomusicology 音乐学 6—151a
民族植物学 ethnobotany 学科 6—150d
民族主义 nationalism 政治 12—38d
民族自由党 National Liberal Party 德国政党 12—16b
岷江 Min Jiang 中国河流 11—240e
岷山 Min Shan 中国山脉 11—241b
旻宁 Minning 中国清代皇帝 11—263b
皿网蛛 sheet-web weaver 节肢动物 15—293e
黾蝽 water strider 昆虫 18—138f
闵采尔 Müntzer, Thomas 欧洲宗教改革运动领袖 11—488a
闵行 Minhang 中国上海市辖区 11—250b
闵科夫斯基 Minkowski, Hermann 德国数学家 11—258e
闵科夫斯基 Minkowski, Oskar 德国生理学家 11—258e
闵希豪生 Münchhausen, Baron 德国乡绅 11—482f
闽方言 Min dialect 汉语方言 11—240e
闽江 Min Jiang 中国河流 11—240f
敏 Min 古埃及神话 11—240d
敏拜尔 minbar 清真寺宣教台 11—243d
敏哈 minhah 犹太教 11—250b
敏哈格 minhag 犹太教习俗 11—250b
敏建 Myingyan 缅甸城镇 11—524d
敏巫 Minbu 缅甸城镇 11—243e
敏彦 minyan 犹太教 11—268f
名 nāman 吠陀教、印度教 11—548c
名单选举制 list system 政治 10—139f
名歌手 meistersinger 德国诗人、音乐家 11—88f
名古屋 nagoya 日本城市 11—540c
名家 Logician 中国先秦哲学流派 10—191e
名人录 Who's Who 名人传记词典 18—242e
名誉晋级 brevet 军官委任形式 3—145f
名祖 eponym 姓名 6—105a
鸣板 crotal 乐器 5—34b
鸣鞭鸟 coachwhipbird (songbird) 鸣禽 4—310c
鸣管 syrinx 鸟发声器官 16—407c
鸣角鸮 screech owl 鸟类 15—155e
鸣门 Naruto 日本城市 12—2b
鸣禽 songbird 鸟类 15—513b
鸣禽类 oscine 鸟类 12—483e
鸣钟术 ringing 英国敲钟技术 14—304f
鸣啭 birdsong 鸟类交际方式 2—490d
明 Ming DYNASTY 中国王朝 11—248f
明暗对比法 chiaroscuro 绘画技法 4—139b
明布雷斯人 Mimbres 史前北美民族 11—237f
明朝帝王 Ming ——: 中国明朝统治者 11—247c
明成祖朱棣 Mingchengzu ZhuDi 中国明朝皇帝 11—247d
明打威群岛 Mentawai Islands 印度尼西亚岛屿 11—120f
明代宗朱祁钰 Mingdaizong Zhu Qiyu 中国明朝皇帝 11—247f
明道加斯 Mindaugas 立陶宛统治者 11—245b
明德冰期 Mindel Glacial Stage 地质学 11—245b
明德卢 Mindelo 佛得角城市 11—245c
明登 Minden 德国城市 11—245c
明登 Minden 美国城市 11—245c
明顿 Minton, Sherman 美国最高法院大法官 11—267e
明顿陶瓷 Minton ware 英国陶器 11—267f
明矾 alum 化合物 1—258c
明矾石 alunite 矿物 1—259c
明盖恰乌尔 Mingechaur 阿塞拜疆城市 11—249c
明戈斯 Mingus, Charles 美国作曲家 11—249f
明格蒂 Minghetti, Marco 意大利政治家 11—249d
明格列尔语 Mingrelian language 黑海沿岸地区语言 11—249e
明古鲁 Bengkulu 印度尼西亚省份 2—384c
明古鲁 Bengkulu 印度尼西亚城市 2—384c
明光宗朱常洛 Mingguangzong Zhu Changluo 中国明朝皇帝 11—248e
明惠帝朱允炆 Minghuidi Zhu Yunwen 中国明朝皇帝 11—247d
明胶 gelatin 动物蛋白质 7—47b
明胶照相法 gelatin process 摄影 7—47c
明教 Mingjiao 摩尼教 11—249d
《明镜》 Spiegel, Der 德国新闻周刊 16—29f
明命 Minh Mang 越南皇帝 11—250a
明穆宗朱载垕 Mingmuzong Zhu Zaihou 中国明朝皇帝 11—248c
明纳 Minna 尼日利亚城镇 11—258f
明纳利 Minnelli, Vincente 美国电影导演 11—259c
明尼阿波利斯 Minneapolis 美国城市 11—259a
明尼阿波利斯西北国民银行 Northwestern National Bank of Minneapolis 美国公司 12—268c
明尼格罗德 Minnigerode, Lucy 美国护士 11—263a
明尼哈哈瀑布 Minnehaha Falls 美国瀑布 11—259c
明尼苏达 Minnesota 美国州名 11—259e
明尼苏达河 Minnesota River 美国河流 11—262f
明尼苏达矿业与制造公司 Minnesota Mining & Manufacturing Company 美国公司 11—262f
明奇 Minch, The 大西洋海峡 11—243e
明器 mingqi 中国古代随葬品 11—249d
明清小说 Ming-Qing xiaoshuo 中国文学 11—249a
明仁 Akihito 日本天皇 1—156b
明仁宗朱高炽 Mingrenzong Zhu Gaochi 中国明朝皇帝 11—247e
明神宗朱翊钧 Mingshenzong Zhu Yijun 中国明朝皇帝 11—248c
明十三陵 Ming Tombs 中国皇室陵墓 11—249b
明石 Akashi 日本城市 1—152e
《明史》 Mingshi 中国纪传体史书 11—249f
明世宗朱厚熜 Mingshizong Zhu Houcong 中国明朝皇帝 11—248b
明式硬木家具 Ming-style furniture of hardwood 中国家具 11—249b
明思宗朱由检 Mingsizong Zhu Youjian 中国明朝皇帝 11—248e
明斯基 Minsky, Marvin 美国数学家、计算机科学家 11—266d
明斯克 Minsk 白俄罗斯州名 11—266b
明斯克 Minsk 白俄罗斯首都 11—266c
明斯特 Münster 德国区名 11—486f
明斯特 Münster 德国城市 11—487a
明斯特 Münster, Sebastian 希伯来学者 11—487b
明斯特尔贝格 Münsterberg, Hugo 美国心理学家 11—487c

明斯特干酪 Münster cheese 食物 11—487c
明斯特兰 Münsterland 德国地区 11—487d
明塔迪 mintadi 非洲艺术 11—267c
明太祖朱元璋 Mingtaizu Zhu Yuanzhang 中国明朝皇帝 11—247c
明堂 Hall of Light 建筑 7—427f
明特 Münter, Gabriele 德国画家 11—487e
明托伯爵(第四) Minto, Gilbert John Elliot-Murray-Kynynmound, 4th earl of 英国官员 11—267d
明托伯爵(第一) Minto, Gilbert Elliot-Murray-Kynynmound, 1st earl of 英国官员 11—267c
明托夫 Mintoff, Dom(inic) 马耳他总理 11—267e
明王 dharmapāla 藏传佛教神祇 5—279b
明王 Myō-ō 日本神灵 11—525a
明武宗朱厚照 Mingwuzong Zhu Houzhao 中国明朝皇帝 11—248a
明西奥 Mincio, Giovanni (pope) 教皇 11—243f
明熹宗朱由校 Mingxizong Zhu Youxiao 中国明朝皇帝 11—248e
明宪宗朱见深 Mingxianzong Zhu Jianshen 中国明朝皇帝 11—248a
明孝宗朱祐樘 Mingxiaozong Zhu Youtang 中国明朝皇帝 11—248a
《明星画刊》 Stern Magazin 德国新闻周刊 16—226b
明宣宗朱瞻基 Mingxuanzong Zhu Zhanji 中国明朝皇帝 11—247f
明亚 Minyā, Al- 埃及省份 11—268f
明亚 Minyā, Al- 埃及城市 11—268f
明洋陶器 Minyan ware 希腊陶器 11—269a
明英宗朱祁镇 Mingyingzong Zhu Qizhen 中国明朝皇帝 11—247f
明喻 simile 文学 15—380e
明曾蒂 Mindszenty, József 匈牙利天主教神职人员 11—245e
明兆 Minchō 日本画家 11—243e
明治天皇 Meiji 日本天皇 11—85c
明治维新 Meiji Restoration 日本历史 11—85f
冥外行星 Planet X 天文学 13—342b
冥王星 Pluto 天文学 13—378a
冥卫一 Charon 天文学 4—84b
铭文学 epigraphy 研究刻写文献的学科 6—100b
螟蛾 pyralid moth 昆虫 14—44c
螟蛉 bollworm 昆虫 3—15b
命 jiva 耆那教 9—36b
命名法 nomenclature 生物学 12—227a
命题函项 propositional function 逻辑学 13—537e
命题演算 propositional calculus 逻辑学 13—537d
命运悲剧 fate tragedy 戏剧 6—248e
命运剧院 Fortune Theatre 英国历史剧院 6—418e
命运女神 Fate 希腊神话中的神 6—248e
命运石 Destiny, Stone of 国王加冕石 5—264d
谬龙属 Apatosaurus 古生物学 1—407b
谬论 fallacy 逻辑学 6—223c
缪尔 Muir, Edwin 苏格兰文学评论家、翻译家 11—471d
缪尔 Muir, John 美国博物学家 11—471e
缪尔树林国家保护区 Muir, Woods National Monument 美国国家保护区 11—471f
缪拉 Murat, Joachim 法国骑兵统帅 11—491c
缪勒 Müller, Karl Alex(ander) 瑞士物理学家 11—476d
缪里斯 Muris, Jean de 法国哲学家、数学家 11—495c
缪塞 Musset, Alfred de 法国诗人、剧作家 11—513a
缪塞 Muset, Colin (poet) 法国诗人 11—502c
缪赛特风笛 musette 乐器 11—502c
缪斯 Muse 希腊女神 11—502a
模仿 imitation 行为 8—342c
模仿诗文 parody 文学 13—60c
模仿作品 parody 音乐 13—60d
模糊逻辑 fuzzy logic 数学 6—536b
模进(继叙咏) sequence 音乐 15—220b
模拟 simulation 科学方法 15—386d
模拟计算机 analog computer 机器 1—309f
模数 module 建筑学 11—308a
模态 modality 逻辑学 11—303d
模态逻辑 modal logic 逻辑学 11—303d
模运算 modular arithmetic 数学 11—307c
摹仿 mimesis 艺术 11—239a
膜 membrane 生物学 11—101f
膜翅目昆虫 hymenopteran 动物学 8—289a
膜蝽 velvet water bug 昆虫 17—496a
膜口虫 hymenostome 原生动物 8—289f
膜鸣乐器 membranophone 乐器 11—102c
摩擦鼓 friction drum 乐器 6—491e
摩擦力 friction 物理学 6—491c
摩擦学 tribology 物理学 17—214e
摩擦轧光印花布 chintz 织物 4—177e
摩德纳 Modena 意大利城市 11—304b
摩尔 Mauer 德国古生物地层 11—34a
摩尔 mole 化学 11—316e
摩尔 Moore, Gordon E. 美国工程师 11—379d
摩尔达维亚 Moldavia 欧洲古地名 11—315f
摩尔多瓦 Moldova 欧洲国家 11—316c
摩尔根 Morgan, Thomas Hunt 美国动物学家 11—393a
摩尔根马 Morgan 马品种 11—391a
摩尔科 Molcho, Solomon 葡萄牙犹太教殉教士 11—315d
摩尔曼斯克 Murmansk 俄罗斯州名 11—495d
摩尔曼斯克 Murmansk 俄罗斯海港 11—495d
摩尔气体常量 molar gas constant 物理常量 11—315a
摩尔人 Moor 民族 11—378d
摩尔式 Moorish style (furniture) 装饰艺术 11—381f
摩尔下颌骨 Mauer jaw 考古化石 11—34a
摩根 Morgan, Anne Tracy 美国慈善家 11—391b
摩根 Morgan, Charles Langbridge 英国小说家、剧作家 11—391d
摩根 Morgan, C(onwy) Lloyd 英国动物学家、心理学家 11—391c
摩根 Morgan, Daniel 美国将领 11—391e
摩根 Morgan, Frederick Edgeworth 英国军官 11—391f
摩根 Morgan, Helen 美国演员、歌手 11—391f
摩根 Morgan, Sir Henry 威尔士海盗 11—392a
摩根 Morgan, John 美国医学教育家 11—392b
摩根 Morgan, John Hunt 美国将军 11—392b
摩根 Morgan, John Pierpont 美国金融家 11—392c
摩根 Morgan, Julia 美国建筑师 11—392f
摩根 Morgan, Lewis Henry 美国人类学家 11—393a
摩根 Morgan, William 基督教主教、宗教改革家 11—393f
摩根 Morgan, William Wilson 美国天文学家 11—393f
摩根(小) Morgan, John Pierpont, Jr. 美国金融家 11—392e
摩根堡 Fort Morgan 美国城市 6—414d
摩根城 Morgan City 美国城市 11—394a
摩根大通公司 JPMorgan Chase & Co. 美国公司 9—95f
摩根敦 Morgantown 美国城市 11—394c
摩根顿 Morganton 美国城市 11—394c
摩根斯顿 Morgenstern, Oskar 美国经济学家 11—394e
摩根索 Morgenthau, Hans J. 美国政治学家、历史学家 11—394e
摩根索(小) Morgenthau, Henry, Jr. 美国政治家 11—394f
摩根韦格 Morgannwg 威尔士历史地区 11—394b
摩诃摩耶 Mahā Māyā 释迦牟尼之母 10—396c
《摩诃婆罗多》 Mahābhārata 印度文学 10—397a
摩诃菩提会 Maha Bodhi Society 印度佛教团体 10—396c
摩亨约-达罗 Mohenjo-daro 巴基斯坦古城市遗址 11—312a
摩加迪沙 Mogadishu 索马里城市 11—309e
摩加多尔 Mogador (Morocco) 摩洛哥城市 11—309f
摩揭陀 Magadha 印度古王国 10—378b
摩羯座 Capricornus 天文学 3—430f
摩科斯 Mokoš 古代斯拉夫神话中女神 11—314d
摩拉瓦河 Morava River 欧洲河流 11—384d

摩拉瓦河 Morava River 塞尔维亚河流 11—384d
摩拉维亚 Moravia 中欧地区 11—384e
摩拉维亚教会 Moravian church 宗教 11—385a
摩拉维亚岩溶 Moravian Karst 捷克岩溶 11—385b
摩勒 Mollet, Guy 法国总理 11—323a
摩里斯湖 Moeris, Lake 埃及古代湖泊 11—308e
摩里斯科人 Morisco 西班牙穆斯林 11—396c
摩里索 Morisot, Berthe 法国油画家 11—396f
摩里亚采邑 Morea, Despotate of 拜占廷采邑 11—388e
摩利甘 Morrígan 凯尔特神话 11—403e
摩利支天 Marīcī 佛教女神 10—509b
摩鹿加 Moluccas (province, Indonesia) 印度尼西亚省份 11—325f
摩鹿加 Moluccas 印度尼西亚群岛 11—325d
摩鹿加海 Molucca Sea 西太平洋海域 11—325d
摩罗乃 Moroni 宗教人物 11—401d
摩洛 Moloch 古代中东神灵 11—324b
摩洛哥 Morocco 非洲国家 11—399f
摩洛哥危机 Moroccan crises 法国历史 11—399e
摩洛哥行动委员会 National Action Bloc 摩洛哥政党 12—10d
摩洛普斯 Mauropous, John 拜占廷学者、教士 11—40e
摩洛人 Moro 菲律宾民族 11—399b
摩洛蜥 moloch (*Moloch horridus*) 蜥蜴 11—324b
摩门教徒 Mormon 宗教 11—398a
《摩门经》 Mormon, Book of 宗教著作 11—398e
摩那娑 Manasā 孟加拉、印度神话 10—446e
摩纳哥 Monaco 欧洲国家 11—328a
摩纳哥亲王 Monaco, Rainier III, prince de 摩洛哥总统 11—328f
摩尼 Mani 摩尼教创始人 10—460b
摩尼教 Manichaeism 波斯宗教 10—460d
摩涅莫恩 Mnemon 波斯国王 11—298d
摩涅莫绪涅 Mnemosyne 希腊神话中女神 11—298f
摩奴 Manu 印度神话 10—476a
《摩奴法典》 Manu-smṛti 印度教法典 10—476b
摩萨山 Mūsā, Jabal (Sinai, Egypt) 埃及山脉 11—500a
摩萨台 Mosaddeq, Mohammad 伊朗政治领袖 11—411d
摩阇衍陀罗那陀 Matsyendranātha 印度宗教领袖 11—29c
摩哂陀 Mahendra 锡兰佛教传播者 10—400e
摩斯科斯 Moschus 希腊诗人、语法学家 11—414a
摩苏尔 Mosul 伊拉克城市 11—429e
摩苏尔画派 Mosul school 伊拉克画派 11—430a
摩苏尔派 Mosul school 伊拉克金属工艺 11—429f
摩索拉斯 Mausolus 波斯总督 11—41d
摩拓法 frottage 艺术技法 6—503e
摩天楼 skyscraper 建筑 15—424a
摩托车 motorcycle 车辆 11—436c
摩托车导引赛 motor-paced race 体育运动 11—435d
摩托车赛 motorcycle racing 体育运动 11—436e
摩托车选拔赛 motorcycle trial 体育运动 11—437a
摩托车越野赛 motocross 体育运动 11—435a
摩托罗拉公司 Motorola, Inc. 美国公司 11—437a
摩托艇 motorboat 船 11—435e
摩陀伐 Madhva 印度教哲学家 10—368a
摩陀伐迦利耶 Mādhavācārya 印度教哲学家、政治家 10—368a
摩西 Moses 希伯来领袖 11—421d
摩西 Moses, Edwin 美国运动员 11—424c
摩西 Moses, Grandma 美国画家 11—424c
摩西 Moses, Robert 美国官员 11—424d
摩西(霍仑的) Moses of Khoren 亚美尼亚作家 11—424a
摩西(莱昂的) Moses de León 西班牙犹太教人士 11—424a
摩西·本·迈蒙 Moses ben Maimon (Jewish philosopher) 犹太教法学家、哲学家 11—424e
摩西·本·拿曼 Moses ben Nahman (Jewish scholar) 西班牙学者、哲学家 11—424e
摩西·本·萨穆埃尔·伊本·提本 Moses ben Samuel ibn Tibbon 犹太内科医生、翻译家 11—424f
摩西莱克 Moses Lake 美国城市 11—424f
《摩西升天记》 Moses, Assumption of 伪经 11—424b
摩西·伊本·埃兹拉 Moses ibn Ezra 犹太诗人 11—424f
摩西之山 Mountain of Moses (Sinai, Egypt) 埃及山脉 11—445b
摩押人 Moabite 约旦中西部古代民族 11—299c
摩押字母 Moabite alphabet 文字 11—299d
摩耶佛塔铭文 Myazedi inscription 碑文 11—522d
摩耶夫人 Māyā (mother of the Buddha) 释迦牟尼之母 11—49e
磨床 grinding machine 机器 7—314e
磨拉石 molasse 岩石 11—315a
磨料 abrasive 机械加工材料 1—28d
磨石 millstone 农具 11—230e
磨蚀台 abrasion platform 地质学 1—28d
磨损 wear 材料损耗 18—154a
蘑菇 mushroom 真菌 11—504d
蘑菇石 mushroom rock 风化石 11—505b
蘑菇中毒 mushroom poisoning 中毒 11—505a
魔叉探物 dowsing 神秘学 5—407f
魔岛 Devils Island 圭亚那岛屿 5—272c
魔方 magic square 智力游戏 10—382b
魔鬼 devil 宗教 5—271f
魔鬼崇拜 devil worship 神秘习俗 5—272b
魔鬼大哥 Diavolo, Fra 意大利匪首 5—291d
魔鬼缝针 devil's arrow 昆虫 5—272c
魔鬼罗伯特 Robert the Devil 传说人物 14—328c
魔幻现实主义 magic realism 拉丁美洲文学 10—382a
魔罗 Māra 佛教名词 10—486e
魔兽 orc 神秘生物 12—446c
魔术 conjuring 文娱节目 4—432e
魔塔国家保护区 Devils Tower National Monument 美国国家保护区 5—272e
魔桩垛国家保护区 Devils Postpile National Monument 美国国家保护区 5—272d
抹圣油 chrismation 基督教圣事 4—202a
抹香鲸 sperm whale (*Physeter catodon*) 哺乳动物 16—22b
末法 mappō 日本佛教 10—485c
末罗汉王国 Mrohaung, Arakanese Kingdom of 下缅甸王国 11—458c
末罗人 Mallas 印度古民族 10—433a
《末日审判书》 Domesday Book 英国历史 5—369e
末世论 eschatology 宗教教义 6—128b
末世圣徒教会 Latter-day Saints 宗教 9—515f
末乐章 finale 音乐 6—317b
没食子酸 gallic acid 植物酸 6—559c
没收 confiscation 法律 4—421f
《没收法案》 Confiscation Acts 美国历史 4—421f
没药 myrrh 树脂 11—527f
茉莉 jasmine 灌木 8—547d
茉莉芬 Madiun 印度尼西亚城市 10—370c
茉莉芬事件 Madiun Affair 印度尼西亚历史 10—370c
沫蝉 froghopper 昆虫 6—499f
莫 Meaux 法国城镇 11—66a
莫阿布 Moab 美国城市 11—299b
莫埃人像 moai figure 复活节岛木雕 11—299e
莫埃特 Mo'ed 犹太教 11—308d
莫贝里 Moberg, (Carl Artur) Vilheim 瑞典小说家、剧作家 11—299f
莫比尔 Mobile 美国城市 11—300a
莫比尔河 Mobile River 美国河流 11—300c
莫比尔湾 Mobile Bay 墨西哥海湾 11—300b
莫比尔湾战役 Mobile Bay, Battle of 美国历史 11—300b

莫比乌斯 Möbius, Karl August 德国动物学家 11—300e
莫伯日 Maubeuge 法国城镇 11—33d
莫泊桑 Maupassant, Guy de 法国小说家 11—35c
莫布雷 Mowbray, Thomas 英格兰贵族 11—449e
莫布里奇 Mobridge 美国城市 11—300f
莫德 Maud (Holy Roman empress) 神圣罗马帝国皇帝 11—33f
莫德尔 Model, Walther 德国陆军元帅 11—303f
莫德尔松-贝克尔 Modersohn-Becker, Paula 德国画家 11—305f
莫德纳 Modena, Leone 意大利犹太教拉比 11—304c
莫德斯托 Modesto 美国城市 11—306a
莫德耶斯基 Modjeski, Ralph 美国桥梁设计师 11—307a
莫德耶斯卡 Modjeska, Helena 美国演员 11—306f
莫迪卡 Modica 意大利城镇 11—306b
莫迪里阿尼 Modigliani, Amedeo 法国画家 11—306b
莫迪利亚尼 Modigliani, Franco 美国经济学家、财政学教师 11—306d
莫迪尼亚 modinha 葡萄牙歌曲 11—306e
莫迪塞恩 Modisane, Bloke 英国作家、演员 11—306e
莫蒂埃 Mortier, Édouard-Adolphe-Casimir-Joseph, DUC DE TREVISE 法国将军 11—409b
莫蒂哈里 Motīhāri 印度城镇 11—431f
莫蒂隆人 Motilón 美洲印第安人 11—431f
莫蒂默 Mortimer, Edmund 英国贵族 11—409d
莫蒂默 Mortimer, John (Clifford) 英国作家、律师 11—409e
莫蒂默 Mortimer, Penelope (Ruth) 英国新闻记者、小说家 11—409f
莫蒂默 Mortimer, Roger 英国贵族 11—409f
莫蒂默伯爵 Mortimer, Robert Harley, Earl 英国政治家 11—409f
莫蒂默家族 Mortimer FAMILY 盎格鲁-诺曼人家族 11—409d
莫顿 Moten, Bennie 美国钢琴家 11—430d
莫顿 Morton, Jelly Roll 美国音乐家 11—410b
莫顿 Morton, John 英国枢机主教 11—410c
莫顿 Morton, J(ulius) Sterling 美国政治家 11—410a
莫顿 Morton, Levi (Parsons) 美国副总统、银行家 11—410c
莫顿 Morton, Oliver H(azard) P(erry) T(hrock) 美国政治家 11—410d
莫顿 Morton, Sarah Wentworth Apthorp 美国诗人 11—410e
莫顿 Morton, Thomas 英国早期移民 11—410e
莫顿 Morton, William Thomas Green 美国牙外科医师 11—410f
莫顿伯爵 Morton, Archibald Douglas, Earl of 苏格兰反叛者 11—410a
莫顿伯爵(第四) Morton, James Douglas, 4th Earl of 苏格兰贵族 11—410a
莫顿岛 Moreton Island 澳大利亚岛屿 11—390f
莫顿国家公园 Morton National Park 澳大利亚公园 11—411a
莫顿湾 Moreton Bay 太平洋海湾 11—390e
莫顿湾松 Moreton Bay pine (species *Araucaria cunninghamii*) 木本植物 11—390f
莫多克人和克拉马特人 Modoc and Klamath 北美印第安人 11—307b
莫厄斯 Morus, Huw 威尔士诗人 11—411b
莫厄特 Mowatt, Anna Cora 美国剧作家、演员 11—449d
莫恩 Monn, Matthias Georg 奥地利作曲家、管风琴家 11—343c
莫恩山 Mourne Mountains 英国山脉 11—447a
莫尔 More, Sir Anthony 荷兰画家 11—386f
莫尔 Mohl, Hugo von 德国植物学家 11—312b
莫尔 More, Hannah 英国作家 11—386f
莫尔 More, Henry 英国诗人、宗教哲学家 11—387b
莫尔 More, Paul Elmer 美国学者 11—387c
莫尔 More, Sir Thomas 英国政治家、大法官 11—387d
莫尔比昂 Morbihan 法国省份 11—386b
莫尔伯勒 Marlborough 英格兰堂区名、城镇 10—523a
莫尔博恩 Malbone, Edward Greene 美国画家 10—426b
莫尔达诺伯爵 Mordano, Dino Grandi, Count (conte) di 意大利官员 11—386c
莫尔道河 Moldau River (Czech Republic) 捷克河流 11—315f
莫尔德 Mold 威尔士城市 11—315d
莫尔德 Molde 挪威城镇 11—316b
莫尔登 Malden 美国城市 10—427b
莫尔登 Maldon 英格兰城镇 10—427f
莫尔登岛 Malden Island 基里巴斯岛屿 10—427c
莫尔登子爵 Malden, Arthur Capel, Viscount 英格兰政治家 10—427c
莫尔蒂耶 Mortillet, (Louis-Laurent-Marie) Gabriel de 法国考古学家 11—409c
莫尔丁 Mauldin, Bill 美国漫画家 11—34e
莫尔顿 Malton 英格兰城镇 10—438b
莫尔顿 Moulton, Ellen Louise Chandler 美国作家 11—439d
莫尔多瓦 Mordvinia 俄罗斯的共和国 11—386e
莫尔多瓦人 Mordvin 俄罗斯民族 11—386d
莫尔多瓦语 Mordvin language 莫尔多瓦民族语言 11—386d
莫尔菲 Morphy, Paul Charles 美国国际象棋大师 11—403d
莫尔费塔 Molfetta 意大利城镇 11—319c
莫尔谷 Mole Valley 英格兰区名 11—317f
莫尔豪斯彗星 Morehouse, Comet 天文学 11—389d
莫尔黑德城 Morehead City 美国海港 11—389d
莫尔会修士 Maurist 天主教莫尔会成员 11—38d
莫尔基奥氏综合征 Morquio's syndrome 疾病 11—403e
莫尔加尼 Morgagni, Giovanni Battista 意大利解剖学家 11—391a
莫尔加滕战役 Morgarten, Battle of 瑞士历史 11—394d
莫尔莱 Morellet, André 法国经济学家、著作家 11—389f
莫尔纳尔 Molnár, Ferenc 匈牙利戏剧家、小说家 11—324a
莫尔奈 Mornay, Philippe de 法国外交家 11—398f
莫尔南阿尔宾峡谷 Glen Mor 英国峡谷 7—157a
莫尔尼公爵 Morny, Charles-Auguste-Louis-Joseph, duc de 法国政治家 11—399a
莫尔帕伯爵 Maurepas, Jean-Frédéric Phélypeaux, comte de 法国大臣 11—36f
莫尔佩克湾 Malpeque Bay 加拿大海湾 10—435e
莫尔群岛 Molle Islands 澳大利亚岛屿 11—322f
莫尔什滕 Morsztyn, Jan Andrzej 波兰诗人、外交家 11—408b
莫尔什滕 Morsztyn, Zbigniew 波兰诗人 11—408b
莫尔斯 Morse, Jedidiah 美国公理会牧师、地理学家 11—407d
莫尔斯 Morse, Samuel F(inley) B(reese) 美国画家、电报发明人 11—407e
莫尔斯电码 Morse Code 通信 11—407f
莫尔泰 Morty (Indonesia) 印度尼西亚岛屿 11—411b
莫尔特克伯爵 Moltke, Adam Gottlob, Lensgreve 丹麦廷臣 11—324f
莫尔特克伯爵 Moltke, Adam Wilhelm, Lensgreve 丹麦政治家 11—324f
莫尔特里 Moultrie, William 美国将军 11—439e
莫尔旺 Morvan 法国中部高原地区 11—411c
莫尔维 Morvi 印度城镇 11—411c
莫尔文 Malvern 英国旧村庄和小村子 10—439d
莫尔文丘陵 Malvern Hills 英国区名 10—439e
莫尔文子爵(第一) Malvern (of Rhodesia and of Bexley), Godfrey (Martin) Huggins, 1st Viscount 南罗得西亚总理 10—439e
莫尔兹比港 Port Moresby 巴布亚新几内亚首都 13—446c
莫耳甫斯 Morpheus 希腊神话人物 11—402d
莫法特 Moffat, David Halliday 美国资本家 11—309b
莫法特 Moffatt, James 苏格兰圣经学家 11—309c
莫法特 Moffat, Robert 苏格兰传教士 11—309b
莫福洛 Mofolo, Thomas Mokopu 莱索托作家 11—309d
莫干山 Mogan Mountain 中国游览区 11—309f
莫高窟 Mogao cave 中国佛教艺术 11—309f
莫戈永山 Mogollon Mountains 美国山脉 11—310c

莫戈永文化 Mogollon culture 北美印第安人文化 11—310b
莫格万迪人 Mogwandi (people) 非洲民族 11—310d
莫根施泰恩 Morgenstern, Christian 德国诗人 11—394d
莫哈卡河 Mohaka River 新西兰河流 11—310f
莫哈莱斯胡克 Mohale's Hoek 莱索托村庄 11—310f
莫哈奇战役 Mohács, Battle of 匈牙利历史 11—310d
莫哈韦人 Mojave 美国印第安农民 11—314a
莫哈韦沙漠 Mojave Desert 美国沙漠 11—314a
莫赫林 Mauchline 英国村庄 11—33e
莫赫纳茨基 Mochnacki, Maurycy 波兰文学评论家 11—302e
莫赫琼克 Mauch Chunk 美国自治镇 11—33e
莫霍克河 Mohawk River 美国河流 11—311d
莫霍克人 Mohawk 北美印第安部落 11—311c
莫霍洛维奇 Mohorovičić, Andrija 克罗地亚气象学家 11—312d
莫霍伊-纳吉 Moholy-Nagy, László 匈牙利画家 11—312c
莫吉恩 Mauguin, Charles 法国矿物学家 11—34d
莫吉拉 Mogila, Peter 俄罗斯神学家 11—310a
莫吉廖夫 Mogilyov 白俄罗斯州名 11—310b
莫吉廖夫 Mogilyov 白俄罗斯城市 11—310b
莫济里 Mozyr 白俄罗斯城市 11—457c
莫杰夫斯基 Modrzewski, Andrzej 波兰作家 11—307c
莫卡 Moca 多米尼加共和国城市 11—301d
莫卡姆 maqām 伊斯兰教音乐 10—485f
莫卡塔 Mocatta, Frederic David 英国犹太慈善家 11—301e
莫卡辛鞋 moccasin 鞋 11—302a
莫考河 Mokau River 新西兰河流 11—314d
莫科阿 Mocoa 哥伦比亚城市 11—303b
莫克 Moke, Camille 法国音乐家 11—314d
莫克瓜 Moquegua 秘鲁省份 11—382c
莫克瓜 Moquegua 秘鲁城市 11—382d
莫克兰 Makran 亚洲地区 10—417c
莫克兰 Makrān 巴基斯坦区名 10—417d
莫克姆湾 Morecambe Bay 爱尔兰海海湾 11—389c
莫拉达巴德 Morādābād 印度城镇 11—382e
莫拉-迪巴里 Mola di Bari 意大利城镇 11—314f
莫拉莱斯 Morales, Cristóbal de 西班牙作曲家 11—383c
莫拉莱斯 Morales, Evo 玻利维亚总统 11—383c
莫拉莱斯 Morales, Luis de 西班牙画家 11—383d
莫拉女衬衫 mola 巴拿马绣花衫 11—314f
莫拉桑 Morazán, Francisco 中美洲联合省总统 11—386a
莫拉斯 Maurras, Charles(-Marie-Photius) 法国作家、政论家 11—40e
莫拉塔岛 Morata (Papua New Guinea) 巴布亚新几内亚岛屿 11—384c
莫拉廷 Moratín, Leandro Fernández de 西班牙作家 11—384c
莫拉维安镇战役 Moraviantown, Battle of (War of 1812) 美国-加拿大历史 11—385c
莫拉维亚 Moravia, Alberto 意大利新闻记者、作家 11—384f
莫拉战役 Morat, Battle of 瑞士历史 11—384c
莫来石 mullite 矿物 11—478b
莫莱 Molay, Jacques de 法国圣殿骑士团头目 11—315c
莫莱伯爵 Molé, Louis-Mathieu, Comte 法国政治家 11—317b
莫赖斯 Morais, Vinícius de 巴西诗人 11—382f
莫兰 Moran, George 美国匪徒 11—383f
莫兰 Morland, George 英国画家 11—397b
莫兰 Morin, Jean 天主教神学家 11—396a
莫兰巴 Moranbah 澳大利亚城镇 11—383f
莫兰迪 Morandi, Giorgio 意大利艺术家 11—384a
莫兰泰 Morante, Elsa 意大利诗人、小说家 11—384b
莫兰特 Morant, Sir Robert Laurie 英国文官 11—384b
莫朗 Morand, Paul 法国外交官、小说家 11—384a
莫朗热 Morhange, Charles-Henri-Valentin 法国画家、作曲家 11—395a
莫勒 Möhler, Johann Adam 德国天主教会史学家 11—312c
莫勒尔 Maurel, Victor 法国歌唱家 11—36e
莫勒圣尼古拉 Môle Saint-Nicolas 海地村庄 11—317f
莫勒斯霍特 Moleschott, Jacob 意大利生理学家 11—319b
莫雷阿岛 Moorea 法属波利尼西亚火山岛 11—381b
莫雷尔 Morel (poet) 法国诗人 11—389d
莫雷尔 Morel, Benedict Augustin 法国心理学家 11—389d
莫雷尔 Morrell, Lady Ottoline (Violet Anne) 英国文艺庇护者 11—403e
莫雷利 Morelli, Giovanni 意大利艺术评论家 11—389f
莫雷利亚 Morelia 墨西哥城市 11—389e
莫雷洛斯 Morelos 墨西哥州名 11—390a
莫雷洛斯(-帕冯) Morelos (y Pavón), José María 墨西哥天主教司铎 11—390a
莫雷纳 Morena 印度城镇 11—390b
莫雷纳山 Morena, Sierra 西班牙山脉 11—390b
莫雷诺 Moreno 阿根廷行政区 11—390c
莫雷诺 Moreno, José Manue 阿根廷足球运动员 11—390c
莫雷诺 Moreno, Mariano 阿根廷爱国者、政治领袖 11—390d
莫雷托 Moreto (y Cabaña), Agustín 西班牙戏剧家 11—390e
莫雷亚斯 Moréas, Jean 法国诗人 11—388e
莫里 Moree 澳大利亚城镇 11—389c
莫里 Maury, Matthew Fontaine 美国海军军官 11—41a
莫里哀 Molière 法国戏剧家 11—319d
莫里哀之家 Maison de Molière, La (theatre) 法国国家剧院 10—412a
莫里埃 Maurier, Sir Gerald Hubert Edward Busson du 英国演员、剧院经理 11—38d
莫里奥里人 Moriori 新西兰已消亡的民族 11—396c
莫里伯爵 Moray, EARLS OF 苏格兰封爵贵族 11—385e
莫里伯爵(第二) Moray, James Stewart, 2nd Earl of 苏格兰摄政 11—385f
莫里伯爵(第一) Moray, James Stewart, 1st Earl of 苏格兰摄政官 11—385f
莫里伯爵(第一) Moray, Thomas Randolph, 1st Earl of 苏格兰摄政 11—385e
莫里茨 Moritz, Karl Philipp 德国小说家 11—397b
莫里尔 Morier, James Justinian 英国外交家、作家 11—395f
莫里尔 Morrill, Justin S(mith) 美国政治家 11—403f
莫里尔顿 Morrilton 美国城市 11—404a
莫里尼人 Morini 欧洲古代民族 11—396b
莫里森 Morrison, Arthur 英国作家 11—406d
莫里森 Morrison, (of Lambeth), Herbert Stanley Morrison, Baron 英国工党政治家 11—406d
莫里森 Morison, James 基督教神学家 11—396c
莫里森 Morison, Robert 苏格兰植物学家 11—396d
莫里森 Morison, Samuel Eliot 美国传记学家、历史学家 11—396d
莫里森 Morison, Stanley 英国印刷术史学家 11—396e
莫里森 Morrison, Toni 美国作家 11—406f
莫里森 Morrison, Van 爱尔兰歌唱家 11—407a
莫里斯 Maurice 统治者之名 11—37d
莫里斯 Maurice 拜占廷皇帝 11—37d
莫里斯 Maurice 荷兰执政 11—37e
莫里斯 Maurice 萨克森公爵 11—37f
莫里斯 Morris, Alexander 加拿大政治家 11—404a
莫里斯 Morris, Clara 美国演员 11—404a
莫里斯 Morris (of St. John's and of Waterford), Edward Patrick Morris, 1st Baron 加拿大政治家、纽芬兰总理 11—404b
莫里斯 Morris, Elizabeth 美国演员 11—404c
莫里斯 Morris, Esther Hobart McQuigg Slack 美国妇女参政主义者 11—404c
莫里斯 Maurice, Furnley 澳大利亚诗人 11—38b
莫里斯 Morris, Gouverneur 美国政治家 11—404d

莫里斯 Maurice, (John) Frederick Denison 英国神学家 11—38b
莫里斯 Morris, Mark 美国舞蹈家 11—404e
莫里斯 Morris, Richard B(randon) 美国教育家、历史学家 11—404f
莫里斯 Morris, Robert 美国商人、政治家 11—404f
莫里斯 Morris, Robert 美国艺术家 11—405a
莫里斯 Morris, William 英国艺术家、诗人 11—405b
莫里斯 Morris, William 美国剧院经理 11—405e
莫里斯 Morris, Wright (Marion) 美国小说家 11—405e
莫里斯 Morris, William Richard 英国工业家 11—405e
莫里斯(拿骚的) Maurice of Nassau 荷兰执政 11—38a
莫里斯，圣 Maurice, Saint 罗马军人 11—38a
莫里斯敦 Morristown 美国城镇 11—407b
莫里斯敦 Morristown 美国城市 11—407c
莫里斯父子 Morris, Thomas and Thomas, Jr. 英国高尔夫球运动员 11—405b
莫里斯宫 Mauritshuis 荷兰绘画陈列馆 11—40d
莫里斯·杰塞普角 Morris Jesup, Cape 格陵兰地区 11—406b
莫里斯-琼斯 Morris-Jones, Sir John 威尔士教师、学者 11—406b
莫里斯舞 Morris dance 舞蹈 11—405f
莫里斯椅 Morris chair 家具 11—405f
莫里亚克 Mauriac, Claude 法国小说家、评论家 11—37a
莫里亚克 Mauriac, François 法国小说家、剧作家 11—37b
莫里兹 Móricz, Zsigmond 匈牙利小说家 11—395e
莫利 Morley, Christopher 美国作家 11—397c
莫利 Morley, Edward Williams 美国化学家 11—397d
莫利 Morley, Margaret Warner 美国生物学家 11—397d
莫利 Moley, Raymond (Charles) 美国新闻记者 11—319b
莫利 Morley, Robert 英国艺术家 11—397e
莫利 Morley, Thomas 英国作曲家 11—397f
莫利昂 Mollien, Gaspard-Théodore 法国探险家 11—323b
莫利昂 Mollien, Nicolas-François, Comte 法国政治家 11—323b
莫利罗 Murillo, Gerardo (painter) 墨西哥画家、作家、革命家 11—495c
莫利纳 Molina, Luis de 西班牙神学家 11—322b
莫利纳 Molina, Mario 美国化学家 11—322c
莫利纳 Molina, Rafael Leónidas Trujillo 多米尼加共和国独裁者 11—322c
莫利纳伯爵 Molina, Carlos María Isidro de Borbón, conde de (count of) 西班牙总统 11—322b
莫利内 Molinet, Jean 法国诗人、编年史家 11—322d
莫利纽克斯 Molyneux, Samuel 英国天文学家、政治家 11—[illegible]
莫利诺斯 Molinos, Miguel de 西班牙神父 11—322d
莫利塞 Molise 意大利区名 11—322e
莫利社 Molly Maguires 美国矿工组织 11—323f
莫莉水壶 Pitcher, Molly 美国英雄 13—327e
莫列讷河谷 Maurienne 法国峡谷 11—38c
莫林 Moline 美国城市 11—322d
莫龙 Morón 阿根廷行政区 11—401b
莫龙 Morón 古巴城市 11—401b
莫龙 Morón 委内瑞拉城镇 11—401c
莫龙-德拉弗龙特拉 Morón de la Frontera 西班牙城市 11—401c
莫龙根 Morungen, Heinrich von 德国诗人 11—411b
莫鲁亚 Moruya 澳大利亚城镇 11—411c
莫伦 Moeran, Ernest John 英国作曲家 11—308d
莫伦贝克·圣·让 Molenbeek-Saint-Jean 比利时城镇 11—319a
莫罗 Moro, Aldo 意大利政治家 11—399d
莫罗 Morrow, Dwight W(hitney) 美国律师、政治家 11—407c
莫罗 Moreau, Gustave 法国画家 11—388f
莫罗 Moreau, Jeanne 法国演员 11—389a
莫罗 Moreau, (Jean-) Victor(-Marie) 法国将领 11—389b
莫罗河 Moreau River 美国河流 11—389c
莫罗莱昂 Moroleón 墨西哥城市 11—401a
莫罗尼 Moroni 科摩罗首都 11—401d
莫罗尼 Moroni, Giovanni Battista 意大利画家 11—401e
莫罗泰 Morotai 印度尼西亚岛屿 11—402b
莫罗托 Moroto 乌干达城镇 11—402b
莫罗西尼家族 Morosini family 意大利贵族世家 11—402a
莫罗佐夫 Morozov, Boris Ivanovich 俄国政治家 11—402b
莫罗佐夫 Morozov, Pavlik 俄罗斯共产主义青年 11—402c
莫洛波河 Molopo River 非洲河流 11—324c
莫洛迪 Molody, Konon Trofimovich 苏联间谍 11—324c
莫洛杰奇诺 Molodechno 白俄罗斯城市 11—324c
莫洛凯 Molokai 美国火山岛 11—324c
莫洛内 Morone, Giovanni 意大利天主教枢机主教 11—401c
莫洛托夫 Molotov (city, Russia) 俄罗斯城市 11—324d
莫洛托夫 Molotov, Vyacheslav Mikhaylovich 苏联政治家、外交家 11—324d
莫洛托夫斯克 Molotovsk (Russia) 俄罗斯城市 11—324e
莫洛亚 Maurois, André 法国传记作家、小说家 11—40d
莫米河 Maumee River 美国河流 11—34e
莫纳 Mona (Wales) 威尔士岛屿 11—327f
莫纳岛 Mona Island 波多黎各岛屿 11—327f
莫纳亨 Monaghan 爱尔兰郡名 11—329a
莫纳加斯 Monagas 委内瑞拉州名 11—329a
莫纳利亚山 Monadhliath Mountains 英国山脉 11—328f
莫纳什 Monash, Sir John 澳大利亚土木工程师 11—329f
莫纳斯提尔 Munastīr, al- 突尼斯城市 11—482a
莫纳斯提尔 Monastir (Macedonia) 马其顿城市 11—330d
莫纳希山脉 Monashee Mountains 加拿大山岭 11—330a
莫奈 Monet, Claude 法国画家 11—333b
莫奈姆瓦夏 Monemvasía 希腊城镇 11—333a
莫内 Mone, Jean 法国雕塑家 11—332e
莫内 Monnet, Jean 法国政治经济学家 11—343d
莫内塔 Moneta, Ernesto Teodoro 意大利新闻记者 11—333d
莫内特 Monett 美国城市 11—334c
莫内特 Monette, Paul 美国作家 11—334d
莫尼埃 Monnier, Henri (Bonaventure) 法国漫画家、作家 11—343e
莫尼埃 Monier, Joseph 法国园艺工 11—339f
莫尼克 Maunick, Édouard J. 非洲诗人、评论家 11—35b
莫尼诺-雷东多 Moñino y Redondo, José 西班牙政治家 11—340a
“莫尼特”号和“梅里麦克”号之战 Monitor and Merrimack, Battle of 美国历史 11—340c
莫宁顿伯爵(第二) Mornington, Richard Colley Wellesley, 2nd earl of 英国政治家 11—399a
莫农加希拉河 Monongahela River 美国河流 11—345d
莫农加希拉河战役 Monongahela, Battle of the 法国-英国战役 11—345d
莫诺 Monod, Adolphe-Théodore 法国牧师 11—344b
莫诺 Monod, Gabriel(-Jean-Jacques) 法国历史学家 11—344b
莫诺 Monod, Jacques (Lucien) 法国生物化学家 11—344c
莫诺河 Mono River 非洲河流 11—343f
莫诺马赫冠 Monomakh's Cap 俄罗斯皇冠 11—345b
莫诺人 Mono 美国印第安人 11—343e
莫诺铸排机 Monotype 印刷 11—348b
莫佩尔蒂 Maupertuis, Pierre-Louis Moreau de 法国数学家、天文学家 11—36d
莫珀斯 Morpeth 英格兰城镇 11—402c
莫珀斯堡 Castle Morpeth 英格兰区名 3—513c
莫普 Maupeou, René-Nicolas-Charles-Augustin de 法国大法官 11—36c
莫普提 Mopti 马里城镇 11—382c
莫奇利 Mauchly, John W. 美国物理学家、工程师 11—33f
莫恰尔 Moczar, Mieczysław 波兰共产党领导人 11—303b
莫恰洛夫 Mochalov, Pavel Stepanovich 俄国演员 11—302c
莫乔普洛斯 Moschopoulos, Manuel 拜占廷语法学家 11—413e

莫切 Moche 南美洲文化 11—302d
莫丘迪 Mochudi 博茨瓦纳村落 11—302e
莫日达斯克鲁济斯 Mogi das Cruzes 巴西城市 11—310a
莫萨德 Mossad 以色列情报组织 11—427e
莫萨法尔王朝 Mosāferīd DYNASTY 伊朗王朝 11—411e
莫萨卡 moussaka 食物 11—448a
莫萨里拉干酪 mozzarella 食品 11—457c
莫塞莱 Moseley, Henry Gwyn Jeffreys 英国物理学家 11—421a
莫塞勒 Moselle 法国省份 11—421b
莫塞勒河 Moselle River 欧洲河流 11—421b
莫塞尼戈家族 Mocenigo FAMILY 意大利贵族世家 11—302b
莫桑比克 Moçambique 莫桑比克城镇 11—301d
莫桑比克 Mozambique 非洲国家 11—450e
莫桑比克岛 Mozambique, Island of 印度洋岛屿 11—452a
莫桑比克海峡 Mozambique Channel 西印度洋水道 11—452b
莫桑比克解放阵线 Frelimo 莫桑比克政党 6—474e
莫桑比克全国抵抗运动 Renamo 游击队组织 14—226b
《莫桑比克协议》 Mozambique Conventions 南非-莫桑比克协议 11—452b
莫桑比克洋流 Mozambique Current 西印度洋洋流 11—452c
莫桑德尔 Mosander, Carl Gustaf 瑞典化学家 11—413a
莫色洛史 Moscherosch, Johann Michael 德国作家 11—413d
莫森 Mawson, Sir Douglas 澳大利亚地质学家、探险家 11—42d
莫舍 Mosher, Eliza Maria 美国医生、教育家 11—425a
莫舍勒斯 Moscheles, Ignaz 捷克钢琴家 11—413b
莫伸 Motion, Andrew 英国诗人、传记作家 11—432b
莫什科夫斯基 Moszkowski, Moritz 德国作曲家 11—430b
莫氏 Mac FAMILY 越南氏族 10—325c
莫氏硬度 Mohs hardness 矿物学 11—312f
莫舒舒二世 Moshoeshoe II 莱索托国王 11—425c
莫斯 Moss 挪威城市 11—426f
莫斯 Moss, Carlton 美国电影导演 11—427a
莫斯 Moss, Howard 美国诗人、编辑 11—427b
莫斯 Mauss, Marcel 法国社会学家、人类学家 11—41d
莫斯比 Mosby, John Singleton 美国领袖 11—413a
莫斯海姆 Mosheim, Johann Lorenz von 德意志神学家 11—425a
莫斯基托海岸 Mosquito Coast 尼加拉瓜-洪都拉斯地区 11—426e
莫斯卡 Mosca, Gaetano 意大利法学家、政治理论家 11—413b
莫斯科 Moscow 俄罗斯州名 11—414c
莫斯科 Moscow 俄罗斯首都 11—414e
莫斯科 Moscow 美国城市 11—420a
莫斯科大公国 Moscow, Grand Principality of 俄罗斯中世纪公国 11—420a
莫斯科动物园 Moscow Zoo 俄罗斯动物园 11—421a
莫斯科公司 Muscovy Company 英国贸易组织 11—501f
莫斯科河 Moskva River 俄罗斯河流 11—425d
莫斯科画派 Moscow school 俄罗斯画派 11—420c
莫斯科模范艺术剧院 Moscow Academic Art Theatre 俄国剧院 11—420b
莫斯科尼 Mosconi, Willie 美国台球运动员 11—414b
莫斯科索 Moscoso, Mireya 巴拿马总统 11—414c
《莫斯科条约》 Moscow, Treaty of 苏联历史 11—420a
莫斯科小剧院 Kamerny Theatre 俄国剧院 9—148e
莫斯科运河 Moscow Canal 俄罗斯运河 11—420c
莫斯克海峡 Mosken Marine Channel (Norway) 挪威海峡 11—425d
莫斯克拉 Mosquera, Tomás Cipriano de 新格拉纳达总统 11—426a
莫斯克斯 Moschus, John 拜占廷修士 11—414a
莫斯克文 Moskvin, Ivan Mikhailovich 俄国演员 11—425d
莫斯利 Mosley, Sir Oswald (Ernald), 6TH BARONET 英国政治活动家 11—425e
莫斯塔尔 Mostar 波斯尼亚和黑塞哥维那城镇 11—429c
莫斯塔特 Mostaert, Jan 荷兰画家 11—429a
莫斯特 Most 捷克城市 11—428f
莫斯提尔 Mostel, Zero 美国艺术家 11—429d
莫索罗 Mossoró 巴西城市 11—428f
莫塔 Motta, Giuseppe 瑞士政治领袖 11—437e
莫塔瓜河 Motagua River 危地马拉河流 11—430c
莫塔帕 Mutapa 非洲帝国 11—516f
莫坦生 Mortensen, Richard 丹麦画家 11—408e
莫特 Mot 古代西闪米特人神话 11—430c
莫特 Mott, Charles Stewart 美国汽车实业家、慈善家 11—437b
莫特(夫人) Mott, Lucretia 美国改革家 11—437d
莫特尔 Mottl, Felix 奥地利指挥家 11—438a
莫特-费奈隆 Mothe-Fénelon, François de Salignac de La 法国大主教、作家 11—431a
莫特利 Motley, Constance Baker 美国律师、法官 11—434d
莫特利 Motley, John Lothrop 美国外交家、历史学家 11—434e
莫特森 Mottelson, Ben R. 丹麦物理学家 11—437f
莫图莫迪河 Madhumati River 孟加拉国河流 10—368a
莫脱 Mott, Sir Nevill F. 英国物理学家 11—437e
莫韦尔 Morwell 澳大利亚城镇 11—411d
莫温克尔 Mowinckel, Johan Ludwig 挪威政治家 11—449e
莫温克尔 Mowinckel, Sigmund (Olaf Plytt) 挪威圣经学家 11—449f
莫卧儿玻璃器皿 Mughal glass 工艺品 11—465d
莫卧儿地毯 Mughal carpet 工艺品 11—465c
莫卧儿绘画 Mughal painting 印度绘画 11—465e
莫卧儿建筑艺术 Mughal architecture 艺术 11—465b
莫卧儿王朝 Mughal DYNASTY 印度王朝 11—465a
莫西人 Mossi 非洲民族 11—428d
莫西亚 Moesia 罗马行省 11—309a
莫西诸邦 Mossi states 西非历史王国 11—428e
莫希干人 Mohegan 美国印第安人 11—311f
莫希齐茨基 Mościcki, Ignacy 波兰政治家 11—414a
莫夏夫 moshav 以色列居民点 11—424f
莫亚诺 Moyano, Sebastián 西班牙征服者 11—450a
莫延多 Mollendo 秘鲁城市 11—322f
莫伊 Moe 澳大利亚城市 11—308c
莫伊 Moi, Daniel arap 肯尼亚总统 11—312f
莫伊尔 Moyle 北爱尔兰区名 11—450b
莫伊拉伯爵(第二) Moira, Francis Rawdon-Hastings, 2nd earl of 英国殖民地官员 11—313a
莫伊尼汉 Moynihan (of Leeds), Berkeley George Andrew Moynihan, 1st Baron 英国外科医生 11—450b
莫伊尼汉 Moynihan, Daniel Patrick 美国学者、政治家 11—450c
莫伊塞维奇 Moiseiwitsch, Benno 英国钢琴家 11—313c
莫伊谢耶夫 Moiseyev, Igor Aleksandrovich 俄罗斯舞蹈编导 11—313c
莫伊兹 Moïse, Isaäc 法国政治家 11—313c
莫约班巴 Moyobamba 秘鲁城市 11—450d
莫泽-普罗尔 Moser-Proell, Annemarie 奥地利滑雪运动员 11—421c
莫扎法尔王朝 Moẓaffarid DYNASTY 伊朗王朝 11—450e
莫扎拉布 Mozarab 西班牙基督教徒 11—452c
莫扎拉布圣咏 Mozarabic chant 音乐 11—452e
莫扎拉布艺术 Mozarabic art 艺术 11—452c
莫扎拉布语 Mozarabic language 西班牙古代方言 11—452e
莫扎特 Mozart, (Johann Georg) Leopold 奥地利作曲家 11—452f
莫扎特 Mozart, Wolfgang Amadeus 奥地利作曲家 11—452f
莫兹利 Maudslay, Henry 英国工程师、发明家 11—34a
秣市骚乱 Haymarket Riot 美国历史 7—533c
秣菟罗艺术 Mathurā art 佛教艺术 11—24e
鹣鹉 macaw 鸟类 10—330b
漠河 Mohe 中国县名 11—311f
漠泽 moor 草地 11—378d
靺鞨 Mohe 中国古代民族 11—311e

墨杜萨 Medusa 希腊神话 11—79a
墨尔本 Melbourne 澳大利亚城市 11—93c
墨尔本 Melbourne 美国城市 11—95c
墨尔本大学 Melbourne, University of 澳大利亚大学 11—95c
墨尔波墨涅 Melpomene 希腊宗教女神 11—100b
墨菲 Murphy, Eddie 美国演员 11—496b
墨菲 Murphy, Frank 美国最高法院大法官 11—496b
墨菲 Murphy, Isaac Burns 美国赛马骑师 11—496e
墨菲 Murphy, William P(arry) 美国医师 11—496e
墨菲夫妇 Murphy, Gerald; and Murphy, Sara 美国画家和舞台设计家 11—496d
墨菲斯托菲里斯 Mephistopheles 虚构的魔鬼精灵 11—122d
墨绘 sumi-e (Japanese painting) 日本绘画 16—332c
墨迹 bokuseki 中国、日本的书法 3—9f
墨迹测验 inkblot test 心理测验 8—389b
墨家 Mohism 中国战国时期学派 11—312b
墨角兰 marjoram (species *Majorana hortensis*) 草本植物 10—519d
墨角藻属 Fucus 藻类植物 6—509c
《墨经》 Mojing 中国哲学著作 11—314c
墨卡托 Mercator, Gerardus 佛兰德地图学家 11—123d
墨卡托投影 Mercator projection 制图学 11—124a
墨兰普斯 Melampus 希腊神话 11—90e
墨勒阿革 Meleager 希腊神话 11—96a
墨勒阿格 Meleager 希腊诗人 11—96b
墨累河 Murray River 澳大利亚河流 11—498a
墨累灰牛 Murray Grey 牛品种 11—498a
墨利索斯(萨摩斯的) Melissus of Samos 希腊哲学家 11—97d
墨林 Merlin 亚瑟王传奇故事人物 11—132c
墨洛维 Merovech 萨利安法兰克人国王 11—133f
墨洛温王朝 Merovingian dynasty 法兰克人王朝 11—133f
墨洛温字体 Merovingian script 法国古代字体 11—134b
墨涅德摩斯(厄立特里亚的) Menedemus of Eretria 希腊哲学家 11—112b
墨涅拉俄斯 Menelaus 希腊神话 11—112b
墨丘利 Mercury 罗马神灵 11—126c
墨萨多 Mussato, Albertino 意大利政治家 11—512d
墨塞 Mussey, Ellen Spencer 美国律师、教育家 11—513b
墨伞菌 inky cap 蘑菇 8—389c
墨水瓶架 inkstand 文具 8—389b
墨水、油墨 ink 书写用品 8—388d
墨索里尼 Mussolini, Benito (Amilcare Andrea) 意大利首相 11—513c
墨西哥 Mexico 拉丁美洲国家 11—165f
墨西哥 México 墨西哥州名 11—167e
墨西哥 Mexico 美国城市 11—167e
墨西哥城 Mexico City 墨西哥首都 11—168b
墨西哥刺木 ocotillo (*Fouquieria splendens*) 植物 12—334b
墨西哥法 Mexican process (silver production) 化学 11—165b
墨西哥革命 Mexican Revolution 墨西哥历史 11—165b
墨西哥革命党 Mexican Revolutionary Party 墨西哥政党 11—165d
墨西哥国立自治大学 Mexico, National Autonomous University of 墨西哥大学 11—168a
墨西哥海盆 Mexico Basin 墨西哥湾洋区 11—168a
墨西哥空运公司 Mexicana Airlines 墨西哥公司 11—165e
墨西哥鹿 brocket 哺乳动物 3—173d
墨西哥帽子舞 Mexican hat dance 舞蹈 11—165a
墨西哥狮 Mexican lion 哺乳动物 11—165b
墨西哥石油公司 Petróleos Mexicanos 墨西哥公司 13—210e
墨西哥跳豆 Mexican jumping bean 木本植物 11—165a
墨西哥湾 Mexico, Gulf of 北美水域 11—167f
墨西哥湾海岸 Gulf Coast 美国地理区 7—367f
墨西哥湾统 Gulf Series 地质学 7—368b
墨西哥无毛狗 Mexican hairless 狗品种 11—165a
墨西哥郁金香罂粟 Mexican tulip poppy 观赏植物 11—165d
墨西哥战争 Mexican War 美国-墨西哥历史 11—165d
墨西卡利 Mexicali 墨西哥城市 11—165a
墨西拿 Messina 意大利城市 11—145b
墨西拿 Messina 南非城镇 11—145c
墨西拿海峡 Messina, Strait of 地中海海峡 11—145c
墨子 Mozi 中国古代思想家 11—457a
墨渍画法 blot drawing 作画技法 2—544f
默庵灵渊 Mokuan Reien 日本禅僧画家 11—314e
默丹杰里 Mattāncheri 印度城镇 11—29d
默德冈 Madgaon 印度城市 10—367f
默德灵 Mödling 奥地利城市 11—307b
默东 Meudon 法国城市 11—164a
默冬周 Metonic cycle 历法 11—159f
默顿 Merton 英格兰自治市 11—136e
默顿 Merton, Robert C. 美国经济学家 11—136f
默顿 Merton, Robert K(ing) 美国社会学家 11—137a
默顿 Merton, Thomas 美国作家 11—137b
默顿斯 Mertens, Pierre 比利时小说家 11—136b
默多克 Murdoch, Dame Iris 英国小说家、哲学家 11—493a
默多克 Murdock, George P(eter) 美国人类学家 11—493f
默多克 Murdoch, James Edward 美国演员 11—493b
默多克 Murdoch, Rupert 澳大利亚出版家 11—493c
默多克 Murdock, William 苏格兰发明家 11—494a
默恩达尔 Mölndal 瑞典城镇 11—324a
默恩岛 Møn 丹麦岛屿 11—327c
默尔恩 Mölln 德国城市 11—323c
默尔克 Merck, Johann Heinrich 德国作家、评论家 11—125f
默尔克海德 Malkhed (India) 印度古城遗址 10—432b
默尔斯 Moers 德国城市 11—309a
默尔特-摩泽尔 Meurthe-et-Moselle 法国省份 11—164b
默弗里 Murfree, Mary Noailles (writer) 美国作家 11—494d
默弗里斯伯勒 Murfreesboro 美国城市 11—494e
默弗里斯伯勒战役 Murfreesboro, Battle of (American Civil War) 美国南北战争 11—494e
默根特勒 Mergenthaler, Ottmar 美国发明家 11—129d
默哈巴利布勒姆 Mahābalipuram 印度城市 10—396e
默哈伯莱什沃尔 Mahābaleshwar 印度城镇 10—396e
默哈讷迪河 Mahānadi River 印度河流 10—398a
默哈嫩达河 Mahānanda River 南亚河流 10—398a
默赫代奥丘陵 Mahādeo Hills 印度丘陵 10—397b
默赫萨纳 Mehsana 印度城镇 11—83e
默赫什沃尔 Maheshwar 印度城镇 10—400f
默吉利伯德讷姆 Machilīpatnam (India) 印度县名 10—347b
默棘连 Mo-chi-lien (Mongol khan) 蒙古皇帝 11—299a
默棘连 Mojilian (Mongol khan) 东突厥可汗 11—314c
默杰贡德河 Machkund (India) 印度河流 10—349e
默克尔 Merkle, Fred 美国棒球运动员 11—132a
默克莱 Mekele 埃塞俄比亚城镇 11—89f
默拉皮火山 Merapi, Mount 印度尼西亚火山峰 11—122f
默朗 Smon-lam chen-mo 中国藏传佛教 15—455f
默朗格舞 merengue 舞蹈 11—128f
默勒 Møller, Poul Martin 丹麦作家 11—322f
默勒·范·登·布鲁克 Moeller van den Bruck, Arthur 德国文化评论家 11—308d
默勒-鲁姆斯达尔 Møre og Romsdal 挪威郡名 11—388d
默里 Murray, (George) Gilbert (Aimé) 英国古典文学学者 11—497a
默里 Murray, George Redmayne 英国医师 11—496f
默里 Murray, James 英国军人 11—497a
默里 Murray, Sir James (Augustus Henry) 苏格兰词典编纂者 11—497b
默里 Murray, Sir John 苏格兰博物学家 11—497c

默里 Murray(of Broughton),Sir John,Baronet 苏格兰詹姆斯党人 11—497d
默里 Murry,John Middleton 英国新闻记者、评论家 11—499a
默里 Murray,Joseph E(dward) 美国外科医生 11—497d
默里 Murray,Judith Sargent Stevens 美国作家 11—497e
默里 Murray,Lord George 苏格兰詹姆斯党人 11—496f
默里 Murray,Philip 美国劳工领袖 11—497f
默里 Murray,William (British chief justice) 英国法官 11—497f
默里布里奇 Murray Bridge 澳大利亚城镇 11—498a
默里迪恩 Meridian 美国城市 11—130d
默里克 Mörike,Eduard Friedrich 德国诗人 11—395f
默伦 Melun 法国城市 11—100e
默伦 Meulen,Adam Frans van der 佛兰德斯画家 11—164a
默伦-塞纳尔 Melun-Sénart 法国城镇 11—100f
默罗 Murrow,Edward (Egbert) R(oscoe) 美国播音员 11—498f
默曼 Merman,Ethel 美国歌唱家 11—133b
默纳沙 Menasha 美国城市 11—106c
默尼耶 Meunier,Constantin (Emile) 比利时雕刻家、画家 11—164a
默念 meditation 宗教哲学 11—78b
默念耶稣圣名 Jesus prayer 东正教 9—6d
默奇森河 Murchison River 澳大利亚河流 11—492c
默奇森瀑布 Murchison Falls (Uganda) 乌干达瀑布 11—492c
默塞德 Merced 美国城市 11—124b
默塞尔 Mercer,David 英国剧作家 11—124e
默塞尔 Mercer,Johnny 美国音乐家 11—124f
默苏利珀德姆 Masulipatam 印度城市 11—16d
《默苏利珀德姆条约》 Masulipatam,Treaty of 印度历史 11—16d
默特尔比奇 Myrtle Beach 美国城市 11—528e
默图伯尼 Madhubani 印度城镇 10—368a
默威伦巴 Murwillumbah 澳大利亚城镇 11—499d
默西河 Mersey,River 澳大利亚河流 11—135f
默西河 Mersey,River 英格兰河流 11—135f
默西赛德 Merseyside 英格兰都会郡 11—136a
默希河 Mahi River 印度河流 10—401a
默泽尔 Möser,Justus 德国政论家、诗人 11—421c
默兹 Meuse 法国省份 11—164c
默兹-阿尔贡战役 Meuse-Argonne,battles of the 第一次世界大战史 11—164c
默兹河 Meuse River 欧洲河流 11—164d
默兹画派 Mosan school 艺术风格 11—412f
貘 tapir 动物 16—476a
貘头兽 Tapinocephalus 古生物学 16—475f
牟宗三 Mou Zongsan 中国现代哲学家 11—438a
谋杀 murder 刑法 11—493a
模版版画 stenciling 视觉艺术 16—217a
模具 die 工具 5—304c
模具 mold 工具 11—315f
模具型腔加工 diesinking 冶金 5—307a
母会 Mother Church 基督教教会 11—431b
母鸡带小鸡草 hen-and-chickens 植物 8—11f
母牛 cow 动物 4—556d
母牛崇拜 cow,sanctity of the 印度教 4—556d
母亲节 Mother's Day 节日 11—431d
母亲神 mother goddess 宗教 11—431b
母亲学校 maternal school 法国教育 11—21b
母权制 matriarchy 社会制度 11—26e
母韵 assonance 韵律学 2—1a
牡丹江 Mudanjiang 中国城市 11—461f
《牡丹亭》 Mudan Ting 中国文学 11—461f
牡蛎 oyster 软体动物 12—526e
牡蛎草 oyster plant 草本植物 12—527b
拇囊肿 bunion 疾病 3—252f
拇指 thumb 解剖学 17—69e
拇指钢琴 thumb piano (musical instrument) 乐器 17—69e
姆巴 M'ba,Léon 加蓬总统 11—59b
姆巴巴内 Mbabane 斯威士兰首都 11—59b
姆巴尔马约 Mbalmayo 喀麦隆城镇 11—59c
姆巴拉拉 Mbarara 乌干达城镇 11—59d
姆巴莱 Mbale 乌干达城镇 11—59c
姆巴里·姆巴约俱乐部 Mbari Mbayo Club 非洲艺术俱乐部 11—59d
姆巴亚人 Mbayá 南美印第安人 11—59f
姆班达卡 Mbandaka 刚果(金)城市 11—59c
姆班扎刚果 M'banza Congo 安哥拉城市 11—59c
姆贝基 Mbeki,Thabo 南非总统 11—60a
姆本贝人 Mbembe 尼日利亚民族 11—60a
姆本杜人 Mbundu 安哥拉民族 11—60d
姆比拉琴 mbira (musical instrument) 乐器 11—60a
姆博穆河 Mbomou River (Africa) 中非河流 11—60b
姆博亚 Mboya,Tom 肯尼亚政治领袖 11—60b
姆布蒂人 Mbuti 刚果(金)民族 11—60d
姆布吉马伊 Mbuji-Mayi 刚果(金)城市 11—60b
姆布卢-恩古卢 mbulu-ngulu 非洲艺术 11—60c
姆查利 Mtshali,Oswald Mbuyiseni 南非诗人 11—459b
姆茨赫塔 Mtskheta 格鲁吉亚城镇 11—459c
姆迪纳 Mdina 马耳他城镇 11—60e
姆菲卡尼 Mfecane 非洲历史 11—173d
姆丰比罗山脉 M'fumbiro Mountains (Africa) 非洲山脉 11—173e
姆丰古人 Mfengu 南非民族 11—173e
姆豪 Mhow 印度城市 11—173f
姆济利卡齐 Mzilikazi 南非国王 11—532c
姆津巴 Mzimba 马拉维城镇 11—532f
姆克哈伊 Mqhayi,S.E.K. 南非诗人、历史学家 11—458a
姆拉达-博莱斯拉夫 Mladá Boleslav 捷克城市 11—298c
姆兰杰 Mulanje 马拉维行政中心 11—473c
姆兰杰山脉 Mulanje Mountains 马拉维山脉 11—473c
姆里丹加鼓 mridanga 乐器 11—458b
姆罗热克 Mrożek,Sławomir 波兰剧作家 11—458d
姆马巴托 Mmabatho 博普塔茨瓦纳城镇 11—298d
姆奈西克里 Mnesicles 古希腊建筑师 11—298f
姆尼安帕拉 Mnyampala,Mathias E. 坦桑尼亚诗人、学者 11—299a
姆佩泽尼 Mpezeni 南非酋长 11—457d
姆蓬多人 Mpondo 南非民族 11—457e
姆普马兰加 Mpumalanga 南非省份 11—458a
姆什韦什韦 Mshweshwe 南非索托国缔造者、酋长 11—458f
姆斯瓦蒂 Mswati 南非酋长 11—459a
姆泰特瓦 Mtetwa 南非帝国 11—459b
姆瓦帕 Nwapa,Flora 尼日利亚小说家 12—307f
姆万盖 Mwangi,Meja 非洲小说家 11—520c
姆韦鲁湖 Mweru,Lake 非洲湖泊 11—520d
姆韦尼·马塔帕 Mwene Matapa ("Ravager of the Lands") 非洲国王 11—520d
姆温达 Mwenda (African ruler) 非洲领袖 11—520c
姆西拉 M'Sila 阿尔及利亚城镇 11—458f
姆西里 Msiri 非洲统治者 11—459a
姆扎卜 M'zab 阿尔及利亚绿洲群 11—532a
姆扎派 M'zabite 伊斯兰教派 11—532b
木板式 Shingle style 美国建筑风格 15—317a
木版画 woodcut 雕制画版的技法 18—322e
木版图书 block book 印刷品 2—538a
木菠萝 jackfruit (species *Artocarpus heterophyllus*) 植物 8—504a
木材 wood 材料 18—317a
木材采运 logging 林学 10—189f
木醇 wood spirit 化合物 18—321b

木底鞋舞 clog dance 舞蹈 4—298b
木鹟 rail-babbler 鸟类 14—125a
木蠹蛾 carpenter moth 昆虫 3—476f
木尔坦 Multān 巴基斯坦城市 11—478e
木耳 tree ear 植物 17—207a
木各具 Pakokku 缅甸城镇 12—554b
木更津 Kisarazu 日本城市 9—306a
木工哥特式 Carpenter Gothic 建筑学 3—476f
木工作业 carpentry 技术 3—477d
木构教堂 stave church 挪威教堂 16—204b
木骨架 timber framing 建筑 17—98a
木瓜 flowering quince 木本植物 6—376b
木瓜蛋白酶 papain 酶 13—20f
木管乐器 woodwind 笛类和簧管类管乐器 18—326b
木户孝允 Kido Takayoshi 日本政治家 9—270e
木黄蜂 wood wasp 昆虫 18—321c
木匠蜂 carpenter bee 昆虫 3—476e
木焦油 wood tar 化工 18—321b
木槿 hibiscus 植物 8—69c
木槿 rose of Sharon (*Hibiscus syriacus*, or *Althaeasyriaca*) 木本植物 14—402a
木精 wood alcohol 化工 18—319e
木口木刻 wood engraving 版画制作技法 18—319f
木兰 magnolia 植物 10—392e
《木兰辞》 Mulanci 中国北朝叙事诗 11—473b
木兰科 Magnoliaceae 植物学 10—392f
木兰目 Magnoliales 植物学 10—393a
木兰亚纲 Magnoliidae 植物学 10—393c
木兰植物门 Magnoliophyta 植物学 10—393c
木蓝 indigo 植物 8—368c
木藜芦属 Leucothoë 植物学 10—43c
木连杆动作装置 tracker action 音乐 17—186c
木螺钻 auger 工具 2—47d
木麻黄目 Casuarinales 植物学 3—517d
木棉 bombax cotton 植物学 3—19f
木棉 kapok 木本植物 9—172e
木棉科 Bombacaceae 植物学 3—19b
木盘 trencher 器皿 17—209e
木浦 Mokp'o 韩国城市 11—314d
木琴 xylophone 乐器 18—399f
木萨米迪什 Moçâmedes (Angolan city) 安哥拉城市 11—301e
木萨米迪什 Mossamedes (city, Angola) 安哥拉城市 11—427f
木萨米迪什沙漠 Moçâmedes Desert 非洲沙漠 11—301e
木虱 jumping plant louse 昆虫 9—108e
木薯 cassava (*Manihot esculenta*) 植物 3—503a
木薯淀粉 tapioca 食品增稠剂 16—476a
木栓 cork 植物学 4—508f
木斯 mousse 食物 11—448a
木通属 Akebia 植物学 1—153d
木卫二 Europa 天文学 6—167b
木卫三 Ganymede 木星的卫星 7—3d
木卫四 Callisto 天文学 3—356c
木卫五 Amalthea 天文学 1—264a
木卫一 Io 天文学 8—429a
木犀 tea olive 木本植物 16—510a
木犀草 mignonette (*Reseda odorata*) 草本植物 11—206d
木犀科 Oleaceae 植物学 12—371e
木下惠介 Kinoshita Keisuke 日本电影导演 9—294f
木下顺二 Kinoshita, Junji 日本戏剧家 9—294f
木鞋 sabot 鞋 14—484c
木星 Jupiter 天文学 9—115a
木雅语 Muya language 中国藏族语言 11—519c
木油 wood oil 化学 18—320d
木油树 wood oil tree 木本植物 18—320d
木贼 horsetail 植物 8—184f
木贼属 Equisetum (plant genus) 植物学 6—108f
木质部 xylem 植物学 18—399d
木质素 lignin 化学 10—94c
目的论 teleology 哲学 16—525b
目的论伦理学 teleological ethics 哲学 16—524f
目录学 bibliography 图书馆学 2—460a
仫佬语 Mulao language 中国民族语言 11—473e
仫佬族 Mulao 中国民族 11—473c
牟利罗 Murillo, Bartolomé Esteban 西班牙画家 11—495a
牟羽可汗 Muyu Khan 中国回纥登里可汗 11—519e
沐浴 bath 卫生保健 2—276e
苜蓿 alfalfa (*Medicago sativa*) 草本植物 1—215a
苜蓿叶象 alfalfa weevil (*Hypera postica*) 昆虫 1—215b
牧场式住宅 ranch house 建筑物 14—146b
牧场占用者 squatter 澳大利亚历史 16—169b
牧地 rangeland 放牧场 14—150a
牧豆树 mesquite 木本植物 11—143b
牧夫座α Alpha Boötis 天文学 1—249f
牧歌 eclogue 田园诗 5—526b
牧歌 madrigal 音乐体裁 10—374c
牧根草 rampion 植物学 14—141e
牧剧 madrigal comedy 音乐体裁 10—374d
牧神节 Lupercalia 古罗马节日 10—289e
牧师案 Parson's Cause 美国殖民时代历史 13—64d
牧师会礼堂 chapter house 教堂建筑 4—58f
牧首 patriarch 基督教教区主教 13—90c
牧童 Pastoureaux 法国民众起义参加者 13—83e
牧童歌 Gītagovinda 古印度抒情诗 7—145d
牧溪法常 Muxi Fachang 中国南宋画家 11—519b
牧羊人朝拜圣婴 shepherds, adoration of the 基督教艺术题材 15—304b
牧杖 pastoral staff 宗教 13—83d
钼(Mo) molybdenum 化学元素 11—326b
钼铅矿 wulfenite 矿物 18—359a
钼酸盐和钨酸盐矿物 molybdate and tungstate minerals 矿物学 11—325f
墓地 necropolis 考古学 12—63c
墓石卧像 gisant 雕塑 7—144a
墓园诗歌 graveyard school 英国诗歌流派 7—264f
墓志铭 epitaph 铭文 6—104b
幕府 shogunate 日本历史 15—329d
幕阜山 Mufu Shan 中国山脉 11—464d
睦邻政策 Good Neighbor Policy 美国外交政策 7—207d
睦仁 Mutsuhito 日本天皇 11—518c
暮祷 maarib 犹太教 10—323e
慕尼黑 Munich 德国城市 11—484b
慕尼黑暴动(1923) Munich Putsch 德国历史 11—484f
慕尼黑大学 Munich, University of 德国大学 11—484d
《慕尼黑协定》 Munich agreement 欧洲历史 11—484e
慕帕赫列列 Mphahlele, Es'kia 南非小说家 11—457d
《慕善集》 Philokalia 希腊正教论文集 13—244e
慕士塔格山 Muztagata Shan 中国山脉 11—520b
穆 Moe, Jørgen Engebretsen (Norwegian folklorist) 挪威作家 11—308c
穆阿斯凯尔 Mascara 阿尔及利亚城镇 10—569b
穆阿台迪德 Muʻtaḍid, al- 阿拔斯王朝哈里发 11—516b
穆阿台绥姆 Muʻtaṣim, al- 阿拔斯王朝哈里发 11—517a
穆阿威叶一世 Muʻāwiyah I 伊斯兰领袖 11—460a
穆安达 Mouanda 加蓬城镇 11—438b
穆奥 Mouhot, (Alexandre-) Henri 法国探险家 11—438d
穆巴拉克 Mubārak, Hosnī 埃及总统 11—460b

穆拜赖德 Mubarrad,al- 阿拉伯语法家、文学学者 11—460d
穆比 Mubi 尼日利亚城镇 11—460d
穆茨瓦伊罗 Mutswairo,Solomon M. 赞比亚作家 11—518c
穆德 Mott,John R. 美国基督教布道家 11—437c
穆德拉 Muttra (India) 印度城镇 11—518d
《穆德洛斯停战协定》 Mudros,Armistice of 土耳其历史 11—463b
穆迪 Moody,Anne 美国民权活动家、作家 11—375d
穆迪 Moody, Dwight L(yman) 美国福音教派传教士 11—375e
穆迪 Moody,Helen Wills 英国管风琴制造家 11—375f
穆迪 Moodie,Susanna Strickland 加拿大作家 11—375d
穆迪 Moody,William 美国最高法院大法官 11—375f
穆迪 Moody,William Vaughn 美国诗人、剧作家 11—375f
穆迪扎尔人 Mudejar 西班牙穆斯林 11—462b
穆蒂 Muti,Riccardo 意大利指挥家 11—517f
穆蒂斯 Mutis,José (Celestino Bruno) 西班牙植物学家 11—518b
穆杜马拉野生动物保护区 Mudumalai Wild Life Sanctuary 印度野生动物保护区 11—463d
穆恩字母 Moon type 盲文书写体系 11—377e
穆尔 Moore,Alfred 美国最高法院大法官 11—378d
穆尔 Moore,Archie 美国拳击运动员 11—378e
穆尔 Moore,Brian 爱尔兰小说家 11—378e
穆尔 Moore,Carl Richard 美国动物学家 11—378f
穆尔 Moore,Clement Clarke 美国学者、教师 11—378f
穆尔 Moore,Douglas Stuart 美国作曲家 11—379a
穆尔 Moore,Ely 美国新闻工作者 11—379a
穆尔 Moore,Grace 美国歌唱家、演员 11—379e
穆尔 Moore,George (Augustus) 爱尔兰小说家 11—379c
穆尔 Moore,G(eorge) E(dward) 英国哲学家 11—379b
穆尔 Moore,George Foot 美国学者、神学家 11—379d
穆尔 Moore,Henry 英国雕刻家 11—380a
穆尔 Moore,Sir John 英国陆军中将 11—380c
穆尔 Moore,John Bassett 美国法学家 11—380c
穆尔 Moore,Marianne 美国诗人 11—380d
穆尔 Moore,Mike 新西兰工党领袖 11—380e
穆尔 Moore,Nicholas 英国诗人 11—380f
穆尔 Moore,Raymond Cecil 美国古生物学家 11—380f
穆尔 Moore, Stanford 美国生物化学家 11—380f
穆尔 Moore,Thomas 爱尔兰诗人、作家 11—381a
穆尔德河 Mulde River 德国河流 11—474d
穆尔蒂纳 Murtına (Turkey) 土耳其城市 11—499c
穆尔河桥战役 Moore's Creek Bridge,Battle of 美国历史 11—381c
穆尔黑德 Moorhead 美国城市 11—381d
穆尔黑德 Moorehead,Agnes 美国演员 11—381c
穆尔吉亚派 Murji'ah 伊斯兰教派别 11—495c
穆尔加布河 Murgab River 亚洲河流 11—494e
穆尔诺 Murnau,F.W. 德国电影导演 11—495e
穆尔萨战役 Mursa,Battle of 罗马历史 11—499a
穆尔塔图里 Multatuli 荷兰作家 11—478f
穆尔太齐赖派 Muʿtazilah 伊斯兰教派别 11—517d
穆尔瓦拉 Murwāra 印度城镇 11—499d
穆尔西利斯二世 Mursilis Ⅱ 赫梯人国王 11—499b
穆尔西利斯一世 Mursilis Ⅰ 赫梯人国王 11—499b
穆尔西亚 Murcia 西班牙王国 11—492d
穆尔西亚 Murcia 西班牙历史地区 11—492d
穆尔西亚 Murcia 西班牙城市 11—492f
穆尔希达巴德 Murshidābād 印度城市 11—499a
穆耳台米德 Muʿtamid,al- 塞尔维亚国王 11—516d
《穆法德勒诗选》 Mufaḍḍalīyāt,al- 阿拉伯古诗集 11—464a
穆法特 Muffat,Georg 德国作曲家 11—464c
穆夫提 mufti 伊斯兰教教法权威 11—464d
穆富利拉 Mufulira 赞比亚城镇 11—464e
穆盖耶尔丘 Tall al-Muqayyar (Iraq) 伊拉克古城 16—445c
穆盖耶尔丘 Muqayyar,Tall al- (Mesopotamian site) 美索不达米亚城市 11—488f
穆格台菲 Muqtafī,al- 阿拔斯王朝的哈里发 11—488f
穆哈 Mocha 也门城镇 11—302b
穆哈 Mucha,Alphonse 捷克画家 11—460e
穆哈拉格 Muḥarraq,Al- 巴林城市 11—470d
穆哈姆默拉 Mohammerah (Iran) 伊朗城市 11—311c
穆哈武拉 Muhavura 非洲火山 11—471a
穆哈西比 Muḥāsibī, al- 伊斯兰教教义学家 11—470f
穆海莱卜 Muhallab ibn Abī Ṣufrā,al- 伍麦叶王朝将军 11—466d
穆罕多 Muhando,Penina O. 坦桑尼亚剧作家 11—470d
穆罕默德 Mehmed 奥斯曼苏丹之名 11—82a
穆罕默德 Muḥammad 统治者之名 11—466d
穆罕默德 Muhammad 伊斯兰教创立者 11—466d
穆罕默德 Mohammed,Warith Deen 美国宗教领袖 11—311b
穆罕默德(时代的马赫迪) Muḥammad al-Mahdī al-Ḥujjah 伊斯兰教末代伊玛目 11—469a
穆罕默德·阿卜杜拉·哈桑 Maxamed Cabdulle Xasan,Sayyid 索马里宗教和民族领袖 11—43a
穆罕默德·阿布杜 ʿAbduh, Muḥammad 埃及宗教学者、法学家 1—15a
穆罕默德·阿伽 Mehmed Ağa 土耳其建筑师 11—83b
穆罕默德·阿里 Muḥammad ʿAlī 埃及总督、帕夏 11—469a
穆罕默德·阿里 Mohammed Ali,F. 美国宗教领袖 11—311b
穆罕默德·阿斯基亚 Muḥammad Askia 西非政治家、军队领袖 11—469c
穆罕默德·埃萨德 Mehmed Esʿad 土耳其作家 11—83c
穆罕默德·宾·哈米德 Muhammed bin Hamid 桑给巴尔商人 11—470d
穆罕默德·狄布 Mohammed Dib 阿尔及利亚作家 11—311c
穆罕默德二世 Mehmed Ⅱ 奥斯曼苏丹 11—82c
穆罕默德二世穆耳台米德 Muḥammad Ⅱ al-Muʿtamid 阿拔斯王朝哈里发 11—468d
穆罕默德·福阿德·克普律吕 Mehmed Fuat Köprülü 土耳其学者、政治家 11—83c
穆罕默德·古里 Muhammad Ghūrī 印度穆斯林创建者 11—469c
穆罕默德·哈桑·本·穆纳斯 Muhammad Hasan bin Munas 马来亚农民领袖 11—469c
穆罕默德·胡达班达 Moḥammad Khudābanda 伊朗统治者 11—310f
穆罕默德会 Muhammadiyah 印度尼西亚宗教团体 11—470c
穆罕默德六世 Mehmed Ⅵ 奥斯曼苏丹 11—83a
穆罕默德三世 Mehmed Ⅲ 奥斯曼苏丹 11—82e
穆罕默德沙 Moḥammed Shāh,Sultan Sir 印度穆斯林领袖 11—311c
穆罕默德沙 Muḥammad Shāh 印度穆斯林领袖 11—470a
穆罕默德·沙姆斯·奥丁·哈菲兹 Moḥammad Shams od-Dīn Ḥāfeẓ 波斯诗人 11—311b
穆罕默德十一世 Muhammad Ⅺ 西班牙奈斯尔王朝统治者 11—468b
穆罕默德四世 Mehmed Ⅳ 奥斯曼苏丹 11—82f
穆罕默德·塔基·拜哈尔 Muḥammad Taqī Bahār 伊朗诗人 11—470a
穆罕默德·塔拉特帕夏 Mehmed Talât Paşa 土耳其政治家 11—83e
穆罕默德五世 Mehmed Ⅴ 奥斯曼苏丹 11—82f
穆罕默德五世 Muhammad Ⅴ 摩洛哥苏丹 11—468c
穆罕默德·西亚-卡莱姆 Mehmed Siyah-Kalem 土耳其艺术家 11—83d
穆罕默德一世 Mehmed Ⅰ 奥斯曼苏丹 11—82b
穆罕默德一世阿斯基亚 Muḥammad Ⅰ Askia 西非政治家、军队领袖 11—468d
穆罕默德·伊本·阿卜杜勒·克里姆·哈塔比 Muḥammad ibn ʿAbd

al-Karīm al-Khaṭṭābī 柏柏尔领袖 11—469d
穆罕默德·伊本·阿卜杜勒·马利克·伊本·穆罕默德·伊本·穆罕默德·伊本·图菲勒·卡伊西 Muḥammad ibn ʿAbd al-Malik ibn Muḥammad ibn Muḥammad ibn Ṭufayl al-Qaysī 摩尔人哲学家、内科医生 11—469d
穆罕默德·伊本·艾布·阿米尔·曼苏尔 Muḥammad ibn Abū ʿĀmir al-Manṣūr (Muslim ruler of Córdoba) 西班牙伍麦叶王朝首相 11—469d
穆罕默德·伊本·艾哈迈德·迈格迪西 Muḥammad ibn Aḥmad al-Maqdisī (Arab geographer) 阿拉伯地理学家、旅行家 11—469d
穆罕默德·伊本·法拉赫 Muḥammad ibn Falāḥ 穆斯林教义学家 11—469e
穆罕默德·伊本·哈乃斐叶赫 Muḥammad ibn al-Ḥanafīyah 伊斯兰教人物 11—469d
穆罕默德·伊本·哈旺德沙哈·伊本·马哈茂德 Muḥammad ibn Khāvandshāh ibn Maḥmūd 波斯编年史作家 11—469e
穆罕默德·伊本·穆罕默德·伊本·塔尔汉·伊本·乌扎拉格赫·法拉比 Muḥammad ibn Muḥammad ibn Ṭarkhān ibn Uzalagh al-Fārābī (Muslim philosopher) 穆斯林哲学家 11—469e
穆罕默德·伊本·穆萨·花拉子密 Muḥammad ibn Mūsā al-Khwārizmī (Muslim mathematician and astronomer) 阿拉伯数学家、天文学家 11—469f
穆罕默德·伊本·图格鲁克 Muḥammad ibn Tughluq 印度图格鲁克王朝苏丹 11—469f
穆罕默德·尤努斯 Muhammad Yunus 孟加拉国经济学家 11—470a
穆罕默德·尤素福·本·阿赫麦德 Muhammad Yusof bin Ahmad 马来伊斯兰教义学家 11—470b
穆罕默迪 Muḥammadī 伊朗画家 11—470b
穆罕默迪耶 Mohammedia 摩洛哥城市 11—311c
穆河 Mu River 缅甸河流 11—459d
穆赫塔尔·伊本·阿布·乌巴德·塞盖菲 Mukhtār ibn Abū ʿUbayd at-Thaqafī, al- 伊斯兰教领袖 11—472f
穆赫辛 Muḥsin, Zuhayr 巴勒斯坦民族主义者 11—471c
穆赫伊丁 Muḥyiʾ ad-Dīn (Iraqi ruler) 白益王朝苏丹 11—471d
穆胡 Muhu 爱沙尼亚群岛、岛屿 11—471d
穆吉布 Mujib, Sheikh (president of Bangladesh) 孟加拉国领导人 11—472b
穆加贝 Mugabe, Robert (Gabriel) 津巴布韦总理 11—464e
穆嘉关 Mu Gia Pass 亚洲山脉山口 11—459c
穆卡拉 Mukallā, Al- 也门港口 11—472e
穆卡切沃 Mukacheve 乌克兰城市 11—472d
穆坎马斯 Mukammas, David al- 叙利亚哲学家 11—472e
穆克 Muck, Karl 德国指挥家 11—460f
穆克台菲 Muktafī, al- 阿拔斯王朝哈里发 11—473a
穆宽纳(蒙面人) Muqannaʿ, al- 宗教领袖 11—488e
穆拉 Muğla 土耳其城市 11—466a
穆拉比特 marabout 伊斯兰教社团成员 10—487a
穆拉比特人 Almoravids 柏柏尔人联合体 1—247d
穆拉德 Murad 奥斯曼苏丹之名 11—489a
穆拉德 Murad, Ferid 美国药理学家 11—490a
穆拉德二世 Murad II 奥斯曼苏丹 11—489c
穆拉德帕夏 Murad Pasha (Polish military officer) 波兰军官 11—490a
穆拉德三世 Murad III 奥斯曼苏丹 11—489d
穆拉德四世 Murad IV 奥斯曼苏丹 11—489e
穆拉德五世 Murad V 奥斯曼苏丹 11—489f
穆拉德一世 Murad I 奥斯曼苏丹 11—489a
穆拉纳 Mawlānā (Persian poet) 苏非派神秘主义者、诗人 11—42c
穆拉诺 Murano 意大利岛屿 11—491a
穆拉人 Mura 巴西印第安人 11—488f
穆拉·萨德拉 Mullā Ṣadrā 伊朗哲学家 11—475b
穆拉·桑卡拉 Mula Sankara (Hindu reformer) 印度领袖 11—473a
穆拉特河 Murat River 土耳其河流 11—491d
穆拉维约夫 Muravyov, Mikhail Nikolayevich, Graf (Count) 俄国外交家、政治家 11—491d
穆拉维约夫 Muravyov, Nikolay Nikolayevich, Count (Graf) Amursky 俄国政治家、探险家 11—491e
穆拉维约夫-阿波斯托尔 Muravyov-Apostol, Sergey Ivanovich 俄国军官 11—491f
穆拉维约娃 Muravyova, Vera Fyodorovna Komissarzhevskaya, Grafinya (Countess) (Russian actress) 俄国演员 11—491f
穆莱达战役 Mulaydah, Battle of al- 阿拉伯历史 11—473f
穆兰 Moulins 法国城镇 11—439a
穆兰 Moulin, Jean 法国文官 11—438e
穆兰彩陶 Moulins faience 陶器 11—439c
穆兰画师 Moulins, Master of 法国画家 11—439b
穆勒 Mill, James 英国哲学家、历史学家、经济学家 11—220e
穆勒 Mill, John Stuart 英国哲学家、经济学家 11—221a
穆里 Muri 尼日利亚城镇 11—494f
穆里泰 Murieta, Joaquín 美国强盗 11—495a
穆列什 Mureş 罗马尼亚县名 11—494b
穆列什河 Mureş River 欧洲河流 11—494c
穆隆 Mouron, Adolphe-Jean-Marie 法国艺术家 11—447c
穆卢干 Murugan 古印度神灵 11—499c
穆卢耶河 Moulouya River 摩洛哥河流 11—439d
穆鲁罗瓦 Mururoa 波利尼西亚环礁 11—499c
穆鲁特人 Murut 婆罗洲民族 11—499c
穆伦贝尔格家族 Muhlenberg family 美国家族 11—471a
穆罗姆 Murom 俄罗斯城市 11—495f
穆米乌斯 Mummius, Lucius 罗马政治家、将军 11—481d
穆姆人 Mum (people) 西非民族 11—481a
穆纳岛 Muna Island 印度尼西亚岛屿 11—481f
穆纳纳 Mounana 加蓬城镇 11—439f
穆尼 Moonie 澳大利亚居民点 11—378b
穆尼 Mooney, James 美国人种志学者 11—377f
穆尼 Mooney, Tom 美国社会活动家 11—377f
穆尼奥斯·里维拉 Muñoz Rivera, Luis 波多黎各政治家、出版家 11—485f
穆尼奥斯·马林 Muñoz Marín, Luis 波多黎各政治家 11—485e
穆侬语 Mnong language 越南、柬埔寨语言 11—298f
穆诺涅 Munonye, John 非洲教育家、小说家 11—485d
穆齐阿努斯 Mucianus, Publius Licinius Crassus Dives 古罗马政治家 11—460f
穆撒尔运动 Musar 犹太教 11—500b
穆撒夫 musaf 犹太教 11—500a
穆萨 Mūsā 马里帝国皇帝 11—499f
穆萨 Musa 安息国王的母亲 11—499f
穆萨西尔 Muṣaṣir 土耳其古代遗址 11—500c
穆塞韦尼 Museveni, Yoweri Kaguta 乌干达总统 11—503e
穆赛义德 Musayʿīd 卡塔尔城镇 11—500d
穆桑代姆半岛 Musandam Peninsula 阿拉伯半岛 11—500b
穆沙拉比窗 moucharaby 建筑学 11—438b
穆沙拉夫 Musharraf, Pervez 巴基斯坦总统 11—504c
穆沙里弗·奥丁·穆斯利赫·奥丁 Musharrif od-Dīn Muṣliḥ od-Dīn (poet) 波斯诗人 11—504d
穆什 Muş 土耳其城市 11—499e
穆斯堡尔 Mössbauer, Rudolf Ludwig 德国物理学家 11—427f
穆斯堡尔效应 Mössbauer effect 物理学 11—428a
穆斯法克特里 Moose Factory 加拿大无建制居民点 11—382a
穆斯河 Moose River 加拿大河流 11—382b
穆斯黑德湖 Moosehead Lake 美国湖泊 11—382b
穆斯捷彩陶 Moustiers faience 法国陶器 11—448b
穆斯克龙 Mouscron 比利时城镇 11—447c
穆斯林历 Muslim calendar 历法 11—512a

穆斯林联盟 Muslim League 印度政治团体 11—512a
穆斯林兄弟会 Muslim Brotherhood 埃及宗教组织 11—511f
穆斯林·伊本·哈加吉 Muslim ibn al-Ḥajjāj 阿拉伯学者 11—512a
穆斯佩尔海姆 Muspelheim 斯堪的纳维亚神话 11—512c
穆斯乔 Moose Jaw 加拿大城市 11—382a
穆斯塔法 Mustafa, Kara 奥斯曼大臣 11—515b
穆斯塔法 Mustafa 奥斯曼苏丹 11—514e
穆斯塔法二世 Mustafa II 奥斯曼苏丹 11—514f
穆斯塔法·凯末尔 Mustafa Kemal 土耳其政治家 11—515c
穆斯塔法·赖希德帕夏 Mustafa Reşid Paşa 奥斯曼政治家 11—515c
穆斯塔法三世 Mustafa III 奥斯曼苏丹 11—515a
穆斯塔法四世 Mustafa IV 奥斯曼苏丹 11—515b
穆斯塔法一世 Mustafa I 奥斯曼苏丹 11—514f
穆斯塔加奈姆 Mostaganem 阿尔及利亚城镇 11—429b
穆斯台绥木 Mustaʿṣim, al- 阿拔斯王朝哈里发 11—515f
穆斯坦绥尔 Mustanṣir, al- 埃及法蒂玛王朝哈里发 11—515c
穆斯特文化期工艺 Mousterian industry 史前文化 11—448b
穆索尔斯基 Mussorgsky, Modest (Petrovich) 俄国作曲家 11—513f
穆索尼 Moosonee 加拿大无建制居民点 11—382b
穆索斯 Musäus, Johann Karl August 德国作家 11—500c
穆塔尔 mutʿah 婚姻制度 11—516c
穆塔拉 Motala 瑞典城镇 11—430c
穆塔雷 Mutare 津巴布韦城镇 11—516f
穆塔瓦基勒 Mutawakkil, al- 阿拔斯王朝哈里发 11—517d
穆太奈比 Mutanabbī, al- 阿拉伯诗人 11—516e
穆特 Mut 埃及神灵 11—516a
穆特萨二世 Mutesa II 布干达国王 11—517e
穆特萨一世 Mutesa I 布干达国王 11—517e
穆通 Mouton, Jean 法国作曲家 11—448d
穆瓦诺 Moineau, Georges-Victor-Marcel 法国作家 11—313a
穆瓦桑 Moissan, (Ferdinand-Frédéric-) Henri 法国化学家 11—313d
穆瓦塔利斯 Muwatallis 赫梯人国王 11—519a
穆乌阿岛 Muyua 巴布亚新几内亚珊瑚岛 11—519f
穆西埃尔 Musial, Stan 美国棒球运动员 11—505b
穆西尔 Musil, Robert 奥地利-德意志小说家 11—510b
穆西河 Musi River 印度尼西亚河流 11—505b
穆希卡·莱内斯 Mujica Láinez, Manuel 阿根廷作家 11—472b
穆希-乌德-丁·穆罕默德 Muḥī-ud-Dīn Muḥammad (Mughal emperor) 印度莫卧儿帝国皇帝 11—471a
穆欣 Mushin 尼日利亚城镇 11—504d
穆伊拉 Mouila 加蓬城镇 11—438e
穆伊斯卡人 Muisca (people) 民族 11—471f
穆伊兹 Muʿizz, al- 法蒂玛王朝哈里发 11—471f
穆伊兹-乌德-丁·穆罕默德·伊本·萨曼 Muʿizz-ud-Dīn Muḥammad ibn Sām 印度穆斯林统治创建者 11—472a
穆宰费尔·阿里 Muẓaffar ʿAlī 波斯画家、书法家 11—519f
穆宰费尔丁·沙阿 Moẓaffar od-Dīn Shāh 波斯统治者 11—450d
穆扎法尔布尔 Muzaffarpur 印度比哈尔邦城市 11—520b
穆扎法尔讷格尔 Muzaffarnagar 印度北方邦城市 11—520a
穆朱尔地毯 Mujur rug 土耳其工艺品 11—472c

N

拿波尼度 Nabonidus 巴比伦国王 11—535a
拿弗他利 Naphtali 犹太人祖先 11—562a
拿哈曼尼 Naḥamani (Jewish scholar) 犹太学者 11—541e
拿马尼德斯 Nahmanides 西班牙学者 11—542b
拿破仑(二世) Napoleon (II) 拿破仑一世之子 11—572b
《拿破仑法典》 Napoleonic Code 法国民法典 11—572e
拿破仑三世 Napoleon III 法兰西总统 11—572c
拿破仑一世 Napoleon I 法国皇帝 11—567b
拿破仑战争 Napoleonic Wars 欧洲历史 11—573a
拿撒勒 Nazareth (Ethiopia) 埃塞俄比亚城镇 12—54f
拿撒勒 Nazareth 以色列城市 12—54f
拿撒勒派 Nazarene 德国艺术团体 12—54d
拿撒勒派教会 Nazarene, Church of the 美国基督教教会 12—54e
拿撒勒人 Nazarene 基督教 12—54d
拿骚 Nassau 巴哈马联邦首都 12—7a
拿骚 Nassau 德意志历史地区 12—7b
拿细耳人 Nazirite 古代希伯来人 12—55f
镎(Np) neptunium 化学元素 12—84c
镎系 neptunium series 化学元素系 12—84c
那霸 Naha 日本城市 11—541d
那波 Nabu 亚述人、巴比伦人的神灵 11—535b
那不勒斯 Naples 意大利城市 11—563c
那不勒斯 Naples 美国城市 11—566c
那不勒斯大学 Naples, University of 意大利大学 11—567a
那不勒斯歌剧 Neapolitan opera 意大利歌剧 12—57f
那不勒斯湾 Naples, Bay of 地中海海湾 11—566c
那不勒斯王国 Naples, Kingdom of 意大利历史国家 11—566d
那伽 naga 印度教神灵 11—537d
那伽里字母 Nāgarī (Indian script) 印度文字体系 11—539a
那格浦尔 Nāgpur 印度城市 11—540d
那鸿书 Nahum, Book of 《旧约》 11—542f
那加兰 Nāgāland 印度邦名 11—538a
那加丘陵 Nāga Hills 亚洲山区 11—537f
那加人 Nāga 印度民族 11—537e
那喀索斯 Narcissus 希腊神话 11—575a
那空叻差是玛 Nakhon Ratchasima 泰国城市 11—547b
那空拍侬 Nakhon Phanom 泰国城镇 11—547b
那空沙旺 Nakhon Sawan 泰国城镇 11—547c
那空是贪玛叻 Nakhon Si Thammarat 泰国城镇 11—547c
那拉提瓦 Narathiwat 泰国城市 11—574c
那烂陀 Nālanda 佛教寺院中心 11—547e
那罗弥迦罗 Narameikhla 缅甸王朝创立者 11—574a
那罗希摩 Narasiṃha 印度教 11—574b
那慕尔 Namur 比利时省份 11—551a
那慕尔 Namur 比利时城市 11—551b
那那·萨希伯 Nana Sahib 印度反叛者 11—552a
那纳克 Nānak 锡克教祖师 11—552c
那婆罗怛罗节 navaratra 印度教节日 12—50b
那曲 Nagqu 中国西藏县名 11—540d
那牙 Naga 菲律宾城市 11—537f
那耶那勒 Nāyanār 古印度诗人-乐师 12—54a
那伊阿得 Naiad 希腊神话 11—543a
那吒罗阇 Naṭarāja 印度教神话 12—8f
那智胜浦 Nachi-katsuura 日本城镇 11—535e
纳 nat 缅甸宗教 12—8d
纳巴科夫 Nabokov, Vladimir (Vladimirovich) 美国小说家 11—534c
纳巴泰人 Nabataean 古代阿拉伯半岛民族 11—533c
纳巴泰字母 Nabataean alphabet 纳巴泰人文字体系 11—533d
纳贝斯克公司 Nabisco 美国公司 11—534c
纳比厄 Nābighah, an- 阿拉伯诗人 11—533f
纳比画派 Nabis 法国艺术家团体 11—534b
纳比迈恩德 Nabī Mind, Tall an- (Syria) 叙利亚城市 11—533f
纳比斯 Nabis 斯巴达统治者 11—534a
纳波河 Napo River 厄瓜多尔河流 11—567a
纳伯勒岛 Narborough Island (Galápagos Islands) 厄瓜多尔岛屿 11—575a
纳博讷 Narbonne 法国城市 11—574f
纳布科·德·阿劳若 Nabuco de Araújo, Joaquim Aurelio Barreto 巴西外交官 11—535c
纳布勒 Nābul 突尼斯城镇 11—535d
纳布卢斯 Nābulus 巴勒斯坦城市 11—535d
纳布斯 Nabbes, Thomas 英国戏剧家 11—533e

纳茨福德 Knutsford 英格兰城镇 9—327a
纳粹党 Nazi Party 德国政党 12—55c
纳粹主义 Nazism 德国政治运动 12—56a
纳达尔 Nadar 法国作家 11—536b
纳德 Nader, Ralph 美国律师 11—536d
纳德尔 Nadel, S(iegfried) F(rederick) 英国人类学家 11—536b
纳德尔曼 Nadelman, Elie 雕刻家 11—536c
纳-德内诸语言 Na-Dené languages 北美印第安语言 11—533a
纳迪尔·沙阿 Nādir Shāh 伊朗统治者 11—536f
纳迪希 Nadig, Marie-Thérèse 瑞士高山滑雪运动员 11—536f
纳蒂埃 Nattier, Jean-Marc 法国画家 12—43d
纳丁 Nutting, Mary Adelaide 美国护士 12—307a
纳尔榜南西斯 Narbonensis 古罗马省份 11—574f
纳尔迪 Nardi, Jacopo 佛罗伦萨政治家 11—575e
纳尔迪尼 Nardini, Pietro 意大利小提琴家 11—575f
纳尔多 Nardò 意大利城镇 11—575f
纳尔尼 Narni 意大利城镇 11—576c
纳尔奇克 Nalchik 俄罗斯城市 11—547f
纳尔萨 Narses 波斯国王 12—1e
纳尔塞斯 Narses 拜占廷将军 12—1f
纳尔森(娃娃脸) Nelson, Baby Face 美国罪犯 12—70d
纳尔斯伯勒 Knaresborough 英格兰城镇 9—320c
纳尔瓦 Narva 爱沙尼亚城市 12—2c
纳尔维克 Narvik 挪威城镇 12—2e
纳尔逊 Nelson 加拿大城市 12—70c
纳尔逊 Nelson 新西兰城市 12—70d
纳尔逊 Nelson, Horatio Nelson, Viscount, DUCA (duke) DI BRONTE 英国海军统帅 12—70e
纳尔逊 Nelson, Samuel 美国高尔夫球运动员 12—72c
纳尔逊 Nelson, William Rockhill 美国新闻记者 12—72d
纳尔逊-阿特金斯美术馆 Nelson-Atkins Museum of Fine Arts 美国艺术博物馆 12—72d
纳尔逊河 Nelson River 加拿大河流 12—72e
纳尔逊湖国家公园 Nelson Lakes National Park 新西兰国家公园 12—72e
纳菲尔德射电天文实验室 Nuffield Radio Astronomy Laboratories (Cheshire, England) 英国柴郡实验室 12—293f
纳菲尔德子爵 Nuffield, William Richard Morris, Viscount, BARON NUFFIELD OF NUFFIELD 英国工业家 12—293d
纳夫拉蒂洛娃 Navratilova, Martina 美国网球运动员 12—52c
纳夫普利翁 Návplion (Greece) 希腊城镇 12—52c
纳夫普利亚 Nauplia 希腊城镇 12—47d
纳盖尔戈伊尔 Nāgercoil 印度城市 11—540a
纳高尔 Nāgaur 印度城市 11—539d
纳戈尔诺-卡拉巴赫 Nagorno-Karabakh 阿塞拜疆地区 11—540b
纳戈斯基 Nagurski, Bronko 美国橄榄球运动员 11—541a
纳格伯蒂讷姆 Nāgappattinam 印度城市 11—538f
纳·格科帕林 na gCopaleen, Myles 爱尔兰小说家 11—533b
纳格斯黑德 Nags Head 美国城镇 11—540f
纳瓜 Nagua 多米尼加共和国城市 11—540f
纳瓜尔 nagual 中美洲印第安人神灵 11—540f
纳哈里亚 Nahariyya 以色列城市 11—541e
纳哈万德战役 Nahāvand, Battle of 伊朗历史 11—541f
纳汉特 Nahant 美国市镇 11—541e
纳赫蒂加尔 Nachtigal, Gustav 德国探险家 11—535f
纳亨 Nāhan 印度城市 11—541e
纳侯姆村 Kefar Naḥum (Israel) 以色列古城 9—212c
纳霍德卡 Nakhodka 俄罗斯城镇 11—547a
纳基托什 Natchitoches 美国城市 12—9c
纳吉 Nagy, Ferenc 匈牙利政治家 11—541b
纳吉 Nagy, Imre 匈牙利政治家 11—541b
纳吉 Nagy, Ivan 匈牙利演员 11—541c
纳吉布 Naguib, Muḥammad 埃及军官 11—541a
纳吉布拉 Najibullah, Mohammad 阿富汗总统 11—545f
纳吉尔 Nakīr (Islāmic myth) 伊斯兰教神话 11—547c
纳济莫娃 Nazimova, Alla 俄国演员 12—55e
纳加杜姆加 Naga Dumka (India) 印度城镇 11—537f
纳加尔哈维利 Nagar Haveli (India) 印度中央直辖区 11—539a
纳加斯瓦拉姆管 nagaswaram 乐器 11—539c
纳贾王朝 Najāḥid DYNASTY 也门王朝 11—545e
纳杰夫 Najaf, an- 伊拉克城市 11—545d
纳杰哈马迪 Najʿ Ḥammādī 埃及城镇 11—545a
纳杰日金斯克 Nadezhdinsk (Russia) 俄罗斯城市 11—536e
纳卡 Nacka 瑞典城镇 11—536a
《纳卡拉克达卡玛》 Nāgarakṛtāgama 爪哇语史诗 11—539a
纳考梅 Nacaome 洪都拉斯城市 11—535e
纳科贝 Nakbe 危地马拉考古遗址 11—546e
纳科多奇斯 Nacogdoches 美国城市 11—536a
纳克-达吉斯坦诸语言 Nakho-Dagestanian languages 高加索东北部语族 11—547a
纳克尔斯 Knuckles 斯里兰卡山脉 9—326e
纳克索斯 Naxos 西西里古希腊殖民地 12—53f
纳克索斯岛 Náxos 希腊岛屿 12—53f
纳克西班底教团 Naqshbandīyah 伊斯兰教 11—573c
纳克诸语言 Nakh languages 俄罗斯、格鲁吉亚的语支 11—546e
纳库鲁 Nakuru 肯尼亚城镇 11—547d
纳库鲁湖 Nakuru, Lake 肯尼亚湖泊 11—547d
纳拉伯平原 Nullarbor Plain 澳大利亚高原 12—294d
纳拉布赖 Narrabri 澳大利亚城镇 11—576f
纳拉甘西特 Narragansett 美国城镇 12—1a
纳拉甘西特人 Narraganset 美国印第安人 11—576f
纳拉甘西特湾 Narragansett Bay 美国海湾 12—1b
纳拉库特 Naracoorte 澳大利亚城镇 11—573f
纳拉渠 Nāra Canal 巴基斯坦水道 11—573d
纳拉亚南 Narayanan, Kocheril Raman 印度总统 11—574d
纳拉扬 Narayan, Jaya Prakash 印度政治领袖 11—574c
纳拉扬 Narayan, R(asipuram) K(rishnaswami) 印度作家 11—574c
纳拉扬甘杰 Nārāyanganj 孟加拉国城市 11—574e
纳腊萱 Naresuan 暹罗国王 11—575f
纳赖 Narai 暹罗国王 11—573f
纳兰德拉 Narrandera 澳大利亚城镇 12—1b
纳兰性德 Nalan Xingde 中国清代词人 11—547e
纳雷夫河 Narew River 欧洲河流 11—576a
纳雷什金娜 Naryshkina, Natalya Kirillovna 俄国彼得大帝之母 12—3a
纳里尼奥 Nariño 哥伦比亚省份 11—576a
纳列克 Narek, Gregory 亚美尼亚诗人 11—575f
纳鲁谢维奇 Naruszewicz, Adam (Stanisław) 波兰史学家 12—2b
纳伦 Naryn 吉尔吉斯斯坦州名 12—2f
纳伦 Naryn 吉尔吉斯斯坦城市 12—3a
纳伦河 Naryn River 亚洲河流 12—3a
纳罗达峰 Narodnaya, Mount 俄罗斯山峰 11—576d
纳罗福明斯克 Naro-Fominsk 俄罗斯城市 11—576c
纳罗金 Narrogin 澳大利亚城镇 12—1d
纳马夸人 Namaqua (African people) 纳米比亚民族 11—548d
纳马人 Nama 纳米比亚民族 11—548b
纳马思 Namath, Joe 美国橄榄球运动员 11—548d
纳马提拉 Namatjira, Albert 澳大利亚土著画家 11—548e
纳曼干 Namangan 乌兹别克斯坦州名 11—548c
纳曼干 Namangan 乌兹别克斯坦城市 11—548c
纳米贝 Namibe 安哥拉城市 11—549e
纳米比亚 Namibia 非洲国家 11—549e
纳米布(沙漠) Namib 西南非洲沙漠 11—549d
纳米尔 Namier, Sir Lewis Bernstein 英国历史学家 11—550f
纳米技术 nanotechnology 量子力学 11—557f
纳木错 Nam Co 中国湖泊 11—547f

纳纳 Nana 阿帕切人领袖 11—551f
纳奈莫 Nanaimo 加拿大城市 11—552b
纳尼顿-贝德沃思 Nuneaton and Bedworth 英格兰自治市 12—300e
纳尼诺 Nanino, Giovanni Maria 意大利音乐家 11—554f
纳帕 Nābha 印度城市 11—533f
纳帕 Napa 美国城市 11—561d
纳帕尼 Nappanee 美国城市 11—573a
纳帕塔 Napata 苏丹古代城市 11—561e
纳蒲 Nabu-rimanni 巴比伦天文学家 11—535c
纳普 Knapp, Seaman Asahel 美国农学家 9—320a
纳普牌 Nap 纸牌戏 11—561d
纳齐姆·希克梅特·让 Nazım Hikmet Ran 土耳其诗人 12—55e
纳齐苏斯 Narcissus 古罗马官员 11—575b
纳奇库夫石器工艺 Nachikufan industry 非洲石器工艺 11—535f
纳奇兹 Natchez 美国城市 12—9b
纳奇兹小道公园路 Natchez Trace Parkway 美国公路 12—9c
纳切斯人 Natchez 北美印第安人 12—9a
纳萨拉瓦 Nasarawa 尼日利亚酋长国 12—3d
纳萨斯河 Nazas River 墨西哥河流 12—55a
纳塞利 Naselli, Alberto 意大利演员 12—4a
纳赛尔 Nasser, Gamal Abdel 埃及总统 12—7c
纳赛尔丁·沙阿 Nāṣer od-Dīn Shāh 埃及总统 12—4a
纳赛尔·霍斯鲁 Nāṣir-i Khusraw 波斯诗人、作家 12—6c
纳赛尔水库 Nasser, Lake 非洲水库 12—7e
纳沙泰尔 Neuchâtel 瑞士州名 12—94f
纳沙泰尔 Neuchâtel 瑞士城市 12—95a
纳沙泰尔湖 Neuchâtel, Lake 瑞士湖泊 12—95a
纳沙泰尔危机 Neuchâtel crisis 瑞士历史事件 12—95b
纳什 Nash, (Frederic) Ogden 美国幽默诗作家 12—4d
纳什 Nash, John 英国建筑师 12—4b
纳什 Nash, John F. 美国数学家 12—4c
纳什 Nash, Paul 英国画家 12—4f
纳什 Nash, Richard Southwell Bourke, Lord 印度总督 12—4f
纳什 Nashe, Thomas 英国诗人 12—5b
纳什 Nash, Sir Walter 新西兰总理 12—5a
纳什维尔 Nashville 美国城市 12—5d
纳什维尔 Nashville 美国城市 12—5e
纳什维尔大会 Nashville Convention 美国历史 12—5f
纳什维尔穹窿 Nashville Dome 地质学 12—6a
纳什维尔战役 Nashville, Battle of 美国历史 12—5f
纳舒厄 Nashua 美国城市 12—5d
纳斯 Nurse Sir Paul M. 英国科学家 12—303d
纳斯比 Nasby, Petroleum V(esuvius) 美国作家 12—3d
纳斯达克 NASDAQ 证券交易市场 12—3f
纳斯尔·伊本·赛雅尔 Naṣr ibn Sayyār 伍麦叶王朝总督 12—6f
纳斯基字体 naskhī script 伊斯兰字母手写体 12—6e
纳斯卡皮人 Naskapi (people) 北美印第安民族 12—6e
纳斯卡文化 Nazca 南美早中间期文化 12—55a
纳斯卡线条图 Nazca Lines 秘鲁考古遗址 12—55b
纳斯拉尼角 Ra's Naṣrānī 埃及西奈半岛海湾、海角 14—156d
纳斯塔利克字体 nasta'līq script 波斯书法字体 12—8a
纳斯塔塞 Nastase, Ilie 罗马尼亚网球运动员 12—8b
纳斯特 Nast, Thomas 美国漫画家 12—7f
纳绥尔 Nāṣir, an- 阿拔斯王朝哈里发 12—6c
纳绥尔-乌德-丁·穆罕默德沙 Nāṣir-ud-Dīn Muḥammad Shāh (emperor of India) 印度皇帝 12—6e
纳塔 Natta, Giulio 意大利化学家 12—43d
纳塔尔 Natal 巴西城市 12—8d
纳塔尔 Natal 南非前省份 12—8d
纳塔尔港 Port Natal (South Africa) 南非城市、海港 13—446d
纳特龙湖 Natron, Lake 非洲湖泊 12—43b
纳图夫文化 Natufian culture 巴勒斯坦、叙利亚石器时代文化 12—43d
纳托尔 Nuttall, George Henry Falkiner 英国生物学家 12—306e
纳托尔 Nuttall, Thomas 英国博物学家 12—306f
纳托尔 Nuttall, Zelia Maria Magdalena 美国考古学家 12—307a
纳陀崇拜 Nātha 印度宗教 12—9d
纳瓦埃斯 Narváez, Panfilo de 西班牙殖民官员 12—2c
纳瓦埃斯 Narváez, Ramón María, duque (duke) de Valencia 西班牙将军 12—2d
纳瓦霍国家保护区 Navajo National Monument 美国保护区 12—49d
纳瓦霍人 Navajo 北美印第安人 12—49a
纳瓦霍语 Navajo language 北美印第安语言 12—49d
纳瓦霍织物 Navajo weaving 北美印第安人织物 12—49f
纳瓦拉 Navarre 西班牙自治区域 12—50d
纳瓦莱特 Navarrete, Juan Fernández de (Spanish painter) 西班牙画家 12—50e
纳瓦里诺 Navarino (Greece) 希腊城市 12—50c
纳瓦里诺战役 Navarino, Battle of 希腊独立战争 12—50c
纳瓦林湾 Navarin, Bay of 希腊海湾 12—50c
纳瓦罗(奥利韦托伯爵) Navarro, Pedro, conde (count) de Olivetto 西班牙将军 12—50e
纳瓦人 Nahua 墨西哥印第安人 11—542b
纳瓦斯-德托洛萨战役 Navas de Tolosa, Battle of Las 西班牙历史 12—50f
纳瓦语 Nahua language 墨西哥语言 11—542c
纳瓦诸语言 Nahuan languages 中美洲语言 11—542d
纳韦尔瓦皮国家公园 Nahuel Huapí National Park 阿根廷国家公园 11—542e
纳韦尔瓦皮湖 Nahuel Huapí, Lake 阿根廷湖泊 11—542d
纳维斯塔国际公司 Navistar International Corporation 美国卡车制造商 12—52a
纳文 Navan 爱尔兰城市 12—50b
纳沃华 Navojoa 墨西哥城市 12—52b
纳沃塔斯 Navotas 菲律宾城镇 12—52b
纳沃伊 Nawoiy 乌兹别克斯坦州名 12—53c
纳乌巴 nawbah 伊斯兰音乐组曲 12—53c
纳西克 Nāsik 印度城镇 12—6a
纳西拉巴德 Nasirābād (Bangladesh) 孟加拉国城市 12—6e
纳西里耶 Nāṣirīyah, An- 伊拉克城市 12—6e
纳西门托 Nascimento, Edson Arantes do 巴西运动员 12—3e
纳西门托 Nascimento, Francisco Manuel do 葡萄牙诗人 12—3e
纳西语 Naxi language 中国语言 12—53e
纳西族 Naxi 中国民族 12—53c
纳希切万 Nakhichevan 阿塞拜疆的共和国 11—546f
纳希切万 Nakhichevan 阿塞拜疆的共和国首府 11—547a
纳辛 Nation, Carry (Amelia) 美国主张禁酒者 12—10a
纳辛哈普尔 Narsimhapur 印度城镇 12—1f
纳辛-乌德-丁·穆罕默德 Nāṣin-ud-Dīn Muḥammad (Mughal ruler) 莫卧儿统治者 12—6c
纳亚尔 Nāyar 印度种姓 12—54a
纳亚里特 Nayarit 墨西哥州名 12—54b
纳伊尔 Nair, Sir Chettur Sankaran (Indian jurist) 印度法官 11—543f
纳伊迈 Na'īmah, Mikhā'īl 黎巴嫩剧作家 11—543c
《纳伊条约》 Neuilly, Treaty of 保加利亚历史和约 12—95f
纳扎尔巴耶夫 Nazarbayev, Nursultan 哈萨克斯坦总统 12—54c
纳扎雷 Nazaré 葡萄牙城镇 12—54c
纳兹雷特 Nazret 埃塞俄比亚城镇 12—56a
纳祖尔 Nador 摩洛哥城市 11—537a
钠(Na) sodium 化学元素 15—483d
钠泵 sodium pump 细胞生理学 15—484a
钠长石 albite 矿物 1—184b
钠沸石 natrolite 矿物 12—43a

钠钙玻璃 soda-lime glass 玻璃 15—482e
钠菱沸石 gmelinite 矿物 7—166f
钠硼解石 ulexite 矿物 17—329b
钠缺乏 sodium deficiency 病理学 15—484a
钠闪石 riebeckite 矿物 14—292d
钠透闪石 richterite 矿物 14—289a
钠云母 paragonite 矿物 13—32a
钠蒸气灯 sodium-vapour lamp 照明灯 15—484b
娜西姆 Nashim 犹太教 12—5d
乃穹 Nechung oracle 藏传佛教巫师 12—62d
奶 milk 食品 11—219a
奶油 butter 食品 3—292b
奶油杯花 creamcups (species *Platystemon californicus*) 植物 4—574d
奶油茶糕 madeleine 食品 10—367b
奶油果 cream nut 坚果 4—574d
奶油硬糖 butterscotch 食品 3—293e
奶粥节 Pongal 印度教节日 13—426b
氖(Ne) neon 化学元素 12—78d
奈 Nye, Bill 美国新闻记者 12—309c
奈阿波利斯 Neapolis (Israeli-occupied Jordan) 巴勒斯坦城市 12—57f
奈阿尔科斯 Nearchus 马其顿军官 12—58a
奈阿克 Nyack 美国村庄 12—308a
奈波尔 Naipaul, V(idiadhar) S(urajprasad) 特立尼达作家 11—543e
奈卜哈佩特雷 Nebhapetre (king of Egypt) 埃及国王 12—58c
奈德哈特·封·罗伊恩塔 Neidhart VON REUENTHAL 中世纪德国骑士诗人 12—68f
奈迪姆 Nedim, Ahmed 奥斯曼诗人 12—64a
奈都(夫人) Naidu, Sarojini 印度政治活动家 11—543a
奈顿 Knighton, Henry 英格兰编年史学家 9—321f
奈厄布拉勒河 Niobrara River 美国河流 12—200a
奈厄布拉勒灰岩 Niobrara Limestone 地质学 12—200a
奈恩 Nairne (of Nairne), Carolina Nairne, Baroness 苏格兰歌词作者 11—544a
奈恩郡 Nairnshire 苏格兰历史郡 11—544a
奈尔 Nair, Mira 印度导演 11—543f
奈尔斯 Niles 美国密歇根州城市 12—194a
奈尔斯 Niles 美国俄亥俄州城市 12—194a
奈尔斯 Niles, Hezekiah 美国报纸主编 12—194a
奈尔斯 Niles, John Jacob 美国民歌手 12—194b
奈耳 Néel, Louis-Eugène-Félix 法国物理学家 12—65a
奈费尔海佩鲁雷·阿孟霍特普 Neferkheperure Amenhotep (Egyptian king) 埃及国王 12—65e
奈费尔提蒂 Nefertiti 埃及王后 12—65f
奈费尔廷 Nefertem 古埃及宗教神祇 12—65e
奈弗尔斯战役 Näfels, Battle of 瑞士历史 11—537b
奈富塞高原 Nafūsah Plateau 利比亚高原 11—537c
奈哈斯帕夏 Naḥḥās Pasha, Muṣṭafā an- 埃及政治家 11—542a
奈哈特 Neihardt, John Gneisenau 美国诗人 12—69a
奈赫贝特 Nekhbet 埃及宗教神祇 12—69f
奈霍夫 Nijhoff, Martinus 荷兰诗人 12—190e
奈基 Nike 希腊宗教神祇 12—191e
奈基导弹 Nike missile 美国武器 12—191f
奈季兰 Najrān 沙特阿拉伯城镇 11—546a
奈加代 Naqādah 上埃及城镇 11—573b
奈加代二期文化 Naqādah II culture 埃及历史 11—573b
奈加代一期文化 Naqādah I culture 埃及历史 11—573b
奈克塔内博 Nectanebo 埃及国王之名 12—63c
奈克塔内博二世 Nectanebo II 埃及国王 12—63d
奈克塔内博一世 Nectanebo I 埃及国王 12—63d
奈拉 naira 尼日利亚货币单位 11—543f
奈良 Nara 日本县名 11—573c
奈良 Nara 日本城市 11—573c
奈良国立博物馆 Nara National Museum 日本博物馆 11—573e
奈良时代 Nara period 日本历史 11—573e
奈迈阿赛会 Nemean Games 古希腊赛会 12—73d
奈迈阿战役 Nemea, Battle of 古希腊科林斯战争 12—73d
奈曼 Neyman, Jerzy 美国数学家 12—158e
奈梅亨 Nijmegen 荷兰城市 12—191c
奈尼达尔 Naini Tāl 印度城镇 11—543d
奈萨姆 Naẓẓām, Ibrāhīm an- 伊斯兰教义学家 12—56a
奈史密斯 Naismith, James A. 美国体育家 11—544d
奈斯尔王朝 Naṣrid DYNASTY 西班牙王朝 12—7a
奈斯特韦兹 Næstved 丹麦城市 11—537a
奈斯托斯河 Néstos River 欧洲河流 12—90d
奈特 Knight, Frank Hyneman 美国经济学家 9—321b
奈特 Knight, John S(hively) 美国新闻工作者 9—321c
奈特 Knight, Margaret E. 美国发明家 9—321d
奈特 Knight, Thomas Andrew 英国园艺学家 9—321d
奈特(夫人) Knight, Sarah Kemble 美国教师 9—321d
奈瓦尔 Nerval, Gérard de 法国诗人 12—86d
奈瓦沙湖 Naivasha, Lake 肯尼亚湖泊 11—544e
奈维尔逊 Nevelson, Louise 美国雕刻家 12—104d
奈维乌斯 Naevius, Gnaeus 拉丁史诗诗人 11—537b
《奈维印》 Nevi'im 希伯来语《圣经》 12—105c
奈西湖 Näsi, Lake 芬兰湖泊 12—6a
奈亚特劳斯 Niatross 美国轻驾车走马 12—165d
奈伊拉 neilah 犹太教节日 12—69c
耐火材料 refractory 工业材料 14—200c
耐火砖 firebrick 耐火材料 6—327c
萘 naphthalene 化合物 11—562a
萘酚 naphthol 化合物 11—562b
男高音 tenor 音乐 16—544e
男爵 baron 贵族称号 2—238c
男女合校教育 coeducation 教育 4—327f
《男童的神奇号角》 Knaben Wunderhorn, Des 德国民歌集 9—320a
男像柱 atlas 建筑 2—29a
男中音 baritone 音乐 2—229d
男子乳房女性化 gynecomastia 病理现象 7—390f
南阿尔卑斯山 Southern Alps 大洋洲最高山脉 15—552f
南阿拉伯语 South Arabic language 语言 15—537c
南阿斯里诸语言 Southern Aslian languages 亚洲语言 15—553a
南安普敦 Southampton 英格兰城市 15—549c
南安普敦 Southampton 美国纽约州城镇 15—549d
南安普敦伯爵 Southampton, William Fitzwilliam, Earl of 英国海军上将 15—549e
南安普敦伯爵(第二) Southampton, Henry Wriothesley, 2nd Earl of 英国贵族 15—549f
南安普敦伯爵(第三) Southampton, Henry Wriothesley, 3rd Earl of 英国贵族 15—549f
南安普敦伯爵(第四) Southampton, Thomas Wriothesley, 4th Earl of 英国贵族 15—550b
南安普敦伯爵(第一) Southampton, Thomas Wriothesley, 1st Earl of 英国国务大臣 15—549e
南安普敦伯爵、女伯爵和公爵 Southampton, EARLS, COUNTESS, AND DUKES OF 英国封爵贵族 15—549d
南安普敦岛 Southampton Island 加拿大岛屿 15—550c
南安普敦公爵(第一) Southampton, Charles Fitzroy, 1st Duke of 英国贵族 15—550b
南安普敦女伯爵 Southampton, Barbara Villiers, Countess of 英国贵族 15—550b
南岸 South Bank 伦敦地区 15—538c
南奥克尼群岛 South Orkney Islands 英属南极洲领地 15—547c
南奥兰治村 South Orange Village 美国新泽西州区名 15—547c

南奥塞梯 South Ossetia 格鲁吉亚中北部地区 15—547d
南澳大利亚 South Australia 澳大利亚州名 15—538a
南巴克斯 South Bucks 英格兰地名 15—538e
南巴拉卡斯 Barracas al Sur (Argentina) 阿根廷城市 2—240a
南邦 Lampang 泰国城镇 9—467f
南北安普顿 South Northamptonshire 英格兰中南部区名 15—547b
南贝德福 South Bedfordshire 英格兰中南部区名 15—538d
南奔 Lamphun 泰国城镇 9—468a
南本德 South Bend 美国城市 15—538e
南布迪里 Nambūdiri 印度种姓 11—548f
南布格河 Yuzhny Bug 乌克兰河流 18—485f
南部邦联 Confederate States of America 美国南北战争史 4—419e
南部邦联女子联合会 United Daughters of the Confederacy (UDC) 美国妇女组织 17—351f
南部非洲 southern Africa 非洲南部地区 15—552b
南部非洲发展协调会议 Southern African Development Coordination Conference (SADCC) 南部非洲国际组织 15—552e
南部海 Southern Ocean 南极洲周围海域 15—553d
南部区 Southland 新西兰南岛行政区 15—554c
南查尔斯顿 South Charleston 美国城市 15—541f
南昌 Nanchang 中国城市 11—552d
南昌起义 Nanchang Uprising 中国历史 11—552f
南朝 Southern Dynasties 中国古代王朝 15—553c
南充 Nanchong 中国城市 11—553b
南达科他 South Dakota 美国州名 15—542b
南岛 South Island 新西兰主要岛屿 15—546b
南德比 South Derbyshire 英格兰德比郡区名 15—544f
《南德意志报》 Süddeutsche Zeitung 德国报纸 16—305f
南迪人 Nandi 肯尼亚民族 11—554a
南迪瓦人 Nandeva (South American Indians) 南美印第安人 11—554a
南蒂科克人 Nanticoke 美国印第安人 11—560a
南丁格尔 Nightingale, Florence 英国护理学先驱 12—189a
南定 Nam Dinh 越南城市 11—548a
南方哥特派 Southern gothic 美国南方作家写作风格 15—553c
南方共同市场 Mercosur 南美洲经济组织 11—126a
南方古猿 Australopithecus 人类学 2—69b
南方横贯大陆邮递公司 Southern Overland Mail Company 美国公司 15—553d
南方基督教领袖会议 Southern Christian Leadership Conference (SCLC) 美国民权组织 15—553b
南方浸礼联会 Southern Baptist Convention 美国教会组织 15—553a
南方佬 scalawag 美国历史 15—99f
南方群岛 Austral Islands 太平洋中南部群岛 2—63e
南方铁路公司 Southern Railway Company 美国铁路系统 15—553e
南方摇滚 Southern rock 美国流行音乐风格 15—553f
南方有蹄目 Notoungulata 古生物学 12—274f
南方越橘 blueberry (*Vaccinium australe*) 灌木 2—549f
南方之星 Star of the South 宝石 16—196d
南方诸语言 Austric languages 假设的语言超系 2—72a
南非 South Africa 非洲国家 15—532a
南非大羚羊 gemsbok 哺乳动物 7—50d
南非党 South African Party 南非政党 15—535a
《南非法》(1909) South Africa Act 南非历史 15—533e
南非共和国 South African Republic, 非洲国家 15—535b
南非国家植物园 National Botanic Gardens of South Africa 南非植物园 12—12d
南非国立动物园 National Zoological Gardens of South Africa 南非动物园 12—38c
南非荷兰归正宣教会 Dutch Reformed Mission Church in South Africa 南非基督教会 5—481b
南非荷兰语 Cape Dutch language 非洲语言 3—420b
南非圣公会 South Africa, Church of the Province of 南非教会 15—533e
南非文学 South African literature 文学 15—533f
南非新国民党 New National Party of South Africa 南非政党 12—122a
南非战争 South African War 英国-南非历史 15—535b
南非之星 Star of South Africa 宝石 16—196d
南伽山 Nānga Parbat 亚洲山峰 11—554c
南竿 Nankan (China) 中国岛屿 11—556d
南高加索诸语言 South Caucasian languages 语言 15—541f
南格拉摩根 South Glamorgan 南威尔士郡名 15—545a
南瓜(大果) pumpkin 草本植物 14—25c
南瓜(小果) squash 草本植物 16—167f
南瓜灯 jack-o'-lantern 美国节日用灯 8—503d
南瓜缘蝽 squash bug (insect) 昆虫 16—168a
南哈德利 South Hadley 美国城镇 15—545b
南哈姆斯 South Hams 英格兰德文郡区名 15—545c
南海 Nan Hai 中国大陆以南海域 11—551d
南海 Nanhai 中国区名 11—554d
南海泡沫 South Sea Bubble 英国历史 15—548c
南海诸岛 South China Sea Islands 中国南海岛屿统称 15—541f
南河三 Procyon 天文学 13—527a
南荷兰 South Holland 英格兰林肯郡区名 15—545d
南荷兰 Zuid-Holland 荷兰省份 18—572a
南赫里福德 South Herefordshire 英格兰西部区名 15—545d
南湖 Nan-hu 中国诗人 11—551e
《南华真经》 Nan Hua Chen Ching 中国经典 11—551e
南画 Nan-ga 日本绘画风格 11—551c
南怀仁 Verbiest, Ferdinand 荷兰耶稣会传教士 17—511d
南怀特 South Wight 英格兰怀特岛自治市 15—549b
南回归线 Capricorn, Tropic of 地理学 3—430e
南回归线 Tropic of Capricorn 地理学 17—234c
南汇 Nanhui 中国区名 11—554e
南霍兰 South Holland 美国库克县村庄 15—545e
南极 South Pole 地轴南端 15—548a
南极半岛 Antarctic Peninsula 南极洲半岛 1—375c
南极光 southern lights 大气现象 15—553d
南极海 Antarctic Ocean 南极洲周围海域 1—375b
南极圈 Antarctic Circle 地理学 1—375a
南极群岛 Antarctic Archipelago (Antarctica) 南极洲岛群 1—375a
《南极条约》 Antarctic Treaty 国际协议 1—375c
南极洲 Antarctica 世界大洲之一 1—375d
南极洲横贯山地 Transantarctic Mountains 南极洲山系 17—194d
南极洲环流 Antarctic Circumpolar Current 南极洲洋流 1—375a
南加里曼丹 Kalimantan Selatan 印度尼西亚省份 9—141b
南剑桥 South Cambridgeshire 英格兰地名 15—539a
南捷克州 Jihočeský 捷克州名 9—21d
南芥 rock cress 草本植物 14—340d
南金斯敦 South Kingstown 美国城镇 15—546e
南京 Nanjing 中国城市 11—554f
南京博物院 Nanjing Museum 中国博物馆 11—555f
南京布 nankeen 棉布 11—556d
南京大屠杀 Nanking Massacre 中国历史 11—556e
南京大学 Nanjing University 中国大学 11—556a
南京受降 Acceptance of Japan's Surrender in Nanjing 中日战争 1—45c
《南京条约》 Nanking, Treaty of 中国历史 11—556f
南喀尔巴阡山 Carpații Meridionali (Romania) 罗马尼亚山脉 3—475e
南喀尔巴阡山 Southern Carpathians (Romania) 罗马尼亚山脉 15—553b
南卡鲁 Southern Karoo (South Africa) 南非高原盆地 15—553d
南卡罗来纳 South Carolina 美国州名 15—539a

南卡舒埃拉 Cachoeira, do Sul 巴西城市 3—310c
南卡希亚斯 Caxias do Sul 巴西城市 3—543f
南开大学 Nankai University 中国大学 11—556c
南凯斯蒂文 South Kesteven 英格兰林肯郡区名 15—546e
南科西嘉 Corse-du-Sud 法国省份 4—522f
南孔瀑布 Khone Falls 老挝瀑布 9—263a
南口 Nankou 中国城镇 11—557a
南莱克兰 South Lakeland 英格兰坎布里亚郡区名 15—546f
南里奥格兰德州 Rio Grande do Sul 巴西州名 14—309f
南里布尔 South Ribble 英格兰兰开夏郡区名 15—548a
南岭 Nan Ling 中国山系 11—551e
南马托格罗索 Mato Grosso do Sul 巴西州名 11—26a
南满铁路 South Manchurian Railway 中国铁路 15—547a
南曼兰 Södermanland 瑞典省份 15—483c
南美刺豚鼠 acouchi 啮齿动物 1—57a
南美大草原 Pampas, the 南美地理区域 12—576e
南美狐 South American fox 哺乳动物 15—537b
南美浣熊 coati 哺乳动物 4—313b
南美巨侧颈龟 arrau 爬行动物 1—514c
南美犰狳 pichi 哺乳动物 13—288e
南美水獭 saro 哺乳动物 15—68e
南美印第安地域人种 South American Indian local race 人类学 15—537b
南美洲 South America 世界第四大洲 15—535c
南摩拉维亚 Jihomoravský 捷克州名 9—21f
南那 Nanna (Mesopotamian deity) 美索不达米亚神祇 11—557b
南尼 Nanni di Banco 佛罗伦萨雕刻家 11—557b
南尼 Nenni, Pietro Sandro 佛罗伦萨雕刻家 12—76b
南鸟岛 Minami-tori Island 日本岛屿 11—241f
南宁 Nanning 中国城市 11—557c
南宁战争 Naning War 英国-马来亚历史 11—554e
南牛津 South Oxfordshire 英格兰牛津郡区名 15—547d
南诺福克 South Norfolk 英格兰诺福克郡区名 15—547b
南帕拉伊巴河 Paraíba do Sul River 巴西河流 13—34b
南帕萨迪纳 South Pasadena 美国城市 15—547f
南彭布罗克夏尔 South Pembrokeshire 威尔士达费德郡区名 15—547f
南平 Nanping 中国城市 11—558a
南浦 Namp'o 朝鲜城市 11—550f
南普拉特河 South Platte River 美国河流 15—548a
南乔治亚 South Georgia 南大西洋荒岛 15—544f
南丘绵羊 Southdown 哺乳动物 15—550e
南曲 nanqu 中国戏曲 11—558b
南日德兰 Sønderjyllands 丹麦州名 15—508e
南萨哈林斯克 Yuzhno-Sakhalinsk 俄罗斯城市 18—485f
南萨默塞特 South Somerset 英格兰萨默塞特郡区名 15—548e
南桑威奇群岛 South Sandwich Islands 英属福克兰群岛岛屿 15—548b
南森 Nansen, Fridtjof 挪威海洋学家 11—558c
南森瓶 Nansen bottle 海水取样瓶 11—559a
南沙赫巴兹布尔岛 Dakhin Shāhbāzpur Island 孟加拉国岛屿 5—114c
南山 South Mountain 美国蓝岭山脉北段 15—547b
南闪米特字母 South Semitic alphabet 阿姆哈拉文字 15—548c
南舍 Nanshe 美索不达米亚女神 11—559a
南设得兰群岛 South Shetland Islands 英属南极洲领地 15—548d
南圣保罗 South Saint Paul 美国城市 15—548b
南圣弗朗西斯科 South San Francisco 美国城市 15—548b
南圣卡埃塔诺 São Caetano do Sul 巴西城市 15—51e
南十字座 Crux 天文学 5—41b
南十字座α Alpha Crucis 天文学 1—250a
南什罗普 South Shropshire 英格兰什罗普郡区名 15—548d
南斯拉夫 Yugoslavia 欧洲国家 18—477e
南斯拉夫反法西斯民族解放委员会 Anti-Fascist Council for the National Liberation of Yugoslavia 欧洲历史 1—381b
南斯匹次卑尔根国家公园 South Spitsbergen National Park 挪威鸟类保护区 15—548f
南斯塔福德 South Staffordshire 英格兰斯塔福德郡区名 15—548f
南斯特伦菲尤尔 Søndre Strømfjord 格陵兰西南部海湾 15—508f
南苏拉威西 Sulawesi Selatan 印度尼西亚省份 16—316b
南苏门答腊 Sumatera Selatan 印度尼西亚省份 16—330f
南太平洋铁路 Southern Pacific Railroad 美国铁路系统 15—553d
南太平洋委员会 South Pacific Commission 国际组织 15—547e
南泰恩赛德 South Tyneside 英格兰自治市 15—548f
南泰利耶 Södertälje 瑞典城镇 15—483d
南特 Nantes 法国城市 11—559b
《南特敕令》 Nantes, Edict of 法国历史 11—559d
南特大学 Nantes, University of 法国大学 11—559d
南特加尔瓷器 Nantgarw porcelain 英国瓷器 11—559e
南特伦德拉格 Sør-Trøndelag 挪威郡名 15—520c
南特伊 Nanteuil, Robert 法国肖像铜版画家 11—559e
南通 Nantong 中国城市 11—560a
南投 Nantou 中国城市 11—560e
南投 Nantou 中国县名 11—560c
南望 Rembang 印度尼西亚城市 14—216f
南乌河 Ou River 老挝河流 12—504a
南西里伯斯 South Celebes (Indonesia) 印度尼西亚省份 15—541f
南西摩岛 South Seymour Island (Galápagos Islands) 东太平洋加拉帕戈斯群岛岛屿 15—548d
南西奈省 Janūb Sīnā' 埃及省份 8—536b
南希尔兹 South Shields 英格兰北海港口 15—548d
南锡 Nancy 法国城市 11—553d
南戏 nanxi 中国历史剧种 11—560f
南下加利福尼亚 Baja California Sur 墨西哥州名 2—152f
南学派 Teṉkalai 印度教派别 16—540c
南亚克河 Yaque del Sur River 多米尼加共和国河流 18—426a
南亚区域合作联盟 South Asian Association for Regional Co-operation (SAARC) 南亚国际组织 15—538a
南亚野鲮 rohu 鱼类 14—356f
南亚艺术 South Asian arts 艺术 15—537c
南阳 Nanyang 中国城市 11—561a
南洋杉属 Araucaria 植物学 1—441d
南伊罗戈 Ilocos Sur 菲律宾省份 8—339c
南印度教会 South India, Church of 印度基督教会 15—545e
南印度青铜像 South Indian bronze 艺术 15—545f
南印度寺庙建筑 South Indian temple architecture 印度教寺庙建筑形式 15—546a
南尤伊斯特岛 South Uist 苏格兰外赫布里底群岛岛屿 15—549a
南鱼座α Alpha Piscis Austrini 天文学 1—250c
南约克 South Yorkshire 英格兰中北部区名 15—549b
南越 Nam Viet 亚洲古代王国 11—548a
南越王墓 King's tomb of Nanyue 中国古墓 9—292a
南泽西玻璃器皿 South Jersey glass 玻璃器皿 15—546c
南诏 Nanzhao 中国古代王国 11—561b
南烛属 Lyonia 植物学 10—316a
难 Nan 泰国城镇 11—551c
难底 Nandi 印度教神话 11—554a
难河 Nan River 泰国河流 11—551f
难接近极 Pole of Inaccessibility 地理术语 13—398e
难近母 Durgā 印度教神话女神名 5—472f
难提弗 Nāmdev 印度诗圣 11—549a
难陀利派 Nāmdhārī 印度锡克教教派 11—549a
难陀王朝 Nanda dynasty 印度王朝 11—553f
楠巴卡黑兹岬 Nambucca Heads 澳大利亚城镇、岬角 11—548e
楠榜 Lampung 印度尼西亚省份 9—468f
楠榜人 Lampong 亚洲民族 9—468b

楠代德 Nānded 印度城镇 11—554a
楠木正成 Kusunoki Masashige 日本军事战略家 9—406b
楠塔哈拉河 Nantahala River 美国河流 11—559a
楠塔基特 Nantucket 大西洋岛屿 11—560e
楠泰尔 Nanterre 法国城市 11—559b
楠特威奇 Nantwich 英格兰城镇 11—560f
难民 refugee 流离失所的移民 14—201a
囊 bladder 动物学 2—522c
囊鼻海豹 bladdernose seal 哺乳动物 2—522d
囊地鼠 gopher 啮齿动物 7—211a
囊泡果 burro-fat (species *Cleome isomeris*) 植物 3—275c
囊胚 blastula 动物学 2—531b
囊鼠 pocket gopher 啮齿动物 13—383b
囊鼠 pouched rat 哺乳动物 13—467d
囊性纤维性骨炎 osteitis fibrosa cystica (disease) 疾病 12—490a
囊咽鱼 gulper 鱼类 7—370a
囊翼蝠 sac-winged bat 哺乳动物 14—485d
囊肿 cyst 病理现象 5—94d
囊状纤维变性 cystic fibrosis (CF) 病理现象 5—94e
挠性轴 flexible shaft 机械零件 6—359d
硇砂 sal ammoniac 化合物 14—536a
蛲虫 pinworm (*Enterobius* or *Oxyuris*, *vermicularis*) 寄生虫 13—316d
脑 brain 解剖学 3—115d
脑癌 brain cancer 疾病 3—115f
脑电描记术 electroencephalography 医学 6—24e
脑回声检查法 echoencephalography 医学 5—523c
脑积水 hydrocephalus 病理现象 8—282c
脑脊膜 meninges 解剖学 11—114f
脑脊髓膜炎 meningitis 疾病 11—115a
脑脊液 cerebrospinal fluid (CSF) 生理学 4—10d
脑梅毒 brain syphilis (disease) 疾病 3—116c
脑膜炎球菌 meningococcus 微生物 11—115c
脑桥 pons 解剖学 13—426e
脑扫描 brain scanning 医学 3—116b
脑上腺 epiphysis cerebri 解剖学 6—101f
脑神经 cranial nerve 解剖学 4—569c
脑血管意外 cerebrovascular accident (medicine) 医学 4—10e
脑炎 encephalitis 疾病 6—69b
脑叶切断术 lobotomy 医学 10—173c
脑震荡 concussion 病理学 4—414b
瑙贡 Nagaon 印度阿萨姆邦城市 11—538f
瑙贡 Nowgong 印度阿萨姆邦城市 12—284c
瑙汉湖 Naujan Lake 菲律宾湖泊 12—47a
瑙吉巴尼奥 Nagybánya (Romania) 罗马尼亚城市 11—541d
瑙吉松博特 Nagyszombat (Slovakia) 斯洛伐克城镇 11—541d
瑙吉瓦劳德 Nagyvárad (Romania) 罗马尼亚城市 11—541d
瑙拉-博马德里 Nowra-Bomaderry 澳大利亚城市区 12—284d
瑙鲁 Nauru 太平洋岛国 12—47e
瑙曼 Naumann, Friedrich 德国政治理论家 12—47b
瑙姆堡 Naumburg 德国城市 12—47c
瑙萨里 Navsāri 印度城市 12—52d
瑙塞特人 Nauset 北美印第安人 12—48c
瑙谢拉 Nowshera 巴基斯坦城镇 12—284d
闹剧 farce 诙谐剧 6—238d
讷巴达 Narbada (India) 印度河流 11—574e
讷伯德维普 Nabadwīp 印度城市 11—533c
讷德林根 Nördlingen 德国城市 12—234b
讷德林根战役 Nördlingen, Battle of 欧洲历史 12—234c
讷德瓦拉 Nāthdwāra 印度城镇 12—9f
讷迪亚 Nadia (town, West Bengal state, India) 印度城镇 11—536e
讷迪亚德 Nadiād 印度城市 11—536f
讷尔布德达河 Nerbudda River (India) 印度河流 12—84d
讷尔默达河 Narmada River 印度河流 11—576c
讷尔沃尔 Narwar 印度古城 12—2e
讷尔辛格格尔 Narsinghgarh 印度城镇 12—2a
讷勒默拉山地 Nallamala Range 印度丘陵、谷地 11—547f
讷瓦布沙阿 Nawābshāh 巴基斯坦城镇 12—53b
讷瓦讷格尔 Nawānagar, Sir Ranjitsinhji Vibhaji, Maharaja Jam Saheb of 印度板球运动员 12—53b
讷韦尔 Nevers 法国城市 12—104e
讷韦尔玻璃小像 Nevers glass figure 法国玻璃工艺品 12—105a
讷韦尔彩陶 Nevers faience 法国陶器 12—104e
内阿米巴属 Entamoeba 生物学 6—87e
内波斯 Nepos, Cornelius 罗马历史学家 12—83f
内波斯 Nepos, Julius 西罗马帝国皇帝 12—83f
内布拉斯加 Nebraska 美国州名 12—58d
内布拉斯加冰期 Nebraskan Glacial Stage 地质学 12—61a
内布拉斯加城 Nebraska City 美国城市 12—60f
内布利纳峰 Neblina Peak 巴西最高峰 12—58c
内插 interpolation 数学 8—422e
内彻 Netscher, Caspar 德国画家 12—94b
内村鉴三 Uchimura Kanzō 日本宗教思想家、评论家 17—318b
内德堡 Nederburgh, Sebastian Cornelius 荷兰政治家 12—63f
内地 Outback 澳大利亚内陆地区 12—508c
内地荒漠 sertão 巴西内陆区 15—228a
内蒂克 Natick 美国城镇 12—9f
内电子偶产生 internal pair production 物理学 8—411a
内殿 cella 建筑 3—556f
内毒素 endotoxin 细菌毒素 6—75b
内尔 Neer, Aert van der 荷兰画家 12—65b
内尔 Neher, Erwin 德国物理学家 12—68b
内尔彻 Närke 瑞典历史省份 11—576b
内尔德克 Nöldeke, Theodor 德国东方学家 12—226b
内尔格勒 Nergal 美索不达米亚宗教神灵 12—85b
内尔瑟斯 Nerthus 古日耳曼女神 12—86a
内尔瓦 Nerva 罗马皇帝 12—86c
内尔维 Nervi, Pier Luigi 意大利工程师 12—86e
内尔沃 Nervo, Amado 墨西哥诗人 12—87b
内耳 inner ear 解剖学 8—389f
内耳迷路 labyrinth of the ear 解剖学 9—434f
内菲 Nef'i 奥斯曼诗人 12—66a
内啡肽 endorphin 生物化学 6—75a
内分泌系统 endocrine system 医学 6—73e
内分泌学 endocrinology 医学 6—74b
内夫 Nef, John Ulric 美国化学家 12—65d
内夫得沙漠 Nafūd, an- 沙特阿拉伯地区 11—537c
内夫塔 Nafṭah 突尼斯城镇 11—537c
内夫谢希尔 Nevşehir 土耳其城市 12—106a
内弗斯 Nevers, Ernie 美国橄榄球 12—104e
内盖夫 Negev 以色列南部地区 12—66c
内盖利侯爵 Neghelli, Rodolfo Graziani, marchese di (marquess of) 意大利陆军元帅 12—66d
内肛动物 entoproct 水生无脊椎动物 6—89c
内阁 cabinet 政治机构 3—305e
内阁 Neige 中国旧行政机关 12—68f
内格尔 Nagel, Ernest 美国哲学家 11—539e
内格拉山 Negra, Cordillera 秘鲁山岭 12—67b
内格雷蒂 Negreti, Jacopo 意大利画家 12—67b
内格里 Nägeli, Hans Franz 瑞士政治家 11—539f
内格里 Nägeli, Karl Wilhelm von 瑞士植物学家 11—539f
内格林 Negrín, Juan 西班牙总理 12—67b
内格罗河 Negro River 阿根廷河流 12—67d
内格罗河 Negro River 南美洲河流 12—67d
内格罗河 Negro River 乌拉圭河流 12—67e
内格罗斯 Negros 菲律宾岛屿 12—67e

内供 nang-mchod 中国藏传佛教礼仪 11—554b
内海航道 Inside Passage 美国航道 8—399a
内涵和外延 intension and extension 逻辑学 8—407a
内赫布里底群岛 Inner Hebrides 苏格兰岛屿 8—390a
内湖 Bay, Laguna de 菲律宾湖泊 2—291e
内华达 Nevada 美国州名 12—101e
内华达 Nevada, Emma 美国演员 12—104b
内华达山 Sierra Nevada 西班牙山脉 15—359a
内华达山 Sierra Nevada 北美洲山脉 15—359a
内华达山国家公园 Sierra Nevada National Park 委内瑞拉国家公园 15—359b
内华达造山运动 Nevadan orogeny 地质学 12—104c
内寄生性黏菌 endoparasitic slime mold 微生物 6—74f
内加拉国家公园 Negara National Park 马来西亚国家公园 12—66a
内加帕塔姆 Negapattam (India) 印度城镇 12—66a
内贾蒂 Necati, İsa 奥斯曼诗人 12—62a
内江 Neijiang 中国城市 12—69b
内角拱 squinch 建筑 16—170a
内景主义 Intimism 绘画 8—424e
内聚假说 cohesion hypothesis 植物学 4—333d
内聚力 cohesion 物理学 4—333d
内卡河 Neckar River 德国河流 12—62e
内科 internal medicine 医学 8—410f
内克 Necker, Jacques 法国政府官员 12—62f
内克(夫人) Necker, Suzanne 法国庇护人 12—63a
内克·德·索叙尔(夫人) Necker de Saussure, Albertine-Adrienne 瑞士作家 12—63b
内克鼓 naker 乐器 11—546e
内克姆 Neckam, Alexander 英国科学家 12—62e
内窥镜检查 endoscopy 医学 6—75a
内勒 Kneller, Sir Godfrey, BARONET 英格兰画家 9—320e
内勒 Nayler, James 英格兰宗教领袖 12—54b
内雷特瓦河 Neretva River 欧洲河流 12—84f
内里 Neri, Saint Philip 意大利奥秘神学家 12—85c
内利冈 Nelligan, Émile 加拿大诗人 12—70c
内陆低地 Interior Lowlands 北美地区 8—409c
内罗毕 Nairobi 肯尼亚首都 11—544b
内罗毕国家公园 Nairobi National Park 肯尼亚国家公园 11—544d
内罗得阿彭策尔 Appenzell Inner-Rhoden 瑞士半州名 1—418c
内马尼奇王朝 Nemanjić DYNASTY 巴尔干历史 12—73a
内毛虫 entodiniomorph 原生动物 6—89a
内梅罗夫 Nemerov, Howard 美国诗人 12—73e
内梅西安努斯 Nemesianus, Marcus Aurelius Olympius 罗马诗人 12—73f
内蒙古 Inner Mongolia 中国自治区 8—390b
内蒙古高原 Inner Mongolian Plateau 中国高原 8—391a
内米湖 Nemi, Lake 意大利火山口湖 12—74b
内米纳塔 Neminātha (Jaina saint) 耆那教圣者 12—74b
内穆尔 Nemours 法国城镇 12—74e
内穆尔公爵 Nemours, DUKES OF 法国贵族称号 12—74e
内穆尔公爵 Nemours, Charles-Amédée de Savoie, duc de 法国贵族 12—75a
内穆尔公爵 Nemours, Charles-Emmanuel de Savoie, duc de, PRINCE DE GENEVOIS 法国贵族 12—74f
内穆尔公爵 Nemours, Giuliano de' Medici, duc de 法国贵族 12—74f
内穆尔公爵 Nemours, Henri I de Savoie, duc de 法国贵族 12—75a
内穆尔公爵 Nemours, Henri II de Savoie, duc de 法国贵族 12—75a
内穆尔公爵 Nemours, Jacques d'Armagnac, duc de 法国贵族 12—74e
内穆尔公爵 Nemours, Jacques de Savoie, duc de 法国贵族 12—74f
内穆尔公爵 Nemours, Louis-Charles-Philippe-Raphaël d'Orléans, duc de 法国贵族 12—75b
内穆尔公爵 Nemours, Louis d'Armagnac, duc de 法国贵族 12—74f
内穆尔公爵夫人 Nemours, Marie d'Orleans-Longueville, duchesse de 纳沙泰尔君主 12—75c
内纳多维奇 Nenadović, Matija 塞尔维亚外交使臣 12—75d
内能 internal energy 物理学 8—410d
内尼厄斯 Nennius 威尔士古文物家 12—76b
内胚层 endoderm 胚胎学 6—74c
内胚层体型 endomorph 生理学 6—74e
内皮尔 Napier 新西兰城市 11—562b
内皮尔 Napier, Sir Charles, CONDE (count) NAPIER DE SÃO VICENTE 英国舰队司令 11—562c
内皮尔 Napier, Sir Charles James 英国将军 11—562d
内皮尔 Napier, John 英国数学家 11—562e
内皮尔 Napier, MacVey 苏格兰法学家 11—562f
内皮尔 Napier (of Magdala), Robert (Cornelis) Napier, 1st Baron 英国陆军元帅 11—562f
内皮尔 Napier, Sir William Francis Patrick 英国将军 11—563b
内珀维尔 Naperville 美国城市 11—561f
内齐钦 Neziqin 犹太教律法汇编 12—159d
内倾 introvert 心理学 8—425f
内燃机 internal-combustion engine 发动机 8—410c
内萨瓦尔科约特尔 Nezahualcóyotl 墨西哥自治区 12—159b
内塞伯尔 Nesebŭr 保加利亚历史城镇 12—88c
内森 Nathan, Daniel (U.S. author) 美国作家 12—9d
内森 Nathan, George Jean 美国作家 12—9d
内森 Nathan, Maud 美国社会福利事业领袖 12—9e
内森斯 Nathans, Daniel 美国微生物学家 12—9f
内沙布尔 Neyshābūr 伊朗城镇 12—158f
内沙布尔陶器 Nishapur pottery 穆斯林陶器 12—202a
内生软骨瘤 enchondroma 疾病 6—69d
内施 Nesch, Rolf 德国-挪威艺术家 12—88c
内什里 Neşri 奥斯曼历史学家 12—88e
内史密斯 Nasmyth, James 英国工程师 12—6f
内收肌 adductor muscle 解剖学 1—74d
内斯 Naas 爱尔兰城镇 11—533b
内斯 Ness, Eliot 美国打击犯罪斗士 12—88e
内斯比特 Nesbit, E(dith) 英国作家 12—88c
内斯特 Nestor, Agnes 美国劳工领袖 12—90a
内斯特罗伊 Nestroy, Johann (Nepomuk Eduard Ambrosius) 奥地利喜剧作家 12—90d
内塔尼亚胡 Netanyahu, Benjamin 以色列总理 12—91a
内坦亚 Netanya 以色列城市 12—91a
内图 Neto, (Antônio) Agostinho 安哥拉总统 12—94a
内瓦 Neiva 哥伦比亚城市 12—69f
内维尔 Neville, John 英格兰贵族 12—105d
内维尔 Neville, Richard 英格兰贵族 12—105d
内维尔骄子 Nevele Pride 美国种马 12—104d
内维尔男爵(第四) Neville, Ralph Neville, 4th Baron 英格兰贵族 12—105d
内维尔十字路口战役 Neville's Cross, Battle of 英国历史 12—105d
内维森 Nevison, John 英国强盗 12—106a
内维斯 Neves 巴西城市 12—105c
内文 Nevin, Ethelbert Woodbridge 美国作曲家 12—105d
内文 Nevin, John Williamson 美国基督教神学家 12—105e
内文斯 Nevins, Allan 美国历史学家 12—105f
内乌肯 Neuquén 阿根廷省份 12—96d
内乌肯 Neuquén 阿根廷城市 12—96d
内务部 MVD 苏联机构 11—520c
内务府 Neiwufu 中国清朝机构 12—69f
内务人民委员部 NKVD 克格勃的前身 12—211f

内西奥特斯 Nesiotes (sculptor) 希腊雕刻家 12—88e
内西米 Nesimi, Seyid İmadeddin 土耳其神秘主义诗人 12—88d
内喜马拉雅山脉 Inner Himalayas (mountains, Asia) 亚洲山脉 8—390a
内心独白 interior monologue 文学 8—409c
内心之光 Inner Light 基督教教义 8—390b
内省 introspection 心理学 8—425d
内伊 Ney, Elisabet 雕塑家 12—158c
内伊 Ney, Michel 法国元帅 12—158d
内伊湖 Neagh, Lough 北爱尔兰湖泊 12—57b
内因子 intrinsic factor 蛋白质 8—425d
内院 patio 建筑 13—88d
内脏利什曼病 visceral leishmaniasis (disease) 疾病 18—16d
内扎米 Neẓāmī 波斯诗人 12—159c
内战 Civil War 国内战争 4—256a
内酯 lactone 化学 9—440c
内志 Najd 沙特阿拉伯地区 11—545e
内质网 endoplasmic reticulum (ER) 生物学 6—74f
内兹比战役 Naseby, Battle of 英国历史 12—3f
内兹佩尔塞人 Nez Percé 北美印第安人 12—158f
内眦褶 epicanthic fold 解剖学 6—97e
嫩江 Nen Jiang 中国河流 12—75d
嫩江 Nenjiang 中国县名 12—76a
能 energy 物理学 6—75d
能阿弥 Nōami 日本诗人 12—212f
能代 Noshiro 日本城市 12—273a
能带论 band theory 固体物理学理论 2—191d
能登半岛 Noto Peninsula 日本半岛 12—274d
能剧 nō theatre 日本戏剧 12—211c
能力倾向测验 aptitude test 心理学 1—424e
能量均分 energy, equipartition of 物理学 6—75e
能量守恒 energy, conservation of 物理学 6—75d
能人 Homo habilis 人类学 8—147c
能斯脱 Nernst, Walther Hermann 德国物理化学家 12—85e
能所 nengsuo 佛教术语 12—75f
能态 energy state 原子物理学 6—75f
妮格尔 Neagle, Dame Anna 英国演员 12—57c
妮特 Neith 希腊诗人 12—69e
尼阿拉米 nialamide 药物 12—164c
尼阿里河 Niari River 刚果河流 12—165c
尼埃尔 Niel, Adolphe 法国元帅 12—180f
尼埃普斯 Niepce, (Joseph-) Nicéphore 法国发明家 12—182d
尼安 Niane, Djibril Tamsir 非洲历史学家 12—164e
尼安德特人 Neanderthal 人类学 12—57e
尼安蒂克人 Niantic 美国印第安人 12—165a
尼安-尼安人 Niam-Niam (people) 中非民族 12—164c
尼安萨省 Nyanza Province 肯尼亚省份 12—308e
尼奥尔 Niort 法国城镇 12—200a
尼奥罗人 Nyoro 乌干达民族 12—312e
尼堡 Nyborg 丹麦城市 12—309b
《尼贝龙根之歌》 Nibelungenlied 德语史诗 12—165e
尼波 Nebo (Mesopotamian deity) 美索不达米亚神灵 12—58c
尼泊尔 Nepal 亚洲国家 12—80a
尼泊尔根杰 Nepālganj 尼泊尔城镇 12—81b
尼泊尔文学 Nepali literature 文学 12—81b
尼泊尔语 Nepali language 亚洲语言 12—81b
尼博山 Nebo, Mount 美国山脉 12—58c
《尼布楚条约》 Nerchinsk, Treaty of 中-俄分界条约 12—84e
尼布尔 Niebuhr, Barthold Georg 德意志历史学家 12—178f
尼布尔 Niebuhr, Carsten 德国旅行家 12—179a
尼布尔 Niebuhr, Helmut Richard 美国神学家 12—179b
尼布尔 Niebuhr, Reinhold 基督教神学家 12—179c
尼布甲尼撒 Nebuchadrezzar 巴比伦国王之名 12—61a
尼布甲尼撒二世 Nebuchadrezzar II 古代迦勒底国王 12—61b
尼布甲尼撒一世 Nebuchadrezzar I 巴比伦国王 12—61a
尼采 Nietzsche, Friedrich 德国哲学家 12—182e
尼查科河 Nechako River 加拿大河流 12—62a
尼查姆·沙希王朝 Niẓām Shāhī DYNASTY 印度王朝 12—209a
尼查姆-乌穆尔克 Niẓām-ul-Mulk 印度王公称号 12—209b
尼达姆 Needham, John Turberville 英国博物学家 12—64a
尼达姆 Needham, Marchamont 英国记者 12—64b
尼代 Niğde 土耳其城市 12—184f
尼德尔斯 Needles 美国城市 12—65a
尼德间冰期 Needian Interglacial Stage 地质学 12—64b
尼德兰东印度群岛 Netherlands East Indies (Indonesia) 荷兰海外领地 12—93e
尼德兰归正会 Netherlands Reformed Church, The 尼德兰基督教会 12—93e
尼德兰归正会 Reformed Churches in The Netherlands 尼德兰基督教新教教会 14—199f
尼德兰联合省 United Provinces of the Netherlands 荷兰历史 17—363e
尼德兰联合省共和国 Netherlands, United Provinces of the 16～18世纪欧洲国家 12—93a
尼德兰学派 Netherlands school (music) 欧洲音乐创作风格 12—94a
尼德兰语 Netherlandic language 语言 12—91c
尼德维勒陶瓷器 Niderviller ware 法国彩陶和瓷器 12—178a
尼蒂 Nitti, Francesco Saverio 意大利政治家 12—206e
尼多斯 Cnidus 古希腊城市 4—309e
尼俄柏 Niobe 希腊神话人物 12—199d
尼俄柏画匠 Niobid Painter 希腊画匠 12—199d
尼恩 Nin, Anaïs 美国小说家 12—195f
尼尔 Neill, A.S. 英国教育家、作家 12—69c
尼尔 Neal, Patricia 美国电影演员 12—57c
尼尔格峡谷 Nirgal Vallis 火星地貌 12—201b
尼尔吉里丘陵 Nīlgiri Hills 印度山区 12—194c
尼尔森 Nielsen, Alice 美国歌唱家 12—181c
尼尔森 Nielsen, A(rthur) C(harles) 美国工程师 12—181b
尼尔森 Nielsen, Carl (August) 丹麦作曲家 12—181d
尼尔森 Neilson, James Beaumont 苏格兰发明家 12—69d
尼尔森 Nielsen, Morten 丹麦诗人 12—181e
尼尔·索尔斯基，圣 Nil Sorsky, SAINT 俄罗斯奥秘修行家 12—193c
尼尔逊 Nilsson, (Märta) Birgit 瑞典女高音歌唱家 12—194e
尼法 Nephi 美国城市 12—83a
尼费尔 Niffer (ancient Mesopotamian city) 美索不达米亚古城 12—184e
尼夫赫人 Nivkh (people) 西伯利亚东部民族 12—207e
尼弗尔海姆 Niflheim 古斯堪的纳维亚神话 12—184e
尼福 Nifo, Agostino 意大利哲学家 12—184e
尼格 Nigg 苏格兰小镇 12—188c
尼格尔 Niger, Pescennius 罗马皇帝 12—186b
尼格利 Niggli, Paul 瑞士矿物学家 12—188c
尼格利陀地域人种 Negrito local race 人类学 12—67b
尼格罗地理人种 Negroid geographic race 人类学 12—67e
尼根 nigun 犹太教无词歌 12—189e
尼古丁 nicotine 化合物 12—177d
尼古拉 Nicholas 统治者之名 12—170a
尼古拉 Nicholas 俄国大公 12—172a
尼古拉 Nicolai, Friedrich 德国作家 12—176a
尼古拉(奥特库尔的) Nicholas OF AUTRECOURT 法国哲学家 12—172c
尼古拉(凡尔登的) Nicholas OF VERDUN 釉画艺人 12—173b
尼古拉(赫里福德的) Nicholas OF HEREFORD 英格兰基督教神学家 12—173a
尼古拉(里拉的) Nicholas OF LYRA 法国天主教神学家 12—173b
尼古拉(洛伦佐的) Nicola DI LORENZO 意大利民众领袖 12—176a

尼古拉(五世) Nicholas (V) 敌对教皇 12—170e
尼古拉二世 Nicholas Ⅱ 俄国末代皇帝 12—171d
尼古拉二世 Nicholas Ⅱ 教皇 12—170c
尼古拉-法弗尔病 Nicolas-Favre disease 疾病 12—176c
尼古拉·卡萨特金,圣 Nikolay Kasatkin, Saint 俄国传教士 12—192d
尼古拉三世 Nicholas Ⅲ 教皇 12—170d
尼古拉三世 Nicholas Ⅲ 君士坦丁堡牧首 12—171b
尼古拉斯 Nikolais, Alwin 美国舞蹈编导 12—192b
尼古拉斯(大马士革的) Nicholas of Damascus 希腊历史学家 12—172f
尼古拉斯(克莱芒热的) Nicholas of Clémanges 法国神学家 12—172e
尼古拉斯(库萨的) Nicholas of Cusa 天主教枢机主教 12—172e
尼古拉斯兄弟 Nicholas Brothers 美国踢踏舞双人搭档 12—173d
尼古拉四世 Nicholas Ⅳ 教皇 12—170e
尼古拉五世 Nicholas Ⅴ 教皇 12—170f
尼古拉耶夫 Mykolayiv 乌克兰州名 11—524d
尼古拉耶夫 Mykolayiv 乌克兰城市 11—524e
尼古拉耶夫 Nikolayev, Andriyan Grigoryevich 苏联航天员 12—192d
尼古拉耶夫斯克 Nikolayevsk-na-Amure 俄罗斯城市 12—192e
尼古拉一世 Nicholas Ⅰ 黑山大公、国王 12—170b
尼古拉一世 Nicholas Ⅰ 君士坦丁堡牧首 12—171a
尼古拉一世 Nicholas Ⅰ 俄国皇帝 12—171b
尼古拉一世,圣 Nicholas Ⅰ, Saint 教皇 12—170b
尼豪 Niihau 美国火山岛 12—190c
尼赫鲁 Nehru, Jawaharlal 印度总理 12—68c
尼赫鲁 Nehru, Motilal 印度独立运动领袖 12—68e
《尼赫鲁-利亚格特协定》 Nehru-Liaqat Pact 印-巴协定 12—68f
尼基施 Nikisch, Arthur 德国音乐指挥家 12—191f
尼济普战役 Nizip, Battle of 奥斯曼与埃及历史事件 12—209f
尼加拉瓜 Nicaragua 中美洲国家 12—166c
尼加拉瓜湖 Nicaragua, Lake 尼加拉瓜湖泊 12—167d
尼加拉瓜湖鲨 Lake Nicaragua shark 鱼类 9—455f
尼卡高原 Nyika Plateau 马拉维高草原台地 12—310a
尼卡罗 Nicaro 古巴城市 12—167e
尼卡人 Nika (people) 非洲民族 12—191d
尼凯宁 Nykänen, Matti 芬兰运动员 12—310c
尼康 Nikon 俄国正教会牧首 12—192f
尼柯莱 Nicolai, Otto 德国作曲家 12—176b
尼科 Necho 埃及统治者之名 12—62b
尼科巴群岛 Nicobar Islands 印度岛群 12—175e
尼科巴诸语言 Nicobarese languages 尼科巴岛语言 12—175e
尼科波尔 Nikopol 保加利亚城镇 12—193b
尼科波尔 Nikopol 乌克兰城市 12—193b
尼科波利斯 Nikópolis (Greece) 希腊城市 12—193b
尼科波利斯战役 Nicopolis, Battle of 土耳其历史事件 12—177b
尼科迪默斯,圣 Nicodemus the Hagiorite, Saint 希腊正教修士 12—175f
尼科尔 Nicol, Davidson 塞拉利昂外交家、作家 12—175f
尼科尔 Nicole, Pierre 法兰西天主教神学家 12—176c
尼科尔森 Nicholson, Ben 英国画家 12—174a
尼科尔森 Nicholson, Eliza Jane Poitevent Holbrook 美国诗人 12—174b
尼科尔森 Nicolson, Sir Harold (George) 英国外交家 12—176f
尼科尔森 Nicholson, Jack 美国电影演员 12—174c
尼科尔森 Nicholson, John 英国军人 12—174c
尼科尔森 Nicholson, Reynold Alleyne 英国东方学专家 12—174d
尼科尔森 Nicholson, Seth Barnes 美国天文学家 12—174e
尼科尔森 Nicholson, William 英国化学家 12—174e
尼科尔森港 Port Nicholson 新西兰小海湾 13—446d
尼科尔斯 Nichols, Clarina Irene Howard 美国记者 12—173d
尼科尔斯 Nicholls, (Erith) Gwyn 威尔士橄榄球运动员 12—173d
尼科尔斯 Nichols, John 英国作家 12—173e
尼科尔斯 Nichols, Mike 美国导演 12—174a
尼科尔斯 Nicolls, Richard 英国殖民地总督 12—176f
尼科二世 Necho Ⅱ 埃及国王 12—62c
尼科莱 Nicolet, Jean 法国探险家 12—176d
尼科莱 Nicollet, Joseph Nicolas 法国数学家、探险家 12—176e
尼科勒 Nicolle, Charles-Jules-Henri 法国细菌学家 12—176d
尼科利 Niccoli, Niccolò 意大利人文主义者 12—167e
尼科洛 Niccolò dell' Arca 意大利雕刻家 12—167f
尼科洛 Niccolo di Giovanni di Massio 意大利画家 12—167f
尼科马科斯 Nicomachus 希腊画家 12—177a
尼科马科斯(杰拉什的) Nicomachus of Gerasa 罗马数学家 12—177a
尼科西亚 Nicosia 塞浦路斯共和国首都 12—177c
尼科亚半岛 Nicoya Peninsula 哥斯达黎加半岛 12—177f
尼科亚湾 Nicoya, Gulf of 哥斯达黎加海湾 12—177f
尼科一世 Necho Ⅰ 埃及总督 12—62b
尼克宾法尔斯特 Nykøbing Falster 丹麦城市 12—310d
尼克劳斯 Nicklaus, Jack (William) 美国高尔夫球运动员 12—175c
尼克斯 Nyx 希腊神话人物 12—313c
尼克松 Nixon, Richard M(ilhous) 美国总统 12—207f
尼克索 Nexø, Martin Andersen 丹麦小说家 12—158b
尼克希奇 Nikšić 黑山城镇 12—193b
尼肯 Nekhen (ancient Egyptian city) 古埃及城市 12—70a
尼奎斯特 Nyquist, Harry 美国物理学家 12—312f
尼奎斯特 Nykvist, Sven 瑞典电影摄影师 12—310d
尼拉贡戈火山 Nyiragongo, Mount 非洲火山 12—310b
尼赖吉哈佐 Nyíregyháza 匈牙利城市 12—310b
尼兰 Nijlen, Jan van 比利时诗人 12—191c
尼朗迦利派 Nirankārī 印度锡克教改革派 12—201a
尼勒 Kniller, Gottfried 英国画家 9—322d
尼雷尔 Nyerere, Julius (Kambarage) 坦桑尼亚总统 12—309d
尼里荒漠 Nyiri Desert 肯尼亚荒漠 12—310c
尼龙 nylon 合成塑料 12—310e
尼卢斯(安卡拉的),圣 Nilus of Ancyra, Saint 拜占廷隐修院院长 12—194f
尼卢斯(罗萨诺的),圣 Nilus of Rossano, Saint 意大利隐修院院长 12—194f
尼禄 Nero 罗马皇帝 12—85e
尼禄金殿 Golden House of Nero 古罗马宫殿 7—190a
尼禄·克劳狄乌斯·德鲁苏斯 Nero Claudius Drusus 古罗马将军 12—86a
尼伦伯格 Nirenberg, Marshall Warren 美国生物化学家 12—201a
尼罗河 Nile River 非洲河流 12—193d
尼罗河鲈 Nile perch (*Lates niloticus*) 鱼类 12—193d
尼罗河战役 Nile, Battle of the 英国与法国历史事件 12—193c
尼罗-撒哈拉诸语言 Nilo-Saharan languages 非洲语言 12—194c
尼罗诸语言 Nilotic languages 语言 12—194e
尼洛波利斯 Nilópolis 巴西城市 12—194d
尼洛特人 Nilot 非洲民族 12—194d
尼迈里 Nimeiri, Gaafar Mohamed el- 苏丹总统 12—195b
尼迈耶尔 Niemeyer (Soares Filho), Oscar 巴西建筑师 12—182a
尼曼-马库斯公司 Neiman Marcus 美国商店 12—69d
尼曼-皮克二氏病 Niemann-Pick disease 疾病 12—181e
尼曼陀派 Niyamānanda (Hindu philosopher) 印度哲学流派 12—208c
尼梅希(埃梅萨的) Nemesius of Emesa 基督教哲学家 12—74a
尼米兹 Nimitz, Chester W(illiam) 美国舰队司令 12—195d
尼默达尔河 Numedalslågen (Norway) 挪威河流 12—297a
尼默杰 Nīmach 印度城镇 12—195a

尼默勒 Niemöller,(Friedrich Gustav Emil) Martin 德国基督教反纳粹牧师 12—182b
尼姆 Nîmes 法国城市 12—195c
尼姆伯施 Niembsch, Nikolaus Franz 奥地利诗人 12—181f
尼姆鲁德 Nimrūd (ancient Assyrian city) 亚述古城 12—195e
尼姆韦根 Nimwegen (The Netherlands) 荷兰城市 12—195e
尼姆佐维奇 Nimzowitsch, Aron 拉脱维亚裔国际象棋大师 12—195f
尼纳 Neenah 美国城市 12—65b
尼纳苏 Ninazu 美索不达米亚神灵 12—196a
尼尼安,圣 Ninian, Saint 凯尔特传教士 12—198f
尼尼微 Nineveh 亚述古城 12—197c
尼宁辛娜 Nininsina (Mesopotamian deity) 美索不达米亚神灵 12—199a
尼努尔塔 Ninurta 美索不达米亚神灵 12—199c
尼努斯 Ninus 希腊神话人物 12—199c
尼欧洞 Niaux 法国考古遗址 12—165d
尼欧可木阶 Neocomian Stage 地质学 12—77f
尼欧肖 Neosho 美国城市 12—79d
尼欧肖河 Neosho River 美国河流 12—79d
尼皮贡湖 Nipigon Lake 加拿大湖泊 12—200b
尼皮辛湖 Nipissing, Lake 加拿大湖泊 12—200b
尼普顿 Neptune 古罗马宗教神灵 12—83f
尼普尔 Nippur 美索不达米亚古城 12—200f
尼普科 Nipkow, Paul Gottlieb 德国工程师 12—200b
尼普穆克人 Nipmuc 北美印第安人 12—200c
尼崎 Amagasaki 日本城市 1—262e
尼切福罗 Niceforo, Alfredo 意大利社会学家 12—168b
尼热哥罗德 Nizhegorod 俄罗斯州名 12—209c
尼任斯基 Nijinsky, Vaslav 俄裔芭蕾舞舞蹈家 12—190f
尼日尔 Niger 非洲国家 12—185a
尼日尔 Niger 尼日利亚州名 12—186b
尼日尔-刚果诸语言 Niger-Congo languages 非洲语言 12—186c
尼日尔河 Niger River 西非河流 12—186d
尼日利亚 Nigeria 非洲国家 12—186e
尼日利亚戏剧 Nigerian theatre 尼日利亚民间歌剧 12—188b
尼萨 Nisa 土库曼斯坦古城 12—201e
尼萨 Niza, Marcos de 法兰西修士 12—208c
尼萨巴 Nissaba 美索不达米亚神灵 12—202f
尼塞塔斯(利米西亚纳的) Nicetas of Remesiana 希腊神学家 12—169c
尼塞塔斯(斯泰塔托斯) Nicetas Stethatos 拜占廷神学家 12—169c
尼什 Niš 塞尔维亚城镇 12—201d
尼思 Neath 威尔士城镇 12—58a
尼思河谷 Nithsdale 苏格兰区名 12—203c
尼思塔尔伯特港 Neath Port Talbot 威尔士自治市 12—58b
尼斯 Nice 法国城市 12—167f
尼斯福鲁斯 Nicephorus 统治者之名 12—168d
尼斯福鲁斯 Nicephorus Callistus Xanthopoulos 拜占廷史学家 12—169b
尼斯福鲁斯·布里恩尼乌斯 Nicephorus Bryennius 拜占廷军人 12—169b
尼斯福鲁斯二世 Nicephorus II Phocas 拜占廷皇帝 12—168e
尼斯福鲁斯三世 Nicephorus III Botaneiates 拜占廷皇帝 12—169a
尼斯福鲁斯一世 Nicephorus I 拜占廷皇帝 12—168d
尼斯福鲁斯一世,圣 Nicephorus I, Saint 希腊正教神学家 12—169a
尼斯河 Neisse River 波兰河流 12—69e
尼斯河畔加布隆茨 Gablonz an der Neisse (Czech Republic) 捷克城市 6—539c
尼斯河畔亚布洛内茨 Jablonec nad Nisou 捷克城市 8—501f
尼斯湖 Ness, Loch 苏格兰水体 12—88f
尼斯莱因-福尔哈德 Nüsslein-Volhard, Christiane 德国发育遗传学家 12—304d
尼斯特鲁尔河 Nistrul River (Ukraine and Moldova) 乌克兰、摩尔多瓦河流 12—203a
尼索斯 Nisus 希腊神话人物 12—203a
尼塔尔 Nithard 法兰克历史学家 12—203b
尼泰罗伊 Niterói 巴西城市 12—203b
尼特拉 Nitra 斯洛伐克城镇 12—203c
尼提 Nitti, Frank 美国匪徒 12—206f
尼瓦尔人 Newar 尼泊尔民族 12—145c
尼韦勒 Nivelle, Robert-Georges 法国总司令 12—207c
尼韦奈 Nivernais 法国地区 12—207e
尼维斯 Mnevis 埃及神话 11—298f
尼文 Niven, David 英国演员 12—207d
尼文 Niven, Frederick John 加拿大小说家 12—207d
尼乌波特 Nieuwpoort 比利时城市 12—184d
尼西比斯学院 Nisibis, School of 叙利亚基督教学术中心 12—202e
尼西宾 Nisibin (Turkey) 土耳其城镇 12—202e
尼西亚 Nicaea (Turkey) 土耳其城镇 12—166a
尼西亚帝国 Nicaea, empire of 亚洲历史国名 12—166c
尼西亚会议(325) Nicaea, Council of 基督教普世会议 12—166a
尼西亚会议(787) Nicaea, Council of 基督教普世会议 12—166b
尼西亚斯 Nicias 雅典政治家 12—174f
尼西亚斯 Nicias 雅典画家 12—175a
《尼西亚信经》 Nicene Creed 基督教信仰宣言 12—168c
尼希米 Nehemiah 犹太人领袖 12—68a
《尼希米记》 Nehemiah, Book of (Bible) 《圣经》 12—68b
尼雪平 Nyköping 瑞典城镇 12—310d
尼雅尔萨迦 Njáls saga 冰岛文学 12—210a
尼亚洞穴 Niah Cave 马来西亚考古遗址 12—164b
尼亚加拉 Niagara (Ontario, Canada) 加拿大城镇 12—163a
尼亚加拉边境区 Niagara Frontier 美国游览区和重工业区 12—163e
尼亚加拉陡崖 Niagara Escarpment 北美洲山脊 12—163a
尼亚加拉河 Niagara River 北美洲河流 12—163f
尼亚加拉瀑布 Niagara Falls 北美洲瀑布 12—163a
尼亚加拉瀑布城 Niagara Falls 加拿大城市 12—163c
尼亚加拉瀑布城 Niagara Falls 美国城市 12—163d
尼亚加拉统 Niagaran Series 地质学 12—164b
尼亚加拉运动 Niagara Movement 美国民权组织 12—163e
尼亚科斯 Niarchos, Stavros (Spyros) 希腊海运大王 12—165c
尼亚库萨人 Nyakyusa 坦桑尼亚民族 12—308a
尼亚拉 Nyala 苏丹城市 12—308b
尼亚美 Niamey 尼日尔首都 12—164c
尼亚姆茨 Neamț 罗马尼亚县名 12—57d
尼亚穆拉吉拉火山 Nyamulagira, Mount 非洲火山 12—308c
尼亚尼 Niani 几内亚村庄 12—164f
尼亚萨湖 Nyasa, Lake 非洲湖泊 12—308e
尼亚萨兰 Nyasaland 马拉维旧称 12—309a
尼亚斯 Nias 印度尼西亚岛屿 12—165c
尼扬科勒人 Nyankole (people) 非洲民族 12—308e
尼扬韦齐人 Nyamwezi 坦桑尼亚民族 12—308c
尼伊卡人 Nyika 非洲民族 12—309f
尼永河 Nyong River 喀麦隆河流 12—312d
尼约尔德 Njörd 古斯堪的纳维亚神话人物 12—210a
尼扎马巴德 Nizāmābād 印度城镇 12—209b
尼札姆·穆尔克 Niẓām al-Mulk 塞尔柱大臣 12—208d
泥笆墙 wattle and daub 建筑 18—147a
泥百灵 mudlark 鸟类 11—462e
泥巢鸟 mudnest builder 鸟类 11—462f
泥盖木屋 hogan 印第安人住宅 8—118e
泥鸽射击 clay-pigeon shooting 体育项目 4—275d
泥龟 mud turtle 淡水龟 11—461d
泥灰岩 marl 岩石 10—522f

泥火山 mud volcano 火山 11—461e
泥鸡 mud hen 鸟类 11—461c
泥蛉 alderfly 昆虫 1—193c
泥流 mudflow 地质学 11—462d
泥煤 peat 矿物燃料 13—115f
泥盆纪 Devonian Period 地质学 5—273d
泥炭取样器 peat sampler 科研仪器 13—116c
泥炭藓 peat moss 草本植物 13—116a
泥小狗 mud puppy 两栖动物 11—461d
泥岩 mudstone 岩石 11—463d
泥质岩 lutite 岩石 10—301d
泥足法庭 piepoudre court 古代英格兰法庭 13—294b
倪瓒 Ni Zan 中国画家 12—162e
铌(Nb) niobium 化学元素 12—199e
铌铁矿 columbite 矿物 4—370b
霓石 aegirine 矿物 1—93a
霓霞岩 ijolite 岩石 8—330b
拟爱神木 jaboticaba 木本植物 8—502a
拟八哥 grackle 鸟类 7—238a
拟步甲 darkling beetle 昆虫 5—150c
拟鹑 mesite 鸟类 11—139c
拟纺锤蜓 Parafusulina 古生物学 13—31f
拟副交感神经药 parasympathomimetic drug 药物 13—39c
拟黄鹂 troupial 鸟类 17—237c
拟黄鹂科 Icteridae 动物学 8—317d
拟蝗蛙 chorus frog 两栖动物 4—200a
拟交配 pseudocopulation 动物行为 13—556d
拟精神病药 psychotomimetic drug 药物 13—565f
拟扣甲 languriid beetle (beetle family) 甲虫 9—486d
拟鲤 roach (*Rutilus rutilus*) 鱼类 14—323a
拟椋鸟 oropendola 鸟类 12—469e
拟猎蝽 nabid bug (insect) 昆虫 11—533f
拟瓢蛤 Modiolopsis 古生物学 11—306e
拟蚺蛇 mussurana (*Clelia clelia*) 毒蛇 11—514d
拟人 personification 辞格 13—186d
拟人化 anthropomorphism 宗教学 1—380d
拟声唱法 scat 音乐 15—106b
拟石莲花属 Echeveria 植物学 5—521f
拟苏铁目 Cycadeoidales 植物学 5—84c
拟态 mimicry 生物学 11—239a
拟天牛 oedemerid beetle 昆虫 12—341d
拟天球场 tlachtli 中美洲宗教性球赛场所 17—120a
拟蚊蠓 biting midge 昆虫 2—503d
拟希瓦格蜓 Paraschwagerina 古生物类 13—38f
拟形诗 pattern poetry 诗体 13—92b
你们看这个人! Ecce Homo 基督教艺术题材 5—519f
逆戟鲸 killer whale (*Orcinus orca*) 哺乳动物 9—279f
逆温 temperature inversion 大气科学 16—533a
逆行 retrograde motion 天文学 14—247b
逆转 peripeteia 戏剧 13—169f
溺河 ria 河流入海口 14—274c
年 year 历法 18—433f
年楚河 Nyang Qu 中国河流 12—308d
年代测定 dating 地质学 5—161f
年代-区域假说 age-area hypothesis 人类学 1—118e
年代学 chronology 计时 4—213f
年号 nian hao 中国古代政权纪年名号 12—164e
年金 annuity 金融 1—367c
年龄分布 age distribution 人口统计学 1—118f
年龄群 age set 社会学 1—118f
黏孢子虫 myxosporidian 原生动物 11—531f
黏病毒 myxovirus 病毒 11—531f
黏度计 viscometer 仪器 18—16e
黏多糖病 mucopolysaccharidosis 疾病 11—461b
黏合集块岩 agglutinate 岩石 1—121b
黏菊 tarweed 草本植物 16—487e
黏菌 slime mold 原始生物 15—432d
黏菌门 Myxomycetes 生物学 11—531d
黏鳗 slime eel 鱼类 15—432d
黏膜 mucous membrane 解剖学 11—461c
黏球藻属 Gloeocapsa 藻类 7—160e
黏土 clay 地质学 4—274b
黏土(坯) adobe 建筑材料 1—83a
黏土矿物 clay mineral 矿物 4—275c
黏土矿物学 clay mineralogy 矿物学 4—275d
黏土岩 claystone 岩石 4—275e
黏性 viscosity 流体力学 18—17d
黏液 mucus 分泌物 11—461c
黏液瘤病 myxomatosis 疾病 11—531d
黏液囊 bursa 解剖学 3—276e
黏液囊炎 bursitis 疾病 3—277a
黏液水肿 myxedema 病理学 11—531c
黏藻门 Myxophyta 生物学 11—531f
黏滞病 mucoviscidosis (metabolic disorder) 疾病 11—461c
黏着法 agglutination 语法 1—121b
鲶鱼 catfish 鱼类 3—524b
捻翅虫 strepsipteran 昆虫 16—275c
捻角羚 kudu 哺乳动物 9—389a
捻角山羊 markhor (*Capra falconeri*) 哺乳动物 10—521e
捻接 splice 绳索接头方法 16—38a
捻军起义 Nian Uprising 中国历史 12—164d
念处 smṛtyupasthāna 佛教哲学 15—456b
念青唐古拉山 Nianqing tanggula Shan 中国山脉 12—164f
念珠 subḥah 伊斯兰教祈祷用珠串 16—297e
念珠豆 rosary pea 草本植物 14—399e
念珠菌病 candidiasis 疾病 3—397f
念珠藻属 Nostoc 植物学 12—273b
鸟巢凤属 Nidularium 植物 12—178b
鸟巢兰 bird's-nest orchid (*Neottia nidus-avis*) 植物 2—490b
鸟岛自然保护区 Niaodao Nature Reserve 中国自然保护区 12—165a
鸟纲 Aves 动物学 2—87e
鸟蛤 cockle 软体动物 4—322f
鸟脚类 ornithopod 古生物学 12—469a
鸟居 torii 日本牌坊 17—160f
鸟居清倍 Torii Kiyomasu 日本画家 17—161a
鸟居清长 Torii Kiyonaga 日本画家 17—161b
鸟居清信 Torii Kiyonobu 日本画家 17—161c
鸟类 bird 鸟纲动物 2—488a
鸟类学 ornithology 动物学 12—468f
鸟女 Bird Woman (Shoshone Indian) 美国印第安妇女 2—490b
鸟嘌呤 guanine 化合物 7—341a
鸟栖 Tosu 日本城市 17—171d
鸟取 Tottori 日本城市 17—173d
鸟热 ornithosis (disease) 疾病 12—469b
鸟舍 aviary 鸟类饲养场 2—88a
鸟身女妖 Harpy 希腊、罗马神话怪物 7—485e
鸟石 bird stone 石刻 2—489f
鸟式 Tori style 日本雕刻艺术 17—160e
鸟兽积粪 guano 堆积的动物排泄物 7—341b
鸟臀类 ornithischian 古生物学 12—468c
鸟羽僧正 Toba Sōjō 日本高僧 17—125d
茑萝 cypress vine (*Ipomoea quamoclit*) 缠绕植物 5—91a
尿 urine 动物排泄物 17—416e
尿崩症 diabetes insipidus 疾病 5—282f
尿道 urethra 解剖学 17—414e

尿道球腺 bulbourethral gland 解剖学 3—240d
尿道炎 urethritis 疾病 17—414e
尿道造口术 urostomy 外科学 17—417f
尿毒症 uremia 疾病 17—414b
尿分析 urinalysis 医学 17—416b
尿黑酸尿症 alkaptonuria 疾病 1—233b
尿路梗阻 urinary tract obstruction 病理现象 17—416c
尿路造影术 urography 医学 17—417e
尿嘧啶 uracil 化合物 17—407a
尿囊 allantois 解剖学 1—236a
尿素 urea 化合物 17—414a
尿酸 uric acid 化合物 17—416a
脲酶 urease 生物化学 17—414b
脲醛树脂 urea-formaldehyde resin 化合物 17—414b
聂耳 Nie Er 中国作曲家 12—178b
聂鲁达 Neruda, Pablo 智利诗人 12—86b
聂姆策维奇 Niemcewicz, Julian Ursyn 波兰剧作家 12—181f
聂荣臻 Nie Rongzhen 中国革命家 12—178d
聂斯脱利 Nestorius 君士坦丁堡主教 12—90c
聂斯脱利派 Nestorian 基督教派别 12—90a
聂卫平 Nie Weiping 中国围棋选手 12—178e
涅比特达格 Nebitdag 土库曼斯坦城市 12—58c
涅俄普托勒摩斯 Neoptolemus 希腊传说人物 12—79a
涅尔琴斯克 Nerchinsk 俄罗斯城镇 12—84e
涅夫勒 Nièvre 法国省份 12—184d
涅夫斯基 Nevsky, Aleksandr (prince of Novgorod) 诺夫哥罗德王公 12—106b
涅甫伊 Navā'ī, (Mir) 'Alī Shīr 突厥诗人 12—49a
涅克拉索夫 Nekrasov, Nikolay Alekseyevich 俄国诗人 12—70a
涅克疏姆契约 nexum 法律史 12—158c
涅里 Nyeri 肯尼亚城镇 12—309f
涅林娜 Nerina, Nadia 南非芭蕾舞演员 12—85d
涅曼河 Neman River 欧洲河流 12—73a
涅米罗维奇-丹钦科 Nemirovich-Danchenko, Vladimir Ivanovich 俄国剧作家 12—74b
涅墨西斯 Nemesis 希腊宗教 12—73f
涅涅茨 Nenets 俄罗斯自治区 12—75f
涅涅茨人 Nenets 俄罗斯民族 12—75e
涅槃 Nirvāṇa 宗教 12—201d
涅磐乐队 Nirvana 美国乐队 12—201c
涅恰也夫 Nechayev, Sergey Gennadiyevich 俄国革命党人 12—62b
涅任 Nizhyn 乌克兰城市 12—209f
涅柔斯 Nereus 希腊宗教海神 12—85a
涅瑞伊得 Nereid 希腊宗教神灵 12—84f
涅斯托尔 Nestor 俄国修士 12—89f
涅斯托耳 Nestor 希腊传说人物 12—89f
涅瓦河 Neva River 俄罗斯河流 12—101e
涅瓦河战役 Neva, Battle of the 欧洲历史 12—101d
涅温诺梅斯克 Nevinnomyssk 俄罗斯城市 12—105e
涅谢尔罗迭 Nesselrode, Karl (Robert) Vasilyevich, Graf (Count) 沙俄外交大臣 12—89a
啮齿类 rodent 动物学 14—346e
啮虫 psocid 昆虫 13—559d
啮龟 snapping turtle 爬行动物 15—459c
啮龙花 snapdragon 植物 15—459a
啮鱼 snapper 鱼类 15—459a
镍(Ni) nickel 化学元素 12—175a
镍华 annabergite 矿物 1—363b
镍黄铁矿 pentlandite 矿物 13—149e
宁巴尔迦 Nimbārka 印度哲学家 12—195a
宁巴山脉 Nimba Range 非洲山脉 12—195a
宁波 Ningbo 中国城市 12—197d
宁芬堡瓷器 Nymphenburg porcelain 德国硬质瓷器 12—312b
宁芬堡府邸 Nymphenburg 德国宫殿 12—312a
宁格雷-汤加语 Ningre-Tongo (creole language) 南美洲语言 12—198a
宁哈尔 Ninhar 美索不达米亚神灵 12—198e
宁河 Ninghe 中国县名 12—197f
宁黑斯 Nienhuys, Jacobus 荷兰商人 12—182c
宁呼尔萨格 Ninhursag 美索不达米亚神灵 12—198f
宁基什西达 Ningishzida 美索不达米亚神灵 12—198a
宁吉尔苏 Ningirsu (Mesopotamian god) 美索不达米亚神灵 12—198a
宁利尔 Ninlil 美索不达米亚神灵 12—196c
宁录 Nimrod 《圣经》人物 12—195e
宁玛派 Rnying-ma-pa 中国藏传佛教教派 14—322e
宁松 Ninsun 美索不达米亚神灵 12—199c
宁夏 Ningxia 中国自治区 12—198a
宁夏地毯 Ningxia carpet 中国工艺品 12—198d
苧烯 limonene 化合物 10—106a
狞猫 caracal (*Felis caracal*) 猫科动物 3—434a
柠檬 lemon (*Citrus limon*) 植物 10—4c
柠檬马鞭草 lemon verbena (*Aloysia triphylla*, or *Lippia citriodora*) 植物 10—4f
柠檬醛 citral 化合物 4—249b
柠檬鲨 Lemon shark 鱼类 10—4f
柠檬酸 citric acid 化合物 4—249b
凝固点 freezing point 液体转变为固体时温度 6—472e
凝灰岩 tuff 岩石 17—259d
凝集素 agglutinin 生物化学 1—121c
凝胶 gel 化学 7—46b
凝胶色谱法 gel chromatography 化学 7—46c
凝结 condensation 物理现象 4—415d
凝结核 condensation nucleus 物理现象 4—415d
凝结尾迹 condensation trail (aerology) 气象学 4—415e
凝结尾迹 contrail (aerology) 气象学 4—471e
凝汽油剂 napalm 化合物 11—561e
凝乳酶 rennin 蛋白消化酶 14—230d
凝血 coagulation 生理学 4—310c
凝血酶原 prothrombin 生物化学 13—545b
牛 ox (*Bos taurus* or *B. taurus primigenius*) 哺乳动物 12—518c
牛鼻鲼 cow-nosed ray 水生动物 4—556d
牛传染性角膜结膜炎 bovine infectious keratoconjunctivitis 动物疾病 3—91b
牛痘 cowpox 免疫学 4—559b
牛顿 Newton 美国艾奥瓦州城市 12—153f
牛顿 Newton 美国堪萨斯州城市 12—153f
牛顿 Newton 美国马萨诸塞州城市 12—154a
牛顿 newton 计量单位 12—154a
牛顿 Newton, Alfred 英国动物学家 12—154a
牛顿 Newton, Sir Charles Thomas 英国考古学家 12—154b
牛顿 Newton, Sir Isaac 英国物理学家 12—154c
牛顿阿伯特 Newton Abbot 英格兰城镇 12—157c
牛顿变换 Newtonian transformations 物理学 12—157d
牛顿环 Newton's rings 光学 12—157f
牛顿万有引力定律 Newton's law of gravitation 物理学 12—157d
牛顿运动定律 Newton's laws of motion 物理学 12—157d
牛轭湖 oxbow lake 地理学 12—518e
牛肝菌科 Boletaceae 植物学 3—11a
牛耕式转行书写法 boustrophedon 书写方法 3—89d
牛海绵状脑病 bovine spongiform encephalopathy 动物疾病 3—91c
牛吼器 bull-roarer 非正式乐器 3—246c
牛祭 Taurobolium 近东宗教祭礼 16—497d
牛角瓜绒 akund floss 植物纤维 1—159b
牛角花 bird's-foot trefoil (*Lotus corniculatus*) 草本植物 2—490b
牛津 Oxford 英国区名 12—519c

牛津 Oxford 美国城市 12—520a
牛津伯爵 Oxford, EARLS OF 英国贵族 12—520a
牛津伯爵(第九) Oxford, Robert de Vere, 9th earl of 英格兰宠臣 12—520a
牛津伯爵(第十七) Oxford, Edward de Vere, 17th Earl of 英国诗人 12—520b
牛津伯爵(第十三) Oxford, John de Vere, 13th Earl of 英格兰军人 12—520b
牛津伯爵(第一) Oxford, Robert Harley, 1st Earl of, EARL MORTIMER, BARON HARLEY OF WIGMORE 英格兰政治家 12—520e
牛津大学 Oxford, University of 英国高等学府 12—520f
牛津和阿斯奎斯伯爵(第一) Oxford and Asquith, H(erbert) H(enry) Asquith, 1st Earl of 英国首相 12—520e
牛津郡 Oxfordshire 英格兰郡名 12—521d
《牛津条例》(1258) Oxford, Provisions of 英格兰改革计划 12—520e
牛津团契 Oxford Group (revivalistic movement) 宗教奋兴运动 12—521c
《牛津英语大词典》 Oxford English Dictionary, The (OED) 英语词典 12—521b
牛津运动 Oxford Movement 宗教运动 12—521c
牛科动物 bovid 哺乳动物 3—91b
牛郎织女 Niulang and Zhinü 中国神话 12—207b
牛鹂 cowbird 鸟类 4—557a
牛椋鸟 oxpecker 鸟类 12—522e
牛泌乳热 milk fever 牛疾病 11—219c
牛鸟 oxbird 鸟类 12—518e
《牛皮书》 Dun Cow, The Book of the 爱尔兰古文献 5—457d
牛皮蝇 cattle grub 昆虫 3—532a
牛肉 beef 食品 2—329e
牛鲨 bull shark 鱼类 3—246e
牛舌草 bugloss 植物 3—236f
牛蛇 bull snake (*Pituophis melanoleucus*) 动物 3—246e
牛栓藤目 Connarales 植物学 4—433b
牛蹄油 neat's-foot oil 油脂 12—58b
牛头刨床 shaper 机械 15—279b
牛头鲖 bullhead 鱼类 3—248f
牛头饰 bucranium 建筑装饰 3—224f
牛蛙 bullfrog (*Rana catesbeiana*) 动物 3—248e
牛瘟 rinderpest 牲畜疾病 14—303e
牛心上尉 Captain Beefheart 美国歌手、歌曲作家 3—432d
牛血红釉 sang-de-boeuf 釉 15—32a
牛眼窗 oeil-de-boeuf window 建筑 12—342c
牛眼鸟 oxeye 鸟类 12—519c
牛羊油脂 tallow 生物化学 16—447f
牛疫 cattle plague 动物疾病 3—532a
牛鱼 cowfish 鱼类 4—557f
牛轧糖 nougat 糖果 12—276d
牛织布鸟 buffalo weaver 鸟类 3—234b
牛至 oregano 草本植物 12—452c
牛仔 cowboy 美国西部牧牛骑手 4—557b
牛仔竞技 RODEO 体育项目 16—127a
扭摆舞 twist 舞蹈 17—303c
扭秤 torsion balance 测量装置 17—167e
扭杆 torsion bar 机械 17—167f
扭角羚 takin (species *Budorcas taxicolor*) 牛科动物 16—441f
扭曲藓 twisted moss 植物 17—303c
扭伤 sprain 病理学 16—160d
扭心珊瑚 Streptelasma 古生物学 16—275d
扭月贝 Strophomena 古生物学 16—282c
纽阿福欧岛 Niuafo'ou 汤加王国岛屿 12—206f
纽阿托普塔普岛 Niuatoputapu 汤加王国岛屿 12—206f
纽埃 Niue 新西兰自治岛邦 12—207a
纽堡 Newburgh 美国城市 12—146b
纽本 Newburn 英格兰工业社区 12—146c
纽波特 Newport 英格兰城镇 12—150e
纽波特 Newport 美国阿肯色州城市 12—150e
纽波特 Newport 美国肯塔基州城市 12—150e
纽波特 Newport 美国俄勒冈州城市 12—150e
纽波特 Newport 美国罗得岛州城市 12—150f
纽波特 Newport 美国佛蒙特州城市 12—151a
纽波特 Newport 威尔士城镇 12—151a
纽波特比奇 Newport Beach 美国城市 12—151b
纽波特纽斯 Newport News 美国城市 12—151c
纽伯格 Newberg 美国城市 12—146a
纽伯里 Newbury 英格兰城镇 12—146c
纽伯里 Newbury 英格兰区名 12—146c
纽伯里波特 Newburyport 美国城市 12—146d
纽伯里奖章 Newbery Medal 美国奖章 12—146a
纽博尔特 Newbolt, Sir Henry (John) 英国诗人 12—146a
纽虫 nemertean 无脊椎动物 12—73f
纽敦 Newtown 英国城镇 12—157f
纽敦阿比 Newtownabbey 英国城镇 12—158a
纽敦纳兹 Newtownards 英国城镇 12—158b
纽厄尔 Newell, Allen 美国计算机科学家 12—148c
纽芬兰狗 Newfoundland 纽芬兰使役狗 12—148d
纽芬兰-拉布拉多 Newfoundland and Labrador 加拿大省份 12—148e
纽汉 Newham 英格兰自治市 12—149b
纽豪斯 Newhouse, S(amuel) I(rving) 美国报纸发行人 12—149c
纽河 New River 美国河流 12—126b
纽黑文 New Haven 美国城市 12—115e
纽黑文 Newhaven 美国城市 12—149b
纽黑文铁路 New Haven Railroad 美国铁路 12—116a
纽霍尔 Newhall, Nancy 美国摄影评论家 12—149b
纽基 Newquay 英格兰海滨胜地 12—151c
纽卡斯尔 Newcastle 澳大利亚城市 12—146e
纽卡斯尔 Newcastle 北爱尔兰城镇 12—146e
纽卡斯尔 Newcastle 加拿大城镇 12—146e
纽卡斯尔 New Castle 美国宾夕法尼亚州城市 12—109f
纽卡斯尔 New Castle 美国特拉华州城市 12—109d
纽卡斯尔 Newcastle 美国南非城镇 12—146f
纽卡斯尔 New Castle 美国印第安纳州城市 12—109e
纽卡斯尔安德莱姆 Newcastle-under-Lyme 英格兰城镇 12—147b
纽卡斯尔公爵(第一) Newcastle(-under-Lyme), Thomas Pelham Holles, 1st Duke of 英国首相 12—146f
纽卡斯尔公爵(第一) Newcastle(-upon-Tyne), William Cavendish, 1st Duke of 英国诗人 12—147a
纽康 Newcomb, Simon 美国天文学家 12—147f
纽科门 Newcomen, Thomas 英国工程师 12—148b
纽科姆 Newcomb, Josephine Louise Le Monnier 美国慈善家 12—147e
纽扣 button 服装 3—293f
纽扣热 boutonneuse fever 疾病 3—90a
纽扣蛛 button spider 蛛类 3—294d
纽兰德 Nieuwland, Julius Arthur 美国化学家 12—184c
纽兰兹 Newlands, John Alexander Reina 英国化学家 12—149d
纽里 Newry 北爱尔兰城镇 12—151d
纽里和莫恩 Newry and Mourne 北爱尔兰区名 12—151d
纽伦堡 Nürnberg 德国城市 12—302e
纽伦堡彩陶 Nürnberg faience 德国锡釉陶器 12—303a
纽伦堡大会 Nürnberg Rally 德国纳粹党大会 12—303b
纽伦堡法令 Nürnberg Laws 德国历史 12—303b
纽伦堡审判 Nürnberg trials 第二次世界大战审判 12—303c
纽伦堡细密铜版画家 Nürnberg Kleinmeister (artists' group) 画家团体 12—303b

纽马基特 New Market 美国城镇 12—119b
纽马基特 Newmarket 英格兰地名 12—150d
纽曼 Newman 澳大利亚城镇 12—149d
纽曼 Newman, Arnold 美国摄影家 12—149e
纽曼 Newman, Barnett 美国画家 12—149f
纽曼 Newman, John Henry 英国教会人士、学者 12—149f
纽曼 Newman, Paul 美国电影演员 12—150b
纽曼 Newman, Randy 美国作曲家 12—150c
纽曼,圣 Neumann, Saint John (Nepomucene) 美国天主教主教 12—96c
纽姆符 neume 音乐记谱法 12—96c
纽塞里 Neuserre 埃及国王 12—98f
纽什凡斯泰恩城堡 Neuschwanstein 德国城堡 12—98e
纽斯河 Neuse River 美国河流 12—98f
纽斯特里亚 Neustria 欧洲历史王国 12—99b
纽瓦克 Newark 美国特拉华州城市 12—145c
纽瓦克 Newark 美国新泽西州城市 12—145c
纽瓦克 Newark 美国俄亥俄州城市 12—145e
纽瓦克-舍伍德 Newark and Sherwood 英格兰区名 12—145f
纽形动物 ribbon worm 无脊椎动物 14—275f
纽因顿 Newington 伦敦一区 12—149c
纽约 New York 美国州名 12—128f
纽约大学 New York University 美国高等学府 12—142e
纽约动物园 New York Zoological Park 美国动物园 12—142f
纽约公共图书馆 New York Public Library 美国图书馆 12—142a
纽约画派 New York school 美国画派 12—142a
《纽约客》 New Yorker, The 美国杂志 12—142f
《纽约每日新闻》 New York Daily News 美国报纸 12—141e
纽约妞儿乐队 New York Dolls 美国乐队 12—141e
纽约-纽黑文-哈特福德铁路公司 New York, New Haven and Hartford Railroad Company 美国公司 12—133b
纽约派 Knickerbocker school 美国作家组织 9—321a
《纽约时报》 New York Times, The 美国报纸 12—142d
《纽约世界报》 New York World 美国报纸 12—142e
纽约市 New York City 美国城市 12—133e
纽约市芭蕾舞团 New York City Ballet 美国芭蕾舞团 12—141d
纽约市立大学 City University of New York, The (CUNY) 美国大学 4—251c
《纽约太阳报》 New York Sun 美国报纸 12—142c
《纽约先驱报》 New York Herald 美国报纸 12—141f
纽约银行公司 Bank of New York Company, Inc., The 美国银行持股公司 2—204f
纽约银行家信托公司 Bankers Trust New York Corporation 美国银行持股公司 2—205b
纽约证券交易所 New York Stock Exchange (NYSE) 美国证券市场 12—142c
纽约-芝加哥-圣路易斯铁路公司 New York, Chicago and St. Louis Railroad Company 美国公司 12—133b
纽约植物园 New York Botanical Garden 美国植物园 12—133d
纽约中央铁路公司 New York Central Railroad Company 美国公司 12—133d
纽约州驳船运河 New York State Barge Canal 美国水道 12—142b
纽约州和新泽西州港务局 Port Authority of New York and New Jersey 美国政府机构 13—444c
纽约州立大学 New York, State University of (SUNY) 美国大学 12—133c
农场主无党派联盟 Farmers' Nonpartisan League 美国农场主组织 6—241d
农村电气化 rural electrification 美国农村建设计划 14—451d
农村免费投递 Rural Free Delivery (RFD) 美国邮政服务 14—451e
农村社会 rural society 社会学 14—451e
农工党 Farmer-Labor Party 美国历史上小政党 6—241b
农河 Nun River 尼日利亚河流 12—299d
农家鲜干酪 cottage cheese 食品 4—537d
农民党 Peasant Party 保加利亚政党 13—115b
农民肺 farmer's lung 肺部疾患 6—241c
农民起义 Peasants' Revolt 英格兰历史 13—115c
农民同盟 Agrarian League 德意志政治组织 1—127b
农牧永租与建造永租 emphyteusis and superficies 罗马法中租赁权 6—63f
农奴制 serfdom 欧洲封建土地制度 15—223c
农诺斯 Nonnus 希腊史诗诗人 12—229c
农业 agriculture 经济 1—129e
《农业法》 Farmer's Law 拜占廷法典 6—241c
农业机械 farm machinery 机械设备 6—240e
农业集体化 collectivization 苏联农业政策 4—346f
农业经济学 agricultural economics 农业 1—128e
农业科学 agricultural sciences 农业 1—129b
农业企业 agribusiness 农业 1—127e
农业调整署 Agricultural Adjustment Administration (AAA) 美国历史 1—128d
农业主 geōmoroi 古希腊社会等级 7—73e
农役租佃 socage 英国封建法律 15—468e
《农用年历》 Farmer's Almanac 美国刊物 6—241c
浓红银矿 pyrargyrite 含硫盐矿物 14—45e
浓密常绿阔叶灌丛 chaparral 植物学 4—56f
脓 pus 发炎时产生的液体 14—35c
脓毒性关节炎 septic arthritis 疾病 15—219d
脓疱病 impetigo 皮肤病 8—347d
脓疱性皮炎 pustular dermatitis 皮肤病 14—37a
脓胸 pyothorax 病理现象 14—44c
脓肿 abscess 病理现象 1—30a
弄臣 jester (comic entertainer) 以逗主子为职业的人 9—5c
弄蝶 skipper 昆虫 15—420f
奴儿干都司 Nu'ergan dusi 中国明代政府机构 12—292f
奴河 Slave River 加拿大河流 15—428a
奴隶法规 slave code 美国历史 15—427e
奴隶海岸 Slave Coast 非洲几内亚湾部分海岸 15—427e
奴隶纪事 slave narrative 美国文学 15—427f
奴隶劳动 slave labour 强迫劳动 15—427f
奴隶起义 slave rebellions 美洲历史 15—428a
奴隶王朝 Slave DYNASTY 印度统治者 15—427d
奴隶制 slavery 社会学 15—428b
努 Nu (Egyptian mythology) 古埃及宗教神祇 12—285e
努埃尔人 Nuer 苏丹民族 12—292f
努埃瓦镇 Villa Nueva 阿根廷门多萨市郊区 17—562f
努埃维塔斯 Nuevitas 古巴城市 12—293b
努奥罗 Nuoro 意大利城市 12—301a
努巴尔帕夏 Nubar Pasha 埃及政治家 12—286b
努巴人 Nuba 苏丹民族 12—286a
努比亚 Nubia 非洲历史地区 12—286d
努比亚沙漠 Nubian Desert 苏丹沙漠 12—287b
努比亚诸语言 Nubian languages 非洲语言 12—287b
努恩 Nun 古埃及宗教神祇 12—299d
努尔·艾尔-希勒米 Nūr al-Hilmī, Burhanuddin bin Muhammad 马来民族主义领袖 12—301d
努尔丁 Nureddin 穆斯林统治者 12—301e
努尔哈赤 Nurhachi 中国清朝统治者 12—302b
努尔海姆 Nordheim, Sondre 挪威滑雪运动员 12—233d
努尔米 Nurmi, Paavo (Johannes) 芬兰径赛运动员 12—302d
努法尔 Nuffar (ancient Mesopotamian city) 美索不达米亚古城 12—293d
努哈 Nukha (Azerbaijan) 阿塞拜疆城市 12—294c
努加尔河谷 Nugaaleed Valley 索马里河谷 12—293f
努克 Nuuk 格陵兰首府 12—307c

努克拉希 Nuqrashi, Mahmud Fahmi al- 埃及政治人物 12—301c
努库阿洛法 Nuku'alofa 汤加王国首都 12—294c
努库斯 Nukus 乌兹别克斯坦城市 12—294d
努里·赛义德 Nuri as-Said 伊拉克政治家 12—302b
努里斯坦 Nūrestān 阿富汗历史地区 12—301e
努里斯坦人 Nūristāni 亚洲民族 12—302d
努里耶夫 Nureyev, Rudolf(Hametovich) 苏联演员 12—301f
努利 Nourrit, Adolphe 法国歌唱家 12—276f
努列克水坝 Nurek Dam 亚洲填土坝 12—301e
努马·庞皮利乌斯 Numa Pompilius 罗马传说人物 12—294e
努曼 Numan 尼日利亚城镇 12—294f
努曼提亚 Numantia 西班牙城镇 12—294f
努梅里安 Numerian 罗马皇帝 12—297c
努美阿 Nouméa 新喀里多尼亚城市 12—276e
努米底亚 Numidia 非洲古代地区 12—299b
努米克诸语言 Numic languages 北美印第安语言 12—299b
努墨尼奥斯(阿帕梅亚的) Numenius OF APAMEA 希腊哲学家 12—297a
努纳武特 Nunavut 加拿大北部领土 12—299e
努内斯 Nunes, Pedro 葡萄牙数学家 12—300e
努尼瓦克岛 Nunivak Island 美国岛屿 12—301a
努涅斯 Núñez, Rafael 哥伦比亚总统 12—300e
努涅斯·德阿尔塞 Núñez de Arce, Gaspar 西班牙诗人 12—301a
努涅斯·卡韦萨·德巴卡 Núñez Cabeza de Vaca, Álvar 西班牙探险家 12—300f
努佩人 Nupe 尼日利亚民族 12—301b
努乔马 Nujoma, Sam 纳米比亚总统 12—294b
努热 Nougé, Paul 比利时诗人 12—276d
努赛宾 Nusaybin 土耳其城镇 12—304d
努森 Knudsen, William S(ignius) 美国工业家 9—326f
努斯库 Nusku 美索不达米亚神灵 12—304d
努特 Nut 埃及宗教女天神 12—304f
努特卡人 Nootka 北美印第安人 12—231b
努特卡湾 Nootka Sound 加拿大海湾 12—231b
努特卡湾争端 Nootka Sound controversy 英国与西班牙之间的争端 12—231c
努瓦迪布 Nouadhibou 毛里塔尼亚城镇 12—276c
努瓦克肖特 Nouakchott 毛里塔尼亚首都 12—276c
努瓦永 Noyon 法国城镇 12—284f
努韦 Nuwe (ancient Egypt) 古埃及都城 12—307e
努沃勒埃利耶 Nuwara Eliya 斯里兰卡城镇 12—307d
努祖 Nuzu 美索不达米亚古城 12—307e
弩弓 crossbow 兵器 5—33c
怒江 Nu Chiang (China) 中国河流 12—286a
怒江 Nu Jiang 中国河流 12—286a
怒苏语 Nusu language 中国民族语言 12—304e
怒族 Nu 中国民族 12—285d
女低音 alto 声乐 1—257c
女低音 contralto 声乐 4—471f
女高音 soprano 声乐 15—520a
女公爵,公爵夫人 duchess 贵族称号 5—445a
《女公民》 Woman Citizen, The 美国女性周刊 18—312c
女帽螺 bonnet shell 海生软体动物 3—33f
女梦淫妖 succubus 中世纪欧洲传说妖怪 16—301f
女亲王 princess 欧洲等级称号 13—515d
女权运动 feminist movement 政治学 6—271f
女权主义 feminism 男女平等的信念 6—271d
女神蛤 geoduck (*Panopea generosa*) 贝类动物 7—70b
女神伊希斯之血 Blood of Isis (Egyptian religion) 埃及宗教 2—541f
女神游乐厅 Folies-Bergère 法国剧场 6—388c
女士 lady 英国贵族称号 9—443a
女式便袍 negligee 服装 12—66e
女童子军 Girl Scouts 儿童组织 7—142e
女娲 Nüwa 中国神话女神 12—307d
女王 queen 女统治者 14—83b
女王美术馆 Queen's Gallery 伦敦公共艺术馆 14—84d
女巫团 coven 巫术 4—554b
女像柱 caryatid 建筑 3—494d
女性同性恋 lesbianism 社会学 10—36b
女妖(布痕瓦尔德的) Witch of Buchenwald 德国战争罪犯 18—298f
女隐修院 convent 天主教 4—474b
女隐修院院长 abbess 天主教 1—8a
女贞 privet 植物 13—521f
女真 Juchen DYNASTY 中国王朝 9—98f
女真 Jurchen DYNASTY 中国古代王朝 9—116d
女真文 Juchen character 中国文字 9—98f
女子无挡板篮球 netball 女子球类运动项目 12—91c
钕(Nd) neodymium 化学元素 12—77f
暖房 conservatory 园艺学 4—446d
暖武里 Nonthaburi 泰国城镇 12—230d
疟疾 malaria 疾病 10—421d
疟疾性血红蛋白尿症 hemoglobinuria, malarial (disease) 疾病 8—10e
疟疾性血红蛋白尿症 malarial hemoglobinuria 疾病 10—422b
疟原虫属 Plasmodium 动物学 13—349d
虐待动物 animals, cruelty to 心理学 1—358e
虐待儿童 child abuse 社会学 4—151b
挪罗齐 Naoroji, Dadabhai 印度民族主义者 11—561c
挪威 Norway 欧洲国家 12—269c
挪威海 Norwegian Sea 大西洋边缘海 12—271e
挪威海螯虾 scampi (*Nephrops norvegicus*) 甲壳动物 15—101c
挪威猎犴狗 Norwegian elkhound 狗品种 12—271c
挪威龙虾 Norway lobster 甲壳动物 12—271c
《挪威民间故事》 Norske folkeeventyr 民间故事集 12—242f
《挪威王列传》 Heimskringla 挪威文学 7—567c
挪威文学 Norwegian literature 文学 12—271e
挪威信义会 Norway, Church of 挪威国定教会 12—271a
挪威洋流 Norway Current 北大西洋洋流 12—271c
挪威语 Norwegian language 语言 12—271d
挪亚 Noah 《圣经》人物 12—212a
挪亚律法 Noahide Laws 犹太教 12—212b
傩舞 nuowu 中国古代舞蹈 12—301b
诺阿卡利 Noākhāli 孟加拉国城市 12—212f
诺阿塔克国家禁猎区 Noatak National Preserve 美国禁猎区 12—212f
诺阿耶 Noailles, Anna de 法国诗人 12—212e
诺阿耶 Noailles, Louis-Antoine de 法国枢机主教 12—212e
诺阿耶公爵(第二) Noailles, Anne-Jules, 2^{e} duc de 法国元帅 12—212c
诺阿耶公爵(第三) Noailles, Adrien-Maurice, 3^{e} duc de 法国贵族 12—212c
诺阿耶公爵(第四) Noailles, Louis, 4^{e} duc de 法国贵族 12—212d
诺阿耶公爵(第五) Noailles, Jean-Paul-François, 5^{e} duc de 法兰西科学院院士 12—212d
诺阿耶公爵(第一) Noailles, Anne, 1^{e}r duc de 法国贵族 12—212c
诺阿耶公爵和子爵 Noailles, DUKES AND VISCOUNTS OF 法国贵族称号 12—212c
诺阿耶子爵 Noailles, Louis-Marie, vicomte de 法国贵族 12—212d
诺埃尔 Nowell, Alexander 英格兰基督教学者 12—284c
诺埃尔-贝克 Noel-Baker (of the City of Derby), Philip John Noel-Baker, Baron 英国政治家 12—224a
诺贝尔 Nobel, Alfred Bernhard 瑞典化学家 12—213a
诺贝尔奖 Nobel Prize 奖项名 12—213c
诺贝尔特,圣 Norbert OF XANTEN, SAINT 马格德堡大主教 12—231e

诺贝尔特会会士 Norbertine (religious order) 天主教普雷蒙特雷会成员 12—231f
诺毕尔 Nobile, Umberto 意大利工程师 12—222b
诺布耳 Noble, Sir Andrew, 1st Baronet 苏格兰物理学家 12—222d
诺布雷 Nobre, António 葡萄牙诗人 12—223b
诺布雷加 Nóbrega, Manuel da 巴西传教士 12—223b
诺达尔 Nordal, Sigurdur Jóhannesson 冰岛语言学家 12—232c
诺德 Naudé, Gabriel 法国医生 12—46f
诺德霍恩 Nordhorn 德国城镇 12—233e
诺德罗克 Nordraak, Rikard 挪威作曲家 12—234c
诺德奈 Norderney 德国岛屿 12—233c
诺登弗利克特 Nordenflycht, Hedvig Charlotta 瑞典诗人 12—232e
诺登舍尔德 Nordenskiöld, (Nils) Adolf Erik, Friherre 瑞典地质学家 12—232f
诺登舍尔德 Nordenskiöld, (Nils) Erland (Herbert) 瑞典人种学家 12—233a
诺登舍尔德 Nordenskjöld, (Nils) Otto (Gustaf) 瑞典地理学家 12—233b
诺狄卡 Nordica, Lillian 美国歌唱家 12—233f
诺迪埃 Nodier, Charles 法国作家 12—223e
诺丁汉 Nottingham 英格兰城市 12—275e
诺丁汉伯爵 Nottingham, earls of 英国贵族 12—275f
诺丁汉伯爵 Nottingham, Thomas Mowbray, earl of 英格兰贵族 12—275f
诺丁汉伯爵(第一) Nottingham, Charles Howard, 1st earl of 英格兰海军大臣 12—276a
诺丁汉伯爵(第一) Nottingham, Heneage Finch, 1st Earl of, Baron Finch of Daventry 英格兰大法官 12—276b
诺丁汉郡 Nottinghamshire 英格兰郡名 12—276b
诺顿 Norton 美国城镇 12—268d
诺顿 Norton 津巴布韦城镇 12—268e
诺顿 Norton, Charles Eliot 美国学者 12—268f
诺顿 Norton, Eleanor Holmes 美国律师 12—269a
诺顿(夫人) Norton, Caroline (Elizabeth Sarah) 英国诗人 12—268e
诺顿湾 Norton Sound 美国海湾 12—269b
诺恩 Norn 日耳曼神话神灵 12—241b
诺尔 Noll, Chuck 美国橄榄球运动员 12—226b
诺尔道 Nordau, Max 犹太民族主义者 12—232d
诺尔迪 Nolde, Emil 德国画家 12—226a
诺尔顿 Knowlton, Charles 美国医生 9—325c
诺尔兰 Nordland 挪威郡名 12—234b
诺尔兰 Norrland 挪威郡名 12—242f
诺尔斯 Knowles, William S. 美国科学家 9—325b
诺尔维德 Norwid, Cyprian Kamil 波兰诗人 12—272b
诺尔雪平 Norrköping 瑞典城镇 12—242f
诺夫哥罗德 Novgorod 俄罗斯州名 12—281d
诺夫哥罗德 Novgorod 俄罗斯城市 12—281e
诺夫哥罗德画派 Novgorod school 俄罗斯中世纪画派 12—282a
《诺夫哥罗德条约》 Novgorod, Treaty of 俄国与挪威之间的和约 12—282a
诺夫哥罗德-谢韦尔斯基 Novgorod-Seversky 乌克兰城市 12—282c
诺福克 Norfolk 英格兰郡名 12—234f
诺福克 Norfolk 美国内布拉斯加州城市 12—235a
诺福克 Norfolk 美国弗吉尼亚州城市 12—235a
诺福克伯爵 Norfolk, Thomas of Brotherton, Earl of 英格兰贵族 12—235c
诺福克伯爵 Norfolk, Thomas Howard, Earl of 英格兰贵族 12—236c
诺福克伯爵和公爵 Norfolk, earls and dukes of 英格兰封爵贵族 12—235c
诺福克岛 Norfolk Island 澳大利亚海外领地 12—236d
诺福克岛松 Norfolk Island pine (*Araucaria excelsa*, or *A. heterophylla*) 木本植物 12—237a
诺福克公爵(第二) Norfolk, Thomas Howard, 2nd Duke of 英格兰贵族 12—235f
诺福克公爵(第三) Norfolk, Thomas Howard, 3rd Duke of 英格兰贵族 12—235f
诺福克公爵(第四) Norfolk, Thomas Howard, 4th Duke of 英格兰贵族 12—236b
诺福克公爵(第一) Norfolk, John Howard, 1st Duke of 英格兰贵族 12—235e
诺福克公爵(第一) Norfolk, Thomas Mowbray, 1st Duke of 英格兰贵族 12—235d
诺福克四区轮作制 Norfolk four-course system 英格兰农业耕作法 12—236c
诺福克-西方铁路公司 Norfolk and Western Railway Company 美国企业 12—236c
诺格拉德 Nógrád 匈牙利州名 12—224f
诺格塔克 Naugatuck 美国城镇 12—47a
诺赫 Norge, Géo 比利时诗人 12—237b
诺华公司 Novartis AG 瑞士公司 12—279a
诺加尔河谷 Nogal Valley (Somalia) 索马里河谷 12—224d
诺加莱斯 Nogales (Mexico) 墨西哥城市 12—224d
诺加莱斯英雄城 Heroica Nogales 墨西哥城市 8—47e
诺加雷 Nogaret, Guillaume de 法国行政官员 12—224d
诺加雷·德·拉瓦莱特 Nogaret de la Valette, Jean-Louis de 法国公爵 12—224e
诺加利斯 Nogales 美国城市 12—224d
诺金斯克 Noginsk 俄罗斯城市 12—224f
诺卡尔氏菌病 nocardiosis 疾病 12—223c
诺克拉提斯 Naukratis 古希腊殖民点 12—47a
诺克罗斯 Norcross, John (American author) 美国作家 12—231f
诺克斯 Knox, Henry 美国将领 9—325d
诺克斯 Knox, John 苏格兰宗教改革家 9—325e
诺克斯 Knox, Philander Chase 美国律师、参议员 9—326b
诺克斯 Knox, Ronald (Arbuthnott) 英国作家、神学家 9—326b
诺克斯 Knox, Rose Markward 美国企业家 9—326c
诺克斯堡 Knox, Fort 美国军事重地 9—325d
《诺克斯礼仪书》 Knox's Liturgy 宗教作品 9—326d
诺克斯维尔 Knoxville 美国城市 9—326d
诺克文化 Nok culture 尼日利亚铁器时代文化 12—225c
诺拉 Nola 意大利城镇 12—225d
诺拉 Nora 意大利城镇 12—231d
诺拉斯科门徒 Nolascan (Christian order) 天主教慈爱圣母会成员 12—226a
诺兰 Nolan, Sir Sidney (Robert) 澳大利亚艺术家 12—225d
诺兰达 Noranda 加拿大城市 12—231e
诺兰德 Noland, Kenneth 美国画家 12—225f
诺勒肯斯 Nollekens, Joseph 英国雕刻家 12—226c
诺雷 Nore, The 英格兰泰晤士河口湾沙岸名 12—234e
诺里尔斯克 Norilsk 俄罗斯城市 12—237e
诺里克阿尔卑斯山 Noric Alps 欧洲山脉 12—237c
诺里库姆 Noricum 欧洲地区 12—237c
诺里奇 Norwich 英格兰城市 12—271f
诺里奇㹴狗 Norwich terrier 狗品种 12—272b
诺里奇画派 Norwich school 英格兰画家团体 12—272a
诺里奇陶器 Norwich ware 英格兰陶器 12—272b
诺里什 Norrish, Ronald George Wreyford 英国化学家 12—242d
诺里斯 Norris 美国城市 12—241e
诺里斯 Norris, Frank 美国小说家 12—241f
诺里斯 Norris, George W. 美国参议员 12—242a
诺里斯 Norris, John 英国牧师、哲学家 12—242b
诺里斯敦 Norristown 美国自治镇 12—242e
《诺里斯-拉瓜迪亚法案》(1932) Norris-La Guardia Act 美国立法法案 12—242d
诺利查基河 Nolichucky River 美国河流 12—226b

诺列加 Noriega (Morena), Manuel (Antonio) 巴拿马军事领导人 12—237d
诺鲁兹节 Nōrūz 琐罗亚斯德教新年 12—269b
诺罗敦 Norodom 柬埔寨国王 12—241b
诺罗敦·西哈努克 Norodom Sihanouk, Prince (Samdech) 柬埔寨国王 12—241c
诺洛斯港 Port Nolloth 南非城镇 13—446d
诺曼 Norman 美国城市 12—238d
诺曼 Norman, Jessye 美国演员 12—238d
诺曼比岛 Normanby Island 巴布亚新几内亚火山岛 12—239b
诺曼德 Normand, Mabel 美国电影演员 12—239b
诺曼底 Normandy 法国历史文化地区 12—239d
诺曼底登陆 Normandy Invasion 第二次世界大战史 12—240c
诺曼底公爵 Normandie, Louis-Charles, duc de (duke of) 法国国王 12—239d
诺曼底群岛 Normandes, Îles 英吉利海峡群岛 12—239c
诺曼底王朝 Normandy, house of 英格兰王朝 12—240a
诺曼风格 Norman style 建筑风格 12—238f
诺曼河 Norman River 澳大利亚河流 12—238f
诺曼人 Norman 北欧民族 12—238b
诺曼征服 Norman Conquest 英国历史 12—238e
诺谟图 nomograph 计算图 12—227d
诺莫斯 nomos 古希腊哲学概念 12—227e
诺莫斯 nomos 音乐旋律类别 12—227e
诺默尔 Normal 美国城镇 12—238a
诺姆 Nome 美国城市 12—227a
诺诺 Nono, Luigi 意大利作曲家 12—229c
诺齐克 Nozick, Robert 美国哲学家 12—285a
诺瑟姆 Northam 澳大利亚城镇 12—258c
诺森伯兰 Northumberland 英格兰郡名 12—265e
诺森伯兰伯爵 Northumberland, John Neville, Earl of, Lord Montagu 英格兰贵族 12—266b
诺森伯兰伯爵(第八) Northumberland, Henry Percy, 8th earl of 英格兰政治人物 12—266e
诺森伯兰伯爵(第九) Northumberland, Henry Percy, 9th earl of 英格兰政治人物 12—266e
诺森伯兰伯爵(第七) Northumberland, Thomas Percy, 7th earl of 英格兰阴谋家 12—266d
诺森伯兰伯爵(第十) Northumberland, Algernon Percy, 10th earl of 英格兰政治人物 12—266f
诺森伯兰伯爵(第一) Northumberland, Henry Percy, 1st Earl of, Baron Percy of Alnwick 英格兰政治家 12—266a
诺森伯兰伯爵和公爵 Northumberland, earls and dukes of 英格兰贵族 12—266a
诺森伯兰公爵 Northumberland, John Dudley, Duke of, Earl of Warwick, Viscount Lisle, Baron Lisle 英格兰政治家 12—266c
诺森布里亚 Northumbria 英国古代王国 12—266f
诺思 North, Sir Dudley 英国商人 12—243c
诺思 North, Douglass C. 美国经济学家 12—243b
诺思 North, Roger 英国律师、作家 12—243e
诺思 North, Simeon 美国枪支制造商 12—243e
诺思布鲁克伯爵(第一) Northbrook, Thomas George Baring, 1st earl of, Viscount Baring of Lee, Baron Northbrook of Stratton 英国政治家 12—259b
诺思科特 Northcote, Sir John, 1st Baronet 英国政治人物 12—259f
诺思科特 Northcote, Sir Stafford Henry, 8th Baronet 英国政治家 12—260a
诺思科特 Northcote, (Thomas) James 英国画家 12—259f
诺思科特男爵(埃克塞特的) Northcote (of Exeter), Henry Stafford Northcote, Baron 英国外交官 12—259e
诺思克利夫子爵 Northcliffe (of Saint Peter), Alfred Charles William Harmsworth, Viscount 英国报纸发行人 12—259c
诺思罗普 Northrop, John Howard 美国生物化学家 12—265b
诺思罗普 Northrop, John Knudsen 美国飞机设计师 12—265c
诺思罗普-格鲁曼公司 Northrop Grumman Corporation 美国公司 12—265d
诺思伍德 Northwood, John 英国玻璃制作师 12—268d
诺思勋爵 North (of Kirtling), Frederick North, Lord 英国首相 12—243c
诺斯 North, Sir Thomas 英国翻译家 12—244b
诺斯贝 North Bay 加拿大城市 12—248d
诺斯黑文 North Haven 美国城镇 12—254e
诺斯克 Noske, Gustav 德国政治家 12—273a
诺斯利 Knowsley 英格兰自治市 9—325c
诺斯塔德 Norstad, Lauris 美国空军上将 12—243a
诺斯特拉达穆斯 Nostradamus 法国占星学家 12—273c
诺斯替教 Gnosticism 宗教 7—168b
诺斯威奇 Northwich 英格兰城镇 12—268c
诺索布河 Nossob River 纳米比亚间歇河 12—273a
诺塔比莱 Notabile (Malta) 马耳他城镇 12—273e
诺特 Noether, (Amalie) Emmy 德国数学家 12—224b
诺特 Noot, Henri van der 比利时律师 12—231a
诺特 Noot, Jan Baptista van der 荷兰诗人 12—231a
诺特 Noth, Martin 德国《圣经》学者 12—273f
诺特夫妇 Knott, Walter; and Knott, Cordelia 美国农场主 9—324f
诺特海姆 Northeim 德国城镇 12—260d
诺特克 Notke, Bernt 德国雕刻家 12—274b
诺特利河 Nottely River 美国河流 12—275e
诺特瓦索加湾 Nottawasaga Bay 加拿大港湾 12—275d
诺特韦河 Nottaway River 加拿大河流 12—275e
诺托 Noto 意大利城镇 12—274c
诺瓦 Nova, João da 西班牙航海家 12—277c
诺瓦埃斯 Novaës, Guiomar 巴西钢琴家 12—278d
诺瓦克 Novák, Vítězslav 捷克作曲家 12—278d
诺瓦拉 Novara 意大利城市 12—278f
诺瓦拉战役 Novara, Battle of 欧洲历史 12—279a
诺瓦利斯 Novalis 德国诗人 12—278e
诺瓦替安 Novatian 敌对教皇 12—279b
诺瓦托 Novato 美国城市 12—279c
诺威奇 Norwich 美国城市 12—272a
诺韦陶器 Nove ware 意大利陶器 12—279d
诺维尔 Noverre, Jean-Georges 法国舞蹈编导 12—281d
诺维科夫 Novikov, Nikolay Ivanovich 俄国作家 12—282e
诺维克 Novykh, Grigory Yefimovich (Russian mystic) 俄国沙皇宠臣 12—284b
诺维利古雷 Novi Ligure 意大利城镇 12—282c
诺维洛 Novello, Antonia 美国公职人员 12—280e
诺维洛 Novello, Ivor 威尔士演员 12—280f
诺维洛 Novello, Vincent 英国作曲家 12—281a
诺维萨德 Novi Sad 塞尔维亚城市 12—282c
诺沃克 Norwalk 美国加利福尼亚州城市 12—269b
诺沃克 Norwalk 美国康涅狄格州城市 12—269c
诺沃克 Norwalk 美国俄亥俄州城市 12—269c
诺沃提尼 Novotný, Antonín 捷克斯洛伐克共产党领袖 12—284a
诺沃西利采夫伯爵 Novosiltsev, Nikolay Nikolayevich, Count (Graf) 俄国政治家 12—283f
诺伍 Nauvoo 美国城市 12—48f
诺伍德 Norwood 美国城镇 12—272c
诺亚德 noiade 北欧拉普人萨满(巫师) 12—225b
诺伊贝尔 Neuber, Caroline 德国演员 12—94d
诺伊霍夫 Neuhof, Theodor, Baron 德意志冒险家 12—95f
诺伊拉特 Neurath, Konstantin, Baron (Freiherr) von 德国外交官 12—97b
诺伊曼 Neumann, Balthasar 德国建筑师 12—96a
诺伊曼线 Neumann line 陨石学 12—96c
诺伊萨茨 Neusatz (Serbia) 塞尔维亚城市 12—98e

诺伊斯 Neuss 德国城市 12—99a
诺伊斯 Noyes, Alfred 英国诗人 12—284e
诺伊斯 Noyes, John Humphrey 美国宗教领袖 12—284e
诺伊索尔 Neusohl (Slovakia) 斯洛伐克城市 12—99a
诺伊特拉 Neutra, Richard Joseph 美国建筑师 12—99d
诺伊特拉 Neutra (Slovakia) 斯洛伐克城镇 12—99c
诺因堡 Neuenburg (Switzerland) 瑞士城市 12—95e
诺因堡湖 Neuenburgersee (Switzerland) 瑞士湖泊 12—95e
诺兹特勒姆 Nordström, Ludvig Anselm 瑞典作家 12—234d
锘(No) nobelium 化学元素 12—213f

O

欧巴涅 Aubagne 法国城镇 2—42c
欧白鱼 bleak (*Alburnus alburnus*) 鱼类 2—532a
欧拜伊德 Ubayyiḍ, al- 苏丹城镇 17—316e
欧宝公司 Opel AG 德国汽车公司 12—427a
欧贝德 'Ubayd, Tall al- 古代遗址 17—316d
欧本 Oeben, Jean-François 法国工匠 12—341b
欧比尼女公爵 Aubigny, Louise-Renée de Kéroualle, duchesse d' (duchess of) 法国公爵 2—43a
欧比松 Aubusson, Pierre d' 耶路撒冷骑士团长 2—43e
欧比松 Aubusson 法国城镇 2—43e
欧比松地毯 Aubusson carpet 法国工艺品 2—43f
欧鳊 bream (*Abramis brama*) 鱼类 3—134e
欧滨草 lyme grass 草本植物 10—311e
欧波利斯 Eupolis 雅典诗人 6—163f
欧布利德斯(米利都的) Eubulides of Miletus 希腊哲学家 6—154d
欧布洛斯 Eubulus 希腊政治家 6—154d
欧茨 Oates, Joyce Carol 美国作家 12—316b
欧茨 Oates, Titus 英国教士 12—316c
欧丹塔普里寺 Odantapurī 印度佛寺 12—336a
欧当归 lovage (*Levisticum officinale*) 植物 10—249a
欧德摩斯(罗得的) Eudemus of Rhodes 希腊哲学家 6—156f
欧登塞 Odense 丹麦城市 12—336d
欧多克索斯(基齐库斯的) Eudoxus of Cyzicus 希腊探险家 6—157e
欧多克索斯(尼多斯的) Eudoxus of Cnidus 古希腊数学家 6—157c
欧多克西亚 Eudoxia 东罗马皇后 6—157b
欧多西亚 Eudocia 东罗马皇后 6—157a
欧多西亚·玛克勒姆玻利提萨 Eudocia Macrembolitissa 拜占廷皇后 6—157b
欧夫罗尼奥斯 Euphronius 希腊画匠、陶工 6—163e
欧弗兰帕克 Overland Park 美国堪萨斯州城市 12—511f
欧弗朗 Øverland, Arnulf 挪威诗人 12—511e
欧福里翁 Euphorion 希腊诗人 6—163b
欧甘草 licorice (species *Glycyrrhiza glabra*) 草本植物 10—82f
欧甘文字 ogham writing 古代文字 12—346b
欧根(萨伏依的) Eugene of Savoy 奥地利帝国将领 6—157f
欧·亨利 Henry, O. 美国作家 8—26e
欧鳇 hausen 鱼类 7—513e
欧几里得 Euclid 古希腊数学家 6—155d
欧几里得 Euclid 美国城市 6—155e
欧几里得几何 Euclidean geometry 数学 6—155f
欧几里得算法 Euclidean algorithm 数学 6—155e
欧加登 Ogaden 埃塞俄比亚地区 12—344e
欧克赫姆 Ockeghem, Jean d' 佛兰德斯作曲家 12—332c
欧克拉提德斯 Eucratides 大夏国王 6—156d
欧克莱尔 Eau Claire 美国城市 5—515a
欧克斯赛 Oaks 英国马赛 12—315d
欧拉 Olah, George A(ndrew) 美国化学家 12—365b
欧拉 Euler, Leonhard 瑞士数学家、物理学家 6—160a
欧拉尔 Aulard, François-Alphonse 法国历史学家 2—56c
欧拉夫峡湾市 Ólafsfjördhur 冰岛城镇 12—365a
欧拉利亚骑士团,圣 Knights of Saint Eulalia (Christian order) 基督教修道会 9—322d
欧拉利亚骑士团,圣 Saint Eulalia, Knights of (Christian order) 基督教修道会 14—510e
欧拉示性数 Euler characteristic 数学 6—160c
欧赖 Auray 法国城镇 2—58a
欧里庇得斯 Euripides 希腊悲剧作家 6—164d
欧里狄克 Eurydice 希腊神话人物 6—173e
欧里纽斯 Ourinhos 巴西城市 12—507e
欧里乌 Hauriou, Maurice-Jean-Claude-Eugène 法国政治学家 7—513a
欧里亚克 Aurillac 法国城市 2—59d
欧鲁普雷图 Ouro Prêto 巴西城市 12—507e
欧伦施莱厄 Oehlenschläger, Adam Gottlob 丹麦作家 12—342b
欧罗巴 Europa 希腊神话人物 6—167a
欧罗普斯 Europus (ancient Syria) 叙利亚古城 6—173d
欧玛尔·海亚姆 Omar Khayyam 波斯诗人 12—413e
欧迈尼斯 Eumenes 希腊将军 6—160f
欧迈尼斯二世 Eumenes II 帕加马国王 6—160f
欧迈尼斯一世 Eumenes I 帕加马统治者 6—160f
欧麦尔 'Umar 穆斯林哈里发之名 17—334e
欧麦尔二世 'Umar II 伍麦叶王朝哈里发 17—334f
欧麦尔·塔尔 'Umar Tal 图库洛尔人领袖 17—335a
欧麦尔一世 'Umar I 穆斯林哈里发 17—334e
欧麦里 'Umarī, al- 大马士革学者、作家 17—335b
欧梅尼乌斯 Eumenius 罗马演说家 6—161a
《欧美插图大百科全书》 Enciclopedia universal ilustrada europeo-americana 西班牙百科全书 6—69d
欧墨尼得斯 Eumenides (Greek mythology) 希腊神话复仇女神 6—161a
欧墨尼斯 Eumenes (Greco-Roman mythology) 希腊神话复仇女神 6—160e
欧姆(Ω) ohm 电阻单位 12—353c
欧姆 Ohm, Georg Simon 德国物理学家 12—353d
欧姆定律 Ohm's law 电学 12—353e
欧纳皮奥斯 Eunapius 希腊历史编纂家 6—161b
欧纳斯阔索阶 Onesquethaw Stage 地质学 12—421b
欧讷男爵 Aulne, Anne-Robert-Jacques Turgot, baron de l' 法国经济学家 2—56d
欧尼斯 Aunis 法国古代地名 2—57c
欧鲇 wels (*Silurus glanis*) 鱼类 18—183d
欧女贞 mock privet 木本植物 11—303a
欧佩莱卡 Opelika 美国城市 12—427a
欧芹 parsley (*Petroselinum crispum* or *Petroselinum sativum*) 植物学 13—63b
欧仁妮 Eugénie 法国皇后 6—158d
欧塞比奥 Eusebio 葡萄牙足球运动员 6—174a
欧塞尔 Auxerre 法国城镇 2—81f
欧申赛德 Oceanside 美国城市 12—331a
欧申斯普林斯 Ocean Springs 美国城市 12—327f
欧什 Auch 法国城镇 2—44a
欧石鸡 chukar 鸟类 4—219f
欧石楠 heath 木本植物 7—544f
欧莳萝 cumin (*Cuminum cyminum*) 草本植物 5—60a
欧坦 Autun 法国城镇 2—81a
欧唐-拉腊 Autant-Lara, Claude 法国电影导演 2—72f
欧忒耳珀 Euterpe 希腊宗教女神 6—175f
欧特克洛克子爵 Hauteclocque, Philippe-Marie, viscomte de (viscount of) 法国军人 7—515d
欧特里沃 Hauterive, Borel d' 法国作家 7—515e
欧特里沃 Hauterive 加拿大城镇 7—515e
欧特里沃阶 Hauterivian Stage 地质学 7—515e
欧特罗庇厄斯 Eutropius 东罗马帝国宦官 6—177a
欧特维尔家族 Hauteville, House of 诺曼贵族、骑士家族 7—516a

欧提基狄斯(西锡安的) Eutychides of Sicyon 希腊雕刻家 6—177b
欧文 Irvine 苏格兰城市 8—454b
欧文 Irvine 美国城市 8—454a
欧文 Owain 威尔士皇族之名 12—514c
欧文 Owen, Alun (Davies) 威尔士剧作家 12—514f
欧文 Owen, Daniel 威尔士作家 12—515a
欧文 Irving, Edward 苏格兰牧师 8—454b
欧文 Irwin, Elisabeth Antoinette 美国教育家 8—455b
欧文 Owen, Goronwy 威尔士诗人 12—515b
欧文 Irving, Sir Henry 英国演员 8—454c
欧文 Irwin, James B. 美国航天员 8—455c
欧文 Owen, John 威尔士诗人 12—515c
欧文 Owen, John 英格兰作家、牧师 12—515c
欧文 Ervine, Saint John (Greer) 英国剧作家 6—124d
欧文 Irwin, May 美国演员 8—455d
欧文 Owen, Robert 英国社会改革家 12—516a
欧文 Owen, Sir Richard 英国解剖学家 12—515d
欧文 Owen, Robert Dale 美国政治家、改革家 12—516b
欧文 Ervin, Samuel J(ames), Jr. 美国参议员 6—124c
欧文 Irving, Washington 美国作家 8—454f
欧文 Owen, Wilfred 美国作家 12—516c
欧文顿 Irvington 美国城镇 8—455b
欧文·圭内斯 Owain Gwynedd 威尔士国王 12—514d
欧文瀑布 Owen Falls 乌干达瀑布 12—516d
欧文·赛菲里奥格 Owain Cyfeiliog 威尔士诗人 12—514c
欧文斯 Owens, Jesse 美国运动员 12—516e
欧文斯伯勒 Owensboro 美国城市 12—516f
欧文·斯坦利岭 Owen Stanley Range 新几内亚高地 12—516d
欧西德莫斯 Euthydemus 大夏国王 6—176b
欧西米德斯 Euthymides 雅典画匠 6—176b
欧阳修 Ouyang Xiu 中国文学家 12—509e
欧阳询 Ouyang Xun 中国书法家 12—509f
欧阳予倩 Ouyang Yuqian 中国戏剧家 12—510a
欧伊伦施皮格尔 Eulenspiegel, Till 德国文学家 6—159f
欧伊迈罗斯 Euhemerus 希腊神话研究者 6—159c
欧元 euro 货币 6—166d
欧扎克山 Ozark Mountains 美国高原地区 12—528a
欧扎克-圣弗朗西斯国家森林 Ozark-Saint Francis National Forest 美国森林地区 12—528b
欧扎克斯湖 Ozarks, Lake of the 美国人工湖 12—528c
欧楂 medlar (species *Mespilus germanica*) 木本植物 11—78f
欧洲 Europe 世界大洲之一 6—167c
欧洲安全与合作组织 Security and Co-operation in Europe, Organization for (OSCE) 国际会议 15—179b
欧洲腭针鱼 garfish 鱼类 7—14d
欧洲法院 European Court of Justice 欧洲共同体司法机构 6—170b
欧洲防风 parsnip (*Pastinaca sativa*) 植物学 13—63c
欧洲防务集团 European Defense Community (EDC) 欧洲军事组织 6—170b
欧洲复兴计划 European Recovery Program 欧洲-美国历史 6—171d
欧洲共产主义 Eurocommunism 政治学 6—166e
欧洲共同体 European Community (EC) 欧洲经济组织 6—169f
欧洲航空防务与航天公司 European Aeronautic Defence and Space Company (EADS) 欧洲航空航天设备生产公司 6—169b
欧洲航天局 European Space Agency (ESA) 欧洲航天机构 6—171e
欧洲核研究组织 CERN 国际组织 4—11e
欧洲鳇 beluga 鱼类 2—372d
欧洲货币单位 ecu 国际金融 5—532e
欧洲经济共同体 European Economic Community (EEC) 欧洲经济组织 6—170c
欧洲经济合作组织 European Economic Co-operation, Organisation for (OEEC) 复兴欧洲经济组织 6—170c
欧洲菊苣 endive (*Cichorium endivia*) 植物 6—73a
欧洲蕨 bracken 植物 3—104d
欧洲联盟 European Union (EU) 西欧经济、政治组织 6—171f
《欧洲联盟条约》 European Union, Treaty on 欧共体成员国国际协定 6—173a
欧洲流行乐 Europop 音乐 6—173c
欧洲煤钢共同体 European Coal and Steel Community (ECSC) 欧洲煤、钢管理机构 6—169e
欧洲美元 Eurodollar 储存在欧洲银行的美元存款 6—167a
欧洲没药 cicely (*Myrrhis odorata*) 草本植物 4—234a
欧洲南天天文台 European Southern Observatory (ESO) 欧洲天体物理学机构 6—171e
欧洲盘羊 mouflon (*Ovis musimon*) 动物 11—438c
欧洲平原 European Plain 世界上面积最大的完整平原之一 6—171c
欧洲人民党 European People's Party (EPP) 跨国政党 6—171b
欧洲人权法院 European Court of Human Rights (ECHR) 国际组织 6—170a
欧洲沙丁鱼 pilchard 鱼类 13—302b
欧洲社会党 European Socialists, Party of (PES) 跨国议会组织 6—171d
欧洲隧道 Eurotunnel 英法间海底铁路隧道 6—173d
欧洲委员会 Europe, Council of 欧洲组织 6—169a
欧洲芽生菌病 European blastomycosis (infection) 传染病 6—169d
欧洲野马 tarpan 哺乳动物 16—484e
欧洲野牛 wisent 哺乳动物 18—297c
欧洲一致 Europe, Concert of 欧洲历史 6—169a
欧洲议会 European Parliament 欧洲共同体立法机构 6—171b
欧洲原子能共同体 European Atomic Energy Community (EURATOM) 欧洲国际组织 6—169d
欧洲越橘 bilberry (*Vaccinium myrtillus*) 灌木 2—471e
欧洲运河 Europa Canal 德国南部水道 6—167c
欧洲紫杉 European yew 木本植物 6—173b
欧洲自由贸易联盟 European Free Trade Association (EFTA) 欧洲七国贸易组织 6—170e
欧洲自由民主改革党 European Liberal Democrat and Reform Party (ELDR) 跨国议会组织 6—171a
鸥科 Laridae 动物学 9—499f
呕吐 vomiting 病理现象 18—47b
偶氮化合物 azo compound 化合物 2—102c
偶氮磺胺 sulfamidochrysoidine (drug) 药物 16—317e
偶氮染料 azo dye 化合物 2—102d
偶极假说 dipolar hypothesis 地球物理学 5—333d
偶然音乐 aleatory music 音乐 1—195c
偶蹄目动物 artiodactyl 哺乳动物 1—531f
偶像崇拜 idolatry 宗教 8—323d
沤麻 retting 纤维与麻杆分离加工过程 14—247d

P

爬虫学 herpetology 动物学 8—49a
爬山虎 Boston ivy (species *Parthenocissus*, or *Ampelopsis*, *tricuspidata*) 藤本植物 3—66f
爬山赛 hill climb 汽车赛 8—82d
爬山运动 mountain climbing 体育活动 11—444d
爬水蝽 creeping water bug 昆虫 5—4b
爬行类 reptile 爬行纲脊椎动物 14—235e
帕 Phrae 泰国城镇 13—268b
帕埃斯人 Páez 哥伦比亚印第安人 12—542a
帕埃斯图姆 Paestum 意大利古代城市 12—541f
帕埃兹 Páez (Xaramillo), Pedro 西班牙神父 12—542c
帕安 Pa-an 缅甸城市 12—530c
帕奥尼乌斯 Paeonius 希腊雕刻家 12—541e

帕比亚尼采 Pabianice 波兰城镇 12—531a
帕波拉玛努七 Paramanuchit 暹罗宗教领袖、作家 13—36a
帕布斯特 Pabst, G(eorg) W(ilhelm) 德国电影导演 12—531a
帕查卡马克 Pachacamac 秘鲁神名 12—531e
帕查卡马克 Pachacamac 秘鲁文化遗址 12—531f
帕查库提·印加·尤潘基 Pachacuti Inca Yupanqui 印加帝国皇帝 12—531f
帕察耶夫 Patsayev, Viktor Ivanovich 苏联航天员 13—92a
帕柴马莱丘陵 Pachaimalai Hills 印度丘陵 12—531f
帕琛 Patchen, Kenneth 美国诗人、画家 13—84f
帕茨 Päts, Konstantin 爱沙尼亚总统 13—91f
帕岱莱夫斯基 Paderewski, Ignacy (Jan) 波兰钢琴家、作曲家 12—539e
帕德巴拉 Bhātpāra 印度城镇 2—451f
帕德博恩 Paderborn 德国城市 12—539c
帕德冈 Bhatgaon (Nepal) 尼泊尔城镇 2—451e
帕德雷港 Puerto Padre 古巴城市 14—16a
帕德里岛 Padre Island 美国岛屿 12—540d
帕迪利亚 Padilla, Heberto 诗人 12—539f
帕迪利亚 Padilla, Juan de 西班牙军事首领 12—540a
帕迪利亚 Padilla, Juan 西班牙天主教传教士 12—540a
帕迪尤卡 Paducah 美国城市 12—541a
帕蒂 Patti, Adelina 意大利歌唱家 13—93a
帕蒂尼奥 Patiño, José Patiño, marqués de 西班牙政治家 13—88c
帕蒂尼尔 Patinir, Joachim (de) 佛兰德斯画家 13—88b
帕丁顿 Paddington 伦敦一区 12—538f
帕杜斯河 Padus (river, Italy) 意大利河流 12—541a
帕顿 Parton, Sara Payson Willis 美国小说家、报纸撰稿人 13—68f
帕多瓦 Padua 意大利城市 12—540e
帕多克 Paddock, Charlie 美国短跑运动员 12—539b
帕多瓦大学 Padua, University of 意大利大学 12—540e
帕尔 Paarl 南非城镇 12—530d
帕尔 Parr, Catherine 英格兰王后 13—60f
帕尔 Paer, Ferdinando 意大利作曲家 12—541e
帕尔 Parr, William 英国贵族 13—60f
帕尔巴蒂人 Parbate (people) 南亚民族 13—39e
帕尔杜比采 Pardubice 捷克城市 13—40b
帕尔多·巴桑 Pardo Bazán, Emilia, Countess (condesa) de 西班牙作家 13—40a
帕尔格雷夫 Palgrave, Francis Turner 英国评论家、诗人 12—565e
帕尔加 Párga 希腊港口 13—41b
帕尔莱日 Parléř, Petr 德国著名石工 13—57c
帕尔马 Palma 西班牙城市 12—570c
帕尔马 Parma 意大利城市 13—58b
帕尔马 Palma, Jacopo 意大利画家 12—570d
帕尔马 Palma, Ricardo 秘鲁作家 12—570e
帕尔马公爵 Parma, Alessandro Farnese, duque de (duke of) 西班牙尼德兰摄政 13—58c
帕尔马公爵 Parme, Jean-Jacques-Régis de Cambacérès, duc de (duke of) 法国政治家 13—58d
帕尔马和皮亚琴察公国 Parma and Piacenza, Duchy of 原意大利公国 13—58c
帕尔马里斯 Palmares 巴西古国名 12—570f
帕尔马-皮亚琴察公爵 Parma e Piacenza, Alessandro Farnese, duca di (duke of) 西班牙尼德兰摄政 13—58d
帕尔马斯 Palmas 巴西城市 12—571a
帕尔马斯角 Cape Palmas (Liberia) 利比里亚城镇、海港 3—421c
帕尔迈拉 Palmyra 美国城镇 12—574b
帕尔梅 Palme, Olof 瑞典首相 12—571a
帕尔梅拉 Palmela, Pedro de Sousa Holstein, Duke (duque) de 葡萄牙政治家 12—571b
帕尔梅尼奥 Parmenio 马其顿将军 13—58e
帕尔梅森干酪 Parmesan 意大利牛奶干酪 13—58f
帕尔米拉 Palmira 哥伦比亚城市 12—573e
帕尔米拉字母 Palmyrenian alphabet 闪米特古文字 12—574c
帕尔默 Palmer, Alice Elvira Freeman 美国教育家 12—571d
帕尔默 Palmer, Arnold (Daniel) 美国高尔夫球运动员 12—571e
帕尔默 Palmer, A. Mitchell 美国律师 12—571b
帕尔默 Palmer, Barbara, Countess of Castlemaine 英国贵族 12—571f
帕尔默 Palmer, Bertha Honoré 美国社会知名人士 12—571f
帕尔默 Palmer, E(dward) H(enry) 英国东方学家 12—572a
帕尔默 Palmer, (Edward) Vance 澳大利亚小说家 12—572e
帕尔默 Palmer, Geoffrey (Winston Russell) 澳大利亚小说家 12—572b
帕尔默 Palmer, Potter 美国商人 12—572d
帕尔默 Palmer, Phoebe Worrall 美国福音布道者 12—572c
帕尔默 Palmer, Roundell 英国大法官 12—572e
帕尔默 Palmer, Samuel 英国画家 12—572e
帕尔默 Palmer, William Henry (magician) 美国魔术师 12—572f
帕尔默 Palmer, William Waldegrave 英国海军大臣 12—572f
帕尔姆格伦 Palmgren, Selim 芬兰钢琴家、作曲家 12—573d
帕尔纳斯派 Parnassian 法国诗人派别 13—59b
帕尔纳索斯草 grass of Parnassus 草本植物 7—261b
帕尔纳索斯山 Parnassus, Mount 希腊山脉 13—59c
帕尔齐法尔 Perceval 英国传奇英雄 13—157c
帕尔萨 Parsa (ancient Persian city) 波斯古都城 13—62f
帕尔萨 Parsa (ancient region, Persia) 波斯古城区 13—62f
帕尔萨乌尼萨 Parthaunisa (ancient city, Parthia) 土库曼斯坦古城 13—65c
帕尔塔人 Palta 厄瓜多尔民族 12—575c
帕尔乌斯 Parvus (Russian-German revolutionary) 俄国-德国社会主义者 13—70b
帕凡舞 pavane 欧洲舞蹈 13—101e
帕夫尔孔 Phaulkon, Constantine 希腊冒险家 13—222a
帕夫拉戈尼亚 Paphlagonia 古安纳托利亚地区 13—24d
帕夫利科夫斯卡-亚斯诺热夫斯卡 Pawlikowska-Jasnorzewska, Maria 波兰诗人 13—104b
帕福斯 Paphos 塞浦路斯城市 13—24d
帕戈尔布尔 Bhāgalpur 印度城市 2—449a
帕戈萨斯普林斯 Pagosa Springs 美国城市 12—546b
帕格尼尼 Paganini, Niccolò 意大利作曲家 12—542e
帕格沃什会议 Pugwash Conferences 世界性会议 14—19b
帕果帕果 Pago Pago 美属萨摩亚港口 12—545d
帕哈里绘画 Pahari painting 印度绘画 12—546f
帕哈里人 Pahārī 南亚民族 12—546d
帕哈里诸语言 Pahari languages 印度-雅利安诸语言 12—546f
帕赫 Pacher, Michael 德国画家 12—532c
帕赫曼 Pachmann, Vladimir von 俄国钢琴家 12—532e
帕黑尔贝尔 Pachelbel, Johann 德国作曲家 12—532b
帕基耶 Pasquier, Étienne 法国律师、作家 13—75c
帕基耶公爵 Pasquier, Étienne(-Denis), duc de 法国政治家 13—75d
帕吉勒提河 Bhāgīrathi River 印度河流 2—449c
帕加迪安 Pagadian 菲律宾城市 12—542c
帕加马 Pergamum 土耳其古城 13—165f
帕加内利·迪·蒙泰马尼奥 Paganelli di Montemagno, Bernardo (pope) 教皇 12—542e
帕加塞湾 Pagasaí, Gulf of 希腊海湾 12—543b
帕金森 Parkinson, C. Northcote 英国历史学家、作家 13—56d
帕金森氏病 Parkinson's disease 疾病 13—56e
帕卡德 Packard, David 美国电气工程师 12—538a
帕卡德 Packard, Sophia B. 美国教育家 12—538b
帕卡赖马山脉 Pacaraima Mountains 南美山脉 12—531c
帕卡斯夸国家公园 Pukaskwa National Park 加拿大公园 14—19e
帕卡图斯·德雷帕尼乌斯 Pacatus Drepanius, Latinius 高卢-罗马演说家 12—531d

帕科罗斯 Pacorus 安息王子 12—538c
帕科罗斯二世 Pacorus II 安息国王 12—538d
帕科米乌斯，圣 Pachomius, SAINT 埃及基督教修士 12—532e
帕克 Parker, Alton B(rooks) 美国法学家 13—54c
帕克 Parker, Bonnie 美国罪犯 13—54d
帕克 Parker, Charlie 美国爵士乐演奏家 13—54d
帕克 Parker, Dorothy 美国作家、诗人 13—54f
帕克 Parker, Francis (Wayland) 美国教育家 13—55b
帕克 Parker, Horatio (William) 美国作曲家、教师 13—55c
帕克 Parker, Matthew 英国坎特伯雷大主教 13—55d
帕克 Park, Mungo 苏格兰探险家 13—53e
帕克 Park, Maud Wood 美国主张妇女参政者 13—53c
帕克 Pack, Otto von 德意志政治家 12—537c
帕克 Parker, Quanah 印第安人领袖 13—55e
帕克 Park, Robert E. 美国社会学家 13—53f
帕克 Parker, Theodore 美国神学家、牧师 13—55f
帕克城 Park City 美国犹他州北部城市 13—54b
帕克福雷斯特 Park Forest 美国村庄 13—54c
帕克赫斯特 Parkhurst, Helen 美国教育家、作家 13—56c
帕克里奇 Park Ridge 美国城市 13—54c
帕克岭 Park Range 落基山脉一部分 13—54c
帕克曼 Parkman, Francis 美国历史学家 13—56e
帕克斯 Parkes 澳大利亚城镇 13—56a
帕克斯 Pax 古罗马神祇 13—105a
帕克斯 Parkes, Alexander 英国化学家、发明家 13—56a
帕克斯 Parkes, Frank Kobina 加纳新闻工作者、诗人 13—56a
帕克斯 Parkes, Sir Henry 澳大利亚政治家 13—56b
帕克斯 Parks, Suzan-Lori 美国剧作家 13—57a
帕克斯堡 Parkersburg 美国城市 13—55f
帕克斯顿 Paxton, Sir Joseph 英国园艺师 13—105b
帕克斯顿青年暴动 Paxton Boys uprising 美国早期历史 13—105d
帕克索斯 Paxos 希腊岛屿 13—105b
帕克西努 Paxinou, Katina 希腊演员 13—105a
帕库维乌斯 Pacuvius, Marcus 罗马戏剧家 12—538d
帕拉 Pará 巴西州名 13—28f
帕拉 Pará (city, Brazil) 巴西城市 13—29b
帕拉 Parra, Nicanor 智利诗人 13—60f
帕拉博拉 Palabora (South Africa) 南非城镇 12—554d
帕拉博鲁瓦 Phalaborwa 南非城镇 13—217e
帕拉茨基 Palacký, František 捷克历史学家、政治家 12—555c
帕拉德 Palade, George E(mil) 美国生物学家 12—555d
帕拉狄昂 Palladium 希腊神像 12—568a
帕拉弟奥 Palladio, Andrea 意大利建筑师 12—568d
帕拉弟奥式窗 Palladian window 建筑 12—567b
帕拉弟奥主义 Palladianism 建筑风格 12—568b
帕拉第乌斯 Palladius 小亚细亚基督教主教、历史学家 12—568c
帕拉蒂诺山 Palatine Hill 意大利罗马丘陵 12—557d
帕拉尔 Parral (Mexico) 墨西哥城市 13—61a
帕拉瓜纳半岛 Paraguaná Peninsula 委内瑞拉半岛 13—32b
帕拉瓜苏河 Paraguaçu River 巴西河流 13—32b
帕拉果 para nut 坚果 13—29c
帕拉河 Pará River 巴西河流 13—29c
帕拉卡斯文化 Paracas 南美古代文化 13—30c
帕拉库 Parakou 贝宁城镇 13—34d
帕拉马里博 Paramaribo 苏里南首都 13—36b
帕拉马斯 Palamás, Kostís 希腊诗人 12—556b
帕拉马斯，圣 Palamas, Saint Gregory 希腊神学家 12—556a
帕拉马塔 Parramatta 澳大利亚城市 13—61a
帕拉墨得斯 Palamedes 希腊传说人物 12—556c
帕拉纳 Palana 俄罗斯城镇 12—556d
帕拉尼亚克 Parañaque 菲律宾城镇 13—38b
帕拉皮纳塞斯 Parapinaces (Byzantine emperor) 拜占廷皇帝 13—38d
帕拉切尔苏斯 Paracelsus 瑞士医师 13—30d
帕拉斯 Pallas, Peter Simon 德国博物学家 12—568d
帕拉斯地毯 palas 工艺品 12—556e
帕拉斯科斯 Paráskhos, Akhilléfs 希腊诗人 13—39b
帕拉瓦王朝 Pallava DYNASTY 印度王朝 12—568f
帕拉乌凯夜鹰 parauque (bird) 鸟类 13—39e
帕拉西奥·巴尔德斯 Palacio Valdés, Armando 西班牙作家 12—555b
帕拉修斯 Parrhasius 古希腊画家 13—61b
帕拉伊巴 Paraíba 巴西州名 13—34a
帕拉佐洛阿克雷德 Palazzolo Acreide 意大利城镇 12—558e
帕莱奥洛格 Paléologue, Maurice-Georges 法国外交家、作家 12—561d
帕莱奥普雷韦扎 Palaiopréveza (Greece) 希腊城市 12—556a
帕莱斯·马托斯 Palés Matos, Luis 波多黎各诗人 12—563b
帕莱斯特里纳 Palestrina, Giovanni Pierluigi da 意大利作曲家 12—564d
帕莱斯特里纳 Palestrina (Italy) 意大利古城 12—564d
帕兰多夫斯基 Parandowski, Jan 波兰作家、翻译家 13—38b
帕兰加巴 Parangaba 巴西城市 13—38c
帕兰科塔 Pālamcottah (India) 印度县名 12—556c
帕朗卡拉亚 Palangkaraya 印度尼西亚城市 12—556d
帕劳 Palau 太平洋西部国家 12—557e
帕劳岛 Palau (Caroline Islands) 加罗林群岛岛屿 12—557e
帕劳语 Palauan language 太平洋帕劳群岛语言 12—558c
帕勒登杜 Bhartendu (Indian author) 印度作家 2—451b
帕勒人 Parni 安息帝国部落 13—59f
帕勒泰恩 Palatine 美国村庄 12—557c
帕雷 Paré, Ambroise 法国外科医生 13—40b
帕雷哈 Pareja, Juan de 西班牙画家 13—40d
帕雷斯 Parys 南非城镇 13—70c
帕雷西斯山 Parecis Mountains 巴西山脉 13—40c
帕累托 Pareto, Vilfredo 意大利经济学家 13—40f
帕里 Pagri 中国城镇 12—546c
帕里 Parry, Sir (Charles) Hubert (Hastings) 英国作曲家、作家 13—62e
帕里奥洛加斯家族 Palaeologus FAMILY 拜占廷家族 12—555e
帕里库廷火山 Parícutin 墨西哥火山 13—42a
帕里马山脉 Parima Mountains 圭亚那山脉 13—42c
帕里桑德 Parry Sound 加拿大城镇 13—62f
帕里什 Parrish, Anne 美国慈善家 13—61c
帕里什 Parrish, Celestia Susannah 美国教育家 13—61d
帕里什 Parrish, (Frederick) Maxfield 美国画家 13—61e
帕里斯 Paris 希腊传说人物 13—42d
帕里斯 Paris 美国肯塔基州城市 13—50d
帕里斯 Paris 美国得克萨斯州城市 13—50d
帕里斯 Parris, Alexander 美国建筑师 13—61b
帕里斯 Paris, (Bruno-Paulin-)Gaston 法国语文学家 13—50f
帕里斯 Paris, Matthew 英格兰修士、编年史家 13—51a
帕里斯岛 Parris Island 美国岛屿 13—61c
帕里斯节 Parilia 古罗马节日 13—42c
帕里乌沙纳节 Paryuṣaṇa 印度耆那教节期 13—70c
帕里亚湾 Paria, Gulf of 加勒比海海湾 13—41d
帕利 Parley, Peter 美国作家 13—57d
帕利梅 Palimé 多哥城镇 12—566a
帕利萨 Palisa, Johann 西里西亚天文学家 12—566d
帕利塞兹丘陵 Palisades, The 美国丘陵 12—566e
帕利西 Palissy, Bernard 法国制陶师、作家 12—566e
帕利亚 pariah 印度低级种姓 13—41e
帕列罗 Pagliero, Marcello 意大利电影导演 12—545a
帕林顿 Parrington, Vernon L(ouis) 美国文学史家 13—61b
帕卢 Palu 印度尼西亚城市 12—575c
帕卢丹 Paludan, (Stig Henning) Jacob (Puggaard) 丹麦小说家

12—575c
帕卢丹-缪勒 Paludan-Müller, Frederik 丹麦诗人 12—575d
帕鲁德 Bhārhut 印度村落 2—450f
帕鲁德雕刻 Bhārhut sculpture 印度古代雕刻 2—451a
帕鲁河 Paru River 巴西河流 13—69e
帕鲁特 Parrott, Robert Parker 美国发明家 13—62d
帕伦贝格 Pallenberg, Max 奥地利演员 12—569a
帕伦克 Palenque 南美州马雅古城遗址 12—559c
帕伦克人 Palenque 委内瑞拉民族 12—559b
帕伦西亚 Palencia 西班牙省份 12—559a
帕伦西亚 palencia 西班牙城市 12—559b
帕罗 Paro 不丹城镇 13—60b
帕罗斯 Páros 希腊岛屿 13—60e
帕罗斯瓷器 Parian ware 英国瓷器 13—41f
帕罗斯大理石 Marmor Parium (ancient Greek document) 古希腊文献 10—526a
帕罗斯年代记 Parian Chronicle 古希腊文献 13—41e
帕洛阿尔托 Palo Alto 美国城市 12—574d
帕洛阿尔托战役 Palo Alto, Battle of 墨西哥历史 12—574d
帕洛马山 Palomar, Mount 美国山峰 12—574f
帕洛马天文台 Palomar Observatory 美国天文台 12—575a
帕洛米诺 Palomino de Castro y Velasco 西班牙画家、学者 12—575b
帕洛米诺马 Palomino 马品种 12—575a
帕马 Parma 美国城市 13—58c
帕芒蒂埃 Parmentier, André 美国园艺家 13—58e
帕米尔高原 Pamirs 亚洲地区 12—576a
帕米贾尼诺 Parmigianino 意大利画家 13—58f
帕米尤特 Paamiut (Greenland) 格陵兰居民点 12—530d
帕默 Palmer, Nathaniel B(rown) 美国船长、探险家 12—572c
帕默半岛 Palmer, Peninsula (Antarctica) 南极洲半岛 12—573a
帕默地 Palmer Land 英属南极领地 12—573a
帕默群岛 Palmer Archipelago 南极岛群 12—573a
帕默斯顿子爵(第三) Palmerston (of Palmerston), Henry John Temple, 3rd Viscount 英国政治家 12—573a
帕姆贝 Palm Bay 美国城市 12—569e
帕姆利科人 Pamlico 北美印第安人 12—576c
帕姆利科湾 Pamlico Sound 美国海湾 12—576d
帕穆卡勒 Pamukkale (ancient Phrygian city) 弗里吉亚古城 13—1f
帕纳吉 Panaji 印度城市 13—4c
帕纳什凯拉 Panasqueira 葡萄牙钨矿区 13—6f
帕奈人 Panayan (people) 菲律宾民族 13—7b
帕奈提奥斯 Panaetius 罗马哲学家 13—4b
帕内东 Panneton, Philippe 加拿大法语小说家 13—14a
帕内尔 Parnell, Thomas 爱尔兰诗人 13—59f
帕内特 Paneth, Friedrich Adolf 奥地利化学家 13—10f
帕内特氏细胞 Paneth cell 细胞学 13—10f
帕内韦日斯 Panevėžys 立陶宛城市 13—11a
帕尼奥尔 Pagnol, Marcel Paul 法国作家、导演 12—545c
帕尼基 Parnicki, Teodor 波兰历史小说家 13—60a
帕尼努斯 Pagninus, Santes 意大利天主教学者 12—545c
帕尼亚尼 Pagnani, Andreina 意大利戏剧演员 12—545b
帕尼亚西斯 Panyassis 爱奥尼亚诗人 13—17b
帕尼泽 Panizzi, Sir Anthony 意大利文学家、图书馆馆长 13—12f
帕宁 Panin, Nikita Ivanovich, Graf (Count) 俄国政治家、伯爵 13—12d
帕努科河 Pánuco River 墨西哥河流 13—17a
帕诺夫斯基 Panofsky, Erwin 美国艺术史学家 13—14e
帕帕迪亚曼托波洛斯 Papadiamantópoulos, Yánnis 法国诗人 13—18f
帕帕戈人 Papago 北美印第安人 13—18f
帕帕戈斯 Papagos, Alexandros 希腊军人、政治家 13—20b
帕帕洛阿潘河 Papaloapan River 墨西哥河流 13—21c
帕帕佐普洛斯 Papadopoulos, Dimitrios (Orthodox patriarch) 希腊东正教牧首 13—18f
帕潘 Papin, Denis 英国物理学家 13—25b
帕潘德里欧 Papandreou, Andreas 希腊总理 13—21c
帕潘德里欧 Papandreou, Georgios 希腊首相、政治家 13—21d
帕潘特拉 Papantla 墨西哥城市 13—21e
帕皮尼 Papini, Giovanni 意大利记者、作家 13—25d
帕皮尼安 Papinian 罗马法学家 13—25e
帕皮尼乌斯·斯塔提乌斯 Papinius Statius, Publius 罗马诗人 13—25e
帕皮诺 Papineau, Louis Joseph 加拿大政治家 13—25c
帕皮提 Papeete 法属波利尼西亚城市 13—22f
帕皮亚门托语 Papiamento 加勒比地区语言 13—24e
帕皮亚斯 Papias 弗里吉亚基督教主教 13—24e
帕普 Papp, Joseph 美国戏剧演出人、导演 13—25f
帕普斯(亚历山大的) Pappus of Alexandria 希腊几何学家 13—26c
帕奇 Partch, Harry 美国作曲家 13—64f
帕奇梅雷斯 Pachymeres, George 拜占廷学者 12—533f
帕奇尼氏小体 pacinian corpuscle 解剖学 12—537b
帕奇诺 Pacino, Al(fredo James) 美国演员 12—537b
帕切科 Pacheco, Francisco 西班牙画家 12—532a
帕切科 Pacheco, José Emilio 墨西哥文学评论家、小说家 12—532a
帕丘卡 Pachuca 墨西哥城市 12—533f
帕容 Pajon, Claude 法国神学家 12—552d
帕茹 Pajou, Augustin 法国雕刻家 12—552d
帕萨迪纳 Pasadena 美国得克萨斯州城市 13—71a
帕萨迪纳 Pasadena 美国加利福尼亚州城市 13—70f
帕萨迪纳剧院 Pasadena Playhouse 美国剧院 13—71a
帕萨尔加德 Pasargadae 伊朗古城 13—71b
帕萨卡里亚 passacaglia 宫廷舞蹈 13—75f
《帕萨罗维茨条约》 Passarowitz, Treaty of 欧洲历史 13—76e
帕萨马科迪人 Passamaquoddy 美国印第安人 13—76c
帕萨马科迪湾 Passamaquoddy Bay 大西洋海湾 13—76d
帕塞克 Pasek, Jan Chryzostom 波兰军人 13—73e
帕塞伊克 Passaic 美国城市 13—76c
帕塞伊克河 Passaic River 美国河流 13—76c
帕赛 Pasay 菲律宾城市 13—71b
帕散 Pascin, Jules 法国画家 13—73c
帕瑟瓦尔克 Pasewalk 德国城镇 13—73e
帕森尼奥斯(尼西亚的) Parthenius of Nicaea 希腊诗人、语法学家 13—65c
帕森斯 Parsons, Sir Charles Algernon 英国工程师 13—63d
帕森斯 Parsons, Elsie (Worthington) Clews 英国社会学家、人类学家 13—63e
帕森斯 Parsons, Louella 美国新闻记者 13—63f
帕森斯 Parsons, Richard D. 美国时代华纳公司首席执行官 13—63f
帕森斯 Parsons, Robert 英格兰耶稣会会士 13—64a
帕森斯 Parsons, Talcott 美国社会学家 13—64b
帕森斯桌 Parsons table 家具 13—64d
帕森特 Poussaint, Alvin 美国精神病学家 13—469e
帕绍 Passau 德国城市 13—76e
帕舍指数 Paasche index 经济学 12—530d
帕什瓦 peshwa 印度马拉塔人首相职位 13—193d
帕斯 Paz, Octavio 墨西哥作家、外交家 13—106e
帕斯·埃斯登索罗 Paz Estenssoro, Víctor 玻利维亚政治家 13—106f
帕斯蒂尔 Pasture, Rogier de la (painter) 佛兰德斯画家 13—84a
帕斯顿信札 Paston Letters 英格兰历史资料 13—82f
帕斯菲尔德男爵 Passfield (of Passfield Corner), Sidney James Webb, Baron (English socialist) 英国社会主义者、经济学家 13—78d
帕斯加尔 Paschal 教皇、敌对教皇的称号 13—72e
帕斯加尔(I) Paschal(I) 敌对教皇 13—72e

帕斯加尔二世 Paschal Ⅱ 教皇 13—72f
帕斯加尔(三世) Paschal(Ⅲ) 敌对教皇 13—73a
帕斯加尔一世,圣 Paschal Ⅰ, SAINT 教皇 13—72e
帕斯捷尔纳克 Pasternak, Boris (Leonidovich) 俄国诗人 13—81b
帕斯卡 pascal 计量单位 13—71b
帕斯卡 Pascal, Blaise 法国科学家、哲学家 13—71c
帕斯卡古拉 Pascagoula 美国城市 13—71b
帕斯卡西乌斯,圣 Paschasius Radbertus, SAINT 法国神学家、作家 13—73b
帕斯卡原理 Pascal's principle 物理学 13—72d
帕斯凯维奇 Paskevich, Ivan Fyodorovich 俄国军官 13—75a
帕斯科 Pasco 秘鲁省份 13—73c
帕斯科 Pasco 美国城市 13—73c
帕斯科里 Pascoli, Giovanni 意大利诗人 13—73d
帕斯克里斯琴 Pass Christian 美国城市 13—75f
帕斯夸谷镇 Valle de la Pascua 委内瑞拉城市 17—454c
帕斯拉 Passerat, Jean 法国诗人 13—77b
帕斯皮耶 passepied 法国舞蹈 13—77b
帕斯塔 Pasta, Giuditta (Maria Costanza) 意大利歌唱家 13—80d
帕斯特 Pastor, Tony 美国歌舞团经理、歌唱家 13—83a
帕斯特罗内 Pastrone, Giovanni 意大利电影导演、制片人 13—83e
帕斯托 Pasto 哥伦比亚城市 13—82e
帕斯托尔 Pastor, Ludwig, FREIHERR (baron) VON CAMPERSFELDEN 德国作家 13—82f
帕斯托拉·戈麦斯 Pastora Gómez, Edén 尼加拉瓜革命者 13—83b
帕斯托里乌斯 Pastorius, Francis Daniel 德国教育家、作家 13—83d
帕斯卓 Pâssjo 北欧民俗 13—79f
帕苏丰杜 Passo Fundo 巴西城市 13—79f
帕苏斯 Passos 巴西城市 13—79f
帕索里尼 Pasolini, Pier Paolo 意大利作家、导演 13—75b
帕塔戈罗人 Patángoro 哥伦比亚印第安人 13—84c
帕台农神庙 Parthenon 希腊神庙 13—65e
帕泰 Pathé, Charles 法国电影业先驱 13—87c
帕泰尔诺 Paternò 意大利城镇 13—86e
帕泰吉 Pategi 尼日利亚城镇 13—85b
帕坦 Pātan 印度城镇 13—84c
帕坦 Pātan (Nepal) 尼泊尔城镇 13—84c
帕坦-索姆纳特 Pātan-Somnāth (India) 印度古城 13—84c
帕特尔 Patel, Vallabhbhai Jhaverbhai 印度政治家 13—85c
帕特尔纳陶器 Paterna ware 西班牙陶器 13 00c
帕特库尔 Patkul, Johann Reinhold von 德意志外交家 13—88f
帕特库洛斯 Paterculus, Velleius 罗马历史学家 13—86e
帕特雷 Pátrai 希腊城市、港口 13—89f
帕特里克 Patrick, Mary Mills 美国传教士、教育家 13—91a
帕特里克兄弟 Patrick, Lester B. and Frank A. 加拿大冰球运动员、领队 13—90f
帕特里奇 Partridge, Eric 英国词典编辑者 13—69b
帕特莫尔 Patmore Coventry (Kersey Dighton) 英国诗人、作家 13—89a
帕特莫斯 Pátmos 希腊岛屿 13—89b
帕特诺珀共和国 Parthenopean Republic 意大利前共和国 13—66a
帕特恰科家族 Parteciaco FAMILY 意大利贵族世家 13—65b
帕特森 Paterson 美国城市 13—86f
帕特森 Patterson, Alicia 美国新闻工作者 13—92c
帕特森 Paterson, A(ndrew) B(arton) 澳大利亚诗人、记者 13—87a
帕特森 Patterson, Eleanor Medill 美国报纸主编、发行人 13—92d
帕特森 Patterson, Floyd 美国拳击运动员 13—92e
帕特森 Patterson, John Henry 美国制造商 13—92f
帕特森 Patterson, Joseph Medill 美国新闻记者 13—93a
帕特森 Paterson, William 美国法理学家 13—87c
帕图卡河 Patuca River 洪都拉斯河流 13—93d
帕图斯 Patos 巴西城市 13—89e
帕图斯 Paetus, Thrasea (Roman senator) 罗马元老 12—542a
帕图斯-迪米纳斯 Patos de Minas 巴西城市 13—89e
帕图斯潟湖 Patos Lagoon 巴西潟湖 13—89f
帕拖拉 paṭolā 印度纱丽服 13—89c
帕脱那拉泰 patralatā 印度艺术 13—90a
帕瓦罗蒂 Pavarotti, Luciano 意大利男高音歌唱家 13—101f
帕韦利奇 Pavelić, Ante 克罗地亚法西斯首脑 13—101f
帕韦泽 Pavese, Cesare 意大利诗人、作家 13—102a
帕维 Pavie, Auguste(-Jean-Marie) 法国探险家、外交家 13—102f
帕维亚 Pavia 意大利城市 13—102c
帕维亚-拉西 Pavía y Lacy, Manuel 西班牙将军 13—102d
帕维亚-罗德里格斯 Pavía y Rodríguez de Alburquerque, Manuel 西班牙将军 13—102e
帕维亚战役 Pavia, Battle of 法国历史 13—102d
帕翁战役 Pavón, Battle of 阿根廷历史 13—104a
帕沃夫斯卡 Pawłowska, Eliza (Polish writer) 波兰作家 13—104c
帕乌拉凯夜鹰 pauraque 鸟类 13—101b
帕乌斯托夫斯基 Paustovsky, Konstantin Georgiyevich 苏联小说家 13—101d
帕西 Passy, Frédéric 法国经济学家 13—80c
帕西菲克格罗夫 Pacific Grove 美国城市 12—533e
帕西格河 Pasig River 菲律宾河流 13—74e
帕西内蒂 Pasinetti, Francesco 意大利电影导演、历史学家 13—74e
帕西珀尼-特洛伊希尔斯 Parsippany-Troy Hills 美国镇区 13—63b
帕西人 Parsi 琐罗亚斯德教徒的后裔 13—63a
帕西特利斯 Pasiteles 希腊雕刻家 13—74f
帕希茨 Pašić, Nikola 塞尔维亚首相 13—74c
帕希亚图阿 Pahiatua 新西兰城市 12—547b
帕夏 pasha 土耳其旧官称 13—73f
帕谢库·佩雷拉 Pacheco Pereira, Duarte 葡萄牙探险家 12—532b
帕亚伦塔国家公园 Padjelanta National Park 瑞典国家公园 12—540c
帕扬 Payen, Anselme 法国化学家 13—105d
帕尧 Phayao 泰国城镇 13—222b
帕耶·达信 Phraya Taksin (Siamese king) 暹罗国王 13—268d
帕伊西埃洛 Paisiello, Giovanni 意大利作曲家 12—551a
帕扎尔吉克 Pazardzhik 保加利亚城镇 13—107b
拍 beat 物理学 2—307f
拍 beat 音乐 2—307f
拍号 time signature 音乐 17—100a
拍毽子 battledore and shuttlecock 儿童游戏 2—283b
拍立得公司 Polaroid Corporation 美国公司 13—398a
拍卖 auction 商业 2—44f
俳句 haiku 日本诗歌形式 7—410e
俳谐 haikai 连歌形式 7—410c
排 platoon 军队编制 13—363d
排比 parallelism 修辞学 13—35d
排冰 pack ice 两极浮冰 12—537c
排斥论者 Exclusive 澳大利亚罪犯殖民区的自由民 6—189e
排灯节 Dīwālī 印度宗教节日 5—348b
排队论 queuing theory 运筹学、管理科学 14—88f
排放-控制系统 emission-control system 汽车工程 6—61c
排粪 defecation 生理学 5—207c
排列与组合 permutations and combinations 数学 13—175a
排卵 ovulation 生理学 12—514a
排尿 urination 生理学 17—416d
排尿酸药 uricosuric 药物 17—416a
排球 VOLLEYBALL 体育项目 16—154a
排球 volleyball 体育项目 18—40a
排水 drainage 农业技术 5—412c
排他主义 particularism 人类学 13—67f

排外性雇佣制企业 closed shop 工会安全保障 4—299f
排湾语 Paiwan language 中国高山族语言 12—552b
排湾族 Paiwan 中国民族 12—552a
排箫 panpipe 乐器 13—15a
排泄 excretion 生理学 6—190a
排犹主义 anti-Semitism 宗教 1—381d
排字 typesetting (the setting of type for use in any of a variety of printing processes) 印刷 17—307d
排字机 typesetting machine 机械 17—307d
"徘徊者"号探测器 Ranger 美国航天探测器 14—150c
迫击炮 mortar 武器 11—408d
哌嗪 piperazine 药物 13—318f
哌替啶 meperidine 药物 11—122d
派埃亚 Paiea (Hawaiian king) 夏威夷国王 12—547e
派安赞歌 paean 希腊抒情诗 12—541a
派迪亚斯河 Pedieos River 塞浦路斯河流 13—119f
派地亚 paideia 古希腊教育体系 12—547d
派恩布拉夫 Pine Bluff 美国城市 13—310c
派恩敦 Pinetown 南非城镇 13—311f
派恩福尔斯 Pine Falls 加拿大村庄 13—310c
派恩山 Pine Mountain 美国山脉 13—310c
派尔 Pyle, Ernie 美国新闻记者 14—42e
派尔 Pyle, Howard 美国画家、作家 14—42f
派尔努 Pärnu 爱沙尼亚城市 13—60a
派尔氏集合淋巴结 Peyer's patch 解剖学 13—215c
派克 Pike, Kenneth L(ee) 美国语言学家、人类学者 13—300f
派克 Pike, Mary Hayden Green 美国小说家 13—301a
派克 Pike, Zebulon Montgomery 美国军官、探险家 13—301b
派克鳄 Euparkeria 古生物学 6—161f
派克斯峰 Pikes Peak 美国山峰 13—301c
派拉蒙传播公司 Paramount Communications Inc. 美国公司 13—36f
派拉蒙影片公司 Paramount Pictures Corporation 美国公司 13—37a
派罗阿 Paeroa 新西兰城市 12—541f
派洛皮德 Pelopidas 第比斯政治家 13—131e
派珀 Piper, William T. 美国飞机制造家 13—318d
派普斯通 Pipestone 美国城市 13—319a
派热克斯耐热硬质玻璃 Pyrex 特种玻璃 14—46d
派桑杜 Paysandú 乌拉圭城市 13—106c
派斯 Páez, José Antonio 委内瑞拉军人、总统 12—542b
派延奈湖 Päijänne, Lake 芬兰湖泊 12—547f
派尤特人 Paiute 美国印第安人 12—551e
蒎烯 pinene 化合物 13—311c
番禺 Panyu 中国城市 13—17b
潘 Pan 希腊神话神名 13—1f
潘查希拉 Pancasila 印度尼西亚哲学 13—7c
潘查耶特 panchayat 印度种姓政府机构 13—7c
潘达洛斯 Pandarus 希腊传说人物 13—9b
潘代岛 Pandai Island (Indonesia) 印度尼西亚岛屿 13—8f
潘代尔高原 Bhānder Plateau 印度中北部高原 2—450a
潘德尔马 Panderma (Turkey) 土耳其城镇 13—9c
潘迪特(夫人) Pandit, Vijaya Lakshmi 印度政治家、外交家 13—9c
潘地亚王朝 Pāṇḍya DYNASTY 印度古代王朝 13—10a
潘杜尔夫 Pandulph 教皇使节、主教 13—9f
潘杜罗 Panduro, Leif 丹麦小说家、戏剧家 13—9f
潘多尔斐 Pandolfi, Vito 意大利评论家、戏剧学者 13—9e
潘多拉 Pandora 希腊神话人物 13—9e
潘恩 Paine, Thomas 美国作家 12—549a
潘菲利亚 Pamphylia 古安纳托利亚地区 13—1c
潘盖翁山 Pangaion, Mount 希腊山区 13—11b
潘古纳 Panguna 巴布亚新几内亚城镇 13—12a
潘光旦 Pan Guangdan 中国社会学家、教育家 13—3b
潘圭奇 Panguitch 美国犹他州中南部城市 13—12a
潘季河 Panj, Āb-e (Central Asia) 中亚河流 13—13a
潘加洛斯 Pangalos, Theodoros 希腊军人、政治家 13—11c
潘加尼 Pangani 坦桑尼亚古城 13—11c
潘克赫斯特 Pankhurst, Dame Christabel Harriette 英国女权运动领袖 13—13d
潘克赫斯特(夫人) Pankhurst, Emmeline 英国女权运动者 13—13d
潘魁 Phan Khoi 越南知识分子领袖 13—218f
潘勒韦 Painlevé, Paul 法国政治家、数学家 12—549d
潘默男爵(第二) Panmure, Fox Maule, 2nd Baron 英国陆军大臣 13—14a
潘尼迦 Panikkar, Kavalam Madhava 印度政治家 13—12c
潘尼尼 Pannini, Giovanni Paolo 意大利画家 13—14c
潘涅吉里斯 panegyris 希腊宗教集会 13—10c
潘诺尼亚 Pannonia 欧洲历史地区 13—14d
潘帕 Pampa 美国城市 12—576d
潘帕斯草 pampas grass (*Cortaderia selloana*) 草本植物 13—1a
潘帕斯猫 pampas cat (*Felis colocolo*) 哺乳动物 12—576f
潘佩珠 Phan Boi Chau 越南爱国者 13—218d
潘普洛纳 Pamplona 哥伦比亚城市 13—1d
潘普洛纳 Pamplona 西班牙自治社区 13—1d
潘奇马尔科 Panchimalco 萨尔瓦多城镇 13—7f
潘清简 Phan Thanh Gian 越南政府官员、外交家 13—218f
潘萨尔斯 Pansaers, Clément 比利时诗人 13—15b
潘塔尔岛 Pantar Island 印度尼西亚岛屿 13—15f
潘塔莱翁 Pantaléon, Jacques (pope) 教皇 13—15d
潘塔隆内 Pantaloon 戏剧人物 13—15d
潘泰莱里亚岛 Pantelleria Island 意大利岛屿 13—16a
潘特尔 Panter, Peter 德国作家 13—16a
潘特克莱尔 Pointe-Claire 加拿大城市 13—389f
潘特纳尔 Pantanal 巴西平原 13—15f
潘天寿 Pan Tianshou 中国画家 13—3e
潘廷逢 Phan Dinh Phung 越南抗法运动领袖 13—218e
潘兴 Pershing, John J(oseph) 美国将军 13—182b
潘扎 Panza, Sancho 文学人物 13—17c
潘周桢 Phan Chau Trinh 越南民族主义领袖 13—218d
攀鲈 climbing perch (species *Anabas testudineus*) 鱼类 4—292e
攀木鸟 woodcreeper 鸟类 18—322d
攀雀科 Remizidae 鸟类 14—222d
攀牙 Phangnga 泰国城镇 13—219b
攀枝花 Panzhihua 中国城市 13—17d
盘 pan 中国古代礼器 13—2a
盘古 Pangu 中国神话 13—11f
盘锦 Panjin 中国城市 13—13b
盘丽鱼 discus fish 鱼类 5—339f
盘龙城 P'an-lung-ch'eng 中国古城遗址 13—3c
盘龙城遗址 Panlongcheng site 中国古城遗址 13—13f
盘舌蟾科 Discoglossidae 动物学 5—339b
盘陀诃罗 bendahara 旧马来首席大臣 2—377c
盘尾丝虫病 onchocerciasis 疾病 12—416e
盘羊 argali (*Ovis ammon*) 哺乳动物 1—461f
磐城 Iwaki 日本城市 8—496a
蟠桃 pantao 中国神话 13—15f
判别式 discriminant 数学 5—339e
判定问题 decision problem 数学、逻辑学 5—203a
判断错误 hamartia 戏剧 7—437c
判断故事 judgment tale (African short story) 非洲短篇故事 9—102a
判决 judgment 法律 9—101e
判决 sentence 法律 15—216a
判例汇编 law report 法律 9—529b
叛道音乐 outlaw music 美国音乐 12—509a

叛国罪 treason 法律 17—204c
叛教 apostasy 基督教 1—415b
庞阿德 Panhard, René 法国工程师 13—12a
庞贝 Pompeii 意大利古城 13—421c
庞德 Pound, Ezra (Loomis) 美国诗人、评论家 13—468e
庞德 Pound, Roscoe 美国法学家、植物学家 13—469b
庞德梅克 Poundmaker 加拿大印第安人首长 13—469d
庞德石英岩 Pound Quartzite 地质学 13—469c
庞蒂弗拉克特 Pontefract 英格兰古集镇 13—428a
庞蒂浦 Pontypool 威尔士城镇 13—429e
庞蒂浦制品 Pontypool ware 英国金属器皿 13—429e
庞蒂亚克 Pontiac 美国印第安人首长 13—428b
庞蒂亚克 Pontiac 美国伊利诺伊州城市 13—428c
庞蒂亚克 Pontiac 美国密歇根州城市 13—428d
庞蒂耶夫尔公爵 Penthièvre, Louis-Joseph, duc de (duke of) 法国将军 13—149d
庞多雷湖 Pend Oreille Lake 美国湖泊 13—135f
庞菲利 Pamphili, Giovanni Battista (pope) 教皇 13—1a
庞加莱 Poincaré, Henri 法国数学家、天文学家 13—387e
庞卡城 Ponca City 美国城市 13—424b
庞尼特 Punnett, Reginald Crundall 英国遗传学家 14—28e
庞帕诺比奇 Pompano Beach 美国城市 13—421b
庞培 Pompey THE GREAT 罗马政治家、将军 13—422f
庞培·马格努斯·庇护 Pompeius Magnus Pius, Sextus 庞培次子 13—422e
庞佩利 Pumpelly, Raphael W. 美国地质学家、科学探险家 14—25b
庞皮利乌斯 Pompilius, Numa (8th-7th-century-BC traditional Roman king) 罗马传说国王 13—423f
庞奇 Punch 木偶戏人物 14—25e
庞恰特雷恩湖 Pontchartrain, Lake 美国湖泊 13—427d
庞乔斗篷 poncho 服饰 13—425c
庞塞·德莱昂 Ponce de León, Juan 西班牙探险家 13—424d
庞塞·德莱昂 Ponce de León, Pedro 西班牙本笃会修士 13—424f
庞瑟尔 Ponselle, Rosa 美国歌唱家 13—426f
庞斯 Pons, Lily 美国歌唱家 13—426e
庞特 Ponte, Antonio da 意大利建筑工程师 13—427d
庞特 Pond, John 英国天文学家 13—425d
庞特道埃 Pontardawe 威尔士地名 13—427c
庞特里亚金 Pontryagin, Lev Semyonovich 俄罗斯数学家 13—429d
庞特普里斯 Pontypridd 威尔士城镇 13—429f
庞廷山脉 Pontic Mountains 土耳其山脉 13—428e
庞勋 Pang Xun 中国唐末起义领袖 13—11a
庞越 Probolinggo 印度尼西亚城市 13—523f
《旁观者》 Spectator, The 英国刊物 16—13e
《旁观者》 Spectator, The 英国周刊 16—13f
旁遮普 Punjab 巴基斯坦省份 14—28a
旁遮普 Punjab 印度邦名 14—27e
旁遮普大学 Punjab, University of the 巴基斯坦大学 14—28c
旁遮普平原 Punjab Plain 印度冲积平原 14—28d
旁遮普语 Punjābī language 印度语言 14—28d
膀胱 urinary bladder 解剖学 17—416b
膀胱癌 bladder cancer 疾病 2—522c
膀胱炎 cystitis 疾病 5—95b
鳑鲏 bitterling 鱼类 2—504a
抛接子游戏 jackstones 游戏 8—508e
抛木杆 caber, tossing the 苏格兰运动项目 3—305b
抛石机 ballista 古代器械 2—177e
抛石索 sling 工具 15—432f
抛物面 paraboloid 数学 13—29f
抛物线 parabola 数学 13—29d
抛物型方程 parabolic equation 数学 13—29e
抛重 weight throw 运动 18—169f
咆哮西风带 roaring forties 气象学 14—324f
狍 roe deer (*Capreolus capreolus*) 哺乳动物 14—350e
庖牺 Pao Hsi 中国神话传说 13—17f
袍剑剧 cloak and sword drama 西班牙文学 4—296c
泡铋矿 bismutite 矿物 2—502c
泡菜 sauerkraut 食品 15—83d
泡蟾 tungara frog (*Physalaemus pustulosus*) 两栖动物 17—268e
泡利 Pauli, Wolfgang 奥地利物理学家 13—99e
泡利不相容原理 Pauli exclusion principle 物理学 13—99f
泡令 Pauling, Linus 美国化学家 13—100a
泡螺 bubble shell 腹足动物 3—217c
泡沫 foam 物理化学 6—383c
泡沫玻璃 foam glass 轻质遮光玻璃 6—383c
泡沫浮选 froth flotation 选矿方法 6—503e
泡沫胶乳 latex foam 化学 9—510f
泡沫珊瑚 Cystiphyllum 古生物学 5—95a
泡沫塑料 foamed plastic 合成树脂材料 6—383d
泡沫橡胶 foam rubber 特种橡胶 6—383d
泡盛草属 Astilbe 植物学 2—5a
疱疹性咽峡炎 herpangina 疾病 8—48e
炮弹 shell 军火 15—295f
炮弹树 cannonball tree (*Couroupita guianensis*) 木本植物 3—405e
炮·是耶暖 Phao Sriyanond 泰国警察总监 13—219c
炮铜 gunmetal 合金 7—372d
胚孔 blastopore 解剖学 2—531b
胚泡 blastocyst 胚胎学 2—531a
胚乳 endosperm 植物学 6—75b
胚胎 embryo 胚胎学 6—58a
胚胎学 embryology 生物学 6—58a
胚珠 ovule 植物学 12—514b
陪衬人物 foil 文学 6—386c
陪审官资格审查 voir dire 法律 18—33e
陪审团 jury 法律 9—117a
陪审推事 assessor 法律 1—561f
培奥尼亚 Paeonia 巴尔干历史地区 12—541d
培尔 Bayle, Pierre 法国哲学家 2—296e
培尔拉美苏 Per Ramessu 古埃及城市 13—155f
培根 Bacon, Albion Fellows 美国改革家、作家 2—119e
培根 Bacon, Delia Salter 美国作家 2—119f
培根 Bacon, Francis, VISCOUNT SAINT ALBAN (or ALBANS), BARON OF VERULAM 英国法学家、政治家、哲学家、语言大师 2—120c
培根 Bacon, Francis 英国画家 2—120a
培根 Bacon, Henry 美国建筑师 2—124a
培根 Bacon, John (theologian) 英国神学家 2—124b
培根 Bacon, John 英国雕刻家 2—124b
培根 Bacon, Nathaniel 北美种植园主 2—124c
培根 Bacon, Sir Nicholas 英格兰大臣 2—124c
培根 Bacon, Roger 英国方济各会修士、科学家 2—124d
培根法 Baconian method 研究自然的方法 2—124e
培根肉 bacon 食品 2—119e
培根索普 Baconthorpe, John 英格兰神学家、哲学家 2—124f
培拉 Pella 希腊古城 13—130f
培拉特 Berat 阿尔巴尼亚城市 2—397e
培雷山 Pelée, Mount 法属马提尼克岛活火山 13—129e
培琉喜阿姆 Pelusium 古埃及城市 13—132f
培刹 peshat 犹太教 13—193a
培养基 culture medium 生物学 5—57b
赔偿金 composition 古日尔曼法律 4—399f
赔偿金 wergild 法律 18—190f
锫(Bk) berkelium 化学元素 2—409d
裴百秋 Perpetua 基督教殉教者 13—177c
裴多菲 Petőfi, Sándor 匈牙利诗人、革命家 13—207b
裴矩 Pei Ju 中国地理学家 13—123f

裴斯泰洛齐 Pestalozzi, Johann Heinrich 瑞士教育改革家 13—194f
裴颉 Pei Wei 中国哲学家 13—124a
裴文中 Pei Wenzhong 中国考古学家、古人类学家 13—124b
裴秀 Pei Xiu 中国地图学家 13—124c
佩埃特河 Payette River 美国河流 13—105d
佩奥特掌 peyote 植物学 13—215c
佩波 Pepo, Bencivieni di (painter) 佛罗伦萨画家 13—153a
佩波利家族 Pepoli FAMILY 意大利贵族世家 13—153b
佩差拉 Phetsarath Ratanavongsa, Prince 老挝亲王、政治领袖 13—225f
佩察莫 Petsamo (Russia) 俄罗斯城镇 13—213d
佩得曼岭 Petermann Ranges 澳大利亚山岭 13—203f
佩德雷尔 Pedrell, Felipe 西班牙作曲家、音乐学者 13—120d
佩德罗 Peter 西班牙卡斯蒂利亚、莱昂国王 13—200d
佩德罗 Pedro, Dom 葡萄牙亲王、摄政 13—121a
佩德罗(残忍者) Peter THE CRUEL 葡萄牙国王 13—202d
佩德罗(讲究礼仪者) Peter THE CEREMONIOUS 阿拉贡国王 13—202d
佩德罗(天主教徒) Peter THE CATHOLIC 阿拉贡国王 13—202d
佩德罗(西班牙人) Petrus HISPANUS 教皇 13—213c
佩德罗(正义者) Peter THE JUST 葡萄牙国王 13—202e
佩德罗二世 Pedro II 巴西皇帝 13—120e
佩德罗二世 Peter II 阿拉贡国王 13—200c
佩德罗二世 Peter II 葡萄牙国王 13—197b
佩德罗胡安-卡瓦列罗 Pedro Juan Caballero 巴拉圭城镇 13—121a
佩德罗利诺 Pedrolino 戏剧中定型人物 13—121a
佩德罗三世 Peter III 阿拉贡国王 13—200c
佩德罗三世 Peter III 葡萄牙女王的丈夫 13—197b
佩德罗四世 Peter IV 阿拉贡国王 13—200c
佩德罗四世 Peter IV 葡萄牙国王 13—197b
佩德罗五世 Peter V 葡萄牙国王 13—197c
佩德罗一世 Pedro I 巴西帝国创始人、皇帝 13—120e
佩德罗一世 Peter I 阿拉贡国王 13—197a
佩德罗一世 Peter I 阿拉贡国王 13—200b
佩德罗一世 Peter I 葡萄牙国王 13—197a
佩德罗一世 Peter I 西西里国王、阿拉贡国王 13—200b
佩德森 Pedersen, Charles J(ohn) 美国化学家 13—119a
佩迪人 Pedi 南非民族 13—119d
佩蒂 Petty, Richard 美国赛车手 13—213e
佩蒂 Petty, Tom 美国歌手、歌曲作家 13—213f
佩蒂-菲茨莫里斯 Petty-Fitzmaurice, Henry Charles Keith 英国外交家 13—214b
佩蒂-菲茨莫里斯 Petty-Fitzmaurice, William 英国首相 13—214b
佩蒂特 Pettit, Bob 美国篮球运动员 13—213d
佩蒂特 Pettit, Katherine 美国居民区工作人员 13—213e
佩蒂翁 Pétion, Alexandre Sabès 海地总统 13—205a
佩蒂翁·德·维尔纳夫 Pétion de Villeneuve, Jérôme 法国政治家 13—205a
佩蒂翁维尔 Pétionville 海地首都郊区 13—205b
佩顿 Paton, Alan (Stewart) 南非作家 13—89d
佩顿 Payton, Walter (Jerry) 美国橄榄球运动员 13—106d
佩多 Pedo, Albinovanus 罗马诗人 13—120b
佩恩 Pesne, Antoine 法国画家 13—193d
佩恩 Penn, Arthur 美国电影导演 13—140d
佩恩 Payne, Humfry (Gilbert Garth) 英国考古学家 13—105f
佩恩 Penn, Irving 美国摄影家 13—140e
佩恩 Payne, John Howard 美国剧作家 13—105f
佩恩 Payne, Peter 英格兰神学家、外交家 13—106a
佩恩 Penn, William 英格兰基督教领袖 13—140f
佩恩 Penn, Sir William 英国海军上将 13—141c
佩恩堡 Fort Payne 美国城市 6—414e
佩恩蒂德沙漠 Painted Desert 美国沙漠 12—550a
佩恩斯维尔 Painesville 美国城市 12—549d
佩尔 Perl, Martin Lewis 美国物理学家 13—172e
佩尔狄卡斯 Perdiccas 马其顿将军、摄政王 13—161a
佩尔蒂埃 Peletier, Jacques 法国诗人 13—129f
佩尔蒂埃 Pelletier, Pierre-Joseph 法国化学家 13—131b
佩尔吉 Perga 土耳其城市 13—165e
佩尔加米诺 Pergamino 阿根廷城市 13—165f
佩尔莱佩 Perlepe (Macedonia) 马其顿城镇 13—172f
佩尔梅克 Permeke, Constant 比利时画家 13—174a
佩尔蒙 Permon, Laure (French author) 法国作家 13—175a
佩尔尼克 Pernik 保加利亚城镇 13—176a
佩尔切人 Puelche 已消亡的南美印第安人 14—14f
佩尔塞 Percé 加拿大城市 13—156e
佩尔什 Perche 法国地区 13—157e
佩尔什马 Percheron 马品种 13—157f
佩尔西尼公爵 Persigny, Jean-Gilbert-Victor Fialin, duc de (duke of) 法国政治家 13—183f
佩尔西乌斯 Persius 罗马诗人 13—184c
佩尔修斯 Perseus 马其顿国王 13—182b
佩夫斯纳 Pevsner, Antoine 法国雕刻家、画家 13—214e
佩夫斯纳 Pevsner, Naum Neemia 俄国雕塑家 13—214e
佩戈莱西 Pergolesi, Giovanni Battista 意大利作曲家 13—166c
佩戈洛蒂 Pegolotti, Francesco Balducci 意大利商人、作者 13—122f
佩格勒 Pegler, (James) Westbrook 美国专栏作家 13—122d
佩吉·古根海姆收藏馆 Peggy Guggenheim Collection (Venice) 意大利艺术收藏馆 13—122d
佩吉特 Paget, Sir James 英国外科医师、生理学家 12—544f
佩季帕 Petipa, Marius 俄国舞蹈家、编导 13—205b
佩剑 sabre 重型军用剑 14—484f
佩金柏 Peckinpah, Sam 美国电影编导 13—118b
佩卡姆 Peckham, Rufus Wheeler 美国最高法院大法官 13—118a
佩科 Peko 爱沙尼亚宗教神祇 13—127f
佩科斯 Pecos 美国城市 13—118b
佩科斯·比尔 Pecos Bill 美国传说人物 13—118c
佩科斯河 Pecos River 美国河流 13—118c
佩科特人 Pequot 美国印第安人 13—155e
佩克 Phek 印度城镇 13—222f
佩克 Peck, Annie Smith 美国登山运动员 13—117f
佩克 Peck, (Eldred) Gregory 美国电影演员 13—118a
佩克堡水坝 Fort Peck Dam 美国水坝 6—414f
佩拉尔塔 Peralta, Pedro de 西班牙殖民地官员 13—156d
佩拉吉娅(安提阿的),圣 Pelagia OF ANTIOCH, SAINT 基督教圣徒 13—127f
佩拉杰群岛 Pelagie Islands 意大利岛群 13—128b
佩拉斯吉人 Pelasgi 古代希腊人 13—128d
佩拉维奇诺 Pelavicino, Oberto 意大利领袖 13—128e
佩拉约 Pelayo 阿斯图里亚斯国王 13—128e
佩莱格里尼 Pellegrini, Carlo 意大利漫画家 13—131a
佩莱格里诺 Pellegrino PELLIGRINI (Italian painter) 意大利画家 13—131a
佩兰 Perrin, Claude 法国将军 13—179c
佩勒代尼耶植物园 Peradeniya Botanic Gardens 斯里兰卡植物园 13—156a
佩勒姆 Pelham, Henry 英国首相 13—130a
佩勒姆-霍利斯 Pelham-Holles, Thomas 英国首相 13—130b
佩雷 Perret, Auguste 法国建筑师 13—179a
佩雷阿尔 Perréal, Jean 法国画家、建筑师 13—178f
佩雷茨 Peretz, Isaac Leib 波兰作家 13—163b
佩雷达 Pereda, José María de 西班牙作家 13—161c
佩雷尔曼 Perelman, S.J. 美国幽默作家 13—162e
佩雷尔斯 Perrers, Alice 英格兰国王情妇 13—179a
佩雷格里尼(马里库尔的) Peregrinus of Maricourt, Peter 法国学者 13—162b

佩雷格里努 Peregrinus 基督教神学家 13—162a
佩雷格里诺斯 Peregrinus Proteus 希腊哲学家 13—162a
佩雷克 Pérec, Marie-José 法国短跑运动员 13—161c
佩雷拉 Pereira 哥伦比亚城市 13—162b
佩雷拉 Pereira, Irene Rice 美国画家 13—162c
佩雷拉 Pereira, Nuno Álvares, Blessed 葡萄牙军事领袖 13—162c
佩雷斯 Pérez, Antonio 西班牙朝臣 13—163d
佩雷斯 Pérez, Carlos Andrés 委内瑞拉总统 13—163e
佩雷斯 Pérez, Manuel Benítez 西班牙斗牛士 13—163e
佩雷斯 Peres, Shimon 以色列总理 13—162e
佩雷斯 Pérez, Tony 美国棒球运动员 13—163e
佩雷斯·埃斯基韦尔 Pérez Esquivel, Adolfo 阿根廷雕刻家、人权运动战士 13—164b
佩雷斯·德·阿亚拉 Pérez de Ayala, Ramón 西班牙小说家、诗人 13—163f
佩雷斯·德古斯曼 Pérez de Guzmán, Fernán 西班牙诗人、历史学家 13—164a
佩雷斯·德奎利亚尔 Pérez de Cuellar, Javier 秘鲁外交家、联合国秘书长 13—164a
佩雷斯·德·伊塔 Pérez de Hita, Ginés 西班牙作家 13—164b
佩雷斯·加尔多斯 Pérez Galdós, Benito 西班牙作家 13—164c
佩雷斯克 Peiresc, Nicolas-Claude Fabri de 法国古物收藏家、人文主义者 13—125b
佩雷斯·希门尼斯 Pérez Jiménez, Marcos 委内瑞拉总统 13—164d
佩里 Perry, Antoinette 美国演员、导演 13—180c
佩里 Perry, Bliss 美国学者、编辑 13—180d
佩里 Peri, Jacopo 意大利作曲家 13—166e
佩里 Perry, Lee ("Scratch") 牙买加音乐制作人 13—180d
佩里 Perry, Lilla Cabot 美国画家 13—180e
佩里 Perry, Matthew C(albraith) 美国海军军官 13—180e
佩里 Perry, Nora 美国记者、诗人 13—181a
佩里 Perry, Oliver Hazard 美国海军军官 13—181a
佩里 Perry, Ralph Barton 美国教育家、哲学家 13—181b
佩里埃 Perier, Casimir(-Pierre) 法国银行家、政治家 13—168b
佩里安德 Periander 希腊科林斯僭主 13—167a
佩里布森 Peribsen 埃及国王 13—167b
佩里戈尔 Périgord 法国历史、文化大区 13—168d
佩里戈尔文化期工艺 Perigordian industry 考古学 13—168d
佩里格 Périgueux 法国城镇 13—168e
佩里哈山脉 Perijá, Mountains of 哥伦比亚、委内瑞拉之间山脉 13—168f
佩里·罗西 Peri Rossi, Cristina 拉美小说家、诗人 13—166f
佩里尼翁侯爵 Pérignon, Dominique-Catherine, marquis de 法国将军、元帅 13—168c
佩里威 periwig 假发 13—171c
《佩里协定》 Perry Convention (Japanese history) 日本历史 13—181c
佩里镇 Vila Pery (Mozambique) 莫桑比克城市 17—560e
佩利 Paley, William 英国牧师、哲学家 12—565b
佩利 Paley, William S. 哥伦比亚广播公司总经理 12—565c
佩利河 Pelly River 加拿大河流 13—131d
佩利科 Pellico, Silvio 意大利爱国者、戏剧家 13—131b
佩利尼人 Paeligni 意大利古民族 12—541c
佩利西耶 Pélissier, Aimable-Jean-Jacques, Duke de Malakoff 法国将军 13—130e
佩列斯韦托夫 Peresvetov, Ivan Semenovich 俄国社会评论家 13—163b
佩列亚斯拉夫-赫梅利尼茨基 Pereyaslav-Khmelnitsky 乌克兰城市 13—163c
《佩列亚斯拉夫协定》 Pereyaslav Agreement 乌克兰归属俄国协定 13—163c
佩林 Perrin, Ami 瑞士基督教人士 13—179b
佩龙 Perron, (Charles) Edgar du 荷兰作家、评论家 13—179e
佩卢 Pelloux, Luigi (Girolamo) 意大利将军、首相 13—131d
佩鲁茨 Perutz, Max Ferdinand 英国生物化学家 13—191e
佩鲁吉诺 Perugino 意大利画家 13—191c
佩鲁贾 Perugia 意大利城市 13—191b
佩鲁贾大学 Perugia, University of 意大利大学 13—191b
佩鲁贾湖 Perugia, Lake of (Italy) 意大利湖泊 13—191b
佩鲁克假发 peruke 男子假发 13—191d
佩鲁齐 Peruzzi, Baldassarre (Tommaso) 意大利建筑师、画家 13—192a
佩鲁齐家族 Peruzzi family 意大利金融家族 13—191f
佩鲁西亚 Perusia (Italy) 意大利城市 13—191e
佩路提埃 Pelloutier, Fernand 法国政治学家 13—131c
佩罗 Perrault, Charles 法国诗人、作家 13—178b
佩罗 Perrault, Claude 法国医生、建筑师 13—178e
佩罗 Perrot, Jules (Joseph) 法国舞蹈演员、编导 13—179f
佩罗 Perrot, Nicolas 法国毛皮商、探险家 13—180b
佩罗 Perrault, Pierre 法国水文学家 13—178f
佩罗 Perot, Ross 美国商人、慈善家 13—176f
佩罗·达·科维良 Covilhã, Pêro da 葡萄牙探险家 4—556a
佩罗内 Perronet, Jean(-Rodolphe) 法国土木工程师 13—179e
佩罗坦 Pérotin 法国作曲家 13—177a
佩罗特 Perrot, Sir John 爱尔兰总督 13—179e
佩洛克 pelog 音乐 13—131d
佩洛塔斯 Pelotas 巴西城市 13—132d
佩洛塔斯河 Pelotas River 巴西河流 13—132e
佩蒙特 Per-Month (town, Egypt) 埃及城镇 13—155f
佩讷明德 Peenemünde 德国村庄 13—122b
佩内杜 Penedo 巴西城市 13—137c
佩尼韦蒂科山系 Penibético Mountain System 西班牙山系 13—139d
佩纽蒂诸语言 Penutian languages 美洲印第安语言 13—150b
佩诺布斯科特河 Penobscot River 美国河流 13—146e
佩诺布斯科特人 Penobscot 美国印第安人 13—146d
佩佩 Pepe, Guglielmo 那不勒斯军人 13—151e
佩佩尔 Pepel 塞拉利昂港口 13—151f
佩皮 Pepi 埃及国王之名 13—152a
佩皮二世 Pepi II Neferkare 埃及国王 13—152b
佩皮尼昂 Perpignan 法国城市 13—177f
佩皮斯 Pepys, Samuel 英国日记作家 13—155c
佩皮一世 Pepi I 埃及国王 13—152a
佩泼洛斯女装 peplos 古希腊女装 13—152f
佩珀雷尔 Pepperrell, Sir William 美洲殖民地商人、政治家 13—154b
佩普什 Pepusch, John Christopher 作曲家 13—155b
佩普西湖 Peipsi, Lake 欧洲湖泊 13—124d
佩奇 Peć 塞尔维亚城镇 13—116d
佩奇 Pécs 匈牙利城市 13—118d
佩奇 Page, Clarence 美国报纸专栏作家 12—543b
佩奇 Page, Sir Earle (Christmas Grafton) 澳大利亚政治家 12—543c
佩奇 Page, Sir Frederick Handley 英国飞机设计家 12—543c
佩奇 Page, Geraldine 美国演员 12—543e
佩奇 Paige, Satchel 美国棒球运动员 12—547e
佩奇 Page, Thomas Nelson 美国作家 12—543e
佩奇 Pecci, Vincenzo Gioacchino (pope) 教皇 13—117a
佩奇 Page, Walter Hines 美国作家、外交家 12—544a
佩奇 Page, William 美国画家 12—544b
佩切涅格人 Pechenegs 突厥游牧民族 13—117b
佩琴加 Pechenga 俄罗斯城镇 13—117b
佩萨克 Pessac 法国城镇 13—193e
佩萨罗 Pesaro 意大利城市 13—192b
佩萨尼亚 Pessanha, Camilo 葡萄牙诗人 13—193f
佩塞利诺 Pesellino 意大利画家 13—192f

佩森 Payson 美国犹他州北部城市 13—106d
佩什蒂戈 Peshtigo 美国城市 13—193d
佩斯 Perse, Saint-John 法国诗人 13—181c
佩斯 Pest 匈牙利州名 13—194a
佩斯卡拉 Pescara 意大利城市 13—192d
佩斯卡拉侯爵 Pescara, Fernando Francesco de Avalos, marchese di (marquess of) 意大利军队首领 13—192d
佩斯利 Paisley 英国城市 12—551b
佩斯利披巾 paisley 纺织品 12—551c
佩斯塞尼乌斯·尼格尔·朱斯图斯 Pescennius Niger Justus, Gaius 罗马皇帝 13—192e
佩索阿 Pessoa, Fernando António Nogueira 葡萄牙诗人 13—193f
佩塔雷 Petare 委内瑞拉城市 13—196c
佩塔卢马 Petaluma 美国城市 13—196b
佩塔索斯帽 petasos 服饰 13—196c
佩塔提克瓦 Petah Tiqwa 以色列城市 13—195f
佩塔佐尼 Pettazzoni, Raffaele 意大利宗教史学家、教育家 13—213d
佩特 Pater, Walter (Horatio) 英国批评家、人文主义者 13—86c
佩特拉 Petra 约旦古城 13—207d
佩特拉基斯 Petrakis, Harry Mark 美国小说家 13—207e
佩特拉里亚斯·达维拉 Pedrarias Dávila 西班牙军人、殖民统治者 13—120d
佩特拉罗纳颅骨 Petralona skull 人类化石 13—207f
佩特拉西 Petrassi, Goffredo 意大利作曲家 13—208c
佩特利 Petri, Laurentius 瑞典基督教教士、宗教改革家 13—209a
佩特利 Petri, Olaus 瑞典基督教教士、宗教改革家 13—209a
佩特鲁奇 Petrucci, Pandolfo 意大利商人、政治家 13—213a
佩特罗波利斯 Petrópolis 巴西城市 13—212e
佩特罗利纳 Petrolina 巴西城市 13—211f
佩特罗纳斯双联大厦 Petronas Twin Towers 马来西亚高层建筑 13—212b
佩特罗尼乌斯 Petronius Arbiter, Gaius 古罗马作家 13—212c
佩特罗尼乌斯·马克西穆斯 Petronius Maximus 罗马皇帝 13—212d
佩特森 Paterson, Sir Alexander (Henry) 英国刑罚学家 13—87b
佩特森 Paterson, William 英格兰银行创办人 13—87b
佩特沃思 Petworth 英格兰城镇 13—214c
佩滕 Petén 危地马拉地区 13—196d
佩滕伊察湖 Petén Itzá, Lake 危地马拉湖泊 13—196d
佩提纳克斯 Pertinax, Publius Helvius 罗马皇帝 13—188e
佩托斯基 Petoskey 美国城市 13—207c
佩文西 Pevensey 英格兰地名 13—214d
佩文西子爵 Pevensey, Spencer Compton, Viscount 英格兰贵族 13—214e
《佩文斋书画谱》 Peiwenzhai Shuhuapu 中国清代书画史论 13—125f
佩西克-劳伦斯(皮斯莱克的) Pethick-Lawrence (of Peaslake), Frederick William Pethick-Lawrence, Baron 英国政治家 13—204f
佩西里克 Petherick, John 英国贸易商、探险家 13—204f
佩西切蒂 Persichetti, Vincent 美国作曲家 13—183e
佩希施泰因 Pechstein, Max 德国画家 13—117e
佩夏 Pescia 意大利城镇 13—192e
佩伊 Pei, Mario (Andrew) 美国语言学家 13—124a
佩因 Paine, John Knowles 美国作曲家 12—548f
佩因 Paine, Robert Treat 美国政治家 12—549a
佩因特 Painter, Theophilus Shickel 美国动物学家 12—550e
佩因特 Painter, William 英国作家 12—550e
佩泽森 Pedersen, Holger 丹麦语言学家 13—119b
佩扎 Pezza, Michele 意大利土匪头子 13—215d
配第 Petty, Sir William 英国政治经济学家 13—214a
配额 quota 经济学 14—97c
配给制 rationing 经济学 14—163a
配克 peck 计量单位 13—117f
配树婚制 tree marriage 社会学 17—207d
配套饰物 parure 整套贵重饰物 13—69f
配位场理论 ligand field theory 化学 10—91a
配位化合物 coordination compound 化学 4—486a
配位数 coordination number 化学 4—486c
配位体 ligand 化学 10—91a
配音 dubbing 电影 5—439a
配子 gamete 生物学 6—569f
配子体 gametophyte 生物学 6—569f
喷赤河 Pyandzh River 中亚河流 14—41b
喷出岩 extrusive rock 岩石学 6—199d
喷醋鞭蝎 vinegarroon 节肢动物 18—1b
喷瓜 squirting cucumber (*Ecballium elaterium*) 草本植物 16—171b
"喷火"式飞机 Spitfire 战斗机 16—37a
喷浆混凝土 Gunite(concrete) 建筑材料 7—372d
喷气发动机 jet engine 机械 9—6d
喷气孔 fumarole 地质学 6—522c
喷泉 fountain 园林建筑 6—424d
喷撒 spraying and dusting 农业 16—161a
喷射混凝土 shotcrete 混凝土 15—336d
喷射剂 propellant 推进剂 13—535c
喷水灭火系统 sprinkler system 消防装置 16—165a
喷丝板 spinneret 纺织学 16—32c
盆地和山脉区 Basin and Range Province 美国地理 2—262f
盆地区 Cuvette 刚果行政区 5—81a
盆会 Bon 日本节日 3—22f
盆景 bonsai 园艺 3—35b
盆腔炎症 pelvic inflammatory disease (PID) 疾病 13—133b
烹饪 cuisine 食品制作 5—53c
烹调法 gastronomy 饮食文化 7—27e
烹调用香料 bouquet garni 调味料 3—83d
朋谔斐尔 Bonhoeffer, Dietrich 德国神学家 3—30a
朋特 Punt 非洲历史地区 14—29a
棚桥 covered bridge 木构架公路桥 4—555e
棚屋 wigwam 美洲印第安人住宅 18—249d
彭伯顿 Pemberton, John Clifford 美国南部邦联将领 13—133c
彭布罗克 Pembroke 威尔士城镇 13—133c
彭布罗克伯爵 Pembroke, EARLS OF 英格兰贵族 13—133d
彭布罗克伯爵 Pembroke, Jasper Tudor, Earl of 威尔士贵族 13—133e
彭布罗克伯爵(第二) Pembroke, Richard FitzGilbert, 2nd Earl of 盎格鲁-诺曼贵族 13—133d
彭布罗克伯爵(第一) Pembroke, William Herbert, 1st Earl of 英格兰贵族 13—133e
彭布罗克伯爵(第一) Pembroke, William Marshal, 1st Earl of 英格兰司令官 13—133e
彭布罗克伯爵夫人 Pembroke, Mary Herbert, Countess of 英格兰翻译家 13—133f
彭布罗克郡 Pembrokeshire 威尔士旧郡 13—134a
彭达 Penda 盎格鲁-撒克逊国王 13—135f
彭达拉 Bhandāra 印度城镇 2—450a
彭代利山 Pendéli Óros (Greece) 希腊山脉 13—136b
彭德尔 Pendle 英格兰区名 13—136f
彭德尔顿 Pendleton 美国城市 13—136f
彭德尔顿 Pendleton, Edmund 美国爱国者 13—137a
彭德尔顿 Pendleton, Ellen Fitz 美国教育家 13—137a
彭德尔顿 Pendleton, George (Hunt) 美国律师、议员 13—137c
《彭德尔顿文官制度法》 Pendleton Civil Service Act 美国立法(1883) 13—137c
彭德格斯特 Pendergast, Thomas J(oseph) 美国政治家 13—136e
彭德怀 Peng Dehuai 中国革命家、军事家 13—137f
彭德雷茨基 Penderecki, Krzysztof 波兰作曲家 13—136d

彭德雷德氏综合征 Pendred's syndrome 疾病 13—137d
彭蒂克顿 Penticton 加拿大城市 13—149e
彭戈拉 bhāngrā 印度舞蹈 2—450b
彭亨 Pahang 马来西亚区名 12—546c
彭亨河 Pahang River 马来西亚河流 12—546d
彭柯夫斯基 Penkovsky, Oleg Vladimirovich 苏联军官 13—140c
彭里斯 Penrith 澳大利亚城市 13—147b
彭里斯 Penrith 英格兰城镇 13—147b
彭林 Penryn 英格兰港口 13—147c
彭罗塞 Penrose, Boies 美国参议员 13—147b
彭罗塞 Penrose, Roger 英国数学家、相对论学者 13—147c
彭纳库克人 Pennacook 美洲印第安人 13—141d
彭南特 Pennant, Thomas 威尔士博物学家、旅行家 13—141d
彭南特氏猫 Pennant's cat 猫品种 13—141e
彭内尔 Pennel, John (Thomas) 美国撑竿跳高运动员 13—141e
彭内尔 Pennell, Joseph 美国版画家、作家 13—141e
彭尼 Penney, J(ames) C(ash) 美国商人 13—141f
彭尼 Penney (of East Hendred), William (George) Penney, Baron 英国核物理学家 13—142a
彭尼阿尔卑斯山 Pennine Alps 意大利－瑞士边境山脉 13—142c
彭尼公司 Penney Company 美国零售业公司 13—142a
彭齐亚斯 Penzias, Arno (Allan) 美国天体物理学家 13—150d
彭萨科拉 Pensacola 美国城市 13—147c
彭赛列 Poncelet, Jean-Victor 法国数学家、工程师 13—424f
彭世洛 Phitsanulok 泰国城镇 13—253a
彭斯 Burns 美国城市 3—273e
彭斯 Burns, Robert 苏格兰诗人 3—274b
彭特科斯特 Pentecost (island, Vanuatu) 瓦努阿图岛屿 13—148e
彭特科特 Pentecôte 瓦努阿图火山岛 13—149c
彭特利库斯山 Pentelicus, Mount 希腊山脉 13—149d
彭托皮丹 Pontoppidan, Henrik 丹麦作家 13—429a
彭威思 Penwith 英格兰区名 13—150b
彭赞斯 Penzance 英格兰城镇 13—150d
彭真 Peng Zhen 中国革命家、政治家 13—138c
蓬巴杜(侯爵夫人) Pompadour, Jeanne-Antoinette Poisson, marquise de 法国贵族 13—420e
蓬巴杜夫人式 pompadour 发式 13—420d
蓬巴尔侯爵 Pombal, Sebastião de Carvalho, marquês de (marquess of) 葡萄牙改革家 13—419b
蓬波纳齐 Pomponazzi, Pietro 意大利哲学家 13—423f
蓬蒂 Ponti, Gio 意大利建筑师、设计师 13—428b
蓬蒂阶 Pontian Stage 地质学 13—428d
蓬蒂内群岛 Pontine Islands (Italy) 意大利岛屿 13—428f
蓬蒂内沼泽 Pontine Marshes 意大利垦荒区 13—428f
蓬多兰 Pondoland 南非地区 13—426a
蓬多人 Pondo (people) 南非民族 13—426a
蓬费拉达 Ponferrada 西班牙城市 13—426a
蓬基耶利 Ponchielli, Amilcare 意大利作曲家 13—425b
蓬莱 Penglai 中国城市 13—139a
蓬莱韦克干酪 Pont-l'Évêque 法国干酪 13—427a
蓬皮杜 Pompidou, Georges(-Jean-Raymond) 法国总理、总统 13—423c
蓬皮杜中心 Pompidou Centre 法国国立文化中心 13—423e
蓬普氏病 Pompe's disease 疾病 13—422f
蓬齐洛 Ponzillo, Rosa Melba (singer) 美国歌唱家 13—430b
蓬塞 Ponce 波多黎各城市、港口 13—424c
蓬塞 Poncet, Charles-Jacques 法国药剂师 13—425a
蓬塔阿雷纳斯 Punta Arenas 智利城市、省会 14—29a
蓬塔德尔加达 Ponta Delgada 葡萄牙港口 13—427b
蓬塔格罗萨 Ponta Grossa 巴西城镇 13—427b
蓬塔雷纳斯 Puntarenas 哥斯达黎加城市 14—29c
蓬塔诺 Pontano, Giovanni 意大利散文家、诗人 13—427c
蓬泰代拉 Pontedera, Andrea da 意大利画家 13—427f
蓬泰科尔沃 Pontecorvo, Guido 意大利遗传学家 13—427f
蓬泰科尔沃亲王 Ponte-Corvo, Jean-Baptiste Bernadotte, prince de 瑞典、挪威国王 13—427e
蓬特赫尼尔 Puente-Genil 西班牙城市 14—15a
蓬特韦德拉 Pontevedra 西班牙省份 13—428a
蓬特韦德拉 Pontevedra 西班牙城市 13—428b
蓬提安,圣 Pontian, Saint 教皇 13—428d
蓬图瓦兹 Pontoise 法国城镇、省会 13—428f
蓬托菲霍 Punto Fijo 委内瑞拉城市 14—29c
蓬托莫 Pontormo, Jacopo da 佛罗伦萨画家 13—429c
蓬尾浣熊 cacomistle 哺乳动物 3—310d
蓬扎群岛 Ponza Islands 意大利火山岛群 13—430a
硼(B) boron 化学元素 3—54f
硼化物 boride 金属化合物 3—51d
硼砂 borax 化合物 3—45a
硼酸(H_3BO_3) boric acid 化合物 3—51d
硼酸盐矿物 borate mineral 矿物 3—43f
硼烷 borane 化学 3—43f
硼族元素 boron group element 化学元素 3—55d
澎湖 Penghu 中国县名 13—138d
澎湖列岛 Penghu Islands 中国岛群 13—138f
篷车队 wagon train 美国马车队 18—63f
篷卡人 Ponca 北美印第安人 13—424a
膨润土 bentonite 矿物 2—395a
膨松剂 leavening agent 食品制作 9—547a
膨羽鴷 puffbird 鸟类 14—17f
膨胀宇宙 expanding universe 天文学 6—194c
碰运气 hazard 掷骰游戏 7—535b
碰撞 collision 物理学 4—350f
碰撞乐队 Clash, the 英国摇滚乐队 4—268d
碰撞理论 collision theory 化学 4—351b
丕林岛 Perim Island 也门岛屿 13—169a
丕平 Pepin 统治者之名 13—152b
丕平 Pepin 意大利国王 13—152e
丕平二世 Pepin II 法国国王 13—152c
丕平二世 Pepin II 法国国王 13—152d
丕平三世 Pepin III 法兰克国王 13—152d
丕平一世 Pepin I 法国国王 13—152c
丕平一世 Pepin I 法国国王 13—152c
丕平赠礼 Pepin, Donation of 意大利历史 13—152f
批发 wholesaling 商业 18—242a
批发价格指数 wholesale price index 经济学 10—242a
披风 mantle 服装 10—475e
披盖病毒 togavirus 病毒 17—129f
披巾 shawl 服装 15—287d
披叻差 Phetracha 泰国大城国王 13—225f
披毛犀 woolly rhinoceros 古生物学 18—328a
披衫剧 fabula palliata 罗马喜剧 6—208f
披水石 label (architecture) 建筑 9—430c
劈 wedge 工具 18—163e
霹雳 Perak, Tun 马来西亚首席部长 13—156d
霹雳 Perak 马来西亚地区 13—156c
霹雳战争 Perak War 马来酋长的反英起事 13—156d
霹隆 Perun 古斯拉夫宗教 13—191d
皮 hide 制革业 8—71e
皮阿 Pyat, (Aimé-)Félix 法国新闻记者、剧作家 14—41c
皮阿萨鸟 Piasa bird 传说 13—280c
皮埃尔(塔朗泰斯的) Pierre de Tarentaise (pope) 教皇 13—296d
皮埃莱奥尼 Pierleoni, Pietro(pope) 教皇 13—295e
皮埃罗(不幸者) Piero the Unfortunate, (Florentine ruler) 意大利统治者 13—296b
皮埃罗齐 Pierozzi, Antonio 佛罗伦萨大主教 13—296b
皮埃蒙特 Piedmont 意大利地区 13—293e

皮埃蒙特-撒丁王国 Piedmont-Sardinia, kingdom of 意大利历史王国 13—294a
皮安德卡尔皮尼 Pian del Carpini, Giovanni da (Franciscan author) 方济各会著作家 13—279e
皮奥里亚 Peoria 美国城市 13—151e
皮奥姆博 Piombo, Sebastiano del (Italian painter) 意大利画家 13—317b
皮奥齐 Piozzi, Hester Lynch 英国作家 13—317c
皮博迪 Peabody 美国城市 13—108b
皮奥伊 Piauí 巴西州名 13—282b
皮博迪 Peabody, Elizabeth Palmer 美国教育家 13—108b
皮博迪 Peabody, George 美国企业家、慈善家 13—108c
皮博迪 Peabody, Josephine Preston 美国诗剧作家、诗人 13—108d
皮博迪 Peabody, Lucy Whitehead McGill Waterbury 美国传教士 13—108d
皮布尔斯 Peebles 苏格兰区城镇 13—121b
皮布尔斯郡 Peeblesshire 苏格兰历史郡 13—121c
皮采尔 Bitzer, Billy 美国电影摄影师 2—505c
皮层 cortex 植物学 4—525c
皮查姆 Peacham, Henry 英国作家 13—109f
皮茨菲尔德 Pittsfield 美国城市 13—331f
皮达尔 Pidal, Ramón Menéndez 西班牙学者 13—292f
皮德蒙特 Piedmont 美国地理区域 13—293f
皮迪河 Pee Dee River 美国河流 13—121b
皮电反应 galvanic skin response 心理、生理现象 6—564c
皮杜尔 Bidault, Georges(-Augustin) 法国外交部长 2—463c
皮蠹 dermestid beetle 昆虫 5—254d
皮尔 Peel 不列颠群岛城镇 13—121c
皮尔 Pierre 美国州首府、县城 13—296b
皮尔 Peale, Charles Willson 美国画家 13—111a
皮尔 Peele, George 英国剧作家 13—122a
皮尔 Peale, Rembrandt 美国画家、作家 13—111b
皮尔 Peel, Sir Robert 英国首相、保守党创始人 13—121d
皮尔巴拉 Pilbara 澳大利亚地区 13—302a
皮尔彻 Pilcher, Percy Sinclair 英国工程师、航空界先驱 13—302b
皮尔夫人 Peel, Lady (entertainer) 英国喜剧演员 13—121d
皮尔戈斯 Pyrgos 希腊城镇 14—464e
皮尔河 Peel River 加拿大河流 13—122a
皮尔姐妹 Peale, Anna Claypoole; and Peale, Sarah Miriam 美国画家 13—110f
皮尔金顿 Pilkington, Francis 英国作曲家 13—303d
皮尔凯 Pirquet, Clemens, Freiherr von 奥地利医师 13—322d
皮尔马森斯 Pirmasens 德国城市 13—322a
皮尔梅 Pirmez, Octave 比利时文学家 13—322b
皮尔斯 Peirce, Benjamin 美国数学家、天文学家 13—124e
皮尔斯 Peirce, Charles Sanders 美国实用主义创始人 13—124f
皮尔斯 Pires, Diogo 犹太教殉教士 13—322a
皮尔斯 Pierce, Franklin 美国总统 13—294c
皮尔斯 Pierce, George Washington 美国无线电话先驱、发明家 13—294d
皮尔斯 Pierce, Jane 美国总统夫人 13—294e
皮尔斯 Pierce, John Davis 美国教育监督 13—294f
皮尔斯 Pierce, John Robinson 美国通信工程师、科学家 13—295a
皮尔斯 Pearse, Patrick Henry 爱尔兰民族主义领袖 13—114b
皮尔斯 Pears, Sir Peter (Neville Luard) 英国男高音歌唱家 13—114a
皮尔斯 Pierce, Sarah 美国教育家 13—295b
皮尔斯堡 Fort Pierce 美国城市 6—414f
皮尔斯伯里 Pillsbury, Charles Alfred 美国企业主 13—304a
皮尔瓦拉 Bhīlwāra 印度城镇 2—452e
皮尔委员会 Peel Commission 英国组织机构 13—121f
皮尔逊 Pearson, Drew 美国专栏作家 13—114c
皮尔逊 Pearson, Hesketh 英国导演、作家 13—114d
皮尔逊 Pearson, Karl 英国数学家 13—114e
皮尔逊 Pearson, Lester B(owles) 加拿大总理 13—114f
皮尔逊 Pearson, Weetman Dickinson 英国工程师 13—115a
皮尔页岩 Pierre Shale 地质学 13—296d
皮肤 skin 解剖学 15—418e
皮肤癌 skin cancer 疾病 15—419c
皮肤病学 dermatology 医学 5—254c
皮肤利什曼病 cutaneous leishmaniasis 疾病 5—78f
皮肤利什曼病 dermal leishmaniasis 疾病 5—254b
皮肤试验 skin test 医学 15—419e
皮肤松垂症 cutis laxa 疾病 5—79b
皮戈特 Pigot (of Patshul), George Pigot, Baron, 1st Baronet 英国商人 13—300a
皮戈特 Piggott, Lester (Keith) 英国骑手 13—299d
皮革 leather 制革业 9—546c
皮格马利翁 Pygmalion 希腊神话 14—42a
皮古 Pigou, Arthur Cecil 英国经济学家 13—300b
皮豪人 Pijao 哥伦比亚印第安人 13—300c
皮划艇运动 canoeing 体育 3—406c
皮簧腔 Pihuangqiang 中国戏曲声腔 13—300c
皮肌炎 dermatomyositis 疾病 5—254d
皮吉勒姆侯爵 Puyguilhem, Antonin-Nompar de Caumont, marquis de 法国军官 14—40d
皮吉特湾 Puget Sound 美国深海湾 14—19a
皮金龟 skin beetle 昆虫 15—419c
皮卡 Picard, (Charles-)Émile 法国数学家 13—283a
皮卡比阿 Picabia, Francis 法国画家、作家 13—282e
皮卡德 Piccard, Auguste 比利时物理学家 13—287a
皮卡德 Pickard, Greenleaf Whittier 美国电气工程师 13—289d
皮卡德 Picard, Jean 法国天文学家 13—283b
皮卡德 Piccard, Jacques(-Ernest-Jean) 瑞士海洋工程学家、经济学家 13—287c
皮卡德 Piccard, Jean-Felix 美国化学工程师 13—287d
皮卡第 Picardy 法国规划大区 13—283c
皮科·德拉·米兰多拉 Pico della Mirandola, Giovanni, Count (conte) di Concordia 意大利学者、哲学家 13—291c
皮科克 Peacock, Thomas Love 英国作家 13—110c
皮科罗米尼 Piccolomini, Francesco Todeschini (pope) 教皇 13—288a
皮科洛米尼家族 Piccolomini family 意大利贵族世家 13—288a
皮科洛米尼-皮里 Piccolomini-Pieri, Ottavio, duca d'Amalfi, Reichsfürst 奥地利将军、外交家 13—288a
皮科马约河 Pilcomayo River 南美河流 13—302b
皮科内里侯爵 Piconnerie, Thomas-Robert Bugeaud, Marquis de la 法国元帅 13—291e
皮克 Peake, Mervyn 英国作家、画家 13—110e
皮克彻罗克斯 Pictured Rocks 美国悬崖 13—292d
皮克当斯 Peak Downs 澳大利亚地区 13—110e
皮克顿 Picton 加拿大城镇 13—292b
皮克顿 Picton 新西兰港口、自治市 13—292c
皮克林 Pickering, Edward Charles 美国物理学家、天文学家 13—289f
皮克林 Pickering, Timothy 美国军官、政治家 13—290a
皮克林 Pickering, William Hayward 美国工程师 13—290b
皮克林 Pickering, William Henry 美国天文学家 13—290c
皮克牌 Piquet 纸牌游戏 13—319f
皮克区 Peak District 英格兰山区 13—110e
皮克氏病 Pick disease 疾病 13—289c
皮克斯基尔 Peekskill 美国城市 13—121c
皮克泰·德罗什蒙 Pictet de Rochemont, Charles 瑞士政治家、作家 13—292a
皮克特 Pickett, Bill 美国运动员 13—290d

皮克特 Pickett, George Edward 美国南部邦联军官 13—290e

皮克特 Pickett, Joseph 美国画家 13—290f

皮克特 Pickett, Wilson 美国歌手、歌曲作者 13—290f

皮克特人 Pict 苏格兰古代民族 13—292a

皮克特语 Pictish language 苏格兰语言 13—292b

皮克图 Pictou 加拿大县城 13—292c

皮克托 Pictor, Quintus Fabius 罗马艺术家、历史学家 13—292c

皮库岛 Pico Island 葡属亚速尔群岛岛屿 13—291d

皮库斯 Picus 罗马神话 13—292f

皮奎 Piqua 美国城市 13—319e

皮拉蒂宁加 Piratininga 巴西城市 13—321d

皮拉尔 Pilar 巴拉圭城镇 13—301e

皮拉米德湖 Pyramid Lake 美国古拉洪坦湖残迹湖 14—45c

皮拉姆·德·康多尔 Pyrame de Candolle, Augustin 瑞士植物学家 14—44f

皮拉姆斯和西斯贝 Pyramus and Thisbe 文学人物 14—45d

皮拉穆斯 Pyramus (river, Turkey) 土耳其河流 14—45d

皮拉内西 Piranesi, Giovanni Battista 意大利画家、建筑师 13—320f

皮拉乌 Pillau (Russia) 俄罗斯城镇 13—304a

皮拉西卡巴 Piracicaba 巴西城市 13—320a

皮莱乌斯帽 pileus 古罗马帽子 13—302d

皮兰 Perrin, Jean(-Baptiste) 法国物理学家 13—179c

皮兰德娄 Pirandello, Luigi 意大利戏剧家、小说家 13—320d

皮朗(埃利斯的) Pyrrhon of Elis 希腊哲学家 14—48e

皮雷利公司 Pirelli SpA 意大利公司 13—321f

皮雷利家族 Pirelli family 意大利企业家家族 13—321e

皮雷纳 Pirenne, Henri 比利时教育家、学者 13—321f

皮里 Peary, Robert Edwin 美国北极探险家 13—115a

皮里 Pirrie (of Belfast), William James Pirrie, Viscount 爱尔兰造船商 13—322e

皮里地 Peary Land 格陵兰地区 13—115b

皮里港 Port Pirie 澳大利亚城市、海港 13—447a

皮里奇战役 Pea Ridge, Battle of 美国历史 13—108b

皮里亚京 Piryatin 乌克兰城市 13—322f

皮利岛 Pelee Island 加拿大岛屿 13—129f

皮利角国家公园 Point Pelee National Park 加拿大公园 13—389c

皮利翁山 Pelion, Mount 希腊山地 13—130d

皮瘤蝇 warble fly 昆虫 18—102f

皮隆 Pilon, Germain 法国雕刻家 13—304c

皮隆 Piron, Alexis 法国戏剧家 13—322c

皮鲁尼特 pirouette 芭蕾舞技巧 13—322c

皮洛蒂 Piloty, Karl (Theodor) von 德国画家 13—304f

皮洛士 Pyrrhus 伊庇鲁斯国王 14—49a

皮洛斯 Pylos 希腊三个地方的名称 14—43b

皮洛要塞大屠杀 Fort Pillow Massacre 美国内战 6—414f

皮马河 Bhīma River 印度河流 2—452e

皮马人 Pima 北美印第安人 13—305e

皮曼河 Pieman River 澳大利亚河流 13—294b

皮姆 Pym, Barbara (Mary Crampton) 英国小说家 14—43c

皮姆 Pym, John 英格兰议员 14—43d

皮纳克尔 pinochle 纸牌游戏 13—315b

皮纳图博山 Pinatubo, Mount 菲律宾火山 13—306e

皮内尔 Pinel, Philippe 法国医师 13—311b

皮内罗洛 Pinerolo 意大利城镇 13—311e

皮尼奥斯河 Piniós River 希腊河流 13—313e

皮尼利亚 Pinilla, Gustavo Rojas 哥伦比亚独裁者 13—313e

皮涅克 Pilnyak, Boris 苏联作家 13—304b

皮涅拉 Piñera, Virgilio 古巴作家 13—311c

皮诺 Pineau, Nicolas 法国木雕家、室内设计师 13—311a

皮诺切特(乌加特) Pinochet (Ugarte), Augusto 智利政治家、总统 13—314f

皮诺斯岛 Pines, Isle of (Cuba) 古巴岛屿 13—311f

皮诺斯岛 Pinos, Isla de (Cuba) 古巴岛屿 13—315b

皮皮 Pippi, Giulio 意大利艺术家、建筑师 13—319c

皮平 Pippin, Horace 美国民间画家 13—319c

皮珀 Piper, Carl, Greve (Count) 瑞典政治家 13—318d

皮奇尼诺 Piccinino, Niccolò 意大利军事冒险家 13—287d

皮契尼 Piccinni, Niccolò 那不勒斯乐派作曲家 13—287e

皮切尼人 Piceni 意大利民族 13—288b

皮钦查 Pichincha 厄瓜多尔省份 13—288e

皮钦查战役 Pichincha, Battle of 南美洲历史 13—288f

皮钦语 pidgin 英语等的变体 13—293a

皮萨卡诸语言 Pisaca languages 东南亚语言 13—323b

皮萨罗 Pizarro, Francisco 西班牙征服者 13—335d

皮萨罗 Pizarro, Gonzalo 西班牙征服者、探险家 13—336a

皮萨内洛 Pisanello, Il 意大利雕刻家、画家 13—323b

皮萨尼 Pisani, Niccolò 意大利海军将领 13—323c

皮萨尼 Pisani, Vettore 意大利海军将领 13—323d

皮萨诺 Pisano, Andrea 意大利雕刻家 13—323d

皮萨诺 Pisano, Antonio 意大利雕刻家、画家 13—323f

皮萨诺 Pisano, Giovanni 意大利雕刻家 13—323f

皮萨诺 Pisano, Nicola 意大利雕刻家 13—324c

皮萨乌鲁姆 Pisaurum (Italy) 意大利城市 13—324f

皮塞勒 Pisseleu, Anne de 法国国王情妇 13—326a

皮塞勒 Pucelle, Jean (Jehan) 法国细密画家、书籍装饰画家 14—12c

皮塞雷古 Pixérécourt, (René-Charles-) Guilbert de 法国戏剧家 13—335a

皮什格吕 Pichegru, (Jean-) Charles 法国将军 13—288b

皮什佩克 Pishpek (Kyrgyzstan) 吉尔吉斯斯坦城市 13—325c

皮斯 Pease, Edward Reynolds 英国作家、费边社创始人之一 13—115e

皮斯顿 Piston, Walter (Hamor) 美国作曲家 13—326e

皮斯河 Peace River 加拿大河流 13—109b

皮斯卡塔韦人 Piscataway (people) 美国印第安人 13—324f

皮斯卡托尔 Piscator, Erwin 德国戏剧演出人、导演 13—324f

皮斯科 Pisco 秘鲁城市 13—325b

皮斯托亚 Pistoia 意大利城市 13—326c

皮斯托亚会议 Pistoia, Synod of 天主教会主教会议(1786) 13—326c

皮斯瓦什瀑布 Pissevache Fall 瑞士瀑布 13—326a

皮松 Python 希腊神话 14—50d

皮索姆 Pithom 古埃及城市 13—328d

皮塔科斯(米蒂利尼的) Pittacus of Mytilene 古希腊政治家 13—331a

皮特 Pitt, Thomas 英国商人 13—329d

皮特(老) Pitt, William, the Elder 英国政治家 13—329e

皮特(小) Pitt, William, the Younger 英国首相 13—330a

皮特奥 Piteå 瑞典城镇、港口 13—328c

皮特岛 Pitt Island (Kiribati) 基里巴斯共和国岛屿 13—330d

皮特尔角城 Pointe-à-Pitre 法国海外省城市 13—389e

皮特金玻璃制品 Pitkin glass 玻璃器皿 13—328f

皮特凯恩岛 Pitcairn Island 太平洋火山岛 13—327b

皮特克 p'Bitek, Okot 乌干达作家、社会人类学家 13—107b

皮特里 Petri, Elio 意大利电影导演、编导 13—208f

皮特里 Petrie, Sir (William Matthew) Flinders 英国考古学家、埃及学家 13—209b

皮特-里弗斯 Pitt-Rivers, Augustus Henry Lane-Fox 英国考古学家 13—330d

皮特里洛 Petrillo, James C(aesar) 美国劳工领袖、音乐家 13—209f

皮特曼 Putman, Andrée 法国设计师 14—37e

皮特曼 Pitman, Sir Isaac 英国教育家 13—328f

皮特曼速记法 Pitman shorthand 快速书写体系 13—329a

皮特尼 Pitney, Mahlon 美国最高法院大法官 13—329b

皮特什蒂 Piteşti 罗马尼亚城市 13—328d

皮特钻石 Pitt diamond 宝石 13—330d
皮图 Pithou, Pierre 法国律师、历史学家 13—328e
皮托 Puteaux 法国城镇、工业区和住宅区 14—37b
皮托 Pitot, Henri 法国水利工程师 13—329c
皮托 Peto, John Frederick 美国静物画家 13—207a
皮托竞技会 Pythian Games 古希腊体育、音乐比赛会 14—50d
皮瓦 Piła 波兰旧省份 13—301e
皮瓦 Piła 波兰城市 13—301e
皮瓦尼 Bhiwāni 印度城市 2—452f
皮维斯·德·夏凡纳 Puvis de Chavannes, Pierre(-Cécile) 法国壁画家 14—39f
皮翁比诺 Piombino 意大利城镇 13—317b
皮乌拉 Piura 秘鲁省份 13—332a
皮乌拉 Piura 秘鲁城市 13—332a
皮西迪亚 Pisidia 古小亚细亚地区 13—325c
皮西亚斯 Pytheas 希腊航海家、天文学家、地理学家 14—50c
皮屑介壳虫 scurfy scale (species *Chionaspis furfura*) 昆虫 15—161d
皮谢姆斯基 Pisemsky, Aleksey Feofilaktovich 俄国小说家、戏剧家 13—325b
皮亚芙 Piaf, Edith 法国歌唱家 13—279a
皮亚季戈尔斯克 Pyatigorsk 俄罗斯城市 14—41d
皮亚诺 Peano, Giuseppe 意大利数学家 13—111c
皮亚诺 Piano, Renzo 意大利建筑师 13—280a
皮亚诺普西昂节 Pyanopsia 希腊宗教节日 14—41b
皮亚诺萨岛 Pianosa Island 意大利岛屿 13—280c
皮亚齐 Piazzi, Giuseppe 意大利天文学家 13—282e
皮亚琴察 Piacenza 意大利城市 13—278f
皮亚琴察公国 Piacenza, duchy of 意大利的两个公国之一 13—279a
皮亚热 Piaget, Jean 瑞士心理学家 13—279b
皮亚斯特王朝 Piast DYNASTY 波兰第一个统治家族 13—280d
皮亚塔科夫 Pyatakov, Georgy Leonidovich 苏联经济学家 14—41c
皮亚特 Piatt, Sarah Morgan Bryan 美国诗人 13—282a
皮亚特拉-尼亚姆茨 Piatra-Neamţ 罗马尼亚城市 13—282a
皮亚韦河 Piave River 意大利河流 13—282c
皮亚扎-阿尔梅里纳 Piazza Armerina 意大利城镇、主教区 13—282c
皮炎 dermatitis 皮肤炎症 5—254b
皮耶 Piye 库施国王 13—335b
皮耶利斯湖 Pielinen, Lake 芬兰湖泊 13—294a
皮耶罗·迪·科西莫 Piero DI COSIMO 意大利画家 13—296a
皮耶罗·迪·乔凡尼 Piero DI GIOVANNI 意大利画家 13—296b
皮耶罗(痛风患者) Piero THE GOUTY (Florentine ruler) 意大利统治者 13—296b
皮耶罗·德拉·弗朗西斯卡 Piero DELLA FRANCESCA 意大利画家 13—295e
皮耶什佳尼 Piešt'any 斯洛伐克城镇 13—296d
皮耶塔尔萨里 Pietarsaari 芬兰城市 13—296f
皮叶克尼斯 Bjerknes, Jacob (Aall Bonnevie) 挪威-美国气象学家 2—507c
皮叶克尼斯 Bjerknes, Vilhelm F(riman) K(oren) 挪威气象学家 2—507d
皮移植术 skin graft 医学 15—419d
皮影戏 shadow play 戏剧 15—252f
皮尤兄弟 Pew, J(ohn) Howard and Joseph N(ewton), Jr. 美国兄弟实业家 13—214f
皮由兹 Pusey, E(dward) B(ouverie) 英国神学家、学者 14—35e
皮脂腺 sebaceous gland 解剖学 15—174e
皮质醇 cortisol 激素 4—526a
皮质激素 corticoid 化合物 4—525d
枇杷 loquat (*Eriobotrya japonica*) 木本植物 10—218a
毗湫帷 pichhwāi 印度教的彩画幕布 13—288d
毗底沙 Vidisha 印度城镇 17—547b
毗诃罗 vihara 佛教寺院 17—559b
毗伽 Bilge 突厥部落首领 2—472e
毗卢遮那 Vairocana 大乘佛教最高佛 17—444d
毗沙门 Bishamon 日本福神 2—495c
毗湿奴 Vishnu 印度教神名 18—18c
毗湿奴教 Vaishnavism 印度教三大派之一 17—445a
毗湿奴自然宗 Vaiṣṇava-Sahajiyā 印度教密宗 17—445b
毗首羯磨 Viśvakarman 印度教神名 18—20e
毗耶娑 Vyāsa 印度圣者 18—56b
毗约 piyyut 犹太教文学 13—335c
铍(Be) beryllium 化学元素 2—434e
铍中毒 berylliosis 疾病 2—434e
疲劳 fatigue 工程力学 6—250b
疲劳 fatigue 生理学、心理学 6—249d
啤酒 beer 饮料 2—330d
啤酒店暴动 Beer Hall Putsch 德国历史事件 2—330f
琵鹭 spoonbill 鸟类 16—41b
琵琶 pipa 中国乐器 13—317e
琵琶湖 Biwa, Lake 日本淡水湖 2—506a
琵琶桶 barrel 容器 2—241d
琵嘴鸭 shoveler 鸟类 15—337c
脾炎 splenitis 病理现象 16—38a
脾脏 spleen 解剖学 16—37f
脾肿大 splenomegaly 病理现象 16—38a
蜱 tick 无脊椎动物 17—85e
蜱螨亚纲 acari 动物学 1—42e
蜱鸟 tickbird 鸟类 17—86a
匹克威克综合征 pickwickian syndrome 疾病 13—291b
匹配禁忌 incompatible mating 生物学 8—353e
匹兹堡 Pittsburg 美国堪萨斯州城市 13—331c
匹兹堡 Pittsburgh 美国宾夕法尼亚州城市 13—331c
匹兹堡板玻璃公司 Pittsburgh Plate Glass Company 美国公司 13—331e
匹兹堡玻璃制品 Pittsburgh glass 玻璃器皿 13—331e
匹兹堡登陆战役 Pittsburg Landing, Battle of 美国历史 13—331c
淠史杭灌区 Pi-Shi-Hang Irrigation Project 中国灌区 13—278e
䴙䴘 grebe 鸟类 7—277b
䴙䴘类 podicipediform 动物学 13—384b
偏跛节奏 aksak 音乐 1—158a
偏硅酸盐 metasilicate (mineralogy) 化合物 11—153b
偏害作用 amensalism 生物学 1—274f
偏口虫 apostome 原生动物 1—416a
偏口鱼 flounder 鱼类 6—374b
偏手性 handedness 心理学、生理学 7—456f
偏瘫 hemiplegia 疾病 8—9f
偏头痛 migraine headache 疾病 11—206e
偏微分方程 partial differential equations 数学 13—66f
偏心圆盘连杆机构 eccentric-and-rod mechanism 机械学 5—520a
偏振 polarization 物理学 13—397f
偏执狂 paranoia 精神病 13—38c
骈文 pianwen 中国文体 13—280c
胼胝 callus 皮肤科学 3—356f
片沸石 heulandite 矿物 8—63f
片麻岩 gneiss 岩石 7—167c
片蚀 sheet erosion 地质学 15—293d
片吸虫病 fascioliasis 疾病 6—245a
片藓 sheet moss 藓类植物 15—293d
片岩 schist 岩石 15—117c
骗局 confidence game 诈骗手段 4—421c
剽窃 plagiarism 欺诈行为 13—338a
漂泊的荷兰人 Flying Dutchman 欧洲传说中的船 6—381e
漂蚕 palolo worm 蠕虫 12—574e

漂浮生物 neuston 生物学 12—99b
漂砾 erratic 地质学 6—122f
漂流者乐队 Drifters,the 美国乐队 5—424c
朴正熙 Park Chung Hee 韩国政治家、总统 13—54a
瓢虫 ladybird beetle 昆虫 9—443c
漂白剂 bleach 化学药品 2—531f
漂白淋溶土 albeluvisol 土壤种类 1—176f
漂白土 fuller's earth 矿物 6—520d
票据交换所 clearinghouse 金融机构 4—277b
嘌呤 purine 有机化合物 14—32f
漂亮的波莉 Pretty Polly 英国赛马 13—500f
氕 protium 氢同位素 13—545d
撇水黾蝽 skimmer (insect) 昆虫 15—418e
拼板玩具 jigsaw puzzle 玩具 9—21c
拼布工艺 patchwork 民间艺术 13—85a
拼猜哑谜 charade 游戏 4—60d
拼读比赛 spelling bee 游戏 16—18f
拼贴 collage 艺术 4—345d
姘居 concubinage 社会学 4—414b
贫齿类 edentate 哺乳动物 5—537e
贫民住房 insula 建筑 8—402b
贫气 dry gas 天然气 5—432c
贫穷 poverty 社会学 13—470d
贫穷克拉雷会 Poor Clare 天主教女修会 13—430f
贫水硼砂 kernite 矿物 9—241f
贫血 anemia 病理现象 1—338a
频带宽度 bandwidth 电子学 2—196c
频率 frequency 物理学 6—482f
频率计 frequency meter 测量电磁波频率装置 6—483a
频率调制 frequency modulation(FM) 电子学 6—483b
频闪观测仪 stroboscope 仪器 16—279a
频耶陀罗 Binnya Dala 下缅甸国王 2—478e
蘋科 Marsileaceae 植物学 10—541f
品达罗斯 Pindar 古希腊诗人 13—308b
品达罗斯颂歌 Pindaric ode 仪节诗歌 13—308e
品都斯山脉 Pindus Mountains 希腊山脉 13—309a
品特 Pinter,Harold 英国剧作家 13—315f
品脱 pint 英美容量单位 13—315d
聘礼 bridewealth 婚姻风俗 3—149e
乒乓球 TABLE TENNIS 体育项目 16—141b
乒乓球 table tennis 体育项目 16—415a
平安时代 Heian period 日本历史 7—564a
平板玻璃 plate glass 玻璃 13—351b
平板马车 dray 运输 5—416f
平版印刷 lithography,offset 印刷 10—147c
平版印刷 litho-offset 印刷 10—147a
平版印刷 planography 印刷 13—344b
平城 P'yŏngsŏng 朝鲜城市 14—44a
平达里 Pindari 印度历史上的非正规骑兵、强盗 13—308d
平代蒙泰 Pindemonte,Ippolito 意大利散文家、诗人、翻译家 13—308f
平德 Bhind 印度城镇 2—452e
平德尔 Pindar,Peter 英国作家 13—308d
平德林 Pindling,Sir Lynden Oscar 巴哈马总理 13—309a
《平等计划》 Iguala Plan 墨西哥历史 8—328b
平等就业机会委员会 Equal Employment Dpportunity Commission(EE-OC) 美国政府机构 6—106a
《平等权利修正案》 Equal Rights Amendment (ERA) 美国宪法修正案 6—106c
平底小渔船 dory 船舶 5—392f
平底雪橇滑雪 tobogganing 体育运动 17—126c
平地铁杉 ground hemlock (shrub) 木本植物 7—323f
平顶海山 guyot 海洋地质学 7—386b
平顶山 Pingdingshan 中国城市 13—312a
平顶山 Tabletop (Canada) 加拿大山名 16—415d
平硐 adit 采矿 1—79c
平方根 square root 数学 16—167d
平房 bungalow 建筑 3—252d
平谷 Pinggu 中国区名 13—312c
平锅菜饭 paella 食物 12—541c
平衡 equilibrium 力学 6—108b
平衡木 balance beam 运动器械 2—160f
平衡税 countervailing duty 抵消税 4—544a
平户 Hirado 日本城市 8—92f
平滑肌 smooth muscle 解剖学 15—456a
《平家物语》 Heike monogatari 日本文学 7—566c
平价 parity 经济学 13—52f
平将门 Taira Masakado 日本叛乱首领 16—434c
平均 mean 数学 11—62e
平均律 equal temperament 音乐 6—106d
平均派 Leveler 英国历史 10—45a
平均寿命 mean life 核物理学 11—63b
平均自由程 mean free path 物理学 11—63a
平卡姆(夫人) Pinkham,Lydia E(stes) 美国家庭药厂老板 13—314c
平卡斯 Pincus,Gregory (Goodwin) 美国内分泌学家 13—308a
平开窗 casement window 建筑 3—498f
平克顿 Pinkerton,Allan 美国侦探 13—314b
平克·弗洛伊德 Pink Floyd 英国乐队 13—314a
平克尼 Pinckney,Charles Cotesworth 美国军人、政治家 13—307d
平克尼 Pinckney,Charles 美国开国元勋、政治领袖 13—307c
平克尼 Pinckney,Thomas 美国军人、政治家 13—307f
平克尼 Pinkney,William 美国政治家、外交家 13—314d
平克尼(夫人) Pinckney,Elizabeth 美国种植园经营家 13—307e
《平克尼条约》 Pinckney's Treaty 西班牙、美国边界的协定(1795) 13—307f
平凉 Pingliang 中国城市 13—312d
平流 advection 大气科学 1—89b
平流层 stratosphere 大气科学 16—268b
平炉炼钢法 open-hearth process 冶炼方法 12—427e
平路机 grader 筑路机械 7—238d
平面设计 graphic design 视觉传播 7—259e
平民 plebeian 古罗马公民 13—367c
平民党 Populares (ancient Roman political group) 古罗马政治集团 13—437e
平民党运动 Populist Movement 美国政治运动 13—439b
平民菲力普 Égalité,Philippe 波旁王子 5—555d
平民税 taille 法国历史 16—431c
平民造反 Comunero Rebellion 西班牙历史 4—408a
平目地 hirameji 日本漆器工艺 8—93e
平纳克尔国家保护地 Pinnacles National Monument 美国地理区 13—314f
平内罗 Pinero,Sir Arthur Wing 英国剧作家 13—311d
平扭贝 Platystrophia 古生物学 13—364e
平奇巴克 Pinchback,Pinckney Benton Stewart 美国黑人政治家、军官 13—307a
平钦 Pynchon,Thomas 美国小说家 14—43f
平清盛 Taira Kiyomori 日本军事独裁者 16—434b
平壤 P'yŏngyang 朝鲜首都 14—44a
平绒 velveteen 纺织品 17—496b
平莳绘 hiramaki-e 日本漆器工艺 8—93d
平氏家族 Taira FAMILY 日本武士家族 16—433f
平斯基 Pinski,David 意第绪语戏剧家、小说家 13—315d
平斯克 Pinsk 白俄罗斯城市 13—315c
平斯克尔 Pinsker,Leo 俄国-波兰医生、论辩家 13—315c
平松岛 Pinzón Island 厄瓜多尔岛屿 13—317a

平松兄弟 Pinzón, Martín Alonso; and Pinzón, Vicente Yáñez 西班牙探险家 13—316f
平台式舞台 platform stage 戏剧舞台 13—353e
平台网球 platform tennis 体育项目 13—353e
平台印刷机 flatbed press 印刷机器 6—349d
平田笃胤 Hirata Atsutane 日本思想家 8—93f
平头鱼 slickhead 鱼类 15—431a
平图里乔 Pinturicchio 意大利画家 13—316c
平托 Pinto, Fernão Mendes 葡萄牙冒险家 13—316c
平纹组织 plain weave 纺织物结构 13—339a
平镶结构 carvel construction 船体结构 3—492f
平肖 Pinchot, Gifford 美国森林和自然保护先驱 13—307b
平胸鸟 ratite 鸟类 14—163b
平遥 Pingyao 中国县名 13—313d
平遥双林寺彩塑 Pingyao Shuanglinsi caisu 中国佛教彩塑 13—313d
平印 lithography 印刷 10—147a
平原 plain 地理学 13—338e
平原派 Plain, The 法国历史 13—338f
平缘线脚 fillet 建筑 6—315b
平扎 Pinza, Ezio 美国歌唱家、演员 13—316f
平针组织 plain stitch 纺织物结构 13—339a
平正盛 Taira Masamori 日本武将 16—434c
平栉田中 Hiragushi Denchū 日本雕刻家 8—93a
平忠盛 Taira Tadamori 日本武将 16—434d
平塚 Hiratsuka 日本城市 8—94a
评剧 pingju 戏曲剧种 13—312f
坪内逍遥 Tsubouchi Shōyō 日本作家 17—250e
苹果 apple 水果 1—419b
苹果计算机公司 Apple Computer, Inc. 美国计算机制造商 1—419d
苹果菊 chamomile 草本植物 4—39b
苹果佬 Appleseed, Johnny 美国传教士、苗圃场主 1—420b
苹果佬 Johnny Appleseed 美国传教士、苗圃场主 9—61b
苹果藓 apple moss (*Bartramia pomiformis*) 苔藓植物 1—420b
苹果汁 cider 食品 4—236b
凭祥 Pingxiang 中国城市 13—313c
屏东 Pingdong 中国台湾县名 13—312b
屏东 Pingdong 中国台湾城市 13—312c
瓶 bottle 容器 3—75a
瓶鼻海雀 bottlenose (bird) 鸟类 3—75c
瓶鼻鲸 bottlenose whale 哺乳动物 3—75c
瓶尔小草科 Ophioglossaceae 植物学 12—430e
瓶口衣属 Verrucaria 植物学 17—524d
瓶树 bottle tree 木本植物 3—75b
瓶子草科 Sarraceniaceae 植物学 15—69e
瓶子草类 pitcher plant 肉食植物 13—327f
萍乡 Pingxiang 中国城市 13—313a
钋(Po) polonium 化学元素 13—410a
坡 Poe, Edgar Allan 美国作家 13—385c
坡尔塔 Porta, Giacomo della 意大利建筑师 13—447e
坡盖盐盒式住宅 saltbox 建筑学 14—555d
坡吕克斯 Pollux, Julius 希腊学者、修辞学家 13—408b
坡缕石 palygorskite 矿物 12—575e
坡莫合金 Permalloy 合金 13—173f
坡普 Pope, John R. 美国建筑师 13—433b
坡斯特 Post, Pieter 荷兰建筑师、画家 13—459c
坡斯特 Post, Wiley 美国第一次环球飞行员 13—459d
坡廷格尔古地图 Peutinger Table 罗马帝国古地图 13—214d
坡印廷 Poynting, John Henry 英国物理学家 13—476e
坡印廷矢量 Poynting vector 物理学 13—476f
泼酒游戏 cottabus 游戏 4—537d
泼墨 pomo 中国绘画技法 13—420c
颇尔人 Peul (people) 穆斯林民族 13—214d
婆利睹梨诃利 Bhartṛhari 印度教哲学家 2—451b
婆罗多舞 bharata natya 印度古典舞蹈 2—450b
《婆罗多舞论》 Bhārata Nāṭya-śāstra 艺术著作 2—450c
婆罗浮屠 Borobuḍur 印度尼西亚佛教古迹 3—54a
婆罗门 Brahman 印度社会等级 3—112e
婆罗门河 Brāhmani River 印度河流 3—113a
婆罗门笈多 Brahmagupta 印度天文学家 3—112d
婆罗门教 Brahmanism 印度宗教 3—113a
婆罗门牛 Brahman 印度牛品种 3—112f
婆罗米文字 Brāhmī 印度古文字 3—113c
婆罗洲 Borneo 亚洲东南部岛屿 3—53a
婆婆纳 speedwell 草本植物 16—18a
婆婆纳属 Veronica (plant) 植物学 17—523b
婆什迦罗第二 Bhāskara II 印度数学家 2—451d
婆什迦罗第一 Bhaskara I 印度天文学家、数学家 2—451c
婆苏提婆 Vāsudeva 印度神话人物 17—479c
婆陀罗波霍第一 Bhadrabāhu I 印度耆那教领袖 2—448f
鄱阳湖 Poyang Hu 中国湖泊 13—476c
钷(Pm) promethium 化学元素 13—533b
珀贝克 Purbeck 英格兰区名 14—30f
珀德拉沃蒂 Bhadrāvati 印度城市 2—449a
珀迪 Purdy, James 美国小说家 14—31e
珀蒂 Petit, Roland 法国舞蹈家、编导 13—205d
珀蒂瓷器 Petit porcelain 法国瓷器 13—206b
珀蒂托 Petitot, Jean 瑞士画家 13—206e
珀丁达 Bhatinda 印度城市 2—451e
珀尔 Pearl, Raymond 美国动物学家 13—112f
珀尔河 Pearl River 美国河流 13—113f
珀尔曼 Perlman, Itzhak 以色列小提琴家 13—173b
珀尔齐格 Poelzig, Hans 德国建筑师 13—385e
珀尔修斯 Perseus 希腊神话 13—181e
珀耳塞福涅 Persephone 希腊宗教故事 13—181c
珀耳帖 Peltier, Jean-Charles-Athanase 法国物理学家 13—132e
珀耳帖效应 Peltier effect 物理学 13—132f
珀伽索斯 Pegasus 希腊神话 13—122c
"珀伽索斯"号卫星 Pegasus 美国科学卫星 13—122c
珀金 Perkin, Sir William Henry 英国化学家 13—172a
珀金斯 Perkins, Frances 美国劳工部长、社会改革家 13—172a
珀金斯 Perkins, George Walbridge 美国金融家 13—172b
珀金斯 Perkins, Jacob 美国发明家 13—172c
珀金斯 Perkins, Lucy Fitch 美国儿童读物作家 13—172c
珀金斯 Perkins, Maxwell (Evarts) 美国编辑 13—172d
珀赖因 Perrine, Charles Dillon 美国天文学家 13—179d
珀勒德布尔 Bharatpur 印度前邦名 2—450d
珀勒德布尔 Bharatpur 印度城镇 2—450e
珀利阿斯 Pelias 希腊神话 13—130b
珀琉斯 Peleus 希腊神话 13—129f
珀鲁 Peru 美国城市 13—190e
珀罗普斯 Pelops 希腊传说 13—132c
珀洛迪 Phalodi 印度城镇 13—218c
珀那忒斯 Penates 古罗马人的家神 13—135b
珀涅罗珀 Penelope 希腊神话 13—137e
珀切斯 Purchas, Samuel 英国游记、探险作品编纂者 14—31d
珀塞耳 Purcell, E(dward) M(ills) 美国物理学家 14—31a
珀斯 Perth 澳大利亚城市 13—187f
珀斯 Perth 加拿大城镇 13—188a
珀斯 Perth 苏格兰城市 13—188b
珀斯安博伊 Perth Amboy 美国城市、港口 13—188b
珀斯-金罗斯 Perth and Kinross 苏格兰政务会辖区 13—188c
珀斯郡 Perthshire 苏格兰历史郡 13—188d
珀斯佩有机玻璃 Perspex (acrylic plastic) 化合物 13—187b
珀瓦尼 Bhawani (India) 印度城市 2—452b

珀维安斯 Purviance, Edna 美国演员 14—35b
珀西 Percy, Algernon 英格兰贵族 13—160d
珀西 Percy, Henry 英格兰贵族 13—160d
珀西 Percy, Sir Henry 英格兰叛乱者 13—160d
珀西 Percy, Lucy 英格兰阴谋家 13—160e
珀西 Percy, Thomas 英格兰贵族 13—160e
珀西 Percy, Thomas 英国古物收藏家 13—160e
珀西 Percy, Walker 美国小说家 13—160f
珀西家族 Percy FAMILY 英格兰家族 13—160b
珀西瓦尔 Perceval, John 英国政治人物 13—157c
珀西瓦尔 Perceval, Spencer 英国首相 13—157c
破布木属 Cordia 植物学 4—502c
破产 bankruptcy 法律 2—205c
破产法 bankruptcy, laws concerning 法律 2—205d
破骨细胞 osteoclast 细胞 12—490e
破骨细胞瘤 osteoclastoma 肿瘤 12—490e
破坏活动 sabotage 破坏性战术 14—484d
破坏名誉 defamation 法律 5—207a
破火山口 caldera 地质学 3—341b
破裂音 plosive (phonetics) 语音学 13—373f
破伤风 tetanus 疾病 16—561c
破晓惜别歌 Tagelied 德国音乐 16—424b
剖腹产术 cesarean section 医学 4—16c
剖析 anatomy 文学 1—320e
扑动䴕 flicker 鸟类 6—360b
扑克牌 playing card 游戏纸牌 13—366c
扑克牌 Poker 纸牌游戏 13—393b
扑克牌大师 Playing Cards, Master of the 德国美术家 13—367a
扑蛲灵 pyrvinium pamoate 根治蛲虫药物 14—49b
扑疟喹啉 pamaquine 药物 12—576a
铺地蜈蚣 cotoneaster (genus *Cotoneaster*) 蔷薇科植物 4—536f
铺那 Bonard, Louis-Adolphe 法国海军上将 3—25b
匍匐冰草 couch grass 草本植物 4—541a
匍匐剪股颖 creeping bent (*Agrostis palustris*) 草坪禾草 5—4a
匍匐浆果鹃 trailing arbutus (*Epigaea repens*) 植物 17—191b
匍匐枝 stolon 生物学 16—247e
莆田 Putian 中国城市 14—37b
菩 Bau 宗教神灵 2—284c
菩橛 phur-bu 藏传佛教密宗法器 13—269e
菩萨 bodhisattva 佛教 2—561e
菩提 bodhi 佛教 2—561d
菩提达摩 Bodhidharma 印度僧人 2—561e
菩提伽耶 Bodh Gayā 印度佛教圣地 2—561c
菩提树 Bo tree 树 2—554b
菩提亚人 Bhutia 喜马拉雅山区民族 2—454e
葡萄 grape 攀缘植物 7—257f
葡萄孢疫病 botrytis blight 植物病害 3—72f
葡萄弹 grapeshot 武器 7—258f
葡萄干 raisin 食品 14—129a
葡萄干树 raisin tree (*Hovenia dulcis*) 木本植物 14—129c
葡萄根瘤蚜 grape phylloxera (*Phylloxera vitifoliae*) 昆虫 7—258d
葡萄酒 wine 含酒精饮料 18—287b
葡萄科 Vitaceae 植物学 18—20f
葡萄膜炎 uveitis 眼部疾病 17—434e
葡萄球菌属 Staphylococcus 生物学 16—194d
葡萄石 prehnite 矿物 13—492e
葡萄胎 hydatidiform mole 病理现象 8—277c
葡萄糖 glucose 生物化学 7—164e
葡萄糖耐量试验 glucose tolerance test 医学 7—164f
葡萄牙 Portugal 欧洲国家 13—454e
《葡萄牙和巴西大百科全书》 Grande Enciclopédia Portuguesa e Brasileira 葡萄牙语百科全书 7—252f
葡萄牙语 Portuguese language 语言 13—456c
葡萄牙语文学 Portuguese literature 以葡萄牙语写作的作品 13—456d
葡萄柚 grapefruit (*Citrus paradisi*) 木本植物 7—258d
葡萄栽培 viticulture 园艺学 18—24d
葡属东非 Portuguese East Africa 莫桑比克的旧称 13—456c
蒲安臣 Burlingame, Anson 美国外交官 3—268e
蒲柏 Pope, Alexander 英国作家 13—432d
蒲福风级 Beaufort scale 气象学 2—312a
蒲甘 Pagan 缅甸国王 12—542d
蒲甘 Pagan 缅甸古城遗址 12—542d
蒲公英 dandelion 多年生杂草 5—133a
蒲郡 Gamagōri 日本城市 6—565f
蒲劳脱 Prout, William 英国化学家 13—549a
蒲鲁东 Proudhon, Pierre-Joseph 法国哲学家、新闻工作者 13—548a
蒲式耳 bushel 计量单位 3—283c
蒲松龄 Pu Songling 中国清代文学家 14—3b
蒲绥里 Būṣīrī, al- 阿拉伯诗人 3—285f
蒲州 Puzhou 中国城镇 14—40f
镤(Pa) protactinium 化学元素 13—541d
镤231-钍230测年法 protactinium-231-thorium-230 dating 地质学 13—541e
濮 Pu 中国古代民族 14—3a
濮阳 Puyang 中国城市 14—40b
朴 hackberry 木本植物 7—399b
朴 pu 中国道家术语 14—3b
朴次茅斯 Portsmouth 英格兰一区(城市) 13—454a
朴次茅斯 Portsmouth 美国新罕布什尔州城市 13—454b
朴次茅斯 Portsmouth 美国俄亥俄州城市 13—454c
朴次茅斯 Portsmouth 美国罗得岛州城镇 13—454c
朴次茅斯 Portsmouth 美国弗吉尼亚州城市、港口 13—454c
《朴次茅斯和约》 Portsmouth, Treaty of 日俄战争和约(1905) 13—454d
朴次茅斯女公爵 Portsmouth, Louise-Renée de Kéroualle, Duchess of 英王查理二世的情妇 13—454d
朴野主义 Brutalism (architecture) 建筑学 3—212f
圃鹀 ortolan (*Emberiza hortulana*) 鸟类 12—476d
圃睡鼠 lerot 啮齿动物 10—35a
浦安 Urayasu 日本城市 17—410c
浦东新区 Pudong Xinqu 中国上海市辖区 14—13a
浦尔契 Pulci, Luigi 意大利诗人 14—20b
浦耳生 Poulsen, Valdemar 丹麦工程师 13—468c
浦和 Urawa 日本城镇 17—410c
浦口 Pukou 中国南京市辖区 14—19e
浦那 Pune 印度城市 14—26d
《浦那协定》 Poona Pact 印度历史(1932) 13—430e
浦品 Pupin, Michael Idvorsky 美国物理学家 14—29f
浦上玉堂 Uragami Gyokudō 日本画家、乐师 17—407a
浦项 P'ohang 韩国城市 13—387c
浦伊尔 Pwyll 凯尔特神话人物 14—41a
普埃布拉 Puebla 墨西哥内陆州 14—13d
普埃布拉 Puebla 墨西哥城市 14—13e
普埃布拉战役 Puebla, Battle of 墨西哥-法国历史 14—13e
普埃托利亚诺 Puertollano 西班牙城市 14—17c
普贝克层 Purbeck Beds 地质学 14—30f
普布利乌斯 Publius 古罗马人名 14—11c
普登汉姆 Puttenham, George 英国廷臣 14—39b
普多夫金 Pudovkin, Vsevolod Illarionovich 苏联电影导演、理论家 14—13b
普恩加来 Poincaré, Raymond 法国政治家、总理 13—388a
普恩特 Puente, Tito 美国乐队指挥 14—15a
普尔 pool 赌博方法 13—430c
普尔 Pool, Maria Louise 美国作家 13—430c

普尔 Poole 英格兰区名 13—430d
普尔 Poole, William Frederick 美国目录学家 13—430d
普尔巴尼 Phūlbani 印度城镇 13—269e
普尔基涅 Purkinje, Jan Evangelista 捷克实验生理学创始人 14—33e
普尔喀 Pulcher, Publius Claudius 罗马执政官 14—20a
普尔喀 Pulcher, Publius Clodius 罗马政客 14—20b
普尔喀丽娅 Pulcheria 罗马女皇 14—20b
普尔科沃天文台 Pulkovo Observatory 俄罗斯天文台 14—21a
普尔曼 Pullman 美国华盛顿州城市 14—21b
普尔曼 Pullman, George M(ortimer) 美国实业家、发明家 14—21b
普尔曼罢工事件 Pullman Strike 美国历史 14—21c
普尔纳普拉吉纳 Pūrṇaprajña (Hindu philosopher) 印度教哲学家 14—34a
普尔热瓦尔斯基 Przhevalsky, Nikolay Mikhaylovich 俄国旅行家 13—554d
普尔热瓦尔斯基氏野马 Przewalski's horse (*Equus caballus przewalskii*) 哺乳动物 13—554c
普尔热瓦尔斯克 Przhevalsk (Kyrgyzstan) 吉尔吉斯斯坦城市 13—554d
普尔特尼 Pulteney, William 英国政治家 14—22e
普尔佐内 Pulzone, Scipione 意大利画家 14—22f
普珥节 Purim 犹太教节日 14—32f
普法尔茨林山 Pfälzer Wald (Germany) 德国山脉 13—215e
普法夫 Pfaff, Johann Friedrich 德国数学家 13—215d
普法战争 Franco-German War 欧洲历史 6—446d
普菲茨纳 Pfitzner, Hans (Erich) 德国作曲家 13—216a
普菲弗 Pfyffer, Ludwig 瑞士军事领袖 13—216a
普费弗尔 Pfeffer, Wilhelm (Friedrich Philipp) 德国植物学家 13—215e
普费弗科恩 Pfefferkorn, Johannes (Joseph) 德国论辩家 13—215f
普芬道夫 Pufendorf, Samuel, Freiherr von 德国国际法专家、历史学家、法理学家 14—17d
普福尔茨海姆 Pforzheim 德国城市 13—216a
普赫塔 Puchta, Georg Friedrich 德国法学家 14—12d
普吉 Phuket 泰国岛屿、城市 13—269d
普加乔夫 Pugachov, Yemelyan Ivanovich 俄国农民起义领袖 14—18d
普杰 Bhuj 印度城镇 2—453c
普杰 Puget, Pierre 法国雕刻家、画家、建筑师 14—18e
普金 Pugin, Augustus Welby Northmore 英国建筑师、作家 14—19a
普京 Putin, Vladimir 俄罗斯总统 14—37d
普救论 Universalism 基督教 17—376f
普卡尔帕 Pucallpa 秘鲁省份 14—11d
普卡基湖 Pukaki, Lake 新西兰冰川堰塞湖 14—19d
普卡拉 Pucará 前哥伦布时期遗址和文化 14—11d
普库库伊 Puu Kukui 美国夏威夷州火山峰 14—39e
普拉 Pula 克罗地亚共和国港口、工业中心 14—19f
普拉班扎 Prapañcā 印度尼西亚诗人、历史学家 13—484e
普拉布帕达 Prabhupada, Swami 印度宗教领袖、作家 13—477f
普拉茨堡 Plattsburgh 美国县城 13—364a
普拉茨茅斯 Plattsmouth 美国县城 13—364b
普拉蒂卡·迪·马雷 Pratica di Mare (Italy) 意大利古市镇 13—485b
普拉蒂亚 Plataea 希腊古代城市 13—351a
普拉东诺夫 Platonov, Sergey Fyodorovich 俄国历史学家 13—363c
普拉多博物馆 Prado Museum 西班牙艺术博物馆 13—478a
普拉多湾 Prudhoe Bay 美国小海湾 13—551d
普拉丰牌 Plafond 纸牌游戏 13—338a
普拉佛塔约法·朱拉罗克 Phraphutthayotfa Chulalok (Siamese king) 暹罗国王 13—268c
普拉河 Pra 加纳河流 13—477e
普拉霍瓦 Prahova 罗马尼亚县名 13—482b
普拉克里特诸语言 Prākrit languages 中古印度-雅利安诸语言 13—483e
普拉克西特利斯 Praxiteles 希腊雕刻家 13—486c
普拉兰岛 Praslin Island 塞舌尔共和国岛屿 13—485b
普拉里河 Purari River 巴布亚新几内亚河流 14—30e
普拉姆迪亚 Pramoedya, Ananta Toer 印度尼西亚小说家 13—484b
普拉姆特里 Plumtree 津巴布韦城镇 13—376f
普拉纳西亚 Planasia (Italy) 意大利岛屿 13—340a
普拉努得斯 Planudes, Maximus 希腊人文学家、编纂家 13—348e
普拉切 Plaatje, Solomon Tshekiso 南非语言学家、新闻工作者、作家 13—336c
普拉萨德 Prasad, Rajendra 印度总统 13—484f
普拉塞塔斯 Placetas 古巴城市 13—337d
普拉森舍 Placentia 加拿大城镇 13—337a
普拉森西亚 Plasencia 西班牙城市 13—348e
普拉绍夫 Plaszow 纳粹德国集中营(在波兰) 13—350f
普拉斯 Plath, Sylvia 美国诗人、小说家 13—353f
普拉斯基特 Plaskett, John Stanley 加拿大天文学家 13—348f
普拉塔港 Puerto Plata 多米尼加共和国城市、港口 14—16b
普拉特 Pratt, E.J. 加拿大诗人 13—485e
普拉特 Pratt, John Jeffreys 英国政治家 13—486a
普拉特 Platt, Orville Hitchcock 美国参议员 13—363d
普拉特 Platt, Thomas Collier 美国众议员、参议员 13—363d
普拉特尔 Platter, Thomas 瑞士作家、人文主义者 13—363f
普拉特河 Platte River 美国河流 13—363f
《普拉特修正案》 Platt Amendment 美国历史 13—363e
普拉滕 Platen(-Hallermünde), August, Graf von 德国诗人、戏剧家 13—352f
普拉托 Prato 意大利城镇 13—485d
普拉托利尼 Pratolini, Vasco 意大利小说家 13—485d
普拉西 Plassey 印度古村庄 13—349e
普拉西德 Placide, Alexander 法国舞蹈、杂技演员 13—337d
普拉西狄亚 Placidia, Aelia Galla 罗马皇帝 13—337e
普拉亚 Praia 佛得角首都、港市 13—482c
普拉佐 prazo 封建庄园 13—487c
普腊蒂哈腊王朝 Pratihāra DYNASTY (Indian Hindu dynasty) 印度历史 13—485b
普莱 Poulet, Georges 法国文学"新批评派"代表 13—468b
普莱埃尔 Pleyel, Ignace Joseph 奥地利裔法国作曲家 13—371a
普莱埃尔 Pleyel, Marie-Félicité-Denise 法国钢琴家 13—371b
普莱恩斯 Plains 美国城市 13—339b
普莱恩维尤 Plainview 美国城市 13—339f
普莱福德 Playford, John 英格兰音乐出版商 13—366b
普莱诺 Plano 美国城市 13—344b
普莱桑 Plethon, George Gemistus 拜占廷哲学家 13—370b
普莱斯 Place, Francis 英国政治人物 13—336c
普莱斯纳 Plessner, Helmuth 德国哲学家 13—370a
普莱西-马尔利 Plessis-Marly, Philippe de Mornay, seigneur du (lord of) 法国外交家 13—370a
普莱西诉弗格森案 Plessy v. Ferguson 美国法院案例 13—370b
普莱耶 Player, Gary (Jim) 南非运动员 13—365e
普赖德 Pride, Sir Thomas 英国军官 13—506c
普赖尔 Pryor 美国县府 13—554a
普赖尔 Pryor, Richard 美国喜剧演员 13—554a
普赖默斯 Primus, Pearl 美国黑人舞蹈家 13—512c
普赖斯 Price 美国城市 13—503c
普赖斯 Price, George 美国漫画家 13—503e
普赖斯 Price, H(enry) H(abberley) 英国哲学家 13—503e
普赖斯 Price, Leontyne 美国歌唱家 13—503f
普赖斯 Price, Lloyd 美国歌手、歌曲作者 13—504a
普赖斯 Price, Richard 英国道德哲学家、财政专家 13—504a
普赖斯 Price, Sterling 美国政治家 13—504b

普赖斯 Price, Thomas 澳大利亚政治家 13—504c
普赖斯 Price, Sir Uvedale, 1st Baronet 英国园林设计家、美学家 13—504c
普赖斯 Price, Vincent 美国演员 13—504e
普赖斯河 Price River 源于美国犹他州中部的河流 13—505c
普兰巴南 Prambanan 印度尼西亚村庄 13—484a
普兰菲尔德 Plainfield 美国城市 13—339a
普朗克 Planck, Max (Karl Ernst Ludwig) 德国物理学家 13—340b
普朗克 Poulenc, Francis 法国作曲家 13—467f
普朗克常量 Planck's constant 物理学 13—341c
普朗克辐射定律 Planck's radiation law 物理学 13—341d
普朗坦 Plantin, Christophe 法国印刷商 13—348d
普朗特 Planté, Francis 法国钢琴家 13—348c
普朗特 Planté, Gaston 法国物理学家 13—348d
普朗特 Prandtl, Ludwig 德国物理学家 13—484d
普劳德 Proud, Joseph 英格兰基督教牧师 13—548a
普劳恩 Plauen 德国城市 13—364e
普劳赖特 Plowright, Joan (Anne) 英国戏剧演员 13—374f
普劳图斯 Plautus 罗马喜剧作家 13—364f
普勒阿得斯 Pleiades 希腊神话 13—367f
普勒尼斯特 Praeneste 意大利古城 13—478b
普雷布尔 Preble, Edward 美国海军司令 13—488b
普雷德 Praed, Winthrop Mackworth 英国作家、政治家 13—478a
普雷科宁努斯 Praeconinus, Lucius Aelius Stilo (Roman philologist) 古罗马学者 13—478a
普雷里德欣 Prairie du Chien 美国城市 13—482f
普雷洛格 Prelog, Vladimir 瑞士化学家 13—492f
普雷蒙特雷会会士 Premonstratensian 天主教成员 13—493e
普雷明杰 Preminger, Otto 美国电影导演 13—493d
普雷塞利-彭布罗克夏尔 Preseli Pembrokeshire 威尔士区名 13—496e
普雷绍夫 Prešov 斯洛伐克城镇 13—497f
普雷斯 Press, Frank 美国地球物理学家 13—498a
普雷斯堡 Pressburg (Slovakia) 斯洛伐克首都德语名称 13—498b
《普雷斯堡条约》 Pressburg, Treaty of 奥法条约(1805) 13—498b
普雷斯蒂克 Prestwick 苏格兰城市 13—500a
普雷斯顿 Preston 英格兰区名 13—499d
普雷斯顿 Preston, Ann 美国医生、教育家 13—499f
普雷斯顿 Preston, May Wilson 美国画家 13—500a
普雷斯科特 Prescott 美国城市 13—496b
普雷斯科特 Prescott, Edward C. 美国经济学家 13—496b
普雷斯科特 Prescott, William H(ickling) 美国历史学家 13—496c
普雷斯克艾尔 Presque Isle 美国城市 13—497f
普雷斯利 Presley, Elvis (Aron) 美国摇滚乐歌唱家 13—497d
普雷斯帕湖 Prespa, Lake 欧洲湖泊 13—497f
普雷斯特阿 Prestea 加纳城镇 13—499b
普雷图河畔圣若泽 São José do Rio Prêto 巴西城市 15—52c
普雷托里乌斯 Praetorius, Michael 德国音乐理论家、作曲家 13—478e
普雷韦 Prévert, Jacques(-Henri-Marie) 法国诗人 13—501c
普雷韦扎 Préveza 希腊城镇、港口 13—501e
普雷文 Previn, André (George) 美国钢琴家 13—501e
普雷沃 Prévost d'Exiles, Antoine-François, Abbé 法国作家 13—502a
普雷沃 Prévost, Françoise 法国芭蕾舞演员 13—501f
普雷沃斯特 Prevost, Sir George 英国军人、加拿大总督 13—501f
普里阿摩斯 Priam 希腊神话 13—502b
普里阿普斯 Priapus 希腊宗教 13—502f
普里阿普斯颂诗 Priapea 拉丁文颂诗 13—502c
普里奥·索卡拉斯 Prío Socarrás, Carlos 古巴总统 13—518d
普里比洛夫群岛 Pribilof Islands 美国岛群 13—503a
普里比洛夫峡谷 Pribilof Canyon 白令海海底峡谷 13—503a
普里比奇维奇 Pribićević, Svetozar 南斯拉夫政治家 13—503a
普里查德 Prichard, H(arold) A(rthur) 英国哲学家 13—505d
普里查德 Prichard, James Cowles 英国医生、人种学家 13—505e
普里查德 Prichard, Katherine Susannah 澳大利亚作家、诗人 13—505e
普里查德 Prichard 美国城市 13—505d
普里道利统 Pridoli Series 地质学 13—506d
普里德沃罗夫 Pridvorov, Yefim Alekseyevich 苏联诗人 13—506e
普里厄 Prieur, Pierre-Louis 法国政界人士 13—508d
普里厄-迪韦尔努瓦 Prieur-Duvernois, Claude-Antoine 法国军事工程师 13—508e
普里恩 Priene 古希腊城市 13—506f
普里尔 Puryear, Martin 美国雕刻家 14—35c
普里盖特 Pridgett, Gertrude 美国歌唱家 13—506c
普里果金 Prigogine, Ilya 比利时物理化学家 13—508e
普里侯爵夫人 Prie, Jeanne-Agnes Berthelot de Pleneuf, marquise de 法国冒险家 13—506e
普里莱普 Prilep 马其顿共和国城镇 13—508f
普里卢基 Priluki 乌克兰城市 13—508f
普里莫·德里维拉 Primo de Rivera, José Antonio, Marqués de Estella 西班牙长枪党创始人 13—511b
普里莫·德里维拉 Primo de Rivera, Miguel 西班牙将军、政治家 13—511c
普里姆罗斯 Primrose, Archibald Philip 英国首相 13—511f
普里姆-普拉茨 Prim(y Prats), Juan 西班牙军事领袖 13—508f
普里尼亚诺 Prignano, Bartolomeo (pope) 教皇 13—508e
普里佩特沼泽地 Pripet Marshes 欧洲水涝地区 13—519a
普里皮亚季河 Pripyat River 乌克兰、白俄罗斯河流 13—519b
普里切特 Pritchett, V.S. 英国作家、评论家 13—520f
普里人和科罗阿多人 Purí and Coroado 南美印第安人部落 14—32e
普里什蒂纳 Priština 塞尔维亚城市 13—520e
普里什凯维奇 Purishkevich, Vladimir Mitrofanovich 俄国政治家、极右分子 14—33a
普里斯 Preece, Warren E(versleigh) 美国编辑 13—490f
普里斯库斯 Priscus, Helvidius 罗马议员 13—519d
普里斯-马尔斯 Price-Mars, Jean 海地医师、外交家 13—505c
普里斯特里弗 Priest River 美国城市 13—507b
普里斯特利 Priestley, J(ohn) B(oynton) 英国小说家、剧作家 13—507d
普里斯特利 Priestley, Joseph 英国教士、科学家 13—507f
普里特维·纳拉扬·沙阿 Prithvi Nārāyaṇ Shah 尼泊尔廓尔喀国王 13—520f
普里西安 Priscian 古罗马拉丁语语法学家 13—519b
普里西利安 Priscillian 西班牙基督教主教 13—519c
普里兹克家族 Pritzker family 美国商业、慈善业家族 13—521a
普里兹克建筑奖 Pritzker Prize 国际奖项 13—521b
普里兹伦 Prizren 塞尔维亚城镇 13—522e
普里兹伦同盟 Prizren, League of 巴尔干历史 13—522f
普利埃 plié 芭蕾舞动作 13—371c
普利策 Pulitzer, Joseph 美国报纸编辑、发行人 14—20d
普利策奖 Pulitzer Prize 美国新闻、文学、音乐奖 14—20e
普利克内斯有奖赛 Preakness Stakes 美国跑马赛 13—488a
普利马蒂乔 Primaticcio, Francesco 意大利画家 13—509f
普利茅斯 Plymouth 英格兰城市 13—378f
普利茅斯 Plymouth 美国印第安纳州城市 13—379a
普利茅斯 Plymouth 美国马萨诸塞州城镇 13—379b
普利茅斯 Plymouth 美国新罕布什尔州城镇 13—379c
普利茅斯 Plymouth 美国佛蒙特州城镇 13—379d
普利茅斯瓷器 Plymouth porcelain 英国瓷器 13—379e
普利茅斯弗吉尼亚殖民地公司 Virginia Colony of Plymouth 英国历史 18—13f
普利茅斯公司 Plymouth Company 英国贸易公司 13—379d
普利茅斯兄弟会 Plymouth Brethren 英格兰基督教会 13—379d
普利尼耶 Plisnier, Charles 比利时小说家、诗人 13—373a

普利斯 Preece, Sir William Henry 英国电气工程师 13—490f
普利特维策湖群 Plitvice Lakes 克罗地亚湖泊群 13—373a
普利维尔 Plievier, Theodor 德国作家 13—371d
普利文 Pleven, René 法国总理 13—370e
普利谢茨卡娅 Plisetskaya, Maya (Mikhaylovna) 俄罗斯芭蕾舞演员 13—372e
普利亚 Puglia 意大利区名 14—19b
普利亚区格拉维纳 Gravina in Puglia 意大利城镇 7—265b
普利子 prion 致病因子 13—518e
普列奥布拉仁斯卡 Preobrajenska, Olga 苏联芭蕾舞演员 13—494a
普列格尔 Pregl, Fritz 奥地利化学家 13—492b
普列汉诺夫 Plekhanov, Georgy Valentinovich 俄国马克思主义奠基人、孟什维克 13—369b
普列克尚斯 Pliekšāns, Jānis 拉脱维亚作家 13—371d
普列克斯玻璃 Plexiglas (acrylic plastic) 有机化合物 13—371a
普列姆昌德 Prem Chand 印度小说家 13—493a
普列舍伦 Prešeren, France 斯洛文尼亚诗人 13—497a
普列韦 Plehve, Vyacheslav Konstantinovich 俄罗斯帝国政治家 13—367e
普列文 Pleven 保加利亚城镇 13—370e
普林 Prynne, William 英格兰清教派作家 13—553f
普林格尔 Pringle, Sir John 英国医师 13—516b
普林格尔 Pringle, Thomas 南非诗人 13—516c
普林利蒙 Plynlimon 威尔士山脉 13—379e
普林尼(老) Pliny THE ELDER 古罗马大科学家、作家 13—371f
普林尼(小) Pliny THE YOUNGER 古罗马作家、行政官 13—372b
普林塞普 Prinsep, James 英国古物收藏家 13—516e
普林塞萨港 Puerto Princesa 菲律宾城市 14—16b
普林塞斯群岛 Princes Islands (Turkey) 土耳其岛群 13—515d
普林斯 Prince, F.T. 英国诗人 13—513d
普林斯 Prince, Harold (Smith) 美国导演、戏剧演出人 13—513d
普林斯 Printz, Johan Björnsson 瑞典军官 13—518c
普林斯巴赫阶 Pliensbachian Stage 地质学 13—371d
普林斯顿 Princeton 美国自治镇、乡 13—515e
普林斯顿大学 Princeton University 美国大学 13—515f
普林斯海姆 Pringsheim, Nathanael 德国植物学家 13—516d
普林西比 Príncipe (island, West Africa) 西非岛屿 13—516b
普林西普 Princip, Gavrilo 南斯拉夫民族主义者 13—516a
普柳里尔琴 pluriarc 西非弦乐器 13—377d
普卢德尼察 poludnitsa 斯拉夫神话 13—410e
普卢默氏病 Plummer's disease 疾病 13—376e
普卢塔克 Plutarch 希腊哲学家、传记作家 13—377e
普鲁登蒂乌斯 Prudentius 基督教诗人 13—551c
普鲁登特总统城 Presidente Prudente 巴西城市 13—497c
普鲁默 Plummer, Christopher 加拿大演员 13—376d
普鲁萨 Prusa 土耳其省份、省首府 13—552a
普鲁士 Prussia 欧洲历史地区 13—552b
普鲁士蓝 Prussian blue 颜料 13—553d
《普鲁士民法典》 Prussian Civil Code 普鲁士普通法 13—553d
普鲁斯 Prus, Bolesław 波兰记者、小说家 13—551f
普鲁斯河 Purus River 南美河流 14—34e
普鲁斯特 Proust, Joseph-Louis 法国化学家 13—548d
普鲁斯特 Proust, Marcel 法国小说家 13—548e
普鲁特河 Prut River 罗马尼亚、摩尔多瓦界河 13—553e
普鲁韦 Prouvé, Jean 法国工程师、建筑师 13—549b
普鲁西纳 Prusiner, Stanley B. 美国神经学家 13—552a
普鲁亚人 Puruhá 厄瓜多尔印第安人 14—34e
普路托 Pluto (Greek god) 希腊神祇 13—378a
普路托斯 Plutus 希腊宗教 13—378e
普吕东 Prud'hon, Pierre-Paul 法国画家 13—551d
普吕克尔 Plücker, Julius 德国数学家、物理学家 13—375a
普律多姆 Prudhomme, René-François-Armand 法国诗人 13—551d
普伦德加斯特 Prendergast, Maurice Brazil 美国画家 13—493f
普伦蒂斯 Prentiss, Elizabeth Payson 美国通俗儿童读物女作家 13—494a
普伦蒂湾 Plenty, Bay of 新西兰海湾 13—369d
普伦蒂湾区 Bay of Plenty 新西兰行政区 2—292c
普伦基特 Plunkett, Edward John Moreton Drax 爱尔兰戏剧家 13—377b
普伦基特 Plunkett, Sir Horace Curzon 爱尔兰农业合作运动先驱 13—377b
普伦基特男爵(第一) Plunket (of Newton), William Conyngham Plunket, 1st Baron 英国-爱尔兰律师 13—377a
普伦基特,圣 Plunket, Saint Oliver 爱尔兰天主教首主教 13—376f
普罗波恩蒂斯 Propontis (Turkey) 土耳其内海 13—537b
普罗布斯 Probus, Marcus Aurelius 罗马皇帝 13—524d
普罗德罗姆斯 Prodromus, Theodore 拜占廷著作家 13—527c
普罗迪 Prodi, Romano 意大利总理 13—527a
普罗蒂奇 Protić, Stojan 塞尔维亚-克罗地亚-斯洛文尼亚首相、政治家 13—545b
普罗尔 Proell, Annemarie (skier) 奥地利运动员 13—527f
普罗夫迪夫 Plovdiv 保加利亚城市 13—374b
普罗富莫事件 Profumo affair 英国政治丑闻 13—528c
普罗格雷索 Progreso 墨西哥城市 13—529b
普罗·胡亚雷斯 Pro Juárez, Miguel (Agustín), BLESSED 天主教司铎 13—522f
普罗霍罗夫 Prokhorov, Aleksandr Mikhaylovich 苏联物理学家 13—531a
普罗科波维奇 Prokopovich, Feofan 俄国正教神学家 13—532b
普罗科菲耶夫 Prokofiev, Sergey (Sergeyevich) 苏联作曲家 13—531b
普罗科鲁斯·西多内斯 Prochorus Cydones 拜占廷东正教修士 13—526a
普罗科皮耶夫斯克 Prokopyevsk 俄罗斯城市 13—532c
普罗科匹厄斯 Procopius 拜占廷历史学家 13—526b
普罗科普(秃顶的) Prokop THE BALD 波希米亚基督教胡斯派领袖 13—532b
普罗克洛斯 Proclus 希腊哲学家 13—526a
普罗克特 Procter, William Cooper 美国工厂主 13—526c
普罗米修斯 Prometheus 希腊宗教 13—533b
普罗奇达岛 Procida, Island of 意大利岛屿 13—526a
普罗瑟 Prosser, Gabriel 美国奴隶暴动领袖 13—540b
普罗斯捷约夫 Prostějov 捷克城镇 13—540f
普罗斯库罗夫 Proskurov (Ukraine) 乌克兰城市 13—539a
普罗斯尼茨 Prossnitz (Czech Republic) 捷克城镇 13—540b
"普罗斯帕罗"号卫星 Prospero 英国人造卫星 13—540b
普罗斯佩克特岛 Prospect Island (Kiribati) 基里巴斯岛屿 13—539f
普罗斯珀(阿基坦的),圣 Prosper OF AQUITAINE, SAINT 基督教教义论辩家 13—540a
普罗塔哥拉 Protagoras 希腊思想家、教师 13—541f
普罗托波波夫 Protopopov, Aleksandr Dmitriyevich 俄国政治家、内政大臣 13—547a
普罗托波波夫和别洛乌索娃 Protopopov, Oleg Alekseyevich; and Belousova, Ludmila Yevgeniyevna 苏联滑冰运动员夫妇 13—547b
普罗托格尼斯 Protogenes 希腊画家 13—546c
普罗万 Provins 法国城镇 13—551b
普罗旺斯 Provence 法国历史文化地区 13—549d
普罗旺斯伯爵 Provence, Louis-Stanislas-Xavier, Comte (count) de 法国国王 13—549f
普罗旺斯地区艾克斯 Aix-en-Provence 法国城市 1—149d
普罗旺斯地区萨隆 Salon-de-Provence 法国城镇 14—551e
普罗旺斯山 Provence Alps 法国山脉 13—550a
普罗旺斯山-蓝岸(地区) Provence-Alpes-Côte d'Azur 法国大区 13—550a

普罗旺斯文学 Provençal literature 法国文学作品 13—549c
普罗旺斯鱼汤 bouillabaisse 法国名菜 3—79c
普罗旺斯语 Provençal language 法国语言 13—549c
普罗维登斯 Providence 美国城市 13—550d
普罗温斯敦 Provincetown 美国城镇 13—550f
普罗温斯敦剧团 Provincetown Players 美国戏剧组织 13—551a
普罗沃 Provo 美国城市 13—551b
普罗伊斯 Preuss, Hugo 德国政治理论家 13—500f
普洛蒂娜 Plotina, Pompeia 罗马皇帝妻子 13—374a
普洛克路斯忒斯 Procrustes 希腊传说中的强盗 13—526c
普洛美尔 Plomer, William (Charles Franklyn) 英国作家 13—373d
普洛佩提乌斯 Propertius, Sextus 古罗马哀歌诗人 13—535e
普洛忒西拉俄斯 Protesilaus 希腊神话 13—543d
普洛透斯 Proteus 希腊神话 13—545a
普洛托斯 Proetus 希腊神话人物 13—527f
普洛耶什蒂 Ploieşti 罗马尼亚城市 13—373d
普米语 Pumi language 中国普米族语言 14—23b
普米族 Pumi 中国民族 14—23a
普密蓬·阿杜德 Bhumibol Adulyadej 泰国国王 2—453d
普那卡 Punakha 不丹城镇 14—25e
普纳岛 Puná Island 厄瓜多尔岛屿 14—25e
普诺 Puno 秘鲁省份 14—28f
普诺 Puno 秘鲁普诺省省会 14—28f
普皮耶努斯·马克西穆斯 Pupienus Maximus 罗马皇帝 14—29e
普奇 Pucci, Emilio, MARCHESE DI BARSENTO 意大利时装设计师、政治家 14—11d
普契尼 Puccini, Giacomo (Antonio Domenico Michele Secondo Maria) 意大利作曲家 14—11e
普热梅希尔 Przemyśl 波兰旧省份 13—554b
普热梅希尔 Przemyśl 波兰省会 13—554b
普热美斯家族 Přemysl, HOUSE OF 捷克统治家族 13—493e
普日贝谢夫斯基 Przybyszewski, Stanisław 波兰散文家、剧作家、诗人 13—554e
普日布拉姆 Příbram 捷克城市 13—503c
普日苏哈 Przysucha, Jacob Isaac ben Asher 波兰犹太教哈西德派领袖 13—554f
普萨沃尔 Bhusāwal 印度城镇 2—453e
普萨伊拉 Psaila, Carmelo (Maltese poet) 马耳他诗人 13—555a
普塞洛斯 Psellus, Michael (Constantine) 拜占廷哲学家、神学家 13—556a
普赛尔 Purcell, Henry 英国作曲家 14—31a
普桑 Poussin, Gaspard 意大利画家 13—470a
普桑 Poussin, Nicolas 法国画家 13—470a
普桑主义者 Poussinist 美术派别 13—470c
普阇 puja 印度教礼拜 14—19d
普什马塔哈 Pushmataha 乔克托印第安人首长 14—36e
普什奇纳 Pszczyna 波兰城市 13—566a
普什图人 Pashtun 阿富汗、巴基斯坦民族 13—74a
普什图语 Pashto language 阿富汗语言 13—73f
普世教会运动 ecumenism 基督教各派联合运动 5—534a
普世全胜教会 Church Universal and Triumphant 宗教 4—224d
普斯科夫 Pskov 俄罗斯州名 13—558f
普斯科夫 Pskov 俄罗斯城市 13—559a
普斯科夫画派 Pskov school 俄罗斯圣像画、壁画画派 13—559b
普塔代哈巴 Phuthaditjhaba 南非城镇 13—270a
普塔霍特普 Ptahhotep 古埃及大臣 13—566c
普泰里亚 Pteria 古安纳托利亚都城 13—566f
普特 Putte, Isaac Dignus Fransen van de 荷兰政治家 14—38f
普特南 Putnam, Emily James Smith 美国教育家 14—37e
普特南 Putnam, Frederic Ward 美国人类学家 14—37f
普特南 Putnam, Herbert 美国图书馆学家 14—38a
普特南 Putnam, Hilary 美国科学哲学家 14—38b
普特南 Putnam, Israel 美国将领 14—38b
普特南 Putnam, Rufus 美国军官 14—38c
普特南 Putnam, Samuel (Whitehall) 美国报纸主编、发行人、作家 14—38d
普特尼克 Putnik, Radomir 塞尔维亚陆军司令 14—38e
普天教 Poch'ongyo 朝鲜宗教 13—383a
普廷贝 Put-in-Bay 美国俄亥俄州村庄 14—37a
普通法 common law 法律 4—387e
普通感冒 common cold 病毒感染 4—387c
普通格律 common metre 诗歌 4—388d
普通工人、市政工人和锅炉制造工人联合会 General, Municipal, and Boilermakers' Union (GMB) 英国工会组织 7—56f
普通话 putonghua 中国汉族共同语 14—38f
普通辉石 augite 矿物 2—48a
普通角闪石 hornblende 矿物 8—176c
普通陪审团 common jury 法律 4—387e
《普通人》 Everyman 英国道德剧 6—184d
普通水泥 portland cement 建筑材料 13—452c
普通特定格律 common particular metre 诗歌 4—388d
普通蛙 common frog (species *Rana temporaria*) 两栖动物 4—387d
普通型汽车赛 stock-car racing 美国汽车比赛 16—242e
普通语义学 general semantics 语言-意义理论 7—57b
普通紫杉 common yew 木本植物 4—388f
普图马约 Putumayo 哥伦比亚州名 14—39d
普图马约河 Putumayo River 南美河流 14—39e
普托拉纳山脉 Putoran Mountains 俄罗斯中西伯利亚山地 14—38f
普陀山 Putuo Shan 中国佛教名山 14—39e
普瓦蒂耶 Poitier, Sidney 巴哈马美国演员、导演 13—391f
普瓦弗尔 Poivre, Pierre 法国传教士、企业家 13—392f
普瓦捷 Poitiers 法国城镇 13—392a
普瓦捷大学 Poitiers, University of 法国大学 13—392d
普瓦捷战役 Poitiers, Battle of 法国历史(732) 13—392b
普瓦捷战役 Poitiers, Battle of 法国历史(1356) 13—392c
普瓦雷 Poiret, Paul 法国时装设计师 13—390c
普瓦斯基 Pułaski, Kazimierz 波兰爱国志士、美国英雄 14—20a
普瓦松 Poisson, Jeanne-Antoinette 法国路易十五情妇 13—391c
普瓦图 Poitou 法国大区 13—392d
普瓦图-夏朗德 Poitou-Charentes 法国大区 13—392f
普瓦西 Poissy 法国城镇 13—391f
普瓦耶 Poyet, Gillaume 法国大法官 13—476d
普韦布洛 Pueblo 美国城市 14—13f
普韦布洛 pueblo 美国印第安人社区 14—13f
"普韦布洛"号事件 Pueblo Incident 美国海军入侵朝鲜事件 14—14a
普韦布洛利布雷 Pueblo Libre 秘鲁社区 14—14d
普韦布洛起义 Pueblo Rebellion 北美历史 14—14f
普韦布洛陶器 Pueblo pottery 美洲印第安人陶瓷艺术 14—14e
普韦布洛印第安人 Pueblo Indians 史前阿纳萨齐诸民族的后裔 14—14a
普沃茨克 Płock 波兰旧省份 13—373b
普沃茨克 Płock 波兰城市 13—373c
普西 Pusey, Nathan (Marsh) 美国教育家 14—35e
普西夏里 Psichari, Ernest 法国作家、士兵 13—557e
普希金 Pushkin 俄罗斯城市 14—36b
普希金 Pushkin, Aleksandr (Sergeyevich) 俄国诗人、小说家、剧作家 14—36b
普希金造型艺术博物馆 Pushkin Fine Arts Museum 莫斯科博物馆 14—36e
《普贤行愿品》 Samantabhadra-caryā-praṇidhāna (Buddhisttext) 佛教经典 14—560b
普贤岳 Fugen-dake (Japan) 日本火山 6—511a
普歇 Pouchet, Félix-Archimède 法国博物学家 13—467d
普绪喀 Psyche 希腊神话 13—559f

普颜笃 Buyantu 中国元朝皇帝 3—295d
《普曜经》 Lalitavistara 佛教经典 9—457e
普耶达 Phya Tak (Siamese king) 暹罗国王 13—270a
普伊格 Puig, Manuel 阿根廷小说家、电影剧本作者 14—19c
普约 Puyo 厄瓜多尔城镇 14—40d
普照国师 Bojo Guksa 高丽高僧 3—8f
溥仪 Puyi (Chinese emperor) 中国清朝末代皇帝 14—40d
溥仪 Puyi 中国清朝末代皇帝 14—65b
谱表 staff 音乐 16—177f
谱分析仪 spectrum analyzer 仪表 16—15f
谱号 clef 音乐 4—278b
谱线系 spectral line series 物理学 16—14a
镨(Pr) praseodymium 化学元素 13—485a
蹼鸡 coot 水栖鸟类 4—486f
蹼足负鼠 yapok 哺乳动物 18—425f
瀑布 waterfall 地理学 18—140b
瀑布线 fall line 地理学 6—222f

Q

七岛市 Sept-Îles 加拿大城市 15—218e
七峰山 Siebengebirge 德国山峰 15—355c
七福神 Shichi-fuku-jin 日本民间神祇 15—311c
七将攻第比斯 Seven Against Thebes 希腊神话 15—236f
七姐妹 Seven Sisters 美国高校联盟 15—237d
七棵松战役 Seven Pines, Battle of 美国历史 15—237c
七氯 heptachlor 化学杀虫剂 8—30c
七摩怛里 Saptamātṛkā 印度教七位女神 15—58e
七年战争 Seven Years' War 欧洲历史 15—238a
七瀑布 Sete Quedas Falls (South America) 南美洲瀑布 15—233c
七七节 Shabuoth 犹太教节日 15—251f
七七事变 July 7 incident 中国历史 9—108a
七人画派 Seven, Group of 加拿大画家团体 15—236e
七日丧期 shivah 犹太教 15—325c
七鳃鳗 lamprey 脊椎动物 9—468c
七声音阶 heptatonic scale 音乐 8—30d
《七十子希腊文本圣经》 Septuagint 《圣经·旧约》 15—219f
七寺城 Seven Pagodas (India) 印度城市 15—237c
七台河 Qitaihe 中国城市 14—69d
七天战役 Seven Days' Battles 美国历史 15—237a
七尾 Nanao 日本城市 11—552d
七五三 Shichi-go-san 日本礼仪 15—311d
《七贤哲》 Seven Wise Masters 连环故事 15—237f
七项全能运动 heptathlon 体育项目 8—30d
七星诗社 Pléiade, La 法国作家团体 13—367f
七伊玛目派 Seveners 伊斯兰教派别 15—238c
七月 July 历法 9—108a
七月二十六日运动 26th of July Movement 古巴历史 17—302d
七月革命 July Revolution 法国历史 9—108b
七月进攻 July Offensive (World War I) 第一次世界大战史 9—108b
七月密谋 July Plot 德国历史 9—108b
七月危机 July Days 俄国历史 9—108a
七周战争 Seven Weeks' War 奥普战争 15—237e
七株橡树大屠杀 Seven Oaks Massacre 加拿大历史 15—237b
栖木鸟 perching bird 鸟类 13—158a
栖鸭 perching duck 水禽 13—158a
桤木 alder 木本植物 1—192f
桤木鼠李 alder buckthorn (*Rhamnus frangula*) 木本植物 1—193b
戚墅堰 Qishuyan 中国常州市辖区 14—69d
期货交易 futures 经济学 6—534c
期刊 periodical 定期出版物 13—169d
期票 promissory note 金融 13—533d
期期地毯 Chichi rug 俄罗斯地毯 4—145d
漆器 lacquerwork 工艺品 9—438a
漆树 varnish tree 木本植物 17—475b
漆树科 Anacardiaceae 植物学 1—307c
槭科 Aceraceae 植物学 1—48e
槭树 maple 木本植物 10—484d
槭糖浆 maple syrup 食品 10—485a
槭糖尿病 maple syrup urine disease 疾病 10—485b
齐 Qi 中国西周分封的诸侯国 14—56b
齐奥尔科夫斯基 Tsiolkovsky, Konstantin Eduardovich 苏联航空和航天科学家 17—249e
齐奥塞斯库 Ceauşescu, Nicolae 罗马尼亚国家元首 3—546f
齐巴人 Ziba (people) 东非民族 18—550a
齐白石 Qi Baishi 中国画家、篆刻家 14—56d
齐柏林伯爵 Zeppelin, Ferdinand (Adolf August Heinrich), Graf von 德国航空界先驱 18—512a
齐柏林飞船 Led Zeppelin 英国乐队 9—552d
齐柏林飞艇 zeppelin 飞艇 18—511d
齐贝吉 Kibaki, Mwai 肯尼亚总统 9—268c
齐布尔达尼泽 Chiburdanidze, Maya 苏联国际象棋大师 4—140b
齐格飞 Ziegfeld, Florenz 美国戏剧演出人 18—550c
齐格菲防线 Siegfried Line 德国历史 15—356b
齐格弗里德 Siegfried 古日耳曼文学 15—356b
齐格勒 Ziegler, Karl 德国化学家 18—550d
齐格勒-纳塔催化剂 Ziegler-Natta catalyst 化工 18—550e
齐赫泽 Chkheidze, Nikolay Semyonovich 孟什维克领袖 4—182f
齐璜 Ch'i Huang 中国画家 4—138b
齐吉家族 Chigi FAMILY 锡耶纳金融家族 4—149b
齐家文化 Qijia culture 中国考古 14—60c
齐克尔 dhikr 伊斯兰教 5—280b
齐克尔 Zirkel, Ferdinand 德国地质学家 18—559a
齐拉特 Szilard, Leo 美国物理学家 16—410e
齐勒尔 Ziller, Tuiskon 德国教育家 18—551e
齐里王朝 Zīrid DYNASTY 穆斯林王朝 18—558f
齐里亚 Cilea, Francesco 意大利作曲家 4—237e
齐米赫蒂人 Tsimihety 非洲民族 17—249c
《齐民要术》 Qimin Yaoshu 中国古代农业百科全书 14—61b
齐莫罗维奇 Zimorowic, Józef Bartłomiej 波兰作家 18—553d
齐默尔曼 Zimmermann, Arthur 德国外交部长 18—553b
齐默尔曼 Zimmermann, Dominikus 巴伐利亚装饰师 18—553c
齐姆良水库 Tsimlyansk Reservoir 俄罗斯水库 17—249c
齐尼亚 Xenia 美国城市 18—374d
齐齐哈尔 Qiqihar 中国城市 14—69a
齐如山 Qi Rushan 中国戏曲作家、理论家 14—57a
齐陶 Zittau 德国城市 18—559d
齐特尔 Zittel, Karl Alfred, Ritter (Knight) von 德国古生物学家 18—559d
齐特琴 zither 乐器 18—559c
齐乌蒂丘特利 Xiuhtecuhtli 阿兹特克神名 18—393b
齐亚 Zia (ur-Rahman), Begum Khaleda 孟加拉国政治家 18—549e
齐亚 Ziya, Mehmed 土耳其社会学家 18—559e
齐亚德王朝 Ziyādid DYNASTY 穆斯林王朝 18—559f
齐亚尔王朝 Zeyārid DYNASTY 伊朗王朝 18—513f
齐亚·哈克 Zia-ul-Haq, Mohammad 巴基斯坦总统 18—549f
齐亚诺 Ciano, Galeazzo, COUNT (conte) DI CORTELLAZZO 意大利政治家 4—232e
祁克 Gierke, Otto Friedrich von 德国法律哲学家 7—123d
祁连山 Qilian Shan 中国青海、甘肃边境山脉 14—60d
祁漫塔格山 Qimantag Shan 中国新疆、青海山脉 14—61b
岐阜 Gifu 日本城市 7—125b
奇阿图拉 Chiatura 格鲁吉亚城市 4—139c
奇班加 Tchibanga 加蓬城镇 16—508e
奇布查人 Chibcha 南美印第安人 4—139f

奇布查诸语言 Chibchan languages 南美印第安语言 4—140a
奇才 prodigy 才华出众的人 13—527b
奇蒂马查人 Chitimacha 北美印第安人 4—181d
奇点 singularity 数学 15—395d
奇恩 Tchien 利比里亚城镇 16—508f
奇尔卡特织物 Chilkat weaving 织物 4—156f
奇尔潘辛戈 Chilpancingo 墨西哥城市 4—157e
奇尔潘辛戈代表大会 Chilpancingo, Congress of 墨西哥历史 4—157e
奇尔奇克 Chirchik 乌兹别克斯坦城市 4—179c
奇尔切奥山 Circeo, Mount 意大利山脊 4—244a
奇尔切乌姆山 Circaeum Promontorium (Italy) 意大利山脉 4—243e
奇尔特恩 Chiltern 英格兰区名 4—157f
奇尔特恩丘陵 Chiltern Hills 英格兰丘陵带 4—158a
奇尔瓦湖 Chilwa, Lake 马拉维湖泊 4—158a
奇夫利 Chifley, Joseph Benedict 澳大利亚政治家 4—148f
奇弗 Cheever, Ezekiel 英属美洲校长 4—102b
奇弗 Cheever, John 美国小说家 4—102b
奇戈利 Cigoli, Ludovico (Cardi da) 意大利画家 4—237d
奇格韦尔 Chigwell 英国城镇 4—149d
奇基穆拉 Chiquimula 危地马拉城镇 4—179a
奇基塔湖 Mar Chiquita, Laguna 阿根廷咸水湖 10—486d
奇迹剧 miracle play 欧洲戏剧 11—271b
奇解 singular solution 数学 15—395c
奇卡科尔 Chicacole (India) 印度县名 4—140b
奇卡马 Chicama (South America) 秘鲁考古遗址 4—144d
奇卡帕 Tshikapa 刚果(金)村庄 17—249a
奇卡亚 Tchicaya U Tam'si 刚果作家 16—508e
奇考梅科特尔 Chicomecóatl 墨西哥女神 4—147c
奇科 Chico 美国城市 4—147b
奇科皮 Chicopee 美国城市 4—147c
奇克拉纳-德拉弗龙特拉 Chiclana de la Frontera 西班牙城市 4—147a
奇克拉约 Chiclayo 秘鲁城市 4—147a
奇克莫加河战役 Chickamauga Creek, Battle of 美国历史 4—146b
奇克索 Chickasaw 美国城市 4—146d
奇克索人 Chickasaw 北美印第安人 4—146c
奇克托瓦加 Cheektowaga 美国城市 4—100c
奇克谢 Chickasha 美国城市 4—146d
奇莱尔 Ciller, Tansu 土耳其经济学家、总理 4—230b
奇兰湖 Chelan, Lake 美国湖泊 4—103d
奇里卡瓦国家保护区 Chiricahua National Monument 美国保护区 4—179d
奇里卡瓦人 Chiricahua 美洲印第安人 4—179c
奇里科夫 Chirikov, Aleksey Ilich 俄国探险家 4—179e
奇里夸人 Chiricoa (people) 南美民族 4—179e
奇利达 Chillida (Juantegui), Eduardo 西班牙雕刻家 4—157c
奇利科西 Chillicothe 美国密苏里州城市 4—157b
奇利科西 Chillicothe 美国俄亥俄州城市 4—157b
奇利拉邦布韦 Chililabombwe 赞比亚城市 4—156f
奇利瓦克 Chilliwack 加拿大自治镇 4—157d
奇利亚地毯 Chilia rug 东高加索地毯 4—156f
奇廉 Chillán 智利城市 4—157a
奇伦布韦 Chilembwe, John 尼亚萨兰传教士 4—156e
奇洛埃岛 Chiloé Island 智利岛屿 4—157d
奇马·达·科内利亚诺 Cima da Conegliano, Giovanni Battista 意大利画家 4—238c
奇马尔特南戈 Chimaltenango 危地马拉省份 4—158c
奇马尔特南戈 Chimaltenango 危地马拉城市 4—158c
奇姆肯特 Chimkent 哈萨克斯坦州名 4—159a
奇姆肯特 Chimkent 哈萨克斯坦城市 4—159a
奇穆人 Chimú 南美印第安人 4—160b
奇南德加 Chinandega 尼加拉瓜城镇 4—166e
奇南特克人 Chinantec 中美印第安人 4—166f
奇尼亚尼 Cignani, Carlo 意大利画家 4—237d
奇努克风 chinook 气象学 4—177a
奇努克鲑 Chinook Salmon 鱼类 4—177a
奇努克人 Chinook 北美印第安人 4—176f
奇诺(皮斯托亚的) Cino da Pistoia 意大利法学家 4—242d
奇诺伊 Chinhoyi 津巴布韦城镇 4—176b
奇帕塔 Chipata 赞比亚城镇 4—178a
奇佩维安人 Chipewyan 北美印第安人 4—178a
奇彭代尔 Chippendale, Thomas 英国家具大师 4—178e
奇彭代尔第二 Chippendale, Thomas II 英国家具大师 4—178f
奇彭代尔式 Chippendale 家具 4—178c
奇彭纳姆 Chippenham 英格兰城镇 4—178f
奇珀瓦人 Chippewa (peoples) 北美印第安人 4—178f
奇珀瓦战役 Chippewa, Battle of 美国历史 4—178f
奇普里亚尼 Cipriani, Giovanni Battista 意大利画家 4—243c
奇普曼 Chipman, John 美国物理化学家 4—178b
奇奇卡斯特南戈 Chichicastenango 危地马拉城镇 4—145f
奇奇梅克人 Chichimec 奇奇梅克人 4—146a
奇切斯特 Chichester 英格兰区名 4—145a
奇切斯特 Chichester 英国城市 4—145a
奇切斯特 Chichester (of Belfast), Arthur Chichester, Baron 英格兰国王驻爱尔兰代表 4—145b
奇切斯特 Chichester, Sir Francis (Charles) 英国探险家 4—145b
奇琴伊察 Chichén Itzá 马雅古城遗址 4—144d
奇趣玻璃品 whimsey glass 无实用价值的玻璃制品 18—223d
奇瑟斯山脉 Chisos Mountains 美国山脉 4—180f
奇斯佳科沃 Chistyakovo (Ukraine) 乌克兰城市 4—181a
奇斯托波尔 Chistopol 俄罗斯城市 4—181a
奇塔尔德鲁格 Chitaldrug (India) 印度城镇 4—181c
奇特姆布韦-姆韦拉高地 Chitembwe-Mwera Highlands (Malaŵi) 马拉维高地 4—181d
奇图尔 Chittoor 印度城镇 4—182d
奇瓦瓦 Chihuahua 墨西哥州名 4—149d
奇瓦瓦 Chihuahua 墨西哥城市 4—149f
奇维达莱-德尔弗留利 Cividale del Friuli 意大利城镇 4—253a
奇维塔卡斯泰拉纳 Civita Castellana 意大利城镇 4—256c
奇维塔诺瓦-马尔凯 Civitanova Marche 意大利城镇 4—256c
奇维塔韦基亚 Civitavecchia 意大利港口 4—256d
奇文顿大屠杀 Chivington Massacre 美国历史 4—182f
奇想 conceit 文学 4—409a
奇想乐队 Kinks, the 英国乐队 9—294b
奇异虫 Paradoxides 古生物学 13—31d
奇异虫统 Paradoxides Series 地质学 13—31e
奇异风格 grotesque 装饰 7—322a
奇异粒子 strange particle 物理学 16—262d
奇泽姆 Chisholm, Caroline 澳大利亚慈善家 4—180a
奇泽姆 Chisholm, Hugh 英国编辑 4—180b
奇泽姆诉佐治亚州案(1793) Chisholm v. Georgia 美国法院案例 4—180c
奇泽姆小径 Chisholm Trail 美国贩牛人小径 4—180b
歧叶节蕨属 Hyenia 古生物学 8—287e
祈祷 prayer 宗教用语 13—486e
祈祷日 Rogation Days 天主教节日 14—352b
祈祷社 Prarthana Samaj 印度教团体 13—484f
祈祷时刻 canonical hours 天主教 3—407e
祈祷时刻 hours, canonical 天主教 8—194c
祈祷书 book of hours 基督教 3—37e
祈祷台 prie-dieu 基督教 13—506f
祈祷毯 prayer rug 伊斯兰教 13—487b
祈祷像 orant 基督教 12—443f
祈雨舞 rain dance 宗教舞蹈 14—126a

耆那教 Jainism 印度宗教 8—518f
耆那教绘画 Jaina painting 印度艺术 8—518f
耆那教经典 Jaina canon 印度耆那教圣典 8—518f
耆英 Qiying 中国清朝大臣 14—70c
脐 navel 解剖学 12—51b
脐带 umbilical cord 解剖学 17—336a
脐花属 Omphalea 植物 12—415d
埼玉 Saitama 日本埼玉县首府 14—532f
埼玉 Saitama 日本县名 14—532e
骑兵 cavalry 兵种 3—538f
骑兵长矛 lance 武器 9—471f
骑警 Mounties 加拿大骑警队 11—446f
骑警 Mounty 加拿大骑警队 11—447a
骑马牧者竞技 rodeo 比赛和表演项目 14—347f
骑牛 bull riding 竞技项目 3—246c
骑士 cavalier 英格兰党派称谓 3—537e
骑士 chevalier 欧洲骑士 4—134f
骑士 knight 荣誉称号 9—321b
骑士堡 Krak des Chevaliers 叙利亚古堡 9—370c
骑士服务 knight service 欧洲封建制度 9—321e
骑士桥 Knightsbridge 英国伦敦居住区 9—322d
骑士诗人 Cavalier poet 英国诗人派系 3—537f
骑士团 chivalry 骑士阶级 4—182e
骑士议会 Cavalier Parliament 英国历史 3—537f
骑无鞍野马 bareback bronc-riding 竞技项目 2—226f
骑野马 bronc-riding 竞技项目 3—177c
骑有鞍野马 saddle bronc-riding 牧马人竞技项目 14—491c
骑装式外衣 redingote 紧身外衣 14—193b
棋盘纹做工 checkerwork 建筑学 4—99e
棋盘形镶砌工艺 opus tessellatum 工艺 12—440d
旗兵 Ch'i-ping (military organization) 军事组织 4—138c
旗队 bandeira 葡萄牙远征队 2—193d
旗腹姬蜂 ensign wasp 昆虫 6—87a
旗会 Palio, The 意大利节日活动 12—566d
旗鸟 flagbird 鸟类 6—343f
旗手 gonfalonier 中世纪意大利官员称号 7—203b
旗鱼 sailfish 鱼类 14—503f
旗帜 flag 标志 6—342d
《旗帜报》 Standard Limited, The 肯尼亚英文日报 16—187c
鲯鳅 dolphin (*Coryphaena hippuras*) 鱼类 5—367f
鳍甲鱼属 Pteraspis 古生物学 13—566f
鳍脚类动物 pinniped 哺乳动物 13—314f
鳍脚鹏 finfoot 鸟类 6—318e
鳍鲸 fin whale (species *Balaenoptera physalus*) 哺乳动物 6—317a
麒麟 qilin 中国神话传说 14—61a
麒麟童 Qilintong 中国京剧表演家 14—61b
麒麟座 R R Monocerotis 天文学 14—100a
乞丐军 Geuzen 荷兰历史 7—105c
乞拉朋齐 Cherrapunji 印度村庄 4—127f
乞力马扎罗 Kilimanjaro 坦桑尼亚火山体 9—278c
企鹅 penguin 鸟类 13—139b
企鹅目 sphenisciform 动物 16—24d
企业财务 business finance 财政 3—285c
企业工会制 enterprise unionism 日本工会组织 6—88e
启定 Khai Dinh 越南皇帝 9—252f
启功 Qi Gong 中国书法家、书画鉴定家 14—56f
启蒙运动 Aufklärung 欧洲历史 2—47c
启蒙运动 Enlightenment 欧洲历史 6—84d
启蒙哲学家 philosophe 法国18世纪思想家、科学家 13—245b
启示 revelation 宗教用语 14—249f
《启示录》 Revelation to John 《新约》最后一卷 14—250b
启示论 apocalypticism 宗教学说 1—410e
启示文学 apocalyptic literature 宗教文学 1—410d
启斯东警察 Keystone Kops 电影人物 9—250f
起爆筒 blasting cap 爆炸装置 2—530f
起搏器 pacemaker 医疗器械 12—531d
起绒织物 pile 纺织品 13—302c
起酥油 shortening 油脂 15—334b
起诉书 indictment 法律 8—367e
起诉资格 standing to sue 法律 16—188b
起重滑车 hoist 机械 8—121f
起重机 crane 机械 4—567f
绮瑟 Iseult (medieval romance) 中世纪爱情传说中人物 8—461c
绮瑟 Isolde 中世纪爱情传说中人物 8—471f
气 qi 中国古代哲学术语 14—56c
气藏 gas reservoir 地质学 7—23c
气笛风琴 calliope 乐器 3—356a
气垫运载器 air-cushion machine 运载工具 1—143a
气动力制动装置 air brake 制动装置 1—142c
气动装置 pneumatic device 气动工具与仪器 13—380a
气缸 cylinder 机械工程 5—88d
气臌病 tympanites (animal disease) 反刍动物疾病 17—306d
气管 trachea 解剖学 17—185d
气管炎 tracheitis 疾病 17—185f
气海界面 air-sea interface 海洋学 1—145d
气候 climate 气候学 4—291a
气候适应 climatic adaptation 体质人类学 4—292a
气候图 climatic map 气候学 4—292b
气候学 climatology 大气科学 4—292c
气辉 airglow 大气科学 1—147a
气精 sylph 假想中生活在空气中的精灵 16—396a
气阱 air pocket 航空学 1—145c
气孔 spiracle 节肢动物器官 16—34c
气孔 stomate 植物学 16—248d
气量计 gas meter 测量装置 7—23a
气轮机列车 turbo train 交通工具 17—277c
气鸣乐器 aerophone 音乐 1—96f
气囊 air sac 解剖学 1—145d
气泡室 bubble chamber 物理学 3—217b
气枪 air gun 武器 1—144c
气球 balloon 航空 2—178b
气球运动 ballooning 体育 2—178f
气溶胶 aerosol 物理化学 1—96f
气体 gas 物质形态 7—22c
气体动理论 kinetic theory of gases 物理学 9—284f
气体燃烧器 gas burner 加热装置 7—22d
气团 air mass 气象学 1—145a
气味 odour 化学 12—340a
气仙沼 Kesennuma 日本城市 9—244c
气相色谱法 gas chromatography 化学 7—22e
气象局 weather bureau 机构 18—155a
气象卫星 weather satellite 气象探测 18—155e
气象学 meteorology 大气科学 11—157d
气象鱼 weatherfish 鱼类 18—155e
气胸 pneumothorax 疾病 13—381e
气旋 cyclone 气象学 5—86e
气压 atmospheric pressure 物理学 2—31a
气压表 barometer 测量气压仪器 2—238a
气压耳炎 baro-otitis 生理学 2—237e
气压耳炎 barotitis 生理学 2—239e
气压计辉光 barometric light 物理现象 2—238b
气压伤 barotrauma 生理学 2—239e
气涌 surge 大气科学 16—353a
气闸室 air lock 机械 1—144f
气质 ethos 文学 6—151b
气质 temperament 心理学 16—532d

气质喜剧 humours, comedy of 戏剧 8—249c
汽车 automobile 运输工具 2—78b
汽车比赛 automobile racing 运动项目 2—78e
汽车驾驶赛 gymkhana 体育 7—389b
汽车俱乐部 automobile club 汽车所有主的组织 2—78e
汽车拉力赛 rally 体育 14—133d
汽车旅馆 motel 旅馆 11—430c
汽车赛 AUTOMOBILE RACING 体育项目 16—51a
汽化 vaporization 物理学 17—470b
汽油 gasoline 燃料 7—24b
汽油机 gasoline engine 工业机械 7—24c
汽转球 aeolipile 汽轮机 1—95a
契丹 Khitan 中国古代民族 9—260a
契尔年科 Chernenko, Konstantin Ustinovich 苏联政治领导人 4—125e
契诃夫 Chekhov, Anton (Pavlovich) 俄国剧作家 4—103b
契卡 Cheka 苏联安全机构 4—103a
契卡洛夫 Chkalov (Russia) 俄罗斯城市 4—182f
契坎工艺 chikan work 印度艺术 4—150c
契克尔德 Tschichold, Jan 德国印刷专家、作家 17—248a
契克斯 Chequers 英国首相别墅 4—124d
契马布埃 Cimabue 佛罗伦萨画家 4—238c
契玛罗萨 Cimarosa, Domenico 意大利作曲家 4—238e
契切林 Chicherin, Boris Nikolayevich 俄国哲学家 4—144f
契切林 Chicherin, Georgy Vasilyevich 苏联外交家 4—144f
契斯提教团 Chishtīyah 宗教 4—180c
契约 contract 法律 4—471c
契约劳动 contract labour 经济学 4—471e
砌合 bond 建筑学 3—25f
器官 organ 解剖学 12—457b
器官发生 organogenesis 生物学 12—458e
器乐曲 instrumental 音乐 8—401b
憩室 diverticulum 病理现象 5—346a
恰 Tziá (Greece) 爱琴海岛屿 17—313f
恰彼克 Čapek, Karel 捷克小说家 3—424c
恰布拉 Chāpra 印度城镇 4—58f
恰布瓦 Jhābua 印度城镇 9—10b
恰达耶夫 Chaadayev, Pyotr Yakovlevich 俄国作家 4—21b
恰当方程 exact equation 数学 6—188c
恰多格 Chhātak 孟加拉国城镇 4—137f
恰尔达什舞 czardas 匈牙利舞蹈 5—90d
恰尔托雷斯基 Czartoryski, Adam Jerzy, Prince 波兰政治家 5—96d
恰尔托雷斯基 Czartoryski, Adam Kazimierz, Prince 波兰王室成员 5—96e
恰尔托雷斯基 Czartoryski, Michał Fryderyk, Prince 波兰政治家 5—96f
恰卡 Shaka 非洲祖鲁帝国缔造者 15—256f
恰克 Chac 马雅雨神 4—22c
恰克马克 Çakmak, Fevzi 土耳其元帅 3—332a
恰克斯特 Čakste, Janis 拉脱维亚共和国总统 3—332a
恰克图 Kyakhta 俄罗斯城镇 9—412d
恰空 chaconne 西班牙舞蹈 4—23a
恰勒瓦尔 Jhālawār 印度城镇 9—10b
恰里卡尔 Chārīkār 阿富汗城市、省会 4—64e
恰纳卡莱 Çanakkale 土耳其城市 3—391b
恰纳卡莱海峡 Çanakkale Boğazı (strait, Turkey) 土耳其海峡 3—391d
《恰纳克条约》 Çanak, Treaty of 欧洲历史 3—391b
恰帕克丘尔 Çapakçur (Turkey) 土耳其城市 3—419c
恰帕斯 Chiapas 墨西哥州名 4—138f
恰帕斯高地 Chiapas Highlands 墨西哥高地 4—139a
恰帕斯州马德雷山脉 Sierra Madre de Chiapas 墨西哥山脉 15—359a
恰帕耶夫斯克 Chapayevsk 俄罗斯城市 4—57a
恰恰舞 cha-cha 舞厅舞 4—21a
恰斯拉夫斯卡 Čáslavská, Věra 捷克体操运动员 3—501d
髂股血栓性静脉炎 iliofemoral thrombophlebitis (medicine) 疾病 8—334b
髂肋肌 iliocostalis muscle 解剖学 8—334a
千岛海沟 Kuril Trench 西太平洋深海沟 9—402d
千岛群岛 Kuril Islands 西太平洋岛群 9—402d
千岛群岛 Thousand Islands 北美圣劳伦斯河岛群 17—61b
千岛洋流 Kuril Current (Pacific Ocean) 太平洋洋流 9—402c
千花玻璃制品 millefiori glass 玻璃器皿 11—224c
千斤顶 jack 机械工具 8—503a
千克 kilogram 计量单位 9—280e
千里光 groundsel 草本植物 7—324f
《千里江山图》 Qianli Jiangshantu 中国北宋画家王希孟作品 14—59f
千里眼 clairvoyance 心理学 4—258c
千利休 Sen Rikyū 日本茶道大师 15—207d
千枚岩 phyllite 岩石 13—270f
千米 kilometre 计量单位 9—280e
千母草 pickaback plant (*Tolmiea menziesii*) 草本植物 13—289d
千年纪 millennium 历法 11—224e
千年穹顶 Millennium Dome 英国建筑 11—225a
《千人请愿书》 Millenary Petition 英格兰历史 11—224d
千人团远征 Thousand, Expedition of the 意大利历史 17—60c
千日红 globe amaranth (Gomphrena globosa) 草本植物 7—160a
千日战争 Thousand Days, The War of a 哥伦比亚历史 17—61a
千岁 Chitose 日本地名 4—182a
千岁兰 tumboa 植物 17—266a
千岁兰科 Welwitschiaceae 植物学 18—185b
千禧年 millennium 基督教神学 11—224e
千叶 Chiba 日本县名 4—139d
千叶 Chiba 日本城市 4—139e
迁飞途径 flyway 动物学 6—382f
迁徙 migration 动物学 11—207c
迁移率 mobility 物理学 11—300c
牵牛花 morning glory 草本植物 11—399a
铅(Pb) lead 化学元素 9—540c
铅白 white lead 含铅无机化合物 18—232f
铅版 stereotype 印刷 16—225d
铅笔 pencil 书画工具 13—135c
铅笔柏 pencil cedar 木本植物 13—135c
铅笔画 pencil drawing 美术 13—135d
铅笔鱼 pencil fish 鱼类 13—135e
铅矾 anglesite 矿物 1—346d
铅黄 massicot 矿物 11—12d
铅晶质玻璃 lead crystal 玻璃 9—541a
铅室法 chamber process 化工 4—34b
铅铁矾 plumbojarosite 矿物 13—376c
铅制品 leadwork 工艺品 9—541d
铅中毒 lead poisoning 病理学 9—541a
铅 210 测年法 lead-210 dating 放射性测年方法 9—541a
谦比西河 Chambeshi River 赞比亚河流 4—37a
谦斋 Kyŏmja (Korean painter) 朝鲜画家 9—414a
骞驴 kiang 动物 9—268c
荨麻科 Urticaceae 植物学 17—418f
荨麻目 Urticales 植物学 17—419b
前北方气候期 Pre-Boreal Climatic Interval 地质学 13—487c
前川国男 Maekawa Kunio 日本建筑师 10—376a
前寒武纪时期 Precambrian time 地质学 13—488b
前蕨类植物 prefern 古植物学 13—492a
前拉斐尔派兄弟会 Pre-Raphaelite Brotherhood 英国艺术团体 13—487c

前廊 narthex 建筑 12—2a
前浪漫主义 Pre-Romanticism 欧洲历史 13—487f
前黎巴嫩山脉 Anti-Lebanon Mountains 叙利亚-黎巴嫩界山 1—381c
前列腺 prostate gland 解剖学 13—540d
前列腺癌 prostate cancer 疾病 13—540c
前列腺疾病 prostatic disorder 疾病 13—540e
前列腺素 prostaglandin 化合物 13—540b
前弥曼差 Pūrva-mīmāṃsā (Indian philosophy) 印度哲学 14—34f
前篇 prequel 文学 13—494c
前桥 Maebashi 日本县名 10—375d
前鳃类 prosobranch 软体动物 13—539a
前鳃类海螺 conch 海生螺 4—411c
前肾 pronephros 解剖学 13—533e
前缩法 foreshortening 作画技法 6—405e
前田家族 Maeda FAMILY 日本大名家族 10—375f
前庭耳蜗神经 vestibulocochlear nerve 解剖学 17—530b
前卫生花 zen'ei ikebana 日本花道 18—507d
前原一诚 Maebara Issei 日本政治家 10—375d
前置胎盘 placenta praevia 病理产科现象 13—336f
前祝圣体礼 Presanctified, Liturgy of the 宗教 13—494e
前奏曲 prelude 音乐 13—493a
虔诚团契 collegia pietatis 新教历史 4—348a
《虔诚者之书》 Sefer-Ḥasidim 犹太教著作 15—186f
虔敬主义 Pietism 宗教运动 13—297b
钱币收藏 coin collecting 钱币学 4—335e
钱伯伦(老) Chamberlen, Hugh, THE ELDER 英国助产士 4—35f
钱伯伦(老彼得) Chamberlen, Peter, THE ELDER 外科医生 4—35f
钱伯斯 Chambers, Dorothea (Katharine) Lambert 英国女子网球运动员 4—36b
钱伯斯 Chambers, Ephraim 英国百科全书编纂者 4—36c
钱伯斯 Chambers, John Graham 英国运动家 4—36c
钱伯斯 Chambers, Robert 苏格兰著作家 4—36c
钱伯斯 Chambers, Whittaker 美国新闻记者 4—36d
钱伯斯 Chambers, Sir William 英国建筑师 4—36d
《钱伯斯百科全书》 Chambers's Encyclopaedia 英国百科全书 4—36e
钱伯斯堡 Chambersburg 美国自治镇 4—36e
钱柏林 Chamberlin, Thomas Chrowder 美国地质学家 4—36a
钱袋花 pocketbook flower 植物学 13—383c
钱德拉布尔 Chandrapur 印度城市 4—45d
钱德拉塞卡 Chandrasekhar, Subrahmanyan 印裔美国天体物理学家 4—45d
钱德拉塞卡极限 Chandrasekhar limit 天体物理学 4—45e
钱德拉·谢卡尔 Chandra Shekhar 印度政治家 4—45c
钱德勒 Chandler, Happy 美国参议员 4—44c
钱德勒 Chandler, Norman 美国报纸发行人 4—44d
钱德勒 Chandler, Raymond 美国侦探小说家 4—44d
钱德勒 Chandler, William Eaton 美国政治家 4—44e
钱德勒 Chandler, Zachariah 美国政治家 4—44f
钱德勒 Chandler 美国城市 4—44b
钱迪达斯 Caṇḍīdās 印度诗人 3—397e
钱端升 Qian Duansheng 中国政治学家、法学家、教育学家 14—57b
钱多斯公爵(第一) Chandos, James Brydges, 1st Duke of, MARQUESS OF CARNARVON, EARL OF CARNARVON, VISCOUNT WILTON, 9TH BARON CHANDOS OF SUDELEY 英国贵族 4—45a
钱多斯 Chandos, Sir John 英格兰陆军上尉 4—45b
钱多斯公爵和伯爵 Chandos, DUKES AND BARONS OF 英国贵族名 4—44f
钱多斯男爵(第五) Chandos (of Sudeley), Grey Brydges, 5th Baron 英国贵族 4—45a
钱多斯男爵(第一) Chandos (of Sudeley), John Brydges, 1st Baron 英格兰著名骑士 4—45a
钱恩 Chain, Sir Ernst Boris 德裔英国生物化学家 4—27f
钱穆 Qian Mu 中国文史学家 14—57c
钱纳尔-巴斯克港 Channel-Port aux Basques 加拿大城镇 4—52c
钱纳尔地区 Channel Country 澳大利亚牧区 4—52b
钱尼 Chaney, Lon 美国电影演员 4—46a
钱宁 Channing, Edward (Perkins) 美国历史学家 4—52d
钱宁 Channing, Walter 美国医师 4—52e
钱宁 Channing, William Ellery 美国作家 4—52e
钱佩里科 Champerico 危地马拉港口 4—41a
钱塞勒 Chancellor, Richard 英国海员 4—43b
钱三强 Qian Sanqiang 中国原子核物理学家 14—57d
钱瑟勒斯维尔战役 Chancellorsville, Battle of 美国历史 4—43c
钱思亮 Qian Siliang 中国教育家、有机化学家 14—57f
钱苔属 Riccia 植物学 14—278e
钱塘江 Qiantang Jiang 中国河流 14—59f
钱特里 Chantrey, Sir Francis Legatt 英国雕刻家 4—54d
钱伟长 Qian Weichang 中国物理学家、社会活动家 14—58a
钱选 Qian Xuan 中国画家、诗人、学者 14—58c
钱学森 Qian Xuesen 中国物理学家、火箭专家 14—58e
钱钟书 Qian Zhongshu 中国文学家 14—59a
钳子 pliers 手工工具 13—371d
乾隆 Ch'ien-lung 中国清代皇帝 4—148c
乾隆 Qianlong 中国清代皇帝 14—59f
乾婆陀瑜伽师 Kānphaṭa Yogi 印度教苦行僧 9—160e
乾山 Kenzan (Japanese potter) 日本陶工 9—236c
乾县 Qian Xian 中国地名 14—58c
潜鸟 loon 鸟类 10—214f
潜热 latent heat 物理学 9—509d
潜水 underwater diving 体育 17—340c
潜水服 diving suit 潜水装备 5—347d
潜水甲 diving beetle 昆虫 5—347c
潜水鸭 diving duck 鸟类 5—347c
潜水钟 diving bell 潜水装备 5—347c
潜鹈鹱 diving petrel 鸟类 5—347d
潜艇 submarine 军舰 16—298e
潜望镜 periscope 光学仪器 13—170a
潜鸭 pochard 鸟类 13—382f
潜叶虫 leaf miner 昆虫 9—542d
潜影 latent image 摄影 9—509e
潜鱼 pearlfish 鱼类 13—114a
浅池泵 sump pump 排水装置 16—334d
浅雕珐琅工艺 basse-taille 彩饰技术 2—268c
浅浮雕 bas-relief 雕刻艺术 2—254f
浅海带 neritic zone 海洋学 12—85d
浅水探海艇 mesoscaphe 潜水船 11—142b
浅水重炮舰 monitor 美国战舰 11—340a
浅滩 shoal 地质学 15—327d
浅野总一郎 Asano Sōichirō 日本实业家 1—538d
遣使会 Mission, Congregation of the 天主教修会 11—278d
遣使会会士 Vincentian 天主教 17—568c
遣兴曲 cassation 音乐 3—502e
茜草 madder 植物 10—366c
茜草科 Rubiaceae 植物学 14—437a
茜素 alizarin 染料 1—231c
堑壕战 trench warfare 军事 17—209b
嵌板椅 panel chair 家具 13—10c
嵌合体 chimera 生物学 4—158f
嵌花 appliqué 工艺品 1—420f
嵌凸缝 tuckpointing 建筑 17—258a
羌塘自然保护区 Qiangtang Nature Reserve 中国野生动物保护区 14—59e
羌语 Qiang language 中国民族语言 14—59d
羌族 Qiang 中国民族 14—59b

枪弹 cartridge 武器 3—491c
枪机 bolt action 武器装置 3—17a
枪木 lancewood 木材 9—473c
枪炮 gun 武器 7—371d
枪炮与玫瑰乐队 Guns N' Roses 美国乐队 7—374a
枪乌贼 squid 软体动物 16—169e
枪鱼 spearfish 鱼类 16—10e
枪支战争 Gun War 非洲历史 7—371e
腔肠动物 coelenterate 动物学 4—328d
腔骨龙属 Coelophysis 古生物学 4—328f
腔棘鱼 coelacanth 鱼类 4—328c
腔静脉 vena cava 解剖学 17—496c
蜣螂 dung beetle 昆虫 5—461b
强盗 gyangu 日本暴力团成员 7—388b
强调重复 ploce 修辞学 13—373b
强核力 strong nuclear force 物理学 16—281c
强击机 attack aircraft 武器 2—37f
强奸 rape 暴力犯罪 14—153f
强力举重 powerlifting 体育运动 13—475a
强音节和弱音节 arsis and thesis 诗歌 1—520e
强硬刑罚 peine forte et dure 法律 13—124d
强占 deforcement 英国财产法 5—209f
强占诉讼 trover 法律 17—238a
强征入伍 impressment 历史 8—348d
《强制法》 Coercive Acts 法律 4—329c
《强制法案》 Force Acts 美国法案 6—400c
强制管理 sequestration 法律 15—220c
《强制劳役法令》 Robotpatent 奥地利法律 14—336e
强制说服 coercive persuasion 洗脑 4—329c
强子 hadron 物理学 7—403d
墙 wall 建筑结构 18—76c
墙板 wallboard 建筑结构 18—80b
墙报 wall newspaper 宣传形式 18—76e
墙角家具 corner furniture 家具 4—514a
墙手球 handball 体育 7—456e
墙树 espalier 园艺 6—132e
墙头花 wallflower 草本植物 18—81c
蔷薇 rose 多年生灌木或藤本植物 14—400c
蔷薇辉石 rhodonite 矿物 14—269d
蔷薇目 Rosales 植物学 14—398e
蔷薇石英 rose quartz 矿物 14—402a
蔷薇藓 rose moss (*Rhodobryum roseum*) 真藓目植物 14—401f
蔷薇亚纲 Rosidae 植物学 14—406b
彊柢 Cuong De 越南亲王 5—64c
抢劫 robbery 刑法 14—325e
羟胺 hydroxylamine 化合物 8—287b
羟胆矾 brochantite 矿物 3—173a
羟钒铅锌石 descloizite 矿物 5—258f
羟钒铜铅石 mottramite 矿物 11—438a
羟脯氨酸 hydroxyproline 生物化学 8—287c
羟赖氨酸 hydroxylysine 生物化学 8—287c
羟磷灰石 hydroxylapatite 矿物 8—287b
羟磷锂铝石 montebrasite 矿物 11—361a
强迫劳动 forced labour 被强制、不自愿的劳动 6—400c
强迫性神经官能症 obsessive-compulsive disorder (OCD) 心理学 12—323e
跷蝽 stilt bug 昆虫 16—238e
锹甲 stag beetle 昆虫 16—179c
敲花工艺 repoussé 金属工艺 14—234b
敲击乐器 percussion instrument 乐器 13—159d
橇 sledge 运输工具 15—429e
乔巴山 Choybalsan 蒙古城镇 4—201d
乔贝蒂 Gioberti, Vincenzo 意大利哲学家、政治家 7—137e
乔布斯 Jobs, Steven P. 美国计算机先驱 9—41e
乔答摩 Gautama, Siddhārtha 佛教 7—35e
乔丹 Jordan, A(rchibald) C. 南非黑人小说家 9—86d
乔丹 Jordan, Barbara C. 美国律师 9—86d
乔丹 Jordan, David Starr 美国博物学家 9—86f
乔丹 Jordan, Michael 美国运动员 9—87a
乔丹 Jordan, Vernon E., Jr. 美国律师、民权领袖 9—87d
乔德 Joad, C(yril) E(dwin) M(itchinson) 英国哲学家、作家、教师 9—37f
乔德地毯 Chaudor carpet 铺地用品 4—94f
乔尔蒂人 Chortí 马雅印第安人 4—199e
乔尔乔涅 Giorgione 意大利画家 7—138d
乔尔人 Chol 马雅印第安人 4—190c
乔尔森 Jolson, Al 美国歌星 9—77e
乔凡尼 Giovanni Acuto 意大利军人 7—139d
乔凡尼 Giovanni da Bologna 意大利艺术家 7—139d
乔凡尼 Giovanni di Fidanza 意大利军人 7—139f
乔凡尼 Giovanni di Paolo (di Grazia) 意大利艺术家 7—139f
乔弗里 Joffrey, Robert 美国舞蹈家 9—43d
乔戈里峰 Chogori (Jammu and Kashmir) 查谟和克什米尔地区山峰 4—189a
乔吉 Giorgi, Giovanni 意大利物理学家 7—138d
乔加-赞比尔 Choghā Zanbīl 古代埃兰人遗址 4—188f
乔科 Choc 哥伦比亚省份 4—187b
乔科瑙伊·维泰兹 Csokonai Vitéz, Mihály 匈牙利诗人 5—45c
乔科人 Chocó 操加勒比语印第安人 4—187a
乔克里弗 Chalk River 加拿大村庄 4—32d
乔克托哈奇河 Choctawhatchee River 美国河流 4—188a
乔克托人 Choctaw 北美印第安人 4—187e
乔克希尔 Chalkhill, John 英国诗人 4—32d
乔奎人 Chokwe 非洲民族 4—190b
乔拉斯夫妇 Jolas, Eugene and Maria 美国期刊创办人、作家 9—76b
乔拉斯米亚 Chorasmia (historic Asian region) 亚洲古地名 4—197f
乔里约斯 Chorrillos 秘鲁城市 4—199e
乔利 Chorley 英格兰自治市 4—199c
乔利 Joly, John 爱尔兰地质学家 9—77f
乔利埃特 Joliet 美国城市 9—76c
乔利亚掌 cholla 植物学 4—191c
乔卢拉 Cholula 墨西哥城市 4—191f
乔卢特卡 Choluteca 洪都拉斯城市 4—192a
乔鲁姆 Çorum 土耳其城市 4—520e
乔罗迦陀 Gorakhnāth 印度瑜伽创始人 7—211d
乔罗特加人 Chorotega 美洲印第安人 4—199d
乔洛 Thyolo 马拉维城镇 17—76a
乔姆利 Cholmondeley, Hugh 英国殖民主义者 4—191e
乔姆斯基 Chomsky, Noam 美国语言学家 4—192a
乔木 tree 植物学 17—206a
乔纳斯 Jonas, Justus 德意志宗教改革家 9—78e
乔纳蟹 Jonah crab 甲壳动物 9—78e
乔诺人 Chono 南美印第安人 4—195d
乔普林 Joplin 美国城市 9—84d
乔普林 Joplin, Scott 美国黑人作曲家 9—84e
乔乔狗 chow chow 狗品种 4—201c
乔乔人 Chocho 中美印第安人 4—187a
乔切尔森 Jochelson, Vladimir Ilich 俄国人种学家 9—42b
乔石 Qiao Shi 中国领导人 14—60a
乔舒亚(柱上苦行者) Joshua the Stylite 隐修院修士 9—91c
乔斯 Jos 尼日利亚城镇 9—88b
乔斯高原 Jos Plateau 尼日利亚高原 9—88c
乔叟 Chaucer, Geoffrey 英国作家 4—92d
乔特 chauth 印度税收 4—96a
乔特-罗斯玛丽学校 Choate Rosemary Hall 美国大学预备学校

4—186f
乔托 Giotto DI BONDONE 意大利画家 7—139a
乔瓦娜二世 Joan II 那不勒斯女王 9—38b
乔瓦娜一世 Joan I 那不勒斯女王 9—38a
乔瓦尼 Giovanni, Agostino di 意大利雕塑家 7—140b
乔万尼(加埃塔的) Giovanni DA GAETA (pope) 教皇 7—139d
乔万尼(皮安德卡尔皮尼的) Giovanni DA PIAN DEL CARPINI 方济各会修士 7—139d
乔伊斯 Joyce, James 爱尔兰小说家 9—95b
乔伊斯 Joyce, William 纳粹英语播音员 9—95d
乔治 George 统治者之名 7—74b
乔治 George 波希米亚国王 7—74c
乔治 George 南非开普省城镇 7—76f
乔治 Giorgio, Francesco di 意大利艺术家 7—138d
乔治 George, Henry 美国经济学家 7—77e
乔治(卡帕多西亚的) George OF CAPPADOCIA 基督教教士 7—77a
乔治(劳迪塞亚的) George OF LAODICEA 基督教教士 7—77b
乔治(牧首秘书) George THE SYNCELLUS 拜占廷历史学家 7—77e
乔治(皮西底亚的) George THE PISIDIAN 拜占廷叙事诗人 7—77d
乔治(塞浦路斯的) George OF CYPRUS (Greek Orthodox leader) 希腊正教会牧首 7—77b
乔治(特拉布宗的) George OF TREBIZOND 拜占廷人文主义者 7—77b
乔治(修士) George THE MONK 拜占廷历史学家 7—77c
乔治,圣 George, SAINT 基督教殉教者 7—77a
乔治堡河 Fort George River (Canada) 加拿大河流 6—413e
乔治敦 Georgetown 冈比亚城市 7—78e
乔治敦 Georgetown 圭亚那首都 7—78e
乔治敦 Georgetown 美国科罗拉多州城市 7—79a
乔治敦 Georgetown 美国华盛顿历史区 7—79a
乔治敦 Georgetown 美国南卡罗来纳州城市 7—79b
乔治二世 George II 大不列颠国王 7—74e
乔治二世 George II 希腊国王 7—76d
乔治风格 Georgian style 建筑学 7—84b
乔治河 George River 加拿大河流 7—78b
乔治湖 George, Lake 澳大利亚湖泊 7—77f
乔治湖 George, Lake 美国湖泊 7—77f
乔治·华盛顿出生地国家纪念馆 George Washington Birthplace National Monument 美国纪念馆 7—78c
乔治奖章 G.M. 英国勋章 7—166f
乔治六世 George VI 英国国王 7—76b
乔治·乔治乌-德治 Gheorghe Gheorghiu-Dej 罗马尼亚城市 7—111e
乔治三世 George III 大不列颠及爱尔兰王国国王 7—75a
乔治十字勋章 George Cross 英国勋章 7—78b
乔治时代诗歌 Georgian poetry 英国文学 7—84b
乔治四世 George IV 大不列颠及爱尔兰王国国王 7—75e
乔治王湾 King George Sound 澳大利亚港口 9—289a
乔治王之战 King George's War 美洲历史 9—289a
乔治王子城 Prince George 加拿大城市 13—514d
乔治·威廉 George William 勃兰登堡选侯 7—78d
乔治乌-德治 Gheorghiu-Dej, Gheorghe 罗马尼亚总理 7—111e
乔治五世 George V 英国国王 7—75f
乔治五世 George V 汉诺威国王 7—76e
乔治修士 George, BROTHER 匈牙利政治家 7—77a
乔治修士 György, FRATER 匈牙利政治家 7—391c
乔治勋章 G.C. 英国勋章 7—40e
乔治亚海峡 Georgia, Strait of 加拿大海峡 7—83c
乔治亚湾 Georgian Bay 加拿大湖湾 7—83d
乔治一世 George I 大不列颠国王 7—74c
乔治一世 George I 希腊国王 7—76c
侨生 Peranakan 印度尼西亚本国与外籍人后代 13—156e
荞麦 buckwheat 草本植物 3—224d
荞麦树 buckwheat tree (*Cliftonia monophylla*) 灌木或乔木 3—224f
桥 bridge 交通 3—149f
桥本病 Hashimoto disease 疾病 7—502f
桥本龙太郎 Hashimoto Ryūtarō 日本首相 7—502f
桥牌 bridge 纸牌游戏 3—151e
桥社 Brücke, Die 德国画家团体 3—200b
巧克力 chocolate 食品 4—187c
巧克力壶 chocolate pot 器皿 4—187d
壳牌石油公司 Shell Oil Company 美国石油公司 15—296f
翘鼻麻鸭 shelduck 鸭科动物 15—295c
鞘翅目昆虫 coleopteran 昆虫 4—341c
鞘膜积液 hydrocele 疾病 8—282b
鞘蕊花属 Coleus 植物学 4—344c
鞘尾蝠 sheath-tailed bat 动物学 15—291c
鞘藻属 Oedogonium 植物学 12—342a
鞘嘴鸥 sheathbill 鸟类 15—291d
切比雪夫 Chebyshev, Pafnuty 俄国数学家 4—98b
切比雪夫不等式 Chebyshev's inequality 数学定理 4—98c
切博克萨雷 Cheboksary 俄罗斯城市 4—98a
切德 Cheddar 英格兰村庄 4—100a
切德尔布尔 Chhatarpur 印度城镇 4—137f
切德干酪 Cheddar 食品 4—100a
切蒂斯格尔 Chhattīsgaṛh 印度邦名 4—138a
切蒂斯格尔平原 Chhattīsgaṛh Plain 印度平原 4—138a
切杜巴岛 Cheduba Island 缅甸岛屿 4—100c
切断术 amputation 医学 1—300e
切多斯贝 Theodossia 古生物学 17—27b
切恩男爵(第一) Cheyne, Sir William Watson, 1ST BARONET 英国外科医生 4—137e
切尔卡瑟 Cherkasy 乌克兰州名 4—125d
切尔卡瑟 Cherkasy 乌克兰城市 4—125e
切尔克斯人 Circassian 高加索民族 4—243e
切尔克斯语 Circassian language 语言学 4—243f
切尔马克·冯·赛塞内格 Tschermak von Seysenegg, Erich 奥地利植物学家 17—247f
切尔马尼克 Csermanek, János (Hungarian premier) 匈牙利首相 5—45b
切尔内 Chelny (Russia) 俄罗斯城市 4—104e
切尔尼戈夫 Chernihiv 乌克兰州名 4—125f
切尔尼戈夫 Chernihiv 乌克兰城市 4—126a
切尔尼乔夫斯基 Tchernichowsky, Saul (Gutmanovich) 希伯来语诗人 16—508d
切尔尼亚耶夫 Chernyayev, Mikhail Grigoryevich 俄国将军 4—126f
切尔宁伯爵 Czernin, Ottokar, Count (Graf) 奥匈帝国外交大臣 5—99f
切尔诺贝利事故 Chernobyl accident 苏联核电站事故 4—126a
切尔诺夫 Chernov, Viktor Mikhaylovich 俄国社会革命党创建人 4—126d
切尔诺夫策 Chernovtsy 乌克兰州名 4—126d
切尔诺夫策 Chernovtsy 乌克兰城市 4—126e
切尔诺戈尔斯克 Chernogorsk 俄罗斯城市 4—126c
切尔诺梅尔金 Chernomyrdin, Viktor Stepanovich 俄罗斯总理 4—126c
切尔诺维茨 Czernowitz (Ukraine) 乌克兰城市 5—100a
切尔斯基岭 Chersky Range 俄罗斯山岭 4—128c
切尔松尼斯(色雷斯的) Chersonese, Thracian 古代地区名 4—128e
切尔松尼斯(陶里人的) Chersonese, Tauric 古克里米亚地区 4—128d
切尔滕纳姆 Cheltenham 英格兰自治市 4—105b
切尔韦泰里 Cerveteri (Italy) 意大利城市 4—15b
切尔维 Cervi, Gino 意大利性格演员 4—15b
切尔西 Chelsea (England) 英格兰城市 4—104e
切尔西瓷器 Chelsea porcelain 英国瓷器 4—104e

切法卢 Cefalù 意大利城镇 3—549f
切分音 syncopation 音乐 16—401e
切腹 seppuku 日本人自杀方式 15—218d
切根虫 wireworm 动物学 18—292f
切哈努夫 Ciechanów 原波兰省份 4—236c
切哈努夫 Ciechanów 波兰城市 4—236d
切赫 Cech,Thomas Robert 美国生物化学家 3—547d
切喉鳟 cutthroat trout (*Salmo clarki*) 鱼类 5—80d
切霍维奇 Czechowicz,Józef 波兰诗人 5—99f
切凯蒂 Cecchetti,Enrico 意大利芭蕾舞演员 3—547e
切克 Cheke,Sir John 英国人文主义者 4—103a
切拉诺湖 Celano,Lago di (Italy) 意大利湖泊 3—551d
切莱斯廷 Celestine 教皇和敌对教皇称号 3—554e
切莱斯廷(二世) Celestine (Ⅱ) 教皇 3—554e
切莱斯廷二世 Celestine Ⅱ 教皇 3—554f
切莱斯廷三世 Celestine Ⅲ 教皇 3—554f
切莱斯廷四世 Celestine Ⅳ 教皇 3—555a
切莱斯廷五世,圣 Celestine V,SAINT 教皇 3—555a
切莱斯廷一世,圣 Celestine I,SAINT 教皇 3—554e
切兰纳 Celaenae 土耳其古城镇 3—551b
切雷肖湖 Ceresio,Lago (Switzerland-Italy) 瑞士-意大利湖泊 4—11a
切里尼奥拉 Cerignola 意大利城镇 4—11b
切里瓦利奇袭 Cherry Valley Raid 美国独立战争史 4—128c
切里亚 Jharia 印度城市 9—10d
切利尼 Cellini,Benvenuto 意大利雕刻家 3—557b
切利尼晕 Cellini's halo 天文学 3—557d
切利诺格勒 Tselinograd 哈萨克斯坦州名 17—248c
切利诺格勒 Tselinograd (Kazakhstan) 哈萨克斯坦城市 17—248d
切列波韦茨 Cherepovets 俄罗斯城市 4—125b
切列梅萨皮科 Ceglie Messapico 意大利城镇 3—550a
切列米斯人 Cheremis (people) 民族 4—125a
切列米斯语 Cheremis language 语言 4—125a
切列姆霍沃 Cheremkhovo 俄罗斯城市 4—125a
切列普宁 Tcherepnin,Alexander (Nikolayevich) 美国音乐家 16—508c
切列普宁 Tcherepnin,Nikolay (Nikolayevich) 俄国作曲家 16—508c
切伦科夫 Cherenkov,Pavel Alekseyevich 苏联物理学家 4—125a
切伦科夫辐射 Cherenkov radiation 物理学 4—125b
切罗基 Cherokee 美国城市 4—127e
切罗基人 Cherokee 北美印第安人 4—127b
切罗基语 Cherokee language 北美印第安语 4—127e
切姆斯福德 Chelmsford 英格兰城镇 4—104b
切姆斯福德 Chelmsford 美国城镇 4—104c
切姆斯福德子爵(第一) Chelmsford (of Chelmsford),Frederic John Napier Thesiger,1st Viscount 英国政治家 4—104d
切尼 Cheney,Charles Edward 基督教人士 4—120b
切尼 Cheney,Dick 美国副总统 4—120b
切普斯托 Chepstow 威尔士集镇 4—124d
切肉刀 cleaver 工具 4—277f
切萨尔皮诺 Cesalpino,Andrea 意大利哲学家 4—16b
切萨罗蒂 Cesarotti,Melchiorre 意大利诗人 4—16e
切萨皮克 Chesapeake 美国城市 4—129e
切萨皮克-俄亥俄铁路公司 Chesapeake and Ohio Railway Company (C&O) 美国铁路公司 4—129f
切萨皮克-俄亥俄运河 Chesapeake and Ohio Canal 美国运河 4—129f
切萨皮克-特拉华运河 Chesapeake and Delaware Canal 美国运河 4—129f
切萨皮克湾 Chesapeake Bay 美国海湾 4—130a
切萨皮克湾隧道桥 Chesapeake Bay Bridge-Tunnel 美国桥 4—130b
切塞纳 Cesenà 意大利城镇 4—16e
切瑟尔海滩 Chesil Beach 英格兰多塞特郡海滩 4—130d
切申 Cieszyn 波兰城市 4—237a
切斯蒂 Cesti,Pietro Antonio 意大利作曲家 4—17e
切斯尔登 Cheselden,William 英国外科医生 4—130c
切斯曼 Chessman,Caryl (Whittier) 美国罪犯 4—132a
切斯纳特 Chesnutt,Charles W(addell) 美国黑人小说家 4—131a
切斯纳特 Chesnut,Mary Boykin Miller 美国作家 4—130f
切斯尼 Chesney,Francis Rawdon 英国陆军军官 4—130e
切斯特 Chester 英格兰城市 4—132e
切斯特 Chester 美国伊利诺伊州城市 4—132f
切斯特 Chester 美国宾夕法尼亚州城市 4—132f
切斯特伯爵 Chester,EARLS OF 英国贵族 4—132f
切斯特伯爵(第六) Chester,Ranulf de Blundeville,6th Earl of 英格兰贵族 4—133a
切斯特伯爵(第四) Chester,Ranulf de Gernons,4th Earl of 英格兰贵族 4—133a
切斯特伯爵(第一) Chester,Hugh of Avranches,1st Earl of 英格兰贵族 4—133a
切斯特顿 Chesterton,G(ilbert) K(eith) 英国诗人 4—133e
切斯特菲尔德 Chesterfield 英格兰自治市 4—133c
切斯特菲尔德伯爵(第四) Chesterfield,Philip Dormer Stanhope,4th Earl of 英国政治家 4—133d
切斯特剧 Chester Plays 英国戏剧 4—133b
切斯特勒斯特里特 Chester-le-Street 英格兰区名 4—133b
切斯特统 Chesterian Series 地质学 4—133e
切特尔 Chettle,Henry 英国剧作家 4—134e
切特里人 Chetrī (people) 南亚民族 4—134e
切特尼克 Chetnik 南斯拉夫武装人员 4—134d
切特韦尔滕斯基家族 Czetwertyński FAMILY 波兰王侯家族 5—100e
切图马尔 Chetumal 墨西哥城市 4—134f
切图马尔城 Ciudad Chetumal (Mexico) 墨西哥城市 4—251e
切瓦人 Chewa 非洲民族 4—136d
切维蔡斯 Chevy Chase (Maryland,U.S.) 美国华盛顿郊区 4—136d
切维厄特绵羊 Cheviot 绵羊品种 4—135d
切维厄特丘陵 Cheviot Hills 英国高地 4—135e
切西系统公司 Chessie System 美国铁路公司 4—132a
切线 tangent 数学 16—463f
切叶蜂 leaf-cutter bee 昆虫 9—542a
切叶蚁 leafcutter ant (Attini) 节肢动物 9—542f
切支丹 Kirishitan 日本天主教徒 9—302a
茄科 Solanaceae 植物学 15—491c
茄类植物 nightshade 植物学 12—189d
茄目 Solanales 植物学 15—491d
茄参 mandrake 植物 10—455a
茄子 eggplant (*Solanum melongena*) 植物 5—557a
窃蠹 borer beetle 昆虫 3—49a
钦巴隆扬琴 cimbalom 乐器 4—239a
钦班古 Kimbangu,Simon 刚果宗教领袖 9—282b
钦班古会 Kimbanguist church 非洲独立基督教会 9—282b
钦博拉索 Chimborazo 厄瓜多尔省份 4—158c
钦博拉索 Chimborazo 厄瓜多尔城市 4—158d
钦博特 Chimbote 秘鲁城市 4—158d
钦查群岛 Chincha Islands 秘鲁群岛 4—167b
钦察人 Kipchak 欧亚大平原古民族 9—298c
钦差 missus dominicus 法兰克国王派出的省督 11—286d
钦德瓦拉 Chhindwāra 印度城镇 4—138a
钦定本英文圣经 King James Version 《圣经》 9—289b
钦戈拉 Chingola 赞比亚城市 4—176a
钦齐奥 Cinzio 意大利作家 4—243a
钦契 Cenci,Beatrice 罗马贵族 3—562b
钦丘陵 Chin Hills 缅甸山区 4—160e
钦人 Chin 蒙古血统部落群体 4—160c

钦西安人 Tsimshian 北美印第安人 17—249d
钦州 Qinzhou 中国海港城市 14—68e
侵略 aggression 国际关系 1—121d
侵权行为法 torts, law of 法律 17—168f
侵蚀 erosion 地貌学 6—122c
侵蚀基准面 baselevel 地理学 2—257d
侵蚀旋回 erosion, cycle of 地貌学 6—122e
侵占 conversion 法律 4—474d
亲岑道夫 Zinzendorf, Nikolaus Ludwig, Graf von 德国宗教改革家 18—556e
亲潮 Oya Current 太平洋洋流 12—525e
亲电子试剂 electrophile 化学 6—30e
亲敦江 Chindwin River 缅甸城镇 4—167c
亲核试剂 nucleophile 化学 12—291b
亲鸾 Shinran 日本哲学家 15—318a
亲属 kin 人类学 9—283c
亲属关系 kinship 社会学 9—296f
亲属关系术语学 kinship terminology 社会学 9—297c
亲同种细胞性抗体 homocytotropic antibody 免疫学 8—147f
亲王 prince 欧洲等级称号 13—512c
芹菜 celery (species *Apium graveolens*) 草本植物 3—553b
芹苴 Can Tho 越南城市 3—385c
芹叶松 celery-top pine (*Phyllocladus asplenifolius*) 针叶乔木 3—553c
秦 Qin DYNASTY 中国王朝 14—62b
秦邦宪 Qin Bangxian 中国共产党领导人 14—62b
秦兵马俑 Qin Terracotta Warriors and Horses 考古 14—63a
秦朝帝王 Qin——: 中国秦朝帝王 14—61e
秦二世胡亥 Qin'ershi Hu Hai 中国秦朝皇帝 14—62a
秦观 Qin Guan 中国词人 14—62c
秦皇岛 Qinhuangdao 中国城市 14—68c
秦九韶 Qin Jiushao 中国数学家 14—62e
秦(始皇)陵 Qin tomb 中国考古遗址 14—63a
秦岭 Qin Ling 中国山脉 14—62e
秦岭山脉 Ch'in Ling Mountains (China) 中国山脉 4—160e
秦岭山脉 Tsinling Mountains (China) 中国山脉 17—249e
秦始皇 Qin shihuang 中国秦朝皇帝 14—61f
秦梯利(法布里亚诺的) Gentile DA FABRIANO 意大利画家 7—68a
秦梯利 Gentile, Giovanni 意大利哲学家 7—68b
秦野 Hadano 日本城市 7—400c
琴 qin 乐器 14—61c
琴楚人 Chenchu 印度民族 4—120a
琴弓 bow 乐器 3—91d
琴尼尼 Cennini, Cennino (di Drea) 佛罗伦萨画家 3—562e
琴鸟 lyrebird 鸟类 10—317b
琴斯托霍瓦 Częstochowa 波兰省份 5—100e
琴斯托霍瓦 Częstochowa 波兰城市 5—100e
琴图里佩 Centuripe 意大利城镇 4—6a
琴托 Cento 意大利城镇 3—565d
琴尾鳉 lyretail 鱼类 10—317c
禽蛋商规律 poulter's measure 诗歌 13—468d
禽流感 bird flu 禽类疾病 2—488f
禽龙 Iguanodon 古生物学 8—328f
禽毯 bird rug 土耳其手织毯 2—489f
擒纵机 escapement 机械学 6—128a
寝殿造 shinden-zukuri 日本建筑式样 15—316f
寝屋川 Neyagawa 日本城市 12—158e
沁河 Qin He 中国河流 14—62d
青春期 adolescence 生理学 1—83d
青瓷 celadon 瓷器 3—550e
青葱 shallot (*Allium ascalonicum*) 草本植物 15—268e
青岛 Qingdao 中国城市 14—65e
青丁 ephebus 古希腊青春期男性 6—94f
青蜂 cuckoo wasp 昆虫 5—50a
青光眼 glaucoma 疾病 7—155c
青海 Qinghai 中国省份 14—65f
青海湖 Blue Lake (China) 中国内陆咸水湖 2—548b
青海湖 Qinghai Hu 中国内陆咸水湖 14—66c
青海南山 Qinghai Nan Shan 中国青海湖西南山岭 14—66d
青函隧道 Seikan Tunnel 日本海底隧道 15—191d
青花瓷 blue-and-white porcelain 中国瓷器 2—546f
青荚叶属 Helwingia 植物学 8—7e
青脚鹬 greenshank (*Tringa nebularia*) 鸟类 7—295e
青金石 lazurite 矿物 9—536a
青卡平 chinquapin 植物学 4—177b
青克纳格尔 Zinkernagel, Rolf M. 瑞士免疫学家 18—555d
青篱竹属 Arundinaria 植物学 1—536b
青梅 Ōme 日本城市 12—414e
青霉属 Penicillium 真菌 13—139e
青霉素 penicillin 药物 13—139d
青尼罗河 Blue Nile River 尼罗河源流 2—548c
青年爱尔兰 Young Ireland 爱尔兰民族主义运动 18—464f
青年奥斯曼党 Young Ottomans 土耳其组织 18—465c
《青年比利时》 Jeune Belgique, La 比利时刊物 9—7c
青年波兰运动 Young Poland movement 波兰文艺运动 18—465d
青年岛 Juventud, Isla de la 古巴岛屿 9—122d
青年德意志 Young Germany 德国社会、文学运动 18—464e
《青年非洲》 Jeune Afrique L'intelligent 法文周刊 9—7c
青年风格 Jugendstil 德国艺术风格 9—103f
青年寄宿舍 youth hostel 旅馆业 18—467b
青年毛利党 Young Maori Party 新西兰毛利人团体 18—465a
青年美国运动 Young America Movement 美国政治运动 18—464d
青年商业社 Junior Achievement 教育组织 9—112a
青年突尼斯党 Young Tunisians 突尼斯政党 18—465e
青年土耳其党 Young Turks 土耳其进步团体联盟 18—465f
青年协会 Burschenschaft 德国学生组织 3—276e
青年新西兰党 Young New Zealand Party 新西兰组织 18—465c
青年意大利 Young Italy 意大利复兴运动 18—464f
青骑士 Blaue Reiter, Der 德国艺术团体 2—531c
青森市 Aomori 日本城市 1—404a
青森县 Aomori 日本县名 1—403f
青少年时期 teens 生理学 16—514e
青铜 bronze 铜锡合金 3—181b
青铜化 bronzing 工艺方法 3—181f
青铜器时代 Bronze Age 历史时代 3—181c
青铜色糖尿病 bronze diabetes 疾病 3—181d
青铜峡 Qingtongxia 中国城市 14—67d
青铜峡水利枢纽工程 Qingtongxia Key Water Control Project 中国水利工程 14—67f
青铜制品 bronze work 器具、艺术品 3—181e
青葙属 Celosia 草本植物 3—558c
青鳕 pollock (*Pollachius*, or *Gadus*, *virens*) 鱼类 13—406f
青阳 Qingyang 中国县名 14—68a
青藏高原 Qinghai-Tibet Plateau 中国最大高原 14—66e
青藏铁路 Qingzhang Tielu 中国铁路 14—68c
青帐突厥字母 Kök Turki alphabet 突厥语文字体系 9—336c
青肿 bruise 医学 3—203a
青贮窖 silo 农业建筑物 15—374a
青贮饲料 silage 农业饲料 15—367b
轻便马车 buggy 两轮或四轮马车 3—236b
轻便雪橇 cutter 运输工具 5—80d
轻便游览马车 wagonette 交通工具 18—64a
轻歌剧 light opera 戏剧 10—93c
轻歌剧 operetta 音乐 12—430a
轻轨运输 light rail transit 交通 10—93c
轻驾车赛马 harness racing 马赛 7—482e

轻捷木骨架 balloon framing 建筑 2—178d
轻快诗 light verse 诗体 10—93c
轻轮马车 bike wagon 四轮马车 2—471b
轻木 balsa (*Ochroma pyramidale*, or *lagopus*) 乔木 2—181c
轻骑兵 hussar 欧洲历史 8—268d
轻桑轻桑科 Cecropia (*Cecropiaceae*) 植物 3—548e
轻雾 mist 气象学 11—286e
轻泻药 laxative 药物 9—533f
轻油 naphtha 化合物 11—562a
轻子 lepton 物理学 10—33a
轻罪 délit 法律 5—227c
轻罪 misdemeanour (law) 法律 11—274f
氢(H) hydrogen 化学元素 8—283b
氢3 hydrogen-3 氢同位素 8—283d
氢弹 H-bomb (hydrogen bomb) 武器 7—394a
氢弹 hydrogen bomb 武器 8—283d
氢化 hydrogenation 化学 8—284b
氢化可的松 hydrocortisone (chemical) 化学 8—282f
氢化物 hydride 化合物 8—281c
氢醌 hydroquinone 化合物 8—286d
氢离子 hydrogen ion 化学 8—284a
氢氧化铵 ammonium hydroxide 化合物 1—293c
氢氧化物 hydroxide 化合物 8—287a
清 Qing DYNASTY 中国古代王朝 14—65c
清唱剧 oratorio 音乐 12—444b
清朝帝王 Qing——: 中国清朝皇帝 14—63c
清川江 Ch'ŏngch'ŏn River 朝鲜河流 4—193d
清党审判 purge trials 苏联历史 14—32b
清德宗载湉 Qingdezong Zaitian 中国清朝皇帝 14—65a
清高宗弘历 Qinggaozong Hongli 中国清朝皇帝 14—64b
清华大学 Qinghua University 中国大学 14—66f
清化 Thanh Hoa 越南城市 17—13f
清教徒前辈移民 Pilgrim Fathers 美洲移民 13—302f
清教主义 Puritanism 宗教改革运动 14—33b
清洁派 Cathari 基督教异端派别 3—524d
清洁行为 cleaning behaviour 修饰 4—276f
清津 Ch'ŏngjin 朝鲜城市 4—193d
清酒 sake 日本烈性米酒 14—534e
清莱 Chiang Rai 泰国城镇 4—138f
清流党 Qingliu dang 中国清代政治派别 14—67b
清六家 Six Masters of the early Qing period 中国清代画家 15—409f
清迈 Chiang Mai 泰国城市 4—138e
《清明上河图》 Qingming Shanghetu 中国北宋画家张择端作品 14—67d
清穆宗载淳 Qingmuzong Zaichun 中国清代皇帝 14—64f
清漆 varnish 化学 17—475b
清仁宗颙琰 Qingrenzong Yongyan 中国清代皇帝 14—64d
清少纳言 Sei Shōnagon 日本诗人 15—190e
清圣祖玄烨 Qingshengzu Xuanye 中国清代皇帝 14—63f
清世宗胤禛 Qingshizong Yinzhen 中国清代皇帝 14—64b
清世祖福临 Qingshizu Fulin 中国清代皇帝 14—63e
清水 Shimizu 日本城市 15—316b
清算 liquidation 商业 10—134a
清太宗皇太极 Qingtaizong Abahai 中国清代皇帝 14—63d
清太祖努尔哈赤 Qingtaizu Nurhachi 中国清王朝的创建者 14—63c
清文宗奕詝 Qingwenzong Yizhu 中国清代皇帝 14—64e
清宣宗旻宁 Qingxuanzong Minning 中国清代皇帝 14—64e
清右卫门 Seiemon (Jepanese potter) 日本陶匠 15—191b
清远 Qingyuan 中国城市 14—68b
清真寺 mosque 穆斯林礼拜场所 11—425e
清真言 shahādah 伊斯兰教 15—255f
清州 Ch'ŏngju 韩国城市 4—193e
蜻蜓 dragonfly 昆虫 5—411e
蜻蜓类 odonate 昆虫 12—338d
鲭 mackerel 鱼类 10—353f
鲭江 Sabae 日本城市 14—481a
鲭鲨 mackerel shark 鱼类 10—354b
情报 intelligence 信息 8—405d
情感 feeling 心理学 6—265b
情感淡漠 apathy 心理学 1—407a
情感论 affections, doctrine of the 音乐美学 1—103b
情感小说 novel of sensibility 小说 12—280d
情感依赖综合征 codependency 心理疾病 4—326c
情感障碍 affective disorder 疾病 1—103c
情节 plot 文学写作技巧 13—373f
情节剧 melodrama 西方戏剧 11—99a
情节舞剧 ballet d'action 艺术 2—176b
情节喜剧 intrigue, comedy of 喜剧 8—425d
情节证据 circumstantial evidence 法律 4—244f
情景喜剧 situation, comedy of 戏剧 15—407d
情侣鹦鹉 lovebird 鸟类 10—249e
情绪 emotion 心理学 6—62d
晴空湍流 clear-air turbulence 大气科学 4—277a
氰钴胺 cyanocobalamin 生物化学 5—83c
氰化氢 hydrogen cyanide 化合物 8—283f
氰化物 cyanide 化合物 5—83b
氰尿酰胺 cyanuramide (chemical compound) 化合物 5—83c
苘麻属 Abutilon 植物学 1—38b
庆典 pageant 盛大演出或列队行进 12—544c
庆法节 Simhath Torah 犹太教节日 15—380d
庆尚北 Kyŏngsang-puk 韩国道名 9—414c
庆尚南 Kyŏngsang-nam 韩国道名 9—414b
庆应大学 Keiō University 日本大学 9—213c
庆州 Kyŏngju 韩国城市 9—414a
庆祝十五周岁 quinceañera 墨西哥社会风俗 14—92e
磬 qing 乐器 14—63b
穷竭法 exhaustion, method of 数学 6—192e
穷理查 Poor Richard 文学人物 13—431b
穹顶 dome 建筑结构 5—368e
穹顶小亭 lantern 建筑 9—489a
穹窿 dome 地质构造 5—368e
穹隅 pendentive 建筑 13—136c
琼 Joan 统治者名 9—38a
琼(纳瓦拉的) Joan of Navarre 英格兰王后 9—41a
琼格拉德 Csongrád 匈牙利州名 5—45c
琼莱 Junqalī 苏丹省份 9—114c
琼琼杵尊 Ninigi 日本传说神名 12—199a
琼丘努 Jhūnjhunun 印度城市 9—10f
琼森 Jonson, Ben 英国剧作家 9—83e
琼森 Jonsson, John Erik 美国仪器制造商 9—84a
琼山 Qiongshan 中国城市 14—68e
琼斯 Jones, (Alfred) Ernest 英国精神分析学家 9—79e
琼斯 Jones, Alfred Gilpin 加拿大政治家 9—79a
琼斯 Jones, Arthur Llewellyn (novelist) 威尔士作家 9—79a
琼斯 Jones, Ben 美国驯马师 9—79b
琼斯 Jones, Bobby 美国运动员 9—79b
琼斯 Jones, Casey 美国火车司机 9—79c
琼斯 Jones, Chuck 美国导演 9—79a
琼斯 Jones, Donald Forsha 美国遗传学家 9—79c
琼斯 Jones, Edward Coley Burne (painter) 画家 9—79d
琼斯 Jones, Edward German (composer) 作曲家 9—79d
琼斯 Jones, Elvin (Ray) 美国爵士乐鼓手 9—79d
琼斯 Jones, (Everett) Leroi 美国作家 9—81c
琼斯 Jones, Henry 英国惠斯特牌权威 9—80a
琼斯 Jones, Henry Arthur 英国戏剧家 9—80a

琼斯 Jones, Sir Harold Spencer 英国天文学家 9—79f
琼斯 Jones, Inigo 英国画家 9—80c
琼斯 Jones, James 美国小说家 9—80d
琼斯 Jones, James Earl 美国演员 9—80e
琼斯 Jones, Jesse H(olman) 美国银行家 9—80f
琼斯 Jones, Jim 美国崇拜体系的领袖 9—80f
琼斯 Jones, John 威尔士语诗人 9—81a
琼斯 Jones, John Paul 美国海军英雄 9—81b
琼斯 Jones, Lewis Ralph 美国植物学家 9—81c
琼斯 Jones, Marion 美国运动员 9—81d
琼斯 Jones, Mary Harris 美国劳工运动组织家 9—81d
琼斯 Jones, Matilda Sissieretta 美国歌剧演员 9—81e
琼斯 Jones, Owen 英国设计师 9—81f
琼斯 Jones, Quincy 美国音乐人 9—81f
琼斯 Jones, R(enato) William 国际篮球运动组织者 9—82a
琼斯 Jones, Richard 英国经济学家、牧师 9—82a
琼斯 Jones, Robert 英国作曲家 9—82b
琼斯 Jones, Robert Edmond 美国戏剧设计师 9—82b
琼斯 Jones, Roy, Jr. 美国拳击手 9—82c
琼斯 Jones, Rufus Matthew 美国宗教领袖 9—82d
琼斯 Jones, Samuel M(ilton) 美国商人 9—82d
琼斯 Jones, Thomas Gwynn 威尔士语诗人 9—82e
琼斯 Jones, Sir William 英国东方学家 9—82e
琼斯伯勒 Jonesboro 美国城市 9—83a
琼斯伯勒 Jonesborough 美国城镇 9—83a
琼斯敦 Jonestown 圭亚那宗教社团旧址 9—83b
《琼斯法案》 Jones Act 法律 9—82f
琼斯兄弟 Jones, Howard (Harding) and T(homas) A(lbert) D(wight) 美国橄榄球教练 9—80b
琼塔尔人 Chontal 马雅印第安人 4—195e
琼脂 agar 海藻制品 1—115e
琼州海峡 Qiongzhou Strait 中国海峡 14—69a
蛩蠊 ice bug 昆虫 8—311c
丘比特 Cupid 罗马神话爱神 5—65e
丘布特 Chubut 阿根廷省份 4—218f
丘布特河 Chubut River 阿根廷河流 4—219a
丘处机 Qiu Chuji 中国道士 14—69e
丘迪 Tschudi, Gilg 瑞士人文主义学者 17—248b
丘顿阶 Chewtonian Stage 地质学 4—137b
丘基卡马塔 Chuquicamata 智利冶炼中心 4—222d
丘基萨卡 Chuquisaca 玻利维亚省份 4—222e
丘基坦他 Chuquitanta (South America) 南美城市 4—222e
丘吉尔 Churchill 加拿大北部海湾 4—225a
丘吉尔 Churchill, Charles 英国诗人 4—225a
丘吉尔 Churchill, John 英国将军 4—225c
丘吉尔 Churchill, Lord Randolph (Henry Spencer) 英国政治家 4—225c
丘吉尔 Churchill, Randolph (Frederick Edward Spencer) 英国作家 4—225e
丘吉尔 Churchill, Winston 美国历史小说家 4—229e
丘吉尔 Churchill, Sir Winston (Leonard Spencer) 英国首相 4—225e
丘吉尔河 Churchill River 加拿大河流 4—230a
丘吉尔瀑布 Churchill Falls 加拿大瀑布 4—229f
丘克 Cukor, George (Dewey) 美国电影导演 5—53d
丘克群岛 Chuuk Islands 太平洋群岛 4—231d
丘拉维斯塔 Chula Vista 美国城市 4—220e
丘雷姆河 Chulym River 俄罗斯河流 4—221a
丘里格拉风格 Churrigueresque 西班牙建筑风格 4—230f
丘里格拉家族 Churriguera FAMILY 西班牙建筑师家族 4—230d
丘林加 tjurunga 宗教礼器和神物 17—122f
丘伦梅鲁瀑布 Churún Merú, Salto (Venezuela) 委内瑞拉瀑布 4—231b
丘马什人 Chumash 北美印第安人 4—221b
丘姆努斯 Chumnus, Nicephorus 拜占廷学者 4—221c
丘脑 thalamus 解剖学 17—11a
丘奇 Church, Frederic Edwin 美国画家 4—223b
丘奇 Church, Sir Richard 英国军人 4—223b
丘奇亚德 Churchyard, Thomas 英格兰作家 4—230b
丘思雷德 Cuthred 西撒克逊国王 5—79a
丘斯滕迪尔 Kyustendil 保加利亚城镇 9—418a
丘索沃伊 Chusovoy 俄罗斯城市 4—231d
丘特切夫 Tyutchev, Fyodor Ivanovich 俄国作家 17—313a
丘瓦洛 Chuvalo, George 加拿大职业拳击手 4—231e
丘鹬 woodcock 鸟类 18—322a
邱吉尔 Churchill, Jennie Jerome 美国社会名流 4—225c
秋巴克 Chūbak, Ṣādeq-i 伊朗作家 4—218c
秋海棠 begonia 植物 2—336f
秋海棠目 Begoniales 植物学 2—337b
秋季 autumn 季节 2—80e
秋季沙龙 Salon d'Automne 法国青年画家作品展 14—551e
秋瑾 Qiu Jin 中国民主革命家 14—69f
秋葵 okra (*Hibiscus esculentus*, or *Abelmoschusesculentus*) 草本植物 12—363b
秋葵汤 gumbo 食品 7—370e
秋明 Tyumen 俄罗斯州名 17—312f
秋明 Tyumen 俄罗斯城市 17—313a
秋沙鸭 merganser 鸟类 11—129c
秋史 Ch'u-sa (Korean calligrapher) 朝鲜书法家 4—217e
秋收起义 Autumn Harvest Uprising 中国历史 2—80f
秋水仙碱 colchicine 药物 4—338d
秋水仙属 Colchicum 植物学 4—338d
秋田 Akita 日本县名 1—156d
秋田犬 akita 狗品种 1—156e
秋英属 Cosmos 植物学 4—531c
蚯蚓 earthworm 环节动物 5—501b
萩 Hagi 日本城市 7—407a
鳅 loach 鱼类 10—171f
仇英 Qiu Ying 中国画家 14—70a
犰狳 armadillo 哺乳动物 1—495f
犰狳蜥 armadillo lizard (species *Cordylus cataphractus*) 爬行动物 1—496a
求恩巡礼 Pilgrimage of Grace 英国历史 13—303a
求幻 vision quest 印第安宗教 18—19a
求积仪 planimeter 数学仪器 13—342f
求降圣灵祈祷文 epiclesis 基督教 6—97f
求面积 quadrature 数学 14—71f
求偶 courtship 动物学 4—550f
求生训练 survival training 训练 16—359a
求主眷念 yizkor 犹太教祷词 18—451e
酋长 chief 政治领袖 4—147f
酋长鸟 cacique 鸟类 3—310c
酋长统治 caciquism 拉丁美洲和西班牙历史 3—310d
球 ball 体育 2—172c
球潮虫 pill bug 甲壳动物 13—303e
球虫病 coccidiosis 传染病 4—319a
球蛋白 globulin 生物化学 7—160d
球果植物 conifer 植物学 4—430d
球果紫堇 fumitory 攀缘植物 6—522e
球海胆 sea urchin 棘皮动物 15—168e
球海绵体肌 bulbocavernosus muscle 解剖学 3—240c
球花 cone 植物学 4—418b
球接子 Agnostus 古生物学 1—125c
球茎 corm 植物学 4—509d
球茎甘蓝 kohlrabi (*Brassica oleracea*, Gongylodes group) 植物 9—335a
球晶占卜术 crystal gazing 占卜 5—44d

球菌 coccus 细菌 4—319a
球粒 chondrule 陨石 4—193b
球粒陨石 chondrite 陨石 4—192e
球菱铁矿 chalybite (mineral) 矿物 4—33d
球面度 steradian 计量单位 16—225a
球面螺旋线 spherical helix (navigation) 导航 16—24f
球拟酵母菌病 torulosis (disease) 疾病 17—170b
球石粒 coccolith 生物学 4—319a
球穗花序 strobilus (botany) 植物学 16—279a
球体蛛 ray spider 节肢动物 14—171c
球窝关节 ball-and-socket joint 解剖学 2—173b
球形瓶 aryballos 希腊瓶 1—537b
球状闪电 ball lightning 气象学 2—173d
球状星团 globular cluster 天文学 7—160d
裘宾 Jobim, Antonio Carlos 巴西词曲作家 9—41e
裘范尼·马利亚·马斯塔伊-费雷提 Mastai-Ferretti, Giovanni Maria (pope) 教皇 11—14b
区别礼 Havdala 犹太教礼仪 7—519a
区间估计 interval estimation 统计学 8—424a
区内租佃制 burgage 英国历史 3—259f
区域 region 社会学 14—204e
区域熔化 zone melting 工业 18—563c
曲柄 crank 机械 4—569e
曲柄滑块机构 slider-crank mechanism 机械 15—431e
曲柄连杆机构 toggle mechanism 机械 17—130b
曲承裕 Khuc Thua Du 越南统治者 9—265f
曲阜 Qufu 中国城市 14—89d
曲棍球 field hockey 体育 6—306a
曲棍球 FIELD HOCKEY 体育项目 16—88a
曲江 Ch'ü-chiang (China) 中国城市韶关旧称 4—217d
曲流 meander 地理学 11—63c
曲率 curvature 数学 5—73d
曲麻莱 Qumarlêb 中国城县 14—96d
曲霉病 aspergillosis 疾病 1—557b
曲霉属 Aspergillus 微生物学 1—557b
曲面 surfaces 数学 16—352a
曲木家具 bentwood furniture 家具 2—395b
曲女城 Kanyakubja (India) 印度城镇 9—170d
曲奇饼 cookie 食品 4—480d
曲线 curve 数学 5—73e
曲线风格 curvilinear style 装饰艺术 5—71e
曲线螺 Loxonema 古生物学 10—256f
佉卢文字 Kharoṣṭī 古印度文字体系 9—257e
驱虫草 bugbane 植物 3—235f
驱力 drive 心理学 5—425d
驱魔 exorcism 宗教仪式 6—194b
驱蠕虫药 anthelmintic 药物 1—377c
驱逐出境 deportation 法律 5—250b
驱逐舰 destroyer 军舰 5—264e
屈恩贝格尔 Kürnberger, Ferdinand 奥地利作家 9—402e
屈尔曼 Kühlmann, Richard von 德国外交部长 9—389f
屈尔珀 Külpe, Oswald 德国心理学家 9—393c
屈夫霍伊瑟山 Kyffhäuser Mountains 德国山岭 9—413a
屈服点 yield point 机械工程学 18—447f
屈光度 diopter 光学 5—330a
屈肌 flexor muscle 解剖学 6—360a
屈家岭文化 Qujialing culture 考古学 14—96c
屈伦贝格 Kürenberger, Der 奥地利爱情歌手 9—402a
屈米 Kymi 芬兰省份 9—413c
屈曲花 candytuft 植物 3—399d
屈赛 Tracy, Spencer 美国演员 17—187a
屈斯阶 Cuisian Stage 地质学 5—53c
屈塔希亚 Kütahya 土耳其城市 9—406c
屈原 Qu Yuan 中国诗人 14—71c
屈折 flection (linguistics) 语言学 6—354c
屈折变化 inflection 语言学 8—382f
趋肤效应 skin effect 电学 15—419d
瞿布罗 gopura 建筑 7—211c
瞿秋白 Qu Qiubai 中国共产党领导人 14—71a
瞿塘峡 Qutang Gorge (China) 长江三峡 14—98c
瞿折罗-普腊蒂哈腊王朝 Gurjara-Pratihāra DYNASTY 印度王朝 7—378d
鼩负鼠 rat opossum 哺乳动物 14—160e
鼩鼱 shrew 哺乳动物 15—338d
鼩鼠 shrew rat 啮齿动物 15—338f
衢州 Quzhou 中国城市 14—99a
蠼螋 earwig 昆虫 5—501d
曲牌联套体 qupai liantaoti 中国戏曲音乐 14—97e
曲言 litotes 文学 10—149c
曲艺 quyi 中国说唱艺术 14—98e
取 upādāna 佛教 17—403d
取代反应 substitution reaction 化学 16—300f
取得 kasb 伊斯兰教教义 9—190a
取景器 viewfinder 取景器 17—557d
取向附生 epitaxy 结晶学 6—104c
取消律师资格 disbarment 法律 5—338c
取消赎回权 foreclosure 法律 6—404a
取岩心 core sampling 地质学 4—504f
龋 caries 疾病 3—459a
去甲肾上腺素 noradrenaline (hormone) 激素 12—231e
去甲肾上腺素 norepinephrine (hormone) 激素 12—234f
去敏灵 tripelennamine 药物 17—224a
趣剧 sotie 戏剧 15—524e
圈 hoop 玩具 8—165b
圈地 enclosure 欧洲历史 6—70a
圈椅(斗鸡椅) cockfighting chair 家具 4—322e
权力主义 authoritarianism 政治 2—73a
权力转移战争 Devolution, War of 法-西历史事件 5—273b
权利保卫协会 Defence of Rights, Associations for the 土耳其爱国同盟 5—208e
《权利法案》 Rights, Bill of 英国宪法 14—299a
权利请愿书 right, petition of 英国法律 14—298d
权利使用费 royalty 法律 14—433b
权能和管辖 competence and jurisdiction 法律 4—398a
权杖 crosier 宗教 5—31b
全北区 Holarctic region 生物学 8—123d
全鞭毛虫属 Holomastigotoides 动物学 8—137f
全才人 universal man (Humanist ideal) 文艺复兴 17—376d
全斗焕 Chun Doo Hwan 韩国将军、总统 4—221c
全俄肃清反革命及怠工特设委员会 Vecheka 苏联政治警察机构 17—484f
全非工会联合会 AATUF 非洲工人组织 1—3e
全非工会联合会 All-African Trade Union Federation (AATUF) 非洲工人组织 1—233d
全氟烃 fluorocarbon 化合物 6—379c
全骨鱼 holostean 硬骨鱼的类群 8—137f
全国棒球联盟 National League 美国体育组织 12—16a
全国棒球名人堂和博物馆 National Baseball Hall of Fame and Museum 美国名人堂 12—12c
全国保守主义和统一主义协会联盟 National Union of Conservative and Unionist Associations (United Kingdom) 英国政党 12—37d
全国冰球联盟 National Hockey League (NHL) 北美体育组织 12—15d
全国步枪协会 National Rifle Association (NRA) 美国和英国组织 12—36b
全国城市联盟 National Urban League 美国组织 12—37d

全国初始浸礼联会 National Primitive Baptist Convention, Inc. 美国黑人教会联会 12—35d
全国大马赛 Grand National 英国马赛 7—250f
全国大学生体育协会 National Collegiate Athletic Association (NCAA) 美国体育组织 12—13c
全国独立人士与农民中心 National Centre of Independents and Peasants 法国政党 12—13b
全国反对妇女选举权协会 National Association Opposed to Woman Suffrage (NAOWS) 美国组织 12—12a
全国福音协会 National Association of Evangelicals 美国基督教组织 12—11f
全国妇女党 National Woman's Party (NWP) 美国政党 12—37f
全国妇女历史项目 National Women's History Project (NWHP) 美国组织 12—38b
全国妇女历史月 National Women's History Month 美国纪念月 12—38a
全国妇女名人堂 National Women's Hall of Fame 美国机构 12—38a
全国妇女选举权协会 National Woman Suffrage Association (NWSA) 美国组织 12—37f
全国妇女政治核心小组 National Women's Political Caucus (NWPC) 美国组织 12—38b
全国妇女组织 National Organization for Women (NOW) 美国民间组织 12—17f
全国橄榄球联盟 National Football League (NFL) 美国体育组织 12—14e
全国广播公司 National Broadcasting Co., Inc. (NBC) 美国广播公司 12—12e
全国黑人妇女委员会 National Council of Negro Women (NCNW) 美国伞式组织 12—14a
全国家长和教师代表大会 National Congress of Parents and Teachers 美国儿童福利组织 12—13d
全国教育协会 National Education Association (NEA) 美国组织 12—14c
全国进步浸礼联会 Progressive National Baptist Convention, Inc. 美国教会联合组织 13—529f
全国科学院 National Academy of Sciences 美国科学家和工程师组织 12—10c
全国拉美裔妇女理事会 National Council of Hispanic Women (NCHW) 美国组织 12—13f
全国篮球协会 National Basketball Association (NBA) 美国体育组织 12—12c
全国劳工关系局 National Labor Relations Board (NLRB) 美国联邦机构 12—16a
全国流产和生育权利行动联盟 National Abortion and Reproductive Rights Action League 美国民间组织 12—10c
全国铁路客运公司 Amtrak 美国运输公司 1—304d
全国托管协会 National Trust 英国国家机构 12—37b
全国无党派联盟 National Nonpartisan League (U.S.) 美国政治组织 12—17f
全国消费者联盟 National Consumers League (NCL) 美国组织 12—13d
全国邀请赛 National Invitation Tournament (NIT) 美国大学篮球比赛 12—15f
全国犹太妇女理事会 National Council of Jewish Women (NCJW) 美国组织 12—13f
全国有色妇女协会 National Association of Colored Women (NACW) 美国妇女组织 12—11e
全国有色人种促进协会 National Association for the Advancement of Colored People (NAACP) 美国种族联合组织 12—11e
全或无定律 all-or-none law 生理学 1—235a
全景电影 Cinerama 电影制式 4—241e
全景画 panorama 美术 13—14f
全卤烃 halocarbon 化合物 7—432e
全氯乙烯 perchloroethylene 化合物 13—158b
全罗北道 Chŏlla-puk 韩国道名 4—191e
全罗南道 Chŏlla-nam 韩国道名 4—191d
全美明星队 All-America team 美国橄榄球队 1—233e
全美女子职业棒球联合会 All-American Girls Professional Baseball League 美国体育组织 1—233e
全民公决和创制权 referendum and initiative 政治 14—197e
全民合作联盟 Co-operative Commonwealth Federation (CCF) 加拿大政党 4—309f
全能体操比赛 combined exercises 体育 4—378b
全球变暖 global warming 气象学 7—159d
全球黑人促进协会 Universal Negro Improvement Association (UNIA) 国际组织 17—376d
全球化 globalization 社会学理论 7—159e
全日本航空公司 All Nippon Airways Co., Ltd. 日本航空企业 1—235a
全身水肿 anasarca 疾病 1—316f
全身肖像光轮 mandorla 宗教艺术 10—454f
全四牌 All-Fours 纸牌游戏 1—234f
全苏基督教福音浸礼会 All-Union Council of Evangelical Christians and Baptists 苏联基督教组织 1—235c
全苏列宁共产主义青年团 Leninist Communist League of Youth, All-Union 苏联组织 10—11f
全体印第安部落妇女 Women of All Red Nations (WARN) 美国组织 18—315a
全息术 holography 摄影 8—136f
全新世 Holocene Epoch 地质学 8—136c
全星赛 All-Star Game 美国棒球比赛 1—235c
《全译本海湾圣诗》 Whole Booke of Psalmes, The 北美出版物 18—241f
全音音阶 whole-tone scale 音乐 18—241f
全音域 gamut 音乐 6—570f
全印度工会大会 All-India Trade Union Congress (AITUC) 印度工人组织 1—235a
全印度穆斯林联盟 All India Muslim League 印度穆斯林团体 1—234f
全英锦标赛 All-England Championships 国际网球锦标赛 1—234f
全真道 Quanzhendao 中国道教教派 14—76e
全州 Chŏnju 韩国城市 4—195c
泉 spring 水文学 16—161f
泉大津 Izumi-Ōtsu 日本城市 8—499e
泉华 sinter 矿物 15—398f
泉镜花 Izumi Kyōka 日本小说家 8—499e
泉藓 fountain moss 植物学 6—424e
泉州 Quanzhou 中国城市 14—76f
泉佐野 Izumi-Sano 日本城市 8—499e
拳击 boxing 体育 3—98b
拳击 BOXING 体育项目 16—67a
醛 aldehyde 化合物 1—192c
醛甾酮 aldosterone 生物化学 1—194a
鬈毛比雄犬 bichon frise 狗品种 2—461c
颧弓 zygomatic arch 解剖学 18—578a
颧骨 zygomatic bone 解剖学 18—578a
犬 canine 哺乳动物 3—401d
犬病毒性肝炎 canine viral hepatitis 动物疾病 3—401e
犬地卷 dog lichen (*Peltigera canina*) 植物 5—360b
犬颌兽 Cynognathus 古生物学 5—89e
犬羚 dik-dik 动物 5—315b
犬儒学派 Cynic 希腊哲学派别 5—89d
犬瘟热 canine distemper 动物疾病 3—401d
犬星 Dog Star 天文学 5—360d
犬牙 canine tooth 哺乳动物尖牙 3—401d

犬养毅 Inukai Tsuyoshi 日本首相 8—426c
劝世静物画 vanitas 绘画 17—468a
缺翅虫 zorapteran 昆虫 18—567d
缺环 missing link 假设的已绝灭动物 11—278b
缺铁性贫血 iron-deficiency anemia 病理现象 8—450f
缺席投票 absentee voting 选举法 1—30b
缺血性心脏病 ischemic heart disease 疾病 8—460a
却克里王朝 Chakkri DYNASTY 泰国王朝 4—29c
雀 sparrow 鸟类 16—8e
雀稗属 Paspalum 植物学 13—75c
雀斑 freckle 皮肤色素斑 6—457f
雀鹎 iora 鸟类 8—433d
雀巢食品公司 Nestlé SA 瑞士食品跨国公司 12—89d
雀鲷 damselfish 鱼类 5—130a
雀科 Paridae 鸟类 13—42b
雀类 finch 动物学 6—317d
雀麦草 bromegrass 植物 3—176b
雀鹛 tit-babbler 鸟类 17—114c
雀鳝 gar 鱼类 7—6f
雀形科 Passeridae 动物学 13—77c
雀形类 passeriform 动物学 13—77c
雀鹰 sparrowhawk 鸟类 16—8f
确认 affirmation 法律 1—103e
鹊鹨科 Grallinidae 动物学 7—244a
鹊鸲 magpie-robin 鸟类 10—395b
鹊雁 magpie goose (*Anseranas semipalmata*) 鸟类 10—395b
裙撑 bustle 女装用品 3—287e
裙环裙 hoop skirt 服装 8—165b
裙脂鲤 tetra 鱼类 16—562e
群 group 数学 7—325c
群岛地区 islands area 英国地区 8—469b
群岛湾 Islands, Bay of 新西兰海湾 8—469b
群岛崖坡 archipelagic apron 地质学 1—451e
群婚 group marriage 人类学 7—325d
群居织布鸟 social weaver 鸟类 15—475b
群落 community 生物学 4—393a
群落交错区 ecotone 生态学 5—531e
群落生态学 community ecology 生物群落 4—393b
群马 Gumma 日本县名 7—371b
群青 ultramarine 染料 17—333c
群山 Kunsan 韩国城市 9—090c
群体 colony 动物学 4—359f
群体生态学 synecology 生态学 16—402c
《群众》 Masses, The 美国杂志 11—12a

R

蚺 boa 爬行动物 2—554b
髯狗 schnauzer 狗品种 15—124c
髯海豹 bearded seal (*Erignathus barbatus*) 哺乳动物 2—306a
髯鹫 lammergeier (species *Gypaetus barbatus*) 鸟类 9—466a
燃灯 Dīpaṅkara (Buddhist reformer) 佛教人物 5—331c
燃料电池 fuel cell 电化学反应装置 6—510a
燃料油 fuel oil 燃油 6—510c
燃烧 combustion 化学 4—378b
燃素 phlogiston 化学 13—253c
燃油炉 oil burner 机械 12—354b
燃油喷射 fuel injection 发动机技术 6—510c
染匠菘蓝 dyerswoad (herb) 植物 5—487f
染料 dye 化合物 5—487b
染料衣属 Roccella 生物学 14—337d
染色体 chromosome 生物学 4—213a
染色体疾病 chromosomal disorder 疾病 4—212d
染印法 dye-transfer process 摄影 5—487c
让-阿列克西斯·蒙柯热 Moncorgé, Jean-Alexis (French actor) 法国演员 11—331e
让·保尔 Jean Paul 德国小说家 8—556c
让步 handicap 体育 7—458b
让·德巴黎 Jean de Paris 法国建筑师 8—556c
让·德·默恩 Jean DE MEUN 法国诗人 8—556b
让蒂尔 Gentil, Émile 法国殖民官员 7—67f
让蒂尔港 Port-Gentil 加蓬城市 13—445a
让娜(纳瓦拉的) Joan OF NAVARRE (French queen) 法国王后 9—41a
让娜一世 Joan I 法国王后 9—38b
让南 Jeannin, Pierre 法国政治家 8—556e
让·勒贝尔 Jean LE BEL 佛兰芒编年史学家 8—556c
让内尔 Jeannel, René 法国生物学家 8—556d
让内雷 Jeanneret, Charles-Édouard (architect) 瑞士建筑学家 8—556e
让桑 Janssen, Pierre(-Jules-César) 法国天文学家 8—535e
让与不动产 feoffment 英国法律 6—278b
饶勒斯 Jaurès, (Auguste-Marie-Joseph-) Jean 法国政治家 8—550c
桡骨 radius 解剖学 14—119a
桡足类 copepod 动物学 4—489a
扰乱治安 disturbing the peace 法律 5—344f
绕口令 tongue twister 民俗学 17—151d
惹尼 Gény, François 法国法学家 7—69c
热 heat 物理学 7—543f
热泵 heat pump 机械 7—544e
热层 thermosphere 大气科学 17—35d
热传导 thermal conduction 物理学 17—32d
热带辐合带 intertropical convergence zone (ITCZ) 气象学 8—423f
热带海牛 manatee 哺乳动物 10—447b
热带莓疱 frambesia (disease) 疾病 6—435c
热带气旋 tropical cyclone 气象学 17—234c
热带性口炎性腹泻 tropical sprue 疾病 17—234e
热带性脾大 tropical splenomegaly (disease) 疾病 17—234e
热带医学 tropical medicine 医学 17—234d
热带雨林 tropical rain forest 生态学 17—234e
热电偶 thermal junction (device) 测温装置 17—32f
热电温度计 thermel (device) 电学 17—33a
热电性 pyroelectricity 电学 14—47b
热尔 Gers 法国省份 7—100c
热尔贝(欧里亚克的) Gerbert OF AURILLAC (pope) 教皇 7—86c
热尔拉什·德戈姆里 Gerlache de Gomery, Adrien-Victor-Joseph, baron de 比利时海军军官 7—88b
热尔拉什男爵 Gerlache, Étienne-Constantin, baron de 比利时政治家 7—88b
热尔曼 Germain, François-Thomas 法国银匠 7—88d
热尔曼 Germain, Lord George 英国政治家、军人 7—88d
热尔曼 Germain, Pierre 法国银匠 7—88d
热尔曼 Germain, Sophie 法国数学家 7—88e
热尔曼 Germain, Thomas 法国银匠 7—88e
热尔松 Gerson, Jean de 法国神学家 7—101a
热尔韦 Gervais, (François-Louis-) Paul 法国古生物学家 7—101c
热辐射 thermal radiation 物理学 17—32f
热管 heat pipe 机械 7—544e
热海 Atami 日本城市 2—12f
热河鸟 Jeholornis 原始鸟类化石 8—562c
热核弹 thermonuclear bomb 武器 17—34e
热核反应 thermonuclear reaction 物理学 17—34f
热基蒂尼奥尼亚河 Jequitinhonha River 巴西河流 8—568a
热基耶 Jequié 巴西城市 8—568a
热交换器 heat exchanger 机械 7—544c
热喀斯特 thermokarst 地质学 17—34c
热拉尔 Gerhardt, Charles(-Frédéric) 法国化学家 7—87b
热拉尔 Gérard, François, Baron 法国画家 7—86a

热拉尔 Gérard, Jean-Ignace-Isidore 法国漫画家 7—86b
热莱 Gellée, Claude (painter) 法国艺术家 7—48b
热兰-拉茹瓦 Gérin-Lajoie, Antoine 加拿大作家 7—87d
热雷米 Jérémie 海地城镇 8—569c
热离子发射 thermionic emission 物理学 17—33b
热离子功率转换器 thermionic power converter 电学 17—33c
热里科 Géricault, (Jean-Louis-André-) Théodore 法国画家 7—87b
热里什山 Gerez Mountains 欧洲山脉 7—86f
热力学 thermodynamics 物理学 17—33f
热力学平衡 thermodynamic equilibrium 物理学 17—33f
热利亚博夫 Zhelyabov, Andrey Ivanovich 俄国革命家 18—528e
热列兹诺戈尔斯克 Zheleznogorsk 俄罗斯城市 18—528e
热罗姆 Gérome, Jean-Léon 法国画家 7—99b
热罗姆 Jérôme (king of Westphalia) 威斯特伐利亚国王 8—569f
热罗姆斯基 Żeromski, Stefan 波兰小说家 18—512e
热敏电阻器 thermistor 电学 17—33d
热那亚 Genoa 意大利城市 7—64e
热那亚花边 Genoese lace 意大利工艺品 7—65e
热那亚湾 Genoa, Gulf of 意大利海湾 7—65d
热内 Genêt (American writer) 美国作家 7—58d
热内 Genet, Edmond-Charles 法国外交官 7—58e
热内 Genet, Jean 法国作家 7—58e
热内事件 Citizen Genêt Affair 法国历史 4—248d
热内瓦亲王 Genevois, Charles-Emmanuel de Savoie, prince de 法国公爵 7—63c
热内维埃夫,圣 Geneviève, SAINT 法国主保圣人 7—63b
热能 thermal energy 物理学 17—32d
热泡 thermal 气象学 17—32d
热膨胀 thermal expansion 物理学 17—32e
"热情之花" Pasionaria, La 伊巴露丽笔名 13—74f
热容 heat capacity 物理学 7—544c
热熔解 thermal fusion 物理学 17—32e
热舒夫 Rzeszów 波兰省份 14—477e
热舒夫 Rzeszów 波兰城市 14—477e
热衰竭 heat exhaustion 疾病 7—544d
热泰 jeté 芭蕾舞 9—7a
热田 Atsuta 日本港口区 2—37e
热调节 heat regulation 生理学 7—544e
热韦尔 Gevers, Marie 比利时小说家 7—105d
热沃当 Gévaudan 法国古地名 7—105c
热液矿床 hydrothermal ore deposit 地质学 8—286f
热月反动 Thermidorian Reaction 法国历史 17—33b
热质说 caloric theory 物理学 3—357d
热致发光 thermoluminescence 物理学 17—34d
热中子 thermal neutron 物理学 17—32f
人 human being (species *Homo sapiens*) 人类学 8—233c
人 man 人类学 10—443e
《人道报》 Humanité, L' 法国报纸 8—242d
人道教 Hito-no-michi 日本宗教教派 8—105d
人道主义事务协调办事处 United Nations Office for the Coordination of Humanitarian Affairs (UNDRO) 联合国机构 17—362f
人的财产 personal property(law) 法律 13—185a
人痘接种 variolation 医学 17—473e
人格 personality 人的思维、情感、行为模式 13—185d
人格解体 depersonalization 心理学 5—249f
人格障碍 personality disorder 精神障碍 13—186c
人格主义 personalism 哲学派别 13—185b
人工处理的宝石 treated gem 工艺品 17—204f
人工岛 crannog 古代不列颠住所 4—570b
人工呼吸 artificial respiration 医学 1—531a
人工降雨 rainmaking 大气科学 14—128c
人工器官 artificial organ 医学 1—530f
人工授精 artificial insemination 医学 1—530c
人工心脏 artificial heart 医学 1—530a
人工选择 artificial selection 生物学 1—531a
人工影响天气 weather modification 大气科学 18—155d
人工智能 artificial intelligence (AI) 计算机科学 1—530d
人机工程学 ergonomics 生物工程学 6—115a
人祭 human sacrifice 宗教 8—241e
人科 Hominidae 动物学 8—146d
人科动物 hominid 人类学 8—146b
人科尼安德特种 Homo neanderthalensis 人类学 8—147d
人口 population 统计学 13—438d
人口普查 census 社会学 3—564a
人口统计学 demography 社会科学 5—237f
人兰 man orchid (species *Aceras anthropophorum*) 植物 10—445a
人类博物馆 Homme, Musée de l' 巴黎机构 8—146f
人类的家园 Manna-heim (Norse mythology) 挪威神话 10—467a
人类基因图谱制图工程 Human Genome Project 生物工程学 8—235a
人类基因组计划 Human Genome Project DNA 研究 8—235a
人类假两性畸形 pseudohermaphroditism 病理现象 13—556e
人类进化 human evolution 人类学 8—234c
人类迁徙 human migration 社会学 8—235e
人类生态学 human ecology 社会学 8—234c
人类文化语言学 ethnolinguistics 语言学 6—151a
人类行为 human behaviour 心理学、社会学 8—232e
人类学 anthropology 社会科学学科 1—380c
人类-因素工程学 human-factors engineering 工程学 8—234f
人类语言学 anthropological linguistics 语言学 1—380b
人力车 ricksha 交通工具 14—290f
人马座 Sagittarius 天文学 14—499a
人马座 A Sagittarius A 天文学 14—499b
人民大会 comitia 古罗马人民集会 4—382b
人民大会堂 Great Hall of the people 中国建筑 7—272b
人民党 Popular Party 西班牙政党 13—437d
人民党人 Popolare 意大利政治团体 13—433f
人民公敌乐队 Public Enemy 美国乐队 14—4d
人民共和运动 Popular Republican Movement 法国政党 13—437d
《人民观察家报》 Völkischer Beobachter 德国报纸 18—39b
人民民主党 People's Democratic Party (PDP) 尼日利亚政党 13—151a
《人民日报》 Renmin Ribao 中国报纸 14—229a
人民圣殿教 Peoples Temple 美国宗教组织 13—151c
人民胜利渠 Renmin Shengli Canal 中国灌溉工程 14—229b
人民议会 Volksraad 印度尼西亚历史 18—39d
人民院 Lok Sabha 印度下院 10—194a
人民阵线 popular front 欧洲联盟 13—437a
人民主权论 popular sovereignty 美国历史上政治学说 13—437e
人命赔偿 diyah 伊斯兰法律 5—349f
人权 human rights 政治学 8—236a
《人权法案》 Rights, Bill of 美国宪法 14—299a
《人权和公民权利宣言》 Rights of Man and of the Citizen, Declaration of the 基本宪章之一 14—299b
人权和公民权利之友社 Friends of the Rights of Man and the Citizen, Society of the 法国大革命群众政治俱乐部 6—493f
人身保护状 habeas corpus 法律 7—397a
人身悬挂广告牌 sandwich board 广告牌 15—31b
《人身自由法》 personal-liberty laws 美国法律 13—185a
人参 ginseng 草本植物 7—137b
人神 hitogami 日本宗教 8—105d
人虱 human louse (*Pediculus humanus*) 昆虫 8—235d
人事管理 personnel administration 人员管理 13—186d
人手自动写字 automatic writing 招魂术 2—76b
人寿保险 life insurance 保险业 10—89a
人属 Homo 生物学 8—147a

人体　human body　生物学、生理学、解剖学　8—233c
人体白细胞抗原　human leukocyte antigen (HLA)　生物化学　8—235d
人体测量学　anthropometry　人类学　1—380c
人头狮身蝎尾兽　manticore　传说中的动物　10—474f
人头税　capitation　法国税制　3—427c
人头税　poll tax　税种　13—405b
人文心理学　humanistic psychology　心理学　8—242a
人文学科　humanities　涉及人类及人类文化的诸学科　8—242d
人文主义　humanism　哲学　8—241f
人心果　sapodilla (*Manilkara*, or *Achras*, *zapota*)　木本植物　15—57a
人鱼　merman　民间传说　11—133b
人猿超科　Hominoidea　动物学　8—146e
人造地球卫星　Earth satellite　航天器　5—498d
人造黄油　margarine　食品　10—504f
人造丝　rayon　纺织纤维　14—173c
人造卫星　Sputnik　苏联人造地球卫星系列　16—166d
人造纤维　man-made fibre　化工　10—444e
人质节戏剧　Hocktide play　英国民间戏剧　8—112d
人种混杂　miscegenation　社会学　11—274e
人种志　ethnography　文化人类学　6—150d
仁　ren　儒学　14—223b
仁爱会　Charity of Saint Vincent de Paul, Daughtersof (D.C.)　天主教女修会　4—65c
仁爱修会　Charity, Sisters of　天主教女修会　4—65c
仁安羌　Yenangyaung　缅甸城镇　18—440f
仁川　Inch'ŏn　韩国城市　8—352a
仁钦桑波　Rin-chen-bzang-po　中国藏传佛经译师　14—303c
仁清　Ninsei　日本陶师　12—199b
壬申之乱　Jinshin-no-ran　日本历史　9—33e
任弼时　Ren Bishi　中国共产党领导人　14—223b
任伯年　Ren Bonian　中国画家　14—223e
任美锷　Ren Mei'e　中国地理学家　14—223e
任抹　Jember　印度尼西亚城市　8—565a
任那　Mimana (Korean confederation)　朝鲜古代民族　11—237f
任新民　Ren Xinmin　中国火箭专家　14—223f
任颐　Ren Yi　中国画家　14—224a
忍冬　honeysuckle　木本植物　8—154e
忍冬科　Caprifoliaceae　植物学　3—431a
忍冬饰　anthemion　装饰　1—377e
刃脊　arête　地质学　1—460e
刃具　cutlery　切削工具　5—79c
认识论　epistemology　哲学　6—103b
认知　cognition　哲学　4—331f
认知失调　cognitive dissonance　心理学　4—332a
认主独一　tawhid　伊斯兰教　16—500a
认罪　confession　宗教　4—420e
任期　tenure　行政学　16—547a
任意变速跑　Fartlek　体育训练　6—244f
韧带　ligament　解剖学　10—90f
韧皮部　phloem　植物组织　13—253b
韧皮纤维　bast fibre　木质软纤维　2—270d
韧藤　supplejack　木本植物　16—348e
韧致辐射　bremsstrahlung　物理学　3—140c
妊娠　pregnancy　生理学　13—492b
妊娠毒血症　toxemia of pregnancy　疾病　17—182a
妊娠期　gestation　生理学　7—103d
日　day　历法　5—181b
日本　Japan　亚洲岛国　8—536c
日本阿尔卑斯山　Japanese Alps　日本山脉　8—540e
日本棒球联盟　Japanese baseball leagues　日本体育组织　8—540f
日本筚篥　hichiriki　日本乐器　8—69d
日本长春藤　Japanese ivy　植物学　8—541d
日本电报电话公司　Nippon Telegraph and Telephone Corporation (NTT)　日本公司　12—200e
日本电气株式会社　NEC Corp.　日本制造商　12—61f
日本法　Japanese law　法律　8—542a
日本榧　Japanese torreya (*Torreya nucifera*)　木本植物　8—544c
日本钢管公司　Nippon Kōkan KK　日本公司　12—200d
日本工会总评议会　Sōhyō　日本组织　15—487f
日本共产党　Japan Communist Party　日本政党　8—540b
日本古琴　koto　日本乐器　9—365b
日本鼓　tsuzumi　乐器　17—252c
日本广播协会　Nippon Hoso Kyokai (NHK)　日本广播电视系统　12—200c
日本国会　Diet　日本立法机构　5—307c
日本国家铁路公司　Japanese National Railways (JNR)　日本公司　8—543b
日本海　Japan, Sea of　西太平洋边缘海　8—540a
日本海沟　Japan Trench　西太平洋海沟　8—540d
日本海流　Japan Current (Pacific Ocean)　太平洋洋流　8—540c
日本航空公司　Japan Air Lines Co., Ltd. (JAL)　日本公司　8—540a
日本红木　Japanese redwood　木本植物　8—544b
日本猎狗　Japanese spaniel　狗品种　8—544b
日本进出口银行　Export-Import Bank of Japan　日本金融机构　6—195f
《日本经济新闻》　Nihon keizai shimbun　日本报纸　12—190a
日本丽金龟　Japanese beetle (species *Popillia japonica*)　昆虫　8—540f
日本柳杉　Japanese cedar (species *Cryptomeria japonica*)　木本植物　8—541a
日本鹿　Japanese deer　哺乳动物　8—541d
《日本民法典》　Japanese Civil Code　法律　8—541b
日本琵琶　biwa　弦乐器　2—506a
日本葡萄干树　Japanese raisin tree　植物　8—544b
日本漆　japan (varnish)　日本清漆　8—540a
日本漆工艺　japanning　装饰艺术　8—544e
日本漆树　Japanese varnish tree　植物　8—544d
日本社会党　Nihon Shakaitō (Japan)　日本政党　12—190a
《日本书纪》　Nihon shoki　日本史籍　12—190a
日本铁路集团公司　Japan Railways Group　日本公司　8—540c
日本文学　Japanese literature　文学　8—542c
日本武尊　Yamato Takeru　日本传说人物　18—411e
日本蟹　Japanese crab　动物　8—541d
日本新党　Japan New Party　日本政党　8—540c
日本新生党　Japan Renewal Party　日本政党　8—540d
日本兴业银行　Industrial Bank of Japan　日本银行　8—376a
日本艺术　Japanese art　艺术　8—540e
日本音乐　Japanese music　音乐　8—542f
日本浴衣　yukata　服饰　18—479c
日本哲学　Japanese philosophy　哲学　8—543c
日本正教会　Japanese Orthodox Church　日本教会　8—543c
日本职业棒球锦标赛　Japan Series　日本赛事　8—540d
日本主义　Japanism　艺术　8—544e
日本紫杉　Japanese yew (*Taxus cuspidata*)　木本植物　8—544d
日本最高法院　Supreme Court of Japan　日本法律　16—349c
日产汽车公司　Nissan Motor Co., Ltd.　日本公司　12—202f
日常语言分析　ordinary language analysis　哲学　12—450c
日丹诺夫　Zhdanov (Ukraine)　乌克兰城市　18—527b
日丹诺夫　Zhdanov, Andrey Aleksandrovich　苏联党政官员　18—527b
日丹诺夫主义　Zhdanovshchina　苏联文化政策　18—527b
日德兰　Jutland　北欧半岛　9—121d
日德兰半岛之战　Jutland, Battle of　第一次世界大战史　9—121e
日俄战争　Russo-Japanese War　俄国-日本战争　14—465d
日耳曼(巴黎的),圣　Germain DE PARIS, SAINT　法国主教　7—88d

日耳曼敦 Germantown 美国居民区 7—94d
日耳曼敦战役 Germantown, Battle of 美国历史 7—94e
日耳曼法 Germanic law 法律 7—92b
日耳曼努斯(巴黎的),圣 Germanus of Paris, Saint 法国主教 7—94f
《日耳曼史文献资料汇编》 Monumenta Germaniae Historica 德国史料汇编 11—374f
日耳曼诸民族 Germanic peoples 欧洲民族 7—92c
日耳曼诸语言 Germanic languages 欧洲语言 7—91e
日耳曼宗教和神话 Germanic religion and mythology 日耳曼历史 7—93f
日珥 solar prominence 天文学 15—492f
日夫科夫 Zhivkov, Todor (Khristov) 保加利亚总统 18—533a
日夫科维奇 Živković, Petar 南斯拉夫首相 18—559e
日夫鲁瓦 Geoffroy, Étienne-François 法国化学家 7—70f
日高山脉 Hidaka Range 日本山脉 8—71a
日光 Nikkō 日本城市 12—192b
日光灯 sunlamp 灯具 16—343a
日光兰 sun orchid 植物 16—336f
日光蛇 sunbeam snake (*Xenopeltis unicolor*) 蛇类 16—339d
日光室 solarium 建筑物 15—494b
日晷 sundial 古老记时装置 16—341f
日活影片公司 Nikkatsu Motion Picture Company 日本公司 12—192a
日记 diary 自传性文体 5—289b
日䴉 sun bittern (species *Eurypyga helias*) 鸟类 16—335f
日界线 date line 历法、地理学 5—161c
日喀则 Xigazê 中国城市 18—385f
日课 divine office 基督教公众礼拜 5—346e
《日课经》 breviary 天主教用书 3—145f
日立 Hitachi 日本城市 8—101c
日立公司 Hitachi, Ltd. 日本公司 8—101d
日利纳 Žilina 斯洛伐克城镇 18—551e
日莲 Nichiren 日本佛教高僧 12—169f
日莲宗 Nichiren Buddhism 日本佛教宗派 12—170a
《日美修好通商条约》 Harris treaty 美国历史 7—489b
日冕 corona 天文学 4—517b
日冕仪 coronagraph 天文学 4—517e
日南 Nichinan 日本城市 12—169e
日内瓦 Geneva 瑞士州名 7—59e
日内瓦 Genève 瑞士城市 7—63b
日内瓦公约 Geneva Conventions 国际条约 7—62e
日内瓦湖 Geneva, Lake 欧洲湖泊 7—62b
《日内瓦教理问答》 Geneva Catechism 基督教著作 7—62d
日内瓦礼仪书 Order of Geneva (religious manual) 宗教作品 12—449d
《日内瓦日报》 Journal de Genève 瑞士日报 9—93c
《日内瓦圣经》 Geneva Bible 基督教著作 7—62d
日内瓦市温室和植物园 Geneva City Conservatory and Botanical Gardens 瑞士植物园 7—62e
《日内瓦协议》 Geneva Accords 印度支那历史 7—62c
日内瓦学院 Geneva, Academy of 瑞士学院 7—62a
日惹 Yogyakarta 印度尼西亚特区 18—452c
日惹 Yogyakarta 印度尼西亚城市 18—452d
日烧病 sunscald 植物病害 16—343f
日索尔 Gisors 法国城镇 7—145a
日索尔公爵 Gisors, Charles (-Louis-Auguste) Fouquet, Duke de 法国元帅 7—145b
日鹛 sun-grebe (bird) 鸟类 16—336b
日田 Hita 日本城市 8—101c
日托儿所 day-care center 幼儿教育 5—182b
日托米尔 Zhitomir 乌克兰州名 18—532f
日托米尔 Zhitomir 乌克兰城市 18—532f
日维茨 Żywiec 波兰城镇 18—578f
日乌河 Jiu River 罗马尼亚河流 9—34f
日乌山口 Jiu Defile 罗马尼亚山口 9—34f
日心体系 heliocentric system 天文学 7—573e
日野 Hino 日本城市 8—90a
日语 Japanese language 日本语言 8—541d
日元 yen 日本货币单位 18—440e
日月潭 Riyue Tan 中国台湾省湖泊 14—321b
日照 Rizhao 中国城市 14—322a
日照 sunlight 太阳辐射 16—343a
日志 journal 日记 9—93b
日蛛 sunspider 蛛形纲动物 16—344a
戎金 Jongkind, Johan Barthold 荷兰油画家 9—83c
戎克罗 Junqueiro, Abílio Manuel Guerra 葡萄牙诗人 9—114d
荣宝斋 Rongbaozhai 中国艺术企业 14—388e
荣加斯 Yungas 玻利维亚地区 18—482e
荣禄 Ronglu 中国清末大臣 14—388f
荣山江 Yŏngsan River 韩国河流 18—455d
荣市 Vinh 越南城市 18—1e
荣松 Jónsson, Arngrímur 冰岛学者 9—84a
荣松 Jónsson, Hjálmar 冰岛诗人 9—84a
荣耀颂 doxology 基督教颂辞 5—408a
荣毅仁 Rong Yiren 中国实业家、国家副主席 14—388d
荣誉爵士 C.H. 英国荣誉勋位成员 4—21a
荣誉勋位 Companions of Honour, Order of the 英国贵族爵位 4—395d
荣誉勋位团 Legion of Honour 法国勋位 9—562a
荣誉勋章 Honor, Medal of 美国勋章 8—159f
狨 marmoset 哺乳动物 10—526a
绒背鹟 puffback flycatcher (bird) 鸟类 14—17e
绒滨蝽 velvety shore bug 昆虫 17—496c
绒毛 villus 解剖学 17—566e
绒毛猴 woolly monkey 哺乳动物 18—327f
绒毛狐猴 avahi (*Avahi laniger*) 灵长类动物 2—82e
绒毛膜 chorion 胚胎学 4—199c
绒毛蜘蛛猴 woolly spider monkey (*Brachyteles arachnoides*) 哺乳动物 18—328b
绒泡菌属 Physarum 生物学 13—272c
绒线刺绣 crewel work 绣制品 5—10d
绒鸭 eider 海鸟类 5—565b
绒叶 velvetleaf 植物 17—496b
绒蚁 velvet ant 昆虫 17—495d
容 Jung, Carl (Gustav) 瑞士心理学家 9—110e
容 Jung, Johann Heinrich 德国作家 9—111a
容庵 Rong'an 中国清末大臣 14—388e
容迪亚伊 Jundiaí 巴西城市 9—110a
容格尔 Jünger, Ernst 德国小说家 9—111c
容闳 Rong Hong 中国学者 14—388c
容基耶尔 Jonquière 加拿大城市 9—83e
容克 Junker 普鲁士、德意志地主 9—113c
容克 Junkers, Hugo 德国飞机设计家 9—113d
容克尔 Junker, (Johann) Wilhelm 俄罗斯探险家 9—113c
容量分析 volumetric analysis 化学 18—46a
容纳量 carrying capacity 生物学 3—485b
《容忍法》 Toleration Act 英格兰法令 17—138c
容-施蒂林 Jung-Stilling, Johann Heinrich 德国作家 9—111b
溶胶 sol 物理化学术语 15—491b
溶菌酶 lysozyme 酶类 10—319b
溶酶体 lysosome 生物学 10—319a
溶蚀丘 haystack hill 地质学 7—534b
溶血 hemolysis 病理现象 8—10e
溶液 solution 化学 15—501d
溶液栽培 hydroponics 农业 8—286c
溶原现象 lysogeny 微生物学 10—318f

榕树 banyan (*Ficus benghalensis* or *F. indica*) 乔木 2—209f
榕属 Ficus 植物学 6—303d
熔点 melting point 物理学 11—100d
熔化 melting 物理学 11—100d
熔剂 flux 冶金学 6—380d
熔结凝灰岩 ignimbrite 岩石 8—327b
熔结凝灰岩 welded tuff 岩石 18—175c
熔炼 smelting 冶金 15—441e
熔模铸造 investment casting 冶金 8—428c
熔岩 lava 地质学 9—524e
熔岩层国家保护区 Lava Beds National Monument 美国自然保护区 9—524f
熔岩洞穴 lava cave 地质学 9—524f
熔岩流错位残体 louderback 地质学 10—232d
熔岩原孤丘 kipuka 地质学 9—299a
蝾螺 turban shell 动物 17—276c
蝾螈 salamander 两栖动物 14—537e
融通念佛宗 Yūzū Nembutsu 日本佛教宗派 18—486a
冗余音节 hypercatalexis 诗歌 8—291e
柔道 judo 日本体育运动 9—103a
柔道 JUDO 体育项目 16—126a
柔佛 Johor 马来西亚州名 9—73f
柔佛海峡 Johore Strait 亚洲海峡 9—74b
柔然 Juan-juan 中国古代民族 9—96f
柔软体操 calisthenics 体育 3—352a
柔若语 Rouruo language 中国怒族语言 14—420d
柔术 jujitsu 日本武术 9—104f
柔性版印刷 flexography 印刷术 6—359e
鞣皮栎 tanbark oak (*Lithocarpus densiflorus*) 木本植物 16—458a
鞣皮制革法 tanning 制革工艺 16—469a
肉孢子虫属 Sarcocystis 动物学 15—63b
肉齿目 Creodonta 古生物学 5—6a
肉冻 aspic 食品 1—557f
肉豆蔻 nutmeg 木本植物 12—305e
肉豆蔻干皮 mace 调味品 10—339b
肉豆蔻科 Myristicaceae 植物学 11—527c
肉毒碱 carnitine 化合物 3—468a
肉毒中毒 botulism 食物中毒 3—75f
肉桂 cassia (*Cinnamomum cassia*) 植物 3—503f
肉红玉髓和缠丝玛瑙 sard and sardonyx 矿物 15—63e
肉类 meat 食品 11—65c
肉瘤 sarcoma 病理学 15—63c
肉食龙 carnosaur 古生物学 3—470a
肉刑 corporal punishment 刑法 4—519a
肉芽肿性甲状腺炎 granulomatous thyroiditis 疾病 7—257c
肉欲诗派 fleshly school of poetry 一批英国诗人 6—357e
肉质植物 succulent 植物学 16—302a
肉足虫 sarcodine 原生动物 15—63b
如来 Tathāgata 佛教 16—494b
如尼字母 runic alphabet 日耳曼民族的文字体系 14—449e
《如是》 Tel Quel 法国文学刊物 16—521f
茹阿泽鲁 Juàzeiro 巴西城市 9—97e
茹弗 Jouve, Pierre-Jean 法国诗人 9—94a
茹弗鲁瓦 Jouffroy d'Abbans, Claude-François-Dorothée, marquis de 法国工程师 9—92e
茹科夫斯基 Zhukovsky, Vasily Andreyevich 俄国诗人 18—548e
茹鲁阿河 Juruá River 南美洲河流 9—116f
茹鲁埃纳河 Juruena River 巴西河流 9—116f
茹瓦约斯公爵 Joyeuse, Anne, Duke de 法国贵族 9—95d
茹沃内 Jouvenet, Jean 法国画家 9—94b
茹伊布 toile de Jouy 纺织品 17—132b
茹伊斯-迪福拉 Juiz de Fore 巴西城市 9—104f
铷(Rb) rubidium 化学元素 14—437b
铷-锶测年法 rubidium-strontium dating 估算岩石、陨石年代方法 14—437c
儒安维尔 Joinville, Jean, sire de 法国编年史作者 9—75e
儒安维尔亲王 Joinville, François-Ferdinand-Philippe-Louis-Marie d'Orléans, prince de 法国海军军官 9—75d
儒奥 Jouhaux, Léon 法国社会党人 9—92e
儒贝尔 Joubert, Barthélemy-Catherine 法国将军 9—92c
儒尔当伯爵 Jourdan, Jean-Baptiste, Count 法国指挥官 9—93b
儒艮 dugong (*Dugong dugon*) 海洋哺乳动物 5—449a
儒家 Confucianism 中国文化 4—422d
《儒林外史》 Rulin Waishi 中国文学 14—447b
儒略历 Julian calendar 历法 9—106d
儒略周期 Julian period 历法 9—106e
儒韦 Jouvet, Louis 法国演员 9—94b
儒学 Ruxue 中国文化 14—471f
濡水 Ru Shui (China) 中国河流 14—434d
蠕虫 worm 无脊椎动物 18—338b
蠕虫石 myrmekite 地质学 11—527c
蠕虫蜥 worm lizard (*Rhineura floridana*) 爬行动物 18—338c
蠕虫状纹样工艺 opus vermiculatum 工艺 12—440e
蠕动 creep 地质学 5—3f
蠕动 peristalsis 解剖学 13—170f
蠕螺 worm shell 腹足纲海产贝类 18—338c
蠕蛇 worm snake 动物 18—338d
汝即彼 tat tvam asi 印度哲学 16—491f
汝拉 Jura 瑞士州名 9—115e
汝窑 Ru kiln 中国古瓷窑 14—434d
乳白玻璃 milk glass 玻璃 11—219c
乳齿象 mastodon 古生物学 11—15e
乳多空病毒 papovavirus 病毒 13—25e
乳房切除术 mastectomy 医学 11—14b
乳杆菌属 Lactobacillus 微生物学 9—440c
乳化剂 emulsifier 化学添加剂 6—66e
乳糜 chyle 生物化学 4—232c
乳糜泻 celiac disease 病理现象 3—555c
乳品业 dairying 农业 5—112f
乳清 whey 化合物 18—223a
乳色玻璃 opaline glass 玻璃 12—425f
乳酸 lactic acid 化学 9—440b
乳酸细菌 lactic-acid bacterium 微生物学 9—440c
乳糖 lactose 化学 9—440d
乳糖酶 lactase 生物化学 9—440a
乳头状瘤病毒 papillomavirus 病理学 13—24f
乳突 mastoid process 解剖学 11—15f
乳突炎 mastoiditis 疾病 11—15f
乳腺 mammary gland 解剖学 10—441f
乳腺癌 breast cancer 疾病 3—135a
乳腺炎 mastitis 疾病 11—15d
乳香 frankincense 芳香树脂 6—450e
乳溢 galactorrhea 内分泌病 6—549c
乳汁草 milkweed 植物学 11—220a
乳脂肪 butterfat 牛奶中主要成分 3—292d
乳状液 emulsion 液体混合物 6—66f
《入阿毗达磨论》 Abhidhammāvatāra 佛教著作 1—23d
入法礼 upanayana 印度教 17—403d
入籍 naturalization 法律 12—46c
入间 Iruma 日本城市 8—454a
入凌 ingress 天文学 8—387a
褥疮 bedsore 疾病 2—327b
褥榻 ottoman 家具 12—502c
阮爱国 Nguyen Ai Quoc (Vietnamese leader) 越南领袖 12—161d
阮宝岛 Nguyen Bun Dao (Vietnamese emperor) 越南皇帝 12—161d
阮必成 Nguyen That Thanh (Vietnamese leader) 越南领袖 12—

162a
阮长祚 Nguyen Truong To 越南改革者 12—162a
阮朝 Nguyen DYNASTY 越南王朝 12—161c
阮福濒 Nguyen Phuoc Tan (Vietnamese ruler) 越南南方统治者 12—161f
阮福洪任 Nguyen Phuoc Hoang Nham (Vietnamese emperor) 越南皇帝 12—161f
阮福皎 Nguyen Phuoc Chi Dam (Vietnamese emperor) 越南皇帝 12—161f
阮冈纳赞 Ranganathan, Shiyali Ramamrita 印度图书馆学家、教育家 14—149d
阮高其 Nguyen Cao Ky 南越军政领袖 12—161d
阮惠 Nguyen Hue (Vietnamese revolutionary leader) 越南革命领袖 12—161e
阮籍 Ruan Ji 中国诗人、思想家 14—434e
阮侣 Nguyen Lu (Vietnamese revolutionary leader) 越南革命领袖 12—161f
阮庆 Nguyen Khanh 南越军政领导人 12—161f
阮堂 Wan-dang (Korean calligrapher) 韩国书法家 18—89e
阮文绍 Nguyen Van Thieu 越南共和国(南越)总统 12—162b
阮文厅 Nguyen Van Thinh 越南政治人物 12—162b
阮映 Nguyen Anh (Vietnamese emperor) 越南皇帝 12—161d
阮永瑞 Nguyen Vinh Thuy (Vietnamese emperor) 越南皇帝 12—162b
阮攸 Nguyen Du 越南诗人 12—161d
阮友寿 Nguyen Huu Tho 越南领袖 12—161e
阮元 Ruan Yuan 中国学者 14—434f
阮岳 Nguyen Nhac (Vietnamese revolutionary leader) 越南革命领袖 12—161f
阮智方 Nguyen Tri Phuong 越南保守派 12—162a
软材 softwood 木材 15—486b
软腭化 velarization 语音学 17—491c
软骨 cartilage 生理学 3—490d
软骨发育不全 achondroplasia 遗传病 1—53f
软骨肉瘤 chondrosarcoma 病理学 4—192f
软骨图案 knorpelwerk (decorative arts) 装饰艺术 9—323c
软骨硬鳞目 Chondrosteiformes 动物学 4—193b
软骨硬鳞鱼 chondrostean 鱼类 4—192f
软骨鱼 chondrichthian 动物学 4—192c
软管 hose 导管 8—187f
软甲龟 softshell turtle 爬行动物 15—485f
软甲类 malacostracan 动物学 10—419c
软件 software 计算机科学 15—486a
软煤 soft coal 矿物 15—485d
软锰矿 pyrolusite 矿物 14—47c
软泥 ooze 地质学 12—425a
软槭 soft maple 植物 15—485e
软钎焊 soldering 冶金 15—494c
软式飞艇 blimp 航空器 2—534f
软式墙网球 SQUASH RACKETS 体育项目 16—138b
软式墙网球 squash rackets 体育项目 16—168b
软水 soft water 化学 15—485e
软水铝石 boehmite 矿物 2—564a
软体动物 mollusk 无脊椎动物 11—323c
软土 mollisol 土壤类型 11—323c
软下疳 chancroid 病理学 4—43e
软饮料 soft drink 非酒精饮料 15—485d
软玉 nephrite 宝石级矿物 12—83b
蚋 black fly 昆虫 2—511f
蚋鹟鹩 gnatcatcher 鸟类 7—167a
蚋鹩科 Polioptilidae (bird family) 动物学 13—401a
锐钛矿 anatase 矿物 1—318b
瑞 Re 古埃及宗教太阳神 14—175a
瑞安 Juin, Alphonse(-Pierre) 法国指挥官 9—104e
瑞安 Ryan, Nolan 美国棒球运动员 14—473f
瑞安 Ryan, T. Claude 美国民航企业家、飞机制造家 14—474a
瑞安 Ryan, Thomas Fortune 美国大金融家 14—474b
瑞保 Shwebo 缅甸城镇 15—345c
瑞典 Sweden 欧洲国家 16—376d
《瑞典日报》 Svenska Dagbladet 瑞典报纸 16—367f
瑞典式自助餐 smorgasbord 斯堪的纳维亚烹饪法 15—456a
瑞典文学 Swedish literature 北欧文学 16—378d
瑞典信义会 Sweden, Church of 瑞典国定教会 16—377f
瑞典语 Swedish language 北欧语言 16—378d
瑞金 Ruijin 中国城市 14—445f
瑞利(特林普莱斯的)男爵(第三) Rayleigh (of Terling Place), John William Strutt, 3rd Baron 英国物理学家 14—171e
瑞利散射 Rayleigh scattering 物理学 14—172a
瑞诺 Junod, Henri Alexandre 瑞士人类学家 9—114a
瑞瑞克 Rerek (Egyptian god) 埃及神祇 14—238e
瑞舍夫 Resheph 古代西闪米特人神灵 14—239b
瑞士 Switzerland 中欧内陆国家 16—388b
瑞士德语 Swiss German language 语言 16—387c
瑞士干酪 Swiss cheese 食品 16—387a
瑞士国家公园 Swiss National Park 瑞士公园 16—387e
瑞士国王 Swiss, King of the 瑞士军事领袖 16—386f
瑞士航空公司 Swissair 瑞士公司 16—387f
瑞士褐牛 Brown Swiss 牛品种 3—195a
瑞士基督教联合会 Swiss Federation of Protestant Churches 瑞士基督教组织 16—387b
瑞士军刀 Swiss Army knife 工具 16—386f
瑞士联邦 Confederaziun Helvetica 中欧内陆国家 4—420c
瑞士联邦 Swiss Confederation 中欧内陆国家 16—387b
瑞士联合银行 Union Bank of Switzerland 瑞士银行 17—345d
《瑞士民法典》 Swiss Civil Code 瑞士法律 16—387a
瑞士人民党 Swiss People's Party 瑞士政党 16—387f
瑞士社会民主党 Social Democratic Party of Switzerland 瑞士政党 15—471b
瑞士卫队 Swiss Guards 梵蒂冈历史 16—387d
瑞士文学 Swiss literature 文学 16—387e
《瑞士信纲》 Helvetic Confession 基督教 8—7b
瑞士银行公司 Swiss Bank Corporation 瑞士商业银行 16—386f
瑞氏综合征 Reye syndrome 疾病 14—254d
瑞穗金融集 Mizuho Financial Group, Inc. 日本金融机构 11—298a
瑞天咸港 Port Swettenham (Malaysia) 马来西亚港口 13—447d
瑞天咸 Swettenham, Sir Frank (Athelstane) 马来亚英国殖民官员 16—381c
瑞香目 Thymelaeales 植物学 17—75d
瑞香属 Daphne 植物学 5—145a
瑞亚 Rhea 希腊女神 14—258e
闰年 leap year 历法 9—545b
润肤剂 emollient 化妆品成分 6—62c
润滑 lubrication 机械 10—265c
润滑脂 grease 润滑剂 7—268d
润湿剂 wetting agent 化工品 18—215d
若安(女教皇) Joan, POPE 传说中的教皇 9—38d
若昂(阿维什的) John OF AVIZ 葡萄牙国王 9—55a
若昂(大帝) John THE GREAT 葡萄牙国王 9—58a
若昂(私生子) John THE BASTARD 葡萄牙国王 9—57f
若昂贝卢 João Belo (Mozambique) 莫桑比克城市 9—41b
若昂二世 John II 葡萄牙国王 9—53b
若昂六世 John VI 葡萄牙国王 9—53d
若昂佩索阿 João Pessoa 巴西港口 9—41b
若昂三世 John III 葡萄牙国王 9—53c
若昂四世 John IV 葡萄牙国王 9—53d
若昂五世 John V 葡萄牙国王 9—53d

若昂一世 John I 葡萄牙国王 9—52f
若虫 nymph 昆虫学 12—310f
若代尔 Jodelle, Étienne 法国戏剧家 9—42d
若尔瑙 Zsolna (Slovakia) 斯洛伐克城镇 18—570a
若弗兰 Geoffrin, Marie-Thérèse Rodet 法国沙龙主持人 7—70e
若弗鲁瓦·圣-蒂莱尔 Geoffroy Saint-Hilaire, Étienne 法国博物学家 7—71a
若弗鲁瓦·圣-蒂莱尔 Geoffroy Saint-Hilaire, Isidore 法国动物学家 7—71b
若弗鲁瓦氏猫 Geoffroy's cat (*Felis geoffroyi*) 哺乳动物 7—71b
若格 Jogues, Saint Isaac 天主教传教士 9—44a
若开 Arakan 缅甸地区 1—436e
若开人 Arakanese 缅甸土著民族 1—436f
若开山脉 Arakan Mountain Range 缅甸山脉 1—436f
若利埃 Jolliet, Louis 法国-加拿大探险家 9—77c
若利韦 Jolivet, André 法国作曲家 9—77b
若瑟 Joseph 葡萄牙国王 9—89d
若斯坎·德普雷 Josquin DES PREZ 欧洲作曲家 9—91f
若斯潘 Jospin, Lionel 法国政治人物 9—91e
若望 Ciudad, Juan 葡萄牙僧侣 4—251d
若因维利 Joinvile 巴西城市 9—75d
弱核力 weak nuclear force 物理学 18—153b
弱视 amblyopia 疾病 1—270c
弱夜鹰 poorwill (*Phalaenoptilus nuttallii*) 鸟类 13—431b